2014/15

THE DIRECTORY OF

GRANT MAKING TRUSTS

23RD EDITION

Tom Traynor, Jude Doherty, Lucy Lernelius-Tonks, Denise Lillya, Jonny Morris and Emma Weston

Additional research by Ged Howells, Liam Lynch, Alan Price and Gabriele Zagnojute

DIRECTORY OF SOCIAL CHANGE

Published by the Directory of Social Change (Registered Charity no. 800517 in England and Wales)
Head office: 24 Stephenson Way, London NW1 2DP
Northern office: Suite 103, 1 Old Hall Street, Liverpool L3 9HG
Tel: 08450 77 77 07

Visit www.dsc.org.uk to find out more about our books, subscription funding websites and training events. You can also sign up for e-newsletters so that you're always the first to hear about what's new.

The publisher welcomes suggestions and comments that will help to inform and improve future versions of this and all of our titles. Please give us your feedback by emailing publications@dsc.org.uk.

It should be understood that this publication is intended for guidance only and is not a substitute for professional or legal advice. No responsibility for loss occasioned as a result of any person acting or refraining from acting can be accepted by the authors or publisher.

First published by Charities Aid Foundation 1968
Second edition 1971
Third edition 1974
Fourth edition 1975
Fifth edition 1977
Sixth edition 1978
Seventh edition 1981
Eighth edition 1983
Ninth edition 1985
Tenth edition 1987
Eleventh edition 1989
Twelfth edition 1991
Thirteenth edition 1993
Fourteenth edition 1995
Fifteenth edition 1997
Sixteenth edition 1999
Seventeenth edition published by Directory of Social Change 2001
Eighteenth edition 2003
Nineteenth edition 2005
Twentieth edition 2007
Twenty-first edition 2010
Twenty-second edition 2012
Twenty-third edition 2014

ISBN 978 1 906294 87 8

British Library Cataloguing in Publication Data
A catalogue record for this book is available from the British Library

Cover design by Kate Bass
Text designed by Eugenie Dodd Typographics, London
Typeset by Marlinzo Services, Frome
Printed and bound in Great Britain by CPI Group, Croydon

FSC
www.fsc.org
MIX
Paper from
responsible sources
FSC® C013604

Contents

About the Directory of Social Change

The Directory of Social Change (DSC) has a vision of an independent voluntary sector at the heart of social change. The activities of independent charities, voluntary organisations and community groups are fundamental to achieve social change. We exist to help these organisations and the people who support them to achieve their goals.

We do this by:

■ providing practical tools that organisations and activists need, including online and printed publications, training courses, and conferences on a huge range of topics;

■ acting as a 'concerned citizen' in public policy debates, often on behalf of smaller charities, voluntary organisations and community groups;

■ leading campaigns and stimulating debate on key policy issues that affect those groups;

■ carrying out research and providing information to influence policymakers.

DSC is the leading provider of information and training for the voluntary sector and publishes an extensive range of guides and handbooks covering subjects such as fundraising, management, communication, finance and law. We have a range of subscription-based websites containing a wealth of information on funding from trusts, companies and government sources. We run more than 300 training courses each year, including bespoke in-house training provided at the client's location. DSC conferences, many of which run on an annual basis, include the Charity Management Conference, the Charity Accountants' Conference and the Charity Law Conference. DSC's major annual event is Charityfair, which provides low-cost training on a wide variety of subjects.

For details of all our activities, and to order publications and book courses, go to www.dsc.org.uk, call 08450 777707 or email publications@dsc.org.uk.

Foreword

When I first started in fundraising over 20 years ago, my then boss at Prisoners Abroad said 'never be afraid to ask: you are doing donors a favour in helping them to give'. There was never a truer word spoken, especially in relation to grant-making trusts and foundations. These wonderful giving charities have one role in life and that is to make donations to causes like yours. How much they give will depend on many factors, but give it away they must and you can help them do just that.

When I first started in fundraising, this publication, which has come on leaps and bounds, was my bible. It was always on my desk, and I always consulted it before a letter asking for a grant left the office. My mantra was: get my hands on the latest edition first and have those letters ready to go the next day! Using this directory, I raised tens of thousands of pounds for one of the hardest causes going. My fundraisers still use the *Directory of Grant Making Trusts* every day to help raise millions of pounds.

The UK fundraising environment is highly competitive. Demand in the individual giving space is outstripping supply, philanthropic funding from companies is becoming almost unheard of and swingeing statutory funding cuts show no signs of reversal. Charities' funds are being squeezed from every direction

In reading this book, you are not only being smart but also wise. Charitable trusts provide a reliable source of income, supporting charities – small to large with a wide range of funding. Trusts are made up of people just like you, passionate about the charitable sector, and if you treat them as part of your family, they can be with you for life. There are still trusts giving to the causes I first fundraised for all those years ago.

Whether you are a small, medium or large charity, the *Directory of Grant Making Trusts* is an essential tool for fundraisers. It will help you reduce that most frustrating experience of receiving rejection after rejection after putting your heart and soul into writing your most compelling proposals.

It will do this by helping you ensure you target funders who are interested in funding the work that you deliver. Regardless of how compelling your appeal is, the work you need funding must match their funding policies to hit the target. Take heart, however, as whatever the cause you can be sure to find the right trust or foundation in this guide.

Mark Astarita
Chair of Trustees, Institute of Fundraising
Director of Fundraising, British Red Cross

Introduction

This book covers the largest 2,500 grant-making trusts in the UK that give grants to organisations. The amounts given by individual funders range from around £25,000 in total each year up to £511.1 million. The combined giving of all these trusts totals over £4.3 billion a year, a significant increase on the previous edition due in no small part to a substantial increase in funding from the Big Lottery Fund. The top 150 are listed at the end of this introduction and include the Big Lottery Fund and Awards for All, as well as more traditional grant-making trusts.

Charities Aid Foundation published the first edition of the Directory of Grant Making Trusts (DGMT) in 1968 and it has been researched and published by the Directory of Social Change since 2001. Over this time the title has gained a notable reputation as a comprehensive guide to UK grant-making trusts and their funding policies. It is designed to provide a bridge between the foundation and fundraising communities in the UK. Today it is hard to imagine the difficulties which must have been encountered in trying to obtain funds from trusts before the DGMT brought together so many of them in one place.

The DGMT is a key source of information on how trusts see themselves and their grant making. Each entry aims to reflect the trust's own view of its policies, priorities and exclusions. Other guides include independent, sometimes critical comment on and analysis of trust activities. The DGMT does not. Rather, it is the trusts' guide to grant-making trusts.

Many charities were hit hard by the recession that took hold several years ago. Thankfully, the trusts and foundations in this book have seen a general improvement in their finances since the last edition of this book, in some cases recovering to pre-recession levels. It must also be noted that the significant increase in the top line figure for total grants in this book – £4.3 billion in total grants in this edition compared to £3.6 billion in the previous – is largely due to the Big Lottery Fund. However, it is still the case that over half of the organisations here increased their grants compare to the previous edition.

This overall trend towards a recovery of the finances does need to be viewed in the wider context of severe cuts or 'efficiency savings' in practically every area of public expenditure, from welfare and the NHS to education and the environment, with the poorest and most disadvantaged in society being hit hardest. With more cuts on the way it is likely that the funders in the guide will see even more demand, which is why getting the right information is critical.

Potential fundraisers should, however, remain optimistic. While many trusts have disappeared from this edition for one reason or another, there are over 200 trusts that are new to this edition; however, the need to focus on well-targeted applications to relevant funders has never been more important, and this book will help you in that endeavour.

We value the opinions of our readers on all aspects of this directory. We are always looking to improve the guide and would welcome any feedback – positive or negative – which could be useful for future editions. Please contact us at: Research Team, Directory of Social Change, Suite 103, 1 Old Hall Street, Liverpool L3 9HG, telephone 0151 708 0136 or email us at: dgmt@dsc.org.uk with any comments you would like to make.

The trusts we have listed This directory aims to include the majority of UK-based trusts that are capable of giving at least £25,000 a year to organisations. Every trust was sent a questionnaire giving them the opportunity to update key information about how they operate.

Many of the trusts are extremely helpful and provide comprehensive information on their current policies via their websites and published material. However, not all trusts are so open. Where a trust does not make this information available, their details have been updated, where possible, using the information on file at the Charity Commission or the Office of the Scottish Charity Regulator. In addition, all contact details were checked. Trusts have been included in the index under the relevant headings according to their own published guidelines. We have placed those trusts for which we do not have such information available under what we believe are the most suitable categories based on the information in their annual reports and accounts.

Some trusts continue to state their wish not to be included in this book. However, we believe that trust directories provide an invaluable bridge between the trust community and the rest of the voluntary sector, and that trusts in receipt of public funds through tax relief should not attempt to draw a veil of secrecy over their activities. Consequently, we have declined requests from trusts to be excluded from this directory.

In general we have included:

■ trusts with a grant-making capacity of at least £25,000 per year which make grants to charities and voluntary organisations, including Big Lottery Fund and Awards for All (which operate like grant-making trusts).

We have excluded:

■ trusts which fund individuals only;

■ trusts which fund one organisation exclusively;

■ trusts which have a grant-making capacity or an income of less than £25,000 (smaller local trusts are included on www.trustfunding.org.uk);

■ trusts which have ceased to exist or are being wound down with remaining funds fully committed.

We continue to include trusts which state that they do not respond to unsolicited applications. We believe that their inclusion benefits fundraisers by giving a broader overview of the grant-making community, and that the information could be important in supporting relationship fundraising activity. We feel it benefits the trusts in helping them to communicate that they do not wish to receive applications, which fundraisers might not know if they identified the trust through other avenues. In this way we are working towards achieving one of our Great Giving campaign goals of reducing the number of ineligible applications that are submitted to trusts (please visit www.dsc.org.uk for more information).

Acknowledgements

We would like to thank Mark Astarita, Director of Fundraising at the British Red Cross and Chair of the Institute of Fundraising, for contributing the foreword to this edition.

We would also like to thank all those trusts which make their information openly available, and all those who replied to our questionnaire.

How to use the DGMT

The directory starts with three indexes:

- trusts by geographical area
- trusts by field of interest and type of beneficiary
- trusts by grant type.

There is a listing of the top 150 trusts by grant total at the end of this introduction. All of these lists are in alphabetical order.

Using these indexes, users should end up with a shortlist of trusts whose funding policies match their needs.

Trusts by geographical area

This index enables you to see which trusts will consider applications from a charity or project in a particular geographical area. It contains two separate listings:

LIST OF GEOGRAPHICAL AREA HEADINGS

This is a complete list of all the geographical area headings used in the DGMT. The page numbers relate to the second listing.

LIST OF TRUSTS BY GEOGRAPHICAL AREA

These pages list trusts under the geographical areas from which they will consider applications for funding.

Trusts by field of interest and type of beneficiary

This index enables you to see which trusts are likely to fund projects doing a particular type of work to benefit a particular type of person. It lists trusts according to:

- the type of activity or work they are willing to fund – their 'fields of interest';
- who they want to benefit – their preferred 'beneficiaries'.

These pages contain two separate listings:

CATEGORISATION OF FIELDS OF INTEREST AND TYPES OF BENEFICIARY

This lists all of the headings used in the DGMT to categorise fields of interest and types of beneficiary. This listing should help you match your project with one – or more – of the categories used. The page numbers relate to the second listing.

LIST OF TRUSTS BY FIELD OF INTEREST AND TYPE OF BENEFICIARY

These pages list trusts under the fields of interest and types of beneficiary they have indicated they have a preference for or might be willing to support.

The index is structured hierarchically. This means that the general heading comes first, followed by more specific subject areas. For example, Education and training is split into eight sub-headings, including Higher education; Informal, continuing and adult education; Primary and secondary school education; and so on. Some of these are then split further. For example, Primary and secondary school education contains a further four categories including Faith schools and Special needs schools.

So, if your project falls under a specific heading such as Special needs schools, it may also be worth looking at the trusts which have expressed a general interest in funding primary and secondary education and, above that, education and training.

Trusts by type of grant

This index enables you to see which trusts will consider making the types of grant you are looking for. Trusts are listed under the types of grant that they have indicated they are willing to make. These pages contain two separate listings:

LIST OF GRANT TYPES

This lists all of the headings used in the DGMT to categorise grant types. Page numbers relate to the second listing.

LIST OF TRUSTS BY GRANT TYPE

These pages list trusts under the types of grant that they are willing to make.

The largest trusts

At the end of these sections, we have listed the largest 150 trusts by grant total in alphabetical order. Between them they account for around £3.75 billion, or about 87% of the funds available in the book. Please do not use this simply as a mailing list: these trusts cover a wide range of specialist interests and many of them will never fund your work.

We recommend that you read each entry carefully and compile your own list of major trusts relevant to you. You can then set this list alongside the other lists generated from the other indexes in the directory. We believe this is the most effective way of ensuring that you do not omit any major trusts.

How to use the DGMT
Key steps

STEP 1

Define the project, programme or work for which you are seeking funding.

STEP 2

Geographical area: find the area most local to your requirements. Note down the names of the trusts listed here.

STEP 3

Field of interest and type of beneficiary: identify the categories that match your project. Note down the names of the trusts listed here.

STEP 4

Type of grant: identify the type of grant you are looking for. Note down the names of the trusts listed here.

STEP 5

Compare the three lists of trusts to produce a list of those whose funding policies most closely match the characteristics of the project for which you are seeking funding.

STEP 6

If your trust list is too short you could include trusts that have a general interest in funding your area.

STEP 7

Look up entries for the trusts identified, study their details carefully and pay close attention to 'What is funded' and 'What is not funded'.

▼

STEP 8

Look at the list of the top 150 trusts. Look up entries for the trusts identified, study their details carefully and again pay close attention to 'What is funded' and 'What is not funded'.

Checklist

STEP 1 **The following checklist will help you assemble the information you need.**

- What is the geographical location of the people who will benefit from any funding received?
- What facilities or services will the funding provide?
- What are the characteristics which best describe the people who will benefit from any funding received?
- What type of grant are you looking for?

EXAMPLE *Funding is being sought for a project in Merseyside to enable unemployed young people to take part in an employment training scheme.*

- The geographical location is: England → North West → Merseyside
- The service to be provided is: Vocational training
- The key characteristic of the people to benefit is that they are: Unemployed
- The type of grant being sought is: Project support

STEP 2 **Look up the area where your project is based in the list of geographical area headings on page 2.**

- Turn to the relevant pages in the list of trusts by geographical area and note down the names of the trusts which have stated that they will consider funding projects in your area.

EXAMPLE *Look up the area most local to your requirements (Merseyside) in the list of geographical area headings. Then turn to the relevant page in the list of trusts by geographical area and look up the names of the trusts listed under Merseyside. You may want to look at the trusts listed under the broader region (North West) as well. Note down the names so that they can be compared with the lists through the indexes by type of grant and by field of interest and type of beneficiary.*

It is also worth looking at trusts listed under England, as a trust listed under a more general heading may be just as willing to fund activity in a specific region as another which states that it has a specific interest in that region.

STEP 3 Using the 'Field of interest and type of beneficiary' category on page 50, identify all the categories that match the project, programme or work for which you are seeking funding.

Turn to the relevant pages in the list of trusts by field of interest and type of beneficiary and look up the headings identified.

Note down the names of the trusts that appear under these headings so that you can compare them with the names identified through the indexes by geographical area and by type of grant.

EXAMPLE *With a project to provide training for work, you will probably look first under the main heading 'Education and training'. Under this heading you will find the sub-heading 'Informal, continuing and adult education' and under this you will find the heading 'Vocational education and training'. Note down the page numbers beside 'Informal, continuing and adult education' and 'Vocational education and training'. Trusts that have expressed an interest in funding vocational training may represent your best prospects, but trusts with a more general interest in funding informal education and training might be worth approaching – particularly if they like to fund projects in your area.*

If you look under 'Beneficial groups' you will find 'People who are poor, on low incomes', which is under 'Social and economic circumstances' and 'Disadvantaged and socially excluded people'. Note down this page number too.

STEP 4 Look up the type of grant that you are seeking in 'Trusts by type of grant' on page 176.

Turn to the relevant pages in the list of trusts by type of grant and note down the names of the trusts which will consider giving the type of grant that you are seeking. Compare these names with those that you identified through the indexes by geographical area and by field of interest and type of beneficiary.

EXAMPLE *Look up the type of grant you are seeking in the list of grant types (in this case 'Project support'). Then turn to the relevant page of the list of trusts by type of grant and look at the names of the trusts listed under 'Project support'. Note down the names of all these trusts.*

STEP 5 Compare the lists of trust names produced via steps 2, 3 and 4, and make a list of all the trusts which appear on more than one list. This will produce a list of trusts whose funding policies most closely match the characteristics of the project for which you are seeking funding.

STEP 6 If the list turns out to be too short it can easily be adjusted.

EXAMPLE *You find that you have ended up with a list of five trusts.*

Going back to step 3, you could include the trusts which come under 'Education and training', or, going back to step 2, you could include trusts which will consider funding projects in the North West.

STEP 7 Look up the entries for the trusts identified and study their details carefully, paying particular attention to 'Where funding can be given', 'What is funded' and 'What is not funded'.

If you feel that there is a good match between the characteristics of the project for which you require support and the funding policies of the trust identified, you could submit an application.

STEP 8 Look at the list of the top 150 trusts.

Check that you have not missed any of the major funders because you have made your search too specific. Some of the largest foundations give to a wide range of organisations and projects, and they tend to give the largest grants. They are also the most over-subscribed.

Look up the entries for each trust and study their details carefully, paying particular attention to 'Where funding can be given', 'What is funded' and 'What is not funded'. If you feel that there is a good match between the characteristics of the project for which you require support and the funding policies of the trust identified, you could submit an application.

However, make sure that there is a good reason for writing to any trust that you select: do not just send off indiscriminate applications to the whole list!

A typical trust entry

A complete entry should contain information under the headings listed below. An explanation of the information which should appear in these fields is given alongside.

CC NO
Charity registration number

WHERE FUNDING CAN BE GIVEN
The village, town, borough, parish or other geographical area the trust is prepared to fund

WHAT IS FUNDED
Details of the types of project or activity the trust plans to fund

WHAT IS NOT FUNDED
The types of projects or causes the trust will definitely not fund, e.g. expeditions, scholarships

SAMPLE GRANTS
The main grants given by the trust in the last financial year

TRUSTEES
Names of the trustees

PUBLICATIONS
Titles of publications the trust has produced which are of interest to grant seekers

WHO TO APPLY TO
The name and address of the person to whom applications should be sent

ESTABLISHED
Year established

WHO CAN BENEFIT
The kinds of people, animals, etc., the trust wishes to ultimately benefit

TYPE OF GRANT
The types of grant or loan the trust is prepared to give, e.g. one-off, recurring, running costs

RANGE OF GRANTS
The smallest, largest and typical size of grant normally given

FINANCES
The most recent financial information, including the total amount of grants given

OTHER INFORMATION
Any other information which might be useful to grant seekers

HOW TO APPLY
Useful information to those preparing their grant application

■ The Fictitious Trust

CC NO 123456   **ESTABLISHED** 1993
WHERE FUNDING CAN BE GIVEN UK.
WHO CAN BENEFIT Charities benefiting children.
WHAT IS FUNDED Education and training.
WHAT IS NOT FUNDED No grants to individuals.
TYPE OF GRANT One-off, capital, running costs.
RANGE OF GRANTS £250–£5,000.
SAMPLE GRANTS A school (£5,000); a university (£1,000); a school library (£800); a school (£600); a grammar school, a further education college and for classroom equipment (£500 each); a university appeal (£400); and a wheelchair ramp (£250).
FINANCES Year 2011 Income £55,000 Grants £50,000 Assets £800,000
TRUSTEES Peter Brown, Chair; Mrs Mary Brown; Alistair Johnson; Lord Great; Lady Good.
PUBLICATIONS The Fictitious Trust – The First 20 Years.
OTHER INFORMATION This trust recently merged with the Fictional Trust.
HOW TO APPLY In writing to the address below. An sae should be enclosed if an acknowledgement is required.
WHO TO APPLY TO A Grant, Secretary, The Old Barn, Main Street, New Town ZC48 2QQ Tel 020 7123 4567 Fax 020 7123 4567 email trust@fictitioustrust.co.uk Website www.fictitioustrust.co.uk

A list of the top 150 trusts by grant total

This is a list of the largest 150 trusts by grant total in alphabetical order. Between them they account for around £3.75 billion, or about 87% of the funds available in the book. Please do not use this simply as a mailing list: these trusts cover a wide range of specialist interests and many of them will never fund your work.

We recommend that you read each entry carefully and compile your own list of major trusts relevant to you. You can then set this list alongside the other lists generated from the other indexes in the directory. We believe this is the most effective way of ensuring that you do not omit any major trusts.

The 29th May 1961 Charitable Trust

A W Charitable Trust

ABF The Soldiers' Charity

Achisomoch Aid Company Limited

Action Medical Research

Age UK

Aid to the Church in Need (UK)

Allchurches Trust Ltd

Amabrill Limited

Arthritis Research UK

Arts Council England

Arts Council of Northern Ireland

Arts Council of Wales

Asthma UK

Awards for All

The Baily Thomas Charitable Fund

The Baring Foundation

BBC Children in Need

The Big Lottery Fund

The Michael Bishop Foundation

The Bowland Charitable Trust

The Liz and Terry Bramall Foundation

The British Gas (Scottish Gas) Energy Trust

British Heart Foundation

The Barrow Cadbury Trust and the Barrow Cadbury Fund

The Cadogan Charity

CAFOD

The Childwick Trust

Christian Aid

The City Bridge Trust

The Clore Duffield Foundation

The Clothworkers' Foundation

The Coalfields Regeneration Trust

Comic Relief

The Comino Foundation

County Durham Community Foundation

Creative Scotland

Diabetes UK

The Dulverton Trust

Dunard Fund

The Dunhill Medical Trust

EDF Energy Trust (EDFET)

The John Ellerman Foundation

The Eranda Foundation

Euro Charity Trust

Esmée Fairbairn Foundation

The Allan and Nesta Ferguson Charitable Settlement

The Fidelity UK Foundation

The Football Foundation

Forever Manchester

The Foyle Foundation

The Freemasons' Grand Charity

The Gatsby Charitable Foundation

The Goldsmiths' Company Charity

The Gosling Foundation Limited

The M and R Gross Charities Limited

Paul Hamlyn Foundation

The Headley Trust

The Helping Foundation

The Hintze Family Charitable Foundation

The Jerusalem Trust

The Elton John Aids Foundation

The Kay Kendall Leukaemia Fund

Kent Community Foundation

Keren Association

Maurice and Hilda Laing Charitable Trust

The Kirby Laing Foundation

The LankellyChase Foundation

The Leeds Community Foundation

Leukaemia and Lymphoma Research Fund

The Leverhulme Trust

The Linbury Trust

Liverpool Charity and Voluntary Services

Lloyds Bank Foundation for England and Wales

The Lolev Charitable Trust

The Trust for London

The London Community Foundation

The London Marathon Charitable Trust

The Lord's Taverners

John Lyon's Charity

Mayfair Charities Ltd

The Medlock Charitable Trust

The Mercers' Charitable Foundation

The Monument Trust

Muslim Hands

The National Art Collections Fund

Nominet Charitable Foundation

Norfolk Community Foundation

The Community Foundation for Northern Ireland

The Northern Rock Foundation

The Nuffield Foundation

Oxfam (GB)

The Pears Family Charitable Foundation

People's Postcode Trust

The Jack Petchey Foundation

The Pilgrim Trust

Porticus UK

The Premier League Charitable Fund

The Prince of Wales's Charitable Foundation

Quartet Community Foundation

Rachel Charitable Trust

The Rank Foundation Limited

The Joseph Rank Trust

The Sigrid Rausing Trust

Ridgesave Limited

The River Farm Foundation

The Robertson Trust

The Joseph Rowntree Charitable Trust

The Joseph Rowntree Foundation

Royal British Legion

Santander UK Foundation Limited

The Schroder Foundation

Foundation Scotland

Seafarers UK

The Samuel Sebba Charitable Trust

The Shetland Charitable Trust

SHINE

The Henry Smith Charity

The Sobell Foundation

The Souter Charitable Trust

Sparks Charity

St James's Place Foundation

The Stewards' Company Limited

The Stobart Newlands Charitable Trust

The Stone Family Foundation

The Bernard Sunley Charitable Foundation

Swansea and Brecon Diocesan Board of Finance Limited

Tearfund

The Tennis Foundation

Tesco Charity Trust

The Thompson Family Charitable Trust

The Sir Jules Thorn Charitable Trust

The Tudor Trust

Community Foundation Serving Tyne and Wear and Northumberland

The Underwood Trust

United Utilities Trust Fund

The Michael Uren Foundation

The Variety Club Children's Charity

The Vodafone Foundation

Voluntary Action Fund

Wales Council for Voluntary Action

Sir Siegmund Warburg's Voluntary Settlement

The Waterloo Foundation

The Wellcome Trust

The Garfield Weston Foundation

The Charles Wolfson Charitable Trust

The Wolfson Foundation

Youth Music

Youth United Foundation

The Zochonis Charitable Trust

Other publications and resources

The following publications and resources may also be of interest to readers of the DGMT. They are all available directly from the Directory of Social Change by ringing 08450 77 77 07 or visiting our website at www.dsc.org.uk.

The Guide to Grants for Individuals in Need
Directory of Social Change

This best-selling funding guide gives details of a wide range of funds and other support available for the relief of individual poverty and hardship. It remains a key reference book for social workers, as well as the individuals themselves and those concerned with their welfare.

■ Details on national and local charitable trusts which collectively around £269 million a year towards the relief of individual poverty and hardship.

■ Essential advice on applications for each source: eligibility; types of grants given; annual grant total; contact details.

■ An example of how to make an effective application, and advice on finding the right sources to apply to.

The Educational Grants Directory
Directory of Social Change

This best-selling guide gives details on a wide range of funds and other support available to schoolchildren and students in need, up to and including first degree level. It is a key reference book for educational social workers, student welfare officers, teachers and advice agencies, and the individuals themselves and their families. It includes:

■ Sources of funding for children and students up to and including first degree level from trusts that collectively give over £50 million each year.

■ Essential advice and information on applications for each source including eligibility, types of grants given, annual grant total and contact details.

■ An example of how to make an effective application, and advice on finding the right sources to apply to.

The Guide to UK Company Giving
Directory of Social Change

This invaluable guide includes details of 550 companies in the UK that give a combined total of around £470 million in cash donations to voluntary and community organisations. It contains:

■ Essential information on who to contact with each company.

■ Details information on cash donations, sponsorship, staff volunteering and gifts in kind.

The Guide to the Major Trusts Volumes 1 & 2
Directory of Social Change

The in-depth research and independent comment that these flagship titles offer has made them an essential reference guide for all fundraisers. These guides are the only source of independent critical analysis of trusts in practice.

Volume 1: concentrates on the 400 largest trusts that give over £300,000 a year.

Volume 2: complements volume 1 to provide a further 1,200 trusts that give between £30,000 and £300,000 each year.

www.trustfunding.org.uk

Packed with information on more than 4,500 UK grant-making trusts, this successful and popular tool for fundraisers lists trusts that collectively give over £4.3 billion each year.

■ Search by geographical area, name of trust, type of grant or by keyword search.

■ Choose to receive notification when information on a particular trust or trusts are updated.

■ Receive monthly bulletins that keep you informed of news and updates.

www.grantsfor individuals.org.uk

A Guide to Grants for Individuals in Need and The Educational Grants Directory come together in this database. It contains over 3,500 trusts and foundations that give to individuals for educational and welfare purposes. Collectively they give over £300 million each year.

■ Search by geographical area, name of trust, type of grant or by keyword search.

■ Choose to receive notification when information on a particular trust or trusts is updated.

■ Receive monthly bulletins that keep you informed of news and updates.

www.companygiving. org.uk

This database contains all those companies in The Guide to UK Company Giving, as well as newly discovered company giving and support. Over 550 companies are featured, giving over £470 million in cash donations. Entries contain full details on the various giving methods (cash donations, in-kind support, employee-led support, sponsorship and commercially-led support), and describe both what the company is prepared to fund and the organisations it has supported in the past.

■ Search by geographical area, name of company, type of grant or keyword.

■ Choose to receive notification when information on a particular company or companies is updated.

■ Receive monthly bulletins that keep you informed of news and updates.

www.government funding.org.uk

This database is an essential tool for anyone looking for information on statutory funding. Continually updated, it provides details on over £2 billion of funding from local, regional, national and European sources.

- Receive notification of funding rounds before they open.
- Use funder ratings for an independent and unique insight into what to expect from over 200 local, regional, national and European sources.
- Search by type of grant, e.g. small grants, loans and contracts.

DSC also offers a range of specialist funding guides. These guides provide essential tailored reference points for fundraisers working in specific areas.

They include:

The Youth Funding Guide
The Sports Funding Guide
The Environmental Funding Guide
And, finally, a trusted source of fundraising advice.
The Complete Fundraising Handbook

Trusts by geographical area

This index contains two separate listings:

Geographical area headings: This lists all of the geographical area headings used in the DGMT.

Trusts by geographical area: This lists the trusts appearing in the DGMT under the geographical area for which they have expressed a funding preference.

Trusts by geographical area

The index contains two separate listings:

Geographical area headings
This lists all of the geographical area headings used in DGMT.

Trusts by geographical area
This lists the trusts appearing in the DGMT under the geographical areas for which they have expressed a funding preference

Type of place

■ Developing world

The A B Charitable Trust
The Pat Allsop Charitable Trust
Anglo American Group
Foundation
The Ardwick Trust
The A S Charitable Trust
Veta Bailey Charitable Trust
The Austin Bailey Foundation
The Balmore Trust
The Baring Foundation
The Bartlett Taylor Charitable
Trust
The Bay Tree Charitable Trust
The John Beckwith Charitable
Trust
The Body Shop Foundation
H E and E L Botteley
Charitable Trust
P G and N J Boulton Trust
The Bower Trust
John and Susan Bowers Fund
Buckland Charitable Trust
The Burden Trust
Burdens Charitable Foundation
The Arnold Burton 1998
Charitable Trust
Edward Cadbury Charitable
Trust
Henry T and Lucy B Cadbury
Charitable Trust
CAFOD
The Calpe Trust
The Canning Trust
The Casey Trust
Christadelphian Samaritan
Fund
Christian Aid
Chrysalis Trust
The Coltstaple Trust
The Conscience Trust
The Gershon Coren Charitable
Foundation
Michael Cornish Charitable
Trust
The Evan Cornish Foundation
The Cotton Trust
The Cumber Family Charitable
Trust
The Dorfred Charitable Trust
Dromintee Trust
The Eagle Charity Trust
The Gilbert and Eileen Edgar
Foundation
The Ellerdale Trust
The Endure Foundation
The Ericson Trust
Euro Charity Trust
The A M Fenton Trust
Allan and Nesta Ferguson
Charitable Settlement
The Forest Hill Charitable Trust
The Donald Forrester Trust

The Anna Rosa Forster
Charitable Trust
The Four Winds Trust
Sydney E Franklin Deceased's
New Second Charity
The Jill Franklin Trust
The Fulmer Charitable Trust
The Fuserna Foundation
General Charitable Trust
The Galanthus Trust
The Generations Foundation
Global Care
The Green Hall Foundation
H C D Memorial Fund
The Haramead Trust
Miss K M Harbinson's
Charitable Trust
Hasluck Charitable Trust
The Headley Trust
Philip Henman Trust
The Hilden Charitable Fund
R G Hills Charitable Trust
The Horne Trust
The Hunter Foundation
The Innocent Foundation
The Jephcott Charitable Trust
The Cyril and Eve Jumbo
Charitable Trust
The Soli and Leah Kelaty Trust
Fund
The Kirby Laing Foundation
The Beatrice Laing Trust
The Langley Charitable Trust
The William Leech Charity
The Leonard Trust
The Linbury Trust
The Marie Helen Luen
Charitable Trust
Paul Lunn-Rockliffe Charitable
Trust
The Lyndhurst Trust
The Mahavir Trust
The Marianne Foundation
Mariapolis Limited
The Marr-Munning Trust
The John Mason Family Trust
Mercury Phoenix Trust
The Metropolitan Drinking
Fountain and Cattle Trough
Association
The Millhouses Charitable
Trust
The Mirianog Trust
The Mizpah Trust
The Monatrea Charitable Trust
The Morel Charitable Trust
Frederick Mulder Charitable
Trust
The George Müller Charitable
Trust
Peter John Murray Trust
Muslim Hands
Nazareth Trust Fund
Network for Social Change
Alice Noakes Memorial
Charitable Trust

The Northern Rock Foundation
The Father O'Mahoney
Memorial Trust
The Odin Charitable Trust
The Paget Charitable Trust
Paraton Trust
The Parthenon Trust
The Pears Family Charitable
Foundation
The Pilkington Charities Fund
The Col W W Pilkington Will
Trusts The General Charity
Fund
The Popocatepetl Trust
The David and Elaine Potter
Foundation
The W L Pratt Charitable Trust
The Bishop Radford Trust
Ranworth Trust
The Eleanor Rathbone
Charitable Trust
The Reed Foundation
The John and Sally Reeve
Charitable Trust
The Rhododendron Trust
The Sir Cliff Richard Charitable
Trust
The Ripple Effect Foundation
The River Farm Foundation
Rivers Foundation
Robyn Charitable Trust
The Rock Foundation
The Roddick Foundation
The Sir James Roll Charitable
Trust
The Rothera Charitable
Settlement
The RRAF Charitable Trust
The Rufford Foundation
Ryklow Charitable Trust 1992
The Saga Charitable Trust
The Alan and Babette
Sainsbury Charitable Fund
The Shanti Charitable Trust
Rita and David Slowe
Charitable Trust
The SMB Charitable Trust
The W F Southall Trust
The Peter Stebbings Memorial
Charity
The Stone Family Foundation
The Sunny Skies Foundation
The Gay and Keith Talbot Trust
The Lady Tangye Charitable
Trust
C B and H H Taylor 1984 Trust
Tearfund
The C Paul Thackray General
Charitable Trust
The Loke Wan Tho Memorial
Foundation
The Tinsley Foundation
The Tisbury Telegraph Trust
The Tolkien Trust
The Tresillian Trust
Ulting Overseas Trust

The United Society for the
Propagation of the Gospel
The Valentine Charitable Trust
The Van Neste Foundation
The Vardy Foundation
The Verdon-Smith Family
Charitable Settlement
The Vodafone Foundation
War on Want
The Westcroft Trust
The Harold Hyam Wingate
Foundation
The Wood Family Trust
The Matthews Wrightson
Charity Trust
The Wyndham Charitable Trust
Zephyr Charitable Trust

■ Areas of social deprivation

The 29th May 1961 Charitable
Trust
The Archer Trust
The Bank of Scotland
Foundation
The Liz and Terry Bramall
Foundation
Church Urban Fund
Stephen Clark 1957
Charitable Trust
The Cray Trust
The Hamilton Davies Trust
The Digbeth Trust Limited
The Drapers' Charitable Fund
The Dulverton Trust
The Football Association
National Sports Centre
Trust
The Forte Charitable Trust
The Hugh Fraser Foundation
The Peter Harrison Foundation
The Heritage of London Trust
Ltd
The Lynn Foundation
Millennium Stadium Charitable
Trust
The Norda Trust
Mrs L D Rope Third Charitable
Settlement
Santander UK Foundation
Limited
The Wood Family Trust

■ Urban areas, inner cities

Access Sport
The Alchemy Foundation
The Pat Allsop Charitable Trust
Viscount Amory's Charitable
Trust
The Anson Charitable Trust
The Archer Trust

AstonMansfield Charitable
Trust
The Austin Bailey Trust
The Barbour Foundation
The Bartlett Taylor Charitable
Trust
The Bay Tree Charitable Trust
The John Beckwith Charitable
Trust
The Bellinger Donnay Trust
Bergqvist Charitable Trust
The Oliver Borthwick Memorial
Trust
P G and N J Boulton Trust
John and Susan Bowers Fund
The Liz and Terry Bramall
Charitable Trust
The Harold and Alice Bridges
Charity
Bristol Archdeaconry Charity
The Burden Trust
The Arnold Burton 1998
Charitable Trust
Edward Cadbury Charitable
Trust
CAFOD
Calouste Gulbenkian
Foundation
The Calpe Trust
Christian Aid
The Church Urban Fund
Stephen Clark 1957
Charitable Trust
The E Alec Colman Charitable
Fund Ltd
The Coltstaple Trust
The Cotton Trust
The Cray Trust
The Hamilton Davies Trust
The Digbeth Trust
The Drapers' Charitable Fund
The Dulverton Trust
The Ellis Campbell Foundation
The Elmgrant Trust
Samuel William Farmer Trust
The Farmers' Company
Charitable Fund
The A M Fenton Trust
The Earl Fitzwilliam Charitable
Trust
The Football Association
National Sports Centre
Trust
The Forest Hill Charitable Trust
The Forte Charitable Trust
The Hugh Fraser Foundation
Generations Charitable Trust
Gloucestershire Community
Foundation
The Alfred Haines Charitable
Trust
The Peter Harrison Foundation
The Heart of England
Community Foundation
The Heritage of London Trust
Ltd

The Hilden Charitable Fund
R G Hills Charitable Trust
The Horne Trust
The Hunter Foundation
The Soli and Leah Kelaty Trust
Fund
The Kiawah Charitable Trust
The William Leech Charity
The Marie Helen Luen
Charitable Trust
The Lynn Foundation
Marr-Munning Trust
Mercury Phoenix Trust
The Millhouses Charitable
Trust
The Morel Charitable Trust
Muslim Hands
Nazareth Trust Fund
The Norda Trust
The Northern Rock Foundation
The Odin Charitable Trust
The David and Elaine Potter
Foundation
The Bishop Radford Trust
The Ripple Effect Foundation
The Rufford Foundation
The J S and E C Rymer
Charitable Trust
Santander UK Foundation
Limited
The SMB Charitable Trust
The Lady Tangye Charitable
Trust
The Westcroft Trust
The Harold Hyam Wingate
Foundation
The Wood Family Trust
The Matthews Wrightson
Charity Trust
The Wyndham Charitable Trust

■ Rural areas

Access Sport
The Alchemy Foundation
The Pat Allsop Charitable Trust
Viscount Amory's Charitable
Trust
The Anson Charitable Trust
The Archer Trust
AstonMansfield Charitable
Trust
The Austin Bailey Trust
The Barbour Foundation
The Bartlett Taylor Charitable
Trust
The Bay Tree Charitable Trust
The John Beckwith Charitable
Trust
The Bellinger Donnay Trust
Bergqvist Charitable Trust
P G and N J Boulton Trust
John and Susan Bowers Fund
The Liz and Terry Bramall
Charitable Trust

The Harold and Alice Bridges
   Charity
Bristol Archdeaconry Charity
The Burden Trust
The Arnold Burton 1998
   Charitable Trust
Edward Cadbury Charitable
   Trust
CAFOD
Calouste Gulbenkian
   Foundation
The Calpe Trust
Christian Aid
The Church Urban Fund
Stephen Clark 1957
   Charitable Trust
The Coalfields Regeneration
   Trust
The E Alec Colman Charitable
   Fund Ltd
The Coltstaple Trust
The Cotton Trust
The Cray Trust
The Hamilton Davies Trust
The Digbeth Trust
The Drapers' Charitable Fund
The Dulverton Trust
The Ellis Campbell Foundation
The Elmgrant Trust
Samuel William Farmer Trust
The Farmers' Company
   Charitable Fund
The A M Fenton Trust
The Earl Fitzwilliam Charitable
   Trust
The Football Association
   National Sports Centre
   Trust
The Forest Hill Charitable Trust
The Forte Charitable Trust
The Hugh Fraser Foundation
Generations Charitable Trust
Gloucestershire Community
   Foundation
The Alfred Haines Charitable
   Trust
The Peter Harrison Foundation
The Heart of England
   Community Foundation
The Heritage of London Trust
   Ltd
The Hilden Charitable Fund
R G Hills Charitable Trust
The Horne Trust
The Hunter Foundation
The Soli and Leah Kelaty Trust
   Fund
The Kiawah Charitable Trust
The William Leech Charity
The Marie Helen Luen
   Charitable Trust
The Lynn Foundation
Marr-Munning Trust
Mercury Phoenix Trust
The Millhouses Charitable
   Trust

The Morel Charitable Trust
Muslim Hands
Nazareth Trust Fund
The Norda Trust
The Northern Rock Foundation
The Odin Charitable Trust
The David and Elaine Potter
   Foundation
The Bishop Radford Trust
The Ripple Effect Foundation
The Rufford Foundation
The J S and E C Rymer
   Charitable Trust
Santander UK Foundation
   Limited
Schroder Charity Trust
The SMB Charitable Trust
The Lady Tangye Charitable
   Trust
The Westcroft Trust
The Harold Hyam Wingate
   Foundation
The Wood Family Trust
The Matthews Wrightson
   Charity Trust
The Wyndham Charitable Trust

Worldwide

4 Charity Foundation
The Acacia Charitable Trust
The Sylvia Adams Charitable
   Trust
The Agger Foundation
Aid to the Church in Need (UK)
Aim to Zero Foundation
The Allen Trust
The Alliance Family Foundation
The Altajir Trust
The Apax Foundation
The Ardwick Trust
Armenian General Benevolent
   Union London Trust
The Arsenal Foundation
The Arts Council of Northern
   Ireland
The Ashden Trust
The Associated Country
   Women of the World
The Scott Bader
   Commonwealth Ltd
The C Alma Baker Trust
The Andrew Balint Charitable
   Trust
The George Balint Charitable
   Trust
The Paul Balint Charitable
   Trust
The Barbour Foundation
The Beaverbrook Foundation
The Victoria and David
   Beckham Children's Charity
The Beit Trust
The Bestway Foundation
BHST
The Bertie Black Foundation
The Blandford Lake Trust
The Breadsticks Foundation
The Brendish Family
   Foundation
British Institute at Ankara
British Ornithologists' Union
Edna Brown Charitable
   Settlement
Bumba Foundation
The Noel Buxton Trust
The James Caan Foundation
The William A Cadbury
   Charitable Trust
Calouste Gulbenkian
   Foundation – UK Branch
The Catholic Charitable Trust
The CH (1980) Charitable
   Trust
Charitworth Limited
The Childwick Trust
Christian Response to Eastern
   Europe
Church of Ireland Priorities
   Fund
The Clear Light Trust
Closehelm Limited
The Vivienne and Samuel
   Cohen Charitable Trust

Col-Reno Ltd
Comic Relief
The Craps Charitable Trust
Itzchok Meyer Cymerman Trust
Ltd
The Daiwa Anglo-Japanese
Foundation
The Wilfrid Bruce Davis
Charitable Trust
The Debmar Benevolent Trust
The Delves Charitable Trust
The Djanogly Foundation
The Novak Djokovic Foundation
(UK) Limited
The DM Charitable Trust
The Dollond Charitable Trust
The Doughty Charity Trust
The Dulverton Trust
Dushinsky Trust Ltd
The James Dyson Foundation
eaga Charitable Trust
The Edith Maud Ellis 1985
Charitable Trust
Embrace the Middle East
The Ericson Trust
The Estelle Trust
Euro Charity Trust
The Family Rich Charities Trust
The Farthing Trust
Federation of Jewish Relief
Organisations
The Fidelity UK Foundation
Mejer and Gertrude Miriam
Frydman Foundation
The Gatsby Charitable
Foundation
The Great Britain Sasakawa
Foundation
Philip and Judith Green Trust
N and R Grunbaum Charitable
Trust
Paul Hamlyn Foundation
The Helen Hamlyn Trust
The Charles Hayward
Foundation
The Christina Mary Hendrie
Trust for Scottish and
Canadian Charities
The Hospital Saturday Fund
The Reta Lila Howard
Foundation
The Daniel Howard Trust
Human Relief Foundation
The Humanitarian Trust
The Hunting Horn General
Charitable Trust
The Huntingdon Foundation
I G O Foundation Limited
The Inland Waterways
Association
Investream Charitable Trust
The Ireland Fund of Great
Britain
The Irish Youth Foundation
(UK) Ltd

The Isaacs Charitable Trust
The J & J Benevolent
Foundation
JCA Charitable Foundation
The Nick Jenkins Foundation
The Norman Joels Charitable
Trust
The Joffe Charitable Trust
The Elton John Aids
Foundation
The J E Joseph Charitable
Fund
The Josh Charitable Trust
The Bernard Kahn Charitable
Trust
The Ian Karten Charitable
Trust
The Kasner Charitable Trust
The Kennedy Charitable
Foundation
Keren Association
Kermaville Ltd
Liudmila Korneenko
Foundation
The Neil Kreitman Foundation
Kupath Gemach Chaim
Bechesed Viznitz Trust
The Lambert Charitable Trust
The Lancaster Foundation
Largsmount Ltd
The Lauffer Family Charitable
Foundation
The Kennedy Leigh Charitable
Trust
The Erica Leonard Trust
The Leverhulme Trust
The Joseph Levy Charitable
Foundation
Lewis Family Charitable Trust
Littlefield Foundation (UK)
Limited
Jack Livingstone Charitable
Trust
The Lo Family Charitable Trust
The Locker Foundation
Lord and Lady Lurgan Trust
The Sir Jack Lyons Charitable
Trust
The Lyras Family Charitable
Trust
Marbeh Torah Trust
Marchig Animal Welfare Trust
The Hilda and Samuel Marks
Foundation
The Marr-Munning Trust
Mayfair Charities Ltd
The Mears Foundation
Melodor Limited
Melow Charitable Trust
Mercaz Torah Vechesed
Limited
Merchant Navy Welfare Board
The Esmé Mitchell Trust
The MITIE Foundation
The Mittal Foundation
The Henry Moore Foundation

Morgan Stanley International
Foundation
The Mount Everest Foundation
Muslim Hands
MYR Charitable Trust
The Eleni Nakou Foundation
Ner Foundation
NJD Charitable Trust
The Community Foundation for
Northern Ireland
Novi Most International
The Nuffield Foundation
The Father O'Mahoney
Memorial Trust
The Old Broad Street Charity
Trust
Open Gate
The Ouseley Trust
Oxfam (GB)
The Paladin Vince-Odozi
Charitable Trust
Ambika Paul Foundation
The Payne Charitable Trust
The Peltz Trust
The Polonsky Foundation
The John Porter Charitable
Trust
The Porter Foundation
The Puri Foundation
The Queen Anne's Gate
Foundation
Rachel Charitable Trust
The Peggy Ramsay Foundation
The Joseph and Lena Randall
Charitable Trust
The Joseph Rank Trust
The Rayne Trust
The Rehoboth Trust
Relief Fund for Romania
Limited
Ridgesave Limited
Robyn Charitable Trust
Rowanville Ltd
William Arthur Rudd Memorial
Trust
Raymond and Beverly Sackler
1988 Foundation
The Ruzin Sadagora Trust
Saint Sarkis Charity Trust
The Samworth Foundation
The Samuel Sebba Charitable
Trust
SEM Charitable Trust
The Archie Sherman Cardiff
Foundation
The Archie Sherman Charitable
Trust
The Shoe Zone Trust
Sino-British Fellowship Trust
The Sobell Foundation
The Solo Charitable
Settlement
Dr Richard Solomon's
Charitable Trust
Songdale Ltd
R H Southern Trust

Rosalyn and Nicholas Springer
  Charitable Trust
St James' Trust Settlement
The Steinberg Family
  Charitable Trust
The Stephen Barry Charitable
  Trust
Sir Halley Stewart Trust
The Sylvanus Charitable Trust
The Tajtelbaum Charitable
  Trust
The David Tannen Charitable
  Trust
C B and H H Taylor 1984 Trust
Rosanna Taylor's 1987 Charity
  Trust
Tegham Limited
The John P. Gommes
  Foundation
Mrs R P Tindall's Charitable
  Trust
Tomchei Torah Charitable
  Trust
The True Colours Trust
The Tsukanov Family
  Foundation
The Tudor Trust
TVML Foundation
Trustees of Tzedakah
The United Society for the
  Propagation of the Gospel
The Vail Foundation
Veneziana Fund
The Scurrah Wainwright Charity
G R Waters Charitable Trust
  2000
Webb Memorial Trust
The Norman Whiteley Trust
The HDH Wills 1965
  Charitable Trust
The Witzenfeld Foundation
The Maurice Wohl Charitable
  Foundation
The Charles Wolfson
  Charitable Trust
The Wolfson Family Charitable
  Trust
The Wolfson Foundation
The Zochonis Charitable Trust
Zurich Community Trust (UK)
  Limited

....

■ **Europe**

The Agger Foundation
Aid to the Church in Need (UK)
The Apax Foundation
Armenian General Benevolent
  Union London Trust
The Arts Council of Northern
  Ireland
The Scott Bader
  Commonwealth Ltd
The Andrew Balint Charitable
  Trust

The George Balint Charitable
  Trust
The Paul Balint Charitable
  Trust
The Blandford Lake Trust
British Institute at Ankara
British Ornithologists' Union
The William A Cadbury
  Charitable Trust
Calouste Gulbenkian
  Foundation – UK Branch
The Catholic Charitable Trust
Christian Response to Eastern
  Europe
Church of Ireland Priorities
  Fund
The Novak Djokovic Foundation
  (UK) Limited
eaga Charitable Trust
The Edith Maud Ellis 1985
  Charitable Trust
The Ericson Trust
The Fidelity UK Foundation
The Headley Trust
The Hospital Saturday Fund
The Reta Lila Howard
  Foundation
The Inland Waterways
  Association
The Ireland Fund of Great
  Britain
The Irish Youth Foundation
  (UK) Ltd
The Elton John Aids
  Foundation
The Kennedy Charitable
  Foundation
Liudmila Korneenko
  Foundation
The Leverhulme Trust
The Lyras Family Charitable
  Trust
Marchig Animal Welfare Trust
The Mears Foundation
Merchant Navy Welfare Board
The Esmé Mitchell Trust
The MITIE Foundation
The Henry Moore Foundation
Morgan Stanley International
  Foundation
The Eleni Nakou Foundation
The Community Foundation for
  Northern Ireland
Novi Most International
The Father O'Mahoney
  Memorial Trust
The Old Broad Street Charity
  Trust
Open Gate
The Ouseley Trust
Oxfam (GB)
Rachel Charitable Trust
The Peggy Ramsay Foundation
The Joseph Rank Trust
Relief Fund for Romania
  Limited

William Arthur Rudd Memorial
  Trust
Saint Sarkis Charity Trust
R H Southern Trust
The Sylvanus Charitable Trust
C B and H H Taylor 1984 Trust
The Tsukanov Family
  Foundation
Veneziana Fund
Webb Memorial Trust
The Norman Whiteley Trust
The HDH Wills 1965
  Charitable Trust

....

■ **Republic of Ireland**

The Arts Council of Northern
  Ireland
The William A Cadbury
  Charitable Trust
Calouste Gulbenkian
  Foundation – UK Branch
Church of Ireland Priorities
  Fund
The Edith Maud Ellis 1985
  Charitable Trust
The Hospital Saturday Fund
The Reta Lila Howard
  Foundation
The Inland Waterways
  Association
The Ireland Fund of Great
  Britain
The Irish Youth Foundation
  (UK) Ltd
The Elton John Aids
  Foundation
The Kennedy Charitable
  Foundation
The Esmé Mitchell Trust
The MITIE Foundation
The Community Foundation for
  Northern Ireland
The Ouseley Trust
The Peggy Ramsay Foundation
The Joseph Rank Trust
R H Southern Trust
C B and H H Taylor 1984 Trust
The HDH Wills 1965
  Charitable Trust

....

■ **Asia**

4 Charity Foundation
The Acacia Charitable Trust
Aid to the Church in Need (UK)
Aim to Zero Foundation
The Alliance Family Foundation
The Altajir Trust
The Apax Foundation
The Ardwick Trust
The Ashden Trust
The Scott Bader
  Commonwealth Ltd

The Andrew Balint Charitable
Trust
The George Balint Charitable
Trust
The Paul Balint Charitable
Trust
The Bestway Foundation
BHST
The Bertie Black Foundation
The Blandford Lake Trust
The Breadsticks Foundation
The Brendish Family
Foundation
British Institute at Ankara
Edna Brown Charitable
Settlement
The James Caan Foundation
The CH (1980) Charitable
Trust
Charitworth Limited
The Clear Light Trust
Closehelm Limited
The Vivienne and Samuel
Cohen Charitable Trust
Col-Reno Ltd
The Craps Charitable Trust
Itzchok Meyer Cymerman Trust
Ltd
The Daiwa Anglo-Japanese
Foundation
The Wilfrid Bruce Davis
Charitable Trust
The Debmar Benevolent Trust
The Djanogly Foundation
The DM Charitable Trust
The Dollond Charitable Trust
The Doughty Charity Trust
Dushinsky Trust Ltd
Embrace the Middle East
Euro Charity Trust
The Family Rich Charities Trust
Federation of Jewish Relief
Organisations
Mejer and Gertrude Miriam
Frydman Foundation
The Great Britain Sasakawa
Foundation
N and R Grunbaum Charitable
Trust
Paul Hamlyn Foundation
The Helen Hamlyn Trust
The Daniel Howard Trust
The Humanitarian Trust
I G O Foundation Limited
Investream Charitable Trust
The Isaacs Charitable Trust
The J & J Benevolent
Foundation
JCA Charitable Foundation
The Nick Jenkins Foundation
The Norman Joels Charitable
Trust
The Elton John Aids
Foundation
The J E Joseph Charitable
Fund

The Josh Charitable Trust
The Bernard Kahn Charitable
Trust
The Ian Karten Charitable
Trust
The Kasner Charitable Trust
Keren Association
Kermaville Ltd
The Neil Kreitman Foundation
Kupath Gemach Chaim
Bechesed Viznitz Trust
The Lambert Charitable Trust
Largsmount Ltd
The Lauffer Family Charitable
Foundation
The Kennedy Leigh Charitable
Trust
The Leverhulme Trust
The Joseph Levy Charitable
Foundation
Lewis Family Charitable Trust
Jack Livingstone Charitable
Trust
The Lo Family Charitable Trust
The Locker Foundation
The Sir Jack Lyons Charitable
Trust
Marbeh Torah Trust
Marchig Animal Welfare Trust
The Hilda and Samuel Marks
Foundation
The Marr-Munning Trust
Mayfair Charities Ltd
The Mears Foundation
Melodor Limited
Melow Charitable Trust
Mercaz Torah Vechesed
Limited
The Mittal Foundation
MYR Charitable Trust
Ner Foundation
NJD Charitable Trust
The Father O'Mahoney
Memorial Trust
Open Gate
Oxfam (GB)
Ambika Paul Foundation
The Payne Charitable Trust
The Peltz Trust
The Polonsky Foundation
The John Porter Charitable
Trust
The Porter Foundation
The Puri Foundation
The Queen Anne's Gate
Foundation
The Rayne Trust
The Rehoboth Trust
Rowanville Ltd
The Ruzin Sadagora Trust
The Samuel Sebba Charitable
Trust
SEM Charitable Trust
The Archie Sherman Cardiff
Foundation

The Archie Sherman Charitable
Trust
The Shoe Zone Trust
Sino-British Fellowship Trust
The Sobell Foundation
The Solo Charitable
Settlement
Songdale Ltd
R H Southern Trust
Rosalyn and Nicholas Springer
Charitable Trust
The Steinberg Family
Charitable Trust
The Stephen Barry Charitable
Trust
The Tajtelbaum Charitable
Trust
The David Tannen Charitable
Trust
Tegham Limited
The John P. Gommes
Foundation
Tomchei Torah Charitable
Trust
TVML Foundation
Trustees of Tzedakah
The Vail Foundation
The Witzenfeld Foundation
The Maurice Wohl Charitable
Foundation
The Charles Wolfson
Charitable Trust
The Wolfson Family Charitable
Trust
The Wolfson Foundation

....

■ Africa

The Sylvia Adams Charitable
Trust
Aid to the Church in Need (UK)
The Allen Trust
The Apax Foundation
The Ashden Trust
The Scott Bader
Commonwealth Ltd
The Beit Trust
The Blandford Lake Trust
The Breadsticks Foundation
British Ornithologists' Union
Bumba Foundation
The Noel Buxton Trust
The Childwick Trust
Comic Relief
The Dulverton Trust
The Estelle Trust
Euro Charity Trust
The Gatsby Charitable
Foundation
Philip and Judith Green Trust
The Charles Hayward
Foundation
The Headley Trust
The Hunting Horn General
Charitable Trust
The Nick Jenkins Foundation

The Joffe Charitable Trust
The Elton John Aids
   Foundation
The Lancaster Foundation
The Lauffer Family Charitable
   Foundation
The Leverhulme Trust
Marchig Animal Welfare Trust
The Marr-Munning Trust
The Mears Foundation
Morgan Stanley International
   Foundation
The Nuffield Foundation
The Father O'Mahoney
   Memorial Trust
Open Gate
Oxfam (GB)
The Paladin Vince-Odozi
   Charitable Trust
The Samworth Foundation
SEM Charitable Trust
The Archie Sherman Cardiff
   Foundation
The Stephen Barry Charitable
   Trust
Sir Halley Stewart Trust
Mrs R P Tindall's Charitable
   Trust
The True Colours Trust
The Tudor Trust
The Scurrah Wainwright Charity
The Zochonis Charitable Trust

■ **America and the
   West Indies**

Aid to the Church in Need (UK)
The Apax Foundation
The Ashden Trust
The Scott Bader
   Commonwealth Ltd
The Beaverbrook Foundation
The Blandford Lake Trust
British Ornithologists' Union
The Catholic Charitable Trust
The Clear Light Trust
Col-Reno Ltd
The Christina Mary Hendrie
   Trust for Scottish and
   Canadian Charities
The Huntingdon Foundation
I G O Foundation Limited
Lludmila Korneenko
   Foundation
The Neil Kreitman Foundation
The Lauffer Family Charitable
   Foundation
The Leverhulme Trust
Littlefield Foundation (UK)
   Limited
Marchig Animal Welfare Trust
The Henry Moore Foundation
MYR Charitable Trust
The Father O'Mahoney
   Memorial Trust
Open Gate

Oxfam (GB)
The Polonsky Foundation
The Archie Sherman Cardiff
   Foundation
St James' Trust Settlement
The Stephen Barry Charitable
   Trust
The Sylvanus Charitable Trust
Rosanna Taylor's 1987 Charity
   Trust
TVML Foundation
G R Waters Charitable Trust
   2000

■ **Australasia**

The C Alma Baker Trust
The Josh Charitable Trust
The Lauffer Family Charitable
   Foundation
The Lo Family Charitable Trust
Marchig Animal Welfare Trust
The Mount Everest Foundation
Open Gate
The Archie Sherman Cardiff
   Foundation
R H Southern Trust

■ **United Kingdom**

The 1970 Trust
The 1989 Willan Charitable
   Trust
The 29th May 1961 Charitable
   Trust
4 Charity Foundation
The A B Charitable Trust
A W Charitable Trust
The Aberbrothock Skea Trust
The Aberdeen Endowments
   Trust
The Aberdeenshire Educational
   Trust Scheme
ABF The Soldiers' Charity
Brian Abrams Charitable Trust
Eric Abrams Charitable Trust
The Acacia Charitable Trust
Access Sport
The ACT Foundation
Action Medical Research
The Company of Actuaries'
   Charitable Trust Fund
The Ad Meliora Charitable
   Trust
The Sylvia Adams Charitable
   Trust
The Adamson Trust
The Victor Adda Foundation
The Adint Charitable Trust
The Adnams Charity
AF Trust Company
Age Scotland
Age UK
The Agger Foundation
The AIM Foundation
Aim to Zero Foundation
The Green and Lilian F M
   Ainsworth and Family
   Benevolent Fund
The Sylvia Aitken Charitable
   Trust
The Al Fayed Charitable
   Foundation
The Alabaster Trust
D G Albright Charitable Trust
The Alchemy Foundation
Aldgate and All Hallows'
   Foundation
The Aldgate Freedom
   Foundation
All Saints Educational Trust
The Derrill Allatt Foundation
The H B Allen Charitable Trust
The Allen Lane Trust
The Allen Trust
The Alliance Family Foundation
Angus Allnatt Charitable
   Foundation
The Pat Allsop Charitable Trust
The Almond Trust
Almondsbury Charity
The Altajir Trust
Alvor Charitable Trust
Amabrill Limited
The Ammco Trust

Sir John and Lady Amory's
Charitable Trust
Viscount Amory's Charitable
Trust
The Bryan and June Amos
Foundation
The Ampelos Trust
The AMW Charitable Trust
The Andrew Anderson Trust
The André Christian Trust
Anguish's Educational
Foundation
The Animal Defence Trust
Philip Anker Trust
The Eric Anker-Petersen
Charity
The Annandale Charitable
Trust
Anpride Ltd
The Anson Charitable Trust
The Apax Foundation
Ambrose and Ann Appelbe
Trust
The Appletree Trust
The John Apthorp Charity
The Arbib Foundation
Archbishop of Wales' Fund for
Children
The Architectural Heritage
Fund
The Ardwick Trust
The Argentarius Foundation
The Argus Appeal
Armenian General Benevolent
Union London Trust
The John Armitage Charitable
Trust
The Armourers' and Brasiers'
Gauntlet Trust
The Arsenal Foundation
The Artemis Charitable Trust
Arthritis Research UK
The Arts and Entertainment
Charitable Trust
Arts Council England
Arts Council of Wales
The A S Charitable Trust
ASCB Charitable Fund
Ashburnham Thanksgiving
Trust
A J H Ashby Will Trust
The Ashden Trust
The Ashendene Trust
The Ashley Family Foundation
The Ian Askew Charitable Trust
The Association of Colleges
Charitable Trust
Asthma UK
AstonMansfield Charitable
Trust
The Astor Foundation
The Astor of Hever Trust
The Atlas Fund
The Aurelius Charitable Trust
The Lord Austin Trust

Autonomous Research
Charitable Trust
The Avenue Charitable Trust
The John Avins Trustees
The Avon and Somerset Police
Community Trust
Awards for All
The Aylesford Family
Charitable Trust
The BAA Communities Trust
Harry Bacon Foundation
The BACTA Charitable Trust
The Scott Bader
Commonwealth Ltd
Bag4Sport Foundation
Veta Bailey Charitable Trust
The Austin Bailey Foundation
The Baily Thomas Charitable
Fund
The Baird Trust
The Roy and Pixie Baker
Charitable Trust
The Balcombe Charitable Trust
The Andrew Balint Charitable
Trust
The George Balint Charitable
Trust
The Paul Balint Charitable
Trust
The Albert Casanova Ballard
Deceased Trust
The Ballinger Charitable Trust
Balmain Charitable Trust
The Balmore Trust
The Balney Charitable Trust
The Baltic Charitable Fund
The Bamford Charitable
Foundation
The Banbury Charities
William P Bancroft (No 2)
Charitable Trust and
Jenepher Gillett Trust
The Band Trust
The Bank of Scotland
Foundation
The Barbers' Company General
Charities
The Barbour Foundation
The Barcapel Foundation
Barchester Healthcare
Foundation
The Barclay Foundation
The Baring Foundation
Peter Barker-Mill Memorial
Charity
The Barleycorn Trust
Lord Barnby's Foundation
Barnes Workhouse Fund
The Barnsbury Charitable Trust
The Barnstaple Bridge Trust
The Barnwood House Trust
The Misses Barrie Charitable
Trust
Barrington Family Charitable
Trust
Bartholomew Charitable Trust

The Bartlett Taylor Charitable
Trust
The Paul Bassham Charitable
Trust
The Bates Charitable Trust
The Louis Baylis (Maidenhead
Advertiser) Charitable Trust
BBC Children in Need
BC Partners Foundation
B-CH 1971 Charitable Trust
The Bearder Charity
The James Beattie Charitable
Trust
The Jack and Ada Beattie
Foundation
The Beaverbrook Foundation
The Beccles Town Lands
Charity
The Becketts and Sargeants
Educational Foundation
The Victoria and David
Beckham Children's Charity
The Peter Beckwith Charitable
Trust
The Bedfordshire and
Hertfordshire Historic
Churches Trust
The Bedfordshire and Luton
Community Foundation
The David and Ruth Behrend
Fund
The Bellahouston Bequest
Fund
Bellasis Trust
The Bellhouse Foundation
The Bellinger Donnay Trust
The Benfield Motors Charitable
Trust
The Benham Charitable
Settlement
The Hervey Benham Charitable
Trust
Michael and Lesley Bennett
Charitable Trust
Bennett Lowell Limited
The Gerald Bentall Charitable
Trust
Bergqvist Charitable Trust
The Berkshire Community
Foundation
The Bertarelli UK Foundation
The Bestway Foundation
BHST
The Mason Bibby 1981 Trust
The Bideford Bridge Trust
The Big Lottery Fund
The Billmeir Charitable Trust
Percy Bilton Charity
The Bingham Trust
The Bintaub Charitable Trust
Birmingham & Black Country
Community Foundation
The Birmingham District
Nursing Charitable Trust

The Birmingham Hospital
Saturday Fund Medical
Charity and Welfare Trust
Birmingham International
Airport Community Trust
The Lord Mayor of
Birmingham's Charity
Birthday House Trust
The Michael Bishop
Foundation
The Bishop's Development
Fund
The Sydney Black Charitable
Trust
The Bertie Black Foundation
Sir Alec Black's Charity
Blackheart Foundation (UK)
Limited
Isabel Blackman Foundation
The BlackRock (UK) Charitable
Trust
The Blagrave Trust
The Blair Foundation
The Blanchminster Trust
The Blandford Lake Trust
The Sir Victor Blank Charitable
Settlement
Blatchington Court Trust
The Bluston Charitable
Settlement
The Nicholas Boas Charitable
Trust
The Marjory Boddy Charitable
Trust
The Body Shop Foundation
The Bonamy Charitable Trust
The John and Celia Bonham
Christie Charitable Trust
The Charlotte Bonham-Carter
Charitable Trust
Bonhomie United Charity
Society
BOOST Charitable Trust
The Booth Charities
The Boots Charitable Trust
The Bordon Liphook
Haslemere Charity
The Oliver Borthwick Memorial
Trust
The Boshier-Hinton Foundation
The Bosson Family Charitable
Trust
The Bothwell Charitable Trust
H E and E L Dottelcy
Charitable Trust
The Harry Bottom Charitable
Trust
Sir Clive Bourne Family Trust
The Anthony Bourne
Foundation
Bourneheights Limited
The Bower Trust
The Bowerman Charitable
Trust
John and Susan Bowers Fund
The Bowland Charitable Trust

The Frank Brake Charitable
Trust
The William Brake Charitable
Trust
The Tony Bramall Charitable
Trust
The Liz and Terry Bramall
Foundation
The Bransford Trust
The Breadsticks Foundation
The Breast Cancer Research
Trust
The Brendish Family
Foundation
The Harold and Alice Bridges
Charity
Briggs Animal Welfare Trust
Bristol Archdeaconry Charity
The Bristol Charities
John Bristow and Thomas
Mason Trust
The British Council for
Prevention of Blindness
The British Dietetic
Association General and
Education Trust Fund
The British Gas (Scottish Gas)
Energy Trust
British Heart Foundation
British Humane Association
British Institute at Ankara
British Olympic Foundation
British Record Industry Trust
The Britten-Pears Foundation
The J and M Britton Charitable
Trust
The Charles and Edna
Broadhurst Charitable Trust
The Roger Brooke Charitable
Trust
The David Brooke Charity
The Charles Brotherton Trust
Joseph Brough Charitable
Trust
The Swinfen Broun Charitable
Trust
Bill Brown 1998 Charitable
Trust
Edna Brown Charitable
Settlement
R S Brownless Charitable
Trust
T B H Brunner's Charitable
Settlement
The Jack Brunton Charitable
Trust
The Bruntwood Charity
Buckinghamshire Community
Foundation
The Buckinghamshire Historic
Churches Trust
The Buckinghamshire Masonic
Centenary Fund
The Buffini Chao Foundation
The Rosemary Bugden
Charitable Trust

The E F Bulmer Benevolent
Fund
Bumba Foundation
The Burden Trust
Burdens Charitable Foundation
The Burdett Trust for Nursing
The Burry Charitable Trust
The Burton Breweries
Charitable Trust
Consolidated Charity of Burton
upon Trent
The Paul Bush Foundation
Trust
The Worshipful Company of
Butchers General Charities
The Noel Buxton Trust
C and F Charitable Trust
C M L Family Foundation
The James Caan Foundation
C J Cadbury Charitable Trust
Edward Cadbury Charitable
Trust
Henry T and Lucy B Cadbury
Charitable Trust
The Christopher Cadbury
Charitable Trust
The Richard Cadbury
Charitable Trust
The William A Cadbury
Charitable Trust
The Cadbury Foundation
The Edward and Dorothy
Cadbury Trust
The George Cadbury Trust
The Barrow Cadbury Trust and
the Barrow Cadbury Fund
The Cadogan Charity
CAF (Charities Aid Foundation)
Community Foundation for
Calderdale
The Callander Charitable Trust
Calouste Gulbenkian
Foundation – UK Branch
Calypso Browning Trust
The Cambridgeshire
Community Foundation
The Cambridgeshire Historic
Churches Trust
The Camelia Trust
The Campden Charities
Trustee
The Frederick and Phyllis Cann
Trust
The Canning Trust
M R Cannon 1998 Charitable
Trust
H and L Cantor Trust
Cardy Beaver Foundation
The Carew Pole Charitable
Trust
The D W T Cargill Fund
The Carlton House Charitable
Trust
The Carmelite Monastery Ware
Trust

The Worshipful Company of
Carmen Benevolent Trust
The Richard Carne Trust
The Carnegie Dunfermline
Trust
The Carnegie Trust for the
Universities of Scotland
The Carpenter Charitable Trust
The Carpenters' Company
Charitable Trust
The Carr-Gregory Trust
The Carrington Charitable
Trust
The Carron Charitable
Settlement
The Leslie Mary Carter
Charitable Trust
Carter's Educational
Foundation
Cash for Kids Radio Clyde
The Cass Foundation
Sir John Cass's Foundation
The Castang Foundation
The Catalyst Charitable Trust
The Catholic Trust for England
and Wales
The Cattanach Charitable Trust
The Joseph and Annie Cattle
Trust
The Thomas Sivewright Catto
Charitable Settlement
The Wilfrid and Constance
Cave Foundation
The Cayo Foundation
Elizabeth Cayzer Charitable
Trust
The B G S Cayzer Charitable
Trust
The Cazenove Charitable Trust
Celtic Charity Fund
The Gaynor Cemlyn-Jones
Trust
The CH (1980) Charitable
Trust
R E Chadwick Charitable Trust
The Amelia Chadwick Trust
The Pamela Champion
Foundation
Champneys Charitable
Foundation
John William Chapman's
Charitable Trust
The Charities Advisory Trust
Charitworth Limited
The Charter 600 Charity
The Chasah Trust
The Chelsea Square 1994
Trust
Cherry Grove Charitable Trust
The Cheruby Trust
Cheshire Freemason's Charity
Chest, Heart and Stroke
Scotland
Chesterhill Charitable Trust
The Chetwode Foundation

Cheviot Asset Management
Charitable Trust
Child Growth Foundation
Children's Liver Disease
Foundation
The Children's Research Fund
The Childwick Trust
The Chippenham Borough
Lands Charity
The Chipping Sodbury Town
Lands Charity
CHK Charities Limited
The Chownes Foundation
The Chrimes Family Charitable
Trust
The Christabella Charitable
Trust
Christadelphian Samaritan
Fund
Christian Aid
The Church and Community
Fund
The Church Burgesses
Educational Foundation
Church Burgesses Trust
Church of Ireland Priorities
Fund
Church Urban Fund
City and County of Swansea
Welsh Church Act Fund
The City Bridge Trust
The City Educational Trust
Fund
CLA Charitable Trust
Stephen Clark 1957
Charitable Trust
J A Clark Charitable Trust
The Hilda and Alice Clark
Charitable Trust
The Roger and Sarah Bancroft
Clark Charitable Trust
The Clarke Charitable
Settlement
The Clear Light Trust
The Cleopatra Trust
Lord Clinton's Charitable Trust
The Clore Duffield Foundation
Miss V L Clore's 1967
Charitable Trust
Closehelm Limited
The Clothworkers' Foundation
Richard Cloudesley's Charity
The Clover Trust
The Robert Clutterbuck
Charitable Trust
Clydpride Ltd
The Francis Coales Charitable
Foundation
The Coalfields Regeneration
Trust
The John Coates Charitable
Trust
The Cobtree Charity Trust Ltd
The Denise Cohen Charitable
Trust

The Vivienne and Samuel
Cohen Charitable Trust
The R and S Cohen
Foundation
The Colchester Catalyst
Charity
John Coldman Charitable Trust
The Cole Charitable Trust
The Colefax Charitable Trust
The John and Freda Coleman
Charitable Trust
The Bernard Coleman
Charitable Trust
The George Henry Collins
Charity
The Sir Jeremiah Colman Gift
Trust
Col-Reno Ltd
The Colt Foundation
Colwinston Charitable Trust
Colyer-Fergusson Charitable
Trust
Comic Relief
The Comino Foundation
Community First (Landfill
Communities Fund)
The Compton Charitable Trust
The Douglas Compton James
Charitable Trust
The Congleton Inclosure Trust
The Congregational and
General Charitable Trust
The Conscience Trust
The Conservation Foundation
The Consolidated Charities for
the Infirm Merchant
Taylors' Company
Gordon Cook Foundation
The Ernest Cook Trust
The Cooks Charity
The Catherine Cookson
Charitable Trust
The Keith Coombs Trust
Harold and Daphne Cooper
Charitable Trust
Mabel Cooper Charity
The Alice Ellen Cooper Dean
Charitable Foundation
The Co-operative Foundation
The Marjorie Coote Animal
Charity Fund
The Marjorie Coote Old
People's Charity
The Helen Jean Cope Trust
The J Reginald Corah
Foundation Fund
The Gershon Coren Charitable
Foundation (also known as
The Muriel and Gus Coren
Charitable Foundation)
Michael Cornish Charitable
Trust
Cornwall Community
Foundation
The Cornwall Historic
Churches Trust

The Duke of Cornwall's
  Benevolent Fund
The Cornwell Charitable Trust
The Sidney and Elizabeth
  Corob Charitable Trust
The Corona Charitable Trust
The Bryan Christopher
  Corrigan Charitable Trust
The Costa Family Charitable
  Trust
The John and Barbara Cotton
  Charitable Foundation
The Cotton Industry War
  Memorial Trust
The Cotton Trust
Country Houses Foundation
County Durham Community
  Foundation
The Augustine Courtauld Trust
The General Charities of the
  City of Coventry
Coventry Building Society
  Charitable Foundation
The John Cowan Foundation
The Sir Tom Cowie Charitable
  Trust
Dudley and Geoffrey Cox
  Charitable Trust
The Sir William Coxen Trust
  Fund
The Lord Cozens-Hardy Trust
The Craignish Trust
The Craps Charitable Trust
Michael Crawford Children's
  Charity
The Cray Trust
Creative Scotland
The Crerar Hotels Trust
The Crescent Trust
Cripplegate Foundation
The Violet and Milo Cripps
  Charitable Trust
The Harry Crook Foundation
The Cross Trust
The Croydon Relief in Need
  Charities
The Peter Cruddas Foundation
Cruden Foundation Ltd
The Ronald Cruickshanks
  Foundation
The Cuby Charitable Trust
Cullum Family Trust
The Culra Charitable Trust
Cumberland Building Society
  Charitable Foundation
Cumbria Community
  Foundation
The Cunningham Trust
The Harry Cureton Charitable
  Trust
The D J H Currie Memorial
  Trust
The Dennis Curry Charitable
  Trust
The Manny Cussins
  Foundation

The Cutler Trust (the
  Worshipful Company of
  Makers of Playing Cards)
The Cwmbran Trust
Itzchok Meyer Cymerman Trust
  Ltd
D C R Allen Charitable Trust
The D G Charitable Settlement
The D'Oyly Carte Charitable
  Trust
Roald Dahl's Marvellous
  Children's Charity
Daily Prayer Union Charitable
  Trust Limited
The Daisy Trust
The Daiwa Anglo-Japanese
  Foundation
The Dr and Mrs A Darlington
  Charitable Trust
Baron Davenport's Charity
The Davidson (Nairn)
  Charitable Trust
The Davidson Family
  Charitable Trust
The Alderman Joe Davidson
  Memorial Trust
Michael Davies Charitable
  Settlement
The Gwendoline and Margaret
  Davies Charity
The Hamilton Davies Trust
The Wilfrid Bruce Davis
  Charitable Trust
Davis-Rubens Charitable Trust
The Dawe Charitable Trust
The De Brye Charitable Trust
The De Clermont Charitable
  Company Ltd
Peter De Haan Charitable
  Trust
The Deakin Charitable Trust
William Dean Countryside and
  Educational Trust
The Debmar Benevolent Trust
The Delius Trust
The Dellal Foundation
The Delves Charitable Trust
The Demigryphon Trust
The Denman Charitable Trust
Dentons UKMEA LLP
  Charitable Trust
The Earl of Derby's Charitable
  Trust
The Derbyshire Churches and
  Chapels Preservation Trust
Derbyshire Community
  Foundation
The J N Derbyshire Trust
Devon Community Foundation
The Devon Educational Trust
The Devon Historic Churches
  Trust
The Duke of Devonshire's
  Charitable Trust
The Sandy Dewhirst Charitable
  Trust

Deymel Charitable Trust
The Laduma Dhamecha
  Charitable Trust
Diabetes UK
Alan and Sheila Diamond
  Charitable Trust
The Dibden Allotments Fund
Diced Cap Charity
The Gillian Dickinson Trust
The Dickon Trust
Grace Dieu Charitable Trust
The Digbeth Trust Limited
The Dinwoodie Settlement
Disability Aid Fund (The Roger
  and Jean Jefcoate Trust)
Dischma Charitable Trust
The Djanogly Foundation
The Novak Djokovic Foundation
  (UK) Limited
The DLM Charitable Trust
The DM Charitable Trust
Louise Dobson Charitable
  Trust
The Derek and Eileen Dodgson
  Foundation
The Dollond Charitable Trust
Domepride Ltd
The Dorcas Trust
Dorset Community Foundation
The Dorset Historic Churches
  Trust
The Dorus Trust
The Doughty Charity Trust
Douglas Arter Foundation
The R M Douglas Charitable
  Trust
Downlands Educational Trust
The Drapers' Charitable Fund
The Drayson Foundation
Dromintee Trust
The Dulverton Trust
The P B Dumbell Charitable
  Trust
The Dumbreck Charity
Dunard Fund
The Dunhill Medical Trust
The Dunn Family Charitable
  Trust
The W E Dunn Trust
The Charles Dunstone
  Charitable Trust
Annette Duvollet Charitable
  Trust
The Dwek Family Charitable
  Trust
The Dyers' Company
  Charitable Trust
The James Dyson Foundation
eaga Charitable Trust
The Eagle Charity Trust
Audrey Earle Charitable Trust
The Earley Charity
Earls Colne and Halstead
  Educational Charity
The Earmark Trust

East End Community Foundation
Eastern Counties Educational Trust Limited
The Sir John Eastwood Foundation
The Ebenezer Trust
The EBM Charitable Trust
The Ecology Trust
Eden Arts Trust
EDF Energy Trust (EDFET)
The Gilbert and Eileen Edgar Foundation
Gilbert Edgar Trust
Edge Fund
Edinburgh Children's Holiday Fund
Edinburgh Trust No 2 Account
Edinburgh Voluntary Organisations' Trust Funds (EVOT)
Educational Foundation of Alderman John Norman
Dr Edwards Bishop King's Fulham Endowment Fund
The W G Edwards Charitable Foundation
The William Edwards Educational Charity
The Eighty Eight Foundation
The Elephant Trust
The George Elias Charitable Trust
The Gerald Palmer Eling Trust Company
The Wilfred and Elsie Elkes Charity Fund
The Maud Elkington Charitable Trust
The John Ellerman Foundation
The Ellinson Foundation Ltd
The Edith Maud Ellis 1985 Charitable Trust
The Ellis Campbell Foundation
James Ellis Charitable Trust
The Elm House Trust
The Elmgrant Trust
The Elmley Foundation
Elshore Ltd
The Vernon N Ely Charitable Trust
The Embleton Trust
The Emerton-Christie Charity
EMI Music Sound Foundation
The Endure Foundation
The Worshipful Company of Engineers Charitable Trust Fund
The Englefield Charitable Trust
The English Schools' Football Association
The Enkalon Foundation
The Epigoni Trust
Epilepsy Research UK
The Equilibrium Foundation
The Equitable Charitable Trust

The Equity Trust Fund
The Eranda Foundation
The Ericson Trust
The Ernest Hecht Charitable Foundation
The Erskine Cunningham Hill Trust
The Essendon Charitable Trust
The Essex and Southend Sports Trust
Essex Community Foundation
The Essex Fairway Charitable Trust
The Essex Heritage Trust
Essex Provincial Charity Fund
The Essex Youth Trust
The Estelle Trust
Euro Charity Trust
The Alan Evans Memorial Trust
Sir John Evelyn's Charity
The Eventhall Family Charitable Trust
The Everard Foundation
The Eveson Charitable Trust
The Beryl Evetts and Robert Luff Animal Welfare Trust Limited
The Exilarch's Foundation
The Expat Foundation
Extonglen Limited
F C Charitable Trust
The F P Limited Charitable Trust
The Faber Charitable Trust
Esmée Fairbairn Foundation
The Fairway Trust
The Lord Faringdon Charitable Trust
Samuel William Farmer Trust
The Farmers' Company Charitable Fund
The Thomas Farr Charity
Walter Farthing (Trust) Limited
The Farthing Trust
The Fassnidge Memorial Trust
Joseph Fattorini Charitable Trust
The February Foundation
The John Feeney Charitable Trust
The George Fentham Birmingham Charity
The A M Fenton Trust
Elizabeth Ferguson Charitable Trust Fund
The Fidelity UK Foundation
The Doris Field Charitable Trust
Fife Council/Common Good Funds and Trusts
The Fifty Fund
Filey Foundation Ltd
Dixie Rose Findlay Charitable Trust
Finnart House School Trust
Gerald Finzi Charitable Trust

Firtree Trust
The Sir John Fisher Foundation
The Fishmongers' Company's Charitable Trust
Marc Fitch Fund
The Fitton Trust
The Earl Fitzwilliam Charitable Trust
The Ian Fleming Charitable Trust
The Joyce Fletcher Charitable Trust
Florence's Charitable Trust
The Flow Foundation
The Gerald Fogel Charitable Trust
The Football Association National Sports Centre Trust
The Football Association Youth Trust
The Football Foundation
The Forbes Charitable Foundation
The Forces Trust (Working Name)
Ford Britain Trust
The Oliver Ford Charitable Trust
Fordeve Limited
The Lady Forester Trust
The Foresters' Fund for Children
The Foresters' Charity Stewards UK Trust
Forever Manchester
The Forman Hardy Charitable Trust
Gwyneth Forrester Trust
The Fort Foundation
The Lord Forte Foundation
The Four Lanes Trust
The Foyle Foundation
The Isaac and Freda Frankel Memorial Charitable Trust
The Elizabeth Frankland Moore and Star Foundation
The Gordon Fraser Charitable Trust
The Hugh Fraser Foundation
The Joseph Strong Frazer Trust
The Louis and Valerie Freedman Charitable Settlement
The Freemasons' Grand Charity
The Thomas Freke and Lady Norton Charity Trust
The Charles S French Charitable Trust
The Anne French Memorial Trust
The Freshfield Foundation
The Freshgate Trust Foundation
The Friarsgate Trust

The Friends Hall Farm Street
Trust
The Friends of Kent Churches
Friends of Muir Group
Friends of Wiznitz Limited
Friends Provident Charitable
Foundation
The Frognal Trust
T F C Frost Charitable Trust
The Patrick & Helena Frost
Foundation
Mejer and Gertrude Miriam
Frydman Foundation
The Fulmer Charitable Trust
Worshipful Company of
Furniture Makers Charitable
Fund
The G I Foundation
G M C Trust
Gableholt Limited
The Galbraith Trust
The Gale Family Charity Trust
Gamlen Charitable Trust
The Gamma Trust
The Gannochy Trust
The Ganzoni Charitable Trust
The Worshipful Company of
Gardeners of London
The Samuel Gardner Memorial
Trust
The Garnett Charitable Trust
Garrick Charitable Trust
Garthgwynion Charities
Garvan Limited
Gatwick Airport Community
Trust
The Robert Gavron Charitable
Trust
Jacqueline and Michael Gee
Charitable Trust
Thomas Betton's Charity for
Pensions and Relief-in-Need
The General Nursing Council
for England and Wales
Trust
The Steven Gerrard Foundation
Get Kids Going
The Gibbons Family Trust
The David Gibbons Foundation
The Gibbs Charitable Trust
Simon Gibson Charitable Trust
The G C Gibson Charitable
Trust
Lady Gibson's Charitable Trust
The Harvey and Hilary Gilbert
Charitable Trust
The Girdlers' Company
Charitable Trust
The B and P Glasser
Charitable Trust
The Glass-House Trust
The Glastonbury Trust Limited
Global Charities
Gloucestershire Community
Foundation

The Gloucestershire Historic
Churches Trust
Worshipful Company of
Glovers of London Charity
Fund
The GNC Trust
The Godinton Charitable Trust
The Sydney and Phyllis
Goldberg Memorial
Charitable Trust
The Golden Bottle Trust
Golden Charitable Trust
The Jack Goldhill Charitable
Trust
The Goldsmiths' Arts Trust
Fund
The Goldsmiths' Company
Charity
The Golf Foundation Limited
The Golsoncott Foundation
Golubovich Foundation
Nicholas and Judith
Goodison's Charitable
Settlement
The Goodman Foundation
The Mike Gooley Trailfinders
Charity
The Gosling Foundation
Limited
The Gough Charitable Trust
The Gould Charitable Trust
The Grace Charitable Trust
A B Grace Trust
The Graff Foundation
E C Graham Belford Charitable
Settlement
A and S Graham Charitable
Trust
The Grahame Charitable
Foundation Limited
The Granada Foundation
Grand Charitable Trust of the
Order of Women
Freemasons
The Grand Order of Water
Rats' Charities Fund
The Grange Farm Centre Trust
Grantham Yorke Trust
GrantScape
The J G Graves Charitable
Trust
The Stanley and Lorna Graves
Charitable Trust
The Gordon Gray Trust
The Gray Trust
The Great Britain Sasakawa
Foundation
The Great Stone Bridge Trust
of Edenbridge
The Great Torrington Town
Lands Charity
The Kenneth & Susan Green
Charitable Foundation
The Haydn Green Charitable
Trust
The Green Hall Foundation

Philip and Judith Green Trust
Mrs H R Greene Charitable
Settlement
Greggs Foundation
The Gretna Charitable Trust
Greys Charitable Trust
The Grimmitt Trust
The Grocers' Charity
The M and R Gross Charities
Limited
The GRP Charitable Trust
The David and Marie Grumitt
Foundation
N and R Grunbaum Charitable
Trust
The Bishop of Guildford's
Foundation
The Guildry Incorporation of
Perth
The Walter Guinness
Charitable Trust
The Gunter Charitable Trust
The Gur Trust
The Gurney Charitable Trust
Dr Guthrie's Association
The H and J Spack Charitable
Trust
The H and M Charitable Trust
H C Foundation
The H P Charitable Trust
The Hackney Parochial
Charities
The Hadfield Trust
The Hadley Trust
The Hadrian Trust
The Alfred Haines Charitable
Trust
E F and M G Hall Charitable
Trust
The Edith Winifred Hall
Charitable Trust
Robert Hall Charity
The Hamamelis Trust
Hamilton Wallace Trust
Paul Hamlyn Foundation
Sue Hammerson Charitable
Trust
The Hampshire and Islands
Historic Churches Trust
Hampshire and Isle of Wight
Community Foundation
The Hampstead Wells and
Campden Trust
Hampton Fuel Allotment
Charity
The W A Handley Charitable
Trust
Beatrice Hankey Foundation
Limited
The Hanley Trust (1987)
The Kathleen Hannay
Memorial Charity
Lord Hanson Foundation
Harbo Charities Limited
The Harborne Parish Lands
Charity

The Harbour Charitable Trust
The Harbour Foundation
The Harding Trust
William Harding's Charity
The Hare of Steep Charitable Trust
The Harebell Centenary Fund
The Kenneth Hargreaves Charitable Trust
The Harpur Trust
The Harris Charitable Trust
The Harris Charity
The Harris Family Charitable Trust
The Edith Lilian Harrison 2000 Foundation
The Harrison and Potter Trust
The John Harrison Charitable Trust
The Peter Harrison Foundation
The Spencer Hart Charitable Trust
The Hartley Charitable Trust
The Alfred And Peggy Harvey Charitable Trust
William Geoffrey Harvey's Discretionary Settlement
The Edward Harvist Trust
Haskel Family Foundation
Hasluck Charitable Trust
The Hathaway Trust
The M A Hawe Settlement
The Hawkins Foundation
The Hawthorne Charitable Trust
The Dorothy Hay-Bolton Charitable Trust
The Charles Hayward Foundation
Headley-Pitt Charitable Trust
Heart of England Community Foundation
Heart Research UK
The Heathcoat Trust
Heathside Charitable Trust
Percy Hedley 1990 Charitable Trust
The Hedley Denton Charitable Trust
The Hedley Foundation
The H J Heinz Company Limited Charitable Trust
The Hellenic Foundation
The Michael Heller Charitable Foundation
The Simon Heller Charitable Settlement
Help for Health
Help the Homeless
The Helping Foundation
The Hemby Trust
The Christina Mary Hendrie Trust for Scottish and Canadian Charities

Henley Educational Trust (formerley Henley Educational Charity)
Esther Hennell Charitable Trust
The G D Herbert Charitable Trust
The Anne Herd Memorial Trust
The Herefordshire Community Foundation
The Herefordshire Historic Churches Trust
The Heritage of London Trust Ltd
The Hertfordshire Community Foundation
The Hesed Trust
The Hesslewood Children's Trust (Hull Seamen's and General Orphanage)
Hexham and Newcastle Diocesan Trust (1947)
The P and C Hickinbotham Charitable Trust
The Rosalind Hicks Charitable Trust
The Higgs Charitable Trust
Alan Edward Higgs Charity
The Graham High Charitable Trust
The High Sheriff's Police Trust for the County of West Midlands (Building Blocks)
Highcroft Charitable Trust
The Hilden Charitable Fund
The Derek Hill Foundation
The Charles Littlewood Hill Trust
The Hillier Trust
The Hillingdon Community Trust
The Hillingdon Partnership Trust
R G Hills Charitable Trust
The Hilmarnach Charitable Trust
Hinchley Charitable Trust
Lady Hind Trust
Stuart Hine Trust
The Hinrichsen Foundation
The Hintze Family Charitable Foundation
The Hiscox Foundation
The Hitchin Educational Foundation
The Henry C Hoare Charitable Trust
The Eleemosynary Charity of William Hobbayne
Hobson Charity Limited
Hockerill Educational Foundation
Matthew Hodder Charitable Trust
The Sir Julian Hodge Charitable Trust
The Jane Hodge Foundation

The J G Hogg Charitable Trust
The Holden Charitable Trust
John Holford's Charity
The Hollands-Warren Fund
The Hollick Family Charitable Trust
The Holliday Foundation
The Dorothy Holmes Charitable Trust
The Holmes Family Trust (Sheffield)
The Holst Foundation
P H Holt Foundation
The Edward Holt Trust
The Holywood Trust
The Homelands Charitable Trust
The Homestead Charitable Trust
Mary Homfray Charitable Trust
Hope for Youth (NI)
HopMarket Charity
The Cuthbert Horn Trust
The Antony Hornby Charitable Trust
The Horne Foundation
The Horne Trust
The Worshipful Company of Horners' Charitable Trusts
The Hornsey Parochial Charities
The Hospital of God at Greatham
The Hospital Saturday Fund
The Sir Joseph Hotung Charitable Settlement
Houblon-Norman/George Fund
The House of Industry Estate
The Reta Lila Howard Foundation
The Daniel Howard Trust
The Huddersfield Common Good Trust
The Hudson Foundation
The Huggard Charitable Trust
The Geoffrey C Hughes Charitable Trust
The Hull and East Riding Charitable Trust
Hulme Trust Estates (Educational)
The Humanitarian Trust
The Michael and Shirley Hunt Charitable Trust
The Albert Hunt Trust
The Hunter Foundation
Miss Agnes H Hunter's Trust
The Huntingdon Foundation
Huntingdon Freemen's Trust
Hurdale Charity Limited
The Nani Huyu Charitable Trust
The P Y N and B Hyams Trust
The Hyde Charitable Trust
I B B Charitable Trust
I G O Foundation Limited
The Idlewild Trust

The Iliffe Family Charitable Trust

Impetus – The Private Equity Foundation (Impetus – PEF)

The Indigo Trust

The Ingram Trust

The Inland Waterways Association

The Inlight Trust

The Inman Charity

The Inner London Magistrates Court Poor Box and Feeder Charity

The International Bankers Charitable Trust (The Worshipful Company of International Bankers)

The Inverforth Charitable Trust

Investream Charitable Trust

The Ireland Fund of Great Britain

The Irish Youth Foundation (UK) Ltd (incorporating The Lawlor Foundation)

The Ironmongers' Foundation

The Charles Irving Charitable Trust

Irwin Trust

The ISA Charity

The Isaacs Charitable Trust

The J Isaacs Charitable Trust

The Isle of Anglesey Charitable Trust

The ITF Seafarers Trust

The Ithaca Trust

The J & J Benevolent Foundation

The J & J Charitable Trust

J A R Charitable Trust

J D R Charitable Trust

The J J Charitable Trust

The J M K Charitable Trust

The J R S S T Charitable Trust

C Richard Jackson Charitable Trust

Elizabeth Jackson Charitable Trust

Jacobs Charitable Trust

The Ruth and Lionel Jacobson Trust (Second Fund) No 2

Jaffe Family Relief Fund

John James Bristol Foundation

The Susan and Stephen James Charitable Settlement

The James Trust

The Jarman Charitable Trust

The John Jarrold Trust

The Jasper Conran Foundation

The Jeffrey Charitable Trust

Rees Jeffreys Road Fund

The Nick Jenkins Foundation

The Jenour Foundation

The Jerusalem Trust

Jerwood Charitable Foundation

Jesus Hospital Charity

Jewish Child's Day

The Jewish Youth Fund

The Jigsaw Foundation

The Harold Joels Charitable Trust

The Nicholas Joels Charitable Trust

The Norman Joels Charitable Trust

The Elton John Aids Foundation

The Dyfrig and Heather John Charitable Trust

The Michael John Trust

The Lillie Johnson Charitable Trust

The Johnson Foundation

The Reginald Johnson Foundation

The Johnnie Johnson Trust

The Johnson Wax Ltd Charitable Trust

The Joicey Trust

The Jones 1986 Charitable Trust

The Dezna Robins Jones Charitable Foundation

The Marjorie and Geoffrey Jones Charitable Trust

The Jordan Charitable Foundation

The Joron Charitable Trust

The J E Joseph Charitable Fund

The Lady Eileen Joseph Foundation

The Josephs Family Charitable Trust

The Josh Charitable Trust

JTH Charitable Trust

The Judith Trust

The Julian Budd Kids in Sport Trust Limited

The Jungels-Winkler Charitable Foundation

The Anton Jurgens Charitable Trust

The Bernard Kahn Charitable Trust

The Stanley Kalms Foundation

The Karenza Foundation

The Boris Karloff Charitable Foundation

The Ian Karten Charitable Trust

The Kasner Charitable Trust

The Kathleen Trust

The Michael and Ilse Katz Foundation

The Katzauer Charitable Settlement

The C S Kaufman Charitable Trust

The Geoffrey John Kaye Charitable Foundation

The Emmanuel Kaye Foundation

The Caron Keating Foundation

The Kelly Family Charitable Trust

Kelsick's Educational Foundation

The KempWelch Charitable Trust

The Kay Kendall Leukaemia Fund

William Kendall's Charity (Wax Chandlers' Company)

The Kennel Club Charitable Trust

Kent Community Foundation

The Nancy Kenyon Charitable Trust

Keren Association

Kermaville Ltd

E and E Kernkraut Charities Limited

The Peter Kershaw Trust

Keswick Hall Trust

Kettering and District Charitable Medical Trust

The Ursula Keyes Trust

The Mr & Mrs Paul Killik Charitable Trust

The Robert Kiln Charitable Trust

The King Henry VIII Endowed Trust Warwick

The King/Cullimore Charitable Trust

Kingdom Way Trust

The Kingsbury Charity

The Mary Kinross Charitable Trust

Kinsurdy Charitable Trust

Kirkley Poor's Lands Estate

The Richard Kirkman Charitable Trust

Kirschel Foundation

Robert Kitchin (Saddlers' Company)

The Marina Kleinwort Charitable Trust

The Sir James Knott Trust

The Kobler Trust

The Kofia Trust

The Kohn Foundation

The KPMG Foundation

The Kreditor Charitable Trust

The Kreitman Foundation

The Neil Kreitman Foundation

The Heinz, Anna and Carol Kroch Foundation

Kupath Gemach Chaim Bechesed Viznitz Trust

The Kyte Charitable Trust

The Late Sir Pierce Lacy Charity Trust

John Laing Charitable Trust

The Christopher Laing Foundation

The Lambert Charitable Trust
Community Foundation for Lancashire
LWS Lancashire Environmental Fund Limited
Duchy of Lancaster Benevolent Fund
The Lancaster Foundation
LandAid Charitable Trust
The Jack Lane Charitable Trust
The Allen Lane Foundation
The Langtree Trust
The LankellyChase Foundation
The R J Larg Family Charitable Trust
Largsmount Ltd
The Lark Trust
Laufer Charitable Trust
The Lauffer Family Charitable Foundation
The Kathleen Laurence Trust
The Edgar E Lawley Foundation
The Herd Lawson and Muriel Lawson Charitable Trust
The Lawson Beckman Charitable Trust
The Raymond and Blanche Lawson Charitable Trust
The Mason Le Page Charitable Trust
The Leach Fourteenth Trust
The David Lean Foundation
The Leathersellers' Company Charitable Fund
The Leche Trust
The Arnold Lee Charitable Trust
The William Leech Charity
The Lord Mayor of Leeds Appeal Fund
Leeds Building Society Charitable Foundation
The Leeds Community Foundation
Leicestershire and Rutland Community Foundation
Leicestershire Historic Churches Trust
The Kennedy Leigh Charitable Trust
Morris Leigh Foundation
Mrs Vera Leigh's Charity
P Leigh-Bramwell Trust 'E'
The Erica Leonard Trust
The Leonard Trust
The Mark Leonard Trust
Lesley Lesley and Mutter Trust
Leukaemia and Lymphoma Research
The Leverhulme Trade Charities Trust
The Leverhulme Trust
Lord Leverhulme's Charitable Trust
The Joseph Levy Charitable Foundation

Lewis Family Charitable Trust
The John Spedan Lewis Foundation
The Sir Edward Lewis Foundation
John Lewis Partnership General Community Fund
The Lewis Ward Trust
Liberum Foundation
Lichfield Conduit Lands
Limoges Charitable Trust
The Lincolnshire Churches Trust
Lincolnshire Community Foundation
The Lind Trust
The Linden Charitable Trust
The Enid Linder Foundation
The Linmardon Trust
The Ruth and Stuart Lipton Charitable Trust
The Lister Charitable Trust
Frank Litchfield Charitable Trust
The Andrew and Mary Elizabeth Little Charitable Trust
Littlefield Foundation (UK) Limited
The Second Joseph Aaron Littman Foundation
The George John and Sheilah Livanos Charitable Trust
Liverpool Charity and Voluntary Services
Liverpool Sailors' Home Trust
Jack Livingstone Charitable Trust
The Ian & Natalie Livingstone Charitable Trust
The Elaine and Angus Lloyd Charitable Trust
Lloyd's Charities Trust
Lloyds Bank Foundation for England and Wales
Lloyds Bank Foundation for Northern Ireland
Lloyds Bank Foundation for the Channel Islands
Lloyds TSB Foundation for Scotland
The Lo Family Charitable Trust
Localtrent Ltd
The Loftus Charitable Trust
The Joyce Lomax Bullock Charitable Trust
The Trust for London
London Catalyst
The London Community Foundation
The London Housing Foundation
The London Law Trust
London Legal Support Trust
The London Marathon Charitable Trust

The William and Katherine Longman Trust
The Lord's Taverners
The Loseley and Guildway Charitable Trust
The Lowy Mitchell Foundation
The C L Loyd Charitable Trust
LSA Charitable Trust
The Marie Helen Luen Charitable Trust
Robert Luff Foundation Ltd
C F Lunoe Trust Fund
The Ruth and Jack Lunzer Charitable Trust
Lord and Lady Lurgan Trust
The Lyndhurst Trust
The Lynn Foundation
The Lynwood Trust
John Lyon's Charity
The Lyons Charitable Trust
The Sir Jack Lyons Charitable Trust
Sylvanus Lyson's Charity
The M and C Trust
The M K Charitable Trust
The E M MacAndrew Trust
The R S Macdonald Charitable Trust
Macdonald-Buchanan Charitable Trust
The Macfarlane Walker Trust
The Mackay and Brewer Charitable Trust
The Mackintosh Foundation
The MacRobert Trust
Ian Mactaggart Trust
James Madison Trust
The Magdalen and Lasher Charity
Magdalen Hospital Trust
The Magen Charitable Trust
Mageni Trust
The Makin Charitable Trust
Man Group plc Charitable Trust
The Manackerman Charitable Trust
Manchester Airport Community Trust Fund
The Manchester Guardian Society Charitable Trust
Lord Mayor of Manchester's Charity Appeal Trust
Mandeville Trust
The Manifold Charitable Trust
W M Mann Foundation
R W Mann Trust
The Leslie and Lilian Manning Trust
Maranatha Christian Trust
Marbeh Torah Trust
The Marcela Trust
Marchig Animal Welfare Trust
The Stella and Alexander Margulies Charitable Trust

Market Harborough and The
  Bowdens Charity
The Marks Family Foundation
The Ann and David Marks
  Foundation
The Hilda and Samuel Marks
  Foundation
J P Marland Charitable Trust
The Michael Marsh Charitable
  Trust
The Marsh Christian Trust
The Charlotte Marshall
  Charitable Trust
The Jim Marshall Charitable
  Trust
The Nora Joan Marshall
  Charitable Trust
The D G Marshall of
  Cambridge Trust
Marshall's Charity
Marshgate Charitable
  Settlement
Sir George Martin Trust
John Martin's Charity
The John Mason Family Trust
The Mason Porter Charitable
  Trust
The Nancie Massey Charitable
  Trust
The Mathew Trust
Matliwala Family Charitable
  Trust
The Matt 6.3 Charitable Trust
The Violet Mauray Charitable
  Trust
The Maxwell Family Foundation
Evelyn May Trust
Mayfair Charities Ltd
The Mayfield Valley Arts Trust
Mazars Charitable Trust
The Robert McAlpine
  Foundation
The McDougall Trust
The A M McGreevy No 5
  Charitable Settlement
The McKenna Charitable Trust
Martin McLaren Memorial
  Trust
The Helen Isabella McMorran
  Charitable Foundation
D D McPhail Charitable
  Settlement
The Mears Foundation
The James Frederick and Ethel
  Anne Measures Charity
The Medlock Charitable Trust
The Anthony and Elizabeth
  Mellows Charitable
  Settlement
Melow Charitable Trust
Meningitis Trust
Menuchar Ltd
Mercaz Torah Vechesed
  Limited
The Mercers' Charitable
  Foundation

Merchant Navy Welfare Board
The Merchant Taylors'
  Company Charities Fund
The Merchant Venturers'
  Charity
The Merchants' House of
  Glasgow
The Mersey Docks and
  Harbour Company
  Charitable Fund
Community Foundation for
  Merseyside
The Zachary Merton and
  George Woofindin
  Convalescent Trust
The Tony Metherell Charitable
  Trust
The Metropolitan Drinking
  Fountain and Cattle Trough
  Association
The Metropolitan Masonic
  Charity
The Mickel Fund
Mickleham Charitable Trust
Gerald Micklem Charitable
  Trust
The Sir John Middlemore
  Charitable Trust
The Masonic Province of
  Middlesex Charitable Trust
Middlesex Sports Foundation
Midhurst Pensions Trust
The Migraine Trust
Miles Trust for the Putney and
  Roehampton Community
Millennium Stadium Charitable
  Trust
The Hugh and Mary Miller
  Bequest Trust
The Ronald Miller Foundation
The Millfield House Foundation
The Millfield Trust
The Millhouses Charitable
  Trust
The Millichope Foundation
The Mills Charity
The Clare Milne Trust
Milton Keynes Community
  Foundation
The Edgar Milward Charity
The Keith and Joan
  Mindelsohn Charitable
  Trust
The Peter Minet Trust
Minge's Gift and the Pooled
  Trusts
Minton Charitable Trust
The Mirfield Educational
  Charity
The Mirianog Trust
The Laurence Misener
  Charitable Trust
The Mishcon Family Charitable
  Trust
The Misselbrook Trust

The Brian Mitchell Charitable
  Settlement
The Mitchell Charitable Trust
The Esmé Mitchell Trust
The MITIE Foundation
The Mittal Foundation
Keren Mitzvah Trust
The Mizpah Trust
The Mobbs Memorial Trust Ltd
The Modiano Charitable Trust
The Moette Charitable Trust
The Mole Charitable Trust
The Mollie Thomas Charitable
  Trust
The Monatrea Charitable Trust
The D C Moncrieff Charitable
  Trust
Monmouthshire County Council
  Welsh Church Act Fund
The Montague Thompson
  Coon Charitable Trust
The Colin Montgomerie
  Charitable Foundation
The Monument Trust
George A Moore Foundation
The Henry Moore Foundation
John Moores Foundation
The Morel Charitable Trust
The Morgan Charitable
  Foundation
The Morgan Foundation
The Mr and Mrs J T Morgan
  Foundation
Morgan Stanley International
  Foundation
The Oliver Morland Charitable
  Trust
S C and M E Morland's
  Charitable Trust
The Bernard Morris Charitable
  Trust
The Morris Charitable Trust
The Willie and Mabel Morris
  Charitable Trust
The Peter Morrison Charitable
  Foundation
G M Morrison Charitable Trust
The Stanley Morrison
  Charitable Trust
Moshal Charitable Trust
The Moshulu Charitable Trust
The Moss Charitable Trust
The Robert and Margaret
  Moss Charitable Trust
The Moss Family Charitable
  Trust
Mosselson Charitable Trust
Mothercare Group Foundation
Moto in the Community
British Motor Sports Training
  Trust
J P Moulton Charitable
  Foundation
The Mount Everest Foundation
Mountbatten Festival of Music
Move On Foundation Limited

Mrs Waterhouse Charitable Trust

The MSE Charity

The Mugdock Children's Trust

The Mulberry Trust

The George Müller Charitable Trust

The Edith Murphy Foundation

Murphy-Neumann Charity Company Limited

The John R Murray Charitable Trust

The Mushroom Fund

The Music Sales Charitable Trust

The Mutual Trust Group

MW (CL) Foundation

MYA Charitable Trust

MYR Charitable Trust

The Kitty and Daniel Nabarro Charitable Trust

The Nadezhda Charitable Trust

The Janet Nash Charitable Settlement

The National Art Collections Fund

The National Churches Trust

The National Express Foundation

The National Hockey Foundation

The National Manuscripts Conservation Trust

The Nationwide Foundation

Needham Market and Barking Welfare Charities

The Worshipful Company of Needlemakers' Charitable Fund

The Neighbourly Charitable Trust

The James Neill Trust Fund

Nemoral Ltd

Ner Foundation

Nesswall Ltd

The New Appeals Organisation for the City and County of Nottingham

Newby Trust Limited

The Newcomen Collett Foundation

The Frances and Augustus Newman Foundation

Newpier Charity Ltd

Alderman Newton's Educational Foundation

The NFU Mutual Charitable Trust

The Night Garden Charity

The Chevras Ezras Nitzrochim Trust

NJD Charitable Trust

The Noon Foundation

The Norda Trust

Norfolk Community Foundation

Norie Charitable Trust

Normalyn Charitable Trust

The Norman Family Charitable Trust

The Duncan Norman Trust Fund

The Normanby Charitable Trust

The North West Cancer Research Fund

The Northampton Municipal Church Charities

The Northampton Queen's Institute Relief in Sickness Fund

The Earl of Northampton's Charity

Northamptonshire Community Foundation

The Northcott Devon Foundation

The Northcott Devon Medical Foundation

The Community Foundation for Northern Ireland

The Northern Rock Foundation

The Northumberland Village Homes Trust

The Northumbria Historic Churches Trust

The Northwood Charitable Trust

The Norton Foundation

The Norwich Church of England Young Men's Society

The Norwich Town Close Estate Charity

The Norwood and Newton Settlement

The Noswad Charity

The Notgrove Trust

The Nottingham General Dispensary

The Nottingham Gordon Memorial Trust for Boys and Girls

Nottinghamshire Community Foundation

The Nottinghamshire Historic Churches Trust

The Nottinghamshire Miners' Welfare Trust Fund

The Nuffield Foundation

The Oak Trust

The Oakley Charitable Trust

The Oakmoor Charitable Trust

The Odin Charitable Trust

The Ofenheim Charitable Trust

Ogilvie Charities Deed No.2 (including the Charity of Mary Catherine Ford Smith)

Oglesby Charitable Trust

Oizer Charitable Trust

The Old Broad Street Charity Trust

Old Possum's Practical Trust

The John Oldacre Foundation

The Oldham Foundation

Open Gate

The Raymond Oppenheimer Foundation

Ormonde Foundation

The Ormsby Charitable Trust

The Orrin Charitable Trust

The Ouseley Trust

The Owen Family Trust

Oxfam (GB)

City of Oxford Charity

The Oxfordshire Community Foundation

The P F Charitable Trust

The Doris Pacey Charitable Foundation

Padwa Charitable Foundation

The Paget Charitable Trust

The Paladin Vince-Odozi Charitable Trust

The Palmer Foundation

Eleanor Palmer Trust

The Panacea Society

The James Pantyfedwen Foundation

The Park Charitable Trust

The Frank Parkinson Agricultural Trust

The Samuel and Freda Parkinson Charitable Trust

Arthur James Paterson Charitable Trust

The Constance Paterson Charitable Trust

Miss M E Swinton Paterson's Charitable Trust

The Patrick Charitable Trust

The Jack Patston Charitable Trust

Ambika Paul Foundation

Paycare Charity Trust

The Payne Charitable Trust

The Harry Payne Trust

The Peacock Charitable Trust

The Susanna Peake Charitable Trust

The David Pearlman Charitable Foundation

The Pedmore Sporting Club Trust Fund

The Dowager Countess Eleanor Peel Trust

Pegasus (Stanley) Trust

The Peltz Trust

The Pen Shell Project

The Pennycress Trust

People's Postcode Trust

The Performing Right Society Foundation

B E Perl Charitable Trust

The Jack Petchey Foundation

The Petplan Charitable Trust

The Philips and Rubens Charitable Trust

The Phillips Charitable Trust

The Phillips Family Charitable Trust

Philological Foundation

The David Pickford Charitable Foundation

The Pickwell Foundation

The Bernard Piggott Charitable Trust

The Pilgrim Trust

The Cecil Pilkington Charitable Trust

The Elise Pilkington Charitable Trust

The Pilkington Charities Fund

The Austin and Hope Pilkington Trust

The Sir Harry Pilkington Trust

The Col W W Pilkington Will Trusts The General Charity Fund

Miss A M Pilkington's Charitable Trust

The DLA Piper Charitable Trust

The Worshipful Company of Plaisterers Charitable Trust

The Platinum Trust

G S Plaut Charitable Trust Limited

Polden-Puckham Charitable Foundation

The George and Esme Pollitzer Charitable Settlement

The Pollywally Charitable Trust

The Polonsky Foundation

The Ponton House Trust

The John Porter Charitable Trust

The Porter Foundation

Porticus UK

The Portishead Nautical Trust

The Portrack Charitable Trust

The Mary Potter Convent Hospital Trust

The Powell Foundation

The W L Pratt Charitable Trust

The Douglas Prestwich Charitable Trust

The William Price Charitable Trust

The Lucy Price Relief-in-Need Charity

Sir John Priestman Charity Trust

The Primrose Trust

The Prince of Wales's Charitable Foundation

Princess Anne's Charities

Prison Service Charity Fund

The Privy Purse Charitable Trust

The Proven Family Trust

The Provincial Grand Charity of the Province of Derbyshire

The Richard and Christine Purchas Charitable Trust

The Puri Foundation

Mr and Mrs J A Pye's Charitable Settlement

Quartet Community Foundation

The Queen Anne's Gate Foundation

Queen Mary's Roehampton Trust

The Queen's Silver Jubilee Trust

Quercus Trust

R S Charitable Trust

The R V W Trust

The Monica Rabagliati Charitable Trust

Rachel Charitable Trust

The Racing Foundation

Racing Welfare

The Mr and Mrs Philip Rackham Charitable Trust

Richard Radcliffe Charitable Trust

The Radcliffe Trust

The Bishop Radford Trust

The Peggy Ramsay Foundation

The Rank Foundation Limited

The Joseph Rank Trust

The Fanny Rapaport Charitable Settlement

The Ratcliff Foundation

The Ratcliff Pension Charity

The Ratcliffe Charitable Trust

The E L Rathbone Charitable Trust

The Ravensdale Trust

The Rawdon-Smith Trust

The Rayden Charitable Trust

The Roger Raymond Charitable Trust

The Rayne Foundation

The Rayne Trust

The John Rayner Charitable Trust

The Sir James Reckitt Charity

The Red Arrows Trust

Red Hill Charitable Trust

The Red Rose Charitable Trust

The C A Redfern Charitable Foundation

The Reed Foundation

The John and Sally Reeve Charitable Trust

Richard Reeve's Foundation

The Rehoboth Trust

The Max Reinhardt Charitable Trust

REMEDI

The Rest Harrow Trust

The Nathaniel Reyner Trust Fund

The Rhondda Cynon Taff Welsh Church Acts Fund

Daisie Rich Trust

The Sir Cliff Richard Charitable Trust

The Clive Richards Charity

The Violet M Richards Charity

The Richmond Parish Lands Charity

Ridgesave Limited

The Ripple Effect Foundation

The Sir John Ritblat Family Foundation

The River Farm Foundation

River Legacy

The River Trust

Rivers Foundation

Rix-Thompson-Rothenberg Foundation

Thomas Roberts Trust

The Robertson Trust

Edwin George Robinson Charitable Trust

Robyn Charitable Trust

The Rochester Bridge Trust

The Rock Solid Trust

The Rofeh Trust

Rokach Family Charitable Trust

The Helen Roll Charitable Trust

The Sir James Roll Charitable Trust

The Roman Research Trust

The C A Rookes Charitable Trust

Mrs L D Rope Third Charitable Settlement

Rosa – the UK fund for women and girls

The Rosca Trust

The Rose Foundation

The Cecil Rosen Foundation

Rosetrees Trust

The Rothera Charitable Settlement

The Rothermere Foundation

The Rotherwick Foundation

The Rothley Trust

The Roughley Charitable Trust

Mrs Gladys Row Fogo Charitable Trust

Rowanville Ltd

The Christopher Rowbotham Charitable Trust

The Rowing Foundation

The Rowlands Trust

The Joseph Rowntree Charitable Trust

The Joseph Rowntree Foundation

Joseph Rowntree Reform Trust Limited

Royal Artillery Charitable Fund

Royal British Legion

Royal Docks Trust (London)

Royal Masonic Trust for Girls and Boys

The Alfred and Frances Rubens Charitable Trust

William Arthur Rudd Memorial Trust

Rugby Football Foundation

The Rugby Group Benevolent Fund Limited

The Russell Trust

The J S and E C Rymer
Charitable Trust
S O Charitable Trust
Raymond and Beverly Sackler
1988 Foundation
The Sackler Trust
The Ruzin Sadagora Trust
The Saddlers' Company
Charitable Fund
The Jean Sainsbury Animal
Welfare Trust
The Sainsbury Family
Charitable Trusts
Saint Luke's College
Foundation
The Saintbury Trust
The Saints and Sinners Trust
The Salamander Charitable
Trust
The Salt Foundation
The Salt Trust
Salters' Charitable Foundation
The Andrew Salvesen
Charitable Trust
Basil Samuel Charitable Trust
Coral Samuel Charitable Trust
The Peter Samuel Charitable
Trust
The Samworth Foundation
The Sandra Charitable Trust
Santander UK Foundation
Limited
The Sants Charitable Trust
The Peter Saunders Trust
The Scarfe Charitable Trust
The Schapira Charitable Trust
The R H Scholes Charitable
Trust
The Schreib Trust
The Schreiber Charitable Trust
The Schuster Charitable Trust
Foundation Scotland
Scott (Eredine) Charitable
Trust
The Francis C Scott Charitable
Trust
The Frieda Scott Charitable
Trust
Sir Samuel Scott of Yews
Trust
The Sir James and Lady Scott
Trust
The Scott Trust Foundation
The Storrow Scott Will Trust
Scottish Coal Industry Special
Welfare Fund
The Scottish International
Education Trust
The Scouloudi Foundation
The Screwfix Foundation
Seamen's Hospital Society
The Searchlight Electric
Charitable Trust
The Searle Charitable Trust
The Samuel Sebba Charitable
Trust

Leslie Sell Charitable Trust
Sellata Ltd
SEM Charitable Trust
The Seneca Trust
The Seven Fifty Trust
SF Group Charitable Fund for
Disabled People
The Cyril Shack Trust
The Jean Shanks Foundation
The Shanti Charitable Trust
ShareGift (The Orr Mackintosh
Foundation)
The Linley Shaw Foundation
The Shears Foundation
The Sheepdrove Trust
The Sheffield and District
Hospital Services
Charitable Fund
The Sheldon Trust
The Patricia and Donald
Shepherd Charitable Trust
The Sylvia and Colin Shepherd
Charitable Trust
The Archie Sherman Cardiff
Foundation
The Archie Sherman Charitable
Trust
The R C Sherriff Trust
The Shetland Charitable Trust
SHINE (Support and Help in
Education)
The Bassil Shippam and
Alsford Trust
The Shipwrights' Company
Charitable Fund
The Shirley Foundation
The Shoe Zone Trust
The J A Shone Memorial Trust
Community Foundation for
Shropshire and Telford
The Barbara A Shuttleworth
Memorial Trust
The Mary Elizabeth Siebel
Charity
David and Jennifer Sieff
Charitable Trust
The Julius Silman Charitable
Trust
The Leslie Silver Charitable
Trust
The Simmons & Simmons
Charitable Foundation
The Simpson Foundation
The Huntly and Margery
Sinclair Charitable Trust
Sino-British Fellowship Trust
Six Point Foundation
The Skelton Bounty
The Charles Skey Charitable
Trust
Skipton Building Society
Charitable Foundation
The John Slater Foundation
Sloane Robinson Foundation
The Smith & Pinching
Charitable Trust

The Mrs Smith and Mount
Trust
The E H Smith Charitable Trust
The Smith Charitable Trust
The Henry Smith Charity
The Leslie Smith Foundation
The Martin Smith Foundation
Philip Smith's Charitable Trust
The R C Snelling Charitable
Trust
The Snowball Trust
The Sobell Foundation
Solev Co Ltd
The Solo Charitable
Settlement
David Solomons Charitable
Trust
Friends of Somerset Churches
and Chapels
Songdale Ltd
The E C Sosnow Charitable
Trust
The Souter Charitable Trust
The South Square Trust
The Stephen R and Philippa H
Southall Charitable Trust
The W F Southall Trust
The Southdown Trust
R H Southern Trust
The Southover Manor General
Education Trust
The Southwold Trust
The Sovereign Health Care
Charitable Trust
Spar Charitable Fund
Sparks Charity (Sport Aiding
Medical Research For Kids)
Sparquote Limited
The Spear Charitable Trust
The Worshipful Company of
Spectacle Makers' Charity
The Jessie Spencer Trust
The Ralph and Irma Sperring
Charity
The Spielman Charitable Trust
Split Infinitive Trust
The Spoore, Merry and Rixman
Foundation
Sported Foundation
Rosalyn and Nicholas Springer
Charitable Trust
Springfields Employees'
Medical Research and
Charity Trust Fund
Springrule Limited
The Spurrell Charitable Trust
The Geoff and Fiona Squire
Foundation
St Andrew's Conservation
Trust
St Christopher's Educational
Trust (incorporating the
Hughes and Stevens
Bequest)
St Hilda's Trust
St James' Trust Settlement

St James's Place Foundation

Sir Walter St John's Educational Charity

The St Laurence Relief In Need Trust

St Michael's and All Saints' Charities Relief Branch (The Church Houses Relief in Need Charity)

St Monica Trust

The Late St Patrick White Charitable Trust

St Peter's Saltley Trust

St Teilo's Trust

The Stafford Trust

The Stanley Foundation Ltd

The Stanton Ballard Charitable Trust

The Staples Trust

The Star Charitable Trust

The Peter Stebbings Memorial Charity

The Steel Charitable Trust

The Steinberg Family Charitable Trust

The Hugh Stenhouse Foundation

The Stephen Barry Charitable Trust

Stervon Ltd

The Stevenage Community Trust

The June Stevens Foundation

The Steventon Allotments and Relief-in-Need Charity

The Stewards' Charitable Trust

Sir Halley Stewart Trust

The Stewarts Law Foundation

The David and Deborah Stileman Charitable Trust

The Leonard Laity Stoate Charitable Trust

The Stobart Newlands Charitable Trust

The Edward Stocks-Massey Bequest Fund

The Stokenchurch Educational Charity

The Stoller Charitable Trust

The M J C Stone Charitable Trust

The Samuel Storey Family Charitable Trust

Peter Stormonth Darling Charitable Trust

Peter Storrs Trust

The Strangward Trust

The Strasser Foundation

Stratford upon Avon Town Trust

The W O Street Charitable Foundation

The A B Strom and R Strom Charitable Trust

The Sudborough Foundation

Suffolk Community Foundation

The Suffolk Historic Churches Trust

The Alan Sugar Foundation

The Summerfield Charitable Trust

The Bernard Sunley Charitable Foundation

The Sunny Skies Foundation Community Foundation for Surrey

The Surrey Historic Buildings Trust Ltd

The Sussex Community Foundation

The Sussex Historic Churches Trust

The Adrienne and Leslie Sussman Charitable Trust

The Sutasoma Trust

Sutton Coldfield Charitable Trust

The Sutton Trust

Swan Mountain Trust

Swansea and Brecon Diocesan Board of Finance Limited

Swimathon Foundation

The John Swire (1989) Charitable Trust

The Swire Charitable Trust

The Hugh and Ruby Sykes Charitable Trust

The Charles and Elsie Sykes Trust

The Sylvanus Charitable Trust

The Stella Symons Charitable Trust

T and S Trust Fund

The Tajtelbaum Charitable Trust

The Talbot Trusts

The Talbot Village Trust

Tallow Chandlers Benevolent Fund

Talteg Ltd

The Tangent Charitable Trust

The Lady Tangye Charitable Trust

The David Tannen Charitable Trust

The Tanner Trust

The Lili Tapper Charitable Foundation

The Mrs A Lacy Tate Trust

The Taurus Foundation

The Tay Charitable Trust

C B and H H Taylor 1984 Trust

Humphrey Richardson Taylor Charitable Trust

The Connie and Albert Taylor Charitable Trust

The Cyril Taylor Charitable Trust

The Taylor Family Foundation

A P Taylor Trust

Rosanna Taylor's 1987 Charity Trust

The Tedworth Charitable Trust

Tees Valley Community Foundation

Tegham Limited

The Templeton Goodwill Trust

The Tennis Foundation

Tesco Charity Trust

The C Paul Thackray General Charitable Trust

The Thames Wharf Charity

The John P. Gommes Foundation

The Thistle Trust

The David Thomas Charitable Trust

The Thomas Lilley Memorial Trust

The Arthur and Margaret Thompson Charitable Trust

The Maurice and Vivien Thompson Charitable Trust

The Thompson Family Charitable Trust

The Thompson Family Foundation

The Thompson6 Charitable Trust

The Len Thomson Charitable Trust

The Sue Thomson Foundation

The Sir Jules Thorn Charitable Trust

The Thornton Foundation

The Thousandth Man – Richard Burns Charitable Trust

The Three Guineas Trust

The Thriplow Charitable Trust

The John Raymond Tijou Charitable Trust

Mrs R P Tindall's Charitable Trust

The Tisbury Telegraph Trust

The Tobacco Pipe Makers and Tobacco Trade Benevolent Fund

The Tolkien Trust

Tollemache (Buckminster) Charitable Trust

Tomchei Torah Charitable Trust

The Tompkins Foundation

Toni and Guy Charitable Foundation Limited

The Torah Temimah Trust

Toras Chesed (London) Trust

Tottenham Grammar School Foundation

The Tower Hill Trust

The Towry Law Charitable Trust (also known as the Castle Educational Trust)

The Toy Trust

The TPO Foundation

The Mayor of Trafford's Charity Fund

Annie Tranmer Charitable Trust
The Constance Travis
   Charitable Trust
The Treeside Trust
The Trefoil Trust
The Triangle Trust (1949) Fund
The True Colours Trust
Truedene Co. Ltd
The Truemark Trust
Truemart Limited
Trumros Limited
The Trusthouse Charitable
   Foundation
The Tsukanov Family
   Foundation
The James Tudor Foundation
Tudor Rose Ltd
The Tudor Trust
The Tufton Charitable Trust
Tuixen Foundation
The R D Turner Charitable
   Trust
The Douglas Turner Trust
The Florence Turner Trust
The G J W Turner Trust
The Turtleton Charitable Trust
Miss S M Tutton Charitable
   Trust
TVML Foundation
Two Ridings Community
   Foundation
Community Foundation Serving
   Tyne and Wear and
   Northumberland
Trustees of Tzedakah
UKI Charitable Foundation
Ulster Garden Villages Ltd
Ultach Trust
Ulverston Town Lands Charity
The Underwood Trust
The Union of Orthodox Hebrew
   Congregation
United Utilities Trust Fund
Unity Theatre Trust
The Michael Uren Foundation
Uxbridge United Welfare Trust
The Vail Foundation
Vale of Glamorgan – Welsh
   Church Fund
The Valentine Charitable Trust
The Valiant Charitable Trust
The Van Neste Foundation
Mrs Maud Van Norden's
   Charitable Foundation
The Vandervell Foundation
The Vardy Foundation
The Variety Club Children's
   Charity
Veneziana Fund
The William and Patricia
   Venton Charitable Trust
The Verdon-Smith Family
   Charitable Settlement
Victoria Homes Trust
The Nigel Vinson Charitable
   Trust

The William and Ellen Vinten
   Trust
The Vintners' Company
   Charitable Foundation
Vintners' Gifts Charity
Vision Charity
Vivdale Ltd
The Viznitz Foundation
The Vodafone Foundation
Voluntary Action Fund (VAF)
Wade's Charity
The Scurrah Wainwright Charity
The Wakefield and Tetley Trust
Wakeham Trust
The Community Foundation in
   Wales
Wales Council for Voluntary
   Action
Robert and Felicity Waley-
   Cohen Charitable Trust
The Walker Trust
The Thomas Wall Trust
Wallace and Gromit's
   Children's Foundation
The F J Wallis Charitable
   Settlement
Sir Siegmund Warburg's
   Voluntary Settlement
The Ward Blenkinsop Trust
The George Ward Charitable
   Trust
The Barbara Ward Children's
   Foundation
The John Warren Foundation
The Waterloo Foundation
G R Waters Charitable Trust
   2000
The Wates Foundation
Blyth Watson Charitable Trust
The Howard Watson Symington
   Memorial Charity
John Watson's Trust
Waynflete Charitable Trust
The Weavers' Company
   Benevolent Fund
Webb Memorial Trust
The David Webster Charitable
   Trust
The William Webster
   Charitable Trust
Weedon Family Trust
The Weinstock Fund
The James Weir Foundation
The Barbara Welby Trust
The Wellcome Trust
Welsh Church Fund Dyfed
   area (Carmarthenshire,
   Ceredigion and
   Pembrokeshire)
The Welton Foundation
The West Derby Wastelands
   Charity
West London Synagogue
   Charitable Fund
West Yorkshire Police
   Community Trust

Mrs S K West's Charitable
   Trust
The Westminster Foundation
The Garfield Weston
   Foundation
The Barbara Whatmore
   Charitable Trust
The Whitaker Charitable Trust
The Colonel W H Whitbread
   Charitable Trust
The Simon Whitbread
   Charitable Trust
White Stuff Foundation
The Whitecourt Charitable
   Trust
A H and B C Whiteley
   Charitable Trust
The Norman Whiteley Trust
The Whitewater Charitable
   Trust
The Whitley Animal Protection
   Trust
The Whittlesey Charity
The Lionel Wigram Memorial
   Trust
The Felicity Wilde Charitable
   Trust
The Wilkinson Charitable
   Foundation
Will to Win Foundation Ltd.
   (previously Tennis for a
   Life)
The William Barrow's Charity
The Charity of William Williams
The Kay Williams Charitable
   Foundation
The Williams Charitable Trust
Williams Serendipity Trust
The HDH Wills 1965
   Charitable Trust
The Dame Violet Wills Will
   Trust
The Wilmcote Charitrust
Sumner Wilson Charitable
   Trust
David Wilson Foundation
The Wilson Foundation
J and J R Wilson Trust
The Community Foundation for
   Wiltshire and Swindon
The Windruff Charitable Trust
The Benjamin Winegarten
   Charitable Trust
The Harold Hyam Wingate
   Foundation
The Francis Winham
   Foundation
Wirral Mayor's Charity
The James Wise Charitable
   Trust
The Witzenfeld Foundation
The Michael and Anna Wix
   Charitable Trust
The Wixamtree Trust
The Woburn 1986 Charitable
   Trust

The Maurice Wohl Charitable
Foundation
The Charles Wolfson
Charitable Trust
The Wolfson Family Charitable
Trust
The Wolfson Foundation
The Wolseley Charitable Trust
The James Wood Bequest
Fund
The Wood Family Trust
The Woodcock Charitable Trust
Wooden Spoon Society
The F Glenister Woodger Trust
Woodlands Trust
Woodroffe Benton Foundation
The Woodward Charitable
Trust
The A and R Woolf Charitable
Trust
Worcester Municipal Charities
The Worcestershire and
Dudley Historic Churches
Trust
The Wragge and Co. Charitable
Trust
The Diana Edgson Wright
Charitable Trust
The Matthews Wrightson
Charity Trust
Miss E B Wrightson's
Charitable Settlement
Wychville Ltd
The Wyndham Charitable Trust
The Wyseliot Charitable Trust
The Xerox (UK) Trust
The Yapp Charitable Trust
The Yardley Great Trust
The W Wing Yip and Brothers
Foundation
Yorkshire Agricultural Society
Yorkshire Building Society
Charitable Foundation
The South Yorkshire
Community Foundation
The Yorkshire Dales
Millennium Trust
The Yorkshire Historic
Churches Trust
You Gossip Foundation
The William Allen Young
Charitable Trust
The John K Young Endowment
Fund
Youth Music (previously known
as National Foundation for
Youth Music)
Youth United Foundation
The Marjorie and Arnold Ziff
Charitable Foundation
Stephen Zimmerman
Charitable Trust
The Zochonis Charitable Trust
Zurich Community Trust (UK)
Limited

UK

England

The 1989 Willan Charitable
Trust
ABF The Soldiers' Charity
The Adnams Charity
AF Trust Company
Aldgate and All Hallows'
Foundation
The Aldgate Freedom
Foundation
The H B Allen Charitable Trust
Almondsbury Charity
Amabrill Limited
The Ammco Trust
Viscount Amory's Charitable
Trust
Anguish's Educational
Foundation
Anpride Ltd
The Arbib Foundation
The Argus Appeal
The Arsenal Foundation
Arts Council England
The Ashendene Trust
AstonMansfield Charitable
Trust
The Lord Austin Trust
The Avenue Charitable Trust
The John Avins Trustees
The Avon and Somerset Police
Community Trust
The Aylesford Family
Charitable Trust
The BAA Communities Trust
The Roy and Pixie Baker
Charitable Trust
The Albert Casanova Ballard
Deceased Trust
The Ballinger Charitable Trust
The Bamford Charitable
Foundation
The Banbury Charities
The Barbour Foundation
Barchester Healthcare
Foundation
The Baring Foundation
The Barleycorn Trust
Barnes Workhouse Fund
The Barnstaple Bridge Trust
The Barnwood House Trust
The Bates Charitable Trust
The Bearder Charity
The James Beattie Charitable
Trust
The Jack and Ada Beattie
Foundation
The Beccles Town Lands
Charity
The Becketts and Sargeants
Educational Foundation
The Bedfordshire and
Hertfordshire Historic
Churches Trust

The Bedfordshire and Luton
Community Foundation
The Bellinger Donnay Trust
The Benfield Motors Charitable
Trust
The Hervey Benham Charitable
Trust
Bergqvist Charitable Trust
The Berkshire Community
Foundation
The Mason Bibby 1981 Trust
The Bideford Bridge Trust
The Bingham Trust
The Bintaub Charitable Trust
Birmingham & Black Country
Community Foundation
The Birmingham District
Nursing Charitable Trust
Birmingham International
Airport Community Trust
The Lord Mayor of
Birmingham's Charity
Birthday House Trust
The Michael Bishop
Foundation
The Bishop's Development
Fund
Isabel Blackman Foundation
The Blagrave Trust
The Blanchminster Trust
The Sir Victor Blank Charitable
Settlement
The Nicholas Boas Charitable
Trust
Bonhomie United Charity
Society
The Booth Charities
The Boots Charitable Trust
The Bordon Liphook
Haslemere Charity
The Boshier-Hinton Foundation
The Bothwell Charitable Trust
H E and E L Botteley
Charitable Trust
The Bowland Charitable Trust
The Frank Brake Charitable
Trust
The Bransford Trust
The Harold and Alice Bridges
Charity
Bristol Archdeaconry Charity
The Bristol Charities
John Bristow and Thomas
Mason Trust
The British Council for
Prevention of Blindness
The British Gas (Scottish Gas)
Energy Trust
The J and M Britton Charitable
Trust
The Charles and Edna
Broadhurst Charitable Trust
The Charles Brotherton Trust
Joseph Brough Charitable
Trust

The Swinfen Broun Charitable
  Trust
The Jack Brunton Charitable
  Trust
Buckinghamshire Community
  Foundation
The Buckinghamshire Historic
  Churches Trust
The Buckinghamshire Masonic
  Centenary Fund
The E F Bulmer Benevolent
  Fund
Bumba Foundation
The Burton Breweries
  Charitable Trust
Consolidated Charity of Burton
  upon Trent
The Worshipful Company of
  Butchers General Charities
The William A Cadbury
  Charitable Trust
Community Foundation for
  Calderdale
The Cambridgeshire
  Community Foundation
The Cambridgeshire Historic
  Churches Trust
The Camelia Trust
The Campden Charities
  Trustee
The Frederick and Phyllis Cann
  Trust
M R Cannon 1998 Charitable
  Trust
Carter's Educational
  Foundation
Sir John Cass's Foundation
The Catholic Trust for England
  and Wales
The Joseph and Annie Cattle
  Trust
John William Chapman's
  Charitable Trust
The Chelsea Square 1994
  Trust
Cheshire Freemason's Charity
The Chippenham Borough
  Lands Charity
The Chipping Sodbury Town
  Lands Charity
The Chrimes Family Charitable
  Trust
The Christabella Charitable
  Trust
Christadelphian Samaritan
  Fund
The Church and Community
  Fund
The Church Burgesses
  Educational Foundation
Church Burgesses Trust
Church Urban Fund
The City Bridge Trust
CLA Charitable Trust
The Hilda and Alice Clark
  Charitable Trust

The Clarke Charitable
  Settlement
Lord Clinton's Charitable Trust
Richard Cloudesley's Charity
The Coalfields Regeneration
  Trust
The Cobtree Charity Trust Ltd
The R and S Cohen
  Foundation
The Colchester Catalyst
  Charity
The Cole Charitable Trust
The Colefax Charitable Trust
The John and Freda Coleman
  Charitable Trust
The George Henry Collins
  Charity
Colyer-Fergusson Charitable
  Trust
Community First (Landfill
  Communities Fund)
The Compton Charitable Trust
The Douglas Compton James
  Charitable Trust
The Congleton Inclosure Trust
The Consolidated Charities for
  the Infirm Merchant
  Taylors' Company
The Catherine Cookson
  Charitable Trust
The Marjorie Coote Animal
  Charity Trust
The Marjorie Coote Old
  People's Charity
The Helen Jean Cope Trust
The J Reginald Corah
  Foundation Fund
Cornwall Community
  Foundation
The Cornwall Historic
  Churches Trust
The Cornwell Charitable Trust
Country Houses Foundation
County Durham Community
  Foundation
The General Charities of the
  City of Coventry
Coventry Building Society
  Charitable Foundation
The John Cowan Foundation
The Sir Tom Cowie Charitable
  Trust
The Sir William Coxen Trust
  Fund
Michael Crawford Children's
  Charity
Cripplegate Foundation
The Harry Crook Foundation
The Croydon Relief in Need
  Charities
Cumberland Building Society
  Charitable Foundation
Cumbria Community
  Foundation
The Harry Cureton Charitable
  Trust

The D J H Currie Memorial
  Trust
D C R Allen Charitable Trust
The Daisy Trust
The Dr and Mrs A Darlington
  Charitable Trust
Baron Davenport's Charity
The Hamilton Davies Trust
The Denman Charitable Trust
Dentons UKMEA LLP
  Charitable Trust
The Earl of Derby's Charitable
  Trust
The Derbyshire Churches and
  Chapels Preservation Trust
Derbyshire Community
  Foundation
The J N Derbyshire Trust
Devon Community Foundation
The Devon Educational Trust
The Devon Historic Churches
  Trust
The Dibden Allotments Fund
The Gillian Dickinson Trust
The Dickon Trust
The Digbeth Trust Limited
Dischma Charitable Trust
The DM Charitable Trust
The Derek and Eileen Dodgson
  Foundation
Dorset Community Foundation
The Dorset Historic Churches
  Trust
The Doughty Charity Trust
Downlands Educational Trust
The Dulverton Trust
The P B Dumbell Charitable
  Trust
The Dumbreck Charity
The W E Dunn Trust
The James Dyson Foundation
The Earley Charity
Earls Colne and Halstead
  Educational Charity
East End Community
  Foundation
The Ebenezer Trust
Eden Arts Trust
The Gilbert and Eileen Edgar
  Foundation
Edinburgh Trust No 2 Account
Educational Foundation of
  Alderman John Norman
Dr Edwards Bishop King's
  Fulham Endowment Fund
The William Edwards
  Educational Charity
The Elephant Trust
The Gerald Palmer Eling Trust
  Company
The Wilfred and Elsie Elkes
  Charity Fund
The Maud Elkington Charitable
  Trust
The Ellinson Foundation Ltd
The Ellis Campbell Foundation

The Elm House Trust
The Elmgrant Trust
The Elmley Foundation
Elshore Ltd
The Vernon N Ely Charitable
Trust
The English Schools' Football
Association
The Ernest Hecht Charitable
Foundation
The Essex and Southend
Sports Trust
Essex Community Foundation
The Essex Fairway Charitable
Trust
The Essex Heritage Trust
Essex Provincial Charity Fund
The Essex Youth Trust
Sir John Evelyn's Charity
The Eventhall Family
Charitable Trust
The Everard Foundation
The Eveson Charitable Trust
The Fairway Trust
Walter Farthing (Trust) Limited
The Farthing Trust
The Fassnidge Memorial Trust
The John Feeney Charitable
Trust
The George Fentham
Birmingham Charity
The A M Fenton Trust
The Fifty Fund
Finnart House School Trust
Firtree Trust
The Joyce Fletcher Charitable
Trust
The Football Foundation
Ford Britain Trust
The Lady Forester Trust
Forever Manchester (The
Community Foundation for
Greater Manchester)
Gwyneth Forrester Trust
The Fort Foundation
The Four Lanes Trust
The Joseph Strong Frazer Trust
The Freemasons' Grand
Charity
The Thomas Freke and Lady
Norton Charity Trust
The Charles S French
Charitable Trust
The Anne French Memorial
Trust
The Freshgate Trust
Foundation
The Friends Hall Farm Street
Trust
The Friends of Kent Churches
Friends of Wiznitz Limited
T F C Frost Charitable Trust
The Fulmer Charitable Trust
The Galbraith Trust
The Ganzoni Charitable Trust

The Worshipful Company of
Gardeners of London
The Samuel Gardner Memorial
Trust
The Garnett Charitable Trust
Gatwick Airport Community
Trust
The General Nursing Council
for England and Wales
Trust
The Gibbons Family Trust
The David Gibbons Foundation
The Girdlers' Company
Charitable Trust
The B and P Glasser
Charitable Trust
The Glass-House Trust
Gloucestershire Community
Foundation
The Gloucestershire Historic
Churches Trust
The GNC Trust
The Godinton Charitable Trust
The Goldsmiths' Company
Charity
The Goodman Foundation
A B Grace Trust
The Graff Foundation
E C Graham Belford Charitable
Settlement
The Grahame Charitable
Foundation Limited
The Granada Foundation
Grand Charitable Trust of the
Order of Women
Freemasons
The Grange Farm Centre Trust
Grantham Yorke Trust
The Gordon Gray Trust
The Gray Trust
The Great Stone Bridge Trust
of Edenbridge
The Great Torrington Town
Lands Charity
The Green Hall Foundation
Greggs Foundation
The Grimmitt Trust
The M and R Gross Charities
Limited
The Bishop of Guildford's
Foundation
The Walter Guinness
Charitable Trust
The Gur Trust
The H and J Spack Charitable
Trust
The Hackney Parochial
Charities
The Hadfield Trust
The Hadrian Trust
The Alfred Haines Charitable
Trust
E F and M G Hall Charitable
Trust
Robert Hall Charity

The Hampshire and Islands
Historic Churches Trust
Hampshire and Isle of Wight
Community Foundation
The Hampstead Wells and
Campden Trust
Hampton Fuel Allotment
Charity
The W A Handley Charitable
Trust
Lord Hanson Foundation
The Harborne Parish Lands
Charity
The Harbour Foundation
William Harding's Charity
The Harpur Trust
The Harris Charity
The Harrison and Potter Trust
The Peter Harrison Foundation
The Spencer Hart Charitable
Trust
The Hartley Charitable Trust
The Edward Harvist Trust
The M A Hawe Settlement
The Dorothy Hay-Bolton
Charitable Trust
Heart of England Community
Foundation
The Heathcoat Trust
The Hedley Denton Charitable
Trust
The Simon Heller Charitable
Settlement
Help for Health
The Helping Foundation
The Hemby Trust
Henley Educational Trust
(formerley Henley
Educational Charity)
The Herefordshire Community
Foundation
The Herefordshire Historic
Churches Trust
The Heritage of London Trust
Ltd
The Hertfordshire Community
Foundation
The Hesed Trust
The Hesslewood Children's
Trust (Hull Seamen's and
General Orphanage)
Hexham and Newcastle
Diocesan Trust (1947)
The Rosalind Hicks Charitable
Trust
Alan Edward Higgs Charity
The High Sheriff's Police Trust
for the County of West
Midlands (Building Blocks)
Highcroft Charitable Trust
The Hillingdon Community
Trust
The Hillingdon Partnership
Trust
R G Hills Charitable Trust
The Hilmarnan Charitable Trust

Lady Hind Trust
Stuart Hine Trust
The Hintze Family Charitable
Foundation
The Hiscox Foundation
The Hitchin Educational
Foundation
The Eleemosynary Charity of
William Hobbayne
Matthew Hodder Charitable
Trust
John Holford's Charity
The Hollands-Warren Fund
The Hollick Family Charitable
Trust
The Edward Holt Trust
HopMarket Charity
The Antony Hornby Charitable
Trust
The Worshipful Company of
Horners' Charitable Trusts
The Hornsey Parochial
Charities
The Hospital of God at
Greatham
The Sir Joseph Hotung
Charitable Settlement
The House of Industry Estate
The Huddersfield Common
Good Trust
The Hull and East Riding
Charitable Trust
Hulme Trust Estates
(Educational)
Huntingdon Freemen's Trust
Hurdale Charity Limited
The P Y N and B Hyams Trust
The Iliffe Family Charitable
Trust
The Ingram Trust
The Inner London Magistrates
Court Poor Box and Feeder
Charity
The Charles Irving Charitable
Trust
The J Isaacs Charitable Trust
The ITF Seafarers Trust
The Ithaca Trust
J A R Charitable Trust
The J J Charitable Trust
The J M K Charitable Trust
C Richard Jackson Charitable
Trust
Elizabeth Jackson Charitable
Trust
Jacobs Charitable Trust
John James Bristol Foundation
The James Trust
The Jarman Charitable Trust
The John Jarrold Trust
The Nick Jenkins Foundation
The Jerusalem Trust
Jesus Hospital Charity
Jewish Child's Day
The Harold Joels Charitable
Trust

The Nicholas Joels Charitable
Trust
The Johnson Foundation
The Johnson Wax Ltd
Charitable Trust
The Jordan Charitable
Foundation
The J E Joseph Charitable
Fund
The Julian Budd Kids in Sport
Trust Limited
The Stanley Kalms Foundation
The Karenza Foundation
The Boris Karloff Charitable
Foundation
The Ian Karten Charitable
Trust
The Michael and Ilse Katz
Foundation
The Geoffrey John Kaye
Charitable Foundation
The Emmanuel Kaye
Foundation
Kelsick's Educational
Foundation
William Kendall's Charity (Wax
Chandlers' Company)
Kent Community Foundation
The Peter Kershaw Trust
Keswick Hall Trust
The Ursula Keyes Trust
The King Henry VIII Endowed
Trust Warwick
The Kingsbury Charity
Kirkley Poor's Lands Estate
Robert Kitchin (Saddlers'
Company)
The Sir James Knott Trust
Community Foundation for
Lancashire
Duchy of Lancaster Benevolent
Fund
The Jack Lane Charitable Trust
The Langtree Trust
Largsmount Ltd
The Herd Lawson and Muriel
Lawson Charitable Trust
The Mason Le Page Charitable
Trust
The Leach Fourteenth Trust
The William Leech Charity
The Lord Mayor of Leeds
Appeal Fund
The Leeds Community
Foundation
Leicestershire and Rutland
Community Foundation
Leicestershire Historic
Churches Trust
Morris Leigh Foundation
The Erica Leonard Trust
The Leonard Trust
Lesley Lesley and Mutter Trust
Lichfield Conduit Lands
The Lincolnshire Churches
Trust

Lincolnshire Community
Foundation
The Ruth and Stuart Lipton
Charitable Trust
Liverpool Charity and Voluntary
Services
Liverpool Sailors' Home Trust
Lloyds Bank Foundation for
England and Wales
The Lo Family Charitable Trust
The Trust for London
London Catalyst
The London Community
Foundation
The London Housing
Foundation
London Legal Support Trust
The London Marathon
Charitable Trust
The Lowy Mitchell Foundation
Lord and Lady Lurgan Trust
The Lynwood Trust
John Lyon's Charity
Sylvanus Lyson's Charity
The Magdalen and Lasher
Charity
The Makin Charitable Trust
Man Group plc Charitable
Trust
Manchester Airport Community
Trust Fund
The Manchester Guardian
Society Charitable Trust
Lord Mayor of Manchester's
Charity Appeal Trust
The Leslie and Lilian Manning
Trust
Market Harborough and The
Bowdens Charity
The Ann and David Marks
Foundation
The Michael Marsh Charitable
Trust
The Jim Marshall Charitable
Trust
Marshall's Charity
Marshgate Charitable
Settlement
John Martin's Charity
The John Mason Family Trust
Matliwala Family Charitable
Trust
The Mayfield Valley Arts Trust
The McDougall Trust
The McKenna Charitable Trust
The James Frederick and Ethel
Anne Measures Charity
The Merchant Venturers'
Charity
The Mersey Docks and
Harbour Company
Charitable Fund
Community Foundation for
Merseyside
The Metropolitan Masonic
Charity

Gerald Micklem Charitable
Trust
The Sir John Middlemore
Charitable Trust
The Masonic Province of
Middlesex Charitable Trust
Middlesex Sports Foundation
Midhurst Pensions Trust
Miles Trust for the Putney and
Roehampton Community
The Millfield House Foundation
The Mills Charity
The Clare Milne Trust
Milton Keynes Community
Foundation
The Keith and Joan
Mindelsohn Charitable
Trust
The Peter Minet Trust
The Mirfield Educational
Charity
The Mobbs Memorial Trust Ltd
The Modiano Charitable Trust
The D C Moncrieff Charitable
Trust
John Moores Foundation
The Morgan Foundation
Morgan Stanley International
Foundation
The Moss Charitable Trust
The Robert and Margaret
Moss Charitable Trust
The Moss Family Charitable
Trust
Mothercare Group Foundation
Moto in the Community
The Mushroom Fund
The Music Sales Charitable
Trust
MYA Charitable Trust
MYR Charitable Trust
The National Churches Trust
Needham Market and Barking
Welfare Charities
The Worshipful Company of
Needlemakers' Charitable
Fund
The Neighbourly Charitable
Trust
The James Neill Trust Fund
Nemoral Ltd
The New Appeals Organisation
for the City and County of
Nottingham
The Newcomen Collett
Foundation
Alderman Newton's
Educational Foundation
The Noon Foundation
Norfolk Community Foundation
The Norman Family Charitable
Trust
The North West Cancer
Research Fund
The Northampton Municipal
Church Charities

The Northampton Queen's
Institute Relief in Sickness
Fund
The Earl of Northampton's
Charity
Northamptonshire Community
Foundation
The Northcott Devon
Foundation
The Northcott Devon Medical
Foundation
The Northern Rock Foundation
The Northumberland Village
Homes Trust
The Northumbria Historic
Churches Trust
The Norwich Church of England
Young Men's Society
The Norwich Town Close
Estate Charity
The Norwood and Newton
Settlement
The Notgrove Trust
The Nottingham General
Dispensary
The Nottingham Gordon
Memorial Trust for Boys
and Girls
Nottinghamshire Community
Foundation
The Nottinghamshire Historic
Churches Trust
The Nottinghamshire Miners'
Welfare Trust Fund
Ogilvie Charities Deed No.2
(including the Charity of
Mary Catherine Ford Smith)
Oglesby Charitable Trust
The Oldham Foundation
Open Gate
The Raymond Oppenheimer
Foundation
The Ouseley Trust
City of Oxford Charity
The Oxfordshire Community
Foundation
The Paget Charitable Trust
The Palmer Foundation
Eleanor Palmer Trust
The Jack Patston Charitable
Trust
The Payne Charitable Trust
The Harry Payne Trust
The Pedmore Sporting Club
Trust Fund
Pegasus (Stanley) Trust
People's Postcode Trust
The Jack Petchey Foundation
Philological Foundation
The David Pickford Charitable
Foundation
The Bernard Piggott Charitable
Trust
The Pilkington Charities Fund
The Sir Harry Pilkington Trust

The Worshipful Company of
Plaisterers Charitable Trust
The Portishead Nautical Trust
The Mary Potter Convent
Hospital Trust
The Powell Foundation
The William Price Charitable
Trust
The Lucy Price Relief-in-Need
Charity
Sir John Priestman Charity
Trust
The Proven Family Trust
The Provincial Grand Charity of
the Province of Derbyshire
The Puri Foundation
Quartet Community Foundation
The Mr and Mrs Philip
Rackham Charitable Trust
The Fanny Rapaport Charitable
Settlement
The Ratcliff Pension Charity
The Ravensdale Trust
The Rawdon-Smith Trust
The John Rayner Charitable
Trust
Red Hill Charitable Trust
Richard Reeve's Foundation
The Nathaniel Reyner Trust
Fund
The Richmond Parish Lands
Charity
The Rochester Bridge Trust
The Rock Solid Trust
The C A Rookes Charitable
Trust
The Rosca Trust
The Rose Foundation
The Rothermere Foundation
The Rotherwick Foundation
The Rothley Trust
The Roughley Charitable Trust
The Christopher Rowbotham
Charitable Trust
Royal British Legion
Royal Docks Trust (London)
Rugby Football Foundation
The Rugby Group Benevolent
Fund Limited
The J S and E C Rymer
Charitable Trust
S O Charitable Trust
Raymond and Beverly Sackler
1988 Foundation
Saint Luke's College
Foundation
The Salt Foundation
Basil Samuel Charitable Trust
The Samworth Foundation
The Sants Charitable Trust
The R H Scholes Charitable
Trust
The Francis C Scott Charitable
Trust
The Frieda Scott Charitable
Trust

The Sir James and Lady Scott Trust
The Storrow Scott Will Trust
SF Group Charitable Fund for Disabled People
ShareGift (The Orr Mackintosh Foundation)
The Shears Foundation
The Sheldon Trust
The Sylvia and Colin Shepherd Charitable Trust
The R C Sherriff Trust
SHINE (Support and Help in Education)
The Shoe Zone Trust
The J A Shone Memorial Trust
Community Foundation for Shropshire and Telford
The Mary Elizabeth Siebel Charity
The Simmons & Simmons Charitable Foundation
The Skelton Bounty
Skipton Building Society Charitable Foundation
The Smith & Pinching Charitable Trust
The Mrs Smith and Mount Trust
The R C Snelling Charitable Trust
The Snowball Trust
The Sobell Foundation
Friends of Somerset Churches and Chapels
R H Southern Trust
The Southover Manor General Education Trust
The Southwold Trust
Sparquote Limited
The Ralph and Irma Sperring Charity
The Spielman Charitable Trust
The Spoore, Merry and Rixman Foundation
Springfields Employees' Medical Research and Charity Trust Fund
Springrule Limited
St Hilda's Trust
Sir Walter St John's Educational Charity
The St Laurence Relief In Need Trust
St Michael's and All Saints' Charities Relief Branch (The Church Houses Relief in Need Charity)
St Monica Trust
St Peter's Saltley Trust
The Stanton Ballard Charitable Trust
The Stevenage Community Trust
The Steventon Allotments and Relief-in-Need Charity

The Leonard Laity Stoate Charitable Trust
The Edward Stocks-Massey Bequest Fund
The Stokenchurch Educational Charity
The Strangward Trust
The Strasser Foundation
Stratford upon Avon Town Trust
Suffolk Community Foundation
The Suffolk Historic Churches Trust
The Summerfield Charitable Trust
Community Foundation for Surrey
The Surrey Historic Buildings Trust Ltd
The Sussex Community Foundation
The Sussex Historic Churches Trust
Sutton Coldfield Charitable Trust
T and S Trust Fund
The Talbot Trusts
The Talbot Village Trust
Tallow Chandlers Benevolent Fund
The Mrs A Lacy Tate Trust
C B and H H Taylor 1984 Trust
Humphrey Richardson Taylor Charitable Trust
The Connie and Albert Taylor Charitable Trust
The Cyril Taylor Charitable Trust
The Taylor Family Foundation
A P Taylor Trust
Tees Valley Community Foundation
Tegham Limited
The C Paul Thackray General Charitable Trust
Mrs R P Tindall's Charitable Trust
The Tobacco Pipe Makers and Tobacco Trade Benevolent Fund
Toni and Guy Charitable Foundation Limited
Tottenham Grammar School Foundation
The Tower Hill Trust
The Mayor of Trafford's Charity Fund
Tuixen Foundation
The G J W Turner Trust
Miss S M Tutton Charitable Trust
Two Ridings Community Foundation
Community Foundation Serving Tyne and Wear and Northumberland

Ulverston Town Lands Charity
United Utilities Trust Fund
Uxbridge United Welfare Trust
The Valentine Charitable Trust
The Verdon-Smith Family Charitable Settlement
The Vintners' Company Charitable Foundation
Vintners' Gifts Charity
The Vodafone Foundation
Wade's Charity
The Scurrah Wainwright Charity
The Wakefield and Tetley Trust
Robert and Felicity Waley-Cohen Charitable Trust
The Walker Trust
The George Ward Charitable Trust
The Barbara Ward Children's Foundation
The John Warren Foundation
The Wates Foundation
The Howard Watson Symington Memorial Charity
The William Webster Charitable Trust
The West Derby Wastelands Charity
West Yorkshire Police Community Trust
A H and B C Whiteley Charitable Trust
The Norman Whiteley Trust
The Whittlesey Charity
The William Barrow's Charity
The Charity of William Williams
The Dame Violet Wills Will Trust
The Wilmcote Charitrust
David Wilson Foundation
The Wilson Foundation
The Community Foundation for Wiltshire and Swindon
The Francis Winham Foundation
Wirral Mayor's Charity
The F Glenister Woodger Trust
Woodlands Trust
The Woodward Charitable Trust
The A and R Woolf Charitable Trust
Worcester Municipal Charities
The Worcestershire and Dudley Historic Churches Trust
The Yapp Charitable Trust
The Yardley Great Trust
The W Wing Yip and Brothers Foundation
Yorkshire Agricultural Society
The South Yorkshire Community Foundation
The Yorkshire Dales Millennium Trust

The Yorkshire Historic
  Churches Trust
Youth Music (previously known
  as National Foundation for
  Youth Music)
The Zochonis Charitable Trust

....

■ Greater London

ABF The Soldiers' Charity
Aldgate and All Hallows'
  Foundation
The Aldgate Freedom
  Foundation
Amabrill Limited
Anpride Ltd
The Arsenal Foundation
The Ashendene Trust
AstonMansfield Charitable
  Trust
The Avenue Charitable Trust
The Barleycorn Trust
Barnes Workhouse Fund
The Bellinger Donnay Trust
Bergqvist Charitable Trust
The Bintaub Charitable Trust
The Sir Victor Blank Charitable
  Settlement
The Nicholas Boas Charitable
  Trust
The British Council for
  Prevention of Blindness
The Worshipful Company of
  Butchers General Charities
The Campden Charities
  Trustee
Sir John Cass's Foundation
The City Bridge Trust
Richard Cloudesley's Charity
The R and S Cohen
  Foundation
The Consolidated Charities for
  the Infirm Merchant
  Taylors' Company
Cripplegate Foundation
The Croydon Relief in Need
  Charities
The Daisy Trust
Dentons UKMEA LLP
  Charitable Trust
Dischma Charitable Trust
East End Community
  Foundation
Edinburgh Trust No 2 Account
Dr Edwards Bishop King's
  Fulham Endowment Fund
Elshore Ltd
The Vernon N Ely Charitable
  Trust
Sir John Evelyn's Charity
The Fassnidge Memorial Trust
Finnart House School Trust
Firtree Trust
Ford Britain Trust
The Charles S French
  Charitable Trust

Friends of Wiznitz Limited
The Worshipful Company of
  Gardeners of London
The Samuel Gardner Memorial
  Trust
The B and P Glasser
  Charitable Trust
The Glass-House Trust
The Goldsmiths' Company
  Charity
The Graff Foundation
The Grahame Charitable
  Foundation Limited
Grand Charitable Trust of the
  Order of Women
  Freemasons
The Grange Farm Centre Trust
The M and R Gross Charities
  Limited
The Gur Trust
The H and J Spack Charitable
  Trust
The Hackney Parochial
  Charities
The Hampstead Wells and
  Campden Trust
Hampton Fuel Allotment
  Charity
Lord Hanson Foundation
The Harbour Foundation
The Spencer Hart Charitable
  Trust
The Edward Harvist Trust
The Simon Heller Charitable
  Settlement
The Helping Foundation
The Heritage of London Trust
  Ltd
Highcroft Charitable Trust
The Hillingdon Community
  Trust
The Hillingdon Partnership
  Trust
The Hiscox Foundation
The Eleemosynary Charity of
  William Hobbayne
The Hollick Family Charitable
  Trust
The Antony Hornby Charitable
  Trust
The Worshipful Company of
  Horners' Charitable Trusts
The Hornsey Parochial
  Charities
The Sir Joseph Hotung
  Charitable Settlement
Hurdale Charity Limited
The P Y N and B Hyams Trust
The Inner London Magistrates
  Court Poor Box and Feeder
  Charity
The ITF Seafarers Trust
The Ithaca Trust
J A R Charitable Trust
The J J Charitable Trust
Jacobs Charitable Trust

The Jerusalem Trust
Jesus Hospital Charity
Jewish Child's Day
The Harold Joels Charitable
  Trust
The Nicholas Joels Charitable
  Trust
The J E Joseph Charitable
  Fund
The Stanley Kalms Foundation
The Boris Karloff Charitable
  Foundation
The Geoffrey John Kaye
  Charitable Foundation
William Kendall's Charity (Wax
  Chandlers' Company)
The Kingsbury Charity
Robert Kitchin (Saddlers'
  Company)
Largsmount Ltd
The Mason Le Page Charitable
  Trust
The Ruth and Stuart Lipton
  Charitable Trust
The Trust for London
London Catalyst
The London Community
  Foundation
The London Housing
  Foundation
London Legal Support Trust
The London Marathon
  Charitable Trust
The Lowy Mitchell Foundation
The Lynwood Trust
John Lyon's Charity
Man Group plc Charitable
  Trust
The McDougall Trust
The Metropolitan Masonic
  Charity
The Masonic Province of
  Middlesex Charitable Trust
Miles Trust for the Putney and
  Roehampton Community
The Peter Minet Trust
The Modiano Charitable Trust
Morgan Stanley International
  Foundation
The Music Sales Charitable
  Trust
MYA Charitable Trust
The Worshipful Company of
  Needlemakers' Charitable
  Fund
Nemoral Ltd
The Newcomen Collett
  Foundation
The Earl of Northampton's
  Charity
Ogilvie Charities Deed No.2
  (including the Charity of
  Mary Catherine Ford Smith)
The Raymond Oppenheimer
  Foundation
The Palmer Foundation

Eleanor Palmer Trust
People's Postcode Trust
The Jack Petchey Foundation
Philological Foundation
The David Pickford Charitable
Foundation
The Ratcliff Pension Charity
Richard Reeve's Foundation
The Richmond Parish Lands
Charity
The Rose Foundation
The Christopher Rowbotham
Charitable Trust
Royal Docks Trust (London)
Basil Samuel Charitable Trust
SF Group Charitable Fund for
Disabled People
ShareGift (The Orr Mackintosh
Foundation)
SHINE (Support and Help in
Education)
The Simmons & Simmons
Charitable Foundation
The Mrs Smith and Mount
Trust
Sir Walter St John's
Educational Charity
T and S Trust Fund
Tallow Chandlers Benevolent
Fund
Humphrey Richardson Taylor
Charitable Trust
The Cyril Taylor Charitable
Trust
The Taylor Family Foundation
A P Taylor Trust
Tegham Limited
The Tobacco Pipe Makers and
Tobacco Trade Benevolent
Fund
Tottenham Grammar School
Foundation
The Tower Hill Trust
Tuixen Foundation
Uxbridge United Welfare Trust
The Vintners' Company
Charitable Foundation
Vintners' Gifts Charity
The Wakefield and Tetley Trust
The Wates Foundation
Woodlands Trust
The Woodward Charitable
Trust
The W Wing Yip and Brothers
Foundation

■ Barking and Dagenham

Ford Britain Trust
The Jack Petchey Foundation

■ Barnet

The Bintaub Charitable Trust
Elshore Ltd
Finnart House School Trust

The Edward Harvist Trust
Highcroft Charitable Trust
Jesus Hospital Charity
Jewish Child's Day
John Lyon's Charity
Eleanor Palmer Trust
Tegham Limited

■ Bexley

Ford Britain Trust

■ Brent

The Edward Harvist Trust
The Kingsbury Charity
John Lyon's Charity
The W Wing Yip and Brothers
Foundation

■ Camden

The British Council for
Prevention of Blindness
Sir John Cass's Foundation
The Grahame Charitable
Foundation Limited
The Hampstead Wells and
Campden Trust
The Edward Harvist Trust
J A R Charitable Trust
The Harold Joels Charitable
Trust
The Lowy Mitchell Foundation
John Lyon's Charity
The Raymond Oppenheimer
Foundation
Philological Foundation
Richard Reeve's Foundation

■ City of London

Aldgate and All Hallows'
Foundation
The Aldgate Freedom
Foundation
Sir John Cass's Foundation
Dentons UKMEA LLP
Charitable Trust
East End Community
Foundation
The B and P Glasser
Charitable Trust
The Spencer Hart Charitable
Trust
The Hiscox Foundation
The Sir Joseph Hotung
Charitable Settlement
John Lyon's Charity
The Modiano Charitable Trust
The Worshipful Company of
Needlemakers' Charitable
Fund
Richard Reeve's Foundation
The Simmons & Simmons
Charitable Foundation

The Tobacco Pipe Makers and
Tobacco Trade Benevolent
Fund
Tuixen Foundation
The Wakefield and Tetley Trust

■ City of Westminster

The Avenue Charitable Trust
The Nicholas Boas Charitable
Trust
Sir John Cass's Foundation
The R and S Cohen
Foundation
Dischma Charitable Trust
Edinburgh Trust No 2 Account
The Glass-House Trust
The Graff Foundation
The M and R Gross Charities
Limited
The H and J Spack Charitable
Trust
The Edward Harvist Trust
The Simon Heller Charitable
Settlement
The Hollick Family Charitable
Trust
The P Y N and B Hyams Trust
The J J Charitable Trust
Jacobs Charitable Trust
The Jerusalem Trust
The Nicholas Joels Charitable
Trust
The Stanley Kalms Foundation
The Boris Karloff Charitable
Foundation
Largsmount Ltd
The Ruth and Stuart Lipton
Charitable Trust
John Lyon's Charity
Nemoral Ltd
Philological Foundation
Basil Samuel Charitable Trust
ShareGift (The Orr Mackintosh
Foundation)
The Woodward Charitable
Trust

■ Croydon

The Croydon Relief in Need
Charities
The W Wing Yip and Brothers
Foundation

■ Ealing

The Eleemosynary Charity of
William Hobbayne
John Lyon's Charity

■ Greenwich

Sir John Cass's Foundation
Sir John Evelyn's Charity
Ford Britain Trust

■ Hackney

East End Community
   Foundation
Friends of Wiznitz Limited
Hurdale Charity Limited
MYA Charitable Trust
Sir John Cass's Foundation
The Gur Trust
The Hackney Parochial
   Charities
The Harbour Foundation
The Hornsey Parochial
   Charities
The Jack Petchey Foundation

■ Hammersmith and Fulham

Sir John Cass's Foundation
The Daisy Trust
Dr Edwards Bishop King's
   Fulham Endowment Fund
John Lyon's Charity

■ Haringey

The Hornsey Parochial
   Charities
Tottenham Grammar School
   Foundation

■ Harrow

Amabrill Limited
The Samuel Gardner Memorial
   Trust
The Edward Harvist Trust
The Geoffrey John Kaye
   Charitable Foundation
John Lyon's Charity

■ Havering

Ford Britain Trust
The Jack Petchey Foundation

■ Hillingdon

The Fassnidge Memorial Trust
The Hillingdon Community
   Trust
The Hillingdon Partnership
   Trust
A P Taylor Trust
Uxbridge United Welfare Trust

■ Islington

Sir John Cass's Foundation
Richard Cloudesley's Charity
Cripplegate Foundation
Richard Reeve's Foundation

■ Kensington and Chelsea

ABF The Soldiers' Charity
The Campden Charities
   Trustee
Sir John Cass's Foundation
Grand Charitable Trust of the
   Order of Women
   Freemasons
Lord Hanson Foundation
John Lyon's Charity
The Christopher Rowbotham
   Charitable Trust

■ Lambeth

Sir John Cass's Foundation
Sir Walter St John's
   Educational Charity

■ Lewisham

Sir John Cass's Foundation
Sir John Evelyn's Charity

■ Merton

The Vernon N Ely Charitable
   Trust

■ Newham

AstonMansfield Charitable
   Trust
Sir John Cass's Foundation
East End Community
   Foundation
Ford Britain Trust
Morgan Stanley International
   Foundation
The Jack Petchey Foundation
Royal Docks Trust (London)

■ Redbridge

Ford Britain Trust
The Jack Petchey Foundation

■ Richmond upon Thames

Barnes Workhouse Fund
Hampton Fuel Allotment
   Charity
The Richmond Parish Lands
   Charity

■ Southwark

The Sir Victor Blank Charitable
   Settlement
Sir John Cass's Foundation
The ITF Seafarers Trust
The McDougall Trust
The Newcomen Collett
   Foundation
The Wakefield and Tetley Trust

■ Sutton

The Barleycorn Trust
Firtree Trust
The Lynwood Trust
Humphrey Richardson Taylor
   Charitable Trust

■ Tower Hamlets

Aldgate and All Hallows'
   Foundation
Sir John Cass's Foundation
East End Community
   Foundation
Morgan Stanley International
   Foundation
The Palmer Foundation
The Jack Petchey Foundation
The Ratcliff Pension Charity
The Simmons & Simmons
   Charitable Foundation
The Tower Hill Trust
The Wakefield and Tetley Trust

■ Waltham Forest

The Jack Petchey Foundation

■ Wandsworth

Sir John Cass's Foundation
Miles Trust for the Putney and
   Roehampton Community
Sir Walter St John's
   Educational Charity

....

■ South Eastern England

The Ammco Trust
The Arbib Foundation
The Argus Appeal
The Ashendene Trust
The BAA Communities Trust
The Banbury Charities
The Bellinger Donnay Trust
Bergqvist Charitable Trust
The Berkshire Community
   Foundation
Isabel Blackman Foundation
The Blagrave Trust
Bonhomie United Charity
   Society
The Bordon Liphook
   Haslemere Charity
The Frank Brake Charitable
   Trust
John Bristow and Thomas
   Mason Trust
Buckinghamshire Community
   Foundation
The Buckinghamshire Historic
   Churches Trust
The Buckinghamshire Masonic
   Centenary Fund

The Chelsea Square 1994
Trust
The Coalfields Regeneration
Trust
The Cobtree Charity Trust Ltd
The Cole Charitable Trust
The Colefax Charitable Trust
The John and Freda Coleman
Charitable Trust
Colyer-Fergusson Charitable
Trust
The John Cowan Foundation
The Dibden Allotments Fund
The Derek and Eileen Dodgson
Foundation
Downlands Educational Trust
The Dulverton Trust
The Earley Charity
The Gilbert and Eileen Edgar
Foundation
The Gerald Palmer Eling Trust
Company
The Ellis Campbell Foundation
The Essex Fairway Charitable
Trust
Ford Britain Trust
The Four Lanes Trust
The Friends of Kent Churches
T F C Frost Charitable Trust
Gatwick Airport Community
Trust
The Gibbons Family Trust
The GNC Trust
The Godinton Charitable Trust
The Great Stone Bridge Trust
of Edenbridge
The Bishop of Guildford's
Foundation
The Walter Guinness
Charitable Trust
E F and M G Hall Charitable
Trust
The Hampshire and Islands
Historic Churches Trust
Hampshire and Isle of Wight
Community Foundation
William Harding's Charity
The Peter Harrison Foundation
The Dorothy Hay-Bolton
Charitable Trust
Henley Educational Trust
(formerley Henley
Educational Charity)
R G Hills Charitable Trust
Stuart Hine Trust
Matthew Hodder Charitable
Trust
The Hollands-Warren Fund
The Antony Hornby Charitable
Trust
The Iliffe Family Charitable
Trust
The Ingram Trust
The J M K Charitable Trust
Elizabeth Jackson Charitable
Trust

The Johnson Wax Ltd
Charitable Trust
The Julian Budd Kids in Sport
Trust Limited
The Emmanuel Kaye
Foundation
Kent Community Foundation
The Leach Fourteenth Trust
The Erica Leonard Trust
The Leonard Trust
London Legal Support Trust
The Magdalen and Lasher
Charity
The Jim Marshall Charitable
Trust
Gerald Micklem Charitable
Trust
The Masonic Province of
Middlesex Charitable Trust
Milton Keynes Community
Foundation
The Mobbs Memorial Trust Ltd
The Moss Charitable Trust
The Robert and Margaret
Moss Charitable Trust
The Earl of Northampton's
Charity
City of Oxford Charity
The Oxfordshire Community
Foundation
The David Pickford Charitable
Foundation
The Powell Foundation
The William Price Charitable
Trust
Red Hill Charitable Trust
The Rochester Bridge Trust
The Rothermere Foundation
The Rotherwick Foundation
The Sants Charitable Trust
SF Group Charitable Fund for
Disabled People
The R C Sherriff Trust
The Mrs Smith and Mount
Trust
The Southover Manor General
Education Trust
The Spoore, Merry and Rixman
Foundation
The St Laurence Relief In
Need Trust
St Michael's and All Saints'
Charities Relief Branch (The
Church Houses Relief in
Need Charity)
The Stanton Ballard Charitable
Trust
The Steventon Allotments and
Relief-in-Need Charity
The Stokenchurch Educational
Charity
Community Foundation for
Surrey
The Surrey Historic Buildings
Trust Ltd

The Sussex Community
Foundation
The Sussex Historic Churches
Trust
The Mrs A Lacy Tate Trust
Humphrey Richardson Taylor
Charitable Trust
The Taylor Family Foundation
The Vodafone Foundation
The Wates Foundation
The William Barrow's Charity
The F Glenister Woodger Trust

■ **Berkshire**

The Ashendene Trust
Bergqvist Charitable Trust
The Berkshire Community
Foundation
The Colefax Charitable Trust
The Earley Charity
The Gilbert and Eileen Edgar
Foundation
The Gerald Palmer Eling Trust
Company
Henley Educational Trust
(formerley Henley
Educational Charity)
The Iliffe Family Charitable
Trust
The J M K Charitable Trust
The Johnson Wax Ltd
Charitable Trust
The Spoore, Merry and Rixman
Foundation
The St Laurence Relief In
Need Trust
The Vodafone Foundation
The Wates Foundation

■ **Buckinghamshire**

Bergqvist Charitable Trust
Buckinghamshire Community
Foundation
The Buckinghamshire Historic
Churches Trust
The Buckinghamshire Masonic
Centenary Fund
William Harding's Charity
London Legal Support Trust
The Jim Marshall Charitable
Trust
Milton Keynes Community
Foundation
The Mobbs Memorial Trust Ltd
The Powell Foundation
The Stokenchurch Educational
Charity
The Wates Foundation

■ **East Sussex**

The Argus Appeal
Isabel Blackman Foundation

The Derek and Eileen Dodgson
 Foundation
Downlands Educational Trust
Gatwick Airport Community
 Trust
Stuart Hine Trust
The Magdalen and Lasher
 Charity
The Moss Charitable Trust
The Rotherwick Foundation
The Southover Manor General
 Education Trust
The Sussex Community
 Foundation
The Sussex Historic Churches
 Trust
The Mrs A Lacy Tate Trust
The Wates Foundation

■ **Hampshire**

The BAA Communities Trust
Bonhomie United Charity
 Society
The Bordon Liphook
 Haslemere Charity
The Colefax Charitable Trust
The John and Freda Coleman
 Charitable Trust
The Dibden Allotments Fund
Downlands Educational Trust
The Ellis Campbell Foundation
Ford Britain Trust
The Four Lanes Trust
The Walter Guinness
 Charitable Trust
The Hampshire and Islands
 Historic Churches Trust
Hampshire and Isle of Wight
 Community Foundation
The Johnson Wax Ltd
 Charitable Trust
The Emmanuel Kaye
 Foundation
The Leonard Trust
Gerald Micklem Charitable
 Trust
The Moss Charitable Trust
The William Price Charitable
 Trust
The Rotherwick Foundation

■ **Isle of Wight**

Hampshire and Isle of Wight
 Community Foundation

■ **Kent**

The Frank Brake Charitable
 Trust
The Coalfields Regeneration
 Trust
The Cobtree Charity Trust Ltd
The Cole Charitable Trust

Colyer-Fergusson Charitable
 Trust
Downlands Educational Trust
The Friends of Kent Churches
Gatwick Airport Community
 Trust
The Gibbons Family Trust
The Godinton Charitable Trust
The Great Stone Bridge Trust
 of Edenbridge
R G Hills Charitable Trust
Matthew Hodder Charitable
 Trust
The Hollands-Warren Fund
Kent Community Foundation
London Legal Support Trust
The David Pickford Charitable
 Foundation
The Rochester Bridge Trust
The Rothermere Foundation
The William Barrow's Charity

■ **Oxfordshire**

The Arbib Foundation
The Ashendene Trust
The Banbury Charities
Bergqvist Charitable Trust
Henley Educational Trust
 (formerley Henley
 Educational Charity)
Elizabeth Jackson Charitable
 Trust
The Robert and Margaret
 Moss Charitable Trust
City of Oxford Charity
The Oxfordshire Community
 Foundation
The Sants Charitable Trust
St Michael's and All Saints'
 Charities Relief Branch (The
 Church Houses Relief in
 Need Charity)
The Stanton Ballard Charitable
 Trust
The Steventon Allotments and
 Relief-in-Need Charity
The Vodafone Foundation
The Wates Foundation

■ **Surrey**

John Bristow and Thomas
 Mason Trust
The John and Freda Coleman
 Charitable Trust
The John Cowan Foundation
Downlands Educational Trust
T F C Frost Charitable Trust
Gatwick Airport Community
 Trust
The Bishop of Guildford's
 Foundation
The Ingram Trust
The Johnson Wax Ltd
 Charitable Trust

The Erica Leonard Trust
London Legal Support Trust
The Masonic Province of
 Middlesex Charitable Trust
The R C Sherriff Trust
Community Foundation for
 Surrey
The Surrey Historic Buildings
 Trust Ltd
Humphrey Richardson Taylor
 Charitable Trust
The Wates Foundation

■ **West Sussex**

The Argus Appeal
The BAA Communities Trust
The Derek and Eileen Dodgson
 Foundation
Downlands Educational Trust
Gatwick Airport Community
 Trust
The Moss Charitable Trust
The Southover Manor General
 Education Trust
The Sussex Community
 Foundation
The Sussex Historic Churches
 Trust
The Wates Foundation
The F Glenister Woodger Trust

■ **South Western
 England**

The H B Allen Charitable Trust
Almondsbury Charity
Viscount Amory's Charitable
 Trust
The Avon and Somerset Police
 Community Trust
The Albert Casanova Ballard
 Deceased Trust
The Barnstaple Bridge Trust
The Barnwood House Trust
The Bellinger Donnay Trust
The Bideford Bridge Trust
The Blagrave Trust
The Blanchminster Trust
Bristol Archdeaconry Charity
The Bristol Charities
The J and M Britton Charitable
 Trust
M R Cannon 1998 Charitable
 Trust
The Chelsea Square 1994
 Trust
The Chippenham Borough
 Lands Charity
The Chipping Sodbury Town
 Lands Charity
The Hilda and Alice Clark
 Charitable Trust
Lord Clinton's Charitable Trust
Community First (Landfill
 Communities Fund)

Cornwall Community
　Foundation
The Cornwall Historic
　Churches Trust
The Cornwell Charitable Trust
The Harry Crook Foundation
The Dr and Mrs A Darlington
　Charitable Trust
The Denman Charitable Trust
Devon Community Foundation
The Devon Educational Trust
The Devon Historic Churches
　Trust
Dorset Community Foundation
The Dorset Historic Churches
　Trust
The Dulverton Trust
The Elmgrant Trust
The Joyce Fletcher Charitable
　Trust
The Thomas Freke and Lady
　Norton Charity Trust
The Fulmer Charitable Trust
The Garnett Charitable Trust
The Gibbons Family Trust
The David Gibbons Foundation
Gloucestershire Community
　Foundation
The Gloucestershire Historic
　Churches Trust
The GNC Trust
The Gordon Gray Trust
The Great Torrington Town
　Lands Charity
The Walter Guinness
　Charitable Trust
The Peter Harrison Foundation
The Heathcoat Trust
The Rosalind Hicks Charitable
　Trust
The Charles Irving Charitable
　Trust
Elizabeth Jackson Charitable
　Trust
John James Bristol Foundation
The Michael and Ilse Katz
　Foundation
The Jack Lane Charitable Trust
The Langtree Trust
The Leach Fourteenth Trust
Lesley Lesley and Mutter Trust
Sylvanus Lyson's Charity
The Merchant Venturers'
　Charity
The Clare Milne Trust
The Moss Charitable Trust
The Norman Family Charitable
　Trust
The Northcott Devon
　Foundation
The Northcott Devon Medical
　Foundation
The Notgrove Trust
The Oldham Foundation
The Portishead Nautical Trust
Quartet Community Foundation

The Rock Solid Trust
Saint Luke's College
　Foundation
SF Group Charitable Fund for
　Disabled People
Friends of Somerset Churches
　and Chapels
The Ralph and Irma Sperring
　Charity
The Spielman Charitable Trust
St Monica Trust
The Summerfield Charitable
　Trust
The Talbot Village Trust
Mrs R P Tindall's Charitable
　Trust
The Valentine Charitable Trust
The Verdon-Smith Family
　Charitable Settlement
The Vodafone Foundation
The Wates Foundation
The Charity of William Williams
The Dame Violet Wills Will
　Trust
The Community Foundation for
　Wiltshire and Swindon

■ **Avon**

Almondsbury Charity
The Avon and Somerset Police
　Community Trust
Bristol Archdeaconry Charity
The Bristol Charities
The J and M Britton Charitable
　Trust
M R Cannon 1998 Charitable
　Trust
The Chipping Sodbury Town
　Lands Charity
The Harry Crook Foundation
The Denman Charitable Trust
John James Bristol Foundation
The Merchant Venturers'
　Charity
The Portishead Nautical Trust
Quartet Community Foundation
The Rock Solid Trust
The Ralph and Irma Sperring
　Charity
The Spielman Charitable Trust
The Wates Foundation
The Dame Violet Wills Will
　Trust

■ **Cornwall and the Scilly
　Isles**

The Blanchminster Trust
Cornwall Community
　Foundation
The Cornwall Historic
　Churches Trust
The Heathcoat Trust
The Michael and Ilse Katz
　Foundation

The Clare Milne Trust

■ **Devon**

The H B Allen Charitable Trust
Viscount Amory's Charitable
　Trust
The Albert Casanova Ballard
　Deceased Trust
The Barnstaple Bridge Trust
The Bideford Bridge Trust
Lord Clinton's Charitable Trust
The Dr and Mrs A Darlington
　Charitable Trust
Devon Community Foundation
The Devon Educational Trust
The Devon Historic Churches
　Trust
The Gibbons Family Trust
The David Gibbons Foundation
The Great Torrington Town
　Lands Charity
The Heathcoat Trust
The Rosalind Hicks Charitable
　Trust
Lesley Lesley and Mutter Trust
The Clare Milne Trust
The Northcott Devon
　Foundation
The Northcott Devon Medical
　Foundation
Saint Luke's College
　Foundation
The Dame Violet Wills Will
　Trust

■ **Dorset**

Dorset Community Foundation
The Dorset Historic Churches
　Trust
The Moss Charitable Trust
The Talbot Village Trust
Mrs R P Tindall's Charitable
　Trust
The Valentine Charitable Trust
The Wates Foundation
The Charity of William Williams

■ **Gloucestershire**

The Barnwood House Trust
Gloucestershire Community
　Foundation
The Gloucestershire Historic
　Churches Trust
The Gordon Gray Trust
The Charles Irving Charitable
　Trust
Elizabeth Jackson Charitable
　Trust
The Jack Lane Charitable Trust
The Langtree Trust
Sylvanus Lyson's Charity
The Notgrove Trust
Quartet Community Foundation

St Monica Trust
The Summerfield Charitable
   Trust
The Wates Foundation

■ **Somerset**

The Avon and Somerset Police
   Community Trust
The Hilda and Alice Clark
   Charitable Trust
Quartet Community Foundation
Friends of Somerset Churches
   and Chapels
St Monica Trust
The Wates Foundation

■ **Wiltshire**

The Bellinger Donnay Trust
The Blagrave Trust
The Chippenham Borough
   Lands Charity
Community First (Landfill
   Communities Fund)
The Thomas Freke and Lady
   Norton Charity Trust
The Fulmer Charitable Trust
The Walter Guinness
   Charitable Trust
The Jack Lane Charitable Trust
St Monica Trust
Mrs R P Tindall's Charitable
   Trust
The Vodafone Foundation
The Community Foundation for
   Wiltshire and Swindon

....

■ **West Midlands
region**

The Lord Austin Trust
The John Avins Trustees
The Aylesford Family
   Charitable Trust
The Bamford Charitable
   Foundation
The James Beattie Charitable
   Trust
The Jack and Ada Beattie
   Foundation
Birmingham & Black Country
   Community Foundation
The Birmingham District
   Nursing Charitable Trust
Birmingham International
   Airport Community Trust
The Lord Mayor of
   Birmingham's Charity
The Michael Bishop
   Foundation
The Bransford Trust
The Charles Brotherton Trust
The Swinfen Broun Charitable
   Trust

The E F Bulmer Benevolent
   Fund
The Burton Breweries
   Charitable Trust
Consolidated Charity of Burton
   upon Trent
The William A Cadbury
   Charitable Trust
Christadelphian Samaritan
   Fund
The Clarke Charitable
   Settlement
The Coalfields Regeneration
   Trust
The Cole Charitable Trust
The George Henry Collins
   Charity
The General Charities of the
   City of Coventry
Coventry Building Society
   Charitable Foundation
Baron Davenport's Charity
The Digbeth Trust Limited
The Dulverton Trust
The P B Dumbell Charitable
   Trust
The Dumbreck Charity
The W E Dunn Trust
The William Edwards
   Educational Charity
The Wilfred and Elsie Elkes
   Charity Fund
The Elmley Foundation
The Eveson Charitable Trust
The John Feeney Charitable
   Trust
The George Fentham
   Birmingham Charity
The Lady Forester Trust
The Friends Hall Farm Street
   Trust
The GNC Trust
Grantham Yorke Trust
The Grimmitt Trust
The Alfred Haines Charitable
   Trust
The Harborne Parish Lands
   Charity
The Peter Harrison Foundation
Heart of England Community
   Foundation
The Herefordshire Community
   Foundation
The Herefordshire Historic
   Churches Trust
Alan Edward Higgs Charity
The High Sheriff's Police Trust
   for the County of West
   Midlands (Building Blocks)
HopMarket Charity
Elizabeth Jackson Charitable
   Trust
The Jarman Charitable Trust
The Jordan Charitable
   Foundation

The King Henry VIII Endowed
   Trust Warwick
Lichfield Conduit Lands
The London Marathon
   Charitable Trust
The Michael Marsh Charitable
   Trust
John Martin's Charity
The James Frederick and Ethel
   Anne Measures Charity
The Sir John Middlemore
   Charitable Trust
The Keith and Joan
   Mindelsohn Charitable
   Trust
Open Gate
The Payne Charitable Trust
The Harry Payne Trust
The Pedmore Sporting Club
   Trust Fund
Pegasus (Stanley) Trust
People's Postcode Trust
The Bernard Piggott Charitable
   Trust
The Lucy Price Relief-in-Need
   Charity
The C A Rookes Charitable
   Trust
The Roughley Charitable Trust
The Rugby Group Benevolent
   Fund Limited
SF Group Charitable Fund for
   Disabled People
The Sheldon Trust
Community Foundation for
   Shropshire and Telford
The Snowball Trust
St Peter's Saltley Trust
The Strasser Foundation
Stratford upon Avon Town
   Trust
Sutton Coldfield Charitable
   Trust
C B and H H Taylor 1984 Trust
The Connie and Albert Taylor
   Charitable Trust
The C Paul Thackray General
   Charitable Trust
The G J W Turner Trust
The Vodafone Foundation
The Walker Trust
The Wilmcote Charitrust
Woodlands Trust
Worcester Municipal Charities
The Worcestershire and
   Dudley Historic Churches
   Trust
The Yardley Great Trust
The W Wing Yip and Brothers
   Foundation

■ **Herefordshire**

The Elmley Foundation
The Eveson Charitable Trust

The Herefordshire Community
  Foundation
The Herefordshire Historic
  Churches Trust
The Jordan Charitable
  Foundation
St Peter's Saltley Trust
The C Paul Thackray General
  Charitable Trust

■ **Shropshire**

Baron Davenport's Charity
The P B Dumbell Charitable
  Trust
The Lady Forester Trust
Pegasus (Stanley) Trust
Community Foundation for
  Shropshire and Telford
The C Paul Thackray General
  Charitable Trust
The Walker Trust

■ **Staffordshire**

The Bamford Charitable
  Foundation
The Swinfen Broun Charitable
  Trust
The Burton Breweries
  Charitable Trust
Consolidated Charity of Burton
  upon Trent
The Clarke Charitable
  Settlement
Baron Davenport's Charity
The Wilfred and Elsie Elkes
  Charity Fund
The Alfred Haines Charitable
  Trust
Lichfield Conduit Lands
The Michael Marsh Charitable
  Trust
Open Gate
St Peter's Saltley Trust
The Strasser Foundation
The Vodafone Foundation

■ **Warwickshire**

The Aylesford Family
  Charitable Trust
Birmingham International
  Airport Community Trust
Baron Davenport's Charity
The Dumbreck Charity
The William Edwards
  Educational Charity
The Alfred Haines Charitable
  Trust
Heart of England Community
  Foundation
Alan Edward Higgs Charity
Elizabeth Jackson Charitable
  Trust

The King Henry VIII Endowed
  Trust Warwick
The Michael Marsh Charitable
  Trust
The Harry Payne Trust
The Lucy Price Relief-in-Need
  Charity
The C A Rookes Charitable
  Trust
The Snowball Trust
Stratford upon Avon Town
  Trust
Woodlands Trust

■ **West Midlands**

The Lord Austin Trust
The John Avins Trustees
The Aylesford Family
  Charitable Trust
The James Beattie Charitable
  Trust
Birmingham & Black Country
  Community Foundation
The Birmingham District
  Nursing Charitable Trust
Birmingham International
  Airport Community Trust
The Charles Brotherton Trust
The William A Cadbury
  Charitable Trust
Christadelphian Samaritan
  Fund
The Cole Charitable Trust
The George Henry Collins
  Charity
The General Charities of the
  City of Coventry
Baron Davenport's Charity
The Digbeth Trust Limited
The P B Dumbell Charitable
  Trust
The Dumbreck Charity
The Eveson Charitable Trust
The John Feeney Charitable
  Trust
The George Fentham
  Birmingham Charity
The Friends Hall Farm Street
  Trust
Grantham Yorke Trust
The Grimmitt Trust
The Alfred Haines Charitable
  Trust
The Harborne Parish Lands
  Charity
Heart of England Community
  Foundation
Alan Edward Higgs Charity
The High Sheriff's Police Trust
  for the County of West
  Midlands (Building Blocks)
Elizabeth Jackson Charitable
  Trust
The Jarman Charitable Trust

The London Marathon
  Charitable Trust
The Michael Marsh Charitable
  Trust
The James Frederick and Ethel
  Anne Measures Charity
The Keith and Joan
  Mindelsohn Charitable
  Trust
Open Gate
The Payne Charitable Trust
The Harry Payne Trust
The Bernard Piggott Charitable
  Trust
The Roughley Charitable Trust
The Sheldon Trust
The Snowball Trust
St Peter's Saltley Trust
Sutton Coldfield Charitable
  Trust
C B and H H Taylor 1984 Trust
Woodlands Trust
The W Wing Yip and Brothers
  Foundation

■ **Worcestershire**

Baron Davenport's Charity
The Dumbreck Charity
The Elmley Foundation
The Eveson Charitable Trust
HopMarket Charity
The Michael Marsh Charitable
  Trust
John Martin's Charity
The Harry Payne Trust
St Peter's Saltley Trust
The C Paul Thackray General
  Charitable Trust
Worcester Municipal Charities
The Worcestershire and
  Dudley Historic Churches
  Trust

....

■ **East Midlands**

The Bamford Charitable
  Foundation
The Bates Charitable Trust
The Jack and Ada Beattie
  Foundation
The Becketts and Sargeants
  Educational Foundation
Bergqvist Charitable Trust
The Bingham Trust
The Michael Bishop
  Foundation
The Boots Charitable Trust
The Burton Breweries
  Charitable Trust
The Frederick and Phyllis Cann
  Trust
Carter's Educational
  Foundation
The Clarke Charitable
  Settlement

The Coalfields Regeneration
    Trust
The Compton Charitable Trust
The Douglas Compton James
    Charitable Trust
The Helen Jean Cope Trust
The J Reginald Corah
    Foundation Fund
Coventry Building Society
    Charitable Foundation
The Derbyshire Churches and
    Chapels Preservation Trust
Derbyshire Community
    Foundation
The J N Derbyshire Trust
The Dulverton Trust
The W E Dunn Trust
The Maud Elkington Charitable
    Trust
The Everard Foundation
The Fifty Fund
Ford Britain Trust
The GNC Trust
The Gray Trust
The Peter Harrison Foundation
The Hartley Charitable Trust
The Hesed Trust
Elizabeth Jackson Charitable
    Trust
Leicestershire and Rutland
    Community Foundation
Leicestershire Historic
    Churches Trust
The Lincolnshire Churches
    Trust
Lincolnshire Community
    Foundation
The London Marathon
    Charitable Trust
Market Harborough and The
    Bowdens Charity
The New Appeals Organisation
    for the City and County of
    Nottingham
Alderman Newton's
    Educational Foundation
The Northampton Municipal
    Church Charities
The Northampton Queen's
    Institute Relief in Sickness
    Fund
Northamptonshire Community
    Foundation
The Nottingham General
    Dispensary
The Nottingham Gordon
    Memorial Trust for Boys
    and Girls
Nottinghamshire Community
    Foundation
The Nottinghamshire Historic
    Churches Trust
The Nottinghamshire Miners'
    Welfare Trust Fund
Open Gate
The Paget Charitable Trust

The Jack Patston Charitable
    Trust
People's Postcode Trust
The Mary Potter Convent
    Hospital Trust
The Provincial Grand Charity of
    the Province of Derbyshire
The Puri Foundation
The Rugby Group Benevolent
    Fund Limited
The Samworth Foundation
SF Group Charitable Fund for
    Disabled People
The Shoe Zone Trust
The Mary Elizabeth Siebel
    Charity
The G J W Turner Trust
The Vodafone Foundation
The George Ward Charitable
    Trust
The John Warren Foundation
The Wates Foundation
The Howard Watson Symington
    Memorial Charity
The Wilmcote Charitrust
David Wilson Foundation
The Wilson Foundation

■ Derbyshire

The Bamford Charitable
    Foundation
The Bates Charitable Trust
The Bingham Trust
The Burton Breweries
    Charitable Trust
The Clarke Charitable
    Settlement
The Helen Jean Cope Trust
The Derbyshire Churches and
    Chapels Preservation Trust
Derbyshire Community
    Foundation
Open Gate
The Provincial Grand Charity of
    the Province of Derbyshire
The Samworth Foundation

■ Leicestershire

The Burton Breweries
    Charitable Trust
The Helen Jean Cope Trust
The J Reginald Corah
    Foundation Fund
The Maud Elkington Charitable
    Trust
The Everard Foundation
The Hesed Trust
Leicestershire and Rutland
    Community Foundation
Leicestershire Historic
    Churches Trust
Market Harborough and The
    Bowdens Charity

Alderman Newton's
    Educational Foundation
Open Gate
The Paget Charitable Trust
The Jack Patston Charitable
    Trust
The Samworth Foundation
The Shoe Zone Trust
The George Ward Charitable
    Trust
The Howard Watson Symington
    Memorial Charity
David Wilson Foundation

■ Lincolnshire

The Lincolnshire Churches
    Trust
Lincolnshire Community
    Foundation
The John Warren Foundation

■ Northamptonshire

The Becketts and Sargeants
    Educational Foundation
Bergqvist Charitable Trust
The Frederick and Phyllis Cann
    Trust
The Compton Charitable Trust
The Douglas Compton James
    Charitable Trust
The Maud Elkington Charitable
    Trust
Ford Britain Trust
Elizabeth Jackson Charitable
    Trust
The London Marathon
    Charitable Trust
The Northampton Municipal
    Church Charities
The Northampton Queen's
    Institute Relief in Sickness
    Fund
Northamptonshire Community
    Foundation
The John Warren Foundation
The Wilson Foundation

■ Nottinghamshire

The Boots Charitable Trust
Carter's Educational
    Foundation
The Helen Jean Cope Trust
The J N Derbyshire Trust
The Fifty Fund
The Gray Trust
The Hartley Charitable Trust
The New Appeals Organisation
    for the City and County of
    Nottingham
The Nottingham General
    Dispensary

The Nottingham Gordon
   Memorial Trust for Boys
   and Girls
Nottinghamshire Community
   Foundation
The Nottinghamshire Historic
   Churches Trust
The Nottinghamshire Miners'
   Welfare Trust Fund
Open Gate
The Mary Potter Convent
   Hospital Trust
The Puri Foundation
The Samworth Foundation
The Mary Elizabeth Siebel
   Charity
The Vodafone Foundation
The John Warren Foundation
The Wates Foundation

....

■ Eastern

The Adnams Charity
Anguish's Educational
   Foundation
The BAA Communities Trust
The Beccles Town Lands
   Charity
The Bedfordshire and
   Hertfordshire Historic
   Churches Trust
The Bedfordshire and Luton
   Community Foundation
The Hervey Benham Charitable
   Trust
Bergqvist Charitable Trust
The Cambridgeshire
   Community Foundation
The Cambridgeshire Historic
   Churches Trust
The Christabella Charitable
   Trust
The Colchester Catalyst
   Charity
The Cole Charitable Trust
The Harry Cureton Charitable
   Trust
The D J H Currie Memorial
   Trust
The Dulverton Trust
Earls Colne and Halstead
   Educational Charity
The Ebenezer Trust
Educational Foundation of
   Alderman John Norman
The Essex and Southend
   Sports Trust
Essex Community Foundation
The Essex Heritage Trust
Essex Provincial Charity Fund
The Essex Youth Trust
Walter Farthing (Trust) Limited
The Farthing Trust
Ford Britain Trust
The Charles S French
   Charitable Trust

The Anne French Memorial
   Trust
The Ganzoni Charitable Trust
The GNC Trust
The Grange Farm Centre Trust
Robert Hall Charity
The Harpur Trust
The Peter Harrison Foundation
The Hertfordshire Community
   Foundation
The Hitchin Educational
   Foundation
The House of Industry Estate
Huntingdon Freemen's Trust
The John Jarrold Trust
Kirkley Poor's Lands Estate
London Legal Support Trust
The Masonic Province of
   Middlesex Charitable Trust
The Mills Charity
The D C Moncrieff Charitable
   Trust
Mothercare Group Foundation
The Music Sales Charitable
   Trust
Needham Market and Barking
   Welfare Charities
The Neighbourly Charitable
   Trust
Norfolk Community Foundation
The Norwich Church of England
   Young Men's Society
The Norwich Town Close
   Estate Charity
Ogilvie Charities Deed No.2
   (including the Charity of
   Mary Catherine Ford Smith)
The Jack Patston Charitable
   Trust
The Jack Petchey Foundation
The Mr and Mrs Philip
   Rackham Charitable Trust
Red Hill Charitable Trust
The Rosca Trust
SF Group Charitable Fund for
   Disabled People
The Smith & Pinching
   Charitable Trust
The R C Snelling Charitable
   Trust
The Southwold Trust
The Stevenage Community
   Trust
The Strangward Trust
Suffolk Community Foundation
The Suffolk Historic Churches
   Trust
The John Warren Foundation
The Whittlesey Charity
The A and R Woolf Charitable
   Trust

■ Bedfordshire

The Bedfordshire and
   Hertfordshire Historic
   Churches Trust
The Bedfordshire and Luton
   Community Foundation
Bergqvist Charitable Trust
The Harpur Trust
The Hitchin Educational
   Foundation
The House of Industry Estate
The Neighbourly Charitable
   Trust
The John Warren Foundation

■ Cambridgeshire

The Cambridgeshire
   Community Foundation
The Cambridgeshire Historic
   Churches Trust
The Cole Charitable Trust
The Harry Cureton Charitable
   Trust
The Farthing Trust
Robert Hall Charity
Huntingdon Freemen's Trust
The Jack Patston Charitable
   Trust
The Smith & Pinching
   Charitable Trust
The Whittlesey Charity

■ Essex

The BAA Communities Trust
The Hervey Benham Charitable
   Trust
The Christabella Charitable
   Trust
The Colchester Catalyst
   Charity
The D J H Currie Memorial
   Trust
Earls Colne and Halstead
   Educational Charity
The Ebenezer Trust
The Essex and Southend
   Sports Trust
Essex Community Foundation
The Essex Heritage Trust
Essex Provincial Charity Fund
The Essex Youth Trust
Walter Farthing (Trust) Limited
Ford Britain Trust
The Charles S French
   Charitable Trust
The Grange Farm Centre Trust
London Legal Support Trust
Ogilvie Charities Deed No.2
   (including the Charity of
   Mary Catherine Ford Smith)
The Jack Petchey Foundation
The Rosca Trust
The Smith & Pinching
   Charitable Trust

■ **Hertfordshire**

The Bedfordshire and
  Hertfordshire Historic
  Churches Trust
Bergqvist Charitable Trust
The Hertfordshire Community
  Foundation
The Hitchin Educational
  Foundation
London Legal Support Trust
The Masonic Province of
  Middlesex Charitable Trust
Mothercare Group Foundation
The Smith & Pinching
  Charitable Trust
The Stevenage Community
  Trust
The A and R Woolf Charitable
  Trust

■ **Norfolk**

Anguish's Educational
  Foundation
Educational Foundation of
  Alderman John Norman
The Anne French Memorial
  Trust
The John Jarrold Trust
The D C Moncrieff Charitable
  Trust
Norfolk Community Foundation
The Norwich Church of England
  Young Men's Society
The Norwich Town Close
  Estate Charity
The Mr and Mrs Philip
  Rackham Charitable Trust
The Smith & Pinching
  Charitable Trust
The R C Snelling Charitable
  Trust

■ **Suffolk**

The Adnams Charity
The Beccles Town Lands
  Charity
The Anne French Memorial
  Trust
The Ganzoni Charitable Trust
Kirkley Poor's Lands Estate
The Mills Charity
The D C Moncrieff Charitable
  Trust
The Music Sales Charitable
  Trust
Needham Market and Barking
  Welfare Charities
Ogilvie Charities Deed No.2
  (including the Charity of
  Mary Catherine Ford Smith)
The Smith & Pinching
  Charitable Trust
The Southwold Trust
Suffolk Community Foundation

The Suffolk Historic Churches
  Trust

....

■ **North West**

The Mason Bibby 1981 Trust
The Booth Charities
The Bowland Charitable Trust
The Harold and Alice Bridges
  Charity
The Charles and Edna
  Broadhurst Charitable Trust
The Charles Brotherton Trust
Bumba Foundation
The Camelia Trust
Cheshire Freemason's Charity
The Chrimes Family Charitable
  Trust
The Coalfields Regeneration
  Trust
The Congleton Inclosure Trust
Cumberland Building Society
  Charitable Foundation
Cumbria Community
  Foundation
The Hamilton Davies Trust
The Earl of Derby's Charitable
  Trust
The Dulverton Trust
Eden Arts Trust
The Eventhall Family
  Charitable Trust
The Fairway Trust
Forever Manchester (The
  Community Foundation for
  Greater Manchester)
The Fort Foundation
The Galbraith Trust
The GNC Trust
A B Grace Trust
The Granada Foundation
The Hadfield Trust
The Harris Charity
The Peter Harrison Foundation
The M A Hawe Settlement
The Helping Foundation
The Hemby Trust
The Hilmarnan Charitable Trust
John Holford's Charity
The Edward Holt Trust
Hulme Trust Estates
  (Educational)
The Johnson Foundation
The J E Joseph Charitable
  Fund
Kelsick's Educational
  Foundation
The Peter Kershaw Trust
The Ursula Keyes Trust
Community Foundation for
  Lancashire
Duchy of Lancaster Benevolent
  Fund
The Herd Lawson and Muriel
  Lawson Charitable Trust

Liverpool Charity and Voluntary
  Services
Liverpool Sailors' Home Trust
The Makin Charitable Trust
Manchester Airport Community
  Trust Fund
The Manchester Guardian
  Society Charitable Trust
Lord Mayor of Manchester's
  Charity Appeal Trust
The Ann and David Marks
  Foundation
The John Mason Family Trust
Matliwala Family Charitable
  Trust
The Mersey Docks and
  Harbour Company
  Charitable Fund
Community Foundation for
  Merseyside
John Moores Foundation
The Morgan Foundation
The Mushroom Fund
The North West Cancer
  Research Fund
The Northern Rock Foundation
Oglesby Charitable Trust
The Oldham Foundation
The Payne Charitable Trust
People's Postcode Trust
The Pilkington Charities Fund
The Sir Harry Pilkington Trust
The Proven Family Trust
The Fanny Rapaport Charitable
  Settlement
The Ravensdale Trust
The Rawdon-Smith Trust
The Nathaniel Reyner Trust
  Fund
The Christopher Rowbotham
  Charitable Trust
The Francis C Scott Charitable
  Trust
The Frieda Scott Charitable
  Trust
The Sir James and Lady Scott
  Trust
SF Group Charitable Fund for
  Disabled People
SHINE (Support and Help in
  Education)
The J A Shone Memorial Trust
The Skelton Bounty
Springfields Employees'
  Medical Research and
  Charity Trust Fund
The Edward Stocks-Massey
  Bequest Fund
T and S Trust Fund
The Mayor of Trafford's Charity
  Fund
Ulverston Town Lands Charity
United Utilities Trust Fund
The Vodafone Foundation
The West Derby Wastelands
  Charity

The Norman Whiteley Trust
Wirral Mayor's Charity
The W Wing Yip and Brothers
Foundation
The Yorkshire Dales
Millennium Trust
The Zochonis Charitable Trust

■ Cheshire

Cheshire Freemason's Charity
The Congleton Inclosure Trust
The Hamilton Davies Trust
John Holford's Charity
The Ursula Keyes Trust
Manchester Airport Community
Trust Fund
John Moores Foundation
The Proven Family Trust
The Christopher Rowbotham
Charitable Trust
The Vodafone Foundation

■ Cumbria

The Harold and Alice Bridges
Charity
Cumberland Building Society
Charitable Foundation
Cumbria Community
Foundation
Eden Arts Trust
The Hadfield Trust
The Hilmarnan Charitable Trust
Kelsick's Educational
Foundation
The Herd Lawson and Muriel
Lawson Charitable Trust
The Northern Rock Foundation
The Payne Charitable Trust
The Proven Family Trust
The Rawdon-Smith Trust
The Francis C Scott Charitable
Trust
The Frieda Scott Charitable
Trust
Ulverston Town Lands Charity
The Norman Whiteley Trust
The Yorkshire Dales
Millennium Trust

■ Greater Manchester

The Booth Charities
The Camelia Trust
Cheshire Freemason's Charity
The Hamilton Davies Trust
Forever Manchester (The
Community Foundation for
Greater Manchester)
The Helping Foundation
The Edward Holt Trust
Hulme Trust Estates
(Educational)
The J E Joseph Charitable
Fund

The Peter Kershaw Trust
Duchy of Lancaster Benevolent
Fund
Manchester Airport Community
Trust Fund
The Manchester Guardian
Society Charitable Trust
Lord Mayor of Manchester's
Charity Appeal Trust
The Ann and David Marks
Foundation
The Christopher Rowbotham
Charitable Trust
The Sir James and Lady Scott
Trust
SHINE (Support and Help in
Education)
The Skelton Bounty
T and S Trust Fund
The Mayor of Trafford's Charity
Fund
The W Wing Yip and Brothers
Foundation
The Zochonis Charitable Trust

■ Lancashire

The Harold and Alice Bridges
Charity
Cumberland Building Society
Charitable Foundation
The Fort Foundation
The Galbraith Trust
A B Grace Trust
The Harris Charity
The M A Hawe Settlement
Community Foundation for
Lancashire
Duchy of Lancaster Benevolent
Fund
Matliwala Family Charitable
Trust
Community Foundation for
Merseyside
John Moores Foundation
The Christopher Rowbotham
Charitable Trust
The Francis C Scott Charitable
Trust
The Skelton Bounty
Springfields Employees'
Medical Research and
Charity Trust Fund
The Edward Stocks-Massey
Bequest Fund
The Yorkshire Dales
Millennium Trust

■ Merseyside

The Mason Bibby 1981 Trust
The Charles and Edna
Broadhurst Charitable Trust
The Charles Brotherton Trust
The Camelia Trust
Cheshire Freemason's Charity

The Chrimes Family Charitable
Trust
The Hemby Trust
The Johnson Foundation
Duchy of Lancaster Benevolent
Fund
Liverpool Charity and Voluntary
Services
Liverpool Sailors' Home Trust
The Makin Charitable Trust
The Mersey Docks and
Harbour Company
Charitable Fund
Community Foundation for
Merseyside
John Moores Foundation
The Mushroom Fund
The Pilkington Charities Fund
The Sir Harry Pilkington Trust
The Proven Family Trust
The Ravensdale Trust
The Nathaniel Reyner Trust
Fund
The J A Shone Memorial Trust
The Skelton Bounty
The West Derby Wastelands
Charity
Wirral Mayor's Charity

■ Yorkshire and the Humber

The Bearder Charity
The Benfield Motors Charitable
Trust
The Bishop's Development
Fund
The Charles Brotherton Trust
The Jack Brunton Charitable
Trust
Community Foundation for
Calderdale
M R Cannon 1998 Charitable
Trust
The Joseph and Annie Cattle
Trust
John William Chapman's
Charitable Trust
The Church Burgesses
Educational Foundation
Church Burgesses Trust
The Coalfields Regeneration
Trust
The Marjorie Coote Animal
Charity Trust
The Marjorie Coote Old
People's Charity
The Dulverton Trust
The Elm House Trust
The A M Fenton Trust
The Freshgate Trust
Foundation
The GNC Trust
The Green Hall Foundation
The Harrison and Potter Trust
The Peter Harrison Foundation

The Hartley Charitable Trust
Help for Health
The Hesslewood Children's
    Trust (Hull Seamen's and
    General Orphanage)
The Huddersfield Common
    Good Trust
The Hull and East Riding
    Charitable Trust
Duchy of Lancaster Benevolent
    Fund
The Lord Mayor of Leeds
    Appeal Fund
The Leeds Community
    Foundation
The Mayfield Valley Arts Trust
The Mirfield Educational
    Charity
The James Neill Trust Fund
Open Gate
People's Postcode Trust
Sir John Priestman Charity
    Trust
The J S and E C Rymer
    Charitable Trust
The Salt Foundation
SF Group Charitable Fund for
    Disabled People
The Shears Foundation
The Sylvia and Colin Shepherd
    Charitable Trust
The Talbot Trusts
Two Ridings Community
    Foundation
Wade's Charity
The Scurrah Wainwright Charity
West Yorkshire Police
    Community Trust
Yorkshire Agricultural Society
The South Yorkshire
    Community Foundation
The Yorkshire Dales
    Millennium Trust
The Yorkshire Historic
    Churches Trust

■ **Humberside, East Riding**

The Joseph and Annie Cattle
    Trust
Help for Health
The Hesslewood Children's
    Trust (Hull Seamen's and
    General Orphanage)
The Hull and East Riding
    Charitable Trust
The J S and E C Rymer
    Charitable Trust
SF Group Charitable Fund for
    Disabled People

■ **North Yorkshire**

The Charles Brotherton Trust
The Jack Brunton Charitable
    Trust

M R Cannon 1998 Charitable
    Trust
The Marjorie Coote Animal
    Charity Trust
The Elm House Trust
Sir John Priestman Charity
    Trust
The Sylvia and Colin Shepherd
    Charitable Trust
Two Ridings Community
    Foundation
The Yorkshire Dales
    Millennium Trust

■ **South Yorkshire**

John William Chapman's
    Charitable Trust
The Church Burgesses
    Educational Foundation
Church Burgesses Trust
The Marjorie Coote Old
    People's Charity
The Freshgate Trust
    Foundation
The Mayfield Valley Arts Trust
The James Neill Trust Fund
Open Gate
The Talbot Trusts
The South Yorkshire
    Community Foundation

■ **West Yorkshire**

The Bearder Charity
The Benfield Motors Charitable
    Trust
The Bishop's Development
    Fund
The Charles Brotherton Trust
Community Foundation for
    Calderdale
The Green Hall Foundation
The Harrison and Potter Trust
The Huddersfield Common
    Good Trust
Duchy of Lancaster Benevolent
    Fund
The Lord Mayor of Leeds
    Appeal Fund
The Leeds Community
    Foundation
The Mirfield Educational
    Charity
The Salt Foundation
The Shears Foundation
Wade's Charity
West Yorkshire Police
    Community Trust

....
■ **North East**

The 1989 Willan Charitable
    Trust
The Roy and Pixie Baker
    Charitable Trust

The Ballinger Charitable Trust
The Barbour Foundation
The Benfield Motors Charitable
    Trust
Joseph Brough Charitable
    Trust
M R Cannon 1998 Charitable
    Trust
The Coalfields Regeneration
    Trust
The Catherine Cookson
    Charitable Trust
County Durham Community
    Foundation
The Sir Tom Cowie Charitable
    Trust
Cumberland Building Society
    Charitable Foundation
The Gillian Dickinson Trust
The Dickon Trust
The Dulverton Trust
The Ellinson Foundation Ltd
The Elm House Trust
The GNC Trust
E C Graham Belford Charitable
    Settlement
Greggs Foundation
The Hadrian Trust
The W A Handley Charitable
    Trust
The Peter Harrison Foundation
The Hedley Denton Charitable
    Trust
Hexham and Newcastle
    Diocesan Trust (1947)
The Hospital of God at
    Greatham
The Sir James Knott Trust
The William Leech Charity
The Leslie and Lilian Manning
    Trust
The Millfield House Foundation
The Northern Rock Foundation
The Northumberland Village
    Homes Trust
The Northumbria Historic
    Churches Trust
People's Postcode Trust
Sir John Priestman Charity
    Trust
The Rothley Trust
The Christopher Rowbotham
    Charitable Trust
S O Charitable Trust
The Storrow Scott Will Trust
SF Group Charitable Fund for
    Disabled People
The Shears Foundation
The Sylvia and Colin Shepherd
    Charitable Trust
St Hilda's Trust
T and S Trust Fund
Tees Valley Community
    Foundation

Community Foundation Serving
Tyne and Wear and
Northumberland
The William Webster
Charitable Trust
Yorkshire Agricultural Society

■ **Cleveland**

The Hadrian Trust
Hexham and Newcastle
Diocesan Trust (1947)
The Hospital of God at
Greatham
The Sir James Knott Trust
The Northern Rock Foundation
The Northumbria Historic
Churches Trust
Tees Valley Community
Foundation
Yorkshire Agricultural Society

■ **Durham**

Joseph Brough Charitable
Trust
M R Cannon 1998 Charitable
Trust
County Durham Community
Foundation
The Sir Tom Cowie Charitable
Trust
The Gillian Dickinson Trust
The Hadrian Trust
Hexham and Newcastle
Diocesan Trust (1947)
The Hospital of God at
Greatham
The Sir James Knott Trust
The William Leech Charity
The Northern Rock Foundation
The Northumbria Historic
Churches Trust
Sir John Priestman Charity
Trust
The Shears Foundation
Yorkshire Agricultural Society

■ **Northumberland**

Joseph Brough Charitable
Trust
Cumberland Building Society
Charitable Foundation
The Gillian Dickinson Trust
E C Graham Belford Charitable
Settlement
The Hadrian Trust
The W A Handley Charitable
Trust
Hexham and Newcastle
Diocesan Trust (1947)
The Hospital of God at
Greatham
The Sir James Knott Trust
The William Leech Charity

The Northern Rock Foundation
The Northumbria Historic
Churches Trust
The Christopher Rowbotham
Charitable Trust
The Shears Foundation
St Hilda's Trust
Community Foundation Serving
Tyne and Wear and
Northumberland
Yorkshire Agricultural Society

■ **Tyne & Wear**

Joseph Brough Charitable
Trust
The Sir Tom Cowie Charitable
Trust
The Gillian Dickinson Trust
The Ellinson Foundation Ltd
The Hadrian Trust
The W A Handley Charitable
Trust
Hexham and Newcastle
Diocesan Trust (1947)
The Hospital of God at
Greatham
The Sir James Knott Trust
The William Leech Charity
The Northern Rock Foundation
The Northumbria Historic
Churches Trust
Sir John Priestman Charity
Trust
The Christopher Rowbotham
Charitable Trust
S O Charitable Trust
The Shears Foundation
St Hilda's Trust
T and S Trust Fund
Community Foundation Serving
Tyne and Wear and
Northumberland

Northern Ireland

Church of Ireland Priorities
Fund
The Enkalon Foundation
The Garnett Charitable Trust
The GNC Trust
The Goodman Foundation
The Peter Harrison Foundation
Hope for Youth (NI)
The Ian Karten Charitable
Trust
Lloyds Bank Foundation for
Northern Ireland
Lord and Lady Lurgan Trust
The Esmé Mitchell Trust
John Moores Foundation
The Community Foundation for
Northern Ireland
Royal British Legion
Ulster Garden Villages Ltd
Ultach Trust

Victoria Homes Trust
The Vodafone Foundation

Scotland

The Aberbrothock Skea Trust
The Aberdeen Endowments
Trust
The Aberdeenshire Educational
Trust Scheme
Age Scotland
The AMW Charitable Trust
The BAA Communities Trust
The Baird Trust
The Bank of Scotland
Foundation
Barchester Healthcare
Foundation
The Bellahouston Bequest
Fund
The Benfield Motors Charitable
Trust
The British Gas (Scottish Gas)
Energy Trust
The Callander Charitable Trust
The Carnegie Dunfermline
Trust
The Carnegie Trust for the
Universities of Scotland
Cash for Kids Radio Clyde
The Cattanach Charitable Trust
Chest, Heart and Stroke
Scotland
The Coalfields Regeneration
Trust
The Craignish Trust
The Cray Trust
Creative Scotland
The Crerar Hotels Trust
The Cross Trust
Cumberland Building Society
Charitable Foundation
The Cunningham Trust
The Davidson (Nairn)
Charitable Trust
Diced Cap Charity
The Dickon Trust
The Dulverton Trust
Edinburgh Children's Holiday
Fund
Edinburgh Voluntary
Organisations' Trust Funds
(EVOT)
The Ellis Campbell Foundation
The Erskine Cunningham Hill
Trust
Fife Council/Common Good
Funds and Trusts
The Gannochy Trust
The GNC Trust
The Guildry Incorporation of
Perth
Dr Guthrie's Association
The Peter Harrison Foundation

The Christina Mary Hendrie
Trust for Scottish and
Canadian Charities
The Anne Herd Memorial Trust
The Holywood Trust
Miss Agnes H Hunter's Trust
The Jeffrey Charitable Trust
The Jordan Charitable
Foundation
JTH Charitable Trust
The Ian Karten Charitable
Trust
The Kelly Family Charitable
Trust
The Late Sir Pierce Lacy
Charity Trust
The Andrew and Mary
Elizabeth Little Charitable
Trust
Lloyds TSB Foundation for
Scotland
The R S Macdonald Charitable
Trust
The Mackintosh Foundation
W M Mann Foundation
The Nancie Massey Charitable
Trust
The Mathew Trust
The Merchants' House of
Glasgow
Morgan Stanley International
Foundation
The Stanley Morrison
Charitable Trust
The Mugdock Children's Trust
The Northwood Charitable
Trust
The Orrin Charitable Trust
Miss M E Swinton Paterson's
Charitable Trust
People's Postcode Trust
The Ponton House Trust
The Robertson Trust
Mrs Gladys Row Fogo
Charitable Trust
Royal British Legion
Foundation Scotland
Scottish Coal Industry Special
Welfare Fund
The Scottish International
Education Trust
The Shetland Charitable Trust
R H Southern Trust
The Hugh Stenhouse
Foundation
The Templeton Goodwill Trust
The Arthur and Margaret
Thompson Charitable Trust
The Len Thomson Charitable
Trust
The Turtleton Charitable Trust
Voluntary Action Fund (VAF)
John Watson's Trust
A H and B C Whiteley
Charitable Trust
J and J R Wilson Trust

The James Wood Bequest
Fund
The John K Young Endowment
Fund

■ Central

The Callander Charitable Trust
Mrs Gladys Row Fogo
Charitable Trust
The James Wood Bequest
Fund

■ Grampian Region

The Aberbrothock Skea Trust
The Aberdeen Endowments
Trust
The Aberdeenshire Educational
Trust Scheme
The BAA Communities Trust
Diced Cap Charity

■ Highlands & Islands

The Davidson (Nairn)
Charitable Trust
The Jordan Charitable
Foundation
The Mackintosh Foundation
The Shetland Charitable Trust

■ Lothians Region

The BAA Communities Trust
The Benfield Motors Charitable
Trust
Edinburgh Children's Holiday
Fund
Edinburgh Voluntary
Organisations' Trust Funds
(EVOT)
The Kelly Family Charitable
Trust
The Ponton House Trust
Mrs Gladys Row Fogo
Charitable Trust
The John K Young Endowment
Fund

■ Southern Scotland

The Callander Charitable Trust
Cumberland Building Society
Charitable Foundation
The Holywood Trust

■ Strathclyde

The BAA Communities Trust
The Bellahouston Bequest
Fund
Cash for Kids Radio Clyde
The Andrew and Mary
Elizabeth Little Charitable
Trust

The Merchants' House of
Glasgow
Morgan Stanley International
Foundation
The Stanley Morrison
Charitable Trust
The Templeton Goodwill Trust
The James Wood Bequest
Fund

■ Tayside & Fife

The Aberbrothock Skea Trust
The Carnegie Dunfermline
Trust
The Ellis Campbell Foundation
Fife Council/Common Good
Funds and Trusts
The Guildry Incorporation of
Perth
The Late Sir Pierce Lacy
Charity Trust
The Mathew Trust
The Northwood Charitable
Trust
The Arthur and Margaret
Thompson Charitable Trust

Wales

Archbishop of Wales' Fund for
Children
Arts Council of Wales (also
known as Cyngor
Celfyddydau Cymru)
The Austin Bailey Foundation
Barchester Healthcare
Foundation
The Baring Foundation
Birthday House Trust
The Blandford Lake Trust
The Boshier-Hinton Foundation
H E and E L Botteley
Charitable Trust
The Bower Trust
The British Gas (Scottish Gas)
Energy Trust
The Catholic Trust for England
and Wales
The Gaynor Cemlyn-Jones
Trust
The Chrimes Family Charitable
Trust
The Church and Community
Fund
City and County of Swansea
Welsh Church Act Fund
CLA Charitable Trust
The Coalfields Regeneration
Trust
The Bernard Coleman
Charitable Trust
Colwinston Charitable Trust
Michael Crawford Children's
Charity
The Cwmbran Trust

D C R Allen Charitable Trust
The DM Charitable Trust
The Dulverton Trust
The James Dyson Foundation
The Elephant Trust
The Ernest Hecht Charitable
  Foundation
Ford Britain Trust
Gwyneth Forrester Trust
The Joseph Strong Frazer Trust
The Freemasons' Grand
  Charity
The General Nursing Council
  for England and Wales
  Trust
The Girdlers' Company
  Charitable Trust
The GNC Trust
The Goodman Foundation
The Peter Harrison Foundation
Lady Hind Trust
The Hintze Family Charitable
  Foundation
The Jane Hodge Foundation
The J Isaacs Charitable Trust
The Isle of Anglesey Charitable
  Trust
C Richard Jackson Charitable
  Trust
The James Trust
The Nick Jenkins Foundation
The Dyfrig and Heather John
  Charitable Trust
The Dezna Robins Jones
  Charitable Foundation
The Karenza Foundation
The Ian Karten Charitable
  Trust
Keswick Hall Trust
Morris Leigh Foundation
Lloyds Bank Foundation for
  England and Wales
Lord and Lady Lurgan Trust
Marshall's Charity
Marshgate Charitable
  Settlement
The McKenna Charitable Trust
Middlesex Sports Foundation
Midhurst Pensions Trust
Millennium Stadium Charitable
  Trust
Monmouthshire County Council
  Welsh Church Act Fund
The Morgan Foundation
The Mr and Mrs J T Morgan
  Foundation
The Moss Family Charitable
  Trust
Moto in the Community
The National Churches Trust
  (formerly the Historic
  Churches Preservation
  Trust with the Incorporated
  Church Building Society)
The Noon Foundation

The North West Cancer
  Research Fund
The Norwood and Newton
  Settlement
The Ouseley Trust
The James Pantyfedwen
  Foundation
The Payne Charitable Trust
People's Postcode Trust
The Bernard Piggott Charitable
  Trust
The Rhondda Cynon Taff
  Welsh Church Acts Fund
Royal British Legion
The Peter Saunders Trust
Skipton Building Society
  Charitable Foundation
The Sobell Foundation
R H Southern Trust
Sparquote Limited
Springrule Limited
St Teilo's Trust
The Leonard Laity Stoate
  Charitable Trust
Swansea and Brecon Diocesan
  Board of Finance Limited
Toni and Guy Charitable
  Foundation Limited
Miss S M Tutton Charitable
  Trust
Vale of Glamorgan – Welsh
  Church Fund
The Community Foundation in
  Wales
Wales Council for Voluntary
  Action
Robert and Felicity Waley-
  Cohen Charitable Trust
The Barbara Ward Children's
  Foundation
Welsh Church Fund Dyfed
  area (Carmarthenshire,
  Ceredigion and
  Pembrokeshire)
A H and B C Whiteley
  Charitable Trust
The Yapp Charitable Trust

■ North Wales

The Blandford Lake Trust
The Gaynor Cemlyn-Jones
  Trust
The Chrimes Family Charitable
  Trust
The Isle of Anglesey Charitable
  Trust
The Morgan Foundation
The North West Cancer
  Research Fund
The Payne Charitable Trust
The Bernard Piggott Charitable
  Trust
The Peter Saunders Trust

■ Mid and West Wales

The North West Cancer
  Research Fund
Swansea and Brecon Diocesan
  Board of Finance Limited
Welsh Church Fund Dyfed
  area (Carmarthenshire,
  Ceredigion and
  Pembrokeshire)

■ South Wales

The Austin Bailey Foundation
City and County of Swansea
  Welsh Church Act Fund
The Cwmbran Trust
Ford Britain Trust
Monmouthshire County Council
  Welsh Church Act Fund
The Rhondda Cynon Taff
  Welsh Church Acts Fund
Swansea and Brecon Diocesan
  Board of Finance Limited
Vale of Glamorgan – Welsh
  Church Fund

Channel Islands

The Freemasons' Grand
  Charity
The Hampshire and Islands
  Historic Churches Trust
Lloyds Bank Foundation for the
  Channel Islands
Lord and Lady Lurgan Trust

Trusts by field of interest and type of beneficiary

This index contains two separate listings:

Categorisation of fields of interest and type of beneficiary: This lists all of the headings used in the DGMT to categorise fields of interest and types of beneficiary.

Trusts by field of interest and type of beneficiary: This lists trusts under the fields of interest and types of beneficiary for which they have expressed a funding preference.

Trusts by field of interest and type of beneficiary

These pages contain two separate listings:

Categorisation of fields of interest and type of beneficiary
This lists all of the headings used in the DGMT to categorise fields of interest and types of beneficiary

Trusts by field of interest and type of beneficiary
This lists trusts under the fields of interest and types of beneficiary for which they have expressed a funding preference

Arts, culture, sport and recreation 56

Arts and culture 60

Access to the arts 63

Amateur and community arts 63

Art and culture of specific countries 63

Arts management, policy and planning 63

Combined arts 63

Crafts 63

Disability arts 63

Libraries 63

Literature 63

Museums and galleries 63

Performing arts 64

Dance 64

Music 64

Theatre 64

Visual arts 65

Fine art 65

Public art/ sculpture 65

Heritage and the built environment 65

Arts and the environment 66

Architecture 66

Landscape 66

Heritage 66

Maintenance and preservation of buildings 67

Religious buildings 67

Restoration and maintenance of inland waterways 68

Built environment – education and research 68

Humanities 68

Archaeology 68

History 68

International understanding 69

Philosophy and ethics 69

Media and communications 69

Recreation and sport 69
Parks and open spaces 70

Recreation facilities 70

Sports for people with a disability 70

Sports 71

Development, housing and employment 71
Community and economic development 73

Housing 74

Specific industries 74

Education and training 75
Higher education 81

Informal, continuing and adult education 81

Vocational education and training 81

Integrated education 82

Management of schools 82

Particular subjects, curriculum development 82

Arts education and training 82

Business education 83

Citizenship, personal and social education 83

Language and literacy education 83

Religious education 83

Science education 83

Technology, engineering and computer education 83

Pre-school education 83

Primary and secondary school education 83

Faith schools 84

Public and independent schools 84

Special needs schools 84

State schools 84

Environment and animals 85
Agriculture and fishing 87

Farming and food production 88

Fishing and fisheries 88

Forestry 88

Horticulture 88

Animal care 88

Animal conservation 88

Climate change 89

Countryside 89

Environmental education and research 89

Natural environment 90

Flora and fauna 90

Water resources 90

Pollution abatement and control 90

Sustainable environment 91

Energy issues 91

Transport 91

General charitable purposes 91

Health 101
Alternative and complementary medicine 107

Health care 107

Medical equipment 108

Medical institutions 108

Nursing 109

Medical research 109

History of medicine 111

Health education/ prevention/ development 111

Overseas aid/ projects 112

Philanthropy and the voluntary sector 113
Voluntarism 114

Community participation 114

Voluntary sector capacity building 114

Religious activities 114
Christianity 119

Christian causes 121

Christian churches 122

Christian social thought 122

Missionary work, evangelism 122

Hinduism 123

Inter-faith activities 123

Islam 123

Judaism 123

Jewish causes, work 125

Orthodox Judaism 126

Religious understanding 126

Rights, law and conflict 126
Citizen participation 127

Conflict resolution 127

Legal advice and services 127

Rights, equality and justice 128

Human rights 128

Civil liberties 128

Cultural equity 128

Disability rights 128

Arts, culture, sport and recreation

The 29th May 1961 Charitable
Trust
The A B Charitable Trust
Access Sport
The Victor Adda Foundation
Allchurches Trust Ltd
The H B Allen Charitable Trust
Angus Allnatt Charitable
Foundation
The Ammco Trust
The AMW Charitable Trust
Andor Charitable Trust
The Eric Anker-Petersen
Charity
The Architectural Heritage
Fund
The Armourers' and Brasiers'
Gauntlet Trust
The Arsenal Foundation
The Arthur Ronald Dyer
Charitable Trust
Arts Council England
The Arts Council of Northern
Ireland
Arts Council of Wales (also
known as Cyngor
Celfyddydau Cymru)
The Ove Arup Foundation
ASCB Charitable Fund
A J H Ashby Will Trust
The Ashden Trust
The Ashendene Trust
The Ashley Family Foundation
The Astor Foundation
The Astor of Hever Trust
The Aurelius Charitable Trust
B W Charitable Trust
Backstage Trust
Bag4Sport Foundation
The Baird Trust
The Roy and Pixie Baker
Charitable Trust
The Ballinger Charitable Trust
The Barcapel Foundation
The Baring Foundation
Barnes Workhouse Fund
Barrington Family Charitable
Trust
BBC Children in Need
BC Partners Foundation
The Beaverbrook Foundation
The John Beckwith Charitable
Trust
The Bedfordshire and
Hertfordshire Historic
Churches Trust
The Bellahouston Bequest
Fund
The Hervey Benham Charitable
Trust
Bergqvist Charitable Trust
Bet365 Foundation
The Big Lottery Fund

Birmingham International
Airport Community Trust
Blackheart Foundation (UK)
Limited
The BlackRock (UK) Charitable
Trust
The Blagrave Trust
The Neville and Elaine Blond
Charitable Trust
The Nicholas Boas Charitable
Trust
The Boltini Trust
BOOST Charitable Trust
The Bowerman Charitable
Trust
John and Susan Bowers Fund
The Liz and Terry Bramall
Foundation
The Harold and Alice Bridges
Charity
British Institute at Ankara
British Olympic Foundation
The Britten-Pears Foundation
The Rory and Elizabeth Brooks
Foundation
Brown-Mellows Trust
The Brownsword Charitable
Foundation
T B H Brunner's Charitable
Settlement
The Buckinghamshire Historic
Churches Trust
The Rosemary Bugden
Charitable Trust
The Arnold Burton 1998
Charitable Trust
The Derek Butler Trust
C J Cadbury Charitable Trust
Edward Cadbury Charitable
Trust
Peter Cadbury Charitable Trust
The G W Cadbury Charitable
Trust
The William A Cadbury
Charitable Trust
The Edward and Dorothy
Cadbury Trust
The Barrow Cadbury Trust and
the Barrow Cadbury Fund
Calouste Gulbenkian
Foundation – UK Branch
The Cambridgeshire Historic
Churches Trust
The Carnegie Dunfermline
Trust
The Carpenters' Company
Charitable Trust
The Carr-Gregory Trust
Carter's Educational
Foundation
The Cass Foundation
The Cayo Foundation
Elizabeth Cayzer Charitable
Trust
The Gaynor Cemlyn-Jones
Trust

The Chapman Charitable Trust
The Chetwode Foundation
The Chipping Sodbury Town
Lands Charity
The City Bridge Trust
Stephen Clark 1957
Charitable Trust
J A Clark Charitable Trust
The Cleopatra Trust
The Clore Duffield Foundation
Miss V L Clore's 1967
Charitable Trust
The Clover Trust
The Robert Clutterbuck
Charitable Trust
The Francis Coales Charitable
Foundation
The Coalfields Regeneration
Trust
The John Coates Charitable
Trust
The Denise Cohen Charitable
Trust
The Vivienne and Samuel
Cohen Charitable Trust
The John S Cohen Foundation
The R and S Cohen
Foundation
The Bernard Coleman
Charitable Trust
Colwinston Charitable Trust
Colyer-Fergusson Charitable
Trust
Community First (Landfill
Communities Fund)
The Congleton Inclosure Trust
The Conservation Foundation
The Ernest Cook Trust
Michael Cornish Charitable
Trust
The Evan Cornish Foundation
The Duke of Cornwall's
Benevolent Fund
Country Houses Foundation
The Craignish Trust
The Craps Charitable Trust
Creative Scotland
The Crescent Trust
Criffel Charitable Trust
The Cross Trust
The Peter Cruddas Foundation
Cruden Foundation Ltd
The Cumber Family Charitable
Trust
The D J H Currie Memorial
Trust
The D'Oyly Carte Charitable
Trust
The Daiwa Anglo-Japanese
Foundation
The Davidson Family
Charitable Trust
The Gwendoline and Margaret
Davies Charity
The Hamilton Davies Trust

Peter De Haan Charitable
    Trust
The De Laszlo Foundation
The Deakin Charitable Trust
The Delius Trust
The Demigryphon Trust
Dentons UKMEA LLP
    Charitable Trust
The Derbyshire Churches and
    Chapels Preservation Trust
The Devon Historic Churches
    Trust
The Sandy Dewhirst Charitable
    Trust
The Gillian Dickinson Trust
Grace Dieu Charitable Trust
Dischma Charitable Trust
The Djanogly Foundation
Dorset Community Foundation
The Dorset Historic Churches
    Trust
The Dorus Trust
The Drapers' Charitable Fund
The Duis Charitable Trust
The Dulverton Trust
Dunard Fund
The Dyers' Company
    Charitable Trust
The Earmark Trust
The Sir John Eastwood
    Foundation
Eden Arts Trust
The Gilbert and Eileen Edgar
    Foundation
Edinburgh Trust No 2 Account
Educational Foundation of
    Alderman John Norman
The Elephant Trust
The John Ellerman Foundation
The Ellis Campbell Foundation
The Elmgrant Trust
The Elmley Foundation
The Vernon N Ely Charitable
    Trust
The Emerton-Christie Charity
The English Schools' Football
    Association
The Epigoni Trust
The Equity Trust Fund
The Eranda Foundation
The Ericson Trust
The Essex and Southend
    Sports Trust
The Essex Heritage Trust
The Alan Evans Memorial Trust
Esmée Fairbairn Foundation
The Fairway Trust
The Family Rich Charities Trust
The Lord Faringdon Charitable
    Trust
Samuel William Farmer Trust
The February Foundation
The John Feeney Charitable
    Trust
The Fidelity UK Foundation

Fife Council/Common Good
    Funds and Trusts
Gerald Finzi Charitable Trust
The Sir John Fisher Foundation
Fisherbeck Charitable Trust
The Fishmongers' Company's
    Charitable Trust
Marc Fitch Fund
The Joyce Fletcher Charitable
    Trust
The Flow Foundation
The Follett Trust
The Football Association
    National Sports Centre
    Trust
The Football Association Youth
    Trust
The Football Foundation
The Forman Hardy Charitable
    Trust
The Donald Forrester Trust
The Fort Foundation
The Four Lanes Trust
The Foyle Foundation
The Jill Franklin Trust
The Gordon Fraser Charitable
    Trust
The Hugh Fraser Foundation
The Joseph Strong Frazer Trust
The Thomas Freke and Lady
    Norton Charity Trust
The Freshgate Trust
    Foundation
Friends of Essex Churches
    Trust
The Friends of Kent Churches
Friends of Muir Group
The Frognal Trust
Maurice Fry Charitable Trust
The Fuserna Foundation
    General Charitable Trust
The Galanthus Trust
Gamlen Charitable Trust
The Gamma Trust
The Gannochy Trust
The Samuel Gardner Memorial
    Trust
The Garnett Charitable Trust
Garrick Charitable Trust
The Gatsby Charitable
    Foundation
Gatwick Airport Community
    Trust
The Robert Gavron Charitable
    Trust
Jacqueline and Michael Gee
    Charitable Trust
The Generations Foundation
Get Kids Going
The Gibbs Charitable Trust
Simon Gibson Charitable Trust
Lady Gibson's Charitable Trust
The Girdlers' Company
    Charitable Trust
The Glass-House Trust

The Gloucestershire Historic
    Churches Trust
The GNC Trust
The Golden Bottle Trust
Golden Charitable Trust
The Jack Goldhill Charitable
    Trust
The Goldsmiths' Arts Trust
    Fund
The Goldsmiths' Company
    Charity
The Golf Foundation Limited
The Golsoncott Foundation
Golubovich Foundation
Nicholas and Judith
    Goodison's Charitable
    Settlement
The Gosling Foundation
    Limited
A and S Graham Charitable
    Trust
The Granada Foundation
The Grand Order of Water
    Rats' Charities Fund
The Grange Farm Centre Trust
The J G Graves Charitable
    Trust
The Great Britain Sasakawa
    Foundation
The Kenneth & Susan Green
    Charitable Foundation
Greenham Common
    Community Trust Limited
Greys Charitable Trust
The Grimmitt Trust
The Grocers' Charity
The Hadfield Trust
The Hadrian Trust
Robert Hall Charity
Paul Hamlyn Foundation
The Helen Hamlyn Trust
The Hampshire and Islands
    Historic Churches Trust
The W A Handley Charitable
    Trust
The Kathleen Hannay
    Memorial Charity
The Harbour Foundation
The Harding Trust
William Harding's Charity
The Hare of Steep Charitable
    Trust
The Kenneth Hargreaves
    Charitable Trust
The Harpur Trust
The Harris Charitable Trust
The Peter Harrison Foundation
Haskel Family Foundation
The Dorothy Hay-Bolton
    Charitable Trust
The Charles Hayward
    Foundation
The Headley Trust
The Charlotte Heber-Percy
    Charitable Trust
The Hellenic Foundation

The Hemby Trust
Henley Educational Trust (formerley Henley Educational Charity)
The Herefordshire Historic Churches Trust
The Heritage of London Trust Ltd
The Derek Hill Foundation
The Charles Littlewood Hill Trust
The Hillier Trust
The Hinrichsen Foundation
The Hintze Family Charitable Foundation
Hobson Charity Limited
Matthew Hodder Charitable Trust
The Holst Foundation
The Homestead Charitable Trust
The Horne Foundation
The Reta Lila Howard Foundation
The Huddersfield Common Good Trust
The Geoffrey C Hughes Charitable Trust
Human Relief Foundation
Huntingdon Freemen's Trust
The Idlewild Trust
The Iliffe Family Charitable Trust
The Inland Waterways Association
The Inlight Trust
The Ireland Fund of Great Britain
The Irish Youth Foundation (UK) Ltd (incorporating The Lawlor Foundation)
The ISA Charity
The J M K Charitable Trust
Jacobs Charitable Trust
The John Jarrold Trust
The Jenour Foundation
Jerwood Charitable Foundation
The Dyfrig and Heather John Charitable Trust
The Johnnie Johnson Trust
The Johnson Wax Ltd Charitable Trust
The Julian Budd Kids in Sport Trust Limited
The Jungels-Winkler Charitable Foundation
Jusaca Charitable Trust
The Stanley Kalms Foundation
The Kalou Foundation
The Boris Karloff Charitable Foundation
The Kathleen Trust
The Michael and Ilse Katz Foundation
The Kelly Family Charitable Trust

The Mr & Mrs Paul Killik Charitable Trust
The Robert Kiln Charitable Trust
The Eric and Margaret Kinder Charitable Trust
The Marina Kleinwort Charitable Trust
The Sir James Knott Trust
The Kobler Trust
The Kohn Foundation
The Neil Kreitman Foundation
The Christopher Laing Foundation
The David Laing Foundation
The Kirby Laing Foundation
LWS Lancashire Environmental Fund Limited
The R J Larg Family Charitable Trust
The Lark Trust
Laslett's (Hinton) Charity
The Lawson Beckman Charitable Trust
The Raymond and Blanche Lawson Charitable Trust
The David Lean Foundation
The Leathersellers' Company Charitable Fund
The Leche Trust
Leeds Building Society Charitable Foundation
Leicestershire and Rutland Community Foundation
Leicestershire Historic Churches Trust
Mrs Vera Leigh's Charity
The Leverhulme Trust
Lord Leverhulme's Charitable Trust
The Joseph Levy Charitable Foundation
John Lewis Partnership General Community Fund
Liberum Foundation
The Limbourne Trust
Limoges Charitable Trust
The Linbury Trust
The Lincolnshire Churches Trust
The Linden Charitable Trust
The Enid Linder Foundation
The Lister Charitable Trust
The George John and Sheilah Livanos Charitable Trust
The Charles Lloyd Foundation
Lloyd's Charities Trust
Lloyds Bank Foundation for Northern Ireland
The London Marathon Charitable Trust
The William and Katherine Longman Trust
The Lord's Taverners
The Ruth and Jack Lunzer Charitable Trust

Lord and Lady Lurgan Trust
The Lynn Foundation
John Lyon's Charity
The Sir Jack Lyons Charitable Trust
The Macfarlane Walker Trust
The Mackintosh Foundation
The MacRobert Trust
Ian Mactaggart Trust
Mageni Trust
Man Group plc Charitable Trust
Manchester Airport Community Trust Fund
The Manifold Charitable Trust
W M Mann Foundation
The Manoukian Charitable Foundation
Maranatha Christian Trust
The Stella and Alexander Margulies Charitable Trust
Market Harborough and The Bowdens Charity
Michael Marks Charitable Trust
The Marks Family Foundation
The Marsh Christian Trust
The Jim Marshall Charitable Trust
Marshall's Charity
Sir George Martin Trust
John Martin's Charity
The Nancie Massey Charitable Trust
The Mayfield Valley Arts Trust
The McKenna Charitable Trust
The Mears Foundation
The Anthony and Elizabeth Mellows Charitable Settlement
Brian Mercer Charitable Trust
The Mercers' Charitable Foundation
The Merchant Venturers' Charity
The Merchants' House of Glasgow
The Metropolitan Drinking Fountain and Cattle Trough Association
The Metropolitan Masonic Charity
Gerald Micklem Charitable Trust
Middlesex Sports Foundation
Miles Trust for the Putney and Roehampton Community
Millennium Stadium Charitable Trust
The Ronald Miller Foundation
The Millichope Foundation
The Millward Charitable Trust
Milton Keynes Community Foundation
The Peter Minet Trust
The Mitchell Charitable Trust

The Esmé Mitchell Trust
The Modiano Charitable Trust
Monmouthshire County Council
  Welsh Church Act Fund
The Monument Trust
The Henry Moore Foundation
The Morel Charitable Trust
Diana and Allan Morgenthau
  Charitable Trust
The Stanley Morrison
  Charitable Trust
Mosselson Charitable Trust
British Motor Sports Training
  Trust
The Mount Everest Foundation
Move On Foundation Limited
Mrs Waterhouse Charitable
  Trust
The Mugdock Children's Trust
The John R Murray Charitable
  Trust
Peter John Murray Trust
The Kitty and Daniel Nabarro
  Charitable Trust
The Naggar Charitable Trust
The Eleni Nakou Foundation
The National Art Collections
  Fund
The National Churches Trust
The National Express
  Foundation
The National Hockey
  Foundation
The National Manuscripts
  Conservation Trust
Needham Market and Barking
  Welfare Charities
Network for Social Change
Nominet Charitable Foundation
Norfolk Community Foundation
The Normanby Charitable Trust
The Community Foundation for
  Northern Ireland
The Northern Rock Foundation
The Northumbria Historic
  Churches Trust
The Northwood Charitable
  Trust
The Norton Foundation
The Norwich Church of England
  Young Men's Society
The Noswad Charity
The Nottinghamshire Historic
  Churches Trust
The Oakdale Trust
The Oakley Charitable Trust
The Ofenheim Charitable Trust
Oglesby Charitable Trust
The Old Broad Street Charity
  Trust
Old Possum's Practical Trust
The Oldham Foundation
The Ouseley Trust
The Owen Family Trust
The James Pantyfedwen
  Foundation

The Parthenon Trust
Miss M E Swinton Paterson's
  Charitable Trust
The Jack Patston Charitable
  Trust
The Pedmore Sporting Club
  Trust Fund
The Pell Charitable Trust
The Peltz Trust
People's Postcode Trust
The Performing Right Society
  Foundation
The Bernard Piggott Charitable
  Trust
The Pilgrim Trust
The Austin and Hope
  Pilkington Trust
The Col W W Pilkington Will
  Trusts The General Charity
  Fund
Polden-Puckham Charitable
  Foundation
The Polonsky Foundation
The John Porter Charitable
  Trust
The Porter Foundation
The Premier League Charitable
  Fund
The Prince of Wales's
  Charitable Foundation
The Puri Foundation
Mr and Mrs J A Pye's
  Charitable Settlement
The Quarry Family Charitable
  Trust
Quartet Community Foundation
Quercus Trust
The R V W Trust
The Racing Foundation
The Radcliffe Trust
The Ragdoll Foundation
The Peggy Ramsay Foundation
The Sigrid Rausing Trust
The Ravensdale Trust
The Rayne Foundation
The Rayne Trust
The Reed Foundation
The Max Reinhardt Charitable
  Trust
The Rhododendron Trust
The Rhondda Cynon Taff
  Welsh Church Acts Fund
The Sir Cliff Richard Charitable
  Trust
The Clive Richards Charity
The Richmond Parish Lands
  Charity
River Legacy
Rix-Thompson-Rothenberg
  Foundation
The Robertson Trust
The Rock Solid Trust
The Roman Research Trust
Mrs L D Rope Third Charitable
  Settlement
The Rose Foundation

The Rotherwick Foundation
The Rothley Trust
The Roughley Charitable Trust
The Rowing Foundation
The Rowlands Trust
The Joseph Rowntree
  Charitable Trust
Royal Docks Trust (London)
The Rubin Foundation
Rugby Football Foundation
The J S and E C Rymer
  Charitable Trust
The Jeremy and John Sacher
  Charitable Trust
The Michael Harry Sacher
  Trust
Raymond and Beverly Sackler
  1988 Foundation
The Sackler Trust
The Saddlers' Company
  Charitable Fund
The Alan and Babette
  Sainsbury Charitable Fund
The Saintbury Trust
The Andrew Salvesen
  Charitable Trust
Basil Samuel Charitable Trust
Coral Samuel Charitable Trust
The Peter Samuel Charitable
  Trust
The Sands Family Trust
The Scarfe Charitable Trust
Schroder Charity Trust
The Frieda Scott Charitable
  Trust
Scottish Coal Industry Special
  Welfare Fund
The Scottish International
  Education Trust
The Scouloudi Foundation
The Searle Charitable Trust
The Shears Foundation
The Archie Sherman Charitable
  Trust
The R C Sherriff Trust
The Shetland Charitable Trust
The Shipwrights' Company
  Charitable Fund
SITA Cornwall Trust Limited
Six Point Foundation
The Smith & Pinching
  Charitable Trust
The N Smith Charitable
  Settlement
The Martin Smith Foundation
The Stanley Smith UK
  Horticultural Trust
Friends of Somerset Churches
  and Chapels
The E C Sosnow Charitable
  Trust
Spears-Stutz Charitable Trust
The Spero Foundation
Split Infinitive Trust
Sported Foundation

St Andrew's Conservation Trust
The Stanley Foundation Ltd
The Steel Charitable Trust
Stevenson Family's Charitable Trust
The Stewards' Charitable Trust
The Stewarts Law Foundation
Peter Stormonth Darling Charitable Trust
The Suffolk Historic Churches Trust
The Summerfield Charitable Trust
The Surrey Historic Buildings Trust Ltd
The Sussex Community Foundation
The Sussex Historic Churches Trust
Sutton Coldfield Charitable Trust
Swimathon Foundation
The John Swire (1989) Charitable Trust
The Connie and Albert Taylor Charitable Trust
A P Taylor Trust
The Ten Ten Charitable Trust
The Tennis Foundation
The Thistle Trust
The Thompson Family Charitable Trust
Mrs R P Tindall's Charitable Trust
The Tinsley Foundation
Annie Tranmer Charitable Trust
The Trefoil Trust
The Tsukanov Family Foundation
The Turtleton Charitable Trust
Miss S M Tutton Charitable Trust
Two Ridings Community Foundation
Community Foundation Serving Tyne and Wear and Northumberland
The Underwood Trust
Unity Theatre Trust
The Michael Uren Foundation
Vale of Glamorgan – Welsh Church Fund
The Valentine Charitable Trust
The Albert Van Den Bergh Charitable Trust
The Vardy Foundation
The Variety Club Children's Charity
Veneziana Fund
The Nigel Vinson Charitable Trust
Wales Council for Voluntary Action
Robert and Felicity Waley-Cohen Charitable Trust

Sir Siegmund Warburg's Voluntary Settlement
The Ward Blenkinsop Trust
The John Warren Foundation
The Waterloo Foundation
The Howard Watson Symington Memorial Charity
Welsh Church Fund Dyfed area (Carmarthenshire, Ceredigion and Pembrokeshire)
The Welton Foundation
The Westcroft Trust
The Garfield Weston Foundation
The Barbara Whatmore Charitable Trust
The Whitaker Charitable Trust
The Colonel W H Whitbread Charitable Trust
Will to Win Foundation Ltd. (previously Tennis for a Life)
The Williams Charitable Trust
Williams Serendipity Trust
The HDH Wills 1965 Charitable Trust
David Wilson Foundation
The Harold Hyam Wingate Foundation
The Winton Charitable Foundation
The Wixamtree Trust
The Maurice Wohl Charitable Foundation
The Wolfson Family Charitable Trust
The Wolfson Foundation
The Woodcock Charitable Trust
Wooden Spoon Society
The Woodward Charitable Trust
The Worcestershire and Dudley Historic Churches Trust
The Matthews Wrightson Charity Trust
Miss E B Wrightson's Charitable Settlement
The Wyseliot Charitable Trust
The W Wing Yip and Brothers Foundation
The Yorkshire Dales Millennium Trust
The Yorkshire Historic Churches Trust
The William Allen Young Charitable Trust
Youth Music (previously known as National Foundation for Youth Music)
Youth United Foundation
The Marjorie and Arnold Ziff Charitable Foundation
The Zochonis Charitable Trust

Arts and culture

The A B Charitable Trust
The Victor Adda Foundation
The H B Allen Charitable Trust
Angus Allnatt Charitable Foundation
The AMW Charitable Trust
Andor Charitable Trust
The Eric Anker-Petersen Charity
The Armourers' and Brasiers' Gauntlet Trust
Arts Council England
The Arts Council of Northern Ireland
Arts Council of Wales (also known as Cyngor Celfyddydau Cymru)
The Ashden Trust
The Ashendene Trust
The Ashley Family Foundation
The Aurelius Charitable Trust
B W Charitable Trust
Backstage Trust
The Ballinger Charitable Trust
The Baring Foundation
Barrington Family Charitable Trust
BC Partners Foundation
The Hervey Benham Charitable Trust
Bergqvist Charitable Trust
The Neville and Elaine Blond Charitable Trust
The Nicholas Boas Charitable Trust
The Boltini Trust
The Bowerman Charitable Trust
John and Susan Bowers Fund
The Liz and Terry Bramall Foundation
British Institute at Ankara
The Britten-Pears Foundation
The Rory and Elizabeth Brooks Foundation
The Brownsword Charitable Foundation
T B H Brunner's Charitable Settlement
The Rosemary Bugden Charitable Trust
The Derek Butler Trust
C J Cadbury Charitable Trust
Edward Cadbury Charitable Trust
Peter Cadbury Charitable Trust
The G W Cadbury Charitable Trust
The William A Cadbury Charitable Trust
The Edward and Dorothy Cadbury Trust
Calouste Gulbenkian Foundation – UK Branch

The Carnegie Dunfermline Trust
The Cayo Foundation
Elizabeth Cayzer Charitable Trust
The Chetwode Foundation
J A Clark Charitable Trust
The Clore Duffield Foundation
Miss V L Clore's 1967 Charitable Trust
The Francis Coales Charitable Foundation
The Denise Cohen Charitable Trust
The John S Cohen Foundation
The R and S Cohen Foundation
Colwinston Charitable Trust
Colyer-Fergusson Charitable Trust
The Ernest Cook Trust
The Craignish Trust
Creative Scotland
The Cross Trust
The Cumber Family Charitable Trust
The D'Oyly Carte Charitable Trust
The Daiwa Anglo-Japanese Foundation
The Davidson Family Charitable Trust
The Gwendoline and Margaret Davies Charity
Peter De Haan Charitable Trust
The Deakin Charitable Trust
The Delius Trust
Dentons UKMEA LLP Charitable Trust
The Djanogly Foundation
The Drapers' Charitable Fund
The Duis Charitable Trust
Dunard Fund
The Dyers' Company Charitable Trust
The Earmark Trust
Eden Arts Trust
The Gilbert and Eileen Edgar Foundation
The Elephant Trust
The John Ellerman Foundation
The Elmgrant Trust
The Elmley Foundation
The Emerton-Christie Charity
The Equity Trust Fund
The Eranda Foundation
The Ericson Trust
Esmée Fairbairn Foundation
The Family Rich Charities Trust
The Lord Faringdon Charitable Trust
The John Feeney Charitable Trust
The Fidelity UK Foundation

Fife Council/Common Good Funds and Trusts
Gerald Finzi Charitable Trust
The Sir John Fisher Foundation
The Joyce Fletcher Charitable Trust
The Follett Trust
The Forman Hardy Charitable Trust
The Fort Foundation
The Four Lanes Trust
The Foyle Foundation
The Gordon Fraser Charitable Trust
The Hugh Fraser Foundation
The Freshgate Trust Foundation
Gamlen Charitable Trust
The Samuel Gardner Memorial Trust
The Garnett Charitable Trust
Garrick Charitable Trust
The Gatsby Charitable Foundation
Gatwick Airport Community Trust
The Robert Gavron Charitable Trust
Jacqueline and Michael Gee Charitable Trust
The Gibbs Charitable Trust
Simon Gibson Charitable Trust
Lady Gibson's Charitable Trust
The Girdlers' Company Charitable Trust
The Glass-House Trust
Golden Charitable Trust
The Jack Goldhill Charitable Trust
The Goldsmiths' Arts Trust Fund
The Goldsmiths' Company Charity
The Golsoncott Foundation
Golubovich Foundation
Nicholas and Judith Goodison's Charitable Settlement
A and S Graham Charitable Trust
The Granada Foundation
The Grand Order of Water Rats' Charities Fund
The J G Graves Charitable Trust
The Great Britain Sasakawa Foundation
The Kenneth & Susan Green Charitable Foundation
Greys Charitable Trust
The Grimmitt Trust
The Grocers' Charity
The Hadfield Trust
The Hadrian Trust
Paul Hamlyn Foundation

The W A Handley Charitable Trust
The Harding Trust
The Kenneth Hargreaves Charitable Trust
The Harris Charitable Trust
Haskel Family Foundation
The Headley Trust
The Hellenic Foundation
The Hemby Trust
Henley Educational Trust (formerley Henley Educational Charity)
The Heritage of London Trust Ltd
The Derek Hill Foundation
The Charles Littlewood Hill Trust
The Hinrichsen Foundation
The Hintze Family Charitable Foundation
Hobson Charity Limited
Matthew Hodder Charitable Trust
The Holst Foundation
The Homestead Charitable Trust
The Horne Foundation
The Reta Lila Howard Foundation
The Huddersfield Common Good Trust
The Geoffrey C Hughes Charitable Trust
Human Relief Foundation
The Idlewild Trust
The Ireland Fund of Great Britain
The ISA Charity
Jacobs Charitable Trust
The John Jarrold Trust
Jerwood Charitable Foundation
The Dyfrig and Heather John Charitable Trust
The Jungels-Winkler Charitable Foundation
The Stanley Kalms Foundation
The Boris Karloff Charitable Foundation
The Kathleen Trust
The Michael and Ilse Katz Foundation
The Robert Kiln Charitable Trust
The Eric and Margaret Kinder Charitable Trust
The Marina Kleinwort Charitable Trust
The Kobler Trust
The Kohn Foundation
The Christopher Laing Foundation
The Kirby Laing Foundation
The Lark Trust
The Leathersellers' Company Charitable Fund

The Leche Trust
Leeds Building Society
   Charitable Foundation
Mrs Vera Leigh's Charity
The Leverhulme Trust
Lord Leverhulme's Charitable
   Trust
The Joseph Levy Charitable
   Foundation
The Limbourne Trust
The Linbury Trust
The Linden Charitable Trust
The Enid Linder Foundation
The Charles Lloyd Foundation
Lloyds Bank Foundation for
   Northern Ireland
The London Marathon
   Charitable Trust
The William and Katherine
   Longman Trust
The Ruth and Jack Lunzer
   Charitable Trust
Lord and Lady Lurgan Trust
John Lyon's Charity
The Sir Jack Lyons Charitable
   Trust
The Mackintosh Foundation
The MacRobert Trust
Ian Mactaggart Trust
Mageni Trust
Man Group plc Charitable
   Trust
The Manifold Charitable Trust
W M Mann Foundation
Market Harborough and The
   Bowdens Charity
Michael Marks Charitable
   Trust
Sir George Martin Trust
John Martin's Charity
The Nancie Massey Charitable
   Trust
The Anthony and Elizabeth
   Mellows Charitable
   Settlement
Brian Mercer Charitable Trust
The Mercers' Charitable
   Foundation
The Merchants' House of
   Glasgow
Miles Trust for the Putney and
   Roehampton Community
Millennium Stadium Charitable
   Trust
The Millward Charitable Trust
The Peter Minet Trust
The Mitchell Charitable Trust
The Esmé Mitchell Trust
The Modiano Charitable Trust
Monmouthshire County Council
   Welsh Church Act Fund
The Monument Trust
The Henry Moore Foundation
The Morel Charitable Trust
Diana and Allan Morgenthau
   Charitable Trust

The John R Murray Charitable
   Trust
The Eleni Nakou Foundation
The National Art Collections
   Fund
The National Manuscripts
   Conservation Trust
Network for Social Change
The Normanby Charitable Trust
The Community Foundation for
   Northern Ireland
The Northwood Charitable
   Trust
The Noswad Charity
The Oakdale Trust
The Oakley Charitable Trust
The Ofenheim Charitable Trust
Oglesby Charitable Trust
The Old Broad Street Charity
   Trust
Old Possum's Practical Trust
The Ouseley Trust
The Owen Family Trust
The James Pantyfedwen
   Foundation
The Parthenon Trust
The Pell Charitable Trust
The Peltz Trust
The Performing Right Society
   Foundation
The Bernard Piggott Charitable
   Trust
The Pilgrim Trust
The Austin and Hope
   Pilkington Trust
The Col W W Pilkington Will
   Trusts The General Charity
   Fund
The Polonsky Foundation
The John Porter Charitable
   Trust
The Porter Foundation
The Prince of Wales's
   Charitable Foundation
Mr and Mrs J A Pye's
   Charitable Settlement
Quercus Trust
The R V W Trust
The Radcliffe Trust
The Ragdoll Foundation
The Peggy Ramsay Foundation
The Sigrid Rausing Trust
The Ravensdale Trust
The Rayne Foundation
The Max Reinhardt Charitable
   Trust
The Rhododendron Trust
The Rhondda Cynon Taff
   Welsh Church Acts Fund
The Clive Richards Charity
Rix-Thompson-Rothenberg
   Foundation
The Robertson Trust
The Rose Foundation
The Roughley Charitable Trust
The Rowlands Trust

Royal Docks Trust (London)
The Rubin Foundation
The Jeremy and John Sacher
   Charitable Trust
The Michael Harry Sacher
   Trust
Raymond and Beverly Sackler
   1988 Foundation
The Sackler Trust
The Alan and Babette
   Sainsbury Charitable Fund
The Andrew Salvesen
   Charitable Trust
Basil Samuel Charitable Trust
Coral Samuel Charitable Trust
The Sands Family Trust
The Scarfe Charitable Trust
Schroder Charity Trust
The Frieda Scott Charitable
   Trust
The Scottish International
   Education Trust
The Archie Sherman Charitable
   Trust
The R C Sherriff Trust
The Shetland Charitable Trust
Six Point Foundation
The N Smith Charitable
   Settlement
The Martin Smith Foundation
The E C Sosnow Charitable
   Trust
Spears-Stutz Charitable Trust
The Stanley Foundation Ltd
Stevenson Family's Charitable
   Trust
The Stewarts Law Foundation
The Summerfield Charitable
   Trust
The John Swire (1989)
   Charitable Trust
A P Taylor Trust
The Ten Ten Charitable Trust
The Thistle Trust
The Trefoil Trust
The Tsukanov Family
   Foundation
Miss S M Tutton Charitable
   Trust
The Underwood Trust
Unity Theatre Trust
The Albert Van Den Bergh
   Charitable Trust
The Vardy Foundation
Veneziana Fund
Robert and Felicity Waley-
   Cohen Charitable Trust
Sir Siegmund Warburg's
   Voluntary Settlement
The Ward Blenkinsop Trust
The Waterloo Foundation
The Barbara Whatmore
   Charitable Trust
The Whitaker Charitable Trust
The Williams Charitable Trust

The Harold Hyam Wingate
Foundation
The Wolfson Foundation
The Woodward Charitable
Trust
Miss E B Wrightson's
Charitable Settlement
The Wyseliot Charitable Trust
The William Allen Young
Charitable Trust
The Marjorie and Arnold Ziff
Charitable Foundation
The Zochonis Charitable Trust

Access to the arts

The Chetwode Foundation
Creative Scotland
Gamlen Charitable Trust
The Robert Gavron Charitable
Trust
Paul Hamlyn Foundation
The Linbury Trust
Lloyds Bank Foundation for
Northern Ireland
Miles Trust for the Putney and
Roehampton Community

Amateur and community arts

The Ashden Trust
Calouste Gulbenkian
Foundation – UK Branch
Eden Arts Trust
The Ericson Trust
The Joyce Fletcher Charitable
Trust
The Robert Gavron Charitable
Trust
The Horne Foundation
The Huddersfield Common
Good Trust
The Joseph Levy Charitable
Foundation
John Martin's Charity
The Monument Trust
The Community Foundation for
Northern Ireland
The Oakdale Trust
The James Pantyfedwen
Foundation
The Ragdoll Foundation
Six Point Foundation
The Woodward Charitable
Trust

Art and culture of specific countries

The Baring Foundation
Calouste Gulbenkian
Foundation – UK Branch

Creative Scotland
The Great Britain Sasakawa
Foundation
The Hellenic Foundation
Miles Trust for the Putney and
Roehampton Community
The Eleni Nakou Foundation

Arts management, policy and planning

The Eric Anker-Petersen
Charity
Creative Scotland
Esmée Fairbairn Foundation
Miles Trust for the Putney and
Roehampton Community

Combined arts

The Earmark Trust
The Joyce Fletcher Charitable
Trust
Jerwood Charitable Foundation

Crafts

The Ernest Cook Trust
The Girdlers' Company
Charitable Trust
The Community Foundation for
Northern Ireland
The Radcliffe Trust

Disability arts

The A B Charitable Trust
Creative Scotland
The Robert Gavron Charitable
Trust
The Jungels-Winkler Charitable
Foundation
Lloyds Bank Foundation for
Northern Ireland
Rix-Thompson-Rothenberg
Foundation
The Woodward Charitable
Trust

Libraries

The Francis Coales Charitable
Foundation
Colwinston Charitable Trust
The J G Graves Charitable
Trust
Paul Hamlyn Foundation
The Headley Trust
The Heritage of London Trust
Ltd

The Mercers' Charitable
Foundation
The John R Murray Charitable
Trust
The Pilgrim Trust

Literature

The Elmgrant Trust
The Joyce Fletcher Charitable
Trust
The Follett Trust
Garrick Charitable Trust
Matthew Hodder Charitable
Trust
The Limbourne Trust
The John R Murray Charitable
Trust

Museums and galleries

The Victor Adda Foundation
The Armourers' and Brasiers'
Gauntlet Trust
The Aurelius Charitable Trust
The Clore Duffield Foundation
The Francis Coales Charitable
Foundation
The Cumber Family Charitable
Trust
The Djanogly Foundation
The Duis Charitable Trust
The Sir John Fisher Foundation
The Joyce Fletcher Charitable
Trust
The Girdlers' Company
Charitable Trust
Golden Charitable Trust
The J G Graves Charitable
Trust
The W A Handley Charitable
Trust
The Headley Trust
The Heritage of London Trust
Ltd
The Idlewild Trust
The Leche Trust
The Linbury Trust
The Manifold Charitable Trust
Sir George Martin Trust
The Mercers' Charitable
Foundation
The Monument Trust
The Henry Moore Foundation
The John R Murray Charitable
Trust
The National Art Collections
Fund
The National Manuscripts
Conservation Trust
The Pilgrim Trust
The Radcliffe Trust
The Sigrid Rausing Trust

Raymond and Beverly Sackler
1988 Foundation
Spears-Stutz Charitable Trust
The Summerfield Charitable
Trust

Performing arts

Angus Allnatt Charitable
Foundation
The Eric Anker-Petersen
Charity
The Hervey Benham Charitable
Trust
The Boltini Trust
The Britten-Pears Foundation
The Rosemary Bugden
Charitable Trust
The Derek Butler Trust
C J Cadbury Charitable Trust
Colwinston Charitable Trust
Creative Scotland
The Deakin Charitable Trust
The Delius Trust
The Duis Charitable Trust
Dunard Fund
The Equity Trust Fund
Esmée Fairbairn Foundation
The Family Rich Charities Trust
Gerald Finzi Charitable Trust
The Sir John Fisher Foundation
The Joyce Fletcher Charitable
Trust
The Fort Foundation
The Gordon Fraser Charitable
Trust
The Hugh Fraser Foundation
The Freshgate Trust
Foundation
Garrick Charitable Trust
The Gatsby Charitable
Foundation
The Gibbs Charitable Trust
The Girdlers' Company
Charitable Trust
The Grand Order of Water
Rats' Charities Fund
The Harding Trust
The Harris Charitable Trust
The Headley Trust
Henley Educational Trust
(formerley Henley
Educational Charity)
The Hinrichsen Foundation
The Holst Foundation
The Huddersfield Common
Good Trust
The Geoffrey C Hughes
Charitable Trust
The Idlewild Trust
Jerwood Charitable Foundation
The Boris Karloff Charitable
Foundation
The Kathleen Trust
The Michael and Ilse Katz
Foundation

The Robert Kiln Charitable
Trust
The Kohn Foundation
The Leche Trust
The Limbourne Trust
The Linbury Trust
The Charles Lloyd Foundation
The Mackintosh Foundation
The MacRobert Trust
The Manifold Charitable Trust
W M Mann Foundation
Sir George Martin Trust
John Martin's Charity
The Mercers' Charitable
Foundation
The Merchants' House of
Glasgow
Miles Trust for the Putney and
Roehampton Community
The Millward Charitable Trust
The Morel Charitable Trust
The Northwood Charitable
Trust
The Oakdale Trust
The Ouseley Trust
The Pell Charitable Trust
The Performing Right Society
Foundation
The Bernard Piggott Charitable
Trust
Mr and Mrs J A Pye's
Charitable Settlement
The R V W Trust
The Radcliffe Trust
The Rhondda Cynon Taff
Welsh Church Acts Fund
The Rowlands Trust
The Sands Family Trust
The Ten Ten Charitable Trust
Miss S M Tutton Charitable
Trust
The Whitaker Charitable Trust
The Williams Charitable Trust

Dance

The Girdlers' Company
Charitable Trust

Music

Angus Allnatt Charitable
Foundation
The Hervey Benham Charitable
Trust
The Boltini Trust
The Britten-Pears Foundation
The Rosemary Bugden
Charitable Trust
The Derek Butler Trust
C J Cadbury Charitable Trust
The Deakin Charitable Trust
The Delius Trust
Dunard Fund
Esmée Fairbairn Foundation

The Family Rich Charities Trust
Gerald Finzi Charitable Trust
The Joyce Fletcher Charitable
Trust
The Hugh Fraser Foundation
The Freshgate Trust
Foundation
The Gatsby Charitable
Foundation
The Harding Trust
The Harris Charitable Trust
The Hinrichsen Foundation
The Holst Foundation
The Huddersfield Common
Good Trust
The Kathleen Trust
The Michael and Ilse Katz
Foundation
The Robert Kiln Charitable
Trust
The Kohn Foundation
The Leche Trust
The Charles Lloyd Foundation
The Mackintosh Foundation
The MacRobert Trust
The Manifold Charitable Trust
W M Mann Foundation
Sir George Martin Trust
John Martin's Charity
The Oakdale Trust
The Ouseley Trust
The Performing Right Society
Foundation
The R V W Trust
The Radcliffe Trust
The Rhondda Cynon Taff
Welsh Church Acts Fund
The Rowlands Trust
Miss S M Tutton Charitable
Trust
The Whitaker Charitable Trust

Theatre

The Eric Anker-Petersen
Charity
The Equity Trust Fund
Esmée Fairbairn Foundation
The Gatsby Charitable
Foundation
The Gibbs Charitable Trust
The Grand Order of Water
Rats' Charities Fund
The Headley Trust
The Huddersfield Common
Good Trust
The Leche Trust
The Mackintosh Foundation
The Morel Charitable Trust
The Bernard Piggott Charitable
Trust
The Williams Charitable Trust

Visual arts

The Ashley Family Foundation
Colwinston Charitable Trust
Creative Scotland
The Duis Charitable Trust
Dunard Fund
The Gilbert and Eileen Edgar
 Foundation
The Elephant Trust
The Joyce Fletcher Charitable
 Trust
The Gordon Fraser Charitable
 Trust
Jerwood Charitable Foundation
John Martin's Charity
Brian Mercer Charitable Trust
The Mercers' Charitable
 Foundation
The Henry Moore Foundation
The National Art Collections
 Fund
The Max Reinhardt Charitable
 Trust
Robert and Felicity Waley-
 Cohen Charitable Trust

Fine art

The Gilbert and Eileen Edgar
 Foundation
The Mercers' Charitable
 Foundation
The Henry Moore Foundation
The National Art Collections
 Fund
The Max Reinhardt Charitable
 Trust
Robert and Felicity Waley-
 Cohen Charitable Trust

Public art/ sculpture

The Henry Moore Foundation

Heritage and the built environment

Allchurches Trust Ltd
The Architectural Heritage
 Fund
The Arthur Ronald Dyer
 Charitable Trust
Arts Council of Wales (also
 known as Cyngor
 Celfyddydau Cymru)
The Ove Arup Foundation
A J H Ashby Will Trust
The Baird Trust
The Barcapel Foundation
The Beaverbrook Foundation
The Bedfordshire and
 Hertfordshire Historic
 Churches Trust
The Bellahouston Bequest
 Fund
The Hervey Benham Charitable
 Trust
Birmingham International
 Airport Community Trust
The Harold and Alice Bridges
 Charity
T B H Brunner's Charitable
 Settlement
The Buckinghamshire Historic
 Churches Trust
The Arnold Burton 1998
 Charitable Trust
The Cambridgeshire Historic
 Churches Trust
The Carpenters' Company
 Charitable Trust
The Cass Foundation
The Chapman Charitable Trust
Stephen Clark 1957
 Charitable Trust
The Francis Coales Charitable
 Foundation
Colyer-Fergusson Charitable
 Trust
The Conservation Foundation
The Duke of Cornwall's
 Benevolent Fund
Country Houses Foundation
The Cumber Family Charitable
 Trust
The Demigryphon Trust
The Derbyshire Churches and
 Chapels Preservation Trust
The Devon Historic Churches
 Trust
The Dorset Historic Churches
 Trust
The Drapers' Charitable Fund
The Dulverton Trust
The Gilbert and Eileen Edgar
 Foundation
Edinburgh Trust No 2 Account
The Elephant Trust
The Ellis Campbell Foundation
The Elmgrant Trust

The Essex Heritage Trust
The Alan Evans Memorial Trust
The Fairway Trust
Fife Council/Common Good
 Funds and Trusts
Fisherbeck Charitable Trust
The Fishmongers' Company's
 Charitable Trust
Marc Fitch Fund
The Jill Franklin Trust
The Gordon Fraser Charitable
 Trust
The Freshgate Trust
 Foundation
Friends of Essex Churches
 Trust
The Friends of Kent Churches
The Frognal Trust
The Galanthus Trust
The Gannochy Trust
The Samuel Gardner Memorial
 Trust
Gatwick Airport Community
 Trust
The Girdlers' Company
 Charitable Trust
The Glass-House Trust
The Gloucestershire Historic
 Churches Trust
The Goldsmiths' Company
 Charity
The Golsoncott Foundation
The Gosling Foundation
 Limited
Greys Charitable Trust
The Grimmitt Trust
The Grocers' Charity
The Hadrian Trust
The Hampshire and Islands
 Historic Churches Trust
The W A Handley Charitable
 Trust
The Harbour Foundation
The Kenneth Hargreaves
 Charitable Trust
The Dorothy Hay-Bolton
 Charitable Trust
The Charles Hayward
 Foundation
The Headley Trust
The Hemby Trust
The Herefordshire Historic
 Churches Trust
The Heritage of London Trust
 Ltd
The Charles Littlewood Hill
 Trust
The Idlewild Trust
The Iliffe Family Charitable
 Trust
The Inland Waterways
 Association
The Johnnie Johnson Trust
Laslett's (Hinton) Charity
The Leche Trust

Leeds Building Society
  Charitable Foundation
Leicestershire Historic
  Churches Trust
Limoges Charitable Trust
The Linbury Trust
The Lincolnshire Churches
  Trust
The Charles Lloyd Foundation
Manchester Airport Community
  Trust Fund
The Manifold Charitable Trust
Market Harborough and The
  Bowdens Charity
Marshall's Charity
The Mears Foundation
The Anthony and Elizabeth
  Mellows Charitable
  Settlement
The Mercers' Charitable
  Foundation
The Metropolitan Drinking
  Fountain and Cattle Trough
  Association
Gerald Micklem Charitable
  Trust
Miles Trust for the Putney and
  Roehampton Community
The Esmé Mitchell Trust
Monmouthshire County Council
  Welsh Church Act Fund
The Monument Trust
Mrs Waterhouse Charitable
  Trust
The John R Murray Charitable
  Trust
The National Churches Trust
The Normanby Charitable Trust
The Northern Rock Foundation
The Northumbria Historic
  Churches Trust
The Nottinghamshire Historic
  Churches Trust
The Owen Family Trust
The James Pantyfedwen
  Foundation
Miss M E Swinton Paterson's
  Charitable Trust
The Jack Patston Charitable
  Trust
The Pilgrim Trust
The Prince of Wales's
  Charitable Foundation
The Radcliffe Trust
The Rhondda Cynon Taff
  Welsh Church Acts Fund
The Robertson Trust
The Rock Solid Trust
Mrs L D Rope Third Charitable
  Settlement
The Roughley Charitable Trust
Royal Docks Trust (London)
The J S and E C Rymer
  Charitable Trust
The Peter Samuel Charitable
  Trust

Schroder Charity Trust
The Shears Foundation
The Shetland Charitable Trust
The Stanley Smith UK
  Horticultural Trust
Friends of Somerset Churches
  and Chapels
St Andrew's Conservation
  Trust
Stevenson Family's Charitable
  Trust
Peter Stormonth Darling
  Charitable Trust
The Suffolk Historic Churches
  Trust
The Surrey Historic Buildings
  Trust Ltd
The Sussex Historic Churches
  Trust
The Connie and Albert Taylor
  Charitable Trust
The Turtleton Charitable Trust
The Michael Uren Foundation
Vale of Glamorgan – Welsh
  Church Fund
Veneziana Fund
The John Warren Foundation
Welsh Church Fund Dyfed
  area (Carmarthenshire,
  Ceredigion and
  Pembrokeshire)
The Colonel W H Whitbread
  Charitable Trust
The Wolfson Foundation
The Worcestershire and
  Dudley Historic Churches
  Trust
The Yorkshire Dales
  Millennium Trust
The Yorkshire Historic
  Churches Trust
The Marjorie and Arnold Ziff
  Charitable Foundation

Arts and the environment

The Carpenters' Company
  Charitable Trust
The Conservation Foundation
The Samuel Gardner Memorial
  Trust
The Glass-House Trust
The Headley Trust
The Heritage of London Trust
  Ltd
Leeds Building Society
  Charitable Foundation
Manchester Airport Community
  Trust Fund
The Metropolitan Drinking
  Fountain and Cattle Trough
  Association
Monmouthshire County Council
  Welsh Church Act Fund

The Monument Trust
The Shetland Charitable Trust
The Stanley Smith UK
  Horticultural Trust
The Marjorie and Arnold Ziff
  Charitable Foundation

Architecture

The Glass-House Trust
The Heritage of London Trust
  Ltd
Monmouthshire County Council
  Welsh Church Act Fund

Landscape

The Conservation Foundation
The Samuel Gardner Memorial
  Trust
Manchester Airport Community
  Trust Fund
The Metropolitan Drinking
  Fountain and Cattle Trough
  Association
The Stanley Smith UK
  Horticultural Trust
The Marjorie and Arnold Ziff
  Charitable Foundation

Heritage

The Architectural Heritage
  Fund
Arts Council of Wales (also
  known as Cyngor
  Celfyddydau Cymru)
A J H Ashby Will Trust
The Hervey Benham Charitable
  Trust
Birmingham International
  Airport Community Trust
T B H Brunner's Charitable
  Settlement
The Arnold Burton 1998
  Charitable Trust
The Carpenters' Company
  Charitable Trust
The Francis Coales Charitable
  Foundation
The Elephant Trust
The Essex Heritage Trust
The Fairway Trust
The Fishmongers' Company's
  Charitable Trust
Marc Fitch Fund
The Freshgate Trust
  Foundation
The Frognal Trust
The Samuel Gardner Memorial
  Trust
The Goldsmiths' Company
  Charity

The Gosling Foundation
  Limited
The Grocers' Charity
The W A Handley Charitable
  Trust
The Headley Trust
The Heritage of London Trust
  Ltd
Leeds Building Society
  Charitable Foundation
The Linbury Trust
The Manifold Charitable Trust
Market Harborough and The
  Bowdens Charity
The Mears Foundation
The Anthony and Elizabeth
  Mellows Charitable
  Settlement
The Mercers' Charitable
  Foundation
Gerald Micklem Charitable
  Trust
Miles Trust for the Putney and
  Roehampton Community
The Esmé Mitchell Trust
Monmouthshire County Council
  Welsh Church Act Fund
The Monument Trust
Mrs Waterhouse Charitable
  Trust
The John R Murray Charitable
  Trust
The Normanby Charitable Trust
The Northern Rock Foundation
The Owen Family Trust
Miss M E Swinton Paterson's
  Charitable Trust
The Pilgrim Trust
The Radcliffe Trust
The Robertson Trust
Mrs L D Rope Third Charitable
  Settlement
The Peter Samuel Charitable
  Trust
The Shears Foundation
Peter Stormonth Darling
  Charitable Trust
The Surrey Historic Buildings
  Trust Ltd
The Connie and Albert Taylor
  Charitable Trust
Veneziana Fund
The Wolfson Foundation

Maintenance and preservation of buildings

The Architectural Heritage
  Fund
The Baird Trust
The Bedfordshire and
  Hertfordshire Historic
  Churches Trust

The Bellahouston Bequest
  Fund
The Buckinghamshire Historic
  Churches Trust
The Cambridgeshire Historic
  Churches Trust
The Carpenters' Company
  Charitable Trust
Stephen Clark 1957
  Charitable Trust
The Francis Coales Charitable
  Foundation
Colyer-Fergusson Charitable
  Trust
The Conservation Foundation
The Duke of Cornwall's
  Benevolent Fund
The Derbyshire Churches and
  Chapels Preservation Trust
The Devon Historic Churches
  Trust
The Dorset Historic Churches
  Trust
The Dulverton Trust
Edinburgh Trust No 2 Account
The Ellis Campbell Foundation
The Essex Heritage Trust
The Alan Evans Memorial Trust
The Fairway Trust
Fife Council/Common Good
  Funds and Trusts
The Fishmongers' Company's
  Charitable Trust
The Jill Franklin Trust
Friends of Essex Churches
  Trust
The Friends of Kent Churches
The Girdlers' Company
  Charitable Trust
The Gloucestershire Historic
  Churches Trust
Greys Charitable Trust
The Grocers' Charity
The Hadrian Trust
The Hampshire and Islands
  Historic Churches Trust
The Dorothy Hay-Bolton
  Charitable Trust
The Headley Trust
The Hemby Trust
The Herefordshire Historic
  Churches Trust
The Heritage of London Trust
  Ltd
The Idlewild Trust
Laslett's (Hinton) Charity
Leicestershire Historic
  Churches Trust
The Lincolnshire Churches
  Trust
The Charles Lloyd Foundation
Manchester Airport Community
  Trust Fund
The Manifold Charitable Trust
Marshall's Charity

Miles Trust for the Putney and
  Roehampton Community
Monmouthshire County Council
  Welsh Church Act Fund
The Monument Trust
The National Churches Trust
The Northumbria Historic
  Churches Trust
The Nottinghamshire Historic
  Churches Trust
The James Pantyfedwen
  Foundation
The Jack Patston Charitable
  Trust
The Pilgrim Trust
The Prince of Wales's
  Charitable Foundation
The Rhondda Cynon Taff
  Welsh Church Acts Fund
The Rock Solid Trust
Royal Docks Trust (London)
Friends of Somerset Churches
  and Chapels
The Suffolk Historic Churches
  Trust
The Surrey Historic Buildings
  Trust Ltd
The Sussex Historic Churches
  Trust
The Connie and Albert Taylor
  Charitable Trust
The Michael Uren Foundation
Vale of Glamorgan – Welsh
  Church Fund
The John Warren Foundation
Welsh Church Fund Dyfed
  area (Carmarthenshire,
  Ceredigion and
  Pembrokeshire)
The Worcestershire and
  Dudley Historic Churches
  Trust
The Yorkshire Historic
  Churches Trust

Religious buildings

The Architectural Heritage
  Fund
The Bedfordshire and
  Hertfordshire Historic
  Churches Trust
The Bellahouston Bequest
  Fund
The Buckinghamshire Historic
  Churches Trust
The Cambridgeshire Historic
  Churches Trust
Stephen Clark 1957
  Charitable Trust
The Francis Coales Charitable
  Foundation
Colyer-Fergusson Charitable
  Trust
The Derbyshire Churches and
  Chapels Preservation Trust

The Devon Historic Churches
  Trust
The Dorset Historic Churches
  Trust
The Alan Evans Memorial Trust
The Fishmongers' Company's
  Charitable Trust
The Jill Franklin Trust
Friends of Essex Churches
  Trust
The Friends of Kent Churches
The Girdlers' Company
  Charitable Trust
The Gloucestershire Historic
  Churches Trust
The Grocers' Charity
The Hadrian Trust
The Hampshire and Islands
  Historic Churches Trust
The Dorothy Hay-Bolton
  Charitable Trust
The Headley Trust
The Hemby Trust
The Herefordshire Historic
  Churches Trust
The Heritage of London Trust
  Ltd
Laslett's (Hinton) Charity
Leicestershire Historic
  Churches Trust
The Lincolnshire Churches
  Trust
The Charles Lloyd Foundation
The Manifold Charitable Trust
Marshall's Charity
Miles Trust for the Putney and
  Roehampton Community
Monmouthshire County Council
  Welsh Church Act Fund
The Monument Trust
The National Churches Trust
The Northumbria Historic
  Churches Trust
The Nottinghamshire Historic
  Churches Trust
The James Pantyfedwen
  Foundation
The Jack Patston Charitable
  Trust
The Pilgrim Trust
The Prince of Wales's
  Charitable Foundation
The Rhondda Cynon Taff
  Welsh Church Acts Fund
The Rock Solid Trust
Friends of Somerset Churches
  and Chapels
The Suffolk Historic Churches
  Trust
The Sussex Historic Churches
  Trust
Vale of Glamorgan – Welsh
  Church Fund
The John Warren Foundation

Welsh Church Fund Dyfed
  area (Carmarthenshire,
  Ceredigion and
  Pembrokeshire)
The Worcestershire and
  Dudley Historic Churches
  Trust
The Yorkshire Historic
  Churches Trust

Restoration and maintenance of inland waterways

The Carpenters' Company
  Charitable Trust
The Inland Waterways
  Association
Leeds Building Society
  Charitable Foundation
Gerald Micklem Charitable
  Trust

Built environment – education and research

The Ove Arup Foundation
The Carpenters' Company
  Charitable Trust
The Gannochy Trust
Leeds Building Society
  Charitable Foundation

Humanities

The Aurelius Charitable Trust
British Institute at Ankara
The Barrow Cadbury Trust and
  the Barrow Cadbury Fund
Calouste Gulbenkian
  Foundation – UK Branch
The Gaynor Cemlyn-Jones
  Trust
The Francis Coales Charitable
  Foundation
The Denise Cohen Charitable
  Trust
The Daiwa Anglo-Japanese
  Foundation
Edinburgh Trust No 2 Account
The Elmgrant Trust
Marc Fitch Fund
The Golsoncott Foundation
The Great Britain Sasakawa
  Foundation
The Inlight Trust
The Robert Kiln Charitable
  Trust
The Neil Kreitman Foundation
Leeds Building Society
  Charitable Foundation
The Mount Everest Foundation
The Kitty and Daniel Nabarro
  Charitable Trust
The Eleni Nakou Foundation
The Peltz Trust
Polden-Puckham Charitable
  Foundation
The Sir Cliff Richard Charitable
  Trust
The Roman Research Trust
Mrs L D Rope Third Charitable
  Settlement
The Rothley Trust
The Joseph Rowntree
  Charitable Trust
The Scouloudi Foundation
The Tinsley Foundation
The Westcroft Trust
The W Wing Yip and Brothers
  Foundation

Archaeology

Marc Fitch Fund
The Robert Kiln Charitable
  Trust
The Roman Research Trust

History

The Gaynor Cemlyn-Jones
  Trust
The Francis Coales Charitable
  Foundation
Marc Fitch Fund
The Neil Kreitman Foundation
The Roman Research Trust

The Scouloudi Foundation

International understanding

The Barrow Cadbury Trust and
the Barrow Cadbury Fund
Calouste Gulbenkian
Foundation – UK Branch
The Daiwa Anglo-Japanese
Foundation
Edinburgh Trust No 2 Account
The Great Britain Sasakawa
Foundation
The Mount Everest Foundation
The Kitty and Daniel Nabarro
Charitable Trust
The Eleni Nakou Foundation
The Rothley Trust
The Tinsley Foundation
The Westcroft Trust
The W Wing Yip and Brothers
Foundation

Philosophy and ethics

The Inlight Trust
Polden-Puckham Charitable
Foundation
The Sir Cliff Richard Charitable
Trust
Mrs L D Rope Third Charitable
Settlement
The Joseph Rowntree
Charitable Trust

Media and communications

The Eric Anker-Petersen
Charity
The Follett Trust
Paul Hamlyn Foundation
The David Lean Foundation
Leeds Building Society
Charitable Foundation
Nominet Charitable Foundation
Unity Theatre Trust

Recreation and sport

Access Sport
Angus Allnatt Charitable
Foundation
The Arsenal Foundation
ASCB Charitable Fund
A J H Ashby Will Trust
Bag4Sport Foundation
BBC Children in Need
The John Beckwith Charitable
Trust
The Bellahouston Bequest
Fund
Bet365 Foundation
The Big Lottery Fund
Birmingham International
Airport Community Trust
Blackheart Foundation (UK)
Limited
The Blagrave Trust
BOOST Charitable Trust
British Olympic Foundation
The Carnegie Dunfermline
Trust
Carter's Educational
Foundation
The Chetwode Foundation
The Chipping Sodbury Town
Lands Charity
The Clover Trust
The Robert Clutterbuck
Charitable Trust
The Coalfields Regeneration
Trust
The Bernard Coleman
Charitable Trust
Community First (Landfill
Communities Fund)
The Congleton Inclosure Trust
Michael Cornish Charitable
Trust
The D J H Currie Memorial
Trust
The Hamilton Davies Trust
The Sir John Eastwood
Foundation
The Vernon N Ely Charitable
Trust
The English Schools' Football
Association
The Essex and Southend
Sports Trust
The February Foundation
The John Feeney Charitable
Trust
Fife Council/Common Good
Funds and Trusts
The Football Association
National Sports Centre
Trust
The Football Association Youth
Trust
The Football Foundation
The Joseph Strong Frazer Trust

The Thomas Freke and Lady Norton Charity Trust

Gatwick Airport Community Trust

The Generations Foundation

Get Kids Going

The Girdlers' Company Charitable Trust

The Golf Foundation Limited

The Granada Foundation

The Grange Farm Centre Trust

The J G Graves Charitable Trust

Robert Hall Charity

The Kenneth Hargreaves Charitable Trust

The Harpur Trust

The Peter Harrison Foundation

The Dorothy Hay-Bolton Charitable Trust

Henley Educational Trust (formerley Henley Educational Charity)

The Heritage of London Trust Ltd

The Huddersfield Common Good Trust

Huntingdon Freemen's Trust

The Inland Waterways Association

The Julian Budd Kids in Sport Trust Limited

The Kalou Foundation

The Boris Karloff Charitable Foundation

The Kelly Family Charitable Trust

LWS Lancashire Environmental Fund Limited

Leeds Building Society Charitable Foundation

The Joseph Levy Charitable Foundation

The George John and Sheilah Livanos Charitable Trust

The London Marathon Charitable Trust

The Lord's Taverners

John Lyon's Charity

Manchester Airport Community Trust Fund

W M Mann Foundation

The Jim Marshall Charitable Trust

The Mears Foundation

The Merchant Venturers' Charity

Gerald Micklem Charitable Trust

Middlesex Sports Foundation

Millennium Stadium Charitable Trust

The Peter Minet Trust

Monmouthshire County Council Welsh Church Act Fund

The Morel Charitable Trust

The Stanley Morrison Charitable Trust

British Motor Sports Training Trust

Move On Foundation Limited

The Mugdock Children's Trust

The National Express Foundation

The National Hockey Foundation

The Community Foundation for Northern Ireland

The Northern Rock Foundation

The Norwich Church of England Young Men's Society

The Pedmore Sporting Club Trust Fund

People's Postcode Trust

The Premier League Charitable Fund

The Puri Foundation

Mr and Mrs J A Pye's Charitable Settlement

The Quarry Family Charitable Trust

Quartet Community Foundation

The Racing Foundation

The Richmond Parish Lands Charity

River Legacy

The Robertson Trust

The Rowing Foundation

Royal Docks Trust (London)

Rugby Football Foundation

The Saddlers' Company Charitable Fund

Scottish Coal Industry Special Welfare Fund

The Searle Charitable Trust

The Shears Foundation

The Shetland Charitable Trust

The Shipwrights' Company Charitable Fund

SITA Cornwall Trust Limited

The Martin Smith Foundation

Sported Foundation

The Stewards' Charitable Trust

Peter Stormonth Darling Charitable Trust

Swimathon Foundation

The Connie and Albert Taylor Charitable Trust

The Tennis Foundation

The Thompson Family Charitable Trust

The Howard Watson Symington Memorial Charity

Will to Win Foundation Ltd

David Wilson Foundation

The Winton Charitable Foundation

Wooden Spoon Society

Miss E B Wrightson's Charitable Settlement

The William Allen Young Charitable Trust

Youth United Foundation

Parks and open spaces

Community First (Landfill Communities Fund)

The John Feeney Charitable Trust

The J G Graves Charitable Trust

The Heritage of London Trust Ltd

The Merchant Venturers' Charity

Recreation facilities

The Carnegie Dunfermline Trust

Carter's Educational Foundation

The Chipping Sodbury Town Lands Charity

Community First (Landfill Communities Fund)

The Football Association National Sports Centre Trust

The Thomas Freke and Lady Norton Charity Trust

The Granada Foundation

The Peter Harrison Foundation

The Huddersfield Common Good Trust

LWS Lancashire Environmental Fund Limited

The Joseph Levy Charitable Foundation

The Community Foundation for Northern Ireland

The Northern Rock Foundation

SITA Cornwall Trust Limited

Wooden Spoon Society

Sports for people with a disability

The Blagrave Trust

BOOST Charitable Trust

The Football Association National Sports Centre Trust

Get Kids Going

The Kenneth Hargreaves Charitable Trust

The Peter Harrison Foundation

The Dorothy Hay-Bolton Charitable Trust

Henley Educational Trust (formerley Henley Educational Charity)

The Huddersfield Common
  Good Trust
The Joseph Levy Charitable
  Foundation
The London Marathon
  Charitable Trust
The Lord's Taverners
Gerald Micklem Charitable
  Trust
The Community Foundation for
  Northern Ireland
Mr and Mrs J A Pye's
  Charitable Settlement
The Rowing Foundation
Wooden Spoon Society

Sports

Access Sport
Angus Allnatt Charitable
  Foundation
A J H Ashby Will Trust
The John Beckwith Charitable
  Trust
BOOST Charitable Trust
The Chetwode Foundation
The Clover Trust
The D J H Currie Memorial
  Trust
The Sir John Eastwood
  Foundation
The Vernon N Ely Charitable
  Trust
The English Schools' Football
  Association
The Football Association
  National Sports Centre
  Trust
The Football Association Youth
  Trust
The Football Foundation
The Golf Foundation Limited
The Peter Harrison Foundation
Henley Educational Trust
  (formerley Henley
  Educational Charity)
The Inland Waterways
  Association
The Boris Karloff Charitable
  Foundation
The Joseph Levy Charitable
  Foundation
The George John and Sheilah
  Livanos Charitable Trust
The London Marathon
  Charitable Trust
The Lord's Taverners
W M Mann Foundation
The Jim Marshall Charitable
  Trust
Millennium Stadium Charitable
  Trust
The Peter Minet Trust
British Motor Sports Training
  Trust

The National Hockey
  Foundation
The Quarry Family Charitable
  Trust
The Racing Foundation
The Richmond Parish Lands
  Charity
The Rowing Foundation
Rugby Football Foundation
The Saddlers' Company
  Charitable Fund
The Searle Charitable Trust
The Shipwrights' Company
  Charitable Fund
The Martin Smith Foundation
The Stewards' Charitable Trust
Peter Stormonth Darling
  Charitable Trust
Swimathon Foundation
The Tennis Foundation
The Thompson Family
  Charitable Trust
Wooden Spoon Society

Development, housing and employment

ABF The Soldiers' Charity
The ACT Foundation
The AIM Foundation
The Ajahma Charitable Trust
The H B Allen Charitable Trust
Anglo American Group
  Foundation
The Ashden Trust
The Ashley Family Foundation
The Associated Country
  Women of the World
The BAA Communities Trust
The Balmore Trust
The Baring Foundation
Barnes Workhouse Fund
BC Partners Foundation
The Bedfordshire and Luton
  Community Foundation
The Big Lottery Fund
Birmingham International
  Airport Community Trust
The BlackRock (UK) Charitable
  Trust
The Boots Charitable Trust
The Oliver Borthwick Memorial
  Trust
The Liz and Terry Bramall
  Foundation
R S Brownless Charitable
  Trust
The Brownsword Charitable
  Foundation
Buckinghamshire Community
  Foundation
Henry T and Lucy B Cadbury
  Charitable Trust
The Cadbury Foundation
The Barrow Cadbury Trust and
  the Barrow Cadbury Fund
CAFOD (Catholic Agency for
  Overseas Development)
Community Foundation for
  Calderdale
Calouste Gulbenkian
  Foundation – UK Branch
Calypso Browning Trust
The Carpenters' Company
  Charitable Trust
The Carr-Gregory Trust
The Church and Community
  Fund
Church Urban Fund
The City Bridge Trust
The Cleopatra Trust
The Clothworkers' Foundation
The Coalfields Regeneration
  Trust
The Cole Charitable Trust
The Coltstaple Trust
Colyer-Fergusson Charitable
  Trust

The Consolidated Charities for the Infirm Merchant Taylors' Company
The Cooks Charity
The Evan Cornish Foundation
The Cotton Industry War Memorial Trust
Dudley and Geoffrey Cox Charitable Trust
Michael Crawford Children's Charity
The Cumber Family Charitable Trust
Cumbria Community Foundation
Baron Davenport's Charity
The Sandy Dewhirst Charitable Trust
The Digbeth Trust Limited
Dorset Community Foundation
The Dorus Trust
The Drapers' Charitable Fund
The Duis Charitable Trust
The Dulverton Trust
The Dyers' Company Charitable Trust
The Ebenezer Trust
The Edith Maud Ellis 1985 Charitable Trust
The Englefield Charitable Trust
The Epigoni Trust
Essex Community Foundation
Sir John Evelyn's Charity
The Expat Foundation
Esmée Fairbairn Foundation
Allan and Nesta Ferguson Charitable Settlement
The Sir John Fisher Foundation
The Football Association National Sports Centre Trust
The Football Foundation
Ford Britain Trust
The Oliver Ford Charitable Trust
The Donald Forrester Trust
Sydney E Franklin Deceased's New Second Charity
Friends Provident Charitable Foundation
The Patrick & Helena Frost Foundation
Worshipful Company of Furniture Makers Charitable Fund
The Fuserna Foundation General Charitable Trust
The G D Charitable Trust
The Gatsby Charitable Foundation
Gatwick Airport Community Trust
Jacqueline and Michael Gee Charitable Trust
The Girdlers' Company Charitable Trust

The Glass-House Trust
Gloucestershire Community Foundation
Grand Charitable Trust of the Order of Women Freemasons
GrantScape
Greenham Common Community Trust Limited
The Grimmitt Trust
The Grocers' Charity
The Hadfield Trust
Hampton Fuel Allotment Charity
The W A Handley Charitable Trust
The Harbour Foundation
William Harding's Charity
The Hare of Steep Charitable Trust
Hasluck Charitable Trust
The Charles Hayward Foundation
The Hemby Trust
Matthew Hodder Charitable Trust
The Horne Trust
The Worshipful Company of Horners' Charitable Trusts
HTA Sheba Foundation UK
The Huddersfield Common Good Trust
The Hyde Charitable Trust
Impetus – The Private Equity Foundation (Impetus – PEF)
The Irish Youth Foundation (UK) Ltd (incorporating The Lawlor Foundation)
The Isle of Anglesey Charitable Trust
The Johnson Foundation
Jusaca Charitable Trust
The Mary Kinross Charitable Trust
The Heinz, Anna and Carol Kroch Foundation
LandAid Charitable Trust
The Allen Lane Foundation
Laslett's (Hinton) Charity
The Lawson Beckman Charitable Trust
The Leathersellers' Company Charitable Fund
The William Leech Charity
Leeds Building Society Charitable Foundation
Mrs Vera Leigh's Charity
Liberum Foundation
Lindenleaf Charitable Trust
Liverpool Sailors' Home Trust
Lloyd's Charities Trust
Lloyds Bank Foundation for England and Wales
Lloyds Bank Foundation for Northern Ireland
The Trust for London

The London Community Foundation
The London Housing Foundation
The Lotus Foundation
C F Lunoe Trust Fund
John Lyon's Charity
The R S Macdonald Charitable Trust
The Macfarlane Walker Trust
Magdalen Hospital Trust
Mandeville Trust
The Hilda and Samuel Marks Foundation
The Charlotte Marshall Charitable Trust
The Jim Marshall Charitable Trust
The Mathew Trust
Matliwala Family Charitable Trust
The Mears Foundation
The Menzies Charity Foundation
The Merchant Venturers' Charity
The Merchants' House of Glasgow
Community Foundation for Merseyside
Mickleham Charitable Trust
Miles Trust for the Putney and Roehampton Community
The Millfield House Foundation
Milton Keynes Community Foundation
The MITIE Foundation
Monmouthshire County Council Welsh Church Act Fund
The Monument Trust
John Moores Foundation
Moto in the Community
The Edwina Mountbatten Trust
Frederick Mulder Charitable Trust
Peter John Murray Trust
Muslim Hands
The Kitty and Daniel Nabarro Charitable Trust
The Nadezhda Charitable Trust
The National Churches Trust
The Nationwide Foundation
Needham Market and Barking Welfare Charities
The Worshipful Company of Needlemakers' Charitable Fund
The Noon Foundation
The Norda Trust
Norfolk Community Foundation
The Community Foundation for Northern Ireland
The Northern Rock Foundation
The Norton Foundation
The Norwich Town Close Estate Charity

Nottinghamshire Community Foundation
The Nottinghamshire Miners' Welfare Trust Fund
Novi Most International
Oizer Charitable Trust
The Oldham Foundation
The Paladin Vince-Odozi Charitable Trust
Panton Trust
Paraton Trust
People's Postcode Trust
The Phillips Charitable Trust
The Pilgrim Trust
The Pilkington Charities Fund
The Worshipful Company of Plaisterers Charitable Trust
The Premier League Charitable Fund
The Puebla Charitable Trust
Mr and Mrs J A Pye's Charitable Settlement
Ranworth Trust
The Eleanor Rathbone Charitable Trust
The Sigrid Rausing Trust
The Rayne Foundation
The Robertson Trust
Mrs L D Rope Third Charitable Settlement
The Joseph Rowntree Charitable Trust
Royal Docks Trust (London)
The Saddlers' Company Charitable Fund
The Peter Saunders Trust
Foundation Scotland
The Scottish International Education Trust
The Screwfix Foundation
The Shanti Charitable Trust
The Sheldon Trust
Dr Richard Solomon's Charitable Trust
The Spero Foundation
St Monica Trust
Sir Halley Stewart Trust
The Stokenchurch Educational Charity
The Sussex Community Foundation
Sutton Coldfield Charitable Trust
The Hugh and Ruby Sykes Charitable Trust
C B and H H Taylor 1984 Trust
Community Foundation Serving Tyne and Wear and Northumberland
Ulster Garden Villages Ltd
The Nigel Vinson Charitable Trust
Volant Charitable Trust
Voluntary Action Fund (VAF)
The Scurrah Wainwright Charity
Wakeham Trust

Wales Council for Voluntary Action
The Thomas Wall Trust
War on Want
The Waterloo Foundation
The Welton Foundation
The Wixamtree Trust
The Wood Family Trust
Woodlands Trust
Woodroffe Benton Foundation
The Yapp Charitable Trust

Community and economic development

The AIM Foundation
The Ashley Family Foundation
The BAA Communities Trust
The Balmore Trust
The Baring Foundation
BC Partners Foundation
The Bedfordshire and Luton Community Foundation
The Big Lottery Fund
Birmingham International Airport Community Trust
The Boots Charitable Trust
The Liz and Terry Bramall Foundation
The Brownsword Charitable Foundation
Buckinghamshire Community Foundation
The Cadbury Foundation
The Barrow Cadbury Trust and the Barrow Cadbury Fund
Community Foundation for Calderdale
Calouste Gulbenkian Foundation – UK Branch
The Church and Community Fund
Church Urban Fund
The Coalfields Regeneration Trust
The Cole Charitable Trust
Colyer-Fergusson Charitable Trust
The Evan Cornish Foundation
Dudley and Geoffrey Cox Charitable Trust
The Cumber Family Charitable Trust
Cumbria Community Foundation
The Digbeth Trust Limited
The Dulverton Trust
The Edith Maud Ellis 1985 Charitable Trust
Essex Community Foundation
Esmée Fairbairn Foundation
Allan and Nesta Ferguson Charitable Settlement

The Football Association National Sports Centre Trust
The Football Foundation
Ford Britain Trust
Sydney E Franklin Deceased's New Second Charity
Friends Provident Charitable Foundation
The Patrick & Helena Frost Foundation
The Gatsby Charitable Foundation
Gatwick Airport Community Trust
The Glass-House Trust
Gloucestershire Community Foundation
GrantScape
The Grimmitt Trust
The Grocers' Charity
The Hadfield Trust
HTA Sheba Foundation UK
The Hyde Charitable Trust
Impetus – The Private Equity Foundation (Impetus – PEF)
The Isle of Anglesey Charitable Trust
The Johnson Foundation
The Mary Kinross Charitable Trust
LandAid Charitable Trust
The Allen Lane Foundation
The William Leech Charity
Leeds Building Society Charitable Foundation
Lindenleaf Charitable Trust
Lloyds Bank Foundation for England and Wales
The Trust for London
The London Community Foundation
The Lotus Foundation
The R S Macdonald Charitable Trust
The Hilda and Samuel Marks Foundation
The Jim Marshall Charitable Trust
The Mathew Trust
Matliwala Family Charitable Trust
The Merchant Venturers' Charity
Community Foundation for Merseyside
Mickleham Charitable Trust
Miles Trust for the Putney and Roehampton Community
The Millfield House Foundation
Milton Keynes Community Foundation
The MITIE Foundation
Monmouthshire County Council Welsh Church Act Fund
John Moores Foundation

The Edwina Mountbatten Trust
Frederick Mulder Charitable
Trust
The Kitty and Daniel Nabarro
Charitable Trust
The National Churches Trust
The Noon Foundation
The Norda Trust
The Community Foundation for
Northern Ireland
The Northern Rock Foundation
The Norwich Town Close
Estate Charity
Novi Most International
The Paladin Vince-Odozi
Charitable Trust
Panton Trust
Paraton Trust
People's Postcode Trust
The Pilkington Charities Fund
The Premier League Charitable
Fund
The Puebla Charitable Trust
Ranworth Trust
The Eleanor Rathbone
Charitable Trust
The Sigrid Rausing Trust
The Robertson Trust
The Joseph Rowntree
Charitable Trust
Royal Docks Trust (London)
The Peter Saunders Trust
Foundation Scotland
The Scottish International
Education Trust
The Screwfix Foundation
The Shanti Charitable Trust
The Sheldon Trust
Dr Richard Solomon's
Charitable Trust
The Spero Foundation
Sir Halley Stewart Trust
The Stokenchurch Educational
Charity
Sutton Coldfield Charitable
Trust
The Hugh and Ruby Sykes
Charitable Trust
C B and H H Taylor 1984 Trust
Community Foundation Serving
Tyne and Wear and
Northumberland
Volant Charitable Trust
Voluntary Action Fund (VAF)
The Scurrah Wainwright Charity
Wakeham Trust
Wales Council for Voluntary
Action
The Thomas Wall Trust
The Welton Foundation
Woodlands Trust

Housing

The H B Allen Charitable Trust
The Oliver Borthwick Memorial
Trust
Henry T and Lucy B Cadbury
Charitable Trust
Calypso Browning Trust
The Carpenters' Company
Charitable Trust
The Carr-Gregory Trust
The Clothworkers' Foundation
The Cole Charitable Trust
The Coltstaple Trust
The Consolidated Charities for
the Infirm Merchant
Taylors' Company
The Evan Cornish Foundation
Michael Crawford Children's
Charity
The Cumber Family Charitable
Trust
Baron Davenport's Charity
The Duis Charitable Trust
The Ebenezer Trust
The Oliver Ford Charitable
Trust
The Patrick & Helena Frost
Foundation
The Girdlers' Company
Charitable Trust
The Glass-House Trust
Greenham Common
Community Trust Limited
Hampton Fuel Allotment
Charity
The W A Handley Charitable
Trust
The Charles Hayward
Foundation
The Hemby Trust
The Horne Trust
The Huddersfield Common
Good Trust
The Hyde Charitable Trust
The Irish Youth Foundation
(UK) Ltd (incorporating The
Lawlor Foundation)
Jusaca Charitable Trust
The Heinz, Anna and Carol
Kroch Foundation
LandAid Charitable Trust
Laslett's (Hinton) Charity
Leeds Building Society
Charitable Foundation
Lloyds Bank Foundation for
Northern Ireland
The Trust for London
The London Community
Foundation
The London Housing
Foundation
John Lyon's Charity
Magdalen Hospital Trust
The Charlotte Marshall
Charitable Trust
The Monument Trust

The Nadezhda Charitable Trust
The Nationwide Foundation
The Norton Foundation
Oizer Charitable Trust
The Pilgrim Trust
Mr and Mrs J A Pye's
Charitable Settlement
The Rayne Foundation
Mrs L D Rope Third Charitable
Settlement
St Monica Trust
The Sussex Community
Foundation
Community Foundation Serving
Tyne and Wear and
Northumberland
Ulster Garden Villages Ltd
Woodlands Trust
Woodroffe Benton Foundation
The Yapp Charitable Trust

Specific industries

The Clothworkers' Foundation
The Cooks Charity
The Cotton Industry War
Memorial Trust
Cumbria Community
Foundation
The Drapers' Charitable Fund
The Sir John Fisher Foundation
The Oliver Ford Charitable
Trust
Worshipful Company of
Furniture Makers Charitable
Fund
The W A Handley Charitable
Trust
Matthew Hodder Charitable
Trust
The Worshipful Company of
Horners' Charitable Trusts
The Leathersellers' Company
Charitable Fund
Liverpool Sailors' Home Trust
C F Lunoe Trust Fund
The Merchants' House of
Glasgow
The Worshipful Company of
Needlemakers' Charitable
Fund
The Phillips Charitable Trust
The Worshipful Company of
Plaisterers Charitable Trust
The Saddlers' Company
Charitable Fund

Education and training

The 1989 Willan Charitable Trust
The Aberdeen Endowments Trust
The Aberdeenshire Educational Trust Scheme
ABF The Soldiers' Charity
The Acacia Charitable Trust
Access Sport
The Sylvia Adams Charitable Trust
AF Trust Company
Aldgate and All Hallows' Foundation
All Saints Educational Trust
Allchurches Trust Ltd
The H B Allen Charitable Trust
The Alliance Family Foundation
Angus Allnatt Charitable Foundation
The Pat Allsop Charitable Trust
Almondsbury Charity
The Altajir Trust
The Ammco Trust
Viscount Amory's Charitable Trust
The AMW Charitable Trust
Anglo American Group Foundation
Anguish's Educational Foundation
Philip Anker Trust
The Apax Foundation
Ambrose and Ann Appelbe Trust
The John Apthorp Charity
The Arbib Foundation
The Ardwick Trust
The John Armitage Charitable Trust
The Armourers' and Brasiers' Gauntlet Trust
The Arsenal Foundation
Arts Council of Wales (also known as Cyngor Celfyddydau Cymru)
A J H Ashby Will Trust
The Associated Country Women of the World
The Association of Colleges Charitable Trust
The Astor of Hever Trust
The Lord Austin Trust
Autonomous Research Charitable Trust
The BAA Communities Trust
The Scott Bader Commonwealth Ltd
The Bagri Foundation
The Baily Thomas Charitable Fund
The Roy and Pixie Baker Charitable Trust

The Balcombe Charitable Trust
The George Balint Charitable Trust
The Bamford Charitable Foundation
The Banbury Charities
The Baring Foundation
The Barleycorn Trust
Barnes Workhouse Fund
Baruch Family Charitable Trust
BC Partners Foundation
BCH Trust
The Becketts and Sargeants Educational Foundation
The John Beckwith Charitable Trust
The Beit Trust
The Bellahouston Bequest Fund
The Ruth Berkowitz Charitable Trust
The Bestway Foundation
The Big Lottery Fund
The Bintaub Charitable Trust
The Sydney Black Charitable Trust
Blackheart Foundation (UK) Limited
The BlackRock (UK) Charitable Trust
The Blanchminster Trust
The Blandford Lake Trust
Blatchington Court Trust
The Neville and Elaine Blond Charitable Trust
The Bluston Charitable Settlement
The Nicholas Boas Charitable Trust
The Boltons Trust
BOOST Charitable Trust
The Booth Charities
The Boots Charitable Trust
The Bosson Family Charitable Trust
The Harry Bottom Charitable Trust
The Bowland Charitable Trust
The Liz and Terry Bramall Foundation
The Breadsticks Foundation
The Brendish Family Foundation
Bridgepoint Charitable Trust
The Bristol Charities
John Bristow and Thomas Mason Trust
British Record Industry Trust
The J and M Britton Charitable Trust
The Rory and Elizabeth Brooks Foundation
The Charles Brotherton Trust
Brown-Mellows Trust
The Brownsword Charitable Foundation

Brushmill Ltd
The Buffini Chao Foundation
The Rosemary Bugden Charitable Trust
Bumba Foundation
The Clara E Burgess Charity
The Arnold Burton 1998 Charitable Trust
The Derek Butler Trust
The James Caan Foundation
Edward Cadbury Charitable Trust
The William A Cadbury Charitable Trust
The Cadbury Foundation
The Edward and Dorothy Cadbury Trust
CAFOD (Catholic Agency for Overseas Development)
Calouste Gulbenkian Foundation – UK Branch
The Campden Charities Trustee
The Carlton House Charitable Trust
The Richard Carne Trust
The Carnegie Trust for the Universities of Scotland
The Carpenters' Company Charitable Trust
The Carr-Gregory Trust
The Carron Charitable Settlement
Carter's Educational Foundation
Sir John Cass's Foundation
The Gaynor Cemlyn-Jones Trust
Charitworth Limited
The Worshipful Company of Chartered Accountants General Charitable Trust (also known as CALC)
The Cheruby Trust
Chesterhill Charitable Trust
The Chetwode Foundation
The Childwick Trust
The Chipping Sodbury Town Lands Charity
The Chrimes Family Charitable Trust
Christie Foundation
Chrysalis Trust
The Church Burgesses Educational Foundation
Church Burgesses Trust
The City Bridge Trust
The City Educational Trust Fund
J A Clark Charitable Trust
The Cleevely Family Charitable Trust
The Cleopatra Trust
The Clore Duffield Foundation
The Robert Clutterbuck Charitable Trust

The Coalfields Regeneration Trust
The John Coates Charitable Trust
The Denise Cohen Charitable Trust
The Vivienne and Samuel Cohen Charitable Trust
The John S Cohen Foundation
The R and S Cohen Foundation
The John and Freda Coleman Charitable Trust
Colyer-Fergusson Charitable Trust
The Comino Foundation
The Douglas Compton James Charitable Trust
The Congleton Inclosure Trust
Gordon Cook Foundation
The Cooks Charity
Michael Cornish Charitable Trust
The Evan Cornish Foundation
The Duke of Cornwall's Benevolent Fund
The Corona Charitable Trust
The Cotton Industry War Memorial Trust
Dudley and Geoffrey Cox Charitable Trust
The Lord Cozens-Hardy Trust
The Craignish Trust
The Craps Charitable Trust
Criffel Charitable Trust
The Harry Crook Foundation
The Cross Trust
The Peter Cruddas Foundation
Cruden Foundation Ltd
The Ronald Cruickshanks Foundation
The Cuby Charitable Trust
Cullum Family Trust
The Cumber Family Charitable Trust
The Cutler Trust (the Worshipful Company of Makers of Playing Cards)
Daily Prayer Union Charitable Trust Limited
The Daiwa Anglo-Japanese Foundation
Oizer Dalim Trust
The Davidson Family Charitable Trust
The Hamilton Davies Trust
The Deakin Charitable Trust
William Dean Countryside and Educational Trust
The Demigryphon Trust
The Desmond Foundation
The Devon Educational Trust
The Sandy Dewhirst Charitable Trust
The Dibden Allotments Fund

The Peter Alan Dickson Foundation
Dischma Charitable Trust
The Djanogly Foundation
The Novak Djokovic Foundation (UK) Limited
The DM Charitable Trust
The Dorcas Trust
Dorset Community Foundation
The Dorus Trust
The Double 'O' Charity Ltd
The Drapers' Charitable Fund
Dromintee Trust
The Duis Charitable Trust
The Royal Foundation of the Duke and Duchess of Cambridge and Prince Harry
The Dyers' Company Charitable Trust
The James Dyson Foundation
Earls Colne and Halstead Educational Charity
East End Community Foundation
Eastern Counties Educational Trust Limited
The Sir John Eastwood Foundation
The Ebenezer Trust
The Gilbert and Eileen Edgar Foundation
Edinburgh Trust No 2 Account
Educational Foundation of Alderman John Norman
Edupoor Limited
The William Edwards Educational Charity
The Elephant Trust
The George Elias Charitable Trust
The Ellinson Foundation Ltd
The Ellis Campbell Foundation
The Elm House Trust
The Elmgrant Trust
Embrace the Middle East
EMI Music Sound Foundation
The Emilienne Charitable Trust
The Worshipful Company of Engineers Charitable Trust Fund
The Epigoni Trust
The Equilibrium Foundation
The Equitable Charitable Trust
The Eranda Foundation
The Ernest Hecht Charitable Foundation
The Essex Youth Trust
Euro Charity Trust
Sir John Evelyn's Charity
The Exilarch's Foundation
The Expat Foundation
Extonglen Limited
The F P Limited Charitable Trust
Esmée Fairbairn Foundation
The Fairway Trust

Famos Foundation Trust
The Lord Faringdon Charitable Trust
Samuel William Farmer Trust
The Farthing Trust
Joseph Fattorini Charitable Trust
The February Foundation
The John Feeney Charitable Trust
The George Fentham Birmingham Charity
Allan and Nesta Ferguson Charitable Settlement
The Doris Field Charitable Trust
Fife Council/Common Good Funds and Trusts
Filey Foundation Ltd
Fisherbeck Charitable Trust
The Fishmongers' Company's Charitable Trust
The Ian Fleming Charitable Trust
The Joyce Fletcher Charitable Trust
Florence's Charitable Trust
The Flow Foundation
The Follett Trust
The Football Association National Sports Centre Trust
The Football Foundation
The Forbes Charitable Foundation
Ford Britain Trust
The Oliver Ford Charitable Trust
The Forest Hill Charitable Trust
The Donald Forrester Trust
The Fort Foundation
The Lord Forte Foundation
The Four Lanes Trust
The Foyle Foundation
The Jill Franklin Trust
The Hugh Fraser Foundation
The Joseph Strong Frazer Trust
The Louis and Valerie Freedman Charitable Settlement
The Freemasons' Grand Charity
The Thomas Freke and Lady Norton Charity Trust
The Freshgate Trust Foundation
The Friarsgate Trust
Friends of Biala Limited
Friends of Muir Group
Friends of Wiznitz Limited
The Patrick & Helena Frost Foundation
Maurice Fry Charitable Trust
Mejer and Gertrude Miriam Frydman Foundation

The Fuserna Foundation
General Charitable Trust
The G I Foundation
Gableholt Limited
The Galanthus Trust
The Gale Family Charity Trust
Gamlen Charitable Trust
The Samuel Gardner Memorial
Trust
The Garnett Charitable Trust
Garrick Charitable Trust
The Gatsby Charitable
Foundation
Gatwick Airport Community
Trust
The Robert Gavron Charitable
Trust
Jacqueline and Michael Gee
Charitable Trust
Thomas Betton's Charity for
Pensions and Relief-in-Need
The Gibbons Family Trust
The G C Gibson Charitable
Trust
The Girdlers' Company
Charitable Trust
The Glastonbury Trust Limited
The GNC Trust
The Golden Bottle Trust
The Goldsmiths' Company
Charity
The Golsoncott Foundation
Nicholas and Judith
Goodison's Charitable
Settlement
The Gosling Foundation
Limited
The Hemraj Goyal Foundation
A and S Graham Charitable
Trust
The Granada Foundation
The J G Graves Charitable
Trust
The Great Britain Sasakawa
Foundation
The Great Stone Bridge Trust
of Edenbridge
The Kenneth & Susan Green
Charitable Foundation
The Green Woodpecker Trust
Greenham Common
Community Trust Limited
Greggs Foundation
The Grimmitt Trust
The Grocers' Charity
The M and R Gross Charities
Limited
The Guildry Incorporation of
Perth
The Gur Trust
The H and M Charitable Trust
H C D Memorial Fund
H C Foundation
The Hadrian Trust
Paul Hamlyn Foundation
The Helen Hamlyn Trust

Sue Hammerson Charitable
Trust
Hampton Fuel Allotment
Charity
Beatrice Hankey Foundation
Limited
The Kathleen Hannay
Memorial Charity
The Haramead Trust
Harbo Charities Limited
The Harbour Charitable Trust
The Harbour Foundation
William Harding's Charity
The Hare of Steep Charitable
Trust
The Harebell Centenary Fund
The Kenneth Hargreaves
Charitable Trust
The Harpur Trust
The Harris Charity
Haskel Family Foundation
The Maurice Hatter Foundation
The Dorothy Hay-Bolton
Charitable Trust
The Charles Hayward
Foundation
The Headley Trust
May Hearnshaw's Charity
The Heathcoat Trust
The Charlotte Heber-Percy
Charitable Trust
The Hedley Foundation
The Michael Heller Charitable
Foundation
The Simon Heller Charitable
Settlement
The Helping Foundation
The Hemby Trust
Henley Educational Trust
(formerley Henley
Educational Charity)
Philip Henman Trust
Alan Edward Higgs Charity
The Charles Littlewood Hill
Trust
The Hillier Trust
R G Hills Charitable Trust
Hinduja Foundation
The Hinrichsen Foundation
The Hintze Family Charitable
Foundation
The Hitchin Educational
Foundation
Hobson Charity Limited
Hockerill Educational
Foundation
Matthew Hodder Charitable
Trust
The Sir Julian Hodge
Charitable Trust
The Jane Hodge Foundation
John Holford's Charity
Hope for Youth (NI)
The Hope Trust
The Horizon Foundation

The Antony Hornby Charitable
Trust
The Horne Foundation
The Hornsey Parochial
Charities
The Reta Lila Howard
Foundation
The Daniel Howard Trust
HTA Sheba Foundation UK
The Huddersfield Common
Good Trust
Hulme Trust Estates
(Educational)
Human Relief Foundation
The Humanitarian Trust
The Hunter Foundation
Miss Agnes H Hunter's Trust
The Huntingdon Foundation
The Hyde Charitable Trust
The Iliffe Family Charitable
Trust
Impetus – The Private Equity
Foundation (Impetus – PEF)
The Inland Waterways
Association
The International Bankers
Charitable Trust (The
Worshipful Company of
International Bankers)
Investream Charitable Trust
The Ireland Fund of Great
Britain
The Irish Youth Foundation
(UK) Ltd (incorporating The
Lawlor Foundation)
The Ironmongers' Foundation
The ISA Charity
The Ithaca Trust
The J & J Benevolent
Foundation
The J & J Charitable Trust
J A R Charitable Trust
The J J Charitable Trust
The Jabbs Foundation
The Ruth and Lionel Jacobson
Trust (Second Fund) No 2
John James Bristol Foundation
The Marjory Jameson Trust
The Jerusalem Trust
Jerwood Charitable Foundation
The Jigsaw Foundation
The Dyfrig and Heather John
Charitable Trust
The Michael John Trust
The Johnson Foundation
The Johnson Wax Ltd
Charitable Trust
The Dezna Robins Jones
Charitable Foundation
The Joron Charitable Trust
The Ian Karten Charitable
Trust
The Soli and Leah Kelaty Trust
Fund
Kelsick's Educational
Foundation

The KempWelch Charitable
    Trust
Kent Community Foundation
E and E Kernkraut Charities
    Limited
The Peter Kershaw Trust
Keswick Hall Trust
The Mr & Mrs Paul Killik
    Charitable Trust
The Robert Kiln Charitable
    Trust
Robert Kitchin (Saddlers'
    Company)
The Sir James Knott Trust
The Kohn Foundation
The KPMG Foundation
The Kreditor Charitable Trust
The Kreitman Foundation
The Neil Kreitman Foundation
The Kyte Charitable Trust
John Laing Charitable Trust
Maurice and Hilda Laing
    Charitable Trust
The David Laing Foundation
The Lambert Charitable Trust
Duchy of Lancaster Benevolent
    Fund
The Allen Lane Foundation
Langdale Trust
The Langley Charitable Trust
The R J Larg Family Charitable
    Trust
The Law Society Charity
The Lawson Beckman
    Charitable Trust
The David Lean Foundation
The Leathersellers' Company
    Charitable Fund
The Leche Trust
The Arnold Lee Charitable
    Trust
Leeds Building Society
    Charitable Foundation
Leicestershire and Rutland
    Community Foundation
The Kennedy Leigh Charitable
    Trust
Morris Leigh Foundation
The Leigh Trust
P Leigh-Bramwell Trust 'E'
The Mark Leonard Trust
The Leverhulme Trade
    Charities Trust
The Leverhulme Trust
Lord Leverhulme's Charitable
    Trust
The Joseph Levy Charitable
    Foundation
Lewis Family Charitable Trust
John Lewis Partnership
    General Community Fund
The Lewis Ward Trust
Liberum Foundation
Lichfield Conduit Lands
Limoges Charitable Trust
The Linbury Trust

Lindale Educational
    Foundation
The Lister Charitable Trust
The Second Joseph Aaron
    Littman Foundation
Lloyd's Charities Trust
Lloyds Bank Foundation for
    Northern Ireland
The Lo Family Charitable Trust
Localtrent Ltd
The Loftus Charitable Trust
The Trust for London
The London Law Trust
The Lord's Taverners
The C L Loyd Charitable Trust
LSA Charitable Trust
The Marie Helen Luen
    Charitable Trust
Henry Lumley Charitable Trust
The Ruth and Jack Lunzer
    Charitable Trust
Lord and Lady Lurgan Trust
The Lynn Foundation
John Lyon's Charity
The Sir Jack Lyons Charitable
    Trust
The Madeline Mabey Trust
Macdonald-Buchanan
    Charitable Trust
The Macfarlane Walker Trust
The Mackintosh Foundation
The MacRobert Trust
Ian Mactaggart Trust
James Madison Trust
Magdalen Hospital Trust
The Magen Charitable Trust
The Mahavir Trust
Malbin Trust
Man Group plc Charitable
    Trust
The Manifold Charitable Trust
W M Mann Foundation
The Manoukian Charitable
    Foundation
Maranatha Christian Trust
Marbeh Torah Trust
The Stella and Alexander
    Margulies Charitable Trust
The Marianne Foundation
Market Harborough and The
    Bowdens Charity
The Ann and David Marks
    Foundation
The Hilda and Samuel Marks
    Foundation
The Marr-Munning Trust
The Michael Marsh Charitable
    Trust
The Marsh Christian Trust
The Charlotte Marshall
    Charitable Trust
The Jim Marshall Charitable
    Trust
Marshgate Charitable
    Settlement
Sir George Martin Trust

John Martin's Charity
The John Mason Family Trust
The Nancie Massey Charitable
    Trust
The Mathew Trust
Matliwala Family Charitable
    Trust
Evelyn May Trust
The Mayfield Valley Arts Trust
The Robert McAlpine
    Foundation
The McKenna Charitable Trust
The Mears Foundation
The Medlock Charitable Trust
Melodor Limited
Melow Charitable Trust
The Menzies Charity
    Foundation
The Mercers' Charitable
    Foundation
The Merchant Taylors'
    Company Charities Fund
The Merchant Venturers'
    Charity
The Merchants' House of
    Glasgow
Community Foundation for
    Merseyside
The Metropolitan Masonic
    Charity
T and J Meyer Family
    Foundation Limited
Mi Yu Foundation
Mickleham Charitable Trust
Gerald Micklem Charitable
    Trust
Miles Trust for the Putney and
    Roehampton Community
The Ronald Miller Foundation
The Millichope Foundation
The Edgar Milward Charity
The Peter Minet Trust
Minge's Gift and the Pooled
    Trusts
Minton Charitable Trust
The Mirfield Educational
    Charity
The Mitchell Charitable Trust
The MITIE Foundation
The Moette Charitable Trust
The Mole Charitable Trust
Monmouthshire County Council
    Welsh Church Act Fund
The Colin Montgomerie
    Charitable Foundation
The Henry Moore Foundation
John Moores Foundation
The Morel Charitable Trust
The Mr and Mrs J T Morgan
    Foundation
Morgan Stanley International
    Foundation
Diana and Allan Morgenthau
    Charitable Trust
The Morris Charitable Trust
G M Morrison Charitable Trust

The Stanley Morrison
Charitable Trust
Vyoel Moshe Charitable Trust
The Moss Charitable Trust
The Robert and Margaret
Moss Charitable Trust
Mosselson Charitable Trust
Moto in the Community
J P Moulton Charitable
Foundation
The Edwina Mountbatten Trust
The Mountbatten Memorial
Trust
The MSE Charity
Peter John Murray Trust
The Music Sales Charitable
Trust
Muslim Hands
The Mutual Trust Group
MW (CL) Foundation
MW (GK) Foundation
MW (HO) Foundation
MW (RH) Foundation
The Kitty and Daniel Nabarro
Charitable Trust
The Eleni Nakou Foundation
The National Express
Foundation
Needham Market and Barking
Welfare Charities
The Worshipful Company of
Needlemakers' Charitable
Fund
Newby Trust Limited
The Newcomen Collett
Foundation
Alderman Newton's
Educational Foundation
Nominet Charitable Foundation
The Noon Foundation
Norfolk Community Foundation
The Normanby Charitable Trust
The Northampton Municipal
Church Charities
Northamptonshire Community
Foundation
The Community Foundation for
Northern Ireland
The Northumberland Village
Homes Trust
The Northwood Charitable
Trust
The Norton Foundation
The Norton Rose Charitable
Foundation
The Norwich Town Close
Estate Charity
The Nottingham Gordon
Memorial Trust for Boys
and Girls
The Nottinghamshire Miners'
Welfare Trust Fund
The Nuffield Foundation
Nutrisport Trust
The Father O'Mahoney
Memorial Trust

The Oakley Charitable Trust
Oglesby Charitable Trust
Oizer Charitable Trust
The Old Broad Street Charity
Trust
Old Possum's Practical Trust
Open Gate
Ormonde Foundation
The Owen Family Trust
City of Oxford Charity
Padwa Charitable Foundation
The Paladin Vince-Odozi
Charitable Trust
The Palmer Foundation
The James Pantyfedwen
Foundation
The Park House Charitable
Trust
The Parthenon Trust
Ambika Paul Foundation
The Dowager Countess
Eleanor Peel Trust
The Peltz Trust
The Performing Right Society
Foundation
The Jack Petchey Foundation
Philological Foundation
The Pickwell Foundation
The Bernard Piggott Charitable
Trust
The Pilgrim Trust
The Worshipful Company of
Plaisterers Charitable Trust
The Pollywally Charitable Trust
The Polonsky Foundation
The Ponton House Trust
The John Porter Charitable
Trust
The Porter Foundation
Porticus UK
The David and Elaine Potter
Foundation
The Praebendo Charitable
Foundation
The Premier League Charitable
Fund
The Tom Press Charitable
Foundation
The William Price Charitable
Trust
The Lucy Price Relief-in-Need
Charity
Sir John Priestman Charity
Trust
The Prince of Wales's
Charitable Foundation
The Puri Foundation
Mr and Mrs J A Pye's
Charitable Settlement
The Quarry Family Charitable
Trust
Quartet Community Foundation
The Queen Anne's Gate
Foundation
The Queen's Silver Jubilee
Trust

The Racing Foundation
Richard Radcliffe Charitable
Trust
The Radcliffe Trust
The Peggy Ramsay Foundation
The Rank Foundation Limited
Ranworth Trust
The Rashbass Family Trust
The Ravensdale Trust
The Roger Raymond Charitable
Trust
The Rayne Foundation
Eva Reckitt Trust Fund
Red Hill Charitable Trust
The Red Rose Charitable Trust
The Reed Foundation
Richard Reeve's Foundation
Relief Fund for Romania
Limited
Reuben Foundation
The Clive Richards Charity
The Violet M Richards Charity
The Richmond Parish Lands
Charity
Ridgesave Limited
Rix-Thompson-Rothenberg
Foundation
The Robertson Trust
Robyn Charitable Trust
The Roddick Foundation
The Sir James Roll Charitable
Trust
Mrs L D Rope Third Charitable
Settlement
The Rose Foundation
The Rothermere Foundation
The Rotherwick Foundation
The Rothley Trust
The Christopher Rowbotham
Charitable Trust
The Rowland Family
Foundation
The Rowlands Trust
Royal Docks Trust (London)
Royal Masonic Trust for Girls
and Boys
Ryklow Charitable Trust 1992
(also known as A B
Williamson Charitable Trust)
The J S and E C Rymer
Charitable Trust
The Michael Harry Sacher
Trust
The Saddlers' Company
Charitable Fund
Erach and Roshan Sadri
Foundation
Saint Luke's College
Foundation
The Saintbury Trust
The Salt Foundation
The Andrew Salvesen
Charitable Trust
Basil Samuel Charitable Trust
Coral Samuel Charitable Trust
The Samworth Foundation

The Sands Family Trust
Santander UK Foundation
  Limited
The Peter Saunders Trust
Schroder Charity Trust
The Scott Trust Foundation
The Scottish International
  Education Trust
The Samuel Sebba Charitable
  Trust
SEM Charitable Trust
The Seneca Trust
The Ayrton Senna Foundation
The Jean Shanks Foundation
The Shears Foundation
The Sheepdrove Trust
The Archie Sherman Cardiff
  Foundation
The Archie Sherman Charitable
  Trust
SHINE (Support and Help in
  Education)
The Bassil Shippam and
  Alsford Trust
The Shoe Zone Trust
The Simmons & Simmons
  Charitable Foundation
Sino-British Fellowship Trust
Sloane Robinson Foundation
The Smith & Pinching
  Charitable Trust
The Leslie Smith Foundation
The Martin Smith Foundation
The R C Snelling Charitable
  Trust
The Solo Charitable
  Settlement
The E C Sosnow Charitable
  Trust
The South Square Trust
The Stephen R and Philippa H
  Southall Charitable Trust
The Southdown Trust
R H Southern Trust
The Southover Manor General
  Education Trust
Sparquote Limited
The Spero Foundation
Split Infinitive Trust
The Spoore, Merry and Rixman
  Foundation
Rosalyn and Nicholas Springer
  Charitable Trust
The Geoff and Fiona Squire
  Foundation
St Christopher's Educational
  Trust (incorporating the
  Hughes and Stevens
  Bequest)
St James's Place Foundation
Sir Walter St John's
  Educational Charity
St Peter's Saltley Trust
The Stanley Foundation Ltd
The Peter Stebbings Memorial
  Charity

Stevenson Family's Charitable
  Trust
The Stewarts Law Foundation
The Stokenchurch Educational
  Charity
The M J C Stone Charitable
  Trust
Stratford upon Avon Town
  Trust
The W O Street Charitable
  Foundation
The Sudborough Foundation
Sueberry Ltd
The Summerfield Charitable
  Trust
The Sussex Community
  Foundation
The Sutasoma Trust
Sutton Coldfield Charitable
  Trust
The Sutton Trust
The Suva Foundation Limited
The John Swire (1989)
  Charitable Trust
The Hugh and Ruby Sykes
  Charitable Trust
Tallow Chandlers Benevolent
  Fund
The Mrs A Lacy Tate Trust
C B and H H Taylor 1984 Trust
Humphrey Richardson Taylor
  Charitable Trust
The Connie and Albert Taylor
  Charitable Trust
The Cyril Taylor Charitable
  Trust
The Ten Ten Charitable Trust
Tesco Charity Trust
The C Paul Thackray General
  Charitable Trust
The Thompson Family
  Charitable Trust
The Thornton Trust
The Thriplow Charitable Trust
Mrs R P Tindall's Charitable
  Trust
The Tobacco Pipe Makers and
  Tobacco Trade Benevolent
  Fund
The Tolkien Trust
The Tory Family Foundation
Tottenham Grammar School
  Foundation
The Towry Law Charitable Trust
  (also known as the Castle
  Educational Trust)
Annie Tranmer Charitable Trust
Truedene Co. Ltd
The Tsukanov Family
  Foundation
The James Tudor Foundation
Miss S M Tutton Charitable
  Trust
TVML Foundation

Community Foundation Serving
  Tyne and Wear and
  Northumberland
Ultach Trust
The Michael Uren Foundation
Uxbridge United Welfare Trust
Vale of Glamorgan – Welsh
  Church Fund
The Vardy Foundation
The Variety Club Children's
  Charity
Roger Vere Foundation
The William and Ellen Vinten
  Trust
The Vintners' Company
  Charitable Foundation
Volant Charitable Trust
Voluntary Action Fund (VAF)
Wakeham Trust
Wales Council for Voluntary
  Action
Robert and Felicity Waley-
  Cohen Charitable Trust
The Walker Trust
The Thomas Wall Trust
The Ward Blenkinsop Trust
The Waterloo Foundation
The Howard Watson Symington
  Memorial Charity
John Watson's Trust
The Weavers' Company
  Benevolent Fund
Webb Memorial Trust
The James Weir Foundation
The Welton Foundation
The Wessex Youth Trust
The Westminster Foundation
The Garfield Weston
  Foundation
The Barbara Whatmore
  Charitable Trust
The Whitaker Charitable Trust
The Colonel W H Whitbread
  Charitable Trust
The Simon Whitbread
  Charitable Trust
The Whittlesey Charity
The William Barrow's Charity
The Charity of William Williams
The Williams Charitable Trust
Williams Serendipity Trust
The HDH Wills 1965
  Charitable Trust
David Wilson Foundation
The Wilson Foundation
The Harold Hyam Wingate
  Foundation
The Winton Charitable
  Foundation
The Michael and Anna Wix
  Charitable Trust
The Wixamtree Trust
The Maurice Wohl Charitable
  Foundation
The Charles Wolfson
  Charitable Trust

The Wolfson Family Charitable
Trust
The Wolfson Foundation
The Wood Family Trust
Woodroffe Benton Foundation
The Woodward Charitable
Trust
ME Woolfe Charitable Trust
Worcester Municipal Charities
The Matthews Wrightson
Charity Trust
Miss E B Wrightson's
Charitable Settlement
The Yapp Charitable Trust
The W Wing Yip and Brothers
Foundation
Youth Music (previously known
as National Foundation for
Youth Music)
Youth United Foundation
Suha Yusuf Charitable Trust
The Marjorie and Arnold Ziff
Charitable Foundation
The Zochonis Charitable Trust

Higher education

AF Trust Company
The Alliance Family Foundation
The Altajir Trust
The Beit Trust
The Harry Bottom Charitable
Trust
The Rory and Elizabeth Brooks
Foundation
The Carlton House Charitable
Trust
The Carnegie Trust for the
Universities of Scotland
Dudley and Geoffrey Cox
Charitable Trust
The Elmgrant Trust
The Essex Youth Trust
The Fairway Trust
The February Foundation
The Football Association
National Sports Centre
Trust
The Hugh Fraser Foundation
The Joseph Strong Frazer Trust
The Gatsby Charitable
Foundation
Paul Hamlyn Foundation
Henley Educational Trust
(formerley Henley
Educational Charity)
Hulme Trust Estates
(Educational)
Impetus – The Private Equity
Foundation (Impetus – PEF)
The Ian Karten Charitable
Trust
Kelsick's Educational
Foundation
Keswick Hall Trust
The Kreitman Foundation

The Leche Trust
The Leverhulme Trade
Charities Trust
The Leverhulme Trust
The Loftus Charitable Trust
John Lyon's Charity
The Sir Jack Lyons Charitable
Trust
James Madison Trust
Miles Trust for the Putney and
Roehampton Community
Monmouthshire County Council
Welsh Church Act Fund
J P Moulton Charitable
Foundation
The Eleni Nakou Foundation
The Northwood Charitable
Trust
The Nuffield Foundation
The Polonsky Foundation
Mr and Mrs J A Pye's
Charitable Settlement
The Red Rose Charitable Trust
Richard Reeve's Foundation
The Robertson Trust
The South Square Trust
Stevenson Family's Charitable
Trust
The Thriplow Charitable Trust
Webb Memorial Trust
The Wilson Foundation
The Winton Charitable
Foundation

Informal, continuing and adult education

The Association of Colleges
Charitable Trust
The Beit Trust
The Big Lottery Fund
The Boots Charitable Trust
The Cadbury Foundation
The John and Freda Coleman
Charitable Trust
Dudley and Geoffrey Cox
Charitable Trust
The Duis Charitable Trust
The Royal Foundation of the
Duke and Duchess of
Cambridge and Prince Harry
The Elmgrant Trust
The Essex Youth Trust
The Fairway Trust
The Hugh Fraser Foundation
The Freemasons' Grand
Charity
The Gatsby Charitable
Foundation
Gatwick Airport Community
Trust
The Girdlers' Company
Charitable Trust
Greggs Foundation

Paul Hamlyn Foundation
The Charles Hayward
Foundation
Hope for Youth (NI)
The Hyde Charitable Trust
Impetus – The Private Equity
Foundation (Impetus – PEF)
Jerwood Charitable Foundation
Kelsick's Educational
Foundation
John Laing Charitable Trust
The Allen Lane Foundation
The Trust for London
John Lyon's Charity
Magdalen Hospital Trust
The Mahavir Trust
The Mathew Trust
The Merchant Venturers'
Charity
Community Foundation for
Merseyside
Miles Trust for the Putney and
Roehampton Community
The Millichope Foundation
The Peter Minet Trust
Monmouthshire County Council
Welsh Church Act Fund
John Moores Foundation
The MSE Charity
Nominet Charitable Foundation
The Community Foundation for
Northern Ireland
The Nuffield Foundation
Mr and Mrs J A Pye's
Charitable Settlement
Richard Reeve's Foundation
The Christopher Rowbotham
Charitable Trust
The Peter Saunders Trust
David Wilson Foundation
The Wilson Foundation
Youth United Foundation

Vocational education and training

The John and Freda Coleman
Charitable Trust
Dudley and Geoffrey Cox
Charitable Trust
The Hugh Fraser Foundation
The Freemasons' Grand
Charity
The Gatsby Charitable
Foundation
The Girdlers' Company
Charitable Trust
Hope for Youth (NI)
The Hyde Charitable Trust
Jerwood Charitable Foundation
Kelsick's Educational
Foundation
The Allen Lane Foundation
John Lyon's Charity

Magdalen Hospital Trust
The Nuffield Foundation
The Christopher Rowbotham
   Charitable Trust

Integrated education

The Beit Trust
The Essex Youth Trust
The Charles Hayward
   Foundation
Hope for Youth (NI)
Impetus – The Private Equity
   Foundation (Impetus – PEF)

Management of schools

Calouste Gulbenkian
   Foundation – UK Branch
The Charles Hayward
   Foundation
The Marjory Jameson Trust
Monmouthshire County Council
   Welsh Church Act Fund
The Kitty and Daniel Nabarro
   Charitable Trust
The Nuffield Foundation

Particular subjects, curriculum development

All Saints Educational Trust
Angus Allnatt Charitable
   Foundation
The Altajir Trust
Arts Council of Wales (also
   known as Cyngor
   Celfyddydau Cymru)
The Beit Trust
The Big Lottery Fund
British Record Industry Trust
The Derek Butler Trust
Calouste Gulbenkian
   Foundation – UK Branch
The Richard Carne Trust
The Gaynor Cemlyn-Jones
   Trust
Church Burgesses Trust
The Clore Duffield Foundation
The Deakin Charitable Trust
The Duis Charitable Trust
The James Dyson Foundation
The Ellis Campbell Foundation
The Elmgrant Trust
EMI Music Sound Foundation
The Worshipful Company of
   Engineers Charitable Trust
   Fund

The Ian Fleming Charitable
   Trust
The Joyce Fletcher Charitable
   Trust
The Lord Forte Foundation
Gamlen Charitable Trust
The Samuel Gardner Memorial
   Trust
The Gatsby Charitable
   Foundation
The Girdlers' Company
   Charitable Trust
The Glastonbury Trust Limited
The Golsoncott Foundation
Nicholas and Judith
   Goodison's Charitable
   Settlement
The J G Graves Charitable
   Trust
Paul Hamlyn Foundation
The Charles Hayward
   Foundation
The Headley Trust
The Michael Heller Charitable
   Foundation
The Hinrichsen Foundation
Hockerill Educational
   Foundation
Matthew Hodder Charitable
   Trust
The Hope Trust
The Hyde Charitable Trust
The International Bankers
   Charitable Trust (The
   Worshipful Company of
   International Bankers)
The J J Charitable Trust
The Ruth and Lionel Jacobson
   Trust (Second Fund) No 2
The Jerusalem Trust
Keswick Hall Trust
The Robert Kiln Charitable
   Trust
Maurice and Hilda Laing
   Charitable Trust
The Law Society Charity
The Leverhulme Trust
The Joseph Levy Charitable
   Foundation
The Linbury Trust
Magdalen Hospital Trust
Miles Trust for the Putney and
   Roehampton Community
The Henry Moore Foundation
The MSE Charity
The Music Sales Charitable
   Trust
The Kitty and Daniel Nabarro
   Charitable Trust
Nominet Charitable Foundation
The Nuffield Foundation
The Old Broad Street Charity
   Trust
Old Possum's Practical Trust
The Performing Right Society
   Foundation

The Pilgrim Trust
Sir John Priestman Charity
   Trust
The Racing Foundation
Richard Radcliffe Charitable
   Trust
The Radcliffe Trust
The Peggy Ramsay Foundation
The Sir James Roll Charitable
   Trust
Mrs L D Rope Third Charitable
   Settlement
Saint Luke's College
   Foundation
The South Square Trust
St Christopher's Educational
   Trust (incorporating the
   Hughes and Stevens
   Bequest)
St Peter's Saltley Trust
Humphrey Richardson Taylor
   Charitable Trust
Ultach Trust
The William and Ellen Vinten
   Trust
Miss E B Wrightson's
   Charitable Settlement
Youth Music (previously known
   as National Foundation for
   Youth Music)

Arts education and training

Angus Allnatt Charitable
   Foundation
Arts Council of Wales (also
   known as Cyngor
   Celfyddydau Cymru)
British Record Industry Trust
The Derek Butler Trust
Calouste Gulbenkian
   Foundation – UK Branch
The Richard Carne Trust
The Gaynor Cemlyn-Jones
   Trust
The Clore Duffield Foundation
The Deakin Charitable Trust
The Duis Charitable Trust
The James Dyson Foundation
The Elmgrant Trust
EMI Music Sound Foundation
The Ian Fleming Charitable
   Trust
The Joyce Fletcher Charitable
   Trust
Gamlen Charitable Trust
The Samuel Gardner Memorial
   Trust
The Golsoncott Foundation
Nicholas and Judith
   Goodison's Charitable
   Settlement
Paul Hamlyn Foundation
The Headley Trust

The Hinrichsen Foundation
Matthew Hodder Charitable
Trust
The Robert Kiln Charitable
Trust
The Linbury Trust
Miles Trust for the Putney and
Roehampton Community
The Henry Moore Foundation
The Music Sales Charitable
Trust
The Performing Right Society
Foundation
The Pilgrim Trust
The Radcliffe Trust
The Peggy Ramsay Foundation
The South Square Trust
Humphrey Richardson Taylor
Charitable Trust
Miss E B Wrightson's
Charitable Settlement
Youth Music (previously known
as National Foundation for
Youth Music)

Business education

The Ellis Campbell Foundation
The Gatsby Charitable
Foundation
The International Bankers
Charitable Trust (The
Worshipful Company of
International Bankers)
The MSE Charity
The Old Broad Street Charity
Trust

Citizenship, personal and social education

The Big Lottery Fund
The Elmgrant Trust
The Kitty and Daniel Nabarro
Charitable Trust
Nominet Charitable Foundation

Language and literacy education

The Duis Charitable Trust
The Elmgrant Trust
The Headley Trust
Matthew Hodder Charitable
Trust
The Hyde Charitable Trust
The J J Charitable Trust
Miles Trust for the Putney and
Roehampton Community
The Kitty and Daniel Nabarro
Charitable Trust

Old Possum's Practical Trust
Ultach Trust

Religious education

All Saints Educational Trust
The Altajir Trust
Church Burgesses Trust
The Girdlers' Company
Charitable Trust
The Glastonbury Trust Limited
Hockerill Educational
Foundation
The Hope Trust
The Ruth and Lionel Jacobson
Trust (Second Fund) No 2
The Jerusalem Trust
Keswick Hall Trust
Maurice and Hilda Laing
Charitable Trust
The Joseph Levy Charitable
Foundation
Miles Trust for the Putney and
Roehampton Community
Sir John Priestman Charity
Trust
Saint Luke's College
Foundation
St Christopher's Educational
Trust (incorporating the
Hughes and Stevens
Bequest)
St Peter's Saltley Trust

Science education

The Gatsby Charitable
Foundation
The J G Graves Charitable
Trust
The Michael Heller Charitable
Foundation
The Kitty and Daniel Nabarro
Charitable Trust
The Nuffield Foundation
The Racing Foundation
Mrs L D Rope Third Charitable
Settlement
The William and Ellen Vinten
Trust

Technology, engineering and computer education

The James Dyson Foundation
The Worshipful Company of
Engineers Charitable Trust
Fund
The Gatsby Charitable
Foundation

The Headley Trust
The Michael Heller Charitable
Foundation
Magdalen Hospital Trust
The Kitty and Daniel Nabarro
Charitable Trust
Richard Radcliffe Charitable
Trust
The Sir James Roll Charitable
Trust
The William and Ellen Vinten
Trust

Pre-school education

Carter's Educational
Foundation
The Elmgrant Trust
The Football Association
National Sports Centre
Trust
The Thomas Freke and Lady
Norton Charity Trust
Gatwick Airport Community
Trust
Hampton Fuel Allotment
Charity
The Charles Hayward
Foundation
The Hemby Trust
Henley Educational Trust
(formerley Henley
Educational Charity)
The Huddersfield Common
Good Trust
Impetus – The Private Equity
Foundation (Impetus – PEF)
John Lyon's Charity
The Madeline Mabey Trust
Miles Trust for the Putney and
Roehampton Community
Monmouthshire County Council
Welsh Church Act Fund
The Edwina Mountbatten Trust
Mr and Mrs J A Pye's
Charitable Settlement
Richard Reeve's Foundation

Primary and secondary school education

The Alliance Family Foundation
The Ammco Trust
A J H Ashby Will Trust
The BAA Communities Trust
The Baily Thomas Charitable
Fund
The Blandford Lake Trust
The Harry Bottom Charitable
Trust
The Bristol Charities
The Cadbury Foundation

Calouste Gulbenkian
   Foundation – UK Branch
Carter's Educational
   Foundation
The Congleton Inclosure Trust
Dudley and Geoffrey Cox
   Charitable Trust
The Hamilton Davies Trust
The Deakin Charitable Trust
The Dibden Allotments Fund
Earls Colne and Halstead
   Educational Charity
Eastern Counties Educational
   Trust Limited
The William Edwards
   Educational Charity
The Ellis Campbell Foundation
The Elmgrant Trust
The Equitable Charitable Trust
The Fairway Trust
The February Foundation
The Joyce Fletcher Charitable
   Trust
The Football Association
   National Sports Centre
   Trust
The Forbes Charitable
   Foundation
The Joseph Strong Frazer Trust
The Thomas Freke and Lady
   Norton Charity Trust
Mejer and Gertrude Miriam
   Frydman Foundation
The Gatsby Charitable
   Foundation
Gatwick Airport Community
   Trust
The Girdlers' Company
   Charitable Trust
Paul Hamlyn Foundation
Hampton Fuel Allotment
   Charity
The Harris Charity
The Charles Hayward
   Foundation
The Headley Trust
The Hedley Foundation
Henley Educational Trust
   (formerley Henley
   Educational Charity)
The Charles Littlewood Hill
   Trust
John Holford's Charity
The Horne Foundation
The Hornsey Parochial
   Charities
Hulme Trust Estates
   (Educational)
Impetus – The Private Equity
   Foundation (Impetus – PEF)
The J J Charitable Trust
The Ruth and Lionel Jacobson
   Trust (Second Fund) No 2
The Ian Karten Charitable
   Trust

Kelsick's Educational
   Foundation
The Peter Kershaw Trust
The Leche Trust
Leeds Building Society
   Charitable Foundation
The Mark Leonard Trust
The Leverhulme Trust
The Joseph Levy Charitable
   Foundation
The Lord's Taverners
John Lyon's Charity
The Madeline Mabey Trust
The Charlotte Marshall
   Charitable Trust
Sir George Martin Trust
The Medlock Charitable Trust
Mickleham Charitable Trust
Gerald Micklem Charitable
   Trust
Miles Trust for the Putney and
   Roehampton Community
The Mirfield Educational
   Charity
Monmouthshire County Council
   Welsh Church Act Fund
The Kitty and Daniel Nabarro
   Charitable Trust
The Newcomen Collett
   Foundation
The Nuffield Foundation
The Owen Family Trust
City of Oxford Charity
The Jack Petchey Foundation
Philological Foundation
Mr and Mrs J A Pye's
   Charitable Settlement
Richard Reeve's Foundation
Relief Fund for Romania
   Limited
Rix-Thompson-Rothenberg
   Foundation
The Robertson Trust
The Salt Foundation
The Leslie Smith Foundation
The South Square Trust
St James's Place Foundation
John Watson's Trust
The Colonel W H Whitbread
   Charitable Trust
The William Barrow's Charity
The Wilson Foundation

Faith schools

The Alliance Family Foundation
Mejer and Gertrude Miriam
   Frydman Foundation
Miles Trust for the Putney and
   Roehampton Community
The Owen Family Trust

Public and independent schools

The Elmgrant Trust
The Equitable Charitable Trust
The Fairway Trust
The Headley Trust
The Peter Kershaw Trust
The Leche Trust
The Leverhulme Trust
Sir George Martin Trust
The Nuffield Foundation
The Owen Family Trust

Special needs schools

The Ammco Trust
The Baily Thomas Charitable
   Fund
Eastern Counties Educational
   Trust Limited
The Ellis Campbell Foundation
The Elmgrant Trust
The Equitable Charitable Trust
The Joyce Fletcher Charitable
   Trust
The Forbes Charitable
   Foundation
The Thomas Freke and Lady
   Norton Charity Trust
The Girdlers' Company
   Charitable Trust
The J J Charitable Trust
The Ruth and Lionel Jacobson
   Trust (Second Fund) No 2
The Ian Karten Charitable
   Trust
Kelsick's Educational
   Foundation
Leeds Building Society
   Charitable Foundation
The Joseph Levy Charitable
   Foundation
The Lord's Taverners
Gerald Micklem Charitable
   Trust
Miles Trust for the Putney and
   Roehampton Community
The Kitty and Daniel Nabarro
   Charitable Trust
Relief Fund for Romania
   Limited
Rix-Thompson-Rothenberg
   Foundation
St James's Place Foundation
John Watson's Trust

State schools

The Deakin Charitable Trust
The Mark Leonard Trust
Richard Reeve's Foundation

Environment and animals

The 1970 Trust
The Aberbrothock Skea Trust
The AIM Foundation
The Alborada Trust
The H B Allen Charitable Trust
Anglo American Group
Foundation
The Animal Defence Trust
The Ardwick Trust
The John Armitage Charitable
Trust
The Arthur Ronald Dyer
Charitable Trust
A J H Ashby Will Trust
The Ashden Trust
The Ashendene Trust
The Associated Country
Women of the World
The Astor Foundation
The Astor of Hever Trust
Autonomous Research
Charitable Trust
The BAA Communities Trust
Harry Bacon Foundation
The Scott Bader
Commonwealth Ltd
The C Alma Baker Trust
The Balcombe Charitable Trust
The Balney Charitable Trust
The Barbour Foundation
The Baring Foundation
Lord Barnby's Foundation
BC Partners Foundation
The Beit Trust
The Bellahouston Bequest
Fund
The Hervey Benham Charitable
Trust
The Big Lottery Fund
Birmingham International
Airport Community Trust
The BlackRock (UK) Charitable
Trust
The Blair Foundation
The Body Shop Foundation
The Bothwell Charitable Trust
John and Susan Bowers Fund
Briggs Animal Welfare Trust
The Bromley Trust
Brown-Mellows Trust
C J Cadbury Charitable Trust
Edward Cadbury Charitable
Trust
The Christopher Cadbury
Charitable Trust
The G W Cadbury Charitable
Trust
The William A Cadbury
Charitable Trust
The Cadbury Foundation
The Edward and Dorothy
Cadbury Trust

CAFOD (Catholic Agency for
Overseas Development)
Calouste Gulbenkian
Foundation – UK Branch
Calypso Browning Trust
M R Cannon 1998 Charitable
Trust
The Carron Charitable
Settlement
The Leslie Mary Carter
Charitable Trust
The Cass Foundation
The Wilfrid and Constance
Cave Foundation
The Gaynor Cemlyn-Jones
Trust
The Chapman Charitable Trust
The Chelsea Square 1994
Trust
The Childwick Trust
The City Bridge Trust
CLA Charitable Trust
Clark Bradbury Charitable
Trust
J A Clark Charitable Trust
The Robert Clutterbuck
Charitable Trust
The John Coates Charitable
Trust
The John S Cohen Foundation
The Cole Charitable Trust
Colyer-Fergusson Charitable
Trust
The Conscience Trust
The Conservation Foundation
The Ernest Cook Trust
The Marjorie Coote Animal
Charity Trust
The Helen Jean Cope Trust
The Gershon Coren Charitable
Foundation (also known as
The Muriel and Gus Coren
Charitable Foundation)
The Duke of Cornwall's
Benevolent Fund
The Craignish Trust
The Craps Charitable Trust
The Crescent Trust
The Ronald Cruickshanks
Foundation
The Cumber Family Charitable
Trust
The D J H Currie Memorial
Trust
The Dennis Curry Charitable
Trust
The D'Oyly Carte Charitable
Trust
The Dr and Mrs A Darlington
Charitable Trust
Peter De Haan Charitable
Trust
William Dean Countryside and
Educational Trust
The Delves Charitable Trust
The Demigryphon Trust

Dischma Charitable Trust
The Dorus Trust
The Duis Charitable Trust
The Royal Foundation of the
Duke and Duchess of
Cambridge and Prince Harry
The Dulverton Trust
The Dumbreck Charity
Dunard Fund
The Dunn Family Charitable
Trust
eaga Charitable Trust
Audrey Earle Charitable Trust
The Sir John Eastwood
Foundation
The EBM Charitable Trust
The Ecology Trust
Edinburgh Trust No 2 Account
The John Ellerman Foundation
The Ellis Campbell Foundation
The Elmgrant Trust
The Epigoni Trust
The Ericson Trust
The Alan Evans Memorial Trust
The Beryl Evetts and Robert
Luff Animal Welfare Trust
Limited
The Matthew Eyton Animal
Welfare Trust
Esmée Fairbairn Foundation
The Lord Faringdon Charitable
Trust
Samuel William Farmer Trust
The Farmers' Company
Charitable Fund
The John Feeney Charitable
Trust
Fife Council/Common Good
Funds and Trusts
The Fishmongers' Company's
Charitable Trust
The Flow Foundation
The Oliver Ford Charitable
Trust
The Donald Forrester Trust
The Anna Rosa Forster
Charitable Trust
Sydney E Franklin Deceased's
New Second Charity
The Gordon Fraser Charitable
Trust
The Hugh Fraser Foundation
The Louis and Valerie
Freedman Charitable
Settlement
The Freshfield Foundation
The Fuserna Foundation
General Charitable Trust
The G D Charitable Trust
The Galanthus Trust
The Gannochy Trust
The Worshipful Company of
Gardeners of London
The Garnett Charitable Trust
The Gatsby Charitable
Foundation

Gatwick Airport Community Trust
The Generations Foundation
The G C Gibson Charitable Trust
The Girdlers' Company Charitable Trust
The Glastonbury Trust Limited
The GNC Trust
The Golden Bottle Trust
The Gosling Foundation Limited
GrantScape
The Stanley and Lorna Graves Charitable Trust
The Gordon Gray Trust
The Green Room Charitable Trust
Greenham Common Community Trust Limited
The Gunter Charitable Trust
H C D Memorial Fund
The Hadfield Trust
The Hadrian Trust
The Doris Louise Hailes Charitable Trust
The Hamamelis Trust
The Kathleen Hannay Memorial Charity
The Harbour Foundation
The Harebell Centenary Fund
The Kenneth Hargreaves Charitable Trust
William Geoffrey Harvey's Discretionary Settlement
Hasluck Charitable Trust
The Charles Hayward Foundation
The Headley Trust
The Charlotte Heber-Percy Charitable Trust
The G D Herbert Charitable Trust
The J G Hogg Charitable Trust
The Homestead Charitable Trust
The Cuthbert Horn Trust
The Reta Lila Howard Foundation
The Geoffrey C Hughes Charitable Trust
The Michael and Shirley Hunt Charitable Trust
The Idlewild Trust
The J J Charitable Trust
The Barbara Joyce Jarrald Charitable Trust
The John Jarrold Trust
Rees Jeffreys Road Fund
The Johnson Wax Ltd Charitable Trust
The Jordan Charitable Foundation
The Kennel Club Charitable Trust

The Robert Kiln Charitable Trust
Ernest Kleinwort Charitable Trust
John Laing Charitable Trust
The Christopher Laing Foundation
The David Laing Foundation
The Martin Laing Foundation
LWS Lancashire Environmental Fund Limited
Mrs F B Laurence Charitable Trust
The Raymond and Blanche Lawson Charitable Trust
The Leach Fourteenth Trust
The Leathersellers' Company Charitable Fund
The Mark Leonard Trust
Lord Leverhulme's Charitable Trust
The John Spedan Lewis Foundation
John Lewis Partnership General Community Fund
The Limbourne Trust
Limoges Charitable Trust
The Linbury Trust
The William and Katherine Longman Trust
The Lotus Foundation
LSA Charitable Trust
The Lynn Foundation
The Lyons Charitable Trust
The R S Macdonald Charitable Trust
Macdonald-Buchanan Charitable Trust
The Macfarlane Walker Trust
The Mackintosh Foundation
The MacRobert Trust
The Mahavir Trust
Manchester Airport Community Trust Fund
The Manifold Charitable Trust
The Marcela Trust
Marchig Animal Welfare Trust
Market Harborough and The Bowdens Charity
Michael Marks Charitable Trust
Marmot Charitable Trust
The Marsh Christian Trust
Sir George Martin Trust
Evelyn May Trust
Martin McLaren Memorial Trust
The Mears Foundation
The Mercers' Charitable Foundation
The Mersey Docks and Harbour Company Charitable Fund
The Metropolitan Drinking Fountain and Cattle Trough Association

T and J Meyer Family Foundation Limited
Millennium Stadium Charitable Trust
The Ronald Miller Foundation
The Millichope Foundation
The Millward Charitable Trust
The Peter Minet Trust
The Minos Trust
The D C Moncrieff Charitable Trust
The Montague Thompson Coon Charitable Trust
The Monument Trust
The Morel Charitable Trust
Moto in the Community
Mrs Waterhouse Charitable Trust
Frederick Mulder Charitable Trust
The Edith Murphy Foundation
The Kitty and Daniel Nabarro Charitable Trust
Network for Social Change
The NFU Mutual Charitable Trust
Alice Noakes Memorial Charitable Trust
Norfolk Community Foundation
The Community Foundation for Northern Ireland
The Nottinghamshire Miners' Welfare Trust Fund
The Sir Peter O'Sullevan Charitable Trust
The Oakdale Trust
The Oakley Charitable Trust
The Ofenheim Charitable Trust
Oglesby Charitable Trust
Old Possum's Practical Trust
The John Oldacre Foundation
The Oldham Foundation
Open Gate
The Owen Family Trust
The Paget Charitable Trust
Panton Trust
The Frank Parkinson Agricultural Trust
The Samuel and Freda Parkinson Charitable Trust
The Jack Patston Charitable Trust
The Peacock Charitable Trust
People's Postcode Trust
The Persula Foundation
The Petplan Charitable Trust
The Phillips Charitable Trust
The Pickwell Foundation
The Pilgrim Trust
The Cecil Pilkington Charitable Trust
The Elise Pilkington Charitable Trust
The Col W W Pilkington Will Trusts The General Charity Fund

Polden-Puckham Charitable
   Foundation
The John Porter Charitable
   Trust
The Porter Foundation
The Primrose Trust
The Prince of Wales's
   Charitable Foundation
Princess Anne's Charities
Mr and Mrs J A Pye's
   Charitable Settlement
Quartet Community Foundation
The Racing Foundation
The Joseph Rank Trust
The Sigrid Rausing Trust
The Rhododendron Trust
The Ripple Effect Foundation
The River Farm Foundation
The Robertson Trust
The Rochester Bridge Trust
The Roddick Foundation
The Rothera Charitable
   Settlement
The Roughley Charitable Trust
The Rowlands Trust
Royal Docks Trust (London)
The Rufford Foundation
Ryklow Charitable Trust 1992
   (also known as A B
   Williamson Charitable Trust)
The Michael Harry Sacher
   Trust
The Jean Sainsbury Animal
   Welfare Trust
The Saintbury Trust
The Saints and Sinners Trust
Salters' Charitable Foundation
The M J Samuel Charitable
   Trust
The Peter Samuel Charitable
   Trust
The Sandra Charitable Trust
The Scarfe Charitable Trust
Schroder Charity Trust
The Scouloudi Foundation
Seafarers UK (King George's
   Fund for Sailors)
The Linley Shaw Foundation
The Shears Foundation
The Sheepdrove Trust
The Sylvia and Colin Shepherd
   Charitable Trust
The Shetland Charitable Trust
The Shipwrights' Company
   Charitable Fund
The Simpson Education and
   Conservation Trust
The John Slater Foundation
Ruth Smart Foundation
The SMB Charitable Trust
The N Smith Charitable
   Settlement
The Stanley Smith UK
   Horticultural Trust
Philip Smith's Charitable Trust

The R C Snelling Charitable
   Trust
The Sobell Foundation
The South Square Trust
The Stephen R and Philippa H
   Southall Charitable Trust
The W F Southall Trust
R H Southern Trust
The Spero Foundation
The Stafford Trust
The Staples Trust
The Steel Charitable Trust
The June Stevens Foundation
Stevenson Family's Charitable
   Trust
The Andy Stewart Charitable
   Foundation
The Stewarts Law Foundation
The M J C Stone Charitable
   Trust
The Stone Family Foundation
The Sylvanus Charitable Trust
The Mrs A Lacy Tate Trust
C B and H H Taylor 1984 Trust
The Connie and Albert Taylor
   Charitable Trust
Tearfund
The C Paul Thackray General
   Charitable Trust
The Loke Wan Tho Memorial
   Foundation
The Three Guineas Trust
Annie Tranmer Charitable Trust
Community Foundation Serving
   Tyne and Wear and
   Northumberland
The Underwood Trust
The Michael Uren Foundation
The Valentine Charitable Trust
The Albert Van Den Bergh
   Charitable Trust
The William and Patricia
   Venton Charitable Trust
Roger Vere Foundation
Wales Council for Voluntary
   Action
The Waterloo Foundation
The David Webster Charitable
   Trust
The Westminster Foundation
The Garfield Weston
   Foundation
The Barbara Whatmore
   Charitable Trust
The Whitaker Charitable Trust
The Colonel W H Whitbread
   Charitable Trust
The Simon Whitbread
   Charitable Trust
The Whitley Animal Protection
   Trust
The HDH Wills 1965
   Charitable Trust
J and J R Wilson Trust
The Wixamtree Trust

The Maurice Wohl Charitable
   Foundation
The Wolfson Family Charitable
   Trust
Woodlands Trust
Woodroffe Benton Foundation
The Woodward Charitable
   Trust
The A and R Woolf Charitable
   Trust
ME Woolfe Charitable Trust
The Diana Edgson Wright
   Charitable Trust
Yorkshire Agricultural Society
The Yorkshire Dales
   Millennium Trust
Youth United Foundation
Zephyr Charitable Trust

Agriculture and fishing

The C Alma Baker Trust
The Baring Foundation
The Chapman Charitable Trust
CLA Charitable Trust
The Ecology Trust
The John Ellerman Foundation
Esmée Fairbairn Foundation
The Farmers' Company
   Charitable Fund
The Fishmongers' Company's
   Charitable Trust
The Oliver Ford Charitable
   Trust
The Worshipful Company of
   Gardeners of London
The Gatsby Charitable
   Foundation
The G C Gibson Charitable
   Trust
The Charles Hayward
   Foundation
The Headley Trust
The J J Charitable Trust
The John Spedan Lewis
   Foundation
The Limbourne Trust
LSA Charitable Trust
The MacRobert Trust
Manchester Airport Community
   Trust Fund
Marchig Animal Welfare Trust
Martin McLaren Memorial
   Trust
The Mears Foundation
The NFU Mutual Charitable
   Trust
The John Oldacre Foundation
The Frank Parkinson
   Agricultural Trust
The Cecil Pilkington Charitable
   Trust
Mr and Mrs J A Pye's
   Charitable Settlement

Quartet Community Foundation
The Peter Samuel Charitable
  Trust
Seafarers UK (King George's
  Fund for Sailors)
The Stanley Smith UK
  Horticultural Trust
The Stewarts Law Foundation
The Waterloo Foundation
The Garfield Weston
  Foundation
Yorkshire Agricultural Society

Farming and food production

CLA Charitable Trust
The Farmers' Company
  Charitable Fund
The Gatsby Charitable
  Foundation
The J J Charitable Trust
The Limbourne Trust
Mr and Mrs J A Pye's
  Charitable Settlement

Fishing and fisheries

The Fishmongers' Company's
  Charitable Trust
The John Spedan Lewis
  Foundation
Seafarers UK (King George's
  Fund for Sailors)

Forestry

CLA Charitable Trust
The Headley Trust
Manchester Airport Community
  Trust Fund
Mr and Mrs J A Pye's
  Charitable Settlement
The Peter Samuel Charitable
  Trust

Horticulture

CLA Charitable Trust
The Oliver Ford Charitable
  Trust
The Worshipful Company of
  Gardeners of London
The Gatsby Charitable
  Foundation
The John Spedan Lewis
  Foundation
LSA Charitable Trust
The MacRobert Trust
Martin McLaren Memorial
  Trust

The Stanley Smith UK
  Horticultural Trust

Animal care

The Alborada Trust
The Animal Defence Trust
The Arthur Ronald Dyer
  Charitable Trust
The Ashden Trust
The Astor Foundation
Harry Bacon Foundation
The Barbour Foundation
The Bellahouston Bequest
  Fund
Briggs Animal Welfare Trust
Calypso Browning Trust
The Wilfrid and Constance
  Cave Foundation
The Gaynor Cemlyn-Jones
  Trust
The Chelsea Square 1994
  Trust
The Childwick Trust
The Robert Clutterbuck
  Charitable Trust
The Marjorie Coote Animal
  Charity Trust
The Dumbreck Charity
The Sir John Eastwood
  Foundation
The EBM Charitable Trust
The Beryl Evetts and Robert
  Luff Animal Welfare Trust
  Limited
The Matthew Eyton Animal
  Welfare Trust
The Anna Rosa Forster
  Charitable Trust
The Stanley and Lorna Graves
  Charitable Trust
The Doris Louise Hailes
  Charitable Trust
William Geoffrey Harvey's
  Discretionary Settlement
The J G Hogg Charitable Trust
The Homestead Charitable
  Trust
The Michael and Shirley Hunt
  Charitable Trust
The Barbara Joyce Jarrald
  Charitable Trust
The Kennel Club Charitable
  Trust
The William and Katherine
  Longman Trust
The Lyons Charitable Trust
The R S Macdonald Charitable
  Trust
Marchig Animal Welfare Trust
The Millward Charitable Trust
The Edith Murphy Foundation
Alice Noakes Memorial
  Charitable Trust
The Sir Peter O'Sullevan
  Charitable Trust

Old Possum's Practical Trust
Open Gate
The Paget Charitable Trust
The Samuel and Freda
  Parkinson Charitable Trust
The Persula Foundation
The Petplan Charitable Trust
The Phillips Charitable Trust
The Elise Pilkington Charitable
  Trust
The Racing Foundation
The Joseph Rank Trust
The Jean Sainsbury Animal
  Welfare Trust
The Saints and Sinners Trust
The Sandra Charitable Trust
The John Slater Foundation
Ruth Smart Foundation
The Andy Stewart Charitable
  Foundation
The Sylvanus Charitable Trust
The William and Patricia
  Venton Charitable Trust
The Whitley Animal Protection
  Trust
The HDH Wills 1965
  Charitable Trust
J and J R Wilson Trust
ME Woolfe Charitable Trust

Animal conservation

A J H Ashby Will Trust
Birmingham International
  Airport Community Trust
The Body Shop Foundation
The Carron Charitable
  Settlement
The Wilfrid and Constance
  Cave Foundation
The Gaynor Cemlyn-Jones
  Trust
The Chapman Charitable Trust
The Robert Clutterbuck
  Charitable Trust
The Conservation Foundation
The Marjorie Coote Animal
  Charity Trust
The Cumber Family Charitable
  Trust
The Dr and Mrs A Darlington
  Charitable Trust
William Dean Countryside and
  Educational Trust
The Dumbreck Charity
The Sir John Eastwood
  Foundation
Sydney E Franklin Deceased's
  New Second Charity
The Stanley and Lorna Graves
  Charitable Trust
William Geoffrey Harvey's
  Discretionary Settlement

The Barbara Joyce Jarrald
Charitable Trust
The John Spedan Lewis
Foundation
The Lotus Foundation
Marchig Animal Welfare Trust
The Oakdale Trust
Old Possum's Practical Trust
The Owen Family Trust
The Paget Charitable Trust
The Samuel and Freda
Parkinson Charitable Trust
The Jack Patston Charitable
Trust
The Primrose Trust
Mr and Mrs J A Pye's
Charitable Settlement
The Joseph Rank Trust
The Rhododendron Trust
The Rufford Foundation
Ryklow Charitable Trust 1992
(also known as A B
Williamson Charitable Trust)
The Michael Harry Sacher
Trust
The Jean Sainsbury Animal
Welfare Trust
The Simpson Education and
Conservation Trust
The Albert Van Den Bergh
Charitable Trust
The David Webster Charitable
Trust
The Garfield Weston
Foundation
The Whitley Animal Protection
Trust
The HDH Wills 1965
Charitable Trust
ME Woolfe Charitable Trust
The Diana Edgson Wright
Charitable Trust

Climate change

The Ashden Trust
The Baring Foundation
The Bromley Trust
The Chapman Charitable Trust
The John Ellerman Foundation
Esmée Fairbairn Foundation
The Charles Hayward
Foundation
The Joseph Rank Trust
The Stewarts Law Foundation
The Three Guineas Trust
The Waterloo Foundation
The Garfield Weston
Foundation

Countryside

The Aberbrothock Skea Trust
The Astor Foundation
The BAA Communities Trust

The Baring Foundation
The Big Lottery Fund
The Blair Foundation
The Bothwell Charitable Trust
The Bromley Trust
The Cadbury Foundation
M R Cannon 1998 Charitable
Trust
The Chapman Charitable Trust
CLA Charitable Trust
Colyer-Fergusson Charitable
Trust
The Ernest Cook Trust
The D J H Currie Memorial
Trust
The D'Oyly Carte Charitable
Trust
The Dr and Mrs A Darlington
Charitable Trust
The Dunn Family Charitable
Trust
The John Ellerman Foundation
The Ellis Campbell Foundation
The Alan Evans Memorial Trust
Esmée Fairbairn Foundation
The Freshfield Foundation
The Galanthus Trust
The Gannochy Trust
Gatwick Airport Community
Trust
The Girdlers' Company
Charitable Trust
The Green Room Charitable
Trust
The Charles Hayward
Foundation
The Idlewild Trust
The John Spedan Lewis
Foundation
Manchester Airport Community
Trust Fund
Sir George Martin Trust
The Mears Foundation
The Kitty and Daniel Nabarro
Charitable Trust
The Pilgrim Trust
The Cecil Pilkington Charitable
Trust
Quartet Community Foundation
The Joseph Rank Trust
The Rufford Foundation
Ryklow Charitable Trust 1992
(also known as A B
Williamson Charitable Trust)
Schroder Charity Trust
The Linley Shaw Foundation
The Shears Foundation
The Stewarts Law Foundation
The Connie and Albert Taylor
Charitable Trust
The Valentine Charitable Trust
The Waterloo Foundation
The David Webster Charitable
Trust
The Garfield Weston
Foundation

The Whitaker Charitable Trust
The Colonel W H Whitbread
Charitable Trust
The Simon Whitbread
Charitable Trust
Woodroffe Benton Foundation
Zephyr Charitable Trust

Environmental education and research

The Ardwick Trust
The Ashden Trust
The BAA Communities Trust
The Barbour Foundation
The Baring Foundation
The Big Lottery Fund
Birmingham International
Airport Community Trust
The Body Shop Foundation
The Cadbury Foundation
The Chapman Charitable Trust
CLA Charitable Trust
The Cole Charitable Trust
The Conservation Foundation
The Ernest Cook Trust
William Dean Countryside and
Educational Trust
The Duis Charitable Trust
The Dulverton Trust
The Dunn Family Charitable
Trust
eaga Charitable Trust
The John Ellerman Foundation
Esmée Fairbairn Foundation
Gatwick Airport Community
Trust
The Green Room Charitable
Trust
The Charles Hayward
Foundation
The J J Charitable Trust
The Mark Leonard Trust
The John Spedan Lewis
Foundation
The Limbourne Trust
Manchester Airport Community
Trust Fund
Marchig Animal Welfare Trust
Marmot Charitable Trust
The Mears Foundation
The Kitty and Daniel Nabarro
Charitable Trust
Network for Social Change
The Community Foundation for
Northern Ireland
Oglesby Charitable Trust
The Cecil Pilkington Charitable
Trust
The Porter Foundation
Quartet Community Foundation
The Joseph Rank Trust
The Rufford Foundation
The Saintbury Trust

The Shears Foundation
The Stanley Smith UK
   Horticultural Trust
The Sobell Foundation
The Spero Foundation
The Staples Trust
The Stewarts Law Foundation
The Waterloo Foundation
The Garfield Weston
   Foundation
The Woodward Charitable
   Trust

Natural environment

A J H Ashby Will Trust
The Ashden Trust
The Ashendene Trust
The BAA Communities Trust
The Balney Charitable Trust
The Baring Foundation
BC Partners Foundation
The Blair Foundation
The Bromley Trust
The Christopher Cadbury
   Charitable Trust
The Cadbury Foundation
The Carron Charitable
   Settlement
The Chapman Charitable Trust
The Robert Clutterbuck
   Charitable Trust
The Conscience Trust
The Conservation Foundation
The Ernest Cook Trust
The D'Oyly Carte Charitable
   Trust
The Dr and Mrs A Darlington
   Charitable Trust
William Dean Countryside and
   Educational Trust
The Demigryphon Trust
The Dulverton Trust
The Dunn Family Charitable
   Trust
The John Ellerman Foundation
The Elmgrant Trust
The Ericson Trust
Esmée Fairbairn Foundation
The Galanthus Trust
The Gannochy Trust
Gatwick Airport Community
   Trust
The Girdlers' Company
   Charitable Trust
The Glastonbury Trust Limited
The Gordon Gray Trust
The Green Room Charitable
   Trust
The Charles Hayward
   Foundation
The Headley Trust
The J J Charitable Trust

The John Spedan Lewis
   Foundation
The Limbourne Trust
Manchester Airport Community
   Trust Fund
Marchig Animal Welfare Trust
The Mears Foundation
The Mercers' Charitable
   Foundation
The Mersey Docks and
   Harbour Company
   Charitable Fund
The Metropolitan Drinking
   Fountain and Cattle Trough
   Association
T and J Meyer Family
   Foundation Limited
Millennium Stadium Charitable
   Trust
The Peter Minet Trust
Mrs Waterhouse Charitable
   Trust
The Oakdale Trust
The Owen Family Trust
The Jack Patston Charitable
   Trust
The Cecil Pilkington Charitable
   Trust
Polden-Puckham Charitable
   Foundation
Mr and Mrs J A Pye's
   Charitable Settlement
Quartet Community Foundation
The Joseph Rank Trust
The Sigrid Rausing Trust
The Rhododendron Trust
The Rufford Foundation
Ryklow Charitable Trust 1992
   (also known as A B
   Williamson Charitable Trust)
The Saintbury Trust
The M J Samuel Charitable
   Trust
The Peter Samuel Charitable
   Trust
Schroder Charity Trust
The Simpson Education and
   Conservation Trust
The Stanley Smith UK
   Horticultural Trust
Stevenson Family's Charitable
   Trust
The Stewarts Law Foundation
The Valentine Charitable Trust
The Waterloo Foundation
The David Webster Charitable
   Trust
The Garfield Weston
   Foundation
The HDH Wills 1965
   Charitable Trust
Woodroffe Benton Foundation
Zephyr Charitable Trust

Flora and fauna

A J H Ashby Will Trust
The Ashendene Trust
The Balney Charitable Trust
The Blair Foundation
The Ernest Cook Trust
The Dulverton Trust
The J J Charitable Trust
Manchester Airport Community
   Trust Fund
Marchig Animal Welfare Trust
The Mercers' Charitable
   Foundation
Mrs Waterhouse Charitable
   Trust
The Jack Patston Charitable
   Trust
Mr and Mrs J A Pye's
   Charitable Settlement
The Peter Samuel Charitable
   Trust
The Simpson Education and
   Conservation Trust
The Stanley Smith UK
   Horticultural Trust
The Valentine Charitable Trust
The HDH Wills 1965
   Charitable Trust

Water resources

The Headley Trust
The Mersey Docks and
   Harbour Company
   Charitable Fund
The Metropolitan Drinking
   Fountain and Cattle Trough
   Association
Mr and Mrs J A Pye's
   Charitable Settlement

Polution abatement and control

The Ashden Trust
The Baring Foundation
BC Partners Foundation
The Chapman Charitable Trust
The John Ellerman Foundation
Esmée Fairbairn Foundation
Gatwick Airport Community
   Trust
The Green Room Charitable
   Trust
The Charles Hayward
   Foundation
LWS Lancashire Environmental
   Fund Limited
The Limbourne Trust
Marmot Charitable Trust
The Mears Foundation

Frederick Mulder Charitable
Trust
Quartet Community Foundation
The Joseph Rank Trust
The Sigrid Rausing Trust
The Saintbury Trust
The Stewarts Law Foundation
The Valentine Charitable Trust
The Waterloo Foundation
The Garfield Weston
Foundation
Woodroffe Benton Foundation
Zephyr Charitable Trust

Sustainable environment

The 1970 Trust
The AIM Foundation
The Ashden Trust
The Associated Country
Women of the World
The BAA Communities Trust
The Baring Foundation
BC Partners Foundation
The Body Shop Foundation
The Bromley Trust
The Cadbury Foundation
Calouste Gulbenkian
Foundation – UK Branch
The Cass Foundation
The Chapman Charitable Trust
J A Clark Charitable Trust
The Conscience Trust
The Dunn Family Charitable
Trust
eaga Charitable Trust
The Ecology Trust
The John Ellerman Foundation
Esmée Fairbairn Foundation
The Freshfield Foundation
The Gannochy Trust
Gatwick Airport Community
Trust
The Generations Foundation
The Glastonbury Trust Limited
The Green Room Charitable
Trust
The Charles Hayward
Foundation
The J J Charitable Trust
John Laing Charitable Trust
LWS Lancashire Environmental
Fund Limited
The Mark Leonard Trust
The Limbourne Trust
Manchester Airport Community
Trust Fund
Marmot Charitable Trust
The Mears Foundation
The Community Foundation for
Northern Ireland
Open Gate
People's Postcode Trust

Polden-Puckham Charitable
Foundation
Quartet Community Foundation
The Joseph Rank Trust
The Sigrid Rausing Trust
The Rufford Foundation
The Saintbury Trust
The Staples Trust
The Stewarts Law Foundation
The Stone Family Foundation
The Waterloo Foundation
The David Webster Charitable
Trust
The Garfield Weston
Foundation
Woodroffe Benton Foundation
Zephyr Charitable Trust

Energy issues

The 1970 Trust
The BAA Communities Trust
eaga Charitable Trust
The Mark Leonard Trust

Transport

The 1970 Trust
The Baring Foundation
The Chapman Charitable Trust
Gatwick Airport Community
Trust
The Gosling Foundation
Limited
The Green Room Charitable
Trust
The Charles Hayward
Foundation
The J J Charitable Trust
Rees Jeffreys Road Fund
The Mears Foundation
Quartet Community Foundation
The Joseph Rank Trust
The Rochester Bridge Trust
Seafarers UK (King George's
Fund for Sailors)
The Shipwrights' Company
Charitable Fund
The Stewarts Law Foundation
The Garfield Weston
Foundation

General charitable purposes

The 101 Foundation
The 1989 Willan Charitable
Trust
The 29th May 1961 Charitable
Trust
A W Charitable Trust
ABF The Soldiers' Charity
The Acacia Charitable Trust
Access Sport
The Adnams Charity
Aim to Zero Foundation
The Green and Lilian F M
Ainsworth and Family
Benevolent Fund
The Sylvia Aitken Charitable
Trust
The Al Fayed Charitable
Foundation
D G Albright Charitable Trust
The Derrill Allatt Foundation
Allchurches Trust Ltd
The H B Allen Charitable Trust
The Allen Trust
The Alliance Family Foundation
The Almond Trust
Almondsbury Charity
The AM Charitable Trust
The Amalur Foundation Limited
Sir John and Lady Amory's
Charitable Trust
The Ampelos Trust
Andor Charitable Trust
The Annandale Charitable
Trust
Anpride Ltd
The Anson Charitable Trust
Ambrose and Ann Appelbe
Trust
The Arbib Foundation
The John M Archer Charitable
Trust
The Ardeola Charitable Trust
The Ardwick Trust
The Argentarius Foundation
The John Armitage Charitable
Trust
The Armourers' and Brasiers'
Gauntlet Trust
The Arsenal Foundation
The Ashendene Trust
The Ashworth Charitable Trust
The Ian Askew Charitable Trust
The Astor Foundation
The Atlas Fund
Autonomous Research
Charitable Trust
The Avenue Charitable Trust
Awards for All
The Aylesford Family
Charitable Trust
B W Charitable Trust
Backstage Trust
The BACTA Charitable Trust

The Scott Bader
  Commonwealth Ltd
The Bagri Foundation
The Andrew Balint Charitable
  Trust
The George Balint Charitable
  Trust
The Paul Balint Charitable
  Trust
The Albert Casanova Ballard
  Deceased Trust
Balmain Charitable Trust
The Bamford Charitable
  Foundation
The Banbury Charities
The Band Trust
The Barham Charitable Trust
Peter Barker-Mill Memorial
  Charity
Lord Barnby's Foundation
The Barnsbury Charitable Trust
The Barnstaple Bridge Trust
The Misses Barrie Charitable
  Trust
The Bartlett Taylor Charitable
  Trust
Baruch Family Charitable Trust
The Paul Bassham Charitable
  Trust
The Batchworth Trust
The Bay Tree Charitable Trust
The Louis Baylis (Maidenhead
  Advertiser) Charitable Trust
BC Partners Foundation
BCH Trust
The Bearder Charity
The James Beattie Charitable
  Trust
The Beaverbrook Foundation
The Beccles Town Lands
  Charity
The Becker Family Charitable
  Trust
The Victoria and David
  Beckham Children's Charity
The Peter Beckwith Charitable
  Trust
The Bedfordshire and Luton
  Community Foundation
The David and Ruth Behrend
  Fund
Bellasis Trust
The Bellinger Donnay Trust
The Benfield Motors Charitable
  Trust
The Benham Charitable
  Settlement
Maurice and Jacqueline
  Bennett Charitable Trust
Michael and Lesley Bennett
  Charitable Trust
Bennett Lowell Limited
The Gerald Bentall Charitable
  Trust
The Ruth Berkowitz Charitable
  Trust

The Berkshire Community
  Foundation
The Bertarelli UK Foundation
Bet365 Foundation
The Bideford Bridge Trust
The Big Lottery Fund
The Billmeir Charitable Trust
The Bingham Trust
Birmingham & Black Country
  Community Foundation
The Lord Mayor of
  Birmingham's Charity
Birthday House Trust
The Michael Bishop
  Foundation
The Bertie Black Foundation
Blackheart Foundation (UK)
  Limited
Isabel Blackman Foundation
The BlackRock (UK) Charitable
  Trust
The Blair Foundation
Blakemore Foundation
The Sir Victor Blank Charitable
  Settlement
The Neville and Elaine Blond
  Charitable Trust
The Bluston Charitable
  Settlement
The Marjory Boddy Charitable
  Trust
The Boltini Trust
The Bonamy Charitable Trust
The John and Celia Bonham
  Christie Charitable Trust
The Charlotte Bonham-Carter
  Charitable Trust
The Linda and Gordon
  Bonnyman Charitable Trust
The Bordon Liphook
  Haslemere Charity
H E and E L Botteley
  Charitable Trust
The Bower Trust
The Bowerman Charitable
  Trust
The Bowland Charitable Trust
The Frank Brake Charitable
  Trust
The William Brake Charitable
  Trust
The Liz and Terry Bramall
  Foundation
The Bransford Trust
The Brendish Family
  Foundation
Bridgepoint Charitable Trust
The J and M Britton Charitable
  Trust
The Charles and Edna
  Broadhurst Charitable Trust
The Roger Brooke Charitable
  Trust
Joseph Brough Charitable
  Trust

The Swinfen Broun Charitable
  Trust
Bill Brown 1998 Charitable
  Trust
Edna Brown Charitable
  Settlement (Mrs E E Brown
  Charitable Settlement)
Brown-Mellows Trust
The Brownsword Charitable
  Foundation
T B H Brunner's Charitable
  Settlement
The Jack Brunton Charitable
  Trust
The Bruntwood Charity
The Buckinghamshire Masonic
  Centenary Fund
Buckland Charitable Trust
The Buffini Chao Foundation
The Bulldog Trust Limited
The Burden Trust
Burdens Charitable Foundation
Consolidated Charity of Burton
  upon Trent
The Paul Bush Foundation
  Trust
The Derek Butler Trust
C M L Family Foundation
Edward Cadbury Charitable
  Trust
Peter Cadbury Charitable Trust
The Christopher Cadbury
  Charitable Trust
The G W Cadbury Charitable
  Trust
The Richard Cadbury
  Charitable Trust
The Edward and Dorothy
  Cadbury Trust
The George Cadbury Trust
The Cadogan Charity
Community Foundation for
  Calderdale
The Callander Charitable Trust
Calleva Foundation
The Camelia Trust
The Frederick and Phyllis Cann
  Trust
The Canning Trust
H and L Cantor Trust
Cardy Beaver Foundation
The Carew Pole Charitable
  Trust
The D W T Cargill Fund
The Carlton House Charitable
  Trust
The Carmelite Monastery Ware
  Trust
The Carpenters' Company
  Charitable Trust
The Carrington Charitable
  Trust
The Casey Trust
The Catalyst Charitable Trust
The Joseph and Annie Cattle
  Trust

The Thomas Sivewright Catto
Charitable Settlement
The Wilfrid and Constance
Cave Foundation
The Cayo Foundation
The B G S Cayzer Charitable
Trust
The Cazenove Charitable Trust
The CBD Charitable Trust
CBRE Charitable Trust
R E Chadwick Charitable Trust
The Amelia Chadwick Trust
The Pamela Champion
Foundation
The Chapman Charitable Trust
The Charities Advisory Trust
Charitworth Limited
The Charter 600 Charity
The Worshipful Company of
Chartered Accountants
General Charitable Trust
(also known as CALC)
Cherry Grove Charitable Trust
The Cheruby Trust
Cheshire Freemason's Charity
The Chetwode Foundation
Cheviot Asset Management
Charitable Trust
Childs Charitable Trust
The Chippenham Borough
Lands Charity
CHK Charities Limited
The Chownes Foundation
Christian Aid
Christie Foundation
Chrysalis Trust
Church Burgesses Trust
City and County of Swansea
Welsh Church Act Fund
Stephen Clark 1957
Charitable Trust
The Hilda and Alice Clark
Charitable Trust
The Roger and Sarah Bancroft
Clark Charitable Trust
The Clear Light Trust
The Cleevely Family Charitable
Trust
The Cleopatra Trust
Lord Clinton's Charitable Trust
Miss V L Clore's 1967
Charitable Trust
Closehelm Limited
The Clothworkers' Foundation
The Clover Trust
Clydpride Ltd
The Coalfields Regeneration
Trust
The John Coates Charitable
Trust
The Cobalt Trust
The Cobtree Charity Trust Ltd
The John S Cohen Foundation
John Coldman Charitable Trust
The Cole Charitable Trust
The Colefax Charitable Trust

The John and Freda Coleman
Charitable Trust
The George Henry Collins
Charity
The Sir Jeremiah Colman Gift
Trust
The Compton Charitable Trust
The Douglas Compton James
Charitable Trust
The Congleton Inclosure Trust
The Catherine Cookson
Charitable Trust
The Cookson Charitable Trust
The Keith Coombs Trust
Mabel Cooper Charity
The Alice Ellen Cooper Dean
Charitable Foundation
The Helen Jean Cope Trust
The Gershon Coren Charitable
Foundation (also known as
The Muriel and Gus Coren
Charitable Foundation)
Michael Cornish Charitable
Trust
The Evan Cornish Foundation
Cornwall Community
Foundation
The Duke of Cornwall's
Benevolent Fund
The Cornwell Charitable Trust
The Sidney and Elizabeth
Corob Charitable Trust
The John and Barbara Cotton
Charitable Foundation
County Durham Community
Foundation
The Augustine Courtauld Trust
The General Charities of the
City of Coventry
Coventry Building Society
Charitable Foundation
The Sir Tom Cowie Charitable
Trust
Cowley Charitable Foundation
The Lord Cozens-Hardy Trust
The Craignish Trust
The Craps Charitable Trust
The Cray Trust
The Crescent Trust
Cripplegate Foundation
The Croydon Relief in Need
Charities
Cruden Foundation Ltd
The Ronald Cruickshanks
Foundation
The Cuby Charitable Trust
Cullum Family Trust
The Culra Charitable Trust
Cumberland Building Society
Charitable Foundation
The Dennis Curry Charitable
Trust
The Manny Cussins
Foundation

The Cutler Trust (the
Worshipful Company of
Makers of Playing Cards)
The Cwmbran Trust
Itzchok Meyer Cymerman Trust
Ltd
D C R Allen Charitable Trust
The D G Charitable Settlement
The Daisy Trust
Oizer Dalim Trust
The Danego Charitable Trust
The Alderman Joe Davidson
Memorial Trust
Michael Davies Charitable
Settlement
The Gwendoline and Margaret
Davies Charity
Davis-Rubens Charitable Trust
The De Brye Charitable Trust
The De Clermont Charitable
Company Ltd
Peter De Haan Charitable
Trust
The De Laszlo Foundation
The Dellal Foundation
The Delves Charitable Trust
The Demigryphon Trust
Dentons UKMEA LLP
Charitable Trust
The Earl of Derby's Charitable
Trust
Derbyshire Community
Foundation
The Desmond Foundation
Devon Community Foundation
The Duke of Devonshire's
Charitable Trust
The Sandy Dewhirst Charitable
Trust
Deymel Charitable Trust
The Laduma Dhamecha
Charitable Trust
Alan and Sheila Diamond
Charitable Trust
The Dibden Allotments Fund
Diced Cap Charity
The Gillian Dickinson Trust
The Dickon Trust
Grace Dieu Charitable Trust
Dischma Charitable Trust
The Djanogly Foundation
The Novak Djokovic Foundation
(UK) Limited
The DLM Charitable Trust
Louise Dobson Charitable
Trust
The Dollond Charitable Trust
Dorset Community Foundation
The Dorus Trust
The Double 'O' Charity Ltd
The R M Douglas Charitable
Trust
The Drapers' Charitable Fund
Dromintee Trust

The Royal Foundation of the Duke and Duchess of Cambridge and Prince Harry
The Dulverton Trust
The P B Dumbell Charitable Trust
The Dumbreck Charity
The Dunn Family Charitable Trust
The Charles Dunstone Charitable Trust
Mildred Duveen Charitable Trust
Annette Duvollet Charitable Trust
The Dwek Family Charitable Trust
The Dyers' Company Charitable Trust
The James Dyson Foundation
The Eagle Charity Trust
Audrey Earle Charitable Trust
The Earley Charity
The Earmark Trust
The Sir John Eastwood Foundation
The Ebenezer Trust
The Gilbert and Eileen Edgar Foundation
Gilbert Edgar Trust
Edinburgh Trust No 2 Account
Edinburgh Voluntary Organisations' Trust Funds (EVOT)
The Eighty Eight Foundation
The George Elias Charitable Trust
The Wilfred and Elsie Elkes Charity Fund
The Maud Elkington Charitable Trust
The Ellerdale Trust
The Edith Maud Ellis 1985 Charitable Trust
The Elm House Trust
The Elmgrant Trust
The Vernon N Ely Charitable Trust
The Emerton-Christie Charity
The Endure Foundation
The Englefield Charitable Trust
The Epigoni Trust
The Equilibrium Foundation
The Erskine Cunningham Hill Trust
Essex Community Foundation
The Essex Fairway Charitable Trust
Essex Provincial Charity Fund
The Estelle Trust
Joseph Ettedgui Charitable Foundation
The Eventhall Family Charitable Trust
The Everard Foundation
The Exilarch's Foundation

The Expat Foundation
The William and Christine Eynon Charity
The Faber Charitable Trust
The Fairstead Trust
The Fairway Trust
Famos Foundation Trust
The Lord Faringdon Charitable Trust
The Thomas Farr Charity
Walter Farthing (Trust) Limited
The Farthing Trust
The Fassnidge Memorial Trust
The John Feeney Charitable Trust
The A M Fenton Trust
The Fidelity UK Foundation
The Doris Field Charitable Trust
Fife Council/Common Good Funds and Trusts
Filey Foundation Ltd
Dixie Rose Findlay Charitable Trust
The Sir John Fisher Foundation
Fisherbeck Charitable Trust
The Earl Fitzwilliam Charitable Trust
The Joyce Fletcher Charitable Trust
Florence's Charitable Trust
The Mrs Yvonne Flux Charitable Trust
The Gerald Fogel Charitable Trust
The Forbes Charitable Foundation
The Forest Hill Charitable Trust
The Foresters' Charity Stewards UK Trust
Forever Manchester (The Community Foundation for Greater Manchester)
Gwyneth Forrester Trust
The Donald Forrester Trust
The Four Lanes Trust
The Isaac and Freda Frankel Memorial Charitable Trust
The Elizabeth Frankland Moore and Star Foundation
The Gordon Fraser Charitable Trust
The Hugh Fraser Foundation
The Joseph Strong Frazer Trust
The Louis and Valerie Freedman Charitable Settlement
The Michael and Clara Freeman Charitable Trust
The Freemasons' Grand Charity
The Charles S French Charitable Trust
The Anne French Memorial Trust

The Freshgate Trust Foundation
The Friarsgate Trust
Sybilla and Leo Friedler Charitable Trust
Friends of Wiznitz Limited
The Patrick & Helena Frost Foundation
Maurice Fry Charitable Trust
The Fulmer Charitable Trust
Worshipful Company of Furniture Makers Charitable Fund
The Fuserna Foundation General Charitable Trust
G M C Trust
The Galbraith Trust
The Gale Family Charity Trust
Gamlen Charitable Trust
The Gamma Trust
The Ganzoni Charitable Trust
The Garennie Charitable Trust
Garrick Charitable Trust
Garthgwynion Charities
The Gatsby Charitable Foundation
The Robert Gavron Charitable Trust
Thomas Betton's Charity for Pensions and Relief-in-Need
Simon Gibson Charitable Trust
The G C Gibson Charitable Trust
Lady Gibson's Charitable Trust
The Harvey and Hilary Gilbert Charitable Trust
Global Charities
Worshipful Company of Glovers of London Charity Fund
The Godinton Charitable Trust
The Golden Bottle Trust
The Goldsmiths' Company Charity
The Mike Gooley Trailfinders Charity
The Gosling Foundation Limited
The Gough Charitable Trust
The Gould Charitable Trust
The Hemraj Goyal Foundation
A B Grace Trust
The Graff Foundation
E C Graham Belford Charitable Settlement
A and S Graham Charitable Trust
Grand Charitable Trust of the Order of Women Freemasons
Grantham Yorke Trust
GrantScape
The J G Graves Charitable Trust
The Stanley and Lorna Graves Charitable Trust

The Gray Trust
The Great Stone Bridge Trust
    of Edenbridge
The Great Torrington Town
    Lands Charity
The Kenneth & Susan Green
    Charitable Foundation
The Haydn Green Charitable
    Trust
The Green Hall Foundation
The Green Room Charitable
    Trust
The Green Woodpecker Trust
Mrs H R Greene Charitable
    Settlement
Greenham Common
    Community Trust Limited
Greggs Foundation
The Gretna Charitable Trust
Greys Charitable Trust
The Grimmitt Trust
The Grocers' Charity
The GRP Charitable Trust
The Bishop of Guildford's
    Foundation
The Walter Guinness
    Charitable Trust
The Gunter Charitable Trust
The Gurney Charitable Trust
The H and J Spack Charitable
    Trust
The H and M Charitable Trust
H and T Clients Charitable
    Trust
H C Foundation
The H P Charitable Trust
The Haley Family Charitable
    Trust
The Edith Winifred Hall
    Charitable Trust
Robert Hall Charity
Hamilton Wallace Trust
Sue Hammerson Charitable
    Trust
Hampshire and Isle of Wight
    Community Foundation
The Hampstead Wells and
    Campden Trust
Hampton Fuel Allotment
    Charity
The W A Handley Charitable
    Trust
The Hanley Trust (1987)
The Kathleen Hannay
    Memorial Charity
The Doughty Hanson
    Charitable Foundation
Lord Hanson Foundation
The Haramead Trust
Miss K M Harbinson's
    Charitable Trust
Harbo Charities Limited
The Harbour Charitable Trust
The Harbour Foundation
William Harding's Charity

The Hare of Steep Charitable
    Trust
The Harebell Centenary Fund
The Hargrave Foundation
The Harpur Trust
The Harris Family Charitable
    Trust
The Edith Lilian Harrison 2000
    Foundation
The Spencer Hart Charitable
    Trust
The Hartley Charitable Trust
The Edward Harvist Trust
Hasluck Charitable Trust
The Maurice Hatter Foundation
The M A Hawe Settlement
The Hawerby Trust
The Hawkins Foundation
The Hawthorne Charitable
    Trust
The Charles Hayward
    Foundation
Headley-Pitt Charitable Trust
May Hearnshaw's Charity
Heart of England Community
    Foundation
The Heathcoat Trust
Heathside Charitable Trust
The Charlotte Heber-Percy
    Charitable Trust
Percy Hedley 1990 Charitable
    Trust
The Hedley Denton Charitable
    Trust
The Hemby Trust
The Christina Mary Hendrie
    Trust for Scottish and
    Canadian Charities
Esther Hennell Charitable
    Trust
The Herefordshire Community
    Foundation
The Hertfordshire Community
    Foundation
The Rosalind Hicks Charitable
    Trust
The Higgs Charitable Trust
The Graham High Charitable
    Trust
The Hilden Charitable Fund
The Hillingdon Partnership
    Trust
R G Hills Charitable Trust
Lady Hind Trust
The Hiscox Foundation
The Henry C Hoare Charitable
    Trust
The Eleemosynary Charity of
    William Hobbayne
The Sir Julian Hodge
    Charitable Trust
The Jane Hodge Foundation
The J G Hogg Charitable Trust
The Hollick Family Charitable
    Trust
The Holliday Foundation

The Dorothy Holmes Charitable
    Trust
The Holmes Family Trust
    (Sheffield)
P H Holt Foundation
Mary Homfray Charitable Trust
The Horizon Foundation
The Cuthbert Horn Trust
The Antony Hornby Charitable
    Trust
The Worshipful Company of
    Horners' Charitable Trusts
The Hornsey Parochial
    Charities
The Hospital of God at
    Greatham
The Sir Joseph Hotung
    Charitable Settlement
The House of Industry Estate
The Daniel Howard Trust
The Howe Family Foundation
HTA Sheba Foundation UK
The Huddersfield Common
    Good Trust
The Hudson Foundation
The Huggard Charitable Trust
The Hull and East Riding
    Charitable Trust
The Hunting Horn General
    Charitable Trust
The Hutton Foundation
The P Y N and B Hyams Trust
I B B Charitable Trust
I G O Foundation Limited
The Iliffe Family Charitable
    Trust
The Indigo Trust
The Ingram Trust
The Inman Charity
The Inverforth Charitable Trust
The Ironmongers' Foundation
The Charles Irving Charitable
    Trust
Irwin Trust
The ISA Charity
The Isaacs Charitable Trust
The J Isaacs Charitable Trust
The Isle of Anglesey Charitable
    Trust
The Ithaca Trust
The J & J Benevolent
    Foundation
The J & J Charitable Trust
J D R Charitable Trust
The Jabbs Foundation
C Richard Jackson Charitable
    Trust
Elizabeth Jackson Charitable
    Trust
John James Bristol Foundation
The Jasper Conran Foundation
The Nick Jenkins Foundation
The Jenour Foundation
The Jephcott Charitable Trust
The Jigsaw Foundation

The Norman Joels Charitable Trust

The Dyfrig and Heather John Charitable Trust

The Reginald Johnson Foundation

The Joicey Trust

The Jones 1986 Charitable Trust

The Dezna Robins Jones Charitable Foundation

The Marjorie and Geoffrey Jones Charitable Trust

The Muriel Jones Foundation

The Jordan Charitable Foundation

The Joron Charitable Trust

The Lady Eileen Joseph Foundation

The Josephs Family Charitable Trust

The Josh Charitable Trust

JTH Charitable Trust

The Anton Jurgens Charitable Trust

The Stanley Kalms Foundation

The Kalou Foundation

The Karenza Foundation

The Boris Karloff Charitable Foundation

The Michael and Ilse Katz Foundation

The Geoffrey John Kaye Charitable Foundation

The Soli and Leah Kelaty Trust Fund

The John Thomas Kennedy Charitable Foundation

The Kennedy Charitable Foundation

Kent Community Foundation

The Nancy Kenyon Charitable Trust

Keren Association

E and E Kernkraut Charities Limited

The Ursula Keyes Trust

The Mr & Mrs Paul Killik Charitable Trust

The King Henry VIII Endowed Trust Warwick

The King/Cullimore Charitable Trust

Kingdom Way Trust

Laura Kinsella Foundation

Kinsurdy Charitable Trust

The Richard Kirkman Charitable Trust

Robert Kitchin (Saddlers' Company)

Ernest Kleinwort Charitable Trust

The Sir James Knott Trust

The Kofia Trust

Liudmila Korneenko Foundation

L P W Limited

The Late Sir Pierce Lacy Charity Trust

John Laing Charitable Trust

The Christopher Laing Foundation

The David Laing Foundation

The Kirby Laing Foundation

The Martin Laing Foundation

Duchy of Lancaster Benevolent Fund

The Jack Lane Charitable Trust

Langdale Trust

The Langley Charitable Trust

The Langtree Trust

Laufer Charitable Trust

The Lauffer Family Charitable Foundation

The Kathleen Laurence Trust

The Lawson Beckman Charitable Trust

The Raymond and Blanche Lawson Charitable Trust

The Leach Fourteenth Trust

The Leathersellers' Company Charitable Fund

The Lord Mayor of Leeds Appeal Fund

Leeds Building Society Charitable Foundation

Leicestershire and Rutland Community Foundation

The Kennedy Leigh Charitable Trust

Morris Leigh Foundation

Mrs Vera Leigh's Charity

P Leigh-Bramwell Trust 'E'

The Lennox and Wyfold Foundation

The Erica Leonard Trust

The Mark Leonard Trust

Lord Leverhulme's Charitable Trust

Lewis Family Charitable Trust

The Sir Edward Lewis Foundation

Liberum Foundation

Lichfield Conduit Lands

Limoges Charitable Trust

The Linbury Trust

Lincolnshire Community Foundation

The Linden Charitable Trust

Lindenleaf Charitable Trust

The Enid Linder Foundation

The Linmardon Trust

The Ruth and Stuart Lipton Charitable Trust

The Lister Charitable Trust

Littlefield Foundation (UK) Limited

The Second Joseph Aaron Littman Foundation

The George John and Sheilah Livanos Charitable Trust

Liverpool Charity and Voluntary Services

Jack Livingstone Charitable Trust

The Ian & Natalie Livingstone Charitable Trust

The Elaine and Angus Lloyd Charitable Trust

Lloyd's Charities Trust

Lloyds Bank Foundation for Northern Ireland

Lloyds Bank Foundation for the Channel Islands

The Lo Family Charitable Trust

The Locker Foundation

The Joyce Lomax Bullock Charitable Trust

The London Community Foundation

The William and Katherine Longman Trust

The Loseley and Guildway Charitable Trust

The Lower Green Foundation

The Lowy Mitchell Foundation

The C L Loyd Charitable Trust

Henry Lumley Charitable Trust

Paul Lunn-Rockliffe Charitable Trust

The Lynn Foundation

The Lyras Family Charitable Trust

The E M MacAndrew Trust

Macdonald-Buchanan Charitable Trust

The Mackay and Brewer Charitable Trust

The Mackintosh Foundation

The MacRobert Trust

The Mactaggart Third Fund

Ian Mactaggart Trust

Magdalen Hospital Trust

The Magen Charitable Trust

The Brian Maguire Charitable Trust

The Mahavir Trust

The Makin Charitable Trust

Malbin Trust

The Mallinckrodt Foundation

Man Group plc Charitable Trust

The Manchester Guardian Society Charitable Trust

Lord Mayor of Manchester's Charity Appeal Trust

Mandeville Trust

The Manifold Charitable Trust

W M Mann Foundation

R W Mann Trust

Maranatha Christian Trust

Marbeh Torah Trust

The Stella and Alexander Margulies Charitable Trust

Market Harborough and The Bowdens Charity

The Marks Family Foundation

The Ann and David Marks
Foundation
The Hilda and Samuel Marks
Foundation
J P Marland Charitable Trust
The Marsh Christian Trust
The Charlotte Marshall
Charitable Trust
The Jim Marshall Charitable
Trust
The D G Marshall of
Cambridge Trust
Sir George Martin Trust
John Martin's Charity
The John Mason Family Trust
The Violet Mauray Charitable
Trust
The Maxwell Family Foundation
Evelyn May Trust
Mazars Charitable Trust
The A M McGreevy No 5
Charitable Settlement
The McKenna Charitable Trust
Martin McLaren Memorial
Trust
The Helen Isabella McMorran
Charitable Foundation
The James Frederick and Ethel
Anne Measures Charity
The Medlock Charitable Trust
Melodor Limited
The Menzies Charity
Foundation
The Mercers' Charitable
Foundation
The Merchant Venturers'
Charity
The Merchants' House of
Glasgow
The Mersey Docks and
Harbour Company
Charitable Fund
Community Foundation for
Merseyside
The Metropolitan Masonic
Charity
Mi Yu Foundation
The Mickel Fund
Mickleham Charitable Trust
Gerald Micklem Charitable
Trust
The Masonic Province of
Middlesex Charitable Trust
Midhurst Pensions Trust
The Hugh and Mary Miller
Bequest Trust
The Ronald Miller Foundation
The Millhouses Charitable
Trust
The Millichope Foundation
The Mills Charity
Milton Keynes Community
Foundation
The Edgar Milward Charity

The Keith and Joan
Mindelsohn Charitable
Trust
The Minos Trust
The Mirianog Trust
The Laurence Misener
Charitable Trust
The Misselbrook Trust
The Brian Mitchell Charitable
Settlement
The Esmé Mitchell Trust
The MITIE Foundation
The Mittal Foundation
Keren Mitzvah Trust
The Mizpah Trust
The Mobbs Memorial Trust Ltd
The Modiano Charitable Trust
The Moette Charitable Trust
The Mole Charitable Trust
The Mollie Thomas Charitable
Trust
The Monatrea Charitable Trust
The D C Moncrieff Charitable
Trust
The Colin Montgomerie
Charitable Foundation
The Monument Trust
The Moonpig Foundation
George A Moore Foundation
The Morgan Charitable
Foundation
The Morgan Foundation
The Mr and Mrs J T Morgan
Foundation
Diana and Allan Morgenthau
Charitable Trust
The Oliver Morland Charitable
Trust
The Bernard Morris Charitable
Trust
The Morris Charitable Trust
The Willie and Mabel Morris
Charitable Trust
The Peter Morrison Charitable
Foundation
G M Morrison Charitable Trust
The Stanley Morrison
Charitable Trust
Vyoel Moshe Charitable Trust
Brian and Jill Moss Charitable
Trust
The Moss Family Charitable
Trust
Moto in the Community
The Mulberry Trust
Peter John Murray Trust
The Mushroom Fund
Muslim Hands
The Kitty and Daniel Nabarro
Charitable Trust
The Naggar Charitable Trust
The Janet Nash Charitable
Settlement
The NDL Foundation
Needham Market and Barking
Welfare Charities

The Worshipful Company of
Needlemakers' Charitable
Fund
The James Neill Trust Fund
Network for Social Change
Newpier Charity Ltd
The Night Garden Charity
The Noon Foundation
Norfolk Community Foundation
Norie Charitable Trust
Normalyn Charitable Trust
The Norman Family Charitable
Trust
The Duncan Norman Trust
Fund
The Normanby Charitable Trust
Northamptonshire Community
Foundation
The Northwood Charitable
Trust
The Notgrove Trust
Nottinghamshire Community
Foundation
The Nottinghamshire Miners'
Welfare Trust Fund
The Oak Trust
The Oakdale Trust
The Oakmoor Charitable Trust
The Odin Charitable Trust
Ogilvie Charities Deed No.2
(including the Charity of
Mary Catherine Ford Smith)
Oglesby Charitable Trust
Oizer Charitable Trust
The Old Broad Street Charity
Trust
Old Possum's Practical Trust
The Raymond Oppenheimer
Foundation
Ormonde Foundation
The Ormsby Charitable Trust
The Orrin Charitable Trust
The Oxfordshire Community
Foundation
The P F Charitable Trust
Padwa Charitable Foundation
The Paget Charitable Trust
Panahpur (previously Panahpur
Charitable Trust)
The James Pantyfedwen
Foundation
The Paphitis Charitable Trust
The Paragon Trust
Paraton Trust
The Samuel and Freda
Parkinson Charitable Trust
Miss M E Swinton Paterson's
Charitable Trust
The Patrick Charitable Trust
The Peacock Charitable Trust
The Susanna Peake Charitable
Trust
The Dowager Countess
Eleanor Peel Trust
Pegasus (Stanley) Trust
The Pell Charitable Trust

The Pennycress Trust
The Pharsalia Charitable Trust
The Philips and Rubens
   Charitable Trust
The Phillips Family Charitable
   Trust
The David Pickford Charitable
   Foundation
The Pickwell Foundation
The Bernard Piggott Charitable
   Trust
The Cecil Pilkington Charitable
   Trust
The Sir Harry Pilkington Trust
Miss A M Pilkington's
   Charitable Trust
The DLA Piper Charitable Trust
The Worshipful Company of
   Plaisterers Charitable Trust
G S Plaut Charitable Trust
   Limited
The Polestar Digital
   Foundation
The George and Esme Pollitzer
   Charitable Settlement
The J S F Pollitzer Charitable
   Settlement
The Pollywally Charitable Trust
The Popocatepetl Trust
Edith and Ferdinand Porjes
   Charitable Trust
The John Porter Charitable
   Trust
The Porter Foundation
The Portrack Charitable Trust
The David and Elaine Potter
   Foundation
The W L Pratt Charitable Trust
The Premier League Charitable
   Fund
Premierquote Ltd
The Primrose Trust
Princess Anne's Charities
Prison Service Charity Fund
The Privy Purse Charitable
   Trust
The Proven Family Trust
The Provincial Grand Charity of
   the Province of Derbyshire
The Puebla Charitable Trust
The Quarry Family Charitable
   Trust
Quartet Community Foundation
The Queen's Silver Jubilee
   Trust
R J M Charitable Trust
The Monica Rabagliati
   Charitable Trust
Rachel Charitable Trust
The Mr and Mrs Philip
   Rackham Charitable Trust
The Rainford Trust
The Joseph and Lena Randall
   Charitable Trust
The Rank Foundation Limited
The Joseph Rank Trust

Ranworth Trust
The Rashbass Family Trust
The Ratcliff Foundation
The Ratcliffe Charitable Trust
The Ravensdale Trust
The Rawdon-Smith Trust
The John Rayner Charitable
   Trust
The Sir James Reckitt Charity
The Red Arrows Trust
The Red Rose Charitable Trust
The C A Redfern Charitable
   Foundation
The Reed Foundation
The John and Sally Reeve
   Charitable Trust
Relief Fund for Romania
   Limited
The Rest Harrow Trust
Reuben Foundation
The Nathaniel Reyner Trust
   Fund
The Rhododendron Trust
The Rhondda Cynon Taff
   Welsh Church Acts Fund
Daisie Rich Trust
The Clive Richards Charity
The Richmond Parish Lands
   Charity
Ridgesave Limited
The Ripple Effect Foundation
The Sir John Ritblat Family
   Foundation
The River Farm Foundation
Rivers Foundation
The Robertson Trust
Robyn Charitable Trust
The Rochester Bridge Trust
The Rofeh Trust
Rokach Family Charitable Trust
The Helen Roll Charitable
   Trust
The Sir James Roll Charitable
   Trust
The Gerald Ronson Foundation
The C A Rookes Charitable
   Trust
Mrs L D Rope Third Charitable
   Settlement
The Rose Foundation
The Rothermere Foundation
The Rothley Trust
The Roughley Charitable Trust
The Rowland Family
   Foundation
The Rowlands Trust
Royal Artillery Charitable Fund
The RRAF Charitable Trust
The Alfred and Frances
   Rubens Charitable Trust
The Rubin Foundation
William Arthur Rudd Memorial
   Trust
The Rugby Group Benevolent
   Fund Limited
The Russell Trust

The J S and E C Rymer
   Charitable Trust
The Jeremy and John Sacher
   Charitable Trust
The Michael Harry Sacher
   Trust
The Sackler Trust
The Saddlers' Company
   Charitable Fund
The Alan and Babette
   Sainsbury Charitable Fund
The Saintbury Trust
The Salamander Charitable
   Trust
The Salt Trust
Salters' Charitable Foundation
The Andrew Salvesen
   Charitable Trust
Basil Samuel Charitable Trust
Coral Samuel Charitable Trust
The Samworth Foundation
The Sandhu Charitable
   Foundation
The Sands Family Trust
Santander UK Foundation
   Limited
The Sants Charitable Trust
The Peter Saunders Trust
The Schmidt-Bodner Charitable
   Trust
The R H Scholes Charitable
   Trust
The Schreib Trust
The Schroder Foundation
The Schuster Charitable Trust
Foundation Scotland
The Frieda Scott Charitable
   Trust
The Storrow Scott Will Trust
The Scouloudi Foundation
The Searchlight Electric
   Charitable Trust
The Samuel Sebba Charitable
   Trust
SEM Charitable Trust
The Cyril Shack Trust
The Shanti Charitable Trust
ShareGift (The Orr Mackintosh
   Foundation)
The Sheepdrove Trust
The Sheldon Trust
The Patricia and Donald
   Shepherd Charitable Trust
The Sylvia and Colin Shepherd
   Charitable Trust
The Archie Sherman Charitable
   Trust
The Barnett and Sylvia Shine
   No 2 Charitable Trust
Community Foundation for
   Shropshire and Telford
David and Jennifer Sieff
   Charitable Trust
The Julius Silman Charitable
   Trust

....

The Leslie Silver Charitable Trust

The Huntly and Margery Sinclair Charitable Trust

The Charles Skey Charitable Trust

Skipton Building Society Charitable Foundation

The John Slater Foundation

Rita and David Slowe Charitable Trust

The SMB Charitable Trust

The Smith & Pinching Charitable Trust

The N Smith Charitable Settlement

The E H Smith Charitable Trust

The Smith Charitable Trust

The Leslie Smith Foundation

Smithcorp Charitable Trust

Social Business Trust (Scale-Up)

The Solo Charitable Settlement

Dr Richard Solomon's Charitable Trust

The South Square Trust

The Stephen R and Philippa H Southall Charitable Trust

The W F Southall Trust

The Southwold Trust

Spar Charitable Fund

Sparquote Limited

The Spear Charitable Trust

Spears-Stutz Charitable Trust

The Worshipful Company of Spectacle Makers' Charity

The Jessie Spencer Trust

The Ralph and Irma Sperring Charity

The Spielman Charitable Trust

Split Infinitive Trust

Rosalyn and Nicholas Springer Charitable Trust

The Spurrell Charitable Trust

The Geoff and Fiona Squire Foundation

St Hilda's Trust

St James' Trust Settlement

The Late St Patrick White Charitable Trust

The Stanton Ballard Charitable Trust

The Star Charitable Trust

The Peter Stebbings Memorial Charity

The Steel Charitable Trust

The Steinberg Family Charitable Trust

The Hugh Stenhouse Foundation

The Stephen Barry Charitable Trust

The Sigmund Sternberg Charitable Foundation

The Stevenage Community Trust

The June Stevens Foundation

Stevenson Family's Charitable Trust

The Steventon Allotments and Relief-in-Need Charity

The Andy Stewart Charitable Foundation

Sir Halley Stewart Trust

The Stewarts Law Foundation

The David and Deborah Stileman Charitable Trust

The Leonard Laity Stoate Charitable Trust

The Edward Stocks-Massey Bequest Fund

The Stoller Charitable Trust

The M J C Stone Charitable Trust

The Samuel Storey Family Charitable Trust

Peter Storrs Trust

The Strasser Foundation

Stratford upon Avon Town Trust

The A B Strom and R Strom Charitable Trust

The Sudborough Foundation

Suffolk Community Foundation

The Alan Sugar Foundation

The Bernard Sunley Charitable Foundation

The Sunny Skies Foundation

Community Foundation for Surrey

The Sussex Community Foundation

The Adrienne and Leslie Sussman Charitable Trust

The Sutasoma Trust

Sutton Coldfield Charitable Trust

The Suva Foundation Limited

Swansea and Brecon Diocesan Board of Finance Limited

The John Swire (1989) Charitable Trust

The Swire Charitable Trust

The Adrian Swire Charitable Trust

The Hugh and Ruby Sykes Charitable Trust

The Charles and Elsie Sykes Trust

The Hugh Symons Charitable Trust

The Stella Symons Charitable Trust

The Talbot Village Trust

Tallow Chandlers Benevolent Fund

The Tangent Charitable Trust

The Lady Tangye Charitable Trust

The Tanner Trust

The Mrs A Lacy Tate Trust

The Taurus Foundation

The Tay Charitable Trust

C B and H H Taylor 1984 Trust

Rosanna Taylor's 1987 Charity Trust

The Tedworth Charitable Trust

Tees Valley Community Foundation

The Templeton Goodwill Trust

The Ten Ten Charitable Trust

The Thames Wharf Charity

The John P. Gommes Foundation

The Loke Wan Tho Memorial Foundation

The David Thomas Charitable Trust

The Thomas Lilley Memorial Trust

The Arthur and Margaret Thompson Charitable Trust

The Maurice and Vivien Thompson Charitable Trust

The Thompson Family Charitable Trust

The Thompson Family Foundation

The Thompson6 Charitable Trust

The Thornton Foundation

The Thousandth Man- Richard Burns Charitable Trust

The John Raymond Tijou Charitable Trust

Mrs R P Tindall's Charitable Trust

The Tisbury Telegraph Trust

The Tolkien Trust

Tollemache (Buckminster) Charitable Trust

Toni and Guy Charitable Foundation Limited

The Tower Hill Trust

The Toy Trust

The Toye Foundation

The TPO Foundation

The Mayor of Trafford's Charity Fund

Annie Tranmer Charitable Trust

The Constance Travis Charitable Trust

The Treeside Trust

The Tresillian Trust

The Truemark Trust

Truemart Limited

The Trusthouse Charitable Foundation

The Tsukanov Family Foundation

The Tudor Trust

Tuixen Foundation

The R D Turner Charitable Trust

The Douglas Turner Trust

The Florence Turner Trust

The G J W Turner Trust
The TUUT Charitable Trust
TVML Foundation
Community Foundation Serving Tyne and Wear and Northumberland
The Udlington Trust
UKI Charitable Foundation
Ulverston Town Lands Charity
The Michael Uren Foundation
The David Uri Memorial Trust
The Vail Foundation
The Valentine Charitable Trust
The Valiant Charitable Trust
The Albert Van Den Bergh Charitable Trust
Mrs Maud Van Norden's Charitable Foundation
The Vandervell Foundation
The Vardy Foundation
The Variety Club Children's Charity
The Verdon-Smith Family Charitable Settlement
Roger Vere Foundation
Victoria Homes Trust
The Nigel Vinson Charitable Trust
The Viznitz Foundation
Volant Charitable Trust
Voluntary Action Fund (VAF)
Wade's Charity
The Wakefield and Tetley Trust
The Community Foundation in Wales
The F J Wallis Charitable Settlement
The Ward Blenkinsop Trust
The George Ward Charitable Trust
G R Waters Charitable Trust 2000
Waynflete Charitable Trust
Weatherley Charitable Trust
The William Webster Charitable Trust
Weedon Family Trust
The Weinberg Foundation
The Weinstock Fund
The James Weir Foundation
The Joir and Kato Weisz Foundation
The Barbara Welby Trust
Welsh Church Fund Dyfed area (Carmarthenshire, Ceredigion and Pembrokeshire)
The Welton Foundation
The Wessex Youth Trust
The West Derby Wastelands Charity
West London Synagogue Charitable Fund
Mrs S K West's Charitable Trust

The Garfield Weston Foundation
The Melanie White Foundation Limited
White Stuff Foundation
The Whitecourt Charitable Trust
A H and B C Whiteley Charitable Trust
The Whitewater Charitable Trust
The Whittlesey Charity
The Lionel Wigram Memorial Trust
The Kay Williams Charitable Foundation
The Williams Charitable Trust
The Williams Family Charitable Trust
Williams Serendipity Trust
The HDH Wills 1965 Charitable Trust
The Dame Violet Wills Will Trust
The Wilmcote Charitrust
Sumner Wilson Charitable Trust
David Wilson Foundation
The Community Foundation for Wiltshire and Swindon
The Windruff Charitable Trust
The Harold Hyam Wingate Foundation
Wirral Mayor's Charity
The James Wise Charitable Trust
The Witzenfeld Foundation
The Michael and Anna Wix Charitable Trust
The Wixamtree Trust
The Woburn 1986 Charitable Trust
The Maurice Wohl Charitable Foundation
The Charles Wolfson Charitable Trust
The Wolseley Charitable Trust
The James Wood Bequest Fund
The Woodcock Charitable Trust
The F Glenister Woodger Trust
Woodroffe Benton Foundation
The Woodward Charitable Trust
The A and R Woolf Charitable Trust
ME Woolfe Charitable Trust
The Wragge and Co. Charitable Trust
The Diana Edgson Wright Charitable Trust
The Wright Vigar Charitable Trust
The Matthews Wrightson Charity Trust

The Joan Wyatt Charitable Trust
Wychville Ltd
The Wyndham Charitable Trust
The Yardley Great Trust
The Dennis Alan Yardy Charitable Trust
Yorkshire Building Society Charitable Foundation
The South Yorkshire Community Foundation
You Gossip Foundation
The John Young Charitable Settlement
The William Allen Young Charitable Trust
The Marjorie and Arnold Ziff Charitable Foundation
The Zochonis Charitable Trust
The Zolfo Cooper Foundation
Zurich Community Trust (UK) Limited

Health

The 1970 Trust
The 1989 Willan Charitable Trust
The Aberbrothock Skea Trust
ABF The Soldiers' Charity
Access Sport
The ACT Foundation
Action Medical Research
The Company of Actuaries' Charitable Trust Fund
The Ad Meliora Charitable Trust
The Adamson Trust
The Victor Adda Foundation
The Adint Charitable Trust
Age UK
The AIM Foundation
The Green and Lilian F M Ainsworth and Family Benevolent Fund
The Sylvia Aitken Charitable Trust
The Ajahma Charitable Trust
The Al Fayed Charitable Foundation
The Alchemy Foundation
The H B Allen Charitable Trust
The Allen Lane Trust
The Alliance Family Foundation
The Pat Allsop Charitable Trust
Almondsbury Charity
The Ammco Trust
Andor Charitable Trust
Anglo American Group Foundation
The Appletree Trust
The Arbib Foundation
The Ardwick Trust
The John Armitage Charitable Trust
The Armourers' and Brasiers' Gauntlet Trust
The Artemis Charitable Trust
Arthritis Research UK
The Arts and Entertainment Charitable Trust
The Associated Country Women of the World
Astellas European Foundation
Asthma UK
The Astor Foundation
The Astor of Hever Trust
The Lord Austin Trust
Autonomous Research Charitable Trust
The John Avins Trustees
The Bacit Foundation
Harry Bacon Foundation
Veta Bailey Charitable Trust
The Baily Thomas Charitable Fund
The Baker Charitable Trust
The Roy and Pixie Baker Charitable Trust
The Balcombe Charitable Trust

The Albert Casanova Ballard Deceased Trust
The Band Trust
The Barbers' Company General Charities
The Barbour Foundation
The Barcapel Foundation
Barchester Healthcare Foundation
The Barclay Foundation
The Baring Foundation
The Barleycorn Trust
Barnes Workhouse Fund
The Barnwood House Trust
The Misses Barrie Charitable Trust
Bartholomew Charitable Trust
The Batchworth Trust
BBC Children in Need
BC Partners Foundation
B-CH 1971 Charitable Trust
The John Beckwith Charitable Trust
The Peter Beckwith Charitable Trust
The Bellahouston Bequest Fund
The Bellhouse Foundation
Bergqvist Charitable Trust
The Ruth Berkowitz Charitable Trust
The Bestway Foundation
The Mason Bibby 1981 Trust
The Big Lottery Fund
The Billmeir Charitable Trust
The Bintaub Charitable Trust
The Birmingham District Nursing Charitable Trust
The Birmingham Hospital Saturday Fund Medical Charity and Welfare Trust
Sir Alec Black's Charity
Blackheart Foundation (UK) Limited
The BlackRock (UK) Charitable Trust
The Neville and Elaine Blond Charitable Trust
The Marjory Boddy Charitable Trust
The Boltons Trust
BOOST Charitable Trust
The Booth Charities
The Boots Charitable Trust
The Boshier-Hinton Foundation
The Bothwell Charitable Trust
The Harry Bottom Charitable Trust
P G and N J Boulton Trust
Sir Clive Bourne Family Trust
The Bowerman Charitable Trust
The Tony Bramall Charitable Trust
The Liz and Terry Bramall Foundation

The Breadsticks Foundation
The Breast Cancer Research Trust
The Brendish Family Foundation
The British Council for Prevention of Blindness
The British Dietetic Association General and Education Trust Fund
British Heart Foundation
The David Brooke Charity
The Rory and Elizabeth Brooks Foundation
The Charles Brotherton Trust
Bill Brown 1998 Charitable Trust
Edna Brown Charitable Settlement (Mrs E E Brown Charitable Settlement)
R S Brownless Charitable Trust
The Brownsword Charitable Foundation
Buckland Charitable Trust
The Burden Trust
The Burdett Trust for Nursing
The Burry Charitable Trust
The Arnold Burton 1998 Charitable Trust
The Derek Butler Trust
Henry T and Lucy B Cadbury Charitable Trust
Peter Cadbury Charitable Trust
The William A Cadbury Charitable Trust
The Cadbury Foundation
The Edward and Dorothy Cadbury Trust
CAFOD (Catholic Agency for Overseas Development)
M R Cannon 1998 Charitable Trust
The Carr-Gregory Trust
The Carron Charitable Settlement
The Elizabeth Casson Trust
The Castang Foundation
The Wilfrid and Constance Cave Foundation
The Cayo Foundation
Celtic Charity Fund
The Gaynor Cemlyn-Jones Trust
Champneys Charitable Foundation
The Chapman Charitable Trust
The Charities Advisory Trust
Chest, Heart and Stroke Scotland
Child Growth Foundation
Children's Liver Disease Foundation
The Children's Research Fund
The Childwick Trust

The Chrimes Family Charitable Trust

The City Bridge Trust

J A Clark Charitable Trust

The Clarke Charitable Settlement

The Cleevely Family Charitable Trust

The Cleopatra Trust

Miss V L Clore's 1967 Charitable Trust

The Clothworkers' Foundation

Richard Cloudesley's Charity

The Clover Trust

The Robert Clutterbuck Charitable Trust

The Coalfields Regeneration Trust

The John Coates Charitable Trust

The Denise Cohen Charitable Trust

The Vivienne and Samuel Cohen Charitable Trust

The Colchester Catalyst Charity

John Coldman Charitable Trust

The Cole Charitable Trust

The Bernard Coleman Charitable Trust

The Colt Foundation

Colyer-Fergusson Charitable Trust

The Congleton Inclosure Trust

The Consolidated Charities for the Infirm Merchant Taylors' Company

Harold and Daphne Cooper Charitable Trust

The Helen Jean Cope Trust

The J Reginald Corah Foundation Fund

The Gershon Coren Charitable Foundation (also known as The Muriel and Gus Coren Charitable Foundation)

Michael Cornish Charitable Trust

The Evan Cornish Foundation

The Bryan Christopher Corrigan Charitable Trust

The Cotton Trust

The John Cowan Foundation

Dudley and Geoffrey Cox Charitable Trust

The Sir William Coxen Trust Fund

The Lord Cozens-Hardy Trust

The Craps Charitable Trust

Michael Crawford Children's Charity

The Crerar Hotels Trust

Criffel Charitable Trust

The Violet and Milo Cripps Charitable Trust

The Peter Cruddas Foundation

Cruden Foundation Ltd

The Cumber Family Charitable Trust

Cumbria Community Foundation

The Cunningham Trust

The Harry Cureton Charitable Trust

The Manny Cussins Foundation

The D'Oyly Carte Charitable Trust

Roald Dahl's Marvellous Children's Charity

The Dr and Mrs A Darlington Charitable Trust

Baron Davenport's Charity

The Davidson Family Charitable Trust

The Wilfrid Bruce Davis Charitable Trust

The De Brye Charitable Trust

The De Clermont Charitable Company Ltd

The Deakin Charitable Trust

The Delves Charitable Trust

The Demigryphon Trust

The Denman Charitable Trust

Dentons UKMEA LLP Charitable Trust

The J N Derbyshire Trust

The Desmond Foundation

The Sandy Dewhirst Charitable Trust

Diabetes UK

The Dinwoodie Settlement

Disability Aid Fund (The Roger and Jean Jefcoate Trust)

Dischma Charitable Trust

The Djanogly Foundation

The Derek and Eileen Dodgson Foundation

Dorset Community Foundation

The Dorus Trust

The Double 'O' Charity Ltd

Douglas Arter Foundation

The Drayson Foundation

Dromintee Trust

The Duis Charitable Trust

The Royal Foundation of the Duke and Duchess of Cambridge and Prince Harry

The Dumbreck Charity

The Dunhill Medical Trust

The Dunn Family Charitable Trust

The W E Dunn Trust

The Dyers' Company Charitable Trust

The James Dyson Foundation

The Earmark Trust

The Sir John Eastwood Foundation

The Ebenezer Trust

The EBM Charitable Trust

The Gilbert and Eileen Edgar Foundation

Gilbert Edgar Trust

Edinburgh Trust No 2 Account

Educational Foundation of Alderman John Norman

The George Elias Charitable Trust

The Gerald Palmer Eling Trust Company

The John Ellerman Foundation

James Ellis Charitable Trust

Embrace the Middle East

The Emerton-Christie Charity

The Englefield Charitable Trust

The Epigoni Trust

Epilepsy Research UK

The Equilibrium Foundation

The Eranda Foundation

The Essendon Charitable Trust

Essex Provincial Charity Fund

The Patrick Evans Foundation

Sir John Evelyn's Charity

The Eventhall Family Charitable Trust

The Eveson Charitable Trust

The Exilarch's Foundation

The F P Limited Charitable Trust

The Family Rich Charities Trust

The Lord Faringdon Charitable Trust

Samuel William Farmer Trust

The Farthing Trust

Joseph Fattorini Charitable Trust

The A M Fenton Trust

Elizabeth Ferguson Charitable Trust Fund

The Fidelity UK Foundation

The Doris Field Charitable Trust

Fife Council/Common Good Funds and Trusts

Dixie Rose Findlay Charitable Trust

The Sir John Fisher Foundation

The Fishmongers' Company's Charitable Trust

The Fitton Trust

The Ian Fleming Charitable Trust

Florence's Charitable Trust

The Flow Foundation

The Follett Trust

The Oliver Ford Charitable Trust

The Forest Hill Charitable Trust

The Lady Forester Trust

The Foresters' Charity Stewards UK Trust

The Forman Hardy Charitable Trust

The Donald Forrester Trust

The Anna Rosa Forster Charitable Trust

The Fort Foundation
The Forte Charitable Trust
The Elizabeth Frankland Moore
and Star Foundation
The Jill Franklin Trust
The Hugh Fraser Foundation
The Joseph Strong Frazer Trust
The Louis and Valerie
Freedman Charitable
Settlement
The Freemasons' Grand
Charity
The Freshfield Foundation
The Freshgate Trust
Foundation
The Friarsgate Trust
The Frognal Trust
T F C Frost Charitable Trust
The Patrick & Helena Frost
Foundation
Maurice Fry Charitable Trust
The Fuserna Foundation
General Charitable Trust
The G I Foundation
G M C Trust
The Galanthus Trust
The Gamma Trust
The Ganzoni Charitable Trust
The Garnett Charitable Trust
Garthgwynion Charities
The Gatsby Charitable
Foundation
Gatwick Airport Community
Trust
The Robert Gavron Charitable
Trust
Jacqueline and Michael Gee
Charitable Trust
The General Nursing Council
for England and Wales
Trust
The Generations Foundation
The David Gibbons Foundation
Simon Gibson Charitable Trust
The G C Gibson Charitable
Trust
The Girdlers' Company
Charitable Trust
The B and P Glasser
Charitable Trust
The GNC Trust
The Sydney and Phyllis
Goldberg Memorial
Charitable Trust
The Golden Bottle Trust
Golden Charitable Trust
The Jack Goldhill Charitable
Trust
The Goldsmiths' Company
Charity
The Goodman Foundation
The Mike Gooley Trailfinders
Charity
The Hemraj Goyal Foundation

Grand Charitable Trust of the
Order of Women
Freemasons
The Grand Order of Water
Rats' Charities Fund
Grantham Yorke Trust
The Stanley and Lorna Graves
Charitable Trust
The Gordon Gray Trust
The Great Britain Sasakawa
Foundation
The Green Hall Foundation
Greenham Common
Community Trust Limited
The Grimmitt Trust
The Grocers' Charity
The Gunter Charitable Trust
The H and M Charitable Trust
H C D Memorial Fund
H C Foundation
The Doris Louise Hailes
Charitable Trust
E F and M G Hall Charitable
Trust
Robert Hall Charity
The Hamamelis Trust
Hamilton Wallace Trust
The Helen Hamlyn Trust
Sue Hammerson Charitable
Trust
Hampton Fuel Allotment
Charity
The W A Handley Charitable
Trust
The Kathleen Hannay
Memorial Charity
The Haramead Trust
Harbo Charities Limited
The Harbour Charitable Trust
The Hare of Steep Charitable
Trust
The Harebell Centenary Fund
The Hargrave Foundation
The Kenneth Hargreaves
Charitable Trust
The Harris Charitable Trust
The Harris Family Charitable
Trust
The John Harrison Charitable
Trust
The Alfred And Peggy Harvey
Charitable Trust
Hasluck Charitable Trust
The Maurice Hatter Foundation
The Charles Hayward
Foundation
The Headley Trust
Heart Research UK
The Charlotte Heber-Percy
Charitable Trust
The Hedley Foundation
The Michael Heller Charitable
Foundation
The Simon Heller Charitable
Settlement
Help for Health

Help the Hospices
The Hemby Trust
The G D Herbert Charitable
Trust
Alan Edward Higgs Charity
The Charles Littlewood Hill
Trust
R G Hills Charitable Trust
The Hilmarnan Charitable Trust
Lady Hind Trust
Hinduja Foundation
The Hintze Family Charitable
Foundation
The Sir Julian Hodge
Charitable Trust
The Jane Hodge Foundation
The Hollands-Warren Fund
The Edward Holt Trust
The Homelands Charitable
Trust
The Homestead Charitable
Trust
The Antony Hornby Charitable
Trust
The Horne Trust
The Hospital Saturday Fund
HTA Sheba Foundation UK
Human Relief Foundation
The Humanitarian Trust
The Albert Hunt Trust
Miss Agnes H Hunter's Trust
Huntingdon Freemen's Trust
The Nani Huyu Charitable Trust
The Iliffe Family Charitable
Trust
Impetus – The Private Equity
Foundation (Impetus – PEF)
The Inman Charity
International Spinal Research
Trust
The ISA Charity
The Isaacs Charitable Trust
The Jabbs Foundation
The Ruth and Lionel Jacobson
Trust (Second Fund) No 2
John James Bristol Foundation
The Marjory Jameson Trust
The Jarman Charitable Trust
The Barbara Joyce Jarrald
Charitable Trust
The John Jarrold Trust
The Jasper Conran Foundation
The Jeffrey Charitable Trust
The Jenour Foundation
The Jigsaw Foundation
The Nicholas Joels Charitable
Trust
The Elton John Aids
Foundation
The Michael John Trust
The Lillie Johnson Charitable
Trust
The Johnson Foundation
The Johnson Wax Ltd
Charitable Trust

The Jones 1986 Charitable Trust
The Dezna Robins Jones Charitable Foundation
The Jordan Charitable Foundation
The Joron Charitable Trust
The Judith Trust
The Kalou Foundation
The Ian Karten Charitable Trust
The Michael and Ilse Katz Foundation
The Emmanuel Kaye Foundation
The Caron Keating Foundation
The Kelly Family Charitable Trust
The KempWelch Charitable Trust
The Kay Kendall Leukaemia Fund
The Kennedy Charitable Foundation
Kent Community Foundation
The Peter Kershaw Trust
Kettering and District Charitable Medical Trust
The Ursula Keyes Trust
The Kingsbury Charity
The Mary Kinross Charitable Trust
Kirschel Foundation
Ernest Kleinwort Charitable Trust
The Kobler Trust
The Kohn Foundation
The KPMG Foundation
The Kreditor Charitable Trust
The Kreitman Foundation
The Heinz, Anna and Carol Kroch Foundation
The Kyte Charitable Trust
Maurice and Hilda Laing Charitable Trust
The Christopher Laing Foundation
The David Laing Foundation
The Beatrice Laing Trust
The Lambert Charitable Trust
Langdale Trust
The Langley Charitable Trust
The R J Larg Family Charitable Trust
Laslett's (Hinton) Charity
Mrs F B Laurence Charitable Trust
The Kathleen Laurence Trust
The Edgar E Lawley Foundation
The Lawson Beckman Charitable Trust
The Raymond and Blanche Lawson Charitable Trust
The Mason Le Page Charitable Trust
The Leach Fourteenth Trust

The Leathersellers' Company Charitable Fund
The Arnold Lee Charitable Trust
The William Leech Charity
Leeds Building Society Charitable Foundation
The Leigh Trust
Mrs Vera Leigh's Charity
The Leonard Trust
Lesley Lesley and Mutter Trust
Leukaemia and Lymphoma Research
Lord Leverhulme's Charitable Trust
The Joseph Levy Charitable Foundation
Lewis Family Charitable Trust
John Lewis Partnership General Community Fund
The Lewis Ward Trust
Liberum Foundation
Lifeline 4 Kids
Limoges Charitable Trust
The Linbury Trust
The Linden Charitable Trust
The Enid Linder Foundation
The Lister Charitable Trust
Frank Litchfield Charitable Trust
The Andrew and Mary Elizabeth Little Charitable Trust
The George John and Sheilah Livanos Charitable Trust
The Elaine and Angus Lloyd Charitable Trust
Lloyds Bank Foundation for Northern Ireland
Lloyds Bank Foundation for the Channel Islands
The Lo Family Charitable Trust
The Locker Foundation
The Loftus Charitable Trust
The Trust for London
London Catalyst
The London Law Trust
The Lord's Taverners
The Lotus Foundation
The C L Loyd Charitable Trust
The Marie Helen Luen Charitable Trust
Robert Luff Foundation Ltd
Henry Lumley Charitable Trust
Lord and Lady Lurgan Trust
The Lynn Foundation
The Lyons Charitable Trust
The Lyras Family Charitable Trust
The Madeline Mabey Trust
The E M MacAndrew Trust
The R S Macdonald Charitable Trust
Macdonald-Buchanan Charitable Trust
The Macfarlane Walker Trust

The Mackintosh Foundation
The MacRobert Trust
Ian Mactaggart Trust
The Mahavir Trust
Malbin Trust
Mandeville Trust
R W Mann Trust
The Leslie and Lilian Manning Trust
The Manoukian Charitable Foundation
Maranatha Christian Trust
The Marcela Trust
The Stella and Alexander Margulies Charitable Trust
Market Harborough and The Bowdens Charity
The Marks Family Foundation
The Ann and David Marks Foundation
The Hilda and Samuel Marks Foundation
The Michael Marsh Charitable Trust
The Marsh Christian Trust
The Charlotte Marshall Charitable Trust
The Jim Marshall Charitable Trust
Marshgate Charitable Settlement
Sir George Martin Trust
John Martin's Charity
The Mason Porter Charitable Trust
The Nancie Massey Charitable Trust
Matliwala Family Charitable Trust
The Violet Mauray Charitable Trust
The Maxwell Family Foundation
Evelyn May Trust
The Robert McAlpine Foundation
The McKenna Charitable Trust
D D McPhail Charitable Settlement
The Medlock Charitable Trust
The Anthony and Elizabeth Mellows Charitable Settlement
Meningitis Trust
Brian Mercer Charitable Trust
The Mercers' Charitable Foundation
The Merchant Taylors' Company Charities Fund
Mercury Phoenix Trust
The Tony Metherell Charitable Trust
The Metropolitan Masonic Charity
T and J Meyer Family Foundation Limited
Mi Yu Foundation

Mickleham Charitable Trust

Gerald Micklem Charitable Trust

Midhurst Pensions Trust

The Migraine Trust

Miles Trust for the Putney and Roehampton Community

The Hugh and Mary Miller Bequest Trust

The Ronald Miller Foundation

The Millichope Foundation

The Millward Charitable Trust

The Peter Minet Trust

Minge's Gift and the Pooled Trusts

The Mishcon Family Charitable Trust

The Mitchell Charitable Trust

Monmouthshire County Council Welsh Church Act Fund

The Montague Thompson Coon Charitable Trust

The Monument Trust

The Morel Charitable Trust

The Morgan Charitable Foundation

The Morgan Foundation

Morgan Stanley International Foundation

Diana and Allan Morgenthau Charitable Trust

The Morris Charitable Trust

The Willie and Mabel Morris Charitable Trust

G M Morrison Charitable Trust

Brian and Jill Moss Charitable Trust

The Moss Charitable Trust

The Robert and Margaret Moss Charitable Trust

The Moss Family Charitable Trust

Mosselson Charitable Trust

Mothercare Group Foundation

Moto in the Community

J P Moulton Charitable Foundation

The Edwina Mountbatten Trust

Mrs Waterhouse Charitable Trust

The Edith Murphy Foundation

Murphy-Neumann Charity Company Limited

Peter John Murray Trust

Muslim Hands

The Naggar Charitable Trust

The Janet Nash Charitable Settlement

Needham Market and Barking Welfare Charities

The Neighbourly Charitable Trust

Network for Social Change

The New Appeals Organisation for the City and County of Nottingham

Newby Trust Limited

The Frances and Augustus Newman Foundation

Norfolk Community Foundation

The Normanby Charitable Trust

The North West Cancer Research Fund

The Northampton Queen's Institute Relief in Sickness Fund

Northamptonshire Community Foundation

The Northcott Devon Medical Foundation

The Community Foundation for Northern Ireland

The Northwood Charitable Trust

The Norton Foundation

The Norton Rose Charitable Foundation

The Nottingham General Dispensary

Nottinghamshire Community Foundation

The Nottinghamshire Miners' Welfare Trust Fund

The Nuffield Foundation

The Father O'Mahoney Memorial Trust

The Oakdale Trust

The Oakley Charitable Trust

The Ofenheim Charitable Trust

Oglesby Charitable Trust

Oizer Charitable Trust

The Olga Charitable Trust

Ormonde Foundation

The Ormsby Charitable Trust

The O'Sullivan Family Charitable Trust

The Owen Family Trust

The Paget Charitable Trust

The Paphitis Charitable Trust

The Park Charitable Trust

The Samuel and Freda Parkinson Charitable Trust

The Parthenon Trust

Arthur James Paterson Charitable Trust

The Constance Paterson Charitable Trust

Paycare Charity Trust

The Harry Payne Trust

The Peacock Charitable Trust

The Pedmore Sporting Club Trust Fund

The Dowager Countess Eleanor Peel Trust

Pegasus (Stanley) Trust

The Peltz Trust

The Pen Shell Project

People's Postcode Trust

The Persula Foundation

The Pharsalia Charitable Trust

The Bernard Piggott Charitable Trust

The Cecil Pilkington Charitable Trust

The Pilkington Charities Fund

The Austin and Hope Pilkington Trust

The Col W W Pilkington Will Trusts The General Charity Fund

G S Plaut Charitable Trust Limited

The John Porter Charitable Trust

The Porter Foundation

The J E Posnansky Charitable Trust

The Mary Potter Convent Hospital Trust

The Praebendo Charitable Foundation

The Premier League Charitable Fund

The Tom Press Charitable Foundation

The Douglas Prestwich Charitable Trust

Sir John Priestman Charity Trust

The Prince of Wales's Charitable Foundation

Princess Anne's Charities

Prison Service Charity Fund

The Richard and Christine Purchas Charitable Trust

Mr and Mrs J A Pye's Charitable Settlement

The Pyne Charitable Trust

The Queen Anne's Gate Foundation

Queen Mary's Roehampton Trust

Quothquan Trust

The Monica Rabagliati Charitable Trust

The Mr and Mrs Philip Rackham Charitable Trust

Richard Radcliffe Charitable Trust

The Rank Foundation Limited

The Joseph Rank Trust

Ranworth Trust

The Fanny Rapaport Charitable Settlement

The Rashbass Family Trust

The Ravensdale Trust

The Roger Raymond Charitable Trust

The Rayne Foundation

The Red Rose Charitable Trust

The C A Redfern Charitable Foundation

The Reed Foundation

The Max Reinhardt Charitable Trust

Relief Fund for Romania Limited

REMEDI

Reuben Foundation
The Violet M Richards Charity
The Richmond Parish Lands Charity
The River Farm Foundation
Thomas Roberts Trust
The Robertson Trust
Edwin George Robinson Charitable Trust
Robyn Charitable Trust
The Roddick Foundation
The Rosca Trust
The Rose Foundation
The Cecil Rosen Foundation
Rosetrees Trust
The Rothera Charitable Settlement
The Rotherwick Foundation
The Rothley Trust
Mrs Gladys Row Fogo Charitable Trust
The Christopher Rowbotham Charitable Trust
The Rowlands Trust
The RRAF Charitable Trust
Ryklow Charitable Trust 1992 (also known as A B Williamson Charitable Trust)
The J S and E C Rymer Charitable Trust
The Jeremy and John Sacher Charitable Trust
The Michael Harry Sacher Trust
Raymond and Beverly Sackler 1988 Foundation
The Sackler Trust
The Alan and Babette Sainsbury Charitable Fund
The Saintbury Trust
The Saints and Sinners Trust
Salters' Charitable Foundation
The Andrew Salvesen Charitable Trust
Basil Samuel Charitable Trust
The Peter Samuel Charitable Trust
The Sandra Charitable Trust
The Sands Family Trust
The Scarfe Charitable Trust
Schroder Charity Trust
Scott (Eredine) Charitable Trust
Sir Samuel Scott of Yews Trust
The Sir James and Lady Scott Trust
The Scouloudi Foundation
The Samuel Sebba Charitable Trust
The Ayrton Senna Foundation
The Jean Shanks Foundation
The Shears Foundation
The Sheepdrove Trust

The Sheffield and District Hospital Services Charitable Fund
The Sylvia and Colin Shepherd Charitable Trust
The Archie Sherman Cardiff Foundation
The Bassil Shippam and Alsford Trust
The Shirley Foundation
The Barbara A Shuttleworth Memorial Trust
The Simpson Education and Conservation Trust
The Huntly and Margery Sinclair Charitable Trust
The John Slater Foundation
The SMB Charitable Trust
The Smith & Pinching Charitable Trust
The N Smith Charitable Settlement
The Henry Smith Charity
The R C Snelling Charitable Trust
The Sobell Foundation
David Solomons Charitable Trust
The E C Sosnow Charitable Trust
The South Square Trust
R H Southern Trust
The Sovereign Health Care Charitable Trust
Sparks Charity (Sport Aiding Medical Research For Kids)
Sparquote Limited
The Worshipful Company of Spectacle Makers' Charity
The Spero Foundation
The Spielman Charitable Trust
Rosalyn and Nicholas Springer Charitable Trust
Springfields Employees' Medical Research and Charity Trust Fund
The Geoff and Fiona Squire Foundation
St James's Place Foundation
St Michael's and All Saints' Charities Relief Branch (The Church Houses Relief in Need Charity)
St Monica Trust
The Stanley Foundation Ltd
The Peter Stebbings Memorial Charity
The Steel Charitable Trust
The Steinberg Family Charitable Trust
Stevenson Family's Charitable Trust
The Andy Stewart Charitable Foundation
Sir Halley Stewart Trust
The Stoller Charitable Trust

The M J C Stone Charitable Trust
Peter Stormonth Darling Charitable Trust
The Strangward Trust
The Strawberry Charitable Trust
The W O Street Charitable Foundation
Sueberry Ltd
The Sussex Community Foundation
The Suva Foundation Limited
Swan Mountain Trust
The John Swire (1989) Charitable Trust
The Hugh and Ruby Sykes Charitable Trust
The Charles and Elsie Sykes Trust
The Tajtelbaum Charitable Trust
The Gay and Keith Talbot Trust
The Talbot Trusts
Tallow Chandlers Benevolent Fund
C B and H H Taylor 1984 Trust
The Connie and Albert Taylor Charitable Trust
The C Paul Thackray General Charitable Trust
Thackray Medical Research Trust
The Loke Wan Tho Memorial Foundation
The Thompson Family Charitable Trust
The Len Thomson Charitable Trust
The Sue Thomson Foundation
The Sir Jules Thorn Charitable Trust
The Thornton Trust
The Three Guineas Trust
The John Raymond Tijou Charitable Trust
Mrs R P Tindall's Charitable Trust
The Tolkien Trust
The Tompkins Foundation
The Tory Family Foundation
The Towry Law Charitable Trust (also known as the Castle Educational Trust)
Annie Tranmer Charitable Trust
The Trefoil Trust
The True Colours Trust
The James Tudor Foundation
The Tyche Charitable Trust
Community Foundation Serving Tyne and Wear and Northumberland
UKI Charitable Foundation
The Ulverscroft Foundation
The Underwood Trust
The Michael Uren Foundation

The Valentine Charitable Trust
The Albert Van Den Bergh
  Charitable Trust
The Variety Club Children's
  Charity
Roger Vere Foundation
The Vintners' Company
  Charitable Foundation
Vision Charity
Volant Charitable Trust
Voluntary Action Fund (VAF)
The Wakefield and Tetley Trust
Robert and Felicity Waley-
  Cohen Charitable Trust
The Walker Trust
Wallace and Gromit's
  Children's Foundation
The Ward Blenkinsop Trust
The Waterloo Foundation
Blyth Watson Charitable Trust
Weedon Family Trust
The Weinstein Foundation
The Wellcome Trust
The Welton Foundation
The Wessex Youth Trust
The Westcroft Trust
The Garfield Weston
  Foundation
The Simon Whitbread
  Charitable Trust
The Felicity Wilde Charitable
  Trust
The Will Charitable Trust
The Kay Williams Charitable
  Foundation
The Williams Charitable Trust
Williams Serendipity Trust
The Harold Hyam Wingate
  Foundation
The Michael and Anna Wix
  Charitable Trust
The Wixamtree Trust
The Maurice Wohl Charitable
  Foundation
The Charles Wolfson
  Charitable Trust
The Wolfson Family Charitable
  Trust
The Wolfson Foundation
The Wood Family Trust
The Woodward Charitable
  Trust
The A and R Woolf Charitable
  Trust
ME Woolfe Charitable Trust
The Wragge and Co. Charitable
  Trust
The Matthews Wrightson
  Charity Trust
Miss E B Wrightson's
  Charitable Settlement
The Wyseliot Charitable Trust
The Xerox (UK) Trust
The Yapp Charitable Trust
The William Allen Young
  Charitable Trust

The John K Young Endowment
  Fund
Suha Yusuf Charitable Trust
Zephyr Charitable Trust
The Marjorie and Arnold Ziff
  Charitable Foundation
The Zochonis Charitable Trust
Zurich Community Trust (UK)
  Limited

Alternative and complementary medicine

The AIM Foundation
Edna Brown Charitable
  Settlement (Mrs E E Brown
  Charitable Settlement)
Disability Aid Fund (The Roger
  and Jean Jefcoate Trust)
The Sir John Fisher Foundation
London Catalyst
The Paget Charitable Trust
Mr and Mrs J A Pye's
  Charitable Settlement
The Joseph Rank Trust
Rosalyn and Nicholas Springer
  Charitable Trust
The Simon Whitbread
  Charitable Trust

Health care

The 1970 Trust
The Aberbrothock Skea Trust
The ACT Foundation
The Alchemy Foundation
Almondsbury Charity
The Artemis Charitable Trust
Veta Bailey Charitable Trust
The Barbers' Company General
  Charities
The Barclay Foundation
The Barnwood House Trust
Bartholomew Charitable Trust
The Birmingham District
  Nursing Charitable Trust
Sir Alec Black's Charity
The Boshier-Hinton Foundation
The Harry Bottom Charitable
  Trust
The Tony Bramall Charitable
  Trust
The Breadsticks Foundation
Edna Brown Charitable
  Settlement (Mrs E E Brown
  Charitable Settlement)
The Burdett Trust for Nursing
The William A Cadbury
  Charitable Trust
The Cadbury Foundation
The Carron Charitable
  Settlement
The Elizabeth Casson Trust

Chest, Heart and Stroke
  Scotland
The Clarke Charitable
  Settlement
The Congleton Inclosure Trust
The John Cowan Foundation
Dudley and Geoffrey Cox
  Charitable Trust
The Sir William Coxen Trust
  Fund
The Manny Cussins
  Foundation
The D'Oyly Carte Charitable
  Trust
Baron Davenport's Charity
The Deakin Charitable Trust
Dentons UKMEA LLP
  Charitable Trust
The Dinwoodie Settlement
Disability Aid Fund (The Roger
  and Jean Jefcoate Trust)
The Duis Charitable Trust
The Dunhill Medical Trust
Gilbert Edgar Trust
James Ellis Charitable Trust
The Eranda Foundation
The Eveson Charitable Trust
The Family Rich Charities Trust
Elizabeth Ferguson Charitable
  Trust Fund
Fife Council/Common Good
  Funds and Trusts
The Lady Forester Trust
The Forte Charitable Trust
The Hugh Fraser Foundation
The Freemasons' Grand
  Charity
The Freshfield Foundation
The Freshgate Trust
  Foundation
G M C Trust
The Ganzoni Charitable Trust
The Gatsby Charitable
  Foundation
Gatwick Airport Community
  Trust
The General Nursing Council
  for England and Wales
  Trust
The Generations Foundation
Simon Gibson Charitable Trust
The Girdlers' Company
  Charitable Trust
The Goldsmiths' Company
  Charity
The Grand Order of Water
  Rats' Charities Fund
The Gordon Gray Trust
The Green Hall Foundation
Robert Hall Charity
Hampton Fuel Allotment
  Charity
The W A Handley Charitable
  Trust
The Kenneth Hargreaves
  Charitable Trust

The Harris Family Charitable
Trust
The Charles Hayward
Foundation
The Hedley Foundation
The Michael Heller Charitable
Foundation
Help the Hospices
The Hemby Trust
The Charles Littlewood Hill
Trust
The Hintze Family Charitable
Foundation
The Hollands-Warren Fund
The Homelands Charitable
Trust
The Horne Trust
The Hospital Saturday Fund
Human Relief Foundation
The Humanitarian Trust
Huntingdon Freemen's Trust
Impetus – The Private Equity
Foundation (Impetus – PEF)
The Ruth and Lionel Jacobson
Trust (Second Fund) No 2
The Jarman Charitable Trust
The Barbara Joyce Jarrald
Charitable Trust
The Johnson Foundation
The Ian Karten Charitable
Trust
The Kennedy Charitable
Foundation
The Peter Kershaw Trust
Kettering and District
Charitable Medical Trust
Ernest Kleinwort Charitable
Trust
Langdale Trust
Laslett's (Hinton) Charity
Leeds Building Society
Charitable Foundation
Lesley Lesley and Mutter Trust
The Joseph Levy Charitable
Foundation
John Lewis Partnership
General Community Fund
Lifeline 4 Kids
The Andrew and Mary
Elizabeth Little Charitable
Trust
Lloyds Bank Foundation for
Northern Ireland
The Trust for London
London Catalyst
The Lord's Taverners
Lord and Lady Lurgan Trust
The MacRobert Trust
Market Harborough and The
Bowdens Charity
Sir George Martin Trust
John Martin's Charity
The Robert McAlpine
Foundation
The Medlock Charitable Trust

The Anthony and Elizabeth
Mellows Charitable
Settlement
The Tony Metherell Charitable
Trust
Gerald Micklem Charitable
Trust
Miles Trust for the Putney and
Roehampton Community
Monmouthshire County Council
Welsh Church Act Fund
The Monument Trust
The Morgan Charitable
Foundation
Morgan Stanley International
Foundation
Brian and Jill Moss Charitable
Trust
The Frances and Augustus
Newman Foundation
The Northampton Queen's
Institute Relief in Sickness
Fund
The Nottingham General
Dispensary
The Nuffield Foundation
The Owen Family Trust
The Paget Charitable Trust
The Park Charitable Trust
The Samuel and Freda
Parkinson Charitable Trust
The Constance Paterson
Charitable Trust
Paycare Charity Trust
The Pen Shell Project
The Mary Potter Convent
Hospital Trust
The Tom Press Charitable
Foundation
The Douglas Prestwich
Charitable Trust
Sir John Priestman Charity
Trust
The Prince of Wales's
Charitable Foundation
The Richard and Christine
Purchas Charitable Trust
Richard Radcliffe Charitable
Trust
The Joseph Rank Trust
Ranworth Trust
The Rayne Foundation
Relief Fund for Romania
Limited
Reuben Foundation
The Violet M Richards Charity
Thomas Roberts Trust
The Rose Foundation
The Rotherwick Foundation
The Christopher Rowbotham
Charitable Trust
The Sackler Trust
The Saintbury Trust
The Sheepdrove Trust

The Sheffield and District
Hospital Services
Charitable Fund
The Sylvia and Colin Shepherd
Charitable Trust
David Solomons Charitable
Trust
The E C Sosnow Charitable
Trust
The South Square Trust
Rosalyn and Nicholas Springer
Charitable Trust
St James's Place Foundation
Stevenson Family's Charitable
Trust
The Strawberry Charitable
Trust
The Tajtelbaum Charitable
Trust
The Connie and Albert Taylor
Charitable Trust
The Trefoil Trust
The True Colours Trust
The Variety Club Children's
Charity
Wallace and Gromit's
Children's Foundation
Blyth Watson Charitable Trust
The Westcroft Trust
The Wixamtree Trust
The Charles Wolfson
Charitable Trust
The Xerox (UK) Trust
The Yapp Charitable Trust

Medical equipment

The Barnwood House Trust
Sir Alec Black's Charity
The Grand Order of Water
Rats' Charities Fund
The Green Hall Foundation
The Hedley Foundation
The Ian Karten Charitable
Trust
Kettering and District
Charitable Medical Trust
The Joseph Levy Charitable
Foundation
Lifeline 4 Kids
London Catalyst
The Lord's Taverners
The Frances and Augustus
Newman Foundation
Paycare Charity Trust
The Sylvia and Colin Shepherd
Charitable Trust

Medical institutions

The Aberbrothock Skea Trust
The Barnwood House Trust
Bartholomew Charitable Trust

The Birmingham District
Nursing Charitable Trust
Sir Alec Black's Charity
The Harry Bottom Charitable
Trust
Chest, Heart and Stroke
Scotland
The Clarke Charitable
Settlement
The John Cowan Foundation
Dudley and Geoffrey Cox
Charitable Trust
The Sir William Coxen Trust
Fund
Baron Davenport's Charity
The Deakin Charitable Trust
The Duis Charitable Trust
The Dunhill Medical Trust
Gilbert Edgar Trust
The Eveson Charitable Trust
Elizabeth Ferguson Charitable
Trust Fund
Fife Council/Common Good
Funds and Trusts
The Hugh Fraser Foundation
The Freemasons' Grand
Charity
The Ganzoni Charitable Trust
Gatwick Airport Community
Trust
The Girdlers' Company
Charitable Trust
The Gordon Gray Trust
The Green Hall Foundation
Robert Hall Charity
Hampton Fuel Allotment
Charity
The Charles Hayward
Foundation
The Hedley Foundation
The Michael Heller Charitable
Foundation
Help the Hospices
The Homelands Charitable
Trust
The Horne Trust
The Hospital Saturday Fund
The Ruth and Lionel Jacobson
Trust (Second Fund) No 2
The Jarman Charitable Trust
The Kennedy Charitable
Foundation
The Peter Kershaw Trust
Ernest Kleinwort Charitable
Trust
Leeds Building Society
Charitable Foundation
The Joseph Levy Charitable
Foundation
Lloyds Bank Foundation for
Northern Ireland
Lord and Lady Lurgan Trust
Sir George Martin Trust
The Robert McAlpine
Foundation
The Medlock Charitable Trust

The Anthony and Elizabeth
Mellows Charitable
Settlement
The Tony Metherell Charitable
Trust
Gerald Micklem Charitable
Trust
Miles Trust for the Putney and
Roehampton Community
Monmouthshire County Council
Welsh Church Act Fund
The Monument Trust
The Morgan Charitable
Foundation
Morgan Stanley International
Foundation
The Northampton Queen's
Institute Relief in Sickness
Fund
The Nottingham General
Dispensary
The Owen Family Trust
The Park Charitable Trust
Paycare Charity Trust
The Douglas Prestwich
Charitable Trust
Sir John Priestman Charity
Trust
The Prince of Wales's
Charitable Foundation
Richard Radcliffe Charitable
Trust
The Rayne Foundation
The Rose Foundation
The Sackler Trust
The Sheffield and District
Hospital Services
Charitable Fund
St James's Place Foundation
The Tajtelbaum Charitable
Trust
The Connie and Albert Taylor
Charitable Trust
Blyth Watson Charitable Trust

Nursing

The Barbers' Company General
Charities
The Birmingham District
Nursing Charitable Trust
The General Nursing Council
for England and Wales
Trust
The Hedley Foundation
Impetus – The Private Equity
Foundation (Impetus – PEF)
The Ruth and Lionel Jacobson
Trust (Second Fund) No 2
The Joseph Levy Charitable
Foundation

Medical research

The 1989 Willan Charitable
Trust
The Aberbrothock Skea Trust
Action Medical Research
The Company of Actuaries'
Charitable Trust Fund
Age UK
The Green and Lilian F M
Ainsworth and Family
Benevolent Fund
The Sylvia Aitken Charitable
Trust
The Alchemy Foundation
The Alliance Family Foundation
The Pat Allsop Charitable Trust
Anglo American Group
Foundation
The Arbib Foundation
The Armourers' and Brasiers'
Gauntlet Trust
Arthritis Research UK
Astellas European Foundation
Asthma UK
The Astor Foundation
The Astor of Hever Trust
The Bacit Foundation
The Baily Thomas Charitable
Fund
The Baker Charitable Trust
The Barbers' Company General
Charities
The Barclay Foundation
The Barleycorn Trust
The Barnwood House Trust
Bartholomew Charitable Trust
The Bellhouse Foundation
Bergqvist Charitable Trust
The Ruth Berkowitz Charitable
Trust
BOOST Charitable Trust
P G and N J Boulton Trust
The Breast Cancer Research
Trust
The British Council for
Prevention of Blindness
British Heart Foundation
The Charles Brotherton Trust
The Brownsword Charitable
Foundation
Buckland Charitable Trust
The Burden Trust
The Burry Charitable Trust
The Arnold Burton 1998
Charitable Trust
The Derek Butler Trust
Peter Cadbury Charitable Trust
The Castang Foundation
The Cayo Foundation
Celtic Charity Fund
The Gaynor Cemlyn-Jones
Trust
The Charities Advisory Trust
Chest, Heart and Stroke
Scotland
Child Growth Foundation

Children's Liver Disease
  Foundation
The Children's Research Fund
The Childwick Trust
The Clarke Charitable
  Settlement
The Clothworkers' Foundation
The Bernard Coleman
  Charitable Trust
The Colt Foundation
The Cotton Trust
The John Cowan Foundation
Dudley and Geoffrey Cox
  Charitable Trust
The Sir William Coxen Trust
  Fund
Cruden Foundation Ltd
The Cunningham Trust
Roald Dahl's Marvellous
  Children's Charity
The De Clermont Charitable
  Company Ltd
The Denman Charitable Trust
Diabetes UK
The Dinwoodie Settlement
The Dunhill Medical Trust
The Dunn Family Charitable
  Trust
The James Dyson Foundation
The Earmark Trust
The EBM Charitable Trust
Gilbert Edgar Trust
James Ellis Charitable Trust
Epilepsy Research UK
The Eranda Foundation
Essex Provincial Charity Fund
The Eveson Charitable Trust
The Family Rich Charities Trust
Elizabeth Ferguson Charitable
  Trust Fund
The Sir John Fisher Foundation
The Fishmongers' Company's
  Charitable Trust
The Ian Fleming Charitable
  Trust
The Follett Trust
The Anna Rosa Forster
  Charitable Trust
The Hugh Fraser Foundation
The Joseph Strong Frazer Trust
The Freemasons' Grand
  Charity
The Frognal Trust
T F C Frost Charitable Trust
G M C Trust
The Garnett Charitable Trust
Garthgwynion Charities
The Gatsby Charitable
  Foundation
The Girdlers' Company
  Charitable Trust
The Sydney and Phyllis
  Goldberg Memorial
  Charitable Trust
Golden Charitable Trust

The Mike Gooley Trailfinders
  Charity
The Gordon Gray Trust
The Great Britain Sasakawa
  Foundation
The Gunter Charitable Trust
The Hamamelis Trust
Hamilton Wallace Trust
The W A Handley Charitable
  Trust
The Harbour Charitable Trust
The Harebell Centenary Fund
The Hargrave Foundation
The Kenneth Hargreaves
  Charitable Trust
The Harris Charitable Trust
The John Harrison Charitable
  Trust
The Alfred And Peggy Harvey
  Charitable Trust
Heart Research UK
The Hedley Foundation
The Michael Heller Charitable
  Foundation
The Simon Heller Charitable
  Settlement
The Sir Julian Hodge
  Charitable Trust
The Jane Hodge Foundation
The Edward Holt Trust
The Homelands Charitable
  Trust
The Homestead Charitable
  Trust
The Antony Hornby Charitable
  Trust
Miss Agnes H Hunter's Trust
International Spinal Research
  Trust
The Jabbs Foundation
The John Jarrold Trust
The Jasper Conran Foundation
The Jeffrey Charitable Trust
The Elton John Aids
  Foundation
The Johnson Foundation
The Jones 1986 Charitable
  Trust
The Jordan Charitable
  Foundation
The Emmanuel Kaye
  Foundation
The Caron Keating Foundation
The KempWelch Charitable
  Trust
The Kay Kendall Leukaemia
  Fund
The Peter Kershaw Trust
The Mary Kinross Charitable
  Trust
Ernest Kleinwort Charitable
  Trust
The Kohn Foundation
The Kathleen Laurence Trust
The Edgar E Lawley Foundation
The William Leech Charity

The Leigh Trust
The Leonard Trust
Leukaemia and Lymphoma
  Research
The Joseph Levy Charitable
  Foundation
Lewis Family Charitable Trust
Liberum Foundation
The Linbury Trust
Frank Litchfield Charitable
  Trust
The George John and Sheilah
  Livanos Charitable Trust
The London Law Trust
The Lotus Foundation
The Marie Helen Luen
  Charitable Trust
Robert Luff Foundation Ltd
Lord and Lady Lurgan Trust
The Madeline Mabey Trust
The R S Macdonald Charitable
  Trust
Macdonald-Buchanan
  Charitable Trust
The Mackintosh Foundation
Mandeville Trust
The Manoukian Charitable
  Foundation
The Marcela Trust
Marshgate Charitable
  Settlement
The Nancie Massey Charitable
  Trust
The Robert McAlpine
  Foundation
D D McPhail Charitable
  Settlement
The Medlock Charitable Trust
Meningitis Trust
Brian Mercer Charitable Trust
The Mercers' Charitable
  Foundation
The Tony Metherell Charitable
  Trust
Mickleham Charitable Trust
Gerald Micklem Charitable
  Trust
The Migraine Trust
The Millward Charitable Trust
Monmouthshire County Council
  Welsh Church Act Fund
The Montague Thompson
  Coon Charitable Trust
The Monument Trust
The Willie and Mabel Morris
  Charitable Trust
G M Morrison Charitable Trust
The Robert and Margaret
  Moss Charitable Trust
Mothercare Group Foundation
J P Moulton Charitable
  Foundation
The Janet Nash Charitable
  Settlement
The Frances and Augustus
  Newman Foundation

The North West Cancer
Research Fund
The Northcott Devon Medical
Foundation
The Northwood Charitable
Trust
The Nottingham General
Dispensary
The Nuffield Foundation
The Oakdale Trust
Oglesby Charitable Trust
Ormonde Foundation
The Ormsby Charitable Trust
The O'Sullivan Family
Charitable Trust
The Owen Family Trust
The Parthenon Trust
Arthur James Paterson
Charitable Trust
The Constance Paterson
Charitable Trust
Paycare Charity Trust
The Harry Payne Trust
The Dowager Countess
Eleanor Peel Trust
The Pen Shell Project
The Persula Foundation
The Cecil Pilkington Charitable
Trust
The Pilkington Charities Fund
The Col W W Pilkington Will
Trusts The General Charity
Fund
The Tom Press Charitable
Foundation
The Richard and Christine
Purchas Charitable Trust
Mr and Mrs J A Pye's
Charitable Settlement
Queen Mary's Roehampton
Trust
The Monica Rabagliati
Charitable Trust
The Mr and Mrs Philip
Rackham Charitable Trust
The Rank Foundation Limited
The Rayne Foundation
The Max Reinhardt Charitable
Trust
REMEDI
The Violet M Richards Charity
The Robertson Trust
Edwin George Robinson
Charitable Trust
Rosetrees Trust
Mrs Gladys Row Fogo
Charitable Trust
The Rowlands Trust
Ryklow Charitable Trust 1992
(also known as A B
Williamson Charitable Trust)
Raymond and Beverly Sackler
1988 Foundation
The Alan and Babette
Sainsbury Charitable Fund

The Andrew Salvesen
Charitable Trust
The Peter Samuel Charitable
Trust
The Scarfe Charitable Trust
Sir Samuel Scott of Yews
Trust
The Jean Shanks Foundation
The Sheepdrove Trust
The Shirley Foundation
The Simpson Education and
Conservation Trust
The SMB Charitable Trust
The N Smith Charitable
Settlement
The Henry Smith Charity
The South Square Trust
Sparks Charity (Sport Aiding
Medical Research For Kids)
The Worshipful Company of
Spectacle Makers' Charity
The Spielman Charitable Trust
Rosalyn and Nicholas Springer
Charitable Trust
The Geoff and Fiona Squire
Foundation
St James's Place Foundation
The Andy Stewart Charitable
Foundation
Sir Halley Stewart Trust
Peter Stormonth Darling
Charitable Trust
Swan Mountain Trust
The John Swire (1989)
Charitable Trust
The Charles and Elsie Sykes
Trust
Tallow Chandlers Benevolent
Fund
The Connie and Albert Taylor
Charitable Trust
The Len Thomson Charitable
Trust
The Sir Jules Thorn Charitable
Trust
The John Raymond Tijou
Charitable Trust
The Towry Law Charitable Trust
(also known as the Castle
Educational Trust)
The Trefoil Trust
The Ulverscroft Foundation
The Michael Uren Foundation
The Variety Club Children's
Charity
Roger Vere Foundation
The Vintners' Company
Charitable Foundation
Vision Charity
Weedon Family Trust
The Wellcome Trust
The Felicity Wilde Charitable
Trust
The Will Charitable Trust
The Kay Williams Charitable
Foundation

The Williams Charitable Trust
The Harold Hyam Wingate
Foundation
The Charles Wolfson
Charitable Trust
The Wolfson Foundation
Miss E B Wrightson's
Charitable Settlement
The John K Young Endowment
Fund

History of medicine

Edna Brown Charitable
Settlement (Mrs E E Brown
Charitable Settlement)
The Paget Charitable Trust
The Joseph Rank Trust
Thackray Medical Research
Trust
The Wellcome Trust

Health education/ prevention/ development

The AIM Foundation
The Alchemy Foundation
The Associated Country
Women of the World
The Big Lottery Fund
BOOST Charitable Trust
The Tony Bramall Charitable
Trust
The British Dietetic
Association General and
Education Trust Fund
Edna Brown Charitable
Settlement (Mrs E E Brown
Charitable Settlement)
The Derek Butler Trust
Henry T and Lucy B Cadbury
Charitable Trust
Chest, Heart and Stroke
Scotland
The Colt Foundation
The Cotton Trust
Disability Aid Fund (The Roger
and Jean Jefcoate Trust)
Gilbert Edgar Trust
The John Ellerman Foundation
Hampton Fuel Allotment
Charity
The Haramead Trust
Human Relief Foundation
The Kelly Family Charitable
Trust
Lloyds Bank Foundation for
Northern Ireland
The Trust for London
London Catalyst
Mercury Phoenix Trust

Monmouthshire County Council
Welsh Church Act Fund
The Robert and Margaret
Moss Charitable Trust
The Community Foundation for
Northern Ireland
The Paget Charitable Trust
The Richard and Christine
Purchas Charitable Trust
Mr and Mrs J A Pye's
Charitable Settlement
The Joseph Rank Trust
Relief Fund for Romania
Limited
The Violet M Richards Charity
The Rosca Trust
Rosalyn and Nicholas Springer
Charitable Trust

Overseas aid/ projects

Aid to the Church in Need (UK)
The Alchemy Foundation
The H B Allen Charitable Trust
The Allen Trust
The Pat Allsop Charitable Trust
The Associated Country
Women of the World
The Balmore Trust
The Barbour Foundation
The Barleycorn Trust
The John Beckwith Charitable
Trust
The BlackRock (UK) Charitable
Trust
The Blandford Lake Trust
The Neville and Elaine Blond
Charitable Trust
The Boltini Trust
H E and E L Botteley
Charitable Trust
The Breadsticks Foundation
The Brendish Family
Foundation
Buckland Charitable Trust
The Calpe Trust
The Cheruby Trust
Christadelphian Samaritan
Fund
The Cleopatra Trust
The Clover Trust
The Vivienne and Samuel
Cohen Charitable Trust
The Coltstaple Trust
Comic Relief
The Conscience Trust
The Gershon Coren Charitable
Foundation (also known as
The Muriel and Gus Coren
Charitable Foundation)
Michael Cornish Charitable
Trust
The Evan Cornish Foundation
The Cotton Trust
The Craps Charitable Trust
Criffel Charitable Trust
The Cumber Family Charitable
Trust
The Delves Charitable Trust
Dischma Charitable Trust
The Dorfred Charitable Trust
The Dorus Trust
The Endure Foundation
The Epigoni Trust
Euro Charity Trust
The Expat Foundation
The Farthing Trust
Allan and Nesta Ferguson
Charitable Settlement
The Forest Hill Charitable Trust
The Donald Forrester Trust
The Four Winds Trust
The Elizabeth Frankland Moore
and Star Foundation

The Freshfield Foundation
The G D Charitable Trust
The Galanthus Trust
The Generations Foundation
Global Care
The GNC Trust
The Golden Bottle Trust
The Goodman Foundation
The Gunter Charitable Trust
H C D Memorial Fund
Beatrice Hankey Foundation
Limited
The Haramead Trust
The Harbour Foundation
Hasluck Charitable Trust
The Charles Hayward
Foundation
The Headley Trust
The Charlotte Heber-Percy
Charitable Trust
The Simon Heller Charitable
Settlement
Philip Henman Trust
Hexham and Newcastle
Diocesan Trust (1947)
Sir Harold Hood's Charitable
Trust
HTA Sheba Foundation UK
The Hunting Horn General
Charitable Trust
The Indigo Trust
The Innocent Foundation
The Marjory Jameson Trust
The Joffe Charitable Trust
The Mr & Mrs Paul Killik
Charitable Trust
The David Laing Foundation
The Kirby Laing Foundation
The Beatrice Laing Trust
Langdale Trust
The Lawson Beckman
Charitable Trust
The William Leech Charity
Mrs Vera Leigh's Charity
The Leonard Trust
Lloyd's Charities Trust
The Mahavir Trust
Maranatha Christian Trust
The Ann and David Marks
Foundation
The Marr-Munning Trust
The Marsh Christian Trust
The John Mason Family Trust
Matliwala Family Charitable
Trust
The Mirianog Trust
The Mittal Foundation
The Morris Charitable Trust
The Edwina Mountbatten Trust
Peter John Murray Trust
Muslim Hands
National Committee of the
Women's World Day of
Prayer for England and
Wales and Northern Ireland
Network for Social Change

The Father O'Mahoney
Memorial Trust
Oizer Charitable Trust
The Olga Charitable Trust
Open Gate
The Paget Charitable Trust
The Paladin Vince-Odozi
Charitable Trust
Pegasus (Stanley) Trust
The Pilkington Charities Fund
The W L Pratt Charitable Trust
The Eleanor Rathbone
Charitable Trust
Eva Reckitt Trust Fund
The Reed Foundation
The John and Sally Reeve
Charitable Trust
The Rhododendron Trust
Robyn Charitable Trust
The Rothera Charitable
Settlement
The Shanley Charitable Trust
Rita and David Slowe
Charitable Trust
The Souter Charitable Trust
The W F Southall Trust
The Staples Trust
The Peter Stebbings Memorial
Charity
The Steinberg Family
Charitable Trust
Sir Halley Stewart Trust
The Stewarts Law Foundation
The Stone Family Foundation
The Sunny Skies Foundation
The Sutasoma Trust
The Gay and Keith Talbot Trust
The Tanner Trust
C B and H H Taylor 1984 Trust
Rosanna Taylor's 1987 Charity
Trust
Tearfund
The C Paul Thackray General
Charitable Trust
The Loke Wan Tho Memorial
Foundation
The Thornton Trust
The Three Oaks Trust
The Tinsley Foundation
The Tisbury Telegraph Trust
The Tolkien Trust
The Toy Trust
The Constance Travis
Charitable Trust
The Tresillian Trust
The True Colours Trust
Truemart Limited
Ulting Overseas Trust
The Valentine Charitable Trust
The Albert Van Den Bergh
Charitable Trust
The Van Neste Foundation
The Vardy Foundation
Volant Charitable Trust
War on Want
The Waterloo Foundation

The Westcroft Trust
Williams Serendipity Trust
The HDH Wills 1965
Charitable Trust
The Wixamtree Trust
The Maurice Wohl Charitable
Foundation
The Matthews Wrightson
Charity Trust

Philanthropy and the voluntary sector

Almondsbury Charity
The Baring Foundation
The Big Lottery Fund
The Edward and Dorothy
Cadbury Trust
CAF (Charities Aid Foundation)
Calouste Gulbenkian
Foundation – UK Branch
The City Bridge Trust
The Digbeth Trust Limited
Esmée Fairbairn Foundation
Samuel William Farmer Trust
The Fidelity UK Foundation
Gatwick Airport Community
Trust
The Hadrian Trust
Paul Hamlyn Foundation
The Kenneth Hargreaves
Charitable Trust
The Charles Hayward
Foundation
The Hemby Trust
Impetus – The Private Equity
Foundation (Impetus – PEF)
The William Leech Charity
The Mark Leonard Trust
Lloyds Bank Foundation for
Northern Ireland
Lloyds Bank Foundation for the
Channel Islands
The Trust for London
The London Community
Foundation
The London Law Trust
The Medlock Charitable Trust
Community Foundation for
Merseyside
Mi Yu Foundation
The Millfield House Foundation
Milton Keynes Community
Foundation
The Moonpig Foundation
John Moores Foundation
The MSE Charity
Nominet Charitable Foundation
The Northern Rock Foundation
The Pears Family Charitable
Foundation
People's Postcode Trust
The Jack Petchey Foundation
The Rashbass Family Trust
Mrs L D Rope Third Charitable
Settlement
The Joseph Rowntree
Charitable Trust
St Hilda's Trust
The Tudor Trust
Two Ridings Community
Foundation
Voluntary Action Fund (VAF)
Wakeham Trust

Wales Council for Voluntary
    Action
The Westcroft Trust
Youth United Foundation

Voluntarism

The Big Lottery Fund
Calouste Gulbenkian
    Foundation – UK Branch
Esmée Fairbairn Foundation
The Hemby Trust
Impetus – The Private Equity
    Foundation (Impetus – PEF)
The William Leech Charity
The Mark Leonard Trust
Lloyds Bank Foundation for
    Northern Ireland
The London Community
    Foundation
The London Law Trust
Milton Keynes Community
    Foundation
Nominet Charitable Foundation
The Jack Petchey Foundation
Mrs L D Rope Third Charitable
    Settlement
Voluntary Action Fund (VAF)
Wakeham Trust
Wales Council for Voluntary
    Action
Youth United Foundation

Community participation

The Big Lottery Fund
Calouste Gulbenkian
    Foundation – UK Branch
The Hemby Trust
Impetus – The Private Equity
    Foundation (Impetus – PEF)
The Mark Leonard Trust
The London Law Trust
Nominet Charitable Foundation
The Jack Petchey Foundation
Wakeham Trust

Voluntary sector capacity building

Almondsbury Charity
The Baring Foundation
CAF (Charities Aid Foundation)
The Digbeth Trust Limited
Gatwick Airport Community
    Trust
The Hadrian Trust
Paul Hamlyn Foundation
Impetus – The Private Equity
    Foundation (Impetus – PEF)
The Trust for London

The London Community
    Foundation
The MSE Charity
The Northern Rock Foundation
Voluntary Action Fund (VAF)
The Westcroft Trust

Religious activities

4 Charity Foundation
A W Charitable Trust
Brian Abrams Charitable Trust
Eric Abrams Charitable Trust
The Acacia Charitable Trust
Achisomoch Aid Company
    Limited
Adenfirst Ltd
The Adint Charitable Trust
Aid to the Church in Need (UK)
The Alabaster Trust
The Alexis Trust
All Saints Educational Trust
Allchurches Trust Ltd
The Allen Trust
The Alliance Family Foundation
The Almond Trust
Almondsbury Charity
The Altajir Trust
Altamont Ltd
Alvor Charitable Trust
The AM Charitable Trust
Amabrill Limited
Viscount Amory's Charitable
    Trust
The Anchor Foundation
The Andrew Anderson Trust
Andor Charitable Trust
The André Christian Trust
Andrews Charitable Trust
Anpride Ltd
The John Apthorp Charity
The Archer Trust
The Ardwick Trust
The John Armitage Charitable
    Trust
The Armourers' and Brasiers'
    Gauntlet Trust
The A S Charitable Trust
Ashburnham Thanksgiving
    Trust
The Ashendene Trust
The Astor of Hever Trust
The Austin Bailey Foundation
The Baird Trust
The Baker Charitable Trust
The Andrew Balint Charitable
    Trust
The George Balint Charitable
    Trust
The Paul Balint Charitable
    Trust
The Balney Charitable Trust
William P Bancroft (No 2)
    Charitable Trust and
    Jenepher Gillett Trust
The Barclay Foundation
The Barleycorn Trust
The Bates Charitable Trust
Bay Charitable Trust
BCH Trust
The Beacon Trust
Bear Mordechai Ltd

Beauland Ltd
The Becker Family Charitable
 Trust
The Bellahouston Bequest
 Fund
Maurice and Jacqueline
 Bennett Charitable Trust
Michael and Lesley Bennett
 Charitable Trust
The Ruth Berkowitz Charitable
 Trust
BHST
The Bintaub Charitable Trust
Miss Jeanne Bisgood's
 Charitable Trust
The Bishop's Development
 Fund
The Sydney Black Charitable
 Trust
The Bertie Black Foundation
The Blandford Lake Trust
The Sir Victor Blank Charitable
 Settlement
The Neville and Elaine Blond
 Charitable Trust
The Bluston Charitable
 Settlement
The Bonamy Charitable Trust
Salo Bordon Charitable Trust
The Bosson Family Charitable
 Trust
H E and E L Botteley
 Charitable Trust
The Harry Bottom Charitable
 Trust
P G and N J Boulton Trust
The A H and E Boulton Trust
Sir Clive Bourne Family Trust
Bourneheights Limited
The Bowerman Charitable
 Trust
The Bowland Charitable Trust
The Liz and Terry Bramall
 Foundation
Bristol Archdeaconry Charity
Edna Brown Charitable
 Settlement (Mrs E E Brown
 Charitable Settlement)
T B H Brunner's Charitable
 Settlement
Brushmill Ltd
Buckingham Trust
The Burden Trust
The Arnold Burton 1998
 Charitable Trust
C and F Charitable Trust
Edward Cadbury Charitable
 Trust
Henry T and Lucy B Cadbury
 Charitable Trust
The William A Cadbury
 Charitable Trust
The Cambridgeshire Historic
 Churches Trust
H and L Cantor Trust
Carlee Ltd

The Carlton House Charitable
 Trust
The Carmelite Monastery Ware
 Trust
The Carpenter Charitable Trust
The Carpenters' Company
 Charitable Trust
The Catholic Charitable Trust
Catholic Foreign Missions
The Catholic Trust for England
 and Wales
The Gaynor Cemlyn-Jones
 Trust
The CH (1980) Charitable
 Trust
Charitworth Limited
The Chasah Trust
Childs Charitable Trust
The Childwick Trust
The Chownes Foundation
The Christabella Charitable
 Trust
Christian Response to Eastern
 Europe
The Church and Community
 Fund
Church Burgesses Trust
Church of Ireland Priorities
 Fund
Church Urban Fund
The Hilda and Alice Clark
 Charitable Trust
The Roger and Sarah Bancroft
 Clark Charitable Trust
The Clarke Charitable
 Settlement
The Clore Duffield Foundation
Miss V L Clore's 1967
 Charitable Trust
Closehelm Limited
Richard Cloudesley's Charity
The Clover Trust
Clydpride Ltd
The Denise Cohen Charitable
 Trust
The Vivienne and Samuel
 Cohen Charitable Trust
John Coldman Charitable Trust
Col-Reno Ltd
The Congregational and
 General Charitable Trust
The Keith Coombs Trust
Harold and Daphne Cooper
 Charitable Trust
The Gershon Coren Charitable
 Foundation (also known as
 The Muriel and Gus Coren
 Charitable Foundation)
The Cornwall Historic
 Churches Trust
The Duke of Cornwall's
 Benevolent Fund
The Sidney and Elizabeth
 Corob Charitable Trust
The Corona Charitable Trust

The Bryan Christopher
 Corrigan Charitable Trust
The Costa Family Charitable
 Trust
The Craps Charitable Trust
Criffel Charitable Trust
The Cuby Charitable Trust
The Cumber Family Charitable
 Trust
The Manny Cussins
 Foundation
Itzchok Meyer Cymerman Trust
 Ltd
Daily Prayer Union Charitable
 Trust Limited
Oizer Dalim Trust
The Davidson Family
 Charitable Trust
The Alderman Joe Davidson
 Memorial Trust
Davis-Rubens Charitable Trust
The Deakin Charitable Trust
The Debmar Benevolent Trust
The Dellal Foundation
The Sandy Dewhirst Charitable
 Trust
Alan and Sheila Diamond
 Charitable Trust
Grace Dieu Charitable Trust
The Djanogly Foundation
The DM Charitable Trust
The Dollond Charitable Trust
Domepride Ltd
The Dorcas Trust
Dorset Community Foundation
The Doughty Charity Trust
The Duis Charitable Trust
The Dulverton Trust
Dushinsky Trust Ltd
The Dyers' Company
 Charitable Trust
The Earmark Trust
The Sir John Eastwood
 Foundation
The Ebenezer Trust
The Gilbert and Eileen Edgar
 Foundation
The George Elias Charitable
 Trust
The Gerald Palmer Eling Trust
 Company
Ellador Ltd
The Ellinson Foundation Ltd
The Edith Maud Ellis 1985
 Charitable Trust
The Elmgrant Trust
Elshore Ltd
The Englefield Charitable Trust
Entindale Ltd
The Ernest Hecht Charitable
 Foundation
The Erskine Cunningham Hill
 Trust
The Esfandi Charitable
 Foundation

The Eventhall Family
  Charitable Trust
The Exilarch's Foundation
Extonglen Limited
F C Charitable Trust
The F P Limited Charitable
  Trust
The Faber Charitable Trust
The Fairway Trust
Famos Foundation Trust
The Farthing Trust
Joseph Fattorini Charitable
  Trust
Federation of Jewish Relief
  Organisations
Finnart House School Trust
Firtree Trust
Fisherbeck Charitable Trust
The Flow Foundation
The Gerald Fogel Charitable
  Trust
Fordeve Limited
The Forest Hill Charitable Trust
The Forman Hardy Charitable
  Trust
The Forte Charitable Trust
The Four Winds Trust
The Isaac and Freda Frankel
  Memorial Charitable Trust
The Hugh Fraser Foundation
The Joseph Strong Frazer Trust
The Thomas Freke and Lady
  Norton Charity Trust
The Anne French Memorial
  Trust
The Friends Hall Farm Street
  Trust
Friends of Biala Limited
Friends of Boyan Trust
Friends of Essex Churches
  Trust
Friends of Wiznitz Limited
Mejer and Gertrude Miriam
  Frydman Foundation
The G I Foundation
Gableholt Limited
The Gale Family Charity Trust
The Gamma Trust
The Ganzoni Charitable Trust
Garvan Limited
Jacqueline and Michael Gee
  Charitable Trust
The Gibbs Charitable Trust
The Girdlers' Company
  Charitable Trust
The B and P Glasser
  Charitable Trust
Global Care
The GNC Trust
The Golden Bottle Trust
Golden Charitable Trust
The Jack Goldhill Charitable
  Trust
The Grace Charitable Trust
The Grahame Charitable
  Foundation Limited

Philip and Judith Green Trust
Greys Charitable Trust
The M and R Gross Charities
  Limited
The GRP Charitable Trust
N and R Grunbaum Charitable
  Trust
The Gunter Charitable Trust
The Gur Trust
The H and J Spack Charitable
  Trust
The H P Charitable Trust
E F and M G Hall Charitable
  Trust
Sue Hammerson Charitable
  Trust
The W A Handley Charitable
  Trust
Beatrice Hankey Foundation
  Limited
The Kathleen Hannay
  Memorial Charity
Harbo Charities Limited
The Harris Charitable Trust
Haskel Family Foundation
The Hathaway Trust
The Maurice Hatter Foundation
The Charles Hayward
  Foundation
Headley-Pitt Charitable Trust
May Hearnshaw's Charity
Heathside Charitable Trust
The Helping Foundation
The Hesed Trust
Hexham and Newcastle
  Diocesan Trust (1947)
The P and C Hickinbotham
  Charitable Trust
Highcroft Charitable Trust
The Charles Littlewood Hill
  Trust
The Hillier Trust
Hinchley Charitable Trust
Hinduja Foundation
Stuart Hine Trust
Hockerill Educational
  Foundation
Matthew Hodder Charitable
  Trust
The Sir Julian Hodge
  Charitable Trust
The Jane Hodge Foundation
The Holden Charitable Trust
The Holmes Family Trust
  (Sheffield)
The Homelands Charitable
  Trust
The Homestead Charitable
  Trust
Sir Harold Hood's Charitable
  Trust
The Hope Trust
The Daniel Howard Trust
The Humanitarian Trust
The Huntingdon Foundation
Hurdale Charity Limited

The Hutton Foundation
The P Y N and B Hyams Trust
I G O Foundation Limited
Infinity Capital Trust
The Inlight Trust
Investream Charitable Trust
Irwin Trust
The Isaacs Charitable Trust
The J & J Benevolent
  Foundation
The J & J Charitable Trust
J A R Charitable Trust
The J M K Charitable Trust
Jacobs Charitable Trust
The Ruth and Lionel Jacobson
  Trust (Second Fund) No 2
The Susan and Stephen
  James Charitable
  Settlement
The James Trust
The Marjory Jameson Trust
The Jarman Charitable Trust
The Barbara Joyce Jarrald
  Charitable Trust
Jay Education Trust
JCA Charitable Foundation
The Jenour Foundation
The Jerusalem Trust
Jewish Child's Day
The Jewish Youth Fund
The Harold Joels Charitable
  Trust
The Nicholas Joels Charitable
  Trust
The Norman Joels Charitable
  Trust
The Joron Charitable Trust
The J E Joseph Charitable
  Fund
The Josephs Family Charitable
  Trust
Jusaca Charitable Trust
The Bernard Kahn Charitable
  Trust
The Stanley Kalms Foundation
The Kasner Charitable Trust
The Michael and Ilse Katz
  Foundation
The Katzauer Charitable
  Settlement
The C S Kaufman Charitable
  Trust
The Geoffrey John Kaye
  Charitable Foundation
The Emmanuel Kaye
  Foundation
The Soli and Leah Kelaty Trust
  Fund
The KempWelch Charitable
  Trust
The Kennedy Charitable
  Foundation
Keren Association
Kermaville Ltd
E and E Kernkraut Charities
  Limited

Keswick Hall Trust
The King Henry VIII Endowed Trust Warwick
Kingdom Way Trust
Kirschel Foundation
The Kobler Trust
The Kohn Foundation
Kollel and Co. Limited
The Kreditor Charitable Trust
Kupath Gemach Chaim Bechesed Viznitz Trust
The Kyte Charitable Trust
L P W Limited
The Late Sir Pierce Lacy Charity Trust
The K P Ladd Charitable Trust
Maurice and Hilda Laing Charitable Trust
The Kirby Laing Foundation
The Beatrice Laing Trust
The Lambert Charitable Trust
Duchy of Lancaster Benevolent Fund
The Lancaster Foundation
Langdale Trust
The Langley Charitable Trust
The R J Larg Family Charitable Trust
Largsmount Ltd
Laslett's (Hinton) Charity
The Lauffer Family Charitable Foundation
The Lawson Beckman Charitable Trust
The Leathersellers' Company Charitable Fund
The Arnold Lee Charitable Trust
The William Leech Charity
The Kennedy Leigh Charitable Trust
Morris Leigh Foundation
Mrs Vera Leigh's Charity
P Leigh-Bramwell Trust 'E'
The Leonard Trust
The Joseph Levy Charitable Foundation
Lewis Family Charitable Trust
The Lind Trust
Lindale Educational Foundation
The Ruth and Stuart Lipton Charitable Trust
The Second Joseph Aaron Littman Foundation
Jack Livingstone Charitable Trust
The Elaine and Angus Lloyd Charitable Trust
The Charles Lloyd Foundation
The Lo Family Charitable Trust
Localtrent Ltd
The Locker Foundation
The Loftus Charitable Trust
The Lolev Charitable Trust
The Lowy Mitchell Foundation

The C L Loyd Charitable Trust
Paul Lunn-Rockliffe Charitable Trust
The Ruth and Jack Lunzer Charitable Trust
The Lyndhurst Trust
The Lynwood Trust
The Sir Jack Lyons Charitable Trust
The Lyras Family Charitable Trust
Sylvanus Lyson's Charity
The M and C Trust
The M K Charitable Trust
The SV and PE Magee Family Charitable Trust
The Magen Charitable Trust
The Mahavir Trust
Malbin Trust
The Manackerman Charitable Trust
Maranatha Christian Trust
Marbeh Torah Trust
The Stella and Alexander Margulies Charitable Trust
Mariapolis Limited
The Marks Family Foundation
The Ann and David Marks Foundation
The Hilda and Samuel Marks Foundation
The Michael Marsh Charitable Trust
The Marsh Christian Trust
The Charlotte Marshall Charitable Trust
The Nora Joan Marshall Charitable Trust
Marshall's Charity
Marshgate Charitable Settlement
Sir George Martin Trust
John Martin's Charity
The John Mason Family Trust
The Mason Porter Charitable Trust
Matliwala Family Charitable Trust
The Matt 6.3 Charitable Trust
The Violet Mauray Charitable Trust
Evelyn May Trust
Mayfair Charities Ltd
Mazars Charitable Trust
The Anthony and Elizabeth Mellows Charitable Settlement
Melodor Limited
Melow Charitable Trust
Menuchar Ltd
Mercaz Torah Vechesed Limited
The Mercers' Charitable Foundation
The Merchant Taylors' Company Charities Fund

The Metropolitan Masonic Charity
Miles Trust for the Putney and Roehampton Community
The Ronald Miller Foundation
The Millfield Trust
The Millhouses Charitable Trust
The Edgar Milward Charity
The Minos Trust
The Laurence Misener Charitable Trust
The Mishcon Family Charitable Trust
The Mitchell Charitable Trust
The Mizpah Trust
The Modiano Charitable Trust
The Mole Charitable Trust
Monmouthshire County Council Welsh Church Act Fund
The Colin Montgomerie Charitable Foundation
The Mr and Mrs J T Morgan Foundation
Diana and Allan Morgenthau Charitable Trust
The Oliver Morland Charitable Trust
S C and M E Morland's Charitable Trust
The Peter Morrison Charitable Foundation
Moshal Charitable Trust
The Moshulu Charitable Trust
Brian and Jill Moss Charitable Trust
The Moss Charitable Trust
The Moss Family Charitable Trust
Mosselson Charitable Trust
Mrs Waterhouse Charitable Trust
The George Müller Charitable Trust
Muslim Hands
The Mutual Trust Group
MW (CL) Foundation
MW (GK) Foundation
MW (HO) Foundation
MW (RH) Foundation
MYA Charitable Trust
MYR Charitable Trust
The Nadezhda Charitable Trust
The Naggar Charitable Trust
National Committee of the Women's World Day of Prayer for England and Wales and Northern Ireland
Nazareth Trust Fund
The Worshipful Company of Needlemakers' Charitable Fund
Nemoral Ltd
Ner Foundation
Nesswall Ltd

The New Appeals Organisation for the City and County of Nottingham
Newpier Charity Ltd
The Chevras Ezras Nitzrochim Trust
NJD Charitable Trust
Normalyn Charitable Trust
The Community Foundation for Northern Ireland
The Northumbria Historic Churches Trust
The Norwich Church of England Young Men's Society
The Norwood and Newton Settlement
The Nottinghamshire Historic Churches Trust
Novi Most International
Ogilvie Charities Deed No.2 (including the Charity of Mary Catherine Ford Smith)
The Ogle Christian Trust
The Oikonomia Trust
Oizer Charitable Trust
Ormonde Foundation
The Owen Family Trust
The Doris Pacey Charitable Foundation
The Paget Charitable Trust
The Panacea Society
Panahpur (previously Panahpur Charitable Trust)
The James Pantyfedwen Foundation
Paraton Trust
The Park Charitable Trust
The Park House Charitable Trust
Miss M E Swinton Paterson's Charitable Trust
The Jack Patston Charitable Trust
The Payne Charitable Trust
The Harry Payne Trust
The David Pearlman Charitable Foundation
The Pears Family Charitable Foundation
The Peltz Trust
B E Perl Charitable Trust
The Persson Charitable Trust
The Philips and Rubens Charitable Trust
The Phillips Family Charitable Trust
The David Pickford Charitable Foundation
The Bernard Piggott Charitable Trust
G S Plaut Charitable Trust Limited
The George and Esme Pollitzer Charitable Settlement
The Pollywally Charitable Trust

Edith and Ferdinand Porjes Charitable Trust
The John Porter Charitable Trust
Porticus UK
The J E Posnansky Charitable Trust
The Praebendo Charitable Foundation
Premierquote Ltd
Premishlaner Charitable Trust
Sir John Priestman Charity Trust
The Pyne Charitable Trust
Quothquan Trust
R J M Charitable Trust
R S Charitable Trust
Rachel Charitable Trust
The Bishop Radford Trust
The Rank Foundation Limited
The Joseph Rank Trust
The Fanny Rapaport Charitable Settlement
The Rashbass Family Trust
The Ravensdale Trust
The Rayden Charitable Trust
The Rayne Trust
The Sir James Reckitt Charity
The Rehoboth Trust
The Rest Harrow Trust
Reuben Foundation
The Nathaniel Reyner Trust Fund
The Sir Cliff Richard Charitable Trust
The Clive Richards Charity
Ridgesave Limited
The Sir John Ritblat Family Foundation
The River Trust
The Rock Foundation
The Rock Solid Trust
The Rofeh Trust
Rokach Family Charitable Trust
The Sir James Roll Charitable Trust
The Gerald Ronson Foundation
Mrs L D Rope Third Charitable Settlement
The Rotherwick Foundation
Rowanville Ltd
The Rowland Family Foundation
The RRAF Charitable Trust
The Alfred and Frances Rubens Charitable Trust
The Rubin Foundation
S F Foundation
S O Charitable Trust
The Jeremy and John Sacher Charitable Trust
The Michael Harry Sacher Trust
The Ruzin Sadagora Trust
Erach and Roshan Sadri Foundation

Saint Sarkis Charity Trust
The Salamander Charitable Trust
Salters' Charitable Foundation
The M J Samuel Charitable Trust
The Peter Samuel Charitable Trust
The Scarfe Charitable Trust
The Schapira Charitable Trust
The Annie Schiff Charitable Trust
The Schmidt-Bodner Charitable Trust
The R H Scholes Charitable Trust
The Schreib Trust
The Schreiber Charitable Trust
The Samuel Sebba Charitable Trust
The Seedfield Trust
Sellata Ltd
SEM Charitable Trust
The Ayrton Senna Foundation
The Seven Fifty Trust
The Cyril Shack Trust
The Shanti Charitable Trust
The Archie Sherman Cardiff Foundation
The Archie Sherman Charitable Trust
The Bassil Shippam and Alsford Trust
Shlomo Memorial Fund Limited
The J A Shone Memorial Trust
The Julius Silman Charitable Trust
The Leslie Silver Charitable Trust
The Simpson Foundation
The SMB Charitable Trust
The R C Snelling Charitable Trust
The Sobell Foundation
Solev Co Ltd
The Solo Charitable Settlement
Songdale Ltd
The Souter Charitable Trust
The W F Southall Trust
Sparquote Limited
Spears-Stutz Charitable Trust
The Spielman Charitable Trust
Rosalyn and Nicholas Springer Charitable Trust
Springrule Limited
St Peter's Saltley Trust
St Teilo's Trust
The Steel Charitable Trust
The Steinberg Family Charitable Trust
C E K Stern Charitable Trust
The Sigmund Sternberg Charitable Foundation
Stervon Ltd

The Stewards' Company
    Limited (incorporating the J
    W Laing Trust and the J W
    Laing Biblical Scholarship
    Trust)
Sir Halley Stewart Trust
The Leonard Laity Stoate
    Charitable Trust
The Stobart Newlands
    Charitable Trust
The Strawberry Charitable
    Trust
The A B Strom and R Strom
    Charitable Trust
Sueberry Ltd
The Alan Sugar Foundation
The Adrienne and Leslie
    Sussman Charitable Trust
Sutton Coldfield Charitable
    Trust
Swansea and Brecon Diocesan
    Board of Finance Limited
The Sylvanus Charitable Trust
T and S Trust Fund
The Tabeel Trust
The Tajtelbaum Charitable
    Trust
Talteg Ltd
The Tangent Charitable Trust
The Lady Tangye Charitable
    Trust
The David Tannen Charitable
    Trust
The Lili Tapper Charitable
    Foundation
C B and H H Taylor 1984 Trust
Tearfund
Tegham Limited
The Thornton Trust
Mrs R P Tindall's Charitable
    Trust
The Tisbury Telegraph Trust
The Tolkien Trust
Tomchei Torah Charitable
    Trust
The Torah Temimah Trust
Toras Chesed (London) Trust
The Tory Family Foundation
Truedene Co. Ltd
Truemart Limited
Trumros Limited
Tudor Rose Ltd
The Tufton Charitable Trust
Community Foundation Serving
    Tyne and Wear and
    Northumberland
Trustees of Tzedakah
UKI Charitable Foundation
Ulting Overseas Trust
The Union of Orthodox Hebrew
    Congregation
The United Society for the
    Propagation of the Gospel
The David Uri Memorial Trust
The Vail Foundation
The Valentine Charitable Trust

The Van Neste Foundation
The Vardy Foundation
Roger Vere Foundation
Vivdale Ltd
The Viznitz Foundation
Robert and Felicity Waley-
    Cohen Charitable Trust
Wallington Missionary Mart
    and Auctions
Weedon Family Trust
The Weinstein Foundation
West London Synagogue
    Charitable Fund
The Westcroft Trust
The Westminster Foundation
The Garfield Weston
    Foundation
The Whitecourt Charitable
    Trust
The Norman Whiteley Trust
The Williams Family Charitable
    Trust
Dame Violet Wills Charitable
    Trust
The Benjamin Winegarten
    Charitable Trust
The Harold Hyam Wingate
    Foundation
The Witzenfeld Foundation
The Michael and Anna Wix
    Charitable Trust
The Wixamtree Trust
The Maurice Wohl Charitable
    Foundation
The Charles Wolfson
    Charitable Trust
The Wolfson Family Charitable
    Trust
The James Wood Bequest
    Fund
Woodlands Green Ltd
The A and R Woolf Charitable
    Trust
The Worcestershire and
    Dudley Historic Churches
    Trust
The Matthews Wrightson
    Charity Trust
Wychdale Ltd
Wychville Ltd
Yankov Charitable Trust
The Yorkshire Historic
    Churches Trust
The Marjorie and Arnold Ziff
    Charitable Foundation
Stephen Zimmerman
    Charitable Trust

Christianity

Aid to the Church in Need (UK)
The Alabaster Trust
The Alexis Trust
Allchurches Trust Ltd
The Almond Trust
Almondsbury Charity

Alvor Charitable Trust
Viscount Amory's Charitable
    Trust
The Anchor Foundation
The Andrew Anderson Trust
The André Christian Trust
Andrews Charitable Trust
The John Apthorp Charity
The Archer Trust
The Armourers' and Brasiers'
    Gauntlet Trust
The A S Charitable Trust
Ashburnham Thanksgiving
    Trust
The Ashendene Trust
The Baird Trust
The Balney Charitable Trust
William P Bancroft (No 2)
    Charitable Trust and
    Jenepher Gillett Trust
The Barleycorn Trust
The Bates Charitable Trust
The Beacon Trust
Miss Jeanne Bisgood's
    Charitable Trust
The Bishop's Development
    Fund
The Sydney Black Charitable
    Trust
The Blandford Lake Trust
The Bosson Family Charitable
    Trust
H E and E L Botteley
    Charitable Trust
The Harry Bottom Charitable
    Trust
P G and N J Boulton Trust
The A H and E Boulton Trust
The Bowland Charitable Trust
The Liz and Terry Bramall
    Foundation
Bristol Archdeaconry Charity
T B H Brunner's Charitable
    Settlement
Buckingham Trust
The Burden Trust
Henry T and Lucy B Cadbury
    Charitable Trust
The William A Cadbury
    Charitable Trust
The Cambridgeshire Historic
    Churches Trust
The Carpenter Charitable Trust
The Carpenters' Company
    Charitable Trust
The Catholic Charitable Trust
Catholic Foreign Missions
The Catholic Trust for England
    and Wales
The Chasah Trust
Childs Charitable Trust
The Christabella Charitable
    Trust
Christian Response to Eastern
    Europe

The Church and Community
Fund
Church Burgesses Trust
Church Urban Fund
The Hilda and Alice Clark
Charitable Trust
The Roger and Sarah Bancroft
Clark Charitable Trust
The Clarke Charitable
Settlement
Richard Cloudesley's Charity
The Clover Trust
John Coldman Charitable Trust
The Congregational and
General Charitable Trust
The Cornwall Historic
Churches Trust
The Costa Family Charitable
Trust
Criffel Charitable Trust
The Cumber Family Charitable
Trust
Daily Prayer Union Charitable
Trust Limited
Grace Dieu Charitable Trust
The Dorcas Trust
The Dulverton Trust
The Dyers' Company
Charitable Trust
The Earmark Trust
The Edith Maud Ellis 1985
Charitable Trust
The Englefield Charitable Trust
The Erskine Cunningham Hill
Trust
F C Charitable Trust
The Fairway Trust
The Farthing Trust
Joseph Fattorini Charitable
Trust
Firtree Trust
Fisherbeck Charitable Trust
The Forest Hill Charitable Trust
The Forman Hardy Charitable
Trust
The Forte Charitable Trust
The Four Winds Trust
The Thomas Freke and Lady
Norton Charity Trust
The Anne French Memorial
Trust
The Friends Hall Farm Street
Trust
The Gale Family Charity Trust
The Gamma Trust
The Ganzoni Charitable Trust
The Gibbs Charitable Trust
The Girdlers' Company
Charitable Trust
Global Care
Golden Charitable Trust
The Grace Charitable Trust
Philip and Judith Green Trust
Greys Charitable Trust
E F and M G Hall Charitable
Trust

The W A Handley Charitable
Trust
Beatrice Hankey Foundation
Limited
The Kathleen Hannay
Memorial Charity
The Harris Charitable Trust
Headley-Pitt Charitable Trust
May Hearnshaw's Charity
The Hesed Trust
Hexham and Newcastle
Diocesan Trust (1947)
The P and C Hickinbotham
Charitable Trust
The Charles Littlewood Hill
Trust
The Hillier Trust
Hinchley Charitable Trust
Stuart Hine Trust
Hockerill Educational
Foundation
Matthew Hodder Charitable
Trust
The Jane Hodge Foundation
The Holmes Family Trust
(Sheffield)
The Homelands Charitable
Trust
The Homestead Charitable
Trust
Sir Harold Hood's Charitable
Trust
The Hope Trust
The Hutton Foundation
Irwin Trust
J A R Charitable Trust
The James Trust
The Marjory Jameson Trust
The Jarman Charitable Trust
The Barbara Joyce Jarrald
Charitable Trust
The Jerusalem Trust
The KempWelch Charitable
Trust
The Kennedy Charitable
Foundation
The King Henry VIII Endowed
Trust Warwick
Kingdom Way Trust
The Late Sir Pierce Lacy
Charity Trust
The K P Ladd Charitable Trust
Maurice and Hilda Laing
Charitable Trust
The Kirby Laing Foundation
The Beatrice Laing Trust
Duchy of Lancaster Benevolent
Fund
The Lancaster Foundation
Langdale Trust
The Langley Charitable Trust
Laslett's (Hinton) Charity
The Leathersellers' Company
Charitable Fund
The William Leech Charity
P Leigh-Bramwell Trust 'E'

The Leonard Trust
The Lind Trust
Lindale Educational
Foundation
The Elaine and Angus Lloyd
Charitable Trust
The Charles Lloyd Foundation
The Lo Family Charitable Trust
Paul Lunn-Rockliffe Charitable
Trust
The Lyndhurst Trust
The Lynwood Trust
Sylvanus Lyson's Charity
Mariapolis Limited
The Marsh Christian Trust
The Charlotte Marshall
Charitable Trust
The Nora Joan Marshall
Charitable Trust
Marshall's Charity
Marshgate Charitable
Settlement
Sir George Martin Trust
John Martin's Charity
The John Mason Family Trust
The Mason Porter Charitable
Trust
The Matt 6.3 Charitable Trust
Evelyn May Trust
Mazars Charitable Trust
The Anthony and Elizabeth
Mellows Charitable
Settlement
The Mercers' Charitable
Foundation
The Merchant Taylors'
Company Charities Fund
Miles Trust for the Putney and
Roehampton Community
The Millfield Trust
The Millhouses Charitable
Trust
The Edgar Milward Charity
The Minos Trust
The Mizpah Trust
Monmouthshire County Council
Welsh Church Act Fund
The Mr and Mrs J T Morgan
Foundation
The Oliver Morland Charitable
Trust
S C and M E Morland's
Charitable Trust
The Moshulu Charitable Trust
The Moss Charitable Trust
Mrs Waterhouse Charitable
Trust
The George Müller Charitable
Trust
The Nadezhda Charitable Trust
National Committee of the
Women's World Day of
Prayer for England and
Wales and Northern Ireland
Nazareth Trust Fund

The New Appeals Organisation
for the City and County of
Nottingham
The Northumbria Historic
Churches Trust
The Norwich Church of England
Young Men's Society
The Norwood and Newton
Settlement
The Nottinghamshire Historic
Churches Trust
The Ogle Christian Trust
The Oikonomia Trust
Ormonde Foundation
The Owen Family Trust
The Paget Charitable Trust
The Panacea Society
Panahpur (previously Panahpur
Charitable Trust)
The James Pantyfedwen
Foundation
Paraton Trust
The Park House Charitable
Trust
Miss M E Swinton Paterson's
Charitable Trust
The Jack Patston Charitable
Trust
The Payne Charitable Trust
The Persson Charitable Trust
The David Pickford Charitable
Foundation
The Bernard Piggott Charitable
Trust
The Praebendo Charitable
Foundation
Sir John Priestman Charity
Trust
The Pyne Charitable Trust
Quothquan Trust
The Bishop Radford Trust
The Rank Foundation Limited
The Ravensdale Trust
The Sir James Reckitt Charity
The Rehoboth Trust
The Nathaniel Reyner Trust
Fund
The Sir Cliff Richard Charitable
Trust
The Clive Richards Charity
The River Trust
The Rock Foundation
The Rock Solid Trust
Mrs L D Rope Third Charitable
Settlement
The Rotherwick Foundation
Saint Sarkis Charity Trust
The Salamander Charitable
Trust
Salters' Charitable Foundation
The Scarfe Charitable Trust
The Seedfield Trust
The Seven Fifty Trust
The Shanti Charitable Trust
The Bassil Shippam and
Alsford Trust

The J A Shone Memorial Trust
The Simpson Foundation
The SMB Charitable Trust
The Souter Charitable Trust
The W F Southall Trust
St Peter's Saltley Trust
St Teilo's Trust
The Stewards' Company
Limited (incorporating the J
W Laing Trust and the J W
Laing Biblical Scholarship
Trust)
Sir Halley Stewart Trust
The Leonard Laity Stoate
Charitable Trust
The Stobart Newlands
Charitable Trust
Swansea and Brecon Diocesan
Board of Finance Limited
The Sylvanus Charitable Trust
The Tabeel Trust
The Lady Tangye Charitable
Trust
C B and H H Taylor 1984 Trust
Tearfund
The Thornton Trust
Mrs R P Tindall's Charitable
Trust
The Tisbury Telegraph Trust
The Tolkien Trust
The Tory Family Foundation
The Tufton Charitable Trust
Ulting Overseas Trust
The United Society for the
Propagation of the Gospel
The Van Neste Foundation
The Vardy Foundation
Wallington Missionary Mart
and Auctions
The Westcroft Trust
The Westminster Foundation
The Whitecourt Charitable
Trust
The Norman Whiteley Trust
Dame Violet Wills Charitable
Trust
The James Wood Bequest
Fund
The Worcestershire and
Dudley Historic Churches
Trust
The Matthews Wrightson
Charity Trust
The Yorkshire Historic
Churches Trust

Christian causes

The Alexis Trust
The Almond Trust
Alvor Charitable Trust
The Andrew Anderson Trust
The Archer Trust
Ashburnham Thanksgiving
Trust
The Baird Trust

The Barleycorn Trust
The Blandford Lake Trust
H E and E L Botteley
Charitable Trust
Bristol Archdeaconry Charity
The Carpenter Charitable Trust
The Carpenters' Company
Charitable Trust
Church Burgesses Trust
Church Urban Fund
The Englefield Charitable Trust
The Farthing Trust
Firtree Trust
The Forest Hill Charitable Trust
The Forte Charitable Trust
The Four Winds Trust
The Anne French Memorial
Trust
The Friends Hall Farm Street
Trust
The Gibbs Charitable Trust
The Girdlers' Company
Charitable Trust
Global Care
Stuart Hine Trust
Matthew Hodder Charitable
Trust
The Jerusalem Trust
The KempWelch Charitable
Trust
Maurice and Hilda Laing
Charitable Trust
Langdale Trust
The William Leech Charity
Sir George Martin Trust
Mazars Charitable Trust
The Mercers' Charitable
Foundation
Miles Trust for the Putney and
Roehampton Community
Nazareth Trust Fund
The Norwood and Newton
Settlement
The Owen Family Trust
The Paget Charitable Trust
The Panacea Society
The Park House Charitable
Trust
The Payne Charitable Trust
The Sir Cliff Richard Charitable
Trust
The River Trust
The Rock Solid Trust
Mrs L D Rope Third Charitable
Settlement
The Salamander Charitable
Trust
Salters' Charitable Foundation
The Seedfield Trust
The Shanti Charitable Trust
The J A Shone Memorial Trust
The Stewards' Company
Limited (incorporating the J
W Laing Trust and the J W
Laing Biblical Scholarship
Trust)

The Stobart Newlands
   Charitable Trust
Tearfund
Mrs R P Tindall's Charitable
   Trust
The Tufton Charitable Trust
The Vardy Foundation
The Whitecourt Charitable
   Trust

Christian churches

Aid to the Church in Need (UK)
Almondsbury Charity
Viscount Amory's Charitable
   Trust
The Ashendene Trust
The Baird Trust
The Balney Charitable Trust
William P Bancroft (No 2)
   Charitable Trust and
   Jenepher Gillett Trust
The Bates Charitable Trust
Miss Jeanne Bisgood's
   Charitable Trust
The Bishop's Development
   Fund
The Sydney Black Charitable
   Trust
The A H and E Boulton Trust
T B H Brunner's Charitable
   Settlement
Henry T and Lucy B Cadbury
   Charitable Trust
The William A Cadbury
   Charitable Trust
The Cambridgeshire Historic
   Churches Trust
The Catholic Charitable Trust
Catholic Foreign Missions
The Catholic Trust for England
   and Wales
The Church and Community
   Fund
Church Burgesses Trust
The Hilda and Alice Clark
   Charitable Trust
The Roger and Sarah Bancroft
   Clark Charitable Trust
Richard Cloudesley's Charity
The Congregational and
   General Charitable Trust
The Cornwall Historic
   Churches Trust
The Edith Maud Ellis 1985
   Charitable Trust
The Erskine Cunningham Hill
   Trust
Joseph Fattorini Charitable
   Trust
The Thomas Freke and Lady
   Norton Charity Trust
The Anne French Memorial
   Trust
The Friends Hall Farm Street
   Trust

The Gale Family Charity Trust
The Gibbs Charitable Trust
The Girdlers' Company
   Charitable Trust
Greys Charitable Trust
E F and M G Hall Charitable
   Trust
The W A Handley Charitable
   Trust
The Harris Charitable Trust
Headley-Pitt Charitable Trust
Hexham and Newcastle
   Diocesan Trust (1947)
The P and C Hickinbotham
   Charitable Trust
Stuart Hine Trust
The Jane Hodge Foundation
The Homelands Charitable
   Trust
Sir Harold Hood's Charitable
   Trust
The Hope Trust
J A R Charitable Trust
The Jarman Charitable Trust
The Kennedy Charitable
   Foundation
The King Henry VIII Endowed
   Trust Warwick
Laslett's (Hinton) Charity
Lindale Educational
   Foundation
The Charles Lloyd Foundation
Sylvanus Lyson's Charity
The Charlotte Marshall
   Charitable Trust
Marshall's Charity
The Anthony and Elizabeth
   Mellows Charitable
   Settlement
Monmouthshire County Council
   Welsh Church Act Fund
The Oliver Morland Charitable
   Trust
S C and M E Morland's
   Charitable Trust
Mrs Waterhouse Charitable
   Trust
Nazareth Trust Fund
The New Appeals Organisation
   for the City and County of
   Nottingham
The Northumbria Historic
   Churches Trust
The Norwood and Newton
   Settlement
The Nottinghamshire Historic
   Churches Trust
The Ogle Christian Trust
Ormonde Foundation
The Owen Family Trust
Miss M E Swinton Paterson's
   Charitable Trust
The Bernard Piggott Charitable
   Trust
Sir John Priestman Charity
   Trust

The Bishop Radford Trust
The Sir James Reckitt Charity
The Nathaniel Reyner Trust
   Fund
The Clive Richards Charity
Mrs L D Rope Third Charitable
   Settlement
The Rotherwick Foundation
Saint Sarkis Charity Trust
The Simpson Foundation
The W F Southall Trust
St Teilo's Trust
The Leonard Laity Stoate
   Charitable Trust
The Sylvanus Charitable Trust
The Lady Tangye Charitable
   Trust
C B and H H Taylor 1984 Trust
The Thornton Trust
The Tolkien Trust
The Westcroft Trust
The Westminster Foundation
The Norman Whiteley Trust
The James Wood Bequest
   Fund
The Worcestershire and
   Dudley Historic Churches
   Trust
The Yorkshire Historic
   Churches Trust

Christian social thought

The Carpenters' Company
   Charitable Trust
The Jerusalem Trust
Sir Halley Stewart Trust

Missionary work, evangelism

The Armourers' and Brasiers'
   Gauntlet Trust
The Barleycorn Trust
The Beacon Trust
P G and N J Boulton Trust
The A H and E Boulton Trust
The Carpenters' Company
   Charitable Trust
The Chasah Trust
Daily Prayer Union Charitable
   Trust Limited
The Fairway Trust
The Farthing Trust
Philip and Judith Green Trust
Beatrice Hankey Foundation
   Limited
The Hesed Trust
Stuart Hine Trust
Hockerill Educational
   Foundation
The Hope Trust
The Jerusalem Trust

Maurice and Hilda Laing Charitable Trust
The Beatrice Laing Trust
The Lancaster Foundation
The Langley Charitable Trust
Paul Lunn-Rockliffe Charitable Trust
The Lyndhurst Trust
The Millhouses Charitable Trust
The Moshulu Charitable Trust
The George Müller Charitable Trust
National Committee of the Women's World Day of Prayer for England and Wales and Northern Ireland
Nazareth Trust Fund
The Ogle Christian Trust
The Owen Family Trust
Panahpur (previously Panahpur Charitable Trust)
The Payne Charitable Trust
The Persson Charitable Trust
The Rank Foundation Limited
The Sir Cliff Richard Charitable Trust
The Rock Foundation
The Seedfield Trust
The J A Shone Memorial Trust
St Teilo's Trust
The Stewards' Company Limited (incorporating the J W Laing Trust and the J W Laing Biblical Scholarship Trust)
The Tabeel Trust
The Thornton Trust
Ulting Overseas Trust
The United Society for the Propagation of the Gospel
Wallington Missionary Mart and Auctions
The Norman Whiteley Trust
Dame Violet Wills Charitable Trust

Hinduism

The Carpenters' Company Charitable Trust

Inter-faith activities

All Saints Educational Trust
The Astor of Hever Trust
The Bowerman Charitable Trust
The Carpenters' Company Charitable Trust
The Duis Charitable Trust
The Edith Maud Ellis 1985 Charitable Trust
The Elmgrant Trust

The Joseph Strong Frazer Trust
The Anne French Memorial Trust
Sue Hammerson Charitable Trust
Hinduja Foundation
The Sir Julian Hodge Charitable Trust
The Inlight Trust
The Soli and Leah Kelaty Trust Fund
The Joseph Levy Charitable Foundation
The C L Loyd Charitable Trust
The Mahavir Trust
The Colin Montgomerie Charitable Foundation
The Community Foundation for Northern Ireland
The Rofeh Trust
The Sir James Roll Charitable Trust
The Rowland Family Foundation
The RRAF Charitable Trust
The Jeremy and John Sacher Charitable Trust
The Sigmund Sternberg Charitable Foundation
Sir Halley Stewart Trust
Roger Vere Foundation
West London Synagogue Charitable Fund

Islam

The Altajir Trust
The Carpenters' Company Charitable Trust
Matliwala Family Charitable Trust
Muslim Hands

Judaism

4 Charity Foundation
A W Charitable Trust
Brian Abrams Charitable Trust
Eric Abrams Charitable Trust
The Acacia Charitable Trust
Achisomoch Aid Company Limited
Adenfirst Ltd
The Adint Charitable Trust
The Alliance Family Foundation
Altamont Ltd
The AM Charitable Trust
Amabrill Limited
Andor Charitable Trust
Anpride Ltd
The Ardwick Trust
The Baker Charitable Trust
The Andrew Balint Charitable Trust

The George Balint Charitable Trust
The Paul Balint Charitable Trust
Bay Charitable Trust
BCH Trust
Bear Mordechai Ltd
Beauland Ltd
The Becker Family Charitable Trust
Maurice and Jacqueline Bennett Charitable Trust
Michael and Lesley Bennett Charitable Trust
The Ruth Berkowitz Charitable Trust
BHST
The Bintaub Charitable Trust
The Bertie Black Foundation
The Sir Victor Blank Charitable Settlement
The Neville and Elaine Blond Charitable Trust
The Bluston Charitable Settlement
The Bonamy Charitable Trust
Salo Bordon Charitable Trust
Sir Clive Bourne Family Trust
Bourneheights Limited
Edna Brown Charitable Settlement (Mrs E E Brown Charitable Settlement)
Brushmill Ltd
The Arnold Burton 1998 Charitable Trust
C and F Charitable Trust
H and L Cantor Trust
Carlee Ltd
The Carlton House Charitable Trust
The Carpenters' Company Charitable Trust
The CH (1980) Charitable Trust
Charitworth Limited
The Childwick Trust
The Clore Duffield Foundation
Miss V L Clore's 1967 Charitable Trust
Closehelm Limited
Clydpride Ltd
The Denise Cohen Charitable Trust
The Vivienne and Samuel Cohen Charitable Trust
Col-Reno Ltd
Harold and Daphne Cooper Charitable Trust
The Gershon Coren Charitable Foundation (also known as The Muriel and Gus Coren Charitable Foundation)
The Sidney and Elizabeth Corob Charitable Trust
The Corona Charitable Trust
The Craps Charitable Trust

The Cuby Charitable Trust
The Manny Cussins
 Foundation
Itzchok Meyer Cymerman Trust
 Ltd
Oizer Dalim Trust
The Davidson Family
 Charitable Trust
The Alderman Joe Davidson
 Memorial Trust
Davis-Rubens Charitable Trust
The Debmar Benevolent Trust
The Dellal Foundation
Alan and Sheila Diamond
 Charitable Trust
The Djanogly Foundation
The DM Charitable Trust
The Dollond Charitable Trust
Domepride Ltd
The Doughty Charity Trust
The Duis Charitable Trust
Dushinsky Trust Ltd
The George Elias Charitable
 Trust
Ellador Ltd
The Ellinson Foundation Ltd
Elshore Ltd
Entindale Ltd
The Esfandi Charitable
 Foundation
The Eventhall Family
 Charitable Trust
The Exilarch's Foundation
Extonglen Limited
The Faber Charitable Trust
Famos Foundation Trust
Federation of Jewish Relief
 Organisations
Finnart House School Trust
The Flow Foundation
The Gerald Fogel Charitable
 Trust
Fordeve Limited
The Isaac and Freda Frankel
 Memorial Charitable Trust
Friends of Biala Limited
Friends of Boyan Trust
Friends of Wiznitz Limited
Mejer and Gertrude Miriam
 Frydman Foundation
The G I Foundation
Gableholt Limited
Garvan Limited
Jacqueline and Michael Gee
 Charitable Trust
The B and P Glasser
 Charitable Trust
Golden Charitable Trust
The Jack Goldhill Charitable
 Trust
The Grahame Charitable
 Foundation Limited
The M and R Gross Charities
 Limited
The GRP Charitable Trust

N and R Grunbaum Charitable
 Trust
The Gur Trust
The H and J Spack Charitable
 Trust
The H P Charitable Trust
Harbo Charities Limited
Haskel Family Foundation
The Hathaway Trust
The Maurice Hatter Foundation
Heathside Charitable Trust
The Helping Foundation
Highcroft Charitable Trust
The Holden Charitable Trust
The Daniel Howard Trust
The Humanitarian Trust
The Huntingdon Foundation
Hurdale Charity Limited
The P Y N and B Hyams Trust
I G O Foundation Limited
Infinity Capital Trust
Investream Charitable Trust
The Isaacs Charitable Trust
The J & J Benevolent
 Foundation
The J & J Charitable Trust
Jacobs Charitable Trust
The Ruth and Lionel Jacobson
 Trust (Second Fund) No 2
The Susan and Stephen
 James Charitable
 Settlement
Jay Education Trust
JCA Charitable Foundation
Jewish Child's Day
The Jewish Youth Fund
The Harold Joels Charitable
 Trust
The Nicholas Joels Charitable
 Trust
The Norman Joels Charitable
 Trust
The Joron Charitable Trust
The J E Joseph Charitable
 Fund
The Josephs Family Charitable
 Trust
Jusaca Charitable Trust
The Bernard Kahn Charitable
 Trust
The Stanley Kalms Foundation
The Kasner Charitable Trust
The Michael and Ilse Katz
 Foundation
The Katzauer Charitable
 Settlement
The C S Kaufman Charitable
 Trust
The Geoffrey John Kaye
 Charitable Foundation
The Emmanuel Kaye
 Foundation
Keren Association
Kermaville Ltd
E and E Kernkraut Charities
 Limited

Kirschel Foundation
The Kobler Trust
The Kohn Foundation
Kollel and Co. Limited
The Kreditor Charitable Trust
Kupath Gemach Chaim
 Bechesed Viznitz Trust
The Kyte Charitable Trust
L P W Limited
The Lambert Charitable Trust
Largsmount Ltd
The Lauffer Family Charitable
 Foundation
The Lawson Beckman
 Charitable Trust
The Arnold Lee Charitable
 Trust
The Kennedy Leigh Charitable
 Trust
Morris Leigh Foundation
The Joseph Levy Charitable
 Foundation
Lewis Family Charitable Trust
The Ruth and Stuart Lipton
 Charitable Trust
The Second Joseph Aaron
 Littman Foundation
Jack Livingstone Charitable
 Trust
Localtrent Ltd
The Locker Foundation
The Loftus Charitable Trust
The Lolev Charitable Trust
The Lowy Mitchell Foundation
The Ruth and Jack Lunzer
 Charitable Trust
The Sir Jack Lyons Charitable
 Trust
The M and C Trust
The M K Charitable Trust
The Magen Charitable Trust
Malbin Trust
The Manackerman Charitable
 Trust
Marbeh Torah Trust
The Stella and Alexander
 Margulies Charitable Trust
The Marks Family Foundation
The Ann and David Marks
 Foundation
The Hilda and Samuel Marks
 Foundation
The Violet Mauray Charitable
 Trust
Mayfair Charities Ltd
Melodor Limited
Melow Charitable Trust
Menuchar Ltd
Mercaz Torah Vechesed
 Limited
The Laurence Misener
 Charitable Trust
The Mishcon Family Charitable
 Trust
The Mitchell Charitable Trust
The Modiano Charitable Trust

The Mole Charitable Trust
Diana and Allan Morgenthau Charitable Trust
The Peter Morrison Charitable Foundation
Moshal Charitable Trust
Brian and Jill Moss Charitable Trust
Mosselson Charitable Trust
The Mutual Trust Group
MW (CL) Foundation
MW (GK) Foundation
MW (HO) Foundation
MW (RH) Foundation
MYA Charitable Trust
MYR Charitable Trust
The Naggar Charitable Trust
Nemoral Ltd
Ner Foundation
Nesswall Ltd
Newpier Charity Ltd
The Chevras Ezras Nitzrochim Trust
NJD Charitable Trust
Normalyn Charitable Trust
Oizer Charitable Trust
The Doris Pacey Charitable Foundation
The Park Charitable Trust
The David Pearlman Charitable Foundation
The Pears Family Charitable Foundation
The Peltz Trust
B E Perl Charitable Trust
The Philips and Rubens Charitable Trust
The Phillips Family Charitable Trust
G S Plaut Charitable Trust Limited
The George and Esme Pollitzer Charitable Settlement
The Pollywally Charitable Trust
Edith and Ferdinand Porjes Charitable Trust
The John Porter Charitable Trust
The J E Posnansky Charitable Trust
Premierquote Ltd
Premishlaner Charitable Trust
R J M Charitable Trust
R S Charitable Trust
Rachel Charitable Trust
The Fanny Rapaport Charitable Settlement
The Rayden Charitable Trust
The Rayne Trust
The Rest Harrow Trust
Reuben Foundation
Ridgesave Limited
The Sir John Ritblat Family Foundation
Rokach Family Charitable Trust
The Gerald Ronson Foundation

Rowanville Ltd
The Alfred and Frances Rubens Charitable Trust
The Rubin Foundation
S F Foundation
S O Charitable Trust
The Ruzin Sadagora Trust
The M J Samuel Charitable Trust
The Peter Samuel Charitable Trust
The Schapira Charitable Trust
The Annie Schiff Charitable Trust
The Schmidt-Bodner Charitable Trust
The Schreib Trust
The Schreiber Charitable Trust
The Samuel Sebba Charitable Trust
Sellata Ltd
SEM Charitable Trust
The Cyril Shack Trust
The Archie Sherman Cardiff Foundation
The Archie Sherman Charitable Trust
Shlomo Memorial Fund Limited
The Julius Silman Charitable Trust
The Leslie Silver Charitable Trust
The Sobell Foundation
Solev Co Ltd
The Solo Charitable Settlement
Songdale Ltd
Sparquote Limited
Spears-Stutz Charitable Trust
The Spielman Charitable Trust
Rosalyn and Nicholas Springer Charitable Trust
Springrule Limited
The Steinberg Family Charitable Trust
C E K Stern Charitable Trust
The Sigmund Sternberg Charitable Foundation
Stervon Ltd
The Strawberry Charitable Trust
The A B Strom and R Strom Charitable Trust
Sueberry Ltd
The Alan Sugar Foundation
The Adrienne and Leslie Sussman Charitable Trust
T and S Trust Fund
The Tajtelbaum Charitable Trust
Talteg Ltd
The Tangent Charitable Trust
The David Tannen Charitable Trust
The Lili Tapper Charitable Foundation

Tegham Limited
Tomchei Torah Charitable Trust
The Torah Temimah Trust
Toras Chesed (London) Trust
Truedene Co. Ltd
Truemart Limited
Trumros Limited
Tudor Rose Ltd
Trustees of Tzedakah
The Union of Orthodox Hebrew Congregation
The David Uri Memorial Trust
The Vail Foundation
Vivdale Ltd
The Viznitz Foundation
Robert and Felicity Waley-Cohen Charitable Trust
The Weinstein Foundation
West London Synagogue Charitable Fund
The Williams Family Charitable Trust
The Benjamin Winegarten Charitable Trust
The Harold Hyam Wingate Foundation
The Witzenfeld Foundation
The Michael and Anna Wix Charitable Trust
The Maurice Wohl Charitable Foundation
The Charles Wolfson Charitable Trust
The Wolfson Family Charitable Trust
Woodlands Green Ltd
The A and R Woolf Charitable Trust
Wychdale Ltd
Wychville Ltd
Yankov Charitable Trust
The Marjorie and Arnold Ziff Charitable Foundation
Stephen Zimmerman Charitable Trust

Jewish causes, work

The Adint Charitable Trust
Altamont Ltd
The Arnold Burton 1998 Charitable Trust
Miss V L Clore's 1967 Charitable Trust
The Duis Charitable Trust
Ellador Ltd
The Faber Charitable Trust
N and R Grunbaum Charitable Trust
The Hathaway Trust
The J & J Charitable Trust

The Susan and Stephen
  James Charitable
  Settlement
The Kyte Charitable Trust
The Lambert Charitable Trust
Malbin Trust
The Modiano Charitable Trust
Normalyn Charitable Trust
The Pears Family Charitable
  Foundation
The Peltz Trust
The Pollywally Charitable Trust
Reuben Foundation
Sellata Ltd
Rosalyn and Nicholas Springer
  Charitable Trust
The Tangent Charitable Trust
The Wolfson Family Charitable
  Trust

Orthodox Judaism

Achisomoch Aid Company
  Limited
Amabrill Limited
The Becker Family Charitable
  Trust
Bourneheights Limited
C and F Charitable Trust
The Doughty Charity Trust
Extonglen Limited
Friends of Boyan Trust
The H P Charitable Trust
The Helping Foundation
The J & J Benevolent
  Foundation
The Lolev Charitable Trust
Mayfair Charities Ltd
Mercaz Torah Vechesed
  Limited
MW (CL) Foundation
MW (GK) Foundation
MW (HO) Foundation
MW (RH) Foundation
Nemoral Ltd
Newpier Charity Ltd
Oizer Charitable Trust
Rowanville Ltd
Sparquote Limited
C E K Stern Charitable Trust
T and S Trust Fund
Tegham Limited
The Torah Temimah Trust
Vivdale Ltd

Religious understanding

The Carpenters' Company
  Charitable Trust
The Doughty Charity Trust
The Gilbert and Eileen Edgar
  Foundation
The Elmgrant Trust

The Anne French Memorial
  Trust
Keswick Hall Trust
The Kennedy Leigh Charitable
  Trust
The Joseph Levy Charitable
  Foundation
Quothquan Trust

Rights, law and conflict

The 1970 Trust
The A B Charitable Trust
ABF The Soldiers' Charity
The Ajahma Charitable Trust
The Alchemy Foundation
The A S Charitable Trust
The Associated Country
  Women of the World
The Scott Bader
  Commonwealth Ltd
The Baring Foundation
The Jack and Ada Beattie
  Foundation
The Body Shop Foundation
John and Susan Bowers Fund
The British Gas (Scottish Gas)
  Energy Trust
The Bromley Trust
The William A Cadbury
  Charitable Trust
The Barrow Cadbury Trust and
  the Barrow Cadbury Fund
CAFOD (Catholic Agency for
  Overseas Development)
Calouste Gulbenkian
  Foundation – UK Branch
The Calpe Trust
Celtic Charity Fund
The Charities Advisory Trust
The Jimmy Choo Foundation
J A Clark Charitable Trust
The Evan Cornish Foundation
The Violet and Milo Cripps
  Charitable Trust
The Daiwa Anglo-Japanese
  Foundation
Dentons UKMEA LLP
  Charitable Trust
The Duis Charitable Trust
The Dulverton Trust
Dunard Fund
EDF Energy Trust (EDFET)
Edge Fund
The Edith Maud Ellis 1985
  Charitable Trust
The Embleton Trust
Esmée Fairbairn Foundation
The Farthing Trust
Allan and Nesta Ferguson
  Charitable Settlement
Sydney E Franklin Deceased's
  New Second Charity
The Jill Franklin Trust
Friends Provident Charitable
  Foundation
Maurice Fry Charitable Trust
The Fuserna Foundation
  General Charitable Trust
The G D Charitable Trust
Gamlen Charitable Trust
The Robert Gavron Charitable
  Trust
The Hemraj Goyal Foundation

Greggs Foundation
The Grimmitt Trust
The Hadley Trust
Paul Hamlyn Foundation
The Helen Hamlyn Trust
The Charles Hayward
    Foundation
The Hilden Charitable Fund
Hope for Youth (NI)
The Ireland Fund of Great
    Britain
The J R S S T Charitable Trust
The Joffe Charitable Trust
The Allen Lane Foundation
The Law Society Charity
The Leigh Trust
The Mark Leonard Trust
The Joseph Levy Charitable
    Foundation
Lloyds Bank Foundation for
    England and Wales
Lloyds Bank Foundation for
    Northern Ireland
The Trust for London
The London Community
    Foundation
London Legal Support Trust
Ian Mactaggart Trust
Mariapolis Limited
Marmot Charitable Trust
Community Foundation for
    Merseyside
The Millfield House Foundation
John Moores Foundation
S C and M E Morland's
    Charitable Trust
Frederick Mulder Charitable
    Trust
Muslim Hands
The Kitty and Daniel Nabarro
    Charitable Trust
The Nadezhda Charitable Trust
Network for Social Change
Newby Trust Limited
The Noon Foundation
Norfolk Community Foundation
The Community Foundation for
    Northern Ireland
The Northern Rock Foundation
Novi Most International
The Nuffield Foundation
The Harry Payne Trust
People's Postcode Trust
The Persula Foundation
The Col W W Pilkington Will
    Trusts The General Charity
    Fund
Polden-Puckham Charitable
    Foundation
The David and Elaine Potter
    Foundation
Quartet Community Foundation
The Monica Rabagliati
    Charitable Trust
The Eleanor Rathbone
    Charitable Trust

The Sigrid Rausing Trust
The Roddick Foundation
Rosa – the UK fund for women
    and girls
The Joseph Rowntree
    Charitable Trust
Joseph Rowntree Reform Trust
    Limited
The Alan and Babette
    Sainsbury Charitable Fund
Santander UK Foundation
    Limited
The Samuel Sebba Charitable
    Trust
The Simmons & Simmons
    Charitable Foundation
The W F Southall Trust
The Staples Trust
The C Paul Thackray General
    Charitable Trust
The Tinsley Foundation
The Tresillian Trust
United Utilities Trust Fund
The Michael Uren Foundation
Voluntary Action Fund (VAF)
The Scurrah Wainwright Charity
War on Want
The Westcroft Trust
The Wolfson Family Charitable
    Trust
Worcester Municipal Charities
The Xerox (UK) Trust
Youth United Foundation

Citizen participation

The Barrow Cadbury Trust and
    the Barrow Cadbury Fund
The Joffe Charitable Trust
The Nuffield Foundation
People's Postcode Trust
The Joseph Rowntree
    Charitable Trust
Joseph Rowntree Reform Trust
    Limited
The Tinsley Foundation
Youth United Foundation

Conflict resolution

The A S Charitable Trust
The Scott Bader
    Commonwealth Ltd
The William A Cadbury
    Charitable Trust
The Barrow Cadbury Trust and
    the Barrow Cadbury Fund
Calouste Gulbenkian
    Foundation – UK Branch
The Charities Advisory Trust
J A Clark Charitable Trust
The Daiwa Anglo-Japanese
    Foundation
The Dulverton Trust

The Edith Maud Ellis 1985
    Charitable Trust
Esmée Fairbairn Foundation
Allan and Nesta Ferguson
    Charitable Settlement
The Hadley Trust
Hope for Youth (NI)
The Ireland Fund of Great
    Britain
The Allen Lane Foundation
Mariapolis Limited
Marmot Charitable Trust
S C and M E Morland's
    Charitable Trust
Frederick Mulder Charitable
    Trust
The Kitty and Daniel Nabarro
    Charitable Trust
The Noon Foundation
The Community Foundation for
    Northern Ireland
Novi Most International
The Harry Payne Trust
People's Postcode Trust
Polden-Puckham Charitable
    Foundation
The Eleanor Rathbone
    Charitable Trust
The Joseph Rowntree
    Charitable Trust
The W F Southall Trust
The Tresillian Trust
The Westcroft Trust

Legal advice and services

The British Gas (Scottish Gas)
    Energy Trust
Dentons UKMEA LLP
    Charitable Trust
EDF Energy Trust (EDFET)
The Embleton Trust
Friends Provident Charitable
    Foundation
The Law Society Charity
Lloyds Bank Foundation for
    England and Wales
Lloyds Bank Foundation for
    Northern Ireland
The London Community
    Foundation
London Legal Support Trust
Community Foundation for
    Merseyside
John Moores Foundation
The Community Foundation for
    Northern Ireland
The Northern Rock Foundation
The Nuffield Foundation
Quartet Community Foundation
Santander UK Foundation
    Limited
The Simmons & Simmons
    Charitable Foundation

United Utilities Trust Fund
Worcester Municipal Charities

Rights, equality and justice

The 1970 Trust
The A B Charitable Trust
The Ajahma Charitable Trust
The Associated Country Women of the World
The Body Shop Foundation
John and Susan Bowers Fund
The Bromley Trust
The Barrow Cadbury Trust and the Barrow Cadbury Fund
Calouste Gulbenkian Foundation – UK Branch
Celtic Charity Fund
The Jimmy Choo Foundation
The Duis Charitable Trust
Dunard Fund
The Farthing Trust
Allan and Nesta Ferguson Charitable Settlement
Sydney E Franklin Deceased's New Second Charity
The G D Charitable Trust
The Hemraj Goyal Foundation
Greggs Foundation
Paul Hamlyn Foundation
The Helen Hamlyn Trust
The Hilden Charitable Fund
Hope for Youth (NI)
The J R S S T Charitable Trust
The Joffe Charitable Trust
The Allen Lane Foundation
The Law Society Charity
The Leigh Trust
The Mark Leonard Trust
The Joseph Levy Charitable Foundation
Lloyds Bank Foundation for England and Wales
The Millfield House Foundation
John Moores Foundation
The Kitty and Daniel Nabarro Charitable Trust
The Nadezhda Charitable Trust
Network for Social Change
Newby Trust Limited
The Noon Foundation
The Community Foundation for Northern Ireland
The Nuffield Foundation
People's Postcode Trust
The Persula Foundation
The Col W W Pilkington Will Trusts The General Charity Fund
Polden-Puckham Charitable Foundation
The Monica Rabagliati Charitable Trust

The Eleanor Rathbone Charitable Trust
The Roddick Foundation
Rosa – the UK fund for women and girls
The Joseph Rowntree Charitable Trust
Joseph Rowntree Reform Trust Limited
The Alan and Babette Sainsbury Charitable Fund
The Staples Trust
The Tinsley Foundation
Voluntary Action Fund (VAF)
The Scurrah Wainwright Charity
The Xerox (UK) Trust

Human rights

The 1970 Trust
The A B Charitable Trust
The Ajahma Charitable Trust
The Body Shop Foundation
The Bromley Trust
The Barrow Cadbury Trust and the Barrow Cadbury Fund
Dunard Fund
The Farthing Trust
The Helen Hamlyn Trust
The Persula Foundation
Polden-Puckham Charitable Foundation
The Monica Rabagliati Charitable Trust
The Roddick Foundation
The Tinsley Foundation

Civil liberties

The 1970 Trust
The Barrow Cadbury Trust and the Barrow Cadbury Fund
The Joseph Rowntree Charitable Trust
Joseph Rowntree Reform Trust Limited
The Tinsley Foundation
Voluntary Action Fund (VAF)

Cultural equity

Calouste Gulbenkian Foundation – UK Branch
Greggs Foundation
Paul Hamlyn Foundation
The Kitty and Daniel Nabarro Charitable Trust

Disability rights

Calouste Gulbenkian Foundation – UK Branch
The G D Charitable Trust

John Moores Foundation
Newby Trust Limited
The Xerox (UK) Trust

Economic justice

Allan and Nesta Ferguson Charitable Settlement
Lloyds Bank Foundation for England and Wales
The Millfield House Foundation
The Joseph Rowntree Charitable Trust
The Tinsley Foundation

Racial justice

The Barrow Cadbury Trust and the Barrow Cadbury Fund
Celtic Charity Fund
The Duis Charitable Trust
The Farthing Trust
The Hilden Charitable Fund
The Leigh Trust
The Joseph Levy Charitable Foundation
John Moores Foundation
The Noon Foundation
The Joseph Rowntree Charitable Trust
The Tinsley Foundation
Voluntary Action Fund (VAF)

Social justice

John and Susan Bowers Fund
The Duis Charitable Trust
Network for Social Change
Joseph Rowntree Reform Trust Limited
The Tinsley Foundation
The Scurrah Wainwright Charity
The Xerox (UK) Trust

Women's rights

The Associated Country Women of the World
The Duis Charitable Trust
The Hemraj Goyal Foundation
John Moores Foundation
Polden-Puckham Charitable Foundation
Rosa – the UK fund for women and girls
The Staples Trust

Young people's rights

Calouste Gulbenkian Foundation – UK Branch

The Duis Charitable Trust
Hope for Youth (NI)
The Mark Leonard Trust
The Nadezhda Charitable Trust
The Xerox (UK) Trust

Science and technology

The 1970 Trust
The Armourers' and Brasiers' Gauntlet Trust
Astellas European Foundation
The Big Lottery Fund
British Ornithologists' Union
The Carlton House Charitable Trust
The Cass Foundation
The John Coates Charitable Trust
The Ernest Cook Trust
The Evan Cornish Foundation
William Dean Countryside and Educational Trust
The Dunn Family Charitable Trust
The James Dyson Foundation
The Gilbert and Eileen Edgar Foundation
The Beryl Evetts and Robert Luff Animal Welfare Trust Limited
The Gamma Trust
The Gatsby Charitable Foundation
The GNC Trust
The Golden Bottle Trust
The Granada Foundation
Paul Hamlyn Foundation
The Charles Hayward Foundation
The Simon Heller Charitable Settlement
The Indigo Trust
The Michael John Trust
The Kohn Foundation
The Leathersellers' Company Charitable Fund
The John Spedan Lewis Foundation
The MacRobert Trust
The Ronald Miller Foundation
The Mountbatten Memorial Trust
The Kitty and Daniel Nabarro Charitable Trust
The Nuffield Foundation
Open Gate
The Petplan Charitable Trust
The David and Elaine Potter Foundation
Ranworth Trust
Mrs L D Rope Third Charitable Settlement
The Rowlands Trust
The Jeremy and John Sacher Charitable Trust
Raymond and Beverly Sackler 1988 Foundation
The Sackler Trust
The Alan and Babette Sainsbury Charitable Fund

The Andrew Salvesen Charitable Trust
The Simpson Education and Conservation Trust
The C Paul Thackray General Charitable Trust
The Thompson Family Charitable Trust
The Waterloo Foundation
The Wellcome Trust
The Wilkinson Charitable Foundation
The Wolfson Family Charitable Trust
The Wolfson Foundation
The John K Young Endowment Fund

Engineering/ technology

The 1970 Trust
The Armourers' and Brasiers' Gauntlet Trust
The Cass Foundation
The Ernest Cook Trust
The James Dyson Foundation
Paul Hamlyn Foundation
The Indigo Trust
The Mountbatten Memorial Trust
The Kitty and Daniel Nabarro Charitable Trust
Open Gate
Ranworth Trust

Life sciences

The Big Lottery Fund
British Ornithologists' Union
The Ernest Cook Trust
William Dean Countryside and Educational Trust
The Dunn Family Charitable Trust
The Beryl Evetts and Robert Luff Animal Welfare Trust Limited
The Gatsby Charitable Foundation
The John Spedan Lewis Foundation
The Petplan Charitable Trust
The Andrew Salvesen Charitable Trust
The Simpson Education and Conservation Trust
The Thompson Family Charitable Trust
The Waterloo Foundation
The Wellcome Trust

Physical/earth sciences

*The Armourers' and Brasiers'
   Gauntlet Trust*
*Mrs L D Rope Third Charitable
   Settlement*
*The John K Young Endowment
   Fund*

Social sciences, policy and research

Age UK
British Institute at Ankara
CAF (Charities Aid Foundation)
The Keith Coombs Trust
*Itzchok Meyer Cymerman Trust
   Ltd*
*The Daiwa Anglo-Japanese
   Foundation*
eaga Charitable Trust
The Elmgrant Trust
*The Gatsby Charitable
   Foundation*
*The Robert Gavron Charitable
   Trust*
The Hadley Trust
The Harbour Foundation
*The Kenneth Hargreaves
   Charitable Trust*
Haskel Family Foundation
Houblon-Norman/George Fund
The Allen Lane Foundation
The LankellyChase Foundation
The Leverhulme Trust
*The Joseph Levy Charitable
   Foundation*
The Trust for London
*The London Housing
   Foundation*
James Madison Trust
The McDougall Trust
The Millfield House Foundation
*Monmouthshire County Council
   Welsh Church Act Fund*
*Frederick Mulder Charitable
   Trust*
*The Kitty and Daniel Nabarro
   Charitable Trust*
The Eleni Nakou Foundation
The Night Garden Charity
The Nuffield Foundation
The Polonsky Foundation
*The Joseph Rowntree
   Charitable Trust*
*The Joseph Rowntree
   Foundation*
The Steel Charitable Trust
The Sutasoma Trust
*The Nigel Vinson Charitable
   Trust*
War on Want
Webb Memorial Trust

Economics

Age UK
CAF (Charities Aid Foundation)
Houblon-Norman/George Fund

Political science

*The Gatsby Charitable
   Foundation*
The Allen Lane Foundation
James Madison Trust
The McDougall Trust
The Eleni Nakou Foundation
*The Joseph Rowntree
   Charitable Trust*
*The Joseph Rowntree
   Foundation*
Webb Memorial Trust

Social policy

Age UK
*The Gatsby Charitable
   Foundation*
*The Robert Gavron Charitable
   Trust*
*The Kenneth Hargreaves
   Charitable Trust*
Haskel Family Foundation
*The Joseph Levy Charitable
   Foundation*
The Trust for London
*The London Housing
   Foundation*
*Monmouthshire County Council
   Welsh Church Act Fund*
*Frederick Mulder Charitable
   Trust*
*The Kitty and Daniel Nabarro
   Charitable Trust*
The Nuffield Foundation
*The Joseph Rowntree
   Foundation*
Webb Memorial Trust

Social welfare

The 1970 Trust
The 1989 Willan Charitable
　Trust
The 29th May 1961 Charitable
　Trust
ABF The Soldiers' Charity
The Acacia Charitable Trust
The ACT Foundation
The Company of Actuaries'
　Charitable Trust Fund
The Ad Meliora Charitable
　Trust
The Sylvia Adams Charitable
　Trust
The Adamson Trust
The Adint Charitable Trust
Age Scotland
Age UK
The Agger Foundation
The Green and Lilian F M
　Ainsworth and Family
　Benevolent Fund
The Sylvia Aitken Charitable
　Trust
The Ajahma Charitable Trust
The Alborada Trust
The Alchemy Foundation
The Allen Lane Trust
The Pat Allsop Charitable Trust
The Almond Trust
Almondsbury Charity
The Ammco Trust
Viscount Amory's Charitable
　Trust
The Bryan and June Amos
　Foundation
The AMW Charitable Trust
The Andrew Anderson Trust
Andrews Charitable Trust
Philip Anker Trust
The Apax Foundation
The Appletree Trust
The John Apthorp Charity
The Arbib Foundation
Archbishop of Wales' Fund for
　Children
The Archer Trust
The Ardwick Trust
The Argus Appeal
The John Armitage Charitable
　Trust
The Armourers' and Brasiers'
　Gauntlet Trust
The Arsenal Foundation
The Artemis Charitable Trust
The Arts and Entertainment
　Charitable Trust
The Ashendene Trust
The Ashworth Charitable Trust
The Associated Country
　Women of the World
AstonMansfield Charitable
　Trust
The Astor Foundation
The Lord Austin Trust

The Avon and Somerset Police
　Community Trust
Awards for All
The Scott Bader
　Commonwealth Ltd
The Roy and Pixie Baker
　Charitable Trust
The Balcombe Charitable Trust
The Paul Balint Charitable
　Trust
The Albert Casanova Ballard
　Deceased Trust
The Ballinger Charitable Trust
The Balmore Trust
The Balney Charitable Trust
The Band Trust
The Bank of Scotland
　Foundation
The Barbour Foundation
Barchester Healthcare
　Foundation
The Barclay Foundation
The Barleycorn Trust
Lord Barnby's Foundation
Barnes Workhouse Fund
The Barnwood House Trust
Baruch Family Charitable Trust
The Batchworth Trust
The Bates Charitable Trust
BBC Children in Need
BCH Trust
The Jack and Ada Beattie
　Foundation
The Victoria and David
　Beckham Children's Charity
The John Beckwith Charitable
　Trust
The Peter Beckwith Charitable
　Trust
The Bedfordshire and Luton
　Community Foundation
The Beit Trust
The Bellahouston Bequest
　Fund
Bergqvist Charitable Trust
The Bestway Foundation
The Mason Bibby 1981 Trust
The Big Lottery Fund
Birmingham & Black Country
　Community Foundation
The Birmingham District
　Nursing Charitable Trust
The Sydney Black Charitable
　Trust
The BlackRock (UK) Charitable
　Trust
The Blagrave Trust
The Blanchminster Trust
The Blandford Lake Trust
The Neville and Elaine Blond
　Charitable Trust
The Bluston Charitable
　Settlement
The Boltini Trust
The Boltons Trust
The Booth Charities

The Boots Charitable Trust
Salo Bordon Charitable Trust
The Bothwell Charitable Trust
P G and N J Boulton Trust
The A H and E Boulton Trust
The Anthony Bourne
　Foundation
The Bowerman Charitable
　Trust
The Liz and Terry Bramall
　Foundation
The Bridging Fund Charitable
　Trust
The Bristol Charities
John Bristow and Thomas
　Mason Trust
British Humane Association
The Bromley Trust
The David Brooke Charity
The Rory and Elizabeth Brooks
　Foundation
Bill Brown 1998 Charitable
　Trust
The Bruntwood Charity
Brushmill Ltd
Buckland Charitable Trust
The E F Bulmer Benevolent
　Fund
Bumba Foundation
The Burden Trust
The Clara E Burgess Charity
The Arnold Burton 1998
　Charitable Trust
The Burton Breweries
　Charitable Trust
The Worshipful Company of
　Butchers General Charities
The Noel Buxton Trust
The James Caan Foundation
Edward Cadbury Charitable
　Trust
The G W Cadbury Charitable
　Trust
The William A Cadbury
　Charitable Trust
The Edward and Dorothy
　Cadbury Trust
The Barrow Cadbury Trust and
　the Barrow Cadbury Fund
CAFOD (Catholic Agency for
　Overseas Development)
Calouste Gulbenkian
　Foundation – UK Branch
The Calpe Trust
The Cambridgeshire
　Community Foundation
The Campden Charities
　Trustee
The Carpenter Charitable Trust
The Carr-Gregory Trust
The Leslie Mary Carter
　Charitable Trust
Carter's Educational
　Foundation
The Cattanach Charitable Trust

The Wilfrid and Constance Cave Foundation
The Cayo Foundation
Celtic Charity Fund
The Chapman Charitable Trust
John William Chapman's Charitable Trust
Charitworth Limited
The Chelsea Square 1994 Trust
The Cheruby Trust
Chesterhill Charitable Trust
The Chipping Sodbury Town Lands Charity
The Jimmy Choo Foundation
The Chrimes Family Charitable Trust
Christadelphian Samaritan Fund
Christian Response to Eastern Europe
Christie Foundation
Chrysalis Trust
The Church and Community Fund
Church Urban Fund
The City Bridge Trust
Clark Bradbury Charitable Trust
The Cleopatra Trust
Miss V L Clore's 1967 Charitable Trust
Closehelm Limited
The Clothworkers' Foundation
Richard Cloudesley's Charity
The Clover Trust
The Robert Clutterbuck Charitable Trust
The Coalfields Regeneration Trust
The John Coates Charitable Trust
The Denise Cohen Charitable Trust
The Vivienne and Samuel Cohen Charitable Trust
The R and S Cohen Foundation
The Cole Charitable Trust
The Coltstaple Trust
Colyer-Fergusson Charitable Trust
Comic Relief
The Douglas Compton James Charitable Trust
The Congleton Inclosure Trust
The Consolidated Charities for the Infirm Merchant Taylors' Company
The Cooks Charity
The Co-operative Foundation
The Helen Jean Cope Trust
The J Reginald Corah Foundation Fund

The Gershon Coren Charitable Foundation (also known as The Muriel and Gus Coren Charitable Foundation)
Michael Cornish Charitable Trust
The Evan Cornish Foundation
Cornwall Community Foundation
The Duke of Cornwall's Benevolent Fund
The Corona Charitable Trust
The Cotton Trust
County Durham Community Foundation
Coutts Charitable Foundation
The John Cowan Foundation
The Lord Cozens-Hardy Trust
The Craps Charitable Trust
Michael Crawford Children's Charity
The Crerar Hotels Trust
Criffel Charitable Trust
The Violet and Milo Cripps Charitable Trust
The Croydon Relief in Need Charities
Cruden Foundation Ltd
The Ronald Cruickshanks Foundation
Cullum Family Trust
Cumbria Community Foundation
The D J H Currie Memorial Trust
Itzchok Meyer Cymerman Trust Ltd
Oizer Dalim Trust
The Dr and Mrs A Darlington Charitable Trust
Baron Davenport's Charity
The Davidson (Nairn) Charitable Trust
The Davidson Family Charitable Trust
The Hamilton Davies Trust
The De Brye Charitable Trust
Peter De Haan Charitable Trust
The Debmar Benevolent Trust
The Denman Charitable Trust
Derbyshire Community Foundation
The J N Derbyshire Trust
The Desmond Foundation
The Sandy Dewhirst Charitable Trust
The Dibden Allotments Fund
The Peter Alan Dickson Foundation
Disability Aid Fund (The Roger and Jean Jefcoate Trust)
Dischma Charitable Trust
The Djanogly Foundation
The Novak Djokovic Foundation (UK) Limited

The DM Charitable Trust
The Derek and Eileen Dodgson Foundation
The Dorcas Trust
Dorset Community Foundation
The Dorus Trust
The Double 'O' Charity Ltd
The R M Douglas Charitable Trust
The Drapers' Charitable Fund
The Royal Foundation of the Duke and Duchess of Cambridge and Prince Harry
The Dulverton Trust
The Dumbreck Charity
The W E Dunn Trust
The James Dyson Foundation
The Eagle Charity Trust
East End Community Foundation
Eastern Counties Educational Trust Limited
The Ebenezer Trust
The EBM Charitable Trust
The Gilbert and Eileen Edgar Foundation
Gilbert Edgar Trust
Edge Fund
Edinburgh Children's Holiday Fund
Edinburgh Trust No 2 Account
Edinburgh Voluntary Organisations' Trust Funds (EVOT)
Edupoor Limited
Dr Edwards Bishop King's Fulham Endowment Fund
The W G Edwards Charitable Foundation
The George Elias Charitable Trust
The Gerald Palmer Eling Trust Company
The Maud Elkington Charitable Trust
The Ellerdale Trust
The John Ellerman Foundation
The Edith Maud Ellis 1985 Charitable Trust
The Emerton-Christie Charity
The Emilienne Charitable Trust
The Englefield Charitable Trust
The Enkalon Foundation
The Epigoni Trust
The Equilibrium Foundation
The Eranda Foundation
The Ericson Trust
The Ernest Hecht Charitable Foundation
The Essendon Charitable Trust
Essex Community Foundation
Euro Charity Trust
Sir John Evelyn's Charity
The Eventhall Family Charitable Trust
The Eveson Charitable Trust

The Exilarch's Foundation
The Expat Foundation
Extonglen Limited
F C Charitable Trust
Esmée Fairbairn Foundation
The Fairway Trust
The Family Rich Charities Trust
Famos Foundation Trust
The Lord Faringdon Charitable Trust
Samuel William Farmer Trust
The Fassnidge Memorial Trust
The February Foundation
The George Fentham Birmingham Charity
Elizabeth Ferguson Charitable Trust Fund
The Doris Field Charitable Trust
Fife Council/Common Good Funds and Trusts
Filey Foundation Ltd
Dixie Rose Findlay Charitable Trust
The Sir John Fisher Foundation
Fisherbeck Charitable Trust
The Fishmongers' Company's Charitable Trust
The Fitton Trust
The Ian Fleming Charitable Trust
Florence's Charitable Trust
The Flow Foundation
The Football Association National Sports Centre Trust
The Forbes Charitable Foundation
The Forces Trust (Working Name)
Ford Britain Trust
The Oliver Ford Charitable Trust
The Forest Hill Charitable Trust
The Lady Forester Trust
The Foresters' Fund for Children
The Foresters' Charity Stewards UK Trust
Forever Manchester (The Community Foundation for Greater Manchester)
The Forman Hardy Charitable Trust
The Donald Forrester Trust
The Fort Foundation
The Four Lanes Trust
Sydney E Franklin Deceased's New Second Charity
The Jill Franklin Trust
The Gordon Fraser Charitable Trust
The Hugh Fraser Foundation
The Joseph Strong Frazer Trust
The Freemasons' Grand Charity

The Thomas Freke and Lady Norton Charity Trust
The Freshgate Trust Foundation
Friends of Biala Limited
Friends of Muir Group
The Frognal Trust
The Patrick & Helena Frost Foundation
Maurice Fry Charitable Trust
The Fuserna Foundation General Charitable Trust
The G D Charitable Trust
Gamlen Charitable Trust
The Gamma Trust
The Gannochy Trust
The Ganzoni Charitable Trust
Garthgwynion Charities
Garvan Limited
The Gatsby Charitable Foundation
Gatwick Airport Community Trust
The Robert Gavron Charitable Trust
The Generations Foundation
The Steven Gerrard Foundation
The Gibbons Family Trust
The David Gibbons Foundation
The Gibbs Charitable Trust
Simon Gibson Charitable Trust
The Girdlers' Company Charitable Trust
The B and P Glasser Charitable Trust
The Glass-House Trust
The Sydney and Phyllis Goldberg Memorial Charitable Trust
The Jack Goldhill Charitable Trust
The Goldsmiths' Company Charity
The Goodman Foundation
The Mike Gooley Trailfinders Charity
The Gosling Foundation Limited
The Hemraj Goyal Foundation
A and S Graham Charitable Trust
Grand Charitable Trust of the Order of Women Freemasons
Grantham Yorke Trust
The Gordon Gray Trust
The Kenneth & Susan Green Charitable Foundation
The Green Hall Foundation
Greggs Foundation
The Grimmitt Trust
The Bishop of Guildford's Foundation
The Guildry Incorporation of Perth
The Gunter Charitable Trust

The Gur Trust
Dr Guthrie's Association
The H and M Charitable Trust
H C D Memorial Fund
H C Foundation
The H P Charitable Trust
The Hackney Parochial Charities
The Hadfield Trust
The Hadley Trust
The Hadrian Trust
The Alfred Haines Charitable Trust
E F and M G Hall Charitable Trust
Robert Hall Charity
Sue Hammerson Charitable Trust
Hampshire and Isle of Wight Community Foundation
The Hampstead Wells and Campden Trust
Hampton Fuel Allotment Charity
The W A Handley Charitable Trust
Beatrice Hankey Foundation Limited
The Hanley Trust (1987)
The Kathleen Hannay Memorial Charity
The Haramead Trust
Miss K M Harbinson's Charitable Trust
Harbo Charities Limited
The Harborne Parish Lands Charity
The Harbour Charitable Trust
The Harbour Foundation
The Harding Trust
William Harding's Charity
The Hargrave Foundation
The Kenneth Hargreaves Charitable Trust
The Harpur Trust
The Harris Charitable Trust
The Harris Charity
The Harrison and Potter Trust
The Alfred And Peggy Harvey Charitable Trust
Hasluck Charitable Trust
The Dorothy Hay-Bolton Charitable Trust
The Charles Hayward Foundation
The Headley Trust
May Hearnshaw's Charity
The Heathcoat Trust
The Hedley Foundation
The H J Heinz Company Limited Charitable Trust
The Helping Foundation
The Hemby Trust
The Christina Mary Hendrie Trust for Scottish and Canadian Charities

Henley Educational Trust (formerley Henley Educational Charity)

Philip Henman Trust

The G D Herbert Charitable Trust

The Hertfordshire Community Foundation

The Hesslewood Children's Trust (Hull Seamen's and General Orphanage)

The P and C Hickinbotham Charitable Trust

Alan Edward Higgs Charity

The High Sheriff's Police Trust for the County of West Midlands (Building Blocks)

The Hilden Charitable Fund

The Charles Littlewood Hill Trust

The Hillier Trust

The Hilmarnan Charitable Trust

Lady Hind Trust

Hinduja Foundation

Hobson Charity Limited

The J G Hogg Charitable Trust

John Holford's Charity

The Edward Holt Trust

The Holywood Trust

The Homelands Charitable Trust

The Homestead Charitable Trust

Hope for Youth (NI)

HopMarket Charity

The Horizon Foundation

The Horne Foundation

The Horne Trust

The Hornsey Parochial Charities

The Reta Lila Howard Foundation

HTA Sheba Foundation UK

The Huddersfield Common Good Trust

Human Relief Foundation

The Humanitarian Trust

The Michael and Shirley Hunt Charitable Trust

The Albert Hunt Trust

Miss Agnes H Hunter's Trust

Huntingdon Freemen's Trust

The Nani Huyu Charitable Trust

The Hyde Charitable Trust

I G O Foundation Limited

Impetus – The Private Equity Foundation (Impetus – PEF)

The Inman Charity

The Inner London Magistrates Court Poor Box and Feeder Charity

Investream Charitable Trust

The Ireland Fund of Great Britain

The Irish Youth Foundation (UK) Ltd (incorporating The Lawlor Foundation)

The ITF Seafarers Trust

The Ithaca Trust

J A R Charitable Trust

The Jabbs Foundation

The Ruth and Lionel Jacobson Trust (Second Fund) No 2

Jaffe Family Relief Fund

The Jarman Charitable Trust

The Barbara Joyce Jarrald Charitable Trust

The John Jarrold Trust

The Jasper Conran Foundation

The Jeffrey Charitable Trust

The Jenour Foundation

Jesus Hospital Charity

Jewish Child's Day

The Jigsaw Foundation

The Nicholas Joels Charitable Trust

The Lillie Johnson Charitable Trust

The Johnson Foundation

The Johnnie Johnson Trust

The Johnson Wax Ltd Charitable Trust

The Jones 1986 Charitable Trust

The Cyril and Eve Jumbo Charitable Trust

The Anton Jurgens Charitable Trust

The Kalou Foundation

The Michael and Ilse Katz Foundation

The Emmanuel Kaye Foundation

The Kelly Family Charitable Trust

Kelsick's Educational Foundation

The KempWelch Charitable Trust

William Kendall's Charity (Wax Chandlers' Company)

Kent Community Foundation

The Peter Kershaw Trust

The Mr & Mrs Paul Killik Charitable Trust

The Kingsbury Charity

The Mary Kinross Charitable Trust

Kirkley Poor's Lands Estate

Ernest Kleinwort Charitable Trust

The Sir James Knott Trust

Kollel and Co. Limited

The KPMG Foundation

The Kreditor Charitable Trust

The Kreitman Foundation

The Neil Kreitman Foundation

The Heinz, Anna and Carol Kroch Foundation

The Kyte Charitable Trust

L P W Limited

John Laing Charitable Trust

Maurice and Hilda Laing Charitable Trust

The Christopher Laing Foundation

The David Laing Foundation

The Beatrice Laing Trust

The Lambert Charitable Trust

Community Foundation for Lancashire

LWS Lancashire Environmental Fund Limited

Duchy of Lancaster Benevolent Fund

LandAid Charitable Trust

The Allen Lane Foundation

Langdale Trust

The Langley Charitable Trust

The LankellyChase Foundation

The R J Larg Family Charitable Trust

The Lark Trust

Laslett's (Hinton) Charity

Mrs F B Laurence Charitable Trust

The Kathleen Laurence Trust

The Edgar E Lawley Foundation

The Lawson Beckman Charitable Trust

The Raymond and Blanche Lawson Charitable Trust

The William Leech Charity

Leeds Building Society Charitable Foundation

The Leeds Community Foundation

The Kennedy Leigh Charitable Trust

The Leigh Trust

Mrs Vera Leigh's Charity

The Mark Leonard Trust

The Leverhulme Trade Charities Trust

Lord Leverhulme's Charitable Trust

The Joseph Levy Charitable Foundation

Lewis Family Charitable Trust

John Lewis Partnership General Community Fund

Liberum Foundation

Lifeline 4 Kids

The Limbourne Trust

The Linbury Trust

Lindenleaf Charitable Trust

The Enid Linder Foundation

The Lister Charitable Trust

The Andrew and Mary Elizabeth Little Charitable Trust

The Second Joseph Aaron Littman Foundation

The Elaine and Angus Lloyd Charitable Trust

Lloyd's Charities Trust

Lloyds Bank Foundation for England and Wales
Lloyds Bank Foundation for Northern Ireland
Lloyds Bank Foundation for the Channel Islands
Lloyds TSB Foundation for Scotland
Localtrent Ltd
The Trust for London
London Catalyst
The London Community Foundation
The London Housing Foundation
The Lotus Foundation
The C L Loyd Charitable Trust
The Marie Helen Luen Charitable Trust
Henry Lumley Charitable Trust
Paul Lunn-Rockliffe Charitable Trust
The Lynn Foundation
The Lynwood Trust
John Lyon's Charity
The Lyons Charitable Trust
The M and C Trust
The R S Macdonald Charitable Trust
The Macfarlane Walker Trust
The MacRobert Trust
Ian Mactaggart Trust
The Magdalen and Lasher Charity
Magdalen Hospital Trust
The Magen Charitable Trust
Mageni Trust
The Mahavir Trust
Malbin Trust
Man Group plc Charitable Trust
The Manifold Charitable Trust
R W Mann Trust
The Leslie and Lilian Manning Trust
The Manoukian Charitable Foundation
Maranatha Christian Trust
Marbeh Torah Trust
The Stella and Alexander Margulies Charitable Trust
Market Harborough and The Bowdens Charity
The Ann and David Marks Foundation
The Hilda and Samuel Marks Foundation
The Marr-Munning Trust
The Michael Marsh Charitable Trust
The Marsh Christian Trust
The Charlotte Marshall Charitable Trust
The Nora Joan Marshall Charitable Trust
Sir George Martin Trust

John Martin's Charity
The John Mason Family Trust
Matliwala Family Charitable Trust
The Maxwell Family Foundation
Evelyn May Trust
The Robert McAlpine Foundation
The McKenna Charitable Trust
The Mears Foundation
The Medlock Charitable Trust
Melodor Limited
Melow Charitable Trust
The Menzies Charity Foundation
Brian Mercer Charitable Trust
The Mercers' Charitable Foundation
Merchant Navy Welfare Board
The Merchant Taylors' Company Charities Fund
The Merchants' House of Glasgow
Community Foundation for Merseyside
The Zachary Merton and George Woofindin Convalescent Trust
The Tony Metherell Charitable Trust
The Metropolitan Masonic Charity
Mi Yu Foundation
Mickleham Charitable Trust
Gerald Micklem Charitable Trust
Midhurst Pensions Trust
Miles Trust for the Putney and Roehampton Community
Millennium Stadium Charitable Trust
The Ronald Miller Foundation
The Mills Charity
The Millward Charitable Trust
Milton Keynes Community Foundation
The Peter Minet Trust
The Mirfield Educational Charity
The Mishcon Family Charitable Trust
The Mitchell Charitable Trust
The Mizpah Trust
The Modiano Charitable Trust
The Moette Charitable Trust
The D C Moncrieff Charitable Trust
Monmouthshire County Council Welsh Church Act Fund
The Monument Trust
John Moores Foundation
The Morel Charitable Trust
The Morgan Charitable Foundation
The Morgan Foundation

Morgan Stanley International Foundation
S C and M E Morland's Charitable Trust
The Morris Charitable Trust
G M Morrison Charitable Trust
Vyoel Moshe Charitable Trust
The Moss Charitable Trust
The Robert and Margaret Moss Charitable Trust
The Moss Family Charitable Trust
Mosselson Charitable Trust
Mothercare Group Foundation
Moto in the Community
Mountbatten Festival of Music
The Mountbatten Memorial Trust
Mrs Waterhouse Charitable Trust
The Mugdock Children's Trust
The George Müller Charitable Trust
The Edith Murphy Foundation
Murphy-Neumann Charity Company Limited
Peter John Murray Trust
Muslim Hands
The Mutual Trust Group
MW (CL) Foundation
MW (GK) Foundation
MW (HO) Foundation
MW (RH) Foundation
The Kitty and Daniel Nabarro Charitable Trust
The Nadezhda Charitable Trust
The Janet Nash Charitable Settlement
The National Express Foundation
The Nationwide Foundation
Needham Market and Barking Welfare Charities
The Worshipful Company of Needlemakers' Charitable Fund
The New Appeals Organisation for the City and County of Nottingham
Newby Trust Limited
Newpier Charity Ltd
Nominet Charitable Foundation
The Norda Trust
Norfolk Community Foundation
The Normanby Charitable Trust
The Northampton Municipal Church Charities
The Northampton Queen's Institute Relief in Sickness Fund
The Earl of Northampton's Charity
Northamptonshire Community Foundation
The Northcott Devon Foundation

The Community Foundation for Northern Ireland
The Northern Rock Foundation
The Northmoor Trust
The Northumberland Village Homes Trust
The Norton Foundation
The Norton Rose Charitable Foundation
The Norwich Town Close Estate Charity
The Nottingham General Dispensary
The Nottingham Gordon Memorial Trust for Boys and Girls
Nottinghamshire Community Foundation
The Nottinghamshire Miners' Welfare Trust Fund
The Nuffield Foundation
The Father O'Mahoney Memorial Trust
The Oakdale Trust
The Oakley Charitable Trust
The Ofenheim Charitable Trust
Ogilvie Charities Deed No.2 (including the Charity of Mary Catherine Ford Smith)
The Oldham Foundation
The Olga Charitable Trust
Open Gate
The O'Sullivan Family Charitable Trust
The Owen Family Trust
The Paget Charitable Trust
The Paladin Vince-Odozi Charitable Trust
Eleanor Palmer Trust
The Panacea Society
The Paphitis Charitable Trust
The Park House Charitable Trust
The Parthenon Trust
The Constance Paterson Charitable Trust
Miss M E Swinton Paterson's Charitable Trust
The Harry Payne Trust
The Peacock Charitable Trust
The Pears Family Charitable Foundation
The Pedmore Sporting Club Trust Fund
Pegasus (Stanley) Trust
People's Postcode Trust
The Persula Foundation
The Jack Petchey Foundation
The Phillips Charitable Trust
The Phillips Family Charitable Trust
The Pickwell Foundation
The Bernard Piggott Charitable Trust
The Pilgrim Trust

The Elise Pilkington Charitable Trust
The Pilkington Charities Fund
The Austin and Hope Pilkington Trust
The Col W W Pilkington Will Trusts The General Charity Fund
G S Plaut Charitable Trust Limited
The Pollywally Charitable Trust
The John Porter Charitable Trust
The Porter Foundation
Porticus UK
The Portishead Nautical Trust
The J E Posnansky Charitable Trust
The Mary Potter Convent Hospital Trust
The Praebendo Charitable Foundation
The Premier League Charitable Fund
The Tom Press Charitable Foundation
The Lucy Price Relief-in-Need Charity
Sir John Priestman Charity Trust
Princess Anne's Charities
The Puri Foundation
Quartet Community Foundation
Queen Mary's Roehampton Trust
The Queen's Silver Jubilee Trust
Quothquan Trust
R S Charitable Trust
The Monica Rabagliati Charitable Trust
The Racing Foundation
The Rainford Trust
The Rank Foundation Limited
The Joseph Rank Trust
The Fanny Rapaport Charitable Settlement
The Rashbass Family Trust
The Ratcliff Pension Charity
The E L Rathbone Charitable Trust
The Eleanor Rathbone Charitable Trust
The Sigrid Rausing Trust
The Ravensdale Trust
The Rayne Foundation
The Rayne Trust
The Sir James Reckitt Charity
Eva Reckitt Trust Fund
The C A Redfern Charitable Foundation
The Reed Foundation
Relief Fund for Romania Limited
The Rhododendron Trust

The Rhondda Cynon Taff Welsh Church Acts Fund
The Sir Cliff Richard Charitable Trust
The Richmond Parish Lands Charity
The Ripple Effect Foundation
The River Farm Foundation
Rix-Thompson-Rothenberg Foundation
Thomas Roberts Trust
The Robertson Trust
Robyn Charitable Trust
The Roddick Foundation
The Sir James Roll Charitable Trust
The C A Rookes Charitable Trust
Mrs L D Rope Third Charitable Settlement
The Rosca Trust
The Cecil Rosen Foundation
The Rothera Charitable Settlement
The Rotherwick Foundation
The Rothley Trust
The Christopher Rowbotham Charitable Trust
The Rowland Family Foundation
The Rowlands Trust
The Joseph Rowntree Foundation
Royal British Legion
Royal Docks Trust (London)
Royal Masonic Trust for Girls and Boys
The RRAF Charitable Trust
Ryklow Charitable Trust 1992 (also known as A B Williamson Charitable Trust)
The Michael Harry Sacher Trust
Erach and Roshan Sadri Foundation
The Saga Charitable Trust
Saint Sarkis Charity Trust
The Saintbury Trust
The Saints and Sinners Trust
Salters' Charitable Foundation
The Andrew Salvesen Charitable Trust
Coral Samuel Charitable Trust
The Peter Samuel Charitable Trust
The Sandra Charitable Trust
The Peter Saunders Trust
Schroder Charity Trust
Foundation Scotland
Scott (Eredine) Charitable Trust
The Francis C Scott Charitable Trust
The Frieda Scott Charitable Trust

The Sir James and Lady Scott Trust

Scottish Coal Industry Special Welfare Fund

The Scottish International Education Trust

The Scouloudi Foundation

Seafarers UK (King George's Fund for Sailors)

The Searle Charitable Trust

The Samuel Sebba Charitable Trust

Leslie Sell Charitable Trust

Sellata Ltd

The Seneca Trust

The Ayrton Senna Foundation

The Shanley Charitable Trust

The Shears Foundation

The Sheffield and District Hospital Services Charitable Fund

The Sheldon Trust

The Sylvia and Colin Shepherd Charitable Trust

The Archie Sherman Cardiff Foundation

The Archie Sherman Charitable Trust

The Shetland Charitable Trust

The Shipwrights' Company Charitable Fund

The Shoe Zone Trust

The J A Shone Memorial Trust

Community Foundation for Shropshire and Telford

The Mary Elizabeth Siebel Charity

The Simmons & Simmons Charitable Foundation

Six Point Foundation

The Skelton Bounty

The SMB Charitable Trust

The Smith & Pinching Charitable Trust

The Mrs Smith and Mount Trust

The N Smith Charitable Settlement

The Henry Smith Charity

The Leslie Smith Foundation

Philip Smith's Charitable Trust

Smithcorp Charitable Trust

The Snowball Trust

The Sobell Foundation

Social Business Trust (Scale-Up)

The E C Sosnow Charitable Trust

The Souter Charitable Trust

The South Square Trust

The W F Southall Trust

R H Southern Trust

Sparquote Limited

Spears-Stutz Charitable Trust

Split Infinitive Trust

Rosalyn and Nicholas Springer Charitable Trust

Springfields Employees' Medical Research and Charity Trust Fund

St Hilda's Trust

St James's Place Foundation

The St Laurence Relief In Need Trust

St Michael's and All Saints' Charities Relief Branch (The Church Houses Relief in Need Charity)

St Monica Trust

The Stafford Trust

The Stanley Foundation Ltd

The Peter Stebbings Memorial Charity

The Steel Charitable Trust

Stevenson Family's Charitable Trust

The Stewarts Law Foundation

The Stokenchurch Educational Charity

The M J C Stone Charitable Trust

The Stone Family Foundation

Stratford upon Avon Town Trust

The W O Street Charitable Foundation

Sueberry Ltd

Suffolk Community Foundation

The Summerfield Charitable Trust

Community Foundation for Surrey

The Sussex Community Foundation

Sutton Coldfield Charitable Trust

Swan Mountain Trust

The John Swire (1989) Charitable Trust

The Gay and Keith Talbot Trust

Talteg Ltd

The Lady Tangye Charitable Trust

The Tanner Trust

C B and H H Taylor 1984 Trust

The Connie and Albert Taylor Charitable Trust

The Taylor Family Foundation

The Tedworth Charitable Trust

Tesco Charity Trust

The C Paul Thackray General Charitable Trust

The Len Thomson Charitable Trust

The Sue Thomson Foundation

The Sir Jules Thorn Charitable Trust

The Three Oaks Trust

Mrs R P Tindall's Charitable Trust

The Tisbury Telegraph Trust

The Tolkien Trust

The Tompkins Foundation

The Tory Family Foundation

The Towry Law Charitable Trust (also known as the Castle Educational Trust)

Annie Tranmer Charitable Trust

The Trefoil Trust

The Triangle Trust (1949) Fund

The True Colours Trust

Truemart Limited

The James Tudor Foundation

The Tudor Trust

TVML Foundation

Two Ridings Community Foundation

The Tyche Charitable Trust

Community Foundation Serving Tyne and Wear and Northumberland

Trustees of Tzedakah

Ulster Garden Villages Ltd

The Underwood Trust

The Valentine Charitable Trust

The Valiant Charitable Trust

The Albert Van Den Bergh Charitable Trust

The Van Neste Foundation

The Vardy Foundation

The Variety Club Children's Charity

The William and Patricia Venton Charitable Trust

Roger Vere Foundation

Vintners' Gifts Charity

The Vodafone Foundation

Volant Charitable Trust

Voluntary Action Fund (VAF)

Wade's Charity

The Wakefield and Tetley Trust

Wakeham Trust

The Community Foundation in Wales

Wales Council for Voluntary Action

The Thomas Wall Trust

The Ward Blenkinsop Trust

The Waterloo Foundation

The Wates Foundation

Blyth Watson Charitable Trust

The Howard Watson Symington Memorial Charity

John Watson's Trust

The Weavers' Company Benevolent Fund

The Weinstein Foundation

The James Weir Foundation

The Wessex Youth Trust

West Yorkshire Police Community Trust

The Westcroft Trust

The Westminster Foundation

The Garfield Weston Foundation

The Simon Whitbread Charitable Trust

White Stuff Foundation
The Whittlesey Charity
The William Barrow's Charity
The Charity of William Williams
Williams Serendipity Trust
The HDH Wills 1965
　Charitable Trust
The Wilson Foundation
J and J R Wilson Trust
The Community Foundation for
　Wiltshire and Swindon
The Francis Winham
　Foundation
The Michael and Anna Wix
　Charitable Trust
The Wixamtree Trust
The Maurice Wohl Charitable
　Foundation
The Wolfson Foundation
The Wood Family Trust
Woodlands Green Ltd
Woodlands Trust
Woodroffe Benton Foundation
The Woodward Charitable
　Trust
Worcester Municipal Charities
The Wragge and Co. Charitable
　Trust
The Diana Edgson Wright
　Charitable Trust
The Matthews Wrightson
　Charity Trust
Miss E B Wrightson's
　Charitable Settlement
The Wyseliot Charitable Trust
The Yapp Charitable Trust
The Yorkshire Dales
　Millennium Trust
The William Allen Young
　Charitable Trust
Youth United Foundation
Zephyr Charitable Trust
The Marjorie and Arnold Ziff
　Charitable Foundation
The Zochonis Charitable Trust
Zurich Community Trust (UK)
　Limited

Community care services

The 1989 Willan Charitable
　Trust
The Company of Actuaries'
　Charitable Trust Fund
Age Scotland
Age UK
The Green and Lilian F M
　Ainsworth and Family
　Benevolent Fund
Archbishop of Wales' Fund for
　Children
The Archer Trust
The Artemis Charitable Trust
The Astor Foundation

The Avon and Somerset Police
　Community Trust
The Ballinger Charitable Trust
The Barnwood House Trust
The Victoria and David
　Beckham Children's Charity
The Big Lottery Fund
The Birmingham District
　Nursing Charitable Trust
The Anthony Bourne
　Foundation
John Bristow and Thomas
　Mason Trust
The David Brooke Charity
The Rory and Elizabeth Brooks
　Foundation
The Burton Breweries
　Charitable Trust
The Noel Buxton Trust
Calouste Gulbenkian
　Foundation – UK Branch
Carter's Educational
　Foundation
The Cattanach Charitable Trust
The J Reginald Corah
　Foundation Fund
The John Cowan Foundation
The D J H Currie Memorial
　Trust
Baron Davenport's Charity
The Hamilton Davies Trust
Disability Aid Fund (The Roger
　and Jean Jefcoate Trust)
The Dulverton Trust
The Dumbreck Charity
Gilbert Edgar Trust
Edinburgh Children's Holiday
　Fund
The Eveson Charitable Trust
Esmée Fairbairn Foundation
The Fairway Trust
The Family Rich Charities Trust
Samuel William Farmer Trust
The Fassnidge Memorial Trust
The February Foundation
Elizabeth Ferguson Charitable
　Trust Fund
The Forbes Charitable
　Foundation
The Oliver Ford Charitable
　Trust
The Foresters' Fund for
　Children
The Jill Franklin Trust
The Gordon Fraser Charitable
　Trust
The Freshgate Trust
　Foundation
The Frognal Trust
The Ganzoni Charitable Trust
The Gatsby Charitable
　Foundation
Gatwick Airport Community
　Trust
The Girdlers' Company
　Charitable Trust

The Glass-House Trust
The Gosling Foundation
　Limited
Grantham Yorke Trust
The Gordon Gray Trust
The Green Hall Foundation
The Grimmitt Trust
Dr Guthrie's Association
The Hadrian Trust
The Alfred Haines Charitable
　Trust
Robert Hall Charity
The W A Handley Charitable
　Trust
The Haramead Trust
The Harbour Charitable Trust
The Kenneth Hargreaves
　Charitable Trust
The Harris Charitable Trust
The Harris Charity
The Alfred And Peggy Harvey
　Charitable Trust
The Charles Hayward
　Foundation
May Hearnshaw's Charity
The H J Heinz Company
　Limited Charitable Trust
The Hemby Trust
The Christina Mary Hendrie
　Trust for Scottish and
　Canadian Charities
Henley Educational Trust
　(formerley Henley
　Educational Charity)
Philip Henman Trust
The Hesslewood Children's
　Trust (Hull Seamen's and
　General Orphanage)
The High Sheriff's Police Trust
　for the County of West
　Midlands (Building Blocks)
The Hilden Charitable Fund
The Holywood Trust
Hope for Youth (NI)
The Horne Trust
The Reta Lila Howard
　Foundation
The Huddersfield Common
　Good Trust
Miss Agnes H Hunter's Trust
Huntingdon Freemen's Trust
The Hyde Charitable Trust
Impetus – The Private Equity
　Foundation (Impetus – PEF)
The Irish Youth Foundation
　(UK) Ltd (incorporating The
　Lawlor Foundation)
The Ruth and Lionel Jacobson
　Trust (Second Fund) No 2
The Jarman Charitable Trust
The Barbara Joyce Jarrald
　Charitable Trust
The Jeffrey Charitable Trust
Jewish Child's Day
The Lillie Johnson Charitable
　Trust

The Johnnie Johnson Trust
The Jones 1986 Charitable Trust
The Kelly Family Charitable Trust
Kelsick's Educational Foundation
The KempWelch Charitable Trust
The Mary Kinross Charitable Trust
The KPMG Foundation
John Laing Charitable Trust
Duchy of Lancaster Benevolent Fund
The Allen Lane Foundation
The Lark Trust
The Edgar E Lawley Foundation
The Raymond and Blanche Lawson Charitable Trust
The William Leech Charity
Leeds Building Society Charitable Foundation
The Mark Leonard Trust
Lord Leverhulme's Charitable Trust
The Joseph Levy Charitable Foundation
Lloyds Bank Foundation for Northern Ireland
Lloyds Bank Foundation for the Channel Islands
London Catalyst
The Lotus Foundation
John Lyon's Charity
The MacRobert Trust
Magdalen Hospital Trust
Mageni Trust
Market Harborough and The Bowdens Charity
Sir George Martin Trust
The Mears Foundation
The Merchants' House of Glasgow
Community Foundation for Merseyside
The Zachary Merton and George Woofindin Convalescent Trust
Gerald Micklem Charitable Trust
Miles Trust for the Putney and Roehampton Community
The Mirfield Educational Charity
Monmouthshire County Council Welsh Church Act Fund
The Monument Trust
John Moores Foundation
The Mugdock Children's Trust
The George Müller Charitable Trust
The Kitty and Daniel Nabarro Charitable Trust
The Nadezhda Charitable Trust

The National Express Foundation
The Northcott Devon Foundation
The Northern Rock Foundation
The Nottingham General Dispensary
The Nottingham Gordon Memorial Trust for Boys and Girls
The Nuffield Foundation
The Paget Charitable Trust
The Panacea Society
The Paphitis Charitable Trust
The Constance Paterson Charitable Trust
Miss M E Swinton Paterson's Charitable Trust
The Pears Family Charitable Foundation
The Persula Foundation
The Jack Petchey Foundation
The Bernard Piggott Charitable Trust
The Pilgrim Trust
The Pilkington Charities Fund
G S Plaut Charitable Trust Limited
The Portishead Nautical Trust
The Mary Potter Convent Hospital Trust
The Lucy Price Relief-in-Need Charity
The Monica Rabagliati Charitable Trust
The Rank Foundation Limited
The Rayne Foundation
The Reed Foundation
Relief Fund for Romania Limited
The Rhondda Cynon Taff Welsh Church Acts Fund
The Richmond Parish Lands Charity
Rix-Thompson-Rothenberg Foundation
The Robertson Trust
The C A Rookes Charitable Trust
Mrs L D Rope Third Charitable Settlement
The Rothley Trust
The Rowlands Trust
Ryklow Charitable Trust 1992 (also known as A B Williamson Charitable Trust)
The Michael Harry Sacher Trust
The Saintbury Trust
The Andrew Salvesen Charitable Trust
The Sandra Charitable Trust
The Francis C Scott Charitable Trust
Scottish Coal Industry Special Welfare Fund

Seafarers UK (King George's Fund for Sailors)
The Searle Charitable Trust
Leslie Sell Charitable Trust
The Shears Foundation
The Sheldon Trust
The Sylvia and Colin Shepherd Charitable Trust
The Shipwrights' Company Charitable Fund
Community Foundation for Shropshire and Telford
The Mary Elizabeth Siebel Charity
The Mrs Smith and Mount Trust
The Leslie Smith Foundation
The Snowball Trust
St Monica Trust
The Connie and Albert Taylor Charitable Trust
The Taylor Family Foundation
The Tedworth Charitable Trust
The Sue Thomson Foundation
The True Colours Trust
The William and Patricia Venton Charitable Trust
Wade's Charity
Wakeham Trust
John Watson's Trust
The Weavers' Company Benevolent Fund
The Simon Whitbread Charitable Trust
The Wilson Foundation
J and J R Wilson Trust
The Francis Winham Foundation
Woodlands Trust
The Woodward Charitable Trust
The Wragge and Co. Charitable Trust
The Marjorie and Arnold Ziff Charitable Foundation

Services for and about children and young people

The 1989 Willan Charitable Trust
The Company of Actuaries' Charitable Trust Fund
The Green and Lilian F M Ainsworth and Family Benevolent Fund
Archbishop of Wales' Fund for Children
The Artemis Charitable Trust
The Victoria and David Beckham Children's Charity
The Big Lottery Fund
The Anthony Bourne Foundation

The David Brooke Charity
The Burton Breweries
   Charitable Trust
The Noel Buxton Trust
Calouste Gulbenkian
   Foundation – UK Branch
Carter's Educational
   Foundation
The Cattanach Charitable Trust
The J Reginald Corah
   Foundation Fund
The John Cowan Foundation
Baron Davenport's Charity
The Dulverton Trust
The Dumbreck Charity
Gilbert Edgar Trust
Edinburgh Children's Holiday
   Fund
The Eveson Charitable Trust
Esmée Fairbairn Foundation
The Fairway Trust
Samuel William Farmer Trust
Elizabeth Ferguson Charitable
   Trust Fund
The Foresters' Fund for
   Children
The Gordon Fraser Charitable
   Trust
The Freshgate Trust
   Foundation
The Frognal Trust
The Ganzoni Charitable Trust
The Gatsby Charitable
   Foundation
Gatwick Airport Community
   Trust
The Girdlers' Company
   Charitable Trust
The Glass-House Trust
The Gosling Foundation
   Limited
Grantham Yorke Trust
The Green Hall Foundation
Dr Guthrie's Association
The Alfred Haines Charitable
   Trust
Robert Hall Charity
The W A Handley Charitable
   Trust
The Haramead Trust
The Harbour Charitable Trust
The Harris Charitable Trust
The Harris Charity
May Hearnshaw's Charity
The H J Heinz Company
   Limited Charitable Trust
The Hemby Trust
The Christina Mary Hendrie
   Trust for Scottish and
   Canadian Charities
Henley Educational Trust
   (formerley Henley
   Educational Charity)
Philip Henman Trust

The Hesslewood Children's
   Trust (Hull Seamen's and
   General Orphanage)
The High Sheriff's Police Trust
   for the County of West
   Midlands (Building Blocks)
The Hilden Charitable Fund
The Holywood Trust
Hope for Youth (NI)
The Reta Lila Howard
   Foundation
The Huddersfield Common
   Good Trust
Miss Agnes H Hunter's Trust
The Hyde Charitable Trust
Impetus – The Private Equity
   Foundation (Impetus – PEF)
The Irish Youth Foundation
   (UK) Ltd (incorporating The
   Lawlor Foundation)
The Ruth and Lionel Jacobson
   Trust (Second Fund) No 2
The Jarman Charitable Trust
The Jeffrey Charitable Trust
The Lillie Johnson Charitable
   Trust
The Johnnie Johnson Trust
The Kelly Family Charitable
   Trust
Kelsick's Educational
   Foundation
The KempWelch Charitable
   Trust
The Mary Kinross Charitable
   Trust
The KPMG Foundation
John Laing Charitable Trust
Duchy of Lancaster Benevolent
   Fund
The William Leech Charity
Leeds Building Society
   Charitable Foundation
The Mark Leonard Trust
Lord Leverhulme's Charitable
   Trust
The Lotus Foundation
John Lyon's Charity
The MacRobert Trust
Magdalen Hospital Trust
Mageni Trust
The Merchants' House of
   Glasgow
Gerald Micklem Charitable
   Trust
Miles Trust for the Putney and
   Roehampton Community
The Mirfield Educational
   Charity
John Moores Foundation
The Mugdock Children's Trust
The George Müller Charitable
   Trust
The Nadezhda Charitable Trust
The National Express
   Foundation
The Northern Rock Foundation

The Nottingham Gordon
   Memorial Trust for Boys
   and Girls
The Nuffield Foundation
The Paget Charitable Trust
The Paphitis Charitable Trust
The Constance Paterson
   Charitable Trust
Miss M E Swinton Paterson's
   Charitable Trust
The Pears Family Charitable
   Foundation
The Persula Foundation
The Jack Petchey Foundation
The Bernard Piggott Charitable
   Trust
The Pilkington Charities Fund
The Portishead Nautical Trust
The Lucy Price Relief-in-Need
   Charity
The Monica Rabagliati
   Charitable Trust
The Rank Foundation Limited
Relief Fund for Romania
   Limited
The Rhondda Cynon Taff
   Welsh Church Acts Fund
The Richmond Parish Lands
   Charity
The Rothley Trust
Ryklow Charitable Trust 1992
   (also known as A B
   Williamson Charitable Trust)
The Andrew Salvesen
   Charitable Trust
The Sandra Charitable Trust
The Francis C Scott Charitable
   Trust
Scottish Coal Industry Special
   Welfare Fund
Seafarers UK (King George's
   Fund for Sailors)
The Searle Charitable Trust
Leslie Sell Charitable Trust
The Shears Foundation
The Sylvia and Colin Shepherd
   Charitable Trust
The Shipwrights' Company
   Charitable Fund
Community Foundation for
   Shropshire and Telford
The Mrs Smith and Mount
   Trust
The Leslie Smith Foundation
The Snowball Trust
The Connie and Albert Taylor
   Charitable Trust
The Taylor Family Foundation
The Tedworth Charitable Trust
Wade's Charity
John Watson's Trust
The Weavers' Company
   Benevolent Fund
The Simon Whitbread
   Charitable Trust
The Wilson Foundation

The Marjorie and Arnold Ziff
Charitable Foundation

Services for and about older people

The Company of Actuaries'
Charitable Trust Fund
Age Scotland
Age UK
The Barnwood House Trust
The Birmingham District
Nursing Charitable Trust
The John Cowan Foundation
The D J H Currie Memorial
Trust
Baron Davenport's Charity
Disability Aid Fund (The Roger
and Jean Jefcoate Trust)
The Dumbreck Charity
The Eveson Charitable Trust
Samuel William Farmer Trust
The Fassnidge Memorial Trust
Gatwick Airport Community
Trust
The Girdlers' Company
Charitable Trust
The Green Hall Foundation
The Alfred Haines Charitable
Trust
The W A Handley Charitable
Trust
The Charles Hayward
Foundation
The Hemby Trust
The Christina Mary Hendrie
Trust for Scottish and
Canadian Charities
The KempWelch Charitable
Trust
The Joseph Levy Charitable
Foundation
Sir George Martin Trust
The Merchants' House of
Glasgow
The Pilkington Charities Fund
G S Plaut Charitable Trust
Limited
Relief Fund for Romania
Limited
The C A Rookes Charitable
Trust
The Rowlands Trust
The Andrew Salvesen
Charitable Trust
Scottish Coal Industry Special
Welfare Fund
Seafarers UK (King George's
Fund for Sailors)
The Sylvia and Colin Shepherd
Charitable Trust
Community Foundation for
Shropshire and Telford
The Mary Elizabeth Siebel
Charity

The Connie and Albert Taylor
Charitable Trust
The William and Patricia
Venton Charitable Trust
J and J R Wilson Trust
The Francis Winham
Foundation

Services for and about vulnerable people/people who are ill

The 1989 Willan Charitable
Trust
The Company of Actuaries'
Charitable Trust Fund
The Green and Lilian F M
Ainsworth and Family
Benevolent Fund
The Archer Trust
The Artemis Charitable Trust
The Birmingham District
Nursing Charitable Trust
The Dumbreck Charity
The Family Rich Charities Trust
Samuel William Farmer Trust
The Forbes Charitable
Foundation
The Oliver Ford Charitable
Trust
The Jill Franklin Trust
The Freshgate Trust
Foundation
Gatwick Airport Community
Trust
The Girdlers' Company
Charitable Trust
The Green Hall Foundation
The Hadrian Trust
The W A Handley Charitable
Trust
May Hearnshaw's Charity
The Hemby Trust
The Horne Trust
Huntingdon Freemen's Trust
The Ruth and Lionel Jacobson
Trust (Second Fund) No 2
The Jeffrey Charitable Trust
The Allen Lane Foundation
The Lark Trust
Leeds Building Society
Charitable Foundation
The Joseph Levy Charitable
Foundation
London Catalyst
John Lyon's Charity
Magdalen Hospital Trust
Market Harborough and The
Bowdens Charity
The Zachary Merton and
George Woofindin
Convalescent Trust
John Moores Foundation
The Mugdock Children's Trust

The Kitty and Daniel Nabarro
Charitable Trust
The Northcott Devon
Foundation
The Nottingham General
Dispensary
The Panacea Society
The Pilkington Charities Fund
G S Plaut Charitable Trust
Limited
The Portishead Nautical Trust
The Mary Potter Convent
Hospital Trust
The Rothley Trust
The Rowlands Trust
The Andrew Salvesen
Charitable Trust
The Sylvia and Colin Shepherd
Charitable Trust
Community Foundation for
Shropshire and Telford
The Leslie Smith Foundation
The Snowball Trust
The Connie and Albert Taylor
Charitable Trust
The Sue Thomson Foundation
The True Colours Trust
Woodlands Trust
The Wragge and Co. Charitable
Trust

Services for carers

The Astor Foundation
The Eveson Charitable Trust
Gatwick Airport Community
Trust
The Girdlers' Company
Charitable Trust
The Harris Charitable Trust
The Hemby Trust
The Ruth and Lionel Jacobson
Trust (Second Fund) No 2
The Joseph Levy Charitable
Foundation
London Catalyst
Gerald Micklem Charitable
Trust
The Northern Rock Foundation
Rix-Thompson-Rothenberg
Foundation

Services for victims of crime

The Girdlers' Company
Charitable Trust
The Hemby Trust

Services for women

The Lotus Foundation
The Northern Rock Foundation
The Reed Foundation
The Woodward Charitable
  Trust

Community centres and activities

The Ballinger Charitable Trust
The Big Lottery Fund
The A H and E Boulton Trust
John Bristow and Thomas
  Mason Trust
The Co-operative Foundation
The John Cowan Foundation
The Hamilton Davies Trust
Disability Aid Fund (The Roger
  and Jean Jefcoate Trust)
Eastern Counties Educational
  Trust Limited
Gilbert Edgar Trust
Dr Edwards Bishop King's
  Fulham Endowment Fund
Samuel William Farmer Trust
The George Fentham
  Birmingham Charity
The Sir John Fisher Foundation
The Football Association
  National Sports Centre
  Trust
The Four Lanes Trust
The Thomas Freke and Lady
  Norton Charity Trust
The Gannochy Trust
Gatwick Airport Community
  Trust
The Mike Gooley Trailfinders
  Charity
Grantham Yorke Trust
Greggs Foundation
The Grimmitt Trust
The Alfred Haines Charitable
  Trust
The W A Handley Charitable
  Trust
The Kenneth Hargreaves
  Charitable Trust
The Hedley Foundation
The Hemby Trust
The Horne Foundation
The Hornsey Parochial
  Charities
The Huddersfield Common
  Good Trust
The Hyde Charitable Trust
Jewish Child's Day
The Jones 1986 Charitable
  Trust
LWS Lancashire Environmental
  Fund Limited

Duchy of Lancaster Benevolent
  Fund
The Edgar E Lawley Foundation
The William Leech Charity
Lord Leverhulme's Charitable
  Trust
Lloyds Bank Foundation for
  Northern Ireland
Lloyds Bank Foundation for the
  Channel Islands
John Lyon's Charity
Magdalen Hospital Trust
The Michael Marsh Charitable
  Trust
John Martin's Charity
The Mears Foundation
Community Foundation for
  Merseyside
Gerald Micklem Charitable
  Trust
Monmouthshire County Council
  Welsh Church Act Fund
Mothercare Group Foundation
The Mountbatten Memorial
  Trust
The Nationwide Foundation
The Northern Rock Foundation
The Owen Family Trust
The Pilgrim Trust
The Pilkington Charities Fund
The Rhododendron Trust
The Richmond Parish Lands
  Charity
The Ripple Effect Foundation
The Robertson Trust
The Sir James Roll Charitable
  Trust
The Rothley Trust
Royal Docks Trust (London)
The Saga Charitable Trust
The Saintbury Trust
The Peter Saunders Trust
Foundation Scotland
The Frieda Scott Charitable
  Trust
The Sheldon Trust
The Sylvia and Colin Shepherd
  Charitable Trust
The Archie Sherman Cardiff
  Foundation
The Stokenchurch Educational
  Charity
The Summerfield Charitable
  Trust
The Len Thomson Charitable
  Trust
Wade's Charity
Wakeham Trust
The Westcroft Trust
The Yorkshire Dales
  Millennium Trust
Youth United Foundation

Community organisations

The Big Lottery Fund
John Bristow and Thomas
  Mason Trust
Disability Aid Fund (The Roger
  and Jean Jefcoate Trust)
The Hornsey Parochial
  Charities
Duchy of Lancaster Benevolent
  Fund
The Rothley Trust
The Saga Charitable Trust
Foundation Scotland
The Len Thomson Charitable
  Trust
Wakeham Trust

Community outings and holidays

The Big Lottery Fund
The Alfred Haines Charitable
  Trust
The Huddersfield Common
  Good Trust
Magdalen Hospital Trust
Wakeham Trust

Emergency response

The Balney Charitable Trust
Bergqvist Charitable Trust
The Blandford Lake Trust
The Boltini Trust
P G and N J Boulton Trust
The Carpenter Charitable Trust
Christadelphian Samaritan
  Fund
Christian Response to Eastern
  Europe
Clark Bradbury Charitable
  Trust
The Robert Clutterbuck
  Charitable Trust
The Peter Alan Dickson
  Foundation
The Dulverton Trust
Edinburgh Trust No 2 Account
The Family Rich Charities Trust
The Sir John Fisher Foundation
The Forces Trust (Working
  Name)
Sydney E Franklin Deceased's
  New Second Charity
The Gibbs Charitable Trust
The Gosling Foundation
  Limited
The Alfred Haines Charitable
  Trust

The W A Handley Charitable
Trust
Miss K M Harbinson's
Charitable Trust
The Kenneth Hargreaves
Charitable Trust
The Horne Trust
The Raymond and Blanche
Lawson Charitable Trust
Lloyds Bank Foundation for
Northern Ireland
The MacRobert Trust
Magdalen Hospital Trust
The Mahavir Trust
Man Group plc Charitable
Trust
The Marr-Munning Trust
The Mears Foundation
Monmouthshire County Council
Welsh Church Act Fund
John Moores Foundation
Mountbatten Festival of Music
The Father O'Mahoney
Memorial Trust
The Parthenon Trust
The Phillips Charitable Trust
The Pilkington Charities Fund
Queen Mary's Roehampton
Trust
The Sigrid Rausing Trust
The Rhododendron Trust
The Robertson Trust
The Sir James Roll Charitable
Trust
The Rothley Trust
The Rowlands Trust
Royal British Legion
The SMB Charitable Trust
The E C Sosnow Charitable
Trust
Stevenson Family's Charitable
Trust
The Gay and Keith Talbot Trust
The Lady Tangye Charitable
Trust
The Tisbury Telegraph Trust
Roger Vere Foundation
Woodroffe Benton Foundation
Miss E B Wrightson's
Charitable Settlement
Youth United Foundation

Armed forces

The Balney Charitable Trust
The Robert Clutterbuck
Charitable Trust
Edinburgh Trust No 2 Account
The Sir John Fisher Foundation
The Forces Trust (Working
Name)
The Gosling Foundation
Limited
The W A Handley Charitable
Trust

The Raymond and Blanche
Lawson Charitable Trust
Mountbatten Festival of Music
Queen Mary's Roehampton
Trust
The Rowlands Trust
Royal British Legion

Relief assistance

Bergqvist Charitable Trust
The Boltini Trust
P G and N J Boulton Trust
The Carpenter Charitable Trust
Christadelphian Samaritan
Fund
Christian Response to Eastern
Europe
The Dulverton Trust
Sydney E Franklin Deceased's
New Second Charity
The Gibbs Charitable Trust
The Alfred Haines Charitable
Trust
The W A Handley Charitable
Trust
Miss K M Harbinson's
Charitable Trust
Magdalen Hospital Trust
The Mahavir Trust
The Marr-Munning Trust
John Moores Foundation
The Father O'Mahoney
Memorial Trust
The Parthenon Trust
The Pilkington Charities Fund
The Sigrid Rausing Trust
The Rhododendron Trust
The Rothley Trust
The SMB Charitable Trust
Stevenson Family's Charitable
Trust
The Gay and Keith Talbot Trust
The Lady Tangye Charitable
Trust
The Tisbury Telegraph Trust
Roger Vere Foundation

Socially preventative schemes

The 1970 Trust
The Ashendene Trust
The Avon and Somerset Police
Community Trust
The Ballinger Charitable Trust
The Bowerman Charitable
Trust
The Bromley Trust
The Noel Buxton Trust
The G W Cadbury Charitable
Trust

The Barrow Cadbury Trust and
the Barrow Cadbury Fund
The Cayo Foundation
The Co-operative Foundation
The Evan Cornish Foundation
The Violet and Milo Cripps
Charitable Trust
The Hamilton Davies Trust
The Emilienne Charitable Trust
The Ericson Trust
Gatwick Airport Community
Trust
The Kenneth Hargreaves
Charitable Trust
The Charles Hayward
Foundation
The Hemby Trust
The High Sheriff's Police Trust
for the County of West
Midlands (Building Blocks)
The Hilden Charitable Fund
The Huddersfield Common
Good Trust
The Hyde Charitable Trust
Impetus – The Private Equity
Foundation (Impetus – PEF)
The Irish Youth Foundation
(UK) Ltd (incorporating The
Lawlor Foundation)
The Jabbs Foundation
Jewish Child's Day
The Kelly Family Charitable
Trust
The Mary Kinross Charitable
Trust
The Leigh Trust
The Joseph Levy Charitable
Foundation
Lloyds Bank Foundation for
Northern Ireland
The London Housing
Foundation
The Lotus Foundation
Magdalen Hospital Trust
The Charlotte Marshall
Charitable Trust
The Merchant Taylors'
Company Charities Fund
Community Foundation for
Merseyside
The Monument Trust
The Kitty and Daniel Nabarro
Charitable Trust
The Nadezhda Charitable Trust
The National Express
Foundation
The Norda Trust
The Nuffield Foundation
The Oakdale Trust
The Persula Foundation
The Pilgrim Trust
The Portishead Nautical Trust
Quothquan Trust
The Ripple Effect Foundation
The Robertson Trust
Saint Sarkis Charity Trust

The Saintbury Trust
Swan Mountain Trust
The Weavers' Company
  Benevolent Fund
West Yorkshire Police
  Community Trust
The Woodward Charitable
  Trust

Crime prevention

The 1970 Trust
The Barrow Cadbury Trust and
  the Barrow Cadbury Fund
The Cayo Foundation
Gatwick Airport Community
  Trust
The Kenneth Hargreaves
  Charitable Trust
The Hemby Trust
The High Sheriff's Police Trust
  for the County of West
  Midlands (Building Blocks)
The Huddersfield Common
  Good Trust
The Hyde Charitable Trust
The Joseph Levy Charitable
  Foundation
Lloyds Bank Foundation for
  Northern Ireland
The London Housing
  Foundation
Magdalen Hospital Trust

Prisons and penal reform

The Bowerman Charitable
  Trust
The Bromley Trust
The Noel Buxton Trust
The Barrow Cadbury Trust and
  the Barrow Cadbury Fund
The Evan Cornish Foundation
The Violet and Milo Cripps
  Charitable Trust
The Ericson Trust
The Charles Hayward
  Foundation
The Hilden Charitable Fund
The Mary Kinross Charitable
  Trust
The Leigh Trust
The London Housing
  Foundation
The Monument Trust
The Oakdale Trust
The Persula Foundation
Saint Sarkis Charity Trust
Swan Mountain Trust
The Woodward Charitable
  Trust

Substance abuse and education

The Ashendene Trust
The Emilienne Charitable Trust
The Lotus Foundation
The Charlotte Marshall
  Charitable Trust
The Merchant Taylors'
  Company Charities Fund
The Portishead Nautical Trust
The Robertson Trust
The Woodward Charitable
  Trust

Beneficial groups

Age

■ Babies

The 1989 Willan Charitable
  Trust
Archbishop of Wales' Fund for
  Children
Lord Barnby's Foundation
The Victoria and David
  Beckham Children's Charity
Children's Liver Disease
  Foundation
The G D Charitable Trust
Impetus – The Private Equity
  Foundation (Impetus – PEF)
Lifeline 4 Kids
The Edwina Mountbatten Trust
The Francis C Scott Charitable
  Trust

■ Children and young people

The 1989 Willan Charitable
  Trust
The Aberbrothock Skea Trust
Access Sport
The ACT Foundation
The Company of Actuaries'
  Charitable Trust Fund
The Ad Meliora Charitable
  Trust
The Sylvia Adams Charitable
  Trust
The Adamson Trust
The Adint Charitable Trust
The Agger Foundation
The Green and Lilian F M
  Ainsworth and Family
  Benevolent Fund
The Al Fayed Charitable
  Foundation
The Allen Lane Trust
The Allen Trust
Angus Allnatt Charitable
  Foundation
The Pat Allsop Charitable Trust
Viscount Amory's Charitable
  Trust
The AMW Charitable Trust
Anglo American Group
  Foundation
Anguish's Educational
  Foundation
Philip Anker Trust
The Arbib Foundation
Archbishop of Wales' Fund for
  Children
The Armourers' and Brasiers'
  Gauntlet Trust
The Arts and Entertainment
  Charitable Trust

A J H Ashby Will Trust
The Associated Country
   Women of the World
The Astor Foundation
The Astor of Hever Trust
The Lord Austin Trust
Autonomous Research
   Charitable Trust
The Albert Casanova Ballard
   Deceased Trust
The Ballinger Charitable Trust
The Balmore Trust
The Band Trust
The Barcapel Foundation
The Barclay Foundation
The Barleycorn Trust
Lord Barnby's Foundation
Barnes Workhouse Fund
The Louis Baylis (Maidenhead
   Advertiser) Charitable Trust
BBC Children in Need
B-CH 1971 Charitable Trust
The Victoria and David
   Beckham Children's Charity
The John Beckwith Charitable
   Trust
The Beit Trust
The Bellinger Donnay Trust
Bennett Lowell Limited
The Gerald Bentall Charitable
   Trust
Bergqvist Charitable Trust
The Ruth Berkowitz Charitable
   Trust
Bet365 Foundation
The Big Lottery Fund
Percy Bilton Charity
The Sydney Black Charitable
   Trust
The BlackRock (UK) Charitable
   Trust
The Blagrave Trust
Blakemore Foundation
The Nicholas Boas Charitable
   Trust
The Boltini Trust
BOOST Charitable Trust
The Bothwell Charitable Trust
H E and E L Botteley
   Charitable Trust
The Anthony Bourne
   Foundation
The Bowland Charitable Trust
The Breadsticks Foundation
The Brendish Family
   Foundation
Bridgepoint Charitable Trust
The Harold and Alice Bridges
   Charity
The David Brooke Charity
The Charles Brotherton Trust
The Brownsword Charitable
   Foundation
The Bruntwood Charity
The Buffini Chao Foundation
Bumba Foundation

The Clara E Burgess Charity
The Burton Breweries
   Charitable Trust
The Noel Buxton Trust
The James Caan Foundation
The William A Cadbury
   Charitable Trust
Calouste Gulbenkian
   Foundation – UK Branch
Carter's Educational
   Foundation
The Casey Trust
Cash for Kids Radio Clyde
The Cattanach Charitable Trust
The Joseph and Annie Cattle
   Trust
The Cayo Foundation
The CBD Charitable Trust
Celtic Charity Fund
Chesterhill Charitable Trust
The Chetwode Foundation
Children's Liver Disease
   Foundation
The Church Burgesses
   Educational Foundation
Church Urban Fund
The City Bridge Trust
The Cleevely Family Charitable
   Trust
The Cleopatra Trust
Lord Clinton's Charitable Trust
The Clore Duffield Foundation
Miss V L Clore's 1967
   Charitable Trust
The Clothworkers' Foundation
The Clover Trust
The Robert Clutterbuck
   Charitable Trust
The John Coates Charitable
   Trust
The Vivienne and Samuel
   Cohen Charitable Trust
John Coldman Charitable Trust
The John and Freda Coleman
   Charitable Trust
The Bernard Coleman
   Charitable Trust
Colyer-Fergusson Charitable
   Trust
Comic Relief
The Comino Foundation
The Douglas Compton James
   Charitable Trust
Gordon Cook Foundation
The Ernest Cook Trust
The Cooks Charity
The Keith Coombs Trust
The Co-operative Foundation
The J Reginald Corah
   Foundation Fund
The Gershon Coren Charitable
   Foundation (also known as
   The Muriel and Gus Coren
   Charitable Foundation)
Michael Cornish Charitable
   Trust

The Evan Cornish Foundation
The Duke of Cornwall's
   Benevolent Fund
The Corona Charitable Trust
The Cotton Trust
Dudley and Geoffrey Cox
   Charitable Trust
The Craps Charitable Trust
Michael Crawford Children's
   Charity
The Cray Trust
The Crerar Hotels Trust
Criffel Charitable Trust
The Cross Trust
The Peter Cruddas Foundation
Cullum Family Trust
The Cumber Family Charitable
   Trust
Cumbria Community
   Foundation
The D J H Currie Memorial
   Trust
The Manny Cussins
   Foundation
Roald Dahl's Marvellous
   Children's Charity
Daily Prayer Union Charitable
   Trust Limited
Oizer Dalim Trust
Baron Davenport's Charity
The Hamilton Davies Trust
The De Brye Charitable Trust
The De Clermont Charitable
   Company Ltd
Peter De Haan Charitable
   Trust
William Dean Countryside and
   Educational Trust
The Desmond Foundation
The Devon Educational Trust
The Sandy Dewhirst Charitable
   Trust
The Dibden Allotments Fund
The Dickon Trust
The Peter Alan Dickson
   Foundation
Grace Dieu Charitable Trust
Dischma Charitable Trust
The Djanogly Foundation
Dorset Community Foundation
The Dorus Trust
Douglas Arter Foundation
Downlands Educational Trust
The Drapers' Charitable Fund
The Drayson Foundation
Dromintee Trust
The Duis Charitable Trust
The Royal Foundation of the
   Duke and Duchess of
   Cambridge and Prince Harry
The Dulverton Trust
The Dumbreck Charity
The Charles Dunstone
   Charitable Trust
Annette Duvollet Charitable
   Trust

The Dyers' Company
Charitable Trust
Earls Colne and Halstead
Educational Charity
The Earmark Trust
Eastern Counties Educational
Trust Limited
The Sir John Eastwood
Foundation
The Ebenezer Trust
The EBM Charitable Trust
The Gilbert and Eileen Edgar
Foundation
Gilbert Edgar Trust
Edinburgh Children's Holiday
Fund
Edinburgh Trust No 2 Account
Educational Foundation of
Alderman John Norman
Dr Edwards Bishop King's
Fulham Endowment Fund
The William Edwards
Educational Charity
The Wilfred and Elsie Elkes
Charity Fund
The Maud Elkington Charitable
Trust
The Ellerdale Trust
The John Ellerman Foundation
The Ellis Campbell Foundation
Embrace the Middle East
EMI Music Sound Foundation
The Endure Foundation
The Englefield Charitable Trust
The English Schools' Football
Association
The Epigoni Trust
The Equilibrium Foundation
The Equitable Charitable Trust
The Erskine Cunningham Hill
Trust
The Essendon Charitable Trust
The Essex Youth Trust
Joseph Ettedgui Charitable
Foundation
Sir John Evelyn's Charity
The Eventhall Family
Charitable Trust
The Eveson Charitable Trust
The Exilarch's Foundation
The Expat Foundation
Esmée Fairbairn Foundation
The Fairway Trust
Samuel William Farmer Trust
Joseph Fattorini Charitable
Trust
The George Fentham
Birmingham Charity
The A M Fenton Trust
Elizabeth Ferguson Charitable
Trust Fund
The Doris Field Charitable
Trust
Dixie Rose Findlay Charitable
Trust

The Joyce Fletcher Charitable
Trust
The Football Association
National Sports Centre
Trust
Ford Britain Trust
The Foresters' Fund for
Children
The Donald Forrester Trust
The Fort Foundation
The Forte Charitable Trust
The Gordon Fraser Charitable
Trust
The Hugh Fraser Foundation
The Joseph Strong Frazer Trust
The Louis and Valerie
Freedman Charitable
Settlement
The Freemasons' Grand
Charity
The Thomas Freke and Lady
Norton Charity Trust
The Friarsgate Trust
Friends of Biala Limited
Friends of Muir Group
Friends of Wiznitz Limited
The Frognal Trust
The Patrick & Helena Frost
Foundation
Maurice Fry Charitable Trust
The Fuserna Foundation
General Charitable Trust
The Gale Family Charity Trust
The Gannochy Trust
The Ganzoni Charitable Trust
Garrick Charitable Trust
The Gatsby Charitable
Foundation
The Robert Gavron Charitable
Trust
Thomas Betton's Charity for
Pensions and Relief-in-Need
The Generations Foundation
The Steven Gerrard Foundation
Get Kids Going
The Gibbons Family Trust
Simon Gibson Charitable Trust
The G C Gibson Charitable
Trust
The Girdlers' Company
Charitable Trust
The Glass-House Trust
Global Care
Global Charities
The GNC Trust
The Mike Gooley Trailfinders
Charity
The Gosling Foundation
Limited
The Hemraj Goyal Foundation
A and S Graham Charitable
Trust
Grand Charitable Trust of the
Order of Women
Freemasons
Grantham Yorke Trust

The Green Hall Foundation
The Green Woodpecker Trust
Greenham Common
Community Trust Limited
Greggs Foundation
The Grimmitt Trust
The Grocers' Charity
The Bishop of Guildford's
Foundation
The Gunter Charitable Trust
The Gur Trust
Dr Guthrie's Association
The H and M Charitable Trust
The Hackney Parochial
Charities
The Hadfield Trust
The Hadrian Trust
The Alfred Haines Charitable
Trust
E F and M G Hall Charitable
Trust
Robert Hall Charity
Hampton Fuel Allotment
Charity
The W A Handley Charitable
Trust
The Kathleen Hannay
Memorial Charity
The Haramead Trust
Harbo Charities Limited
The Harbour Foundation
William Harding's Charity
The Hare of Steep Charitable
Trust
The Harebell Centenary Fund
The Kenneth Hargreaves
Charitable Trust
The Harris Charitable Trust
The Harris Charity
The Harris Family Charitable
Trust
The Peter Harrison Foundation
The Alfred And Peggy Harvey
Charitable Trust
Hasluck Charitable Trust
The Hawthorne Charitable
Trust
The Dorothy Hay-Bolton
Charitable Trust
The Headley Trust
May Hearnshaw's Charity
Heart of England Community
Foundation
The Charlotte Heber-Percy
Charitable Trust
The Hedley Foundation
The H J Heinz Company
Limited Charitable Trust
The Hemby Trust
The Christina Mary Hendrie
Trust for Scottish and
Canadian Charities
Henley Educational Trust
(formerley Henley
Educational Charity)

The Hesslewood Children's Trust (Hull Seamen's and General Orphanage)
Alan Edward Higgs Charity
The Graham High Charitable Trust
The Hilden Charitable Fund
The Charles Littlewood Hill Trust
The Hillier Trust
The Jane Hodge Foundation
The Holmes Family Trust (Sheffield)
The Holywood Trust
The Homelands Charitable Trust
Hope for Youth (NI)
The Horizon Foundation
The Horne Foundation
The Hospital of God at Greatham
The Reta Lila Howard Foundation
The Huddersfield Common Good Trust
The Hull and East Riding Charitable Trust
The Humanitarian Trust
The Albert Hunt Trust
The Hunter Foundation
Miss Agnes H Hunter's Trust
The Hyde Charitable Trust
I B B Charitable Trust
I G O Foundation Limited
Impetus – The Private Equity Foundation (Impetus – PEF)
The Irish Youth Foundation (UK) Ltd (incorporating The Lawlor Foundation)
The Ironmongers' Foundation
The J & J Charitable Trust
The Ruth and Lionel Jacobson Trust (Second Fund) No 2
The James Trust
The Jasper Conran Foundation
The Jeffrey Charitable Trust
The Nick Jenkins Foundation
The Jenour Foundation
Jewish Child's Day
The Jewish Youth Fund
The Jigsaw Foundation
The Dyfrig and Heather John Charitable Trust
The Lillie Johnson Charitable Trust
The Johnson Foundation
The Johnnie Johnson Trust
The Jones 1986 Charitable Trust
The Dezna Robins Jones Charitable Foundation
The Julian Budd Kids in Sport Trust Limited
The Cyril and Eve Jumbo Charitable Trust

The Anton Jurgens Charitable Trust
The Kathleen Trust
The Michael and Ilse Katz Foundation
Kelsick's Educational Foundation
The KempWelch Charitable Trust
The Peter Kershaw Trust
The Mr & Mrs Paul Killik Charitable Trust
The Eric and Margaret Kinder Charitable Trust
The Mary Kinross Charitable Trust
Ernest Kleinwort Charitable Trust
The Sir James Knott Trust
The KPMG Foundation
John Laing Charitable Trust
Maurice and Hilda Laing Charitable Trust
The Christopher Laing Foundation
The David Laing Foundation
The Kirby Laing Foundation
The Martin Laing Foundation
The Beatrice Laing Trust
The Lambert Charitable Trust
LWS Lancashire Environmental Fund Limited
Duchy of Lancaster Benevolent Fund
LandAid Charitable Trust
Langdale Trust
The Langley Charitable Trust
The R J Larg Family Charitable Trust
The Edgar E Lawley Foundation
The Raymond and Blanche Lawson Charitable Trust
The David Lean Foundation
The Leathersellers' Company Charitable Fund
The Leche Trust
Leicestershire and Rutland Community Foundation
The Leigh Trust
Mrs Vera Leigh's Charity
P Leigh-Bramwell Trust 'E'
The Mark Leonard Trust
Lord Leverhulme's Charitable Trust
The Joseph Levy Charitable Foundation
Lewis Family Charitable Trust
John Lewis Partnership General Community Fund
The Lewis Ward Trust
Liberum Foundation
Lifeline 4 Kids
Limoges Charitable Trust
Lincolnshire Community Foundation

Lindale Educational Foundation
Lindenleaf Charitable Trust
The Enid Linder Foundation
The Lister Charitable Trust
The Second Joseph Aaron Littman Foundation
The George John and Sheilah Livanos Charitable Trust
The Ian & Natalie Livingstone Charitable Trust
The Elaine and Angus Lloyd Charitable Trust
Lloyd's Charities Trust
Lloyds Bank Foundation for England and Wales
Lloyds Bank Foundation for Northern Ireland
Lloyds TSB Foundation for Scotland
The London Law Trust
The Lord's Taverners
The Loseley and Guildway Charitable Trust
The Lotus Foundation
Henry Lumley Charitable Trust
Paul Lunn-Rockliffe Charitable Trust
The Ruth and Jack Lunzer Charitable Trust
Lord and Lady Lurgan Trust
The Lynn Foundation
John Lyon's Charity
The Lyons Charitable Trust
The Sir Jack Lyons Charitable Trust
The M and C Trust
The Madeline Mabey Trust
The R S Macdonald Charitable Trust
Macdonald-Buchanan Charitable Trust
The Macfarlane Walker Trust
The Mackintosh Foundation
The MacRobert Trust
Magdalen Hospital Trust
The Magen Charitable Trust
Malbin Trust
The Mallinckrodt Foundation
Man Group plc Charitable Trust
Mandeville Trust
R W Mann Trust
Maranatha Christian Trust
The Stella and Alexander Margulies Charitable Trust
The Marianne Foundation
The Marks Family Foundation
The Ann and David Marks Foundation
The Michael Marsh Charitable Trust
The Marsh Christian Trust
The Charlotte Marshall Charitable Trust

The Jim Marshall Charitable
Trust
The Nora Joan Marshall
Charitable Trust
John Martin's Charity
The Nancie Massey Charitable
Trust
Matliwala Family Charitable
Trust
The Violet Mauray Charitable
Trust
Evelyn May Trust
The Robert McAlpine
Foundation
The McKenna Charitable Trust
D D McPhail Charitable
Settlement
Melodor Limited
The Menzies Charity
Foundation
The Mercers' Charitable
Foundation
The Merchant Taylors'
Company Charities Fund
The Merchant Venturers'
Charity
The Metropolitan Masonic
Charity
Mi Yu Foundation
Mickleham Charitable Trust
The Sir John Middlemore
Charitable Trust
Miles Trust for the Putney and
Roehampton Community
Milton Keynes Community
Foundation
The Peter Minet Trust
The Mirfield Educational
Charity
The MITIE Foundation
The Mittal Foundation
The Mole Charitable Trust
Monmouthshire County Council
Welsh Church Act Fund
The Montague Thompson
Coon Charitable Trust
The Monument Trust
The Moonpig Foundation
John Moores Foundation
The Morgan Foundation
Morgan Stanley International
Foundation
The Peter Morrison Charitable
Foundation
The Stanley Morrison
Charitable Trust
The Moss Family Charitable
Trust
Mosselson Charitable Trust
Moto in the Community
The Edwina Mountbatten Trust
The Mountbatten Memorial
Trust
The Mugdock Children's Trust
The Edith Murphy Foundation

Murphy-Neumann Charity
Company Limited
Peter John Murray Trust
The Music Sales Charitable
Trust
Muslim Hands
The National Express
Foundation
The National Hockey
Foundation
Needham Market and Barking
Welfare Charities
Newby Trust Limited
The Newcomen Collett
Foundation
Nominet Charitable Foundation
Norfolk Community Foundation
The Northampton Queen's
Institute Relief in Sickness
Fund
Northamptonshire Community
Foundation
The Northcott Devon
Foundation
The Northern Rock Foundation
The Northumberland Village
Homes Trust
The Norton Foundation
The Norton Rose Charitable
Foundation
The Norwich Church of England
Young Men's Society
The Notgrove Trust
The Nottingham Gordon
Memorial Trust for Boys
and Girls
Nottinghamshire Community
Foundation
Novi Most International
The Nuffield Foundation
Nutrisport Trust
The Oakley Charitable Trust
Ogilvie Charities Deed No.2
(including the Charity of
Mary Catherine Ford Smith)
Oizer Charitable Trust
Old Possum's Practical Trust
The Oldham Foundation
The Olga Charitable Trust
Open Gate
Ormonde Foundation
The O'Sullivan Family
Charitable Trust
Padwa Charitable Foundation
The Paget Charitable Trust
The Paladin Vince-Odozi
Charitable Trust
The Palmer Foundation
The Paphitis Charitable Trust
Paraton Trust
Arthur James Paterson
Charitable Trust
The Constance Paterson
Charitable Trust
Miss M E Swinton Paterson's
Charitable Trust

Ambika Paul Foundation
Paycare Charity Trust
The Peacock Charitable Trust
The Pears Family Charitable
Foundation
The Pedmore Sporting Club
Trust Fund
Pegasus (Stanley) Trust
The Jack Petchey Foundation
The Phillips Charitable Trust
Philological Foundation
The Pickwell Foundation
The Pilkington Charities Fund
The Austin and Hope
Pilkington Trust
The Platinum Trust
G S Plaut Charitable Trust
Limited
The Ponton House Trust
The Popocatepetl Trust
The Portishead Nautical Trust
The Praebendo Charitable
Foundation
The Premier League Charitable
Fund
The Tom Press Charitable
Foundation
The William Price Charitable
Trust
The Lucy Price Relief-in-Need
Charity
Sir John Priestman Charity
Trust
The Prince of Wales's
Charitable Foundation
Princess Anne's Charities
The Proven Family Trust
The Provincial Grand Charity of
the Province of Derbyshire
The Puri Foundation
Mr and Mrs J A Pye's
Charitable Settlement
The Quarry Family Charitable
Trust
The Queen's Silver Jubilee
Trust
Quothquan Trust
The Monica Rabagliati
Charitable Trust
The Ragdoll Foundation
The Rank Foundation Limited
The Joseph Rank Trust
The Rashbass Family Trust
The Ratcliff Pension Charity
The Ravensdale Trust
The Rawdon-Smith Trust
The Rayne Foundation
The Rayne Trust
The Sir James Reckitt Charity
Red Hill Charitable Trust
The Red Rose Charitable Trust
The Reed Foundation
The John and Sally Reeve
Charitable Trust
Richard Reeve's Foundation

The Rhondda Cynon Taff Welsh Church Acts Fund
The Clive Richards Charity
The Richmond Parish Lands Charity
The Ripple Effect Foundation
The Robertson Trust
Robyn Charitable Trust
Mrs L D Rope Third Charitable Settlement
The Rosca Trust
The Rotherwick Foundation
The Christopher Rowbotham Charitable Trust
Royal Docks Trust (London)
Royal Masonic Trust for Girls and Boys
The RRAF Charitable Trust
Ryklow Charitable Trust 1992 (also known as A B Williamson Charitable Trust)
The Alan and Babette Sainsbury Charitable Fund
Salters' Charitable Foundation
The Andrew Salvesen Charitable Trust
Basil Samuel Charitable Trust
The Sandra Charitable Trust
The R H Scholes Charitable Trust
Schroder Charity Trust
The Francis C Scott Charitable Trust
The Searle Charitable Trust
The Samuel Sebba Charitable Trust
SEM Charitable Trust
The Seneca Trust
The Ayrton Senna Foundation
The Shears Foundation
The Patricia and Donald Shepherd Charitable Trust
The Sylvia and Colin Shepherd Charitable Trust
SHINE (Support and Help in Education)
The Bassil Shippam and Alsford Trust
The Shipwrights' Company Charitable Fund
The Shoe Zone Trust
Community Foundation for Shropshire and Telford
The Barbara A Shuttleworth Memorial Trust
The Leslie Silver Charitable Trust
Skipton Building Society Charitable Foundation
Sloane Robinson Foundation
The Smith & Pinching Charitable Trust
The Henry Smith Charity
The Leslie Smith Foundation
Philip Smith's Charitable Trust

The R C Snelling Charitable Trust
The Snowball Trust
The Sobell Foundation
The E C Sosnow Charitable Trust
The Southdown Trust
The Southover Manor General Education Trust
Spar Charitable Fund
Sparquote Limited
The Spero Foundation
The Spielman Charitable Trust
The Geoff and Fiona Squire Foundation
St Hilda's Trust
St James's Place Foundation
Sir Walter St John's Educational Charity
The St Laurence Relief In Need Trust
The Stafford Trust
The Stanton Ballard Charitable Trust
The Steinberg Family Charitable Trust
The June Stevens Foundation
The Andy Stewart Charitable Foundation
Sir Halley Stewart Trust
The Stoller Charitable Trust
The Strawberry Charitable Trust
The W O Street Charitable Foundation
Sueberry Ltd
The Summerfield Charitable Trust
The Bernard Sunley Charitable Foundation
The Sutton Trust
The Connie and Albert Taylor Charitable Trust
The Taylor Family Foundation
A P Taylor Trust
The Tedworth Charitable Trust
The Ten Ten Charitable Trust
Tesco Charity Trust
The John P. Gommes Foundation
The Len Thomson Charitable Trust
The Sue Thomson Foundation
The Thornton Trust
The Thousandth Man- Richard Burns Charitable Trust
Mrs R P Tindall's Charitable Trust
The Tolkien Trust
Toni and Guy Charitable Foundation Limited
The Tory Family Foundation
The Toy Trust
Annie Tranmer Charitable Trust
The Trefoil Trust
The Tresillian Trust

The True Colours Trust
The Tsukanov Family Foundation
The Tyche Charitable Trust
Community Foundation Serving Tyne and Wear and Northumberland
The Valentine Charitable Trust
The Albert Van Den Bergh Charitable Trust
The Vardy Foundation
The Variety Club Children's Charity
Victoria Homes Trust
The Viznitz Foundation
The Vodafone Foundation
Volant Charitable Trust
Voluntary Action Fund (VAF)
Wade's Charity
Wales Council for Voluntary Action
Wallace and Gromit's Children's Foundation
The Barbara Ward Children's Foundation
The Waterloo Foundation
The Wates Foundation
John Watson's Trust
The Weavers' Company Benevolent Fund
Weedon Family Trust
The James Weir Foundation
The Welton Foundation
The Wessex Youth Trust
The Garfield Weston Foundation
The Barbara Whatmore Charitable Trust
White Stuff Foundation
The Felicity Wilde Charitable Trust
Will to Win Foundation Ltd. (previously Tennis for a Life)
The Charity of William Williams
Williams Serendipity Trust
The HDH Wills 1965 Charitable Trust
Dame Violet Wills Charitable Trust
The Wilson Foundation
The Community Foundation for Wiltshire and Swindon
The Wixamtree Trust
The Maurice Wohl Charitable Foundation
The Charles Wolfson Charitable Trust
The Wolfson Family Charitable Trust
The Wood Family Trust
The Woodcock Charitable Trust
Woodlands Trust
The Woodward Charitable Trust

The A and R Woolf Charitable Trust
The Matthews Wrightson Charity Trust
Miss E B Wrightson's Charitable Settlement
The Xerox (UK) Trust
The Yapp Charitable Trust
Yorkshire Building Society Charitable Foundation
The South Yorkshire Community Foundation
The John K Young Endowment Fund
Youth Music (previously known as National Foundation for Youth Music)
Youth United Foundation
The Marjorie and Arnold Ziff Charitable Foundation
The Zochonis Charitable Trust

....

■ Older people

The A B Charitable Trust
The ACT Foundation
The Company of Actuaries' Charitable Trust Fund
The Ad Meliora Charitable Trust
Age Scotland
Age UK
The Green and Lilian F M Ainsworth and Family Benevolent Fund
The Allen Lane Trust
Viscount Amory's Charitable Trust
The Bryan and June Amos Foundation
The Argus Appeal
The Lord Austin Trust
Autonomous Research Charitable Trust
The Baker Charitable Trust
The Paul Balint Charitable Trust
The Ballinger Charitable Trust
The Balney Charitable Trust
The Band Trust
Barchester Healthcare Foundation
The Barclay Foundation
The Barleycorn Trust
Barnes Workhouse Fund
The Barnwood House Trust
The Louis Baylis (Maidenhead Advertiser) Charitable Trust
The Beaverbrook Foundation
The Bellinger Donnay Trust
The Benfield Motors Charitable Trust
Bennett Lowell Limited
The Gerald Bentall Charitable Trust
Bet365 Foundation

The Mason Bibby 1981 Trust
Percy Bilton Charity
Miss Jeanne Bisgood's Charitable Trust
The BlackRock (UK) Charitable Trust
The Blagrave Trust
Blakemore Foundation
The Bothwell Charitable Trust
H E and E L Botteley Charitable Trust
P G and N J Boulton Trust
The Harold and Alice Bridges Charity
The David Brooke Charity
The Charles Brotherton Trust
The Brownsword Charitable Foundation
The William A Cadbury Charitable Trust
The Joseph and Annie Cattle Trust
The Childwick Trust
The City Bridge Trust
The Cleopatra Trust
Lord Clinton's Charitable Trust
The Clore Duffield Foundation
Miss V L Clore's 1967 Charitable Trust
The Clothworkers' Foundation
The Clover Trust
The Robert Clutterbuck Charitable Trust
The John Coates Charitable Trust
The Vivienne and Samuel Cohen Charitable Trust
Colyer-Fergusson Charitable Trust
Comic Relief
The Consolidated Charities for the Infirm Merchant Taylors' Company
The Marjorie Coote Old People's Charity
The Gershon Coren Charitable Foundation (also known as The Muriel and Gus Coren Charitable Foundation)
The Evan Cornish Foundation
The Duke of Cornwall's Benevolent Fund
The Corona Charitable Trust
The Cotton Industry War Memorial Trust
The Cotton Trust
Dudley and Geoffrey Cox Charitable Trust
The Craps Charitable Trust
The Crerar Hotels Trust
Criffel Charitable Trust
The Cumber Family Charitable Trust
Cumbria Community Foundation

The Manny Cussins Foundation
Oizer Dalim Trust
The Dr and Mrs A Darlington Charitable Trust
Baron Davenport's Charity
The De Brye Charitable Trust
William Dean Countryside and Educational Trust
The Desmond Foundation
The Sandy Dewhirst Charitable Trust
Grace Dieu Charitable Trust
Dischma Charitable Trust
The Djanogly Foundation
The Derek and Eileen Dodgson Foundation
Dorset Community Foundation
The Dorus Trust
Douglas Arter Foundation
The Drapers' Charitable Fund
The Dulverton Trust
The P B Dumbell Charitable Trust
The Dumbreck Charity
The Dunhill Medical Trust
The Sir John Eastwood Foundation
The Ebenezer Trust
The Gilbert and Eileen Edgar Foundation
The W G Edwards Charitable Foundation
The Wilfred and Elsie Elkes Charity Fund
The Maud Elkington Charitable Trust
The John Ellerman Foundation
The Endure Foundation
The Englefield Charitable Trust
The Epigoni Trust
The Equilibrium Foundation
The Ericson Trust
The Erskine Cunningham Hill Trust
Sir John Evelyn's Charity
The Eventhall Family Charitable Trust
The Eveson Charitable Trust
The Expat Foundation
Esmée Fairbairn Foundation
The Fairway Trust
The Lord Faringdon Charitable Trust
Samuel William Farmer Trust
The Fassnidge Memorial Trust
Joseph Fattorini Charitable Trust
The A M Fenton Trust
Dixie Rose Findlay Charitable Trust
The Football Association National Sports Centre Trust
The Donald Forrester Trust
The Hugh Fraser Foundation

The Joseph Strong Frazer Trust
The Freemasons' Grand
Charity
The Friarsgate Trust
Friends of Biala Limited
Friends of Muir Group
The Frognal Trust
The Patrick & Helena Frost
Foundation
Maurice Fry Charitable Trust
The Fuserna Foundation
General Charitable Trust
The G D Charitable Trust
The Gale Family Charity Trust
The David Gibbons Foundation
The Girdlers' Company
Charitable Trust
The GNC Trust
The Gosling Foundation
Limited
Grand Charitable Trust of the
Order of Women
Freemasons
The Green Hall Foundation
Greenham Common
Community Trust Limited
Greggs Foundation
The Grimmitt Trust
The Grocers' Charity
The Bishop of Guildford's
Foundation
The Guildry Incorporation of
Perth
The Gunter Charitable Trust
The H and M Charitable Trust
The Hadfield Trust
The Hadrian Trust
The Alfred Haines Charitable
Trust
E F and M G Hall Charitable
Trust
The Helen Hamlyn Trust
Hampton Fuel Allotment
Charity
The W A Handley Charitable
Trust
The Kathleen Hannay
Memorial Charity
Harbo Charities Limited
The Harbour Foundation
William Harding's Charity
The Hare of Steep Charitable
Trust
The Harebell Centenary Fund
The Kenneth Hargreaves
Charitable Trust
The Harris Family Charitable
Trust
The Harrison and Potter Trust
The Alfred And Peggy Harvey
Charitable Trust
Hasluck Charitable Trust
The Dorothy Hay-Bolton
Charitable Trust
The Headley Trust
Headley-Pitt Charitable Trust

Heart of England Community
Foundation
The Charlotte Heber-Percy
Charitable Trust
The Hemby Trust
The Christina Mary Hendrie
Trust for Scottish and
Canadian Charities
The Graham High Charitable
Trust
The Hillier Trust
The Hilmarnan Charitable Trust
The Sir Julian Hodge
Charitable Trust
The Jane Hodge Foundation
The Edward Holt Trust
The Cuthbert Horn Trust
The Hospital of God at
Greatham
The Huddersfield Common
Good Trust
The Hudson Foundation
The Albert Hunt Trust
Miss Agnes H Hunter's Trust
Huntingdon Freemen's Trust
I B B Charitable Trust
I G O Foundation Limited
The Inman Charity
The Charles Irving Charitable
Trust
The Ruth and Lionel Jacobson
Trust (Second Fund) No 2
John James Bristol Foundation
The Jenour Foundation
The Johnson Foundation
The Jones 1986 Charitable
Trust
The Dezna Robins Jones
Charitable Foundation
The Cyril and Eve Jumbo
Charitable Trust
The Anton Jurgens Charitable
Trust
The Michael and Ilse Katz
Foundation
The KempWelch Charitable
Trust
The Peter Kershaw Trust
The Mr & Mrs Paul Killik
Charitable Trust
Ernest Kleinwort Charitable
Trust
The Sir James Knott Trust
The David Laing Foundation
The Martin Laing Foundation
The Beatrice Laing Trust
The Lambert Charitable Trust
Duchy of Lancaster Benevolent
Fund
The Allen Lane Foundation
Langdale Trust
The Edgar E Lawley Foundation
The Herd Lawson and Muriel
Lawson Charitable Trust
The Raymond and Blanche
Lawson Charitable Trust

Leicestershire and Rutland
Community Foundation
The Joseph Levy Charitable
Foundation
The Linbury Trust
Lincolnshire Community
Foundation
The Linden Charitable Trust
Jack Livingstone Charitable
Trust
Lloyds Bank Foundation for
England and Wales
Lloyds Bank Foundation for
Northern Ireland
Lloyds TSB Foundation for
Scotland
Paul Lunn-Rockliffe Charitable
Trust
Lord and Lady Lurgan Trust
The Lynn Foundation
The M and C Trust
Macdonald-Buchanan
Charitable Trust
The Macfarlane Walker Trust
Man Group plc Charitable
Trust
The Stella and Alexander
Margulies Charitable Trust
The Marks Family Foundation
The Ann and David Marks
Foundation
The Michael Marsh Charitable
Trust
The Marsh Christian Trust
The Charlotte Marshall
Charitable Trust
John Martin's Charity
The Nancie Massey Charitable
Trust
Matliwala Family Charitable
Trust
The Violet Mauray Charitable
Trust
The Maxwell Family Foundation
Evelyn May Trust
The Robert McAlpine
Foundation
D D McPhail Charitable
Settlement
The Mercers' Charitable
Foundation
The Merchant Taylors'
Company Charities Fund
The Merchant Venturers'
Charity
The Zachary Merton and
George Woofindin
Convalescent Trust
The Tony Metherell Charitable
Trust
The Metropolitan Masonic
Charity
Midhurst Pensions Trust
Miles Trust for the Putney and
Roehampton Community

Milton Keynes Community Foundation

The Peter Minet Trust

The Mitchell Charitable Trust

The MITIE Foundation

Monmouthshire County Council Welsh Church Act Fund

The Peter Morrison Charitable Foundation

The Moss Family Charitable Trust

Mosselson Charitable Trust

The Edith Murphy Foundation

Murphy-Neumann Charity Company Limited

Muslim Hands

Needham Market and Barking Welfare Charities

Nominet Charitable Foundation

Norfolk Community Foundation

The Northampton Queen's Institute Relief in Sickness Fund

Northamptonshire Community Foundation

The Northern Rock Foundation

The Northwood Charitable Trust

Nottinghamshire Community Foundation

The Nuffield Foundation

The Oakley Charitable Trust

Ogilvie Charities Deed No.2 (including the Charity of Mary Catherine Ford Smith)

Oizer Charitable Trust

The Oldham Foundation

Ormonde Foundation

Paraton Trust

Arthur James Paterson Charitable Trust

The Constance Paterson Charitable Trust

Paycare Charity Trust

The Harry Payne Trust

The Pedmore Sporting Club Trust Fund

The Dowager Countess Eleanor Peel Trust

Pegasus (Stanley) Trust

The Elise Pilkington Charitable Trust

The Pilkington Charities Fund

The Austin and Hope Pilkington Trust

G S Plaut Charitable Trust Limited

The Ponton House Trust

The Powell Foundation

The Praebendo Charitable Foundation

The Douglas Prestwich Charitable Trust

Sir John Priestman Charity Trust

The Proven Family Trust

The Provincial Grand Charity of the Province of Derbyshire

The Puri Foundation

Mr and Mrs J A Pye's Charitable Settlement

The Quarry Family Charitable Trust

The Queen's Silver Jubilee Trust

Quothquan Trust

The Rank Foundation Limited

The Joseph Rank Trust

The Rashbass Family Trust

The Ratcliff Pension Charity

The Ravensdale Trust

The Roger Raymond Charitable Trust

The Rayne Foundation

The Rayne Trust

The Sir James Reckitt Charity

The Red Rose Charitable Trust

The John and Sally Reeve Charitable Trust

Relief Fund for Romania Limited

The Violet M Richards Charity

The Richmond Parish Lands Charity

The Robertson Trust

Robyn Charitable Trust

The C A Rookes Charitable Trust

The Rosca Trust

The Cecil Rosen Foundation

The Rotherwick Foundation

Mrs Gladys Row Fogo Charitable Trust

The Rowlands Trust

The RRAF Charitable Trust

The Andrew Salvesen Charitable Trust

The Sylvia and Colin Shepherd Charitable Trust

The Bassil Shippam and Alsford Trust

Community Foundation for Shropshire and Telford

The Mary Elizabeth Siebel Charity

Skipton Building Society Charitable Foundation

The Henry Smith Charity

Philip Smith's Charitable Trust

The R C Snelling Charitable Trust

The Sobell Foundation

The Sovereign Health Care Charitable Trust

Sparquote Limited

The Spero Foundation

The Spielman Charitable Trust

The St Laurence Relief In Need Trust

St Monica Trust

The Stafford Trust

The Stanley Foundation Ltd

The Stanton Ballard Charitable Trust

The June Stevens Foundation

Sir Halley Stewart Trust

The Summerfield Charitable Trust

The Bernard Sunley Charitable Foundation

A P Taylor Trust

The Ten Ten Charitable Trust

Tesco Charity Trust

The Thousandth Man- Richard Burns Charitable Trust

The Tolkien Trust

Annie Tranmer Charitable Trust

The Trusthouse Charitable Foundation

The Tyche Charitable Trust

Community Foundation Serving Tyne and Wear and Northumberland

The Valiant Charitable Trust

The Albert Van Den Bergh Charitable Trust

The Van Neste Foundation

The William and Patricia Venton Charitable Trust

The Viznitz Foundation

Voluntary Action Fund (VAF)

The Wakefield and Tetley Trust

Wales Council for Voluntary Action

The James Weir Foundation

The Welton Foundation

The Garfield Weston Foundation

Williams Serendipity Trust

The HDH Wills 1965 Charitable Trust

Dame Violet Wills Charitable Trust

J and J R Wilson Trust

The Community Foundation for Wiltshire and Swindon

The Francis Winham Foundation

The Michael and Anna Wix Charitable Trust

The Wixamtree Trust

The Maurice Wohl Charitable Foundation

The Charles Wolfson Charitable Trust

Woodlands Trust

Woodroffe Benton Foundation

The Matthews Wrightson Charity Trust

The Wyseliot Charitable Trust

The Yapp Charitable Trust

Yorkshire Building Society Charitable Foundation

The Marjorie and Arnold Ziff Charitable Foundation

Class, group, occupation or former occupation

■ Armed forces

ABF The Soldiers' Charity
The Ammco Trust
The Armourers' and Brasiers' Gauntlet Trust
ASCB Charitable Fund
The Balney Charitable Trust
The Baltic Charitable Fund
The Band Trust
The BlackRock (UK) Charitable Trust
The Robert Clutterbuck Charitable Trust
The De Clermont Charitable Company Ltd
The Royal Foundation of the Duke and Duchess of Cambridge and Prince Harry
The Dulverton Trust
Edinburgh Trust No 2 Account
The Erskine Cunningham Hill Trust
The Sir John Fisher Foundation
The Forces Trust (Working Name)
The Donald Forrester Trust
The Fuserna Foundation General Charitable Trust
The Girdlers' Company Charitable Trust
The Mike Gooley Trailfinders Charity
The Gosling Foundation Limited
The W A Handley Charitable Trust
The Christina Mary Hendrie Trust for Scottish and Canadian Charities
The Charles Littlewood Hill Trust
The Inman Charity
The Sir James Knott Trust
The Beatrice Laing Trust
The Raymond and Blanche Lawson Charitable Trust
Henry Lumley Charitable Trust
The MacRobert Trust
Mountbatten Festival of Music
The Noswad Charity
The Prince of Wales's Charitable Foundation
Princess Anne's Charities
Queen Mary's Roehampton Trust
The Red Arrows Trust
The Rowlands Trust
Royal Artillery Charitable Fund
Royal British Legion
Salters' Charitable Foundation

Scott (Eredine) Charitable Trust
Seafarers UK (King George's Fund for Sailors)
The Leslie Smith Foundation
Philip Smith's Charitable Trust
The Stafford Trust
The Trefoil Trust
The Albert Van Den Bergh Charitable Trust
The Westminster Foundation

■ Arts, culture, sports and recreation

Arts Council of Wales (also known as Cyngor Celfyddydau Cymru)
The Band Trust
The Richard Carne Trust
The Equity Trust Fund
The Follett Trust
The Goldsmiths' Company Charity
Paul Hamlyn Foundation
The Derek Hill Foundation
The Hinrichsen Foundation
The Horne Foundation
The Boris Karloff Charitable Foundation
The Kathleen Trust
The David Lean Foundation
The Leverhulme Trust
The Anthony and Elizabeth Mellows Charitable Settlement
The R V W Trust
The Racing Foundation
Racing Welfare
The Peggy Ramsay Foundation
The Rayne Foundation
Miss S M Tutton Charitable Trust
Unity Theatre Trust

■ Environment and agriculture

The C Alma Baker Trust
Sir Alec Black's Charity
The Farmers' Company Charitable Fund
The Fishmongers' Company's Charitable Trust
The Girdlers' Company Charitable Trust
The Joicey Trust
Frank Litchfield Charitable Trust
The NFU Mutual Charitable Trust
The Racing Foundation
Racing Welfare
Yorkshire Agricultural Society

The Yorkshire Dales Millennium Trust

■ Law

The Law Society Charity

■ Manufacturing and service industries

The Clothworkers' Foundation
The Cotton Industry War Memorial Trust
Florence's Charitable Trust
Worshipful Company of Glovers of London Charity Fund
The Leverhulme Trade Charities Trust
Minge's Gift and the Pooled Trusts

■ Medicine and health

The John Avins Trustees
Veta Bailey Charitable Trust
B-CH 1971 Charitable Trust
The British Dietetic Association General and Education Trust Fund
British Heart Foundation
The Carron Charitable Settlement
The Dinwoodie Settlement
The General Nursing Council for England and Wales Trust
The Kenneth Hargreaves Charitable Trust
The John Harrison Charitable Trust
The Michael Heller Charitable Foundation
The Emmanuel Kaye Foundation
John Lewis Partnership General Community Fund
The Northcott Devon Medical Foundation
The Rayne Foundation
The Sandra Charitable Trust

■ Religion

All Saints Educational Trust
Ashburnham Thanksgiving Trust
The Anne French Memorial Trust
The Hope Trust
The James Trust
The Langley Charitable Trust
The Lyndhurst Trust

Sylvanus Lyson's Charity
Marshall's Charity
Sir John Priestman Charity
 Trust
The Bishop Radford Trust
The Rehoboth Trust
St Teilo's Trust
Swansea and Brecon Diocesan
 Board of Finance Limited
Ulting Overseas Trust
Wallington Missionary Mart
 and Auctions
The James Wood Bequest
 Fund

....

■ Science, technology and engineering

The Colt Foundation
The Michael Heller Charitable
 Foundation
The Emmanuel Kaye
 Foundation
The Leverhulme Trade
 Charities Trust
The Leverhulme Trust
The Kitty and Daniel Nabarro
 Charitable Trust
The Nottinghamshire Miners'
 Welfare Trust Fund
Scottish Coal Industry Special
 Welfare Fund

....

■ Sporting or social clubs (inc. Masons)

Essex Provincial Charity Fund
The Freemasons' Grand
 Charity
Grand Charitable Trust of the
 Order of Women
 Freemasons
The Provincial Grand Charity of
 the Province of Derbyshire

....

■ Transport

The Baltic Charitable Fund
The Worshipful Company of
 Carmen Benevolent Trust
The Erskine Cunningham Hill
 Trust
Dixie Rose Findlay Charitable
 Trust
The Donald Forrester Trust
The Gosling Foundation
 Limited
The W A Handley Charitable
 Trust
The ITF Seafarers Trust
The Joicey Trust
The George John and Sheilah
 Livanos Charitable Trust

Merchant Navy Welfare Board
The Merchants' House of
 Glasgow
The Mersey Docks and
 Harbour Company
 Charitable Fund
The Phillips Charitable Trust
Seafarers UK (King George's
 Fund for Sailors)
Seamen's Hospital Society
The Shipwrights' Company
 Charitable Fund

Disability

■ People with a mental impairment

The 1989 Willan Charitable
 Trust
The Aberbrothock Skea Trust
The Sylvia Adams Charitable
 Trust
The Adamson Trust
The Green and Lilian F M
 Ainsworth and Family
 Benevolent Fund
The Archer Trust
The Baily Thomas Charitable
 Fund
Blakemore Foundation
The Joseph and Annie Cattle
 Trust
The J Reginald Corah
 Foundation Fund
Douglas Arter Foundation
The Drapers' Charitable Fund
The Dumbreck Charity
The W E Dunn Trust
Eastern Counties Educational
 Trust Limited
The EBM Charitable Trust
The John Ellerman Foundation
James Ellis Charitable Trust
The Eveson Charitable Trust
Esmée Fairbairn Foundation
The Forbes Charitable
 Foundation
Ford Britain Trust
The Oliver Ford Charitable
 Trust
The Jill Franklin Trust
The Hugh Fraser Foundation
The Joseph Strong Frazer Trust
The Freemasons' Grand
 Charity
The Gatsby Charitable
 Foundation
The Robert Gavron Charitable
 Trust
Simon Gibson Charitable Trust
The Girdlers' Company
 Charitable Trust
The Gosling Foundation
 Limited

The Green Hall Foundation
Greggs Foundation
The Grocers' Charity
The Alfred Haines Charitable
 Trust
The W A Handley Charitable
 Trust
The Hawthorne Charitable
 Trust
The Headley Trust
The Hedley Foundation
The Charles Littlewood Hill
 Trust
The Hilmarnan Charitable Trust
The Hull and East Riding
 Charitable Trust
Miss Agnes H Hunter's Trust
The Iliffe Family Charitable
 Trust
The J J Charitable Trust
The Jeffrey Charitable Trust
The Jones 1986 Charitable
 Trust
The Judith Trust
The Ian Karten Charitable
 Trust
The Sir James Knott Trust
The KPMG Foundation
The Kirby Laing Foundation
The Beatrice Laing Trust
Duchy of Lancaster Benevolent
 Fund
The Linbury Trust
The Enid Linder Foundation
Lloyds Bank Foundation for
 England and Wales
London Catalyst
The Lord's Taverners
Ian Mactaggart Trust
Magdalen Hospital Trust
The Michael Marsh Charitable
 Trust
The Tony Metherell Charitable
 Trust
Miles Trust for the Putney and
 Roehampton Community
The Hugh and Mary Miller
 Bequest Trust
The Peter Minet Trust
John Moores Foundation
Morgan Stanley International
 Foundation
Murphy-Neumann Charity
 Company Limited
The Kitty and Daniel Nabarro
 Charitable Trust
The Neighbourly Charitable
 Trust
The Northern Rock Foundation
The Noswad Charity
The Nottingham General
 Dispensary
The Nuffield Foundation
The Parthenon Trust
The Susanna Peake Charitable
 Trust

The Persula Foundation
The Pilkington Charities Fund
The Platinum Trust
The Ponton House Trust
The Douglas Prestwich
   Charitable Trust
The Red Rose Charitable Trust
Relief Fund for Romania
   Limited
The Clive Richards Charity
The Richmond Parish Lands
   Charity
Rix-Thompson-Rothenberg
   Foundation
The Robertson Trust
The Cecil Rosen Foundation
The Rowlands Trust
The Saddlers' Company
   Charitable Fund
The Sylvia and Colin Shepherd
   Charitable Trust
The Shirley Foundation
Community Foundation for
   Shropshire and Telford
The Mrs Smith and Mount
   Trust
David Solomons Charitable
   Trust
St James's Place Foundation
The Strangward Trust
The Summerfield Charitable
   Trust
The C Paul Thackray General
   Charitable Trust
The Three Guineas Trust
Vision Charity
John Watson's Trust
The Will Charitable Trust
Woodlands Trust
The Woodward Charitable
   Trust
The Xerox (UK) Trust

■ **People with autism**

The Girdlers' Company
   Charitable Trust
The Headley Trust
Magdalen Hospital Trust
The Shirley Foundation
The Three Guineas Trust

■ **People with
   dyslexia**

The Joseph and Annie Cattle
   Trust
The J J Charitable Trust
The KPMG Foundation
The Linbury Trust
Vision Charity

■ **People with
learning difficulties**

The Aberbrothock Skea Trust
The Sylvia Adams Charitable
   Trust
The Green and Lilian F M
   Ainsworth and Family
   Benevolent Fund
The Baily Thomas Charitable
   Fund
Blakemore Foundation
The J Reginald Corah
   Foundation Fund
Douglas Arter Foundation
The Drapers' Charitable Fund
The Dumbreck Charity
The W E Dunn Trust
Eastern Counties Educational
   Trust Limited
The EBM Charitable Trust
The John Ellerman Foundation
James Ellis Charitable Trust
The Eveson Charitable Trust
Esmée Fairbairn Foundation
The Forbes Charitable
   Foundation
Ford Britain Trust
The Oliver Ford Charitable
   Trust
The Jill Franklin Trust
The Hugh Fraser Foundation
The Joseph Strong Frazer Trust
The Freemasons' Grand
   Charity
The Gatsby Charitable
   Foundation
The Robert Gavron Charitable
   Trust
Simon Gibson Charitable Trust
The Gosling Foundation
   Limited
The Green Hall Foundation
Greggs Foundation
The Grocers' Charity
The Alfred Haines Charitable
   Trust
The W A Handley Charitable
   Trust
The Hawthorne Charitable
   Trust
The Hedley Foundation
The Charles Littlewood Hill
   Trust
The Hilmarnan Charitable Trust
The Hull and East Riding
   Charitable Trust
The Iliffe Family Charitable
   Trust
The Jeffrey Charitable Trust
The Jones 1986 Charitable
   Trust
The Judith Trust
The Ian Karten Charitable
   Trust
The Sir James Knott Trust
The Kirby Laing Foundation

Duchy of Lancaster Benevolent
   Fund
The Enid Linder Foundation
Lloyds Bank Foundation for
   England and Wales
London Catalyst
The Lord's Taverners
Ian Mactaggart Trust
Magdalen Hospital Trust
The Michael Marsh Charitable
   Trust
The Tony Metherell Charitable
   Trust
Miles Trust for the Putney and
   Roehampton Community
The Hugh and Mary Miller
   Bequest Trust
The Peter Minet Trust
John Moores Foundation
Morgan Stanley International
   Foundation
Murphy-Neumann Charity
   Company Limited
The Kitty and Daniel Nabarro
   Charitable Trust
The Neighbourly Charitable
   Trust
The Northern Rock Foundation
The Noswad Charity
The Nottingham General
   Dispensary
The Nuffield Foundation
The Parthenon Trust
The Susanna Peake Charitable
   Trust
The Persula Foundation
The Pilkington Charities Fund
The Platinum Trust
The Ponton House Trust
The Douglas Prestwich
   Charitable Trust
Relief Fund for Romania
   Limited
The Clive Richards Charity
The Richmond Parish Lands
   Charity
Rix-Thompson-Rothenberg
   Foundation
The Robertson Trust
The Cecil Rosen Foundation
The Rowlands Trust
The Saddlers' Company
   Charitable Fund
The Sylvia and Colin Shepherd
   Charitable Trust
Community Foundation for
   Shropshire and Telford
The Mrs Smith and Mount
   Trust
St James's Place Foundation
The Summerfield Charitable
   Trust
The C Paul Thackray General
   Charitable Trust
The Will Charitable Trust
Woodlands Trust

The Woodward Charitable Trust

The Xerox (UK) Trust

....

■ People with a physical impairment

The 1989 Willan Charitable Trust

The Aberbrothock Skea Trust

The Sylvia Adams Charitable Trust

The Adamson Trust

The Green and Lilian F M Ainsworth and Family Benevolent Fund

The Ajahma Charitable Trust

Blakemore Foundation

The De Brye Charitable Trust

The Dibden Allotments Fund

Douglas Arter Foundation

The Drapers' Charitable Fund

The Dumbreck Charity

The W E Dunn Trust

The EBM Charitable Trust

The John Ellerman Foundation

James Ellis Charitable Trust

The Emerton-Christie Charity

The Eveson Charitable Trust

Esmée Fairbairn Foundation

The Follett Trust

Ford Britain Trust

The Donald Forrester Trust

The Jill Franklin Trust

The Hugh Fraser Foundation

The Freemasons' Grand Charity

The Frognal Trust

The Gatsby Charitable Foundation

The Robert Gavron Charitable Trust

Simon Gibson Charitable Trust

The Girdlers' Company Charitable Trust

The Gosling Foundation Limited

The Green Hall Foundation

Greggs Foundation

The Grocers' Charity

H C D Memorial Fund

The Hadley Trust

The Hadrian Trust

The Alfred Haines Charitable Trust

The W A Handley Charitable Trust

The Peter Harrison Foundation

The Hawthorne Charitable Trust

The Headley Trust

The Hedley Foundation

The Charles Littlewood Hill Trust

The Hilmarnan Charitable Trust

The Hospital Saturday Fund

The Hull and East Riding Charitable Trust

Miss Agnes H Hunter's Trust

The Iliffe Family Charitable Trust

The Jones 1986 Charitable Trust

The Anton Jurgens Charitable Trust

The Ian Karten Charitable Trust

The Sir James Knott Trust

The Kirby Laing Foundation

The Beatrice Laing Trust

Duchy of Lancaster Benevolent Fund

Mrs F B Laurence Charitable Trust

Lifeline 4 Kids

The Enid Linder Foundation

Lloyds Bank Foundation for England and Wales

London Catalyst

The Lord's Taverners

The R S Macdonald Charitable Trust

Ian Mactaggart Trust

The Michael Marsh Charitable Trust

The Mercers' Charitable Foundation

The Tony Metherell Charitable Trust

Miles Trust for the Putney and Roehampton Community

The Hugh and Mary Miller Bequest Trust

Milton Keynes Community Foundation

The Peter Minet Trust

John Moores Foundation

Morgan Stanley International Foundation

Murphy-Neumann Charity Company Limited

The Neighbourly Charitable Trust

Newby Trust Limited

The Northern Rock Foundation

The Noswad Charity

The Nottingham General Dispensary

The Parthenon Trust

The Peacock Charitable Trust

The Susanna Peake Charitable Trust

The Dowager Countess Eleanor Peel Trust

The Persula Foundation

The Pilkington Charities Fund

The Platinum Trust

The Ponton House Trust

The Douglas Prestwich Charitable Trust

Richard Radcliffe Charitable Trust

The Red Rose Charitable Trust

Relief Fund for Romania Limited

The Clive Richards Charity

The Richmond Parish Lands Charity

The Robertson Trust

Mrs L D Rope Third Charitable Settlement

The Cecil Rosen Foundation

The Rowlands Trust

Royal Docks Trust (London)

The Saddlers' Company Charitable Fund

The Sylvia and Colin Shepherd Charitable Trust

Community Foundation for Shropshire and Telford

St James's Place Foundation

The Strangward Trust

The Summerfield Charitable Trust

Woodlands Trust

The Woodward Charitable Trust

The Xerox (UK) Trust

....

■ People with a sensory impairment

Blakemore Foundation

Blatchington Court Trust

The British Council for Prevention of Blindness

The Charities Advisory Trust

The John Cowan Foundation

The De Brye Charitable Trust

The Wilfred and Elsie Elkes Charity Fund

James Ellis Charitable Trust

The Eveson Charitable Trust

The Joseph Strong Frazer Trust

The Frognal Trust

The Girdlers' Company Charitable Trust

The Dorothy Hay-Bolton Charitable Trust

The Anne Herd Memorial Trust

Miss Agnes H Hunter's Trust

The Lillie Johnson Charitable Trust

The Jungels-Winkler Charitable Foundation

The Anton Jurgens Charitable Trust

The John Spedan Lewis Foundation

The R S Macdonald Charitable Trust

Brian Mercer Charitable Trust

The Tony Metherell Charitable Trust

Mickleham Charitable Trust

Gerald Micklem Charitable Trust

The Northwood Charitable
  Trust
The Persula Foundation
Richard Radcliffe Charitable
  Trust
The Max Reinhardt Charitable
  Trust
The Worshipful Company of
  Spectacle Makers' Charity
The Ulverscroft Foundation
Vision Charity
The Will Charitable Trust

....

■ Hearing loss

The Wilfred and Elsie Elkes
  Charity Fund
The Eveson Charitable Trust
The Joseph Strong Frazer Trust
The Girdlers' Company
  Charitable Trust
The Northwood Charitable
  Trust
The Persula Foundation
The Max Reinhardt Charitable
  Trust

....

■ Sight loss

Blatchington Court Trust
The British Council for
  Prevention of Blindness
The John Cowan Foundation
The De Brye Charitable Trust
The Wilfred and Elsie Elkes
  Charity Fund
The Eveson Charitable Trust
The Joseph Strong Frazer Trust
The Frognal Trust
The Girdlers' Company
  Charitable Trust
The Anne Herd Memorial Trust
Miss Agnes H Hunter's Trust
The Jungels-Winkler Charitable
  Foundation
The R S Macdonald Charitable
  Trust
Brian Mercer Charitable Trust
Mickleham Charitable Trust
The Persula Foundation
The Worshipful Company of
  Spectacle Makers' Charity
The Ulverscroft Foundation
Vision Charity
The Will Charitable Trust

Ethnicity

The Big Lottery Fund
Cherry Grove Charitable Trust
The Evan Cornish Foundation
The Desmond Foundation
Dorset Community Foundation
The Englefield Charitable Trust

The Football Association
  National Sports Centre
  Trust
The Gamma Trust
Greenham Common
  Community Trust Limited
Greggs Foundation
The Hadrian Trust
Hampton Fuel Allotment
  Charity
The Harris Family Charitable
  Trust
The Graham High Charitable
  Trust
The Hospital of God at
  Greatham
The LankellyChase Foundation
Leicestershire and Rutland
  Community Foundation
The Joseph Levy Charitable
  Foundation
Lincolnshire Community
  Foundation
Lloyds Bank Foundation for
  England and Wales
Lloyds TSB Foundation for
  Scotland
The Trust for London
The Ann and David Marks
  Foundation
The Marsh Christian Trust
John Moores Foundation
Norfolk Community Foundation
Northamptonshire Community
  Foundation
The Northern Rock Foundation
The Jack Petchey Foundation
The Popocatepetl Trust
The Rashbass Family Trust
The Eleanor Rathbone
  Charitable Trust
The Sigrid Rausing Trust
The Alan and Babette
  Sainsbury Charitable Fund
Sparquote Limited
The Spero Foundation
The Sussex Community
  Foundation
Community Foundation Serving
  Tyne and Wear and
  Northumberland
The Valentine Charitable Trust
The Viznitz Foundation
Voluntary Action Fund (VAF)
The Wixamtree Trust

Faith

4 Charity Foundation
A W Charitable Trust
Achisomoch Aid Company
  Limited
Adenfirst Ltd
Aid to the Church in Need (UK)
All Saints Educational Trust
Alvor Charitable Trust

Amabrill Limited
Andrews Charitable Trust
Anpride Ltd
Ashburnham Thanksgiving
  Trust
B E Perl Charitable Trust
Bay Charitable Trust
BCH Trust
Bear Mordechai Ltd
Beatrice Hankey Foundation
  Limited
Beauland Ltd
Bourneheights Limited
Brian Abrams Charitable Trust
Brian and Jill Moss Charitable
  Trust
Bristol Archdeaconry Charity
Buckingham Trust
C and F Charitable Trust
C B and H H Taylor 1984 Trust
C E K Stern Charitable Trust
Carlee Ltd
Charitworth Limited
Cherry Grove Charitable Trust
Childs Charitable Trust
Closehelm Limited
Clydpride Ltd
Col-Reno Ltd
Community Foundation Serving
  Tyne and Wear and
  Northumberland
Daily Prayer Union Charitable
  Trust Limited
Dame Violet Wills Charitable
  Trust
Davis-Rubens Charitable Trust
Domepride Ltd
Dorset Community Foundation
Dushinsky Trust Ltd
E and E Kernkraut Charities
  Limited
Edna Brown Charitable
  Settlement (Mrs E E Brown
  Charitable Settlement)
Ellador Ltd
Elshore Ltd
Embrace the Middle East
Entindale Ltd
Erach and Roshan Sadri
  Foundation
Eric Abrams Charitable Trust
Evelyn May Trust
Extonglen Limited
Federation of Jewish Relief
  Organisations
Finnart House School Trust
Fordeve Limited
Friends of Biala Limited
Friends of Boyan Trust
Friends of Wiznitz Limited
G S Plaut Charitable Trust
  Limited
Garvan Limited
Global Care
Grace Dieu Charitable Trust
H and L Cantor Trust

Harbo Charities Limited
Haskel Family Foundation
Henry T and Lucy B Cadbury
    Charitable Trust
Hexham and Newcastle
    Diocesan Trust (1947)
Highcroft Charitable Trust
Hinchley Charitable Trust
Hurdale Charity Limited
I G O Foundation Limited
Infinity Capital Trust
Investream Charitable Trust
Itzchok Meyer Cymerman Trust
    Ltd
Jack Livingstone Charitable
    Trust
Jacobs Charitable Trust
Jay Education Trust
JCA Charitable Foundation
Jewish Child's Day
John Martin's Charity
Joseph Fattorini Charitable
    Trust
Keren Association
Keren Mitzvah Trust
Kermaville Ltd
Kirschel Foundation
Kollel and Co. Limited
Kupath Gemach Chaim
    Bechesed Viznitz Trust
L P W Limited
Largsmount Ltd
Lewis Family Charitable Trust
Lindale Educational
    Foundation
Localtrent Ltd
Macdonald-Buchanan
    Charitable Trust
Malbin Trust
Marbeh Torah Trust
Mariapolis Limited
Maurice and Hilda Laing
    Charitable Trust
Mayfair Charities Ltd
Mejer and Gertrude Miriam
    Frydman Foundation
Melodor Limited
Melow Charitable Trust
Menuchar Ltd
Mercaz Torah Vechesed
    Limited
Michael Cornish Charitable
    Trust
Miles Trust for the Putney and
    Roehampton Community
Morris Leigh Foundation
Moshal Charitable Trust
Mrs Vera Leigh's Charity
Muslim Hands
MW (CL) Foundation
MW (GK) Foundation
MW (HO) Foundation
MW (RH) Foundation
MYA Charitable Trust
MYR Charitable Trust

National Committee of the
    Women's World Day of
    Prayer for England and
    Wales and Northern Ireland
Nemoral Ltd
Ner Foundation
Nesswall Ltd
NJD Charitable Trust
Normalyn Charitable Trust
Novi Most International
Oizer Charitable Trust
Oizer Dalim Trust
P G and N J Boulton Trust
Porticus UK
Premishlaner Charitable Trust
Quothquan Trust
R J M Charitable Trust
R S Charitable Trust
Richard Cloudesley's Charity
Rosalyn and Nicholas Springer
    Charitable Trust
Rowanville Ltd
S C and M E Morland's
    Charitable Trust
S F Foundation
S O Charitable Trust
Saint Luke's College
    Foundation
Salo Bordon Charitable Trust
Sellata Ltd
Shlomo Memorial Fund Limited
Sir Clive Bourne Family Trust
Sir Halley Stewart Trust
Sir Harold Hood's Charitable
    Trust
Sir John Priestman Charity
    Trust
Six Point Foundation
Sparquote Limited
Springrule Limited
St Christopher's Educational
    Trust (incorporating the
    Hughes and Stevens
    Bequest)
St Hilda's Trust
Stephen Zimmerman
    Charitable Trust
Stervon Ltd
Swansea and Brecon Diocesan
    Board of Finance Limited
Sylvanus Lyson's Charity
T and S Trust Fund
The A B Strom and R Strom
    Charitable Trust
The Acacia Charitable Trust
The Adint Charitable Trust
The Adrienne and Leslie
    Sussman Charitable Trust
The Alexis Trust
The Alliance Family Foundation
The Almond Trust
The AMW Charitable Trust
The Anchor Foundation
The Andrew Anderson Trust
The Ann and David Marks
    Foundation

The Annie Schiff Charitable
    Trust
The Archie Sherman Charitable
    Trust
The Arnold Burton 1998
    Charitable Trust
The Arnold Lee Charitable
    Trust
The B and P Glasser
    Charitable Trust
The Baker Charitable Trust
The Benjamin Winegarten
    Charitable Trust
The Bernard Kahn Charitable
    Trust
The Bishop Radford Trust
The Bonamy Charitable Trust
The C L Loyd Charitable Trust
The C S Kaufman Charitable
    Trust
The Catholic Trust for England
    and Wales
The CH (1980) Charitable
    Trust
The Charles Lloyd Foundation
The Charles Wolfson
    Charitable Trust
The Childwick Trust
The Christabella Charitable
    Trust
The Clive Richards Charity
The Clore Duffield Foundation
The Clover Trust
The Corona Charitable Trust
The Costa Family Charitable
    Trust
The Craps Charitable Trust
The Cuby Charitable Trust
The Cumber Family Charitable
    Trust
The Cyril Shack Trust
The Daniel Howard Trust
The David Pearlman Charitable
    Foundation
The David Pickford Charitable
    Foundation
The David Tannen Charitable
    Trust
The David Uri Memorial Trust
The Davidson Family
    Charitable Trust
The Debmar Benevolent Trust
The Dellal Foundation
The Djanogly Foundation
The DM Charitable Trust
The Dollond Charitable Trust
The Doris Pacey Charitable
    Foundation
The Doughty Charity Trust
The Duke of Cornwall's
    Benevolent Fund
The Edith Maud Ellis 1985
    Charitable Trust
The Ellinson Foundation Ltd
The Emmanuel Kaye
    Foundation

The Englefield Charitable Trust
The Esfandi Charitable
 Foundation
The Exilarch's Foundation
The Fanny Rapaport Charitable
 Settlement
The Forest Hill Charitable Trust
The Forte Charitable Trust
The Friends Hall Farm Street
 Trust
The G I Foundation
The Gamma Trust
The Geoffrey John Kaye
 Charitable Foundation
The George Balint Charitable
 Trust
The George Elias Charitable
 Trust
The George Müller Charitable
 Trust
The Gerald Fogel Charitable
 Trust
The Gerald Ronson Foundation
The Gershon Coren Charitable
 Foundation (also known as
 The Muriel and Gus Coren
 Charitable Foundation)
The GNC Trust
The Grahame Charitable
 Foundation Limited
The Gur Trust
The H P Charitable Trust
The Harold Hyam Wingate
 Foundation
The Harold Joels Charitable
 Trust
The Harry Bottom Charitable
 Trust
The Helping Foundation
The Herd Lawson and Muriel
 Lawson Charitable Trust
The Hilda and Samuel Marks
 Foundation
The Holden Charitable Trust
The Hope Trust
The Humanitarian Trust
The Huntingdon Foundation
The Isaac and Freda Frankel
 Memorial Charitable Trust
The Isaacs Charitable Trust
The J E Joseph Charitable
 Fund
The J E Posnansky Charitable
 Trust
The J & J Benevolent
 Foundation
The J M K Charitable Trust
The James Trust
The Jane Hodge Foundation
The Jerusalem Trust
The Jewish Youth Fund
The John Warren Foundation
The Joseph Rank Trust
The Josephs Family Charitable
 Trust
The Judith Trust

The Kasner Charitable Trust
The Katzauer Charitable
 Settlement
The Kennedy Charitable
 Foundation
The Kohn Foundation
The Kreditor Charitable Trust
The Kyte Charitable Trust
The Lambert Charitable Trust
The Late Sir Pierce Lacy
 Charity Trust
The Lauffer Family Charitable
 Foundation
The Lawson Beckman
 Charitable Trust
The Leslie Silver Charitable
 Trust
The Lili Tapper Charitable
 Foundation
The Lincolnshire Churches
 Trust
The Lind Trust
The Lo Family Charitable Trust
The Locker Foundation
The Loftus Charitable Trust
The Lolev Charitable Trust
The Lowy Mitchell Foundation
The Lynwood Trust
The M and C Trust
The M and R Gross Charities
 Limited
The M J Samuel Charitable
 Trust
The M K Charitable Trust
The Magen Charitable Trust
The Mallinckrodt Foundation
The Manackerman Charitable
 Trust
The Manny Cussins
 Foundation
The Marjorie and Arnold Ziff
 Charitable Foundation
The Marjory Jameson Trust
The Marsh Christian Trust
The Mason Porter Charitable
 Trust
The Matt 6.3 Charitable Trust
The Maurice Hatter Foundation
The Maurice Wohl Charitable
 Foundation
The Metropolitan Masonic
 Charity
The Michael and Ilse Katz
 Foundation
The Minos Trust
The Mishcon Family Charitable
 Trust
The Mitchell Charitable Trust
The Modiano Charitable Trust
The Moette Charitable Trust
The Mole Charitable Trust
The Morgan Charitable
 Foundation
The Moss Family Charitable
 Trust
The Mutual Trust Group

The Nadezhda Charitable Trust
The Naggar Charitable Trust
The Neville and Elaine Blond
 Charitable Trust
The Nicholas Joels Charitable
 Trust
The Nora Joan Marshall
 Charitable Trust
The Norman Joels Charitable
 Trust
The Northampton Municipal
 Church Charities
The Norwood and Newton
 Settlement
The Ogle Christian Trust
The Oliver Morland Charitable
 Trust
The Owen Family Trust
The P B Dumbell Charitable
 Trust
The P Y N and B Hyams Trust
The Payne Charitable Trust
The Persson Charitable Trust
The Peter Morrison Charitable
 Foundation
The Phillips Family Charitable
 Trust
The Pollywally Charitable Trust
The Ravensdale Trust
The Rayden Charitable Trust
The Rayne Trust
The Rehoboth Trust
The Rest Harrow Trust
The Rhondda Cynon Taff
 Welsh Church Acts Fund
The Rock Solid Trust
The Roger and Sarah Bancroft
 Clark Charitable Trust
The Rubin Foundation
The Ruth and Jack Lunzer
 Charitable Trust
The Ruth Berkowitz Charitable
 Trust
The Ruzin Sadagora Trust
The Samuel Sebba Charitable
 Trust
The Sandy Dewhirst Charitable
 Trust
The Schmidt-Bodner Charitable
 Trust
The Schreib Trust
The Schreiber Charitable Trust
The Second Joseph Aaron
 Littman Foundation
The Sidney and Elizabeth
 Corob Charitable Trust
The Simpson Foundation
The Sir Jack Lyons Charitable
 Trust
The Sir James Reckitt Charity
The Sir John Ritblat Family
 Foundation
The Sir Victor Blank Charitable
 Settlement
The Solo Charitable
 Settlement

The Stanley Kalms Foundation
The Steinberg Family Charitable Trust
The Stella and Alexander Margulies Charitable Trust
The Stewards' Company Limited (incorporating the J W Laing Trust and the J W Laing Biblical Scholarship Trust)
The Strawberry Charitable Trust
The Susan and Stephen James Charitable Settlement
The Sussex Community Foundation
The SV and PE Magee Family Charitable Trust
The Tajtelbaum Charitable Trust
The Thomas Freke and Lady Norton Charity Trust
The Torah Temimah Trust
The Trust for London
The Tufton Charitable Trust
The Union of Orthodox Hebrew Congregation
The United Society for the Propagation of the Gospel
The Vail Foundation
The Valentine Charitable Trust
The Vardy Foundation
The Violet Mauray Charitable Trust
The Vivienne and Samuel Cohen Charitable Trust
The Weinstein Foundation
The William A Cadbury Charitable Trust
The Wixamtree Trust
The Wolfson Family Charitable Trust
Toras Chesed (London) Trust
Truedene Co. Ltd
Truemart Limited
Trustees of Tzedakah
Vivdale Ltd
William P Bancroft (No 2) Charitable Trust and Jenepher Gillett Trust
Woodlands Green Ltd
Wychdale Ltd
Wychville Ltd
Yankov Charitable Trust

....

■ **Christians**

Aid to the Church in Need (UK)
The Alexis Trust
All Saints Educational Trust
The Almond Trust
Alvor Charitable Trust
The AMW Charitable Trust
The Anchor Foundation
The Andrew Anderson Trust

Andrews Charitable Trust
Ashburnham Thanksgiving Trust
William P Bancroft (No 2) Charitable Trust and Jenepher Gillett Trust
The Harry Bottom Charitable Trust
P G and N J Boulton Trust
Bristol Archdeaconry Charity
Buckingham Trust
Henry T and Lucy B Cadbury Charitable Trust
The William A Cadbury Charitable Trust
The Catholic Trust for England and Wales
Childs Charitable Trust
The Christabella Charitable Trust
The Roger and Sarah Bancroft Clark Charitable Trust
Richard Cloudesley's Charity
The Clover Trust
Michael Cornish Charitable Trust
The Costa Family Charitable Trust
The Cumber Family Charitable Trust
Daily Prayer Union Charitable Trust Limited
Grace Dieu Charitable Trust
The P B Dumbell Charitable Trust
The Edith Maud Ellis 1985 Charitable Trust
Embrace the Middle East
The Englefield Charitable Trust
Joseph Fattorini Charitable Trust
The Forest Hill Charitable Trust
The Forte Charitable Trust
The Thomas Freke and Lady Norton Charity Trust
The Friends Hall Farm Street Trust
The Gamma Trust
Global Care
Beatrice Hankey Foundation Limited
Hexham and Newcastle Diocesan Trust (1947)
Hinchley Charitable Trust
The Jane Hodge Foundation
Sir Harold Hood's Charitable Trust
The Hope Trust
The James Trust
The Marjory Jameson Trust
The Jerusalem Trust
The Kennedy Charitable Foundation
The Late Sir Pierce Lacy Charity Trust

Maurice and Hilda Laing Charitable Trust
The Herd Lawson and Muriel Lawson Charitable Trust
The Lincolnshire Churches Trust
The Lind Trust
Lindale Educational Foundation
The Charles Lloyd Foundation
The Lo Family Charitable Trust
The Lynwood Trust
Sylvanus Lyson's Charity
Macdonald-Buchanan Charitable Trust
The SV and PE Magee Family Charitable Trust
The Mallinckrodt Foundation
Mariapolis Limited
The Marsh Christian Trust
The Nora Joan Marshall Charitable Trust
John Martin's Charity
The Mason Porter Charitable Trust
The Matt 6.3 Charitable Trust
Evelyn May Trust
Miles Trust for the Putney and Roehampton Community
The Minos Trust
The Oliver Morland Charitable Trust
S C and M E Morland's Charitable Trust
The George Müller Charitable Trust
The Nadezhda Charitable Trust
National Committee of the Women's World Day of Prayer for England and Wales and Northern Ireland
The Norwood and Newton Settlement
The Ogle Christian Trust
The Owen Family Trust
The Payne Charitable Trust
The Persson Charitable Trust
The David Pickford Charitable Foundation
G S Plaut Charitable Trust Limited
Sir John Priestman Charity Trust
Quothquan Trust
The Bishop Radford Trust
The Joseph Rank Trust
The Ravensdale Trust
The Sir James Reckitt Charity
The Rehoboth Trust
The Rhondda Cynon Taff Welsh Church Acts Fund
The Clive Richards Charity
The Rock Solid Trust
The Simpson Foundation

St Christopher's Educational Trust (incorporating the Hughes and Stevens Bequest)
St Hilda's Trust
The Stewards' Company Limited (incorporating the J W Laing Trust and the J W Laing Biblical Scholarship Trust)
Swansea and Brecon Diocesan Board of Finance Limited
C B and H H Taylor 1984 Trust
The Tufton Charitable Trust
The United Society for the Propagation of the Gospel
The John Warren Foundation
Dame Violet Wills Charitable Trust

....

■ People of the Jewish faith

4 Charity Foundation
A W Charitable Trust
Brian Abrams Charitable Trust
Eric Abrams Charitable Trust
The Acacia Charitable Trust
Achisomoch Aid Company Limited
Adenfirst Ltd
The Adint Charitable Trust
The Alliance Family Foundation
Amabrill Limited
Anpride Ltd
The Baker Charitable Trust
The George Balint Charitable Trust
Bay Charitable Trust
BCH Trust
Bear Mordechai Ltd
Beauland Ltd
The Ruth Berkowitz Charitable Trust
The Sir Victor Blank Charitable Settlement
The Neville and Elaine Blond Charitable Trust
The Bonamy Charitable Trust
Salo Bordon Charitable Trust
Sir Clive Bourne Family Trust
Bourneheights Limited
Edna Brown Charitable Settlement (Mrs E E Brown Charitable Settlement)
The Arnold Burton 1998 Charitable Trust
C and F Charitable Trust
H and L Cantor Trust
Carlee Ltd
The CH (1980) Charitable Trust
Charitworth Limited
The Childwick Trust
The Clore Duffield Foundation
Closehelm Limited

Clydpride Ltd
The Vivienne and Samuel Cohen Charitable Trust
Col-Reno Ltd
The Gershon Coren Charitable Foundation (also known as The Muriel and Gus Coren Charitable Foundation)
The Sidney and Elizabeth Corob Charitable Trust
The Corona Charitable Trust
The Manny Cussins Foundation
Itzchok Meyer Cymerman Trust Ltd
Oizer Dalim Trust
The Davidson Family Charitable Trust
Davis-Rubens Charitable Trust
The Debmar Benevolent Trust
The Dellal Foundation
The Djanogly Foundation
The DM Charitable Trust
The Dollond Charitable Trust
Domepride Ltd
The Doughty Charity Trust
Dushinsky Trust Ltd
The George Elias Charitable Trust
Ellador Ltd
The Ellinson Foundation Ltd
Elshore Ltd
Entindale Ltd
The Esfandi Charitable Foundation
The Exilarch's Foundation
Extonglen Limited
Federation of Jewish Relief Organisations
Finnart House School Trust
The Gerald Fogel Charitable Trust
Fordeve Limited
The Isaac and Freda Frankel Memorial Charitable Trust
Friends of Biala Limited
Friends of Boyan Trust
Friends of Wiznitz Limited
Mejer and Gertrude Miriam Frydman Foundation
The G I Foundation
Garvan Limited
The B and P Glasser Charitable Trust
The Grahame Charitable Foundation Limited
The M and R Gross Charities Limited
The Gur Trust
The H P Charitable Trust
Harbo Charities Limited
Haskel Family Foundation
The Maurice Hatter Foundation
The Helping Foundation
Highcroft Charitable Trust
The Holden Charitable Trust

The Daniel Howard Trust
The Humanitarian Trust
The Huntingdon Foundation
Hurdale Charity Limited
The P Y N and B Hyams Trust
I G O Foundation Limited
Infinity Capital Trust
Investream Charitable Trust
The Isaacs Charitable Trust
The J & J Benevolent Foundation
Jacobs Charitable Trust
The Susan and Stephen James Charitable Settlement
Jay Education Trust
JCA Charitable Foundation
Jewish Child's Day
The Jewish Youth Fund
The Harold Joels Charitable Trust
The Nicholas Joels Charitable Trust
The Norman Joels Charitable Trust
The J E Joseph Charitable Fund
The Josephs Family Charitable Trust
The Judith Trust
The Bernard Kahn Charitable Trust
The Stanley Kalms Foundation
The Kasner Charitable Trust
The Michael and Ilse Katz Foundation
The Katzauer Charitable Settlement
The C S Kaufman Charitable Trust
The Geoffrey John Kaye Charitable Foundation
The Emmanuel Kaye Foundation
Keren Association
Kermaville Ltd
E and E Kernkraut Charities Limited
Kirschel Foundation
The Kohn Foundation
Kollel and Co. Limited
The Kreditor Charitable Trust
Kupath Gemach Chaim Bechesed Viznitz Trust
The Kyte Charitable Trust
L P W Limited
The Lambert Charitable Trust
Largsmount Ltd
The Lauffer Family Charitable Foundation
The Lawson Beckman Charitable Trust
The Arnold Lee Charitable Trust
Morris Leigh Foundation
Lewis Family Charitable Trust

The Second Joseph Aaron Littman Foundation
Jack Livingstone Charitable Trust
Localtrent Ltd
The Locker Foundation
The Loftus Charitable Trust
The Lolev Charitable Trust
The Lowy Mitchell Foundation
The Ruth and Jack Lunzer Charitable Trust
The Sir Jack Lyons Charitable Trust
The M and C Trust
The M K Charitable Trust
The Magen Charitable Trust
Malbin Trust
The Manackerman Charitable Trust
Marbeh Torah Trust
The Stella and Alexander Margulies Charitable Trust
The Ann and David Marks Foundation
The Hilda and Samuel Marks Foundation
The Violet Mauray Charitable Trust
Mayfair Charities Ltd
Melodor Limited
Melow Charitable Trust
Menuchar Ltd
Mercaz Torah Vechesed Limited
The Mishcon Family Charitable Trust
The Mitchell Charitable Trust
Keren Mitzvah Trust
The Modiano Charitable Trust
The Moette Charitable Trust
The Mole Charitable Trust
The Morgan Charitable Foundation
The Peter Morrison Charitable Foundation
Moshal Charitable Trust
Brian and Jill Moss Charitable Trust
The Moss Family Charitable Trust
The Mutual Trust Group
MW (CL) Foundation
MW (GK) Foundation
MW (HO) Foundation
MW (RH) Foundation
MYA Charitable Trust
MYR Charitable Trust
The Naggar Charitable Trust
Nemoral Ltd
Ner Foundation
Nesswall Ltd
NJD Charitable Trust
Normalyn Charitable Trust
Oizer Charitable Trust
The Doris Pacey Charitable Foundation

The David Pearlman Charitable Foundation
B E Perl Charitable Trust
The Phillips Family Charitable Trust
G S Plaut Charitable Trust Limited
The Pollywally Charitable Trust
The J E Posnansky Charitable Trust
Premishlaner Charitable Trust
R J M Charitable Trust
R S Charitable Trust
The Fanny Rapaport Charitable Settlement
The Rayden Charitable Trust
The Rayne Trust
The Rest Harrow Trust
The Sir John Ritblat Family Foundation
The Gerald Ronson Foundation
Rowanville Ltd
The Rubin Foundation
S F Foundation
S O Charitable Trust
The Ruzin Sadagora Trust
The M J Samuel Charitable Trust
The Annie Schiff Charitable Trust
The Schmidt-Bodner Charitable Trust
The Schreib Trust
The Schreiber Charitable Trust
The Samuel Sebba Charitable Trust
Sellata Ltd
The Cyril Shack Trust
The Archie Sherman Charitable Trust
Shlomo Memorial Fund Limited
The Leslie Silver Charitable Trust
Six Point Foundation
The Solo Charitable Settlement
Sparquote Limited
Rosalyn and Nicholas Springer Charitable Trust
Springrule Limited
The Steinberg Family Charitable Trust
C E K Stern Charitable Trust
Stervon Ltd
The Strawberry Charitable Trust
The A B Strom and R Strom Charitable Trust
The Adrienne and Leslie Sussman Charitable Trust
T and S Trust Fund
The Tajtelbaum Charitable Trust
The David Tannen Charitable Trust

The Lili Tapper Charitable Foundation
The Torah Temimah Trust
Toras Chesed (London) Trust
Truedene Co. Ltd
Truemart Limited
Trustees of Tzedakah
The Union of Orthodox Hebrew Congregation
The David Uri Memorial Trust
The Vail Foundation
Vivdale Ltd
The Weinstein Foundation
The Benjamin Winegarten Charitable Trust
The Harold Hyam Wingate Foundation
The Maurice Wohl Charitable Foundation
The Wolfson Family Charitable Trust
Woodlands Green Ltd
Wychdale Ltd
Wychville Ltd
Yankov Charitable Trust
The Marjorie and Arnold Ziff Charitable Foundation
Stephen Zimmerman Charitable Trust

Gender and relationships

■ Adopted or fostered children

The Girdlers' Company Charitable Trust
Hampton Fuel Allotment Charity
The Hemby Trust
The Hospital of God at Greatham
The Hyde Charitable Trust
The Anton Jurgens Charitable Trust
John Lyon's Charity

■ Bereaved

Baron Davenport's Charity
The Hemby Trust
The Hospital of God at Greatham

■ Carers

The Alchemy Foundation
The Dulverton Trust
Esmée Fairbairn Foundation
The Fishmongers' Company's Charitable Trust
The Hugh Fraser Foundation

The Girdlers' Company
Charitable Trust
The Harris Charitable Trust
The Headley Trust
Heart of England Community
Foundation
The Hemby Trust
The Hospital of God at
Greatham
The Huddersfield Common
Good Trust
The Anton Jurgens Charitable
Trust
Lloyds Bank Foundation for
England and Wales
London Catalyst
John Lyon's Charity
The Zachary Merton and
George Woofindin
Convalescent Trust
John Moores Foundation
Norfolk Community Foundation
The Olga Charitable Trust
Mr and Mrs J A Pye's
Charitable Settlement
Rix-Thompson-Rothenberg
Foundation
The True Colours Trust

■ Families

Archbishop of Wales' Fund for
Children
Children's Liver Disease
Foundation
Hampton Fuel Allotment
Charity
Impetus – The Private Equity
Foundation (Impetus – PEF)
The Jigsaw Foundation
The Kelly Family Charitable
Trust
The Leverhulme Trade
Charities Trust
The Limbourne Trust
Lloyds Bank Foundation for
England and Wales
Lloyds Bank Foundation for
Northern Ireland
The R S Macdonald Charitable
Trust
Mariapolis Limited
The Charlotte Marshall
Charitable Trust
The Nottingham Gordon
Memorial Trust for Boys
and Girls
Porticus UK
Quothquan Trust
Relief Fund for Romania
Limited
Ryklow Charitable Trust 1992
(also known as A B
Williamson Charitable Trust)

■ Lesbians and gay men

Heart of England Community
Foundation
The Hospital of God at
Greatham
The Allen Lane Foundation
Voluntary Action Fund (VAF)

■ Men

The Premier League Charitable
Fund

■ Orphans

Archbishop of Wales' Fund for
Children
The De Brye Charitable Trust
The Girdlers' Company
Charitable Trust
The Hospital of God at
Greatham
Muslim Hands

■ Parents

The Girdlers' Company
Charitable Trust
The Glass-House Trust
Greggs Foundation
The Alfred Haines Charitable
Trust
Heart of England Community
Foundation
The Hemby Trust
The Hospital of God at
Greatham
The Hyde Charitable Trust
Lloyds Bank Foundation for
England and Wales
Lloyds Bank Foundation for
Northern Ireland
John Lyon's Charity
Mothercare Group Foundation
Quothquan Trust
The Tedworth Charitable Trust

■ Lone parents

The Girdlers' Company
Charitable Trust
The Alfred Haines Charitable
Trust
Heart of England Community
Foundation
The Hemby Trust
The Hospital of God at
Greatham
The Hyde Charitable Trust
John Lyon's Charity
Quothquan Trust

■ Women

The 1970 Trust
The A B Charitable Trust
The Ajahma Charitable Trust
The Associated Country
Women of the World
The Balmore Trust
The Jimmy Choo Foundation
Michael Cornish Charitable
Trust
Baron Davenport's Charity
The Freemasons' Grand
Charity
The Hemraj Goyal Foundation
Greggs Foundation
The Hadrian Trust
Heart of England Community
Foundation
The Horizon Foundation
The Hospital of God at
Greatham
The Judith Trust
The Allen Lane Foundation
The LankellyChase Foundation
Lloyds Bank Foundation for
Northern Ireland
The Lotus Foundation
R W Mann Trust
John Moores Foundation
Mosselson Charitable Trust
The Pilgrim Trust
The Eleanor Rathbone
Charitable Trust
The Sigrid Rausing Trust
The Reed Foundation
Rosa – the UK fund for women
and girls
The Staples Trust
The Tresillian Trust
Volant Charitable Trust

Ill health

The A B Charitable Trust
The Aberbrothock Skea Trust
The Sylvia Adams Charitable
Trust
The AMW Charitable Trust
Anglo American Group
Foundation
The Appletree Trust
Arthritis Research UK
The Arthur Ronald Dyer
Charitable Trust
Asthma UK
Autonomous Research
Charitable Trust
The Baker Charitable Trust
The Band Trust
The Barleycorn Trust
B-CH 1971 Charitable Trust
The Benfield Motors Charitable
Trust
The Ruth Berkowitz Charitable
Trust

The Big Lottery Fund
The BlackRock (UK) Charitable
    Trust
The Blagrave Trust
BOOST Charitable Trust
H E and E L Botteley
    Charitable Trust
The Tony Bramall Charitable
    Trust
John Bristow and Thomas
    Mason Trust
British Heart Foundation
The Charles Brotherton Trust
R S Brownless Charitable
    Trust
Buckingham Trust
The E F Bulmer Benevolent
    Fund
The Derek Butler Trust
Peter Cadbury Charitable Trust
Celtic Charity Fund
Champneys Charitable
    Foundation
Cherry Grove Charitable Trust
Child Growth Foundation
The City Bridge Trust
The Clover Trust
The Robert Clutterbuck
    Charitable Trust
Colyer-Fergusson Charitable
    Trust
The Consolidated Charities for
    the Infirm Merchant
    Taylors' Company
The Gershon Coren Charitable
    Foundation (also known as
    The Muriel and Gus Coren
    Charitable Foundation)
Michael Cornish Charitable
    Trust
The John Cowan Foundation
The Craps Charitable Trust
Michael Crawford Children's
    Charity
Criffel Charitable Trust
The Violet and Milo Cripps
    Charitable Trust
The Cumber Family Charitable
    Trust
Roald Dahl's Marvellous
    Children's Charity
The Sandy Dewhirst Charitable
    Trust
Diabetes UK
The Dorus Trust
Dromintee Trust
The W E Dunn Trust
Eastern Counties Educational
    Trust Limited
Gilbert Edgar Trust
The Wilfred and Elsie Elkes
    Charity Fund
The Ellerdale Trust
The John Ellerman Foundation
The Emerton-Christie Charity
The Englefield Charitable Trust

Epilepsy Research UK
The Patrick Evans Foundation
Sir John Evelyn's Charity
The Exilarch's Foundation
Esmée Fairbairn Foundation
The Family Rich Charities Trust
Joseph Fattorini Charitable
    Trust
The February Foundation
The A M Fenton Trust
Dixie Rose Findlay Charitable
    Trust
The Ian Fleming Charitable
    Trust
Florence's Charitable Trust
The Follett Trust
The Forte Charitable Trust
The Jill Franklin Trust
The Hugh Fraser Foundation
Maurice Fry Charitable Trust
The Fuserna Foundation
    General Charitable Trust
The Gamma Trust
Garthgwynion Charities
The Gatsby Charitable
    Foundation
The Generations Foundation
The David Gibbons Foundation
The Girdlers' Company
    Charitable Trust
The B and P Glasser
    Charitable Trust
Global Charities
The Gosling Foundation
    Limited
The Grand Order of Water
    Rats' Charities Fund
The J G Graves Charitable
    Trust
The Green Hall Foundation
Greenham Common
    Community Trust Limited
The Grimmitt Trust
The Bishop of Guildford's
    Foundation
The Hadley Trust
The Doris Louise Hailes
    Charitable Trust
Hampton Fuel Allotment
    Charity
The W A Handley Charitable
    Trust
The Harborne Parish Lands
    Charity
The Kenneth Hargreaves
    Charitable Trust
The Harris Family Charitable
    Trust
The John Harrison Charitable
    Trust
The Peter Harrison Foundation
May Hearnshaw's Charity
Heart of England Community
    Foundation
Heart Research UK

The Charlotte Heber-Percy
    Charitable Trust
The Hedley Foundation
The Hemby Trust
The High Sheriff's Police Trust
    for the County of West
    Midlands (Building Blocks)
R G Hills Charitable Trust
The Hilmarnan Charitable Trust
The Hintze Family Charitable
    Foundation
The Hospital of God at
    Greatham
HTA Sheba Foundation UK
The Hull and East Riding
    Charitable Trust
Human Relief Foundation
The Humanitarian Trust
The Albert Hunt Trust
Miss Agnes H Hunter's Trust
Huntingdon Freemen's Trust
The Iliffe Family Charitable
    Trust
The Inman Charity
The Charles Irving Charitable
    Trust
The Ruth and Lionel Jacobson
    Trust (Second Fund) No 2
The Jasper Conran Foundation
The Jenour Foundation
The Elton John Aids
    Foundation
The Johnson Foundation
The Jones 1986 Charitable
    Trust
The Dezna Robins Jones
    Charitable Foundation
The Judith Trust
The Anton Jurgens Charitable
    Trust
The Kalou Foundation
The Ian Karten Charitable
    Trust
The Michael and Ilse Katz
    Foundation
The Caron Keating Foundation
The Peter Kershaw Trust
Kettering and District
    Charitable Medical Trust
The Mary Kinross Charitable
    Trust
The Kohn Foundation
The Heinz, Anna and Carol
    Kroch Foundation
The Kirby Laing Foundation
The Beatrice Laing Trust
The Allen Lane Foundation
Langdale Trust
The Langley Charitable Trust
The LankellyChase Foundation
The R J Larg Family Charitable
    Trust
The Kathleen Laurence Trust
The Mason Le Page Charitable
    Trust
The Leach Fourteenth Trust

The Leigh Trust
Mrs Vera Leigh's Charity
Leukaemia and Lymphoma
 Research
The Joseph Levy Charitable
 Foundation
The Lewis Ward Trust
The Linbury Trust
Lincolnshire Community
 Foundation
The Linden Charitable Trust
Lloyds Bank Foundation for
 Northern Ireland
Lloyds TSB Foundation for
 Scotland
The Loftus Charitable Trust
John Lyon's Charity
The E M MacAndrew Trust
The Macfarlane Walker Trust
The Mackintosh Foundation
Ian Mactaggart Trust
Magdalen Hospital Trust
Malbin Trust
The Stella and Alexander
 Margulies Charitable Trust
The Marsh Christian Trust
The Charlotte Marshall
 Charitable Trust
The Jim Marshall Charitable
 Trust
John Martin's Charity
Matliwala Family Charitable
 Trust
The Maxwell Family Foundation
Evelyn May Trust
The McKenna Charitable Trust
Brian Mercer Charitable Trust
The Mercers' Charitable
 Foundation
The Merchants' House of
 Glasgow
Mercury Phoenix Trust
The Zachary Merton and
 George Woofindin
 Convalescent Trust
The Tony Metherell Charitable
 Trust
The Metropolitan Masonic
 Charity
Gerald Micklem Charitable
 Trust
Midhurst Pensions Trust
The Ronald Miller Foundation
The Montague Thompson
 Coon Charitable Trust
The Monument Trust
John Moores Foundation
The Peter Morrison Charitable
 Foundation
Moto in the Community
The Mugdock Children's Trust
The Edith Murphy Foundation
Peter John Murray Trust
Needham Market and Barking
 Welfare Charities
Norfolk Community Foundation

The Northampton Queen's
 Institute Relief in Sickness
 Fund
The Northern Rock Foundation
The Northwood Charitable
 Trust
The Owen Family Trust
The Panacea Society
The Park Charitable Trust
The Constance Paterson
 Charitable Trust
Paycare Charity Trust
The Pedmore Sporting Club
 Trust Fund
Pegasus (Stanley) Trust
The Pilgrim Trust
G S Plaut Charitable Trust
 Limited
The Pollywally Charitable Trust
The Mary Potter Convent
 Hospital Trust
Sir John Priestman Charity
 Trust
The Provincial Grand Charity of
 the Province of Derbyshire
Mr and Mrs J A Pye's
 Charitable Settlement
Quothquan Trust
Richard Radcliffe Charitable
 Trust
The Ravensdale Trust
Relief Fund for Romania
 Limited
Thomas Roberts Trust
The Robertson Trust
Robyn Charitable Trust
The Christopher Rowbotham
 Charitable Trust
The Rowlands Trust
The Andrew Salvesen
 Charitable Trust
The M J Samuel Charitable
 Trust
The Seneca Trust
Community Foundation for
 Shropshire and Telford
The Smith & Pinching
 Charitable Trust
The Snowball Trust
The Sovereign Health Care
 Charitable Trust
Sparquote Limited
Split Infinitive Trust
St James's Place Foundation
Sir Halley Stewart Trust
The Sussex Community
 Foundation
Swan Mountain Trust
The Talbot Trusts
The Connie and Albert Taylor
 Charitable Trust
The Thornton Trust
The John Raymond Tijou
 Charitable Trust
The Tory Family Foundation
The True Colours Trust

The James Tudor Foundation
The Valentine Charitable Trust
The Variety Club Children's
 Charity
The Vintners' Company
 Charitable Foundation
Volant Charitable Trust
Voluntary Action Fund (VAF)
The Weinstein Foundation
The Welton Foundation
The Garfield Weston
 Foundation
The Lionel Wigram Memorial
 Trust
The Will Charitable Trust
The HDH Wills 1965
 Charitable Trust
The Wixamtree Trust
The Charles Wolfson
 Charitable Trust
The Wolfson Family Charitable
 Trust
Woodlands Trust
The Woodward Charitable
 Trust
ME Woolfe Charitable Trust
The Matthews Wrightson
 Charity Trust
The Wyseliot Charitable Trust
The Xerox (UK) Trust

....

■ **People with
 cardiovascular
 disorders**

British Heart Foundation
The John Cowan Foundation
The Girdlers' Company
 Charitable Trust
Heart Research UK
The Kathleen Laurence Trust
Gerald Micklem Charitable
 Trust
The Park Charitable Trust

....

■ **People with
 glandular and
 endocrine disorders**

Child Growth Foundation
Diabetes UK
The Girdlers' Company
 Charitable Trust

....

■ **People with
 immune system
 disorders**

Anglo American Group
 Foundation
The Derek Butler Trust
The Jasper Conran Foundation
The Elton John Aids
 Foundation

Lloyds Bank Foundation for
 Northern Ireland
The Mackintosh Foundation
Magdalen Hospital Trust
Mercury Phoenix Trust
Gerald Micklem Charitable
 Trust
The Monument Trust
John Moores Foundation
The True Colours Trust

■ People with a mental impairment

The A B Charitable Trust
The Sylvia Adams Charitable
 Trust
Eastern Counties Educational
 Trust Limited
The John Ellerman Foundation
The Hugh Fraser Foundation
The Fuserna Foundation
 General Charitable Trust
The Gatsby Charitable
 Foundation
The Girdlers' Company
 Charitable Trust
The Hadley Trust
The Peter Harrison Foundation
The Iliffe Family Charitable
 Trust
The Inman Charity
The Charles Irving Charitable
 Trust
The Judith Trust
The Ian Karten Charitable
 Trust
The Mary Kinross Charitable
 Trust
The Kohn Foundation
The Kirby Laing Foundation
The Beatrice Laing Trust
The Allen Lane Foundation
The LankellyChase Foundation
John Lyon's Charity
The Mercers' Charitable
 Foundation
Norfolk Community Foundation
The Northern Rock Foundation
The Pilgrim Trust
Relief Fund for Romania
 Limited
The M J Samuel Charitable
 Trust
Swan Mountain Trust
Woodlands Trust

■ People with musculoskeletal disorders

Arthritis Research UK
The John Cowan Foundation
Miss Agnes H Hunter's Trust
The Kathleen Laurence Trust

■ People with neurological disorders

The John Cowan Foundation
Roald Dahl's Marvellous
 Children's Charity
The Wilfred and Elsie Elkes
 Charity Fund
Epilepsy Research UK
Dixie Rose Findlay Charitable
 Trust
The Forte Charitable Trust
The Girdlers' Company
 Charitable Trust
The John Harrison Charitable
 Trust
The Hospital of God at
 Greatham
Gerald Micklem Charitable
 Trust
The Monument Trust
The Owen Family Trust

■ People with oncological disorders

Peter Cadbury Charitable Trust
The John Cowan Foundation
The Patrick Evans Foundation
The Girdlers' Company
 Charitable Trust
Miss Agnes H Hunter's Trust
The Caron Keating Foundation
The R J Larg Family Charitable
 Trust
Leukaemia and Lymphoma
 Research
The Mackintosh Foundation
Brian Mercer Charitable Trust
The Tony Metherell Charitable
 Trust
The Owen Family Trust
The Park Charitable Trust
The Will Charitable Trust

■ People with respiratory disorders

The Girdlers' Company
 Charitable Trust
Miss Agnes H Hunter's Trust
Relief Fund for Romania
 Limited

■ People with skin disorders

The Lewis Ward Trust

■ People who are substance misusers

Celtic Charity Fund
Gilbert Edgar Trust
Esmée Fairbairn Foundation
The High Sheriff's Police Trust
 for the County of West
 Midlands (Building Blocks)
The Leigh Trust
The Linbury Trust
John Lyon's Charity
The Mercers' Charitable
 Foundation
John Moores Foundation
Norfolk Community Foundation
The Northern Rock Foundation
The Pilgrim Trust
The Robertson Trust
The Vintners' Company
 Charitable Foundation
Woodlands Trust
The Woodward Charitable
 Trust

■ Palliative care

Peter Cadbury Charitable Trust
The John Cowan Foundation
Joseph Fattorini Charitable
 Trust
The Girdlers' Company
 Charitable Trust
The Green Hall Foundation
The Peter Harrison Foundation
The Hedley Foundation
The Caron Keating Foundation
The Zachary Merton and
 George Woofindin
 Convalescent Trust
The Mugdock Children's Trust
Norfolk Community Foundation
Richard Radcliffe Charitable
 Trust
St James's Place Foundation
The Connie and Albert Taylor
 Charitable Trust
The True Colours Trust
The James Tudor Foundation
The Xerox (UK) Trust

Nationality

■ Asian

Matliwala Family Charitable
 Trust
Sino-British Fellowship Trust

The W Wing Yip and Brothers
Foundation

....

■ Eastern European

Armenian General Benevolent
Union London Trust
The Armenian Relief Society of
Great Britain Trust
Golubovich Foundation
The Manoukian Charitable
Foundation
Saint Sarkis Charity Trust

....

■ Southern European

Calouste Gulbenkian
Foundation – UK Branch
The Lyras Family Charitable
Trust

Social or economic circumstances

The 1970 Trust
The 1989 Willan Charitable
Trust
The 29th May 1961 Charitable
Trust
The A B Charitable Trust
Access Sport
The ACT Foundation
The Company of Actuaries'
Charitable Trust Fund
The Sylvia Adams Charitable
Trust
The Green and Lilian F M
Ainsworth and Family
Benevolent Fund
The Ajahma Charitable Trust
The Alchemy Foundation
The Aldgate Freedom
Foundation
The Allen Lane Trust
The Alliance Family Foundation
The Pat Allsop Charitable Trust
The Bryan and June Amos
Foundation
Andrews Charitable Trust
The Appletree Trust
The John Apthorp Charity
The Archer Trust
The Ashden Trust
The Ashendene Trust
AstonMansfield Charitable
Trust
Autonomous Research
Charitable Trust
Awards for All
The Scott Bader
Commonwealth Ltd
The George Balint Charitable
Trust
The Band Trust

The Bank of Scotland
Foundation
The Barleycorn Trust
Barnes Workhouse Fund
Baruch Family Charitable Trust
The Jack and Ada Beattie
Foundation
The Beit Trust
The Bellahouston Bequest
Fund
The Bellinger Donnay Trust
The Benfield Motors Charitable
Trust
Bennett Lowell Limited
Bergqvist Charitable Trust
The Big Lottery Fund
Percy Bilton Charity
The BlackRock (UK) Charitable
Trust
The Boltini Trust
The Oliver Borthwick Memorial
Trust
H E and E L Botteley
Charitable Trust
P G and N J Boulton Trust
The Breadsticks Foundation
The Bridging Fund Charitable
Trust
John Bristow and Thomas
Mason Trust
The Bromley Trust
R S Brownless Charitable
Trust
Buckingham Trust
The E F Bulmer Benevolent
Fund
Bumba Foundation
Consolidated Charity of Burton
upon Trent
The Worshipful Company of
Butchers General Charities
The Noel Buxton Trust
Henry T and Lucy B Cadbury
Charitable Trust
The William A Cadbury
Charitable Trust
The Barrow Cadbury Trust and
the Barrow Cadbury Fund
CAFOD (Catholic Agency for
Overseas Development)
The Calpe Trust
Calypso Browning Trust
The Campden Charities
Trustee
The Charities Advisory Trust
Cherry Grove Charitable Trust
Chesterhill Charitable Trust
The Chetwode Foundation
The Chrimes Family Charitable
Trust
Christadelphian Samaritan
Fund
Christian Aid
Chrysalis Trust
Church Urban Fund
The City Bridge Trust

CLA Charitable Trust
The Cleopatra Trust
The Clore Duffield Foundation
Closehelm Limited
Richard Cloudesley's Charity
The Clover Trust
The Vivienne and Samuel
Cohen Charitable Trust
The R and S Cohen
Foundation
The Coltstaple Trust
Colyer-Fergusson Charitable
Trust
Comic Relief
The Consolidated Charities for
the Infirm Merchant
Taylors' Company
The Cooks Charity
The Helen Jean Cope Trust
Michael Cornish Charitable
Trust
The Evan Cornish Foundation
The Duke of Cornwall's
Benevolent Fund
The Cotton Trust
Coutts Charitable Foundation
The Craps Charitable Trust
Michael Crawford Children's
Charity
The Crerar Hotels Trust
Criffel Charitable Trust
The Violet and Milo Cripps
Charitable Trust
The Cumber Family Charitable
Trust
Cumbria Community
Foundation
The Dawe Charitable Trust
The Sandy Dewhirst Charitable
Trust
The Peter Alan Dickson
Foundation
Disability Aid Fund (The Roger
and Jean Jefcoate Trust)
The Novak Djokovic Foundation
(UK) Limited
The Dorfred Charitable Trust
Dorset Community Foundation
The Dorus Trust
The Double 'O' Charity Ltd
The Doughty Charity Trust
The Drapers' Charitable Fund
Dromintee Trust
The Duis Charitable Trust
The Royal Foundation of the
Duke and Duchess of
Cambridge and Prince Harry
The P B Dumbell Charitable
Trust
The W E Dunn Trust
Eastern Counties Educational
Trust Limited
The Ebenezer Trust
The EBM Charitable Trust
The Gilbert and Eileen Edgar
Foundation

Gilbert Edgar Trust
Edge Fund
Dr Edwards Bishop King's
Fulham Endowment Fund
The George Elias Charitable
Trust
The Wilfred and Elsie Elkes
Charity Fund
The Ellerdale Trust
The John Ellerman Foundation
The Ellinson Foundation Ltd
The Edith Maud Ellis 1985
Charitable Trust
The Ellis Campbell Foundation
The Emerton-Christie Charity
The Endure Foundation
The Englefield Charitable Trust
The Enkalon Foundation
The Epigoni Trust
The Ericson Trust
Euro Charity Trust
Sir John Evelyn's Charity
The Eveson Charitable Trust
The Exilarch's Foundation
The Expat Foundation
Esmée Fairbairn Foundation
The George Fentham
Birmingham Charity
The Doris Field Charitable
Trust
The Fifty Fund
Fisherbeck Charitable Trust
The Fishmongers' Company's
Charitable Trust
The Ian Fleming Charitable
Trust
The Follett Trust
The Anna Rosa Forster
Charitable Trust
Sydney E Franklin Deceased's
New Second Charity
The Jill Franklin Trust
The Hugh Fraser Foundation
The Freemasons' Grand
Charity
Friends Provident Charitable
Foundation
The Patrick & Helena Frost
Foundation
Maurice Fry Charitable Trust
The Fuserna Foundation
General Charitable Trust
The G D Charitable Trust
The G I Foundation
Gamlen Charitable Trust
The Gannochy Trust
Garthgwynion Charities
The Gatsby Charitable
Foundation
The Robert Gavron Charitable
Trust
Jacqueline and Michael Gee
Charitable Trust
The Generations Foundation
The Steven Gerrard Foundation
The David Gibbons Foundation

The G C Gibson Charitable
Trust
The Girdlers' Company
Charitable Trust
Global Care
Global Charities
The GNC Trust
The Goodman Foundation
The J G Graves Charitable
Trust
The Green Hall Foundation
Mrs H R Greene Charitable
Settlement
Greggs Foundation
The Grocers' Charity
The David and Marie Grumitt
Foundation
The Bishop of Guildford's
Foundation
H C D Memorial Fund
The Hackney Parochial
Charities
The Hadley Trust
The Alfred Haines Charitable
Trust
Paul Hamlyn Foundation
The Helen Hamlyn Trust
Sue Hammerson Charitable
Trust
Hampton Fuel Allotment
Charity
Beatrice Hankey Foundation
Limited
The Kathleen Hannay
Memorial Charity
The Haramead Trust
The Harbour Foundation
William Harding's Charity
The Kenneth Hargreaves
Charitable Trust
The Harpur Trust
The Harrison and Potter Trust
The Peter Harrison Foundation
The Charles Hayward
Foundation
May Hearnshaw's Charity
Heart of England Community
Foundation
Help the Homeless
The Hemby Trust
Henley Educational Trust
(formerley Henley
Educational Charity)
The High Sheriff's Police Trust
for the County of West
Midlands (Building Blocks)
Highcroft Charitable Trust
The Hilden Charitable Fund
R G Hills Charitable Trust
The Hilmarnan Charitable Trust
Hobson Charity Limited
The Horne Foundation
The Horne Trust
The Hornsey Parochial
Charities

The Hospital of God at
Greatham
HTA Sheba Foundation UK
The Huddersfield Common
Good Trust
Human Relief Foundation
The Humanitarian Trust
The Michael and Shirley Hunt
Charitable Trust
The Albert Hunt Trust
The Hunter Foundation
Miss Agnes H Hunter's Trust
The Hyde Charitable Trust
I G O Foundation Limited
Impetus – The Private Equity
Foundation (Impetus – PEF)
Investream Charitable Trust
The Ireland Fund of Great
Britain
The Irish Youth Foundation
(UK) Ltd (incorporating The
Lawlor Foundation)
The Charles Irving Charitable
Trust
The J & J Benevolent
Foundation
The J J Charitable Trust
The Jenour Foundation
The Jephcott Charitable Trust
The Jigsaw Foundation
The Joffe Charitable Trust
The Johnson Foundation
The Jones 1986 Charitable
Trust
The Lady Eileen Joseph
Foundation
The Kalou Foundation
The Michael and Ilse Katz
Foundation
The Emmanuel Kaye
Foundation
The Peter Kershaw Trust
The Mary Kinross Charitable
Trust
The Kohn Foundation
The KPMG Foundation
The Heinz, Anna and Carol
Kroch Foundation
L P W Limited
John Laing Charitable Trust
Maurice and Hilda Laing
Charitable Trust
The Martin Laing Foundation
The Beatrice Laing Trust
LandAid Charitable Trust
The Allen Lane Foundation
The Langley Charitable Trust
The LankellyChase Foundation
The R J Larg Family Charitable
Trust
Mrs F B Laurence Charitable
Trust
The Law Society Charity
The Raymond and Blanche
Lawson Charitable Trust

The Leathersellers' Company
    Charitable Fund
The Leche Trust
Leicestershire and Rutland
    Community Foundation
The Leigh Trust
Mrs Vera Leigh's Charity
The Leonard Trust
The Mark Leonard Trust
The Joseph Levy Charitable
    Foundation
John Lewis Partnership
    General Community Fund
The Limbourne Trust
The Linbury Trust
Lincolnshire Community
    Foundation
The Enid Linder Foundation
The Lister Charitable Trust
The Andrew and Mary
    Elizabeth Little Charitable
    Trust
The Second Joseph Aaron
    Littman Foundation
The Elaine and Angus Lloyd
    Charitable Trust
Lloyd's Charities Trust
Lloyds Bank Foundation for
    England and Wales
Lloyds Bank Foundation for
    Northern Ireland
Lloyds TSB Foundation for
    Scotland
The Lo Family Charitable Trust
Localtrent Ltd
The Loftus Charitable Trust
The Trust for London
The London Housing
    Foundation
The Lord's Taverners
The Loseley and Guildway
    Charitable Trust
The Lotus Foundation
The C L Loyd Charitable Trust
LSA Charitable Trust
The Marie Helen Luen
    Charitable Trust
Henry Lumley Charitable Trust
Paul Lunn-Rockliffe Charitable
    Trust
John Lyon's Charity
The M and C Trust
The Mackintosh Foundation
Ian Mactaggart Trust
Magdalen Hospital Trust
The Magen Charitable Trust
The Mahavir Trust
Malbin Trust
Man Group plc Charitable
    Trust
R W Mann Trust
Maranatha Christian Trust
Marmot Charitable Trust
The Michael Marsh Charitable
    Trust
The Marsh Christian Trust

The Charlotte Marshall
    Charitable Trust
The Nora Joan Marshall
    Charitable Trust
John Martin's Charity
The Mathew Trust
Matliwala Family Charitable
    Trust
Evelyn May Trust
The McKenna Charitable Trust
The Mears Foundation
Melodor Limited
The Menzies Charity
    Foundation
The Mercers' Charitable
    Foundation
The Merchant Taylors'
    Company Charities Fund
The Merchant Venturers'
    Charity
The Metropolitan Masonic
    Charity
Mickleham Charitable Trust
Gerald Micklem Charitable
    Trust
The Sir John Middlemore
    Charitable Trust
Miles Trust for the Putney and
    Roehampton Community
The Millfield House Foundation
Milton Keynes Community
    Foundation
The Peter Minet Trust
Minge's Gift and the Pooled
    Trusts
Monmouthshire County Council
    Welsh Church Act Fund
The Colin Montgomerie
    Charitable Foundation
The Monument Trust
John Moores Foundation
The Morel Charitable Trust
The Moss Charitable Trust
The Robert and Margaret
    Moss Charitable Trust
The Moss Family Charitable
    Trust
The Mountbatten Memorial
    Trust
The Edith Murphy Foundation
Murphy-Neumann Charity
    Company Limited
Peter John Murray Trust
Muslim Hands
The Kitty and Daniel Nabarro
    Charitable Trust
The Nationwide Foundation
Needham Market and Barking
    Welfare Charities
Network for Social Change
Nominet Charitable Foundation
The Norda Trust
Norfolk Community Foundation
The Northcott Devon
    Foundation
The Northern Rock Foundation

The Northmoor Trust
The Norton Foundation
Novi Most International
The Nuffield Foundation
The Odin Charitable Trust
Ogilvie Charities Deed No.2
    (including the Charity of
    Mary Catherine Ford Smith)
Oglesby Charitable Trust
Old Possum's Practical Trust
The Olga Charitable Trust
Oxfam (GB)
The Palmer Foundation
The Parthenon Trust
Paycare Charity Trust
The Harry Payne Trust
Pegasus (Stanley) Trust
The Persula Foundation
The Pilgrim Trust
The Elise Pilkington Charitable
    Trust
The Pilkington Charities Fund
The Pollywally Charitable Trust
The Portishead Nautical Trust
The W L Pratt Charitable Trust
Sir John Priestman Charity
    Trust
The Puebla Charitable Trust
The Puri Foundation
Mr and Mrs J A Pye's
    Charitable Settlement
The Queen Anne's Gate
    Foundation
Quothquan Trust
The Eleanor Rathbone
    Charitable Trust
The Ravensdale Trust
The Rayne Foundation
The Rayne Trust
The Sir James Reckitt Charity
Eva Reckitt Trust Fund
The Reed Foundation
Relief Fund for Romania
    Limited
The Rhondda Cynon Taff
    Welsh Church Acts Fund
The Clive Richards Charity
The Richmond Parish Lands
    Charity
The River Farm Foundation
Thomas Roberts Trust
The Robertson Trust
Mrs L D Rope Third Charitable
    Settlement
The Rotherwick Foundation
The Rowland Family
    Foundation
The Rowlands Trust
The Joseph Rowntree
    Charitable Trust
Royal Docks Trust (London)
Ryklow Charitable Trust 1992
    (also known as A B
    Williamson Charitable Trust)
Erach and Roshan Sadri
    Foundation

The Alan and Babette
   Sainsbury Charitable Fund
Saint Sarkis Charity Trust
The Salamander Charitable
   Trust
Salters' Charitable Foundation
The Sandra Charitable Trust
Santander UK Foundation
   Limited
Scottish Coal Industry Special
   Welfare Fund
The Samuel Sebba Charitable
   Trust
The Seedfield Trust
The Shanley Charitable Trust
The Simmons & Simmons
   Charitable Foundation
Six Point Foundation
The Smith & Pinching
   Charitable Trust
The Mrs Smith and Mount
   Trust
The Sobell Foundation
Social Business Trust (Scale-
   Up)
The E C Sosnow Charitable
   Trust
R H Southern Trust
The Sovereign Health Care
   Charitable Trust
Sparquote Limited
Spears-Stutz Charitable Trust
The Spero Foundation
Split Infinitive Trust
Sir Walter St John's
   Educational Charity
The St Laurence Relief In
   Need Trust
Sir Halley Stewart Trust
The Stone Family Foundation
The Summerfield Charitable
   Trust
The Bernard Sunley Charitable
   Foundation
The Sunny Skies Foundation
The Sussex Community
   Foundation
Sutton Coldfield Charitable
   Trust
The Sutton Trust
Swan Mountain Trust
Tegham Limited
The Ten Ten Charitable Trust
The C Paul Thackray General
   Charitable Trust
The Thornton Trust
Mrs R P Tindall's Charitable
   Trust
The Tinsley Foundation
The Tolkien Trust
The Tory Family Foundation
Annie Tranmer Charitable Trust
The Tresillian Trust
The Triangle Trust (1949) Fund
TVML Foundation

Community Foundation Serving
   Tyne and Wear and
   Northumberland
UKI Charitable Foundation
The Underwood Trust
The United Society for the
   Propagation of the Gospel
Uxbridge United Welfare Trust
The Valentine Charitable Trust
The Vardy Foundation
The Variety Club Children's
   Charity
Volant Charitable Trust
Voluntary Action Fund (VAF)
The Scurrah Wainwright Charity
The Wakefield and Tetley Trust
Wakeham Trust
Wales Council for Voluntary
   Action
The Wates Foundation
John Watson's Trust
The Weavers' Company
   Benevolent Fund
The James Weir Foundation
The Welton Foundation
The Wessex Youth Trust
The Garfield Weston
   Foundation
The Barbara Whatmore
   Charitable Trust
White Stuff Foundation
The Will Charitable Trust
Will to Win Foundation Ltd.
   (previously Tennis for a
   Life)
Williams Serendipity Trust
The HDH Wills 1965
   Charitable Trust
The Community Foundation for
   Wiltshire and Swindon
The Michael and Anna Wix
   Charitable Trust
The Wixamtree Trust
The Maurice Wohl Charitable
   Foundation
The Charles Wolfson
   Charitable Trust
The Wolfson Family Charitable
   Trust
The Wood Family Trust
Woodlands Trust
Woodroffe Benton Foundation
The Woodward Charitable
   Trust
The Matthews Wrightson
   Charity Trust
Miss E B Wrightson's
   Charitable Settlement
The Wyseliot Charitable Trust
The Yapp Charitable Trust
Zurich Community Trust (UK)
   Limited

....
■ **People with an
alternative lifestyle
(inc/ travellers)**

The Allen Lane Foundation
The Odin Charitable Trust
The Woodward Charitable
   Trust

....
■ **People who are
educationally
disadvantaged**

Eastern Counties Educational
   Trust Limited
The Ellis Campbell Foundation
The Girdlers' Company
   Charitable Trust
Global Care
H C D Memorial Fund
The Hadley Trust
Human Relief Foundation
The KPMG Foundation
John Lyon's Charity
The Michael Marsh Charitable
   Trust
The Simmons & Simmons
   Charitable Foundation
The Sutton Trust
Mrs R P Tindall's Charitable
   Trust
White Stuff Foundation

....
■ **People who are
homeless**

The 29th May 1961 Charitable
   Trust
The A B Charitable Trust
The Sylvia Adams Charitable
   Trust
The Aldgate Freedom
   Foundation
The Ashden Trust
The Beit Trust
The Oliver Borthwick Memorial
   Trust
Henry T and Lucy B Cadbury
   Charitable Trust
Calypso Browning Trust
The Charities Advisory Trust
Christian Aid
The Coltstaple Trust
The Dawe Charitable Trust
The Drapers' Charitable Fund
Gilbert Edgar Trust
The Wilfred and Elsie Elkes
   Charity Fund
The John Ellerman Foundation
The Ellinson Foundation Ltd
The Ericson Trust
The Eveson Charitable Trust
Esmée Fairbairn Foundation
Fisherbeck Charitable Trust

The Fishmongers' Company's
Charitable Trust
The Hugh Fraser Foundation
The Freemasons' Grand
Charity
The G D Charitable Trust
The Girdlers' Company
Charitable Trust
Global Care
The Green Hall Foundation
Greggs Foundation
The David and Marie Grumitt
Foundation
The Bishop of Guildford's
Foundation
The Alfred Haines Charitable
Trust
Hampton Fuel Allotment
Charity
The Harbour Foundation
The Kenneth Hargreaves
Charitable Trust
The Harpur Trust
The Harrison and Potter Trust
The Peter Harrison Foundation
Help the Homeless
The Hemby Trust
The Hilden Charitable Fund
The Horne Foundation
The Horne Trust
The Hospital of God at
Greatham
The Huddersfield Common
Good Trust
The Hyde Charitable Trust
The Irish Youth Foundation
(UK) Ltd (incorporating The
Lawlor Foundation)
The Charles Irving Charitable
Trust
John Laing Charitable Trust
Maurice and Hilda Laing
Charitable Trust
The Beatrice Laing Trust
LandAid Charitable Trust
The Joseph Levy Charitable
Foundation
The London Housing
Foundation
The Marie Helen Luen
Charitable Trust
Paul Lunn-Rockliffe Charitable
Trust
John Lyon's Charity
The Mackintosh Foundation
Miles Trust for the Putney and
Roehampton Community
The Peter Minet Trust
The Monument Trust
John Moores Foundation
The Kitty and Daniel Nabarro
Charitable Trust
Network for Social Change
Norfolk Community Foundation
The Odin Charitable Trust
The Persula Foundation

The Pilgrim Trust
The Portishead Nautical Trust
Relief Fund for Romania
Limited
The Robertson Trust
Mrs L D Rope Third Charitable
Settlement
Erach and Roshan Sadri
Foundation
The Mrs Smith and Mount
Trust
The Sobell Foundation
The Summerfield Charitable
Trust
Woodlands Trust
The Woodward Charitable
Trust
The Matthews Wrightson
Charity Trust

....

■ People who are housebound

Paycare Charity Trust
The Elise Pilkington Charitable
Trust

....

■ Migrants

The 29th May 1961 Charitable
Trust
The Barrow Cadbury Trust and
the Barrow Cadbury Fund

....

■ Offenders

The 29th May 1961 Charitable
Trust
The A B Charitable Trust
The Alchemy Foundation
The Ashendene Trust
The Bromley Trust
The Noel Buxton Trust
The William A Cadbury
Charitable Trust
The Barrow Cadbury Trust and
the Barrow Cadbury Fund
Chesterhill Charitable Trust
The Chetwode Foundation
The Cooks Charity
The Evan Cornish Foundation
The Violet and Milo Cripps
Charitable Trust
The Drapers' Charitable Fund
Esmée Fairbairn Foundation
The Jill Franklin Trust
The Gatsby Charitable
Foundation
The Robert Gavron Charitable
Trust
The Girdlers' Company
Charitable Trust
Mrs H R Greene Charitable
Settlement
Greggs Foundation

H C D Memorial Fund
The Hadley Trust
Paul Hamlyn Foundation
The Helen Hamlyn Trust
The Charles Hayward
Foundation
The Hemby Trust
The High Sheriff's Police Trust
for the County of West
Midlands (Building Blocks)
The Hilden Charitable Fund
The Michael and Shirley Hunt
Charitable Trust
The J J Charitable Trust
The Mary Kinross Charitable
Trust
The KPMG Foundation
The Allen Lane Foundation
The LankellyChase Foundation
The Mark Leonard Trust
The Linbury Trust
John Lyon's Charity
The Mercers' Charitable
Foundation
The Monument Trust
The Norda Trust
The Nuffield Foundation
The Odin Charitable Trust
The Pilgrim Trust
The Portishead Nautical Trust
Mr and Mrs J A Pye's
Charitable Settlement
The Rhondda Cynon Taff
Welsh Church Acts Fund
Saint Sarkis Charity Trust
Swan Mountain Trust
The Ten Ten Charitable Trust
The Triangle Trust (1949) Fund
The Underwood Trust
The Weavers' Company
Benevolent Fund
Woodlands Trust

....

■ Ex-offenders

The 29th May 1961 Charitable
Trust
The Ashendene Trust
Esmée Fairbairn Foundation
The Girdlers' Company
Charitable Trust
Greggs Foundation
Paul Hamlyn Foundation
The Hemby Trust
The Michael and Shirley Hunt
Charitable Trust
The J J Charitable Trust
The Allen Lane Foundation
The Linbury Trust
John Lyon's Charity
The Mercers' Charitable
Foundation
The Norda Trust
The Odin Charitable Trust
Mr and Mrs J A Pye's
Charitable Settlement

The Weavers' Company
  Benevolent Fund

....

■ Prisoners and their families

The A B Charitable Trust
The Noel Buxton Trust
The Michael and Shirley Hunt
  Charitable Trust
The Norda Trust
The Odin Charitable Trust
The Weavers' Company
  Benevolent Fund

....

■ Young people at risk of offending

The Gatsby Charitable
  Foundation
Mrs H R Greene Charitable
  Settlement
Paul Hamlyn Foundation
The Hemby Trust
The High Sheriff's Police Trust
  for the County of West
  Midlands (Building Blocks)
The J J Charitable Trust
The KPMG Foundation
The Mark Leonard Trust
The Nuffield Foundation
The Portishead Nautical Trust
The Rhondda Cynon Taff
  Welsh Church Acts Fund
The Weavers' Company
  Benevolent Fund
Woodlands Trust

....

■ People who are poor, on low incomes

The 1989 Willan Charitable
  Trust
The 29th May 1961 Charitable
  Trust
The Sylvia Adams Charitable
  Trust
The Ajahma Charitable Trust
The Aldgate Freedom
  Foundation
The Alliance Family Foundation
The Pat Allsop Charitable Trust
The Bryan and June Amos
  Foundation
The Appletree Trust
The Archer Trust
AstonMansfield Charitable
  Trust
The George Balint Charitable
  Trust
Baruch Family Charitable Trust
The Bellahouston Bequest
  Fund

The Bellinger Donnay Trust
The Benfield Motors Charitable
  Trust
P G and N J Boulton Trust
The Bridging Fund Charitable
  Trust
John Bristow and Thomas
  Mason Trust
Buckingham Trust
The E F Bulmer Benevolent
  Fund
The Worshipful Company of
  Butchers General Charities
CAFOD (Catholic Agency for
  Overseas Development)
The Chetwode Foundation
The Chrimes Family Charitable
  Trust
Christian Aid
Church Urban Fund
CLA Charitable Trust
Closehelm Limited
The R and S Cohen
  Foundation
Michael Crawford Children's
  Charity
The Novak Djokovic Foundation
  (UK) Limited
The Double 'O' Charity Ltd
The Doughty Charity Trust
The Drapers' Charitable Fund
Eastern Counties Educational
  Trust Limited
The EBM Charitable Trust
Euro Charity Trust
The Eveson Charitable Trust
The George Fentham
  Birmingham Charity
The Fifty Fund
The Fishmongers' Company's
  Charitable Trust
Sydney E Franklin Deceased's
  New Second Charity
The Hugh Fraser Foundation
The G I Foundation
The David Gibbons Foundation
The Girdlers' Company
  Charitable Trust
Global Care
The J G Graves Charitable
  Trust
Mrs H R Greene Charitable
  Settlement
Greggs Foundation
The Grocers' Charity
The Bishop of Guildford's
  Foundation
H C D Memorial Fund
The Hadley Trust
Hampton Fuel Allotment
  Charity
The Haramead Trust
May Hearnshaw's Charity
The Hemby Trust

Henley Educational Trust
  (formerley Henley
  Educational Charity)
Highcroft Charitable Trust
R G Hills Charitable Trust
The Hilmarnan Charitable Trust
The Hornsey Parochial
  Charities
The Hospital of God at
  Greatham
The Huddersfield Common
  Good Trust
Human Relief Foundation
The Hunter Foundation
The Hyde Charitable Trust
I G O Foundation Limited
The Ireland Fund of Great
  Britain
The J & J Benevolent
  Foundation
The Jephcott Charitable Trust
The Jones 1986 Charitable
  Trust
The Lady Eileen Joseph
  Foundation
The Kohn Foundation
The Heinz, Anna and Carol
  Kroch Foundation
L P W Limited
Maurice and Hilda Laing
  Charitable Trust
The Beatrice Laing Trust
LandAid Charitable Trust
The Leathersellers' Company
  Charitable Fund
John Lewis Partnership
  General Community Fund
The Enid Linder Foundation
The Andrew and Mary
  Elizabeth Little Charitable
  Trust
Localtrent Ltd
LSA Charitable Trust
The Marie Helen Luen
  Charitable Trust
Paul Lunn-Rockliffe Charitable
  Trust
Ian Mactaggart Trust
Magdalen Hospital Trust
The Mahavir Trust
The Michael Marsh Charitable
  Trust
The Metropolitan Masonic
  Charity
Gerald Micklem Charitable
  Trust
Miles Trust for the Putney and
  Roehampton Community
Monmouthshire County Council
  Welsh Church Act Fund
The Colin Montgomerie
  Charitable Foundation
The Morel Charitable Trust
The Moss Charitable Trust
The Robert and Margaret
  Moss Charitable Trust

The Edith Murphy Foundation
Muslim Hands
The Kitty and Daniel Nabarro
Charitable Trust
Norfolk Community Foundation
The Northmoor Trust
The Odin Charitable Trust
The Olga Charitable Trust
Oxfam (GB)
The Elise Pilkington Charitable
Trust
The Pollywally Charitable Trust
The Portishead Nautical Trust
Sir John Priestman Charity
Trust
The Puebla Charitable Trust
The Puri Foundation
Mr and Mrs J A Pye's
Charitable Settlement
Quothquan Trust
The Rhondda Cynon Taff
Welsh Church Acts Fund
The Clive Richards Charity
The Richmond Parish Lands
Charity
Mrs L D Rope Third Charitable
Settlement
The Rowland Family
Foundation
The Rowlands Trust
The Joseph Rowntree
Charitable Trust
Royal Docks Trust (London)
The Sandra Charitable Trust
Scottish Coal Industry Special
Welfare Fund
The Seedfield Trust
The Shanley Charitable Trust
The Simmons & Simmons
Charitable Foundation
R H Southern Trust
Spears-Stutz Charitable Trust
The Summerfield Charitable
Trust
The Sunny Skies Foundation
Tegham Limited
The Thornton Trust
Mrs R P Tindall's Charitable
Trust
The Tinsley Foundation
UKI Charitable Foundation
Uxbridge United Welfare Trust
The Barbara Whatmore
Charitable Trust
White Stuff Foundation
The Maurice Wohl Charitable
Foundation
The Matthews Wrightson
Charity Trust

■ Prostitutes, sex workers

The LankellyChase Foundation

■ Refugees and asylum seekers

The 29th May 1961 Charitable
Trust
The A B Charitable Trust
The Bromley Trust
The Barrow Cadbury Trust and
the Barrow Cadbury Fund
The Charities Advisory Trust
The Edith Maud Ellis 1985
Charitable Trust
The Ericson Trust
The Jill Franklin Trust
H C D Memorial Fund
The Harbour Foundation
The Hilden Charitable Fund
The KPMG Foundation
The Allen Lane Foundation
The LankellyChase Foundation
The Leigh Trust
The Mackintosh Foundation
John Moores Foundation
Network for Social Change
The Norda Trust
The Odin Charitable Trust
The Pilgrim Trust
The Pilkington Charities Fund
Mr and Mrs J A Pye's
Charitable Settlement
Eva Reckitt Trust Fund
The Reed Foundation
The Alan and Babette
Sainsbury Charitable Fund
Six Point Foundation
The Woodward Charitable
Trust

■ Victims, oppressed people

The 1970 Trust
The Alchemy Foundation
Bergqvist Charitable Trust
The Bromley Trust
The Barrow Cadbury Trust and
the Barrow Cadbury Fund
CAFOD (Catholic Agency for
Overseas Development)
The Charities Advisory Trust
Christadelphian Samaritan
Fund
Christian Aid
The Coltstaple Trust
The Dorfred Charitable Trust
The Follett Trust
The Anna Rosa Forster
Charitable Trust
Sydney E Franklin Deceased's
New Second Charity

The Jill Franklin Trust
The Freemasons' Grand
Charity
The Girdlers' Company
Charitable Trust
Global Care
Greggs Foundation
Heart of England Community
Foundation
The Hemby Trust
The Horne Trust
The Hospital of God at
Greatham
The Huddersfield Common
Good Trust
Human Relief Foundation
The Hyde Charitable Trust
The Charles Irving Charitable
Trust
The Heinz, Anna and Carol
Kroch Foundation
The Allen Lane Foundation
The LankellyChase Foundation
The Law Society Charity
The Leathersellers' Company
Charitable Fund
The Leigh Trust
The Leonard Trust
The Joseph Levy Charitable
Foundation
The Loseley and Guildway
Charitable Trust
The Lotus Foundation
Monmouthshire County Council
Welsh Church Act Fund
The Morel Charitable Trust
Muslim Hands
Network for Social Change
Novi Most International
Oxfam (GB)
The Parthenon Trust
The Pilkington Charities Fund
The Portishead Nautical Trust
The W L Pratt Charitable Trust
Mr and Mrs J A Pye's
Charitable Settlement
The Sir James Reckitt Charity
Eva Reckitt Trust Fund
The Joseph Rowntree
Charitable Trust
Ryklow Charitable Trust 1992
(also known as A B
Williamson Charitable Trust)
Six Point Foundation
The C Paul Thackray General
Charitable Trust
The Tinsley Foundation
The Tresillian Trust
The Wolfson Family Charitable
Trust
Woodroffe Benton Foundation
The Woodward Charitable
Trust

■ People who have suffered abuse, violence or torture

The Girdlers' Company Charitable Trust
Global Care
Greggs Foundation
The Hemby Trust
The Hospital of God at Greatham
The Huddersfield Common Good Trust
The Hyde Charitable Trust
The Charles Irving Charitable Trust
The Heinz, Anna and Carol Kroch Foundation
The Allen Lane Foundation
The LankellyChase Foundation
The Lotus Foundation
The Portishead Nautical Trust
Mr and Mrs J A Pye's Charitable Settlement
Ryklow Charitable Trust 1992 (also known as A B Williamson Charitable Trust)
The Woodward Charitable Trust

■ Victims of crime

Bergqvist Charitable Trust
Christadelphian Samaritan Fund
Christian Aid
The Dorfred Charitable Trust
The Follett Trust
Sydney E Franklin Deceased's New Second Charity
The Freemasons' Grand Charity
Human Relief Foundation
The Leathersellers' Company Charitable Fund
The Leonard Trust
The Loseley and Guildway Charitable Trust
Monmouthshire County Council Welsh Church Act Fund
Muslim Hands
Oxfam (GB)
The Parthenon Trust
The Pilkington Charities Fund
The W L Pratt Charitable Trust
The Sir James Reckitt Charity
Woodroffe Benton Foundation

■ Victims of disasters

Bergqvist Charitable Trust
Christadelphian Samaritan Fund
Christian Aid
The Dorfred Charitable Trust

The Follett Trust
Sydney E Franklin Deceased's New Second Charity
The Freemasons' Grand Charity
Human Relief Foundation
The Leathersellers' Company Charitable Fund
The Leonard Trust
The Loseley and Guildway Charitable Trust
Monmouthshire County Council Welsh Church Act Fund
Muslim Hands
Oxfam (GB)
The Parthenon Trust
The Pilkington Charities Fund
The W L Pratt Charitable Trust
The Sir James Reckitt Charity
Woodroffe Benton Foundation

■ People suffering from famine

The Alchemy Foundation
Bergqvist Charitable Trust
CAFOD (Catholic Agency for Overseas Development)
Christadelphian Samaritan Fund
The Coltstaple Trust
The Dorfred Charitable Trust
The Anna Rosa Forster Charitable Trust
Sydney E Franklin Deceased's New Second Charity
Global Care
The Leonard Trust
The Joseph Levy Charitable Foundation
The Morel Charitable Trust
Oxfam (GB)
The Parthenon Trust
Ryklow Charitable Trust 1992 (also known as A B Williamson Charitable Trust)

■ People suffering injustice

The Charities Advisory Trust
Sydney E Franklin Deceased's New Second Charity
Global Care
The LankellyChase Foundation
The Law Society Charity
The Leigh Trust
Network for Social Change
The Joseph Rowntree Charitable Trust

■ Victims of war or conflict

CAFOD (Catholic Agency for Overseas Development)
The Dorfred Charitable Trust
Global Care
Human Relief Foundation
The Heinz, Anna and Carol Kroch Foundation
Muslim Hands
Novi Most International
Oxfam (GB)
The Pilkington Charities Fund
The Wolfson Family Charitable Trust

Trusts by type of grant

This index contains two separate listings:

List of types of grant: This lists all the headings used in the DGMT to categorise types of grant.

Trusts by type of grant: This lists trusts under the types of grant for which they have expressed a funding preference.

Trusts by type of grants

These pages contain two separate listings

List of type of grants
This lists all of the headings used in the DGMT to categorise types of grants

Trusts by type of grants
This lists trusts under the types of grants for which they have expressed a funding preference

Type of support 178

Capital support 178

- Building/renovation 178

- Collections and acquisitions 189

- Computer systems and equipment 201

- Equipment 213

- Vehicles 225

Core support 237

- Core costs 237

- Development funding 240

- Replacement of statutory funding 255

- Salaries 256

- Strategic funding 258

Project support 273

- Full project funding 273

- Project funding (excluding overheads) 286

- Seed funding 298

Campaigning 310

Loan finance 312

Duration of grant 312

Trusts listed here have expressly stated on a questionniare used as part of the research for this book that they give grants for the specified time period. Other trusts in this book which did not respond to the questionnaire may also give grants as stated below.

- One-off donation 312

- One year 315

- Two years 316

- Three years 317

- Longer than three years 317

Average time to pay grant 317

- Less than one month 317

- Two months 318

- Three months 319

- Four months 320

- Five months 320

- Six months or more 320

Type of support

Capital support

■ Building/renovation

The 1970 Trust
The 1989 Willan Charitable Trust
The 29th May 1961 Charitable Trust
A W Charitable Trust
The Aberbrothock Skea Trust
The Aberdeen Endowments Trust
The Aberdeenshire Educational Trust Scheme
Access Sport
Achisomoch Aid Company Limited
The ACT Foundation
Action Medical Research
The Sylvia Adams Charitable Trust
The Victor Adda Foundation
The Adint Charitable Trust
The Adnams Charity
Age UK
Aid to the Church in Need (UK)
The Sylvia Aitken Charitable Trust
The Al Fayed Charitable Foundation
The Aldgate Freedom Foundation
Allchurches Trust Ltd
The H B Allen Charitable Trust
The Alliance Family Foundation
Angus Allnatt Charitable Foundation
The Pat Allsop Charitable Trust
Almondsbury Charity
Altamont Ltd
Alvor Charitable Trust
The Ammco Trust
Viscount Amory's Charitable Trust
The AMW Charitable Trust
The Anchor Foundation
The Andrew Anderson Trust
The André Christian Trust
Anglo American Group Foundation
Anguish's Educational Foundation
The Animal Defence Trust
Anpride Ltd
The Appletree Trust
The Arbib Foundation
The John M Archer Charitable Trust
The Archer Trust
The Architectural Heritage Fund
The Ardwick Trust
The Argus Appeal

The Armenian Relief Society of Great Britain Trust
The Arsenal Foundation
The Artemis Charitable Trust
The Arts and Entertainment Charitable Trust
Arts Council England
The Arts Council of Northern Ireland
Arts Council of Wales (also known as Cyngor Celfyddydau Cymru)
The Ove Arup Foundation
The A S Charitable Trust
The Ashden Trust
The Ashendene Trust
The Ashworth Charitable Trust
The Ian Askew Charitable Trust
The Associated Country Women of the World
The Association of Colleges Charitable Trust
Astellas European Foundation
The Astor Foundation
The Astor of Hever Trust
The Aurelius Charitable Trust
The John Avins Trustees
The Aylesford Family Charitable Trust
The BAA Communities Trust
The Scott Bader Commonwealth Ltd
The Bagri Foundation
The Austin Bailey Foundation
The Baily Thomas Charitable Fund
The Baird Trust
The Baker Charitable Trust
The Balcombe Charitable Trust
The Albert Casanova Ballard Deceased Trust
The Ballinger Charitable Trust
The Balmore Trust
The Balney Charitable Trust
The Baltic Charitable Fund
The Bamford Charitable Foundation
The Banbury Charities
William P Bancroft (No 2) Charitable Trust and Jenepher Gillett Trust
The Band Trust
The Barbers' Company General Charities
Barchester Healthcare Foundation
The Barclay Foundation
The Baring Foundation
Peter Barker-Mill Memorial Charity
Barnes Workhouse Fund
The Barnsbury Charitable Trust
The Barnstaple Bridge Trust
The Misses Barrie Charitable Trust
Barrington Family Charitable Trust

The Bartlett Taylor Charitable Trust
The Paul Bassham Charitable Trust
The Batchworth Trust
The Bates Charitable Trust
The Bay Tree Charitable Trust
The Louis Baylis (Maidenhead Advertiser) Charitable Trust
BBC Children in Need
B-CH 1971 Charitable Trust
The Beacon Trust
The Bearder Charity
The James Beattie Charitable Trust
The Beaverbrook Foundation
The Beccles Town Lands Charity
The Becker Family Charitable Trust
The Becketts and Sargeants Educational Foundation
The John Beckwith Charitable Trust
The Peter Beckwith Charitable Trust
The Bedfordshire and Hertfordshire Historic Churches Trust
The David and Ruth Behrend Fund
The Beit Trust
The Bellahouston Bequest Fund
The Bellinger Donnay Trust
The Benfield Motors Charitable Trust
The Benham Charitable Settlement
The Hervey Benham Charitable Trust
Maurice and Jacqueline Bennett Charitable Trust
The Gerald Bentall Charitable Trust
Bergqvist Charitable Trust
The Berkshire Community Foundation
The Bestway Foundation
The Mason Bibby 1981 Trust
The Bideford Bridge Trust
The Big Lottery Fund
The Billmeir Charitable Trust
Percy Bilton Charity
The Bingham Trust
The Bintaub Charitable Trust
The Birmingham District Nursing Charitable Trust
The Birmingham Hospital Saturday Fund Medical Charity and Welfare Trust
Birmingham International Airport Community Trust
The Lord Mayor of Birmingham's Charity
Miss Jeanne Bisgood's Charitable Trust

The Michael Bishop
Foundation
The Bishop's Development
Fund
The Bertie Black Foundation
Isabel Blackman Foundation
The Blagrave Trust
The Blair Foundation
Blakemore Foundation
The Blanchminster Trust
The Blandford Lake Trust
The Sir Victor Blank Charitable
Settlement
The Neville and Elaine Blond
Charitable Trust
The Bluston Charitable
Settlement
The Marjory Boddy Charitable
Trust
The Boltons Trust
The Bonamy Charitable Trust
The John and Celia Bonham
Christie Charitable Trust
The Charlotte Bonham-Carter
Charitable Trust
Bonhomie United Charity
Society
The Boots Charitable Trust
The Bordon Liphook
Haslemere Charity
The Oliver Borthwick Memorial
Trust
The Bosson Family Charitable
Trust
The Bothwell Charitable Trust
H E and E L Botteley
Charitable Trust
The Harry Bottom Charitable
Trust
The Anthony Bourne
Foundation
The Bower Trust
The Bowerman Charitable
Trust
John and Susan Bowers Fund
The Bowland Charitable Trust
The Frank Brake Charitable
Trust
The William Brake Charitable
Trust
The Tony Bramall Charitable
Trust
The Harold and Alice Bridges
Charity
Bristol Archdeaconry Charity
John Bristow and Thomas
Mason Trust
The British Council for
Prevention of Blindness
The British Dietetic
Association General and
Education Trust Fund
British Humane Association
British Record Industry Trust
The J and M Britton Charitable
Trust

The Roger Brooke Charitable
Trust
The David Brooke Charity
The Charles Brotherton Trust
Joseph Brough Charitable
Trust
The Swinfen Broun Charitable
Trust
Edna Brown Charitable
Settlement (Mrs E E Brown
Charitable Settlement)
Brown-Mellows Trust
The Jack Brunton Charitable
Trust
Buckinghamshire Community
Foundation
The Buckinghamshire Historic
Churches Trust
The Bulldog Trust Limited
The E F Bulmer Benevolent
Fund
Bumba Foundation
Burdens Charitable Foundation
The Clara E Burgess Charity
The Burry Charitable Trust
The Arnold Burton 1998
Charitable Trust
The Burton Breweries
Charitable Trust
Consolidated Charity of Burton
upon Trent
The Worshipful Company of
Butchers General Charities
Henry T and Lucy B Cadbury
Charitable Trust
The Christopher Cadbury
Charitable Trust
The G W Cadbury Charitable
Trust
The Richard Cadbury
Charitable Trust
The Edward and Dorothy
Cadbury Trust
The George Cadbury Trust
CAF (Charities Aid Foundation)
CAFOD (Catholic Agency for
Overseas Development)
Community Foundation for
Calderdale
The Callander Charitable Trust
Calleva Foundation
Calypso Browning Trust
The Cambridgeshire Historic
Churches Trust
The Campden Charities
Trustee
The Canning Trust
The Carew Pole Charitable
Trust
The D W T Cargill Fund
Carlee Ltd
The Carlton House Charitable
Trust
The Carmelite Monastery Ware
Trust
The Worshipful Company of
Carmen Benevolent Trust

The Carnegie Dunfermline
Trust
The Carpenter Charitable Trust
The Carpenters' Company
Charitable Trust
The Carrington Charitable
Trust
The Carron Charitable
Settlement
The Leslie Mary Carter
Charitable Trust
The Casey Trust
Cash for Kids Radio Clyde
The Cass Foundation
The Catalyst Charitable Trust
The Catholic Charitable Trust
Catholic Foreign Missions
The Catholic Trust for England
and Wales
The Joseph and Annie Cattle
Trust
The Thomas Sivewright Catto
Charitable Settlement
The Wilfrid and Constance
Cave Foundation
The Cayo Foundation
Elizabeth Cayzer Charitable
Trust
The B G S Cayzer Charitable
Trust
The Cazenove Charitable Trust
Celtic Charity Fund
The Pamela Champion
Foundation
The Chapman Charitable Trust
John William Chapman's
Charitable Trust
The Charities Advisory Trust
Charitworth Limited
The Charter 600 Charity
The Worshipful Company of
Chartered Accountants
General Charitable Trust
(also known as CALC)
The Chelsea Square 1994
Trust
The Cheruby Trust
Cheshire Freemason's Charity
The Chetwode Foundation
Cheviot Asset Management
Charitable Trust
Childs Charitable Trust
The Childwick Trust
The Chippenham Borough
Lands Charity
The Chipping Sodbury Town
Lands Charity
CHK Charities Limited
The Chownes Foundation
The Chrimes Family Charitable
Trust
Christadelphian Samaritan
Fund
Christian Aid
Christian Response to Eastern
Europe
Chrysalis Trust

The Church and Community
Fund
The Church Burgesses
Educational Foundation
Church Burgesses Trust
City and County of Swansea
Welsh Church Act Fund
The City Bridge Trust
Stephen Clark 1957
Charitable Trust
The Hilda and Alice Clark
Charitable Trust
The Roger and Sarah Bancroft
Clark Charitable Trust
The Clarke Charitable
Settlement
The Cleopatra Trust
Lord Clinton's Charitable Trust
The Clore Duffield Foundation
Miss V L Clore's 1967
Charitable Trust
Closehelm Limited
The Clothworkers' Foundation
Richard Cloudesley's Charity
The Clover Trust
The Robert Clutterbuck
Charitable Trust
Clydpride Ltd
The Francis Coales Charitable
Foundation
The Coalfields Regeneration
Trust
The John Coates Charitable
Trust
The Cobtree Charity Trust Ltd
The Denise Cohen Charitable
Trust
The Vivienne and Samuel
Cohen Charitable Trust
The John S Cohen Foundation
The R and S Cohen
Foundation
The Colchester Catalyst
Charity
The Cole Charitable Trust
The Colefax Charitable Trust
The John and Freda Coleman
Charitable Trust
The George Henry Collins
Charity
The Sir Jeremiah Colman Gift
Trust
The Coltstaple Trust
Colwinston Charitable Trust
Colyer-Fergusson Charitable
Trust
Community First (Landfill
Communities Fund)
The Compton Charitable Trust
The Congleton Inclosure Trust
The Congregational and
General Charitable Trust
The Conservation Foundation
The Cooks Charity
The Catherine Cookson
Charitable Trust
Mabel Cooper Charity

The Alice Ellen Cooper Dean
Charitable Foundation
The Marjorie Coote Animal
Charity Trust
The Marjorie Coote Old
People's Charity
The Helen Jean Cope Trust
The J Reginald Corah
Foundation Fund
The Gershon Coren Charitable
Foundation (also known as
The Muriel and Gus Coren
Charitable Foundation)
The Cornwall Historic
Churches Trust
The Duke of Cornwall's
Benevolent Fund
The Cornwell Charitable Trust
The Sidney and Elizabeth
Corob Charitable Trust
The Corona Charitable Trust
The Costa Family Charitable
Trust
The Cotton Industry War
Memorial Trust
Country Houses Foundation
County Durham Community
Foundation
The General Charities of the
City of Coventry
Coventry Building Society
Charitable Foundation
The John Cowan Foundation
Dudley and Geoffrey Cox
Charitable Trust
The Sir William Coxen Trust
Fund
The Lord Cozens-Hardy Trust
The Craignish Trust
The Craps Charitable Trust
Michael Crawford Children's
Charity
The Cray Trust
The Crerar Hotels Trust
The Crescent Trust
Cripplegate Foundation
The Violet and Milo Cripps
Charitable Trust
The Cross Trust
Cruden Foundation Ltd
The Ronald Cruickshanks
Foundation
The Culra Charitable Trust
The Cumber Family Charitable
Trust
Cumberland Building Society
Charitable Foundation
Cumbria Community
Foundation
The D J H Currie Memorial
Trust
The Dennis Curry Charitable
Trust
The Manny Cussins
Foundation
The Cwmbran Trust

Itzchok Meyer Cymerman Trust
Ltd
The D G Charitable Settlement
The D'Oyly Carte Charitable
Trust
The Dr and Mrs A Darlington
Charitable Trust
Baron Davenport's Charity
The Davidson Family
Charitable Trust
The Alderman Joe Davidson
Memorial Trust
Michael Davies Charitable
Settlement
The Gwendoline and Margaret
Davies Charity
The Hamilton Davies Trust
The Wilfrid Bruce Davis
Charitable Trust
Davis-Rubens Charitable Trust
The Dawe Charitable Trust
The De Brye Charitable Trust
The De Clermont Charitable
Company Ltd
The Deakin Charitable Trust
William Dean Countryside and
Educational Trust
The Debmar Benevolent Trust
The Dellal Foundation
The Delves Charitable Trust
The Demigryphon Trust
The Denman Charitable Trust
Dentons UKMEA LLP
Charitable Trust
The Earl of Derby's Charitable
Trust
The Derbyshire Churches and
Chapels Preservation Trust
Derbyshire Community
Foundation
The J N Derbyshire Trust
The Desmond Foundation
The Devon Educational Trust
The Devon Historic Churches
Trust
The Duke of Devonshire's
Charitable Trust
The Sandy Dewhirst Charitable
Trust
The Laduma Dhamecha
Charitable Trust
The Dibden Allotments Fund
Diced Cap Charity
The Dickon Trust
The Peter Alan Dickson
Foundation
The Digbeth Trust Limited
The Dinwoodie Settlement
Dischma Charitable Trust
The DLM Charitable Trust
Louise Dobson Charitable
Trust
The Derek and Eileen Dodgson
Foundation
The Dollond Charitable Trust
Domepride Ltd
The Dorcas Trust

The Dorset Historic Churches
Trust
The Dorus Trust
The Doughty Charity Trust
The R M Douglas Charitable
Trust
The Drapers' Charitable Fund
The Duis Charitable Trust
The P B Dumbell Charitable
Trust
The Dumbreck Charity
Dunard Fund
The Dunn Family Charitable
Trust
The W E Dunn Trust
Dushinsky Trust Ltd
The Dwek Family Charitable
Trust
The Dyers' Company
Charitable Trust
The Eagle Charity Trust
The Earley Charity
Earls Colne and Halstead
Educational Charity
The Earmark Trust
Eastern Counties Educational
Trust Limited
The Sir John Eastwood
Foundation
The Ebenezer Trust
The EBM Charitable Trust
Eden Arts Trust
The Gilbert and Eileen Edgar
Foundation
Edinburgh Trust No 2 Account
The W G Edwards Charitable
Foundation
The William Edwards
Educational Charity
The Elephant Trust
The George Elias Charitable
Trust
The Gerald Palmer Eling Trust
Company
The Wilfred and Elsie Elkes
Charity Fund
The Maud Elkington Charitable
Trust
The Ellerdale Trust
The John Ellerman Foundation
The Ellinson Foundation Ltd
The Ellis Campbell Foundation
The Elmgrant Trust
The Vernon N Ely Charitable
Trust
The Embleton Trust
Embrace the Middle East
The Emerton-Christie Charity
The Worshipful Company of
Engineers Charitable Trust
Fund
The Englefield Charitable Trust
The Enkalon Foundation
Entindale Ltd
The Epigoni Trust
The Equitable Charitable Trust
The Equity Trust Fund

The Ericson Trust
The Erskine Cunningham Hill
Trust
Essex Community Foundation
The Essex Fairway Charitable
Trust
The Essex Heritage Trust
Essex Provincial Charity Fund
The Essex Youth Trust
Euro Charity Trust
Sir John Evelyn's Charity
The Eventhall Family
Charitable Trust
The Everard Foundation
The Eveson Charitable Trust
The Beryl Evetts and Robert
Luff Animal Welfare Trust
Limited
The Exilarch's Foundation
F C Charitable Trust
The F P Limited Charitable
Trust
The Faber Charitable Trust
The Fairway Trust
The Lord Faringdon Charitable
Trust
Samuel William Farmer Trust
The Farmers' Company
Charitable Fund
The Thomas Farr Charity
Walter Farthing (Trust) Limited
The Fassnidge Memorial Trust
Joseph Fattorini Charitable
Trust
The February Foundation
Federation of Jewish Relief
Organisations
The John Feeney Charitable
Trust
The George Fentham
Birmingham Charity
The A M Fenton Trust
Allan and Nesta Ferguson
Charitable Settlement
The Fidelity UK Foundation
The Doris Field Charitable
Trust
Fife Council/Common Good
Funds and Trusts
Firtree Trust
The Fishmongers' Company's
Charitable Trust
The Fitton Trust
The Earl Fitzwilliam Charitable
Trust
The Ian Fleming Charitable
Trust
The Joyce Fletcher Charitable
Trust
The Flow Foundation
The Gerald Fogel Charitable
Trust
The Follett Trust
The Football Association
National Sports Centre
Trust

The Football Association Youth
Trust
The Football Foundation
The Forbes Charitable
Foundation
The Forces Trust (Working
Name)
Ford Britain Trust
The Oliver Ford Charitable
Trust
The Forest Hill Charitable Trust
The Foresters' Charity
Stewards UK Trust
The Forman Hardy Charitable
Trust
Gwyneth Forrester Trust
The Forte Charitable Trust
The Four Lanes Trust
The Foyle Foundation
The Isaac and Freda Frankel
Memorial Charitable Trust
The Elizabeth Frankland Moore
and Star Foundation
The Gordon Fraser Charitable
Trust
The Hugh Fraser Foundation
The Joseph Strong Frazer Trust
The Louis and Valerie
Freedman Charitable
Settlement
The Thomas Freke and Lady
Norton Charity Trust
The Charles S French
Charitable Trust
The Anne French Memorial
Trust
The Freshfield Foundation
The Freshgate Trust
Foundation
The Friarsgate Trust
The Friends Hall Farm Street
Trust
Friends of Essex Churches
Trust
The Friends of Kent Churches
The Frognal Trust
The Patrick & Helena Frost
Foundation
Maurice Fry Charitable Trust
The Fulmer Charitable Trust
G M C Trust
Gableholt Limited
The Galbraith Trust
The Gale Family Charity Trust
Gamlen Charitable Trust
The Gamma Trust
The Gannochy Trust
The Worshipful Company of
Gardeners of London
The Samuel Gardner Memorial
Trust
The Garnett Charitable Trust
Garvan Limited
The Gatsby Charitable
Foundation
Gatwick Airport Community
Trust

The Robert Gavron Charitable
  Trust
Thomas Betton's Charity for
  Pensions and Relief-in-Need
The Gibbs Charitable Trust
Simon Gibson Charitable Trust
The G C Gibson Charitable
  Trust
Lady Gibson's Charitable Trust
The Harvey and Hilary Gilbert
  Charitable Trust
The Girdlers' Company
  Charitable Trust
The B and P Glasser
  Charitable Trust
The Glass-House Trust
Global Care
Global Charities
Gloucestershire Community
  Foundation
The Gloucestershire Historic
  Churches Trust
Worshipful Company of
  Glovers of London Charity
  Fund
The GNC Trust
The Godinton Charitable Trust
The Sydney and Phyllis
  Goldberg Memorial
  Charitable Trust
The Golden Bottle Trust
The Jack Goldhill Charitable
  Trust
The Goldsmiths' Company
  Charity
The Golsoncott Foundation
The Mike Gooley Trailfinders
  Charity
The Gosling Foundation
  Limited
The Gough Charitable Trust
The Gould Charitable Trust
The Grace Charitable Trust
A B Grace Trust
The Graff Foundation
E C Graham Belford Charitable
  Settlement
The Grahame Charitable
  Foundation Limited
The Granada Foundation
Grand Charitable Trust of the
  Order of Women
  Freemasons
The Grand Order of Water
  Rats' Charities Fund
The Grange Farm Centre Trust
Grantham Yorke Trust
The J G Graves Charitable
  Trust
The Gordon Gray Trust
The Gray Trust
The Great Stone Bridge Trust
  of Edenbridge
The Great Torrington Town
  Lands Charity
The Green Hall Foundation

Greenham Common
  Community Trust Limited
Greggs Foundation
The Gretna Charitable Trust
The Grimmitt Trust
The Grocers' Charity
The M and R Gross Charities
  Limited
The GRP Charitable Trust
The David and Marie Grumitt
  Foundation
The Bishop of Guildford's
  Foundation
The Guildry Incorporation of
  Perth
The Walter Guinness
  Charitable Trust
The Gunter Charitable Trust
The Gur Trust
The Gurney Charitable Trust
Dr Guthrie's Association
The H and M Charitable Trust
H C D Memorial Fund
The H P Charitable Trust
The Hackney Parochial
  Charities
The Hadfield Trust
The Hadley Trust
The Hadrian Trust
E F and M G Hall Charitable
  Trust
The Edith Winifred Hall
  Charitable Trust
Robert Hall Charity
The Hamamelis Trust
The Hampshire and Islands
  Historic Churches Trust
Hampshire and Isle of Wight
  Community Foundation
Hampton Fuel Allotment
  Charity
The W A Handley Charitable
  Trust
Beatrice Hankey Foundation
  Limited
The Hanley Trust (1987)
The Kathleen Hannay
  Memorial Charity
The Doughty Hanson
  Charitable Foundation
Lord Hanson Foundation
The Haramead Trust
Miss K M Harbinson's
  Charitable Trust
The Harborne Parish Lands
  Charity
The Harbour Charitable Trust
The Harbour Foundation
The Harding Trust
William Harding's Charity
The Hare of Steep Charitable
  Trust
The Harebell Centenary Fund
The Kenneth Hargreaves
  Charitable Trust
The Harpur Trust
The Harris Charity

The Harrison and Potter Trust
The John Harrison Charitable
  Trust
The Peter Harrison Foundation
The Spencer Hart Charitable
  Trust
The Hartley Charitable Trust
William Geoffrey Harvey's
  Discretionary Settlement
The Edward Harvist Trust
The Hathaway Trust
The Maurice Hatter Foundation
The M A Hawe Settlement
The Hawthorne Charitable
  Trust
The Dorothy Hay-Bolton
  Charitable Trust
The Headley Trust
Headley-Pitt Charitable Trust
Heart of England Community
  Foundation
The Heathcoat Trust
Heathside Charitable Trust
The Charlotte Heber-Percy
  Charitable Trust
The Hedley Denton Charitable
  Trust
The Hedley Foundation
The H J Heinz Company
  Limited Charitable Trust
The Hellenic Foundation
The Michael Heller Charitable
  Foundation
The Simon Heller Charitable
  Settlement
Help the Homeless
The Hemby Trust
The Christina Mary Hendrie
  Trust for Scottish and
  Canadian Charities
Henley Educational Trust
  (formerley Henley
  Educational Charity)
Esther Hennell Charitable
  Trust
The G D Herbert Charitable
  Trust
The Anne Herd Memorial Trust
The Herefordshire Historic
  Churches Trust
The Heritage of London Trust
  Ltd
The Hesed Trust
The Hesslewood Children's
  Trust (Hull Seamen's and
  General Orphanage)
Hexham and Newcastle
  Diocesan Trust (1947)
The P and C Hickinbotham
  Charitable Trust
The Higgs Charitable Trust
Alan Edward Higgs Charity
The High Sheriff's Police Trust
  for the County of West
  Midlands (Building Blocks)
Highcroft Charitable Trust

The Charles Littlewood Hill
Trust
The Hillingdon Partnership
Trust
The Hiscox Foundation
The Eleemosynary Charity of
William Hobbayne
Hobson Charity Limited
Matthew Hodder Charitable
Trust
The Sir Julian Hodge
Charitable Trust
The J G Hogg Charitable Trust
The Holden Charitable Trust
The Hollick Family Charitable
Trust
The Dorothy Holmes Charitable
Trust
The Holywood Trust
The Homelands Charitable
Trust
The Homestead Charitable
Trust
Sir Harold Hood's Charitable
Trust
Hope for Youth (NI)
HopMarket Charity
The Cuthbert Horn Trust
The Antony Hornby Charitable
Trust
The Horne Foundation
The Horne Trust
The Worshipful Company of
Horners' Charitable Trusts
The Hornsey Parochial
Charities
The Hospital Saturday Fund
Houblon-Norman/George Fund
The House of Industry Estate
The Reta Lila Howard
Foundation
The Daniel Howard Trust
The Huddersfield Common
Good Trust
The Hudson Foundation
The Geoffrey C Hughes
Charitable Trust
The Hull and East Riding
Charitable Trust
Hulme Trust Estates
(Educational)
Human Relief Foundation
The Humanitarian Trust
The Michael and Shirley Hunt
Charitable Trust
The Hunter Foundation
Miss Agnes H Hunter's Trust
The Huntingdon Foundation
Huntingdon Freemen's Trust
Hurdale Charity Limited
The Nani Huyu Charitable Trust
The P Y N and B Hyams Trust
The Hyde Charitable Trust
The Idlewild Trust
The Iliffe Family Charitable
Trust
The Indigo Trust

The Ingram Trust
The Inman Charity
The Inner London Magistrates
Court Poor Box and Feeder
Charity
The Ireland Fund of Great
Britain
The Irish Youth Foundation
(UK) Ltd (incorporating The
Lawlor Foundation)
The Ironmongers' Foundation
The Charles Irving Charitable
Trust
Irwin Trust
The ISA Charity
The Isaacs Charitable Trust
The J Isaacs Charitable Trust
The Isle of Anglesey Charitable
Trust
The ITF Seafarers Trust
The J M K Charitable Trust
The J R S S T Charitable Trust
C Richard Jackson Charitable
Trust
Elizabeth Jackson Charitable
Trust
The Ruth and Lionel Jacobson
Trust (Second Fund) No 2
Jaffe Family Relief Fund
The Susan and Stephen
James Charitable
Settlement
The James Trust
The Marjory Jameson Trust
The John Jarrold Trust
JCA Charitable Foundation
The Jeffrey Charitable Trust
The Jenour Foundation
The Jephcott Charitable Trust
Jesus Hospital Charity
The Jewish Youth Fund
The Harold Joels Charitable
Trust
The Nicholas Joels Charitable
Trust
The Norman Joels Charitable
Trust
The Lillie Johnson Charitable
Trust
The Johnson Foundation
The Reginald Johnson
Foundation
The Johnnie Johnson Trust
The Johnson Wax Ltd
Charitable Trust
The Joicey Trust
The Jones 1986 Charitable
Trust
The Marjorie and Geoffrey
Jones Charitable Trust
The Jordan Charitable
Foundation
The J E Joseph Charitable
Fund
The Lady Eileen Joseph
Foundation

The Josephs Family Charitable
Trust
JTH Charitable Trust
The Julian Budd Kids in Sport
Trust Limited
The Anton Jurgens Charitable
Trust
The Bernard Kahn Charitable
Trust
The Stanley Kalms Foundation
The Karenza Foundation
The Boris Karloff Charitable
Foundation
The Ian Karten Charitable
Trust
The Kasner Charitable Trust
The Kathleen Trust
The Michael and Ilse Katz
Foundation
The Katzauer Charitable
Settlement
The C S Kaufman Charitable
Trust
The Geoffrey John Kaye
Charitable Foundation
The Emmanuel Kaye
Foundation
Kelsick's Educational
Foundation
The KempWelch Charitable
Trust
The Kay Kendall Leukaemia
Fund
The John Thomas Kennedy
Charitable Foundation
The Kennedy Charitable
Foundation
Kent Community Foundation
The Nancy Kenyon Charitable
Trust
Keren Association
Kermaville Ltd
The Ursula Keyes Trust
The King Henry VIII Endowed
Trust Warwick
The King/Cullimore Charitable
Trust
The Kingsbury Charity
The Mary Kinross Charitable
Trust
Kirkley Poor's Lands Estate
The Richard Kirkman
Charitable Trust
Kirschel Foundation
Robert Kitchin (Saddlers'
Company)
Ernest Kleinwort Charitable
Trust
The Marina Kleinwort
Charitable Trust
The Sir James Knott Trust
The Kobler Trust
The Kohn Foundation
The Kreditor Charitable Trust
The Kreitman Foundation
The Neil Kreitman Foundation

The Heinz, Anna and Carol
Kroch Foundation
The Kyte Charitable Trust
The Late Sir Pierce Lacy
Charity Trust
John Laing Charitable Trust
Maurice and Hilda Laing
Charitable Trust
The Christopher Laing
Foundation
The Kirby Laing Foundation
The Martin Laing Foundation
The Beatrice Laing Trust
The Lambert Charitable Trust
LWS Lancashire Environmental
Fund Limited
Duchy of Lancaster Benevolent
Fund
The Lancaster Foundation
Langdale Trust
The Langley Charitable Trust
The Langtree Trust
The LankellyChase Foundation
The R J Larg Family Charitable
Trust
Largsmount Ltd
The Lark Trust
Laslett's (Hinton) Charity
The Lauffer Family Charitable
Foundation
The Kathleen Laurence Trust
The Edgar E Lawley Foundation
The Herd Lawson and Muriel
Lawson Charitable Trust
The Lawson Beckman
Charitable Trust
The Raymond and Blanche
Lawson Charitable Trust
The Leach Fourteenth Trust
The David Lean Foundation
The Leathersellers' Company
Charitable Fund
The Arnold Lee Charitable
Trust
The William Leech Charity
The Lord Mayor of Leeds
Appeal Fund
Leicestershire Historic
Churches Trust
The Kennedy Leigh Charitable
Trust
The Leigh Trust
Mrs Vera Leigh's Charity
P Leigh-Bramwell Trust 'E'
The Lennox and Wyfold
Foundation
The Erica Leonard Trust
The Leonard Trust
The Mark Leonard Trust
Lesley Lesley and Mutter Trust
The Leverhulme Trade
Charities Trust
The Leverhulme Trust
Lord Leverhulme's Charitable
Trust
The Joseph Levy Charitable
Foundation

The Sir Edward Lewis
Foundation
John Lewis Partnership
General Community Fund
Lichfield Conduit Lands
Lifeline 4 Kids
The Linbury Trust
The Lincolnshire Churches
Trust
The Lind Trust
Lindale Educational
Foundation
The Linden Charitable Trust
The Enid Linder Foundation
The Linmardon Trust
The Ruth and Stuart Lipton
Charitable Trust
The Lister Charitable Trust
The Andrew and Mary
Elizabeth Little Charitable
Trust
The Second Joseph Aaron
Littman Foundation
The George John and Sheilah
Livanos Charitable Trust
Liverpool Charity and Voluntary
Services
Liverpool Sailors' Home Trust
The Elaine and Angus Lloyd
Charitable Trust
The Charles Lloyd Foundation
Lloyd's Charities Trust
Lloyds Bank Foundation for
Northern Ireland
Lloyds Bank Foundation for the
Channel Islands
The Locker Foundation
The Loftus Charitable Trust
The Lolev Charitable Trust
London Catalyst
The London Community
Foundation
The London Housing
Foundation
The London Law Trust
The London Marathon
Charitable Trust
The William and Katherine
Longman Trust
The Loseley and Guildway
Charitable Trust
The Lotus Foundation
The C L Loyd Charitable Trust
The Marie Helen Luen
Charitable Trust
Henry Lumley Charitable Trust
C F Lunoe Trust Fund
The Ruth and Jack Lunzer
Charitable Trust
Lord and Lady Lurgan Trust
The Lynn Foundation
The Lynwood Trust
John Lyon's Charity
The Lyons Charitable Trust
The Sir Jack Lyons Charitable
Trust

The Lyras Family Charitable
Trust
The M and C Trust
The M K Charitable Trust
The Madeline Mabey Trust
The E M MacAndrew Trust
The R S Macdonald Charitable
Trust
Macdonald-Buchanan
Charitable Trust
The Macfarlane Walker Trust
The Mackay and Brewer
Charitable Trust
The Mackintosh Foundation
The MacRobert Trust
Magdalen Hospital Trust
The Magen Charitable Trust
Man Group plc Charitable
Trust
The Manackerman Charitable
Trust
The Manchester Guardian
Society Charitable Trust
Lord Mayor of Manchester's
Charity Appeal Trust
Mandeville Trust
The Manifold Charitable Trust
W M Mann Foundation
The Leslie and Lilian Manning
Trust
Marbeh Torah Trust
Marchig Animal Welfare Trust
The Stella and Alexander
Margulies Charitable Trust
Market Harborough and The
Bowdens Charity
The Ann and David Marks
Foundation
The Hilda and Samuel Marks
Foundation
J P Marland Charitable Trust
The Michael Marsh Charitable
Trust
The Charlotte Marshall
Charitable Trust
The Jim Marshall Charitable
Trust
The Nora Joan Marshall
Charitable Trust
The D G Marshall of
Cambridge Trust
Marshall's Charity
Marshgate Charitable
Settlement
Sir George Martin Trust
John Martin's Charity
The Mason Porter Charitable
Trust
The Nancie Massey Charitable
Trust
The Matt 6.3 Charitable Trust
The Violet Mauray Charitable
Trust
Evelyn May Trust
Mayfair Charities Ltd
The Mayfield Valley Arts Trust
Mazars Charitable Trust

The Robert McAlpine
Foundation
The McKenna Charitable Trust
The Helen Isabella McMorran
Charitable Foundation
The Mears Foundation
The James Frederick and Ethel
Anne Measures Charity
The Medlock Charitable Trust
The Anthony and Elizabeth
Mellows Charitable
Settlement
Melow Charitable Trust
The Mercers' Charitable
Foundation
The Merchant Taylors'
Company Charities Fund
The Merchant Venturers'
Charity
The Merchants' House of
Glasgow
The Mersey Docks and
Harbour Company
Charitable Fund
Community Foundation for
Merseyside
The Zachary Merton and
George Woofindin
Convalescent Trust
The Tony Metherell Charitable
Trust
The Metropolitan Drinking
Fountain and Cattle Trough
Association
The Mickel Fund
Gerald Micklem Charitable
Trust
Midhurst Pensions Trust
The Migraine Trust
Miles Trust for the Putney and
Roehampton Community
The Hugh and Mary Miller
Bequest Trust
The Ronald Miller Foundation
The Millfield Trust
The Millhouses Charitable
Trust
The Millichope Foundation
The Mills Charity
The Millward Charitable Trust
The Clare Milne Trust
Milton Keynes Community
Foundation
The Edgar Milward Charity
The Keith and Joan
Mindelsohn Charitable
Trust
The Peter Minet Trust
The Minos Trust
The Laurence Misener
Charitable Trust
The Mishcon Family Charitable
Trust
The Misselbrook Trust
The Mitchell Charitable Trust
The Esmé Mitchell Trust
Keren Mitzvah Trust

The Mizpah Trust
The Mobbs Memorial Trust Ltd
The Modiano Charitable Trust
The Moette Charitable Trust
The Mole Charitable Trust
The D C Moncrieff Charitable
Trust
Monmouthshire County Council
Welsh Church Act Fund
The Montague Thompson
Coon Charitable Trust
The Colin Montgomerie
Charitable Foundation
The Monument Trust
George A Moore Foundation
The Morel Charitable Trust
The Morgan Charitable
Foundation
The Mr and Mrs J T Morgan
Foundation
Morgan Stanley International
Foundation
The Oliver Morland Charitable
Trust
The Bernard Morris Charitable
Trust
The Morris Charitable Trust
The Willie and Mabel Morris
Charitable Trust
The Peter Morrison Charitable
Foundation
The Stanley Morrison
Charitable Trust
Vyoel Moshe Charitable Trust
The Moss Charitable Trust
The Moss Family Charitable
Trust
Mosselson Charitable Trust
The Edwina Mountbatten Trust
Mountbatten Festival of Music
The Mountbatten Memorial
Trust
Mrs Waterhouse Charitable
Trust
The Mugdock Children's Trust
The Mulberry Trust
The Edith Murphy Foundation
The Mushroom Fund
The Music Sales Charitable
Trust
Muslim Hands
The Mutual Trust Group
The Kitty and Daniel Nabarro
Charitable Trust
The Nadezhda Charitable Trust
The Naggar Charitable Trust
The Eleni Nakou Foundation
The Janet Nash Charitable
Settlement
The National Hockey
Foundation
The National Manuscripts
Conservation Trust
The Nationwide Foundation
Needham Market and Barking
Welfare Charities

The Worshipful Company of
Needlemakers' Charitable
Fund
The Neighbourly Charitable
Trust
The James Neill Trust Fund
Nemoral Ltd
Alderman Newton's
Educational Foundation
The Chevras Ezras Nitzrochim
Trust
The Noon Foundation
The Norda Trust
Norfolk Community Foundation
Norie Charitable Trust
The Norman Family Charitable
Trust
The Duncan Norman Trust
Fund
The Normanby Charitable Trust
The Northampton Municipal
Church Charities
The Earl of Northampton's
Charity
The Northcott Devon
Foundation
The Community Foundation for
Northern Ireland
The Northumberland Village
Homes Trust
The Northumbria Historic
Churches Trust
The Northwood Charitable
Trust
The Norton Foundation
The Norwich Church of England
Young Men's Society
The Norwich Town Close
Estate Charity
The Norwood and Newton
Settlement
The Notgrove Trust
Nottinghamshire Community
Foundation
The Nottinghamshire Historic
Churches Trust
The Nottinghamshire Miners'
Welfare Trust Fund
Novi Most International
The Father O'Mahoney
Memorial Trust
The Sir Peter O'Sullevan
Charitable Trust
The Oak Trust
The Oakdale Trust
The Oakley Charitable Trust
The Oakmoor Charitable Trust
The Odin Charitable Trust
The Ofenheim Charitable Trust
Ogilvie Charities Deed No.2
(including the Charity of
Mary Catherine Ford Smith)
Oglesby Charitable Trust
The Oikonomia Trust
Oizer Charitable Trust
The Old Broad Street Charity
Trust

The John Oldacre Foundation
The Oldham Foundation
Open Gate
Ormonde Foundation
The Ormsby Charitable Trust
The Orrin Charitable Trust
The Owen Family Trust
Oxfam (GB)
The Oxfordshire Community
  Foundation
The P F Charitable Trust
Padwa Charitable Foundation
The Paget Charitable Trust
The Palmer Foundation
The Panacea Society
Panton Trust
The James Pantyfedwen
  Foundation
The Paragon Trust
Paraton Trust
The Park House Charitable
  Trust
The Frank Parkinson
  Agricultural Trust
The Samuel and Freda
  Parkinson Charitable Trust
The Parthenon Trust
The Constance Paterson
  Charitable Trust
The Patrick Charitable Trust
The Jack Patston Charitable
  Trust
Paycare Charity Trust
The Susanna Peake Charitable
  Trust
The Pedmore Sporting Club
  Trust Fund
The Dowager Countess
  Eleanor Peel Trust
The Pennycress Trust
The Performing Right Society
  Foundation
The Persson Charitable Trust
The Jack Petchey Foundation
The Petplan Charitable Trust
The Philips and Rubens
  Charitable Trust
The Phillips Charitable Trust
The Phillips Family Charitable
  Trust
Philological Foundation
The Bernard Piggott Charitable
  Trust
The Pilgrim Trust
The Cecil Pilkington Charitable
  Trust
The Pilkington Charities Fund
The Austin and Hope
  Pilkington Trust
The Sir Harry Pilkington Trust
The Col W W Pilkington Will
  Trusts The General Charity
  Fund
The DLA Piper Charitable Trust
The Worshipful Company of
  Plaisterers Charitable Trust
The Platinum Trust

The George and Esme Pollitzer
  Charitable Settlement
The J S F Pollitzer Charitable
  Settlement
Edith and Ferdinand Porjes
  Charitable Trust
The John Porter Charitable
  Trust
The Porter Foundation
The Portishead Nautical Trust
The Portrack Charitable Trust
The J E Posnansky Charitable
  Trust
The Powell Foundation
Premierquote Ltd
Premishlaner Charitable Trust
The Tom Press Charitable
  Foundation
The William Price Charitable
  Trust
Sir John Priestman Charity
  Trust
The Primrose Trust
The Prince of Wales's
  Charitable Foundation
Prison Service Charity Fund
The Privy Purse Charitable
  Trust
The Proven Family Trust
The Provincial Grand Charity of
  the Province of Derbyshire
The Puebla Charitable Trust
The Richard and Christine
  Purchas Charitable Trust
The Puri Foundation
Mr and Mrs J A Pye's
  Charitable Settlement
Quartet Community Foundation
Queen Mary's Roehampton
  Trust
The Queen's Silver Jubilee
  Trust
R S Charitable Trust
The Monica Rabagliati
  Charitable Trust
Rachel Charitable Trust
The Mr and Mrs Philip
  Rackham Charitable Trust
Richard Radcliffe Charitable
  Trust
The Radcliffe Trust
The Ragdoll Foundation
The Rainford Trust
The Peggy Ramsay Foundation
The Joseph and Lena Randall
  Charitable Trust
The Rank Foundation Limited
The Fanny Rapaport Charitable
  Settlement
The Ratcliff Foundation
The Ratcliff Pension Charity
The Ratcliffe Charitable Trust
The Eleanor Rathbone
  Charitable Trust
The Sigrid Rausing Trust
The Ravensdale Trust
The Rawdon-Smith Trust

The Rayden Charitable Trust
The Roger Raymond Charitable
  Trust
The Rayne Foundation
The Rayne Trust
The Sir James Reckitt Charity
The Red Arrows Trust
The Red Rose Charitable Trust
The C A Redfern Charitable
  Foundation
The Reed Foundation
Richard Reeve's Foundation
The Max Reinhardt Charitable
  Trust
Relief Fund for Romania
  Limited
The Rest Harrow Trust
Reuben Foundation
The Nathaniel Reyner Trust
  Fund
The Rhododendron Trust
The Rhondda Cynon Taff
  Welsh Church Acts Fund
The Clive Richards Charity
The Richmond Parish Lands
  Charity
Ridgesave Limited
The Ripple Effect Foundation
The Sir John Ritblat Family
  Foundation
Thomas Roberts Trust
The Robertson Trust
The Rochester Bridge Trust
The Rock Foundation
The Rock Solid Trust
The Rofeh Trust
Rokach Family Charitable Trust
The Helen Roll Charitable
  Trust
The Sir James Roll Charitable
  Trust
The C A Rookes Charitable
  Trust
The Rosca Trust
The Rose Foundation
The Cecil Rosen Foundation
The Rothermere Foundation
The Rotherwick Foundation
The Rothley Trust
The Roughley Charitable Trust
Rowanville Ltd
The Rowlands Trust
Royal Artillery Charitable Fund
Royal British Legion
Royal Docks Trust (London)
Royal Masonic Trust for Girls
  and Boys
The Alfred and Frances
  Rubens Charitable Trust
The Rubin Foundation
William Arthur Rudd Memorial
  Trust
Rugby Football Foundation
The Russell Trust
The J S and E C Rymer
  Charitable Trust
S O Charitable Trust

The Jeremy and John Sacher
Charitable Trust
The Michael Harry Sacher
Trust
Raymond and Beverly Sackler
1988 Foundation
The Sackler Trust
The Ruzin Sadagora Trust
The Saddlers' Company
Charitable Fund
The Saga Charitable Trust
The Jean Sainsbury Animal
Welfare Trust
The Alan and Babette
Sainsbury Charitable Fund
The Sainsbury Family
Charitable Trusts
The Saintbury Trust
The Saints and Sinners Trust
The Salt Foundation
Basil Samuel Charitable Trust
The M J Samuel Charitable
Trust
The Peter Samuel Charitable
Trust
The Samworth Foundation
The Sandra Charitable Trust
The Scarfe Charitable Trust
The Schapira Charitable Trust
The Schmidt-Bodner Charitable
Trust
The R H Scholes Charitable
Trust
The Schreib Trust
The Schreiber Charitable Trust
The Schuster Charitable Trust
Foundation Scotland
The Francis C Scott Charitable
Trust
The Frieda Scott Charitable
Trust
The Storrow Scott Will Trust
Scottish Coal Industry Special
Welfare Fund
The Scouloudi Foundation
The Screwfix Foundation
Seafarers UK (King George's
Fund for Sailors)
Seamen's Hospital Society
The Searchlight Electric
Charitable Trust
The Samuel Sebba Charitable
Trust
The Seedfield Trust
Leslie Sell Charitable Trust
The Ayrton Senna Foundation
The Seven Fifty Trust
The Cyril Shack Trust
The Shanti Charitable Trust
ShareGift (The Orr Mackintosh
Foundation)
The Linley Shaw Foundation
The Shears Foundation
The Sheffield and District
Hospital Services
Charitable Fund

The Patricia and Donald
Shepherd Charitable Trust
The Sylvia and Colin Shepherd
Charitable Trust
The Archie Sherman Cardiff
Foundation
The Archie Sherman Charitable
Trust
The Shetland Charitable Trust
SHINE (Support and Help in
Education)
The Barnett and Sylvia Shine
No 2 Charitable Trust
The Bassil Shippam and
Alsford Trust
The Shipwrights' Company
Charitable Fund
The Shirley Foundation
Shlomo Memorial Fund Limited
The J A Shone Memorial Trust
The Barbara A Shuttleworth
Memorial Trust
The Mary Elizabeth Siebel
Charity
David and Jennifer Sieff
Charitable Trust
The Julius Silman Charitable
Trust
The Leslie Silver Charitable
Trust
The Simpson Education and
Conservation Trust
The Simpson Foundation
The Huntly and Margery
Sinclair Charitable Trust
Sino-British Fellowship Trust
SITA Cornwall Trust Limited
The Skelton Bounty
The Charles Skey Charitable
Trust
The John Slater Foundation
Sloane Robinson Foundation
The SMB Charitable Trust
The Mrs Smith and Mount
Trust
The N Smith Charitable
Settlement
The E H Smith Charitable Trust
The Smith Charitable Trust
The Henry Smith Charity
The Leslie Smith Foundation
The Martin Smith Foundation
The Stanley Smith UK
Horticultural Trust
The Solo Charitable
Settlement
Dr Richard Solomon's
Charitable Trust
Friends of Somerset Churches
and Chapels
The E C Sosnow Charitable
Trust
The South Square Trust
The Stephen R and Philippa H
Southall Charitable Trust
The W F Southall Trust

The Southover Manor General
Education Trust
The Southwold Trust
The Sovereign Health Care
Charitable Trust
Sparquote Limited
The Spear Charitable Trust
The Worshipful Company of
Spectacle Makers' Charity
The Jessie Spencer Trust
The Ralph and Irma Sperring
Charity
The Spielman Charitable Trust
Springrule Limited
The Spurrell Charitable Trust
The Geoff and Fiona Squire
Foundation
St Andrew's Conservation
Trust
St James' Trust Settlement
St James's Place Foundation
St Michael's and All Saints'
Charities Relief Branch (The
Church Houses Relief in
Need Charity)
The Late St Patrick White
Charitable Trust
The Stanley Foundation Ltd
The Stanton Ballard Charitable
Trust
The Staples Trust
The Star Charitable Trust
The Steel Charitable Trust
The Steinberg Family
Charitable Trust
The Hugh Stenhouse
Foundation
The Stephen Barry Charitable
Trust
The Sigmund Sternberg
Charitable Foundation
Stervon Ltd
The Stevenage Community
Trust
The June Stevens Foundation
The Steventon Allotments and
Relief-in-Need Charity
The Stewards' Company
Limited (incorporating the J
W Laing Trust and the J W
Laing Biblical Scholarship
Trust)
The Leonard Laity Stoate
Charitable Trust
The Stobart Newlands
Charitable Trust
The Edward Stocks-Massey
Bequest Fund
The Stokenchurch Educational
Charity
The Stoller Charitable Trust
The M J C Stone Charitable
Trust
The Samuel Storey Family
Charitable Trust
Peter Stormonth Darling
Charitable Trust

....

The Strangward Trust
The Strasser Foundation
Stratford upon Avon Town
  Trust
The W O Street Charitable
  Foundation
The Sudborough Foundation
The Suffolk Historic Churches
  Trust
The Summerfield Charitable
  Trust
The Bernard Sunley Charitable
  Foundation
The Surrey Historic Buildings
  Trust Ltd
The Sussex Historic Churches
  Trust
The Sutasoma Trust
Sutton Coldfield Charitable
  Trust
Swansea and Brecon Diocesan
  Board of Finance Limited
The John Swire (1989)
  Charitable Trust
The Swire Charitable Trust
The Adrian Swire Charitable
  Trust
The Hugh and Ruby Sykes
  Charitable Trust
The Charles and Elsie Sykes
  Trust
The Sylvanus Charitable Trust
The Stella Symons Charitable
  Trust
The Tabeel Trust
The Tajtelbaum Charitable
  Trust
The Talbot Trusts
The Talbot Village Trust
Tallow Chandlers Benevolent
  Fund
The Tangent Charitable Trust
The Lady Tangye Charitable
  Trust
The David Tannen Charitable
  Trust
The Tanner Trust
The Lili Tapper Charitable
  Foundation
The Mrs A Lacy Tate Trust
The Tay Charitable Trust
Humphrey Richardson Taylor
  Charitable Trust
The Connie and Albert Taylor
  Charitable Trust
The Cyril Taylor Charitable
  Trust
A P Taylor Trust
Tearfund
The Tedworth Charitable Trust
Tees Valley Community
  Foundation
The Templeton Goodwill Trust
Tesco Charity Trust
The C Paul Thackray General
  Charitable Trust
The Thames Wharf Charity

The John P. Gommes
  Foundation
The Thistle Trust
The Loke Wan Tho Memorial
  Foundation
The Thomas Lilley Memorial
  Trust
The Arthur and Margaret
  Thompson Charitable Trust
The Thompson Family
  Charitable Trust
The Len Thomson Charitable
  Trust
The Sir Jules Thorn Charitable
  Trust
The Thornton Foundation
The Thornton Trust
The Thousandth Man- Richard
  Burns Charitable Trust
The Three Guineas Trust
The Three Oaks Trust
The Thriplow Charitable Trust
Mrs R P Tindall's Charitable
  Trust
The Tinsley Foundation
The Tobacco Pipe Makers and
  Tobacco Trade Benevolent
  Fund
The Tolkien Trust
Tollemache (Buckminster)
  Charitable Trust
Tomchei Torah Charitable
  Trust
The Tompkins Foundation
The Tory Family Foundation
Tottenham Grammar School
  Foundation
The Tower Hill Trust
The Towry Law Charitable Trust
  (also known as the Castle
  Educational Trust)
The Toy Trust
The Mayor of Trafford's Charity
  Fund
The Constance Travis
  Charitable Trust
The Treeside Trust
The Triangle Trust (1949) Fund
The True Colours Trust
Truedene Co. Ltd
The Truemark Trust
Truemart Limited
Trumros Limited
The Trusthouse Charitable
  Foundation
Tudor Rose Ltd
The Tudor Trust
The Tufton Charitable Trust
The R D Turner Charitable
  Trust
The Douglas Turner Trust
The Florence Turner Trust
The G J W Turner Trust
The Turtleton Charitable Trust
Miss S M Tutton Charitable
  Trust
The TUUT Charitable Trust

Community Foundation Serving
  Tyne and Wear and
  Northumberland
Trustees of Tzedakah
Ulster Garden Villages Ltd
Ulverston Town Lands Charity
The Underwood Trust
The Union of Orthodox Hebrew
  Congregation
The United Society for the
  Propagation of the Gospel
The David Uri Memorial Trust
Uxbridge United Welfare Trust
Vale of Glamorgan – Welsh
  Church Fund
The Valentine Charitable Trust
The Van Neste Foundation
Mrs Maud Van Norden's
  Charitable Foundation
The Vandervell Foundation
The Vardy Foundation
The Variety Club Children's
  Charity
Veneziana Fund
The Verdon-Smith Family
  Charitable Settlement
Victoria Homes Trust
The Nigel Vinson Charitable
  Trust
Vintners' Gifts Charity
Vision Charity
Vivdale Ltd
The Viznitz Foundation
Voluntary Action Fund (VAF)
Wade's Charity
The Community Foundation in
  Wales
Wales Council for Voluntary
  Action
Robert and Felicity Waley-
  Cohen Charitable Trust
The F J Wallis Charitable
  Settlement
War on Want
The Ward Blenkinsop Trust
The George Ward Charitable
  Trust
The Barbara Ward Children's
  Foundation
The John Warren Foundation
G R Waters Charitable Trust
  2000
John Watson's Trust
Waynflete Charitable Trust
Weatherley Charitable Trust
The Weavers' Company
  Benevolent Fund
The William Webster
  Charitable Trust
The Weinberg Foundation
The Weinstein Foundation
The James Weir Foundation
The Barbara Welby Trust
The Wellcome Trust

Welsh Church Fund Dyfed area (Carmarthenshire, Ceredigion and Pembrokeshire)
The Welton Foundation
The Wessex Youth Trust
The West Derby Wastelands Charity
West London Synagogue Charitable Fund
The Westminster Foundation
The Garfield Weston Foundation
The Colonel W H Whitbread Charitable Trust
The Simon Whitbread Charitable Trust
The Whitecourt Charitable Trust
The Norman Whiteley Trust
The Whitley Animal Protection Trust
The Whittlesey Charity
The Lionel Wigram Memorial Trust
The Felicity Wilde Charitable Trust
The Wilkinson Charitable Foundation
Will to Win Foundation Ltd. (previously Tennis for a Life)
The William Barrow's Charity
The Charity of William Williams
The Kay Williams Charitable Foundation
The Williams Family Charitable Trust
The HDH Wills 1965 Charitable Trust
The Dame Violet Wills Will Trust
The Wilmcote Charitrust
David Wilson Foundation
The Wilson Foundation
J and J R Wilson Trust
The Community Foundation for Wiltshire and Swindon
The Benjamin Winegarten Charitable Trust
The Francis Winham Foundation
Wirral Mayor's Charity
The James Wise Charitable Trust
The Michael and Anna Wix Charitable Trust
The Wixamtree Trust
The Woburn 1986 Charitable Trust
The Maurice Wohl Charitable Foundation
The Charles Wolfson Charitable Trust
The Wolfson Family Charitable Trust
The Wolfson Foundation

The James Wood Bequest Fund
Wooden Spoon Society
Woodlands Green Ltd
The Woodward Charitable Trust
Worcester Municipal Charities
The Worcestershire and Dudley Historic Churches Trust
The Diana Edgson Wright Charitable Trust
The Matthews Wrightson Charity Trust
Miss E B Wrightson's Charitable Settlement
Wychdale Ltd
Wychville Ltd
The Wyndham Charitable Trust
The Wyseliot Charitable Trust
The Yardley Great Trust
The Dennis Alan Yardy Charitable Trust
Yorkshire Agricultural Society
Yorkshire Building Society Charitable Foundation
The South Yorkshire Community Foundation
The Yorkshire Dales Millennium Trust
The Yorkshire Historic Churches Trust
The John Young Charitable Settlement
The William Allen Young Charitable Trust
The John K Young Endowment Fund
Zephyr Charitable Trust
The Marjorie and Arnold Ziff Charitable Foundation
Stephen Zimmerman Charitable Trust
The Zochonis Charitable Trust
Zurich Community Trust (UK) Limited

....

■ Collections and acquisitions

The 1970 Trust
The 1989 Willan Charitable Trust
The 29th May 1961 Charitable Trust
A W Charitable Trust
The Aberbrothock Skea Trust
The Aberdeen Endowments Trust
Achisomoch Aid Company Limited
The ACT Foundation
Action Medical Research
The Company of Actuaries' Charitable Trust Fund

The Sylvia Adams Charitable Trust
The Victor Adda Foundation
The Adint Charitable Trust
Aid to the Church in Need (UK)
The Sylvia Aitken Charitable Trust
The Al Fayed Charitable Foundation
Aldgate and All Hallows' Foundation
The Aldgate Freedom Foundation
Allchurches Trust Ltd
The H B Allen Charitable Trust
The Alliance Family Foundation
The Pat Allsop Charitable Trust
Almondsbury Charity
Altamont Ltd
Alvor Charitable Trust
The Ammco Trust
Viscount Amory's Charitable Trust
The AMW Charitable Trust
The André Christian Trust
Anguish's Educational Foundation
The Animal Defence Trust
The Eric Anker-Petersen Charity
Anpride Ltd
Ambrose and Ann Appelbe Trust
The Appletree Trust
The Arbib Foundation
The John M Archer Charitable Trust
The Archer Trust
The Ardwick Trust
The Argus Appeal
The Armenian Relief Society of Great Britain Trust
The Armourers' and Brasiers' Gauntlet Trust
The Arsenal Foundation
The Arts and Entertainment Charitable Trust
Arts Council England
The Arts Council of Northern Ireland
Arts Council of Wales (also known as Cyngor Celfyddydau Cymru)
The Ove Arup Foundation
The A S Charitable Trust
The Ashden Trust
The Ashendene Trust
The Ashley Family Foundation
The Ashworth Charitable Trust
The Ian Askew Charitable Trust
The Associated Country Women of the World
The Association of Colleges Charitable Trust
Astellas European Foundation
Asthma UK
The Astor Foundation

The Astor of Hever Trust
The Aurelius Charitable Trust
The John Avins Trustees
The Avon and Somerset Police
Community Trust
The Aylesford Family
Charitable Trust
The BAA Communities Trust
The Bagri Foundation
Veta Bailey Charitable Trust
The Austin Bailey Foundation
The Baird Trust
The Baker Charitable Trust
The Balcombe Charitable Trust
The Albert Casanova Ballard
Deceased Trust
The Ballinger Charitable Trust
The Balmore Trust
The Balney Charitable Trust
The Baltic Charitable Fund
The Bamford Charitable
Foundation
The Banbury Charities
William P Bancroft (No 2)
Charitable Trust and
Jenepher Gillett Trust
The Band Trust
The Barbers' Company General
Charities
The Barbour Foundation
Barchester Healthcare
Foundation
The Barclay Foundation
Peter Barker-Mill Memorial
Charity
The Barleycorn Trust
Barnes Workhouse Fund
The Barnsbury Charitable Trust
The Barnstaple Bridge Trust
The Misses Barrie Charitable
Trust
Barrington Family Charitable
Trust
Bartholomew Charitable Trust
The Bartlett Taylor Charitable
Trust
The Paul Bassham Charitable
Trust
The Batchworth Trust
The Bates Charitable Trust
The Bay Tree Charitable Trust
The Louis Baylis (Maidenhead
Advertiser) Charitable Trust
BBC Children in Need
B-CH 1971 Charitable Trust
The Beacon Trust
The Bearder Charity
The James Beattie Charitable
Trust
The Beaverbrook Foundation
The Beccles Town Lands
Charity
The Becker Family Charitable
Trust
The Becketts and Sargeants
Educational Foundation

The Peter Beckwith Charitable
Trust
The David and Ruth Behrend
Fund
The Beit Trust
The Bellahouston Bequest
Fund
The Bellinger Donnay Trust
The Benfield Motors Charitable
Trust
The Benham Charitable
Settlement
Maurice and Jacqueline
Bennett Charitable Trust
The Gerald Bentall Charitable
Trust
Bergqvist Charitable Trust
The Berkshire Community
Foundation
The Bestway Foundation
BHST
The Mason Bibby 1981 Trust
The Bideford Bridge Trust
The Big Lottery Fund
The Billmeir Charitable Trust
The Bingham Trust
The Bintaub Charitable Trust
The Birmingham District
Nursing Charitable Trust
The Birmingham Hospital
Saturday Fund Medical
Charity and Welfare Trust
Birmingham International
Airport Community Trust
The Lord Mayor of
Birmingham's Charity
Miss Jeanne Bisgood's
Charitable Trust
The Michael Bishop
Foundation
The Bishop's Development
Fund
The Bertie Black Foundation
Isabel Blackman Foundation
The Blagrave Trust
The Blair Foundation
Blakemore Foundation
The Blanchminster Trust
The Blandford Lake Trust
The Sir Victor Blank
Settlement
The Neville and Elaine Blond
Charitable Trust
The Bluston Charitable
Settlement
The Bonamy Charitable Trust
The John and Celia Bonham
Christie Charitable Trust
The Charlotte Bonham-Carter
Charitable Trust
Bonhomie United Charity
Society
The Boots Charitable Trust
The Bordon Liphook
Haslemere Charity
The Oliver Borthwick Memorial
Trust

The Bosson Family Charitable
Trust
The Bothwell Charitable Trust
H E and E L Botteley
Charitable Trust
The Harry Bottom Charitable
Trust
The Anthony Bourne
Foundation
The Bower Trust
The Bowerman Charitable
Trust
John and Susan Bowers Fund
The Bowland Charitable Trust
The Frank Brake Charitable
Trust
The William Brake Charitable
Trust
The Tony Bramall Charitable
Trust
The Harold and Alice Bridges
Charity
Bristol Archdeaconry Charity
John Bristow and Thomas
Mason Trust
The British Council for
Prevention of Blindness
The British Dietetic
Association General and
Education Trust Fund
The British Gas (Scottish Gas)
Energy Trust
British Heart Foundation
British Humane Association
British Ornithologists' Union
British Record Industry Trust
The J and M Britton Charitable
Trust
The Roger Brooke Charitable
Trust
The David Brooke Charity
The Charles Brotherton Trust
Joseph Brough Charitable
Trust
The Swinfen Broun Charitable
Trust
Edna Brown Charitable
Settlement (Mrs E E Brown
Charitable Settlement)
The Jack Brunton Charitable
Trust
Buckinghamshire Community
Foundation
The Rosemary Bugden
Charitable Trust
The Bulldog Trust Limited
The E F Bulmer Benevolent
Fund
Burdens Charitable Foundation
The Clara E Burgess Charity
The Burry Charitable Trust
The Arnold Burton 1998
Charitable Trust
The Burton Breweries
Charitable Trust
Consolidated Charity of Burton
upon Trent

The Worshipful Company of
Butchers General Charities
The Noel Buxton Trust
Henry T and Lucy B Cadbury
Charitable Trust
The Christopher Cadbury
Charitable Trust
The G W Cadbury Charitable
Trust
The Richard Cadbury
Charitable Trust
The Edward and Dorothy
Cadbury Trust
The George Cadbury Trust
CAFOD (Catholic Agency for
Overseas Development)
Community Foundation for
Calderdale
The Callander Charitable Trust
Calypso Browning Trust
The Canning Trust
The Carew Pole Charitable
Trust
The D W T Cargill Fund
Carlee Ltd
The Carlton House Charitable
Trust
The Carmelite Monastery Ware
Trust
The Worshipful Company of
Carmen Benevolent Trust
The Carnegie Dunfermline
Trust
The Carpenter Charitable Trust
The Carpenters' Company
Charitable Trust
The Carrington Charitable
Trust
The Carron Charitable
Settlement
The Leslie Mary Carter
Charitable Trust
The Casey Trust
The Elizabeth Casson Trust
The Catalyst Charitable Trust
The Catholic Charitable Trust
Catholic Foreign Missions
The Catholic Trust for England
and Wales
The Joseph and Annie Cattle
Trust
The Thomas Sivewright Catto
Charitable Settlement
The Wilfrid and Constance
Cave Foundation
The Cayo Foundation
Elizabeth Cayzer Charitable
Trust
The B G S Cayzer Charitable
Trust
The Cazenove Charitable Trust
Celtic Charity Fund
The Pamela Champion
Foundation
The Chapman Charitable Trust
John William Chapman's
Charitable Trust

The Charities Advisory Trust
Charitworth Limited
The Charter 600 Charity
The Worshipful Company of
Chartered Accountants
General Charitable Trust
(also known as CALC)
The Chasah Trust
The Chelsea Square 1994
Trust
The Cheruby Trust
Cheshire Freemason's Charity
The Chetwode Foundation
Cheviot Asset Management
Charitable Trust
Childs Charitable Trust
The Childwick Trust
The Chippenham Borough
Lands Charity
The Chipping Sodbury Town
Lands Charity
CHK Charities Limited
The Chownes Foundation
The Chrimes Family Charitable
Trust
The Christabella Charitable
Trust
Christadelphian Samaritan
Fund
Christian Aid
Christian Response to Eastern
Europe
The Church and Community
Fund
The Church Burgesses
Educational Foundation
Church Burgesses Trust
City and County of Swansea
Welsh Church Act Fund
The City Educational Trust
Fund
Stephen Clark 1957
Charitable Trust
J A Clark Charitable Trust
The Hilda and Alice Clark
Charitable Trust
The Roger and Sarah Bancroft
Clark Charitable Trust
The Clarke Charitable
Settlement
The Cleopatra Trust
Lord Clinton's Charitable Trust
The Clore Duffield Foundation
Miss V L Clore's 1967
Charitable Trust
Closehelm Limited
The Clothworkers' Foundation
The Clover Trust
The Robert Clutterbuck
Charitable Trust
Clydpride Ltd
The John Coates Charitable
Trust
The Cobtree Charity Trust Ltd
The Denise Cohen Charitable
Trust

The Vivienne and Samuel
Cohen Charitable Trust
The John S Cohen Foundation
The R and S Cohen
Foundation
The Colchester Catalyst
Charity
The Cole Charitable Trust
The Colefax Charitable Trust
The John and Freda Coleman
Charitable Trust
The George Henry Collins
Charity
The Sir Jeremiah Colman Gift
Trust
The Coltstaple Trust
Colwinston Charitable Trust
Colyer-Fergusson Charitable
Trust
Community First (Landfill
Communities Fund)
The Compton Charitable Trust
The Congleton Inclosure Trust
The Conservation Foundation
The Consolidated Charities for
the Infirm Merchant
Taylors' Company
The Cooks Charity
The Catherine Cookson
Charitable Trust
Mabel Cooper Charity
The Alice Ellen Cooper Dean
Charitable Foundation
The Marjorie Coote Animal
Charity Trust
The Marjorie Coote Old
People's Charity
The Helen Jean Cope Trust
The J Reginald Corah
Foundation Fund
The Gershon Coren Charitable
Foundation (also known as
The Muriel and Gus Coren
Charitable Foundation)
The Duke of Cornwall's
Benevolent Fund
The Cornwell Charitable Trust
The Sidney and Elizabeth
Corob Charitable Trust
The Corona Charitable Trust
The Costa Family Charitable
Trust
The Cotton Industry War
Memorial Trust
The Cotton Trust
County Durham Community
Foundation
The Augustine Courtauld Trust
The General Charities of the
City of Coventry
Coventry Building Society
Charitable Foundation
The John Cowan Foundation
Dudley and Geoffrey Cox
Charitable Trust
The Sir William Coxen Trust
Fund

The Lord Cozens-Hardy Trust
The Craignish Trust
The Craps Charitable Trust
Michael Crawford Children's
  Charity
The Cray Trust
Creative Scotland
The Crescent Trust
The Violet and Milo Cripps
  Charitable Trust
The Harry Crook Foundation
The Cross Trust
The Croydon Relief in Need
  Charities
Cruden Foundation Ltd
The Ronald Cruickshanks
  Foundation
The Culra Charitable Trust
The Cumber Family Charitable
  Trust
Cumberland Building Society
  Charitable Foundation
Cumbria Community
  Foundation
The D J H Currie Memorial
  Trust
The Dennis Curry Charitable
  Trust
The Manny Cussins
  Foundation
The Cwmbran Trust
Itzchok Meyer Cymerman Trust
  Ltd
The D G Charitable Settlement
The D'Oyly Carte Charitable
  Trust
Daily Prayer Union Charitable
  Trust Limited
The Daiwa Anglo-Japanese
  Foundation
The Dr and Mrs A Darlington
  Charitable Trust
The Davidson (Nairn)
  Charitable Trust
The Davidson Family
  Charitable Trust
The Alderman Joe Davidson
  Memorial Trust
Michael Davies Charitable
  Settlement
The Gwendoline and Margaret
  Davies Charity
The Wilfrid Bruce Davis
  Charitable Trust
Davis-Rubens Charitable Trust
The Dawe Charitable Trust
The De Brye Charitable Trust
The De Clermont Charitable
  Company Ltd
The Deakin Charitable Trust
The Debmar Benevolent Trust
The Delius Trust
The Dellal Foundation
The Delves Charitable Trust
The Demigryphon Trust
The Denman Charitable Trust

Dentons UKMEA LLP
  Charitable Trust
The Earl of Derby's Charitable
  Trust
Derbyshire Community
  Foundation
The J N Derbyshire Trust
The Desmond Foundation
Devon Community Foundation
The Devon Educational Trust
The Duke of Devonshire's
  Charitable Trust
The Sandy Dewhirst Charitable
  Trust
The Laduma Dhamecha
  Charitable Trust
The Dibden Allotments Fund
Diced Cap Charity
The Dickon Trust
The Digbeth Trust Limited
The Dinwoodie Settlement
Dischma Charitable Trust
The DLM Charitable Trust
Louise Dobson Charitable
  Trust
The Derek and Eileen Dodgson
  Foundation
The Dollond Charitable Trust
Domepride Ltd
The Dorcas Trust
The Dorus Trust
The Doughty Charity Trust
Douglas Arter Foundation
The R M Douglas Charitable
  Trust
The Drapers' Charitable Fund
The Duis Charitable Trust
The P B Dumbell Charitable
  Trust
The Dumbreck Charity
Dunard Fund
The Dunn Family Charitable
  Trust
The W E Dunn Trust
Dushinsky Trust Ltd
The Dwek Family Charitable
  Trust
The Dyers' Company
  Charitable Trust
The Eagle Charity Trust
The Earley Charity
Earls Colne and Halstead
  Educational Charity
The Earmark Trust
East End Community
  Foundation
Eastern Counties Educational
  Trust Limited
The Ebenezer Trust
The EBM Charitable Trust
Eden Arts Trust
EDF Energy Trust (EDFET)
The Gilbert and Eileen Edgar
  Foundation
Edinburgh Trust No 2 Account

Edinburgh Voluntary
  Organisations' Trust Funds
  (EVOT)
The W G Edwards Charitable
  Foundation
The William Edwards
  Educational Charity
The Elephant Trust
The George Elias Charitable
  Trust
The Gerald Palmer Eling Trust
  Company
The Wilfred and Elsie Elkes
  Charity Fund
The Ellerdale Trust
The John Ellerman Foundation
The Ellinson Foundation Ltd
The Ellis Campbell Foundation
James Ellis Charitable Trust
The Elmgrant Trust
The Elmley Foundation
The Vernon N Ely Charitable
  Trust
The Embleton Trust
Embrace the Middle East
The Emerton-Christie Charity
EMI Music Sound Foundation
The Worshipful Company of
  Engineers Charitable Trust
  Fund
The Englefield Charitable Trust
The Enkalon Foundation
Entindale Ltd
The Epigoni Trust
The Equity Trust Fund
The Ericson Trust
The Erskine Cunningham Hill
  Trust
Essex Community Foundation
The Essex Fairway Charitable
  Trust
The Essex Heritage Trust
Essex Provincial Charity Fund
The Essex Youth Trust
Euro Charity Trust
Sir John Evelyn's Charity
The Eventhall Family
  Charitable Trust
The Everard Foundation
The Beryl Evetts and Robert
  Luff Animal Welfare Trust
  Limited
The Exilarch's Foundation
F C Charitable Trust
The F P Limited Charitable
  Trust
The Faber Charitable Trust
The Fairway Trust
The Family Rich Charities Trust
The Lord Faringdon Charitable
  Trust
Samuel William Farmer Trust
The Farmers' Company
  Charitable Fund
The Thomas Farr Charity
Walter Farthing (Trust) Limited
The Fassnidge Memorial Trust

Joseph Fattorini Charitable Trust

Federation of Jewish Relief Organisations

The John Feeney Charitable Trust

The George Fentham Birmingham Charity

The A M Fenton Trust

Allan and Nesta Ferguson Charitable Settlement

The Fidelity UK Foundation

The Doris Field Charitable Trust

Fife Council/Common Good Funds and Trusts

Firtree Trust

The Fitton Trust

The Earl Fitzwilliam Charitable Trust

The Ian Fleming Charitable Trust

The Joyce Fletcher Charitable Trust

The Flow Foundation

The Gerald Fogel Charitable Trust

The Follett Trust

The Football Association National Sports Centre Trust

The Football Foundation

The Forbes Charitable Foundation

The Forces Trust (Working Name)

The Oliver Ford Charitable Trust

The Forest Hill Charitable Trust

The Foresters' Charity Stewards UK Trust

Forever Manchester (The Community Foundation for Greater Manchester)

The Forman Hardy Charitable Trust

Gwyneth Forrester Trust

The Forte Charitable Trust

The Four Lanes Trust

The Four Winds Trust

The Foyle Foundation

The Isaac and Freda Frankel Memorial Charitable Trust

The Elizabeth Frankland Moore and Star Foundation

The Jill Franklin Trust

The Gordon Fraser Charitable Trust

The Hugh Fraser Foundation

The Joseph Strong Frazer Trust

The Louis and Valerie Freedman Charitable Settlement

The Thomas Freke and Lady Norton Charity Trust

The Charles S French Charitable Trust

The Anne French Memorial Trust

The Freshfield Foundation

The Freshgate Trust Foundation

The Friarsgate Trust

The Friends Hall Farm Street Trust

Friends Provident Charitable Foundation

The Frognal Trust

The Patrick & Helena Frost Foundation

Maurice Fry Charitable Trust

The Fulmer Charitable Trust

Worshipful Company of Furniture Makers Charitable Fund

Gableholt Limited

The Galbraith Trust

The Gale Family Charity Trust

Gamlen Charitable Trust

The Gamma Trust

The Gannochy Trust

The Worshipful Company of Gardeners of London

The Samuel Gardner Memorial Trust

The Garnett Charitable Trust

Garthgwynion Charities

Garvan Limited

The Gatsby Charitable Foundation

Gatwick Airport Community Trust

The Robert Gavron Charitable Trust

Thomas Betton's Charity for Pensions and Relief-in-Need

The Gibbs Charitable Trust

Simon Gibson Charitable Trust

The G C Gibson Charitable Trust

Lady Gibson's Charitable Trust

The Harvey and Hilary Gilbert Charitable Trust

The Girdlers' Company Charitable Trust

The B and P Glasser Charitable Trust

The Glass-House Trust

Global Care

Global Charities

Gloucestershire Community Foundation

Worshipful Company of Glovers of London Charity Fund

The GNC Trust

The Godinton Charitable Trust

The Sydney and Phyllis Goldberg Memorial Charitable Trust

The Golden Bottle Trust

The Jack Goldhill Charitable Trust

The Goldsmiths' Arts Trust Fund

The Goldsmiths' Company Charity

The Mike Gooley Trailfinders Charity

The Gosling Foundation Limited

The Gough Charitable Trust

The Gould Charitable Trust

The Grace Charitable Trust

A B Grace Trust

The Graff Foundation

E C Graham Belford Charitable Settlement

The Grahame Charitable Foundation Limited

The Granada Foundation

Grand Charitable Trust of the Order of Women Freemasons

The Grand Order of Water Rats' Charities Fund

The Grange Farm Centre Trust

Grantham Yorke Trust

The Gordon Gray Trust

The Gray Trust

The Great Stone Bridge Trust of Edenbridge

The Great Torrington Town Lands Charity

Greenham Common Community Trust Limited

The Gretna Charitable Trust

The Grimmitt Trust

The Grocers' Charity

The M and R Gross Charities Limited

The GRP Charitable Trust

The David and Marie Grumitt Foundation

The Bishop of Guildford's Foundation

The Guildry Incorporation of Perth

The Walter Guinness Charitable Trust

The Gunter Charitable Trust

The Gur Trust

The Gurney Charitable Trust

Dr Guthrie's Association

The H and M Charitable Trust

H C D Memorial Fund

The H P Charitable Trust

The Hackney Parochial Charities

The Hadfield Trust

The Hadrian Trust

The Alfred Haines Charitable Trust

E F and M G Hall Charitable Trust

The Edith Winifred Hall Charitable Trust

Robert Hall Charity

The Hamamelis Trust

Hamilton Wallace Trust

Paul Hamlyn Foundation
The W A Handley Charitable
Trust
Beatrice Hankey Foundation
Limited
The Hanley Trust (1987)
The Kathleen Hannay
Memorial Charity
The Doughty Hanson
Charitable Foundation
Lord Hanson Foundation
The Haramead Trust
Miss K M Harbinson's
Charitable Trust
The Harborne Parish Lands
Charity
The Harbour Charitable Trust
The Harbour Foundation
The Harding Trust
William Harding's Charity
The Hare of Steep Charitable
Trust
The Harebell Centenary Fund
The Kenneth Hargreaves
Charitable Trust
The Harris Charity
The Harrison and Potter Trust
The John Harrison Charitable
Trust
The Spencer Hart Charitable
Trust
The Hartley Charitable Trust
William Geoffrey Harvey's
Discretionary Settlement
The Edward Harvist Trust
Haskel Family Foundation
The Hathaway Trust
The M A Hawe Settlement
The Hawthorne Charitable
Trust
The Dorothy Hay-Bolton
Charitable Trust
The Headley Trust
Headley-Pitt Charitable Trust
Heart of England Community
Foundation
The Heathcoat Trust
Heathside Charitable Trust
The Charlotte Heber-Percy
Charitable Trust
The Hedley Denton Charitable
Trust
The Hedley Foundation
The H J Heinz Company
Limited Charitable Trust
The Hellenic Foundation
The Michael Heller Charitable
Foundation
The Simon Heller Charitable
Settlement
Help the Homeless
The Hemby Trust
The Christina Mary Hendrie
Trust for Scottish and
Canadian Charities

Henley Educational Trust
(formerley Henley
Educational Charity)
Esther Hennell Charitable
Trust
The G D Herbert Charitable
Trust
The Anne Herd Memorial Trust
The Herefordshire Historic
Churches Trust
The Heritage of London Trust
Ltd
The Hesed Trust
The Hesslewood Children's
Trust (Hull Seamen's and
General Orphanage)
Hexham and Newcastle
Diocesan Trust (1947)
The P and C Hickinbotham
Charitable Trust
The Higgs Charitable Trust
The High Sheriff's Police Trust
for the County of West
Midlands (Building Blocks)
Highcroft Charitable Trust
The Charles Littlewood Hill
Trust
The Hillingdon Partnership
Trust
The Hilmarnan Charitable Trust
The Hiscox Foundation
The Hitchin Educational
Foundation
The Eleemosynary Charity of
William Hobbayne
Hobson Charity Limited
Matthew Hodder Charitable
Trust
The Sir Julian Hodge
Charitable Trust
The J G Hogg Charitable Trust
The Holden Charitable Trust
John Holford's Charity
The Hollick Family Charitable
Trust
The Dorothy Holmes Charitable
Trust
The Holywood Trust
The Homelands Charitable
Trust
The Homestead Charitable
Trust
Sir Harold Hood's Charitable
Trust
Hope for Youth (NI)
The Hope Trust
HopMarket Charity
The Cuthbert Horn Trust
The Antony Hornby Charitable
Trust
The Horne Trust
The Worshipful Company of
Horners' Charitable Trusts
The Hornsey Parochial
Charities
The Hospital of God at
Greatham

The Hospital Saturday Fund
Houblon-Norman/George Fund
The House of Industry Estate
The Reta Lila Howard
Foundation
The Daniel Howard Trust
The Hudson Foundation
The Geoffrey C Hughes
Charitable Trust
The Hull and East Riding
Charitable Trust
Hulme Trust Estates
(Educational)
Human Relief Foundation
The Humanitarian Trust
The Michael and Shirley Hunt
Charitable Trust
The Hunter Foundation
Miss Agnes H Hunter's Trust
The Huntingdon Foundation
Huntingdon Freemen's Trust
Hurdale Charity Limited
The Nani Huyu Charitable Trust
The P Y N and B Hyams Trust
The Hyde Charitable Trust
The Idlewild Trust
The Iliffe Family Charitable
Trust
The Indigo Trust
The Ingram Trust
The Inlight Trust
The Inman Charity
The Inner London Magistrates
Court Poor Box and Feeder
Charity
The Ireland Fund of Great
Britain
The Irish Youth Foundation
(UK) Ltd (incorporating The
Lawlor Foundation)
The Ironmongers' Foundation
The Charles Irving Charitable
Trust
Irwin Trust
The ISA Charity
The Isaacs Charitable Trust
The J Isaacs Charitable Trust
The ITF Seafarers Trust
The J M K Charitable Trust
The J R S S T Charitable Trust
C Richard Jackson Charitable
Trust
Elizabeth Jackson Charitable
Trust
The Ruth and Lionel Jacobson
Trust (Second Fund) No 2
Jaffe Family Relief Fund
The Susan and Stephen
James Charitable
Settlement
The James Trust
The Jarman Charitable Trust
The John Jarrold Trust
JCA Charitable Foundation
The Jeffrey Charitable Trust
The Nick Jenkins Foundation
The Jenour Foundation

The Jephcott Charitable Trust
Jesus Hospital Charity
Jewish Child's Day
The Jewish Youth Fund
The Harold Joels Charitable
Trust
The Nicholas Joels Charitable
Trust
The Norman Joels Charitable
Trust
The Lillie Johnson Charitable
Trust
The Johnson Foundation
The Reginald Johnson
Foundation
The Johnnie Johnson Trust
The Johnson Wax Ltd
Charitable Trust
The Joicey Trust
The Jones 1986 Charitable
Trust
The Marjorie and Geoffrey
Jones Charitable Trust
The Jordan Charitable
Foundation
The J E Joseph Charitable
Fund
The Lady Eileen Joseph
Foundation
The Josephs Family Charitable
Trust
JTH Charitable Trust
The Julian Budd Kids in Sport
Trust Limited
The Jungels-Winkler Charitable
Foundation
The Anton Jurgens Charitable
Trust
The Bernard Kahn Charitable
Trust
The Stanley Kalms Foundation
The Karenza Foundation
The Boris Karloff Charitable
Foundation
The Kasner Charitable Trust
The Kathleen Trust
The Michael and Ilse Katz
Foundation
The Katzauer Charitable
Settlement
The C S Kaufman Charitable
Trust
The Geoffrey John Kaye
Charitable Foundation
The Emmanuel Kaye
Foundation
Kelsick's Educational
Foundation
The KempWelch Charitable
Trust
William Kendall's Charity (Wax
Chandlers' Company)
The John Thomas Kennedy
Charitable Foundation
The Kennel Club Charitable
Trust

The Nancy Kenyon Charitable
Trust
Keren Association
Kermaville Ltd
The Peter Kershaw Trust
The Ursula Keyes Trust
The Robert Kiln Charitable
Trust
The King Henry VIII Endowed
Trust Warwick
The King/Cullimore Charitable
Trust
The Kingsbury Charity
Kirkley Poor's Lands Estate
The Richard Kirkman
Charitable Trust
Kirschel Foundation
Robert Kitchin (Saddlers'
Company)
Ernest Kleinwort Charitable
Trust
The Marina Kleinwort
Charitable Trust
The Kobler Trust
The Kohn Foundation
The Kreditor Charitable Trust
The Kreitman Foundation
The Neil Kreitman Foundation
The Heinz, Anna and Carol
Kroch Foundation
The Kyte Charitable Trust
The Late Sir Pierce Lacy
Charity Trust
The Christopher Laing
Foundation
The Martin Laing Foundation
The Lambert Charitable Trust
LWS Lancashire Environmental
Fund Limited
Duchy of Lancaster Benevolent
Fund
Langdale Trust
The Langley Charitable Trust
The Langtree Trust
The LankellyChase Foundation
The R J Larg Family Charitable
Trust
Largsmount Ltd
The Lark Trust
Laslett's (Hinton) Charity
The Lauffer Family Charitable
Foundation
The Kathleen Laurence Trust
The Edgar E Lawley Foundation
The Herd Lawson and Muriel
Lawson Charitable Trust
The Lawson Beckman
Charitable Trust
The Raymond and Blanche
Lawson Charitable Trust
The Mason Le Page Charitable
Trust
The Leach Fourteenth Trust
The David Lean Foundation
The Arnold Lee Charitable
Trust

The Lord Mayor of Leeds
Appeal Fund
Leeds Building Society
Charitable Foundation
The Kennedy Leigh Charitable
Trust
The Leigh Trust
Mrs Vera Leigh's Charity
P Leigh-Bramwell Trust 'E'
The Lennox and Wyfold
Foundation
The Erica Leonard Trust
The Leonard Trust
The Mark Leonard Trust
Lesley Lesley and Mutter Trust
The Leverhulme Trust
The Joseph Levy Charitable
Foundation
The John Spedan Lewis
Foundation
The Sir Edward Lewis
Foundation
John Lewis Partnership
General Community Fund
Lichfield Conduit Lands
Lifeline 4 Kids
The Linbury Trust
The Lind Trust
Lindale Educational
Foundation
The Linden Charitable Trust
The Linmardon Trust
The Ruth and Stuart Lipton
Charitable Trust
The Lister Charitable Trust
Frank Litchfield Charitable
Trust
The Andrew and Mary
Elizabeth Little Charitable
Trust
The Second Joseph Aaron
Littman Foundation
Liverpool Charity and Voluntary
Services
Liverpool Sailors' Home Trust
The Elaine and Angus Lloyd
Charitable Trust
The Charles Lloyd Foundation
Lloyd's Charities Trust
Lloyds Bank Foundation for the
Channel Islands
The Locker Foundation
The Loftus Charitable Trust
The Lolev Charitable Trust
The Trust for London
London Catalyst
The London Community
Foundation
The London Housing
Foundation
The London Law Trust
The William and Katherine
Longman Trust
The Loseley and Guildway
Charitable Trust
The Lotus Foundation
The C L Loyd Charitable Trust

The Marie Helen Luen
Charitable Trust
Robert Luff Foundation Ltd
Henry Lumley Charitable Trust
C F Lunoe Trust Fund
The Ruth and Jack Lunzer
Charitable Trust
Lord and Lady Lurgan Trust
The Lyndhurst Trust
The Lynn Foundation
The Lynwood Trust
John Lyon's Charity
The Lyons Charitable Trust
The Sir Jack Lyons Charitable
Trust
The Lyras Family Charitable
Trust
Sylvanus Lyson's Charity
The M and C Trust
The M K Charitable Trust
The Madeline Mabey Trust
The E M MacAndrew Trust
The R S Macdonald Charitable
Trust
Macdonald-Buchanan
Charitable Trust
The Macfarlane Walker Trust
The Mackay and Brewer
Charitable Trust
The Mackintosh Foundation
The MacRobert Trust
Magdalen Hospital Trust
The Magen Charitable Trust
Man Group plc Charitable
Trust
The Manackerman Charitable
Trust
The Manchester Guardian
Society Charitable Trust
Lord Mayor of Manchester's
Charity Appeal Trust
Mandeville Trust
The Manifold Charitable Trust
W M Mann Foundation
The Leslie and Lilian Manning
Trust
Marbeh Torah Trust
Marchig Animal Welfare Trust
The Stella and Alexander
Margulies Charitable Trust
Market Harborough and The
Bowdens Charity
The Ann and David Marks
Foundation
The Hilda and Samuel Marks
Foundation
J P Marland Charitable Trust
The Michael Marsh Charitable
Trust
The Marsh Christian Trust
The Charlotte Marshall
Charitable Trust
The Jim Marshall Charitable
Trust
The Nora Joan Marshall
Charitable Trust

The D G Marshall of
Cambridge Trust
Marshall's Charity
Marshgate Charitable
Settlement
Sir George Martin Trust
The Mason Porter Charitable
Trust
The Nancie Massey Charitable
Trust
The Mathew Trust
The Matt 6.3 Charitable Trust
The Violet Mauray Charitable
Trust
The Maxwell Family Foundation
Evelyn May Trust
The Mayfield Valley Arts Trust
Mazars Charitable Trust
The Robert McAlpine
Foundation
The McDougall Trust
The McKenna Charitable Trust
The Helen Isabella McMorran
Charitable Foundation
The James Frederick and Ethel
Anne Measures Charity
The Anthony and Elizabeth
Mellows Charitable
Settlement
Melow Charitable Trust
The Mercers' Charitable
Foundation
The Merchant Taylors'
Company Charities Fund
The Merchant Venturers'
Charity
The Merchants' House of
Glasgow
The Mersey Docks and
Harbour Company
Charitable Fund
Community Foundation for
Merseyside
The Zachary Merton and
George Woofindin
Convalescent Trust
The Tony Metherell Charitable
Trust
The Metropolitan Drinking
Fountain and Cattle Trough
Association
The Mickel Fund
Gerald Micklem Charitable
Trust
Midhurst Pensions Trust
The Migraine Trust
Miles Trust for the Putney and
Roehampton Community
The Hugh and Mary Miller
Bequest Trust
The Ronald Miller Foundation
The Millfield Trust
The Millhouses Charitable
Trust
The Millichope Foundation
The Mills Charity
The Millward Charitable Trust

The Clare Milne Trust
Milton Keynes Community
Foundation
The Edgar Milward Charity
The Keith and Joan
Mindelsohn Charitable
Trust
The Peter Minet Trust
The Minos Trust
The Mirfield Educational
Charity
The Laurence Misener
Charitable Trust
The Mishcon Family Charitable
Trust
The Misselbrook Trust
The Mitchell Charitable Trust
The Esmé Mitchell Trust
Keren Mitzvah Trust
The Mizpah Trust
The Mobbs Memorial Trust Ltd
The Modiano Charitable Trust
The Moette Charitable Trust
The Mole Charitable Trust
The D C Moncrieff Charitable
Trust
Monmouthshire County Council
Welsh Church Act Fund
The Montague Thompson
Coon Charitable Trust
The Colin Montgomerie
Charitable Foundation
The Monument Trust
The Henry Moore Foundation
The Morel Charitable Trust
The Morgan Charitable
Foundation
The Mr and Mrs J T Morgan
Foundation
Morgan Stanley International
Foundation
The Oliver Morland Charitable
Trust
The Bernard Morris Charitable
Trust
The Morris Charitable Trust
The Willie and Mabel Morris
Charitable Trust
The Peter Morrison Charitable
Foundation
The Stanley Morrison
Charitable Trust
Vyoel Moshe Charitable Trust
The Moss Charitable Trust
The Robert and Margaret
Moss Charitable Trust
The Moss Family Charitable
Trust
Mosselson Charitable Trust
The Mount Everest Foundation
The Edwina Mountbatten Trust
Mountbatten Festival of Music
The Mountbatten Memorial
Trust
Mrs Waterhouse Charitable
Trust
The Mugdock Children's Trust

The Mulberry Trust
The Edith Murphy Foundation
The Mushroom Fund
The Music Sales Charitable Trust
Muslim Hands
The Mutual Trust Group
The Kitty and Daniel Nabarro Charitable Trust
The Nadezhda Charitable Trust
The Naggar Charitable Trust
The Eleni Nakou Foundation
The Janet Nash Charitable Settlement
The National Art Collections Fund
The National Churches Trust
National Committee of the Women's World Day of Prayer for England and Wales and Northern Ireland
The National Hockey Foundation
The National Manuscripts Conservation Trust
The Nationwide Foundation
Needham Market and Barking Welfare Charities
The Worshipful Company of Needlemakers' Charitable Fund
The Neighbourly Charitable Trust
The James Neill Trust Fund
Nemoral Ltd
The Newcomen Collett Foundation
Alderman Newton's Educational Foundation
The Chevras Ezras Nitzrochim Trust
The Noon Foundation
The Norda Trust
Norie Charitable Trust
The Norman Family Charitable Trust
The Duncan Norman Trust Fund
The Normanby Charitable Trust
The Northampton Municipal Church Charities
The Northampton Queen's Institute Relief in Sickness Fund
The Earl of Northampton's Charity
The Northcott Devon Foundation
The Northcott Devon Medical Foundation
The Northmoor Trust
The Northumberland Village Homes Trust
The Northumbria Historic Churches Trust
The Northwood Charitable Trust

The Norton Foundation
The Norwich Church of England Young Men's Society
The Norwich Town Close Estate Charity
The Norwood and Newton Settlement
The Noswad Charity
The Nottingham General Dispensary
The Nottingham Gordon Memorial Trust for Boys and Girls
Nottinghamshire Community Foundation
The Nottinghamshire Historic Churches Trust
The Nottinghamshire Miners' Welfare Trust Fund
Novi Most International
The Father O'Mahoney Memorial Trust
The Sir Peter O'Sullevan Charitable Trust
The Oak Trust
The Oakdale Trust
The Oakley Charitable Trust
The Oakmoor Charitable Trust
The Odin Charitable Trust
The Ofenheim Charitable Trust
Ogilvie Charities Deed No.2 (including the Charity of Mary Catherine Ford Smith)
The Ogle Christian Trust
The Oikonomia Trust
Oizer Charitable Trust
The Old Broad Street Charity Trust
The John Oldacre Foundation
The Oldham Foundation
Open Gate
The Raymond Oppenheimer Foundation
Ormonde Foundation
The Ormsby Charitable Trust
The Orrin Charitable Trust
The Ouseley Trust
The Owen Family Trust
Oxfam (GB)
The Oxfordshire Community Foundation
The P F Charitable Trust
Padwa Charitable Foundation
The Paget Charitable Trust
The Palmer Foundation
The Panacea Society
Panton Trust
The James Pantyfedwen Foundation
The Paragon Trust
The Park House Charitable Trust
The Frank Parkinson Agricultural Trust
The Samuel and Freda Parkinson Charitable Trust
The Parthenon Trust

The Constance Paterson Charitable Trust
The Patrick Charitable Trust
The Jack Patston Charitable Trust
Paycare Charity Trust
The Payne Charitable Trust
The Harry Payne Trust
The Susanna Peake Charitable Trust
The Pedmore Sporting Club Trust Fund
The Pennycress Trust
The Performing Right Society Foundation
The Persson Charitable Trust
The Persula Foundation
The Jack Petchey Foundation
The Petplan Charitable Trust
The Philips and Rubens Charitable Trust
The Phillips Charitable Trust
The Phillips Family Charitable Trust
Philological Foundation
The David Pickford Charitable Foundation
The Bernard Piggott Charitable Trust
The Pilgrim Trust
The Cecil Pilkington Charitable Trust
The Austin and Hope Pilkington Trust
The Sir Harry Pilkington Trust
The Col W W Pilkington Will Trusts The General Charity Fund
The DLA Piper Charitable Trust
The Worshipful Company of Plaisterers Charitable Trust
The Platinum Trust
The George and Esme Pollitzer Charitable Settlement
The J S F Pollitzer Charitable Settlement
The Ponton House Trust
Edith and Ferdinand Porjes Charitable Trust
The John Porter Charitable Trust
The Porter Foundation
The Portishead Nautical Trust
The Portrack Charitable Trust
The J E Posnansky Charitable Trust
The Powell Foundation
The W L Pratt Charitable Trust
Premierquote Ltd
Premishlaner Charitable Trust
The Tom Press Charitable Foundation
The William Price Charitable Trust
The Lucy Price Relief-in-Need Charity

Sir John Priestman Charity
  Trust
The Primrose Trust
The Prince of Wales's
  Charitable Foundation
Prison Service Charity Fund
The Privy Purse Charitable
  Trust
The Proven Family Trust
The Provincial Grand Charity of
  the Province of Derbyshire
The Puebla Charitable Trust
The Richard and Christine
  Purchas Charitable Trust
The Puri Foundation
The Queen's Silver Jubilee
  Trust
R S Charitable Trust
The R V W Trust
The Monica Rabagliati
  Charitable Trust
Rachel Charitable Trust
The Mr and Mrs Philip
  Rackham Charitable Trust
Richard Radcliffe Charitable
  Trust
The Radcliffe Trust
The Ragdoll Foundation
The Rainford Trust
The Peggy Ramsay Foundation
The Joseph and Lena Randall
  Charitable Trust
The Fanny Rapaport Charitable
  Settlement
The Ratcliff Foundation
The Ratcliff Pension Charity
The Ratcliffe Charitable Trust
The Eleanor Rathbone
  Charitable Trust
The Sigrid Rausing Trust
The Ravensdale Trust
The Rawdon-Smith Trust
The Rayden Charitable Trust
The Roger Raymond Charitable
  Trust
The Rayne Foundation
The Rayne Trust
The Sir James Reckitt Charity
The Red Arrows Trust
The Red Rose Charitable Trust
The C A Redfern Charitable
  Foundation
The Reed Foundation
Richard Reeve's Foundation
The Max Reinhardt Charitable
  Trust
Relief Fund for Romania
  Limited
The Rest Harrow Trust
Reuben Foundation
The Nathaniel Reyner Trust
  Fund
The Rhododendron Trust
The Rhondda Cynon Taff
  Welsh Church Acts Fund
The Clive Richards Charity

The Richmond Parish Lands
  Charity
Ridgesave Limited
The Ripple Effect Foundation
The Sir John Ritblat Family
  Foundation
The River Trust
Thomas Roberts Trust
The Robertson Trust
The Rochester Bridge Trust
The Rock Foundation
The Rock Solid Trust
The Rofeh Trust
Rokach Family Charitable Trust
The Helen Roll Charitable
  Trust
The Sir James Roll Charitable
  Trust
The Roman Research Trust
The C A Rookes Charitable
  Trust
The Rosca Trust
The Cecil Rosen Foundation
The Rothermere Foundation
The Rotherwick Foundation
The Rothley Trust
The Roughley Charitable Trust
Mrs Gladys Row Fogo
  Charitable Trust
Rowanville Ltd
The Christopher Rowbotham
  Charitable Trust
The Rowing Foundation
The Rowlands Trust
Royal Artillery Charitable Fund
Royal British Legion
Royal Docks Trust (London)
Royal Masonic Trust for Girls
  and Boys
The Alfred and Frances
  Rubens Charitable Trust
The Rubin Foundation
William Arthur Rudd Memorial
  Trust
The Russell Trust
The J S and E C Rymer
  Charitable Trust
S O Charitable Trust
The Jeremy and John Sacher
  Charitable Trust
The Michael Harry Sacher
  Trust
Raymond and Beverly Sackler
  1988 Foundation
The Sackler Trust
The Ruzin Sadagora Trust
The Saddlers' Company
  Charitable Fund
The Saga Charitable Trust
The Jean Sainsbury Animal
  Welfare Trust
The Alan and Babette
  Sainsbury Charitable Fund
The Sainsbury Family
  Charitable Trusts
The Saintbury Trust
The Saints and Sinners Trust

The Salt Foundation
The Salt Trust
Basil Samuel Charitable Trust
The M J Samuel Charitable
  Trust
The Peter Samuel Charitable
  Trust
The Samworth Foundation
The Sandra Charitable Trust
The Scarfe Charitable Trust
The Schapira Charitable Trust
The Schmidt-Bodner Charitable
  Trust
The R H Scholes Charitable
  Trust
The Schreib Trust
The Schreiber Charitable Trust
The Schuster Charitable Trust
Foundation Scotland
The Francis C Scott Charitable
  Trust
The Frieda Scott Charitable
  Trust
The Scott Trust Foundation
The Storrow Scott Will Trust
Scottish Coal Industry Special
  Welfare Fund
The Scouloudi Foundation
Seamen's Hospital Society
The Searchlight Electric
  Charitable Trust
The Searle Charitable Trust
The Samuel Sebba Charitable
  Trust
The Seedfield Trust
Leslie Sell Charitable Trust
The Ayrton Senna Foundation
The Seven Fifty Trust
The Cyril Shack Trust
The Shanti Charitable Trust
ShareGift (The Orr Mackintosh
  Foundation)
The Linley Shaw Foundation
The Sheepdrove Trust
The Sheffield and District
  Hospital Services
  Charitable Fund
The Sheldon Trust
The Patricia and Donald
  Shepherd Charitable Trust
The Sylvia and Colin Shepherd
  Charitable Trust
The Archie Sherman Cardiff
  Foundation
The Archie Sherman Charitable
  Trust
The R C Sherriff Trust
The Shetland Charitable Trust
SHINE (Support and Help in
  Education)
The Barnett and Sylvia Shine
  No 2 Charitable Trust
The Bassil Shippam and
  Alsford Trust
The Shipwrights' Company
  Charitable Fund
The Shirley Foundation

Shlomo Memorial Fund Limited
The J A Shone Memorial Trust
Community Foundation for
 Shropshire and Telford
The Barbara A Shuttleworth
 Memorial Trust
David and Jennifer Sieff
 Charitable Trust
The Julius Silman Charitable
 Trust
The Leslie Silver Charitable
 Trust
The Simpson Education and
 Conservation Trust
The Simpson Foundation
The Huntly and Margery
 Sinclair Charitable Trust
Sino-British Fellowship Trust
SITA Cornwall Trust Limited
The Skelton Bounty
The Charles Skey Charitable
 Trust
Skipton Building Society
 Charitable Foundation
The John Slater Foundation
The SMB Charitable Trust
The Mrs Smith and Mount
 Trust
The N Smith Charitable
 Settlement
The E H Smith Charitable Trust
The Smith Charitable Trust
The Leslie Smith Foundation
The Martin Smith Foundation
The Stanley Smith UK
 Horticultural Trust
The Snowball Trust
The Solo Charitable
 Settlement
Dr Richard Solomon's
 Charitable Trust
The E C Sosnow Charitable
 Trust
The Souter Charitable Trust
The South Square Trust
The W F Southall Trust
The Southwold Trust
The Sovereign Health Care
 Charitable Trust
Sparquote Limited
The Spear Charitable Trust
The Worshipful Company of
 Spectacle Makers' Charity
The Jessie Spencer Trust
The Ralph and Irma Sperring
 Charity
The Spielman Charitable Trust
The Spoore, Merry and Rixman
 Foundation
Springfields Employees'
 Medical Research and
 Charity Trust Fund
Springrule Limited
The Spurrell Charitable Trust
The Geoff and Fiona Squire
 Foundation
St James' Trust Settlement

St James's Place Foundation
Sir Walter St John's
 Educational Charity
St Michael's and All Saints'
 Charities Relief Branch (The
 Church Houses Relief in
 Need Charity)
The Late St Patrick White
 Charitable Trust
The Stanley Foundation Ltd
The Stanton Ballard Charitable
 Trust
The Star Charitable Trust
The Steel Charitable Trust
The Steinberg Family
 Charitable Trust
The Hugh Stenhouse
 Foundation
The Stephen Barry Charitable
 Trust
The Sigmund Sternberg
 Charitable Foundation
Stervon Ltd
The Stevenage Community
 Trust
The June Stevens Foundation
The Steventon Allotments and
 Relief-in-Need Charity
The Leonard Laity Stoate
 Charitable Trust
The Edward Stocks-Massey
 Bequest Fund
The Stokenchurch Educational
 Charity
The Stoller Charitable Trust
The M J C Stone Charitable
 Trust
The Samuel Storey Family
 Charitable Trust
Peter Stormonth Darling
 Charitable Trust
The Strangward Trust
The Strasser Foundation
The Sudborough Foundation
The Suffolk Historic Churches
 Trust
The Summerfield Charitable
 Trust
The Bernard Sunley Charitable
 Foundation
The Surrey Historic Buildings
 Trust Ltd
The Sussex Historic Churches
 Trust
The Sutasoma Trust
Swansea and Brecon Diocesan
 Board of Finance Limited
The John Swire (1989)
 Charitable Trust
The Swire Charitable Trust
The Adrian Swire Charitable
 Trust
The Hugh and Ruby Sykes
 Charitable Trust
The Charles and Elsie Sykes
 Trust
The Sylvanus Charitable Trust

The Stella Symons Charitable
 Trust
The Tabeel Trust
The Tajtelbaum Charitable
 Trust
The Talbot Trusts
The Talbot Village Trust
Tallow Chandlers Benevolent
 Fund
The Tangent Charitable Trust
The Lady Tangye Charitable
 Trust
The David Tannen Charitable
 Trust
The Tanner Trust
The Lili Tapper Charitable
 Foundation
The Mrs A Lacy Tate Trust
The Tay Charitable Trust
The Connie and Albert Taylor
 Charitable Trust
The Cyril Taylor Charitable
 Trust
A P Taylor Trust
Tearfund
The Tedworth Charitable Trust
The Templeton Goodwill Trust
Tesco Charity Trust
The C Paul Thackray General
 Charitable Trust
The Thames Wharf Charity
The John P. Gommes
 Foundation
The Thistle Trust
The Loke Wan Tho Memorial
 Foundation
The Thomas Lilley Memorial
 Trust
The Arthur and Margaret
 Thompson Charitable Trust
The Thompson Family
 Charitable Trust
The Len Thomson Charitable
 Trust
The Thornton Foundation
The Thornton Trust
The Thousandth Man –
 Richard Burns Charitable
 Trust
The Three Guineas Trust
The Three Oaks Trust
The Thriplow Charitable Trust
The Tinsley Foundation
The Tobacco Pipe Makers and
 Tobacco Trade Benevolent
 Fund
The Tolkien Trust
Tollemache (Buckminster)
 Charitable Trust
Tomchei Torah Charitable
 Trust
The Tompkins Foundation
The Tory Family Foundation
Tottenham Grammar School
 Foundation
The Tower Hill Trust

The Towry Law Charitable Trust
(also known as the Castle
Educational Trust)
The Toy Trust
The Mayor of Trafford's Charity
Fund
The Constance Travis
Charitable Trust
The Treeside Trust
The True Colours Trust
Truedene Co. Ltd
The Truemark Trust
Truemart Limited
Trumros Limited
Tudor Rose Ltd
The Tudor Trust
The Tufton Charitable Trust
The R D Turner Charitable
Trust
The Douglas Turner Trust
The Florence Turner Trust
The G J W Turner Trust
Miss S M Tutton Charitable
Trust
The TUUT Charitable Trust
Trustees of Tzedakah
Ulster Garden Villages Ltd
Ultach Trust
The Ulverscroft Foundation
Ulverston Town Lands Charity
The Underwood Trust
The Union of Orthodox Hebrew
Congregation
The United Society for the
Propagation of the Gospel
The David Uri Memorial Trust
Uxbridge United Welfare Trust
Vale of Glamorgan – Welsh
Church Fund
The Valentine Charitable Trust
The Van Neste Foundation
Mrs Maud Van Norden's
Charitable Foundation
The Vandervell Foundation
The Vardy Foundation
Veneziana Fund
The Verdon-Smith Family
Charitable Settlement
Victoria Homes Trust
The Nigel Vinson Charitable
Trust
The William and Ellen Vinten
Trust
The Vintners' Company
Charitable Foundation
Vintners' Gifts Charity
Vision Charity
Vivdale Ltd
The Viznitz Foundation
Wade's Charity
The Scurrah Wainwright Charity
Wakeham Trust
The Community Foundation in
Wales
Wales Council for Voluntary
Action

Robert and Felicity Waley-
Cohen Charitable Trust
The F J Wallis Charitable
Settlement
War on Want
The Ward Blenkinsop Trust
The George Ward Charitable
Trust
The Barbara Ward Children's
Foundation
G R Waters Charitable Trust
2000
The Howard Watson Symington
Memorial Charity
John Watson's Trust
Waynflete Charitable Trust
Weatherley Charitable Trust
The Weavers' Company
Benevolent Fund
The William Webster
Charitable Trust
The Weinberg Foundation
The Weinstein Foundation
The James Weir Foundation
The Barbara Welby Trust
Welsh Church Fund Dyfed
area (Carmarthenshire,
Ceredigion and
Pembrokeshire)
The Welton Foundation
The Wessex Youth Trust
The West Derby Wastelands
Charity
West London Synagogue
Charitable Fund
West Yorkshire Police
Community Trust
The Westminster Foundation
The Garfield Weston
Foundation
The Whitaker Charitable Trust
The Colonel W H Whitbread
Charitable Trust
The Simon Whitbread
Charitable Trust
The Whitecourt Charitable
Trust
The Norman Whiteley Trust
The Whitley Animal Protection
Trust
The Whittlesey Charity
The Lionel Wigram Memorial
Trust
The Felicity Wilde Charitable
Trust
The Wilkinson Charitable
Foundation
The William Barrow's Charity
The Charity of William Williams
The Kay Williams Charitable
Foundation
The Williams Family Charitable
Trust
The HDH Wills 1965
Charitable Trust
The Dame Violet Wills Will
Trust

The Wilmcote Charitrust
David Wilson Foundation
The Wilson Foundation
J and J R Wilson Trust
The Benjamin Winegarten
Charitable Trust
The Francis Winham
Foundation
Wirral Mayor's Charity
The James Wise Charitable
Trust
The Michael and Anna Wix
Charitable Trust
The Wixamtree Trust
The Woburn 1986 Charitable
Trust
The Maurice Wohl Charitable
Foundation
The Charles Wolfson
Charitable Trust
The Wolfson Family Charitable
Trust
The Wolfson Foundation
The James Wood Bequest
Fund
Wooden Spoon Society
Woodlands Green Ltd
Woodlands Trust
The Woodward Charitable
Trust
Worcester Municipal Charities
The Wragge and Co. Charitable
Trust
The Diana Edgson Wright
Charitable Trust
The Matthews Wrightson
Charity Trust
Miss E B Wrightson's
Charitable Settlement
Wychdale Ltd
Wychville Ltd
The Wyndham Charitable Trust
The Wyseliot Charitable Trust
The Xerox (UK) Trust
The Yardley Great Trust
The Dennis Alan Yardy
Charitable Trust
The W Wing Yip and Brothers
Foundation
Yorkshire Agricultural Society
Yorkshire Building Society
Charitable Foundation
The Yorkshire Dales
Millennium Trust
The John Young Charitable
Settlement
The William Allen Young
Charitable Trust
The John K Young Endowment
Fund
Zephyr Charitable Trust
The Marjorie and Arnold Ziff
Charitable Foundation
Stephen Zimmerman
Charitable Trust
The Zochonis Charitable Trust

Zurich Community Trust (UK)
Limited

....

■ Computer systems and equipment

The 1970 Trust
The 1989 Willan Charitable
Trust
The 29th May 1961 Charitable
Trust
A W Charitable Trust
The Aberbrothock Skea Trust
The Aberdeen Endowments
Trust
The Aberdeenshire Educational
Trust Scheme
Achisomoch Aid Company
Limited
The ACT Foundation
Action Medical Research
The Company of Actuaries'
Charitable Trust Fund
The Sylvia Adams Charitable
Trust
The Victor Adda Foundation
The Adint Charitable Trust
Age Scotland
Age UK
Aid to the Church in Need (UK)
The Sylvia Aitken Charitable
Trust
The Al Fayed Charitable
Foundation
Aldgate and All Hallows'
Foundation
The Aldgate Freedom
Foundation
Allchurches Trust Ltd
The H B Allen Charitable Trust
The Alliance Family Foundation
Angus Allnatt Charitable
Foundation
The Pat Allsop Charitable Trust
Almondsbury Charity
Altamont Ltd
Alvor Charitable Trust
The Ammco Trust
Viscount Amory's Charitable
Trust
The AMW Charitable Trust
The André Christian Trust
Anguish's Educational
Foundation
The Animal Defence Trust
Anpride Ltd
Ambrose and Ann Appelbe
Trust
The Appletree Trust
Archbishop of Wales' Fund for
Children
The John M Archer Charitable
Trust
The Archer Trust
The Ardwick Trust
The Argus Appeal

The Armenian Relief Society of
Great Britain Trust
The Armourers' and Brasiers'
Gauntlet Trust
The Arsenal Foundation
The Artemis Charitable Trust
The Arts and Entertainment
Charitable Trust
Arts Council England
The Arts Council of Northern
Ireland
Arts Council of Wales (also
known as Cyngor
Celfyddydau Cymru)
The Ove Arup Foundation
The A S Charitable Trust
The Ashden Trust
The Ashendene Trust
The Ashley Family Foundation
The Ashworth Charitable Trust
The Ian Askew Charitable Trust
The Associated Country
Women of the World
The Association of Colleges
Charitable Trust
Astellas European Foundation
Asthma UK
The Astor Foundation
The Astor of Hever Trust
The Aurelius Charitable Trust
The John Avins Trustees
The Avon and Somerset Police
Community Trust
The Aylesford Family
Charitable Trust
The BAA Communities Trust
The Scott Bader
Commonwealth Ltd
Bag4Sport Foundation
The Bagri Foundation
Veta Bailey Charitable Trust
The Austin Bailey Foundation
The Baily Thomas Charitable
Fund
The Baker Charitable Trust
The Balcombe Charitable Trust
The Albert Casanova Ballard
Deceased Trust
The Ballinger Charitable Trust
The Balmore Trust
The Balney Charitable Trust
The Baltic Charitable Fund
The Bamford Charitable
Foundation
The Banbury Charities
William P Bancroft (No 2)
Charitable Trust and
Jenepher Gillett Trust
The Band Trust
The Barbers' Company General
Charities
The Barbour Foundation
Barchester Healthcare
Foundation
The Barclay Foundation
The Baring Foundation

Peter Barker-Mill Memorial
Charity
The Barleycorn Trust
Barnes Workhouse Fund
The Barnsbury Charitable Trust
The Barnstaple Bridge Trust
The Barnwood House Trust
The Misses Barrie Charitable
Trust
Barrington Family Charitable
Trust
Bartholomew Charitable Trust
The Bartlett Taylor Charitable
Trust
The Paul Bassham Charitable
Trust
The Batchworth Trust
The Bates Charitable Trust
The Bay Tree Charitable Trust
The Louis Baylis (Maidenhead
Advertiser) Charitable Trust
BBC Children in Need
B-CH 1971 Charitable Trust
The Beacon Trust
The Bearder Charity
The James Beattie Charitable
Trust
The Beaverbrook Foundation
The Beccles Town Lands
Charity
The Becker Family Charitable
Trust
The Becketts and Sargeants
Educational Foundation
The John Beckwith Charitable
Trust
The Peter Beckwith Charitable
Trust
The David and Ruth Behrend
Fund
The Beit Trust
The Bellahouston Bequest
Fund
The Bellinger Donnay Trust
The Benfield Motors Charitable
Trust
The Benham Charitable
Settlement
The Hervey Benham Charitable
Trust
Maurice and Jacqueline
Bennett Charitable Trust
The Gerald Bentall Charitable
Trust
Bergqvist Charitable Trust
The Berkshire Community
Foundation
The Bestway Foundation
BHST
The Mason Bibby 1981 Trust
The Bideford Bridge Trust
The Big Lottery Fund
The Billmeir Charitable Trust
Percy Bilton Charity
The Bingham Trust
The Bintaub Charitable Trust

The Birmingham District
Nursing Charitable Trust
The Birmingham Hospital
Saturday Fund Medical
Charity and Welfare Trust
Birmingham International
Airport Community Trust
The Lord Mayor of
Birmingham's Charity
Miss Jeanne Bisgood's
Charitable Trust
The Michael Bishop
Foundation
The Bishop's Development
Fund
The Bertie Black Foundation
Isabel Blackman Foundation
The Blagrave Trust
The Blair Foundation
Blakemore Foundation
The Blanchminster Trust
The Blandford Lake Trust
The Sir Victor Blank Charitable
Settlement
The Neville and Elaine Blond
Charitable Trust
The Bluston Charitable
Settlement
The Boltons Trust
The Bonamy Charitable Trust
The John and Celia Bonham
Christie Charitable Trust
The Charlotte Bonham-Carter
Charitable Trust
Bonhomie United Charity
Society
The Boots Charitable Trust
The Bordon Liphook
Haslemere Charity
The Oliver Borthwick Memorial
Trust
The Bothwell Charitable Trust
H E and E L Botteley
Charitable Trust
The Harry Bottom Charitable
Trust
The Anthony Bourne
Foundation
The Bower Trust
The Bowerman Charitable
Trust
John and Susan Bowers Fund
The Bowland Charitable Trust
The Frank Brake Charitable
Trust
The William Brake Charitable
Trust
The Tony Bramall Charitable
Trust
The Harold and Alice Bridges
Charity
Bristol Archdeaconry Charity
John Bristow and Thomas
Mason Trust
The British Council for
Prevention of Blindness

The British Dietetic
Association General and
Education Trust Fund
The British Gas (Scottish Gas)
Energy Trust
British Heart Foundation
British Humane Association
British Ornithologists' Union
British Record Industry Trust
The J and M Britton Charitable
Trust
The Roger Brooke Charitable
Trust
The David Brooke Charity
The Charles Brotherton Trust
Joseph Brough Charitable
Trust
The Swinfen Broun Charitable
Trust
Edna Brown Charitable
Settlement (Mrs E E Brown
Charitable Settlement)
The Jack Brunton Charitable
Trust
Buckinghamshire Community
Foundation
The Rosemary Bugden
Charitable Trust
The Bulldog Trust Limited
The E F Bulmer Benevolent
Fund
Burdens Charitable Foundation
The Clara E Burgess Charity
The Burry Charitable Trust
The Arnold Burton 1998
Charitable Trust
The Burton Breweries
Charitable Trust
Consolidated Charity of Burton
upon Trent
The Worshipful Company of
Butchers General Charities
The Noel Buxton Trust
Henry T and Lucy B Cadbury
Charitable Trust
The Christopher Cadbury
Charitable Trust
The G W Cadbury Charitable
Trust
The Richard Cadbury
Charitable Trust
The Edward and Dorothy
Cadbury Trust
The George Cadbury Trust
CAF (Charities Aid Foundation)
CAFOD (Catholic Agency for
Overseas Development)
Community Foundation for
Calderdale
The Callander Charitable Trust
Calleva Foundation
Calypso Browning Trust
The Campden Charities
Trustee
The Canning Trust
The Carew Pole Charitable
Trust

The D W T Cargill Fund
Carlee Ltd
The Carlton House Charitable
Trust
The Carmelite Monastery Ware
Trust
The Worshipful Company of
Carmen Benevolent Trust
The Carnegie Dunfermline
Trust
The Carpenter Charitable Trust
The Carpenters' Company
Charitable Trust
The Carrington Charitable
Trust
The Carron Charitable
Settlement
The Leslie Mary Carter
Charitable Trust
The Casey Trust
Sir John Cass's Foundation
The Elizabeth Casson Trust
The Castang Foundation
The Catalyst Charitable Trust
The Catholic Charitable Trust
Catholic Foreign Missions
The Catholic Trust for England
and Wales
The Joseph and Annie Cattle
Trust
The Thomas Sivewright Catto
Charitable Settlement
The Wilfrid and Constance
Cave Foundation
The Cayo Foundation
The B G S Cayzer Charitable
Trust
The Cazenove Charitable Trust
Celtic Charity Fund
The Pamela Champion
Foundation
The Chapman Charitable Trust
John William Chapman's
Charitable Trust
The Charities Advisory Trust
Charitworth Limited
The Charter 600 Charity
The Worshipful Company of
Chartered Accountants
General Charitable Trust
(also known as CALC)
The Chasah Trust
The Chelsea Square 1994
Trust
The Cheruby Trust
Cheshire Freemason's Charity
The Chetwode Foundation
Cheviot Asset Management
Charitable Trust
Childs Charitable Trust
The Childwick Trust
The Chippenham Borough
Lands Charity
The Chipping Sodbury Town
Lands Charity
CHK Charities Limited
The Chownes Foundation

The Chrimes Family Charitable Trust
The Christabella Charitable Trust
Christadelphian Samaritan Fund
Christian Aid
Christian Response to Eastern Europe
The Church and Community Fund
The Church Burgesses Educational Foundation
Church Burgesses Trust
Church Urban Fund
City and County of Swansea Welsh Church Act Fund
The City Bridge Trust
The City Educational Trust Fund
Stephen Clark 1957 Charitable Trust
J A Clark Charitable Trust
The Hilda and Alice Clark Charitable Trust
The Roger and Sarah Bancroft Clark Charitable Trust
The Clarke Charitable Settlement
The Cleopatra Trust
Lord Clinton's Charitable Trust
The Clore Duffield Foundation
Miss V L Clore's 1967 Charitable Trust
Closehelm Limited
The Clothworkers' Foundation
Richard Cloudesley's Charity
The Clover Trust
The Robert Clutterbuck Charitable Trust
Clydpride Ltd
The Coalfields Regeneration Trust
The John Coates Charitable Trust
The Cobtree Charity Trust Ltd
The Denise Cohen Charitable Trust
The Vivienne and Samuel Cohen Charitable Trust
The John S Cohen Foundation
The R and S Cohen Foundation
The Colchester Catalyst Charity
The Cole Charitable Trust
The Colefax Charitable Trust
The John and Freda Coleman Charitable Trust
The George Henry Collins Charity
The Sir Jeremiah Colman Gift Trust
The Coltstaple Trust
Colwinston Charitable Trust
Colyer-Fergusson Charitable Trust

Comic Relief
The Comino Foundation
The Compton Charitable Trust
The Congleton Inclosure Trust
The Consolidated Charities for the Infirm Merchant Taylors' Company
The Ernest Cook Trust
The Cooks Charity
The Catherine Cookson Charitable Trust
Mabel Cooper Charity
The Alice Ellen Cooper Dean Charitable Foundation
The Marjorie Coote Animal Charity Trust
The Marjorie Coote Old People's Charity
The Helen Jean Cope Trust
The J Reginald Corah Foundation Fund
The Gershon Coren Charitable Foundation (also known as The Muriel and Gus Coren Charitable Foundation)
The Duke of Cornwall's Benevolent Fund
The Cornwell Charitable Trust
The Sidney and Elizabeth Corob Charitable Trust
The Corona Charitable Trust
The Costa Family Charitable Trust
The Cotton Industry War Memorial Trust
The Augustine Courtauld Trust
The General Charities of the City of Coventry
Coventry Building Society Charitable Foundation
The John Cowan Foundation
Dudley and Geoffrey Cox Charitable Trust
The Sir William Coxen Trust Fund
The Lord Cozens-Hardy Trust
The Craignish Trust
The Craps Charitable Trust
Michael Crawford Children's Charity
The Cray Trust
Creative Scotland
The Crerar Hotels Trust
The Crescent Trust
Cripplegate Foundation
The Violet and Milo Cripps Charitable Trust
The Harry Crook Foundation
The Cross Trust
The Croydon Relief in Need Charities
Cruden Foundation Ltd
The Ronald Cruickshanks Foundation
The Culra Charitable Trust
The Cumber Family Charitable Trust

Cumbria Community Foundation
The D J H Currie Memorial Trust
The Dennis Curry Charitable Trust
The Manny Cussins Foundation
The Cwmbran Trust
Itzchok Meyer Cymerman Trust Ltd
The D G Charitable Settlement
The D'Oyly Carte Charitable Trust
Daily Prayer Union Charitable Trust Limited
The Daiwa Anglo-Japanese Foundation
The Dr and Mrs A Darlington Charitable Trust
Baron Davenport's Charity
The Davidson (Nairn) Charitable Trust
The Davidson Family Charitable Trust
The Alderman Joe Davidson Memorial Trust
Michael Davies Charitable Settlement
The Gwendoline and Margaret Davies Charity
The Wilfrid Bruce Davis Charitable Trust
Davis-Rubens Charitable Trust
The Dawe Charitable Trust
The De Brye Charitable Trust
The De Clermont Charitable Company Ltd
The Deakin Charitable Trust
William Dean Countryside and Educational Trust
The Debmar Benevolent Trust
The Dellal Foundation
The Delves Charitable Trust
The Demigryphon Trust
The Denman Charitable Trust
Dentons UKMEA LLP Charitable Trust
The Earl of Derby's Charitable Trust
Derbyshire Community Foundation
The J N Derbyshire Trust
The Desmond Foundation
Devon Community Foundation
The Devon Educational Trust
The Duke of Devonshire's Charitable Trust
The Sandy Dewhirst Charitable Trust
The Laduma Dhamecha Charitable Trust
Diabetes UK
The Dibden Allotments Fund
Diced Cap Charity
The Dickon Trust
The Digbeth Trust Limited

The Dinwoodie Settlement
Dischma Charitable Trust
The DLM Charitable Trust
Louise Dobson Charitable
	Trust
The Derek and Eileen Dodgson
	Foundation
The Dollond Charitable Trust
Domepride Ltd
The Dorcas Trust
The Dorus Trust
The Doughty Charity Trust
Douglas Arter Foundation
The R M Douglas Charitable
	Trust
Downlands Educational Trust
The Drapers' Charitable Fund
The Duis Charitable Trust
The Dulverton Trust
The P B Dumbell Charitable
	Trust
The Dumbreck Charity
The Dunn Family Charitable
	Trust
The W E Dunn Trust
Dushinsky Trust Ltd
The Dwek Family Charitable
	Trust
The Dyers' Company
	Charitable Trust
The Eagle Charity Trust
The Earley Charity
Earls Colne and Halstead
	Educational Charity
The Earmark Trust
East End Community
	Foundation
Eastern Counties Educational
	Trust Limited
The Sir John Eastwood
	Foundation
The Ebenezer Trust
The EBM Charitable Trust
Eden Arts Trust
EDF Energy Trust (EDFET)
The Gilbert and Eileen Edgar
	Foundation
Edinburgh Trust No 2 Account
Edinburgh Voluntary
	Organisations' Trust Funds
	(EVOT)
The W G Edwards Charitable
	Foundation
The William Edwards
	Educational Charity
The Elephant Trust
The George Elias Charitable
	Trust
The Gerald Palmer Eling Trust
	Company
The Wilfred and Elsie Elkes
	Charity Fund
The Maud Elkington Charitable
	Trust
The Ellerdale Trust
The John Ellerman Foundation
The Ellinson Foundation Ltd

The Ellis Campbell Foundation
James Ellis Charitable Trust
The Elmgrant Trust
The Elmley Foundation
The Vernon N Ely Charitable
	Trust
The Embleton Trust
Embrace the Middle East
The Emerton-Christie Charity
EMI Music Sound Foundation
The Worshipful Company of
	Engineers Charitable Trust
	Fund
The Englefield Charitable Trust
The Enkalon Foundation
Entindale Ltd
The Epigoni Trust
The Equitable Charitable Trust
The Equity Trust Fund
The Ericson Trust
The Erskine Cunningham Hill
	Trust
Essex Community Foundation
The Essex Fairway Charitable
	Trust
Essex Provincial Charity Fund
The Essex Youth Trust
Euro Charity Trust
Sir John Evelyn's Charity
The Eventhall Family
	Charitable Trust
The Everard Foundation
The Eveson Charitable Trust
The Beryl Evetts and Robert
	Luff Animal Welfare Trust
	Limited
The Exilarch's Foundation
F C Charitable Trust
The F P Limited Charitable
	Trust
The Faber Charitable Trust
The Fairway Trust
The Family Rich Charities Trust
The Lord Faringdon Charitable
	Trust
Samuel William Farmer Trust
The Farmers' Company
	Charitable Fund
The Thomas Farr Charity
Walter Farthing (Trust) Limited
The Fassnidge Memorial Trust
Joseph Fattorini Charitable
	Trust
Federation of Jewish Relief
	Organisations
The John Feeney Charitable
	Trust
The George Fentham
	Birmingham Charity
The A M Fenton Trust
Allan and Nesta Ferguson
	Charitable Settlement
The Fidelity UK Foundation
The Doris Field Charitable
	Trust
Fife Council/Common Good
	Funds and Trusts

Firtree Trust
The Fishmongers' Company's
	Charitable Trust
The Fitton Trust
The Earl Fitzwilliam Charitable
	Trust
The Ian Fleming Charitable
	Trust
The Joyce Fletcher Charitable
	Trust
The Flow Foundation
The Gerald Fogel Charitable
	Trust
The Follett Trust
The Football Association
	National Sports Centre
	Trust
The Forbes Charitable
	Foundation
The Forces Trust (Working
	Name)
The Oliver Ford Charitable
	Trust
The Forest Hill Charitable Trust
The Foresters' Charity
	Stewards UK Trust
Forever Manchester (The
	Community Foundation for
	Greater Manchester)
The Forman Hardy Charitable
	Trust
Gwyneth Forrester Trust
The Forte Charitable Trust
The Four Lanes Trust
The Four Winds Trust
The Isaac and Freda Frankel
	Memorial Charitable Trust
The Elizabeth Frankland Moore
	and Star Foundation
The Jill Franklin Trust
The Gordon Fraser Charitable
	Trust
The Hugh Fraser Foundation
The Joseph Strong Frazer Trust
The Louis and Valerie
	Freedman Charitable
	Settlement
The Thomas Freke and Lady
	Norton Charity Trust
The Charles S French
	Charitable Trust
The Anne French Memorial
	Trust
The Freshfield Foundation
The Freshgate Trust
	Foundation
The Friarsgate Trust
The Friends Hall Farm Street
	Trust
Friends Provident Charitable
	Foundation
The Frognal Trust
The Patrick & Helena Frost
	Foundation
Maurice Fry Charitable Trust
The Fulmer Charitable Trust

Worshipful Company of
Furniture Makers Charitable
Fund
Gableholt Limited
The Galbraith Trust
The Gale Family Charity Trust
Gamlen Charitable Trust
The Gamma Trust
The Gannochy Trust
The Worshipful Company of
Gardeners of London
The Samuel Gardner Memorial
Trust
The Garnett Charitable Trust
Garthgwynion Charities
Garvan Limited
The Gatsby Charitable
Foundation
Gatwick Airport Community
Trust
The Robert Gavron Charitable
Trust
Thomas Betton's Charity for
Pensions and Relief-in-Need
The Gibbs Charitable Trust
Simon Gibson Charitable Trust
The G C Gibson Charitable
Trust
Lady Gibson's Charitable Trust
The Harvey and Hilary Gilbert
Charitable Trust
The Girdlers' Company
Charitable Trust
The B and P Glasser
Charitable Trust
The Glass-House Trust
Global Care
Global Charities
Gloucestershire Community
Foundation
Worshipful Company of
Glovers of London Charity
Fund
The GNC Trust
The Sydney and Phyllis
Goldberg Memorial
Charitable Trust
The Golden Bottle Trust
The Jack Goldhill Charitable
Trust
The Goldsmiths' Arts Trust
Fund
The Goldsmiths' Company
Charity
The Golsoncott Foundation
The Mike Gooley Trailfinders
Charity
The Gosling Foundation
Limited
The Gough Charitable Trust
The Gould Charitable Trust
The Grace Charitable Trust
A B Grace Trust
The Graff Foundation
E C Graham Belford Charitable
Settlement

The Grahame Charitable
Foundation Limited
The Granada Foundation
Grand Charitable Trust of the
Order of Women
Freemasons
The Grand Order of Water
Rats' Charities Fund
The Grange Farm Centre Trust
Grantham Yorke Trust
The J G Graves Charitable
Trust
The Gordon Gray Trust
The Gray Trust
The Great Stone Bridge Trust
of Edenbridge
The Great Torrington Town
Lands Charity
The Green Hall Foundation
Greenham Common
Community Trust Limited
Greggs Foundation
The Gretna Charitable Trust
The Grocers' Charity
The M and R Gross Charities
Limited
The GRP Charitable Trust
The David and Marie Grumitt
Foundation
The Bishop of Guildford's
Foundation
The Guildry Incorporation of
Perth
The Walter Guinness
Charitable Trust
The Gunter Charitable Trust
The Gur Trust
The Gurney Charitable Trust
Dr Guthrie's Association
The H and M Charitable Trust
H C D Memorial Fund
The H P Charitable Trust
The Hackney Parochial
Charities
The Hadfield Trust
The Hadley Trust
The Hadrian Trust
The Alfred Haines Charitable
Trust
E F and M G Hall Charitable
Trust
The Edith Winifred Hall
Charitable Trust
Robert Hall Charity
The Hamamelis Trust
Hamilton Wallace Trust
Paul Hamlyn Foundation
Hampton Fuel Allotment
Charity
The W A Handley Charitable
Trust
Beatrice Hankey Foundation
Limited
The Hanley Trust (1987)
The Kathleen Hannay
Memorial Charity

The Doughty Hanson
Charitable Foundation
Lord Hanson Foundation
The Haramead Trust
Miss K M Harbinson's
Charitable Trust
The Harborne Parish Lands
Charity
The Harbour Charitable Trust
The Harbour Foundation
The Harding Trust
William Harding's Charity
The Hare of Steep Charitable
Trust
The Harebell Centenary Fund
The Kenneth Hargreaves
Charitable Trust
The Harpur Trust
The Harris Charity
The Harrison and Potter Trust
The John Harrison Charitable
Trust
The Spencer Hart Charitable
Trust
The Hartley Charitable Trust
William Geoffrey Harvey's
Discretionary Settlement
The Edward Harvist Trust
Haskel Family Foundation
The Hathaway Trust
The M A Hawe Settlement
The Hawthorne Charitable
Trust
The Dorothy Hay-Bolton
Charitable Trust
The Headley Trust
Headley-Pitt Charitable Trust
Heart of England Community
Foundation
The Heathcoat Trust
Heathside Charitable Trust
The Charlotte Heber-Percy
Charitable Trust
The Hedley Denton Charitable
Trust
The Hedley Foundation
The H J Heinz Company
Limited Charitable Trust
The Hellenic Foundation
The Michael Heller Charitable
Foundation
The Simon Heller Charitable
Settlement
Help the Homeless
The Hemby Trust
The Christina Mary Hendrie
Trust for Scottish and
Canadian Charities
Henley Educational Trust
(formerley Henley
Educational Charity)
Esther Hennell Charitable
Trust
The G D Herbert Charitable
Trust
The Anne Herd Memorial Trust
The Hesed Trust

The Hesslewood Children's
Trust (Hull Seamen's and
General Orphanage)

Hexham and Newcastle
Diocesan Trust (1947)

The P and C Hickinbotham
Charitable Trust

The Higgs Charitable Trust

Alan Edward Higgs Charity

The High Sheriff's Police Trust
for the County of West
Midlands (Building Blocks)

Highcroft Charitable Trust

The Charles Littlewood Hill
Trust

The Hillingdon Partnership
Trust

The Hilmarnan Charitable Trust

The Hiscox Foundation

The Hitchin Educational
Foundation

The Eleemosynary Charity of
William Hobbayne

Hobson Charity Limited

Matthew Hodder Charitable
Trust

The Sir Julian Hodge
Charitable Trust

The J G Hogg Charitable Trust

The Holden Charitable Trust

John Holford's Charity

The Hollick Family Charitable
Trust

The Dorothy Holmes Charitable
Trust

The Holywood Trust

The Homelands Charitable
Trust

The Homestead Charitable
Trust

Sir Harold Hood's Charitable
Trust

Hope for Youth (NI)

The Hope Trust

HopMarket Charity

The Cuthbert Horn Trust

The Antony Hornby Charitable
Trust

The Horne Foundation

The Horne Trust

The Worshipful Company of
Horners' Charitable Trusts

The Hornsey Parochial
Charities

The Hospital of God at
Greatham

The Hospital Saturday Fund

Houblon-Norman/George Fund

The House of Industry Estate

The Reta Lila Howard
Foundation

The Daniel Howard Trust

The Huddersfield Common
Good Trust

The Hudson Foundation

The Geoffrey C Hughes
Charitable Trust

The Hull and East Riding
Charitable Trust

Hulme Trust Estates
(Educational)

Human Relief Foundation

The Humanitarian Trust

The Michael and Shirley Hunt
Charitable Trust

The Hunter Foundation

Miss Agnes H Hunter's Trust

The Huntingdon Foundation

Huntingdon Freemen's Trust

Hurdale Charity Limited

The Nani Huyu Charitable Trust

The P Y N and B Hyams Trust

The Hyde Charitable Trust

The Idlewild Trust

The Iliffe Family Charitable
Trust

The Indigo Trust

The Ingram Trust

The Inlight Trust

The Inman Charity

The Inner London Magistrates
Court Poor Box and Feeder
Charity

The Ireland Fund of Great
Britain

The Irish Youth Foundation
(UK) Ltd (incorporating The
Lawlor Foundation)

The Ironmongers' Foundation

Irwin Trust

The ISA Charity

The Isaacs Charitable Trust

The J Isaacs Charitable Trust

The Isle of Anglesey Charitable
Trust

The ITF Seafarers Trust

The J M K Charitable Trust

The J R S S T Charitable Trust

C Richard Jackson Charitable
Trust

Elizabeth Jackson Charitable
Trust

The Ruth and Lionel Jacobson
Trust (Second Fund) No 2

Jaffe Family Relief Fund

The Susan and Stephen
James Charitable
Settlement

The James Trust

The Jarman Charitable Trust

The John Jarrold Trust

JCA Charitable Foundation

The Jeffrey Charitable Trust

The Jenour Foundation

The Jephcott Charitable Trust

Jesus Hospital Charity

Jewish Child's Day

The Jewish Youth Fund

The Harold Joels Charitable
Trust

The Nicholas Joels Charitable
Trust

The Norman Joels Charitable
Trust

The Lillie Johnson Charitable
Trust

The Johnson Foundation

The Reginald Johnson
Foundation

The Johnnie Johnson Trust

The Johnson Wax Ltd
Charitable Trust

The Joicey Trust

The Jones 1986 Charitable
Trust

The Marjorie and Geoffrey
Jones Charitable Trust

The Jordan Charitable
Foundation

The J E Joseph Charitable
Fund

The Lady Eileen Joseph
Foundation

The Josephs Family Charitable
Trust

JTH Charitable Trust

The Jungels-Winkler Charitable
Foundation

The Anton Jurgens Charitable
Trust

The Bernard Kahn Charitable
Trust

The Stanley Kalms Foundation

The Karenza Foundation

The Boris Karloff Charitable
Foundation

The Ian Karten Charitable
Trust

The Kasner Charitable Trust

The Kathleen Trust

The Michael and Ilse Katz
Foundation

The Katzauer Charitable
Settlement

The C S Kaufman Charitable
Trust

The Geoffrey John Kaye
Charitable Foundation

The Emmanuel Kaye
Foundation

Kelsick's Educational
Foundation

The KempWelch Charitable
Trust

The Kay Kendall Leukaemia
Fund

William Kendall's Charity (Wax
Chandlers' Company)

The John Thomas Kennedy
Charitable Foundation

The Kennedy Charitable
Foundation

The Kennel Club Charitable
Trust

Kent Community Foundation

The Nancy Kenyon Charitable
Trust

Keren Association

Kermaville Ltd

The Peter Kershaw Trust

Keswick Hall Trust

Kettering and District
   Charitable Medical Trust
The Ursula Keyes Trust
The Robert Kiln Charitable
   Trust
The King Henry VIII Endowed
   Trust Warwick
The King/Cullimore Charitable
   Trust
The Kingsbury Charity
The Mary Kinross Charitable
   Trust
Kirkley Poor's Lands Estate
The Richard Kirkman
   Charitable Trust
Kirschel Foundation
Robert Kitchin (Saddlers'
   Company)
Ernest Kleinwort Charitable
   Trust
The Marina Kleinwort
   Charitable Trust
The Sir James Knott Trust
The Kobler Trust
The Kohn Foundation
The Kreditor Charitable Trust
The Kreitman Foundation
The Neil Kreitman Foundation
The Heinz, Anna and Carol
   Kroch Foundation
The Kyte Charitable Trust
The Late Sir Pierce Lacy
   Charity Trust
John Laing Charitable Trust
Maurice and Hilda Laing
   Charitable Trust
The Christopher Laing
   Foundation
The Kirby Laing Foundation
The Martin Laing Foundation
The Beatrice Laing Trust
The Lambert Charitable Trust
LWS Lancashire Environmental
   Fund Limited
Duchy of Lancaster Benevolent
   Fund
The Lancaster Foundation
Langdale Trust
The Langley Charitable Trust
The Langtree Trust
The LankellyChase Foundation
The R J Larg Family Charitable
   Trust
Largsmount Ltd
The Lark Trust
Laslett's (Hinton) Charity
The Lauffer Family Charitable
   Foundation
The Kathleen Laurence Trust
The Edgar E Lawley Foundation
The Herd Lawson and Muriel
   Lawson Charitable Trust
The Lawson Beckman
   Charitable Trust
The Raymond and Blanche
   Lawson Charitable Trust

The Mason Le Page Charitable
   Trust
The Leach Fourteenth Trust
The David Lean Foundation
The Leathersellers' Company
   Charitable Fund
The Arnold Lee Charitable
   Trust
The William Leech Charity
The Lord Mayor of Leeds
   Appeal Fund
Leeds Building Society
   Charitable Foundation
The Kennedy Leigh Charitable
   Trust
The Leigh Trust
Mrs Vera Leigh's Charity
P Leigh-Bramwell Trust 'E'
The Lennox and Wyfold
   Foundation
The Erica Leonard Trust
The Leonard Trust
The Mark Leonard Trust
Lesley Lesley and Mutter Trust
Leukaemia and Lymphoma
   Research
The Leverhulme Trade
   Charities Trust
Lord Leverhulme's Charitable
   Trust
The Joseph Levy Charitable
   Foundation
The John Spedan Lewis
   Foundation
The Sir Edward Lewis
   Foundation
John Lewis Partnership
   General Community Fund
Lichfield Conduit Lands
Lifeline 4 Kids
The Linbury Trust
The Lind Trust
Lindale Educational
   Foundation
The Linden Charitable Trust
The Enid Linder Foundation
The Linmardon Trust
The Ruth and Stuart Lipton
   Charitable Trust
The Lister Charitable Trust
Frank Litchfield Charitable
   Trust
The Andrew and Mary
   Elizabeth Little Charitable
   Trust
The Second Joseph Aaron
   Littman Foundation
The George John and Sheilah
   Livanos Charitable Trust
Liverpool Charity and Voluntary
   Services
Liverpool Sailors' Home Trust
The Elaine and Angus Lloyd
   Charitable Trust
The Charles Lloyd Foundation
Lloyd's Charities Trust

Lloyds Bank Foundation for
   England and Wales
Lloyds Bank Foundation for
   Northern Ireland
Lloyds Bank Foundation for the
   Channel Islands
The Locker Foundation
The Loftus Charitable Trust
The Lolev Charitable Trust
The Trust for London
London Catalyst
The London Community
   Foundation
The London Housing
   Foundation
The London Law Trust
The William and Katherine
   Longman Trust
The Lord's Taverners
The Loseley and Guildway
   Charitable Trust
The Lotus Foundation
The C L Loyd Charitable Trust
The Marie Helen Luen
   Charitable Trust
Robert Luff Foundation Ltd
Henry Lumley Charitable Trust
C F Lunoe Trust Fund
The Ruth and Jack Lunzer
   Charitable Trust
Lord and Lady Lurgan Trust
The Lyndhurst Trust
The Lynn Foundation
The Lynwood Trust
The Lyons Charitable Trust
The Sir Jack Lyons Charitable
   Trust
The Lyras Family Charitable
   Trust
Sylvanus Lyson's Charity
The M and C Trust
The M K Charitable Trust
The Madeline Mabey Trust
The E M MacAndrew Trust
The R S Macdonald Charitable
   Trust
Macdonald-Buchanan
   Charitable Trust
The Macfarlane Walker Trust
The Mackay and Brewer
   Charitable Trust
The Mackintosh Foundation
The MacRobert Trust
The Magdalen and Lasher
   Charity
Magdalen Hospital Trust
The Magen Charitable Trust
Man Group plc Charitable
   Trust
The Manackerman Charitable
   Trust
Manchester Airport Community
   Trust Fund
The Manchester Guardian
   Society Charitable Trust
Lord Mayor of Manchester's
   Charity Appeal Trust

Mandeville Trust
The Manifold Charitable Trust
W M Mann Foundation
The Leslie and Lilian Manning
Trust
Marbeh Torah Trust
Marchig Animal Welfare Trust
The Stella and Alexander
Margulies Charitable Trust
Market Harborough and The
Bowdens Charity
The Ann and David Marks
Foundation
The Hilda and Samuel Marks
Foundation
J P Marland Charitable Trust
The Michael Marsh Charitable
Trust
The Marsh Christian Trust
The Charlotte Marshall
Charitable Trust
The Jim Marshall Charitable
Trust
The Nora Joan Marshall
Charitable Trust
The D G Marshall of
Cambridge Trust
Marshgate Charitable
Settlement
Sir George Martin Trust
John Martin's Charity
The Mason Porter Charitable
Trust
The Nancie Massey Charitable
Trust
The Mathew Trust
The Matt 6.3 Charitable Trust
The Violet Mauray Charitable
Trust
The Maxwell Family Foundation
Evelyn May Trust
Mayfair Charities Ltd
The Mayfield Valley Arts Trust
Mazars Charitable Trust
The Robert McAlpine
Foundation
The McKenna Charitable Trust
The Helen Isabella McMorran
Charitable Foundation
The James Frederick and Ethel
Anne Measures Charity
The Medlock Charitable Trust
The Anthony and Elizabeth
Mellows Charitable
Settlement
Melow Charitable Trust
The Mercers' Charitable
Foundation
The Merchant Taylors'
Company Charities Fund
The Merchant Venturers'
Charity
The Merchants' House of
Glasgow
The Mersey Docks and
Harbour Company
Charitable Fund

Community Foundation for
Merseyside
The Zachary Merton and
George Woofindin
Convalescent Trust
The Tony Metherell Charitable
Trust
The Metropolitan Drinking
Fountain and Cattle Trough
Association
The Mickel Fund
Gerald Micklem Charitable
Trust
Midhurst Pensions Trust
The Migraine Trust
Miles Trust for the Putney and
Roehampton Community
The Hugh and Mary Miller
Bequest Trust
The Ronald Miller Foundation
The Millfield Trust
The Millhouses Charitable
Trust
The Millichope Foundation
The Mills Charity
The Millward Charitable Trust
The Clare Milne Trust
Milton Keynes Community
Foundation
The Edgar Milward Charity
The Keith and Joan
Mindelsohn Charitable
Trust
The Peter Minet Trust
The Minos Trust
The Mirfield Educational
Charity
The Laurence Misener
Charitable Trust
The Mishcon Family Charitable
Trust
The Misselbrook Trust
The Mitchell Charitable Trust
The Esmé Mitchell Trust
Keren Mitzvah Trust
The Mizpah Trust
The Mobbs Memorial Trust Ltd
The Modiano Charitable Trust
The Moette Charitable Trust
The Mole Charitable Trust
The D C Moncrieff Charitable
Trust
Monmouthshire County Council
Welsh Church Act Fund
The Montague Thompson
Coon Charitable Trust
The Colin Montgomerie
Charitable Foundation
The Monument Trust
John Moores Foundation
The Morel Charitable Trust
The Morgan Charitable
Foundation
The Mr and Mrs J T Morgan
Foundation
Morgan Stanley International
Foundation

The Oliver Morland Charitable
Trust
The Bernard Morris Charitable
Trust
The Morris Charitable Trust
The Willie and Mabel Morris
Charitable Trust
The Peter Morrison Charitable
Foundation
The Stanley Morrison
Charitable Trust
Vyoel Moshe Charitable Trust
The Moss Charitable Trust
The Robert and Margaret
Moss Charitable Trust
The Moss Family Charitable
Trust
Mosselson Charitable Trust
The Mount Everest Foundation
The Edwina Mountbatten Trust
Mountbatten Festival of Music
The Mountbatten Memorial
Trust
Mrs Waterhouse Charitable
Trust
The Mugdock Children's Trust
The Mulberry Trust
The Edith Murphy Foundation
The Mushroom Fund
The Music Sales Charitable
Trust
Muslim Hands
The Mutual Trust Group
The Kitty and Daniel Nabarro
Charitable Trust
The Nadezhda Charitable Trust
The Naggar Charitable Trust
The Eleni Nakou Foundation
The Janet Nash Charitable
Settlement
The National Churches Trust
The National Manuscripts
Conservation Trust
Needham Market and Barking
Welfare Charities
The Worshipful Company of
Needlemakers' Charitable
Fund
The Neighbourly Charitable
Trust
The James Neill Trust Fund
Nemoral Ltd
The Newcomen Collett
Foundation
Alderman Newton's
Educational Foundation
The Chevras Ezras Nitzrochim
Trust
Nominet Charitable Foundation
The Noon Foundation
The Norda Trust
Norfolk Community Foundation
Norie Charitable Trust
The Norman Family Charitable
Trust
The Duncan Norman Trust
Fund

The Normanby Charitable Trust
The North West Cancer
Research Fund
The Northampton Municipal
Church Charities
The Northampton Queen's
Institute Relief in Sickness
Fund
The Earl of Northampton's
Charity
The Northcott Devon
Foundation
The Northcott Devon Medical
Foundation
The Community Foundation for
Northern Ireland
The Northmoor Trust
The Northumberland Village
Homes Trust
The Northwood Charitable
Trust
The Norton Foundation
The Norwich Church of England
Young Men's Society
The Norwich Town Close
Estate Charity
The Norwood and Newton
Settlement
The Noswad Charity
The Notgrove Trust
The Nottingham General
Dispensary
The Nottingham Gordon
Memorial Trust for Boys
and Girls
Nottinghamshire Community
Foundation
The Nottinghamshire Miners'
Welfare Trust Fund
Novi Most International
The Father O'Mahoney
Memorial Trust
The Sir Peter O'Sullevan
Charitable Trust
The Oak Trust
The Oakdale Trust
The Oakley Charitable Trust
The Oakmoor Charitable Trust
The Odin Charitable Trust
The Ofenheim Charitable Trust
Ogilvie Charities Deed No.2
(including the Charity of
Mary Catherine Ford Smith)
The Ogle Christian Trust
The Oikonomia Trust
Oizer Charitable Trust
The Old Broad Street Charity
Trust
The John Oldacre Foundation
The Oldham Foundation
Open Gate
The Raymond Oppenheimer
Foundation
Ormonde Foundation
The Ormsby Charitable Trust
The Orrin Charitable Trust
The Ouseley Trust

The Owen Family Trust
Oxfam (GB)
The Oxfordshire Community
Foundation
The P F Charitable Trust
Padwa Charitable Foundation
The Paget Charitable Trust
The Palmer Foundation
The Panacea Society
Panton Trust
The James Pantyfedwen
Foundation
The Paragon Trust
The Park House Charitable
Trust
The Frank Parkinson
Agricultural Trust
The Samuel and Freda
Parkinson Charitable Trust
The Parthenon Trust
The Constance Paterson
Charitable Trust
The Patrick Charitable Trust
The Jack Patston Charitable
Trust
Paycare Charity Trust
The Payne Charitable Trust
The Harry Payne Trust
The Susanna Peake Charitable
Trust
The Pedmore Sporting Club
Trust Fund
The Dowager Countess
Eleanor Peel Trust
The Pennycress Trust
The Performing Right Society
Foundation
The Persson Charitable Trust
The Persula Foundation
The Jack Petchey Foundation
The Petplan Charitable Trust
The Philips and Rubens
Charitable Trust
The Phillips Charitable Trust
The Phillips Family Charitable
Trust
Philological Foundation
The David Pickford Charitable
Foundation
The Bernard Piggott Charitable
Trust
The Cecil Pilkington Charitable
Trust
The Pilkington Charities Fund
The Austin and Hope
Pilkington Trust
The Sir Harry Pilkington Trust
The Col W W Pilkington Will
Trusts The General Charity
Fund
The DLA Piper Charitable Trust
The Worshipful Company of
Plaisterers Charitable Trust
The Platinum Trust
The George and Esme Pollitzer
Charitable Settlement

The J S F Pollitzer Charitable
Settlement
The Ponton House Trust
Edith and Ferdinand Porjes
Charitable Trust
The John Porter Charitable
Trust
The Porter Foundation
The Portishead Nautical Trust
The Portrack Charitable Trust
The J E Posnansky Charitable
Trust
The Powell Foundation
The W L Pratt Charitable Trust
Premierquote Ltd
Premishlaner Charitable Trust
The Tom Press Charitable
Foundation
The William Price Charitable
Trust
The Lucy Price Relief-in-Need
Charity
Sir John Priestman Charity
Trust
The Primrose Trust
The Prince of Wales's
Charitable Foundation
Prison Service Charity Fund
The Privy Purse Charitable
Trust
The Proven Family Trust
The Provincial Grand Charity of
the Province of Derbyshire
The Puebla Charitable Trust
The Richard and Christine
Purchas Charitable Trust
The Puri Foundation
Mr and Mrs J A Pye's
Charitable Settlement
Quartet Community Foundation
Queen Mary's Roehampton
Trust
The Queen's Silver Jubilee
Trust
R S Charitable Trust
The R V W Trust
The Monica Rabagliati
Charitable Trust
Rachel Charitable Trust
The Mr and Mrs Philip
Rackham Charitable Trust
Richard Radcliffe Charitable
Trust
The Radcliffe Trust
The Ragdoll Foundation
The Rainford Trust
The Peggy Ramsay Foundation
The Joseph and Lena Randall
Charitable Trust
The Rank Foundation Limited
The Fanny Rapaport Charitable
Settlement
The Ratcliff Foundation
The Ratcliff Pension Charity
The Ratcliffe Charitable Trust
The Eleanor Rathbone
Charitable Trust

The Sigrid Rausing Trust
The Ravensdale Trust
The Rawdon-Smith Trust
The Rayden Charitable Trust
The Roger Raymond Charitable
  Trust
The Rayne Foundation
The Rayne Trust
The Sir James Reckitt Charity
The Red Arrows Trust
The Red Rose Charitable Trust
The C A Redfern Charitable
  Foundation
The Reed Foundation
Richard Reeve's Foundation
The Max Reinhardt Charitable
  Trust
Relief Fund for Romania
  Limited
REMEDI
The Rest Harrow Trust
Reuben Foundation
The Nathaniel Reyner Trust
  Fund
The Rhododendron Trust
The Rhondda Cynon Taff
  Welsh Church Acts Fund
The Clive Richards Charity
The Richmond Parish Lands
  Charity
Ridgesave Limited
The Ripple Effect Foundation
The Sir John Ritblat Family
  Foundation
The River Trust
Thomas Roberts Trust
The Robertson Trust
Edwin George Robinson
  Charitable Trust
The Rochester Bridge Trust
The Rock Foundation
The Rock Solid Trust
The Rofeh Trust
Rokach Family Charitable Trust
The Helen Roll Charitable
  Trust
The Sir James Roll Charitable
  Trust
The Roman Research Trust
The C A Rookes Charitable
  Trust
The Rosca Trust
The Cecil Rosen Foundation
The Rothermere Foundation
The Rotherwick Foundation
The Rothley Trust
The Roughley Charitable Trust
Mrs Gladys Row Fogo
  Charitable Trust
Rowanville Ltd
The Christopher Rowbotham
  Charitable Trust
The Rowlands Trust
The Joseph Rowntree
  Charitable Trust
Royal Artillery Charitable Fund
Royal British Legion

Royal Docks Trust (London)
Royal Masonic Trust for Girls
  and Boys
The Alfred and Frances
  Rubens Charitable Trust
The Rubin Foundation
William Arthur Rudd Memorial
  Trust
The Russell Trust
The J S and E C Rymer
  Charitable Trust
S O Charitable Trust
The Jeremy and John Sacher
  Charitable Trust
The Michael Harry Sacher
  Trust
Raymond and Beverly Sackler
  1988 Foundation
The Sackler Trust
The Ruzin Sadagora Trust
The Saddlers' Company
  Charitable Fund
The Saga Charitable Trust
The Jean Sainsbury Animal
  Welfare Trust
The Alan and Babette
  Sainsbury Charitable Fund
The Sainsbury Family
  Charitable Trusts
The Saintbury Trust
The Saints and Sinners Trust
The Salt Foundation
The Salt Trust
Basil Samuel Charitable Trust
The M J Samuel Charitable
  Trust
The Peter Samuel Charitable
  Trust
The Samworth Foundation
The Sandra Charitable Trust
Santander UK Foundation
  Limited
The Scarfe Charitable Trust
The Schapira Charitable Trust
The Schmidt-Bodner Charitable
  Trust
The R H Scholes Charitable
  Trust
The Schreib Trust
The Schreiber Charitable Trust
The Schuster Charitable Trust
Foundation Scotland
The Francis C Scott Charitable
  Trust
The Frieda Scott Charitable
  Trust
Sir Samuel Scott of Yews
  Trust
The Scott Trust Foundation
The Storrow Scott Will Trust
Scottish Coal Industry Special
  Welfare Fund
The Scouloudi Foundation
Seafarers UK (King George's
  Fund for Sailors)
Seamen's Hospital Society

The Searchlight Electric
  Charitable Trust
The Searle Charitable Trust
The Samuel Sebba Charitable
  Trust
The Seedfield Trust
Leslie Sell Charitable Trust
The Ayrton Senna Foundation
The Seven Fifty Trust
The Cyril Shack Trust
The Shanti Charitable Trust
ShareGift (The Orr Mackintosh
  Foundation)
The Linley Shaw Foundation
The Shears Foundation
The Sheepdrove Trust
The Sheffield and District
  Hospital Services
  Charitable Fund
The Sheldon Trust
The Patricia and Donald
  Shepherd Charitable Trust
The Sylvia and Colin Shepherd
  Charitable Trust
The Archie Sherman Cardiff
  Foundation
The Archie Sherman Charitable
  Trust
The R C Sherriff Trust
The Shetland Charitable Trust
SHINE (Support and Help in
  Education)
The Barnett and Sylvia Shine
  No 2 Charitable Trust
The Bassil Shippam and
  Alsford Trust
The Shirley Foundation
Shlomo Memorial Fund Limited
The J A Shone Memorial Trust
Community Foundation for
  Shropshire and Telford
The Barbara A Shuttleworth
  Memorial Trust
The Mary Elizabeth Siebel
  Charity
David and Jennifer Sieff
  Charitable Trust
The Julius Silman Charitable
  Trust
The Leslie Silver Charitable
  Trust
The Simpson Education and
  Conservation Trust
The Simpson Foundation
The Huntly and Margery
  Sinclair Charitable Trust
Sino-British Fellowship Trust
The Skelton Bounty
The Charles Skey Charitable
  Trust
Skipton Building Society
  Charitable Foundation
The John Slater Foundation
Sloane Robinson Foundation
The SMB Charitable Trust
The Mrs Smith and Mount
  Trust

The N Smith Charitable Settlement
The E H Smith Charitable Trust
The Smith Charitable Trust
The Henry Smith Charity
The Leslie Smith Foundation
The Martin Smith Foundation
The Stanley Smith UK Horticultural Trust
The Snowball Trust
The Sobell Foundation
The Solo Charitable Settlement
Dr Richard Solomon's Charitable Trust
The E C Sosnow Charitable Trust
The Souter Charitable Trust
The South Square Trust
The W F Southall Trust
The Southover Manor General Education Trust
The Southwold Trust
The Sovereign Health Care Charitable Trust
Sparquote Limited
The Spear Charitable Trust
The Worshipful Company of Spectacle Makers' Charity
The Jessie Spencer Trust
The Ralph and Irma Sperring Charity
The Spielman Charitable Trust
The Spoore, Merry and Rixman Foundation
Springfields Employees' Medical Research and Charity Trust Fund
Springrule Limited
The Spurrell Charitable Trust
The Geoff and Fiona Squire Foundation
St James' Trust Settlement
St James's Place Foundation
Sir Walter St John's Educational Charity
St Michael's and All Saints' Charities Relief Branch (The Church Houses Relief in Need Charity)
The Late St Patrick White Charitable Trust
The Stanley Foundation Ltd
The Stanton Ballard Charitable Trust
The Staples Trust
The Star Charitable Trust
The Steel Charitable Trust
The Steinberg Family Charitable Trust
The Hugh Stenhouse Foundation
The Stephen Barry Charitable Trust
The Sigmund Sternberg Charitable Foundation
Stervon Ltd

The Stevenage Community Trust
The June Stevens Foundation
The Steventon Allotments and Relief-in-Need Charity
The Stewards' Company Limited (incorporating the J W Laing Trust and the J W Laing Biblical Scholarship Trust)
The Leonard Laity Stoate Charitable Trust
The Stobart Newlands Charitable Trust
The Edward Stocks-Massey Bequest Fund
The Stokenchurch Educational Charity
The Stoller Charitable Trust
The M J C Stone Charitable Trust
The Samuel Storey Family Charitable Trust
Peter Stormonth Darling Charitable Trust
The Strangward Trust
The Strasser Foundation
Stratford upon Avon Town Trust
The W O Street Charitable Foundation
The Sudborough Foundation
The Suffolk Historic Churches Trust
The Summerfield Charitable Trust
The Bernard Sunley Charitable Foundation
The Surrey Historic Buildings Trust Ltd
The Sussex Historic Churches Trust
The Sutasoma Trust
Sutton Coldfield Charitable Trust
Swansea and Brecon Diocesan Board of Finance Limited
The John Swire (1989) Charitable Trust
The Swire Charitable Trust
The Adrian Swire Charitable Trust
The Hugh and Ruby Sykes Charitable Trust
The Charles and Elsie Sykes Trust
The Sylvanus Charitable Trust
The Stella Symons Charitable Trust
The Tabeel Trust
The Tajtelbaum Charitable Trust
The Talbot Trusts
The Talbot Village Trust
Tallow Chandlers Benevolent Fund
The Tangent Charitable Trust

The Lady Tangye Charitable Trust
The David Tannen Charitable Trust
The Tanner Trust
The Lili Tapper Charitable Foundation
The Mrs A Lacy Tate Trust
The Tay Charitable Trust
The Connie and Albert Taylor Charitable Trust
The Cyril Taylor Charitable Trust
A P Taylor Trust
Tearfund
The Tedworth Charitable Trust
Tees Valley Community Foundation
The Templeton Goodwill Trust
Tesco Charity Trust
The C Paul Thackray General Charitable Trust
The Thames Wharf Charity
The John P. Gommes Foundation
The Thistle Trust
The Loke Wan Tho Memorial Foundation
The Thomas Lilley Memorial Trust
The Arthur and Margaret Thompson Charitable Trust
The Thompson Family Charitable Trust
The Len Thomson Charitable Trust
The Sir Jules Thorn Charitable Trust
The Thornton Foundation
The Thornton Trust
The Thousandth Man – Richard Burns Charitable Trust
The Three Guineas Trust
The Three Oaks Trust
The Thriplow Charitable Trust
The Tinsley Foundation
The Tobacco Pipe Makers and Tobacco Trade Benevolent Fund
The Tolkien Trust
Tollemache (Buckminster) Charitable Trust
Tomchei Torah Charitable Trust
The Tompkins Foundation
The Tory Family Foundation
Tottenham Grammar School Foundation
The Tower Hill Trust
The Towry Law Charitable Trust (also known as the Castle Educational Trust)
The Toy Trust
The Mayor of Trafford's Charity Fund

The Constance Travis
  Charitable Trust
The Treeside Trust
The Triangle Trust (1949) Fund
The True Colours Trust
Truedene Co. Ltd
The Truemark Trust
Truemart Limited
Trumros Limited
Tudor Rose Ltd
The Tudor Trust
The Tufton Charitable Trust
The R D Turner Charitable
  Trust
The Douglas Turner Trust
The Florence Turner Trust
The G J W Turner Trust
Miss S M Tutton Charitable
  Trust
The TUUT Charitable Trust
Community Foundation Serving
  Tyne and Wear and
  Northumberland
Trustees of Tzedakah
Ulster Garden Villages Ltd
Ultach Trust
The Ulverscroft Foundation
Ulverston Town Lands Charity
The Underwood Trust
The Union of Orthodox Hebrew
  Congregation
The United Society for the
  Propagation of the Gospel
The David Uri Memorial Trust
Uxbridge United Welfare Trust
Vale of Glamorgan – Welsh
  Church Fund
The Valentine Charitable Trust
The Van Neste Foundation
Mrs Maud Van Norden's
  Charitable Foundation
The Vandervell Foundation
The Vardy Foundation
The Variety Club Children's
  Charity
Veneziana Fund
The Verdon-Smith Family
  Charitable Settlement
Victoria Homes Trust
The Nigel Vinson Charitable
  Trust
The William and Ellen Vinten
  Trust
The Vintners' Company
  Charitable Foundation
Vintners' Gifts Charity
Vision Charity
Vivdale Ltd
The Viznitz Foundation
Wade's Charity
The Scurrah Wainwright Charity
Wakeham Trust
The Community Foundation in
  Wales
Wales Council for Voluntary
  Action

Robert and Felicity Waley-
  Cohen Charitable Trust
The F J Wallis Charitable
  Settlement
War on Want
The Ward Blenkinsop Trust
The George Ward Charitable
  Trust
The Barbara Ward Children's
  Foundation
G R Waters Charitable Trust
  2000
The Howard Watson Symington
  Memorial Charity
John Watson's Trust
Waynflete Charitable Trust
Weatherley Charitable Trust
The Weavers' Company
  Benevolent Fund
The William Webster
  Charitable Trust
The Weinberg Foundation
The Weinstein Foundation
The James Weir Foundation
The Barbara Welby Trust
The Wellcome Trust
Welsh Church Fund Dyfed
  area (Carmarthenshire,
  Ceredigion and
  Pembrokeshire)
The Welton Foundation
The Wessex Youth Trust
The West Derby Wastelands
  Charity
West London Synagogue
  Charitable Fund
West Yorkshire Police
  Community Trust
The Westminster Foundation
The Garfield Weston
  Foundation
The Whitaker Charitable Trust
The Colonel W H Whitbread
  Charitable Trust
The Simon Whitbread
  Charitable Trust
The Whitecourt Charitable
  Trust
The Norman Whiteley Trust
The Whitley Animal Protection
  Trust
The Whittlesey Charity
The Lionel Wigram Memorial
  Trust
The Felicity Wilde Charitable
  Trust
The Wilkinson Charitable
  Foundation
The William Barrow's Charity
The Charity of William Williams
The Kay Williams Charitable
  Foundation
The Williams Family Charitable
  Trust
The HDH Wills 1965
  Charitable Trust

The Dame Violet Wills Will
  Trust
The Wilmcote Charitrust
David Wilson Foundation
The Wilson Foundation
J and J R Wilson Trust
The Community Foundation for
  Wiltshire and Swindon
The Benjamin Winegarten
  Charitable Trust
The Francis Winham
  Foundation
Wirral Mayor's Charity
The James Wise Charitable
  Trust
The Michael and Anna Wix
  Charitable Trust
The Wixamtree Trust
The Woburn 1986 Charitable
  Trust
The Maurice Wohl Charitable
  Foundation
The Charles Wolfson
  Charitable Trust
The Wolfson Family Charitable
  Trust
The Wolfson Foundation
The James Wood Bequest
  Fund
Woodlands Green Ltd
Woodlands Trust
The Woodward Charitable
  Trust
Worcester Municipal Charities
The Wragge and Co. Charitable
  Trust
The Diana Edgson Wright
  Charitable Trust
The Matthews Wrightson
  Charity Trust
Miss E B Wrightson's
  Charitable Settlement
Wychdale Ltd
Wychville Ltd
The Wyndham Charitable Trust
The Wyseliot Charitable Trust
The Xerox (UK) Trust
The Yardley Great Trust
The Dennis Alan Yardy
  Charitable Trust
The W Wing Yip and Brothers
  Foundation
Yorkshire Agricultural Society
Yorkshire Building Society
  Charitable Foundation
The South Yorkshire
  Community Foundation
The Yorkshire Dales
  Millennium Trust
The John Young Charitable
  Settlement
The William Allen Young
  Charitable Trust
The John K Young Endowment
  Fund
Zephyr Charitable Trust

The Marjorie and Arnold Ziff
  Charitable Foundation
Stephen Zimmerman
  Charitable Trust
The Zochonis Charitable Trust
Zurich Community Trust (UK)
  Limited

....

■ Equipment

The 1970 Trust
The 1989 Willan Charitable
  Trust
The 29th May 1961 Charitable
  Trust
A W Charitable Trust
The Aberbrothock Skea Trust
The Aberdeen Endowments
  Trust
The Aberdeenshire Educational
  Trust Scheme
Access Sport
Achisomoch Aid Company
  Limited
The ACT Foundation
Action Medical Research
The Company of Actuaries'
  Charitable Trust Fund
The Sylvia Adams Charitable
  Trust
The Victor Adda Foundation
The Adint Charitable Trust
The Adnams Charity
Age Scotland
Age UK
Aid to the Church in Need (UK)
The Sylvia Aitken Charitable
  Trust
The Al Fayed Charitable
  Foundation
Aldgate and All Hallows'
  Foundation
The Aldgate Freedom
  Foundation
Allchurches Trust Ltd
The H B Allen Charitable Trust
The Alliance Family Foundation
Angus Allnatt Charitable
  Foundation
The Pat Allsop Charitable Trust
Almondsbury Charity
Altamont Ltd
Alvor Charitable Trust
The Ammco Trust
Viscount Amory's Charitable
  Trust
The AMW Charitable Trust
The Anchor Foundation
The Andrew Anderson Trust
The André Christian Trust
Anglo American Group
  Foundation
Anguish's Educational
  Foundation
The Animal Defence Trust

The Eric Anker-Petersen
  Charity
Anpride Ltd
Ambrose and Ann Appelbe
  Trust
The Appletree Trust
The Arbib Foundation
Archbishop of Wales' Fund for
  Children
The John M Archer Charitable
  Trust
The Archer Trust
The Ardwick Trust
The Argus Appeal
The Armenian Relief Society of
  Great Britain Trust
The Armourers' and Brasiers'
  Gauntlet Trust
The Arsenal Foundation
The Artemis Charitable Trust
The Arts and Entertainment
  Charitable Trust
Arts Council England
The Arts Council of Northern
  Ireland
Arts Council of Wales (also
  known as Cyngor
  Celfyddydau Cymru)
The Ove Arup Foundation
The A S Charitable Trust
ASCB Charitable Fund
The Ashden Trust
The Ashendene Trust
The Ashley Family Foundation
The Ashworth Charitable Trust
The Ian Askew Charitable Trust
The Associated Country
  Women of the World
The Association of Colleges
  Charitable Trust
Astellas European Foundation
Asthma UK
The Astor Foundation
The Astor of Hever Trust
The Aurelius Charitable Trust
The John Avins Trustees
The Avon and Somerset Police
  Community Trust
The Aylesford Family
  Charitable Trust
The BAA Communities Trust
The BACTA Charitable Trust
The Scott Bader
  Commonwealth Ltd
Bag4Sport Foundation
The Bagri Foundation
Veta Bailey Charitable Trust
The Austin Bailey Foundation
The Baily Thomas Charitable
  Fund
The Baird Trust
The Baker Charitable Trust
The Balcombe Charitable Trust
The Albert Casanova Ballard
  Deceased Trust
The Ballinger Charitable Trust
The Balmore Trust

The Balney Charitable Trust
The Baltic Charitable Fund
The Bamford Charitable
  Foundation
The Banbury Charities
William P Bancroft (No 2)
  Charitable Trust and
  Jenepher Gillett Trust
The Band Trust
The Barbers' Company General
  Charities
The Barbour Foundation
Barchester Healthcare
  Foundation
The Barclay Foundation
The Baring Foundation
Peter Barker-Mill Memorial
  Charity
The Barleycorn Trust
Barnes Workhouse Fund
The Barnsbury Charitable Trust
The Barnstaple Bridge Trust
The Barnwood House Trust
The Misses Barrie Charitable
  Trust
Barrington Family Charitable
  Trust
Bartholomew Charitable Trust
The Bartlett Taylor Charitable
  Trust
The Paul Bassham Charitable
  Trust
The Batchworth Trust
The Bates Charitable Trust
The Bay Tree Charitable Trust
The Louis Baylis (Maidenhead
  Advertiser) Charitable Trust
BBC Children in Need
B-CH 1971 Charitable Trust
The Beacon Trust
The Bearder Charity
The James Beattie Charitable
  Trust
The Beaverbrook Foundation
The Beccles Town Lands
  Charity
The Becker Family Charitable
  Trust
The Becketts and Sargeants
  Educational Foundation
The John Beckwith Charitable
  Trust
The Peter Beckwith Charitable
  Trust
The David and Ruth Behrend
  Fund
The Beit Trust
The Bellahouston Bequest
  Fund
The Bellinger Donnay Trust
The Benfield Motors Charitable
  Trust
The Benham Charitable
  Settlement
The Hervey Benham Charitable
  Trust

Maurice and Jacqueline
Bennett Charitable Trust
The Gerald Bentall Charitable
Trust
Bergqvist Charitable Trust
The Berkshire Community
Foundation
The Bestway Foundation
BHST
The Mason Bibby 1981 Trust
The Bideford Bridge Trust
The Big Lottery Fund
The Billmeir Charitable Trust
Percy Bilton Charity
The Bingham Trust
The Bintaub Charitable Trust
The Birmingham District
Nursing Charitable Trust
The Birmingham Hospital
Saturday Fund Medical
Charity and Welfare Trust
Birmingham International
Airport Community Trust
The Lord Mayor of
Birmingham's Charity
Miss Jeanne Bisgood's
Charitable Trust
The Michael Bishop
Foundation
The Bishop's Development
Fund
The Bertie Black Foundation
Sir Alec Black's Charity
Isabel Blackman Foundation
The Blagrave Trust
The Blair Foundation
Blakemore Foundation
The Blanchminster Trust
The Blandford Lake Trust
The Sir Victor Blank Charitable
Settlement
The Neville and Elaine Blond
Charitable Trust
The Bluston Charitable
Settlement
The Boltons Trust
The Bonamy Charitable Trust
The John and Celia Bonham
Christie Charitable Trust
The Charlotte Bonham-Carter
Charitable Trust
Bonhomie United Charity
Society
The Boots Charitable Trust
The Bordon Liphook
Haslemere Charity
The Oliver Borthwick Memorial
Trust
The Bothwell Charitable Trust
H E and E L Botteley
Charitable Trust
The Harry Bottom Charitable
Trust
The Anthony Bourne
Foundation
The Bower Trust

The Bowerman Charitable
Trust
John and Susan Bowers Fund
The Bowland Charitable Trust
The Frank Brake Charitable
Trust
The William Brake Charitable
Trust
The Tony Bramall Charitable
Trust
The Harold and Alice Bridges
Charity
The Bridging Fund Charitable
Trust
Bristol Archdeaconry Charity
John Bristow and Thomas
Mason Trust
The British Council for
Prevention of Blindness
The British Dietetic
Association General and
Education Trust Fund
British Heart Foundation
British Humane Association
British Record Industry Trust
The J and M Britton Charitable
Trust
The Roger Brooke Charitable
Trust
The David Brooke Charity
The Charles Brotherton Trust
Joseph Brough Charitable
Trust
The Swinfen Broun Charitable
Trust
Edna Brown Charitable
Settlement (Mrs E E Brown
Charitable Settlement)
The Jack Brunton Charitable
Trust
Buckinghamshire Community
Foundation
The Rosemary Bugden
Charitable Trust
The Bulldog Trust Limited
The E F Bulmer Benevolent
Fund
Bumba Foundation
Burdens Charitable Foundation
The Clara E Burgess Charity
The Burry Charitable Trust
The Arnold Burton 1998
Charitable Trust
The Burton Breweries
Charitable Trust
Consolidated Charity of Burton
upon Trent
The Worshipful Company of
Butchers General Charities
The Noel Buxton Trust
Henry T and Lucy B Cadbury
Charitable Trust
The Christopher Cadbury
Charitable Trust
The G W Cadbury Charitable
Trust

The Richard Cadbury
Charitable Trust
The Edward and Dorothy
Cadbury Trust
The George Cadbury Trust
The Barrow Cadbury Trust and
the Barrow Cadbury Fund
CAF (Charities Aid Foundation)
CAFOD (Catholic Agency for
Overseas Development)
Community Foundation for
Calderdale
The Callander Charitable Trust
Calleva Foundation
Calypso Browning Trust
The Campden Charities
Trustee
The Canning Trust
The Carew Pole Charitable
Trust
The D W T Cargill Fund
Carlee Ltd
The Carlton House Charitable
Trust
The Carmelite Monastery Ware
Trust
The Worshipful Company of
Carmen Benevolent Trust
The Carnegie Dunfermline
Trust
The Carpenter Charitable Trust
The Carpenters' Company
Charitable Trust
The Carrington Charitable
Trust
The Carron Charitable
Settlement
The Leslie Mary Carter
Charitable Trust
The Casey Trust
Sir John Cass's Foundation
The Elizabeth Casson Trust
The Castang Foundation
The Catalyst Charitable Trust
The Catholic Charitable Trust
Catholic Foreign Missions
The Catholic Trust for England
and Wales
The Joseph and Annie Cattle
Trust
The Thomas Sivewright Catto
Charitable Settlement
The Wilfrid and Constance
Cave Foundation
The Cayo Foundation
Elizabeth Cayzer Charitable
Trust
The B G S Cayzer Charitable
Trust
The Cazenove Charitable Trust
Celtic Charity Fund
The Gaynor Cemlyn-Jones
Trust
The Pamela Champion
Foundation
Champneys Charitable
Foundation

The Chapman Charitable Trust
John William Chapman's
	Charitable Trust
The Charities Advisory Trust
Charitworth Limited
The Charter 600 Charity
The Worshipful Company of
	Chartered Accountants
	General Charitable Trust
	(also known as CALC)
The Chasah Trust
The Chelsea Square 1994
	Trust
The Cheruby Trust
Cheshire Freemason's Charity
The Chetwode Foundation
Cheviot Asset Management
	Charitable Trust
Children's Liver Disease
	Foundation
Childs Charitable Trust
The Childwick Trust
The Chippenham Borough
	Lands Charity
The Chipping Sodbury Town
	Lands Charity
CHK Charities Limited
The Chownes Foundation
The Chrimes Family Charitable
	Trust
The Christabella Charitable
	Trust
Christadelphian Samaritan
	Fund
Christian Aid
Christian Response to Eastern
	Europe
Chrysalis Trust
The Church and Community
	Fund
The Church Burgesses
	Educational Foundation
Church Burgesses Trust
Church Urban Fund
City and County of Swansea
	Welsh Church Act Fund
The City Bridge Trust
The City Educational Trust
	Fund
Stephen Clark 1957
	Charitable Trust
J A Clark Charitable Trust
The Hilda and Alice Clark
	Charitable Trust
The Roger and Sarah Bancroft
	Clark Charitable Trust
The Clarke Charitable
	Settlement
The Cleopatra Trust
Lord Clinton's Charitable Trust
The Clore Duffield Foundation
Miss V L Clore's 1967
	Charitable Trust
Closehelm Limited
Richard Cloudesley's Charity
The Clover Trust

The Robert Clutterbuck
	Charitable Trust
Clydpride Ltd
The Coalfields Regeneration
	Trust
The John Coates Charitable
	Trust
The Cobtree Charity Trust Ltd
The Denise Cohen Charitable
	Trust
The Vivienne and Samuel
	Cohen Charitable Trust
The John S Cohen Foundation
The R and S Cohen
	Foundation
The Colchester Catalyst
	Charity
The Cole Charitable Trust
The Colefax Charitable Trust
The John and Freda Coleman
	Charitable Trust
The George Henry Collins
	Charity
The Sir Jeremiah Colman Gift
	Trust
The Coltstaple Trust
Colwinston Charitable Trust
Colyer-Fergusson Charitable
	Trust
The Comino Foundation
Community First (Landfill
	Communities Fund)
The Compton Charitable Trust
The Congleton Inclosure Trust
The Conservation Foundation
The Consolidated Charities for
	the Infirm Merchant
	Taylors' Company
The Ernest Cook Trust
The Cooks Charity
The Catherine Cookson
	Charitable Trust
Mabel Cooper Charity
The Alice Ellen Cooper Dean
	Charitable Foundation
The Marjorie Coote Animal
	Charity Trust
The Marjorie Coote Old
	People's Charity
The Helen Jean Cope Trust
The J Reginald Corah
	Foundation Fund
The Gershon Coren Charitable
	Foundation (also known as
	The Muriel and Gus Coren
	Charitable Foundation)
The Duke of Cornwall's
	Benevolent Fund
The Cornwell Charitable Trust
The Sidney and Elizabeth
	Corob Charitable Trust
The Corona Charitable Trust
The Costa Family Charitable
	Trust
The Cotton Industry War
	Memorial Trust
The Cotton Trust

County Durham Community
	Foundation
The General Charities of the
	City of Coventry
Coventry Building Society
	Charitable Foundation
The John Cowan Foundation
Dudley and Geoffrey Cox
	Charitable Trust
The Sir William Coxen Trust
	Fund
The Lord Cozens-Hardy Trust
The Craignish Trust
The Craps Charitable Trust
Michael Crawford Children's
	Charity
The Cray Trust
Creative Scotland
The Crerar Hotels Trust
The Crescent Trust
Cripplegate Foundation
The Violet and Milo Cripps
	Charitable Trust
The Harry Crook Foundation
The Cross Trust
The Croydon Relief in Need
	Charities
Cruden Foundation Ltd
The Ronald Cruickshanks
	Foundation
The Culra Charitable Trust
The Cumber Family Charitable
	Trust
Cumberland Building Society
	Charitable Foundation
Cumbria Community
	Foundation
The Cunningham Trust
The D J H Currie Memorial
	Trust
The Dennis Curry Charitable
	Trust
The Manny Cussins
	Foundation
The Cwmbran Trust
Itzchok Meyer Cymerman Trust
	Ltd
The D G Charitable Settlement
The D'Oyly Carte Charitable
	Trust
Daily Prayer Union Charitable
	Trust Limited
The Daiwa Anglo-Japanese
	Foundation
The Dr and Mrs A Darlington
	Charitable Trust
Baron Davenport's Charity
The Davidson (Nairn)
	Charitable Trust
The Davidson Family
	Charitable Trust
The Alderman Joe Davidson
	Memorial Trust
Michael Davies Charitable
	Settlement
The Gwendoline and Margaret
	Davies Charity

The Hamilton Davies Trust
The Wilfrid Bruce Davis
Charitable Trust
Davis-Rubens Charitable Trust
The Dawe Charitable Trust
The De Brye Charitable Trust
The De Clermont Charitable
Company Ltd
The Deakin Charitable Trust
William Dean Countryside and
Educational Trust
The Debmar Benevolent Trust
The Dellal Foundation
The Delves Charitable Trust
The Demigryphon Trust
The Denman Charitable Trust
Dentons UKMEA LLP
Charitable Trust
The Earl of Derby's Charitable
Trust
The Derbyshire Churches and
Chapels Preservation Trust
Derbyshire Community
Foundation
The J N Derbyshire Trust
The Desmond Foundation
Devon Community Foundation
The Devon Educational Trust
The Devon Historic Churches
Trust
The Duke of Devonshire's
Charitable Trust
The Sandy Dewhirst Charitable
Trust
The Laduma Dhamecha
Charitable Trust
Diabetes UK
The Dibden Allotments Fund
Diced Cap Charity
The Dickon Trust
The Peter Alan Dickson
Foundation
The Digbeth Trust Limited
The Dinwoodie Settlement
Disability Aid Fund (The Roger
and Jean Jefcoate Trust)
Dischma Charitable Trust
The DLM Charitable Trust
Louise Dobson Charitable
Trust
The Derek and Eileen Dodgson
Foundation
The Dollond Charitable Trust
Domepride Ltd
The Dorcas Trust
The Dorset Historic Churches
Trust
The Dorus Trust
The Doughty Charity Trust
The R M Douglas Charitable
Trust
Downlands Educational Trust
The Drapers' Charitable Fund
The Duis Charitable Trust
The Dulverton Trust
The P B Dumbell Charitable
Trust

The Dumbreck Charity
Dunard Fund
The Dunn Family Charitable
Trust
The W E Dunn Trust
Dushinsky Trust Ltd
The Dwek Family Charitable
Trust
The Dyers' Company
Charitable Trust
The Eagle Charity Trust
The Earley Charity
Earls Colne and Halstead
Educational Charity
The Earmark Trust
East End Community
Foundation
Eastern Counties Educational
Trust Limited
The Sir John Eastwood
Foundation
The Ebenezer Trust
The EBM Charitable Trust
Eden Arts Trust
EDF Energy Trust (EDFET)
The Gilbert and Eileen Edgar
Foundation
Edinburgh Children's Holiday
Fund
Edinburgh Trust No 2 Account
Edinburgh Voluntary
Organisations' Trust Funds
(EVOT)
The W G Edwards Charitable
Foundation
The William Edwards
Educational Charity
The Elephant Trust
The George Elias Charitable
Trust
The Gerald Palmer Eling Trust
Company
The Wilfred and Elsie Elkes
Charity Fund
The Maud Elkington Charitable
Trust
The Ellerdale Trust
The John Ellerman Foundation
The Ellinson Foundation Ltd
The Ellis Campbell Foundation
James Ellis Charitable Trust
The Elmgrant Trust
The Elmley Foundation
The Vernon N Ely Charitable
Trust
The Embleton Trust
Embrace the Middle East
The Emerton-Christie Charity
EMI Music Sound Foundation
The Worshipful Company of
Engineers Charitable Trust
Fund
The Englefield Charitable Trust
The English Schools' Football
Association
The Enkalon Foundation
Entindale Ltd

The Epigoni Trust
The Equitable Charitable Trust
The Equity Trust Fund
The Ericson Trust
The Erskine Cunningham Hill
Trust
The Essex and Southend
Sports Trust
Essex Community Foundation
The Essex Fairway Charitable
Trust
The Essex Heritage Trust
Essex Provincial Charity Fund
The Essex Youth Trust
Euro Charity Trust
Sir John Evelyn's Charity
The Eventhall Family
Charitable Trust
The Everard Foundation
The Eveson Charitable Trust
The Beryl Evetts and Robert
Luff Animal Welfare Trust
Limited
The Exilarch's Foundation
F C Charitable Trust
The F P Limited Charitable
Trust
The Faber Charitable Trust
The Fairway Trust
The Family Rich Charities Trust
The Lord Faringdon Charitable
Trust
Samuel William Farmer Trust
The Farmers' Company
Charitable Fund
The Thomas Farr Charity
Walter Farthing (Trust) Limited
The Fassnidge Memorial Trust
Joseph Fattorini Charitable
Trust
Federation of Jewish Relief
Organisations
The John Feeney Charitable
Trust
The George Fentham
Birmingham Charity
The A M Fenton Trust
Allan and Nesta Ferguson
Charitable Settlement
The Fidelity UK Foundation
The Doris Field Charitable
Trust
Fife Council/Common Good
Funds and Trusts
Firtree Trust
The Fishmongers' Company's
Charitable Trust
The Fitton Trust
The Earl Fitzwilliam Charitable
Trust
The Ian Fleming Charitable
Trust
The Joyce Fletcher Charitable
Trust
The Flow Foundation
The Gerald Fogel Charitable
Trust

The Follett Trust
The Football Association
National Sports Centre
Trust
The Football Association Youth
Trust
The Football Foundation
The Forbes Charitable
Foundation
The Forces Trust (Working
Name)
Ford Britain Trust
The Oliver Ford Charitable
Trust
The Forest Hill Charitable Trust
The Foresters' Charity
Stewards UK Trust
Forever Manchester (The
Community Foundation for
Greater Manchester)
The Forman Hardy Charitable
Trust
Gwyneth Forrester Trust
The Forte Charitable Trust
The Four Lanes Trust
The Four Winds Trust
The Foyle Foundation
The Isaac and Freda Frankel
Memorial Charitable Trust
The Elizabeth Frankland Moore
and Star Foundation
The Jill Franklin Trust
The Gordon Fraser Charitable
Trust
The Hugh Fraser Foundation
The Joseph Strong Frazer Trust
The Louis and Valerie
Freedman Charitable
Settlement
The Thomas Freke and Lady
Norton Charity Trust
The Charles S French
Charitable Trust
The Anne French Memorial
Trust
The Freshfield Foundation
The Freshgate Trust
Foundation
The Friarsgate Trust
The Friends Hall Farm Street
Trust
Friends Provident Charitable
Foundation
The Frognal Trust
The Patrick & Helena Frost
Foundation
Maurice Fry Charitable Trust
The Fulmer Charitable Trust
Worshipful Company of
Furniture Makers Charitable
Fund
G M C Trust
Gableholt Limited
The Galbraith Trust
The Gale Family Charity Trust
Gamlen Charitable Trust
The Gamma Trust

The Gannochy Trust
The Worshipful Company of
Gardeners of London
The Samuel Gardner Memorial
Trust
The Garnett Charitable Trust
Garthgwynion Charities
Garvan Limited
The Gatsby Charitable
Foundation
Gatwick Airport Community
Trust
The Robert Gavron Charitable
Trust
Thomas Betton's Charity for
Pensions and Relief-in-Need
Get Kids Going
The Gibbs Charitable Trust
Simon Gibson Charitable Trust
The G C Gibson Charitable
Trust
Lady Gibson's Charitable Trust
The Harvey and Hilary Gilbert
Charitable Trust
The Girdlers' Company
Charitable Trust
The B and P Glasser
Charitable Trust
The Glass-House Trust
Global Care
Global Charities
Gloucestershire Community
Foundation
Worshipful Company of
Glovers of London Charity
Fund
The GNC Trust
The Sydney and Phyllis
Goldberg Memorial
Charitable Trust
The Golden Bottle Trust
The Jack Goldhill Charitable
Trust
The Goldsmiths' Arts Trust
Fund
The Goldsmiths' Company
Charity
The Golsoncott Foundation
The Mike Gooley Trailfinders
Charity
The Gosling Foundation
Limited
The Gough Charitable Trust
The Gould Charitable Trust
The Grace Charitable Trust
A B Grace Trust
The Graff Foundation
E C Graham Belford Charitable
Settlement
The Grahame Charitable
Foundation Limited
The Granada Foundation
Grand Charitable Trust of the
Order of Women
Freemasons
The Grand Order of Water
Rats' Charities Fund

The Grange Farm Centre Trust
Grantham Yorke Trust
The J G Graves Charitable
Trust
The Gordon Gray Trust
The Gray Trust
The Great Stone Bridge Trust
of Edenbridge
The Great Torrington Town
Lands Charity
The Green Hall Foundation
Greenham Common
Community Trust Limited
Greggs Foundation
The Gretna Charitable Trust
The Grimmitt Trust
The Grocers' Charity
The M and R Gross Charities
Limited
The GRP Charitable Trust
The David and Marie Grumitt
Foundation
The Bishop of Guildford's
Foundation
The Guildry Incorporation of
Perth
The Walter Guinness
Charitable Trust
The Gunter Charitable Trust
The Gur Trust
The Gurney Charitable Trust
Dr Guthrie's Association
The H and M Charitable Trust
H C D Memorial Fund
The H P Charitable Trust
The Hackney Parochial
Charities
The Hadfield Trust
The Hadley Trust
The Hadrian Trust
The Alfred Haines Charitable
Trust
E F and M G Hall Charitable
Trust
The Edith Winifred Hall
Charitable Trust
Robert Hall Charity
The Hamamelis Trust
Hamilton Wallace Trust
The Hampshire and Islands
Historic Churches Trust
Hampshire and Isle of Wight
Community Foundation
Hampton Fuel Allotment
Charity
The W A Handley Charitable
Trust
Beatrice Hankey Foundation
Limited
The Hanley Trust (1987)
The Kathleen Hannay
Memorial Charity
The Doughty Hanson
Charitable Foundation
Lord Hanson Foundation
The Haramead Trust

Miss K M Harbinson's
  Charitable Trust
The Harborne Parish Lands
  Charity
The Harbour Charitable Trust
The Harbour Foundation
The Harding Trust
William Harding's Charity
The Hare of Steep Charitable
  Trust
The Harebell Centenary Fund
The Kenneth Hargreaves
  Charitable Trust
The Harpur Trust
The Harris Charity
The Harrison and Potter Trust
The John Harrison Charitable
  Trust
The Peter Harrison Foundation
The Spencer Hart Charitable
  Trust
The Hartley Charitable Trust
William Geoffrey Harvey's
  Discretionary Settlement
The Edward Harvist Trust
Haskel Family Foundation
The Hathaway Trust
The M A Hawe Settlement
The Hawthorne Charitable
  Trust
The Dorothy Hay-Bolton
  Charitable Trust
The Headley Trust
Headley-Pitt Charitable Trust
Heart of England Community
  Foundation
The Heathcoat Trust
Heathside Charitable Trust
The Charlotte Heber-Percy
  Charitable Trust
The Hedley Denton Charitable
  Trust
The Hedley Foundation
The H J Heinz Company
  Limited Charitable Trust
The Hellenic Foundation
The Michael Heller Charitable
  Foundation
The Simon Heller Charitable
  Settlement
Help for Health
Help the Homeless
The Hemby Trust
The Christina Mary Hendrie
  Trust for Scottish and
  Canadian Charities
Henley Educational Trust
  (formerley Henley
  Educational Charity)
Philip Henman Trust
Esther Hennell Charitable
  Trust
The G D Herbert Charitable
  Trust
The Anne Herd Memorial Trust
The Herefordshire Historic
  Churches Trust

The Heritage of London Trust
  Ltd
The Hesed Trust
The Hesslewood Children's
  Trust (Hull Seamen's and
  General Orphanage)
Hexham and Newcastle
  Diocesan Trust (1947)
The P and C Hickinbotham
  Charitable Trust
The Higgs Charitable Trust
Alan Edward Higgs Charity
The High Sheriff's Police Trust
  for the County of West
  Midlands (Building Blocks)
Highcroft Charitable Trust
The Charles Littlewood Hill
  Trust
The Hillingdon Partnership
  Trust
The Hilmarnan Charitable Trust
The Hiscox Foundation
The Hitchin Educational
  Foundation
The Eleemosynary Charity of
  William Hobbayne
Hobson Charity Limited
Matthew Hodder Charitable
  Trust
The Sir Julian Hodge
  Charitable Trust
The J G Hogg Charitable Trust
The Holden Charitable Trust
John Holford's Charity
The Hollick Family Charitable
  Trust
The Dorothy Holmes Charitable
  Trust
The Holywood Trust
The Homelands Charitable
  Trust
The Homestead Charitable
  Trust
Sir Harold Hood's Charitable
  Trust
Hope for Youth (NI)
The Hope Trust
HopMarket Charity
The Cuthbert Horn Trust
The Antony Hornby Charitable
  Trust
The Horne Foundation
The Horne Trust
The Worshipful Company of
  Horners' Charitable Trusts
The Hornsey Parochial
  Charities
The Hospital of God at
  Greatham
The Hospital Saturday Fund
Houblon-Norman/George Fund
The House of Industry Estate
The Reta Lila Howard
  Foundation
The Daniel Howard Trust
The Huddersfield Common
  Good Trust

The Hudson Foundation
The Geoffrey C Hughes
  Charitable Trust
The Hull and East Riding
  Charitable Trust
Hulme Trust Estates
  (Educational)
Human Relief Foundation
The Humanitarian Trust
The Michael and Shirley Hunt
  Charitable Trust
The Hunter Foundation
Miss Agnes H Hunter's Trust
The Huntingdon Foundation
Huntingdon Freemen's Trust
Hurdale Charity Limited
The Nani Huyu Charitable Trust
The P Y N and B Hyams Trust
The Hyde Charitable Trust
The Idlewild Trust
The Iliffe Family Charitable
  Trust
The Indigo Trust
The Ingram Trust
The Inlight Trust
The Inman Charity
The Inner London Magistrates
  Court Poor Box and Feeder
  Charity
The Ireland Fund of Great
  Britain
The Irish Youth Foundation
  (UK) Ltd (incorporating The
  Lawlor Foundation)
The Ironmongers' Foundation
Irwin Trust
The ISA Charity
The Isaacs Charitable Trust
The J Isaacs Charitable Trust
The Isle of Anglesey Charitable
  Trust
The ITF Seafarers Trust
The J M K Charitable Trust
The J R S S T Charitable Trust
C Richard Jackson Charitable
  Trust
Elizabeth Jackson Charitable
  Trust
The Ruth and Lionel Jacobson
  Trust (Second Fund) No 2
Jaffe Family Relief Fund
The Susan and Stephen
  James Charitable
  Settlement
The James Trust
The Marjory Jameson Trust
The Jarman Charitable Trust
The John Jarrold Trust
JCA Charitable Foundation
The Jeffrey Charitable Trust
Rees Jeffreys Road Fund
The Nick Jenkins Foundation
The Jenour Foundation
The Jephcott Charitable Trust
Jesus Hospital Charity
The Jewish Youth Fund

The Harold Joels Charitable
Trust
The Nicholas Joels Charitable
Trust
The Norman Joels Charitable
Trust
The Lillie Johnson Charitable
Trust
The Johnson Foundation
The Reginald Johnson
Foundation
The Johnnie Johnson Trust
The Johnson Wax Ltd
Charitable Trust
The Joicey Trust
The Jones 1986 Charitable
Trust
The Marjorie and Geoffrey
Jones Charitable Trust
The Jordan Charitable
Foundation
The J E Joseph Charitable
Fund
The Lady Eileen Joseph
Foundation
The Josephs Family Charitable
Trust
JTH Charitable Trust
The Julian Budd Kids in Sport
Trust Limited
The Jungels-Winkler Charitable
Foundation
The Anton Jurgens Charitable
Trust
The Bernard Kahn Charitable
Trust
The Stanley Kalms Foundation
The Karenza Foundation
The Boris Karloff Charitable
Foundation
The Ian Karten Charitable
Trust
The Kasner Charitable Trust
The Kathleen Trust
The Michael and Ilse Katz
Foundation
The Katzauer Charitable
Settlement
The C S Kaufman Charitable
Trust
The Geoffrey John Kaye
Charitable Foundation
The Emmanuel Kaye
Foundation
Kelsick's Educational
Foundation
The KempWelch Charitable
Trust
The Kay Kendall Leukaemia
Fund
William Kendall's Charity (Wax
Chandlers' Company)
The John Thomas Kennedy
Charitable Foundation
The Kennedy Charitable
Foundation

The Kennel Club Charitable
Trust
Kent Community Foundation
The Nancy Kenyon Charitable
Trust
Keren Association
Kermaville Ltd
The Peter Kershaw Trust
Keswick Hall Trust
Kettering and District
Charitable Medical Trust
The Ursula Keyes Trust
The Robert Kiln Charitable
Trust
The King Henry VIII Endowed
Trust Warwick
The King/Cullimore Charitable
Trust
The Kingsbury Charity
The Mary Kinross Charitable
Trust
Kirkley Poor's Lands Estate
The Richard Kirkman
Charitable Trust
Kirschel Foundation
Robert Kitchin (Saddlers'
Company)
Ernest Kleinwort Charitable
Trust
The Marina Kleinwort
Charitable Trust
The Sir James Knott Trust
The Kobler Trust
The Kohn Foundation
The Kreditor Charitable Trust
The Kreitman Foundation
The Neil Kreitman Foundation
The Heinz, Anna and Carol
Kroch Foundation
The Kyte Charitable Trust
The Late Sir Pierce Lacy
Charity Trust
John Laing Charitable Trust
Maurice and Hilda Laing
Charitable Trust
The Christopher Laing
Foundation
The Kirby Laing Foundation
The Martin Laing Foundation
The Beatrice Laing Trust
The Lambert Charitable Trust
LWS Lancashire Environmental
Fund Limited
Duchy of Lancaster Benevolent
Fund
The Lancaster Foundation
Langdale Trust
The Langley Charitable Trust
The Langtree Trust
The LankellyChase Foundation
The R J Larg Family Charitable
Trust
Largsmount Ltd
The Lark Trust
Laslett's (Hinton) Charity
The Lauffer Family Charitable
Foundation

The Kathleen Laurence Trust
The Edgar E Lawley Foundation
The Herd Lawson and Muriel
Lawson Charitable Trust
The Lawson Beckman
Charitable Trust
The Raymond and Blanche
Lawson Charitable Trust
The Mason Le Page Charitable
Trust
The Leach Fourteenth Trust
The David Lean Foundation
The Leathersellers' Company
Charitable Fund
The Arnold Lee Charitable
Trust
The William Leech Charity
The Lord Mayor of Leeds
Appeal Fund
Leeds Building Society
Charitable Foundation
The Kennedy Leigh Charitable
Trust
The Leigh Trust
Mrs Vera Leigh's Charity
P Leigh-Bramwell Trust 'E'
The Lennox and Wyfold
Foundation
The Erica Leonard Trust
The Leonard Trust
The Mark Leonard Trust
Lesley Lesley and Mutter Trust
Leukaemia and Lymphoma
Research
The Leverhulme Trade
Charities Trust
Lord Leverhulme's Charitable
Trust
The Joseph Levy Charitable
Foundation
The John Spedan Lewis
Foundation
The Sir Edward Lewis
Foundation
John Lewis Partnership
General Community Fund
Lichfield Conduit Lands
Lifeline 4 Kids
The Linbury Trust
The Lind Trust
Lindale Educational
Foundation
The Linden Charitable Trust
The Enid Linder Foundation
The Linmardon Trust
The Ruth and Stuart Lipton
Charitable Trust
The Lister Charitable Trust
Frank Litchfield Charitable
Trust
The Andrew and Mary
Elizabeth Little Charitable
Trust
The Second Joseph Aaron
Littman Foundation
The George John and Sheilah
Livanos Charitable Trust

Liverpool Charity and Voluntary
Services
Liverpool Sailors' Home Trust
The Elaine and Angus Lloyd
Charitable Trust
The Charles Lloyd Foundation
Lloyd's Charities Trust
Lloyds Bank Foundation for
England and Wales
Lloyds Bank Foundation for
Northern Ireland
Lloyds Bank Foundation for the
Channel Islands
The Locker Foundation
The Loftus Charitable Trust
The Lolev Charitable Trust
London Catalyst
The London Community
Foundation
The London Housing
Foundation
The London Law Trust
The London Marathon
Charitable Trust
The William and Katherine
Longman Trust
The Lord's Taverners
The Loseley and Guildway
Charitable Trust
The Lotus Foundation
The C L Loyd Charitable Trust
The Marie Helen Luen
Charitable Trust
Robert Luff Foundation Ltd
Henry Lumley Charitable Trust
C F Lunoe Trust Fund
The Ruth and Jack Lunzer
Charitable Trust
Lord and Lady Lurgan Trust
The Lyndhurst Trust
The Lynn Foundation
The Lynwood Trust
John Lyon's Charity
The Lyons Charitable Trust
The Sir Jack Lyons Charitable
Trust
The Lyras Family Charitable
Trust
Sylvanus Lyson's Charity
The M and C Trust
The M K Charitable Trust
The Madeline Mabey Trust
The E M MacAndrew Trust
The R S Macdonald Charitable
Trust
Macdonald-Buchanan
Charitable Trust
The Macfarlane Walker Trust
The Mackay and Brewer
Charitable Trust
The Mackintosh Foundation
The MacRobert Trust
The Magdalen and Lasher
Charity
Magdalen Hospital Trust
The Magen Charitable Trust

Man Group plc Charitable
Trust
The Manackerman Charitable
Trust
The Manchester Guardian
Society Charitable Trust
Lord Mayor of Manchester's
Charity Appeal Trust
Mandeville Trust
The Manifold Charitable Trust
W M Mann Foundation
The Leslie and Lilian Manning
Trust
Marbeh Torah Trust
Marchig Animal Welfare Trust
The Stella and Alexander
Margulies Charitable Trust
Market Harborough and The
Bowdens Charity
The Ann and David Marks
Foundation
The Hilda and Samuel Marks
Foundation
J P Marland Charitable Trust
The Michael Marsh Charitable
Trust
The Marsh Christian Trust
The Charlotte Marshall
Charitable Trust
The Jim Marshall Charitable
Trust
The Nora Joan Marshall
Charitable Trust
The D G Marshall of
Cambridge Trust
Marshall's Charity
Marshgate Charitable
Settlement
Sir George Martin Trust
John Martin's Charity
The Mason Porter Charitable
Trust
The Nancie Massey Charitable
Trust
The Mathew Trust
The Matt 6.3 Charitable Trust
The Violet Mauray Charitable
Trust
The Maxwell Family Foundation
Evelyn May Trust
Mayfair Charities Ltd
The Mayfield Valley Arts Trust
Mazars Charitable Trust
The Robert McAlpine
Foundation
The McKenna Charitable Trust
The Helen Isabella McMorran
Charitable Foundation
The James Frederick and Ethel
Anne Measures Charity
The Medlock Charitable Trust
The Anthony and Elizabeth
Mellows Charitable
Settlement
Melow Charitable Trust
The Mercers' Charitable
Foundation

The Merchant Taylors'
Company Charities Fund
The Merchant Venturers'
Charity
The Merchants' House of
Glasgow
The Mersey Docks and
Harbour Company
Charitable Fund
Community Foundation for
Merseyside
The Zachary Merton and
George Woofindin
Convalescent Trust
The Tony Metherell Charitable
Trust
The Metropolitan Drinking
Fountain and Cattle Trough
Association
The Mickel Fund
Gerald Micklem Charitable
Trust
Middlesex Sports Foundation
Midhurst Pensions Trust
The Migraine Trust
Miles Trust for the Putney and
Roehampton Community
The Hugh and Mary Miller
Bequest Trust
The Ronald Miller Foundation
The Millfield Trust
The Millhouses Charitable
Trust
The Millichope Foundation
The Mills Charity
The Millward Charitable Trust
The Clare Milne Trust
Milton Keynes Community
Foundation
The Edgar Milward Charity
The Keith and Joan
Mindelsohn Charitable
Trust
The Peter Minet Trust
The Minos Trust
The Mirfield Educational
Charity
The Laurence Misener
Charitable Trust
The Mishcon Family Charitable
Trust
The Misselbrook Trust
The Mitchell Charitable Trust
The Esmé Mitchell Trust
Keren Mitzvah Trust
The Mizpah Trust
The Mobbs Memorial Trust Ltd
The Modiano Charitable Trust
The Moette Charitable Trust
The Mole Charitable Trust
The D C Moncrieff Charitable
Trust
Monmouthshire County Council
Welsh Church Act Fund
The Montague Thompson
Coon Charitable Trust

The Colin Montgomerie
Charitable Foundation
The Monument Trust
George A Moore Foundation
John Moores Foundation
The Morel Charitable Trust
The Morgan Charitable
Foundation
The Mr and Mrs J T Morgan
Foundation
Morgan Stanley International
Foundation
The Oliver Morland Charitable
Trust
The Bernard Morris Charitable
Trust
The Morris Charitable Trust
The Willie and Mabel Morris
Charitable Trust
The Peter Morrison Charitable
Foundation
The Stanley Morrison
Charitable Trust
Vyoel Moshe Charitable Trust
The Moss Charitable Trust
The Robert and Margaret
Moss Charitable Trust
The Moss Family Charitable
Trust
Mosselson Charitable Trust
The Mount Everest Foundation
The Edwina Mountbatten Trust
Mountbatten Festival of Music
The Mountbatten Memorial
Trust
Mrs Waterhouse Charitable
Trust
The Mugdock Children's Trust
The Mulberry Trust
The Edith Murphy Foundation
The Mushroom Fund
The Music Sales Charitable
Trust
Muslim Hands
The Mutual Trust Group
The Kitty and Daniel Nabarro
Charitable Trust
The Nadezhda Charitable Trust
The Naggar Charitable Trust
The Eleni Nakou Foundation
The Janet Nash Charitable
Settlement
The National Hockey
Foundation
The National Manuscripts
Conservation Trust
Needham Market and Barking
Welfare Charities
The Worshipful Company of
Needlemakers' Charitable
Fund
The Neighbourly Charitable
Trust
The James Neill Trust Fund
Nemoral Ltd
The Newcomen Collett
Foundation

The Frances and Augustus
Newman Foundation
Alderman Newton's
Educational Foundation
The Chevras Ezras Nitzrochim
Trust
The Noon Foundation
The Norda Trust
Norfolk Community Foundation
Norie Charitable Trust
The Norman Family Charitable
Trust
The Duncan Norman Trust
Fund
The Normanby Charitable Trust
The Northampton Municipal
Church Charities
The Northampton Queen's
Institute Relief in Sickness
Fund
The Earl of Northampton's
Charity
The Northcott Devon
Foundation
The Northcott Devon Medical
Foundation
The Community Foundation for
Northern Ireland
The Northmoor Trust
The Northumberland Village
Homes Trust
The Northumbria Historic
Churches Trust
The Northwood Charitable
Trust
The Norton Foundation
The Norwich Church of England
Young Men's Society
The Norwich Town Close
Estate Charity
The Norwood and Newton
Settlement
The Noswad Charity
The Notgrove Trust
The Nottingham General
Dispensary
The Nottingham Gordon
Memorial Trust for Boys
and Girls
Nottinghamshire Community
Foundation
The Nottinghamshire Historic
Churches Trust
The Nottinghamshire Miners'
Welfare Trust Fund
Novi Most International
The Father O'Mahoney
Memorial Trust
The Sir Peter O'Sullevan
Charitable Trust
The Oak Trust
The Oakdale Trust
The Oakley Charitable Trust
The Oakmoor Charitable Trust
The Odin Charitable Trust
The Ofenheim Charitable Trust

Ogilvie Charities Deed No.2
(including the Charity of
Mary Catherine Ford Smith)
The Ogle Christian Trust
The Oikonomia Trust
Oizer Charitable Trust
The Old Broad Street Charity
Trust
The John Oldacre Foundation
The Oldham Foundation
Open Gate
The Raymond Oppenheimer
Foundation
Ormonde Foundation
The Ormsby Charitable Trust
The Orrin Charitable Trust
The Owen Family Trust
Oxfam (GB)
The Oxfordshire Community
Foundation
The P F Charitable Trust
Padwa Charitable Foundation
The Paget Charitable Trust
The Palmer Foundation
The Panacea Society
Panton Trust
The James Pantyfedwen
Foundation
The Paragon Trust
The Park House Charitable
Trust
The Frank Parkinson
Agricultural Trust
The Samuel and Freda
Parkinson Charitable Trust
The Parthenon Trust
The Constance Paterson
Charitable Trust
The Patrick Charitable Trust
The Jack Patston Charitable
Trust
Paycare Charity Trust
The Payne Charitable Trust
The Harry Payne Trust
The Susanna Peake Charitable
Trust
The Pedmore Sporting Club
Trust Fund
The Dowager Countess
Eleanor Peel Trust
The Pennycress Trust
The Performing Right Society
Foundation
The Persson Charitable Trust
The Persula Foundation
The Jack Petchey Foundation
The Petplan Charitable Trust
The Philips and Rubens
Charitable Trust
The Phillips Charitable Trust
The Phillips Family Charitable
Trust
Philological Foundation
The David Pickford Charitable
Foundation
The Bernard Piggott Charitable
Trust

The Cecil Pilkington Charitable Trust
The Pilkington Charities Fund
The Austin and Hope Pilkington Trust
The Sir Harry Pilkington Trust
The Col W W Pilkington Will Trusts The General Charity Fund
The DLA Piper Charitable Trust
The Worshipful Company of Plaisterers Charitable Trust
The Platinum Trust
The George and Esme Pollitzer Charitable Settlement
The J S F Pollitzer Charitable Settlement
The Ponton House Trust
Edith and Ferdinand Porjes Charitable Trust
The John Porter Charitable Trust
The Porter Foundation
The Portishead Nautical Trust
The Portrack Charitable Trust
The J E Posnansky Charitable Trust
The Powell Foundation
The W L Pratt Charitable Trust
Premierquote Ltd
Premishlaner Charitable Trust
The Tom Press Charitable Foundation
The William Price Charitable Trust
The Lucy Price Relief-in-Need Charity
Sir John Priestman Charity Trust
The Primrose Trust
The Prince of Wales's Charitable Foundation
Prison Service Charity Fund
The Privy Purse Charitable Trust
The Proven Family Trust
The Provincial Grand Charity of the Province of Derbyshire
The Puebla Charitable Trust
The Richard and Christine Purchas Charitable Trust
The Puri Foundation
Mr and Mrs J A Pye's Charitable Settlement
Quartet Community Foundation
Queen Mary's Roehampton Trust
The Queen's Silver Jubilee Trust
Quothquan Trust
R S Charitable Trust
The R V W Trust
The Monica Rabagliati Charitable Trust
Rachel Charitable Trust
The Mr and Mrs Philip Rackham Charitable Trust

Richard Radcliffe Charitable Trust
The Radcliffe Trust
The Ragdoll Foundation
The Rainford Trust
The Peggy Ramsay Foundation
The Joseph and Lena Randall Charitable Trust
The Rank Foundation Limited
The Fanny Rapaport Charitable Settlement
The Ratcliff Foundation
The Ratcliff Pension Charity
The Ratcliffe Charitable Trust
The Eleanor Rathbone Charitable Trust
The Sigrid Rausing Trust
The Ravensdale Trust
The Rawdon-Smith Trust
The Rayden Charitable Trust
The Roger Raymond Charitable Trust
The Rayne Foundation
The Rayne Trust
The Sir James Reckitt Charity
The Red Arrows Trust
The Red Rose Charitable Trust
The C A Redfern Charitable Foundation
The Reed Foundation
Richard Reeve's Foundation
The Max Reinhardt Charitable Trust
Relief Fund for Romania Limited
REMEDI
The Rest Harrow Trust
Reuben Foundation
The Nathaniel Reyner Trust Fund
The Rhododendron Trust
The Rhondda Cynon Taff Welsh Church Acts Fund
The Clive Richards Charity
The Richmond Parish Lands Charity
Ridgesave Limited
The Ripple Effect Foundation
The Sir John Ritblat Family Foundation
River Legacy
The River Trust
Thomas Roberts Trust
The Robertson Trust
Edwin George Robinson Charitable Trust
The Rochester Bridge Trust
The Rock Foundation
The Rock Solid Trust
The Rofeh Trust
Rokach Family Charitable Trust
The Helen Roll Charitable Trust
The Sir James Roll Charitable Trust
The Roman Research Trust

The C A Rookes Charitable Trust
Mrs L D Rope Third Charitable Settlement
The Rosca Trust
The Cecil Rosen Foundation
The Rothermere Foundation
The Rotherwick Foundation
The Rothley Trust
The Roughley Charitable Trust
Mrs Gladys Row Fogo Charitable Trust
Rowanville Ltd
The Christopher Rowbotham Charitable Trust
The Rowing Foundation
The Rowlands Trust
The Joseph Rowntree Charitable Trust
Royal Artillery Charitable Fund
Royal British Legion
Royal Docks Trust (London)
Royal Masonic Trust for Girls and Boys
The Alfred and Frances Rubens Charitable Trust
The Rubin Foundation
William Arthur Rudd Memorial Trust
Rugby Football Foundation
The Russell Trust
The J S and E C Rymer Charitable Trust
S O Charitable Trust
The Jeremy and John Sacher Charitable Trust
The Michael Harry Sacher Trust
Raymond and Beverly Sackler 1988 Foundation
The Sackler Trust
The Ruzin Sadagora Trust
The Saddlers' Company Charitable Fund
The Saga Charitable Trust
The Jean Sainsbury Animal Welfare Trust
The Alan and Babette Sainsbury Charitable Fund
The Sainsbury Family Charitable Trusts
The Saintbury Trust
The Saints and Sinners Trust
The Salt Foundation
The Salt Trust
Basil Samuel Charitable Trust
The M J Samuel Charitable Trust
The Peter Samuel Charitable Trust
The Samworth Foundation
The Sandra Charitable Trust
Santander UK Foundation Limited
The Scarfe Charitable Trust
The Schapira Charitable Trust

The Schmidt-Bodner Charitable Trust
The Schreib Trust
The Schreiber Charitable Trust
The Schuster Charitable Trust Foundation Scotland
The Francis C Scott Charitable Trust
The Frieda Scott Charitable Trust
The Scott Trust Foundation
The Storrow Scott Will Trust
Scottish Coal Industry Special Welfare Fund
The Scouloudi Foundation
Seafarers UK (King George's Fund for Sailors)
Seamen's Hospital Society
The Searchlight Electric Charitable Trust
The Samuel Sebba Charitable Trust
The Seedfield Trust
Leslie Sell Charitable Trust
The Ayrton Senna Foundation
The Seven Fifty Trust
The Cyril Shack Trust
The Shanti Charitable Trust
ShareGift (The Orr Mackintosh Foundation)
The Linley Shaw Foundation
The Shears Foundation
The Sheepdrove Trust
The Sheffield and District Hospital Services Charitable Fund
The Sheldon Trust
The Patricia and Donald Shepherd Charitable Trust
The Sylvia and Colin Shepherd Charitable Trust
The Archie Sherman Cardiff Foundation
The Archie Sherman Charitable Trust
The R C Sherriff Trust
The Shetland Charitable Trust
SHINE (Support and Help in Education)
The Barnett and Sylvia Shine No 2 Charitable Trust
The Bassil Shippam and Alsford Trust
The Shipwrights' Company Charitable Fund
The Shirley Foundation
Shlomo Memorial Fund Limited
The J A Shone Memorial Trust
Community Foundation for Shropshire and Telford
The Barbara A Shuttleworth Memorial Trust
The Mary Elizabeth Siebel Charity
David and Jennifer Sieff Charitable Trust

The Julius Silman Charitable Trust
The Leslie Silver Charitable Trust
The Simpson Education and Conservation Trust
The Simpson Foundation
The Huntly and Margery Sinclair Charitable Trust
Sino-British Fellowship Trust
SITA Cornwall Trust Limited
The Skelton Bounty
The Charles Skey Charitable Trust
Skipton Building Society Charitable Foundation
The John Slater Foundation
Sloane Robinson Foundation
The SMB Charitable Trust
The Mrs Smith and Mount Trust
The N Smith Charitable Settlement
The E H Smith Charitable Trust
The Smith Charitable Trust
The Henry Smith Charity
The Leslie Smith Foundation
The Martin Smith Foundation
The Stanley Smith UK Horticultural Trust
The Snowball Trust
The Sobell Foundation
The Solo Charitable Settlement
Dr Richard Solomon's Charitable Trust
The E C Sosnow Charitable Trust
The Souter Charitable Trust
The South Square Trust
The Stephen R and Philippa H Southall Charitable Trust
The W F Southall Trust
The Southover Manor General Education Trust
The Southwold Trust
The Sovereign Health Care Charitable Trust
Sparks Charity (Sport Aiding Medical Research For Kids)
Sparquote Limited
The Spear Charitable Trust
The Worshipful Company of Spectacle Makers' Charity
The Jessie Spencer Trust
The Ralph and Irma Sperring Charity
The Spielman Charitable Trust
The Spoore, Merry and Rixman Foundation
Sported Foundation
Springfields Employees' Medical Research and Charity Trust Fund
Springrule Limited
The Spurrell Charitable Trust

The Geoff and Fiona Squire Foundation
St James' Trust Settlement
St James's Place Foundation
Sir Walter St John's Educational Charity
St Michael's and All Saints' Charities Relief Branch (The Church Houses Relief in Need Charity)
The Late St Patrick White Charitable Trust
The Stanley Foundation Ltd
The Stanton Ballard Charitable Trust
The Staples Trust
The Star Charitable Trust
The Steel Charitable Trust
The Steinberg Family Charitable Trust
The Hugh Stenhouse Foundation
The Stephen Barry Charitable Trust
The Sigmund Sternberg Charitable Foundation
Stervon Ltd
The Stevenage Community Trust
The June Stevens Foundation
The Steventon Allotments and Relief-in-Need Charity
The Stewards' Company Limited (incorporating the J W Laing Trust and the J W Laing Biblical Scholarship Trust)
The Leonard Laity Stoate Charitable Trust
The Stobart Newlands Charitable Trust
The Edward Stocks-Massey Bequest Fund
The Stokenchurch Educational Charity
The Stoller Charitable Trust
The M J C Stone Charitable Trust
The Samuel Storey Family Charitable Trust
Peter Stormonth Darling Charitable Trust
The Strangward Trust
The Strasser Foundation
Stratford upon Avon Town Trust
The W O Street Charitable Foundation
The Sudborough Foundation
The Suffolk Historic Churches Trust
The Summerfield Charitable Trust
The Bernard Sunley Charitable Foundation
The Surrey Historic Buildings Trust Ltd

The Sussex Historic Churches
Trust
The Sutasoma Trust
Sutton Coldfield Charitable
Trust
Swansea and Brecon Diocesan
Board of Finance Limited
Swimathon Foundation
The John Swire (1989)
Charitable Trust
The Swire Charitable Trust
The Adrian Swire Charitable
Trust
The Hugh and Ruby Sykes
Charitable Trust
The Charles and Elsie Sykes
Trust
The Sylvanus Charitable Trust
The Stella Symons Charitable
Trust
The Tabeel Trust
The Tajtelbaum Charitable
Trust
The Talbot Trusts
The Talbot Village Trust
Tallow Chandlers Benevolent
Fund
The Tangent Charitable Trust
The Lady Tangye Charitable
Trust
The David Tannen Charitable
Trust
The Tanner Trust
The Lili Tapper Charitable
Foundation
The Mrs A Lacy Tate Trust
The Tay Charitable Trust
Humphrey Richardson Taylor
Charitable Trust
The Connie and Albert Taylor
Charitable Trust
The Cyril Taylor Charitable
Trust
A P Taylor Trust
Tearfund
The Tedworth Charitable Trust
Tees Valley Community
Foundation
The Templeton Goodwill Trust
Tesco Charity Trust
The C Paul Thackray General
Charitable Trust
Thackray Medical Research
Trust
The Thames Wharf Charity
The John P. Gommes
Foundation
The Thistle Trust
The Loke Wan Tho Memorial
Foundation
The Thomas Lilley Memorial
Trust
The Arthur and Margaret
Thompson Charitable Trust
The Thompson Family
Charitable Trust

The Len Thomson Charitable
Trust
The Sir Jules Thorn Charitable
Trust
The Thornton Foundation
The Thornton Trust
The Thousandth Man –
Richard Burns Charitable
Trust
The Three Guineas Trust
The Three Oaks Trust
The Thriplow Charitable Trust
Mrs R P Tindall's Charitable
Trust
The Tinsley Foundation
The Tobacco Pipe Makers and
Tobacco Trade Benevolent
Fund
The Tolkien Trust
Tollemache (Buckminster)
Charitable Trust
Tomchei Torah Charitable
Trust
The Tompkins Foundation
The Tory Family Foundation
Tottenham Grammar School
Foundation
The Tower Hill Trust
The Towry Law Charitable Trust
(also known as the Castle
Educational Trust)
The Toy Trust
The Mayor of Trafford's Charity
Fund
The Constance Travis
Charitable Trust
The Treeside Trust
The Triangle Trust (1949) Fund
The True Colours Trust
Truedene Co. Ltd
The Truemark Trust
Truemart Limited
Trumros Limited
The Trusthouse Charitable
Foundation
The James Tudor Foundation
Tudor Rose Ltd
The Tudor Trust
The Tufton Charitable Trust
The R D Turner Charitable
Trust
The Douglas Turner Trust
The Florence Turner Trust
The G J W Turner Trust
Miss S M Tutton Charitable
Trust
The TUUT Charitable Trust
Community Foundation Serving
Tyne and Wear and
Northumberland
Trustees of Tzedakah
Ulster Garden Villages Ltd
Ultach Trust
The Ulverscroft Foundation
Ulverston Town Lands Charity
The Underwood Trust

The Union of Orthodox Hebrew
Congregation
The United Society for the
Propagation of the Gospel
The David Uri Memorial Trust
Uxbridge United Welfare Trust
Vale of Glamorgan – Welsh
Church Fund
The Valentine Charitable Trust
The Van Neste Foundation
Mrs Maud Van Norden's
Charitable Foundation
The Vandervell Foundation
The Vardy Foundation
The Variety Club Children's
Charity
Veneziana Fund
The Verdon-Smith Family
Charitable Settlement
Victoria Homes Trust
The Nigel Vinson Charitable
Trust
The William and Ellen Vinten
Trust
The Vintners' Company
Charitable Foundation
Vintners' Gifts Charity
Vision Charity
Vivdale Ltd
The Viznitz Foundation
Voluntary Action Fund (VAF)
Wade's Charity
The Scurrah Wainwright Charity
Wakeham Trust
The Community Foundation in
Wales
Wales Council for Voluntary
Action
Robert and Felicity Waley-
Cohen Charitable Trust
The F J Wallis Charitable
Settlement
War on Want
The Ward Blenkinsop Trust
The George Ward Charitable
Trust
The Barbara Ward Children's
Foundation
G R Waters Charitable Trust
2000
The Howard Watson Symington
Memorial Charity
John Watson's Trust
Waynflete Charitable Trust
Weatherley Charitable Trust
The Weavers' Company
Benevolent Fund
The William Webster
Charitable Trust
The Weinberg Foundation
The Weinstein Foundation
The James Weir Foundation
The Barbara Welby Trust
The Wellcome Trust

Welsh Church Fund Dyfed area (Carmarthenshire, Ceredigion and Pembrokeshire)
The Welton Foundation
The Wessex Youth Trust
The West Derby Wastelands Charity
West London Synagogue Charitable Fund
West Yorkshire Police Community Trust
The Westminster Foundation
The Garfield Weston Foundation
The Whitaker Charitable Trust
The Colonel W H Whitbread Charitable Trust
The Simon Whitbread Charitable Trust
The Whitecourt Charitable Trust
The Norman Whiteley Trust
The Whitley Animal Protection Trust
The Whittlesey Charity
The Lionel Wigram Memorial Trust
The Felicity Wilde Charitable Trust
The Wilkinson Charitable Foundation
Will to Win Foundation Ltd. (previously Tennis for a Life)
The William Barrow's Charity
The Charity of William Williams
The Kay Williams Charitable Foundation
The Williams Family Charitable Trust
The HDH Wills 1965 Charitable Trust
The Dame Violet Wills Will Trust
The Wilmcote Charitrust
David Wilson Foundation
The Wilson Foundation
J and J R Wilson Trust
The Community Foundation for Wiltshire and Swindon
The Benjamin Winegarten Charitable Trust
The Francis Winham Foundation
Wirral Mayor's Charity
The James Wise Charitable Trust
The Michael and Anna Wix Charitable Trust
The Wixamtree Trust
The Woburn 1986 Charitable Trust
The Maurice Wohl Charitable Foundation
The Charles Wolfson Charitable Trust

The Wolfson Family Charitable Trust
The Wolfson Foundation
The James Wood Bequest Fund
Wooden Spoon Society
Woodlands Green Ltd
Woodlands Trust
The Woodward Charitable Trust
Worcester Municipal Charities
The Worcestershire and Dudley Historic Churches Trust
The Wragge and Co. Charitable Trust
The Diana Edgson Wright Charitable Trust
The Matthews Wrightson Charity Trust
Miss E B Wrightson's Charitable Settlement
Wychdale Ltd
Wychville Ltd
The Wyndham Charitable Trust
The Wyseliot Charitable Trust
The Xerox (UK) Trust
The Yardley Great Trust
The Dennis Alan Yardy Charitable Trust
The W Wing Yip and Brothers Foundation
Yorkshire Agricultural Society
Yorkshire Building Society Charitable Foundation
The South Yorkshire Community Foundation
The Yorkshire Dales Millennium Trust
The John Young Charitable Settlement
The William Allen Young Charitable Trust
The John K Young Endowment Fund
Zephyr Charitable Trust
The Marjorie and Arnold Ziff Charitable Foundation
Stephen Zimmerman Charitable Trust
The Zochonis Charitable Trust
Zurich Community Trust (UK) Limited

....

■ Vehicles

The 1970 Trust
The 1989 Willan Charitable Trust
The 29th May 1961 Charitable Trust
A W Charitable Trust
The Aberbrothock Skea Trust
The Aberdeen Endowments Trust

The Aberdeenshire Educational Trust Scheme
Achisomoch Aid Company Limited
The ACT Foundation
Action Medical Research
The Company of Actuaries' Charitable Trust Fund
The Sylvia Adams Charitable Trust
The Victor Adda Foundation
The Adint Charitable Trust
Age UK
Aid to the Church in Need (UK)
The Sylvia Aitken Charitable Trust
The Al Fayed Charitable Foundation
Aldgate and All Hallows' Foundation
The Aldgate Freedom Foundation
Allchurches Trust Ltd
The H B Allen Charitable Trust
The Alliance Family Foundation
Angus Allnatt Charitable Foundation
The Pat Allsop Charitable Trust
Almondsbury Charity
Altamont Ltd
Alvor Charitable Trust
The Ammco Trust
Viscount Amory's Charitable Trust
The AMW Charitable Trust
The André Christian Trust
Anguish's Educational Foundation
The Animal Defence Trust
Anpride Ltd
Ambrose and Ann Appelbe Trust
The Appletree Trust
Archbishop of Wales' Fund for Children
The John M Archer Charitable Trust
The Archer Trust
The Ardwick Trust
The Argus Appeal
The Armenian Relief Society of Great Britain Trust
The Armourers' and Brasiers' Gauntlet Trust
The Arsenal Foundation
The Artemis Charitable Trust
The Arts and Entertainment Charitable Trust
Arts Council England
The Arts Council of Northern Ireland
Arts Council of Wales (also known as Cyngor Celfyddydau Cymru)
The Ove Arup Foundation
The A S Charitable Trust
The Ashden Trust

The Ashendene Trust
The Ashley Family Foundation
The Ashworth Charitable Trust
The Ian Askew Charitable Trust
The Association of Colleges
    Charitable Trust
Astellas European Foundation
Asthma UK
The Astor Foundation
The Astor of Hever Trust
The Aurelius Charitable Trust
The John Avins Trustees
The Avon and Somerset Police
    Community Trust
The Aylesford Family
    Charitable Trust
The BAA Communities Trust
The Scott Bader
    Commonwealth Ltd
The Bagri Foundation
Veta Bailey Charitable Trust
The Austin Bailey Foundation
The Baily Thomas Charitable
    Fund
The Baker Charitable Trust
The Balcombe Charitable Trust
The Albert Casanova Ballard
    Deceased Trust
The Ballinger Charitable Trust
The Balmore Trust
The Balney Charitable Trust
The Baltic Charitable Fund
The Bamford Charitable
    Foundation
The Banbury Charities
William P Bancroft (No 2)
    Charitable Trust and
    Jenepher Gillett Trust
The Band Trust
The Barbers' Company General
    Charities
The Barbour Foundation
Barchester Healthcare
    Foundation
The Barclay Foundation
The Baring Foundation
Peter Barker-Mill Memorial
    Charity
The Barleycorn Trust
Barnes Workhouse Fund
The Barnsbury Charitable Trust
The Barnstaple Bridge Trust
The Barnwood House Trust
The Misses Barrie Charitable
    Trust
Barrington Family Charitable
    Trust
Bartholomew Charitable Trust
The Bartlett Taylor Charitable
    Trust
The Paul Bassham Charitable
    Trust
The Batchworth Trust
The Bates Charitable Trust
The Bay Tree Charitable Trust
The Louis Baylis (Maidenhead
    Advertiser) Charitable Trust

BBC Children in Need
B-CH 1971 Charitable Trust
The Beacon Trust
The Bearder Charity
The James Beattie Charitable
    Trust
The Beaverbrook Foundation
The Beccles Town Lands
    Charity
The Becker Family Charitable
    Trust
The Becketts and Sargeants
    Educational Foundation
The John Beckwith Charitable
    Trust
The Peter Beckwith Charitable
    Trust
The David and Ruth Behrend
    Fund
The Beit Trust
The Bellahouston Bequest
    Fund
The Bellinger Donnay Trust
The Benfield Motors Charitable
    Trust
The Benham Charitable
    Settlement
The Hervey Benham Charitable
    Trust
Maurice and Jacqueline
    Bennett Charitable Trust
The Gerald Bentall Charitable
    Trust
Bergqvist Charitable Trust
The Berkshire Community
    Foundation
The Bestway Foundation
BHST
The Mason Bibby 1981 Trust
The Bideford Bridge Trust
The Big Lottery Fund
The Billmeir Charitable Trust
Percy Bilton Charity
The Bingham Trust
The Bintaub Charitable Trust
The Birmingham District
    Nursing Charitable Trust
Birmingham International
    Airport Community Trust
The Lord Mayor of
    Birmingham's Charity
Miss Jeanne Bisgood's
    Charitable Trust
The Michael Bishop
    Foundation
The Bishop's Development
    Fund
The Bertie Black Foundation
Isabel Blackman Foundation
The Blagrave Trust
The Blair Foundation
Blakemore Foundation
The Blanchminster Trust
The Blandford Lake Trust
The Sir Victor Blank Charitable
    Settlement

The Neville and Elaine Blond
    Charitable Trust
The Bluston Charitable
    Settlement
The Boltons Trust
The Bonamy Charitable Trust
The John and Celia Bonham
    Christie Charitable Trust
The Charlotte Bonham-Carter
    Charitable Trust
Bonhomie United Charity
    Society
The Boots Charitable Trust
The Bordon Liphook
    Haslemere Charity
The Oliver Borthwick Memorial
    Trust
The Bothwell Charitable Trust
H E and E L Botteley
    Charitable Trust
The Harry Bottom Charitable
    Trust
The Anthony Bourne
    Foundation
The Bower Trust
The Bowerman Charitable
    Trust
John and Susan Bowers Fund
The Bowland Charitable Trust
The Frank Brake Charitable
    Trust
The William Brake Charitable
    Trust
The Tony Bramall Charitable
    Trust
The Harold and Alice Bridges
    Charity
Bristol Archdeaconry Charity
John Bristow and Thomas
    Mason Trust
The British Council for
    Prevention of Blindness
The British Dietetic
    Association General and
    Education Trust Fund
British Humane Association
British Record Industry Trust
The J and M Britton Charitable
    Trust
The Roger Brooke Charitable
    Trust
The David Brooke Charity
The Charles Brotherton Trust
Joseph Brough Charitable
    Trust
The Swinfen Broun Charitable
    Trust
Edna Brown Charitable
    Settlement (Mrs E E Brown
    Charitable Settlement)
The Jack Brunton Charitable
    Trust
Buckinghamshire Community
    Foundation
The Rosemary Bugden
    Charitable Trust
The Bulldog Trust Limited

The E F Bulmer Benevolent
Fund
Burdens Charitable Foundation
The Clara E Burgess Charity
The Burry Charitable Trust
The Arnold Burton 1998
Charitable Trust
The Burton Breweries
Charitable Trust
Consolidated Charity of Burton
upon Trent
The Worshipful Company of
Butchers General Charities
The Noel Buxton Trust
Henry T and Lucy B Cadbury
Charitable Trust
The Christopher Cadbury
Charitable Trust
The G W Cadbury Charitable
Trust
The Richard Cadbury
Charitable Trust
The Edward and Dorothy
Cadbury Trust
The George Cadbury Trust
CAF (Charities Aid Foundation)
CAFOD (Catholic Agency for
Overseas Development)
Community Foundation for
Calderdale
The Callander Charitable Trust
Calleva Foundation
Calypso Browning Trust
The Campden Charities
Trustee
The Canning Trust
The Carew Pole Charitable
Trust
The D W T Cargill Fund
Carlee Ltd
The Carlton House Charitable
Trust
The Carmelite Monastery Ware
Trust
The Worshipful Company of
Carmen Benevolent Trust
The Carnegie Dunfermline
Trust
The Carpenter Charitable Trust
The Carpenters' Company
Charitable Trust
The Carrington Charitable
Trust
The Carron Charitable
Settlement
The Leslie Mary Carter
Charitable Trust
The Casey Trust
The Catalyst Charitable Trust
The Catholic Charitable Trust
Catholic Foreign Missions
The Catholic Trust for England
and Wales
The Joseph and Annie Cattle
Trust
The Thomas Sivewright Catto
Charitable Settlement

The Wilfrid and Constance
Cave Foundation
The Cayo Foundation
The B G S Cayzer Charitable
Trust
The Cazenove Charitable Trust
Celtic Charity Fund
The Gaynor Cemlyn-Jones
Trust
The Pamela Champion
Foundation
The Chapman Charitable Trust
John William Chapman's
Charitable Trust
The Charities Advisory Trust
Charitworth Limited
The Charter 600 Charity
The Worshipful Company of
Chartered Accountants
General Charitable Trust
(also known as CALC)
The Chasah Trust
The Chelsea Square 1994
Trust
The Cheruby Trust
Cheshire Freemason's Charity
The Chetwode Foundation
Cheviot Asset Management
Charitable Trust
Childs Charitable Trust
The Childwick Trust
The Chippenham Borough
Lands Charity
The Chipping Sodbury Town
Lands Charity
CHK Charities Limited
The Chownes Foundation
The Chrimes Family Charitable
Trust
The Christabella Charitable
Trust
Christadelphian Samaritan
Fund
Christian Aid
Christian Response to Eastern
Europe
The Church and Community
Fund
The Church Burgesses
Educational Foundation
Church Burgesses Trust
Church Urban Fund
City and County of Swansea
Welsh Church Act Fund
Stephen Clark 1957
Charitable Trust
J A Clark Charitable Trust
The Hilda and Alice Clark
Charitable Trust
The Roger and Sarah Bancroft
Clark Charitable Trust
The Clarke Charitable
Settlement
The Cleopatra Trust
Lord Clinton's Charitable Trust
The Clore Duffield Foundation

Miss V L Clore's 1967
Charitable Trust
Closehelm Limited
The Clothworkers' Foundation
Richard Cloudesley's Charity
The Clover Trust
The Robert Clutterbuck
Charitable Trust
Clydpride Ltd
The Coalfields Regeneration
Trust
The John Coates Charitable
Trust
The Cobtree Charity Trust Ltd
The Denise Cohen Charitable
Trust
The Vivienne and Samuel
Cohen Charitable Trust
The John S Cohen Foundation
The R and S Cohen
Foundation
The Colchester Catalyst
Charity
The Cole Charitable Trust
The Colefax Charitable Trust
The John and Freda Coleman
Charitable Trust
The George Henry Collins
Charity
The Sir Jeremiah Colman Gift
Trust
The Coltstaple Trust
Colwinston Charitable Trust
Community First (Landfill
Communities Fund)
The Compton Charitable Trust
The Congleton Inclosure Trust
The Consolidated Charities for
the Infirm Merchant
Taylors' Company
The Ernest Cook Trust
The Cooks Charity
The Catherine Cookson
Charitable Trust
Mabel Cooper Charity
The Alice Ellen Cooper Dean
Charitable Foundation
The Marjorie Coote Animal
Charity Trust
The Marjorie Coote Old
People's Charity
The Helen Jean Cope Trust
The J Reginald Corah
Foundation Fund
The Gershon Coren Charitable
Foundation (also known as
The Muriel and Gus Coren
Charitable Foundation)
The Duke of Cornwall's
Benevolent Fund
The Cornwell Charitable Trust
The Sidney and Elizabeth
Corob Charitable Trust
The Corona Charitable Trust
The Costa Family Charitable
Trust

The Cotton Industry War
Memorial Trust
The Cotton Trust
The Augustine Courtauld Trust
The General Charities of the
City of Coventry
Coventry Building Society
Charitable Foundation
The John Cowan Foundation
Dudley and Geoffrey Cox
Charitable Trust
The Sir William Coxen Trust
Fund
The Lord Cozens-Hardy Trust
The Craignish Trust
The Craps Charitable Trust
Michael Crawford Children's
Charity
The Cray Trust
Creative Scotland
The Crerar Hotels Trust
The Crescent Trust
Cripplegate Foundation
The Violet and Milo Cripps
Charitable Trust
The Harry Crook Foundation
The Cross Trust
The Croydon Relief in Need
Charities
Cruden Foundation Ltd
The Ronald Cruickshanks
Foundation
The Culra Charitable Trust
The Cumber Family Charitable
Trust
Cumberland Building Society
Charitable Foundation
Cumbria Community
Foundation
The D J H Currie Memorial
Trust
The Dennis Curry Charitable
Trust
The Manny Cussins
Foundation
The Cwmbran Trust
Itzchok Meyer Cymerman Trust
Ltd
The D G Charitable Settlement
The D'Oyly Carte Charitable
Trust
Daily Prayer Union Charitable
Trust Limited
The Dr and Mrs A Darlington
Charitable Trust
Baron Davenport's Charity
The Davidson (Nairn)
Charitable Trust
The Davidson Family
Charitable Trust
The Alderman Joe Davidson
Memorial Trust
Michael Davies Charitable
Settlement
The Gwendoline and Margaret
Davies Charity

The Wilfrid Bruce Davis
Charitable Trust
Davis-Rubens Charitable Trust
The Dawe Charitable Trust
The De Brye Charitable Trust
The De Clermont Charitable
Company Ltd
The Deakin Charitable Trust
William Dean Countryside and
Educational Trust
The Debmar Benevolent Trust
The Dellal Foundation
The Delves Charitable Trust
The Demigryphon Trust
The Denman Charitable Trust
Dentons UKMEA LLP
Charitable Trust
The Earl of Derby's Charitable
Trust
Derbyshire Community
Foundation
The J N Derbyshire Trust
The Desmond Foundation
The Devon Educational Trust
The Duke of Devonshire's
Charitable Trust
The Sandy Dewhirst Charitable
Trust
The Laduma Dhamecha
Charitable Trust
The Dibden Allotments Fund
Diced Cap Charity
The Dickon Trust
The Digbeth Trust Limited
The Dinwoodie Settlement
Dischma Charitable Trust
The DLM Charitable Trust
Louise Dobson Charitable
Trust
The Derek and Eileen Dodgson
Foundation
The Dollond Charitable Trust
Domepride Ltd
The Dorcas Trust
The Dorus Trust
The Doughty Charity Trust
Douglas Arter Foundation
The R M Douglas Charitable
Trust
Downlands Educational Trust
The Drapers' Charitable Fund
The Duis Charitable Trust
The Dulverton Trust
The P B Dumbell Charitable
Trust
The Dumbreck Charity
Dunard Fund
The Dunn Family Charitable
Trust
The W E Dunn Trust
Dushinsky Trust Ltd
The Dwek Family Charitable
Trust
The Dyers' Company
Charitable Trust
The Eagle Charity Trust
The Earley Charity

Earls Colne and Halstead
Educational Charity
The Earmark Trust
Eastern Counties Educational
Trust Limited
The Sir John Eastwood
Foundation
The Ebenezer Trust
The EBM Charitable Trust
Eden Arts Trust
The Gilbert and Eileen Edgar
Foundation
Edinburgh Trust No 2 Account
Edinburgh Voluntary
Organisations' Trust Funds
(EVOT)
The W G Edwards Charitable
Foundation
The William Edwards
Educational Charity
The Elephant Trust
The George Elias Charitable
Trust
The Gerald Palmer Eling Trust
Company
The Wilfred and Elsie Elkes
Charity Fund
The Maud Elkington Charitable
Trust
The Ellerdale Trust
The Ellinson Foundation Ltd
The Ellis Campbell Foundation
The Elmgrant Trust
The Elmley Foundation
The Vernon N Ely Charitable
Trust
The Embleton Trust
Embrace the Middle East
The Emerton-Christie Charity
The Worshipful Company of
Engineers Charitable Trust
Fund
The Englefield Charitable Trust
The English Schools' Football
Association
The Enkalon Foundation
Entindale Ltd
The Epigoni Trust
The Equitable Charitable Trust
The Equity Trust Fund
The Ericson Trust
The Erskine Cunningham Hill
Trust
Essex Community Foundation
The Essex Fairway Charitable
Trust
Essex Provincial Charity Fund
The Essex Youth Trust
Euro Charity Trust
Sir John Evelyn's Charity
The Eventhall Family
Charitable Trust
The Everard Foundation
The Eveson Charitable Trust
The Beryl Evetts and Robert
Luff Animal Welfare Trust
Limited

The Exilarch's Foundation

F C Charitable Trust

The F P Limited Charitable Trust

The Faber Charitable Trust

The Fairway Trust

The Family Rich Charities Trust

The Lord Faringdon Charitable Trust

Samuel William Farmer Trust

The Farmers' Company Charitable Fund

The Thomas Farr Charity

Walter Farthing (Trust) Limited

The Fassnidge Memorial Trust

Joseph Fattorini Charitable Trust

Federation of Jewish Relief Organisations

The John Feeney Charitable Trust

The George Fentham Birmingham Charity

The A M Fenton Trust

Allan and Nesta Ferguson Charitable Settlement

The Fidelity UK Foundation

The Doris Field Charitable Trust

Fife Council/Common Good Funds and Trusts

Firtree Trust

The Fishmongers' Company's Charitable Trust

The Fitton Trust

The Earl Fitzwilliam Charitable Trust

The Ian Fleming Charitable Trust

The Joyce Fletcher Charitable Trust

The Flow Foundation

The Gerald Fogel Charitable Trust

The Follett Trust

The Football Association National Sports Centre Trust

The Football Association Youth Trust

The Forbes Charitable Foundation

The Forces Trust (Working Name)

Ford Britain Trust

The Oliver Ford Charitable Trust

The Forest Hill Charitable Trust

The Foresters' Charity Stewards UK Trust

Forever Manchester (The Community Foundation for Greater Manchester)

The Forman Hardy Charitable Trust

Gwyneth Forrester Trust

The Forte Charitable Trust

The Four Lanes Trust

The Four Winds Trust

The Isaac and Freda Frankel Memorial Charitable Trust

The Elizabeth Frankland Moore and Star Foundation

The Jill Franklin Trust

The Gordon Fraser Charitable Trust

The Hugh Fraser Foundation

The Joseph Strong Frazer Trust

The Louis and Valerie Freedman Charitable Settlement

The Thomas Freke and Lady Norton Charity Trust

The Charles S French Charitable Trust

The Anne French Memorial Trust

The Freshfield Foundation

The Freshgate Trust Foundation

The Friarsgate Trust

The Friends Hall Farm Street Trust

The Frognal Trust

The Patrick & Helena Frost Foundation

Maurice Fry Charitable Trust

The Fulmer Charitable Trust

Worshipful Company of Furniture Makers Charitable Fund

Gableholt Limited

The Galbraith Trust

The Gale Family Charity Trust

Gamlen Charitable Trust

The Gamma Trust

The Gannochy Trust

The Worshipful Company of Gardeners of London

The Samuel Gardner Memorial Trust

The Garnett Charitable Trust

Garthgwynion Charities

Garvan Limited

The Gatsby Charitable Foundation

Gatwick Airport Community Trust

The Robert Gavron Charitable Trust

Thomas Betton's Charity for Pensions and Relief-in-Need

Get Kids Going

The Gibbs Charitable Trust

Simon Gibson Charitable Trust

The G C Gibson Charitable Trust

Lady Gibson's Charitable Trust

The Harvey and Hilary Gilbert Charitable Trust

The Girdlers' Company Charitable Trust

The B and P Glasser Charitable Trust

The Glass-House Trust

Global Care

Gloucestershire Community Foundation

Worshipful Company of Glovers of London Charity Fund

The GNC Trust

The Sydney and Phyllis Goldberg Memorial Charitable Trust

The Golden Bottle Trust

The Jack Goldhill Charitable Trust

The Goldsmiths' Arts Trust Fund

The Goldsmiths' Company Charity

The Golsoncott Foundation

The Mike Gooley Trailfinders Charity

The Gosling Foundation Limited

The Gough Charitable Trust

The Gould Charitable Trust

The Grace Charitable Trust

A B Grace Trust

The Graff Foundation

E C Graham Belford Charitable Settlement

The Grahame Charitable Foundation Limited

The Granada Foundation

Grand Charitable Trust of the Order of Women Freemasons

The Grand Order of Water Rats' Charities Fund

The Grange Farm Centre Trust

Grantham Yorke Trust

The J G Graves Charitable Trust

The Gordon Gray Trust

The Gray Trust

The Great Stone Bridge Trust of Edenbridge

The Great Torrington Town Lands Charity

The Green Hall Foundation

Greenham Common Community Trust Limited

Greggs Foundation

The Gretna Charitable Trust

The Grimmitt Trust

The Grocers' Charity

The M and R Gross Charities Limited

The GRP Charitable Trust

The David and Marie Grumitt Foundation

The Bishop of Guildford's Foundation

The Guildry Incorporation of Perth

The Walter Guinness Charitable Trust

The Gunter Charitable Trust

The Gur Trust
The Gurney Charitable Trust
Dr Guthrie's Association
The H and M Charitable Trust
H C D Memorial Fund
The H P Charitable Trust
The Hackney Parochial
  Charities
The Hadfield Trust
The Hadley Trust
The Hadrian Trust
The Alfred Haines Charitable
  Trust
E F and M G Hall Charitable
  Trust
The Edith Winifred Hall
  Charitable Trust
Robert Hall Charity
The Hamamelis Trust
Hamilton Wallace Trust
Paul Hamlyn Foundation
Hampton Fuel Allotment
  Charity
The W A Handley Charitable
  Trust
Beatrice Hankey Foundation
  Limited
The Hanley Trust (1987)
The Kathleen Hannay
  Memorial Charity
The Doughty Hanson
  Charitable Foundation
Lord Hanson Foundation
The Haramead Trust
Miss K M Harbinson's
  Charitable Trust
The Harborne Parish Lands
  Charity
The Harbour Charitable Trust
The Harbour Foundation
The Harding Trust
William Harding's Charity
The Hare of Steep Charitable
  Trust
The Harebell Centenary Fund
The Kenneth Hargreaves
  Charitable Trust
The Harpur Trust
The Harris Charity
The Harrison and Potter Trust
The John Harrison Charitable
  Trust
The Spencer Hart Charitable
  Trust
The Hartley Charitable Trust
William Geoffrey Harvey's
  Discretionary Settlement
The Edward Harvist Trust
Haskel Family Foundation
The Hathaway Trust
The M A Hawe Settlement
The Hawthorne Charitable
  Trust
The Dorothy Hay-Bolton
  Charitable Trust
The Headley Trust
Headley-Pitt Charitable Trust

Heart of England Community
  Foundation
The Heathcoat Trust
Heathside Charitable Trust
The Charlotte Heber-Percy
  Charitable Trust
The Hedley Denton Charitable
  Trust
The H J Heinz Company
  Limited Charitable Trust
The Hellenic Foundation
The Michael Heller Charitable
  Foundation
The Simon Heller Charitable
  Settlement
Help the Homeless
The Hemby Trust
The Christina Mary Hendrie
  Trust for Scottish and
  Canadian Charities
Henley Educational Trust
  (formerley Henley
  Educational Charity)
Esther Hennell Charitable
  Trust
The G D Herbert Charitable
  Trust
The Anne Herd Memorial Trust
The Hesed Trust
The Hesslewood Children's
  Trust (Hull Seamen's and
  General Orphanage)
Hexham and Newcastle
  Diocesan Trust (1947)
The P and C Hickinbotham
  Charitable Trust
The Higgs Charitable Trust
Alan Edward Higgs Charity
The High Sheriff's Police Trust
  for the County of West
  Midlands (Building Blocks)
Highcroft Charitable Trust
The Charles Littlewood Hill
  Trust
The Hillingdon Partnership
  Trust
The Hilmarnan Charitable Trust
The Hiscox Foundation
The Hitchin Educational
  Foundation
The Eleemosynary Charity of
  William Hobbayne
Hobson Charity Limited
Matthew Hodder Charitable
  Trust
The Sir Julian Hodge
  Charitable Trust
The J G Hogg Charitable Trust
The Holden Charitable Trust
John Holford's Charity
The Hollick Family Charitable
  Trust
The Dorothy Holmes Charitable
  Trust
The Holywood Trust
The Homelands Charitable
  Trust

The Homestead Charitable
  Trust
Sir Harold Hood's Charitable
  Trust
Hope for Youth (NI)
The Hope Trust
HopMarket Charity
The Cuthbert Horn Trust
The Antony Hornby Charitable
  Trust
The Horne Foundation
The Horne Trust
The Worshipful Company of
  Horners' Charitable Trusts
The Hornsey Parochial
  Charities
The Hospital of God at
  Greatham
The Hospital Saturday Fund
Houblon-Norman/George Fund
The House of Industry Estate
The Reta Lila Howard
  Foundation
The Daniel Howard Trust
The Huddersfield Common
  Good Trust
The Hudson Foundation
The Geoffrey C Hughes
  Charitable Trust
The Hull and East Riding
  Charitable Trust
Hulme Trust Estates
  (Educational)
Human Relief Foundation
The Humanitarian Trust
The Michael and Shirley Hunt
  Charitable Trust
The Hunter Foundation
Miss Agnes H Hunter's Trust
Huntingdon Freemen's Trust
Hurdale Charity Limited
The Nani Huyu Charitable Trust
The P Y N and B Hyams Trust
The Hyde Charitable Trust
The Idlewild Trust
The Iliffe Family Charitable
  Trust
The Indigo Trust
The Ingram Trust
The Inlight Trust
The Inman Charity
The Inner London Magistrates
  Court Poor Box and Feeder
  Charity
The Ireland Fund of Great
  Britain
The Irish Youth Foundation
  (UK) Ltd (incorporating The
  Lawlor Foundation)
The Ironmongers' Foundation
The Charles Irving Charitable
  Trust
Irwin Trust
The ISA Charity
The Isaacs Charitable Trust
The J Isaacs Charitable Trust

The Isle of Anglesey Charitable Trust
The ITF Seafarers Trust
The J M K Charitable Trust
The J R S S T Charitable Trust
C Richard Jackson Charitable Trust
Elizabeth Jackson Charitable Trust
The Ruth and Lionel Jacobson Trust (Second Fund) No 2
Jaffe Family Relief Fund
The Susan and Stephen James Charitable Settlement
The James Trust
The Jarman Charitable Trust
The John Jarrold Trust
JCA Charitable Foundation
The Jeffrey Charitable Trust
The Nick Jenkins Foundation
The Jenour Foundation
The Jephcott Charitable Trust
Jesus Hospital Charity
Jewish Child's Day
The Jewish Youth Fund
The Harold Joels Charitable Trust
The Nicholas Joels Charitable Trust
The Norman Joels Charitable Trust
The Lillie Johnson Charitable Trust
The Johnson Foundation
The Reginald Johnson Foundation
The Johnnie Johnson Trust
The Johnson Wax Ltd Charitable Trust
The Joicey Trust
The Jones 1986 Charitable Trust
The Marjorie and Geoffrey Jones Charitable Trust
The Jordan Charitable Foundation
The J E Joseph Charitable Fund
The Lady Eileen Joseph Foundation
The Josephs Family Charitable Trust
JTH Charitable Trust
The Julian Budd Kids in Sport Trust Limited
The Jungels-Winkler Charitable Foundation
The Anton Jurgens Charitable Trust
The Bernard Kahn Charitable Trust
The Stanley Kalms Foundation
The Karenza Foundation
The Boris Karloff Charitable Foundation

The Ian Karten Charitable Trust
The Kasner Charitable Trust
The Kathleen Trust
The Michael and Ilse Katz Foundation
The Katzauer Charitable Settlement
The C S Kaufman Charitable Trust
The Geoffrey John Kaye Charitable Foundation
The Emmanuel Kaye Foundation
Kelsick's Educational Foundation
The KempWelch Charitable Trust
The Kay Kendall Leukaemia Fund
William Kendall's Charity (Wax Chandlers' Company)
The John Thomas Kennedy Charitable Foundation
The Kennedy Charitable Foundation
The Kennel Club Charitable Trust
The Nancy Kenyon Charitable Trust
Keren Association
Kermaville Ltd
The Peter Kershaw Trust
Kettering and District Charitable Medical Trust
The Ursula Keyes Trust
The Robert Kiln Charitable Trust
The King Henry VIII Endowed Trust Warwick
The King/Cullimore Charitable Trust
The Kingsbury Charity
The Mary Kinross Charitable Trust
Kirkley Poor's Lands Estate
The Richard Kirkman Charitable Trust
Kirschel Foundation
Robert Kitchin (Saddlers' Company)
Ernest Kleinwort Charitable Trust
The Marina Kleinwort Charitable Trust
The Sir James Knott Trust
The Kobler Trust
The Kohn Foundation
The Kreditor Charitable Trust
The Kreitman Foundation
The Neil Kreitman Foundation
The Heinz, Anna and Carol Kroch Foundation
The Kyte Charitable Trust
The Late Sir Pierce Lacy Charity Trust
John Laing Charitable Trust

Maurice and Hilda Laing Charitable Trust
The Christopher Laing Foundation
The Kirby Laing Foundation
The Martin Laing Foundation
The Beatrice Laing Trust
The Lambert Charitable Trust
LWS Lancashire Environmental Fund Limited
Duchy of Lancaster Benevolent Fund
The Lancaster Foundation
Langdale Trust
The Langley Charitable Trust
The Langtree Trust
The LankellyChase Foundation
The R J Larg Family Charitable Trust
Largsmount Ltd
The Lark Trust
Laslett's (Hinton) Charity
The Lauffer Family Charitable Foundation
The Kathleen Laurence Trust
The Edgar E Lawley Foundation
The Herd Lawson and Muriel Lawson Charitable Trust
The Lawson Beckman Charitable Trust
The Raymond and Blanche Lawson Charitable Trust
The Mason Le Page Charitable Trust
The Leach Fourteenth Trust
The David Lean Foundation
The Leathersellers' Company Charitable Fund
The Arnold Lee Charitable Trust
The William Leech Charity
The Lord Mayor of Leeds Appeal Fund
Leeds Building Society Charitable Foundation
The Kennedy Leigh Charitable Trust
The Leigh Trust
Mrs Vera Leigh's Charity
P Leigh-Bramwell Trust 'E'
The Lennox and Wyfold Foundation
The Erica Leonard Trust
The Leonard Trust
The Mark Leonard Trust
Lesley Lesley and Mutter Trust
The Leverhulme Trade Charities Trust
Lord Leverhulme's Charitable Trust
The Joseph Levy Charitable Foundation
The John Spedan Lewis Foundation
The Sir Edward Lewis Foundation

John Lewis Partnership
General Community Fund
Lichfield Conduit Lands
Lifeline 4 Kids
The Linbury Trust
The Lind Trust
Lindale Educational
Foundation
The Linden Charitable Trust
The Enid Linder Foundation
The Linmardon Trust
The Ruth and Stuart Lipton
Charitable Trust
The Lister Charitable Trust
Frank Litchfield Charitable
Trust
The Andrew and Mary
Elizabeth Little Charitable
Trust
The Second Joseph Aaron
Littman Foundation
The George John and Sheilah
Livanos Charitable Trust
Liverpool Charity and Voluntary
Services
Liverpool Sailors' Home Trust
The Elaine and Angus Lloyd
Charitable Trust
The Charles Lloyd Foundation
Lloyd's Charities Trust
Lloyds Bank Foundation for
England and Wales
Lloyds Bank Foundation for
Northern Ireland
Lloyds Bank Foundation for the
Channel Islands
The Locker Foundation
The Loftus Charitable Trust
The Lolev Charitable Trust
The Trust for London
London Catalyst
The London Community
Foundation
The London Housing
Foundation
The London Law Trust
The William and Katherine
Longman Trust
The Lord's Taverners
The Loseley and Guildway
Charitable Trust
The Lotus Foundation
The C L Loyd Charitable Trust
The Marie Helen Luen
Charitable Trust
Henry Lumley Charitable Trust
C F Lunoe Trust Fund
The Ruth and Jack Lunzer
Charitable Trust
Lord and Lady Lurgan Trust
The Lyndhurst Trust
The Lynn Foundation
The Lynwood Trust
John Lyon's Charity
The Lyons Charitable Trust
The Sir Jack Lyons Charitable
Trust

The Lyras Family Charitable
Trust
Sylvanus Lyson's Charity
The M and C Trust
The M K Charitable Trust
The Madeline Mabey Trust
The E M MacAndrew Trust
The R S Macdonald Charitable
Trust
Macdonald-Buchanan
Charitable Trust
The Macfarlane Walker Trust
The Mackay and Brewer
Charitable Trust
The Mackintosh Foundation
The MacRobert Trust
The Magdalen and Lasher
Charity
Magdalen Hospital Trust
The Magen Charitable Trust
Man Group plc Charitable
Trust
The Manackerman Charitable
Trust
The Manchester Guardian
Society Charitable Trust
Lord Mayor of Manchester's
Charity Appeal Trust
Mandeville Trust
The Manifold Charitable Trust
The Leslie and Lilian Manning
Trust
Marbeh Torah Trust
Marchig Animal Welfare Trust
The Stella and Alexander
Margulies Charitable Trust
Market Harborough and The
Bowdens Charity
The Ann and David Marks
Foundation
The Hilda and Samuel Marks
Foundation
J P Marland Charitable Trust
The Michael Marsh Charitable
Trust
The Marsh Christian Trust
The Charlotte Marshall
Charitable Trust
The Jim Marshall Charitable
Trust
The Nora Joan Marshall
Charitable Trust
The D G Marshall of
Cambridge Trust
Marshgate Charitable
Settlement
Sir George Martin Trust
John Martin's Charity
The Mason Porter Charitable
Trust
The Nancie Massey Charitable
Trust
The Mathew Trust
The Matt 6.3 Charitable Trust
The Violet Mauray Charitable
Trust
Evelyn May Trust

Mayfair Charities Ltd
The Mayfield Valley Arts Trust
Mazars Charitable Trust
The Robert McAlpine
Foundation
The McKenna Charitable Trust
The Helen Isabella McMorran
Charitable Foundation
The James Frederick and Ethel
Anne Measures Charity
The Medlock Charitable Trust
The Anthony and Elizabeth
Mellows Charitable
Settlement
Melow Charitable Trust
The Mercers' Charitable
Foundation
The Merchant Taylors'
Company Charities Fund
The Merchant Venturers'
Charity
The Merchants' House of
Glasgow
The Mersey Docks and
Harbour Company
Charitable Fund
Community Foundation for
Merseyside
The Zachary Merton and
George Woofindin
Convalescent Trust
The Tony Metherell Charitable
Trust
The Metropolitan Drinking
Fountain and Cattle Trough
Association
The Mickel Fund
Gerald Micklem Charitable
Trust
Midhurst Pensions Trust
The Migraine Trust
Miles Trust for the Putney and
Roehampton Community
The Hugh and Mary Miller
Bequest Trust
The Ronald Miller Foundation
The Millfield Trust
The Millhouses Charitable
Trust
The Millichope Foundation
The Mills Charity
The Millward Charitable Trust
The Clare Milne Trust
Milton Keynes Community
Foundation
The Edgar Milward Charity
The Keith and Joan
Mindelsohn Charitable
Trust
The Peter Minet Trust
The Minos Trust
The Mirfield Educational
Charity
The Laurence Misener
Charitable Trust
The Mishcon Family Charitable
Trust

The Misselbrook Trust
The Mitchell Charitable Trust
The Esmé Mitchell Trust
Keren Mitzvah Trust
The Mizpah Trust
The Mobbs Memorial Trust Ltd
The Modiano Charitable Trust
The Moette Charitable Trust
The Mole Charitable Trust
The D C Moncrieff Charitable
   Trust
Monmouthshire County Council
   Welsh Church Act Fund
The Montague Thompson
   Coon Charitable Trust
The Colin Montgomerie
   Charitable Foundation
The Monument Trust
The Morel Charitable Trust
The Morgan Charitable
   Foundation
The Mr and Mrs J T Morgan
   Foundation
Morgan Stanley International
   Foundation
The Oliver Morland Charitable
   Trust
The Bernard Morris Charitable
   Trust
The Morris Charitable Trust
The Willie and Mabel Morris
   Charitable Trust
The Peter Morrison Charitable
   Foundation
The Stanley Morrison
   Charitable Trust
Vyoel Moshe Charitable Trust
The Moss Charitable Trust
The Robert and Margaret
   Moss Charitable Trust
The Moss Family Charitable
   Trust
Mosselson Charitable Trust
The Mount Everest Foundation
The Edwina Mountbatten Trust
Mountbatten Festival of Music
The Mountbatten Memorial
   Trust
Mrs Waterhouse Charitable
   Trust
The Mugdock Children's Trust
The Mulberry Trust
The Edith Murphy Foundation
The Mushroom Fund
The Music Sales Charitable
   Trust
Muslim Hands
The Mutual Trust Group
The Kitty and Daniel Nabarro
   Charitable Trust
The Nadezhda Charitable Trust
The Naggar Charitable Trust
The Eleni Nakou Foundation
The Janet Nash Charitable
   Settlement
The National Churches Trust

The National Manuscripts
   Conservation Trust
Needham Market and Barking
   Welfare Charities
The Worshipful Company of
   Needlemakers' Charitable
   Fund
The Neighbourly Charitable
   Trust
The James Neill Trust Fund
Nemoral Ltd
The Newcomen Collett
   Foundation
Alderman Newton's
   Educational Foundation
The Chevras Ezras Nitzrochim
   Trust
The Noon Foundation
The Norda Trust
Norie Charitable Trust
The Norman Family Charitable
   Trust
The Duncan Norman Trust
   Fund
The Normanby Charitable Trust
The Northampton Municipal
   Church Charities
The Northampton Queen's
   Institute Relief in Sickness
   Fund
The Earl of Northampton's
   Charity
The Northcott Devon
   Foundation
The Northmoor Trust
The Northumberland Village
   Homes Trust
The Northwood Charitable
   Trust
The Norton Foundation
The Norwich Church of England
   Young Men's Society
The Norwich Town Close
   Estate Charity
The Noswad Charity
The Notgrove Trust
The Nottingham General
   Dispensary
The Nottingham Gordon
   Memorial Trust for Boys
   and Girls
Nottinghamshire Community
   Foundation
The Nottinghamshire Miners'
   Welfare Trust Fund
Novi Most International
The Father O'Mahoney
   Memorial Trust
The Sir Peter O'Sullevan
   Charitable Trust
The Oak Trust
The Oakdale Trust
The Oakley Charitable Trust
The Oakmoor Charitable Trust
The Odin Charitable Trust
The Ofenheim Charitable Trust

Ogilvie Charities Deed No.2
   (including the Charity of
   Mary Catherine Ford Smith)
The Ogle Christian Trust
The Oikonomia Trust
Oizer Charitable Trust
The Old Broad Street Charity
   Trust
The John Oldacre Foundation
The Oldham Foundation
Open Gate
The Raymond Oppenheimer
   Foundation
Ormonde Foundation
The Ormsby Charitable Trust
The Orrin Charitable Trust
The Ouseley Trust
The Owen Family Trust
Oxfam (GB)
The Oxfordshire Community
   Foundation
The P F Charitable Trust
Padwa Charitable Foundation
The Paget Charitable Trust
The Panacea Society
Panton Trust
The James Pantyfedwen
   Foundation
The Paragon Trust
The Park House Charitable
   Trust
The Frank Parkinson
   Agricultural Trust
The Samuel and Freda
   Parkinson Charitable Trust
The Parthenon Trust
The Constance Paterson
   Charitable Trust
The Patrick Charitable Trust
The Jack Patston Charitable
   Trust
The Payne Charitable Trust
The Harry Payne Trust
The Susanna Peake Charitable
   Trust
The Pedmore Sporting Club
   Trust Fund
The Dowager Countess
   Eleanor Peel Trust
The Pennycress Trust
The Performing Right Society
   Foundation
The Persson Charitable Trust
The Persula Foundation
The Jack Petchey Foundation
The Petplan Charitable Trust
The Philips and Rubens
   Charitable Trust
The Phillips Charitable Trust
The Phillips Family Charitable
   Trust
Philological Foundation
The David Pickford Charitable
   Foundation
The Bernard Piggott Charitable
   Trust

The Cecil Pilkington Charitable
Trust
The Pilkington Charities Fund
The Austin and Hope
Pilkington Trust
The Sir Harry Pilkington Trust
The Col W W Pilkington Will
Trusts The General Charity
Fund
The DLA Piper Charitable Trust
The Worshipful Company of
Plaisterers Charitable Trust
The Platinum Trust
The George and Esme Pollitzer
Charitable Settlement
The J S F Pollitzer Charitable
Settlement
The Ponton House Trust
Edith and Ferdinand Porjes
Charitable Trust
The John Porter Charitable
Trust
The Porter Foundation
The Portishead Nautical Trust
The Portrack Charitable Trust
The J E Posnansky Charitable
Trust
The Powell Foundation
The W L Pratt Charitable Trust
Premierquote Ltd
Premishlaner Charitable Trust
The Tom Press Charitable
Foundation
The William Price Charitable
Trust
The Lucy Price Relief-in-Need
Charity
Sir John Priestman Charity
Trust
The Primrose Trust
The Prince of Wales's
Charitable Foundation
Prison Service Charity Fund
The Privy Purse Charitable
Trust
The Proven Family Trust
The Provincial Grand Charity of
the Province of Derbyshire
The Puebla Charitable Trust
The Richard and Christine
Purchas Charitable Trust
The Puri Foundation
Mr and Mrs J A Pye's
Charitable Settlement
Queen Mary's Roehampton
Trust
The Queen's Silver Jubilee
Trust
R S Charitable Trust
The R V W Trust
The Monica Rabagliati
Charitable Trust
Rachel Charitable Trust
The Mr and Mrs Philip
Rackham Charitable Trust
Richard Radcliffe Charitable
Trust

The Radcliffe Trust
The Rainford Trust
The Peggy Ramsay Foundation
The Joseph and Lena Randall
Charitable Trust
The Rank Foundation Limited
The Fanny Rapaport Charitable
Settlement
The Ratcliff Foundation
The Ratcliff Pension Charity
The Ratcliffe Charitable Trust
The Eleanor Rathbone
Charitable Trust
The Sigrid Rausing Trust
The Ravensdale Trust
The Rawdon-Smith Trust
The Rayden Charitable Trust
The Roger Raymond Charitable
Trust
The Rayne Foundation
The Rayne Trust
The Sir James Reckitt Charity
The Red Arrows Trust
The Red Rose Charitable Trust
The C A Redfern Charitable
Foundation
The Reed Foundation
Richard Reeve's Foundation
The Max Reinhardt Charitable
Trust
Relief Fund for Romania
Limited
The Rest Harrow Trust
Reuben Foundation
The Nathaniel Reyner Trust
Fund
The Rhododendron Trust
The Rhondda Cynon Taff
Welsh Church Acts Fund
The Clive Richards Charity
The Richmond Parish Lands
Charity
Ridgesave Limited
The Ripple Effect Foundation
The Sir John Ritblat Family
Foundation
The River Trust
Thomas Roberts Trust
The Robertson Trust
Edwin George Robinson
Charitable Trust
The Rochester Bridge Trust
The Rock Foundation
The Rock Solid Trust
The Rofeh Trust
Rokach Family Charitable Trust
The Helen Roll Charitable
Trust
The Sir James Roll Charitable
Trust
The C A Rookes Charitable
Trust
Mrs L D Rope Third Charitable
Settlement
The Rosca Trust
The Cecil Rosen Foundation
The Rothermere Foundation

The Rotherwick Foundation
The Rothley Trust
The Roughley Charitable Trust
Rowanville Ltd
The Christopher Rowbotham
Charitable Trust
The Rowing Foundation
The Rowlands Trust
Royal Artillery Charitable Fund
Royal British Legion
Royal Docks Trust (London)
Royal Masonic Trust for Girls
and Boys
The Alfred and Frances
Rubens Charitable Trust
The Rubin Foundation
William Arthur Rudd Memorial
Trust
The Russell Trust
The J S and E C Rymer
Charitable Trust
S O Charitable Trust
The Jeremy and John Sacher
Charitable Trust
The Michael Harry Sacher
Trust
The Sackler Trust
The Ruzin Sadagora Trust
The Saddlers' Company
Charitable Fund
The Saga Charitable Trust
The Jean Sainsbury Animal
Welfare Trust
The Alan and Babette
Sainsbury Charitable Fund
The Sainsbury Family
Charitable Trusts
The Saintbury Trust
The Saints and Sinners Trust
The Salt Foundation
The Salt Trust
Basil Samuel Charitable Trust
The M J Samuel Charitable
Trust
The Peter Samuel Charitable
Trust
The Samworth Foundation
The Sandra Charitable Trust
Santander UK Foundation
Limited
The Scarfe Charitable Trust
The Schapira Charitable Trust
The Schmidt-Bodner Charitable
Trust
The R H Scholes Charitable
Trust
The Schreib Trust
The Schreiber Charitable Trust
The Schuster Charitable Trust
Foundation Scotland
The Francis C Scott Charitable
Trust
The Frieda Scott Charitable
Trust
Scottish Coal Industry Special
Welfare Fund
The Scouloudi Foundation

Seafarers UK (King George's
Fund for Sailors)
Seamen's Hospital Society
The Searchlight Electric
Charitable Trust
The Samuel Sebba Charitable
Trust
The Seedfield Trust
Leslie Sell Charitable Trust
The Ayrton Senna Foundation
The Seven Fifty Trust
The Cyril Shack Trust
The Shanti Charitable Trust
ShareGift (The Orr Mackintosh
Foundation)
The Linley Shaw Foundation
The Shears Foundation
The Sheepdrove Trust
The Sheffield and District
Hospital Services
Charitable Fund
The Patricia and Donald
Shepherd Charitable Trust
The Sylvia and Colin Shepherd
Charitable Trust
The Archie Sherman Cardiff
Foundation
The Archie Sherman Charitable
Trust
The R C Sherriff Trust
The Shetland Charitable Trust
SHINE (Support and Help in
Education)
The Barnett and Sylvia Shine
No 2 Charitable Trust
The Bassil Shippam and
Alsford Trust
The Shipwrights' Company
Charitable Fund
The Shirley Foundation
Shlomo Memorial Fund Limited
The J A Shone Memorial Trust
Community Foundation for
Shropshire and Telford
The Barbara A Shuttleworth
Memorial Trust
David and Jennifer Sieff
Charitable Trust
The Julius Silman Charitable
Trust
The Leslie Silver Charitable
Trust
The Simpson Education and
Conservation Trust
The Simpson Foundation
The Huntly and Margery
Sinclair Charitable Trust
Sino-British Fellowship Trust
The Skelton Bounty
The Charles Skey Charitable
Trust
The John Slater Foundation
The SMB Charitable Trust
The Mrs Smith and Mount
Trust
The N Smith Charitable
Settlement

The E H Smith Charitable Trust
The Smith Charitable Trust
The Henry Smith Charity
The Leslie Smith Foundation
The Martin Smith Foundation
The Stanley Smith UK
Horticultural Trust
The Snowball Trust
The Sobell Foundation
The Solo Charitable
Settlement
Dr Richard Solomon's
Charitable Trust
The E C Sosnow Charitable
Trust
The Souter Charitable Trust
The South Square Trust
The Stephen R and Philippa H
Southall Charitable Trust
The W F Southall Trust
The Southover Manor General
Education Trust
The Southwold Trust
The Sovereign Health Care
Charitable Trust
Sparquote Limited
The Spear Charitable Trust
The Worshipful Company of
Spectacle Makers' Charity
The Jessie Spencer Trust
The Ralph and Irma Sperring
Charity
The Spielman Charitable Trust
Springfields Employees'
Medical Research and
Charity Trust Fund
Springrule Limited
The Spurrell Charitable Trust
The Geoff and Fiona Squire
Foundation
St James' Trust Settlement
St James's Place Foundation
Sir Walter St John's
Educational Charity
St Michael's and All Saints'
Charities Relief Branch (The
Church Houses Relief in
Need Charity)
The Late St Patrick White
Charitable Trust
The Stanley Foundation Ltd
The Stanton Ballard Charitable
Trust
The Staples Trust
The Star Charitable Trust
The Steel Charitable Trust
The Steinberg Family
Charitable Trust
The Hugh Stenhouse
Foundation
The Stephen Barry Charitable
Trust
The Sigmund Sternberg
Charitable Foundation
Stervon Ltd
The Stevenage Community
Trust

The June Stevens Foundation
The Steventon Allotments and
Relief-in-Need Charity
The Stewards' Company
Limited (incorporating the J
W Laing Trust and the J W
Laing Biblical Scholarship
Trust)
The Leonard Laity Stoate
Charitable Trust
The Stobart Newlands
Charitable Trust
The Edward Stocks-Massey
Bequest Fund
The Stokenchurch Educational
Charity
The Stoller Charitable Trust
The M J C Stone Charitable
Trust
The Samuel Storey Family
Charitable Trust
Peter Stormonth Darling
Charitable Trust
The Strangward Trust
The Strasser Foundation
Stratford upon Avon Town
Trust
The W O Street Charitable
Foundation
The Sudborough Foundation
The Suffolk Historic Churches
Trust
The Summerfield Charitable
Trust
The Bernard Sunley Charitable
Foundation
The Surrey Historic Buildings
Trust Ltd
The Sussex Historic Churches
Trust
The Sutasoma Trust
Sutton Coldfield Charitable
Trust
Swansea and Brecon Diocesan
Board of Finance Limited
Swimathon Foundation
The John Swire (1989)
Charitable Trust
The Swire Charitable Trust
The Adrian Swire Charitable
Trust
The Hugh and Ruby Sykes
Charitable Trust
The Charles and Elsie Sykes
Trust
The Sylvanus Charitable Trust
The Stella Symons Charitable
Trust
The Tabeel Trust
The Tajtelbaum Charitable
Trust
The Talbot Trusts
The Talbot Village Trust
Tallow Chandlers Benevolent
Fund
The Tangent Charitable Trust

The Lady Tangye Charitable Trust

The David Tannen Charitable Trust

The Tanner Trust

The Lili Tapper Charitable Foundation

The Mrs A Lacy Tate Trust

The Tay Charitable Trust

The Connie and Albert Taylor Charitable Trust

The Cyril Taylor Charitable Trust

A P Taylor Trust

Tearfund

The Tedworth Charitable Trust

Tees Valley Community Foundation

The Templeton Goodwill Trust

Tesco Charity Trust

The C Paul Thackray General Charitable Trust

The John P. Gommes Foundation

The Thistle Trust

The Loke Wan Tho Memorial Foundation

The Thomas Lilley Memorial Trust

The Arthur and Margaret Thompson Charitable Trust

The Thompson Family Charitable Trust

The Len Thomson Charitable Trust

The Sir Jules Thorn Charitable Trust

The Thornton Foundation

The Thornton Trust

The Thousandth Man – Richard Burns Charitable Trust

The Three Guineas Trust

The Three Oaks Trust

The Thriplow Charitable Trust

The Tinsley Foundation

The Tobacco Pipe Makers and Tobacco Trade Benevolent Fund

The Tolkien Trust

Tollemache (Buckminster) Charitable Trust

Tomchei Torah Charitable Trust

The Tompkins Foundation

The Tory Family Foundation

Tottenham Grammar School Foundation

The Tower Hill Trust

The Towry Law Charitable Trust (also known as the Castle Educational Trust)

The Mayor of Trafford's Charity Fund

The Constance Travis Charitable Trust

The Treeside Trust

The Triangle Trust (1949) Fund

The True Colours Trust

Truedene Co. Ltd

The Truemark Trust

Truemart Limited

Trumros Limited

The Trusthouse Charitable Foundation

Tudor Rose Ltd

The Tudor Trust

The Tufton Charitable Trust

The R D Turner Charitable Trust

The Douglas Turner Trust

The Florence Turner Trust

The G J W Turner Trust

Miss S M Tutton Charitable Trust

The TUUT Charitable Trust

Community Foundation Serving Tyne and Wear and Northumberland

Trustees of Tzedakah

Ulster Garden Villages Ltd

Ultach Trust

The Ulverscroft Foundation

Ulverston Town Lands Charity

The Union of Orthodox Hebrew Congregation

The United Society for the Propagation of the Gospel

The David Uri Memorial Trust

Uxbridge United Welfare Trust

Vale of Glamorgan – Welsh Church Fund

The Valentine Charitable Trust

The Van Neste Foundation

Mrs Maud Van Norden's Charitable Foundation

The Vandervell Foundation

The Vardy Foundation

The Variety Club Children's Charity

Veneziana Fund

The Verdon-Smith Family Charitable Settlement

Victoria Homes Trust

The Nigel Vinson Charitable Trust

The William and Ellen Vinten Trust

The Vintners' Company Charitable Foundation

Vintners' Gifts Charity

Vision Charity

Vivdale Ltd

The Viznitz Foundation

Wade's Charity

The Scurrah Wainwright Charity

The Community Foundation in Wales

Wales Council for Voluntary Action

Robert and Felicity Waley-Cohen Charitable Trust

The F J Wallis Charitable Settlement

War on Want

The Ward Blenkinsop Trust

The George Ward Charitable Trust

The Barbara Ward Children's Foundation

G R Waters Charitable Trust 2000

The Howard Watson Symington Memorial Charity

John Watson's Trust

Waynflete Charitable Trust

Weatherley Charitable Trust

The Weavers' Company Benevolent Fund

The William Webster Charitable Trust

The Weinberg Foundation

The Weinstein Foundation

The James Weir Foundation

The Barbara Welby Trust

Welsh Church Fund Dyfed area (Carmarthenshire, Ceredigion and Pembrokeshire)

The Welton Foundation

The Wessex Youth Trust

The West Derby Wastelands Charity

West London Synagogue Charitable Fund

West Yorkshire Police Community Trust

The Westminster Foundation

The Garfield Weston Foundation

The Whitaker Charitable Trust

The Colonel W H Whitbread Charitable Trust

The Simon Whitbread Charitable Trust

The Whitecourt Charitable Trust

The Norman Whiteley Trust

The Whitley Animal Protection Trust

The Whittlesey Charity

The Lionel Wigram Memorial Trust

The Felicity Wilde Charitable Trust

The William Barrow's Charity

The Kay Williams Charitable Foundation

The Williams Family Charitable Trust

The HDH Wills 1965 Charitable Trust

The Dame Violet Wills Will Trust

The Wilmcote Charitrust

David Wilson Foundation

The Wilson Foundation

J and J R Wilson Trust

The Community Foundation for Wiltshire and Swindon

The Benjamin Winegarten
   Charitable Trust
The Francis Winham
   Foundation
Wirral Mayor's Charity
The James Wise Charitable
   Trust
The Michael and Anna Wix
   Charitable Trust
The Wixamtree Trust
The Woburn 1986 Charitable
   Trust
The Maurice Wohl Charitable
   Foundation
The Charles Wolfson
   Charitable Trust
The Wolfson Family Charitable
   Trust
The Wolfson Foundation
The James Wood Bequest
   Fund
Woodlands Green Ltd
Woodlands Trust
The Woodward Charitable
   Trust
Worcester Municipal Charities
The Wragge and Co. Charitable
   Trust
The Diana Edgson Wright
   Charitable Trust
The Matthews Wrightson
   Charity Trust
Miss E B Wrightson's
   Charitable Settlement
Wychdale Ltd
Wychville Ltd
The Wyndham Charitable Trust
The Wyseliot Charitable Trust
The Xerox (UK) Trust
The Yardley Great Trust
The Dennis Alan Yardy
   Charitable Trust
The W Wing Yip and Brothers
   Foundation
Yorkshire Agricultural Society
Yorkshire Building Society
   Charitable Foundation
The South Yorkshire
   Community Foundation
The Yorkshire Dales
   Millennium Trust
The John Young Charitable
   Settlement
The William Allen Young
   Charitable Trust
The John K Young Endowment
   Fund
Zephyr Charitable Trust
The Marjorie and Arnold Ziff
   Charitable Foundation
Stephen Zimmerman
   Charitable Trust
The Zochonis Charitable Trust
Zurich Community Trust (UK)
   Limited

Core support

■ Core costs

The 29th May 1961 Charitable
   Trust
The A B Charitable Trust
ABF The Soldiers' Charity
The Sylvia Adams Charitable
   Trust
The Adint Charitable Trust
The AIM Foundation
The Ajahma Charitable Trust
The Alchemy Foundation
The Aldgate Freedom
   Foundation
All Saints Educational Trust
The H B Allen Charitable Trust
The Almond Trust
The Ammco Trust
The Anchor Foundation
The Andrew Anderson Trust
Anglo American Group
   Foundation
The Animal Defence Trust
Archbishop of Wales' Fund for
   Children
The Ardwick Trust
The Armourers' and Brasiers'
   Gauntlet Trust
The Ashley Family Foundation
The Ian Askew Charitable Trust
The Astor Foundation
The Lord Austin Trust
The Aylesford Family
   Charitable Trust
Bag4Sport Foundation
The Baily Thomas Charitable
   Fund
The Baker Charitable Trust
The Balmore Trust
The Barham Charitable Trust
Lord Barnby's Foundation
Barnes Workhouse Fund
The Paul Bassham Charitable
   Trust
BBC Children in Need
The Bedfordshire and Luton
   Community Foundation
The Bellahouston Bequest
   Fund
The Bellinger Donnay Trust
The Gerald Bentall Charitable
   Trust
The Berkshire Community
   Foundation
The Bingham Trust
Miss Jeanne Bisgood's
   Charitable Trust
The Sydney Black Charitable
   Trust
Sir Alec Black's Charity
The Marjory Boddy Charitable
   Trust
The Body Shop Foundation
The Harry Bottom Charitable
   Trust

The Bower Trust
John and Susan Bowers Fund
The Breadsticks Foundation
The British Dietetic
   Association General and
   Education Trust Fund
The J and M Britton Charitable
   Trust
The Bromley Trust
The Charles Brotherton Trust
The Swinfen Broun Charitable
   Trust
Brown-Mellows Trust
Buckinghamshire Community
   Foundation
The E F Bulmer Benevolent
   Fund
The Clara E Burgess Charity
Consolidated Charity of Burton
   upon Trent
Peter Cadbury Charitable Trust
The William A Cadbury
   Charitable Trust
The Cadbury Foundation
The Barrow Cadbury Trust and
   the Barrow Cadbury Fund
CAF (Charities Aid Foundation)
The Calpe Trust
The Cambridgeshire
   Community Foundation
The Camelia Trust
The Campden Charities
   Trustee
Carter's Educational
   Foundation
The Casey Trust
Cash for Kids Radio Clyde
The Cattanach Charitable Trust
The Chapman Charitable Trust
The Childwick Trust
Chrysalis Trust
The Church and Community
   Fund
The City Bridge Trust
Stephen Clark 1957
   Charitable Trust
The Robert Clutterbuck
   Charitable Trust
The Cobtree Charity Trust Ltd
The Cole Charitable Trust
The John and Freda Coleman
   Charitable Trust
The Sir Jeremiah Colman Gift
   Trust
The Colt Foundation
Community First (Landfill
   Communities Fund)
The Congleton Inclosure Trust
Gordon Cook Foundation
The Ernest Cook Trust
Harold and Daphne Cooper
   Charitable Trust
The Alice Ellen Cooper Dean
   Charitable Foundation
The J Reginald Corah
   Foundation Fund

Michael Cornish Charitable
   Trust
County Durham Community
   Foundation
The Augustine Courtauld Trust
Cripplegate Foundation
The Peter Cruddas Foundation
Cruden Foundation Ltd
Cullum Family Trust
The Cumber Family Charitable
   Trust
Cumberland Building Society
   Charitable Foundation
The Cwmbran Trust
The D'Oyly Carte Charitable
   Trust
Roald Dahl's Marvellous
   Children's Charity
The Gwendoline and Margaret
   Davies Charity
The Hamilton Davies Trust
William Dean Countryside and
   Educational Trust
Devon Community Foundation
The Dibden Allotments Fund
Disability Aid Fund (The Roger
   and Jean Jefcoate Trust)
The Djanogly Foundation
The Derek and Eileen Dodgson
   Foundation
Dorset Community Foundation
The Double 'O' Charity Ltd
The Drapers' Charitable Fund
The Dulverton Trust
The Dunhill Medical Trust
The W E Dunn Trust
The Charles Dunstone
   Charitable Trust
The Ebenezer Trust
Edge Fund
The Ellerdale Trust
The John Ellerman Foundation
James Ellis Charitable Trust
The Elmley Foundation
The Englefield Charitable Trust
Epilepsy Research UK
The Essendon Charitable Trust
The Essex and Southend
   Sports Trust
The Essex Fairway Charitable
   Trust
The Essex Youth Trust
Joseph Ettedgui Charitable
   Foundation
The Eveson Charitable Trust
The Expat Foundation
Esmée Fairbairn Foundation
Famos Foundation Trust
Samuel William Farmer Trust
The February Foundation
The John Feeney Charitable
   Trust
The George Fentham
   Birmingham Charity
Fife Council/Common Good
   Funds and Trusts
The Fifty Fund

Gerald Finzi Charitable Trust
The Fishmongers' Company's
   Charitable Trust
The Joyce Fletcher Charitable
   Trust
Ford Britain Trust
Gwyneth Forrester Trust
The Donald Forrester Trust
The Fort Foundation
The Forte Charitable Trust
The Foyle Foundation
Sydney E Franklin Deceased's
   New Second Charity
The Freemasons' Grand
   Charity
The Thomas Freke and Lady
   Norton Charity Trust
T F C Frost Charitable Trust
The Patrick & Helena Frost
   Foundation
Maurice Fry Charitable Trust
The Fuserna Foundation
General Charitable Trust
Gamlen Charitable Trust
The Ganzoni Charitable Trust
Garrick Charitable Trust
The Gibbs Charitable Trust
Simon Gibson Charitable Trust
The G C Gibson Charitable
   Trust
The Girdlers' Company
   Charitable Trust
The Glass-House Trust
Gloucestershire Community
   Foundation
The Goldsmiths' Company
   Charity
The Golsoncott Foundation
Nicholas and Judith
   Goodison's Charitable
   Settlement
The Gosling Foundation
   Limited
The Great Britain Sasakawa
   Foundation
Greggs Foundation
H C D Memorial Fund
The Hadfield Trust
The Hadley Trust
The Hadrian Trust
The Hamamelis Trust
Paul Hamlyn Foundation
Hampshire and Isle of Wight
   Community Foundation
The Haramead Trust
The Harborne Parish Lands
   Charity
William Harding's Charity
The Harebell Centenary Fund
The Kenneth Hargreaves
   Charitable Trust
The Harpur Trust
The Harris Charitable Trust
The Peter Harrison Foundation
The Headley Trust
Heart of England Community
   Foundation

Percy Hedley 1990 Charitable
   Trust
The Hedley Denton Charitable
   Trust
The Hertfordshire Community
   Foundation
Alan Edward Higgs Charity
The Charles Littlewood Hill
   Trust
Hinchley Charitable Trust
Lady Hind Trust
The Hintze Family Charitable
   Foundation
Matthew Hodder Charitable
   Trust
The Holmes Family Trust
   (Sheffield)
The Holst Foundation
The Edward Holt Trust
The Homelands Charitable
   Trust
The Homestead Charitable
   Trust
Mary Homfray Charitable Trust
The Worshipful Company of
   Horners' Charitable Trusts
The Hospital Saturday Fund
The House of Industry Estate
The Huggard Charitable Trust
The Hull and East Riding
   Charitable Trust
The Hunter Foundation
The Inland Waterways
   Association
John James Bristol Foundation
The Barbara Joyce Jarrald
   Charitable Trust
The John Jarrold Trust
The Jephcott Charitable Trust
The Jerusalem Trust
Jesus Hospital Charity
The Dyfrig and Heather John
   Charitable Trust
The Jordan Charitable
   Foundation
The Joron Charitable Trust
The Boris Karloff Charitable
   Foundation
The Kelly Family Charitable
   Trust
The Kay Kendall Leukaemia
   Fund
The Kennel Club Charitable
   Trust
Kent Community Foundation
The Peter Kershaw Trust
Keswick Hall Trust
The Robert Kiln Charitable
   Trust
Kingdom Way Trust
The Mary Kinross Charitable
   Trust
The Sir James Knott Trust
The Heinz, Anna and Carol
   Kroch Foundation
The K P Ladd Charitable Trust
The Allen Lane Foundation

The Lark Trust
Mrs F B Laurence Charitable
  Trust
The Edgar E Lawley Foundation
The Leathersellers' Company
  Charitable Fund
The William Leech Charity
The Erica Leonard Trust
The Leonard Trust
The Joseph Levy Charitable
  Foundation
The Sir Edward Lewis
  Foundation
Lincolnshire Community
  Foundation
The Second Joseph Aaron
  Littman Foundation
Lloyds Bank Foundation for
  England and Wales
Lloyds Bank Foundation for
  Northern Ireland
Lloyds TSB Foundation for
  Scotland
John Lyon's Charity
The R S Macdonald Charitable
  Trust
The MacRobert Trust
W M Mann Foundation
R W Mann Trust
The Leslie and Lilian Manning
  Trust
The Marcela Trust
The Ann and David Marks
  Foundation
The Marr-Munning Trust
The Marsh Christian Trust
The Jim Marshall Charitable
  Trust
John Martin's Charity
The John Mason Family Trust
The Nancie Massey Charitable
  Trust
Matliwala Family Charitable
  Trust
The Matt 6.3 Charitable Trust
Mayfair Charities Ltd
The Mears Foundation
Meningitis Trust
The Menzies Charity
  Foundation
The Mercers' Charitable
  Foundation
Mercury Phoenix Trust
The Tony Metherell Charitable
  Trust
The Mickel Fund
Gerald Micklem Charitable
  Trust
Middlesex Sports Foundation
The Clare Milne Trust
The Mitchell Charitable Trust
The Modiano Charitable Trust
George A Moore Foundation
John Moores Foundation
The Morgan Charitable
  Foundation
The Morgan Foundation

G M Morrison Charitable Trust
The Stanley Morrison
  Charitable Trust
Mothercare Group Foundation
The Mugdock Children's Trust
Frederick Mulder Charitable
  Trust
Murphy-Neumann Charity
  Company Limited
The Kitty and Daniel Nabarro
  Charitable Trust
National Committee of the
  Women's World Day of
  Prayer for England and
  Wales and Northern Ireland
The National Express
  Foundation
The National Hockey
  Foundation
The Nationwide Foundation
Nazareth Trust Fund
Needham Market and Barking
  Welfare Charities
The Neighbourly Charitable
  Trust
Network for Social Change
The Frances and Augustus
  Newman Foundation
The Night Garden Charity
Norfolk Community Foundation
Normalyn Charitable Trust
The Northern Rock Foundation
The Northmoor Trust
The Notgrove Trust
The Oakdale Trust
The Oakley Charitable Trust
The Odin Charitable Trust
The Old Broad Street Charity
  Trust
Open Gate
The Owen Family Trust
The P F Charitable Trust
The Paget Charitable Trust
The Paladin Vince-Odozi
  Charitable Trust
The Frank Parkinson
  Agricultural Trust
The Harry Payne Trust
The Peacock Charitable Trust
The Dowager Countess
  Eleanor Peel Trust
The Pennycress Trust
The Pilgrim Trust
The Pilkington Charities Fund
The Col W W Pilkington Will
  Trusts The General Charity
  Fund
Polden-Puckham Charitable
  Foundation
The Mary Potter Convent
  Hospital Trust
The Powell Foundation
The Tom Press Charitable
  Foundation
Princess Anne's Charities
Mr and Mrs J A Pye's
  Charitable Settlement

Queen Mary's Roehampton
  Trust
The Racing Foundation
The Ravensdale Trust
The Rayne Trust
The John Rayner Charitable
  Trust
The Sir James Reckitt Charity
Relief Fund for Romania
  Limited
REMEDI
The Rhododendron Trust
The Richmond Parish Lands
  Charity
The Ripple Effect Foundation
The Helen Roll Charitable
  Trust
The Rosca Trust
Mrs Gladys Row Fogo
  Charitable Trust
The Christopher Rowbotham
  Charitable Trust
The Joseph Rowntree
  Charitable Trust
Royal British Legion
The Alfred and Frances
  Rubens Charitable Trust
The Saddlers' Company
  Charitable Fund
The Alan and Babette
  Sainsbury Charitable Fund
The Saintbury Trust
The Salt Foundation
Santander UK Foundation
  Limited
The R H Scholes Charitable
  Trust
The Frieda Scott Charitable
  Trust
The Sir James and Lady Scott
  Trust
Seafarers UK (King George's
  Fund for Sailors)
The Sheldon Trust
SHINE (Support and Help in
  Education)
The Shirley Foundation
The Simmons & Simmons
  Charitable Foundation
The Simpson Education and
  Conservation Trust
SITA Cornwall Trust Limited
The Charles Skey Charitable
  Trust
Rita and David Slowe
  Charitable Trust
The Mrs Smith and Mount
  Trust
The Sobell Foundation
Social Business Trust (Scale-
  Up)
The Souter Charitable Trust
R H Southern Trust
The Sovereign Health Care
  Charitable Trust
The Jessie Spencer Trust
Sported Foundation

St Christopher's Educational
    Trust (incorporating the
    Hughes and Stevens
    Bequest)
St Hilda's Trust
Sir Walter St John's
    Educational Charity
The St Laurence Relief In
    Need Trust
The Staples Trust
The Peter Stebbings Memorial
    Charity
The Steel Charitable Trust
The Samuel Storey Family
    Charitable Trust
Peter Storrs Trust
Stratford upon Avon Town
    Trust
Sutton Coldfield Charitable
    Trust
Swimathon Foundation
The Stella Symons Charitable
    Trust
The Talbot Trusts
Tallow Chandlers Benevolent
    Fund
The Sue Thomson Foundation
The Sir Jules Thorn Charitable
    Trust
Mrs R P Tindall's Charitable
    Trust
The Tisbury Telegraph Trust
The Tolkien Trust
The Tompkins Foundation
The Towry Law Charitable Trust
    (also known as the Castle
    Educational Trust)
The Constance Travis
    Charitable Trust
The Treeside Trust
The Triangle Trust (1949) Fund
The Trusthouse Charitable
    Foundation
The James Tudor Foundation
The Tudor Trust
Tuixen Foundation
The R D Turner Charitable
    Trust
The Douglas Turner Trust
The Valentine Charitable Trust
The Valiant Charitable Trust
The Vandervell Foundation
Volant Charitable Trust
Voluntary Action Fund (VAF)
The Scurrah Wainwright Charity
Wallington Missionary Mart
    and Auctions
Sir Siegmund Warburg's
    Voluntary Settlement
The Waterloo Foundation
The Wates Foundation
Webb Memorial Trust
The Weinstock Fund
The Barbara Welby Trust
The Westminster Foundation
The Whitaker Charitable Trust

The Simon Whitbread
    Charitable Trust
White Stuff Foundation
The Norman Whiteley Trust
The Whittlesey Charity
The William Barrow's Charity
The Dame Violet Wills Will
    Trust
The Community Foundation for
    Wiltshire and Swindon
The Wixamtree Trust
The Wolfson Family Charitable
    Trust
The Wood Family Trust
Wooden Spoon Society
Woodlands Trust
Woodroffe Benton Foundation
The Wright Vigar Charitable
    Trust
The Joan Wyatt Charitable
    Trust
The Wyndham Charitable Trust
The Yapp Charitable Trust
Youth Music (previously known
    as National Foundation for
    Youth Music)
Youth United Foundation
Stephen Zimmerman
    Charitable Trust
Zurich Community Trust (UK)
    Limited

....

■ Development
funding

The 101 Foundation
The 1970 Trust
The 1989 Willan Charitable
    Trust
The 29th May 1961 Charitable
    Trust
The A B Charitable Trust
A W Charitable Trust
The Aberbrothock Skea Trust
ABF The Soldiers' Charity
Brian Abrams Charitable Trust
Eric Abrams Charitable Trust
The Acacia Charitable Trust
Access Sport
Achisomoch Aid Company
    Limited
The ACT Foundation
Action Medical Research
The Company of Actuaries'
    Charitable Trust Fund
The Ad Meliora Charitable
    Trust
The Sylvia Adams Charitable
    Trust
The Adamson Trust
The Victor Adda Foundation
Adenfirst Ltd
The Adint Charitable Trust
The Adnams Charity
AF Trust Company
Age Scotland

Age UK
The Agger Foundation
Aid to the Church in Need (UK)
Aim to Zero Foundation
The Green and Lilian F M
    Ainsworth and Family
    Benevolent Fund
The Sylvia Aitken Charitable
    Trust
The Ajahma Charitable Trust
The Al Fayed Charitable
    Foundation
The Alabaster Trust
The Alborada Trust
D G Albright Charitable Trust
The Alchemy Foundation
Aldgate and All Hallows'
    Foundation
The Aldgate Freedom
    Foundation
The Alexis Trust
All Saints Educational Trust
The Derrill Allatt Foundation
Allchurches Trust Ltd
The H B Allen Charitable Trust
The Allen Lane Trust
The Allen Trust
The Alliance Family Foundation
Angus Allnatt Charitable
    Foundation
The Pat Allsop Charitable Trust
The Almond Trust
Almondsbury Charity
The Altajir Trust
Altamont Ltd
Alvor Charitable Trust
The AM Charitable Trust
The Ammco Trust
Viscount Amory's Charitable
    Trust
The Bryan and June Amos
    Foundation
The Ampelos Trust
The AMW Charitable Trust
The Anchor Foundation
The Andrew Anderson Trust
Andor Charitable Trust
Andrews Charitable Trust
Anglo American Group
    Foundation
Anguish's Educational
    Foundation
The Animal Defence Trust
Philip Anker Trust
The Eric Anker-Petersen
    Charity
The Annandale Charitable
    Trust
Anpride Ltd
The Anson Charitable Trust
The Apax Foundation
Ambrose and Ann Appelbe
    Trust
The Appletree Trust
The Arbib Foundation
Archbishop of Wales' Fund for
    Children

The John M Archer Charitable
Trust
The Archer Trust
The Architectural Heritage
Fund
The Ardeola Charitable Trust
The Argentarius Foundation
The Argus Appeal
Armenian General Benevolent
Union London Trust
The Armenian Relief Society of
Great Britain Trust
The Armourers' and Brasiers'
Gauntlet Trust
The Arsenal Foundation
The Artemis Charitable Trust
The Arts and Entertainment
Charitable Trust
Arts Council England
The Arts Council of Northern
Ireland
Arts Council of Wales (also
known as Cyngor
Celfyddydau Cymru)
The Ove Arup Foundation
The A S Charitable Trust
Ashburnham Thanksgiving
Trust
A J H Ashby Will Trust
The Ashden Trust
The Ashendene Trust
The Ashley Family Foundation
The Ian Askew Charitable Trust
The Associated Country
Women of the World
The Association of Colleges
Charitable Trust
Astellas European Foundation
Asthma UK
AstonMansfield Charitable
Trust
The Astor Foundation
The Astor of Hever Trust
The Aurelius Charitable Trust
The Avenue Charitable Trust
The Avon and Somerset Police
Community Trust
The BAA Communities Trust
The Bacit Foundation
Harry Bacon Foundation
The BACTA Charitable Trust
The Scott Bader
Commonwealth Ltd
The Bagri Foundation
Veta Bailey Charitable Trust
The Austin Bailey Foundation
The Baily Thomas Charitable
Fund
The Baird Trust
The Baker Charitable Trust
The Roy and Pixie Baker
Charitable Trust
The Balcombe Charitable Trust
The Albert Casanova Ballard
Deceased Trust
The Ballinger Charitable Trust
Balmain Charitable Trust

The Balmore Trust
The Balney Charitable Trust
The Baltic Charitable Fund
The Bamford Charitable
Foundation
The Banbury Charities
William P Bancroft (No 2)
Charitable Trust and
Jenepher Gillett Trust
The Band Trust
The Bank of Scotland
Foundation
The Barbers' Company General
Charities
The Barbour Foundation
The Barcapel Foundation
Barchester Healthcare
Foundation
The Barclay Foundation
The Barham Charitable Trust
The Baring Foundation
Peter Barker-Mill Memorial
Charity
The Barleycorn Trust
Lord Barnby's Foundation
Barnes Workhouse Fund
The Barnsbury Charitable Trust
The Barnwood House Trust
The Misses Barrie Charitable
Trust
Barrington Family Charitable
Trust
Bartholomew Charitable Trust
The Bartlett Taylor Charitable
Trust
Baruch Family Charitable Trust
The Paul Bassham Charitable
Trust
The Batchworth Trust
The Bates Charitable Trust
Bay Charitable Trust
The Bay Tree Charitable Trust
The Louis Baylis (Maidenhead
Advertiser) Charitable Trust
BBC Children in Need
BC Partners Foundation
B-CH 1971 Charitable Trust
BCH Trust
The Beacon Trust
Bear Mordechai Ltd
The Bearder Charity
The James Beattie Charitable
Trust
The Jack and Ada Beattie
Foundation
Beauland Ltd
The Beaverbrook Foundation
The Beccles Town Lands
Charity
The Becker Family Charitable
Trust
The Becketts and Sargeants
Educational Foundation
The John Beckwith Charitable
Trust
The Peter Beckwith Charitable
Trust

The Bedfordshire and Luton
Community Foundation
The David and Ruth Behrend
Fund
The Beit Trust
The Bellahouston Bequest
Fund
Bellasis Trust
The Bellhouse Foundation
The Bellinger Donnay Trust
The Benfield Motors Charitable
Trust
The Benham Charitable
Settlement
Maurice and Jacqueline
Bennett Charitable Trust
Michael and Lesley Bennett
Charitable Trust
Bennett Lowell Limited
The Ruth Berkowitz Charitable
Trust
The Berkshire Community
Foundation
The Bertarelli UK Foundation
The Bestway Foundation
Bet365 Foundation
BHST
The Mason Bibby 1981 Trust
The Bideford Bridge Trust
The Big Lottery Fund
The Billmeir Charitable Trust
The Bingham Trust
The Bintaub Charitable Trust
Birmingham & Black Country
Community Foundation
The Birmingham District
Nursing Charitable Trust
The Birmingham Hospital
Saturday Fund Medical
Charity and Welfare Trust
Birmingham International
Airport Community Trust
The Lord Mayor of
Birmingham's Charity
Birthday House Trust
The Michael Bishop
Foundation
The Bishop's Development
Fund
The Bertie Black Foundation
Blackheart Foundation (UK)
Limited
Isabel Blackman Foundation
The BlackRock (UK) Charitable
Trust
The Blagrave Trust
The Blair Foundation
Blakemore Foundation
The Blanchminster Trust
The Blandford Lake Trust
The Sir Victor Blank Charitable
Settlement
Blatchington Court Trust
The Neville and Elaine Blond
Charitable Trust
The Bluston Charitable
Settlement

The Nicholas Boas Charitable
Trust
The Marjory Boddy Charitable
Trust
The Body Shop Foundation
The Boltons Trust
The Bonamy Charitable Trust
The John and Celia Bonham
Christie Charitable Trust
The Charlotte Bonham-Carter
Charitable Trust
Bonhomie United Charity
Society
The Linda and Gordon
Bonnyman Charitable Trust
The Booth Charities
The Boots Charitable Trust
Salo Bordon Charitable Trust
The Bordon Liphook
Haslemere Charity
The Oliver Borthwick Memorial
Trust
The Boshier-Hinton Foundation
The Bothwell Charitable Trust
H E and E L Botteley
Charitable Trust
The Harry Bottom Charitable
Trust
P G and N J Boulton Trust
The A H and E Boulton Trust
Sir Clive Bourne Family Trust
The Anthony Bourne
Foundation
Bourneheights Limited
The Bower Trust
The Bowerman Charitable
Trust
John and Susan Bowers Fund
The Bowland Charitable Trust
The Frank Brake Charitable
Trust
The William Brake Charitable
Trust
The Tony Bramall Charitable
Trust
The Liz and Terry Bramall
Foundation
The Bransford Trust
The Breadsticks Foundation
The Brendish Family
Foundation
Bridgepoint Charitable Trust
The Harold and Alice Bridges
Charity
Briggs Animal Welfare Trust
Bristol Archdeaconry Charity
The Bristol Charities
John Bristow and Thomas
Mason Trust
The British Council for
Prevention of Blindness
The British Dietetic
Association General and
Education Trust Fund
The British Gas (Scottish Gas)
Energy Trust
British Heart Foundation

British Humane Association
British Institute at Ankara
British Ornithologists' Union
British Record Industry Trust
The J and M Britton Charitable
Trust
The Bromley Trust
The Roger Brooke Charitable
Trust
The David Brooke Charity
The Rory and Elizabeth Brooks
Foundation
The Charles Brotherton Trust
Joseph Brough Charitable
Trust
The Swinfen Broun Charitable
Trust
Bill Brown 1998 Charitable
Trust
Edna Brown Charitable
Settlement (Mrs E E Brown
Charitable Settlement)
R S Brownless Charitable
Trust
Brown-Mellows Trust
The Brownsword Charitable
Foundation
T B H Brunner's Charitable
Settlement
The Bruntwood Charity
Brushmill Ltd
Buckingham Trust
Buckinghamshire Community
Foundation
The Buckinghamshire Masonic
Centenary Fund
Buckland Charitable Trust
The Rosemary Bugden
Charitable Trust
The Bulldog Trust Limited
The E F Bulmer Benevolent
Fund
Bumba Foundation
The Burden Trust
Burdens Charitable Foundation
The Burdett Trust for Nursing
The Clara E Burgess Charity
The Burry Charitable Trust
The Arnold Burton 1998
Charitable Trust
The Burton Breweries
Charitable Trust
Consolidated Charity of Burton
upon Trent
The Paul Bush Foundation
Trust
The Worshipful Company of
Butchers General Charities
The Derek Butler Trust
The Noel Buxton Trust
C and F Charitable Trust
C M L Family Foundation
The James Caan Foundation
C J Cadbury Charitable Trust
Edward Cadbury Charitable
Trust

Henry T and Lucy B Cadbury
Charitable Trust
Peter Cadbury Charitable Trust
The Christopher Cadbury
Charitable Trust
The G W Cadbury Charitable
Trust
The Richard Cadbury
Charitable Trust
The William A Cadbury
Charitable Trust
The Cadbury Foundation
The Edward and Dorothy
Cadbury Trust
The George Cadbury Trust
The Barrow Cadbury Trust and
the Barrow Cadbury Fund
The Cadogan Charity
CAF (Charities Aid Foundation)
CAFOD (Catholic Agency for
Overseas Development)
Community Foundation for
Calderdale
The Callander Charitable Trust
Calleva Foundation
Calouste Gulbenkian
Foundation – UK Branch
Calypso Browning Trust
The Cambridgeshire
Community Foundation
The Camelia Trust
The Campden Charities
Trustee
The Canning Trust
M R Cannon 1998 Charitable
Trust
H and L Cantor Trust
Cardy Beaver Foundation
The Carew Pole Charitable
Trust
The D W T Cargill Fund
Carlee Ltd
The Carlton House Charitable
Trust
The Carmelite Monastery Ware
Trust
The Worshipful Company of
Carmen Benevolent Trust
The Carnegie Dunfermline
Trust
The Carnegie Trust for the
Universities of Scotland
The Carpenter Charitable Trust
The Carpenters' Company
Charitable Trust
The Carrington Charitable
Trust
The Carron Charitable
Settlement
The Leslie Mary Carter
Charitable Trust
The Casey Trust
Cash for Kids Radio Clyde
The Cass Foundation
Sir John Cass's Foundation
The Elizabeth Casson Trust
The Castang Foundation

The Catalyst Charitable Trust
The Catholic Charitable Trust
Catholic Foreign Missions
The Catholic Trust for England and Wales
The Cattanach Charitable Trust
The Joseph and Annie Cattle Trust
The Thomas Sivewright Catto Charitable Settlement
The Wilfrid and Constance Cave Foundation
The Cayo Foundation
Elizabeth Cayzer Charitable Trust
The B G S Cayzer Charitable Trust
The Cazenove Charitable Trust
The CBD Charitable Trust
CBRE Charitable Trust
Celtic Charity Fund
The Gaynor Cemlyn-Jones Trust
The CH (1980) Charitable Trust
R E Chadwick Charitable Trust
The Amelia Chadwick Trust
The Pamela Champion Foundation
The Chapman Charitable Trust
John William Chapman's Charitable Trust
The Charities Advisory Trust
Charitworth Limited
The Charter 600 Charity
The Worshipful Company of Chartered Accountants General Charitable Trust (also known as CALC)
The Chasah Trust
The Chelsea Square 1994 Trust
Cherry Grove Charitable Trust
The Cheruby Trust
Cheshire Freemason's Charity
Chesterhill Charitable Trust
The Chetwode Foundation
Cheviot Asset Management Charitable Trust
Child Growth Foundation
Childs Charitable Trust
The Childwick Trust
The Chipping Sodbury Town Lands Charity
CHK Charities Limited
The Jimmy Choo Foundation
The Chownes Foundation
The Chrimes Family Charitable Trust
The Christabella Charitable Trust
Christadelphian Samaritan Fund
Christian Aid
Christian Response to Eastern Europe
Christie Foundation

Chrysalis Trust
The Church and Community Fund
The Church Burgesses Educational Foundation
Church Burgesses Trust
Church Urban Fund
City and County of Swansea Welsh Church Act Fund
The City Bridge Trust
The City Educational Trust Fund
CLA Charitable Trust
Stephen Clark 1957 Charitable Trust
J A Clark Charitable Trust
The Hilda and Alice Clark Charitable Trust
The Roger and Sarah Bancroft Clark Charitable Trust
The Clarke Charitable Settlement
The Clear Light Trust
The Cleevely Family Charitable Trust
The Cleopatra Trust
Lord Clinton's Charitable Trust
The Clore Duffield Foundation
Miss V L Clore's 1967 Charitable Trust
The Clothworkers' Foundation
Richard Cloudesley's Charity
The Clover Trust
The Robert Clutterbuck Charitable Trust
Clydpride Ltd
The Coalfields Regeneration Trust
The John Coates Charitable Trust
The Cobalt Trust
The Cobtree Charity Trust Ltd
The Denise Cohen Charitable Trust
The Vivienne and Samuel Cohen Charitable Trust
The John S Cohen Foundation
The R and S Cohen Foundation
John Coldman Charitable Trust
The Cole Charitable Trust
The Colefax Charitable Trust
The John and Freda Coleman Charitable Trust
The Bernard Coleman Charitable Trust
The Sir Jeremiah Colman Gift Trust
Col-Reno Ltd
The Colt Foundation
The Coltstaple Trust
Colwinston Charitable Trust
Colyer-Fergusson Charitable Trust
Comic Relief
The Comino Foundation
The Compton Charitable Trust

The Congleton Inclosure Trust
The Conscience Trust
The Conservation Foundation
The Consolidated Charities for the Infirm Merchant Taylors' Company
Gordon Cook Foundation
The Ernest Cook Trust
The Cooks Charity
The Catherine Cookson Charitable Trust
The Cookson Charitable Trust
The Keith Coombs Trust
Harold and Daphne Cooper Charitable Trust
Mabel Cooper Charity
The Alice Ellen Cooper Dean Charitable Foundation
The Co-operative Foundation
The Marjorie Coote Animal Charity Trust
The Marjorie Coote Old People's Charity
The Helen Jean Cope Trust
The J Reginald Corah Foundation Fund
The Gershon Coren Charitable Foundation (also known as The Muriel and Gus Coren Charitable Foundation)
The Evan Cornish Foundation
The Duke of Cornwall's Benevolent Fund
The Cornwell Charitable Trust
The Sidney and Elizabeth Corob Charitable Trust
The Corona Charitable Trust
The Bryan Christopher Corrigan Charitable Trust
The Costa Family Charitable Trust
The Cotton Industry War Memorial Trust
The Cotton Trust
County Durham Community Foundation
The Augustine Courtauld Trust
Coutts Charitable Foundation
The General Charities of the City of Coventry
Coventry Building Society Charitable Foundation
The John Cowan Foundation
Cowley Charitable Foundation
Dudley and Geoffrey Cox Charitable Trust
The Sir William Coxen Trust Fund
The Lord Cozens-Hardy Trust
The Craignish Trust
The Craps Charitable Trust
Michael Crawford Children's Charity
The Cray Trust
Creative Scotland
The Crerar Hotels Trust
The Crescent Trust

Cripplegate Foundation
The Violet and Milo Cripps
    Charitable Trust
The Harry Crook Foundation
The Cross Trust
The Croydon Relief in Need
    Charities
The Peter Cruddas Foundation
Cruden Foundation Ltd
The Ronald Cruickshanks
    Foundation
The Cuby Charitable Trust
The Culra Charitable Trust
The Cumber Family Charitable
    Trust
Cumberland Building Society
    Charitable Foundation
Cumbria Community
    Foundation
The D J H Currie Memorial
    Trust
The Dennis Curry Charitable
    Trust
The Manny Cussins
    Foundation
The Cutler Trust (the
    Worshipful Company of
    Makers of Playing Cards)
The Cwmbran Trust
Itzchok Meyer Cymerman Trust
    Ltd
The D G Charitable Settlement
Roald Dahl's Marvellous
    Children's Charity
Daily Prayer Union Charitable
    Trust Limited
Oizer Dalim Trust
The Dr and Mrs A Darlington
    Charitable Trust
Baron Davenport's Charity
The Davidson (Nairn)
    Charitable Trust
The Davidson Family
    Charitable Trust
The Alderman Joe Davidson
    Memorial Trust
Michael Davies Charitable
    Settlement
The Gwendoline and Margaret
    Davies Charity
The Wilfrid Bruce Davis
    Charitable Trust
Davis-Rubens Charitable Trust
The Dawe Charitable Trust
The De Brye Charitable Trust
The De Clermont Charitable
    Company Ltd
Peter De Haan Charitable
    Trust
The De Laszlo Foundation
The Deakin Charitable Trust
The Debmar Benevolent Trust
The Dellal Foundation
The Delves Charitable Trust
The Demigryphon Trust
The Denman Charitable Trust

Dentons UKMEA LLP
    Charitable Trust
The Earl of Derby's Charitable
    Trust
Derbyshire Community
    Foundation
The J N Derbyshire Trust
The Desmond Foundation
Devon Community Foundation
The Devon Educational Trust
The Duke of Devonshire's
    Charitable Trust
The Sandy Dewhirst Charitable
    Trust
The Laduma Dhamecha
    Charitable Trust
Diabetes UK
Alan and Sheila Diamond
    Charitable Trust
Diced Cap Charity
The Dickon Trust
The Peter Alan Dickson
    Foundation
Grace Dieu Charitable Trust
The Digbeth Trust Limited
The Dinwoodie Settlement
Dischma Charitable Trust
The Djanogly Foundation
The Novak Djokovic Foundation
    (UK) Limited
The DLM Charitable Trust
The DM Charitable Trust
Louise Dobson Charitable
    Trust
The Derek and Eileen Dodgson
    Foundation
The Dollond Charitable Trust
Domepride Ltd
The Dorcas Trust
Dorset Community Foundation
The Dorus Trust
The Double 'O' Charity Ltd
The Doughty Charity Trust
Douglas Arter Foundation
The R M Douglas Charitable
    Trust
The Drapers' Charitable Fund
Dromintee Trust
The Duis Charitable Trust
The Royal Foundation of the
    Duke and Duchess of
    Cambridge and Prince Harry
The Dulverton Trust
The P B Dumbell Charitable
    Trust
The Dumbreck Charity
Dunard Fund
The Dunhill Medical Trust
The Dunn Family Charitable
    Trust
The W E Dunn Trust
The Charles Dunstone
    Charitable Trust
Dushinsky Trust Ltd
Mildred Duveen Charitable
    Trust

Annette Duvollet Charitable
    Trust
The Dwek Family Charitable
    Trust
The Dyers' Company
    Charitable Trust
The James Dyson Foundation
The Eagle Charity Trust
Audrey Earle Charitable Trust
The Earley Charity
Earls Colne and Halstead
    Educational Charity
The Earmark Trust
East End Community
    Foundation
Eastern Counties Educational
    Trust Limited
The Sir John Eastwood
    Foundation
The Ebenezer Trust
The EBM Charitable Trust
Eden Arts Trust
EDF Energy Trust (EDFET)
The Gilbert and Eileen Edgar
    Foundation
Gilbert Edgar Trust
Edge Fund
Edinburgh Children's Holiday
    Fund
Edinburgh Trust No 2 Account
Edinburgh Voluntary
    Organisations' Trust Funds
    (EVOT)
Educational Foundation of
    Alderman John Norman
The William Edwards
    Educational Charity
The Eighty Eight Foundation
The Elephant Trust
The George Elias Charitable
    Trust
The Gerald Palmer Eling Trust
    Company
The Wilfred and Elsie Elkes
    Charity Fund
The Maud Elkington Charitable
    Trust
Ellador Ltd
The Ellerdale Trust
The John Ellerman Foundation
The Ellinson Foundation Ltd
The Ellis Campbell Foundation
James Ellis Charitable Trust
The Elmgrant Trust
The Elmley Foundation
Elshore Ltd
The Vernon N Ely Charitable
    Trust
The Embleton Trust
Embrace the Middle East
The Emerton-Christie Charity
The Emilienne Charitable Trust
The Endure Foundation
The Worshipful Company of
    Engineers Charitable Trust
    Fund
The Englefield Charitable Trust

The English Schools' Football Association

The Enkalon Foundation

Entindale Ltd

The Epigoni Trust

The Equitable Charitable Trust

The Equity Trust Fund

The Ericson Trust

The Erskine Cunningham Hill Trust

The Essendon Charitable Trust

The Essex and Southend Sports Trust

Essex Community Foundation

The Essex Fairway Charitable Trust

The Essex Heritage Trust

Essex Provincial Charity Fund

The Essex Youth Trust

Joseph Ettedgui Charitable Foundation

Euro Charity Trust

The Alan Evans Memorial Trust

Sir John Evelyn's Charity

The Eventhall Family Charitable Trust

The Eveson Charitable Trust

The Beryl Evetts and Robert Luff Animal Welfare Trust Limited

The Exilarch's Foundation

The Matthew Eyton Animal Welfare Trust

F C Charitable Trust

The F P Limited Charitable Trust

The Faber Charitable Trust

Esmée Fairbairn Foundation

The Fairstead Trust

The Fairway Trust

The Family Rich Charities Trust

Famos Foundation Trust

The Lord Faringdon Charitable Trust

Samuel William Farmer Trust

The Farmers' Company Charitable Fund

The Thomas Farr Charity

Walter Farthing (Trust) Limited

The Farthing Trust

The Fassnidge Memorial Trust

Joseph Fattorini Charitable Trust

The February Foundation

Federation of Jewish Relief Organisations

The John Feeney Charitable Trust

The George Fentham Birmingham Charity

The A M Fenton Trust

Allan and Nesta Ferguson Charitable Settlement

Elizabeth Ferguson Charitable Trust Fund

The Fidelity UK Foundation

The Doris Field Charitable Trust

Fife Council/Common Good Funds and Trusts

Filey Foundation Ltd

Dixie Rose Findlay Charitable Trust

Finnart House School Trust

Gerald Finzi Charitable Trust

Firtree Trust

The Sir John Fisher Foundation

The Fishmongers' Company's Charitable Trust

Marc Fitch Fund

The Fitton Trust

The Earl Fitzwilliam Charitable Trust

The Ian Fleming Charitable Trust

The Joyce Fletcher Charitable Trust

Florence's Charitable Trust

The Flow Foundation

The Gerald Fogel Charitable Trust

The Follett Trust

The Football Association National Sports Centre Trust

The Football Association Youth Trust

The Football Foundation

The Forbes Charitable Foundation

The Forces Trust (Working Name)

Ford Britain Trust

The Oliver Ford Charitable Trust

Fordeve Limited

The Forest Hill Charitable Trust

The Foresters' Charity Stewards UK Trust

Forever Manchester (The Community Foundation for Greater Manchester)

The Forman Hardy Charitable Trust

Gwyneth Forrester Trust

The Donald Forrester Trust

The Anna Rosa Forster Charitable Trust

The Forte Charitable Trust

The Lord Forte Foundation

The Four Lanes Trust

The Four Winds Trust

The Foyle Foundation

The Isaac and Freda Frankel Memorial Charitable Trust

The Elizabeth Frankland Moore and Star Foundation

Sydney E Franklin Deceased's New Second Charity

The Jill Franklin Trust

The Gordon Fraser Charitable Trust

The Hugh Fraser Foundation

The Joseph Strong Frazer Trust

The Louis and Valerie Freedman Charitable Settlement

The Michael and Clara Freeman Charitable Trust

The Freemasons' Grand Charity

The Charles S French Charitable Trust

The Anne French Memorial Trust

The Freshfield Foundation

The Freshgate Trust Foundation

The Friarsgate Trust

Sybilla and Leo Friedler Charitable Trust

The Friends Hall Farm Street Trust

Friends of Biala Limited

Friends of Wiznitz Limited

Friends Provident Charitable Foundation

The Frognal Trust

T F C Frost Charitable Trust

The Patrick & Helena Frost Foundation

Maurice Fry Charitable Trust

Mejer and Gertrude Miriam Frydman Foundation

The Fulmer Charitable Trust

Worshipful Company of Furniture Makers Charitable Fund

The Fuserna Foundation General Charitable Trust

The G I Foundation

G M C Trust

Gableholt Limited

The Galbraith Trust

The Gale Family Charity Trust

Gamlen Charitable Trust

The Gamma Trust

The Gannochy Trust

The Worshipful Company of Gardeners of London

The Samuel Gardner Memorial Trust

The Garennie Charitable Trust

The Garnett Charitable Trust

Garrick Charitable Trust

Garthgwynion Charities

Garvan Limited

The Gatsby Charitable Foundation

Gatwick Airport Community Trust

The Robert Gavron Charitable Trust

Jacqueline and Michael Gee Charitable Trust

Thomas Betton's Charity for Pensions and Relief-in-Need

The General Nursing Council for England and Wales Trust

The Generations Foundation
The Steven Gerrard Foundation
The Gibbons Family Trust
The Gibbs Charitable Trust
Simon Gibson Charitable Trust
The G C Gibson Charitable
Trust
Lady Gibson's Charitable Trust
The Harvey and Hilary Gilbert
Charitable Trust
The Girdlers' Company
Charitable Trust
The B and P Glasser
Charitable Trust
The Glass-House Trust
The Glastonbury Trust Limited
Global Care
Global Charities
Gloucestershire Community
Foundation
Worshipful Company of
Glovers of London Charity
Fund
The GNC Trust
The Godinton Charitable Trust
The Sydney and Phyllis
Goldberg Memorial
Charitable Trust
The Golden Bottle Trust
Golden Charitable Trust
The Jack Goldhill Charitable
Trust
The Goldsmiths' Arts Trust
Fund
The Goldsmiths' Company
Charity
The Golsoncott Foundation
Golubovich Foundation
Nicholas and Judith
Goodison's Charitable
Settlement
The Mike Gooley Trailfinders
Charity
The Gosling Foundation
Limited
The Gough Charitable Trust
The Gould Charitable Trust
The Hemraj Goyal Foundation
The Grace Charitable Trust
A B Grace Trust
The Graff Foundation
E C Graham Belford Charitable
Settlement
A and S Graham Charitable
Trust
The Grahame Charitable
Foundation Limited
The Granada Foundation
Grand Charitable Trust of the
Order of Women
Freemasons
The Grand Order of Water
Rats' Charities Fund
The Grange Farm Centre Trust
Grantham Yorke Trust
The Stanley and Lorna Graves
Charitable Trust

The Gordon Gray Trust
The Gray Trust
The Great Britain Sasakawa
Foundation
The Great Stone Bridge Trust
of Edenbridge
The Great Torrington Town
Lands Charity
The Kenneth & Susan Green
Charitable Foundation
The Haydn Green Charitable
Trust
The Green Hall Foundation
The Green Room Charitable
Trust
The Green Woodpecker Trust
Mrs H R Greene Charitable
Settlement
Greenham Common
Community Trust Limited
Greggs Foundation
The Gretna Charitable Trust
Greys Charitable Trust
The Grimmitt Trust
The Grocers' Charity
The M and R Gross Charities
Limited
The GRP Charitable Trust
The David and Marie Grumitt
Foundation
N and R Grunbaum Charitable
Trust
The Bishop of Guildford's
Foundation
The Guildry Incorporation of
Perth
The Walter Guinness
Charitable Trust
The Gunter Charitable Trust
The Gur Trust
The Gurney Charitable Trust
Dr Guthrie's Association
The H and M Charitable Trust
H C D Memorial Fund
H C Foundation
The H P Charitable Trust
The Hackney Parochial
Charities
The Hadfield Trust
The Hadley Trust
The Hadrian Trust
The Alfred Haines Charitable
Trust
The Haley Family Charitable
Trust
E F and M G Hall Charitable
Trust
The Edith Winifred Hall
Charitable Trust
Robert Hall Charity
The Hamamelis Trust
Hamilton Wallace Trust
Paul Hamlyn Foundation
Sue Hammerson Charitable
Trust
The Hampstead Wells and
Campden Trust

Hampton Fuel Allotment
Charity
The W A Handley Charitable
Trust
Beatrice Hankey Foundation
Limited
The Hanley Trust (1987)
The Kathleen Hannay
Memorial Charity
The Doughty Hanson
Charitable Foundation
Lord Hanson Foundation
Miss K M Harbinson's
Charitable Trust
Harbo Charities Limited
The Harborne Parish Lands
Charity
The Harbour Charitable Trust
The Harbour Foundation
The Harding Trust
William Harding's Charity
The Hare of Steep Charitable
Trust
The Harebell Centenary Fund
The Kenneth Hargreaves
Charitable Trust
The Harpur Trust
The Harris Charity
The Harris Family Charitable
Trust
The Edith Lilian Harrison 2000
Foundation
The Harrison and Potter Trust
The John Harrison Charitable
Trust
The Spencer Hart Charitable
Trust
The Hartley Charitable Trust
The Alfred And Peggy Harvey
Charitable Trust
William Geoffrey Harvey's
Discretionary Settlement
Haskel Family Foundation
The Hathaway Trust
The Maurice Hatter Foundation
The M A Hawe Settlement
The Hawerby Trust
The Hawkins Foundation
The Hawthorne Charitable
Trust
The Dorothy Hay-Bolton
Charitable Trust
The Headley Trust
Headley-Pitt Charitable Trust
May Hearnshaw's Charity
Heart of England Community
Foundation
The Heathcoat Trust
Heathside Charitable Trust
The Charlotte Heber-Percy
Charitable Trust
Percy Hedley 1990 Charitable
Trust
The Hedley Denton Charitable
Trust
The Hedley Foundation

The H J Heinz Company
Limited Charitable Trust
The Hellenic Foundation
The Michael Heller Charitable
Foundation
The Simon Heller Charitable
Settlement
The Hemby Trust
The Christina Mary Hendrie
Trust for Scottish and
Canadian Charities
Henley Educational Trust
(formerley Henley
Educational Charity)
Philip Henman Trust
Esther Hennell Charitable
Trust
The G D Herbert Charitable
Trust
The Anne Herd Memorial Trust
The Herefordshire Historic
Churches Trust
The Heritage of London Trust
Ltd
The Hertfordshire Community
Foundation
The Hesed Trust
The Hesslewood Children's
Trust (Hull Seamen's and
General Orphanage)
Hexham and Newcastle
Diocesan Trust (1947)
The Higgs Charitable Trust
Alan Edward Higgs Charity
The Graham High Charitable
Trust
The High Sheriff's Police Trust
for the County of West
Midlands (Building Blocks)
Highcroft Charitable Trust
The Hilden Charitable Fund
The Derek Hill Foundation
The Charles Littlewood Hill
Trust
The Hillier Trust
The Hillingdon Partnership
Trust
R G Hills Charitable Trust
The Hilmarnan Charitable Trust
Hinchley Charitable Trust
Lady Hind Trust
Hinduja Foundation
Stuart Hine Trust
The Hinrichsen Foundation
The Hintze Family Charitable
Foundation
The Hiscox Foundation
The Hitchin Educational
Foundation
The Eleemosynary Charity of
William Hobbayne
Hobson Charity Limited
Hockerill Educational
Foundation
Matthew Hodder Charitable
Trust

The Sir Julian Hodge
Charitable Trust
The Jane Hodge Foundation
The J G Hogg Charitable Trust
The Holden Charitable Trust
John Holford's Charity
The Hollick Family Charitable
Trust
The Holliday Foundation
The Dorothy Holmes Charitable
Trust
The Holmes Family Trust
(Sheffield)
The Holst Foundation
P H Holt Foundation
The Edward Holt Trust
The Holywood Trust
The Homelands Charitable
Trust
The Homestead Charitable
Trust
Mary Homfray Charitable Trust
Sir Harold Hood's Charitable
Trust
Hope for Youth (NI)
The Hope Trust
HopMarket Charity
The Horizon Foundation
The Cuthbert Horn Trust
The Antony Hornby Charitable
Trust
The Horne Foundation
The Horne Trust
The Worshipful Company of
Horners' Charitable Trusts
The Hornsey Parochial
Charities
The Hospital of God at
Greatham
The Hospital Saturday Fund
The Sir Joseph Hotung
Charitable Settlement
Houblon-Norman/George Fund
The House of Industry Estate
The Reta Lila Howard
Foundation
The Daniel Howard Trust
HTA Sheba Foundation UK
The Huddersfield Common
Good Trust
The Hudson Foundation
The Huggard Charitable Trust
The Geoffrey C Hughes
Charitable Trust
The Hull and East Riding
Charitable Trust
Hulme Trust Estates
(Educational)
Human Relief Foundation
The Humanitarian Trust
The Michael and Shirley Hunt
Charitable Trust
The Albert Hunt Trust
The Hunter Foundation
Miss Agnes H Hunter's Trust
The Hunting Horn General
Charitable Trust

The Huntingdon Foundation
Huntingdon Freemen's Trust
Hurdale Charity Limited
The Hutton Foundation
The Nani Huyu Charitable Trust
The P Y N and B Hyams Trust
The Hyde Charitable Trust
I B B Charitable Trust
I G O Foundation Limited
The Idlewild Trust
The Iliffe Family Charitable
Trust
Impetus – The Private Equity
Foundation (Impetus – PEF)
The Indigo Trust
Infinity Capital Trust
The Ingram Trust
The Inlight Trust
The Inman Charity
The Inner London Magistrates
Court Poor Box and Feeder
Charity
The Innocent Foundation
The Ireland Fund of Great
Britain
The Irish Youth Foundation
(UK) Ltd (incorporating The
Lawlor Foundation)
The Ironmongers' Foundation
The Charles Irving Charitable
Trust
Irwin Trust
The ISA Charity
The Isaacs Charitable Trust
The J Isaacs Charitable Trust
The Isle of Anglesey Charitable
Trust
The ITF Seafarers Trust
The Ithaca Trust
The J & J Charitable Trust
J A R Charitable Trust
J D R Charitable Trust
The J J Charitable Trust
The J M K Charitable Trust
The J R S S T Charitable Trust
The Jabbs Foundation
C Richard Jackson Charitable
Trust
Elizabeth Jackson Charitable
Trust
Jacobs Charitable Trust
The Ruth and Lionel Jacobson
Trust (Second Fund) No 2
Jaffe Family Relief Fund
John James Bristol Foundation
The Susan and Stephen
James Charitable
Settlement
The James Trust
The Marjory Jameson Trust
The Jarman Charitable Trust
The Barbara Joyce Jarrald
Charitable Trust
The Jasper Conran Foundation
Jay Education Trust
JCA Charitable Foundation
The Jeffrey Charitable Trust

Rees Jeffreys Road Fund
The Jenour Foundation
The Jerusalem Trust
Jesus Hospital Charity
Jewish Child's Day
The Jewish Youth Fund
The Jigsaw Foundation
The Harold Joels Charitable
 Trust
The Nicholas Joels Charitable
 Trust
The Norman Joels Charitable
 Trust
The Joffe Charitable Trust
The Elton John Aids
 Foundation
The Dyfrig and Heather John
 Charitable Trust
The Lillie Johnson Charitable
 Trust
The Johnson Foundation
The Reginald Johnson
 Foundation
The Johnnie Johnson Trust
The Johnson Wax Ltd
 Charitable Trust
The Joicey Trust
The Jones 1986 Charitable
 Trust
The Marjorie and Geoffrey
 Jones Charitable Trust
The Muriel Jones Foundation
The Jordan Charitable
 Foundation
The Joron Charitable Trust
The J E Joseph Charitable
 Fund
The Lady Eileen Joseph
 Foundation
The Josephs Family Charitable
 Trust
JTH Charitable Trust
The Cyril and Eve Jumbo
 Charitable Trust
The Jungels-Winkler Charitable
 Foundation
The Anton Jurgens Charitable
 Trust
Jusaca Charitable Trust
The Bernard Kahn Charitable
 Trust
The Stanley Kalms Foundation
The Kalou Foundation
The Karenza Foundation
The Boris Karloff Charitable
 Foundation
The Ian Karten Charitable
 Trust
The Kasner Charitable Trust
The Kathleen Trust
The Michael and Ilse Katz
 Foundation
The Katzauer Charitable
 Settlement
The C S Kaufman Charitable
 Trust

The Geoffrey John Kaye
 Charitable Foundation
The Emmanuel Kaye
 Foundation
The Kelly Family Charitable
 Trust
Kelsick's Educational
 Foundation
The KempWelch Charitable
 Trust
The Kay Kendall Leukaemia
 Fund
The John Thomas Kennedy
 Charitable Foundation
The Kennel Club Charitable
 Trust
Kent Community Foundation
The Nancy Kenyon Charitable
 Trust
Keren Association
Kermaville Ltd
E and E Kernkraut Charities
 Limited
The Peter Kershaw Trust
Keswick Hall Trust
The Ursula Keyes Trust
The Mr & Mrs Paul Killik
 Charitable Trust
The King/Cullimore Charitable
 Trust
Kingdom Way Trust
The Kingsbury Charity
The Mary Kinross Charitable
 Trust
Kinsurdy Charitable Trust
Kirkley Poor's Lands Estate
The Richard Kirkman
 Charitable Trust
Kirschel Foundation
Robert Kitchin (Saddlers'
 Company)
Ernest Kleinwort Charitable
 Trust
The Marina Kleinwort
 Charitable Trust
The Kobler Trust
The Kofia Trust
The Kohn Foundation
Kollel and Co. Limited
Liudmila Korneenko
 Foundation
The Kreditor Charitable Trust
The Kreitman Foundation
The Neil Kreitman Foundation
The Heinz, Anna and Carol
 Kroch Foundation
Kupath Gemach Chaim
 Bechesed Viznitz Trust
The Kyte Charitable Trust
L P W Limited
The Late Sir Pierce Lacy
 Charity Trust
The K P Ladd Charitable Trust
John Laing Charitable Trust
Maurice and Hilda Laing
 Charitable Trust

The Christopher Laing
 Foundation
The Kirby Laing Foundation
The Martin Laing Foundation
The Beatrice Laing Trust
The Lambert Charitable Trust
Community Foundation for
 Lancashire
Duchy of Lancaster Benevolent
 Fund
The Lancaster Foundation
The Allen Lane Foundation
Langdale Trust
The Langley Charitable Trust
The LankellyChase Foundation
The R J Larg Family Charitable
 Trust
Largsmount Ltd
The Lark Trust
Laslett's (Hinton) Charity
Laufer Charitable Trust
The Lauffer Family Charitable
 Foundation
Mrs F B Laurence Charitable
 Trust
The Kathleen Laurence Trust
The Law Society Charity
The Edgar E Lawley Foundation
The Herd Lawson and Muriel
 Lawson Charitable Trust
The Lawson Beckman
 Charitable Trust
The Raymond and Blanche
 Lawson Charitable Trust
The Leach Fourteenth Trust
The David Lean Foundation
The Leathersellers' Company
 Charitable Fund
The Arnold Lee Charitable
 Trust
The Lord Mayor of Leeds
 Appeal Fund
Leeds Building Society
 Charitable Foundation
The Leeds Community
 Foundation
The Kennedy Leigh Charitable
 Trust
Morris Leigh Foundation
The Leigh Trust
Mrs Vera Leigh's Charity
P Leigh-Bramwell Trust 'E'
The Lennox and Wyfold
 Foundation
The Erica Leonard Trust
The Leonard Trust
The Mark Leonard Trust
Lesley Lesley and Mutter Trust
Leukaemia and Lymphoma
 Research
The Leverhulme Trade
 Charities Trust
The Leverhulme Trust
The Joseph Levy Charitable
 Foundation
Lewis Family Charitable Trust

The John Spedan Lewis Foundation
The Sir Edward Lewis Foundation
John Lewis Partnership General Community Fund
Lichfield Conduit Lands
Lifeline 4 Kids
Limoges Charitable Trust
The Linbury Trust
The Lincolnshire Churches Trust
Lindale Educational Foundation
The Linden Charitable Trust
Lindenleaf Charitable Trust
The Enid Linder Foundation
The Linmardon Trust
The Ruth and Stuart Lipton Charitable Trust
The Lister Charitable Trust
Frank Litchfield Charitable Trust
The Andrew and Mary Elizabeth Little Charitable Trust
Littlefield Foundation (UK) Limited
The Second Joseph Aaron Littman Foundation
The George John and Sheilah Livanos Charitable Trust
Liverpool Charity and Voluntary Services
Liverpool Sailors' Home Trust
Jack Livingstone Charitable Trust
The Ian & Natalie Livingstone Charitable Trust
The Elaine and Angus Lloyd Charitable Trust
The Charles Lloyd Foundation
Lloyd's Charities Trust
Lloyds Bank Foundation for England and Wales
Lloyds Bank Foundation for Northern Ireland
Lloyds Bank Foundation for the Channel Islands
Lloyds TSB Foundation for Scotland
The Lo Family Charitable Trust
Localtrent Ltd
The Locker Foundation
The Loftus Charitable Trust
The Lolev Charitable Trust
The Trust for London
London Catalyst
The London Community Foundation
The London Housing Foundation
The London Law Trust
The William and Katherine Longman Trust
The Loseley and Guildway Charitable Trust

The Lotus Foundation
The Lowy Mitchell Foundation
The C L Loyd Charitable Trust
LSA Charitable Trust
The Marie Helen Luen Charitable Trust
Robert Luff Foundation Ltd
Henry Lumley Charitable Trust
Paul Lunn-Rockliffe Charitable Trust
C F Lunoe Trust Fund
The Ruth and Jack Lunzer Charitable Trust
Lord and Lady Lurgan Trust
The Lyndhurst Trust
The Lynn Foundation
The Lynwood Trust
John Lyon's Charity
The Lyons Charitable Trust
The Sir Jack Lyons Charitable Trust
The Lyras Family Charitable Trust
Sylvanus Lyson's Charity
The M and C Trust
The M K Charitable Trust
The Madeline Mabey Trust
The E M MacAndrew Trust
The R S Macdonald Charitable Trust
Macdonald-Buchanan Charitable Trust
The Mackay and Brewer Charitable Trust
The Mackintosh Foundation
The MacRobert Trust
Ian Mactaggart Trust
Magdalen Hospital Trust
The SV and PE Magee Family Charitable Trust
The Magen Charitable Trust
Mageni Trust
The Brian Maguire Charitable Trust
The Mahavir Trust
The Makin Charitable Trust
Man Group plc Charitable Trust
The Manackerman Charitable Trust
Manchester Airport Community Trust Fund
The Manchester Guardian Society Charitable Trust
Lord Mayor of Manchester's Charity Appeal Trust
Mandeville Trust
The Manifold Charitable Trust
W M Mann Foundation
The Leslie and Lilian Manning Trust
Maranatha Christian Trust
Marbeh Torah Trust
Marchig Animal Welfare Trust
The Stella and Alexander Margulies Charitable Trust
The Marianne Foundation

Mariapolis Limited
Market Harborough and The Bowdens Charity
Michael Marks Charitable Trust
The Ann and David Marks Foundation
The Hilda and Samuel Marks Foundation
J P Marland Charitable Trust
The Marr-Munning Trust
The Michael Marsh Charitable Trust
The Marsh Christian Trust
The Charlotte Marshall Charitable Trust
The Jim Marshall Charitable Trust
The Nora Joan Marshall Charitable Trust
The D G Marshall of Cambridge Trust
Marshgate Charitable Settlement
John Martin's Charity
The John Mason Family Trust
The Mason Porter Charitable Trust
The Nancie Massey Charitable Trust
The Mathew Trust
Matliwala Family Charitable Trust
The Matt 6.3 Charitable Trust
The Violet Mauray Charitable Trust
The Maxwell Family Foundation
Evelyn May Trust
The Mayfield Valley Arts Trust
Mazars Charitable Trust
The McDougall Trust
The A M McGreevy No 5 Charitable Settlement
The McKenna Charitable Trust
Martin McLaren Memorial Trust
The Helen Isabella McMorran Charitable Foundation
D D McPhail Charitable Settlement
The Mears Foundation
The James Frederick and Ethel Anne Measures Charity
The Medlock Charitable Trust
The Anthony and Elizabeth Mellows Charitable Settlement
Melodor Limited
Melow Charitable Trust
Meningitis Trust
Menuchar Ltd
The Menzies Charity Foundation
The Mercers' Charitable Foundation
The Merchant Taylors' Company Charities Fund

The Merchant Venturers' Charity

The Merchants' House of Glasgow

Mercury Phoenix Trust

The Mersey Docks and Harbour Company Charitable Fund

Community Foundation for Merseyside

The Zachary Merton and George Woofindin Convalescent Trust

The Tony Metherell Charitable Trust

The Metropolitan Drinking Fountain and Cattle Trough Association

The Metropolitan Masonic Charity

T and J Meyer Family Foundation Limited

The Mickel Fund

Mickleham Charitable Trust

Gerald Micklem Charitable Trust

The Sir John Middlemore Charitable Trust

Middlesex Sports Foundation

Midhurst Pensions Trust

The Migraine Trust

Miles Trust for the Putney and Roehampton Community

Millennium Stadium Charitable Trust

The Hugh and Mary Miller Bequest Trust

The Ronald Miller Foundation

The Millfield Trust

The Millhouses Charitable Trust

The Millichope Foundation

The Mills Charity

The Millward Charitable Trust

The Clare Milne Trust

Milton Keynes Community Foundation

The Edgar Milward Charity

The Peter Minet Trust

Minge's Gift and the Pooled Trusts

The Minos Trust

Minton Charitable Trust

The Mirfield Educational Charity

The Mirianog Trust

The Laurence Misener Charitable Trust

The Mishcon Family Charitable Trust

The Misselbrook Trust

The Brian Mitchell Charitable Settlement

The Mitchell Charitable Trust

The Esmé Mitchell Trust

The MITIE Foundation

The Mittal Foundation

Keren Mitzvah Trust

The Mizpah Trust

The Mobbs Memorial Trust Ltd

The Modiano Charitable Trust

The Moette Charitable Trust

The Mole Charitable Trust

The Mollie Thomas Charitable Trust

The Monatrea Charitable Trust

The D C Moncrieff Charitable Trust

Monmouthshire County Council Welsh Church Act Fund

The Montague Thompson Coon Charitable Trust

The Colin Montgomerie Charitable Foundation

The Monument Trust

George A Moore Foundation

The Henry Moore Foundation

The Morel Charitable Trust

The Morgan Charitable Foundation

The Morgan Foundation

The Mr and Mrs J T Morgan Foundation

Morgan Stanley International Foundation

Diana and Allan Morgenthau Charitable Trust

The Oliver Morland Charitable Trust

S C and M E Morland's Charitable Trust

The Bernard Morris Charitable Trust

The Morris Charitable Trust

The Willie and Mabel Morris Charitable Trust

The Peter Morrison Charitable Foundation

The Stanley Morrison Charitable Trust

Moshal Charitable Trust

Vyoel Moshe Charitable Trust

The Moshulu Charitable Trust

Brian and Jill Moss Charitable Trust

The Moss Charitable Trust

The Robert and Margaret Moss Charitable Trust

The Moss Family Charitable Trust

Mosselson Charitable Trust

The Mount Everest Foundation

The Edwina Mountbatten Trust

Mountbatten Festival of Music

The Mountbatten Memorial Trust

Mrs Waterhouse Charitable Trust

The Mugdock Children's Trust

The Mulberry Trust

Frederick Mulder Charitable Trust

The Edith Murphy Foundation

Murphy-Neumann Charity Company Limited

Peter John Murray Trust

The Mushroom Fund

The Music Sales Charitable Trust

Muslim Hands

The Mutual Trust Group

MW (CL) Foundation

MW (GK) Foundation

MW (HO) Foundation

MW (RH) Foundation

MYA Charitable Trust

The Kitty and Daniel Nabarro Charitable Trust

The Nadezhda Charitable Trust

The Naggar Charitable Trust

The Eleni Nakou Foundation

The Janet Nash Charitable Settlement

The National Churches Trust

The National Manuscripts Conservation Trust

The Nationwide Foundation

Needham Market and Barking Welfare Charities

The Worshipful Company of Needlemakers' Charitable Fund

The Neighbourly Charitable Trust

The James Neill Trust Fund

Nemoral Ltd

Nesswall Ltd

The New Appeals Organisation for the City and County of Nottingham

Newby Trust Limited

The Newcomen Collett Foundation

Newpier Charity Ltd

The Night Garden Charity

The Chevras Ezras Nitzrochim Trust

NJD Charitable Trust

Alice Noakes Memorial Charitable Trust

Nominet Charitable Foundation

The Noon Foundation

The Norda Trust

Norie Charitable Trust

Normalyn Charitable Trust

The Norman Family Charitable Trust

The Duncan Norman Trust Fund

The Normanby Charitable Trust

The North West Cancer Research Fund

The Northampton Municipal Church Charities

The Northampton Queen's Institute Relief in Sickness Fund

The Earl of Northampton's Charity

The Northcott Devon Medical
  Foundation
The Community Foundation for
  Northern Ireland
The Northern Rock Foundation
The Northmoor Trust
The Northumberland Village
  Homes Trust
The Northwood Charitable
  Trust
The Norton Foundation
The Norwich Church of England
  Young Men's Society
The Norwich Town Close
  Estate Charity
The Norwood and Newton
  Settlement
The Noswad Charity
The Nottingham General
  Dispensary
The Nottingham Gordon
  Memorial Trust for Boys
  and Girls
Nottinghamshire Community
  Foundation
The Nottinghamshire Historic
  Churches Trust
The Nottinghamshire Miners'
  Welfare Trust Fund
Novi Most International
The Nuffield Foundation
Nutrisport Trust
The Father O'Mahoney
  Memorial Trust
The Sir Peter O'Sullevan
  Charitable Trust
The Oak Trust
The Oakdale Trust
The Oakmoor Charitable Trust
The Odin Charitable Trust
The Ofenheim Charitable Trust
Ogilvie Charities Deed No.2
  (including the Charity of
  Mary Catherine Ford Smith)
The Ogle Christian Trust
The Oikonomia Trust
Oizer Charitable Trust
The Old Broad Street Charity
  Trust
Old Possum's Practical Trust
The John Oldacre Foundation
The Oldham Foundation
The Olga Charitable Trust
Open Gate
The Raymond Oppenheimer
  Foundation
Ormonde Foundation
The Ormsby Charitable Trust
The Orrin Charitable Trust
The O'Sullivan Family
  Charitable Trust
The Ouseley Trust
The Owen Family Trust
Oxfam (GB)
The Oxfordshire Community
  Foundation
The P F Charitable Trust

Padwa Charitable Foundation
The Paget Charitable Trust
The Paladin Vince-Odozi
  Charitable Trust
The Palmer Foundation
The Panacea Society
Panahpur (previously Panahpur
  Charitable Trust)
Panton Trust
The Paphitis Charitable Trust
The Paragon Trust
Paraton Trust
The Park Charitable Trust
The Park House Charitable
  Trust
The Frank Parkinson
  Agricultural Trust
The Samuel and Freda
  Parkinson Charitable Trust
The Parthenon Trust
Arthur James Paterson
  Charitable Trust
The Constance Paterson
  Charitable Trust
Miss M E Swinton Paterson's
  Charitable Trust
The Patrick Charitable Trust
The Jack Patston Charitable
  Trust
Ambika Paul Foundation
Paycare Charity Trust
The Payne Charitable Trust
The Harry Payne Trust
The Peacock Charitable Trust
The Susanna Peake Charitable
  Trust
The Pears Family Charitable
  Foundation
The Pedmore Sporting Club
  Trust Fund
The Dowager Countess
  Eleanor Peel Trust
Pegasus (Stanley) Trust
The Pell Charitable Trust
The Peltz Trust
The Pen Shell Project
The Pennycress Trust
People's Postcode Trust
The Performing Right Society
  Foundation
B E Perl Charitable Trust
The Persson Charitable Trust
The Persula Foundation
The Jack Petchey Foundation
The Petplan Charitable Trust
The Pharsalia Charitable Trust
The Philips and Rubens
  Charitable Trust
The Phillips Charitable Trust
The Phillips Family Charitable
  Trust
Philological Foundation
The David Pickford Charitable
  Foundation
The Pickwell Foundation
The Pilgrim Trust

The Cecil Pilkington Charitable
  Trust
The Elise Pilkington Charitable
  Trust
The Pilkington Charities Fund
The Austin and Hope
  Pilkington Trust
The Sir Harry Pilkington Trust
The Col W W Pilkington Will
  Trusts The General Charity
  Fund
Miss A M Pilkington's
  Charitable Trust
The DLA Piper Charitable Trust
The Worshipful Company of
  Plaisterers Charitable Trust
The Platinum Trust
G S Plaut Charitable Trust
  Limited
Polden-Puckham Charitable
  Foundation
The Polestar Digital
  Foundation
The George and Esme Pollitzer
  Charitable Settlement
The J S F Pollitzer Charitable
  Settlement
The Polonsky Foundation
The Ponton House Trust
Edith and Ferdinand Porjes
  Charitable Trust
The John Porter Charitable
  Trust
The Porter Foundation
Porticus UK
The Portrack Charitable Trust
The J E Posnansky Charitable
  Trust
The Mary Potter Convent
  Hospital Trust
The David and Elaine Potter
  Foundation
The Powell Foundation
The W L Pratt Charitable Trust
The Premier League Charitable
  Fund
Premierquote Ltd
Premishlaner Charitable Trust
The Lucy Price Relief-in-Need
  Charity
Sir John Priestman Charity
  Trust
The Primrose Trust
The Prince of Wales's
  Charitable Foundation
Princess Anne's Charities
Prison Service Charity Fund
The Privy Purse Charitable
  Trust
The Proven Family Trust
The Provincial Grand Charity of
  the Province of Derbyshire
The Puebla Charitable Trust
The Richard and Christine
  Purchas Charitable Trust
The Puri Foundation

Mr and Mrs J A Pye's
   Charitable Settlement
The Quarry Family Charitable
   Trust
Quartet Community Foundation
The Queen Anne's Gate
   Foundation
The Queen's Silver Jubilee
   Trust
Quercus Trust
Quothquan Trust
R J M Charitable Trust
R S Charitable Trust
The R V W Trust
The Monica Rabagliati
   Charitable Trust
Rachel Charitable Trust
The Racing Foundation
The Mr and Mrs Philip
   Rackham Charitable Trust
Richard Radcliffe Charitable
   Trust
The Radcliffe Trust
The Bishop Radford Trust
The Ragdoll Foundation
The Rainford Trust
The Peggy Ramsay Foundation
The Joseph and Lena Randall
   Charitable Trust
The Rank Foundation Limited
The Joseph Rank Trust
Ranworth Trust
The Fanny Rapaport Charitable
   Settlement
The Ratcliff Foundation
The Ratcliff Pension Charity
The Ratcliffe Charitable Trust
The E L Rathbone Charitable
   Trust
The Eleanor Rathbone
   Charitable Trust
The Sigrid Rausing Trust
The Ravensdale Trust
The Rawdon-Smith Trust
The Rayden Charitable Trust
The Roger Raymond Charitable
   Trust
The Rayne Foundation
The Rayne Trust
The Sir James Reckitt Charity
Eva Reckitt Trust Fund
The Red Arrows Trust
The Red Rose Charitable Trust
The C A Redfern Charitable
   Foundation
The Reed Foundation
The John and Sally Reeve
   Charitable Trust
Richard Reeve's Foundation
The Max Reinhardt Charitable
   Trust
Relief Fund for Romania
   Limited
REMEDI
The Rest Harrow Trust
Reuben Foundation

The Nathaniel Reyner Trust
   Fund
The Rhododendron Trust
Daisie Rich Trust
The Clive Richards Charity
The Richmond Parish Lands
   Charity
Ridgesave Limited
The Ripple Effect Foundation
The Sir John Ritblat Family
   Foundation
The River Trust
Thomas Roberts Trust
The Robertson Trust
Robyn Charitable Trust
The Rochester Bridge Trust
The Rock Foundation
The Rock Solid Trust
The Roddick Foundation
The Rofeh Trust
Rokach Family Charitable Trust
The Helen Roll Charitable
   Trust
The Sir James Roll Charitable
   Trust
The Roman Research Trust
The C A Rookes Charitable
   Trust
The Rosca Trust
The Cecil Rosen Foundation
Rosetrees Trust
The Rothermere Foundation
The Rotherwick Foundation
The Roughley Charitable Trust
Mrs Gladys Row Fogo
   Charitable Trust
Rowanville Ltd
The Christopher Rowbotham
   Charitable Trust
The Rowing Foundation
The Rowlands Trust
The Joseph Rowntree
   Charitable Trust
The Joseph Rowntree
   Foundation
Royal Artillery Charitable Fund
Royal British Legion
Royal Docks Trust (London)
Royal Masonic Trust for Girls
   and Boys
The Rubin Foundation
William Arthur Rudd Memorial
   Trust
The Russell Trust
Ryklow Charitable Trust 1992
   (also known as A B
   Williamson Charitable Trust)
The J S and E C Rymer
   Charitable Trust
S F Foundation
S O Charitable Trust
The Jeremy and John Sacher
   Charitable Trust
The Michael Harry Sacher
   Trust
The Sackler Trust
The Ruzin Sadagora Trust

The Saddlers' Company
   Charitable Fund
The Saga Charitable Trust
The Jean Sainsbury Animal
   Welfare Trust
The Alan and Babette
   Sainsbury Charitable Fund
The Sainsbury Family
   Charitable Trusts
Saint Sarkis Charity Trust
The Saintbury Trust
The Saints and Sinners Trust
The Salamander Charitable
   Trust
The Salt Trust
Salters' Charitable Foundation
The Andrew Salvesen
   Charitable Trust
Basil Samuel Charitable Trust
Coral Samuel Charitable Trust
The M J Samuel Charitable
   Trust
The Peter Samuel Charitable
   Trust
The Samworth Foundation
The Sandra Charitable Trust
Santander UK Foundation
   Limited
The Peter Saunders Trust
The Scarfe Charitable Trust
The Schapira Charitable Trust
The Annie Schiff Charitable
   Trust
The Schmidt-Bodner Charitable
   Trust
The R H Scholes Charitable
   Trust
The Schreib Trust
The Schreiber Charitable Trust
Schroder Charity Trust
The Schuster Charitable Trust
Foundation Scotland
Scott (Eredine) Charitable
   Trust
The Francis C Scott Charitable
   Trust
The Frieda Scott Charitable
   Trust
Sir Samuel Scott of Yews
   Trust
The Sir James and Lady Scott
   Trust
The Scott Trust Foundation
The Storrow Scott Will Trust
Scottish Coal Industry Special
   Welfare Fund
The Scottish International
   Education Trust
The Scouloudi Foundation
Seafarers UK (King George's
   Fund for Sailors)
Seamen's Hospital Society
The Searchlight Electric
   Charitable Trust
The Searle Charitable Trust
The Samuel Sebba Charitable
   Trust

The Seedfield Trust
Sellata Ltd
SEM Charitable Trust
The Seneca Trust
The Ayrton Senna Foundation
The Seven Fifty Trust
The Cyril Shack Trust
The Jean Shanks Foundation
The Shanti Charitable Trust
ShareGift (The Orr Mackintosh
    Foundation)
The Linley Shaw Foundation
The Shears Foundation
The Sheepdrove Trust
The Sheffield and District
    Hospital Services
    Charitable Fund
The Sheldon Trust
The Patricia and Donald
    Shepherd Charitable Trust
The Sylvia and Colin Shepherd
    Charitable Trust
The Archie Sherman Cardiff
    Foundation
The Archie Sherman Charitable
    Trust
The R C Sherriff Trust
The Shetland Charitable Trust
SHINE (Support and Help in
    Education)
The Barnett and Sylvia Shine
    No 2 Charitable Trust
The Bassil Shippam and
    Alsford Trust
The Shipwrights' Company
    Charitable Fund
The Shirley Foundation
Shlomo Memorial Fund Limited
The J A Shone Memorial Trust
Community Foundation for
    Shropshire and Telford
The Barbara A Shuttleworth
    Memorial Trust
The Mary Elizabeth Siebel
    Charity
David and Jennifer Sieff
    Charitable Trust
The Julius Silman Charitable
    Trust
The Leslie Silver Charitable
    Trust
The Simmons & Simmons
    Charitable Foundation
The Simpson Foundation
The Huntly and Margery
    Sinclair Charitable Trust
Sino-British Fellowship Trust
The Skelton Bounty
The Charles Skey Charitable
    Trust
Skipton Building Society
    Charitable Foundation
The John Slater Foundation
Rita and David Slowe
    Charitable Trust
Ruth Smart Foundation
The SMB Charitable Trust

The Mrs Smith and Mount
    Trust
The N Smith Charitable
    Settlement
The E H Smith Charitable Trust
The Smith Charitable Trust
The Henry Smith Charity
The Leslie Smith Foundation
The Martin Smith Foundation
The Stanley Smith UK
    Horticultural Trust
Philip Smith's Charitable Trust
Smithcorp Charitable Trust
The R C Snelling Charitable
    Trust
The Snowball Trust
The Sobell Foundation
Solev Co Ltd
The Solo Charitable
    Settlement
Dr Richard Solomon's
    Charitable Trust
David Solomons Charitable
    Trust
Songdale Ltd
The E C Sosnow Charitable
    Trust
The Souter Charitable Trust
The South Square Trust
The Stephen R and Philippa H
    Southall Charitable Trust
The W F Southall Trust
R H Southern Trust
The Southwold Trust
The Sovereign Health Care
    Charitable Trust
Spar Charitable Fund
Sparks Charity (Sport Aiding
    Medical Research For Kids)
Sparquote Limited
The Spear Charitable Trust
Spears-Stutz Charitable Trust
The Jessie Spencer Trust
The Ralph and Irma Sperring
    Charity
The Spielman Charitable Trust
The Spoore, Merry and Rixman
    Foundation
Sported Foundation
Rosalyn and Nicholas Springer
    Charitable Trust
Springfields Employees'
    Medical Research and
    Charity Trust Fund
Springrule Limited
The Spurrell Charitable Trust
The Geoff and Fiona Squire
    Foundation
St Hilda's Trust
St James' Trust Settlement
Sir Walter St John's
    Educational Charity
St Michael's and All Saints'
    Charities Relief Branch (The
    Church Houses Relief in
    Need Charity)

The Late St Patrick White
    Charitable Trust
St Teilo's Trust
The Stafford Trust
The Stanley Foundation Ltd
The Stanton Ballard Charitable
    Trust
The Staples Trust
The Star Charitable Trust
The Peter Stebbings Memorial
    Charity
The Steinberg Family
    Charitable Trust
The Hugh Stenhouse
    Foundation
The Stephen Barry Charitable
    Trust
C E K Stern Charitable Trust
The Sigmund Sternberg
    Charitable Foundation
Stervon Ltd
The Stevenage Community
    Trust
The June Stevens Foundation
Stevenson Family's Charitable
    Trust
The Steventon Allotments and
    Relief-in-Need Charity
The Stewards' Charitable Trust
The Stewards' Company
    Limited (incorporating the J
    W Laing Trust and the J W
    Laing Biblical Scholarship
    Trust)
Sir Halley Stewart Trust
The David and Deborah
    Stileman Charitable Trust
The Stobart Newlands
    Charitable Trust
The Edward Stocks-Massey
    Bequest Fund
The Stokenchurch Educational
    Charity
The Stoller Charitable Trust
The M J C Stone Charitable
    Trust
The Samuel Storey Family
    Charitable Trust
Peter Stormonth Darling
    Charitable Trust
Peter Storrs Trust
The Strangward Trust
The Strasser Foundation
Stratford upon Avon Town
    Trust
The W O Street Charitable
    Foundation
The A B Strom and R Strom
    Charitable Trust
The Sudborough Foundation
Sueberry Ltd
Suffolk Community Foundation
The Suffolk Historic Churches
    Trust
The Alan Sugar Foundation
The Summerfield Charitable
    Trust

The Sunny Skies Foundation
The Surrey Historic Buildings
    Trust Ltd
The Sussex Historic Churches
    Trust
The Adrienne and Leslie
    Sussman Charitable Trust
The Sutasoma Trust
The Sutton Trust
Swan Mountain Trust
Swansea and Brecon Diocesan
    Board of Finance Limited
The John Swire (1989)
    Charitable Trust
The Swire Charitable Trust
The Adrian Swire Charitable
    Trust
The Hugh and Ruby Sykes
    Charitable Trust
The Charles and Elsie Sykes
    Trust
The Sylvanus Charitable Trust
The Stella Symons Charitable
    Trust
The Tabeel Trust
The Tajtelbaum Charitable
    Trust
The Talbot Trusts
Tallow Chandlers Benevolent
    Fund
Talteg Ltd
The Tangent Charitable Trust
The Lady Tangye Charitable
    Trust
The David Tannen Charitable
    Trust
The Tanner Trust
The Lili Tapper Charitable
    Foundation
The Mrs A Lacy Tate Trust
The Taurus Foundation
The Tay Charitable Trust
C B and H H Taylor 1984 Trust
Humphrey Richardson Taylor
    Charitable Trust
The Connie and Albert Taylor
    Charitable Trust
The Cyril Taylor Charitable
    Trust
A P Taylor Trust
Rosanna Taylor's 1987 Charity
    Trust
Tearfund
The Tedworth Charitable Trust
Tees Valley Community
    Foundation
Tegham Limited
The Templeton Goodwill Trust
The Ten Ten Charitable Trust
Tesco Charity Trust
The C Paul Thackray General
    Charitable Trust
Thackray Medical Research
    Trust
The Thames Wharf Charity
The John P. Gommes
    Foundation

The Thistle Trust
The Loke Wan Tho Memorial
    Foundation
The David Thomas Charitable
    Trust
The Thomas Lilley Memorial
    Trust
The Arthur and Margaret
    Thompson Charitable Trust
The Maurice and Vivien
    Thompson Charitable Trust
The Thompson Family
    Charitable Trust
The Thompson Family
    Foundation
The Thompson6 Charitable
    Trust
The Len Thomson Charitable
    Trust
The Sir Jules Thorn Charitable
    Trust
The Thornton Foundation
The Thornton Trust
The Thousandth Man –
    Richard Burns Charitable
    Trust
The Three Guineas Trust
The Three Oaks Trust
The Thriplow Charitable Trust
The John Raymond Tijou
    Charitable Trust
Mrs R P Tindall's Charitable
    Trust
The Tinsley Foundation
The Tisbury Telegraph Trust
The Tobacco Pipe Makers and
    Tobacco Trade Benevolent
    Fund
The Tolkien Trust
Tomchei Torah Charitable
    Trust
The Tompkins Foundation
The Torah Temimah Trust
Toras Chesed (London) Trust
The Tory Family Foundation
Tottenham Grammar School
    Foundation
The Tower Hill Trust
The Towry Law Charitable Trust
    (also known as the Castle
    Educational Trust)
The Toye Foundation
The TPO Foundation
The Mayor of Trafford's Charity
    Fund
Annie Tranmer Charitable Trust
The Constance Travis
    Charitable Trust
The Treeside Trust
The Trefoil Trust
The Tresillian Trust
The Triangle Trust (1949) Fund
The True Colours Trust
Truedene Co. Ltd
The Truemark Trust
Truemart Limited
Trumros Limited

The Trusthouse Charitable
    Foundation
The Tsukanov Family
    Foundation
The James Tudor Foundation
Tudor Rose Ltd
The Tudor Trust
The Tufton Charitable Trust
Tuixen Foundation
The R D Turner Charitable
    Trust
The Douglas Turner Trust
The Florence Turner Trust
The G J W Turner Trust
Miss S M Tutton Charitable
    Trust
The TUUT Charitable Trust
Two Ridings Community
    Foundation
The Tyche Charitable Trust
Community Foundation Serving
    Tyne and Wear and
    Northumberland
Trustees of Tzedakah
The Udlington Trust
UKI Charitable Foundation
Ulster Garden Villages Ltd
Ultach Trust
The Ulverscroft Foundation
Ulverston Town Lands Charity
The Underwood Trust
The Union of Orthodox Hebrew
    Congregation
The United Society for the
    Propagation of the Gospel
The David Uri Memorial Trust
Uxbridge United Welfare Trust
Vale of Glamorgan – Welsh
    Church Fund
The Valentine Charitable Trust
The Valiant Charitable Trust
The Albert Van Den Bergh
    Charitable Trust
The Van Neste Foundation
Mrs Maud Van Norden's
    Charitable Foundation
The Vandervell Foundation
The Vardy Foundation
The Variety Club Children's
    Charity
The Verdon-Smith Family
    Charitable Settlement
Roger Vere Foundation
Victoria Homes Trust
The Nigel Vinson Charitable
    Trust
The William and Ellen Vinten
    Trust
The Vintners' Company
    Charitable Foundation
Vintners' Gifts Charity
Vivdale Ltd
The Viznitz Foundation
Volant Charitable Trust
Wade's Charity
The Scurrah Wainwright Charity
The Wakefield and Tetley Trust

Wakeham Trust
The Community Foundation in Wales
Wales Council for Voluntary Action
Robert and Felicity Waley-Cohen Charitable Trust
The Thomas Wall Trust
Wallace and Gromit's Children's Foundation
The F J Wallis Charitable Settlement
War on Want
Sir Siegmund Warburg's Voluntary Settlement
The Ward Blenkinsop Trust
The George Ward Charitable Trust
The Barbara Ward Children's Foundation
G R Waters Charitable Trust 2000
The Wates Foundation
Blyth Watson Charitable Trust
The Howard Watson Symington Memorial Charity
John Watson's Trust
Waynflete Charitable Trust
Weatherley Charitable Trust
The Weavers' Company Benevolent Fund
The David Webster Charitable Trust
Weedon Family Trust
The Weinberg Foundation
The Weinstein Foundation
The Weinstock Fund
The Joir and Kato Weisz Foundation
The Wellcome Trust
Welsh Church Fund Dyfed area (Carmarthenshire, Ceredigion and Pembrokeshire)
The Welton Foundation
The Wessex Youth Trust
The West Derby Wastelands Charity
West London Synagogue Charitable Fund
West Yorkshire Police Community Trust
Mrs S K West's Charitable Trust
The Westcroft Trust
The Westminster Foundation
The Garfield Weston Foundation
The Barbara Whatmore Charitable Trust
The Whitaker Charitable Trust
The Colonel W H Whitbread Charitable Trust
The Simon Whitbread Charitable Trust
The Melanie White Foundation Limited

White Stuff Foundation
The Whitecourt Charitable Trust
A H and B C Whiteley Charitable Trust
The Norman Whiteley Trust
The Whitewater Charitable Trust
The Whitley Animal Protection Trust
The Whittlesey Charity
The Lionel Wigram Memorial Trust
The Felicity Wilde Charitable Trust
The Wilkinson Charitable Foundation
The Will Charitable Trust
The Charity of William Williams
The Kay Williams Charitable Foundation
The Williams Charitable Trust
The Williams Family Charitable Trust
Williams Serendipity Trust
The HDH Wills 1965 Charitable Trust
The Dame Violet Wills Will Trust
The Wilmcote Charitrust
Sumner Wilson Charitable Trust
David Wilson Foundation
The Wilson Foundation
J and J R Wilson Trust
The Community Foundation for Wiltshire and Swindon
The Windruff Charitable Trust
The Benjamin Winegarten Charitable Trust
The Harold Hyam Wingate Foundation
The Francis Winham Foundation
Wirral Mayor's Charity
The James Wise Charitable Trust
The Witzenfeld Foundation
The Michael and Anna Wix Charitable Trust
The Wixamtree Trust
The Woburn 1986 Charitable Trust
The Maurice Wohl Charitable Foundation
The Charles Wolfson Charitable Trust
The James Wood Bequest Fund
The Wood Family Trust
The Woodcock Charitable Trust
Woodlands Green Ltd
Woodlands Trust
Woodroffe Benton Foundation
The Woodward Charitable Trust

The A and R Woolf Charitable Trust
ME Woolfe Charitable Trust
Worcester Municipal Charities
The Worcestershire and Dudley Historic Churches Trust
The Wragge and Co. Charitable Trust
The Diana Edgson Wright Charitable Trust
The Wright Vigar Charitable Trust
The Matthews Wrightson Charity Trust
Miss E B Wrightson's Charitable Settlement
The Joan Wyatt Charitable Trust
Wychdale Ltd
Wychville Ltd
The Wyndham Charitable Trust
The Wyseliot Charitable Trust
The Xerox (UK) Trust
Yankov Charitable Trust
The Dennis Alan Yardy Charitable Trust
The W Wing Yip and Brothers Foundation
Yorkshire Agricultural Society
The South Yorkshire Community Foundation
The Yorkshire Dales Millennium Trust
You Gossip Foundation
The John Young Charitable Settlement
The William Allen Young Charitable Trust
The John K Young Endowment Fund
Youth United Foundation
Zephyr Charitable Trust
The Marjorie and Arnold Ziff Charitable Foundation
Stephen Zimmerman Charitable Trust
The Zochonis Charitable Trust
The Zolfo Cooper Foundation

....

■ Replacement of statutory funding

The 1970 Trust
The 29th May 1961 Charitable Trust
The Aberdeen Endowments Trust
The Sylvia Adams Charitable Trust
The Sylvia Aitken Charitable Trust
The Archer Trust
The Ardwick Trust
The Ashden Trust
The Ashworth Charitable Trust

Lord Barnby's Foundation
The Paul Bassham Charitable
Trust
The Jack and Ada Beattie
Foundation
The Bellinger Donnay Trust
The Bingham Trust
The Blagrave Trust
John and Susan Bowers Fund
The Tony Bramall Charitable
Trust
Edna Brown Charitable
Settlement (Mrs E E Brown
Charitable Settlement)
Buckinghamshire Community
Foundation
The G W Cadbury Charitable
Trust
CAF (Charities Aid Foundation)
The Campden Charities
Trustee
The Worshipful Company of
Carmen Benevolent Trust
The Cattanach Charitable Trust
The Charities Advisory Trust
Christian Aid
The City Educational Trust
Fund
Colyer-Fergusson Charitable
Trust
The Ernest Cook Trust
The Alice Ellen Cooper Dean
Charitable Foundation
The General Charities of the
City of Coventry
Cruden Foundation Ltd
The Cwmbran Trust
The D G Charitable Settlement
The Demigryphon Trust
Dorset Community Foundation
The Double 'O' Charity Ltd
The W E Dunn Trust
Earls Colne and Halstead
Educational Charity
The Vernon N Ely Charitable
Trust
The Essex Fairway Charitable
Trust
Federation of Jewish Relief
Organisations
The Doris Field Charitable
Trust
The Fifty Fund
The Fitton Trust
The Football Foundation
The Oliver Ford Charitable
Trust
The Foresters' Fund for
Children
Garrick Charitable Trust
The Girdlers' Company
Charitable Trust
Global Care
The Goldsmiths' Company
Charity
The Graff Foundation
The Grange Farm Centre Trust

Grantham Yorke Trust
The Great Stone Bridge Trust
of Edenbridge
The Great Torrington Town
Lands Charity
Greenham Common
Community Trust Limited
The Hadrian Trust
E F and M G Hall Charitable
Trust
The Hamamelis Trust
The W A Handley Charitable
Trust
Miss K M Harbinson's
Charitable Trust
The Harding Trust
Headley-Pitt Charitable Trust
The Hesslewood Children's
Trust (Hull Seamen's and
General Orphanage)
The Hilden Charitable Fund
Hope for Youth (NI)
Hulme Trust Estates
(Educational)
Miss Agnes H Hunter's Trust
Huntingdon Freemen's Trust
The Nani Huyu Charitable Trust
C Richard Jackson Charitable
Trust
The Jarman Charitable Trust
The Karenza Foundation
The Robert Kiln Charitable
Trust
The Mary Kinross Charitable
Trust
Mrs Vera Leigh's Charity
Lesley Lesley and Mutter Trust
The Enid Linder Foundation
The Second Joseph Aaron
Littman Foundation
The MacRobert Trust
The Leslie and Lilian Manning
Trust
The D C Moncrieff Charitable
Trust
Mothercare Group Foundation
Muslim Hands
The Northmoor Trust
The Odin Charitable Trust
The Old Broad Street Charity
Trust
The Owen Family Trust
The Harry Payne Trust
The Mary Potter Convent
Hospital Trust
The Prince of Wales's
Charitable Foundation
The Provincial Grand Charity of
the Province of Derbyshire
The Mr and Mrs Philip
Rackham Charitable Trust
The Ragdoll Foundation
The Joseph and Lena Randall
Charitable Trust
The E L Rathbone Charitable
Trust
The Ravensdale Trust

The Rayne Trust
The Rest Harrow Trust
The Rhododendron Trust
The Rosca Trust
Sir Samuel Scott of Yews
Trust
The John Slater Foundation
The St Laurence Relief In
Need Trust
The Summerfield Charitable
Trust
C B and H H Taylor 1984 Trust
The Cyril Taylor Charitable
Trust
Tesco Charity Trust
The Thousandth Man –
Richard Burns Charitable
Trust
The Tobacco Pipe Makers and
Tobacco Trade Benevolent
Fund
Tottenham Grammar School
Foundation
The Tower Hill Trust
War on Want
The Whitaker Charitable Trust
The Norman Whiteley Trust
The Wilmcote Charitrust
The Community Foundation for
Wiltshire and Swindon
The Woburn 1986 Charitable
Trust
Woodlands Trust
The Wyndham Charitable Trust
The W Wing Yip and Brothers
Foundation
The John K Young Endowment
Fund
Stephen Zimmerman
Charitable Trust

....

■ Salaries

The 29th May 1961 Charitable
Trust
ABF The Soldiers' Charity
The Sylvia Adams Charitable
Trust
The AIM Foundation
The Alchemy Foundation
The Almond Trust
The Anchor Foundation
Anglo American Group
Foundation
The Ardwick Trust
The Armourers' and Brasiers'
Gauntlet Trust
The Ashley Family Foundation
The Ian Askew Charitable Trust
The Associated Country
Women of the World
AstonMansfield Charitable
Trust
The Aylesford Family
Charitable Trust

The Baily Thomas Charitable Fund

The Baker Charitable Trust

Lord Barnby's Foundation

Barnes Workhouse Fund

The Paul Bassham Charitable Trust

BBC Children in Need

The Jack and Ada Beattie Foundation

The Bedfordshire and Luton Community Foundation

The Bellhouse Foundation

The Berkshire Community Foundation

The Bingham Trust

The Boshier-Hinton Foundation

The Bower Trust

John and Susan Bowers Fund

The Breadsticks Foundation

The Breast Cancer Research Trust

The British Dietetic Association General and Education Trust Fund

The J and M Britton Charitable Trust

The Charles Brotherton Trust

Brown-Mellows Trust

Buckinghamshire Community Foundation

The E F Bulmer Benevolent Fund

The Clara E Burgess Charity

Peter Cadbury Charitable Trust

The Cadbury Foundation

CAF (Charities Aid Foundation)

The Cambridgeshire Community Foundation

The Camelia Trust

The Campden Charities Trustee

Cash for Kids Radio Clyde

The Cattanach Charitable Trust

The Chippenham Borough Lands Charity

The Church and Community Fund

Church Urban Fund

The City Bridge Trust

The Sir Jeremiah Colman Gift Trust

The Colt Foundation

Colwinston Charitable Trust

The Ernest Cook Trust

The Alice Ellen Cooper Dean Charitable Foundation

Michael Cornish Charitable Trust

County Durham Community Foundation

Cripplegate Foundation

The Peter Cruddas Foundation

The Cunningham Trust

Roald Dahl's Marvellous Children's Charity

The Hamilton Davies Trust

The J N Derbyshire Trust

Devon Community Foundation

The Dibden Allotments Fund

The Digbeth Trust Limited

Disability Aid Fund (The Roger and Jean Jefcoate Trust)

The Derek and Eileen Dodgson Foundation

Dorset Community Foundation

The Drapers' Charitable Fund

The Dunhill Medical Trust

Eastern Counties Educational Trust Limited

The Ellerdale Trust

The John Ellerman Foundation

Epilepsy Research UK

The Equitable Charitable Trust

The Essendon Charitable Trust

The Essex Fairway Charitable Trust

The Essex Youth Trust

Joseph Ettedgui Charitable Foundation

The Eveson Charitable Trust

Esmée Fairbairn Foundation

The John Feeney Charitable Trust

Fife Council/Common Good Funds and Trusts

Ford Britain Trust

The Donald Forrester Trust

The Foyle Foundation

Sydney E Franklin Deceased's New Second Charity

The Gordon Fraser Charitable Trust

The Freemasons' Grand Charity

The Fuserna Foundation General Charitable Trust

Gamlen Charitable Trust

Garrick Charitable Trust

The Gibbs Charitable Trust

Simon Gibson Charitable Trust

The Girdlers' Company Charitable Trust

The Goldsmiths' Company Charity

Greggs Foundation

The Hadfield Trust

The Hadley Trust

The Hadrian Trust

The Hamamelis Trust

Paul Hamlyn Foundation

Hampshire and Isle of Wight Community Foundation

The Harborne Parish Lands Charity

William Harding's Charity

The Kenneth Hargreaves Charitable Trust

The Harpur Trust

The Peter Harrison Foundation

Heart of England Community Foundation

Percy Hedley 1990 Charitable Trust

The P and C Hickinbotham Charitable Trust

Alan Edward Higgs Charity

The Holmes Family Trust (Sheffield)

P H Holt Foundation

The Edward Holt Trust

The Worshipful Company of Horners' Charitable Trusts

The Hunter Foundation

Miss Agnes H Hunter's Trust

International Spinal Research Trust

The Irish Youth Foundation (UK) Ltd (incorporating The Lawlor Foundation)

The ITF Seafarers Trust

The Barbara Joyce Jarrald Charitable Trust

Rees Jeffreys Road Fund

The Judith Trust

The Julian Budd Kids in Sport Trust Limited

The Boris Karloff Charitable Foundation

The Kelly Family Charitable Trust

The Kay Kendall Leukaemia Fund

William Kendall's Charity (Wax Chandlers' Company)

The Kennel Club Charitable Trust

The Peter Kershaw Trust

Keswick Hall Trust

Kingdom Way Trust

The Mary Kinross Charitable Trust

The Sir James Knott Trust

The K P Ladd Charitable Trust

LandAid Charitable Trust

The Allen Lane Foundation

The Edgar E Lawley Foundation

The Leathersellers' Company Charitable Fund

The Leverhulme Trust

The Joseph Levy Charitable Foundation

The Sir Edward Lewis Foundation

Lincolnshire Community Foundation

Lloyds Bank Foundation for England and Wales

Lloyds Bank Foundation for Northern Ireland

Lloyds TSB Foundation for Scotland

London Catalyst

John Lyon's Charity

The R S Macdonald Charitable Trust

The MacRobert Trust

W M Mann Foundation

The Jim Marshall Charitable Trust

John Martin's Charity

The John Mason Family Trust
The Nancie Massey Charitable Trust
The Mathew Trust
The Robert McAlpine Foundation
Meningitis Trust
The Menzies Charity Foundation
The Mercers' Charitable Foundation
The Mickel Fund
Gerald Micklem Charitable Trust
The Clare Milne Trust
The Mirianog Trust
The Modiano Charitable Trust
John Moores Foundation
The Morgan Charitable Foundation
Mothercare Group Foundation
The Mugdock Children's Trust
The Kitty and Daniel Nabarro Charitable Trust
The National Hockey Foundation
Nazareth Trust Fund
Needham Market and Barking Welfare Charities
Network for Social Change
The Frances and Augustus Newman Foundation
Alderman Newton's Educational Foundation
The Night Garden Charity
Normalyn Charitable Trust
The Northampton Municipal Church Charities
The Northcott Devon Foundation
The Northern Rock Foundation
The Northmoor Trust
The Nuffield Foundation
The Oakdale Trust
The Odin Charitable Trust
The Old Broad Street Charity Trust
The Paget Charitable Trust
The Paladin Vince-Odozi Charitable Trust
The Harry Payne Trust
People's Postcode Trust
The Pilgrim Trust
The Pilkington Charities Fund
The Col W W Pilkington Will Trusts The General Charity Fund
Polden-Puckham Charitable Foundation
The Powell Foundation
Princess Anne's Charities
The Racing Foundation
The Rainford Trust
The Rayne Trust
Relief Fund for Romania Limited
REMEDI

The Rhododendron Trust
The Roddick Foundation
The Joseph Rowntree Charitable Trust
Joseph Rowntree Reform Trust Limited
Royal British Legion
The Saddlers' Company Charitable Fund
The Saintbury Trust
The Salt Foundation
Santander UK Foundation Limited
The Frieda Scott Charitable Trust
The Sir James and Lady Scott Trust
Seafarers UK (King George's Fund for Sailors)
The Sheldon Trust
SHINE (Support and Help in Education)
The Shirley Foundation
The Simpson Education and Conservation Trust
Rita and David Slowe Charitable Trust
The Mrs Smith and Mount Trust
Social Business Trust (Scale-Up)
David Solomons Charitable Trust
R H Southern Trust
Sported Foundation
St Christopher's Educational Trust (incorporating the Hughes and Stevens Bequest)
St Hilda's Trust
St James's Place Foundation
Sir Walter St John's Educational Charity
The St Laurence Relief In Need Trust
The Steel Charitable Trust
Sir Halley Stewart Trust
Stratford upon Avon Town Trust
The Talbot Trusts
Tallow Chandlers Benevolent Fund
The Connie and Albert Taylor Charitable Trust
The Three Guineas Trust
The Thriplow Charitable Trust
Mrs R P Tindall's Charitable Trust
The Tolkien Trust
The Tompkins Foundation
The Constance Travis Charitable Trust
The Triangle Trust (1949) Fund
The Trusthouse Charitable Foundation
The James Tudor Foundation
The Tudor Trust

The Douglas Turner Trust
The Valiant Charitable Trust
Victoria Homes Trust
Volant Charitable Trust
Voluntary Action Fund (VAF)
The Scurrah Wainwright Charity
The Thomas Wall Trust
Sir Siegmund Warburg's Voluntary Settlement
The Waterloo Foundation
The Wates Foundation
The Weinstock Fund
The Westminster Foundation
The Whitaker Charitable Trust
The Simon Whitbread Charitable Trust
White Stuff Foundation
The Norman Whiteley Trust
The Whittlesey Charity
The Lionel Wigram Memorial Trust
Dame Violet Wills Charitable Trust
The Community Foundation for Wiltshire and Swindon
The Wixamtree Trust
The Wood Family Trust
Woodlands Trust
The Woodward Charitable Trust
The Wright Vigar Charitable Trust
The Joan Wyatt Charitable Trust
The Yapp Charitable Trust
The Yardley Great Trust
Youth Music (previously known as National Foundation for Youth Music)
Zurich Community Trust (UK) Limited

....

■ Strategic funding

The 1970 Trust
The 1989 Willan Charitable Trust
The 29th May 1961 Charitable Trust
The A B Charitable Trust
A W Charitable Trust
The Aberbrothock Skea Trust
ABF The Soldiers' Charity
Brian Abrams Charitable Trust
Eric Abrams Charitable Trust
The Acacia Charitable Trust
Achisomoch Aid Company Limited
The ACT Foundation
Action Medical Research
The Company of Actuaries' Charitable Trust Fund
The Sylvia Adams Charitable Trust
The Adamson Trust
The Victor Adda Foundation

Adenfirst Ltd
The Adint Charitable Trust
The Adnams Charity
AF Trust Company
Age Scotland
Age UK
Aid to the Church in Need (UK)
The Green and Lilian F M
    Ainsworth and Family
    Benevolent Fund
The Sylvia Aitken Charitable
    Trust
The Alabaster Trust
The Alborada Trust
D G Albright Charitable Trust
The Alchemy Foundation
Aldgate and All Hallows'
    Foundation
The Aldgate Freedom
    Foundation
The Alexis Trust
All Saints Educational Trust
Allchurches Trust Ltd
The H B Allen Charitable Trust
The Alliance Family Foundation
Angus Allnatt Charitable
    Foundation
The Pat Allsop Charitable Trust
The Almond Trust
Almondsbury Charity
The Altajir Trust
Altamont Ltd
Alvor Charitable Trust
The AM Charitable Trust
The Ammco Trust
Viscount Amory's Charitable
    Trust
The Ampelos Trust
The AMW Charitable Trust
The Anchor Foundation
The Andrew Anderson Trust
Andor Charitable Trust
Anglo American Group
    Foundation
Anguish's Educational
    Foundation
The Animal Defence Trust
The Eric Anker-Petersen
    Charity
The Annandale Charitable
    Trust
Anpride Ltd
The Anson Charitable Trust
The Apax Foundation
Ambrose and Ann Appelbe
    Trust
The Appletree Trust
Archbishop of Wales' Fund for
    Children
The John M Archer Charitable
    Trust
The Archer Trust
The Ardwick Trust
The Argentarius Foundation
The Argus Appeal
Armenian General Benevolent
    Union London Trust

The Armenian Relief Society of
    Great Britain Trust
The Armourers' and Brasiers'
    Gauntlet Trust
The Arsenal Foundation
The Artemis Charitable Trust
The Arts and Entertainment
    Charitable Trust
Arts Council England
The Arts Council of Northern
    Ireland
Arts Council of Wales (also
    known as Cyngor
    Celfyddydau Cymru)
The Ove Arup Foundation
The A S Charitable Trust
Ashburnham Thanksgiving
    Trust
A J H Ashby Will Trust
The Ashden Trust
The Ashendene Trust
The Ashley Family Foundation
The Ian Askew Charitable Trust
The Associated Country
    Women of the World
The Association of Colleges
    Charitable Trust
Astellas European Foundation
Asthma UK
The Astor Foundation
The Astor of Hever Trust
The Aurelius Charitable Trust
The Avon and Somerset Police
    Community Trust
The BAA Communities Trust
Harry Bacon Foundation
The Scott Bader
    Commonwealth Ltd
Bag4Sport Foundation
The Bagri Foundation
Veta Bailey Charitable Trust
The Austin Bailey Foundation
The Baily Thomas Charitable
    Fund
The Baird Trust
The Baker Charitable Trust
The Roy and Pixie Baker
    Charitable Trust
The Balcombe Charitable Trust
The Albert Casanova Ballard
    Deceased Trust
The Ballinger Charitable Trust
Balmain Charitable Trust
The Balmore Trust
The Balney Charitable Trust
The Baltic Charitable Fund
The Bamford Charitable
    Foundation
The Banbury Charities
William P Bancroft (No 2)
    Charitable Trust and
    Jenepher Gillett Trust
The Band Trust
The Barbers' Company General
    Charities
The Barbour Foundation
The Barcapel Foundation

Barchester Healthcare
    Foundation
The Barclay Foundation
The Baring Foundation
Peter Barker-Mill Memorial
    Charity
The Barleycorn Trust
Lord Barnby's Foundation
Barnes Workhouse Fund
The Barnsbury Charitable Trust
The Barnwood House Trust
The Misses Barrie Charitable
    Trust
Barrington Family Charitable
    Trust
Bartholomew Charitable Trust
The Bartlett Taylor Charitable
    Trust
The Paul Bassham Charitable
    Trust
The Bates Charitable Trust
Bay Charitable Trust
The Bay Tree Charitable Trust
The Louis Baylis (Maidenhead
    Advertiser) Charitable Trust
BBC Children in Need
BC Partners Foundation
B-CH 1971 Charitable Trust
The Beacon Trust
Bear Mordechai Ltd
The Bearder Charity
The James Beattie Charitable
    Trust
The Jack and Ada Beattie
    Foundation
Beauland Ltd
The Beaverbrook Foundation
The Beccles Town Lands
    Charity
The Becker Family Charitable
    Trust
The Becketts and Sargeants
    Educational Foundation
The John Beckwith Charitable
    Trust
The Peter Beckwith Charitable
    Trust
The Bedfordshire and Luton
    Community Foundation
The David and Ruth Behrend
    Fund
The Beit Trust
The Bellahouston Bequest
    Fund
Bellasis Trust
The Bellhouse Foundation
The Bellinger Donnay Trust
The Benfield Motors Charitable
    Trust
The Benham Charitable
    Settlement
Maurice and Jacqueline
    Bennett Charitable Trust
Michael and Lesley Bennett
    Charitable Trust
The Gerald Bentall Charitable
    Trust

Bergqvist Charitable Trust

The Ruth Berkowitz Charitable Trust

The Berkshire Community Foundation

The Bestway Foundation

BHST

The Mason Bibby 1981 Trust

The Bideford Bridge Trust

The Big Lottery Fund

The Billmeir Charitable Trust

The Bingham Trust

The Bintaub Charitable Trust

Birmingham & Black Country Community Foundation

The Birmingham District Nursing Charitable Trust

The Birmingham Hospital Saturday Fund Medical Charity and Welfare Trust

Birmingham International Airport Community Trust

The Lord Mayor of Birmingham's Charity

Birthday House Trust

The Michael Bishop Foundation

The Bishop's Development Fund

The Bertie Black Foundation

Blackheart Foundation (UK) Limited

Isabel Blackman Foundation

The BlackRock (UK) Charitable Trust

The Blagrave Trust

The Blair Foundation

Blakemore Foundation

The Blanchminster Trust

The Blandford Lake Trust

The Sir Victor Blank Charitable Settlement

The Neville and Elaine Blond Charitable Trust

The Bluston Charitable Settlement

The Nicholas Boas Charitable Trust

The Body Shop Foundation

The Boltons Trust

The Bonamy Charitable Trust

The John and Celia Bonham Christie Charitable Trust

The Charlotte Bonham-Carter Charitable Trust

Bonhomie United Charity Society

The Booth Charities

The Boots Charitable Trust

Salo Bordon Charitable Trust

The Bordon Liphook Haslemere Charity

The Oliver Borthwick Memorial Trust

The Boshier-Hinton Foundation

The Bothwell Charitable Trust

H E and E L Botteley Charitable Trust

The Harry Bottom Charitable Trust

P G and N J Boulton Trust

The A H and E Boulton Trust

Sir Clive Bourne Family Trust

The Anthony Bourne Foundation

Bourneheights Limited

The Bower Trust

The Bowerman Charitable Trust

John and Susan Bowers Fund

The Bowland Charitable Trust

The Frank Brake Charitable Trust

The William Brake Charitable Trust

The Tony Bramall Charitable Trust

The Bransford Trust

The Breadsticks Foundation

Bridgepoint Charitable Trust

The Harold and Alice Bridges Charity

Briggs Animal Welfare Trust

Bristol Archdeaconry Charity

The Bristol Charities

John Bristow and Thomas Mason Trust

The British Council for Prevention of Blindness

The British Dietetic Association General and Education Trust Fund

The British Gas (Scottish Gas) Energy Trust

British Heart Foundation

British Humane Association

British Institute at Ankara

British Ornithologists' Union

British Record Industry Trust

The J and M Britton Charitable Trust

The Bromley Trust

The Roger Brooke Charitable Trust

The David Brooke Charity

The Rory and Elizabeth Brooks Foundation

Joseph Brough Charitable Trust

The Swinfen Broun Charitable Trust

Bill Brown 1998 Charitable Trust

Edna Brown Charitable Settlement (Mrs E E Brown Charitable Settlement)

R S Brownless Charitable Trust

Brown-Mellows Trust

The Brownsword Charitable Foundation

T B H Brunner's Charitable Settlement

The Bruntwood Charity

Brushmill Ltd

Buckingham Trust

Buckinghamshire Community Foundation

The Rosemary Bugden Charitable Trust

The Bulldog Trust Limited

The E F Bulmer Benevolent Fund

The Burden Trust

Burdens Charitable Foundation

The Burdett Trust for Nursing

The Clara E Burgess Charity

The Burry Charitable Trust

The Arnold Burton 1998 Charitable Trust

The Burton Breweries Charitable Trust

Consolidated Charity of Burton upon Trent

The Worshipful Company of Butchers General Charities

The Derek Butler Trust

The Noel Buxton Trust

C and F Charitable Trust

C J Cadbury Charitable Trust

Edward Cadbury Charitable Trust

Henry T and Lucy B Cadbury Charitable Trust

Peter Cadbury Charitable Trust

The Christopher Cadbury Charitable Trust

The G W Cadbury Charitable Trust

The Richard Cadbury Charitable Trust

The William A Cadbury Charitable Trust

The Cadbury Foundation

The Edward and Dorothy Cadbury Trust

The George Cadbury Trust

The Barrow Cadbury Trust and the Barrow Cadbury Fund

The Cadogan Charity

CAFOD (Catholic Agency for Overseas Development)

Community Foundation for Calderdale

The Callander Charitable Trust

Calleva Foundation

Calouste Gulbenkian Foundation – UK Branch

The Calpe Trust

Calypso Browning Trust

The Cambridgeshire Community Foundation

The Campden Charities Trustee

The Canning Trust

M R Cannon 1998 Charitable Trust

H and L Cantor Trust

Cardy Beaver Foundation

The Carew Pole Charitable
Trust
The D W T Cargill Fund
Carlee Ltd
The Carlton House Charitable
Trust
The Carmelite Monastery Ware
Trust
The Worshipful Company of
Carmen Benevolent Trust
The Carnegie Dunfermline
Trust
The Carnegie Trust for the
Universities of Scotland
The Carpenter Charitable Trust
The Carpenters' Company
Charitable Trust
The Carrington Charitable
Trust
The Carron Charitable
Settlement
The Leslie Mary Carter
Charitable Trust
The Casey Trust
Cash for Kids Radio Clyde
Sir John Cass's Foundation
The Elizabeth Casson Trust
The Castang Foundation
The Catalyst Charitable Trust
The Catholic Charitable Trust
Catholic Foreign Missions
The Catholic Trust for England
and Wales
The Cattanach Charitable Trust
The Joseph and Annie Cattle
Trust
The Thomas Sivewright Catto
Charitable Settlement
The Wilfrid and Constance
Cave Foundation
The Cayo Foundation
Elizabeth Cayzer Charitable
Trust
The B G S Cayzer Charitable
Trust
The Cazenove Charitable Trust
The CBD Charitable Trust
CBRE Charitable Trust
Celtic Charity Fund
The CH (1980) Charitable
Trust
R E Chadwick Charitable Trust
The Amelia Chadwick Trust
The Pamela Champion
Foundation
The Chapman Charitable Trust
John William Chapman's
Charitable Trust
The Charities Advisory Trust
Charitworth Limited
The Charter 600 Charity
The Worshipful Company of
Chartered Accountants
General Charitable Trust
(also known as CALC)
The Chasah Trust

The Chelsea Square 1994
Trust
The Cheruby Trust
Cheshire Freemason's Charity
The Chetwode Foundation
Cheviot Asset Management
Charitable Trust
Childs Charitable Trust
The Childwick Trust
The Chipping Sodbury Town
Lands Charity
CHK Charities Limited
The Chownes Foundation
The Chrimes Family Charitable
Trust
The Christabella Charitable
Trust
Christadelphian Samaritan
Fund
Christian Aid
Christian Response to Eastern
Europe
Chrysalis Trust
The Church and Community
Fund
The Church Burgesses
Educational Foundation
Church Burgesses Trust
Church Urban Fund
City and County of Swansea
Welsh Church Act Fund
The City Bridge Trust
The City Educational Trust
Fund
CLA Charitable Trust
Stephen Clark 1957
Charitable Trust
J A Clark Charitable Trust
The Hilda and Alice Clark
Charitable Trust
The Roger and Sarah Bancroft
Clark Charitable Trust
The Clarke Charitable
Settlement
The Cleevely Family Charitable
Trust
The Cleopatra Trust
Lord Clinton's Charitable Trust
The Clore Duffield Foundation
Miss V L Clore's 1967
Charitable Trust
The Clothworkers' Foundation
Richard Cloudesley's Charity
The Clover Trust
The Robert Clutterbuck
Charitable Trust
Clydpride Ltd
The Coalfields Regeneration
Trust
The John Coates Charitable
Trust
The Cobalt Trust
The Cobtree Charity Trust Ltd
The Denise Cohen Charitable
Trust
The Vivienne and Samuel
Cohen Charitable Trust

The John S Cohen Foundation
The R and S Cohen
Foundation
John Coldman Charitable Trust
The Cole Charitable Trust
The Colefax Charitable Trust
The John and Freda Coleman
Charitable Trust
The Bernard Coleman
Charitable Trust
The George Henry Collins
Charity
The Sir Jeremiah Colman Gift
Trust
Col-Reno Ltd
The Colt Foundation
The Coltstaple Trust
Colwinston Charitable Trust
Colyer-Fergusson Charitable
Trust
Comic Relief
Community First (Landfill
Communities Fund)
The Compton Charitable Trust
The Congleton Inclosure Trust
The Conscience Trust
The Conservation Foundation
The Consolidated Charities for
the Infirm Merchant
Taylors' Company
Gordon Cook Foundation
The Ernest Cook Trust
The Cooks Charity
The Catherine Cookson
Charitable Trust
The Cookson Charitable Trust
Harold and Daphne Cooper
Charitable Trust
Mabel Cooper Charity
The Alice Ellen Cooper Dean
Charitable Foundation
The Co-operative Foundation
The Marjorie Coote Animal
Charity Trust
The Marjorie Coote Old
People's Charity
The Helen Jean Cope Trust
The J Reginald Corah
Foundation Fund
The Gershon Coren Charitable
Foundation (also known as
The Muriel and Gus Coren
Charitable Foundation)
The Evan Cornish Foundation
The Cornwell Charitable Trust
The Sidney and Elizabeth
Corob Charitable Trust
The Corona Charitable Trust
The Costa Family Charitable
Trust
The Cotton Industry War
Memorial Trust
The Cotton Trust
County Durham Community
Foundation
The Augustine Courtauld Trust

The General Charities of the City of Coventry
Coventry Building Society Charitable Foundation
The John Cowan Foundation
Cowley Charitable Foundation
Dudley and Geoffrey Cox Charitable Trust
The Sir William Coxen Trust Fund
The Lord Cozens-Hardy Trust
The Craignish Trust
The Craps Charitable Trust
Michael Crawford Children's Charity
The Cray Trust
Creative Scotland
The Crerar Hotels Trust
The Crescent Trust
Cripplegate Foundation
The Violet and Milo Cripps Charitable Trust
The Harry Crook Foundation
The Cross Trust
The Croydon Relief in Need Charities
Cruden Foundation Ltd
The Ronald Cruickshanks Foundation
The Cuby Charitable Trust
The Culra Charitable Trust
The Cumber Family Charitable Trust
Cumberland Building Society Charitable Foundation
Cumbria Community Foundation
The D J H Currie Memorial Trust
The Dennis Curry Charitable Trust
The Manny Cussins Foundation
The Cutler Trust (the Worshipful Company of Makers of Playing Cards)
The Cwmbran Trust
Itzchok Meyer Cymerman Trust Ltd
The D G Charitable Settlement
The D'Oyly Carte Charitable Trust
Roald Dahl's Marvellous Children's Charity
Daily Prayer Union Charitable Trust Limited
Oizer Dalim Trust
The Dr and Mrs A Darlington Charitable Trust
Baron Davenport's Charity
The Davidson (Nairn) Charitable Trust
The Davidson Family Charitable Trust
The Alderman Joe Davidson Memorial Trust

Michael Davies Charitable Settlement
The Gwendoline and Margaret Davies Charity
The Wilfrid Bruce Davis Charitable Trust
Davis-Rubens Charitable Trust
The Dawe Charitable Trust
The De Brye Charitable Trust
The De Clermont Charitable Company Ltd
Peter De Haan Charitable Trust
The De Laszlo Foundation
The Deakin Charitable Trust
The Debmar Benevolent Trust
The Dellal Foundation
The Delves Charitable Trust
The Demigryphon Trust
The Denman Charitable Trust
Dentons UKMEA LLP Charitable Trust
The Earl of Derby's Charitable Trust
Derbyshire Community Foundation
The J N Derbyshire Trust
The Desmond Foundation
Devon Community Foundation
The Devon Educational Trust
The Duke of Devonshire's Charitable Trust
The Sandy Dewhirst Charitable Trust
The Laduma Dhamecha Charitable Trust
Alan and Sheila Diamond Charitable Trust
The Dibden Allotments Fund
Diced Cap Charity
The Dickon Trust
The Digbeth Trust Limited
The Dinwoodie Settlement
Dischma Charitable Trust
The DM Charitable Trust
Louise Dobson Charitable Trust
The Derek and Eileen Dodgson Foundation
The Dollond Charitable Trust
Domepride Ltd
The Dorcas Trust
Dorset Community Foundation
The Double 'O' Charity Ltd
The Doughty Charity Trust
Douglas Arter Foundation
The R M Douglas Charitable Trust
The Drapers' Charitable Fund
Dromintee Trust
The Duis Charitable Trust
The Dulverton Trust
The P B Dumbell Charitable Trust
The Dumbreck Charity
Dunard Fund
The Dunhill Medical Trust

The Dunn Family Charitable Trust
The W E Dunn Trust
The Charles Dunstone Charitable Trust
Dushinsky Trust Ltd
Mildred Duveen Charitable Trust
Annette Duvollet Charitable Trust
The Dwek Family Charitable Trust
The Dyers' Company Charitable Trust
The James Dyson Foundation
The Eagle Charity Trust
Audrey Earle Charitable Trust
The Earley Charity
Earls Colne and Halstead Educational Charity
The Earmark Trust
East End Community Foundation
Eastern Counties Educational Trust Limited
The Sir John Eastwood Foundation
The Ebenezer Trust
The EBM Charitable Trust
Eden Arts Trust
EDF Energy Trust (EDFET)
The Gilbert and Eileen Edgar Foundation
Gilbert Edgar Trust
Edinburgh Trust No 2 Account
Edinburgh Voluntary Organisations' Trust Funds (EVOT)
Educational Foundation of Alderman John Norman
The William Edwards Educational Charity
The Elephant Trust
The George Elias Charitable Trust
The Gerald Palmer Eling Trust Company
The Wilfred and Elsie Elkes Charity Fund
Ellador Ltd
The Ellerdale Trust
The John Ellerman Foundation
The Ellinson Foundation Ltd
The Edith Maud Ellis 1985 Charitable Trust
The Ellis Campbell Foundation
James Ellis Charitable Trust
The Elmgrant Trust
The Elmley Foundation
Elshore Ltd
The Vernon N Ely Charitable Trust
The Embleton Trust
Embrace the Middle East
The Emerton-Christie Charity
The Emilienne Charitable Trust

The Worshipful Company of Engineers Charitable Trust Fund

The Englefield Charitable Trust

The English Schools' Football Association

The Enkalon Foundation

Entindale Ltd

The Epigoni Trust

The Equitable Charitable Trust

The Equity Trust Fund

The Ericson Trust

The Erskine Cunningham Hill Trust

Essex Community Foundation

The Essex Fairway Charitable Trust

The Essex Heritage Trust

Essex Provincial Charity Fund

The Essex Youth Trust

Joseph Ettedgui Charitable Foundation

Euro Charity Trust

The Alan Evans Memorial Trust

Sir John Evelyn's Charity

The Eventhall Family Charitable Trust

The Eveson Charitable Trust

The Beryl Evetts and Robert Luff Animal Welfare Trust Limited

The Exilarch's Foundation

The Matthew Eyton Animal Welfare Trust

F C Charitable Trust

The F P Limited Charitable Trust

The Faber Charitable Trust

Esmée Fairbairn Foundation

The Fairstead Trust

The Fairway Trust

The Family Rich Charities Trust

Famos Foundation Trust

The Lord Faringdon Charitable Trust

Samuel William Farmer Trust

The Farmers' Company Charitable Fund

The Thomas Farr Charity

Walter Farthing (Trust) Limited

The Farthing Trust

The Fassnidge Memorial Trust

Joseph Fattorini Charitable Trust

The February Foundation

Federation of Jewish Relief Organisations

The John Feeney Charitable Trust

The George Fentham Birmingham Charity

The A M Fenton Trust

Allan and Nesta Ferguson Charitable Settlement

Elizabeth Ferguson Charitable Trust Fund

The Fidelity UK Foundation

The Doris Field Charitable Trust

Fife Council/Common Good Funds and Trusts

Dixie Rose Findlay Charitable Trust

Finnart House School Trust

Firtree Trust

The Sir John Fisher Foundation

The Fishmongers' Company's Charitable Trust

The Fitton Trust

The Earl Fitzwilliam Charitable Trust

The Ian Fleming Charitable Trust

The Joyce Fletcher Charitable Trust

Florence's Charitable Trust

The Flow Foundation

The Gerald Fogel Charitable Trust

The Follett Trust

The Football Association National Sports Centre Trust

The Football Foundation

The Forbes Charitable Foundation

The Forces Trust (Working Name)

Ford Britain Trust

The Oliver Ford Charitable Trust

Fordeve Limited

The Forest Hill Charitable Trust

The Foresters' Charity Stewards UK Trust

Forever Manchester (The Community Foundation for Greater Manchester)

The Forman Hardy Charitable Trust

Gwyneth Forrester Trust

The Donald Forrester Trust

The Anna Rosa Forster Charitable Trust

The Forte Charitable Trust

The Lord Forte Foundation

The Four Lanes Trust

The Four Winds Trust

The Foyle Foundation

The Isaac and Freda Frankel Memorial Charitable Trust

The Elizabeth Frankland Moore and Star Foundation

Sydney E Franklin Deceased's New Second Charity

The Jill Franklin Trust

The Gordon Fraser Charitable Trust

The Hugh Fraser Foundation

The Joseph Strong Frazer Trust

The Louis and Valerie Freedman Charitable Settlement

The Freemasons' Grand Charity

The Charles S French Charitable Trust

The Anne French Memorial Trust

The Freshfield Foundation

The Freshgate Trust Foundation

The Friarsgate Trust

The Friends Hall Farm Street Trust

Friends of Biala Limited

Friends of Wiznitz Limited

Friends Provident Charitable Foundation

The Frognal Trust

T F C Frost Charitable Trust

The Patrick & Helena Frost Foundation

Maurice Fry Charitable Trust

Mejer and Gertrude Miriam Frydman Foundation

The Fulmer Charitable Trust

Worshipful Company of Furniture Makers Charitable Fund

G M C Trust

Gableholt Limited

The Galbraith Trust

The Gale Family Charity Trust

Gamlen Charitable Trust

The Gamma Trust

The Gannochy Trust

The Worshipful Company of Gardeners of London

The Samuel Gardner Memorial Trust

The Garnett Charitable Trust

Garrick Charitable Trust

Garthgwynion Charities

Garvan Limited

The Gatsby Charitable Foundation

Gatwick Airport Community Trust

The Robert Gavron Charitable Trust

Thomas Betton's Charity for Pensions and Relief-in-Need

The General Nursing Council for England and Wales Trust

The Generations Foundation

The Gibbs Charitable Trust

Simon Gibson Charitable Trust

The G C Gibson Charitable Trust

Lady Gibson's Charitable Trust

The Harvey and Hilary Gilbert Charitable Trust

The Girdlers' Company Charitable Trust

The B and P Glasser Charitable Trust

The Glass-House Trust

The Glastonbury Trust Limited

Global Care
Global Charities
Gloucestershire Community
 Foundation
Worshipful Company of
 Glovers of London Charity
 Fund
The GNC Trust
The Sydney and Phyllis
 Goldberg Memorial
 Charitable Trust
The Golden Bottle Trust
Golden Charitable Trust
The Jack Goldhill Charitable
 Trust
The Goldsmiths' Arts Trust
 Fund
The Goldsmiths' Company
 Charity
The Golsoncott Foundation
Golubovich Foundation
Nicholas and Judith
 Goodison's Charitable
 Settlement
The Mike Gooley Trailfinders
 Charity
The Gosling Foundation
 Limited
The Gough Charitable Trust
The Gould Charitable Trust
The Hemraj Goyal Foundation
The Grace Charitable Trust
A B Grace Trust
The Graff Foundation
E C Graham Belford Charitable
 Settlement
The Grahame Charitable
 Foundation Limited
The Granada Foundation
Grand Charitable Trust of the
 Order of Women
 Freemasons
The Grand Order of Water
 Rats' Charities Fund
The Grange Farm Centre Trust
Grantham Yorke Trust
The Gordon Gray Trust
The Gray Trust
The Great Britain Sasakawa
 Foundation
The Great Stone Bridge Trust
 of Edenbridge
The Great Torrington Town
 Lands Charity
The Green Hall Foundation
The Green Room Charitable
 Trust
Mrs H R Greene Charitable
 Settlement
Greenham Common
 Community Trust Limited
Greggs Foundation
The Gretna Charitable Trust
Greys Charitable Trust
The Grimmitt Trust
The Grocers' Charity

The M and R Gross Charities
 Limited
The GRP Charitable Trust
The David and Marie Grumitt
 Foundation
The Bishop of Guildford's
 Foundation
The Guildry Incorporation of
 Perth
The Walter Guinness
 Charitable Trust
The Gunter Charitable Trust
The Gur Trust
The Gurney Charitable Trust
Dr Guthrie's Association
The H and M Charitable Trust
H C D Memorial Fund
The H P Charitable Trust
The Hackney Parochial
 Charities
The Hadfield Trust
The Hadley Trust
The Hadrian Trust
The Alfred Haines Charitable
 Trust
E F and M G Hall Charitable
 Trust
The Edith Winifred Hall
 Charitable Trust
Robert Hall Charity
The Hamamelis Trust
Hamilton Wallace Trust
Paul Hamlyn Foundation
Sue Hammerson Charitable
 Trust
The Hampstead Wells and
 Campden Trust
Hampton Fuel Allotment
 Charity
The W A Handley Charitable
 Trust
Beatrice Hankey Foundation
 Limited
The Hanley Trust (1987)
The Kathleen Hannay
 Memorial Charity
The Doughty Hanson
 Charitable Foundation
Lord Hanson Foundation
Miss K M Harbinson's
 Charitable Trust
Harbo Charities Limited
The Harborne Parish Lands
 Charity
The Harbour Charitable Trust
The Harbour Foundation
The Harding Trust
William Harding's Charity
The Hare of Steep Charitable
 Trust
The Harebell Centenary Fund
The Kenneth Hargreaves
 Charitable Trust
The Harpur Trust
The Harris Charity
The Harris Family Charitable
 Trust

The Harrison and Potter Trust
The John Harrison Charitable
 Trust
The Spencer Hart Charitable
 Trust
The Hartley Charitable Trust
The Alfred And Peggy Harvey
 Charitable Trust
William Geoffrey Harvey's
 Discretionary Settlement
Haskel Family Foundation
The Hathaway Trust
The Maurice Hatter Foundation
The M A Hawe Settlement
The Hawerby Trust
The Hawthorne Charitable
 Trust
The Dorothy Hay-Bolton
 Charitable Trust
The Headley Trust
Headley-Pitt Charitable Trust
May Hearnshaw's Charity
Heart of England Community
 Foundation
The Heathcoat Trust
Heathside Charitable Trust
The Charlotte Heber-Percy
 Charitable Trust
Percy Hedley 1990 Charitable
 Trust
The Hedley Denton Charitable
 Trust
The Hedley Foundation
The H J Heinz Company
 Limited Charitable Trust
The Hellenic Foundation
The Michael Heller Charitable
 Foundation
The Simon Heller Charitable
 Settlement
The Hemby Trust
The Christina Mary Hendrie
 Trust for Scottish and
 Canadian Charities
Henley Educational Trust
 (formerley Henley
 Educational Charity)
Philip Henman Trust
Esther Hennell Charitable
 Trust
The G D Herbert Charitable
 Trust
The Anne Herd Memorial Trust
The Herefordshire Historic
 Churches Trust
The Heritage of London Trust
 Ltd
The Hertfordshire Community
 Foundation
The Hesed Trust
The Hesslewood Children's
 Trust (Hull Seamen's and
 General Orphanage)
Hexham and Newcastle
 Diocesan Trust (1947)
The Higgs Charitable Trust
Alan Edward Higgs Charity

The High Sheriff's Police Trust
for the County of West
Midlands (Building Blocks)
Highcroft Charitable Trust
The Hilden Charitable Fund
The Derek Hill Foundation
The Charles Littlewood Hill
Trust
The Hillingdon Partnership
Trust
R G Hills Charitable Trust
The Hilmarnan Charitable Trust
Hinchley Charitable Trust
Lady Hind Trust
Hinduja Foundation
Stuart Hine Trust
The Hiscox Foundation
The Hitchin Educational
Foundation
The Eleemosynary Charity of
William Hobbayne
Hobson Charity Limited
Hockerill Educational
Foundation
Matthew Hodder Charitable
Trust
The Sir Julian Hodge
Charitable Trust
The Jane Hodge Foundation
The J G Hogg Charitable Trust
The Holden Charitable Trust
John Holford's Charity
The Hollick Family Charitable
Trust
The Holliday Foundation
The Dorothy Holmes Charitable
Trust
The Holmes Family Trust
(Sheffield)
The Holst Foundation
P H Holt Foundation
The Holywood Trust
The Homelands Charitable
Trust
The Homestead Charitable
Trust
Mary Homfray Charitable Trust
Sir Harold Hood's Charitable
Trust
Hope for Youth (NI)
The Hope Trust
HopMarket Charity
The Cuthbert Horn Trust
The Antony Hornby Charitable
Trust
The Horne Foundation
The Horne Trust
The Worshipful Company of
Horners' Charitable Trusts
The Hornsey Parochial
Charities
The Hospital of God at
Greatham
The Hospital Saturday Fund
The Sir Joseph Hotung
Charitable Settlement
Houblon-Norman/George Fund

The House of Industry Estate
The Reta Lila Howard
Foundation
The Daniel Howard Trust
HTA Sheba Foundation UK
The Huddersfield Common
Good Trust
The Hudson Foundation
The Huggard Charitable Trust
The Geoffrey C Hughes
Charitable Trust
The Hull and East Riding
Charitable Trust
Hulme Trust Estates
(Educational)
Human Relief Foundation
The Humanitarian Trust
The Michael and Shirley Hunt
Charitable Trust
The Albert Hunt Trust
The Hunter Foundation
Miss Agnes H Hunter's Trust
The Huntingdon Foundation
Huntingdon Freemen's Trust
Hurdale Charity Limited
The Hutton Foundation
The Nani Huyu Charitable Trust
The P Y N and B Hyams Trust
The Hyde Charitable Trust
The Idlewild Trust
The Iliffe Family Charitable
Trust
Impetus – The Private Equity
Foundation (Impetus – PEF)
The Indigo Trust
Infinity Capital Trust
The Ingram Trust
The Inlight Trust
The Inman Charity
The Inner London Magistrates
Court Poor Box and Feeder
Charity
The Innocent Foundation
The Ireland Fund of Great
Britain
The Irish Youth Foundation
(UK) Ltd (incorporating The
Lawlor Foundation)
The Ironmongers' Foundation
The Charles Irving Charitable
Trust
Irwin Trust
The ISA Charity
The Isaacs Charitable Trust
The J Isaacs Charitable Trust
The Isle of Anglesey Charitable
Trust
The ITF Seafarers Trust
J A R Charitable Trust
The J J Charitable Trust
The J M K Charitable Trust
The J R S S T Charitable Trust
The Jabbs Foundation
C Richard Jackson Charitable
Trust
Elizabeth Jackson Charitable
Trust

Jacobs Charitable Trust
The Ruth and Lionel Jacobson
Trust (Second Fund) No 2
Jaffe Family Relief Fund
John James Bristol Foundation
The Susan and Stephen
James Charitable
Settlement
The James Trust
The Jarman Charitable Trust
The Barbara Joyce Jarrald
Charitable Trust
Jay Education Trust
JCA Charitable Foundation
The Jeffrey Charitable Trust
Rees Jeffreys Road Fund
The Jenour Foundation
The Jerusalem Trust
Jesus Hospital Charity
Jewish Child's Day
The Jewish Youth Fund
The Harold Joels Charitable
Trust
The Nicholas Joels Charitable
Trust
The Norman Joels Charitable
Trust
The Joffe Charitable Trust
The Elton John Aids
Foundation
The Lillie Johnson Charitable
Trust
The Johnson Foundation
The Reginald Johnson
Foundation
The Johnnie Johnson Trust
The Johnson Wax Ltd
Charitable Trust
The Joicey Trust
The Jones 1986 Charitable
Trust
The Marjorie and Geoffrey
Jones Charitable Trust
The Muriel Jones Foundation
The Jordan Charitable
Foundation
The J E Joseph Charitable
Fund
The Lady Eileen Joseph
Foundation
The Josephs Family Charitable
Trust
JTH Charitable Trust
The Cyril and Eve Jumbo
Charitable Trust
The Anton Jurgens Charitable
Trust
Jusaca Charitable Trust
The Bernard Kahn Charitable
Trust
The Stanley Kalms Foundation
The Kalou Foundation
The Karenza Foundation
The Boris Karloff Charitable
Foundation
The Ian Karten Charitable
Trust

The Kasner Charitable Trust
The Kathleen Trust
The Michael and Ilse Katz
    Foundation
The Katzauer Charitable
    Settlement
The C S Kaufman Charitable
    Trust
The Geoffrey John Kaye
    Charitable Foundation
The Emmanuel Kaye
    Foundation
The Kelly Family Charitable
    Trust
Kelsick's Educational
    Foundation
The KempWelch Charitable
    Trust
The Kay Kendall Leukaemia
    Fund
The John Thomas Kennedy
    Charitable Foundation
The Kennedy Charitable
    Foundation
The Kennel Club Charitable
    Trust
Kent Community Foundation
The Nancy Kenyon Charitable
    Trust
Keren Association
Kermaville Ltd
E and E Kernkraut Charities
    Limited
The Peter Kershaw Trust
The Ursula Keyes Trust
The King/Cullimore Charitable
    Trust
Kingdom Way Trust
The Kingsbury Charity
The Mary Kinross Charitable
    Trust
Kinsurdy Charitable Trust
Kirkley Poor's Lands Estate
The Richard Kirkman
    Charitable Trust
Kirschel Foundation
Robert Kitchin (Saddlers'
    Company)
Ernest Kleinwort Charitable
    Trust
The Marina Kleinwort
    Charitable Trust
The Sir James Knott Trust
The Kobler Trust
The Kohn Foundation
Kollel and Co. Limited
The Kreditor Charitable Trust
The Kreitman Foundation
The Neil Kreitman Foundation
The Heinz, Anna and Carol
    Kroch Foundation
Kupath Gemach Chaim
    Bechesed Viznitz Trust
The Kyte Charitable Trust
The Late Sir Pierce Lacy
    Charity Trust
The K P Ladd Charitable Trust

John Laing Charitable Trust
Maurice and Hilda Laing
    Charitable Trust
The Christopher Laing
    Foundation
The Kirby Laing Foundation
The Martin Laing Foundation
The Beatrice Laing Trust
The Lambert Charitable Trust
Community Foundation for
    Lancashire
Duchy of Lancaster Benevolent
    Fund
The Lancaster Foundation
The Allen Lane Foundation
Langdale Trust
The Langley Charitable Trust
The LankellyChase Foundation
The R J Larg Family Charitable
    Trust
Largsmount Ltd
The Lark Trust
Laslett's (Hinton) Charity
Laufer Charitable Trust
The Lauffer Family Charitable
    Foundation
Mrs F B Laurence Charitable
    Trust
The Kathleen Laurence Trust
The Law Society Charity
The Edgar E Lawley Foundation
The Herd Lawson and Muriel
    Lawson Charitable Trust
The Lawson Beckman
    Charitable Trust
The Raymond and Blanche
    Lawson Charitable Trust
The Leach Fourteenth Trust
The David Lean Foundation
The Leathersellers' Company
    Charitable Fund
The Arnold Lee Charitable
    Trust
The Lord Mayor of Leeds
    Appeal Fund
Leeds Building Society
    Charitable Foundation
The Leeds Community
    Foundation
The Kennedy Leigh Charitable
    Trust
Morris Leigh Foundation
The Leigh Trust
Mrs Vera Leigh's Charity
P Leigh-Bramwell Trust 'E'
The Lennox and Wyfold
    Foundation
The Erica Leonard Trust
The Leonard Trust
The Mark Leonard Trust
Lesley Lesley and Mutter Trust
Leukaemia and Lymphoma
    Research
The Leverhulme Trade
    Charities Trust
The Joseph Levy Charitable
    Foundation

Lewis Family Charitable Trust
The John Spedan Lewis
    Foundation
The Sir Edward Lewis
    Foundation
John Lewis Partnership
    General Community Fund
Lichfield Conduit Lands
Lifeline 4 Kids
Limoges Charitable Trust
The Linbury Trust
The Lincolnshire Churches
    Trust
Lindale Educational
    Foundation
The Linden Charitable Trust
The Enid Linder Foundation
The Linmardon Trust
The Ruth and Stuart Lipton
    Charitable Trust
The Lister Charitable Trust
Frank Litchfield Charitable
    Trust
The Andrew and Mary
    Elizabeth Little Charitable
    Trust
The Second Joseph Aaron
    Littman Foundation
The George John and Sheilah
    Livanos Charitable Trust
Liverpool Charity and Voluntary
    Services
Liverpool Sailors' Home Trust
Jack Livingstone Charitable
    Trust
The Elaine and Angus Lloyd
    Charitable Trust
The Charles Lloyd Foundation
Lloyd's Charities Trust
Lloyds Bank Foundation for
    England and Wales
Lloyds Bank Foundation for
    Northern Ireland
Lloyds Bank Foundation for the
    Channel Islands
Lloyds TSB Foundation for
    Scotland
Localtrent Ltd
The Locker Foundation
The Loftus Charitable Trust
The Lolev Charitable Trust
The Trust for London
London Catalyst
The London Community
    Foundation
The London Housing
    Foundation
The London Law Trust
The William and Katherine
    Longman Trust
The Loseley and Guildway
    Charitable Trust
The Lotus Foundation
The Lowy Mitchell Foundation
The C L Loyd Charitable Trust
LSA Charitable Trust

The Marie Helen Luen Charitable Trust
Robert Luff Foundation Ltd
Henry Lumley Charitable Trust
Paul Lunn-Rockliffe Charitable Trust
C F Lunoe Trust Fund
The Ruth and Jack Lunzer Charitable Trust
Lord and Lady Lurgan Trust
The Lyndhurst Trust
The Lynn Foundation
The Lynwood Trust
John Lyon's Charity
The Lyons Charitable Trust
The Sir Jack Lyons Charitable Trust
The Lyras Family Charitable Trust
Sylvanus Lyson's Charity
The M and C Trust
The M K Charitable Trust
The Madeline Mabey Trust
The E M MacAndrew Trust
The R S Macdonald Charitable Trust
Macdonald-Buchanan Charitable Trust
The Mackay and Brewer Charitable Trust
The Mackintosh Foundation
The MacRobert Trust
Ian Mactaggart Trust
Magdalen Hospital Trust
The SV and PE Magee Family Charitable Trust
The Magen Charitable Trust
Mageni Trust
The Brian Maguire Charitable Trust
The Mahavir Trust
The Makin Charitable Trust
Man Group plc Charitable Trust
The Manackerman Charitable Trust
Manchester Airport Community Trust Fund
The Manchester Guardian Society Charitable Trust
Lord Mayor of Manchester's Charity Appeal Trust
Mandeville Trust
The Manifold Charitable Trust
W M Mann Foundation
The Leslie and Lilian Manning Trust
Maranatha Christian Trust
Marbeh Torah Trust
Marchig Animal Welfare Trust
Mariapolis Limited
Market Harborough and The Bowdens Charity
Michael Marks Charitable Trust
The Ann and David Marks Foundation

The Hilda and Samuel Marks Foundation
J P Marland Charitable Trust
The Marr-Munning Trust
The Michael Marsh Charitable Trust
The Marsh Christian Trust
The Charlotte Marshall Charitable Trust
The Jim Marshall Charitable Trust
The Nora Joan Marshall Charitable Trust
The D G Marshall of Cambridge Trust
Marshgate Charitable Settlement
John Martin's Charity
The John Mason Family Trust
The Mason Porter Charitable Trust
The Nancie Massey Charitable Trust
The Mathew Trust
Matliwala Family Charitable Trust
The Matt 6.3 Charitable Trust
The Violet Mauray Charitable Trust
The Maxwell Family Foundation
Evelyn May Trust
The Mayfield Valley Arts Trust
Mazars Charitable Trust
The Robert McAlpine Foundation
The McDougall Trust
The A M McGreevy No 5 Charitable Settlement
The McKenna Charitable Trust
Martin McLaren Memorial Trust
The Helen Isabella McMorran Charitable Foundation
D D McPhail Charitable Settlement
The Mears Foundation
The James Frederick and Ethel Anne Measures Charity
The Medlock Charitable Trust
The Anthony and Elizabeth Mellows Charitable Settlement
Melodor Limited
Melow Charitable Trust
Meningitis Trust
Menuchar Ltd
The Menzies Charity Foundation
The Mercers' Charitable Foundation
The Merchant Taylors' Company Charities Fund
The Merchant Venturers' Charity
The Merchants' House of Glasgow
Mercury Phoenix Trust

The Mersey Docks and Harbour Company Charitable Fund
Community Foundation for Merseyside
The Zachary Merton and George Woofindin Convalescent Trust
The Tony Metherell Charitable Trust
The Metropolitan Drinking Fountain and Cattle Trough Association
The Metropolitan Masonic Charity
T and J Meyer Family Foundation Limited
The Mickel Fund
Mickleham Charitable Trust
Gerald Micklem Charitable Trust
Middlesex Sports Foundation
Midhurst Pensions Trust
The Migraine Trust
Miles Trust for the Putney and Roehampton Community
Millennium Stadium Charitable Trust
The Hugh and Mary Miller Bequest Trust
The Ronald Miller Foundation
The Millfield Trust
The Millhouses Charitable Trust
The Millichope Foundation
The Mills Charity
The Millward Charitable Trust
The Clare Milne Trust
Milton Keynes Community Foundation
The Edgar Milward Charity
The Peter Minet Trust
Minge's Gift and the Pooled Trusts
The Minos Trust
Minton Charitable Trust
The Mirfield Educational Charity
The Mirianog Trust
The Laurence Misener Charitable Trust
The Mishcon Family Charitable Trust
The Misselbrook Trust
The Mitchell Charitable Trust
The Esmé Mitchell Trust
Keren Mitzvah Trust
The Mizpah Trust
The Mobbs Memorial Trust Ltd
The Modiano Charitable Trust
The Moette Charitable Trust
The Mole Charitable Trust
The Monatrea Charitable Trust
The D C Moncrieff Charitable Trust
Monmouthshire County Council Welsh Church Act Fund

The Montague Thompson
Coon Charitable Trust
The Colin Montgomerie
Charitable Foundation
The Monument Trust
George A Moore Foundation
The Morel Charitable Trust
The Morgan Charitable
Foundation
The Morgan Foundation
The Mr and Mrs J T Morgan
Foundation
Morgan Stanley International
Foundation
Diana and Allan Morgenthau
Charitable Trust
The Oliver Morland Charitable
Trust
S C and M E Morland's
Charitable Trust
The Bernard Morris Charitable
Trust
The Morris Charitable Trust
The Willie and Mabel Morris
Charitable Trust
The Peter Morrison Charitable
Foundation
The Stanley Morrison
Charitable Trust
Moshal Charitable Trust
Vyoel Moshe Charitable Trust
The Moshulu Charitable Trust
Brian and Jill Moss Charitable
Trust
The Moss Charitable Trust
The Robert and Margaret
Moss Charitable Trust
The Moss Family Charitable
Trust
Mosselson Charitable Trust
The Mount Everest Foundation
The Edwina Mountbatten Trust
Mountbatten Festival of Music
The Mountbatten Memorial
Trust
Mrs Waterhouse Charitable
Trust
The Mugdock Children's Trust
The Mulberry Trust
Frederick Mulder Charitable
Trust
The Edith Murphy Foundation
Murphy-Neumann Charity
Company Limited
Peter John Murray Trust
The Mushroom Fund
The Music Sales Charitable
Trust
Muslim Hands
The Mutual Trust Group
MW (CL) Foundation
MW (GK) Foundation
MW (HO) Foundation
MW (RH) Foundation
MYA Charitable Trust
The Kitty and Daniel Nabarro
Charitable Trust

The Nadezhda Charitable Trust
The Naggar Charitable Trust
The Eleni Nakou Foundation
The Janet Nash Charitable
Settlement
The National Churches Trust
The National Hockey
Foundation
The National Manuscripts
Conservation Trust
Needham Market and Barking
Welfare Charities
The Worshipful Company of
Needlemakers' Charitable
Fund
The Neighbourly Charitable
Trust
The James Neill Trust Fund
Nemoral Ltd
Nesswall Ltd
Network for Social Change
Newby Trust Limited
The Newcomen Collett
Foundation
Newpier Charity Ltd
Alderman Newton's
Educational Foundation
The Night Garden Charity
The Chevras Ezras Nitzrochim
Trust
NJD Charitable Trust
Alice Noakes Memorial
Charitable Trust
The Noon Foundation
The Norda Trust
Norie Charitable Trust
The Norman Family Charitable
Trust
The Duncan Norman Trust
Fund
The Normanby Charitable Trust
The North West Cancer
Research Fund
The Northampton Municipal
Church Charities
The Northampton Queen's
Institute Relief in Sickness
Fund
The Earl of Northampton's
Charity
The Northcott Devon Medical
Foundation
The Community Foundation for
Northern Ireland
The Northern Rock Foundation
The Northmoor Trust
The Northumberland Village
Homes Trust
The Northwood Charitable
Trust
The Norton Foundation
The Norwich Church of England
Young Men's Society
The Norwich Town Close
Estate Charity
The Norwood and Newton
Settlement

The Noswad Charity
The Nottingham General
Dispensary
The Nottingham Gordon
Memorial Trust for Boys
and Girls
Nottinghamshire Community
Foundation
The Nottinghamshire Historic
Churches Trust
The Nottinghamshire Miners'
Welfare Trust Fund
Novi Most International
The Father O'Mahoney
Memorial Trust
The Sir Peter O'Sullevan
Charitable Trust
The Oak Trust
The Oakdale Trust
The Oakley Charitable Trust
The Oakmoor Charitable Trust
The Odin Charitable Trust
The Ofenheim Charitable Trust
Ogilvie Charities Deed No.2
(including the Charity of
Mary Catherine Ford Smith)
The Ogle Christian Trust
The Oikonomia Trust
Oizer Charitable Trust
The Old Broad Street Charity
Trust
Old Possum's Practical Trust
The John Oldacre Foundation
The Oldham Foundation
The Olga Charitable Trust
Open Gate
The Raymond Oppenheimer
Foundation
Ormonde Foundation
The Ormsby Charitable Trust
The Orrin Charitable Trust
The Ouseley Trust
The Owen Family Trust
Oxfam (GB)
The Oxfordshire Community
Foundation
The P F Charitable Trust
Padwa Charitable Foundation
The Paget Charitable Trust
The Palmer Foundation
The Panacea Society
Panahpur (previously Panahpur
Charitable Trust)
Panton Trust
The Paphitis Charitable Trust
The Paragon Trust
The Park Charitable Trust
The Park House Charitable
Trust
The Frank Parkinson
Agricultural Trust
The Samuel and Freda
Parkinson Charitable Trust
The Parthenon Trust
Arthur James Paterson
Charitable Trust

The Constance Paterson
  Charitable Trust
Miss M E Swinton Paterson's
  Charitable Trust
The Patrick Charitable Trust
The Jack Patston Charitable
  Trust
Ambika Paul Foundation
Paycare Charity Trust
The Payne Charitable Trust
The Harry Payne Trust
The Susanna Peake Charitable
  Trust
The Pears Family Charitable
  Foundation
The Pedmore Sporting Club
  Trust Fund
The Dowager Countess
  Eleanor Peel Trust
Pegasus (Stanley) Trust
The Pell Charitable Trust
The Peltz Trust
The Pennycress Trust
The Performing Right Society
  Foundation
B E Perl Charitable Trust
The Persson Charitable Trust
The Persula Foundation
The Jack Petchey Foundation
The Petplan Charitable Trust
The Pharsalia Charitable Trust
The Philips and Rubens
  Charitable Trust
The Phillips Charitable Trust
The Phillips Family Charitable
  Trust
Philological Foundation
The David Pickford Charitable
  Foundation
The Pilgrim Trust
The Cecil Pilkington Charitable
  Trust
The Elise Pilkington Charitable
  Trust
The Pilkington Charities Fund
The Austin and Hope
  Pilkington Trust
The Sir Harry Pilkington Trust
The Col W W Pilkington Will
  Trusts The General Charity
  Fund
Miss A M Pilkington's
  Charitable Trust
The DLA Piper Charitable Trust
The Worshipful Company of
  Plaisterers Charitable Trust
The Platinum Trust
G S Plaut Charitable Trust
  Limited
Polden-Puckham Charitable
  Foundation
The George and Esme Pollitzer
  Charitable Settlement
The J S F Pollitzer Charitable
  Settlement
The Polonsky Foundation
The Ponton House Trust

Edith and Ferdinand Porjes
  Charitable Trust
The John Porter Charitable
  Trust
The Porter Foundation
Porticus UK
The Portrack Charitable Trust
The J E Posnansky Charitable
  Trust
The Mary Potter Convent
  Hospital Trust
The David and Elaine Potter
  Foundation
The Powell Foundation
The W L Pratt Charitable Trust
The Premier League Charitable
  Fund
Premierquote Ltd
Premishlaner Charitable Trust
The Lucy Price Relief-in-Need
  Charity
Sir John Priestman Charity
  Trust
The Primrose Trust
The Prince of Wales's
  Charitable Foundation
Princess Anne's Charities
Prison Service Charity Fund
The Privy Purse Charitable
  Trust
The Proven Family Trust
The Puebla Charitable Trust
The Richard and Christine
  Purchas Charitable Trust
The Puri Foundation
Mr and Mrs J A Pye's
  Charitable Settlement
Quartet Community Foundation
The Queen Anne's Gate
  Foundation
Queen Mary's Roehampton
  Trust
The Queen's Silver Jubilee
  Trust
Quercus Trust
Quothquan Trust
R J M Charitable Trust
R S Charitable Trust
The R V W Trust
The Monica Rabagliati
  Charitable Trust
Rachel Charitable Trust
The Racing Foundation
The Mr and Mrs Philip
  Rackham Charitable Trust
Richard Radcliffe Charitable
  Trust
The Radcliffe Trust
The Bishop Radford Trust
The Ragdoll Foundation
The Rainford Trust
The Peggy Ramsay Foundation
The Joseph and Lena Randall
  Charitable Trust
The Rank Foundation Limited
The Joseph Rank Trust
Ranworth Trust

The Fanny Rapaport Charitable
  Settlement
The Ratcliff Foundation
The Ratcliff Pension Charity
The Ratcliffe Charitable Trust
The Eleanor Rathbone
  Charitable Trust
The Sigrid Rausing Trust
The Ravensdale Trust
The Rawdon-Smith Trust
The Rayden Charitable Trust
The Roger Raymond Charitable
  Trust
The Rayne Foundation
The Rayne Trust
The Sir James Reckitt Charity
Eva Reckitt Trust Fund
The Red Arrows Trust
The Red Rose Charitable Trust
The C A Redfern Charitable
  Foundation
The Reed Foundation
Richard Reeve's Foundation
The Max Reinhardt Charitable
  Trust
Relief Fund for Romania
  Limited
REMEDI
The Rest Harrow Trust
Reuben Foundation
The Nathaniel Reyner Trust
  Fund
The Rhododendron Trust
Daisie Rich Trust
The Sir Cliff Richard Charitable
  Trust
The Clive Richards Charity
The Richmond Parish Lands
  Charity
Ridgesave Limited
The Ripple Effect Foundation
The Sir John Ritblat Family
  Foundation
The River Trust
Thomas Roberts Trust
The Robertson Trust
Robyn Charitable Trust
The Rochester Bridge Trust
The Rock Foundation
The Rock Solid Trust
The Roddick Foundation
The Rofeh Trust
Rokach Family Charitable Trust
The Helen Roll Charitable
  Trust
The Sir James Roll Charitable
  Trust
The Roman Research Trust
The C A Rookes Charitable
  Trust
The Rosca Trust
The Cecil Rosen Foundation
Rosetrees Trust
The Rothermere Foundation
The Rotherwick Foundation
The Roughley Charitable Trust

Mrs Gladys Row Fogo
Charitable Trust
Rowanville Ltd
The Christopher Rowbotham
Charitable Trust
The Rowing Foundation
The Rowlands Trust
The Joseph Rowntree
Charitable Trust
Joseph Rowntree Reform Trust
Limited
Royal Artillery Charitable Fund
Royal British Legion
Royal Docks Trust (London)
Royal Masonic Trust for Girls
and Boys
The Alfred and Frances
Rubens Charitable Trust
The Rubin Foundation
William Arthur Rudd Memorial
Trust
Rugby Football Foundation
The Russell Trust
Ryklow Charitable Trust 1992
(also known as A B
Williamson Charitable Trust)
The J S and E C Rymer
Charitable Trust
S F Foundation
S O Charitable Trust
The Jeremy and John Sacher
Charitable Trust
The Michael Harry Sacher
Trust
The Sackler Trust
The Ruzin Sadagora Trust
The Saga Charitable Trust
The Jean Sainsbury Animal
Welfare Trust
The Alan and Babette
Sainsbury Charitable Fund
The Sainsbury Family
Charitable Trusts
Saint Sarkis Charity Trust
The Saintbury Trust
The Saints and Sinners Trust
The Salt Trust
Salters' Charitable Foundation
The Andrew Salvesen
Charitable Trust
Basil Samuel Charitable Trust
Coral Samuel Charitable Trust
The M J Samuel Charitable
Trust
The Peter Samuel Charitable
Trust
The Samworth Foundation
The Sandra Charitable Trust
Santander UK Foundation
Limited
The Scarfe Charitable Trust
The Schapira Charitable Trust
The Annie Schiff Charitable
Trust
The Schmidt-Bodner Charitable
Trust

The R H Scholes Charitable
Trust
The Schreib Trust
The Schreiber Charitable Trust
Schroder Charity Trust
The Schuster Charitable Trust
Foundation Scotland
Scott (Eredine) Charitable
Trust
The Francis C Scott Charitable
Trust
The Scott Trust Foundation
The Storrow Scott Will Trust
Scottish Coal Industry Special
Welfare Fund
The Scottish International
Education Trust
The Scouloudi Foundation
Seafarers UK (King George's
Fund for Sailors)
Seamen's Hospital Society
The Searchlight Electric
Charitable Trust
The Samuel Sebba Charitable
Trust
The Seedfield Trust
Sellata Ltd
SEM Charitable Trust
The Seneca Trust
The Ayrton Senna Foundation
The Seven Fifty Trust
The Cyril Shack Trust
The Jean Shanks Foundation
The Shanti Charitable Trust
ShareGift (The Orr Mackintosh
Foundation)
The Linley Shaw Foundation
The Shears Foundation
The Sheepdrove Trust
The Sheffield and District
Hospital Services
Charitable Fund
The Sheldon Trust
The Patricia and Donald
Shepherd Charitable Trust
The Sylvia and Colin Shepherd
Charitable Trust
The Archie Sherman Cardiff
Foundation
The Archie Sherman Charitable
Trust
The R C Sherriff Trust
The Shetland Charitable Trust
SHINE (Support and Help in
Education)
The Barnett and Sylvia Shine
No 2 Charitable Trust
The Bassil Shippam and
Alsford Trust
The Shipwrights' Company
Charitable Fund
The Shirley Foundation
Shlomo Memorial Fund Limited
The J A Shone Memorial Trust
Community Foundation for
Shropshire and Telford

The Barbara A Shuttleworth
Memorial Trust
The Mary Elizabeth Siebel
Charity
David and Jennifer Sieff
Charitable Trust
The Julius Silman Charitable
Trust
The Leslie Silver Charitable
Trust
The Simmons & Simmons
Charitable Foundation
The Simpson Education and
Conservation Trust
The Simpson Foundation
The Huntly and Margery
Sinclair Charitable Trust
Sino-British Fellowship Trust
SITA Cornwall Trust Limited
The Skelton Bounty
Skipton Building Society
Charitable Foundation
The John Slater Foundation
Rita and David Slowe
Charitable Trust
Ruth Smart Foundation
The SMB Charitable Trust
The Mrs Smith and Mount
Trust
The N Smith Charitable
Settlement
The E H Smith Charitable Trust
The Smith Charitable Trust
The Henry Smith Charity
The Leslie Smith Foundation
The Martin Smith Foundation
The Stanley Smith UK
Horticultural Trust
Philip Smith's Charitable Trust
The R C Snelling Charitable
Trust
The Snowball Trust
The Sobell Foundation
Solev Co Ltd
The Solo Charitable
Settlement
Dr Richard Solomon's
Charitable Trust
David Solomons Charitable
Trust
Songdale Ltd
The E C Sosnow Charitable
Trust
The Souter Charitable Trust
The South Square Trust
The W F Southall Trust
R H Southern Trust
The Southwold Trust
Spar Charitable Fund
Sparquote Limited
The Spear Charitable Trust
Spears-Stutz Charitable Trust
The Jessie Spencer Trust
The Ralph and Irma Sperring
Charity
The Spielman Charitable Trust

The Spoore, Merry and Rixman Foundation

Rosalyn and Nicholas Springer Charitable Trust

Springfields Employees' Medical Research and Charity Trust Fund

Springrule Limited

The Spurrell Charitable Trust

St Hilda's Trust

St James' Trust Settlement

Sir Walter St John's Educational Charity

St Michael's and All Saints' Charities Relief Branch (The Church Houses Relief in Need Charity)

The Late St Patrick White Charitable Trust

St Teilo's Trust

The Stafford Trust

The Stanley Foundation Ltd

The Stanton Ballard Charitable Trust

The Staples Trust

The Star Charitable Trust

The Steinberg Family Charitable Trust

The Hugh Stenhouse Foundation

The Stephen Barry Charitable Trust

C E K Stern Charitable Trust

The Sigmund Sternberg Charitable Foundation

Stervon Ltd

The Stevenage Community Trust

The June Stevens Foundation

Stevenson Family's Charitable Trust

The Steventon Allotments and Relief-in-Need Charity

The Stewards' Charitable Trust

The Stewards' Company Limited (incorporating the J W Laing Trust and the J W Laing Biblical Scholarship Trust)

The Stobart Newlands Charitable Trust

The Edward Stocks-Massey Bequest Fund

The Stokenchurch Educational Charity

The Stoller Charitable Trust

The M J C Stone Charitable Trust

The Samuel Storey Family Charitable Trust

Peter Stormonth Darling Charitable Trust

Peter Storrs Trust

The Strangward Trust

The Strasser Foundation

Stratford upon Avon Town Trust

The W O Street Charitable Foundation

The A B Strom and R Strom Charitable Trust

The Sudborough Foundation

Sueberry Ltd

The Suffolk Historic Churches Trust

The Alan Sugar Foundation

The Summerfield Charitable Trust

The Surrey Historic Buildings Trust Ltd

The Sussex Historic Churches Trust

The Adrienne and Leslie Sussman Charitable Trust

The Sutasoma Trust

Swan Mountain Trust

Swansea and Brecon Diocesan Board of Finance Limited

Swimathon Foundation

The John Swire (1989) Charitable Trust

The Swire Charitable Trust

The Adrian Swire Charitable Trust

The Hugh and Ruby Sykes Charitable Trust

The Charles and Elsie Sykes Trust

The Sylvanus Charitable Trust

The Stella Symons Charitable Trust

The Tabeel Trust

The Tajtelbaum Charitable Trust

Tallow Chandlers Benevolent Fund

Talteg Ltd

The Tangent Charitable Trust

The Lady Tangye Charitable Trust

The David Tannen Charitable Trust

The Tanner Trust

The Lili Tapper Charitable Foundation

The Mrs A Lacy Tate Trust

The Taurus Foundation

The Tay Charitable Trust

C B and H H Taylor 1984 Trust

Humphrey Richardson Taylor Charitable Trust

The Connie and Albert Taylor Charitable Trust

The Cyril Taylor Charitable Trust

A P Taylor Trust

Rosanna Taylor's 1987 Charity Trust

Tearfund

The Tedworth Charitable Trust

Tees Valley Community Foundation

Tegham Limited

The Templeton Goodwill Trust

Tesco Charity Trust

The C Paul Thackray General Charitable Trust

Thackray Medical Research Trust

The Thames Wharf Charity

The John P. Gommes Foundation

The Thistle Trust

The Loke Wan Tho Memorial Foundation

The David Thomas Charitable Trust

The Thomas Lilley Memorial Trust

The Arthur and Margaret Thompson Charitable Trust

The Maurice and Vivien Thompson Charitable Trust

The Thompson Family Charitable Trust

The Thompson6 Charitable Trust

The Len Thomson Charitable Trust

The Sir Jules Thorn Charitable Trust

The Thornton Foundation

The Thornton Trust

The Thousandth Man – Richard Burns Charitable Trust

The Three Oaks Trust

The Thriplow Charitable Trust

Mrs R P Tindall's Charitable Trust

The Tinsley Foundation

The Tisbury Telegraph Trust

The Tobacco Pipe Makers and Tobacco Trade Benevolent Fund

The Tolkien Trust

Tomchei Torah Charitable Trust

The Tompkins Foundation

The Torah Temimah Trust

Toras Chesed (London) Trust

The Tory Family Foundation

Tottenham Grammar School Foundation

The Tower Hill Trust

The Towry Law Charitable Trust (also known as the Castle Educational Trust)

The Mayor of Trafford's Charity Fund

Annie Tranmer Charitable Trust

The Constance Travis Charitable Trust

The Treeside Trust

The Trefoil Trust

The Tresillian Trust

The Triangle Trust (1949) Fund

The True Colours Trust

Truedene Co. Ltd

The Truemark Trust

Truemart Limited

Trumros Limited
The Trusthouse Charitable
  Foundation
Tudor Rose Ltd
The Tudor Trust
The Tufton Charitable Trust
The R D Turner Charitable
  Trust
The Douglas Turner Trust
The Florence Turner Trust
The G J W Turner Trust
Miss S M Tutton Charitable
  Trust
The TUUT Charitable Trust
Two Ridings Community
  Foundation
Community Foundation Serving
  Tyne and Wear and
  Northumberland
Trustees of Tzedakah
UKI Charitable Foundation
Ulster Garden Villages Ltd
Ultach Trust
The Ulverscroft Foundation
Ulverston Town Lands Charity
The Underwood Trust
The Union of Orthodox Hebrew
  Congregation
The United Society for the
  Propagation of the Gospel
The David Uri Memorial Trust
Uxbridge United Welfare Trust
Vale of Glamorgan – Welsh
  Church Fund
The Valentine Charitable Trust
The Valiant Charitable Trust
The Albert Van Den Bergh
  Charitable Trust
The Van Neste Foundation
Mrs Maud Van Norden's
  Charitable Foundation
The Vandervell Foundation
The Vardy Foundation
The Variety Club Children's
  Charity
Veneziana Fund
The Verdon-Smith Family
  Charitable Settlement
Roger Vere Foundation
Victoria Homes Trust
The Nigel Vinson Charitable
  Trust
The William and Ellen Vinten
  Trust
The Vintners' Company
  Charitable Foundation
Vintners' Gifts Charity
Vivdale Ltd
The Viznitz Foundation
Wade's Charity
The Scurrah Wainwright Charity
Wakeham Trust
The Community Foundation in
  Wales
Wales Council for Voluntary
  Action

Robert and Felicity Waley-
  Cohen Charitable Trust
The Thomas Wall Trust
Wallace and Gromit's
  Children's Foundation
The F J Wallis Charitable
  Settlement
War on Want
Sir Siegmund Warburg's
  Voluntary Settlement
The Ward Blenkinsop Trust
The George Ward Charitable
  Trust
The Barbara Ward Children's
  Foundation
G R Waters Charitable Trust
  2000
The Wates Foundation
Blyth Watson Charitable Trust
The Howard Watson Symington
  Memorial Charity
John Watson's Trust
Waynflete Charitable Trust
Weatherley Charitable Trust
The Weavers' Company
  Benevolent Fund
The David Webster Charitable
  Trust
The Weinberg Foundation
The Weinstein Foundation
The James Weir Foundation
The Joir and Kato Weisz
  Foundation
The Wellcome Trust
Welsh Church Fund Dyfed
  area (Carmarthenshire,
  Ceredigion and
  Pembrokeshire)
The Welton Foundation
The Wessex Youth Trust
The West Derby Wastelands
  Charity
West London Synagogue
  Charitable Fund
West Yorkshire Police
  Community Trust
Mrs S K West's Charitable
  Trust
The Westcroft Trust
The Westminster Foundation
The Garfield Weston
  Foundation
The Barbara Whatmore
  Charitable Trust
The Whitaker Charitable Trust
The Colonel W H Whitbread
  Charitable Trust
The Simon Whitbread
  Charitable Trust
The Melanie White Foundation
  Limited
White Stuff Foundation
The Whitecourt Charitable
  Trust
A H and B C Whiteley
  Charitable Trust
The Norman Whiteley Trust

The Whitley Animal Protection
  Trust
The Whittlesey Charity
The Lionel Wigram Memorial
  Trust
The Felicity Wilde Charitable
  Trust
The Wilkinson Charitable
  Foundation
The Charity of William Williams
The Kay Williams Charitable
  Foundation
The Williams Charitable Trust
The Williams Family Charitable
  Trust
Williams Serendipity Trust
The HDH Wills 1965
  Charitable Trust
The Dame Violet Wills Will
  Trust
The Wilmcote Charitrust
Sumner Wilson Charitable
  Trust
David Wilson Foundation
The Wilson Foundation
J and J R Wilson Trust
The Benjamin Winegarten
  Charitable Trust
The Harold Hyam Wingate
  Foundation
The Francis Winham
  Foundation
Wirral Mayor's Charity
The James Wise Charitable
  Trust
The Witzenfeld Foundation
The Michael and Anna Wix
  Charitable Trust
The Wixamtree Trust
The Woburn 1986 Charitable
  Trust
The Maurice Wohl Charitable
  Foundation
The Charles Wolfson
  Charitable Trust
The James Wood Bequest
  Fund
The Wood Family Trust
The Woodcock Charitable Trust
Wooden Spoon Society
Woodlands Green Ltd
Woodlands Trust
Woodroffe Benton Foundation
The Woodward Charitable
  Trust
The A and R Woolf Charitable
  Trust
ME Woolfe Charitable Trust
Worcester Municipal Charities
The Worcestershire and
  Dudley Historic Churches
  Trust
The Wragge and Co. Charitable
  Trust
The Diana Edgson Wright
  Charitable Trust

The Matthews Wrightson
   Charity Trust
Miss E B Wrightson's
   Charitable Settlement
The Joan Wyatt Charitable
   Trust
Wychdale Ltd
Wychville Ltd
The Wyndham Charitable Trust
The Wyseliot Charitable Trust
The Xerox (UK) Trust
Yankov Charitable Trust
The Dennis Alan Yardy
   Charitable Trust
The W Wing Yip and Brothers
   Foundation
Yorkshire Agricultural Society
The South Yorkshire
   Community Foundation
The Yorkshire Dales
   Millennium Trust
The John Young Charitable
   Settlement
The William Allen Young
   Charitable Trust
The John K Young Endowment
   Fund
Zephyr Charitable Trust
The Marjorie and Arnold Ziff
   Charitable Foundation
Stephen Zimmerman
   Charitable Trust
The Zochonis Charitable Trust
The Zolfo Cooper Foundation

Project support

■ Full project funding

The 101 Foundation
The 1970 Trust
The 1989 Willan Charitable
   Trust
The 29th May 1961 Charitable
   Trust
A W Charitable Trust
The Aberbrothock Skea Trust
The Aberdeen Endowments
   Trust
ABF The Soldiers' Charity
Achisomoch Aid Company
   Limited
The ACT Foundation
Action Medical Research
The Ad Meliora Charitable
   Trust
The Sylvia Adams Charitable
   Trust
The Victor Adda Foundation
The Adint Charitable Trust
Age UK
The Agger Foundation
Aid to the Church in Need (UK)
Aim to Zero Foundation

The Sylvia Aitken Charitable
   Trust
The Ajahma Charitable Trust
The Al Fayed Charitable
   Foundation
Aldgate and All Hallows'
   Foundation
The Aldgate Freedom
   Foundation
All Saints Educational Trust
The Derrill Allatt Foundation
Allchurches Trust Ltd
The H B Allen Charitable Trust
The Allen Lane Trust
The Alliance Family Foundation
Angus Allnatt Charitable
   Foundation
The Pat Allsop Charitable Trust
Almondsbury Charity
Altamont Ltd
Alvor Charitable Trust
The Ammco Trust
The Bryan and June Amos
   Foundation
The AMW Charitable Trust
The Anchor Foundation
Andrews Charitable Trust
Anglo American Group
   Foundation
Anguish's Educational
   Foundation
The Animal Defence Trust
Philip Anker Trust
The Eric Anker-Petersen
   Charity
Anpride Ltd
Ambrose and Ann Appelbe
   Trust
The Appletree Trust
The Arbib Foundation
The John M Archer Charitable
   Trust
The Archer Trust
The Architectural Heritage
   Fund
The Argus Appeal
The Armenian Relief Society of
   Great Britain Trust
The Armourers' and Brasiers'
   Gauntlet Trust
The Arsenal Foundation
The Artemis Charitable Trust
Arthritis Research UK
The Arts and Entertainment
   Charitable Trust
Arts Council England
The Arts Council of Northern
   Ireland
Arts Council of Wales (also
   known as Cyngor
   Celfyddydau Cymru)
The Ove Arup Foundation
The A S Charitable Trust
The Ashden Trust
The Ashendene Trust
The Ashley Family Foundation
The Ashworth Charitable Trust

The Ian Askew Charitable Trust
The Associated Country
   Women of the World
The Association of Colleges
   Charitable Trust
Astellas European Foundation
Asthma UK
AstonMansfield Charitable
   Trust
The Astor Foundation
The Astor of Hever Trust
The Aurelius Charitable Trust
The Avenue Charitable Trust
Awards for All
The BAA Communities Trust
The Bacit Foundation
The BACTA Charitable Trust
The Scott Bader
   Commonwealth Ltd
The Bagri Foundation
Veta Bailey Charitable Trust
The Austin Bailey Foundation
The Baily Thomas Charitable
   Fund
The Baird Trust
The Baker Charitable Trust
The Balcombe Charitable Trust
The Andrew Balint Charitable
   Trust
The Albert Casanova Ballard
   Deceased Trust
The Ballinger Charitable Trust
The Balmore Trust
The Balney Charitable Trust
The Baltic Charitable Fund
The Bamford Charitable
   Foundation
The Banbury Charities
William P Bancroft (No 2)
   Charitable Trust and
   Jenepher Gillett Trust
The Band Trust
The Barbers' Company General
   Charities
The Barbour Foundation
Barchester Healthcare
   Foundation
The Barclay Foundation
The Baring Foundation
Peter Barker-Mill Memorial
   Charity
The Barleycorn Trust
Barnes Workhouse Fund
The Barnsbury Charitable Trust
The Barnwood House Trust
The Misses Barrie Charitable
   Trust
Barrington Family Charitable
   Trust
Bartholomew Charitable Trust
The Bartlett Taylor Charitable
   Trust
The Paul Bassham Charitable
   Trust
The Batchworth Trust
The Bates Charitable Trust
The Bay Tree Charitable Trust

The Louis Baylis (Maidenhead Advertiser) Charitable Trust
BBC Children in Need
B-CH 1971 Charitable Trust
The Beacon Trust
The Bearder Charity
The James Beattie Charitable Trust
The Beaverbrook Foundation
The Beccles Town Lands Charity
The Becker Family Charitable Trust
The Becketts and Sargeants Educational Foundation
The John Beckwith Charitable Trust
The Peter Beckwith Charitable Trust
The Bedfordshire and Luton Community Foundation
The David and Ruth Behrend Fund
The Beit Trust
The Bellahouston Bequest Fund
The Bellinger Donnay Trust
The Benfield Motors Charitable Trust
The Benham Charitable Settlement
Maurice and Jacqueline Bennett Charitable Trust
Bennett Lowell Limited
The Berkshire Community Foundation
The Bertarelli UK Foundation
The Bestway Foundation
Bet365 Foundation
BHST
The Mason Bibby 1981 Trust
The Bideford Bridge Trust
The Big Lottery Fund
The Billmeir Charitable Trust
The Bingham Trust
The Bintaub Charitable Trust
The Birmingham District Nursing Charitable Trust
The Birmingham Hospital Saturday Fund Medical Charity and Welfare Trust
Birmingham International Airport Community Trust
The Lord Mayor of Birmingham's Charity
The Michael Bishop Foundation
The Bishop's Development Fund
The Bertie Black Foundation
Isabel Blackman Foundation
The Blagrave Trust
The Blair Foundation
Blakemore Foundation
The Blanchminster Trust
The Blandford Lake Trust

The Sir Victor Blank Charitable Settlement
The Neville and Elaine Blond Charitable Trust
The Bluston Charitable Settlement
The Body Shop Foundation
The Boltons Trust
The Bonamy Charitable Trust
The John and Celia Bonham Christie Charitable Trust
The Charlotte Bonham-Carter Charitable Trust
Bonhomie United Charity Society
The Boots Charitable Trust
The Bordon Liphook Haslemere Charity
The Oliver Borthwick Memorial Trust
The Boshier-Hinton Foundation
The Bothwell Charitable Trust
H E and E L Botteley Charitable Trust
The Harry Bottom Charitable Trust
The Anthony Bourne Foundation
The Bower Trust
The Bowerman Charitable Trust
John and Susan Bowers Fund
The Bowland Charitable Trust
The Frank Brake Charitable Trust
The William Brake Charitable Trust
The Tony Bramall Charitable Trust
The Breast Cancer Research Trust
The Harold and Alice Bridges Charity
Bristol Archdeaconry Charity
John Bristow and Thomas Mason Trust
The British Council for Prevention of Blindness
The British Dietetic Association General and Education Trust Fund
The British Gas (Scottish Gas) Energy Trust
British Heart Foundation
British Humane Association
British Institute at Ankara
British Ornithologists' Union
The Britten-Pears Foundation
The J and M Britton Charitable Trust
The Bromley Trust
The Roger Brooke Charitable Trust
The David Brooke Charity
The Charles Brotherton Trust
Joseph Brough Charitable Trust

The Swinfen Broun Charitable Trust
Edna Brown Charitable Settlement (Mrs E E Brown Charitable Settlement)
Buckinghamshire Community Foundation
The Buckinghamshire Masonic Centenary Fund
The Bulldog Trust Limited
The E F Bulmer Benevolent Fund
Bumba Foundation
Burdens Charitable Foundation
The Clara E Burgess Charity
The Burry Charitable Trust
The Arnold Burton 1998 Charitable Trust
The Burton Breweries Charitable Trust
Consolidated Charity of Burton upon Trent
The Paul Bush Foundation Trust
The Worshipful Company of Butchers General Charities
The Noel Buxton Trust
C M L Family Foundation
Henry T and Lucy B Cadbury Charitable Trust
The Christopher Cadbury Charitable Trust
The G W Cadbury Charitable Trust
The Edward and Dorothy Cadbury Trust
CAF (Charities Aid Foundation)
CAFOD (Catholic Agency for Overseas Development)
Community Foundation for Calderdale
The Callander Charitable Trust
Calleva Foundation
The Calpe Trust
Calypso Browning Trust
The Cambridgeshire Community Foundation
The Camelia Trust
The Campden Charities Trustee
The Canning Trust
H and L Cantor Trust
The Carew Pole Charitable Trust
The D W T Cargill Fund
Carlee Ltd
The Carlton House Charitable Trust
The Carmelite Monastery Ware Trust
The Worshipful Company of Carmen Benevolent Trust
The Carnegie Dunfermline Trust
The Carpenter Charitable Trust
The Carpenters' Company Charitable Trust

The Carrington Charitable
Trust
The Carron Charitable
Settlement
The Leslie Mary Carter
Charitable Trust
The Casey Trust
Cash for Kids Radio Clyde
Sir John Cass's Foundation
The Elizabeth Casson Trust
The Castang Foundation
The Catalyst Charitable Trust
The Catholic Charitable Trust
Catholic Foreign Missions
The Catholic Trust for England
and Wales
The Cattanach Charitable Trust
The Joseph and Annie Cattle
Trust
The Thomas Sivewright Catto
Charitable Settlement
The Wilfrid and Constance
Cave Foundation
The Cayo Foundation
The B G S Cayzer Charitable
Trust
The Cazenove Charitable Trust
Celtic Charity Fund
The Gaynor Cemlyn-Jones
Trust
The Pamela Champion
Foundation
The Chapman Charitable Trust
John William Chapman's
Charitable Trust
The Charities Advisory Trust
Charitworth Limited
The Charter 600 Charity
The Worshipful Company of
Chartered Accountants
General Charitable Trust
(also known as CALC)
The Chasah Trust
The Chelsea Square 1994
Trust
Cherry Grove Charitable Trust
The Cheruby Trust
Cheshire Freemason's Charity
The Chetwode Foundation
Cheviot Asset Management
Charitable Trust
Childs Charitable Trust
The Childwick Trust
The Chipping Sodbury Town
Lands Charity
CHK Charities Limited
The Chownes Foundation
The Chrimes Family Charitable
Trust
The Christabella Charitable
Trust
Christadelphian Samaritan
Fund
Christian Aid
Christian Response to Eastern
Europe
Christie Foundation

Chrysalis Trust
The Church and Community
Fund
The Church Burgesses
Educational Foundation
Church Burgesses Trust
Church of Ireland Priorities
Fund
Church Urban Fund
City and County of Swansea
Welsh Church Act Fund
The City Bridge Trust
The City Educational Trust
Fund
Stephen Clark 1957
Charitable Trust
J A Clark Charitable Trust
The Hilda and Alice Clark
Charitable Trust
The Roger and Sarah Bancroft
Clark Charitable Trust
The Clarke Charitable
Settlement
The Clear Light Trust
The Cleopatra Trust
Lord Clinton's Charitable Trust
The Clore Duffield Foundation
Miss V L Clore's 1967
Charitable Trust
Closehelm Limited
Richard Cloudesley's Charity
The Clover Trust
The Robert Clutterbuck
Charitable Trust
Clydpride Ltd
The Coalfields Regeneration
Trust
The John Coates Charitable
Trust
The Cobtree Charity Trust Ltd
The Denise Cohen Charitable
Trust
The Vivienne and Samuel
Cohen Charitable Trust
The John S Cohen Foundation
The R and S Cohen
Foundation
The Cole Charitable Trust
The Colefax Charitable Trust
The John and Freda Coleman
Charitable Trust
The George Henry Collins
Charity
The Coltstaple Trust
Colwinston Charitable Trust
Colyer-Fergusson Charitable
Trust
Comic Relief
The Comino Foundation
The Compton Charitable Trust
The Congleton Inclosure Trust
The Conservation Foundation
The Consolidated Charities for
the Infirm Merchant
Taylors' Company
Gordon Cook Foundation
The Ernest Cook Trust

The Cooks Charity
The Catherine Cookson
Charitable Trust
The Keith Coombs Trust
Mabel Cooper Charity
The Alice Ellen Cooper Dean
Charitable Foundation
The Co-operative Foundation
The Marjorie Coote Animal
Charity Trust
The Marjorie Coote Old
People's Charity
The Helen Jean Cope Trust
The J Reginald Corah
Foundation Fund
The Gershon Coren Charitable
Foundation (also known as
The Muriel and Gus Coren
Charitable Foundation)
The Cornwell Charitable Trust
The Sidney and Elizabeth
Corob Charitable Trust
The Corona Charitable Trust
The Bryan Christopher
Corrigan Charitable Trust
The Costa Family Charitable
Trust
The Cotton Industry War
Memorial Trust
The Cotton Trust
County Durham Community
Foundation
The Augustine Courtauld Trust
Coutts Charitable Foundation
The General Charities of the
City of Coventry
Coventry Building Society
Charitable Foundation
The John Cowan Foundation
Dudley and Geoffrey Cox
Charitable Trust
The Sir William Coxen Trust
Fund
The Lord Cozens-Hardy Trust
The Craignish Trust
The Craps Charitable Trust
Michael Crawford Children's
Charity
The Cray Trust
Creative Scotland
The Crerar Hotels Trust
The Crescent Trust
Cripplegate Foundation
The Violet and Milo Cripps
Charitable Trust
The Cross Trust
The Croydon Relief in Need
Charities
Cruden Foundation Ltd
The Ronald Cruickshanks
Foundation
Cullum Family Trust
The Culra Charitable Trust
Cumberland Building Society
Charitable Foundation
Cumbria Community
Foundation

The D J H Currie Memorial Trust

The Dennis Curry Charitable Trust

The Manny Cussins Foundation

The Cwmbran Trust

Itzchok Meyer Cymerman Trust Ltd

The D G Charitable Settlement

The D'Oyly Carte Charitable Trust

Roald Dahl's Marvellous Children's Charity

Daily Prayer Union Charitable Trust Limited

The Daiwa Anglo-Japanese Foundation

The Dr and Mrs A Darlington Charitable Trust

Baron Davenport's Charity

The Davidson (Nairn) Charitable Trust

The Davidson Family Charitable Trust

The Alderman Joe Davidson Memorial Trust

Michael Davies Charitable Settlement

The Gwendoline and Margaret Davies Charity

The Wilfrid Bruce Davis Charitable Trust

Davis-Rubens Charitable Trust

The Dawe Charitable Trust

The De Brye Charitable Trust

The De Clermont Charitable Company Ltd

Peter De Haan Charitable Trust

The Deakin Charitable Trust

The Debmar Benevolent Trust

The Delius Trust

The Dellal Foundation

The Delves Charitable Trust

The Demigryphon Trust

The Denman Charitable Trust

Dentons UKMEA LLP Charitable Trust

The Earl of Derby's Charitable Trust

Derbyshire Community Foundation

The J N Derbyshire Trust

The Desmond Foundation

The Devon Educational Trust

The Sandy Dewhirst Charitable Trust

The Laduma Dhamecha Charitable Trust

Diabetes UK

Diced Cap Charity

The Gillian Dickinson Trust

The Dickon Trust

The Peter Alan Dickson Foundation

Grace Dieu Charitable Trust

The Digbeth Trust Limited

The Dinwoodie Settlement

Dischma Charitable Trust

The Djanogly Foundation

The Novak Djokovic Foundation (UK) Limited

The DLM Charitable Trust

Louise Dobson Charitable Trust

The Derek and Eileen Dodgson Foundation

The Dollond Charitable Trust

Domepride Ltd

The Dorcas Trust

The Dorus Trust

The Doughty Charity Trust

The R M Douglas Charitable Trust

The Drapers' Charitable Fund

The P B Dumbell Charitable Trust

The Dumbreck Charity

Dunard Fund

The Dunhill Medical Trust

The Dunn Family Charitable Trust

The W E Dunn Trust

Dushinsky Trust Ltd

Annette Duvollet Charitable Trust

The Dwek Family Charitable Trust

The Dyers' Company Charitable Trust

The James Dyson Foundation

eaga Charitable Trust

The Eagle Charity Trust

The Earley Charity

Earls Colne and Halstead Educational Charity

The Earmark Trust

East End Community Foundation

The Sir John Eastwood Foundation

The Ebenezer Trust

The EBM Charitable Trust

Eden Arts Trust

EDF Energy Trust (EDFET)

The Gilbert and Eileen Edgar Foundation

Edinburgh Children's Holiday Fund

Edinburgh Trust No 2 Account

Edinburgh Voluntary Organisations' Trust Funds (EVOT)

The William Edwards Educational Charity

The Eighty Eight Foundation

The Elephant Trust

The George Elias Charitable Trust

The Gerald Palmer Eling Trust Company

The Wilfred and Elsie Elkes Charity Fund

The Maud Elkington Charitable Trust

The Ellerdale Trust

The John Ellerman Foundation

The Ellinson Foundation Ltd

James Ellis Charitable Trust

The Elmgrant Trust

The Elmley Foundation

The Vernon N Ely Charitable Trust

The Embleton Trust

Embrace the Middle East

The Emerton-Christie Charity

The Endure Foundation

The Worshipful Company of Engineers Charitable Trust Fund

The Englefield Charitable Trust

The English Schools' Football Association

The Enkalon Foundation

Entindale Ltd

The Epigoni Trust

Epilepsy Research UK

The Equitable Charitable Trust

The Equity Trust Fund

The Ericson Trust

The Erskine Cunningham Hill Trust

The Essendon Charitable Trust

Essex Community Foundation

The Essex Fairway Charitable Trust

Essex Provincial Charity Fund

The Essex Youth Trust

Euro Charity Trust

Sir John Evelyn's Charity

The Eventhall Family Charitable Trust

The Eveson Charitable Trust

The Beryl Evetts and Robert Luff Animal Welfare Trust Limited

The Exilarch's Foundation

F C Charitable Trust

The F P Limited Charitable Trust

The Faber Charitable Trust

Esmée Fairbairn Foundation

The Fairway Trust

The Family Rich Charities Trust

The Lord Faringdon Charitable Trust

Samuel William Farmer Trust

The Farmers' Company Charitable Fund

The Thomas Farr Charity

Walter Farthing (Trust) Limited

The Fassnidge Memorial Trust

Joseph Fattorini Charitable Trust

Federation of Jewish Relief Organisations

The John Feeney Charitable Trust

The George Fentham Birmingham Charity

The A M Fenton Trust
Allan and Nesta Ferguson
  Charitable Settlement
The Doris Field Charitable
  Trust
The Fifty Fund
Filey Foundation Ltd
Firtree Trust
The Fishmongers' Company's
  Charitable Trust
The Fitton Trust
The Earl Fitzwilliam Charitable
  Trust
The Ian Fleming Charitable
  Trust
The Flow Foundation
The Gerald Fogel Charitable
  Trust
The Follett Trust
The Football Association
  National Sports Centre
  Trust
The Football Association Youth
  Trust
The Football Foundation
The Forbes Charitable
  Foundation
The Forces Trust (Working
  Name)
The Oliver Ford Charitable
  Trust
The Forest Hill Charitable Trust
Forever Manchester (The
  Community Foundation for
  Greater Manchester)
The Forman Hardy Charitable
  Trust
Gwyneth Forrester Trust
The Forte Charitable Trust
The Four Lanes Trust
The Four Winds Trust
The Foyle Foundation
The Isaac and Freda Frankel
  Memorial Charitable Trust
The Elizabeth Frankland Moore
  and Star Foundation
Sydney E Franklin Deceased's
  New Second Charity
The Jill Franklin Trust
The Gordon Fraser Charitable
  Trust
The Hugh Fraser Foundation
The Joseph Strong Frazer Trust
The Louis and Valerie
  Freedman Charitable
  Settlement
The Freemasons' Grand
  Charity
The Charles S French
  Charitable Trust
The Anne French Memorial
  Trust
The Freshfield Foundation
The Freshgate Trust
  Foundation
The Friarsgate Trust

Sybilla and Leo Friedler
  Charitable Trust
The Friends Hall Farm Street
  Trust
Friends Provident Charitable
  Foundation
The Frognal Trust
Maurice Fry Charitable Trust
The Fulmer Charitable Trust
Worshipful Company of
  Furniture Makers Charitable
  Fund
The Fuserna Foundation
  General Charitable Trust
The G I Foundation
Gableholt Limited
The Galbraith Trust
The Gale Family Charity Trust
Gamlen Charitable Trust
The Gamma Trust
The Gannochy Trust
The Worshipful Company of
  Gardeners of London
The Samuel Gardner Memorial
  Trust
The Garennie Charitable Trust
The Garnett Charitable Trust
Garthgwynion Charities
Garvan Limited
The Gatsby Charitable
  Foundation
The Robert Gavron Charitable
  Trust
Thomas Betton's Charity for
  Pensions and Relief-in-Need
The General Nursing Council
  for England and Wales
  Trust
The Gibbs Charitable Trust
Simon Gibson Charitable Trust
The G C Gibson Charitable
  Trust
Lady Gibson's Charitable Trust
The Harvey and Hilary Gilbert
  Charitable Trust
The Girdlers' Company
  Charitable Trust
The B and P Glasser
  Charitable Trust
The Glass-House Trust
Global Care
Global Charities
Gloucestershire Community
  Foundation
Worshipful Company of
  Glovers of London Charity
  Fund
The GNC Trust
The Godinton Charitable Trust
The Sydney and Phyllis
  Goldberg Memorial
  Charitable Trust
The Golden Bottle Trust
The Jack Goldhill Charitable
  Trust
The Goldsmiths' Arts Trust
  Fund

The Goldsmiths' Company
  Charity
The Golsoncott Foundation
The Mike Gooley Trailfinders
  Charity
The Gosling Foundation
  Limited
The Gough Charitable Trust
The Gould Charitable Trust
The Grace Charitable Trust
A B Grace Trust
The Graff Foundation
E C Graham Belford Charitable
  Settlement
The Grahame Charitable
  Foundation Limited
The Granada Foundation
Grand Charitable Trust of the
  Order of Women
  Freemasons
The Grand Order of Water
  Rats' Charities Fund
The Grange Farm Centre Trust
Grantham Yorke Trust
The Stanley and Lorna Graves
  Charitable Trust
The Gordon Gray Trust
The Gray Trust
The Great Stone Bridge Trust
  of Edenbridge
The Great Torrington Town
  Lands Charity
The Kenneth & Susan Green
  Charitable Foundation
The Haydn Green Charitable
  Trust
The Green Hall Foundation
The Green Woodpecker Trust
Greenham Common
  Community Trust Limited
Greggs Foundation
The Gretna Charitable Trust
The Grimmitt Trust
The Grocers' Charity
The M and R Gross Charities
  Limited
The GRP Charitable Trust
The David and Marie Grumitt
  Foundation
N and R Grunbaum Charitable
  Trust
The Bishop of Guildford's
  Foundation
The Guildry Incorporation of
  Perth
The Walter Guinness
  Charitable Trust
The Gunter Charitable Trust
The Gur Trust
The Gurney Charitable Trust
Dr Guthrie's Association
The H and M Charitable Trust
H C D Memorial Fund
H C Foundation
The H P Charitable Trust
The Hackney Parochial
  Charities

The Hadfield Trust
The Hadley Trust
The Hadrian Trust
The Alfred Haines Charitable Trust
The Haley Family Charitable Trust
E F and M G Hall Charitable Trust
The Edith Winifred Hall Charitable Trust
Robert Hall Charity
The Hamamelis Trust
Hamilton Wallace Trust
Paul Hamlyn Foundation
The Hampshire and Islands Historic Churches Trust
Hampshire and Isle of Wight Community Foundation
Hampton Fuel Allotment Charity
The W A Handley Charitable Trust
Beatrice Hankey Foundation Limited
The Hanley Trust (1987)
The Kathleen Hannay Memorial Charity
The Doughty Hanson Charitable Foundation
Lord Hanson Foundation
Miss K M Harbinson's Charitable Trust
The Harborne Parish Lands Charity
The Harbour Charitable Trust
The Harbour Foundation
The Harding Trust
William Harding's Charity
The Hare of Steep Charitable Trust
The Harebell Centenary Fund
The Kenneth Hargreaves Charitable Trust
The Harpur Trust
The Harris Charity
The Harrison and Potter Trust
The John Harrison Charitable Trust
The Peter Harrison Foundation
The Spencer Hart Charitable Trust
The Hartley Charitable Trust
William Geoffrey Harvey's Discretionary Settlement
Haskel Family Foundation
The Hathaway Trust
The Maurice Hatter Foundation
The M A Hawe Settlement
The Hawkins Foundation
The Hawthorne Charitable Trust
The Dorothy Hay-Bolton Charitable Trust
The Headley Trust
Headley-Pitt Charitable Trust

Heart of England Community Foundation
The Heathcoat Trust
Heathside Charitable Trust
The Charlotte Heber-Percy Charitable Trust
The Hedley Denton Charitable Trust
The Hedley Foundation
The H J Heinz Company Limited Charitable Trust
The Hellenic Foundation
The Michael Heller Charitable Foundation
The Simon Heller Charitable Settlement
The Hemby Trust
The Christina Mary Hendrie Trust for Scottish and Canadian Charities
Henley Educational Trust (formerley Henley Educational Charity)
Esther Hennell Charitable Trust
The G D Herbert Charitable Trust
The Anne Herd Memorial Trust
The Herefordshire Historic Churches Trust
The Heritage of London Trust Ltd
The Hesed Trust
The Hesslewood Children's Trust (Hull Seamen's and General Orphanage)
Hexham and Newcastle Diocesan Trust (1947)
The Higgs Charitable Trust
Alan Edward Higgs Charity
The Graham High Charitable Trust
The High Sheriff's Police Trust for the County of West Midlands (Building Blocks)
Highcroft Charitable Trust
The Charles Littlewood Hill Trust
The Hillier Trust
The Hillingdon Partnership Trust
The Hilmarnan Charitable Trust
Lady Hind Trust
The Hiscox Foundation
The Hitchin Educational Foundation
The Eleemosynary Charity of William Hobbayne
Hobson Charity Limited
Matthew Hodder Charitable Trust
The Sir Julian Hodge Charitable Trust
The J G Hogg Charitable Trust
The Holden Charitable Trust
John Holford's Charity

The Hollick Family Charitable Trust
The Dorothy Holmes Charitable Trust
The Holst Foundation
The Edward Holt Trust
The Holywood Trust
The Homelands Charitable Trust
The Homestead Charitable Trust
Mary Homfray Charitable Trust
Sir Harold Hood's Charitable Trust
Hope for Youth (NI)
The Hope Trust
HopMarket Charity
The Cuthbert Horn Trust
The Antony Hornby Charitable Trust
The Horne Foundation
The Horne Trust
The Worshipful Company of Horners' Charitable Trusts
The Hornsey Parochial Charities
The Hospital of God at Greatham
The Hospital Saturday Fund
Houblon-Norman/George Fund
The House of Industry Estate
The Reta Lila Howard Foundation
The Daniel Howard Trust
The Huddersfield Common Good Trust
The Hudson Foundation
The Huggard Charitable Trust
The Geoffrey C Hughes Charitable Trust
Hulme Trust Estates (Educational)
Human Relief Foundation
The Humanitarian Trust
The Michael and Shirley Hunt Charitable Trust
The Hunter Foundation
Miss Agnes H Hunter's Trust
The Hunting Horn General Charitable Trust
The Huntingdon Foundation
Huntingdon Freemen's Trust
Hurdale Charity Limited
The Nani Huyu Charitable Trust
The P Y N and B Hyams Trust
The Hyde Charitable Trust
I B B Charitable Trust
I G O Foundation Limited
The Idlewild Trust
The Iliffe Family Charitable Trust
The Indigo Trust
The Ingram Trust
The Inland Waterways Association
The Inlight Trust
The Inman Charity

The Inner London Magistrates
Court Poor Box and Feeder
Charity
The Innocent Foundation
The International Bankers
Charitable Trust (The
Worshipful Company of
International Bankers)
International Spinal Research
Trust
Investream Charitable Trust
The Ireland Fund of Great
Britain
The Irish Youth Foundation
(UK) Ltd (incorporating The
Lawlor Foundation)
The Ironmongers' Foundation
The Charles Irving Charitable
Trust
Irwin Trust
The ISA Charity
The Isaacs Charitable Trust
The J Isaacs Charitable Trust
The ITF Seafarers Trust
The Ithaca Trust
The J & J Benevolent
Foundation
The J M K Charitable Trust
The J R S S T Charitable Trust
C Richard Jackson Charitable
Trust
Elizabeth Jackson Charitable
Trust
The Ruth and Lionel Jacobson
Trust (Second Fund) No 2
Jaffe Family Relief Fund
John James Bristol Foundation
The Susan and Stephen
James Charitable
Settlement
The James Trust
The Jarman Charitable Trust
The Jasper Conran Foundation
JCA Charitable Foundation
The Jeffrey Charitable Trust
Rees Jeffreys Road Fund
The Jenour Foundation
The Jephcott Charitable Trust
Jerwood Charitable Foundation
Jesus Hospital Charity
Jewish Child's Day
The Jewish Youth Fund
The Jigsaw Foundation
The Harold Joels Charitable
Trust
The Nicholas Joels Charitable
Trust
The Norman Joels Charitable
Trust
The Elton John Aids
Foundation
The Dyfrig and Heather John
Charitable Trust
The Lillie Johnson Charitable
Trust
The Johnson Foundation

The Reginald Johnson
Foundation
The Johnnie Johnson Trust
The Johnson Wax Ltd
Charitable Trust
The Joicey Trust
The Jones 1986 Charitable
Trust
The Marjorie and Geoffrey
Jones Charitable Trust
The Jordan Charitable
Foundation
The J E Joseph Charitable
Fund
The Lady Eileen Joseph
Foundation
The Josephs Family Charitable
Trust
JTH Charitable Trust
The Judith Trust
The Jungels-Winkler Charitable
Foundation
The Anton Jurgens Charitable
Trust
The Bernard Kahn Charitable
Trust
The Stanley Kalms Foundation
The Karenza Foundation
The Boris Karloff Charitable
Foundation
The Ian Karten Charitable
Trust
The Kasner Charitable Trust
The Kathleen Trust
The Michael and Ilse Katz
Foundation
The Katzauer Charitable
Settlement
The C S Kaufman Charitable
Trust
The Geoffrey John Kaye
Charitable Foundation
The Emmanuel Kaye
Foundation
Kelsick's Educational
Foundation
The KempWelch Charitable
Trust
The Kay Kendall Leukaemia
Fund
The John Thomas Kennedy
Charitable Foundation
The Kennedy Charitable
Foundation
The Kennel Club Charitable
Trust
Kent Community Foundation
The Nancy Kenyon Charitable
Trust
Keren Association
Kermaville Ltd
The Peter Kershaw Trust
Keswick Hall Trust
The Ursula Keyes Trust
The Mr & Mrs Paul Killik
Charitable Trust

The Robert Kiln Charitable
Trust
The King Henry VIII Endowed
Trust Warwick
The King/Cullimore Charitable
Trust
The Kingsbury Charity
The Mary Kinross Charitable
Trust
Kirkley Poor's Lands Estate
The Richard Kirkman
Charitable Trust
Kirschel Foundation
Robert Kitchin (Saddlers'
Company)
Ernest Kleinwort Charitable
Trust
The Marina Kleinwort
Charitable Trust
The Kobler Trust
The Kofia Trust
The Kohn Foundation
Liudmila Korneenko
Foundation
The Kreditor Charitable Trust
The Kreitman Foundation
The Neil Kreitman Foundation
The Heinz, Anna and Carol
Kroch Foundation
The Kyte Charitable Trust
L P W Limited
The Late Sir Pierce Lacy
Charity Trust
John Laing Charitable Trust
Maurice and Hilda Laing
Charitable Trust
The Christopher Laing
Foundation
The Kirby Laing Foundation
The Martin Laing Foundation
The Beatrice Laing Trust
The Lambert Charitable Trust
Duchy of Lancaster Benevolent
Fund
The Lancaster Foundation
LandAid Charitable Trust
The Allen Lane Foundation
Langdale Trust
The Langley Charitable Trust
The LankellyChase Foundation
The R J Larg Family Charitable
Trust
Largsmount Ltd
The Lark Trust
Laslett's (Hinton) Charity
The Lauffer Family Charitable
Foundation
The Kathleen Laurence Trust
The Law Society Charity
The Edgar E Lawley Foundation
The Herd Lawson and Muriel
Lawson Charitable Trust
The Lawson Beckman
Charitable Trust
The Raymond and Blanche
Lawson Charitable Trust
The Leach Fourteenth Trust

....

279

The David Lean Foundation
The Leathersellers' Company
Charitable Fund
The Leche Trust
The Arnold Lee Charitable
Trust
The Lord Mayor of Leeds
Appeal Fund
Leeds Building Society
Charitable Foundation
The Kennedy Leigh Charitable
Trust
Morris Leigh Foundation
The Leigh Trust
Mrs Vera Leigh's Charity
P Leigh-Bramwell Trust 'E'
The Lennox and Wyfold
Foundation
The Erica Leonard Trust
The Leonard Trust
The Mark Leonard Trust
Lesley Lesley and Mutter Trust
Leukaemia and Lymphoma
Research
The Leverhulme Trade
Charities Trust
The Joseph Levy Charitable
Foundation
The John Spedan Lewis
Foundation
The Sir Edward Lewis
Foundation
John Lewis Partnership
General Community Fund
Lichfield Conduit Lands
Lifeline 4 Kids
The Linbury Trust
Lincolnshire Community
Foundation
Lindale Educational
Foundation
The Linden Charitable Trust
The Enid Linder Foundation
The Linmardon Trust
The Ruth and Stuart Lipton
Charitable Trust
The Lister Charitable Trust
Frank Litchfield Charitable
Trust
The Andrew and Mary
Elizabeth Little Charitable
Trust
Littlefield Foundation (UK)
Limited
The Second Joseph Aaron
Littman Foundation
The George John and Sheilah
Livanos Charitable Trust
Liverpool Charity and Voluntary
Services
Liverpool Sailors' Home Trust
The Ian & Natalie Livingstone
Charitable Trust
The Elaine and Angus Lloyd
Charitable Trust
The Charles Lloyd Foundation
Lloyd's Charities Trust

Lloyds Bank Foundation for
England and Wales
Lloyds Bank Foundation for
Northern Ireland
Lloyds Bank Foundation for the
Channel Islands
Lloyds TSB Foundation for
Scotland
The Lo Family Charitable Trust
The Locker Foundation
The Loftus Charitable Trust
The Lolev Charitable Trust
The Trust for London
The London Community
Foundation
The London Housing
Foundation
The London Law Trust
The William and Katherine
Longman Trust
The Loseley and Guildway
Charitable Trust
The Lotus Foundation
The Lowy Mitchell Foundation
The C L Loyd Charitable Trust
LSA Charitable Trust
The Marie Helen Luen
Charitable Trust
Robert Luff Foundation Ltd
Henry Lumley Charitable Trust
C F Lunoe Trust Fund
The Ruth and Jack Lunzer
Charitable Trust
Lord and Lady Lurgan Trust
The Lyndhurst Trust
The Lynn Foundation
The Lynwood Trust
John Lyon's Charity
The Lyons Charitable Trust
The Sir Jack Lyons Charitable
Trust
The Lyras Family Charitable
Trust
Sylvanus Lyson's Charity
The M and C Trust
The M K Charitable Trust
The Madeline Mabey Trust
The E M MacAndrew Trust
Macdonald-Buchanan
Charitable Trust
The Mackay and Brewer
Charitable Trust
The Mackintosh Foundation
The MacRobert Trust
James Madison Trust
The Magen Charitable Trust
Man Group plc Charitable
Trust
The Manackerman Charitable
Trust
Manchester Airport Community
Trust Fund
The Manchester Guardian
Society Charitable Trust
Lord Mayor of Manchester's
Charity Appeal Trust
Mandeville Trust

The Manifold Charitable Trust
W M Mann Foundation
R W Mann Trust
The Leslie and Lilian Manning
Trust
Marbeh Torah Trust
Marchig Animal Welfare Trust
The Stella and Alexander
Margulies Charitable Trust
Market Harborough and The
Bowdens Charity
The Ann and David Marks
Foundation
The Hilda and Samuel Marks
Foundation
J P Marland Charitable Trust
The Michael Marsh Charitable
Trust
The Marsh Christian Trust
The Charlotte Marshall
Charitable Trust
The Jim Marshall Charitable
Trust
The Nora Joan Marshall
Charitable Trust
The D G Marshall of
Cambridge Trust
Marshall's Charity
Marshgate Charitable
Settlement
The Mason Porter Charitable
Trust
The Mathew Trust
The Matt 6.3 Charitable Trust
The Violet Mauray Charitable
Trust
The Maxwell Family Foundation
Evelyn May Trust
The Mayfield Valley Arts Trust
Mazars Charitable Trust
The McDougall Trust
The McKenna Charitable Trust
The Helen Isabella McMorran
Charitable Foundation
The James Frederick and Ethel
Anne Measures Charity
The Medlock Charitable Trust
The Anthony and Elizabeth
Mellows Charitable
Settlement
Melow Charitable Trust
The Mercers' Charitable
Foundation
The Merchant Taylors'
Company Charities Fund
The Merchant Venturers'
Charity
The Merchants' House of
Glasgow
The Mersey Docks and
Harbour Company
Charitable Fund
Community Foundation for
Merseyside
The Zachary Merton and
George Woofindin
Convalescent Trust

The Tony Metherell Charitable
   Trust
The Metropolitan Drinking
   Fountain and Cattle Trough
   Association
The Mickel Fund
Gerald Micklem Charitable
   Trust
The Masonic Province of
   Middlesex Charitable Trust
Midhurst Pensions Trust
The Migraine Trust
Miles Trust for the Putney and
   Roehampton Community
Millennium Stadium Charitable
   Trust
The Hugh and Mary Miller
   Bequest Trust
The Ronald Miller Foundation
The Millfield House Foundation
The Millfield Trust
The Millhouses Charitable
   Trust
The Millichope Foundation
The Mills Charity
The Millward Charitable Trust
The Clare Milne Trust
Milton Keynes Community
   Foundation
The Edgar Milward Charity
The Peter Minet Trust
The Minos Trust
Minton Charitable Trust
The Mirfield Educational
   Charity
The Laurence Misener
   Charitable Trust
The Mishcon Family Charitable
   Trust
The Misselbrook Trust
The Brian Mitchell Charitable
   Settlement
The Esmé Mitchell Trust
The MITIE Foundation
Keren Mitzvah Trust
The Mizpah Trust
The Mobbs Memorial Trust Ltd
The Modiano Charitable Trust
The Moette Charitable Trust
The Mole Charitable Trust
The Mollie Thomas Charitable
   Trust
The D C Moncrieff Charitable
   Trust
Monmouthshire County Council
   Welsh Church Act Fund
The Montague Thompson
   Coon Charitable Trust
The Colin Montgomerie
   Charitable Foundation
The Monument Trust
John Moores Foundation
The Morel Charitable Trust
The Morgan Charitable
   Foundation
The Mr and Mrs J T Morgan
   Foundation

Morgan Stanley International
   Foundation
The Oliver Morland Charitable
   Trust
The Bernard Morris Charitable
   Trust
The Morris Charitable Trust
The Willie and Mabel Morris
   Charitable Trust
The Peter Morrison Charitable
   Foundation
The Stanley Morrison
   Charitable Trust
Vyoel Moshe Charitable Trust
The Moss Charitable Trust
The Robert and Margaret
   Moss Charitable Trust
The Moss Family Charitable
   Trust
Mosselson Charitable Trust
The Mount Everest Foundation
The Edwina Mountbatten Trust
Mountbatten Festival of Music
The Mountbatten Memorial
   Trust
Mrs Waterhouse Charitable
   Trust
The Mugdock Children's Trust
The Mulberry Trust
The Edith Murphy Foundation
The Mushroom Fund
The Music Sales Charitable
   Trust
Muslim Hands
The Mutual Trust Group
The Kitty and Daniel Nabarro
   Charitable Trust
The Nadezhda Charitable Trust
The Naggar Charitable Trust
The Eleni Nakou Foundation
The Janet Nash Charitable
   Settlement
The National Churches Trust
National Committee of the
   Women's World Day of
   Prayer for England and
   Wales and Northern Ireland
The National Express
   Foundation
The National Manuscripts
   Conservation Trust
Needham Market and Barking
   Welfare Charities
The Worshipful Company of
   Needlemakers' Charitable
   Fund
The Neighbourly Charitable
   Trust
The James Neill Trust Fund
Nemoral Ltd
The Frances and Augustus
   Newman Foundation
Alderman Newton's
   Educational Foundation
The Chevras Ezras Nitzrochim
   Trust
The Noon Foundation

The Norda Trust
Norfolk Community Foundation
Norie Charitable Trust
Normalyn Charitable Trust
The Norman Family Charitable
   Trust
The Duncan Norman Trust
   Fund
The Normanby Charitable Trust
The North West Cancer
   Research Fund
The Earl of Northampton's
   Charity
The Northcott Devon
   Foundation
The Northcott Devon Medical
   Foundation
The Community Foundation for
   Northern Ireland
The Northern Rock Foundation
The Northmoor Trust
The Northumberland Village
   Homes Trust
The Northwood Charitable
   Trust
The Norton Foundation
The Norwich Church of England
   Young Men's Society
The Norwich Town Close
   Estate Charity
The Noswad Charity
The Nottingham General
   Dispensary
The Nottingham Gordon
   Memorial Trust for Boys
   and Girls
Nottinghamshire Community
   Foundation
The Nottinghamshire Historic
   Churches Trust
The Nottinghamshire Miners'
   Welfare Trust Fund
Novi Most International
The Nuffield Foundation
Nutrisport Trust
The Father O'Mahoney
   Memorial Trust
The Sir Peter O'Sullevan
   Charitable Trust
The Oak Trust
The Oakdale Trust
The Oakmoor Charitable Trust
The Odin Charitable Trust
The Ofenheim Charitable Trust
Ogilvie Charities Deed No.2
   (including the Charity of
   Mary Catherine Ford Smith)
The Ogle Christian Trust
Oglesby Charitable Trust
Oizer Charitable Trust
The Old Broad Street Charity
   Trust
The John Oldacre Foundation
The Oldham Foundation
The Olga Charitable Trust
Open Gate

The Raymond Oppenheimer
Foundation
Ormonde Foundation
The Ormsby Charitable Trust
The Ouseley Trust
The Owen Family Trust
Oxfam (GB)
City of Oxford Charity
The Oxfordshire Community
Foundation
The P F Charitable Trust
Padwa Charitable Foundation
The Paget Charitable Trust
The Paladin Vince-Odozi
Charitable Trust
The Palmer Foundation
Eleanor Palmer Trust
The Panacea Society
Panton Trust
The Paragon Trust
Paraton Trust
The Park House Charitable
Trust
The Frank Parkinson
Agricultural Trust
The Samuel and Freda
Parkinson Charitable Trust
The Parthenon Trust
The Constance Paterson
Charitable Trust
The Patrick Charitable Trust
The Jack Patston Charitable
Trust
Paycare Charity Trust
The Payne Charitable Trust
The Harry Payne Trust
The Susanna Peake Charitable
Trust
The Pedmore Sporting Club
Trust Fund
The Dowager Countess
Eleanor Peel Trust
The Pen Shell Project
The Pennycress Trust
The Performing Right Society
Foundation
The Persson Charitable Trust
The Persula Foundation
The Jack Petchey Foundation
The Petplan Charitable Trust
The Philips and Rubens
Charitable Trust
The Phillips Charitable Trust
The Phillips Family Charitable
Trust
Philological Foundation
The David Pickford Charitable
Foundation
The Pickwell Foundation
The Pilgrim Trust
The Cecil Pilkington Charitable
Trust
The Pilkington Charities Fund
The Austin and Hope
Pilkington Trust
The Sir Harry Pilkington Trust

The Col W W Pilkington Will
Trusts The General Charity
Fund
The DLA Piper Charitable Trust
The Worshipful Company of
Plaisterers Charitable Trust
The Platinum Trust
Polden-Puckham Charitable
Foundation
The Polestar Digital
Foundation
The George and Esme Pollitzer
Charitable Settlement
The J S F Pollitzer Charitable
Settlement
The Ponton House Trust
Edith and Ferdinand Porjes
Charitable Trust
The John Porter Charitable
Trust
The Porter Foundation
The Portrack Charitable Trust
The J E Posnansky Charitable
Trust
The Mary Potter Convent
Hospital Trust
The David and Elaine Potter
Foundation
The Powell Foundation
The W L Pratt Charitable Trust
Premierquote Ltd
Premishlaner Charitable Trust
The Tom Press Charitable
Foundation
The Lucy Price Relief-in-Need
Charity
Sir John Priestman Charity
Trust
The Primrose Trust
The Prince of Wales's
Charitable Foundation
Prison Service Charity Fund
The Privy Purse Charitable
Trust
The Proven Family Trust
The Provincial Grand Charity of
the Province of Derbyshire
The Puebla Charitable Trust
The Richard and Christine
Purchas Charitable Trust
The Puri Foundation
Mr and Mrs J A Pye's
Charitable Settlement
Quartet Community Foundation
Queen Mary's Roehampton
Trust
The Queen's Silver Jubilee
Trust
Quothquan Trust
R S Charitable Trust
The R V W Trust
The Monica Rabagliati
Charitable Trust
Rachel Charitable Trust
The Racing Foundation
The Mr and Mrs Philip
Rackham Charitable Trust

Richard Radcliffe Charitable
Trust
The Radcliffe Trust
The Ragdoll Foundation
The Rainford Trust
The Peggy Ramsay Foundation
The Joseph and Lena Randall
Charitable Trust
The Rank Foundation Limited
The Fanny Rapaport Charitable
Settlement
The Ratcliff Foundation
The Ratcliff Pension Charity
The Ratcliffe Charitable Trust
The Eleanor Rathbone
Charitable Trust
The Sigrid Rausing Trust
The Ravensdale Trust
The Rawdon-Smith Trust
The Rayden Charitable Trust
The Roger Raymond Charitable
Trust
The Rayne Foundation
The Rayne Trust
The Sir James Reckitt Charity
The Red Arrows Trust
Red Hill Charitable Trust
The Red Rose Charitable Trust
The C A Redfern Charitable
Foundation
The Reed Foundation
The John and Sally Reeve
Charitable Trust
Richard Reeve's Foundation
The Max Reinhardt Charitable
Trust
Relief Fund for Romania
Limited
The Rest Harrow Trust
Reuben Foundation
The Nathaniel Reyner Trust
Fund
The Rhododendron Trust
The Sir Cliff Richard Charitable
Trust
The Clive Richards Charity
The Violet M Richards Charity
The Richmond Parish Lands
Charity
Ridgesave Limited
The Ripple Effect Foundation
The Sir John Ritblat Family
Foundation
The River Trust
Thomas Roberts Trust
The Robertson Trust
The Rochester Bridge Trust
The Rock Foundation
The Rock Solid Trust
The Rofeh Trust
Rokach Family Charitable Trust
The Helen Roll Charitable
Trust
The Sir James Roll Charitable
Trust
The Roman Research Trust

The C A Rookes Charitable
Trust
Mrs L D Rope Third Charitable
Settlement
The Rosca Trust
The Rose Foundation
The Cecil Rosen Foundation
Rosetrees Trust
The Rothermere Foundation
The Rotherwick Foundation
The Roughley Charitable Trust
Mrs Gladys Row Fogo
Charitable Trust
Rowanville Ltd
The Christopher Rowbotham
Charitable Trust
The Rowlands Trust
The Joseph Rowntree
Charitable Trust
The Joseph Rowntree
Foundation
Joseph Rowntree Reform Trust
Limited
Royal Artillery Charitable Fund
Royal Docks Trust (London)
Royal Masonic Trust for Girls
and Boys
The Rubin Foundation
William Arthur Rudd Memorial
Trust
The Russell Trust
The J S and E C Rymer
Charitable Trust
S O Charitable Trust
The Jeremy and John Sacher
Charitable Trust
The Michael Harry Sacher
Trust
Raymond and Beverly Sackler
1988 Foundation
The Sackler Trust
The Ruzin Sadagora Trust
Erach and Roshan Sadri
Foundation
The Saga Charitable Trust
The Jean Sainsbury Animal
Welfare Trust
The Alan and Babette
Sainsbury Charitable Fund
The Sainsbury Family
Charitable Trusts
The Saintbury Trust
The Saints and Sinners Trust
The Salamander Charitable
Trust
The Salt Foundation
The Salt Trust
Basil Samuel Charitable Trust
The M J Samuel Charitable
Trust
The Peter Samuel Charitable
Trust
The Samworth Foundation
The Sandra Charitable Trust
Santander UK Foundation
Limited
The Scarfe Charitable Trust

The Schapira Charitable Trust
The Schmidt-Bodner Charitable
Trust
The Schreib Trust
The Schreiber Charitable Trust
The Schuster Charitable Trust
Foundation Scotland
The Francis C Scott Charitable
Trust
The Frieda Scott Charitable
Trust
The Sir James and Lady Scott
Trust
The Scott Trust Foundation
The Storrow Scott Will Trust
Scottish Coal Industry Special
Welfare Fund
The Scottish International
Education Trust
The Scouloudi Foundation
Seafarers UK (King George's
Fund for Sailors)
Seamen's Hospital Society
The Searchlight Electric
Charitable Trust
The Searle Charitable Trust
The Samuel Sebba Charitable
Trust
The Seedfield Trust
Leslie Sell Charitable Trust
The Ayrton Senna Foundation
The Seven Fifty Trust
The Cyril Shack Trust
The Jean Shanks Foundation
The Shanti Charitable Trust
ShareGift (The Orr Mackintosh
Foundation)
The Linley Shaw Foundation
The Shears Foundation
The Sheepdrove Trust
The Sheffield and District
Hospital Services
Charitable Fund
The Sheldon Trust
The Patricia and Donald
Shepherd Charitable Trust
The Sylvia and Colin Shepherd
Charitable Trust
The Archie Sherman Cardiff
Foundation
The Archie Sherman Charitable
Trust
The R C Sherriff Trust
The Shetland Charitable Trust
SHINE (Support and Help in
Education)
The Barnett and Sylvia Shine
No 2 Charitable Trust
The Bassil Shippam and
Alsford Trust
The Shipwrights' Company
Charitable Fund
The Shirley Foundation
Shlomo Memorial Fund Limited
The J A Shone Memorial Trust
Community Foundation for
Shropshire and Telford

The Barbara A Shuttleworth
Memorial Trust
The Mary Elizabeth Siebel
Charity
David and Jennifer Sieff
Charitable Trust
The Julius Silman Charitable
Trust
The Leslie Silver Charitable
Trust
The Simpson Education and
Conservation Trust
The Simpson Foundation
The Huntly and Margery
Sinclair Charitable Trust
Sino-British Fellowship Trust
The Skelton Bounty
The Charles Skey Charitable
Trust
Skipton Building Society
Charitable Foundation
The John Slater Foundation
The SMB Charitable Trust
The Mrs Smith and Mount
Trust
The N Smith Charitable
Settlement
The E H Smith Charitable Trust
The Smith Charitable Trust
The Henry Smith Charity
The Leslie Smith Foundation
The Martin Smith Foundation
The Stanley Smith UK
Horticultural Trust
Smithcorp Charitable Trust
The Snowball Trust
The Sobell Foundation
Social Business Trust (Scale-
Up)
The Solo Charitable
Settlement
Dr Richard Solomon's
Charitable Trust
The E C Sosnow Charitable
Trust
The Souter Charitable Trust
The South Square Trust
The Stephen R and Philippa H
Southall Charitable Trust
The W F Southall Trust
The Southwold Trust
The Sovereign Health Care
Charitable Trust
Sparks Charity (Sport Aiding
Medical Research For Kids)
Sparquote Limited
The Spear Charitable Trust
The Worshipful Company of
Spectacle Makers' Charity
The Jessie Spencer Trust
The Ralph and Irma Sperring
Charity
The Spielman Charitable Trust
Split Infinitive Trust
The Spoore, Merry and Rixman
Foundation

Springfields Employees'
Medical Research and
Charity Trust Fund
Springrule Limited
The Spurrell Charitable Trust
The Geoff and Fiona Squire
Foundation
St Christopher's Educational
Trust (incorporating the
Hughes and Stevens
Bequest)
St Hilda's Trust
St James' Trust Settlement
St James's Place Foundation
Sir Walter St John's
Educational Charity
St Michael's and All Saints'
Charities Relief Branch (The
Church Houses Relief in
Need Charity)
St Monica Trust
The Late St Patrick White
Charitable Trust
St Peter's Saltley Trust
St Teilo's Trust
The Stanley Foundation Ltd
The Stanton Ballard Charitable
Trust
The Staples Trust
The Star Charitable Trust
The Peter Stebbings Memorial
Charity
The Steinberg Family
Charitable Trust
The Hugh Stenhouse
Foundation
The Stephen Barry Charitable
Trust
The Sigmund Sternberg
Charitable Foundation
Stervon Ltd
The Stevenage Community
Trust
The June Stevens Foundation
The Steventon Allotments and
Relief-in-Need Charity
The Stewards' Charitable Trust
The Stewards' Company
Limited (incorporating the J
W Laing Trust and the J W
Laing Biblical Scholarship
Trust)
Sir Halley Stewart Trust
The David and Deborah
Stileman Charitable Trust
The Stobart Newlands
Charitable Trust
The Edward Stocks-Massey
Bequest Fund
The Stokenchurch Educational
Charity
The Stoller Charitable Trust
The M J C Stone Charitable
Trust
The Samuel Storey Family
Charitable Trust

Peter Stormonth Darling
Charitable Trust
The Strangward Trust
The Strasser Foundation
The W O Street Charitable
Foundation
The Sudborough Foundation
Suffolk Community Foundation
The Suffolk Historic Churches
Trust
The Summerfield Charitable
Trust
The Sunny Skies Foundation
The Surrey Historic Buildings
Trust Ltd
The Sussex Historic Churches
Trust
The Sutasoma Trust
Sutton Coldfield Charitable
Trust
Swansea and Brecon Diocesan
Board of Finance Limited
The John Swire (1989)
Charitable Trust
The Swire Charitable Trust
The Adrian Swire Charitable
Trust
The Hugh and Ruby Sykes
Charitable Trust
The Charles and Elsie Sykes
Trust
The Sylvanus Charitable Trust
The Stella Symons Charitable
Trust
The Tabeel Trust
The Tajtelbaum Charitable
Trust
Tallow Chandlers Benevolent
Fund
The Tangent Charitable Trust
The Lady Tangye Charitable
Trust
The David Tannen Charitable
Trust
The Tanner Trust
The Lili Tapper Charitable
Foundation
The Mrs A Lacy Tate Trust
The Tay Charitable Trust
Humphrey Richardson Taylor
Charitable Trust
The Connie and Albert Taylor
Charitable Trust
The Cyril Taylor Charitable
Trust
A P Taylor Trust
Tearfund
The Tedworth Charitable Trust
Tees Valley Community
Foundation
The Templeton Goodwill Trust
The Ten Ten Charitable Trust
Tesco Charity Trust
The C Paul Thackray General
Charitable Trust
The Thames Wharf Charity

The John P. Gommes
Foundation
The Thistle Trust
The Loke Wan Tho Memorial
Foundation
The Thomas Lilley Memorial
Trust
The Arthur and Margaret
Thompson Charitable Trust
The Thompson Family
Charitable Trust
The Thompson Family
Foundation
The Len Thomson Charitable
Trust
The Sue Thomson Foundation
The Sir Jules Thorn Charitable
Trust
The Thornton Foundation
The Thornton Trust
The Thousandth Man- Richard
Burns Charitable Trust
The Three Guineas Trust
The Three Oaks Trust
The Thriplow Charitable Trust
The John Raymond Tijou
Charitable Trust
The Tinsley Foundation
The Tisbury Telegraph Trust
The Tobacco Pipe Makers and
Tobacco Trade Benevolent
Fund
The Tolkien Trust
Tollemache (Buckminster)
Charitable Trust
Tomchei Torah Charitable
Trust
The Tompkins Foundation
The Tory Family Foundation
Tottenham Grammar School
Foundation
The Tower Hill Trust
The Towry Law Charitable Trust
(also known as the Castle
Educational Trust)
The Toy Trust
The Toye Foundation
The TPO Foundation
The Mayor of Trafford's Charity
Fund
The Constance Travis
Charitable Trust
The Treeside Trust
The Triangle Trust (1949) Fund
The True Colours Trust
Truedene Co. Ltd
The Truemark Trust
Truemart Limited
Trumros Limited
The Trusthouse Charitable
Foundation
The Tsukanov Family
Foundation
Tudor Rose Ltd
The Tudor Trust
The Tufton Charitable Trust

The R D Turner Charitable
Trust
The Douglas Turner Trust
The Florence Turner Trust
The G J W Turner Trust
Miss S M Tutton Charitable
Trust
The TUUT Charitable Trust
The Tyche Charitable Trust
Community Foundation Serving
Tyne and Wear and
Northumberland
Trustees of Tzedakah
The Udlington Trust
Ulster Garden Villages Ltd
Ultach Trust
The Ulverscroft Foundation
Ulverston Town Lands Charity
The Underwood Trust
The Union of Orthodox Hebrew
Congregation
The United Society for the
Propagation of the Gospel
Unity Theatre Trust
The David Uri Memorial Trust
Uxbridge United Welfare Trust
Vale of Glamorgan – Welsh
Church Fund
The Valentine Charitable Trust
The Van Neste Foundation
Mrs Maud Van Norden's
Charitable Foundation
The Vandervell Foundation
The Vardy Foundation
The Variety Club Children's
Charity
Veneziana Fund
The Verdon-Smith Family
Charitable Settlement
Victoria Homes Trust
The Nigel Vinson Charitable
Trust
The William and Ellen Vinten
Trust
The Vintners' Company
Charitable Foundation
Vintners' Gifts Charity
Vivdale Ltd
The Viznitz Foundation
Voluntary Action Fund (VAF)
Wade's Charity
The Scurrah Wainwright Charity
The Community Foundation in
Wales
Wales Council for Voluntary
Action
Robert and Felicity Waley-
Cohen Charitable Trust
The F J Wallis Charitable
Settlement
War on Want
The Ward Blenkinsop Trust
The George Ward Charitable
Trust
The Barbara Ward Children's
Foundation
The Waterloo Foundation

G R Waters Charitable Trust
2000
The Wates Foundation
The Howard Watson Symington
Memorial Charity
John Watson's Trust
Waynflete Charitable Trust
Weatherley Charitable Trust
The Weavers' Company
Benevolent Fund
Webb Memorial Trust
Weedon Family Trust
The Weinberg Foundation
The Weinstein Foundation
The Weinstock Fund
The Wellcome Trust
Welsh Church Fund Dyfed
area (Carmarthenshire,
Ceredigion and
Pembrokeshire)
The Welton Foundation
The Wessex Youth Trust
The West Derby Wastelands
Charity
West London Synagogue
Charitable Fund
West Yorkshire Police
Community Trust
The Westminster Foundation
The Garfield Weston
Foundation
The Whitaker Charitable Trust
The Colonel W H Whitbread
Charitable Trust
The Simon Whitbread
Charitable Trust
The Whitecourt Charitable
Trust
The Norman Whiteley Trust
The Whitley Animal Protection
Trust
The Whittlesey Charity
The Lionel Wigram Memorial
Trust
The Felicity Wilde Charitable
Trust
The Will Charitable Trust
The Charity of William Williams
The Kay Williams Charitable
Foundation
The Williams Family Charitable
Trust
The HDH Wills 1965
Charitable Trust
The Dame Violet Wills Will
Trust
The Wilmcote Charitrust
David Wilson Foundation
The Wilson Foundation
J and J R Wilson Trust
The Community Foundation for
Wiltshire and Swindon
The Windruff Charitable Trust
The Benjamin Winegarten
Charitable Trust
The Francis Winham
Foundation

Wirral Mayor's Charity
The James Wise Charitable
Trust
The Michael and Anna Wix
Charitable Trust
The Wixamtree Trust
The Woburn 1986 Charitable
Trust
The Maurice Wohl Charitable
Foundation
The Charles Wolfson
Charitable Trust
The James Wood Bequest
Fund
Woodlands Green Ltd
Woodlands Trust
The Woodward Charitable
Trust
Worcester Municipal Charities
The Worcestershire and
Dudley Historic Churches
Trust
The Wragge and Co. Charitable
Trust
The Diana Edgson Wright
Charitable Trust
The Wright Vigar Charitable
Trust
The Matthews Wrightson
Charity Trust
Miss E B Wrightson's
Charitable Settlement
Wychdale Ltd
Wychville Ltd
The Wyndham Charitable Trust
The Wyseliot Charitable Trust
The Xerox (UK) Trust
The Yapp Charitable Trust
The Dennis Alan Yardy
Charitable Trust
The W Wing Yip and Brothers
Foundation
Yorkshire Agricultural Society
The South Yorkshire
Community Foundation
The Yorkshire Dales
Millennium Trust
You Gossip Foundation
The John Young Charitable
Settlement
The William Allen Young
Charitable Trust
The John K Young Endowment
Fund
Zephyr Charitable Trust
The Marjorie and Arnold Ziff
Charitable Foundation
Stephen Zimmerman
Charitable Trust
The Zochonis Charitable Trust
Zurich Community Trust (UK)
Limited

....
■ Project funding (excluding overheads)

The 1970 Trust
The 1989 Willan Charitable Trust
The 29th May 1961 Charitable Trust
A W Charitable Trust
The Aberbrothock Skea Trust
The Aberdeenshire Educational Trust Scheme
ABF The Soldiers' Charity
Achisomoch Aid Company Limited
The ACT Foundation
Action Medical Research
The Company of Actuaries' Charitable Trust Fund
The Sylvia Adams Charitable Trust
The Victor Adda Foundation
The Adint Charitable Trust
Age Scotland
Age UK
Aid to the Church in Need (UK)
The Sylvia Aitken Charitable Trust
The Ajahma Charitable Trust
The Al Fayed Charitable Foundation
Aldgate and All Hallows' Foundation
The Aldgate Freedom Foundation
All Saints Educational Trust
Allchurches Trust Ltd
The H B Allen Charitable Trust
The Alliance Family Foundation
Angus Allnatt Charitable Foundation
The Pat Allsop Charitable Trust
Almondsbury Charity
Altamont Ltd
Alvor Charitable Trust
The Ammco Trust
Viscount Amory's Charitable Trust
The AMW Charitable Trust
Anguish's Educational Foundation
The Animal Defence Trust
The Eric Anker-Petersen Charity
Anpride Ltd
Ambrose and Ann Appelbe Trust
The Appletree Trust
The John M Archer Charitable Trust
The Archer Trust
The Argus Appeal
The Armenian Relief Society of Great Britain Trust
The Armourers' and Brasiers' Gauntlet Trust

The Arsenal Foundation
The Artemis Charitable Trust
The Arts and Entertainment Charitable Trust
Arts Council England
The Arts Council of Northern Ireland
Arts Council of Wales (also known as Cyngor Celfyddydau Cymru)
The Ove Arup Foundation
The A S Charitable Trust
The Ashden Trust
The Ashendene Trust
The Ashley Family Foundation
The Ian Askew Charitable Trust
The Associated Country Women of the World
The Association of Colleges Charitable Trust
Astellas European Foundation
Asthma UK
AstonMansfield Charitable Trust
The Astor Foundation
The Astor of Hever Trust
The Aurelius Charitable Trust
The BAA Communities Trust
The BACTA Charitable Trust
The Scott Bader Commonwealth Ltd
The Bagri Foundation
Veta Bailey Charitable Trust
The Austin Bailey Foundation
The Baily Thomas Charitable Fund
The Baird Trust
The Baker Charitable Trust
The Balcombe Charitable Trust
The Albert Casanova Ballard Deceased Trust
The Ballinger Charitable Trust
The Balmore Trust
The Balney Charitable Trust
The Baltic Charitable Fund
The Bamford Charitable Foundation
The Banbury Charities
William P Bancroft (No 2) Charitable Trust and Jenepher Gillett Trust
The Band Trust
The Barbers' Company General Charities
The Barbour Foundation
Barchester Healthcare Foundation
The Barclay Foundation
The Baring Foundation
Peter Barker-Mill Memorial Charity
The Barleycorn Trust
Barnes Workhouse Fund
The Barnsbury Charitable Trust
The Barnwood House Trust
The Misses Barrie Charitable Trust

Barrington Family Charitable Trust
Bartholomew Charitable Trust
The Bartlett Taylor Charitable Trust
The Paul Bassham Charitable Trust
The Batchworth Trust
The Bates Charitable Trust
The Bay Tree Charitable Trust
The Louis Baylis (Maidenhead Advertiser) Charitable Trust
BBC Children in Need
B-CH 1971 Charitable Trust
The Beacon Trust
The Bearder Charity
The James Beattie Charitable Trust
The Beaverbrook Foundation
The Beccles Town Lands Charity
The Becker Family Charitable Trust
The Becketts and Sargeants Educational Foundation
The John Beckwith Charitable Trust
The Peter Beckwith Charitable Trust
The David and Ruth Behrend Fund
The Beit Trust
The Bellahouston Bequest Fund
The Bellinger Donnay Trust
The Benfield Motors Charitable Trust
The Benham Charitable Settlement
Maurice and Jacqueline Bennett Charitable Trust
The Berkshire Community Foundation
The Bestway Foundation
BHST
The Mason Bibby 1981 Trust
The Bideford Bridge Trust
The Big Lottery Fund
The Billmeir Charitable Trust
The Bingham Trust
The Bintaub Charitable Trust
The Birmingham District Nursing Charitable Trust
The Birmingham Hospital Saturday Fund Medical Charity and Welfare Trust
Birmingham International Airport Community Trust
The Lord Mayor of Birmingham's Charity
The Michael Bishop Foundation
The Bishop's Development Fund
The Bertie Black Foundation
Isabel Blackman Foundation
The Blagrave Trust

The Blair Foundation
Blakemore Foundation
The Blanchminster Trust
The Blandford Lake Trust
The Sir Victor Blank Charitable
  Settlement
The Neville and Elaine Blond
  Charitable Trust
The Bluston Charitable
  Settlement
The Nicholas Boas Charitable
  Trust
The Boltons Trust
The Bonamy Charitable Trust
The John and Celia Bonham
  Christie Charitable Trust
The Charlotte Bonham-Carter
  Charitable Trust
Bonhomie United Charity
  Society
The Boots Charitable Trust
The Bordon Liphook
  Haslemere Charity
The Oliver Borthwick Memorial
  Trust
The Bothwell Charitable Trust
H E and E L Botteley
  Charitable Trust
The Harry Bottom Charitable
  Trust
The Anthony Bourne
  Foundation
The Bower Trust
The Bowerman Charitable
  Trust
John and Susan Bowers Fund
The Bowland Charitable Trust
The Frank Brake Charitable
  Trust
The William Brake Charitable
  Trust
The Tony Bramall Charitable
  Trust
The Liz and Terry Bramall
  Foundation
The Harold and Alice Bridges
  Charity
Bristol Archdeaconry Charity
John Bristow and Thomas
  Mason Trust
The British Council for
  Prevention of Blindness
The British Dietetic
  Association General and
  Education Trust Fund
The British Gas (Scottish Gas)
  Energy Trust
British Heart Foundation
British Humane Association
British Institute at Ankara
British Ornithologists' Union
British Record Industry Trust
The Britten-Pears Foundation
The J and M Britton Charitable
  Trust
The Bromley Trust

The Roger Brooke Charitable
  Trust
The David Brooke Charity
The Charles Brotherton Trust
Joseph Brough Charitable
  Trust
The Swinfen Broun Charitable
  Trust
Edna Brown Charitable
  Settlement (Mrs E E Brown
  Charitable Settlement)
Buckinghamshire Community
  Foundation
Buckland Charitable Trust
The Rosemary Bugden
  Charitable Trust
The Bulldog Trust Limited
The E F Bulmer Benevolent
  Fund
Burdens Charitable Foundation
The Clara E Burgess Charity
The Burry Charitable Trust
The Arnold Burton 1998
  Charitable Trust
The Burton Breweries
  Charitable Trust
Consolidated Charity of Burton
  upon Trent
The Worshipful Company of
  Butchers General Charities
The Noel Buxton Trust
Henry T and Lucy B Cadbury
  Charitable Trust
The Christopher Cadbury
  Charitable Trust
The G W Cadbury Charitable
  Trust
The Richard Cadbury
  Charitable Trust
The Edward and Dorothy
  Cadbury Trust
The George Cadbury Trust
CAF (Charities Aid Foundation)
CAFOD (Catholic Agency for
  Overseas Development)
Community Foundation for
  Calderdale
The Callander Charitable Trust
Calleva Foundation
Calouste Gulbenkian
  Foundation – UK Branch
The Calpe Trust
Calypso Browning Trust
The Campden Charities
  Trustee
The Canning Trust
The Carew Pole Charitable
  Trust
The D W T Cargill Fund
Carlee Ltd
The Carlton House Charitable
  Trust
The Carmelite Monastery Ware
  Trust
The Worshipful Company of
  Carmen Benevolent Trust

The Carnegie Dunfermline
  Trust
The Carpenter Charitable Trust
The Carpenters' Company
  Charitable Trust
The Carrington Charitable
  Trust
The Carron Charitable
  Settlement
The Leslie Mary Carter
  Charitable Trust
The Casey Trust
Cash for Kids Radio Clyde
Sir John Cass's Foundation
The Elizabeth Casson Trust
The Castang Foundation
The Catalyst Charitable Trust
The Catholic Charitable Trust
Catholic Foreign Missions
The Catholic Trust for England
  and Wales
The Cattanach Charitable Trust
The Joseph and Annie Cattle
  Trust
The Thomas Sivewright Catto
  Charitable Settlement
The Wilfrid and Constance
  Cave Foundation
The Cayo Foundation
The B G S Cayzer Charitable
  Trust
The Cazenove Charitable Trust
Celtic Charity Fund
The Gaynor Cemlyn-Jones
  Trust
The Pamela Champion
  Foundation
The Chapman Charitable Trust
John William Chapman's
  Charitable Trust
The Charities Advisory Trust
Charitworth Limited
The Charter 600 Charity
The Worshipful Company of
  Chartered Accountants
  General Charitable Trust
  (also known as CALC)
The Chasah Trust
The Chelsea Square 1994
  Trust
The Cheruby Trust
Cheshire Freemason's Charity
The Chetwode Foundation
Cheviot Asset Management
  Charitable Trust
Childs Charitable Trust
The Childwick Trust
The Chipping Sodbury Town
  Lands Charity
CHK Charities Limited
The Chownes Foundation
The Chrimes Family Charitable
  Trust
The Christabella Charitable
  Trust
Christadelphian Samaritan
  Fund

Christian Aid

Christian Response to Eastern
Europe

The Church and Community
Fund

The Church Burgesses
Educational Foundation

Church Burgesses Trust

Church of Ireland Priorities
Fund

Church Urban Fund

City and County of Swansea
Welsh Church Act Fund

The City Bridge Trust

The City Educational Trust
Fund

CLA Charitable Trust

Stephen Clark 1957
Charitable Trust

J A Clark Charitable Trust

The Hilda and Alice Clark
Charitable Trust

The Roger and Sarah Bancroft
Clark Charitable Trust

The Clarke Charitable
Settlement

The Cleopatra Trust

Lord Clinton's Charitable Trust

The Clore Duffield Foundation

Miss V L Clore's 1967
Charitable Trust

Richard Cloudesley's Charity

The Clover Trust

The Robert Clutterbuck
Charitable Trust

Clydpride Ltd

The Coalfields Regeneration
Trust

The John Coates Charitable
Trust

The Cobtree Charity Trust Ltd

The Denise Cohen Charitable
Trust

The Vivienne and Samuel
Cohen Charitable Trust

The John S Cohen Foundation

The R and S Cohen
Foundation

The Cole Charitable Trust

The Colefax Charitable Trust

The John and Freda Coleman
Charitable Trust

The George Henry Collins
Charity

The Sir Jeremiah Colman Gift
Trust

The Colt Foundation

The Coltstaple Trust

Colwinston Charitable Trust

Colyer-Fergusson Charitable
Trust

Comic Relief

The Comino Foundation

Community First (Landfill
Communities Fund)

The Compton Charitable Trust

The Congleton Inclosure Trust

The Conservation Foundation

The Consolidated Charities for
the Infirm Merchant
Taylors' Company

The Ernest Cook Trust

The Cooks Charity

The Catherine Cookson
Charitable Trust

Mabel Cooper Charity

The Alice Ellen Cooper Dean
Charitable Foundation

The Co-operative Foundation

The Marjorie Coote Animal
Charity Trust

The Marjorie Coote Old
People's Charity

The Helen Jean Cope Trust

The J Reginald Corah
Foundation Fund

The Gershon Coren Charitable
Foundation (also known as
The Muriel and Gus Coren
Charitable Foundation)

The Cornwell Charitable Trust

The Sidney and Elizabeth
Corob Charitable Trust

The Corona Charitable Trust

The Costa Family Charitable
Trust

The Cotton Industry War
Memorial Trust

The Cotton Trust

County Durham Community
Foundation

The Augustine Courtauld Trust

The General Charities of the
City of Coventry

Coventry Building Society
Charitable Foundation

The John Cowan Foundation

Dudley and Geoffrey Cox
Charitable Trust

The Sir William Coxen Trust
Fund

The Lord Cozens-Hardy Trust

The Craignish Trust

The Craps Charitable Trust

Michael Crawford Children's
Charity

The Cray Trust

The Crerar Hotels Trust

The Crescent Trust

Cripplegate Foundation

The Violet and Milo Cripps
Charitable Trust

The Harry Crook Foundation

The Cross Trust

The Croydon Relief in Need
Charities

Cruden Foundation Ltd

The Ronald Cruickshanks
Foundation

The Culra Charitable Trust

Cumberland Building Society
Charitable Foundation

Cumbria Community
Foundation

The Cunningham Trust

The D J H Currie Memorial
Trust

The Dennis Curry Charitable
Trust

The Manny Cussins
Foundation

The Cwmbran Trust

Itzchok Meyer Cymerman Trust
Ltd

The D G Charitable Settlement

Roald Dahl's Marvellous
Children's Charity

Daily Prayer Union Charitable
Trust Limited

The Daisy Trust

The Daiwa Anglo-Japanese
Foundation

The Dr and Mrs A Darlington
Charitable Trust

Baron Davenport's Charity

The Davidson (Nairn)
Charitable Trust

The Davidson Family
Charitable Trust

The Alderman Joe Davidson
Memorial Trust

Michael Davies Charitable
Settlement

The Gwendoline and Margaret
Davies Charity

The Wilfrid Bruce Davis
Charitable Trust

Davis-Rubens Charitable Trust

The Dawe Charitable Trust

The De Brye Charitable Trust

The De Clermont Charitable
Company Ltd

Peter De Haan Charitable
Trust

The Deakin Charitable Trust

The Debmar Benevolent Trust

The Dellal Foundation

The Delves Charitable Trust

The Demigryphon Trust

The Denman Charitable Trust

Dentons UKMEA LLP
Charitable Trust

The Earl of Derby's Charitable
Trust

Derbyshire Community
Foundation

The J N Derbyshire Trust

The Desmond Foundation

Devon Community Foundation

The Devon Educational Trust

The Duke of Devonshire's
Charitable Trust

The Sandy Dewhirst Charitable
Trust

The Laduma Dhamecha
Charitable Trust

Diabetes UK

Diced Cap Charity

The Dickon Trust

The Digbeth Trust Limited

The Dinwoodie Settlement

Dischma Charitable Trust
The DLM Charitable Trust
Louise Dobson Charitable
Trust
The Derek and Eileen Dodgson
Foundation
The Dollond Charitable Trust
Domepride Ltd
The Dorcas Trust
The Dorus Trust
The Doughty Charity Trust
Douglas Arter Foundation
The R M Douglas Charitable
Trust
The Drapers' Charitable Fund
The Duis Charitable Trust
The Dulverton Trust
The P B Dumbell Charitable
Trust
The Dumbreck Charity
Dunard Fund
The Dunn Family Charitable
Trust
The W E Dunn Trust
Dushinsky Trust Ltd
Annette Duvollet Charitable
Trust
The Dwek Family Charitable
Trust
The Dyers' Company
Charitable Trust
The Eagle Charity Trust
The Earley Charity
Earls Colne and Halstead
Educational Charity
The Earmark Trust
East End Community
Foundation
Eastern Counties Educational
Trust Limited
The Sir John Eastwood
Foundation
The Ebenezer Trust
The EBM Charitable Trust
Eden Arts Trust
EDF Energy Trust (EDFET)
The Gilbert and Eileen Edgar
Foundation
Edinburgh Children's Holiday
Fund
Edinburgh Trust No 2 Account
Edinburgh Voluntary
Organisations' Trust Funds
(EVOT)
The William Edwards
Educational Charity
The Elephant Trust
The George Elias Charitable
Trust
The Gerald Palmer Eling Trust
Company
The Wilfred and Elsie Elkes
Charity Fund
The Maud Elkington Charitable
Trust
The Ellerdale Trust
The John Ellerman Foundation

The Ellinson Foundation Ltd
James Ellis Charitable Trust
The Elmgrant Trust
The Elmley Foundation
The Vernon N Ely Charitable
Trust
The Embleton Trust
Embrace the Middle East
The Emerton-Christie Charity
The Worshipful Company of
Engineers Charitable Trust
Fund
The Englefield Charitable Trust
The English Schools' Football
Association
The Enkalon Foundation
Entindale Ltd
The Epigoni Trust
Epilepsy Research UK
The Equitable Charitable Trust
The Equity Trust Fund
The Ericson Trust
The Erskine Cunningham Hill
Trust
Essex Community Foundation
The Essex Fairway Charitable
Trust
The Essex Heritage Trust
Essex Provincial Charity Fund
The Essex Youth Trust
Euro Charity Trust
Sir John Evelyn's Charity
The Eventhall Family
Charitable Trust
The Eveson Charitable Trust
The Beryl Evetts and Robert
Luff Animal Welfare Trust
Limited
The Exilarch's Foundation
F C Charitable Trust
The F P Limited Charitable
Trust
The Faber Charitable Trust
Esmée Fairbairn Foundation
The Fairway Trust
The Family Rich Charities Trust
The Lord Faringdon Charitable
Trust
Samuel William Farmer Trust
The Farmers' Company
Charitable Fund
The Thomas Farr Charity
Walter Farthing (Trust) Limited
The Fassnidge Memorial Trust
Joseph Fattorini Charitable
Trust
Federation of Jewish Relief
Organisations
The John Feeney Charitable
Trust
The George Fentham
Birmingham Charity
The A M Fenton Trust
Allan and Nesta Ferguson
Charitable Settlement
The Fidelity UK Foundation

The Doris Field Charitable
Trust
The Fifty Fund
Firtree Trust
The Fishmongers' Company's
Charitable Trust
The Fitton Trust
The Earl Fitzwilliam Charitable
Trust
The Ian Fleming Charitable
Trust
The Joyce Fletcher Charitable
Trust
The Flow Foundation
The Gerald Fogel Charitable
Trust
The Follett Trust
The Football Association
National Sports Centre
Trust
The Football Association Youth
Trust
The Football Foundation
The Forbes Charitable
Foundation
The Forces Trust (Working
Name)
The Oliver Ford Charitable
Trust
The Forest Hill Charitable Trust
Forever Manchester (The
Community Foundation for
Greater Manchester)
The Forman Hardy Charitable
Trust
Gwyneth Forrester Trust
The Forte Charitable Trust
The Four Lanes Trust
The Four Winds Trust
The Foyle Foundation
The Isaac and Freda Frankel
Memorial Charitable Trust
The Elizabeth Frankland Moore
and Star Foundation
The Jill Franklin Trust
The Gordon Fraser Charitable
Trust
The Hugh Fraser Foundation
The Joseph Strong Frazer Trust
The Louis and Valerie
Freedman Charitable
Settlement
The Freemasons' Grand
Charity
The Charles S French
Charitable Trust
The Anne French Memorial
Trust
The Freshfield Foundation
The Freshgate Trust
Foundation
The Friarsgate Trust
The Friends Hall Farm Street
Trust
Friends Provident Charitable
Foundation
The Frognal Trust

Maurice Fry Charitable Trust
The Fulmer Charitable Trust
Worshipful Company of
Furniture Makers Charitable
Fund
The Fuserna Foundation
General Charitable Trust
Gableholt Limited
The Galbraith Trust
The Gale Family Charity Trust
Gamlen Charitable Trust
The Gamma Trust
The Gannochy Trust
The Worshipful Company of
Gardeners of London
The Samuel Gardner Memorial
Trust
Garthgwynion Charities
Garvan Limited
The Gatsby Charitable
Foundation
Gatwick Airport Community
Trust
The Robert Gavron Charitable
Trust
Jacqueline and Michael Gee
Charitable Trust
Thomas Betton's Charity for
Pensions and Relief-in-Need
The General Nursing Council
for England and Wales
Trust
The Gibbs Charitable Trust
Simon Gibson Charitable Trust
The G C Gibson Charitable
Trust
Lady Gibson's Charitable Trust
The Harvey and Hilary Gilbert
Charitable Trust
The Girdlers' Company
Charitable Trust
The B and P Glasser
Charitable Trust
The Glass-House Trust
Global Care
Global Charities
Gloucestershire Community
Foundation
Worshipful Company of
Glovers of London Charity
Fund
The GNC Trust
The Godinton Charitable Trust
The Sydney and Phyllis
Goldberg Memorial
Charitable Trust
The Golden Bottle Trust
The Jack Goldhill Charitable
Trust
The Goldsmiths' Arts Trust
Fund
The Goldsmiths' Company
Charity
The Golsoncott Foundation
The Mike Gooley Trailfinders
Charity

The Gosling Foundation
Limited
The Gough Charitable Trust
The Gould Charitable Trust
The Grace Charitable Trust
A B Grace Trust
The Graff Foundation
E C Graham Belford Charitable
Settlement
The Grahame Charitable
Foundation Limited
The Granada Foundation
Grand Charitable Trust of the
Order of Women
Freemasons
The Grand Order of Water
Rats' Charities Fund
The Grange Farm Centre Trust
Grantham Yorke Trust
The Gordon Gray Trust
The Gray Trust
The Great Britain Sasakawa
Foundation
The Great Stone Bridge Trust
of Edenbridge
The Great Torrington Town
Lands Charity
The Green Hall Foundation
Greenham Common
Community Trust Limited
Greggs Foundation
The Gretna Charitable Trust
The Grocers' Charity
The M and R Gross Charities
Limited
The GRP Charitable Trust
The David and Marie Grumitt
Foundation
N and R Grunbaum Charitable
Trust
The Bishop of Guildford's
Foundation
The Guildry Incorporation of
Perth
The Walter Guinness
Charitable Trust
The Gunter Charitable Trust
The Gur Trust
The Gurney Charitable Trust
Dr Guthrie's Association
The H and M Charitable Trust
H C D Memorial Fund
The H P Charitable Trust
The Hackney Parochial
Charities
The Hadfield Trust
The Hadley Trust
The Hadrian Trust
The Alfred Haines Charitable
Trust
E F and M G Hall Charitable
Trust
Robert Hall Charity
The Hamamelis Trust
Hamilton Wallace Trust
Paul Hamlyn Foundation

The Hampshire and Islands
Historic Churches Trust
Hampton Fuel Allotment
Charity
The W A Handley Charitable
Trust
Beatrice Hankey Foundation
Limited
The Hanley Trust (1987)
The Kathleen Hannay
Memorial Charity
The Doughty Hanson
Charitable Foundation
Lord Hanson Foundation
Miss K M Harbinson's
Charitable Trust
The Harborne Parish Lands
Charity
The Harbour Charitable Trust
The Harbour Foundation
The Harding Trust
William Harding's Charity
The Hare of Steep Charitable
Trust
The Harebell Centenary Fund
The Kenneth Hargreaves
Charitable Trust
The Harpur Trust
The Harris Charity
The Harrison and Potter Trust
The John Harrison Charitable
Trust
The Peter Harrison Foundation
The Spencer Hart Charitable
Trust
The Hartley Charitable Trust
William Geoffrey Harvey's
Discretionary Settlement
Haskel Family Foundation
The Hathaway Trust
The Maurice Hatter Foundation
The M A Hawe Settlement
The Hawthorne Charitable
Trust
The Dorothy Hay-Bolton
Charitable Trust
The Charles Hayward
Foundation
The Headley Trust
Headley-Pitt Charitable Trust
Heart of England Community
Foundation
The Heathcoat Trust
Heathside Charitable Trust
The Charlotte Heber-Percy
Charitable Trust
The Hedley Denton Charitable
Trust
The Hedley Foundation
The H J Heinz Company
Limited Charitable Trust
The Hellenic Foundation
The Michael Heller Charitable
Foundation
The Simon Heller Charitable
Settlement
The Hemby Trust

The Christina Mary Hendrie
  Trust for Scottish and
  Canadian Charities
Henley Educational Trust
  (formerley Henley
  Educational Charity)
Philip Henman Trust
Esther Hennell Charitable
  Trust
The G D Herbert Charitable
  Trust
The Anne Herd Memorial Trust
The Herefordshire Historic
  Churches Trust
The Heritage of London Trust
  Ltd
The Hesed Trust
The Hesslewood Children's
  Trust (Hull Seamen's and
  General Orphanage)
Hexham and Newcastle
  Diocesan Trust (1947)
The Higgs Charitable Trust
Alan Edward Higgs Charity
The High Sheriff's Police Trust
  for the County of West
  Midlands (Building Blocks)
Highcroft Charitable Trust
The Charles Littlewood Hill
  Trust
The Hillingdon Partnership
  Trust
The Hilmarnan Charitable Trust
Lady Hind Trust
The Hinrichsen Foundation
The Hiscox Foundation
The Hitchin Educational
  Foundation
The Henry C Hoare Charitable
  Trust
The Eleemosynary Charity of
  William Hobbayne
Hobson Charity Limited
Matthew Hodder Charitable
  Trust
The Sir Julian Hodge
  Charitable Trust
The J G Hogg Charitable Trust
The Holden Charitable Trust
John Holford's Charity
The Hollick Family Charitable
  Trust
The Dorothy Holmes Charitable
  Trust
The Holst Foundation
The Edward Holt Trust
The Holywood Trust
The Homelands Charitable
  Trust
The Homestead Charitable
  Trust
Sir Harold Hood's Charitable
  Trust
Hope for Youth (NI)
The Hope Trust
HopMarket Charity
The Cuthbert Horn Trust

The Antony Hornby Charitable
  Trust
The Horne Foundation
The Horne Trust
The Worshipful Company of
  Horners' Charitable Trusts
The Hornsey Parochial
  Charities
The Hospital of God at
  Greatham
The Hospital Saturday Fund
Houblon-Norman/George Fund
The House of Industry Estate
The Reta Lila Howard
  Foundation
The Daniel Howard Trust
The Huddersfield Common
  Good Trust
The Hudson Foundation
The Huggard Charitable Trust
The Geoffrey C Hughes
  Charitable Trust
The Hull and East Riding
  Charitable Trust
Hulme Trust Estates
  (Educational)
Human Relief Foundation
The Humanitarian Trust
The Michael and Shirley Hunt
  Charitable Trust
The Hunter Foundation
Miss Agnes H Hunter's Trust
The Huntingdon Foundation
Huntingdon Freemen's Trust
Hurdale Charity Limited
The Nani Huyu Charitable Trust
The P Y N and B Hyams Trust
The Hyde Charitable Trust
The Idlewild Trust
The Iliffe Family Charitable
  Trust
The Indigo Trust
The Ingram Trust
The Inland Waterways
  Association
The Inlight Trust
The Inman Charity
The Inner London Magistrates
  Court Poor Box and Feeder
  Charity
The International Bankers
  Charitable Trust (The
  Worshipful Company of
  International Bankers)
The Ireland Fund of Great
  Britain
The Irish Youth Foundation
  (UK) Ltd (incorporating The
  Lawlor Foundation)
The Ironmongers' Foundation
The Charles Irving Charitable
  Trust
Irwin Trust
The ISA Charity
The Isaacs Charitable Trust
The J Isaacs Charitable Trust

The Isle of Anglesey Charitable
  Trust
The ITF Seafarers Trust
The J M K Charitable Trust
The J R S S T Charitable Trust
C Richard Jackson Charitable
  Trust
Elizabeth Jackson Charitable
  Trust
The Ruth and Lionel Jacobson
  Trust (Second Fund) No 2
Jaffe Family Relief Fund
John James Bristol Foundation
The Susan and Stephen
  James Charitable
  Settlement
The James Trust
The Marjory Jameson Trust
The Jarman Charitable Trust
JCA Charitable Foundation
The Jeffrey Charitable Trust
The Jenour Foundation
The Jephcott Charitable Trust
Jerwood Charitable Foundation
Jesus Hospital Charity
Jewish Child's Day
The Jewish Youth Fund
The Harold Joels Charitable
  Trust
The Nicholas Joels Charitable
  Trust
The Norman Joels Charitable
  Trust
The Elton John Aids
  Foundation
The Lillie Johnson Charitable
  Trust
The Johnson Foundation
The Reginald Johnson
  Foundation
The Johnson Wax Ltd
  Charitable Trust
The Joicey Trust
The Jones 1986 Charitable
  Trust
The Marjorie and Geoffrey
  Jones Charitable Trust
The Jordan Charitable
  Foundation
The J E Joseph Charitable
  Fund
The Lady Eileen Joseph
  Foundation
The Josephs Family Charitable
  Trust
JTH Charitable Trust
The Judith Trust
The Jungels-Winkler Charitable
  Foundation
The Anton Jurgens Charitable
  Trust
The Bernard Kahn Charitable
  Trust
The Stanley Kalms Foundation
The Karenza Foundation
The Boris Karloff Charitable
  Foundation

The Ian Karten Charitable
Trust
The Kasner Charitable Trust
The Kathleen Trust
The Michael and Ilse Katz
Foundation
The Katzauer Charitable
Settlement
The C S Kaufman Charitable
Trust
The Geoffrey John Kaye
Charitable Foundation
The Emmanuel Kaye
Foundation
Kelsick's Educational
Foundation
The KempWelch Charitable
Trust
The Kay Kendall Leukaemia
Fund
The John Thomas Kennedy
Charitable Foundation
The Kennedy Charitable
Foundation
The Nancy Kenyon Charitable
Trust
Keren Association
Kermaville Ltd
The Peter Kershaw Trust
Keswick Hall Trust
The Ursula Keyes Trust
The Robert Kiln Charitable
Trust
The King/Cullimore Charitable
Trust
The Kingsbury Charity
The Mary Kinross Charitable
Trust
Kirkley Poor's Lands Estate
The Richard Kirkman
Charitable Trust
Kirschel Foundation
Robert Kitchin (Saddlers'
Company)
Ernest Kleinwort Charitable
Trust
The Marina Kleinwort
Charitable Trust
The Kobler Trust
The Kohn Foundation
The Kreditor Charitable Trust
The Kreitman Foundation
The Neil Kreitman Foundation
The Kyte Charitable Trust
The Late Sir Pierce Lacy
Charity Trust
John Laing Charitable Trust
Maurice and Hilda Laing
Charitable Trust
The Christopher Laing
Foundation
The Kirby Laing Foundation
The Martin Laing Foundation
The Beatrice Laing Trust
The Lambert Charitable Trust
Duchy of Lancaster Benevolent
Fund

The Lancaster Foundation
The Allen Lane Foundation
Langdale Trust
The Langley Charitable Trust
The LankellyChase Foundation
The R J Larg Family Charitable
Trust
Largsmount Ltd
The Lark Trust
Laslett's (Hinton) Charity
The Lauffer Family Charitable
Foundation
The Kathleen Laurence Trust
The Law Society Charity
The Edgar E Lawley Foundation
The Herd Lawson and Muriel
Lawson Charitable Trust
The Lawson Beckman
Charitable Trust
The Raymond and Blanche
Lawson Charitable Trust
The Leach Fourteenth Trust
The David Lean Foundation
The Leathersellers' Company
Charitable Fund
The Leche Trust
The Arnold Lee Charitable
Trust
The Lord Mayor of Leeds
Appeal Fund
Leeds Building Society
Charitable Foundation
The Kennedy Leigh Charitable
Trust
The Leigh Trust
Mrs Vera Leigh's Charity
P Leigh-Bramwell Trust 'E'
The Lennox and Wyfold
Foundation
The Erica Leonard Trust
The Leonard Trust
The Mark Leonard Trust
Lesley Lesley and Mutter Trust
Leukaemia and Lymphoma
Research
The Leverhulme Trade
Charities Trust
The Leverhulme Trust
The Joseph Levy Charitable
Foundation
The John Spedan Lewis
Foundation
The Sir Edward Lewis
Foundation
John Lewis Partnership
General Community Fund
Lichfield Conduit Lands
Lifeline 4 Kids
The Linbury Trust
Lindale Educational
Foundation
The Linden Charitable Trust
The Enid Linder Foundation
The Linmardon Trust
The Ruth and Stuart Lipton
Charitable Trust
The Lister Charitable Trust

Frank Litchfield Charitable
Trust
The Andrew and Mary
Elizabeth Little Charitable
Trust
The Second Joseph Aaron
Littman Foundation
The George John and Sheilah
Livanos Charitable Trust
Liverpool Sailors' Home Trust
The Elaine and Angus Lloyd
Charitable Trust
The Charles Lloyd Foundation
Lloyd's Charities Trust
Lloyds Bank Foundation for
England and Wales
Lloyds Bank Foundation for
Northern Ireland
Lloyds Bank Foundation for the
Channel Islands
Lloyds TSB Foundation for
Scotland
The Locker Foundation
The Loftus Charitable Trust
The Lolev Charitable Trust
The Trust for London
London Catalyst
The London Community
Foundation
The London Housing
Foundation
The London Law Trust
The William and Katherine
Longman Trust
The Loseley and Guildway
Charitable Trust
The Lotus Foundation
The C L Loyd Charitable Trust
LSA Charitable Trust
The Marie Helen Luen
Charitable Trust
Robert Luff Foundation Ltd
Henry Lumley Charitable Trust
C F Lunoe Trust Fund
The Ruth and Jack Lunzer
Charitable Trust
Lord and Lady Lurgan Trust
The Lyndhurst Trust
The Lynn Foundation
The Lynwood Trust
John Lyon's Charity
The Lyons Charitable Trust
The Sir Jack Lyons Charitable
Trust
The Lyras Family Charitable
Trust
Sylvanus Lyson's Charity
The M and C Trust
The M K Charitable Trust
The Madeline Mabey Trust
The E M MacAndrew Trust
Macdonald-Buchanan
Charitable Trust
The Mackay and Brewer
Charitable Trust
The Mackintosh Foundation
The MacRobert Trust

James Madison Trust
The Magen Charitable Trust
Man Group plc Charitable Trust
The Manackerman Charitable Trust
Manchester Airport Community Trust Fund
The Manchester Guardian Society Charitable Trust
Lord Mayor of Manchester's Charity Appeal Trust
Mandeville Trust
The Manifold Charitable Trust
W M Mann Foundation
The Leslie and Lilian Manning Trust
Marbeh Torah Trust
Marchig Animal Welfare Trust
The Stella and Alexander Margulies Charitable Trust
Market Harborough and The Bowdens Charity
The Ann and David Marks Foundation
The Hilda and Samuel Marks Foundation
J P Marland Charitable Trust
The Michael Marsh Charitable Trust
The Marsh Christian Trust
The Charlotte Marshall Charitable Trust
The Jim Marshall Charitable Trust
The Nora Joan Marshall Charitable Trust
The D G Marshall of Cambridge Trust
Marshgate Charitable Settlement
Sir George Martin Trust
The Mason Porter Charitable Trust
The Nancie Massey Charitable Trust
The Mathew Trust
The Matt 6.3 Charitable Trust
The Violet Mauray Charitable Trust
The Maxwell Family Foundation
Evelyn May Trust
The Mayfield Valley Arts Trust
Mazars Charitable Trust
The McDougall Trust
The McKenna Charitable Trust
The Helen Isabella McMorran Charitable Foundation
The James Frederick and Ethel Anne Measures Charity
The Medlock Charitable Trust
The Anthony and Elizabeth Mellows Charitable Settlement
Melow Charitable Trust
The Mercers' Charitable Foundation

The Merchant Taylors' Company Charities Fund
The Merchant Venturers' Charity
The Merchants' House of Glasgow
The Mersey Docks and Harbour Company Charitable Fund
Community Foundation for Merseyside
The Zachary Merton and George Woofindin Convalescent Trust
The Tony Metherell Charitable Trust
The Metropolitan Drinking Fountain and Cattle Trough Association
The Mickel Fund
Gerald Micklem Charitable Trust
Midhurst Pensions Trust
The Migraine Trust
Miles Trust for the Putney and Roehampton Community
Millennium Stadium Charitable Trust
The Hugh and Mary Miller Bequest Trust
The Ronald Miller Foundation
The Millfield Trust
The Millhouses Charitable Trust
The Millichope Foundation
The Mills Charity
The Millward Charitable Trust
The Clare Milne Trust
Milton Keynes Community Foundation
The Edgar Milward Charity
The Peter Minet Trust
The Minos Trust
The Mirfield Educational Charity
The Laurence Misener Charitable Trust
The Mishcon Family Charitable Trust
The Misselbrook Trust
The Esmé Mitchell Trust
Keren Mitzvah Trust
The Mizpah Trust
The Mobbs Memorial Trust Ltd
The Modiano Charitable Trust
The Moette Charitable Trust
The Mole Charitable Trust
The D C Moncrieff Charitable Trust
Monmouthshire County Council Welsh Church Act Fund
The Montague Thompson Coon Charitable Trust
The Colin Montgomerie Charitable Foundation
The Monument Trust
The Henry Moore Foundation

John Moores Foundation
The Morel Charitable Trust
The Morgan Charitable Foundation
The Mr and Mrs J T Morgan Foundation
Morgan Stanley International Foundation
The Oliver Morland Charitable Trust
The Bernard Morris Charitable Trust
The Morris Charitable Trust
The Willie and Mabel Morris Charitable Trust
The Peter Morrison Charitable Foundation
The Stanley Morrison Charitable Trust
Vyoel Moshe Charitable Trust
The Moss Charitable Trust
The Robert and Margaret Moss Charitable Trust
The Moss Family Charitable Trust
Mosselson Charitable Trust
The Mount Everest Foundation
The Edwina Mountbatten Trust
Mountbatten Festival of Music
The Mountbatten Memorial Trust
Mrs Waterhouse Charitable Trust
The Mugdock Children's Trust
The Mulberry Trust
The Edith Murphy Foundation
The Mushroom Fund
The Music Sales Charitable Trust
Muslim Hands
The Mutual Trust Group
The Kitty and Daniel Nabarro Charitable Trust
The Nadezhda Charitable Trust
The Naggar Charitable Trust
The Eleni Nakou Foundation
The Janet Nash Charitable Settlement
The National Churches Trust
The National Hockey Foundation
The National Manuscripts Conservation Trust
Needham Market and Barking Welfare Charities
The Worshipful Company of Needlemakers' Charitable Fund
The Neighbourly Charitable Trust
The James Neill Trust Fund
Nemoral Ltd
The Newcomen Collett Foundation
The Frances and Augustus Newman Foundation

Alderman Newton's Educational Foundation

The Chevras Ezras Nitzrochim Trust

The Noon Foundation

The Norda Trust

Norie Charitable Trust

Normalyn Charitable Trust

The Norman Family Charitable Trust

The Duncan Norman Trust Fund

The Normanby Charitable Trust

The North West Cancer Research Fund

The Northampton Municipal Church Charities

The Northampton Queen's Institute Relief in Sickness Fund

The Earl of Northampton's Charity

The Northcott Devon Medical Foundation

The Community Foundation for Northern Ireland

The Northern Rock Foundation

The Northmoor Trust

The Northumberland Village Homes Trust

The Northwood Charitable Trust

The Norton Foundation

The Norwich Church of England Young Men's Society

The Norwich Town Close Estate Charity

The Norwood and Newton Settlement

The Noswad Charity

The Nottingham General Dispensary

The Nottingham Gordon Memorial Trust for Boys and Girls

Nottinghamshire Community Foundation

The Nottinghamshire Historic Churches Trust

The Nottinghamshire Miners' Welfare Trust Fund

Novi Most International

The Father O'Mahoney Memorial Trust

The Sir Peter O'Sullevan Charitable Trust

The Oak Trust

The Oakdale Trust

The Oakmoor Charitable Trust

The Odin Charitable Trust

The Ofenheim Charitable Trust

Ogilvie Charities Deed No.2 (including the Charity of Mary Catherine Ford Smith)

The Ogle Christian Trust

Oglesby Charitable Trust

Oizer Charitable Trust

The Old Broad Street Charity Trust

The John Oldacre Foundation

The Oldham Foundation

The Olga Charitable Trust

Open Gate

The Raymond Oppenheimer Foundation

Ormonde Foundation

The Ormsby Charitable Trust

The Orrin Charitable Trust

The Ouseley Trust

The Owen Family Trust

Oxfam (GB)

The Oxfordshire Community Foundation

The P F Charitable Trust

Padwa Charitable Foundation

The Paget Charitable Trust

The Palmer Foundation

The Panacea Society

Panton Trust

The Paragon Trust

The Park House Charitable Trust

The Frank Parkinson Agricultural Trust

The Samuel and Freda Parkinson Charitable Trust

The Parthenon Trust

The Constance Paterson Charitable Trust

The Patrick Charitable Trust

The Jack Patston Charitable Trust

Paycare Charity Trust

The Payne Charitable Trust

The Harry Payne Trust

The Susanna Peake Charitable Trust

The Pedmore Sporting Club Trust Fund

The Dowager Countess Eleanor Peel Trust

The Pennycress Trust

The Performing Right Society Foundation

The Persson Charitable Trust

The Persula Foundation

The Jack Petchey Foundation

The Petplan Charitable Trust

The Philips and Rubens Charitable Trust

The Phillips Charitable Trust

The Phillips Family Charitable Trust

Philological Foundation

The David Pickford Charitable Foundation

The Pilgrim Trust

The Cecil Pilkington Charitable Trust

The Pilkington Charities Fund

The Austin and Hope Pilkington Trust

The Sir Harry Pilkington Trust

The Col W W Pilkington Will Trusts The General Charity Fund

The DLA Piper Charitable Trust

The Worshipful Company of Plaisterers Charitable Trust

The Platinum Trust

Polden-Puckham Charitable Foundation

The George and Esme Pollitzer Charitable Settlement

The J S F Pollitzer Charitable Settlement

The Ponton House Trust

Edith and Ferdinand Porjes Charitable Trust

The John Porter Charitable Trust

The Porter Foundation

The Portrack Charitable Trust

The J E Posnansky Charitable Trust

The Mary Potter Convent Hospital Trust

The David and Elaine Potter Foundation

The Powell Foundation

The W L Pratt Charitable Trust

Premierquote Ltd

Premishlaner Charitable Trust

The Lucy Price Relief-in-Need Charity

Sir John Priestman Charity Trust

The Primrose Trust

The Prince of Wales's Charitable Foundation

Prison Service Charity Fund

The Privy Purse Charitable Trust

The Proven Family Trust

The Provincial Grand Charity of the Province of Derbyshire

The Puebla Charitable Trust

The Richard and Christine Purchas Charitable Trust

The Puri Foundation

Mr and Mrs J A Pye's Charitable Settlement

Quartet Community Foundation

Queen Mary's Roehampton Trust

The Queen's Silver Jubilee Trust

R S Charitable Trust

The R V W Trust

The Monica Rabagliati Charitable Trust

Rachel Charitable Trust

The Mr and Mrs Philip Rackham Charitable Trust

Richard Radcliffe Charitable Trust

The Radcliffe Trust

The Ragdoll Foundation

The Rainford Trust

The Peggy Ramsay Foundation

The Joseph and Lena Randall
Charitable Trust
The Rank Foundation Limited
The Fanny Rapaport Charitable
Settlement
The Ratcliff Foundation
The Ratcliffe Pension Charity
The Ratcliffe Charitable Trust
The Eleanor Rathbone
Charitable Trust
The Sigrid Rausing Trust
The Ravensdale Trust
The Rawdon-Smith Trust
The Rayden Charitable Trust
The Roger Raymond Charitable
Trust
The Rayne Foundation
The Rayne Trust
The Sir James Reckitt Charity
The Red Arrows Trust
The Red Rose Charitable Trust
The C A Redfern Charitable
Foundation
The Reed Foundation
Richard Reeve's Foundation
The Max Reinhardt Charitable
Trust
Relief Fund for Romania
Limited
The Rest Harrow Trust
Reuben Foundation
The Nathaniel Reyner Trust
Fund
The Rhododendron Trust
The Sir Cliff Richard Charitable
Trust
The Clive Richards Charity
The Violet M Richards Charity
The Richmond Parish Lands
Charity
Ridgesave Limited
The Ripple Effect Foundation
The Sir John Ritblat Family
Foundation
The River Trust
Thomas Roberts Trust
The Robertson Trust
The Rochester Bridge Trust
The Rock Foundation
The Rock Solid Trust
The Rofeh Trust
Rokach Family Charitable Trust
The Helen Roll Charitable
Trust
The Sir James Roll Charitable
Trust
The Roman Research Trust
The C A Rookes Charitable
Trust
The Rosca Trust
The Rose Foundation
The Cecil Rosen Foundation
Rosetrees Trust
The Rothermere Foundation
The Rotherwick Foundation
The Roughley Charitable Trust

Mrs Gladys Row Fogo
Charitable Trust
Rowanville Ltd
The Christopher Rowbotham
Charitable Trust
The Rowing Foundation
The Rowlands Trust
The Joseph Rowntree
Charitable Trust
The Joseph Rowntree
Foundation
Joseph Rowntree Reform Trust
Limited
Royal Artillery Charitable Fund
Royal British Legion
Royal Docks Trust (London)
Royal Masonic Trust for Girls
and Boys
The Rubin Foundation
William Arthur Rudd Memorial
Trust
The Rufford Foundation
Rugby Football Foundation
The Russell Trust
The J S and E C Rymer
Charitable Trust
S O Charitable Trust
The Jeremy and John Sacher
Charitable Trust
The Michael Harry Sacher
Trust
The Sackler Trust
The Ruzin Sadagora Trust
The Saga Charitable Trust
The Jean Sainsbury Animal
Welfare Trust
The Alan and Babette
Sainsbury Charitable Fund
The Sainsbury Family
Charitable Trusts
Saint Sarkis Charity Trust
The Saintbury Trust
The Saints and Sinners Trust
The Salt Trust
Basil Samuel Charitable Trust
The M J Samuel Charitable
Trust
The Peter Samuel Charitable
Trust
The Samworth Foundation
The Sandra Charitable Trust
Santander UK Foundation
Limited
The Scarfe Charitable Trust
The Schapira Charitable Trust
The Schmidt-Bodner Charitable
Trust
The R H Scholes Charitable
Trust
The Schreib Trust
The Schreiber Charitable Trust
The Schuster Charitable Trust
Foundation Scotland
The Francis C Scott Charitable
Trust
The Sir James and Lady Scott
Trust

The Scott Trust Foundation
The Storrow Scott Will Trust
Scottish Coal Industry Special
Welfare Fund
The Scottish International
Education Trust
The Scouloudi Foundation
Seafarers UK (King George's
Fund for Sailors)
Seamen's Hospital Society
The Searchlight Electric
Charitable Trust
The Samuel Sebba Charitable
Trust
The Seedfield Trust
The Ayrton Senna Foundation
The Seven Fifty Trust
The Cyril Shack Trust
The Jean Shanks Foundation
The Shanti Charitable Trust
ShareGift (The Orr Mackintosh
Foundation)
The Linley Shaw Foundation
The Shears Foundation
The Sheepdrove Trust
The Sheffield and District
Hospital Services
Charitable Fund
The Sheldon Trust
The Patricia and Donald
Shepherd Charitable Trust
The Sylvia and Colin Shepherd
Charitable Trust
The Archie Sherman Cardiff
Foundation
The Archie Sherman Charitable
Trust
The R C Sherriff Trust
The Shetland Charitable Trust
SHINE (Support and Help in
Education)
The Barnett and Sylvia Shine
No 2 Charitable Trust
The Bassil Shippam and
Alsford Trust
The Shipwrights' Company
Charitable Fund
The Shirley Foundation
Shlomo Memorial Fund Limited
The J A Shone Memorial Trust
Community Foundation for
Shropshire and Telford
The Barbara A Shuttleworth
Memorial Trust
The Mary Elizabeth Siebel
Charity
David and Jennifer Sieff
Charitable Trust
The Julius Silman Charitable
Trust
The Leslie Silver Charitable
Trust
The Simpson Education and
Conservation Trust
The Simpson Foundation
The Huntly and Margery
Sinclair Charitable Trust

Sino-British Fellowship Trust
Six Point Foundation
The Skelton Bounty
The Charles Skey Charitable
Trust
Skipton Building Society
Charitable Foundation
The John Slater Foundation
The SMB Charitable Trust
The Mrs Smith and Mount
Trust
The N Smith Charitable
Settlement
The E H Smith Charitable Trust
The Smith Charitable Trust
The Henry Smith Charity
The Leslie Smith Foundation
The Martin Smith Foundation
The Stanley Smith UK
Horticultural Trust
The Snowball Trust
The Sobell Foundation
The Solo Charitable
Settlement
Dr Richard Solomon's
Charitable Trust
The E C Sosnow Charitable
Trust
The Souter Charitable Trust
The South Square Trust
The W F Southall Trust
The Southwold Trust
The Sovereign Health Care
Charitable Trust
Sparks Charity (Sport Aiding
Medical Research For Kids)
Sparquote Limited
The Spear Charitable Trust
The Jessie Spencer Trust
The Ralph and Irma Sperring
Charity
The Spielman Charitable Trust
The Spoore, Merry and Rixman
Foundation
Sported Foundation
Springrule Limited
The Spurrell Charitable Trust
The Geoff and Fiona Squire
Foundation
St Andrew's Conservation
Trust
St Hilda's Trust
St James' Trust Settlement
St James's Place Foundation
Sir Walter St John's
Educational Charity
St Michael's and All Saints'
Charities Relief Branch (The
Church Houses Relief in
Need Charity)
The Late St Patrick White
Charitable Trust
St Peter's Saltley Trust
St Teilo's Trust
The Stanley Foundation Ltd
The Stanton Ballard Charitable
Trust

The Staples Trust
The Star Charitable Trust
The Peter Stebbings Memorial
Charity
The Steinberg Family
Charitable Trust
The Hugh Stenhouse
Foundation
The Stephen Barry Charitable
Trust
The Sigmund Sternberg
Charitable Foundation
Stervon Ltd
The Stevenage Community
Trust
The June Stevens Foundation
The Steventon Allotments and
Relief-in-Need Charity
The Stewards' Charitable Trust
The Stewards' Company
Limited (incorporating the J
W Laing Trust and the J W
Laing Biblical Scholarship
Trust)
Sir Halley Stewart Trust
The Leonard Laity Stoate
Charitable Trust
The Stobart Newlands
Charitable Trust
The Edward Stocks-Massey
Bequest Fund
The Stokenchurch Educational
Charity
The Stoller Charitable Trust
The M J C Stone Charitable
Trust
The Samuel Storey Family
Charitable Trust
Peter Stormonth Darling
Charitable Trust
The Strangward Trust
The Strasser Foundation
Stratford upon Avon Town
Trust
The W O Street Charitable
Foundation
The Sudborough Foundation
The Suffolk Historic Churches
Trust
The Summerfield Charitable
Trust
The Surrey Historic Buildings
Trust Ltd
The Sussex Historic Churches
Trust
The Sutasoma Trust
The Sutton Trust
Swansea and Brecon Diocesan
Board of Finance Limited
The John Swire (1989)
Charitable Trust
The Swire Charitable Trust
The Adrian Swire Charitable
Trust
The Hugh and Ruby Sykes
Charitable Trust

The Charles and Elsie Sykes
Trust
The Sylvanus Charitable Trust
The Stella Symons Charitable
Trust
The Tabeel Trust
The Tajtelbaum Charitable
Trust
Tallow Chandlers Benevolent
Fund
The Tangent Charitable Trust
The Lady Tangye Charitable
Trust
The David Tannen Charitable
Trust
The Tanner Trust
The Lili Tapper Charitable
Foundation
The Mrs A Lacy Tate Trust
The Tay Charitable Trust
Humphrey Richardson Taylor
Charitable Trust
The Connie and Albert Taylor
Charitable Trust
The Cyril Taylor Charitable
Trust
A P Taylor Trust
Tearfund
The Tedworth Charitable Trust
Tees Valley Community
Foundation
The Templeton Goodwill Trust
Tesco Charity Trust
The C Paul Thackray General
Charitable Trust
The Thames Wharf Charity
The John P. Gommes
Foundation
The Thistle Trust
The Loke Wan Tho Memorial
Foundation
The Thomas Lilley Memorial
Trust
The Arthur and Margaret
Thompson Charitable Trust
The Thompson Family
Charitable Trust
The Len Thomson Charitable
Trust
The Sue Thomson Foundation
The Sir Jules Thorn Charitable
Trust
The Thornton Foundation
The Thornton Trust
The Thousandth Man –
Richard Burns Charitable
Trust
The Three Guineas Trust
The Three Oaks Trust
The Thriplow Charitable Trust
The Tinsley Foundation
The Tisbury Telegraph Trust
The Tobacco Pipe Makers and
Tobacco Trade Benevolent
Fund
The Tolkien Trust

Tollemache (Buckminster) Charitable Trust

Tomchei Torah Charitable Trust

The Tompkins Foundation

The Tory Family Foundation

Tottenham Grammar School Foundation

The Tower Hill Trust

The Towry Law Charitable Trust (also known as the Castle Educational Trust)

The Toy Trust

The Mayor of Trafford's Charity Fund

The Constance Travis Charitable Trust

The Treeside Trust

The Triangle Trust (1949) Fund

The True Colours Trust

Truedene Co. Ltd

The Truemark Trust

Truemart Limited

Trumros Limited

The Trusthouse Charitable Foundation

Tudor Rose Ltd

The Tudor Trust

The Tufton Charitable Trust

The R D Turner Charitable Trust

The Douglas Turner Trust

The Florence Turner Trust

The G J W Turner Trust

Miss S M Tutton Charitable Trust

The TUUT Charitable Trust

Community Foundation Serving Tyne and Wear and Northumberland

Trustees of Tzedakah

Ulster Garden Villages Ltd

Ultach Trust

Ulting Overseas Trust

The Ulverscroft Foundation

Ulverston Town Lands Charity

The Underwood Trust

The Union of Orthodox Hebrew Congregation

The United Society for the Propagation of the Gospel

The David Uri Memorial Trust

Uxbridge United Welfare Trust

Vale of Glamorgan – Welsh Church Fund

The Valentine Charitable Trust

The Van Neste Foundation

Mrs Maud Van Norden's Charitable Foundation

The Vandervell Foundation

The Vardy Foundation

The Variety Club Children's Charity

Veneziana Fund

The Verdon-Smith Family Charitable Settlement

Victoria Homes Trust

The Nigel Vinson Charitable Trust

The William and Ellen Vinten Trust

The Vintners' Company Charitable Foundation

Vintners' Gifts Charity

Vivdale Ltd

The Viznitz Foundation

Wade's Charity

The Scurrah Wainwright Charity

Wakeham Trust

The Community Foundation in Wales

Wales Council for Voluntary Action

Robert and Felicity Waley-Cohen Charitable Trust

The Thomas Wall Trust

The F J Wallis Charitable Settlement

War on Want

The Ward Blenkinsop Trust

The George Ward Charitable Trust

The Barbara Ward Children's Foundation

G R Waters Charitable Trust 2000

The Wates Foundation

The Howard Watson Symington Memorial Charity

John Watson's Trust

Waynflete Charitable Trust

Weatherley Charitable Trust

The Weavers' Company Benevolent Fund

The Weinberg Foundation

The Weinstein Foundation

The Wellcome Trust

Welsh Church Fund Dyfed area (Carmarthenshire, Ceredigion and Pembrokeshire)

The Welton Foundation

The Wessex Youth Trust

The West Derby Wastelands Charity

West London Synagogue Charitable Fund

West Yorkshire Police Community Trust

The Westminster Foundation

The Garfield Weston Foundation

The Whitaker Charitable Trust

The Colonel W H Whitbread Charitable Trust

The Simon Whitbread Charitable Trust

The Whitecourt Charitable Trust

The Norman Whiteley Trust

The Whitley Animal Protection Trust

The Whittlesey Charity

The Lionel Wigram Memorial Trust

The Felicity Wilde Charitable Trust

The Will Charitable Trust

The Charity of William Williams

The Kay Williams Charitable Foundation

The Williams Family Charitable Trust

The HDH Wills 1965 Charitable Trust

The Dame Violet Wills Will Trust

The Wilmcote Charitrust

David Wilson Foundation

The Wilson Foundation

J and J R Wilson Trust

The Community Foundation for Wiltshire and Swindon

The Benjamin Winegarten Charitable Trust

The Harold Hyam Wingate Foundation

The Francis Winham Foundation

Wirral Mayor's Charity

The James Wise Charitable Trust

The Michael and Anna Wix Charitable Trust

The Wixamtree Trust

The Woburn 1986 Charitable Trust

The Maurice Wohl Charitable Foundation

The Charles Wolfson Charitable Trust

The James Wood Bequest Fund

Wooden Spoon Society

Woodlands Green Ltd

Woodlands Trust

The Woodward Charitable Trust

Worcester Municipal Charities

The Worcestershire and Dudley Historic Churches Trust

The Wragge and Co. Charitable Trust

The Diana Edgson Wright Charitable Trust

The Matthews Wrightson Charity Trust

Miss E B Wrightson's Charitable Settlement

Wychdale Ltd

Wychville Ltd

The Wyndham Charitable Trust

The Wyseliot Charitable Trust

The Xerox (UK) Trust

The Dennis Alan Yardy Charitable Trust

The W Wing Yip and Brothers Foundation

Yorkshire Agricultural Society

The South Yorkshire
Community Foundation
The Yorkshire Dales
Millennium Trust
The John Young Charitable
Settlement
The William Allen Young
Charitable Trust
The John K Young Endowment
Fund
Zephyr Charitable Trust
The Marjorie and Arnold Ziff
Charitable Foundation
Stephen Zimmerman
Charitable Trust
The Zochonis Charitable Trust
Zurich Community Trust (UK)
Limited

....

■ **Seed funding**

The 1970 Trust
The 1989 Willan Charitable
Trust
The 29th May 1961 Charitable
Trust
A W Charitable Trust
The Aberbrothock Skea Trust
The Aberdeen Endowments
Trust
The Aberdeenshire Educational
Trust Scheme
ABF The Soldiers' Charity
Achisomoch Aid Company
Limited
Action Medical Research
The Sylvia Adams Charitable
Trust
The Victor Adda Foundation
The Adint Charitable Trust
Age Scotland
Age UK
Aid to the Church in Need (UK)
The Sylvia Aitken Charitable
Trust
The Al Fayed Charitable
Foundation
Aldgate and All Hallows'
Foundation
The Aldgate Freedom
Foundation
All Saints Educational Trust
Allchurches Trust Ltd
The Alliance Family Foundation
Angus Allnatt Charitable
Foundation
The Pat Allsop Charitable Trust
The Almond Trust
Almondsbury Charity
Altamont Ltd
Alvor Charitable Trust
The Ammco Trust
Viscount Amory's Charitable
Trust
The AMW Charitable Trust
The Anchor Foundation

Anguish's Educational
Foundation
The Animal Defence Trust
The Eric Anker-Petersen
Charity
Anpride Ltd
Ambrose and Ann Appelbe
Trust
The Appletree Trust
The Arbib Foundation
Archbishop of Wales' Fund for
Children
The John M Archer Charitable
Trust
The Archer Trust
The Ardwick Trust
The Argus Appeal
The Armenian Relief Society of
Great Britain Trust
The Armourers' and Brasiers'
Gauntlet Trust
The Arsenal Foundation
The Artemis Charitable Trust
The Arts and Entertainment
Charitable Trust
Arts Council England
The Arts Council of Northern
Ireland
Arts Council of Wales (also
known as Cyngor
Celfyddydau Cymru)
The Ove Arup Foundation
The A S Charitable Trust
The Ashden Trust
The Ashendene Trust
The Ashley Family Foundation
The Ashworth Charitable Trust
The Ian Askew Charitable Trust
The Associated Country
Women of the World
The Association of Colleges
Charitable Trust
Astellas European Foundation
Asthma UK
AstonMansfield Charitable
Trust
The Astor Foundation
The Astor of Hever Trust
The Aurelius Charitable Trust
The BAA Communities Trust
The Scott Bader
Commonwealth Ltd
The Bagri Foundation
Veta Bailey Charitable Trust
The Austin Bailey Foundation
The Baily Thomas Charitable
Fund
The Baird Trust
The Baker Charitable Trust
The Balcombe Charitable Trust
The Albert Casanova Ballard
Deceased Trust
The Ballinger Charitable Trust
The Balmore Trust
The Balney Charitable Trust
The Baltic Charitable Fund

The Bamford Charitable
Foundation
The Banbury Charities
William P Bancroft (No 2)
Charitable Trust and
Jenepher Gillett Trust
The Band Trust
The Barbers' Company General
Charities
The Barbour Foundation
Barchester Healthcare
Foundation
The Barclay Foundation
The Baring Foundation
Peter Barker-Mill Memorial
Charity
The Barleycorn Trust
Barnes Workhouse Fund
The Barnsbury Charitable Trust
The Barnwood House Trust
The Misses Barrie Charitable
Trust
Barrington Family Charitable
Trust
Bartholomew Charitable Trust
The Bartlett Taylor Charitable
Trust
The Paul Bassham Charitable
Trust
The Batchworth Trust
The Bates Charitable Trust
The Bay Tree Charitable Trust
The Louis Baylis (Maidenhead
Advertiser) Charitable Trust
BBC Children in Need
B-CH 1971 Charitable Trust
The Beacon Trust
The Bearder Charity
The James Beattie Charitable
Trust
The Beaverbrook Foundation
The Beccles Town Lands
Charity
The Becker Family Charitable
Trust
The Becketts and Sargeants
Educational Foundation
The John Beckwith Charitable
Trust
The Peter Beckwith Charitable
Trust
The David and Ruth Behrend
Fund
The Beit Trust
The Bellahouston Bequest
Fund
The Bellinger Donnay Trust
The Benfield Motors Charitable
Trust
The Benham Charitable
Settlement
Maurice and Jacqueline
Bennett Charitable Trust
The Berkshire Community
Foundation
The Bestway Foundation
BHST

The Mason Bibby 1981 Trust
The Bideford Bridge Trust
The Big Lottery Fund
The Billmeir Charitable Trust
The Bingham Trust
The Bintaub Charitable Trust
The Birmingham District
  Nursing Charitable Trust
The Birmingham Hospital
  Saturday Fund Medical
  Charity and Welfare Trust
Birmingham International
  Airport Community Trust
The Lord Mayor of
  Birmingham's Charity
The Michael Bishop
  Foundation
The Bishop's Development
  Fund
The Bertie Black Foundation
Isabel Blackman Foundation
The Blagrave Trust
The Blair Foundation
Blakemore Foundation
The Blanchminster Trust
The Blandford Lake Trust
The Sir Victor Blank Charitable
  Settlement
The Neville and Elaine Blond
  Charitable Trust
The Bluston Charitable
  Settlement
The Nicholas Boas Charitable
  Trust
The Body Shop Foundation
The Boltons Trust
The Bonamy Charitable Trust
The John and Celia Bonham
  Christie Charitable Trust
The Charlotte Bonham-Carter
  Charitable Trust
Bonhomie United Charity
  Society
The Boots Charitable Trust
The Bordon Liphook
  Haslemere Charity
The Oliver Borthwick Memorial
  Trust
The Boshier-Hinton Foundation
The Bothwell Charitable Trust
H E and E L Botteley
  Charitable Trust
The Harry Bottom Charitable
  Trust
The Anthony Bourne
  Foundation
The Bower Trust
The Bowerman Charitable
  Trust
John and Susan Bowers Fund
The Bowland Charitable Trust
The Frank Brake Charitable
  Trust
The William Brake Charitable
  Trust
The Tony Bramall Charitable
  Trust

The Liz and Terry Bramall
  Foundation
The Harold and Alice Bridges
  Charity
Bristol Archdeaconry Charity
John Bristow and Thomas
  Mason Trust
The British Council for
  Prevention of Blindness
The British Dietetic
  Association General and
  Education Trust Fund
The British Gas (Scottish Gas)
  Energy Trust
British Heart Foundation
British Humane Association
British Institute at Ankara
British Ornithologists' Union
British Record Industry Trust
The J and M Britton Charitable
  Trust
The Bromley Trust
The Roger Brooke Charitable
  Trust
The David Brooke Charity
The Charles Brotherton Trust
Joseph Brough Charitable
  Trust
The Swinfen Broun Charitable
  Trust
Edna Brown Charitable
  Settlement (Mrs E E Brown
  Charitable Settlement)
Buckinghamshire Community
  Foundation
The Rosemary Bugden
  Charitable Trust
The Bulldog Trust Limited
The E F Bulmer Benevolent
  Fund
Burdens Charitable Foundation
The Clara E Burgess Charity
The Burry Charitable Trust
The Arnold Burton 1998
  Charitable Trust
The Burton Breweries
  Charitable Trust
Consolidated Charity of Burton
  upon Trent
The Paul Bush Foundation
  Trust
The Worshipful Company of
  Butchers General Charities
The Noel Buxton Trust
Henry T and Lucy B Cadbury
  Charitable Trust
The Christopher Cadbury
  Charitable Trust
The G W Cadbury Charitable
  Trust
The Richard Cadbury
  Charitable Trust
The Edward and Dorothy
  Cadbury Trust
The George Cadbury Trust
CAF (Charities Aid Foundation)

CAFOD (Catholic Agency for
  Overseas Development)
Community Foundation for
  Calderdale
The Callander Charitable Trust
Calleva Foundation
Calouste Gulbenkian
  Foundation – UK Branch
The Calpe Trust
Calypso Browning Trust
The Campden Charities
  Trustee
The Canning Trust
The Carew Pole Charitable
  Trust
The D W T Cargill Fund
Carlee Ltd
The Carlton House Charitable
  Trust
The Carmelite Monastery Ware
  Trust
The Worshipful Company of
  Carmen Benevolent Trust
The Carnegie Dunfermline
  Trust
The Carpenter Charitable Trust
The Carpenters' Company
  Charitable Trust
The Carrington Charitable
  Trust
The Carron Charitable
  Settlement
The Leslie Mary Carter
  Charitable Trust
The Casey Trust
Cash for Kids Radio Clyde
Sir John Cass's Foundation
The Elizabeth Casson Trust
The Castang Foundation
The Catalyst Charitable Trust
The Catholic Charitable Trust
Catholic Foreign Missions
The Catholic Trust for England
  and Wales
The Cattanach Charitable Trust
The Joseph and Annie Cattle
  Trust
The Thomas Sivewright Catto
  Charitable Settlement
The Wilfrid and Constance
  Cave Foundation
The Cayo Foundation
The B G S Cayzer Charitable
  Trust
The Cazenove Charitable Trust
Celtic Charity Fund
The Gaynor Cemlyn-Jones
  Trust
The Pamela Champion
  Foundation
The Chapman Charitable Trust
John William Chapman's
  Charitable Trust
The Charities Advisory Trust
Charitworth Limited
The Charter 600 Charity

The Worshipful Company of
Chartered Accountants
General Charitable Trust
(also known as CALC)
The Chasah Trust
The Chelsea Square 1994
Trust
The Cheruby Trust
Cheshire Freemason's Charity
The Chetwode Foundation
Cheviot Asset Management
Charitable Trust
Childs Charitable Trust
The Childwick Trust
The Chipping Sodbury Town
Lands Charity
CHK Charities Limited
The Chownes Foundation
The Chrimes Family Charitable
Trust
The Christabella Charitable
Trust
Christadelphian Samaritan
Fund
Christian Aid
Christian Response to Eastern
Europe
Chrysalis Trust
The Church and Community
Fund
The Church Burgesses
Educational Foundation
Church Burgesses Trust
Church of Ireland Priorities
Fund
Church Urban Fund
City and County of Swansea
Welsh Church Act Fund
The City Bridge Trust
The City Educational Trust
Fund
Stephen Clark 1957
Charitable Trust
J A Clark Charitable Trust
The Hilda and Alice Clark
Charitable Trust
The Roger and Sarah Bancroft
Clark Charitable Trust
The Clarke Charitable
Settlement
The Cleopatra Trust
Lord Clinton's Charitable Trust
The Clore Duffield Foundation
Miss V L Clore's 1967
Charitable Trust
Closehelm Limited
Richard Cloudesley's Charity
The Clover Trust
The Robert Clutterbuck
Charitable Trust
Clydpride Ltd
The Coalfields Regeneration
Trust
The John Coates Charitable
Trust
The Cobtree Charity Trust Ltd

The Denise Cohen Charitable
Trust
The Vivienne and Samuel
Cohen Charitable Trust
The John S Cohen Foundation
The R and S Cohen
Foundation
The Colchester Catalyst
Charity
The Cole Charitable Trust
The Colefax Charitable Trust
The John and Freda Coleman
Charitable Trust
The George Henry Collins
Charity
The Sir Jeremiah Colman Gift
Trust
The Coltstaple Trust
Colwinston Charitable Trust
Colyer-Fergusson Charitable
Trust
Comic Relief
The Comino Foundation
The Compton Charitable Trust
The Congleton Inclosure Trust
The Conservation Foundation
The Consolidated Charities for
the Infirm Merchant
Taylors' Company
The Ernest Cook Trust
The Cooks Charity
The Catherine Cookson
Charitable Trust
Mabel Cooper Charity
The Alice Ellen Cooper Dean
Charitable Foundation
The Marjorie Coote Animal
Charity Trust
The Marjorie Coote Old
People's Charity
The Helen Jean Cope Trust
The J Reginald Corah
Foundation Fund
The Gershon Coren Charitable
Foundation (also known as
The Muriel and Gus Coren
Charitable Foundation)
The Cornwell Charitable Trust
The Sidney and Elizabeth
Corob Charitable Trust
The Corona Charitable Trust
The Costa Family Charitable
Trust
The Cotton Industry War
Memorial Trust
County Durham Community
Foundation
The Augustine Courtauld Trust
Coutts Charitable Foundation
The General Charities of the
City of Coventry
Coventry Building Society
Charitable Foundation
The John Cowan Foundation
Dudley and Geoffrey Cox
Charitable Trust

The Sir William Coxen Trust
Fund
The Lord Cozens-Hardy Trust
The Craignish Trust
The Craps Charitable Trust
Michael Crawford Children's
Charity
The Cray Trust
Creative Scotland
The Crerar Hotels Trust
The Crescent Trust
Cripplegate Foundation
The Violet and Milo Cripps
Charitable Trust
The Harry Crook Foundation
The Cross Trust
The Croydon Relief in Need
Charities
Cruden Foundation Ltd
The Ronald Cruickshanks
Foundation
The Culra Charitable Trust
Cumberland Building Society
Charitable Foundation
Cumbria Community
Foundation
The D J H Currie Memorial
Trust
The Dennis Curry Charitable
Trust
The Manny Cussins
Foundation
The Cwmbran Trust
Itzchok Meyer Cymerman Trust
Ltd
The D G Charitable Settlement
The D'Oyly Carte Charitable
Trust
Roald Dahl's Marvellous
Children's Charity
Daily Prayer Union Charitable
Trust Limited
The Daisy Trust
The Daiwa Anglo-Japanese
Foundation
The Dr and Mrs A Darlington
Charitable Trust
Baron Davenport's Charity
The Davidson (Nairn)
Charitable Trust
The Davidson Family
Charitable Trust
The Alderman Joe Davidson
Memorial Trust
Michael Davies Charitable
Settlement
The Gwendoline and Margaret
Davies Charity
The Hamilton Davies Trust
The Wilfrid Bruce Davis
Charitable Trust
Davis-Rubens Charitable Trust
The Dawe Charitable Trust
The De Brye Charitable Trust
The De Clermont Charitable
Company Ltd
The Deakin Charitable Trust

The Debmar Benevolent Trust
The Dellal Foundation
The Delves Charitable Trust
The Demigryphon Trust
The Denman Charitable Trust
Dentons UKMEA LLP
    Charitable Trust
The Earl of Derby's Charitable
    Trust
Derbyshire Community
    Foundation
The J N Derbyshire Trust
The Desmond Foundation
Devon Community Foundation
The Devon Educational Trust
The Duke of Devonshire's
    Charitable Trust
The Sandy Dewhirst Charitable
    Trust
The Laduma Dhamecha
    Charitable Trust
Diabetes UK
The Dibden Allotments Fund
Diced Cap Charity
The Dickon Trust
The Digbeth Trust Limited
Disability Aid Fund (The Roger
    and Jean Jefcoate Trust)
Dischma Charitable Trust
The DLM Charitable Trust
Louise Dobson Charitable
    Trust
The Derek and Eileen Dodgson
    Foundation
The Dollond Charitable Trust
Domepride Ltd
The Dorcas Trust
The Dorus Trust
The Doughty Charity Trust
Douglas Arter Foundation
The R M Douglas Charitable
    Trust
The Drapers' Charitable Fund
The Duis Charitable Trust
The Dulverton Trust
The P B Dumbell Charitable
    Trust
The Dumbreck Charity
Dunard Fund
The Dunn Family Charitable
    Trust
The W E Dunn Trust
Dushinsky Trust Ltd
The Dwek Family Charitable
    Trust
The Dyers' Company
    Charitable Trust
The Eagle Charity Trust
The Earley Charity
Earls Colne and Halstead
    Educational Charity
The Earmark Trust
East End Community
    Foundation
Eastern Counties Educational
    Trust Limited

The Sir John Eastwood
    Foundation
The Ebenezer Trust
The EBM Charitable Trust
Eden Arts Trust
EDF Energy Trust (EDFET)
The Gilbert and Eileen Edgar
    Foundation
Edinburgh Trust No 2 Account
Edinburgh Voluntary
    Organisations' Trust Funds
    (EVOT)
The William Edwards
    Educational Charity
The Elephant Trust
The George Elias Charitable
    Trust
The Gerald Palmer Eling Trust
    Company
The Wilfred and Elsie Elkes
    Charity Fund
The Maud Elkington Charitable
    Trust
The Ellerdale Trust
The John Ellerman Foundation
The Ellinson Foundation Ltd
The Edith Maud Ellis 1985
    Charitable Trust
James Ellis Charitable Trust
The Elmgrant Trust
The Elmley Foundation
The Vernon N Ely Charitable
    Trust
The Embleton Trust
Embrace the Middle East
The Emerton-Christie Charity
The Worshipful Company of
    Engineers Charitable Trust
    Fund
The Englefield Charitable Trust
The English Schools' Football
    Association
The Enkalon Foundation
Entindale Ltd
The Epigoni Trust
The Equitable Charitable Trust
The Equity Trust Fund
The Ericson Trust
The Erskine Cunningham Hill
    Trust
The Essendon Charitable Trust
Essex Community Foundation
The Essex Fairway Charitable
    Trust
The Essex Heritage Trust
Essex Provincial Charity Fund
The Essex Youth Trust
Euro Charity Trust
Sir John Evelyn's Charity
The Eventhall Family
    Charitable Trust
The Eveson Charitable Trust
The Beryl Evetts and Robert
    Luff Animal Welfare Trust
    Limited
The Exilarch's Foundation
The Expat Foundation

F C Charitable Trust
The F P Limited Charitable
    Trust
The Faber Charitable Trust
Esmée Fairbairn Foundation
The Fairway Trust
The Family Rich Charities Trust
The Lord Faringdon Charitable
    Trust
Samuel William Farmer Trust
The Farmers' Company
    Charitable Fund
The Thomas Farr Charity
Walter Farthing (Trust) Limited
The Fassnidge Memorial Trust
Joseph Fattorini Charitable
    Trust
Federation of Jewish Relief
    Organisations
The John Feeney Charitable
    Trust
The George Fentham
    Birmingham Charity
The A M Fenton Trust
Allan and Nesta Ferguson
    Charitable Settlement
The Doris Field Charitable
    Trust
Fife Council/Common Good
    Funds and Trusts
Firtree Trust
The Fishmongers' Company's
    Charitable Trust
The Fitton Trust
The Earl Fitzwilliam Charitable
    Trust
The Ian Fleming Charitable
    Trust
The Joyce Fletcher Charitable
    Trust
The Flow Foundation
The Gerald Fogel Charitable
    Trust
The Follett Trust
The Football Association
    National Sports Centre
    Trust
The Football Foundation
The Forbes Charitable
    Foundation
The Forces Trust (Working
    Name)
The Oliver Ford Charitable
    Trust
The Forest Hill Charitable Trust
The Foresters' Fund for
    Children
The Foresters' Charity
    Stewards UK Trust
Forever Manchester (The
    Community Foundation for
    Greater Manchester)
The Forman Hardy Charitable
    Trust
Gwyneth Forrester Trust
The Forte Charitable Trust
The Four Lanes Trust

The Four Winds Trust
The Foyle Foundation
The Isaac and Freda Frankel Memorial Charitable Trust
The Elizabeth Frankland Moore and Star Foundation
The Jill Franklin Trust
The Gordon Fraser Charitable Trust
The Hugh Fraser Foundation
The Joseph Strong Frazer Trust
The Louis and Valerie Freedman Charitable Settlement
The Freemasons' Grand Charity
The Charles S French Charitable Trust
The Anne French Memorial Trust
The Freshfield Foundation
The Freshgate Trust Foundation
The Friarsgate Trust
The Friends Hall Farm Street Trust
Friends Provident Charitable Foundation
The Frognal Trust
Maurice Fry Charitable Trust
The Fulmer Charitable Trust
Worshipful Company of Furniture Makers Charitable Fund
Gableholt Limited
The Galbraith Trust
The Gale Family Charity Trust
Gamlen Charitable Trust
The Gamma Trust
The Gannochy Trust
The Ganzoni Charitable Trust
The Worshipful Company of Gardeners of London
The Samuel Gardner Memorial Trust
The Garnett Charitable Trust
Garrick Charitable Trust
Garthgwynion Charities
Garvan Limited
The Gatsby Charitable Foundation
Gatwick Airport Community Trust
The Robert Gavron Charitable Trust
Thomas Betton's Charity for Pensions and Relief-in-Need
The General Nursing Council for England and Wales Trust
The Gibbs Charitable Trust
Simon Gibson Charitable Trust
The G C Gibson Charitable Trust
Lady Gibson's Charitable Trust
The Harvey and Hilary Gilbert Charitable Trust

The Girdlers' Company Charitable Trust
The B and P Glasser Charitable Trust
The Glass-House Trust
The Glastonbury Trust Limited
Global Care
Global Charities
Gloucestershire Community Foundation
Worshipful Company of Glovers of London Charity Fund
The GNC Trust
The Godinton Charitable Trust
The Sydney and Phyllis Goldberg Memorial Charitable Trust
The Golden Bottle Trust
The Jack Goldhill Charitable Trust
The Goldsmiths' Arts Trust Fund
The Goldsmiths' Company Charity
The Mike Gooley Trailfinders Charity
The Gosling Foundation Limited
The Gough Charitable Trust
The Gould Charitable Trust
The Grace Charitable Trust
A B Grace Trust
The Graff Foundation
E C Graham Belford Charitable Settlement
The Grahame Charitable Foundation Limited
The Granada Foundation
Grand Charitable Trust of the Order of Women Freemasons
The Grand Order of Water Rats' Charities Fund
The Grange Farm Centre Trust
Grantham Yorke Trust
The Gordon Gray Trust
The Gray Trust
The Great Stone Bridge Trust of Edenbridge
The Great Torrington Town Lands Charity
The Green Hall Foundation
Greenham Common Community Trust Limited
Greggs Foundation
The Gretna Charitable Trust
The Grocers' Charity
The M and R Gross Charities Limited
The GRP Charitable Trust
The David and Marie Grumitt Foundation
The Bishop of Guildford's Foundation
The Guildry Incorporation of Perth

The Walter Guinness Charitable Trust
The Gunter Charitable Trust
The Gur Trust
The Gurney Charitable Trust
Dr Guthrie's Association
The H and M Charitable Trust
H C D Memorial Fund
The H P Charitable Trust
The Hackney Parochial Charities
The Hadfield Trust
The Hadley Trust
The Hadrian Trust
The Alfred Haines Charitable Trust
E F and M G Hall Charitable Trust
The Edith Winifred Hall Charitable Trust
Robert Hall Charity
The Hamamelis Trust
Hamilton Wallace Trust
Paul Hamlyn Foundation
Hampshire and Isle of Wight Community Foundation
Hampton Fuel Allotment Charity
The W A Handley Charitable Trust
Beatrice Hankey Foundation Limited
The Hanley Trust (1987)
The Kathleen Hannay Memorial Charity
The Doughty Hanson Charitable Foundation
Lord Hanson Foundation
Miss K M Harbinson's Charitable Trust
The Harborne Parish Lands Charity
The Harbour Charitable Trust
The Harbour Foundation
The Harding Trust
William Harding's Charity
The Hare of Steep Charitable Trust
The Harebell Centenary Fund
The Kenneth Hargreaves Charitable Trust
The Harpur Trust
The Harris Charity
The Harrison and Potter Trust
The John Harrison Charitable Trust
The Peter Harrison Foundation
The Spencer Hart Charitable Trust
The Hartley Charitable Trust
William Geoffrey Harvey's Discretionary Settlement
Haskel Family Foundation
The Hathaway Trust
The Maurice Hatter Foundation
The M A Hawe Settlement

The Hawthorne Charitable
Trust
The Dorothy Hay-Bolton
Charitable Trust
The Headley Trust
Headley-Pitt Charitable Trust
Heart of England Community
Foundation
The Heathcoat Trust
Heathside Charitable Trust
The Charlotte Heber-Percy
Charitable Trust
The Hedley Denton Charitable
Trust
The Hedley Foundation
The H J Heinz Company
Limited Charitable Trust
The Hellenic Foundation
The Michael Heller Charitable
Foundation
The Simon Heller Charitable
Settlement
The Hemby Trust
The Christina Mary Hendrie
Trust for Scottish and
Canadian Charities
Henley Educational Trust
(formerley Henley
Educational Charity)
Esther Hennell Charitable
Trust
The G D Herbert Charitable
Trust
The Anne Herd Memorial Trust
The Herefordshire Historic
Churches Trust
The Heritage of London Trust
Ltd
The Hesed Trust
The Hesslewood Children's
Trust (Hull Seamen's and
General Orphanage)
Hexham and Newcastle
Diocesan Trust (1947)
The P and C Hickinbotham
Charitable Trust
The Higgs Charitable Trust
Alan Edward Higgs Charity
The High Sheriff's Police Trust
for the County of West
Midlands (Building Blocks)
Highcroft Charitable Trust
The Charles Littlewood Hill
Trust
The Hillingdon Partnership
Trust
The Hilmarnan Charitable Trust
Lady Hind Trust
The Hiscox Foundation
The Hitchin Educational
Foundation
The Eleemosynary Charity of
William Hobbayne
Hobson Charity Limited
Matthew Hodder Charitable
Trust

The Sir Julian Hodge
Charitable Trust
The J G Hogg Charitable Trust
The Holden Charitable Trust
John Holford's Charity
The Hollick Family Charitable
Trust
The Dorothy Holmes Charitable
Trust
The Holst Foundation
The Edward Holt Trust
The Holywood Trust
The Homelands Charitable
Trust
The Homestead Charitable
Trust
Sir Harold Hood's Charitable
Trust
Hope for Youth (NI)
The Hope Trust
HopMarket Charity
The Cuthbert Horn Trust
The Antony Hornby Charitable
Trust
The Horne Foundation
The Horne Trust
The Worshipful Company of
Horners' Charitable Trusts
The Hornsey Parochial
Charities
The Hospital of God at
Greatham
The Hospital Saturday Fund
Houblon-Norman/George Fund
The House of Industry Estate
The Reta Lila Howard
Foundation
The Daniel Howard Trust
The Huddersfield Common
Good Trust
The Hudson Foundation
The Huggard Charitable Trust
The Geoffrey C Hughes
Charitable Trust
The Hull and East Riding
Charitable Trust
Hulme Trust Estates
(Educational)
Human Relief Foundation
The Humanitarian Trust
The Michael and Shirley Hunt
Charitable Trust
The Hunter Foundation
Miss Agnes H Hunter's Trust
The Huntingdon Foundation
Huntingdon Freemen's Trust
Hurdale Charity Limited
The Nani Huyu Charitable Trust
The P Y N and B Hyams Trust
The Hyde Charitable Trust
The Idlewild Trust
The Iliffe Family Charitable
Trust
The Indigo Trust
The Ingram Trust
The Inlight Trust
The Inman Charity

The Inner London Magistrates
Court Poor Box and Feeder
Charity
The Ireland Fund of Great
Britain
The Irish Youth Foundation
(UK) Ltd (incorporating The
Lawlor Foundation)
The Ironmongers' Foundation
The Charles Irving Charitable
Trust
Irwin Trust
The ISA Charity
The Isaacs Charitable Trust
The J Isaacs Charitable Trust
The Isle of Anglesey Charitable
Trust
The ITF Seafarers Trust
The J M K Charitable Trust
The J R S S T Charitable Trust
C Richard Jackson Charitable
Trust
Elizabeth Jackson Charitable
Trust
The Ruth and Lionel Jacobson
Trust (Second Fund) No 2
Jaffe Family Relief Fund
John James Bristol Foundation
The Susan and Stephen
James Charitable
Settlement
The James Trust
The Jarman Charitable Trust
The John Jarrold Trust
JCA Charitable Foundation
The Jeffrey Charitable Trust
The Jenour Foundation
Jesus Hospital Charity
Jewish Child's Day
The Jewish Youth Fund
The Harold Joels Charitable
Trust
The Nicholas Joels Charitable
Trust
The Norman Joels Charitable
Trust
The Elton John Aids
Foundation
The Lillie Johnson Charitable
Trust
The Johnson Foundation
The Reginald Johnson
Foundation
The Johnson Wax Ltd
Charitable Trust
The Joicey Trust
The Jones 1986 Charitable
Trust
The Marjorie and Geoffrey
Jones Charitable Trust
The Jordan Charitable
Foundation
The J E Joseph Charitable
Fund
The Lady Eileen Joseph
Foundation

The Josephs Family Charitable
Trust
JTH Charitable Trust
The Jungels-Winkler Charitable
Foundation
The Anton Jurgens Charitable
Trust
The Bernard Kahn Charitable
Trust
The Stanley Kalms Foundation
The Karenza Foundation
The Boris Karloff Charitable
Foundation
The Ian Karten Charitable
Trust
The Kasner Charitable Trust
The Kathleen Trust
The Michael and Ilse Katz
Foundation
The Katzauer Charitable
Settlement
The C S Kaufman Charitable
Trust
The Geoffrey John Kaye
Charitable Foundation
The Emmanuel Kaye
Foundation
Kelsick's Educational
Foundation
The KempWelch Charitable
Trust
The Kay Kendall Leukaemia
Fund
The John Thomas Kennedy
Charitable Foundation
The Kennedy Charitable
Foundation
The Nancy Kenyon Charitable
Trust
Keren Association
Kermaville Ltd
The Peter Kershaw Trust
The Ursula Keyes Trust
The Robert Kiln Charitable
Trust
The King/Cullimore Charitable
Trust
The Kingsbury Charity
The Mary Kinross Charitable
Trust
Kirkley Poor's Lands Estate
The Richard Kirkman
Charitable Trust
Kirschel Foundation
Robert Kitchin (Saddlers'
Company)
Ernest Kleinwort Charitable
Trust
The Marina Kleinwort
Charitable Trust
The Kobler Trust
The Kohn Foundation
The Kreditor Charitable Trust
The Kreitman Foundation
The Neil Kreitman Foundation
The Heinz, Anna and Carol
Kroch Foundation

The Kyte Charitable Trust
The Late Sir Pierce Lacy
Charity Trust
John Laing Charitable Trust
Maurice and Hilda Laing
Charitable Trust
The Christopher Laing
Foundation
The Kirby Laing Foundation
The Martin Laing Foundation
The Beatrice Laing Trust
The Lambert Charitable Trust
Duchy of Lancaster Benevolent
Fund
The Lancaster Foundation
The Allen Lane Foundation
Langdale Trust
The Langley Charitable Trust
The Langtree Trust
The LankellyChase Foundation
The R J Larg Family Charitable
Trust
Largsmount Ltd
The Lark Trust
Laslett's (Hinton) Charity
The Lauffer Family Charitable
Foundation
The Kathleen Laurence Trust
The Law Society Charity
The Edgar E Lawley Foundation
The Herd Lawson and Muriel
Lawson Charitable Trust
The Lawson Beckman
Charitable Trust
The Raymond and Blanche
Lawson Charitable Trust
The Leach Fourteenth Trust
The David Lean Foundation
The Leathersellers' Company
Charitable Fund
The Arnold Lee Charitable
Trust
The William Leech Charity
The Lord Mayor of Leeds
Appeal Fund
Leeds Building Society
Charitable Foundation
The Kennedy Leigh Charitable
Trust
Morris Leigh Foundation
The Leigh Trust
Mrs Vera Leigh's Charity
P Leigh-Bramwell Trust 'E'
The Lennox and Wyfold
Foundation
The Erica Leonard Trust
The Leonard Trust
The Mark Leonard Trust
Lesley Lesley and Mutter Trust
The Leverhulme Trade
Charities Trust
Lord Leverhulme's Charitable
Trust
The Joseph Levy Charitable
Foundation
The John Spedan Lewis
Foundation

The Sir Edward Lewis
Foundation
John Lewis Partnership
General Community Fund
Lichfield Conduit Lands
Lifeline 4 Kids
The Linbury Trust
Lindale Educational
Foundation
The Linden Charitable Trust
The Enid Linder Foundation
The Linmardon Trust
The Ruth and Stuart Lipton
Charitable Trust
The Lister Charitable Trust
Frank Litchfield Charitable
Trust
The Andrew and Mary
Elizabeth Little Charitable
Trust
The Second Joseph Aaron
Littman Foundation
The George John and Sheilah
Livanos Charitable Trust
Liverpool Charity and Voluntary
Services
Liverpool Sailors' Home Trust
The Elaine and Angus Lloyd
Charitable Trust
The Charles Lloyd Foundation
Lloyd's Charities Trust
Lloyds Bank Foundation for
England and Wales
Lloyds Bank Foundation for
Northern Ireland
Lloyds Bank Foundation for the
Channel Islands
Lloyds TSB Foundation for
Scotland
The Locker Foundation
The Loftus Charitable Trust
The Lolev Charitable Trust
The Trust for London
The London Community
Foundation
The London Housing
Foundation
The London Law Trust
The William and Katherine
Longman Trust
The Loseley and Guildway
Charitable Trust
The Lotus Foundation
The C L Loyd Charitable Trust
LSA Charitable Trust
The Marie Helen Luen
Charitable Trust
Robert Luff Foundation Ltd
Henry Lumley Charitable Trust
C F Lunoe Trust Fund
The Ruth and Jack Lunzer
Charitable Trust
Lord and Lady Lurgan Trust
The Lyndhurst Trust
The Lynn Foundation
The Lynwood Trust
John Lyon's Charity

The Lyons Charitable Trust
The Sir Jack Lyons Charitable
Trust
The Lyras Family Charitable
Trust
Sylvanus Lyson's Charity
The M and C Trust
The M K Charitable Trust
The Madeline Mabey Trust
The E M MacAndrew Trust
The R S Macdonald Charitable
Trust
Macdonald-Buchanan
Charitable Trust
The Mackay and Brewer
Charitable Trust
The Mackintosh Foundation
The MacRobert Trust
The Magen Charitable Trust
Man Group plc Charitable
Trust
The Manackerman Charitable
Trust
Manchester Airport Community
Trust Fund
The Manchester Guardian
Society Charitable Trust
Lord Mayor of Manchester's
Charity Appeal Trust
Mandeville Trust
The Manifold Charitable Trust
W M Mann Foundation
The Leslie and Lilian Manning
Trust
Marbeh Torah Trust
Marchig Animal Welfare Trust
The Stella and Alexander
Margulies Charitable Trust
Market Harborough and The
Bowdens Charity
The Ann and David Marks
Foundation
The Hilda and Samuel Marks
Foundation
J P Marland Charitable Trust
The Michael Marsh Charitable
Trust
The Marsh Christian Trust
The Charlotte Marshall
Charitable Trust
The Jim Marshall Charitable
Trust
The Nora Joan Marshall
Charitable Trust
The D G Marshall of
Cambridge Trust
Marshgate Charitable
Settlement
Sir George Martin Trust
The Mason Porter Charitable
Trust
The Mathew Trust
The Matt 6.3 Charitable Trust
The Violet Mauray Charitable
Trust
The Maxwell Family Foundation
Evelyn May Trust

The Mayfield Valley Arts Trust
Mazars Charitable Trust
The McDougall Trust
The McKenna Charitable Trust
The Helen Isabella McMorran
Charitable Foundation
The James Frederick and Ethel
Anne Measures Charity
The Medlock Charitable Trust
The Anthony and Elizabeth
Mellows Charitable
Settlement
Melow Charitable Trust
The Mercers' Charitable
Foundation
The Merchant Taylors'
Company Charities Fund
The Merchant Venturers'
Charity
The Merchants' House of
Glasgow
The Mersey Docks and
Harbour Company
Charitable Fund
Community Foundation for
Merseyside
The Zachary Merton and
George Woofindin
Convalescent Trust
The Tony Metherell Charitable
Trust
The Metropolitan Drinking
Fountain and Cattle Trough
Association
The Mickel Fund
Gerald Micklem Charitable
Trust
Midhurst Pensions Trust
The Migraine Trust
Miles Trust for the Putney and
Roehampton Community
Millennium Stadium Charitable
Trust
The Hugh and Mary Miller
Bequest Trust
The Ronald Miller Foundation
The Millfield Trust
The Millhouses Charitable
Trust
The Millichope Foundation
The Mills Charity
The Millward Charitable Trust
The Clare Milne Trust
Milton Keynes Community
Foundation
The Edgar Milward Charity
The Peter Minet Trust
The Minos Trust
The Mirfield Educational
Charity
The Mirianog Trust
The Laurence Misener
Charitable Trust
The Mishcon Family Charitable
Trust
The Misselbrook Trust
The Esmé Mitchell Trust

Keren Mitzvah Trust
The Mizpah Trust
The Mobbs Memorial Trust Ltd
The Modiano Charitable Trust
The Moette Charitable Trust
The Mole Charitable Trust
The D C Moncrieff Charitable
Trust
Monmouthshire County Council
Welsh Church Act Fund
The Montague Thompson
Coon Charitable Trust
The Colin Montgomerie
Charitable Foundation
The Monument Trust
The Morel Charitable Trust
The Morgan Charitable
Foundation
The Mr and Mrs J T Morgan
Foundation
Morgan Stanley International
Foundation
The Oliver Morland Charitable
Trust
The Bernard Morris Charitable
Trust
The Morris Charitable Trust
The Willie and Mabel Morris
Charitable Trust
The Peter Morrison Charitable
Foundation
The Stanley Morrison
Charitable Trust
Vyoel Moshe Charitable Trust
The Moss Charitable Trust
The Robert and Margaret
Moss Charitable Trust
The Moss Family Charitable
Trust
Mosselson Charitable Trust
The Mount Everest Foundation
The Edwina Mountbatten Trust
Mountbatten Festival of Music
The Mountbatten Memorial
Trust
Mrs Waterhouse Charitable
Trust
The Mugdock Children's Trust
The Mulberry Trust
The Edith Murphy Foundation
The Mushroom Fund
The Music Sales Charitable
Trust
Muslim Hands
The Mutual Trust Group
The Kitty and Daniel Nabarro
Charitable Trust
The Nadezhda Charitable Trust
The Naggar Charitable Trust
The Eleni Nakou Foundation
The Janet Nash Charitable
Settlement
The National Churches Trust
National Committee of the
Women's World Day of
Prayer for England and
Wales and Northern Ireland

The National Hockey
Foundation
The National Manuscripts
Conservation Trust
Needham Market and Barking
Welfare Charities
The Worshipful Company of
Needlemakers' Charitable
Fund
The Neighbourly Charitable
Trust
The James Neill Trust Fund
Nemoral Ltd
Network for Social Change
The Newcomen Collett
Foundation
Alderman Newton's
Educational Foundation
The Chevras Ezras Nitzrochim
Trust
The Noon Foundation
The Norda Trust
Norie Charitable Trust
Normalyn Charitable Trust
The Norman Family Charitable
Trust
The Duncan Norman Trust
Fund
The Normanby Charitable Trust
The North West Cancer
Research Fund
The Northampton Municipal
Church Charities
The Northampton Queen's
Institute Relief in Sickness
Fund
The Earl of Northampton's
Charity
The Northcott Devon Medical
Foundation
The Community Foundation for
Northern Ireland
The Northern Rock Foundation
The Northmoor Trust
The Northumberland Village
Homes Trust
The Northwood Charitable
Trust
The Norton Foundation
The Norwich Church of England
Young Men's Society
The Norwich Town Close
Estate Charity
The Norwood and Newton
Settlement
The Noswad Charity
The Nottingham General
Dispensary
The Nottingham Gordon
Memorial Trust for Boys
and Girls
Nottinghamshire Community
Foundation
The Nottinghamshire Historic
Churches Trust
The Nottinghamshire Miners'
Welfare Trust Fund

Novi Most International
The Father O'Mahoney
Memorial Trust
The Sir Peter O'Sullevan
Charitable Trust
The Oak Trust
The Oakdale Trust
The Oakmoor Charitable Trust
The Odin Charitable Trust
The Ofenheim Charitable Trust
Ogilvie Charities Deed No.2
(including the Charity of
Mary Catherine Ford Smith)
The Ogle Christian Trust
Oglesby Charitable Trust
The Oikonomia Trust
Oizer Charitable Trust
The Old Broad Street Charity
Trust
The John Oldacre Foundation
The Oldham Foundation
The Olga Charitable Trust
Open Gate
The Raymond Oppenheimer
Foundation
Ormonde Foundation
The Ormsby Charitable Trust
The Ouseley Trust
The Owen Family Trust
Oxfam (GB)
The Oxfordshire Community
Foundation
The P F Charitable Trust
Padwa Charitable Foundation
The Paget Charitable Trust
The Palmer Foundation
The Panacea Society
Panton Trust
The Paragon Trust
The Park House Charitable
Trust
The Frank Parkinson
Agricultural Trust
The Samuel and Freda
Parkinson Charitable Trust
The Parthenon Trust
The Constance Paterson
Charitable Trust
The Patrick Charitable Trust
The Jack Patston Charitable
Trust
Paycare Charity Trust
The Payne Charitable Trust
The Harry Payne Trust
The Susanna Peake Charitable
Trust
The Pedmore Sporting Club
Trust Fund
The Dowager Countess
Eleanor Peel Trust
The Pennycress Trust
The Performing Right Society
Foundation
The Persson Charitable Trust
The Persula Foundation
The Jack Petchey Foundation
The Petplan Charitable Trust

The Philips and Rubens
Charitable Trust
The Phillips Charitable Trust
The Phillips Family Charitable
Trust
Philological Foundation
The David Pickford Charitable
Foundation
The Pilgrim Trust
The Cecil Pilkington Charitable
Trust
The Pilkington Charities Fund
The Austin and Hope
Pilkington Trust
The Sir Harry Pilkington Trust
The Col W W Pilkington Will
Trusts The General Charity
Fund
The DLA Piper Charitable Trust
The Worshipful Company of
Plaisterers Charitable Trust
The Platinum Trust
Polden-Puckham Charitable
Foundation
The George and Esme Pollitzer
Charitable Settlement
The J S F Pollitzer Charitable
Settlement
The Ponton House Trust
Edith and Ferdinand Porjes
Charitable Trust
The John Porter Charitable
Trust
The Porter Foundation
The Portrack Charitable Trust
The J E Posnansky Charitable
Trust
The Mary Potter Convent
Hospital Trust
The David and Elaine Potter
Foundation
The Powell Foundation
The W L Pratt Charitable Trust
Premierquote Ltd
Premishlaner Charitable Trust
The Lucy Price Relief-in-Need
Charity
Sir John Priestman Charity
Trust
The Primrose Trust
The Prince of Wales's
Charitable Foundation
Prison Service Charity Fund
The Privy Purse Charitable
Trust
The Proven Family Trust
The Provincial Grand Charity of
the Province of Derbyshire
The Puebla Charitable Trust
The Richard and Christine
Purchas Charitable Trust
The Puri Foundation
Mr and Mrs J A Pye's
Charitable Settlement
Quartet Community Foundation
Queen Mary's Roehampton
Trust

The Queen's Silver Jubilee
Trust
Quothquan Trust
R S Charitable Trust
The R V W Trust
The Monica Rabagliati
Charitable Trust
Rachel Charitable Trust
The Mr and Mrs Philip
Rackham Charitable Trust
Richard Radcliffe Charitable
Trust
The Radcliffe Trust
The Ragdoll Foundation
The Rainford Trust
The Peggy Ramsay Foundation
The Joseph and Lena Randall
Charitable Trust
The Rank Foundation Limited
The Fanny Rapaport Charitable
Settlement
The Ratcliff Foundation
The Ratcliff Pension Charity
The Ratcliffe Charitable Trust
The Eleanor Rathbone
Charitable Trust
The Sigrid Rausing Trust
The Ravensdale Trust
The Rawdon-Smith Trust
The Rayden Charitable Trust
The Roger Raymond Charitable
Trust
The Rayne Foundation
The Rayne Trust
The Sir James Reckitt Charity
The Red Arrows Trust
The Red Rose Charitable Trust
The C A Redfern Charitable
Foundation
The Reed Foundation
Richard Reeve's Foundation
The Max Reinhardt Charitable
Trust
Relief Fund for Romania
Limited
The Rest Harrow Trust
Reuben Foundation
The Nathaniel Reyner Trust
Fund
The Rhododendron Trust
The Sir Cliff Richard Charitable
Trust
The Clive Richards Charity
The Violet M Richards Charity
The Richmond Parish Lands
Charity
Ridgesave Limited
The Ripple Effect Foundation
The Sir John Ritblat Family
Foundation
The River Trust
Thomas Roberts Trust
The Robertson Trust
The Rochester Bridge Trust
The Rock Foundation
The Rock Solid Trust
The Rofeh Trust

Rokach Family Charitable Trust
The Helen Roll Charitable
Trust
The Sir James Roll Charitable
Trust
The Roman Research Trust
The C A Rookes Charitable
Trust
The Rosca Trust
The Cecil Rosen Foundation
Rosetrees Trust
The Rothermere Foundation
The Rotherwick Foundation
The Roughley Charitable Trust
Mrs Gladys Row Fogo
Charitable Trust
Rowanville Ltd
The Christopher Rowbotham
Charitable Trust
The Rowing Foundation
The Rowlands Trust
The Joseph Rowntree
Charitable Trust
The Joseph Rowntree
Foundation
Joseph Rowntree Reform Trust
Limited
Royal Artillery Charitable Fund
Royal Docks Trust (London)
Royal Masonic Trust for Girls
and Boys
The Rubin Foundation
William Arthur Rudd Memorial
Trust
The Russell Trust
The J S and E C Rymer
Charitable Trust
S O Charitable Trust
The Jeremy and John Sacher
Charitable Trust
The Michael Harry Sacher
Trust
The Sackler Trust
The Ruzin Sadagora Trust
The Saddlers' Company
Charitable Fund
Erach and Roshan Sadri
Foundation
The Saga Charitable Trust
The Jean Sainsbury Animal
Welfare Trust
The Alan and Babette
Sainsbury Charitable Fund
The Sainsbury Family
Charitable Trusts
The Saintbury Trust
The Saints and Sinners Trust
The Salt Foundation
The Salt Trust
Basil Samuel Charitable Trust
The M J Samuel Charitable
Trust
The Peter Samuel Charitable
Trust
The Samworth Foundation
The Sandra Charitable Trust

Santander UK Foundation
Limited
The Scarfe Charitable Trust
The Schapira Charitable Trust
The Schmidt-Bodner Charitable
Trust
The R H Scholes Charitable
Trust
The Schreib Trust
The Schreiber Charitable Trust
The Schuster Charitable Trust
Foundation Scotland
The Francis C Scott Charitable
Trust
The Frieda Scott Charitable
Trust
The Sir James and Lady Scott
Trust
The Scott Trust Foundation
The Storrow Scott Will Trust
Scottish Coal Industry Special
Welfare Fund
The Scottish International
Education Trust
The Scouloudi Foundation
Seafarers UK (King George's
Fund for Sailors)
Seamen's Hospital Society
The Searchlight Electric
Charitable Trust
The Searle Charitable Trust
The Samuel Sebba Charitable
Trust
The Seedfield Trust
Leslie Sell Charitable Trust
The Ayrton Senna Foundation
The Seven Fifty Trust
The Cyril Shack Trust
The Jean Shanks Foundation
The Shanti Charitable Trust
ShareGift (The Orr Mackintosh
Foundation)
The Linley Shaw Foundation
The Shears Foundation
The Sheepdrove Trust
The Sheffield and District
Hospital Services
Charitable Fund
The Sheldon Trust
The Patricia and Donald
Shepherd Charitable Trust
The Sylvia and Colin Shepherd
Charitable Trust
The Archie Sherman Cardiff
Foundation
The Archie Sherman Charitable
Trust
The R C Sherriff Trust
The Shetland Charitable Trust
SHINE (Support and Help in
Education)
The Barnett and Sylvia Shine
No 2 Charitable Trust
The Bassil Shippam and
Alsford Trust
The Shipwrights' Company
Charitable Fund

The Shirley Foundation

Shlomo Memorial Fund Limited

The J A Shone Memorial Trust

Community Foundation for Shropshire and Telford

The Barbara A Shuttleworth Memorial Trust

The Mary Elizabeth Siebel Charity

David and Jennifer Sieff Charitable Trust

The Julius Silman Charitable Trust

The Leslie Silver Charitable Trust

The Simpson Education and Conservation Trust

The Simpson Foundation

The Huntly and Margery Sinclair Charitable Trust

Sino-British Fellowship Trust

The Skelton Bounty

The Charles Skey Charitable Trust

Skipton Building Society Charitable Foundation

The John Slater Foundation

The SMB Charitable Trust

The Mrs Smith and Mount Trust

The N Smith Charitable Settlement

The E H Smith Charitable Trust

The Smith Charitable Trust

The Henry Smith Charity

The Leslie Smith Foundation

The Martin Smith Foundation

The Stanley Smith UK Horticultural Trust

The Snowball Trust

The Sobell Foundation

The Solo Charitable Settlement

Dr Richard Solomon's Charitable Trust

The E C Sosnow Charitable Trust

The Souter Charitable Trust

The South Square Trust

The Stephen R and Philippa H Southall Charitable Trust

The W F Southall Trust

The Southwold Trust

The Sovereign Health Care Charitable Trust

Sparquote Limited

The Spear Charitable Trust

The Jessie Spencer Trust

The Ralph and Irma Sperring Charity

The Spielman Charitable Trust

The Spoore, Merry and Rixman Foundation

Springfields Employees' Medical Research and Charity Trust Fund

Springrule Limited

The Spurrell Charitable Trust

The Geoff and Fiona Squire Foundation

St Hilda's Trust

St James' Trust Settlement

Sir Walter St John's Educational Charity

St Michael's and All Saints' Charities Relief Branch (The Church Houses Relief in Need Charity)

The Late St Patrick White Charitable Trust

St Teilo's Trust

The Stanley Foundation Ltd

The Stanton Ballard Charitable Trust

The Staples Trust

The Star Charitable Trust

The Peter Stebbings Memorial Charity

The Steinberg Family Charitable Trust

The Hugh Stenhouse Foundation

The Stephen Barry Charitable Trust

The Sigmund Sternberg Charitable Foundation

Stervon Ltd

The Stevenage Community Trust

The June Stevens Foundation

The Steventon Allotments and Relief-in-Need Charity

The Stewards' Charitable Trust

The Stewards' Company Limited (incorporating the J W Laing Trust and the J W Laing Biblical Scholarship Trust)

Sir Halley Stewart Trust

The Stobart Newlands Charitable Trust

The Edward Stocks-Massey Bequest Fund

The Stokenchurch Educational Charity

The Stoller Charitable Trust

The M J C Stone Charitable Trust

The Samuel Storey Family Charitable Trust

Peter Stormonth Darling Charitable Trust

The Strangward Trust

The Strasser Foundation

Stratford upon Avon Town Trust

The W O Street Charitable Foundation

The Sudborough Foundation

The Suffolk Historic Churches Trust

The Summerfield Charitable Trust

The Surrey Historic Buildings Trust Ltd

The Sussex Historic Churches Trust

The Sutasoma Trust

Swansea and Brecon Diocesan Board of Finance Limited

Swimathon Foundation

The John Swire (1989) Charitable Trust

The Swire Charitable Trust

The Adrian Swire Charitable Trust

The Hugh and Ruby Sykes Charitable Trust

The Charles and Elsie Sykes Trust

The Sylvanus Charitable Trust

The Stella Symons Charitable Trust

The Tabeel Trust

The Tajtelbaum Charitable Trust

Tallow Chandlers Benevolent Fund

The Tangent Charitable Trust

The Lady Tangye Charitable Trust

The David Tannen Charitable Trust

The Tanner Trust

The Lili Tapper Charitable Foundation

The Mrs A Lacy Tate Trust

The Tay Charitable Trust

Humphrey Richardson Taylor Charitable Trust

The Connie and Albert Taylor Charitable Trust

The Cyril Taylor Charitable Trust

A P Taylor Trust

Tearfund

The Tedworth Charitable Trust

Tees Valley Community Foundation

The Templeton Goodwill Trust

Tesco Charity Trust

The C Paul Thackray General Charitable Trust

The Thames Wharf Charity

The John P. Gommes Foundation

The Thistle Trust

The Loke Wan Tho Memorial Foundation

The Thomas Lilley Memorial Trust

The Arthur and Margaret Thompson Charitable Trust

The Thompson Family Charitable Trust

The Len Thomson Charitable Trust

The Sue Thomson Foundation

The Sir Jules Thorn Charitable Trust

The Thornton Foundation
The Thornton Trust
The Thousandth Man –
    Richard Burns Charitable
    Trust
The Three Guineas Trust
The Three Oaks Trust
The Thriplow Charitable Trust
The Tinsley Foundation
The Tisbury Telegraph Trust
The Tobacco Pipe Makers and
    Tobacco Trade Benevolent
    Fund
The Tolkien Trust
Tollemache (Buckminster)
    Charitable Trust
Tomchei Torah Charitable
    Trust
The Tompkins Foundation
The Tory Family Foundation
Tottenham Grammar School
    Foundation
The Tower Hill Trust
The Towry Law Charitable Trust
    (also known as the Castle
    Educational Trust)
The Mayor of Trafford's Charity
    Fund
The Constance Travis
    Charitable Trust
The Treeside Trust
The Triangle Trust (1949) Fund
The True Colours Trust
Truedene Co. Ltd
The Truemark Trust
Truemart Limited
Trumros Limited
Tudor Rose Ltd
The Tudor Trust
The Tufton Charitable Trust
Tuixen Foundation
The R D Turner Charitable
    Trust
The Douglas Turner Trust
The Florence Turner Trust
The G J W Turner Trust
Miss S M Tutton Charitable
    Trust
The TUUT Charitable Trust
Community Foundation Serving
    Tyne and Wear and
    Northumberland
Trustees of Tzedakah
Ulster Garden Villages Ltd
Ultach Trust
The Ulverscroft Foundation
Ulverston Town Lands Charity
The Underwood Trust
The Union of Orthodox Hebrew
    Congregation
The United Society for the
    Propagation of the Gospel
The David Uri Memorial Trust
Uxbridge United Welfare Trust
Vale of Glamorgan – Welsh
    Church Fund
The Valentine Charitable Trust

The Van Neste Foundation
Mrs Maud Van Norden's
    Charitable Foundation
The Vandervell Foundation
The Vardy Foundation
The Variety Club Children's
    Charity
Veneziana Fund
The Verdon-Smith Family
    Charitable Settlement
Victoria Homes Trust
The Nigel Vinson Charitable
    Trust
The William and Ellen Vinten
    Trust
The Vintners' Company
    Charitable Foundation
Vintners' Gifts Charity
Vivdale Ltd
The Viznitz Foundation
Wade's Charity
The Scurrah Wainwright Charity
Wakeham Trust
The Community Foundation in
    Wales
Wales Council for Voluntary
    Action
Robert and Felicity Waley-
    Cohen Charitable Trust
The Thomas Wall Trust
The F J Wallis Charitable
    Settlement
War on Want
The Ward Blenkinsop Trust
The George Ward Charitable
    Trust
The Barbara Ward Children's
    Foundation
G R Waters Charitable Trust
    2000
The Wates Foundation
The Howard Watson Symington
    Memorial Charity
John Watson's Trust
Waynflete Charitable Trust
Weatherley Charitable Trust
The Weavers' Company
    Benevolent Fund
The Weinberg Foundation
The Weinstein Foundation
The Wellcome Trust
Welsh Church Fund Dyfed
    area (Carmarthenshire,
    Ceredigion and
    Pembrokeshire)
The Welton Foundation
The Wessex Youth Trust
The West Derby Wastelands
    Charity
West London Synagogue
    Charitable Fund
West Yorkshire Police
    Community Trust
The Westcroft Trust
The Westminster Foundation
The Garfield Weston
    Foundation

The Whitaker Charitable Trust
The Colonel W H Whitbread
    Charitable Trust
The Simon Whitbread
    Charitable Trust
The Whitecourt Charitable
    Trust
The Norman Whiteley Trust
The Whitley Animal Protection
    Trust
The Whittlesey Charity
The Lionel Wigram Memorial
    Trust
The Felicity Wilde Charitable
    Trust
The Will Charitable Trust
The Charity of William Williams
The Kay Williams Charitable
    Foundation
The Williams Family Charitable
    Trust
The HDH Wills 1965
    Charitable Trust
The Dame Violet Wills Will
    Trust
The Wilmcote Charitrust
David Wilson Foundation
The Wilson Foundation
J and J R Wilson Trust
The Community Foundation for
    Wiltshire and Swindon
The Benjamin Winegarten
    Charitable Trust
The Harold Hyam Wingate
    Foundation
The Francis Winham
    Foundation
Wirral Mayor's Charity
The James Wise Charitable
    Trust
The Michael and Anna Wix
    Charitable Trust
The Wixamtree Trust
The Woburn 1986 Charitable
    Trust
The Maurice Wohl Charitable
    Foundation
The Charles Wolfson
    Charitable Trust
The James Wood Bequest
    Fund
Woodlands Green Ltd
Woodlands Trust
Woodroffe Benton Foundation
The Woodward Charitable
    Trust
Worcester Municipal Charities
The Worcestershire and
    Dudley Historic Churches
    Trust
The Wragge and Co. Charitable
    Trust
The Diana Edgson Wright
    Charitable Trust
The Matthews Wrightson
    Charity Trust

Miss E B Wrightson's
  Charitable Settlement
Wychdale Ltd
Wychville Ltd
The Wyndham Charitable Trust
The Wyseliot Charitable Trust
The Xerox (UK) Trust
The Yapp Charitable Trust
The Dennis Alan Yardy
  Charitable Trust
The W Wing Yip and Brothers
  Foundation
Yorkshire Agricultural Society
The South Yorkshire
  Community Foundation
The Yorkshire Dales
  Millennium Trust
The John Young Charitable
  Settlement
The William Allen Young
  Charitable Trust
The John K Young Endowment
  Fund
Zephyr Charitable Trust
The Marjorie and Arnold Ziff
  Charitable Foundation
Stephen Zimmerman
  Charitable Trust
The Zochonis Charitable Trust
Zurich Community Trust (UK)
  Limited

Campaigning

The 1970 Trust
The A B Charitable Trust
A W Charitable Trust
ABF The Soldiers' Charity
Access Sport
Action Medical Research
The Sylvia Adams Charitable
  Trust
The Adamson Trust
The Adint Charitable Trust
Age Scotland
Age UK
Aid to the Church in Need (UK)
The Green and Lilian F M
  Ainsworth and Family
  Benevolent Fund
The Alborada Trust
The H B Allen Charitable Trust
The Ammco Trust
The AMW Charitable Trust
Anglo American Group
  Foundation
The Animal Defence Trust
The Armenian Relief Society of
  Great Britain Trust
Arts Council England
Arts Council of Wales (also
  known as Cyngor
  Celfyddydau Cymru)
The A S Charitable Trust
The Ashden Trust
The Ashendene Trust

The Associated Country
  Women of the World
The Avon and Somerset Police
  Community Trust
The Balcombe Charitable Trust
The Baring Foundation
The Barnsbury Charitable Trust
The Louis Baylis (Maidenhead
  Advertiser) Charitable Trust
The Big Lottery Fund
Birmingham International
  Airport Community Trust
The BlackRock (UK) Charitable
  Trust
The Blandford Lake Trust
The Bluston Charitable
  Settlement
The Body Shop Foundation
The Harry Bottom Charitable
  Trust
The Harold and Alice Bridges
  Charity
British Record Industry Trust
The Bromley Trust
The Roger Brooke Charitable
  Trust
The David Brooke Charity
The Brownsword Charitable
  Foundation
Henry T and Lucy B Cadbury
  Charitable Trust
The Edward and Dorothy
  Cadbury Trust
The Barrow Cadbury Trust and
  the Barrow Cadbury Fund
CAF (Charities Aid Foundation)
CAFOD (Catholic Agency for
  Overseas Development)
Calouste Gulbenkian
  Foundation – UK Branch
The D W T Cargill Fund
The Carmelite Monastery Ware
  Trust
The B G S Cayzer Charitable
  Trust
Celtic Charity Fund
The Charities Advisory Trust
Christian Aid
Church Urban Fund
Stephen Clark 1957
  Charitable Trust
J A Clark Charitable Trust
The Cobalt Trust
The Coltstaple Trust
Colwinston Charitable Trust
Comic Relief
The Compton Charitable Trust
The Conscience Trust
The Conservation Foundation
The Cooks Charity
The Catherine Cookson
  Charitable Trust
The Marjorie Coote Animal
  Charity Trust
Michael Cornish Charitable
  Trust
The Corona Charitable Trust

The Costa Family Charitable
  Trust
Dudley and Geoffrey Cox
  Charitable Trust
The Craignish Trust
The Craps Charitable Trust
The Crescent Trust
The Violet and Milo Cripps
  Charitable Trust
The D G Charitable Settlement
Davis-Rubens Charitable Trust
Peter De Haan Charitable
  Trust
The De Laszlo Foundation
The Dellal Foundation
The Dollond Charitable Trust
The Dorcas Trust
Dorset Community Foundation
The Drapers' Charitable Fund
The Dulverton Trust
The Earmark Trust
The EBM Charitable Trust
The Elephant Trust
The Ellerdale Trust
The John Ellerman Foundation
Entindale Ltd
The Erskine Cunningham Hill
  Trust
Essex Community Foundation
Esmée Fairbairn Foundation
Allan and Nesta Ferguson
  Charitable Settlement
Elizabeth Ferguson Charitable
  Trust Fund
The Doris Field Charitable
  Trust
The Fishmongers' Company's
  Charitable Trust
The Hugh Fraser Foundation
The Freshfield Foundation
The Gatsby Charitable
  Foundation
The Glastonbury Trust Limited
Global Care
The Graff Foundation
The Great Britain Sasakawa
  Foundation
The Green Hall Foundation
The Guildry Incorporation of
  Perth
H C D Memorial Fund
The Hadley Trust
Paul Hamlyn Foundation
The Kathleen Hannay
  Memorial Charity
The Doughty Hanson
  Charitable Foundation
Miss K M Harbinson's
  Charitable Trust
The Hare of Steep Charitable
  Trust
The Harebell Centenary Fund
The John Harrison Charitable
  Trust
The Dorothy Hay-Bolton
  Charitable Trust

Heart of England Community
  Foundation
The Hedley Foundation
The Michael Heller Charitable
  Foundation
The G D Herbert Charitable
  Trust
Hinduja Foundation
Hobson Charity Limited
Hope for Youth (NI)
The Hudson Foundation
The Indigo Trust
The Ingram Trust
The Inland Waterways
  Association
The Inman Charity
The Innocent Foundation
The J J Charitable Trust
The J R S S T Charitable Trust
C Richard Jackson Charitable
  Trust
The Jarman Charitable Trust
Jay Education Trust
Rees Jeffreys Road Fund
The Jerusalem Trust
The Elton John Aids
  Foundation
The Marjorie and Geoffrey
  Jones Charitable Trust
The Jordan Charitable
  Foundation
The John Thomas Kennedy
  Charitable Foundation
The Nancy Kenyon Charitable
  Trust
Keren Association
Kermaville Ltd
The Mary Kinross Charitable
  Trust
Kirkley Poor's Lands Estate
The KPMG Foundation
Maurice and Hilda Laing
  Charitable Trust
The Martin Laing Foundation
The Allen Lane Foundation
The Langley Charitable Trust
The LankellyChase Foundation
The Leathersellers' Company
  Charitable Fund
The Leigh Trust
The Mark Leonard Trust
Leukaemia and Lymphoma
  Research
The Joseph Levy Charitable
  Foundation
The Linbury Trust
The Enid Linder Foundation
The Andrew and Mary
  Elizabeth Little Charitable
  Trust
Lloyds Bank Foundation for
  England and Wales
Lloyds Bank Foundation for the
  Channel Islands
The Trust for London
The London Housing
  Foundation

The Lotus Foundation
Marchig Animal Welfare Trust
The Nora Joan Marshall
  Charitable Trust
The James Frederick and Ethel
  Anne Measures Charity
The Metropolitan Masonic
  Charity
The Millfield House Foundation
The Mitchell Charitable Trust
Keren Mitzvah Trust
The Mizpah Trust
The D C Moncrieff Charitable
  Trust
The Colin Montgomerie
  Charitable Foundation
The Monument Trust
The Oliver Morland Charitable
  Trust
S C and M E Morland's
  Charitable Trust
Vyoel Moshe Charitable Trust
Mrs Waterhouse Charitable
  Trust
Frederick Mulder Charitable
  Trust
The Eleni Nakou Foundation
The National Churches Trust
The National Manuscripts
  Conservation Trust
The Neighbourly Charitable
  Trust
Nemoral Ltd
Network for Social Change
The Noon Foundation
The Norman Family Charitable
  Trust
The Duncan Norman Trust
  Fund
The Northern Rock Foundation
The Northwood Charitable
  Trust
The Norton Foundation
The Sir Peter O'Sullevan
  Charitable Trust
The Oakmoor Charitable Trust
The Ofenheim Charitable Trust
Oxfam (GB)
The Park Charitable Trust
The Constance Paterson
  Charitable Trust
Pegasus (Stanley) Trust
The Persula Foundation
The Jack Petchey Foundation
The Petplan Charitable Trust
The Pilgrim Trust
The Pilkington Charities Fund
The Col W W Pilkington Will
  Trusts The General Charity
  Fund
Polden-Puckham Charitable
  Foundation
The David and Elaine Potter
  Foundation
The Prince of Wales's
  Charitable Foundation
The Puebla Charitable Trust

Quartet Community Foundation
Queen Mary's Roehampton
  Trust
The Queen's Silver Jubilee
  Trust
Rachel Charitable Trust
The Sigrid Rausing Trust
The Rawdon-Smith Trust
The Rayne Foundation
The Reed Foundation
REMEDI
Reuben Foundation
The Helen Roll Charitable
  Trust
Rosa – the UK fund for women
  and girls
The Joseph Rowntree
  Charitable Trust
The Joseph Rowntree
  Foundation
Joseph Rowntree Reform Trust
  Limited
Royal British Legion
The Rubin Foundation
S F Foundation
S O Charitable Trust
The Michael Harry Sacher
  Trust
The Alan and Babette
  Sainsbury Charitable Fund
The Samuel Sebba Charitable
  Trust
ShareGift (The Orr Mackintosh
  Foundation)
The Shears Foundation
The Sheepdrove Trust
The Barbara A Shuttleworth
  Memorial Trust
The Julius Silman Charitable
  Trust
The Souter Charitable Trust
Springrule Limited
Swansea and Brecon Diocesan
  Board of Finance Limited
The Sylvanus Charitable Trust
The Cyril Taylor Charitable
  Trust
The C Paul Thackray General
  Charitable Trust
The Thomas Lilley Memorial
  Trust
The Thousandth Man –
  Richard Burns Charitable
  Trust
The Tobacco Pipe Makers and
  Tobacco Trade Benevolent
  Fund
The Tolkien Trust
The Triangle Trust (1949) Fund
The Tudor Trust
The Douglas Turner Trust
Miss S M Tutton Charitable
  Trust
Trustees of Tzedakah
Ultach Trust
The Ulverscroft Foundation
The Underwood Trust

The United Society for the
Propagation of the Gospel
The David Uri Memorial Trust
The Vardy Foundation
Wales Council for Voluntary
Action
Robert and Felicity Waley-
Cohen Charitable Trust
G R Waters Charitable Trust
2000
The Wates Foundation
The Wessex Youth Trust
The Whitaker Charitable Trust
The Felicity Wilde Charitable
Trust
Yankov Charitable Trust
The Yorkshire Dales
Millennium Trust
The Marjorie and Arnold Ziff
Charitable Foundation

Loan finance

The ACT Foundation
The Architectural Heritage
Fund
The Bridging Fund Charitable
Trust
The Burton Breweries
Charitable Trust
The Cambridgeshire Historic
Churches Trust
The Coalfields Regeneration
Trust
The Edith Maud Ellis 1985
Charitable Trust
The February Foundation
The Nick Jenkins Foundation
The John Thomas Kennedy
Charitable Foundation
The Christopher Laing
Foundation
Marshall's Charity
Rugby Football Foundation
The Edward Stocks-Massey
Bequest Fund
Ulster Garden Villages Ltd

Duration of grant

Trusts listed here have
expressly stated on a
questionniare used as part
of the research for this
book that they give grants
for the specified time
period. Other trusts in this
book which did not respond
to the questionnaire may
also give grants as stated
below.

■ One-off donation

The 1989 Willan Charitable
Trust
The Aberdeen Endowments
Trust
ABF The Soldiers' Charity
The Sylvia Adams Charitable
Trust
The Adamson Trust
The AIM Foundation
The Aldgate Freedom
Foundation
Allchurches Trust Ltd
The H B Allen Charitable Trust
The Almond Trust
Sir John and Lady Amory's
Charitable Trust
Viscount Amory's Charitable
Trust
The Animal Defence Trust
Archbishop of Wales' Fund for
Children
The Ardwick Trust
The Ashley Family Foundation
The Association of Colleges
Charitable Trust
AstonMansfield Charitable
Trust
The Astor Foundation
The Austin Bailey Foundation
The Baily Thomas Charitable
Fund
The Barleycorn Trust
Lord Barnby's Foundation
The Misses Barrie Charitable
Trust
The Paul Bassham Charitable
Trust
The Jack and Ada Beattie
Foundation
The Beaverbrook Foundation
The Bedfordshire and Luton
Community Foundation
The Beit Trust
The Bellhouse Foundation
The Bellinger Donnay Trust
The Gerald Bentall Charitable
Trust
Percy Bilton Charity
The Bingham Trust

The Sydney Black Charitable
Trust
Sir Alec Black's Charity
Isabel Blackman Foundation
The Nicholas Boas Charitable
Trust
The Body Shop Foundation
The Charlotte Bonham-Carter
Charitable Trust
BOOST Charitable Trust
The Boshier-Hinton Foundation
The Harry Bottom Charitable
Trust
The Bower Trust
John and Susan Bowers Fund
The Tony Bramall Charitable
Trust
The Charles and Edna
Broadhurst Charitable Trust
Buckinghamshire Community
Foundation
The E F Bulmer Benevolent
Fund
Consolidated Charity of Burton
upon Trent
Peter Cadbury Charitable Trust
The Richard Cadbury
Charitable Trust
CAF (Charities Aid Foundation)
Calleva Foundation
The Calpe Trust
The Carew Pole Charitable
Trust
The Carnegie Dunfermline
Trust
The Carnegie Trust for the
Universities of Scotland
The Carpenter Charitable Trust
The Carrington Charitable
Trust
The Leslie Mary Carter
Charitable Trust
Carter's Educational
Foundation
R E Chadwick Charitable Trust
The Chapman Charitable Trust
The Childwick Trust
The Christabella Charitable
Trust
Chrysalis Trust
The Church and Community
Fund
Church Urban Fund
Stephen Clark 1957
Charitable Trust
The Clothworkers' Foundation
Richard Cloudesley's Charity
The Robert Clutterbuck
Charitable Trust
The Cobtree Charity Trust Ltd
The Colchester Catalyst
Charity
The John and Freda Coleman
Charitable Trust
The Comino Foundation
The Alice Ellen Cooper Dean
Charitable Foundation

The Helen Jean Cope Trust
The Corona Charitable Trust
The Cotton Trust
The Lord Cozens-Hardy Trust
The Cray Trust
Cruden Foundation Ltd
The Culra Charitable Trust
Cumberland Building Society
  Charitable Foundation
Roald Dahl's Marvellous
  Children's Charity
The Daiwa Anglo-Japanese
  Foundation
The Gwendoline and Margaret
  Davies Charity
The Delius Trust
The Earl of Derby's Charitable
  Trust
The Derbyshire Churches and
  Chapels Preservation Trust
The Devon Educational Trust
The Devon Historic Churches
  Trust
The Duke of Devonshire's
  Charitable Trust
The Dibden Allotments Fund
The Digbeth Trust Limited
Disability Aid Fund (The Roger
  and Jean Jefcoate Trust)
The DLM Charitable Trust
The Derek and Eileen Dodgson
  Foundation
Douglas Arter Foundation
The Drapers' Charitable Fund
The Dulverton Trust
The Dumbreck Charity
The Dunhill Medical Trust
The W E Dunn Trust
The Dwek Family Charitable
  Trust
eaga Charitable Trust
The Ebenezer Trust
The W G Edwards Charitable
  Foundation
The Elephant Trust
The Maud Elkington Charitable
  Trust
The Ellerdale Trust
The Equitable Charitable Trust
The Erskine Cunningham Hill
  Trust
The Everard Foundation
The Eveson Charitable Trust
Esmée Fairbairn Foundation
The Thomas Farr Charity
The February Foundation
Fife Council/Common Good
  Funds and Trusts
The Fifty Fund
Gerald Finzi Charitable Trust
The Forces Trust (Working
  Name)
Gwyneth Forrester Trust
The Donald Forrester Trust
The Fort Foundation
Sydney E Franklin Deceased's
  New Second Charity

The Gordon Fraser Charitable
  Trust
The Thomas Freke and Lady
  Norton Charity Trust
The Freshgate Trust
  Foundation
Friends of Essex Churches
  Trust
The Patrick & Helena Frost
  Foundation
Maurice Fry Charitable Trust
G M C Trust
The Galanthus Trust
The Gale Family Charity Trust
The Gannochy Trust
The Ganzoni Charitable Trust
Garrick Charitable Trust
The Generations Foundation
Simon Gibson Charitable Trust
The Girdlers' Company
  Charitable Trust
The GNC Trust
The Goldsmiths' Arts Trust
  Fund
The Golsoncott Foundation
Nicholas and Judith
  Goodison's Charitable
  Settlement
The J G Graves Charitable
  Trust
The Green Hall Foundation
The Green Room Charitable
  Trust
The Grocers' Charity
The Hadfield Trust
The Hadrian Trust
William Harding's Charity
The Harebell Centenary Fund
The Kenneth Hargreaves
  Charitable Trust
The Harris Charitable Trust
Hasluck Charitable Trust
Percy Hedley 1990 Charitable
  Trust
The Hedley Denton Charitable
  Trust
The Hedley Foundation
Help the Homeless
The Hesslewood Children's
  Trust (Hull Seamen's and
  General Orphanage)
The Hilden Charitable Fund
The Charles Littlewood Hill
  Trust
Lady Hind Trust
Stuart Hine Trust
The Hintze Family Charitable
  Foundation
Matthew Hodder Charitable
  Trust
The Jane Hodge Foundation
The Holst Foundation
The Homestead Charitable
  Trust
The Hope Trust
The Worshipful Company of
  Horners' Charitable Trusts

The Hospital of God at
  Greatham
The Hull and East Riding
  Charitable Trust
The Humanitarian Trust
The ITF Seafarers Trust
John James Bristol Foundation
The James Trust
The John Jarrold Trust
Jerwood Charitable Foundation
Jewish Child's Day
The Michael John Trust
The Joicey Trust
The Kelly Family Charitable
  Trust
Kelsick's Educational
  Foundation
Keswick Hall Trust
The Robert Kiln Charitable
  Trust
The King/Cullimore Charitable
  Trust
The Mary Kinross Charitable
  Trust
The Sir James Knott Trust
The K P Ladd Charitable Trust
LandAid Charitable Trust
The Jack Lane Charitable Trust
The Allen Lane Foundation
The Langtree Trust
The Lark Trust
The Edgar E Lawley Foundation
The Mason Le Page Charitable
  Trust
The Leathersellers' Company
  Charitable Fund
The Leonard Trust
The Joseph Levy Charitable
  Foundation
The Lincolnshire Churches
  Trust
The Lind Trust
Liverpool Charity and Voluntary
  Services
London Catalyst
Henry Lumley Charitable Trust
The Lynn Foundation
John Lyon's Charity
The R S Macdonald Charitable
  Trust
The Macfarlane Walker Trust
The MacRobert Trust
The Magdalen and Lasher
  Charity
Magdalen Hospital Trust
Mageni Trust
W M Mann Foundation
The Leslie and Lilian Manning
  Trust
Marshall's Charity
Sir George Martin Trust
The Nancie Massey Charitable
  Trust
The Mathew Trust
The Matt 6.3 Charitable Trust
The Mears Foundation

The Mercers' Charitable Foundation

The Metropolitan Drinking Fountain and Cattle Trough Association

The Millfield House Foundation

The Keith and Joan Mindelsohn Charitable Trust

The Mitchell Charitable Trust

The Esmé Mitchell Trust

The Mobbs Memorial Trust Ltd

George A Moore Foundation

The Morgan Foundation

The Stanley Morrison Charitable Trust

The Mulberry Trust

Frederick Mulder Charitable Trust

The Edith Murphy Foundation

Murphy-Neumann Charity Company Limited

The John R Murray Charitable Trust

National Committee of the Women's World Day of Prayer for England and Wales and Northern Ireland

Nazareth Trust Fund

The Neighbourly Charitable Trust

Network for Social Change

The Newcomen Collett Foundation

The Frances and Augustus Newman Foundation

Alderman Newton's Educational Foundation

Norie Charitable Trust

Normalyn Charitable Trust

The Northmoor Trust

The Northumbria Historic Churches Trust

The Norton Foundation

The Norwich Church of England Young Men's Society

The Notgrove Trust

The Oakdale Trust

The Oakley Charitable Trust

The Ogle Christian Trust

The Old Broad Street Charity Trust

Open Gate

The Ouseley Trust

City of Oxford Charity

The Oxfordshire Community Foundation

Eleanor Palmer Trust

The James Pantyfedwen Foundation

The Payne Charitable Trust

The Harry Payne Trust

The Dowager Countess Eleanor Peel Trust

The Pennycress Trust

The Phillips Family Charitable Trust

The Bernard Piggott Charitable Trust

The Elise Pilkington Charitable Trust

The Pilkington Charities Fund

The Col W W Pilkington Will Trusts The General Charity Fund

The DLA Piper Charitable Trust

G S Plaut Charitable Trust Limited

Polden-Puckham Charitable Foundation

The Ponton House Trust

The Mary Potter Convent Hospital Trust

The W L Pratt Charitable Trust

The Tom Press Charitable Foundation

The Provincial Grand Charity of the Province of Derbyshire

Mr and Mrs J A Pye's Charitable Settlement

Quartet Community Foundation

The R V W Trust

The Rainford Trust

The Peggy Ramsay Foundation

The Joseph Rank Trust

The Ravensdale Trust

The John Rayner Charitable Trust

The Sir James Reckitt Charity

The Red Arrows Trust

Red Hill Charitable Trust

The Clive Richards Charity

Thomas Roberts Trust

The Rochester Bridge Trust

The Christopher Rowbotham Charitable Trust

The Rowing Foundation

The Joseph Rowntree Charitable Trust

Joseph Rowntree Reform Trust Limited

William Arthur Rudd Memorial Trust

Ryklow Charitable Trust 1992 (also known as A B Williamson Charitable Trust)

The Saddlers' Company Charitable Fund

The Jean Sainsbury Animal Welfare Trust

Saint Sarkis Charity Trust

The Salamander Charitable Trust

Santander UK Foundation Limited

The Scarfe Charitable Trust

The Scottish International Education Trust

Seafarers UK (King George's Fund for Sailors)

Seamen's Hospital Society

The Searchlight Electric Charitable Trust

The Seedfield Trust

Leslie Sell Charitable Trust

SF Group Charitable Fund for Disabled People

The Shipwrights' Company Charitable Fund

Sino-British Fellowship Trust

The Charles Skey Charitable Trust

The Mrs Smith and Mount Trust

Philip Smith's Charitable Trust

Social Business Trust (Scale-Up)

The Southdown Trust

The Southover Manor General Education Trust

The Worshipful Company of Spectacle Makers' Charity

The Jessie Spencer Trust

Rosalyn and Nicholas Springer Charitable Trust

The Spurrell Charitable Trust

Sir Walter St John's Educational Charity

The St Laurence Relief In Need Trust

The Steel Charitable Trust

Sir Halley Stewart Trust

The Leonard Laity Stoate Charitable Trust

Peter Storrs Trust

Stratford upon Avon Town Trust

The Summerfield Charitable Trust

The Bernard Sunley Charitable Foundation

The Sussex Community Foundation

Swan Mountain Trust

The Stella Symons Charitable Trust

The Talbot Trusts

The Talbot Village Trust

Tallow Chandlers Benevolent Fund

C B and H H Taylor 1984 Trust

The Templeton Goodwill Trust

The Sue Thomson Foundation

The Sir Jules Thorn Charitable Trust

The Thriplow Charitable Trust

Mrs R P Tindall's Charitable Trust

The Tobacco Pipe Makers and Tobacco Trade Benevolent Fund

The Constance Travis Charitable Trust

The Treeside Trust

The Trefoil Trust

The Triangle Trust (1949) Fund

The James Tudor Foundation

The Tudor Trust

The R D Turner Charitable Trust

Veneziana Fund

Victoria Homes Trust
Vision Charity
Vivdale Ltd
Wade's Charity
The Scurrah Wainwright Charity
The Walker Trust
Wallington Missionary Mart
and Auctions
The Barbara Ward Children's
Foundation
The Waterloo Foundation
Blyth Watson Charitable Trust
Webb Memorial Trust
The Weinstock Fund
Mrs S K West's Charitable
Trust
The Westcroft Trust
The Westminster Foundation
The Whitecourt Charitable
Trust
The Whitley Animal Protection
Trust
The Whittlesey Charity
The Wilkinson Charitable
Foundation
Dame Violet Wills Charitable
Trust
The Wilson Foundation
The Harold Hyam Wingate
Foundation
The Wolfson Family Charitable
Trust
The Wolfson Foundation
Woodlands Trust
The Woodward Charitable
Trust
The Matthews Wrightson
Charity Trust
The Wyndham Charitable Trust
Yorkshire Building Society
Charitable Foundation

....

■ One year

The 1989 Willan Charitable
Trust
The Sylvia Adams Charitable
Trust
The Ashley Family Foundation
The Associated Country
Women of the World
The Baily Thomas Charitable
Fund
The Baird Trust
The Barbour Foundation
The Barleycorn Trust
The Bedfordshire and Luton
Community Foundation
The Bingham Trust
The Body Shop Foundation
BOOST Charitable Trust
The Harry Bottom Charitable
Trust
John and Susan Bowers Fund
Buckinghamshire Community
Foundation

CAF (Charities Aid Foundation)
The Carnegie Dunfermline
Trust
The Carnegie Trust for the
Universities of Scotland
The Coalfields Regeneration
Trust
The John and Freda Coleman
Charitable Trust
The Comino Foundation
The Lord Cozens-Hardy Trust
Cruden Foundation Ltd
Cumberland Building Society
Charitable Foundation
Roald Dahl's Marvellous
Children's Charity
The Dulverton Trust
The Dunhill Medical Trust
eaga Charitable Trust
East End Community
Foundation
Eastern Counties Educational
Trust Limited
The Ellerdale Trust
The Equitable Charitable Trust
The Essex Heritage Trust
The Eveson Charitable Trust
Esmée Fairbairn Foundation
The George Fentham
Birmingham Charity
The Fort Foundation
The Freemasons' Grand
Charity
The Galanthus Trust
The Gannochy Trust
The Generations Foundation
Gloucestershire Community
Foundation
The Goldsmiths' Company
Charity
The J G Graves Charitable
Trust
The Hadrian Trust
Hampshire and Isle of Wight
Community Foundation
The Harborne Parish Lands
Charity
William Harding's Charity
The Herefordshire Community
Foundation
The Hilden Charitable Fund
The Hintze Family Charitable
Foundation
Hockerill Educational
Foundation
The Jane Hodge Foundation
The Hospital of God at
Greatham
The Hull and East Riding
Charitable Trust
The ITF Seafarers Trust
Jerwood Charitable Foundation
Jewish Child's Day
The Heinz, Anna and Carol
Kroch Foundation
LandAid Charitable Trust
The Allen Lane Foundation

The Leathersellers' Company
Charitable Fund
The Joseph Levy Charitable
Foundation
Lloyds Bank Foundation for
Northern Ireland
London Catalyst
John Lyon's Charity
The R S Macdonald Charitable
Trust
The Macfarlane Walker Trust
The MacRobert Trust
R W Mann Trust
The Nancie Massey Charitable
Trust
The Morgan Foundation
The Mulberry Trust
Frederick Mulder Charitable
Trust
Murphy-Neumann Charity
Company Limited
Network for Social Change
The Frances and Augustus
Newman Foundation
The Notgrove Trust
The Ogle Christian Trust
Open Gate
The Ouseley Trust
The Oxfordshire Community
Foundation
Eleanor Palmer Trust
The Dowager Countess
Eleanor Peel Trust
The Pennycress Trust
The Philips and Rubens
Charitable Trust
The Elise Pilkington Charitable
Trust
The Col W W Pilkington Will
Trusts The General Charity
Fund
G S Plaut Charitable Trust
Limited
Polden-Puckham Charitable
Foundation
Mr and Mrs J A Pye's
Charitable Settlement
Quartet Community Foundation
The Sigrid Rausing Trust
The Sir James Reckitt Charity
The Rhododendron Trust
The Clive Richards Charity
The Christopher Rowbotham
Charitable Trust
The Joseph Rowntree
Charitable Trust
Joseph Rowntree Reform Trust
Limited
The Alfred and Frances
Rubens Charitable Trust
The Saddlers' Company
Charitable Fund
The Salamander Charitable
Trust
The Frieda Scott Charitable
Trust

The Sir James and Lady Scott
Trust
The Scottish International
Education Trust
Seafarers UK (King George's
Fund for Sailors)
The Shipwrights' Company
Charitable Fund
Sino-British Fellowship Trust
The Skelton Bounty
The Mrs Smith and Mount
Trust
The Sovereign Health Care
Charitable Trust
St Hilda's Trust
Sir Walter St John's
Educational Charity
Sir Halley Stewart Trust
The Leonard Laity Stoate
Charitable Trust
Stratford upon Avon Town
Trust
The Sussex Community
Foundation
The Templeton Goodwill Trust
The Sue Thomson Foundation
The Tobacco Pipe Makers and
Tobacco Trade Benevolent
Fund
The Constance Travis
Charitable Trust
The Triangle Trust (1949) Fund
The James Tudor Foundation
The Tudor Trust
The R D Turner Charitable
Trust
The Douglas Turner Trust
Vision Charity
Vivdale Ltd
The Scurrah Wainwright Charity
The Walker Trust
The Barbara Ward Children's
Foundation
The Waterloo Foundation
Blyth Watson Charitable Trust
The Weinstock Fund
The Whitley Animal Protection
Trust
The Whittlesey Charity
The Lionel Wigram Memorial
Trust
The Community Foundation for
Wiltshire and Swindon
The Harold Hyam Wingate
Foundation
The Wixamtree Trust
Woodlands Trust
Youth Music (previously known
as National Foundation for
Youth Music)

■ **Two years**

The Sylvia Adams Charitable
Trust
The Ajahma Charitable Trust

The Ashley Family Foundation
The Baily Thomas Charitable
Fund
The Barleycorn Trust
The Body Shop Foundation
The Harry Bottom Charitable
Trust
The Breast Cancer Research
Trust
The J and M Britton Charitable
Trust
The Bromley Trust
The Swinfen Broun Charitable
Trust
Buckinghamshire Community
Foundation
CAF (Charities Aid Foundation)
The John and Freda Coleman
Charitable Trust
The Comino Foundation
The Lord Cozens-Hardy Trust
The Cunningham Trust
Roald Dahl's Marvellous
Children's Charity
The Dulverton Trust
The Dunhill Medical Trust
eaga Charitable Trust
The Ellerdale Trust
The Equitable Charitable Trust
The Eveson Charitable Trust
Esmée Fairbairn Foundation
The Foresters' Fund for
Children
The Fort Foundation
The Freemasons' Grand
Charity
The Galanthus Trust
The Gannochy Trust
The Generations Foundation
The J G Graves Charitable
Trust
The Hilden Charitable Fund
The Hintze Family Charitable
Foundation
The Jane Hodge Foundation
The Hospital of God at
Greatham
The Hull and East Riding
Charitable Trust
The ITF Seafarers Trust
LandAid Charitable Trust
The Allen Lane Foundation
The Leathersellers' Company
Charitable Fund
The Kennedy Leigh Charitable
Trust
The Joseph Levy Charitable
Foundation
London Catalyst
John Lyon's Charity
The R S Macdonald Charitable
Trust
The Macfarlane Walker Trust
The MacRobert Trust
The Nancie Massey Charitable
Trust

Milton Keynes Community
Foundation
The Mirianog Trust
The Morgan Foundation
The Mulberry Trust
Frederick Mulder Charitable
Trust
Murphy-Neumann Charity
Company Limited
The Ogle Christian Trust
Open Gate
The Ouseley Trust
Eleanor Palmer Trust
The Dowager Countess
Eleanor Peel Trust
The Elise Pilkington Charitable
Trust
The Col W W Pilkington Will
Trusts The General Charity
Fund
G S Plaut Charitable Trust
Limited
Polden-Puckham Charitable
Foundation
Mr and Mrs J A Pye's
Charitable Settlement
The Sir James Reckitt Charity
The Clive Richards Charity
The Helen Roll Charitable
Trust
The Christopher Rowbotham
Charitable Trust
The Joseph Rowntree
Charitable Trust
Joseph Rowntree Reform Trust
Limited
Ryklow Charitable Trust 1992
(also known as A B
Williamson Charitable Trust)
The Saddlers' Company
Charitable Fund
The Scottish International
Education Trust
Sino-British Fellowship Trust
The Mrs Smith and Mount
Trust
Philip Smith's Charitable Trust
David Solomons Charitable
Trust
Sir Walter St John's
Educational Charity
Sir Halley Stewart Trust
Stratford upon Avon Town
Trust
The Sue Thomson Foundation
The Tobacco Pipe Makers and
Tobacco Trade Benevolent
Fund
The Triangle Trust (1949) Fund
The James Tudor Foundation
The Tudor Trust
The Barbara Ward Children's
Foundation
The Waterloo Foundation
Blyth Watson Charitable Trust
The Weinstock Fund

The Whitecourt Charitable
Trust
The Whitley Animal Protection
Trust
The Whittlesey Charity
The Harold Hyam Wingate
Foundation
Woodlands Trust
Youth Music (previously known
as National Foundation for
Youth Music)

....

■ **Three years**

The Ajahma Charitable Trust
The Anchor Foundation
Anglo American Group
Foundation
The Bromley Trust
The Camelia Trust
The Casey Trust
Cash for Kids Radio Clyde
The Cattanach Charitable Trust
Church Burgesses Trust
The City Bridge Trust
The Francis Coales Charitable
Foundation
The Sir Jeremiah Colman Gift
Trust
The Peter Cruddas Foundation
The Cumber Family Charitable
Trust
The Hamilton Davies Trust
James Ellis Charitable Trust
Epilepsy Research UK
Samuel William Farmer Trust
Marc Fitch Fund
The Forbes Charitable
Foundation
The Foyle Foundation
The Gloucestershire Historic
Churches Trust
Greggs Foundation
The Haramead Trust
The Charles Hayward
Foundation
The Inland Waterways
Association
The Innocent Foundation
The Joffe Charitable Trust
The Boris Karloff Charitable
Foundation
The Peter Kershaw Trust
The Medlock Charitable Trust
John Moores Foundation
The Norman Family Charitable
Trust
The Norwich Town Close
Estate Charity
The Nuffield Foundation
The Sigrid Rausing Trust
Richard Reeve's Foundation
The Richmond Parish Lands
Charity
Edwin George Robinson
Charitable Trust

Saint Luke's College
Foundation
The Henry Smith Charity
Sutton Coldfield Charitable
Trust
The Tabeel Trust
Tuixen Foundation
The Wates Foundation
The Weavers' Company
Benevolent Fund
White Stuff Foundation
Youth Music (previously known
as National Foundation for
Youth Music)
Stephen Zimmerman
Charitable Trust

....

■ **Longer than three
years**

The Architectural Heritage
Fund
The Balmore Trust
Bergqvist Charitable Trust
The Campden Charities
Trustee
The Wilfrid and Constance
Cave Foundation
The Charities Advisory Trust
Gordon Cook Foundation
Criffel Charitable Trust
Finnart House School Trust
Friends Provident Charitable
Foundation
Philip Henman Trust
The Herefordshire Historic
Churches Trust
The Hunter Foundation
Jesus Hospital Charity
The Elton John Aids
Foundation
The Sir Edward Lewis
Foundation
The Marsh Christian Trust
The Mushroom Fund
The Owen Family Trust
The Jack Petchey Foundation
The William Price Charitable
Trust
The Joseph and Lena Randall
Charitable Trust
The Sigrid Rausing Trust
The R H Scholes Charitable
Trust
The Francis C Scott Charitable
Trust
The Shirley Foundation
Solev Co Ltd
The Tay Charitable Trust
White Stuff Foundation
The Wyseliot Charitable Trust
Youth Music (previously known
as National Foundation for
Youth Music)

■ **Average time to
pay grant**

■ **Less than one
month**

ABF The Soldiers' Charity
The AIM Foundation
Sir John and Lady Amory's
Charitable Trust
Anglo American Group
Foundation
The Animal Defence Trust
The Architectural Heritage
Fund
The Ashley Family Foundation
The Austin Bailey Foundation
The Barbour Foundation
The Barleycorn Trust
Lord Barnby's Foundation
Barnes Workhouse Fund
The Bellhouse Foundation
The Bellinger Donnay Trust
The Bingham Trust
The Boshier-Hinton Foundation
The Harry Bottom Charitable
Trust
The Bower Trust
The J and M Britton Charitable
Trust
Consolidated Charity of Burton
upon Trent
The Richard Cadbury
Charitable Trust
The Calpe Trust
The Campden Charities
Trustee
The Carew Pole Charitable
Trust
The Carpenter Charitable Trust
The Carrington Charitable
Trust
The Casey Trust
The Charities Advisory Trust
The Childwick Trust
The Christabella Charitable
Trust
Chrysalis Trust
Church Urban Fund
Richard Cloudesley's Charity
The Robert Clutterbuck
Charitable Trust
The Coalfields Regeneration
Trust
The Alice Ellen Cooper Dean
Charitable Foundation
The Helen Jean Cope Trust
The Cray Trust
Cruden Foundation Ltd
Cumberland Building Society
Charitable Foundation
The Daisy Trust
The Gwendoline and Margaret
Davies Charity
The De Laszlo Foundation

The Duke of Devonshire's
   Charitable Trust
The Dibden Allotments Fund
Disability Aid Fund (The Roger
   and Jean Jefcoate Trust)
The Derek and Eileen Dodgson
   Foundation
Douglas Arter Foundation
The Drapers' Charitable Fund
The Dulverton Trust
The W E Dunn Trust
The Elephant Trust
The Maud Elkington Charitable
   Trust
James Ellis Charitable Trust
The Erskine Cunningham Hill
   Trust
The Eveson Charitable Trust
The George Fentham
   Birmingham Charity
The Fifty Fund
Marc Fitch Fund
The Joyce Fletcher Charitable
   Trust
The Foresters' Fund for
   Children
The Fort Foundation
The Gordon Fraser Charitable
   Trust
The Gannochy Trust
The Ganzoni Charitable Trust
Garrick Charitable Trust
Gloucestershire Community
   Foundation
The Gloucestershire Historic
   Churches Trust
Nicholas and Judith
   Goodison's Charitable
   Settlement
The J G Graves Charitable
   Trust
The Green Hall Foundation
William Harding's Charity
Percy Hedley 1990 Charitable
   Trust
The Hedley Denton Charitable
   Trust
The Charles Littlewood Hill
   Trust
Stuart Hine Trust
The Hintze Family Charitable
   Foundation
Matthew Hodder Charitable
   Trust
The Jane Hodge Foundation
The Hospital of God at
   Greatham
The ITF Seafarers Trust
John James Bristol Foundation
The John Jarrold Trust
Jesus Hospital Charity
The Michael John Trust
Kelsick's Educational
   Foundation
The Peter Kershaw Trust
The Mary Kinross Charitable
   Trust

The Heinz, Anna and Carol
   Kroch Foundation
The Jack Lane Charitable Trust
The Allen Lane Foundation
The Langtree Trust
The Sir Edward Lewis
   Foundation
Liverpool Charity and Voluntary
   Services
The Lynn Foundation
The Magdalen and Lasher
   Charity
W M Mann Foundation
R W Mann Trust
Sir George Martin Trust
The Nancie Massey Charitable
   Trust
Community Foundation for
   Merseyside
The Millfield House Foundation
Milton Keynes Community
   Foundation
The John R Murray Charitable
   Trust
The Mushroom Fund
Nazareth Trust Fund
The Frances and Augustus
   Newman Foundation
The Norwich Town Close
   Estate Charity
The Notgrove Trust
The Harry Payne Trust
The Philips and Rubens
   Charitable Trust
The Pilkington Charities Fund
The Col W W Pilkington Will
   Trusts The General Charity
   Fund
The DLA Piper Charitable Trust
The Mary Potter Convent
   Hospital Trust
The Rainford Trust
The John Rayner Charitable
   Trust
The Sir James Reckitt Charity
Red Hill Charitable Trust
The Richmond Parish Lands
   Charity
Thomas Roberts Trust
The Helen Roll Charitable
   Trust
The Alfred and Frances
   Rubens Charitable Trust
William Arthur Rudd Memorial
   Trust
Santander UK Foundation
   Limited
The Scarfe Charitable Trust
The Francis C Scott Charitable
   Trust
Seamen's Hospital Society
The Searchlight Electric
   Charitable Trust
Solev Co Ltd
The Southover Manor General
   Education Trust
The Jessie Spencer Trust

Rosalyn and Nicholas Springer
   Charitable Trust
St Hilda's Trust
The St Laurence Relief In
   Need Trust
The Summerfield Charitable
   Trust
Swan Mountain Trust
The Talbot Trusts
C B and H H Taylor 1984 Trust
The Sir Jules Thorn Charitable
   Trust
The Constance Travis
   Charitable Trust
The Treeside Trust
Vivdale Ltd
The Scurrah Wainwright Charity
The Walker Trust
The Thomas Wall Trust
Wallington Missionary Mart
   and Auctions
The Weinstock Fund
Mrs S K West's Charitable
   Trust
The Whitecourt Charitable
   Trust
The Whitley Animal Protection
   Trust
The Whittlesey Charity
Dame Violet Wills Charitable
   Trust
The Community Foundation for
   Wiltshire and Swindon
The Harold Hyam Wingate
   Foundation
The Woodward Charitable
   Trust
Stephen Zimmerman
   Charitable Trust

....

■ Two months

The Aberdeen Endowments
   Trust
The Adamson Trust
The Ajahma Charitable Trust
Viscount Amory's Charitable
   Trust
The Architectural Heritage
   Fund
The Ardwick Trust
AstonMansfield Charitable
   Trust
The Astor Foundation
The Baily Thomas Charitable
   Fund
The Paul Bassham Charitable
   Trust
The Bedfordshire and Luton
   Community Foundation
The Sydney Black Charitable
   Trust
Isabel Blackman Foundation
The Nicholas Boas Charitable
   Trust

The Charlotte Bonham-Carter
  Charitable Trust
The Tony Bramall Charitable
  Trust
Buckinghamshire Community
  Foundation
The E F Bulmer Benevolent
  Fund
Peter Cadbury Charitable Trust
Carter's Educational
  Foundation
Church Burgesses Trust
The Colchester Catalyst
  Charity
The Comino Foundation
Gordon Cook Foundation
Michael Cornish Charitable
  Trust
The Corona Charitable Trust
Cripplegate Foundation
The Peter Cruddas Foundation
The Cumber Family Charitable
  Trust
Roald Dahl's Marvellous
  Children's Charity
The De Laszlo Foundation
The Denman Charitable Trust
The Devon Educational Trust
The DLM Charitable Trust
Eastern Counties Educational
  Trust Limited
The Ebenezer Trust
The W G Edwards Charitable
  Foundation
The Ericson Trust
The Everard Foundation
The February Foundation
Sydney E Franklin Deceased's
  New Second Charity
Friends of Essex Churches
  Trust
The Patrick & Helena Frost
  Foundation
The Galanthus Trust
The Gannochy Trust
The Goldsmiths' Company
  Charity
The Grocers' Charity
The Hadfield Trust
The Hadrian Trust
The Harebell Centenary Fund
The Kenneth Hargreaves
  Charitable Trust
The Charles Hayward
  Foundation
The Hedley Foundation
The Herefordshire Community
  Foundation
The Hilden Charitable Fund
The Holst Foundation
The Hunter Foundation
The James Trust
Jewish Child's Day
The Robert Kiln Charitable
  Trust
The Edgar E Lawley Foundation
The Leonard Trust

The Erica Leonard Trust
Lloyds Bank Foundation for
  Northern Ireland
London Catalyst
The R S Macdonald Charitable
  Trust
The Mathew Trust
The Medlock Charitable Trust
The Esmé Mitchell Trust
National Committee of the
  Women's World Day of
  Prayer for England and
  Wales and Northern Ireland
The Newcomen Collett
  Foundation
Alderman Newton's
  Educational Foundation
Normalyn Charitable Trust
The Norman Family Charitable
  Trust
The Norton Foundation
The Ogle Christian Trust
The Old Broad Street Charity
  Trust
The James Pantyfedwen
  Foundation
The Jack Petchey Foundation
The Bernard Piggott Charitable
  Trust
The Elise Pilkington Charitable
  Trust
Polden-Puckham Charitable
  Foundation
The Ponton House Trust
Quartet Community Foundation
The Red Arrows Trust
Joseph Rowntree Reform Trust
  Limited
Saint Sarkis Charity Trust
The R H Scholes Charitable
  Trust
The Frieda Scott Charitable
  Trust
The Mrs Smith and Mount
  Trust
David Solomons Charitable
  Trust
The Sovereign Health Care
  Charitable Trust
Sir Walter St John's
  Educational Charity
The Steel Charitable Trust
Stratford upon Avon Town
  Trust
The Sussex Community
  Foundation
The Sue Thomson Foundation
The Tobacco Pipe Makers and
  Tobacco Trade Benevolent
  Fund
The Toy Trust
The Trefoil Trust
The R D Turner Charitable
  Trust
The Douglas Turner Trust
Veneziana Fund
Vision Charity

The Waterloo Foundation
Webb Memorial Trust
The Westcroft Trust
The Wilkinson Charitable
  Foundation
The Wilson Foundation
Woodlands Trust
The Matthews Wrightson
  Charity Trust
Yorkshire Building Society
  Charitable Foundation

....

■ Three months

The 1989 Willan Charitable
  Trust
The Aldgate Freedom
  Foundation
Archbishop of Wales' Fund for
  Children
The Balmore Trust
The Jack and Ada Beattie
  Foundation
Bergqvist Charitable Trust
Sir Alec Black's Charity
The Body Shop Foundation
BOOST Charitable Trust
The Charles and Edna
  Broadhurst Charitable Trust
The Swinfen Broun Charitable
  Trust
The Carnegie Trust for the
  Universities of Scotland
Cash for Kids Radio Clyde
The Cattanach Charitable Trust
The Chapman Charitable Trust
The Church and Community
  Fund
The Cobtree Charity Trust Ltd
The John and Freda Coleman
  Charitable Trust
The Cotton Trust
The Lord Cozens-Hardy Trust
The Daiwa Anglo-Japanese
  Foundation
The Delius Trust
The Digbeth Trust Limited
The Dwek Family Charitable
  Trust
Esmée Fairbairn Foundation
The Forces Trust (Working
  Name)
The Foyle Foundation
The Thomas Freke and Lady
  Norton Charity Trust
The Freshgate Trust
  Foundation
Maurice Fry Charitable Trust
The Generations Foundation
Greggs Foundation
Hampshire and Isle of Wight
  Community Foundation
The Haramead Trust
Help the Homeless
The Inland Waterways
  Association

The Innocent Foundation
Jerwood Charitable Foundation
The Elton John Aids
  Foundation
The Boris Karloff Charitable
  Foundation
The Kelly Family Charitable
  Trust
Keswick Hall Trust
The King/Cullimore Charitable
  Trust
The Sir James Knott Trust
The K P Ladd Charitable Trust
The Lark Trust
The Leathersellers' Company
  Charitable Fund
The Leche Trust
The Lind Trust
Lloyds TSB Foundation for
  Scotland
The Macfarlane Walker Trust
Mageni Trust
The Matt 6.3 Charitable Trust
The Mears Foundation
The Mercers' Charitable
  Foundation
The Metropolitan Drinking
  Fountain and Cattle Trough
  Association
The Mobbs Memorial Trust Ltd
George A Moore Foundation
John Moores Foundation
The Stanley Morrison
  Charitable Trust
The Edith Murphy Foundation
The Northmoor Trust
The Oakdale Trust
Open Gate
The Oxfordshire Community
  Foundation
Eleanor Palmer Trust
The Phillips Family Charitable
  Trust
The Tom Press Charitable
  Foundation
The William Price Charitable
  Trust
Richard Reeve's Foundation
Edwin George Robinson
  Charitable Trust
Ryklow Charitable Trust 1992
  (also known as A B
  Williamson Charitable Trust)
Saint Luke's College
  Foundation
The Sir James and Lady Scott
  Trust
SF Group Charitable Fund for
  Disabled People
The Skelton Bounty
The Southdown Trust
The Leonard Laity Stoate
  Charitable Trust
The Bernard Sunley Charitable
  Foundation
Sutton Coldfield Charitable
  Trust

Tallow Chandlers Benevolent
  Fund
The Thriplow Charitable Trust
The Triangle Trust (1949) Fund
Wade's Charity
The Barbara Ward Children's
  Foundation
The Wates Foundation
The Westminster Foundation
White Stuff Foundation
The Wixamtree Trust

....

■ **Four months**

Allchurches Trust Ltd
The Architectural Heritage
  Fund
The Misses Barrie Charitable
  Trust
The Carnegie Dunfermline
  Trust
The De Laszlo Foundation
The Essex Heritage Trust
The Thomas Farr Charity
Finnart House School Trust
Gerald Finzi Charitable Trust
The Forbes Charitable
  Foundation
The Freemasons' Grand
  Charity
Friends Provident Charitable
  Foundation
The Gale Family Charity Trust
The GNC Trust
Lady Hind Trust
The Joffe Charitable Trust
The Joicey Trust
The Mason Le Page Charitable
  Trust
The Joseph Levy Charitable
  Foundation
John Lyon's Charity
The Leslie and Lilian Manning
  Trust
The Marsh Christian Trust
The Keith and Joan
  Mindelsohn Charitable
  Trust
The Morgan Foundation
The Mulberry Trust
The Neighbourly Charitable
  Trust
Network for Social Change
The Owen Family Trust
The Dowager Countess
  Eleanor Peel Trust
The Pennycress Trust
The Provincial Grand Charity of
  the Province of Derbyshire
Mr and Mrs J A Pye's
  Charitable Settlement
The Joseph Rank Trust
The Joseph Rowntree
  Charitable Trust
The Scottish International
  Education Trust

Seafarers UK (King George's
  Fund for Sailors)
The Seedfield Trust
Leslie Sell Charitable Trust
The Shipwrights' Company
  Charitable Fund
The Shirley Foundation
The Charles Skey Charitable
  Trust
Social Business Trust (Scale-
  Up)
The Trusthouse Charitable
  Foundation
The James Tudor Foundation
The Tudor Trust
The Weavers' Company
  Benevolent Fund

....

■ **Five months**

The Sylvia Adams Charitable
  Trust
The Anchor Foundation
The Architectural Heritage
  Fund
The Leslie Mary Carter
  Charitable Trust
The De Laszlo Foundation
The Donald Forrester Trust
Hasluck Charitable Trust
The Hope Trust
The Joseph Levy Charitable
  Foundation
John Lyon's Charity
Murphy-Neumann Charity
  Company Limited
The Ouseley Trust
The Paget Charitable Trust
The W L Pratt Charitable Trust
The Rowing Foundation
Philip Smith's Charitable Trust
Sir Halley Stewart Trust
The Tabeel Trust
The Sir Jules Thorn Charitable
  Trust
Mrs R P Tindall's Charitable
  Trust
The Wolfson Foundation

....

■ **Six months or more**

The H B Allen Charitable Trust
The Associated Country
  Women of the World
The Beit Trust
The Gerald Bentall Charitable
  Trust
The Breast Cancer Research
  Trust
The Bromley Trust
The Camelia Trust
The Wilfrid and Constance
  Cave Foundation
R E Chadwick Charitable Trust

Stephen Clark 1957
   Charitable Trust
The Clothworkers' Foundation
The Francis Coales Charitable
   Foundation
The Sir Jeremiah Colman Gift
   Trust
The Culra Charitable Trust
The Cunningham Trust
The Derbyshire Churches and
   Chapels Preservation Trust
The Dumbreck Charity
The Ellerdale Trust
Epilepsy Research UK
Samuel William Farmer Trust
G M C Trust
The Green Room Charitable
   Trust
The Charles Hayward
   Foundation
Philip Henman Trust
Hockerill Educational
   Foundation
The Homestead Charitable
   Trust
The Worshipful Company of
   Horners' Charitable Trusts
LandAid Charitable Trust
The Kennedy Leigh Charitable
   Trust
The Lincolnshire Churches
   Trust
Henry Lumley Charitable Trust
The MacRobert Trust
Marshall's Charity
The Mitchell Charitable Trust
Murphy-Neumann Charity
   Company Limited
Norie Charitable Trust
The Norwich Church of England
   Young Men's Society
The Nuffield Foundation
The Oakley Charitable Trust
The Payne Charitable Trust
The David Pickford Charitable
   Foundation
The Joseph and Lena Randall
   Charitable Trust
The Ravensdale Trust
The Clive Richards Charity
The Rochester Bridge Trust
The Christopher Rowbotham
   Charitable Trust
The Henry Smith Charity
The Worshipful Company of
   Spectacle Makers' Charity
The Spurrell Charitable Trust
Peter Storrs Trust
The Stella Symons Charitable
   Trust
The Talbot Village Trust
The Tay Charitable Trust
The Templeton Goodwill Trust
Tuixen Foundation
Victoria Homes Trust
Blyth Watson Charitable Trust

The Lionel Wigram Memorial
   Trust
The Wolfson Family Charitable
   Trust
Youth Music (previously known
   as National Foundation for
   Youth Music)

Percentage of grants to new applicants

■ Less than 10%

ABF The Soldiers' Charity
The AIM Foundation
The Aldgate Freedom
   Foundation
The Almond Trust
Anglo American Group
   Foundation
The Balmore Trust
The Barbour Foundation
The Bellinger Donnay Trust
The Gerald Bentall Charitable
   Trust
Bergqvist Charitable Trust
The Sydney Black Charitable
   Trust
Sir Alec Black's Charity
The Swinfen Broun Charitable
   Trust
Peter Cadbury Charitable Trust
Calleva Foundation
The Calpe Trust
The Campden Charities
   Trustee
The Carpenter Charitable Trust
The Leslie Mary Carter
   Charitable Trust
Cash for Kids Radio Clyde
The Cobtree Charity Trust Ltd
The Sir Jeremiah Colman Gift
   Trust
The Comino Foundation
Gordon Cook Foundation
The Lord Cozens-Hardy Trust
The Cray Trust
Cruden Foundation Ltd
The De Laszlo Foundation
The Earl of Derby's Charitable
   Trust
The Dwek Family Charitable
   Trust
The Ebenezer Trust
The Ellerdale Trust
The Ericson Trust
The Eveson Charitable Trust
Fisherbeck Charitable Trust
The Forces Trust (Working
   Name)
The Donald Forrester Trust
The Thomas Freke and Lady
   Norton Charity Trust
Maurice Fry Charitable Trust
The Galanthus Trust
The Haramead Trust
The Harris Charitable Trust
The Hedley Denton Charitable
   Trust
The Holst Foundation
The Hope Trust
The Humanitarian Trust

The Hunter Foundation
The Inland Waterways
    Association
The Innocent Foundation
John James Bristol Foundation
The James Trust
Jewish Child's Day
The K P Ladd Charitable Trust
The Langtree Trust
The Lark Trust
The Kennedy Leigh Charitable
    Trust
The Leonard Trust
The Joseph Levy Charitable
    Foundation
The Sir Edward Lewis
    Foundation
The Lind Trust
The Marsh Christian Trust
The Matt 6.3 Charitable Trust
The Metropolitan Drinking
    Fountain and Cattle Trough
    Association
Milton Keynes Community
    Foundation
The Stanley Morrison
    Charitable Trust
Murphy-Neumann Charity
    Company Limited
The Mushroom Fund
Nazareth Trust Fund
Normalyn Charitable Trust
The Northmoor Trust
The Norwich Church of England
    Young Men's Society
The Oakley Charitable Trust
The Paget Charitable Trust
Eleanor Palmer Trust
The Payne Charitable Trust
The Philips and Rubens
    Charitable Trust
The Phillips Family Charitable
    Trust
The W L Pratt Charitable Trust
The William Price Charitable
    Trust
Mr and Mrs J A Pye's
    Charitable Settlement
Richard Reeve's Foundation
Thomas Roberts Trust
The Helen Roll Charitable
    Trust
The Alfred and Frances
    Rubens Charitable Trust
William Arthur Rudd Memorial
    Trust
The Salamander Charitable
    Trust
The Searchlight Electric
    Charitable Trust
SF Group Charitable Fund for
    Disabled People
The Charles Skey Charitable
    Trust
The Worshipful Company of
    Spectacle Makers' Charity
The Jessie Spencer Trust

Rosalyn and Nicholas Springer
    Charitable Trust
Sutton Coldfield Charitable
    Trust
The Talbot Trusts
The Templeton Goodwill Trust
The Sue Thomson Foundation
Mrs R P Tindall's Charitable
    Trust
The Tobacco Pipe Makers and
    Tobacco Trade Benevolent
    Fund
The Treeside Trust
The Weinstock Fund
Mrs S K West's Charitable
    Trust
The Westcroft Trust
White Stuff Foundation
The Whitley Animal Protection
    Trust
The Whittlesey Charity
The Harold Hyam Wingate
    Foundation
The Wixamtree Trust
The Wyndham Charitable Trust
The Wyseliot Charitable Trust

....

■ 10–20%

The H B Allen Charitable Trust
The Ardwick Trust
The Barleycorn Trust
Lord Barnby's Foundation
The Misses Barrie Charitable
    Trust
The Bedfordshire and Luton
    Community Foundation
The Beit Trust
The Boshier-Hinton Foundation
The Harry Bottom Charitable
    Trust
John and Susan Bowers Fund
The Tony Bramall Charitable
    Trust
The Bromley Trust
Buckinghamshire Community
    Foundation
The Buckinghamshire Historic
    Churches Trust
The E F Bulmer Benevolent
    Fund
Consolidated Charity of Burton
    upon Trent
The Richard Cadbury
    Charitable Trust
The Carnegie Dunfermline
    Trust
The Carrington Charitable
    Trust
R E Chadwick Charitable Trust
The Chapman Charitable Trust
The Charities Advisory Trust
The Childwick Trust
Richard Cloudesley's Charity
The Francis Coales Charitable
    Foundation

The Alice Ellen Cooper Dean
    Charitable Foundation
The Corona Charitable Trust
Cripplegate Foundation
The Gwendoline and Margaret
    Davies Charity
The Derek and Eileen Dodgson
    Foundation
The Dulverton Trust
James Ellis Charitable Trust
The Thomas Farr Charity
The George Fentham
    Birmingham Charity
The Fifty Fund
The Joyce Fletcher Charitable
    Trust
The Gordon Fraser Charitable
    Trust
The Patrick & Helena Frost
    Foundation
G M C Trust
The Gannochy Trust
The Gloucestershire Historic
    Churches Trust
Nicholas and Judith
    Goodison's Charitable
    Settlement
William Harding's Charity
The Harebell Centenary Fund
Percy Hedley 1990 Charitable
    Trust
Philip Henman Trust
The Charles Littlewood Hill
    Trust
Lady Hind Trust
Matthew Hodder Charitable
    Trust
The ITF Seafarers Trust
The John Jarrold Trust
Jesus Hospital Charity
Kelsick's Educational
    Foundation
The Robert Kiln Charitable
    Trust
The Sir James Knott Trust
Lloyds Bank Foundation for
    Northern Ireland
Lloyds TSB Foundation for
    Scotland
The Macfarlane Walker Trust
The MacRobert Trust
Mageni Trust
The Medlock Charitable Trust
Community Foundation for
    Merseyside
The Keith and Joan
    Mindelsohn Charitable
    Trust
The Mobbs Memorial Trust Ltd
The Mulberry Trust
Norie Charitable Trust
The Norman Family Charitable
    Trust
The Norton Foundation
The Norwich Town Close
    Estate Charity
The Ogle Christian Trust

Open Gate
The Owen Family Trust
The Pennycress Trust
The Jack Petchey Foundation
The David Pickford Charitable
Foundation
The Pilkington Charities Fund
The Col W W Pilkington Will
Trusts The General Charity
Fund
G S Plaut Charitable Trust
Limited
The Ponton House Trust
The Provincial Grand Charity of
the Province of Derbyshire
The Ravensdale Trust
The John Rayner Charitable
Trust
The Sir James Reckitt Charity
The Red Arrows Trust
The Rhododendron Trust
The Richmond Parish Lands
Charity
Edwin George Robinson
Charitable Trust
Saint Sarkis Charity Trust
The Scarfe Charitable Trust
Seafarers UK (King George's
Fund for Sailors)
The Seedfield Trust
The Skelton Bounty
Philip Smith's Charitable Trust
Solev Co Ltd
Stratford upon Avon Town
Trust
The Sussex Community
Foundation
The Tabeel Trust
The Constance Travis
Charitable Trust
Vision Charity
Vivdale Ltd
Wallington Missionary Mart
and Auctions
Webb Memorial Trust
The Westminster Foundation
The Wilkinson Charitable
Foundation
The Wilson Foundation
Yorkshire Building Society
Charitable Foundation
Stephen Zimmerman
Charitable Trust

....
■ **20–30%**

Viscount Amory's Charitable
Trust
The Animal Defence Trust
The Ashley Family Foundation
The Austin Bailey Foundation
The Paul Bassham Charitable
Trust
The Nicholas Boas Charitable
Trust

The Charlotte Bonham-Carter
Charitable Trust
The Charles and Edna
Broadhurst Charitable Trust
The Camelia Trust
The Carew Pole Charitable
Trust
The Wilfrid and Constance
Cave Foundation
Church Burgesses Trust
The John and Freda Coleman
Charitable Trust
The Helen Jean Cope Trust
The Cotton Trust
The Cumber Family Charitable
Trust
The Derbyshire Churches and
Chapels Preservation Trust
The Devon Educational Trust
Disability Aid Fund (The Roger
and Jean Jefcoate Trust)
The W E Dunn Trust
eaga Charitable Trust
The Maud Elkington Charitable
Trust
The Everard Foundation
The Fort Foundation
Sydney E Franklin Deceased's
New Second Charity
The Freshgate Trust
Foundation
Simon Gibson Charitable Trust
The J G Graves Charitable
Trust
The Green Hall Foundation
The Hadrian Trust
Hampshire and Isle of Wight
Community Foundation
The Kenneth Hargreaves
Charitable Trust
The Herefordshire Community
Foundation
The Hesslewood Children's
Trust (Hull Seamen's and
General Orphanage)
Jerwood Charitable Foundation
The Peter Kershaw Trust
The King/Cullimore Charitable
Trust
The Mary Kinross Charitable
Trust
The Mason Le Page Charitable
Trust
The Leche Trust
Liverpool Charity and Voluntary
Services
Lloyds Bank Foundation for
Northern Ireland
The Lynn Foundation
W M Mann Foundation
The Leslie and Lilian Manning
Trust
The Nancie Massey Charitable
Trust
The Mears Foundation
The Millfield House Foundation
The Mitchell Charitable Trust

George A Moore Foundation
Frederick Mulder Charitable
Trust
The Frances and Augustus
Newman Foundation
The Notgrove Trust
The Oakdale Trust
The Ouseley Trust
The Bernard Piggott Charitable
Trust
The Elise Pilkington Charitable
Trust
Polden-Puckham Charitable
Foundation
The Mary Potter Convent
Hospital Trust
Quartet Community Foundation
The Rainford Trust
The Joseph and Lena Randall
Charitable Trust
Red Hill Charitable Trust
The Christopher Rowbotham
Charitable Trust
The Joseph Rowntree
Charitable Trust
Saint Luke's College
Foundation
The Sir James and Lady Scott
Trust
Leslie Sell Charitable Trust
The Shipwrights' Company
Charitable Fund
The Talbot Village Trust
C B and H H Taylor 1984 Trust
The Thriplow Charitable Trust
The James Tudor Foundation
Tuixen Foundation
The R D Turner Charitable
Trust
The Douglas Turner Trust
The Barbara Ward Children's
Foundation
Blyth Watson Charitable Trust
The Lionel Wigram Memorial
Trust
Dame Violet Wills Charitable
Trust
The Community Foundation for
Wiltshire and Swindon
The Matthews Wrightson
Charity Trust

....
■ **30–40%**

Sir John and Lady Amory's
Charitable Trust
The Associated Country
Women of the World
AstonMansfield Charitable
Trust
The Baily Thomas Charitable
Fund
The Bingham Trust
BOOST Charitable Trust
The Breast Cancer Research
Trust

The Carnegie Trust for the
Universities of Scotland
Carter's Educational
Foundation
The Casey Trust
The Christabella Charitable
Trust
The City Bridge Trust
Stephen Clark 1957
Charitable Trust
The Robert Clutterbuck
Charitable Trust
The Colchester Catalyst
Charity
Michael Cornish Charitable
Trust
The Cunningham Trust
The Daisy Trust
The Denman Charitable Trust
The Dibden Allotments Fund
The DLM Charitable Trust
Eastern Counties Educational
Trust Limited
Samuel William Farmer Trust
Fife Council/Common Good
Funds and Trusts
Finnart House School Trust
The Gale Family Charity Trust
Gloucestershire Community
Foundation
The Golsoncott Foundation
The Hintze Family Charitable
Foundation
The Worshipful Company of
Horners' Charitable Trusts
The Elton John Aids
Foundation
The Heinz, Anna and Carol
Kroch Foundation
The Jack Lane Charitable Trust
R W Mann Trust
The Mercers' Charitable
Foundation
The Mirianog Trust
The Neighbourly Charitable
Trust
The Harry Payne Trust
The R V W Trust
Joseph Rowntree Reform Trust
Limited
The Saddlers' Company
Charitable Fund
The Frieda Scott Charitable
Trust
The Francis C Scott Charitable
Trust
The Sovereign Health Care
Charitable Trust
St Hilda's Trust
Sir Walter St John's
Educational Charity
The St Laurence Relief In
Need Trust
The Leonard Laity Stoate
Charitable Trust
Peter Storrs Trust

Tallow Chandlers Benevolent
Fund
The Tay Charitable Trust
The Sir Jules Thorn Charitable
Trust
The Trefoil Trust
The Tudor Trust
Wade's Charity

....

■ **40–50%**

The 1989 Willan Charitable
Trust
The Aberdeen Endowments
Trust
The Sylvia Adams Charitable
Trust
The Adamson Trust
The Anchor Foundation
Archbishop of Wales' Fund for
Children
The Association of Colleges
Charitable Trust
The Baird Trust
The Jack and Ada Beattie
Foundation
The Beaverbrook Foundation
The Body Shop Foundation
The Bower Trust
The J and M Britton Charitable
Trust
The Cattanach Charitable Trust
Chrysalis Trust
The Coalfields Regeneration
Trust
The Culra Charitable Trust
Roald Dahl's Marvellous
Children's Charity
The Daiwa Anglo-Japanese
Foundation
The Delius Trust
The Devon Historic Churches
Trust
The Drapers' Charitable Fund
The Dumbreck Charity
The Dunhill Medical Trust
The Equitable Charitable Trust
Esmée Fairbairn Foundation
Gerald Finzi Charitable Trust
Marc Fitch Fund
The Foyle Foundation
The Generations Foundation
The Grocers' Charity
The Hadfield Trust
The Harborne Parish Lands
Charity
Hasluck Charitable Trust
The Hedley Foundation
Help the Homeless
The Hilden Charitable Fund
Hockerill Educational
Foundation
The Jane Hodge Foundation
The Hospital of God at
Greatham
The Joffe Charitable Trust

The Joicey Trust
The Boris Karloff Charitable
Foundation
The Kelly Family Charitable
Trust
The Edgar E Lawley Foundation
The Leathersellers' Company
Charitable Fund
The Lincolnshire Churches
Trust
London Catalyst
Magdalen Hospital Trust
Marshall's Charity
Sir George Martin Trust
The Morgan Foundation
National Committee of the
Women's World Day of
Prayer for England and
Wales and Northern Ireland
The Newcomen Collett
Foundation
Alderman Newton's
Educational Foundation
The Old Broad Street Charity
Trust
The Oxfordshire Community
Foundation
The James Pantyfedwen
Foundation
The DLA Piper Charitable Trust
The Clive Richards Charity
Ryklow Charitable Trust 1992
(also known as A B
Williamson Charitable Trust)
Santander UK Foundation
Limited
The Shirley Foundation
Social Business Trust (Scale-
Up)
David Solomons Charitable
Trust
The Southover Manor General
Education Trust
The Steel Charitable Trust
Sir Halley Stewart Trust
Swan Mountain Trust
The Toy Trust
Victoria Homes Trust
The Weavers' Company
Benevolent Fund
The Wolfson Family Charitable
Trust
The Wolfson Foundation
Woodlands Trust
Youth Music (previously known
as National Foundation for
Youth Music)

....

■ **Over 50%**

The Church and Community
Fund
Church Urban Fund
The Clothworkers' Foundation
The Duke of Devonshire's
Charitable Trust

The Digbeth Trust Limited
*The W G Edwards Charitable
   Foundation*
Epilepsy Research UK
The Essex Heritage Trust
*The Forbes Charitable
   Foundation*
*The Foresters' Fund for
   Children*
*Friends of Essex Churches
   Trust*
*Friends Provident Charitable
   Foundation*
*The Green Room Charitable
   Trust*
The Harpur Trust
*The Charles Hayward
   Foundation*
*The Herefordshire Historic
   Churches Trust*
Keswick Hall Trust
LandAid Charitable Trust
*The R S Macdonald Charitable
   Trust*
The Mathew Trust
The Edith Murphy Foundation
*The Dowager Countess
   Eleanor Peel Trust*
*The Tom Press Charitable
   Foundation*
The Joseph Rank Trust
The Rochester Bridge Trust
*The Scottish International
   Education Trust*
*The Mrs Smith and Mount
   Trust*
*The Bernard Sunley Charitable
   Foundation*
*The Trusthouse Charitable
   Foundation*
Veneziana Fund
The Scurrah Wainwright Charity
The Walker Trust
*The Whitecourt Charitable
   Trust*
*The Woodward Charitable
   Trust*

The alphabetical register of grant-making trusts

This section lists the individual entries for the grant-making trusts.

■ The 101 Foundation

CC NO 1146808   **ESTABLISHED** 2012
WHERE FUNDING CAN BE GIVEN UK.
WHO CAN BENEFIT Registered charities.
WHAT IS FUNDED General charitable purposes, with a particular interest in children and young people.
FINANCES *Year* 2012–13 *Income* £1,254,551 *Grants* £700,000
TRUSTEES Angela Dawes; David Dawes; Coutts and Co.
OTHER INFORMATION The foundation was established by David and Angela Dawes, who won £101 million on the EuroMillions lottery in October 2011. The foundation's first annual report and accounts were submitted to the Charity Commission towards the end of January 2014, but were not available to view as this book went to press. However, figures available from the Charity Commission record show that during its first year of operation the foundation had an income of almost £1.3 million and a total expenditure of £739,000.
HOW TO APPLY In writing to the correspondent.
WHO TO APPLY TO Coutts and Co, Trustee Department, 440 Strand, London WC2R 0QS *Tel.* 020 7663 6826

■ The 1970 Trust

SC NO SC008788   **ESTABLISHED** 1970
WHERE FUNDING CAN BE GIVEN UK.
WHO CAN BENEFIT Charities which support disadvantaged minorities.
WHAT IS FUNDED The trust states it supports small UK charities 'doing innovative, educational, or experimental work' in the following fields: civil liberties (e.g. freedom of information; constitutional reform; humanising work; children's welfare); the public interest in the face of vested interest groups (such as the advertising, alcohol, road, war, pharmaceuticals, and tobacco industries); disadvantaged minorities, multiracial work, prison reform; new economics and intermediate technology; public transport, pedestrians, bicycling, road crash prevention, traffic-calming, low-energy lifestyles; and preventative health.
WHAT IS NOT FUNDED No support for larger charities, those with religious connections, or individuals (except in rare cases – and then only through registered charities or educational bodies). No support to central or local government agencies.
TYPE OF GRANT Usually one to three years; sometimes longer.
RANGE OF GRANTS £1,000–£4,000
SAMPLE GRANTS Previous beneficiaries include: Scarman Trust; Roadpeace; Public Interest Research Centre; Earth Resources; Parents for Children; Parent to Parent; Slower Speeds Trust; Prisoners' Wives; Pesticide Action Network; BackCare; and Shelter Winter Night.
FINANCES *Year* 2011–12 *Income* £22,129 *Grants* £65,000
TRUSTEE David Rennie.
HOW TO APPLY In writing to the correspondent. Proposals should be summarised on one page with one or two more pages of supporting information. The trust states that it regrettably only has time to reply to the very few applications it is able to fund.
WHO TO APPLY TO David Rennie, Trustee, 12 St Catherine Street, Cupar, Fife KY15 4HN *Tel.* 01334 653777 *email* enquiries@pagan.co.uk

■ The 1989 Willan Charitable Trust

CC NO 802749   **ESTABLISHED** 1989
WHERE FUNDING CAN BE GIVEN Worldwide, in practice mainly the north east of England.
WHO CAN BENEFIT Registered charities for the benefit of children; disabled people; carers; volunteers; refugees; and offenders.
WHAT IS FUNDED Grants are given to: advance the education of children and help children in need; benefit people with physical or mental disabilities and alleviate hardship and distress either generally or individually; and further medical research.
WHAT IS NOT FUNDED Grants are not given directly to individuals. Grants for gap year students may be considered if the individual will be working for a charity (in this case the grant would be paid to the charity).
RANGE OF GRANTS £500–£10,000.
SAMPLE GRANTS Previous beneficiaries include: SAFC Foundation and Cancer Connexions (£10,000 each); Amble Multi Agency Crime Prevention Initiative (£6,000); Durham City Centre Youth Project, The Children's Society and the Calvert Trust (£5,000 each); Chester le Street Youth Centre (£4,000); Different Strokes North East, Northern Roots and People and Drugs (£3,000 each); Leukaemia Research and Coast Video Club (£2,000 each); Northumberland Mountain Rescue and the Association of British Poles (£1,000 each); and Healthwise and Newcastle Gang Show (£500).
FINANCES *Year* 2011–12 *Income* £445,031 *Grants* £506,397 *Assets* £15,930,313
TRUSTEES Francis A. Chapman; Alex Ohlsson; Willan Trustee Ltd.
HOW TO APPLY In writing to the correspondent at the Community Foundation Serving Tyne and Wear. 'Applicants should provide a letter of application not exceeding 2,000 words in length (approx. Two sides of A4). The letter of application should provide: contact details for the applicant organisation, and a named individual with whom we may discuss the funding proposal in more detail; a brief description of the applicant organisation, its track record and current activities; details of the activities for which funding is sought and why they are needed; a budget for the activities and details of any match funding provided by the applicant or other funders; details of the charity's bank account (a copy of a recent bank statement will suffice). Applicants should provide their charity registration number and recent accounts if these are not held on the Charity Commission website. Where the applicant is asking a registered charity to hold the grant on its behalf, details of that charity must be provided and also recent accounts or financial statements for the group itself. The trustees will meet in March, June, September and December. Applications will generally be considered at the next scheduled trustee meeting provided they are received by the 15th of the preceding month. However applicants are encouraged to submit their applications as early as possible to ensure they are considered at the next available trustees' meeting.'
WHO TO APPLY TO Mark Pierce, Head of Policy, Projects and Programmes, Community Foundation Tyne and Wear and Northumberland, 9th Floor, Cale Cross, 156 Pilgrim Street, Newcastle upon Tyne NE1 6SU *Tel.* 01912 220945 *Fax* 01912 300689 *email* mp@communityfoundation.org.uk

■ The 29th May 1961 Charitable Trust

CC NO 200198   **ESTABLISHED** 1961

WHERE FUNDING CAN BE GIVEN UK, with a special interest in the Warwickshire/Birmingham/Coventry area.

WHO CAN BENEFIT Charitable organisations in the UK. People who are socially disadvantaged may be favoured.

WHAT IS FUNDED General charitable purposes across a broad spectrum, including: art, leisure and youth; health; social welfare; education and training; homelessness and housing; offenders; and conservation and protection.

WHAT IS NOT FUNDED Grants only to registered charities. No grants to individuals.

TYPE OF GRANT One-off, recurring and some spread over two to three years. Grants are given for capital and revenue purposes.

RANGE OF GRANTS £500–£250,000, but the great majority are less than £10,000.

FINANCES *Year* 2011–12 *Income* £3,144,195 *Grants* £3,401,700 *Assets* £99,434,452

TRUSTEES Vanni Emanuele Treves; Andrew C. Jones; Anthony J. Mead; Paul Varney.

HOW TO APPLY To the secretary in writing, enclosing in triplicate the most recent annual report and accounts. Trustees normally meet in February, May, August and November. Due to the large number of applications received, they cannot be acknowledged.

WHO TO APPLY TO Vanni Emanuele Treves, Trustee, Ryder Court, 14 Ryder Street, London SW1 Y. 6QB *Tel.* 020 7024 9034 *email* enquiries@29may1961charity.org.uk

■ 4 Charity Foundation

CC NO 1077143   **ESTABLISHED** 1999

WHERE FUNDING CAN BE GIVEN UK and Israel.

WHO CAN BENEFIT Jewish charities and causes.

WHAT IS FUNDED Religious activities and education.

SAMPLE GRANTS Previous grants include those to: the American Jewish Joint Distribution Committee (£78,000); the Millennium Trust (£66,000); Keren Yehoshua V'Yisroel (£43,000); Project Seed (£35,000); World Jewish Relief (£29,000); Menorah Grammar School (£27,000); British Friends of Jaffa Institute (£23,000); Friends of Mir (£19,000); Heichal Hatorah Foundation (£15,000); Chai Life Line Cancer Care (£12,000); Jewish Care (£11,000); and British Friends of Ezer Mizion (£10,000).

FINANCES *Year* 2011–12 *Income* £7,025,791 *Grants* £975,603 *Assets* £13,126,785

TRUSTEES Jacob Schimmel; Marc Schimmel; D. Rabson; A. Schimmel.

HOW TO APPLY This trust does not respond to unsolicited applications.

WHO TO APPLY TO Jacob Schimmel, Trustee, UK I. Ltd, 54–56 Euston Street, London NW1 2ES *Tel.* 020 7387 0155

■ The A. B. Charitable Trust

CC NO 1000147   **ESTABLISHED** 1990
WHERE FUNDING CAN BE GIVEN Mainly UK.
WHO CAN BENEFIT Charities registered and working in the UK. The trust favours those charities with an annual income between £150,000 and £1.5 million, which do not have substantial investments or surpluses.
WHAT IS FUNDED Charities working where human dignity is imperilled and where there are opportunities for human dignity to be affirmed. Priority is given to charities working to support: refugees and victims of torture; prisoners; older people; people with mental health problems. In relation to these areas, the following cross-cutting themes are of interest to the trustees: women; homelessness; therapeutic art.
WHAT IS NOT FUNDED No grants are made to organisations principally concerned with: animals; children; environment; formal education; individuals; medicine; religion; and research. Capital appeals are not normally supported, nor are charities with large national or international links, or areas which should reasonably be funded by government.
RANGE OF GRANTS £2,500–£50,000.
SAMPLE GRANTS Asylum Aid (£20,000); Detention Advice Service, Law Centres Network and Revolving Doors Agency (£15,000 each); Action on Elder Abuse, Circles UK, Prisoners' Education Trust and Prisoners of Conscience Appeal Fund (£10,000 each); UK Drugs Policy Commission (£6,000); and Finsbury Park Homeless Families Project, Music in Detention, Magic Me, Strong Roots and Zimbabwe Association (£5,000 each).
FINANCES *Year* 2012–13 *Income* £429,786 *Grants* £468,500 *Assets* £10,187
TRUSTEES Claire Bonavero; Olivier Bonavero; Philippe Bonavero; Anne Bonavero; Yves Bonavero; Athol Harley; Alison Swan Parente; Peter Day.
HOW TO APPLY Applications can be completed online at the trust's website. As well as administrative and financial details, the online application form will ask for a two page summary of the organisation's work, including: background; aims and objectives; activities; achievements. After filling in the online application form you will be sent a reference number. Send the director the following documents in hard copy quoting the reference number: the two page overview of the organisation's work; a signed copy of the latest certified accounts/statements, with a reporting date that is no more than 12 months prior to the application deadline chosen (the trustees meet four times a year, in January, April, July and October – see the website for exact deadline dates); up to two items of publicity material that illustrate the work of the organisation, such as annual reviews or leaflets.
WHO TO APPLY TO Sara Harrity, Director, Monmouth House, 87–93 Westbourne Grove, London W2 4UL *Tel.* 020 7313 8070 *Fax* 020 7313 9607 *email* mail@abcharitabletrust.org.uk *Website* www.abcharitabletrust.org.uk

■ A. W. Charitable Trust

CC NO 283322   **ESTABLISHED** 1961
WHERE FUNDING CAN BE GIVEN Unrestricted.
WHO CAN BENEFIT Jewish educational and religious organisations; registered charities.
WHAT IS FUNDED General charitable purposes.
SAMPLE GRANTS Previous beneficiaries include: TET; Asser Bishvil Foundation; Chevras Oneg Shabbos-Yomtov; Friends of Mir; CML; Toimchei Shabbos Manchester; British Friends of Kupat Hair; Purim Fund; Beenstock Home; and Zoreya Tzedokos.
FINANCES *Year* 2011–12 *Income* £29,466,507 *Grants* £4,289,516 *Assets* £100,203,261
TRUSTEES Rabbi Aubrey Weis; Rachel Weis.
HOW TO APPLY In writing to the correspondent. The trust considers 'all justified applications for support of educational establishments, places of worship and other charitable actives.' Each application and request is considered on its own merit.
WHO TO APPLY TO Rabbi Aubrey Weis, Trustee, 1 Allandale Court, Waterpark Road, Manchester M7 4JL *Tel.* 01617 400116

■ The Aberbrothock Skea Trust (formerly known as Aberbrothock Charitable Trust)

SC NO SC039202   **ESTABLISHED** 1971/ 2008
WHERE FUNDING CAN BE GIVEN East of Scotland, north of the Firth of Tay.
WHO CAN BENEFIT Organisations benefiting the community with charitable status.
WHAT IS FUNDED Children/young people; disability; environment/conservation; hospitals/hospices; and medical research are all considered.
WHAT IS NOT FUNDED The geographical restriction is strictly adhered to. Applications from outside the area, and/or from individuals, will not be considered.
TYPE OF GRANT One-off, including project, research, capital and core costs.
RANGE OF GRANTS Up to £2,500.
SAMPLE GRANTS Previous beneficiaries have included Red Cross, Colon Cancer Care, Princess Royal Trust, International League of Horses, Kids Out and Dundee Heritage Trust.
FINANCES *Year* 2011–12 *Income* £114,787
TRUSTEES G. McNicol; A. T. L. Grant; G. G. M. D. Dunlop; E. Steven; I. Townsend; Lady F. Fraser.
OTHER INFORMATION Although the income remains around the same, the grant total changes every year.
HOW TO APPLY In writing to the correspondent. Trustees meet to consider grants in March, July and December.
WHO TO APPLY TO The Trustees, Thorntons Law LLP, Brothockbank House, Arbroath, Angus DD11 1NE

■ The Aberdeen Endowments Trust

SC NO SC010507   **ESTABLISHED** 1909
WHERE FUNDING CAN BE GIVEN The former City and Royal Burgh of Aberdeen (i.e. pre-1975).
WHO CAN BENEFIT Persons of organisations which belong to the former City and Royal Burgh of Aberdeen.
WHAT IS FUNDED Education and the arts. The main purpose of the trust is to give financial

assistance to individuals for educational purposes.

WHAT IS NOT FUNDED No grants to people or organisations from outside the former City and Royal Burgh of Aberdeen.

RANGE OF GRANTS Average grant is less than £1,000

FINANCES *Year* 2012 *Income* £1,011,000

TRUSTEES Three persons elected by Aberdeen City Council; one by the Senatus Academicus of the University of Aberdeen; two by the governors of Robert Gordon's College, Aberdeen; two by the Church of Scotland Presbytery of Aberdeen; one by the churches of Aberdeen other than the Church of Scotland; one by the Society of Advocates in Aberdeen; one by the Convener Court of the Seven Incorporated Trades of Aberdeen; one by the trade unions having branches in Aberdeen; one by the Aberdeen Local Association of the Educational Institute of Scotland; plus not less than two and not more than four co-optees.

HOW TO APPLY Application forms are available from the correspondent. The Benefactions Committee of the trust, which makes financial awards, normally meets nine or ten times a year.

WHO TO APPLY TO David Murdoch, Clerk, 19 Albert Street, Aberdeen AB9 1QF *Tel.* 01224 640194

....

■ The Aberdeenshire Educational Trust Scheme

SC NO SC028382   **ESTABLISHED** 1999

WHERE FUNDING CAN BE GIVEN The former county of Aberdeen.

WHO CAN BENEFIT Individuals in education, schools and further education centres, as well as to clubs and other organisations.

WHAT IS FUNDED Providing and maintaining playing fields and other sports facilities including equipment; schools and further education centres to assist in providing special equipment; clubs, societies and organisations which include amongst their activities work of an educational nature; schools and organisations to assist education in art, music and drama; individuals and bodies to undertake educational experiments and research which will be for the benefit of people belonging to Aberdeen County. Help may also be given towards 'regional and national enterprises of an educational nature'.

FINANCES *Year* 2011–12 *Income* £70,000
Grants £70,000

HOW TO APPLY On a form available from the correspondent. Full guidelines are also available upon request.

WHO TO APPLY TO The Administrator, St Leonards-Aberdeenshire Council, Sandyhill Road, Banff, Aberdeenshire AB45 1BH

....

■ ABF The Soldiers' Charity

CC NO 1146420   **ESTABLISHED** 1944

WHERE FUNDING CAN BE GIVEN Worldwide.

WHO CAN BENEFIT Support and benefit of people serving, or who have served, in the British Army, or their families/dependants.

WHAT IS FUNDED Supporting individuals through the Regimental and Corps Benevolence Funds, and other military and national charities which look after the needs of the serving and retired army community.

TYPE OF GRANT One-off grants.

RANGE OF GRANTS Between £1,000–£5,000

SAMPLE GRANTS Scottish Veterans Residences (£250,000); Royal Commonwealth Ex-Services

League (£245,000); SSAFA Forces Help (£225,500); Combat Stress (£195,000); Erskine Hospital (£150,000); Community Housing and Therapy (£64,000); Victory Services Club (£60,000); Queen Alexandra Hospital Home (£40,000); The Warrior Programme (£30,000); Timebank (£25,000); STUBS (£10,000); West Indian Association of Service Personnel (£5,000); and Ulster Defence Regiment Benevolent Fund (£500).

FINANCES *Year* 2011–12 *Income* £16,859,126
Grants £8,578,717 *Assets* £43,070,602

TRUSTEES Maj. Gen. George Kennedy; Maj. Sir Michael Parker; Stephen Clark; Guy Davies; Maj. Gen. Peter Sheppard; Maj. Gen. Richard Nugee; Brig. Andrew Freemantle; Allison M. Gallico; Damien Francis; Andrew Vernon.

OTHER INFORMATION £3.3 million went to charities; £5.3 million was awarded for the benefit of individuals.

HOW TO APPLY Individual cases should be referred initially to the appropriate Corps or Regimental Association. Charities should apply in writing and enclose the latest annual report and accounts. Also refer to the charity's website for current eligibility criteria and application processes. Initial telephone enquiries are welcome.

WHO TO APPLY TO Roger Musson, Director of Finance and Resources, Mountbarrow House, 12 Elizabeth Street, London SW1W 9RB *Tel.* 0845 241 4820 *Fax* 0845 241 4821 *email* rmusson@soldierscharity.org *Website* www.soldierscharity.org

....

■ Eric Abrams Charitable Trust

CC NO 275939   **ESTABLISHED** 1968

WHERE FUNDING CAN BE GIVEN UK.

WHO CAN BENEFIT Jewish organisations.

WHAT IS FUNDED Jewish causes.

WHAT IS NOT FUNDED No grants to individuals.

SAMPLE GRANTS Previous beneficiaries have included: Friends of Ohr Akiva Institution, Centre for Torah Education Trust, Halacha Lemoshe Trust, Hale Adult Hebrew Education Trust, the Heathlands Village, Manchester Jewish Federation, Rabbi Nachman of Breslov Charitable Foundation, UK Friends of Magen David Adom and United Jewish Israel Appeal.

FINANCES *Year* 2011–12 *Income* £35,897
Grants £27,560 *Assets* £1,020,275

TRUSTEES Brian Abrams; Eric Abrams; Marcia Anne Jacobs; Susan Melanie Abrams.

HOW TO APPLY The trustees do not invite appeals.

WHO TO APPLY TO The Trustees, c/o Lyon Griffiths Limited, Unit 17, Alvaston Business Park, Middlewich Road, Nantwich, Cheshire CW5 6PF *Tel.* 01270 624445

....

■ Brian Abrams Charitable Trust

CC NO 275941   **ESTABLISHED** 1978

WHERE FUNDING CAN BE GIVEN UK

WHO CAN BENEFIT Jewish organisations.

WHAT IS FUNDED Jewish causes.

WHAT IS NOT FUNDED No grants to individuals.

SAMPLE GRANTS Previous beneficiaries have included Centre for Torah Education Trust, Friends of Ohr Akiva Institution, Halacha Lemoshe Trust, Hale Adult Hebrew Education Trust, the Heathlands Village, Manchester Jewish Federation, Rabbi Nachman of Breslov Charitable Foundation, Rainsough Charitable Trust, UK Friends of Magen David Adom and United Jewish Israel Appeal.

FINANCES *Year* 2011–12 *Income* £36,790 *Grants* £27,510 *Assets* £1,036,331

TRUSTEES Betty Abrams; Brian Abrams; Eric Abrams; Gail Gabbie.

HOW TO APPLY The trust has stated that its funds are fully committed and applications are not invited.

WHO TO APPLY TO The Trustees, c/o Lyon Griffiths Limited, Unit 17, Alvaston Business Park, Middlewich Road, Nantwich, Cheshire CW5 6PF *Tel.* 01270 624445

■ The Acacia Charitable Trust

CC NO 274275   ESTABLISHED 1977

WHERE FUNDING CAN BE GIVEN UK and Israel.

WHO CAN BENEFIT Registered charities.

WHAT IS FUNDED Educational and medical charities in the UK. Jewish charities, both in the UK and the State of Israel.

WHAT IS NOT FUNDED No grants to individuals.

TYPE OF GRANT Core and project costs will be considered.

RANGE OF GRANTS Up to £30,000, although most for under £5,000.

SAMPLE GRANTS Previous beneficiaries included: The Jewish Museum (£41,000); Community Security Trust (£5,000); Norwood and Yad Vashem (£1,000 each); Royal National Theatre (£500); Nightingale House (£250); and Shelter, Jewish Council for Racial Equality and Riding for the Disabled (£100 each).

FINANCES *Year* 2011–12 *Income* £70,244 *Grants* £59,696 *Assets* £1,730,236

TRUSTEES Kenneth Rubens; Angela Gillian Rubens; Simon Rubens; Paul Rubens.

HOW TO APPLY In writing to the correspondent.

WHO TO APPLY TO The Secretary, c/o H. W. Fisher and Co, Acre House, 11–15 William Road, London NW1 3ER *Tel.* 020 7486 1884 *email* acacia@dircon.co.uk

■ Access Sport

CC NO 1104687   ESTABLISHED 2004

WHERE FUNDING CAN BE GIVEN Throughout the UK.

WHO CAN BENEFIT Children and young people; disability; socially and economically disadvantaged people.

WHAT IS FUNDED Promotion of health' by increasing sport participation opportunities for young people in the UK through local sports clubs in order to tackle social exclusion, inactivity and obesity, particularly in disadvantaged areas'.

TYPE OF GRANT One – off and ongoing grants to organisations.

FINANCES *Year* 2011–12 *Income* £466,845 *Grants* £80,347 *Assets* £59,861

TRUSTEES Natalie Pinkham; Fraser Hardie; John Sarsby; Michael Allen; Neil Robinson; Neil Goulden; Grace Clancey; David Rigney; Tina Kokkinos; Phil Veasey; Timothy Jones; Greg Searle; Keith Wishart; Mark Donnelly.

HOW TO APPLY Contact details for each of the projects can be found on the trust's website. General inquiries should be directed to the correspondent.

WHO TO APPLY TO Sue Wheeler, Administrator, 3 Durham Yard, Teesdale Street, London E2 6QF *Tel.* 020 7993 9883 *email* mark. hardie@accesssport.co.uk *Website* www. accesssport.co.uk

■ Achisomoch Aid Company Limited

CC NO 278387   ESTABLISHED 1979

WHERE FUNDING CAN BE GIVEN Unrestricted.

WHO CAN BENEFIT Jewish religious charities.

WHAT IS FUNDED The advancement of religion in accordance with the Jewish faith.

SAMPLE GRANTS Previous beneficiaries have included: the Ah Trust, Beis Malka Trust, Chevras Maoz Ladol, Comet Charities Ltd, Davis Elias Charitable Trust, Havenpoint Ltd, Heritage Retreats, Jewish Educational Trust, Lolev Charitable Trust, Menorah Primary School, Michlala Jerusalem College, SOFT, Tomchei Cholim Trust and Yad Eliezer – Israel.

FINANCES *Year* 2011–12 *Income* £8,014,831 *Grants* £7,690,638 *Assets* £2,581,425

TRUSTEES David Chontow; Jack Emanuel; Yitzchock Katz; Michael Hockenbroch.

OTHER INFORMATION The following information about how the trust operates is given on the its website: 'Achisomoch is a charity voucher agency – it is like a bank. You open an account with us and then pay money into the account. You are given a cheque (voucher) book and can then make (charitable) payments by using these vouchers. As a charity in its own right, we can reclaim the tax rebate under Gift Aid to increase the money in your account and available for distribution to charities. Donations, via vouchers can be made only to registered charities. You get regular statements and can arrange to speak to client services for any help or special instructions.'

HOW TO APPLY In writing to the correspondent.

WHO TO APPLY TO Yitzchock Katz, Trustee, 26 Hoop Lane, London NW11 0NU *Tel.* 020 8731 8988 *email* admin@achisomoch.org *Website* www. achisomoch.org

■ The ACT Foundation

CC NO 1068617   ESTABLISHED 1998

WHERE FUNDING CAN BE GIVEN UK and overseas.

WHO CAN BENEFIT Health, welfare and housing.

WHAT IS FUNDED Grants generally fall into the following areas: building – funding modifications to homes, schools, hospices etc.; equipment – provision of specialised wheelchairs, other mobility aids and equipment including medical equipment to assist independent living; financial assistance – towards the cost of short-term respite breaks at a registered respite centre. Projects that intend to be a platform for continuing services will be expected to demonstrate sustainability. ACT would be concerned to be a sole funder of projects that require ongoing support.

WHAT IS NOT FUNDED The foundation will not make grants: to replace statutory funding; to pay for work that has already commenced or equipment already purchased or on order; towards the operating costs of other charities except in connection with setting up new services; to charities that have not been registered for at least three years; for projects which promote a particular religion or faith; to community centres and youth clubs except where those served are in special need of help (e.g. the elderly or persons with special needs); to Local Authorities; to umbrella or grantmaking organisations except where they undertake special assessments not readily available from the foundation's own resources; to universities and colleges, and grant-maintained, private or local education authority schools or their Parent

Teacher Associations, except if those schools are for students with special needs; for costs associated with political or publicity campaigns.

SAMPLE GRANTS Treloar Trust – grants to outreach projects (£500,000); Livability – grants towards 'Lifestyle Choices' project (£100,000); Theatre Royal Stratford East (£20,000); Aspire, Diverse Abilities Plus, HTF Kent, Outreach 3 Way and Swindon Therapy Centre for Multiple Sclerosis (£10,000 each); Build IT International – Zambia, Disability Action Yorkshire, Family Care Trust and PHAB (£5,000 each); Calvert Trust (£4,500); Scottish Huntington's Association and Special Educational Needs Families Support Group (£2,000 each) and Goldhill Adventure Playground (£1,000).

FINANCES *Year* 2011–12 *Income* £15,568,841 *Grants* £1,371,710 *Assets* £46,645,056

TRUSTEES Paul Nield; John J. O'Sullivan; Michael Street; Christine Erwood; Robert F. White; Denis Taylor.

OTHER INFORMATION The grant total includes £489,500 to 447 individuals.

HOW TO APPLY The following information is taken from the foundation's helpful website: 'Application by registered charities and overseas charitable organisations has to be by way of letter on the organisation's headed paper and should: give a brief description of your organisation including any statutory or voluntary registration; provide a summary of the work you plan to undertake with the grant, together with a cost breakdown, plans and/or specification if available and a summary of the key milestones for the work; provide information on why you need to do this work and what would happen if you were unable to do it; give details of any other UK-based support received or pledged for your project; specify what you expect the results of the work to be and the number of beneficiaries helped; tell us how you plan to evaluate whether the work achieved its goals; tell us if the work will require capital and/or ongoing operational funding and if so how you plan to meet these costs. In addition you need to attach the following financial information to the letter: a cashflow projection of income and expenditure budget for the work; details of any income already raised for the work and income outstanding and where you plan to raise it from; your latest annual report and accounts. You can apply for a grant at any time. Trustees meet four times a year, but you do not need to time your application to coincide with these meetings. Procedures exist to give approvals between meeting dates, where necessary. We do not publish the dates of Trustees' meetings. We will send you an acknowledgement letter within one week of receiving your application. If your proposal is either in an unacceptable form, or ineligible, or a low priority, we will tell you in this letter. We will assess all acceptable applications and we may contact you for further information and/or make a personal visit. In the case of charitable bodies we may also ask for a presentation. We aim to make decisions on grants of up to £50,000 within one month of receiving your application. Decisions on grants over £50,000 can take up to three months. If the application is for an emergency you may request a faster timescale and we will do our best to assist.'

WHO TO APPLY TO James Kerr, Grants Manager, 61 Thames Street, Windsor, Berkshire SL4 1QW *Tel.* 01753 753900 *Fax* 01753 753901 *email* info@theactfoundation.co.uk *Website* www.theactfoundation.co.uk

■ Action Medical Research

CC NO 208701 **ESTABLISHED** 1952

WHERE FUNDING CAN BE GIVEN UK.

WHO CAN BENEFIT University departments, hospitals and research institutes for specific research projects.

WHAT IS FUNDED Research focusing on child health including problems affecting pregnancy, childbirth, babies, children and young people. Within this a broad spectrum of research is supported with the objective of preventing disease and disability and of alleviating physical disability.

WHAT IS NOT FUNDED The charity does not provide: grants towards service provision or audit studies; grants purely for higher education, e.g. BSc/MSc/PhD course fees and subsistence costs; grants for medical or dental electives; grants for work undertaken outside the UK; any indirect costs such as administrative or other overheads imposed by the university or other institution; costs associated with advertising and recruitment; 'top up' funding for work supported by other funding bodies; costs to attend conferences and meetings (current Action Medical Research grantholders may apply separately); grants to other charities – applications would normally come directly from research teams and projects need to be passed through Action Medical Research's scientific peer review system; grants for research into complementary/alternative medicine; grants on how best to train clinical staff; grants for psychosocial aspects of treatment; grants on social research, family relationships or socioeconomic research; grants for very basic research with little likelihood of clinical impact within the short to medium term. Applicants based in core funded units can apply but need to demonstrate added value.

TYPE OF GRANT Research comprising: project grants and Research Training Fellowship scheme.

RANGE OF GRANTS The average award is about £80,000. It is unusual to fund projects over £150,000 in their entirety.

SAMPLE GRANTS University Hospital Southampton and Southampton University (£200,000); Universities of Oxford and Oxford University Hospitals NHS Trust £173,000); King's College London (£170,000); University of Glasgow (£52,000); and Swansea University (£10,000).

FINANCES *Year* 2012 *Income* £6,946,837 *Grants* £2,959,133 *Assets* £6,695,526

TRUSTEES Valerie Remington-Hobbs; Prof. Sarah Bray; Charles Jackson; Prof. Andrew George; Richard Price; Sir John Wickerson; David Gibbs; Mark Gardiner; Philip Hodkinson; Esther Alderson.

PUBLICATIONS Newsletter; medical conditions leaflets.

HOW TO APPLY The following information is taken from the charity's website: '**Outline proposal:** All applicants should complete a two page outline proposal form [available from the charity's website] summarising the research and giving an estimation of costs, and email it to the Research Department. The details on the outline form should include the potential clinical application of the work, how it fits the remit of the charity and a description of the work in sufficient detail that our scientific advisors can understand what is proposed. The purpose of the outline is to establish that your proposed work clearly falls within our remit and priorities. The work should also be of sufficient quality to be recommended for further assessment. If your work is considered peripheral to our aims and in cases where demand on our funds is high, we may be unable to request an application from you. **Full application:** if the outline proposal is acceptable, you will be invited to complete a full application form online and you will be advised of the timetable. Applications are assessed by peer review, first by independent external referees and then by our scientific advisory panel. The decision to approve a grant is made by the council on the recommendations of the panel. Closing dates for proposals and applications are available on the charity's website.'

WHO TO APPLY TO Martin Richardson, Vincent House, 31 North Parade, Horsham, West Sussex RH12 2DP *Tel.* 01403 210406 *Fax* 01403 210541 *email* info@action.org.uk *Website* www.action.org.uk

■ The Company of Actuaries' Charitable Trust Fund

CC NO 280702 **ESTABLISHED** 1980
WHERE FUNDING CAN BE GIVEN UK, with a preference for the City of London.
WHO CAN BENEFIT Charitable organisations and individuals involved in, or training for, a career in actuary.
WHAT IS FUNDED Support for people who are elderly or who have disabilities; charities helping children and young people; those involved in treating medical conditions or funding medical research; other worthy charities, such as those working with people who are in need.
WHAT IS NOT FUNDED No grants for the propagation of religious or political beliefs, the maintenance of historic buildings or for conservation. The trustees do not usually support an organisation which has received a grant from the fund in the previous 24 months.
RANGE OF GRANTS £500–£5,000, with larger amounts given where liverymen have a significant connection.
SAMPLE GRANTS Royal Society (£54,000); Children's Liver Disease Foundation (£5,000); Edmonton Sea Cadets (£4,000); Rainbow Trust (£3,500); Guildhall School of Music and Drama (£2,500); Fenland Association for Community Transport and Marine Society and Sea Cadets (£2,000 each); Just Different, Sailors' Families Society and Spadework (£1,000 each); and Carefree Kids, Gambia UpCountry and Traffic of the Stage (£500 each).
FINANCES *Year* 2011–12 *Income* £180,308 *Grants* £141,404 *Assets* £350,234
TRUSTEES Jeff Medlock; Michael Turner; Sally Bridgeland; Geraldine Kaye; Michael Pomery; Alan Smith.
HOW TO APPLY On a form which can be downloaded from the fund's website. Further information about the trust can be obtained from the correspondent.
WHO TO APPLY TO Patrick O'Keeffe, Honorary Almoner, Broomyhurst, Shobley, Ringwood, Hampshire BH24 3HT *Tel.* 01425 472810 *email* almoner.cact@btinternet.com *Website* www.companyofactuaries.co.uk/charitabletrust

■ The Ad Meliora Charitable Trust

CC NO 1148079 **ESTABLISHED** 2012
WHERE FUNDING CAN BE GIVEN UK.
WHO CAN BENEFIT Charities and community groups.
WHAT IS FUNDED Health, social welfare, relief of poverty, the armed forces and emergency services.
TRUSTEES Barclays Bank Trust Company Ltd (Walter Coxon; David Currie; Graham Nicoll; Thomas Rostron; David Blizzard).
HOW TO APPLY In writing to the correspondent.
WHO TO APPLY TO Nigel Williams, Barclays Bank Trust Co. Ltd, Osborne Court, Gadbrook Park, Rudheath, Cheshire CW9 7UE *Tel.* 01606 313386

■ The Sylvia Adams Charitable Trust

CC NO 1050678 **ESTABLISHED** 1995
WHERE FUNDING CAN BE GIVEN Hertfordshire; work in the UK which has a national impact; and Kenya, Tanzania and Uganda.
WHO CAN BENEFIT All grants are made through UK registered charities.
WHAT IS FUNDED Projects benefiting people with disabilities, people living in poverty, children and young people. It is particularly interested in helping people to become self-supporting and self-help projects.
WHAT IS NOT FUNDED The trust does not give grants to: individuals; projects in the Middle East or Eastern Europe or the countries of the ex-Soviet Union; work that solely benefits elderly people; or organisations helping animals, medical research or environmental causes.
TYPE OF GRANT One off and recurring for up to three years. Project and core costs including capital and unrestricted funding.
RANGE OF GRANTS Up to £50,000. Grants generally average £10,000–£15,000.
SAMPLE GRANTS UK beneficiaries included: Down Syndrome Association (£50,000), for an employment project; Raleigh International (£30,000); towards its Youth Agency Partnership Programme; Jubilee Sailing Trust (£26,500), for the costs of an additional fundraiser; Stonewall (£20,000), for a youth programme; Volunteer Reading Project (£15,000), to fund reading support for an additional 90 children; Unique (£10,000), towards IT and fundraising costs; London Youth (£10,000), towards the renovation of Woodrow House (£10,000); Housing Justice (£6,000), towards project work; and Host (£5,000), core funding. Beneficiaries in Hertfordshire included: YMCA Central Hertfordshire (£25,000), for the SPACE project in Hatfield; Groundwork Herts (£12,500), towards a summer holiday scheme; Letchworth Arts Centre (£7,500), for two arts interns; Greenside Studio (£5,000), towards the purchase of a vehicle; and React (£2,500), towards equipment.
FINANCES *Year* 2011–12 *Income* £209,304 *Grants* £1,200,000 *Assets* £7,942,511
TRUSTEES Richard J. Golland; Mark Heasman; Timothy Lawler.
HOW TO APPLY There is a two stage application process: Stage 1 can **only** be made through the trust's website; Applicants who successfully get through this stage will be asked to submit a fuller Stage 2 application. Telephone queries about the guidelines and application process are welcome in advance of applications being made

WHO TO APPLY TO Jane Young, Director, Sylvia AdaHouse, 24 The Common, Hatfield, Hertfordshire AL10 0NB *Tel.* 01707 259259 *Fax* 01707 259268 *email* info@sylvia-adams. org.uk *Website* www.sylvia-adams.org.uk

■ The Adamson Trust

SC NO SC016517 **ESTABLISHED** 1946

WHERE FUNDING CAN BE GIVEN UK, but preference will be given to requests on behalf of Scottish children.

WHO CAN BENEFIT Children under 18 with a physical or mental disability, both groups and individuals.

WHAT IS FUNDED Assistance with holidays – grants may be given to the parent(s) of children or as block grants; for example, to the special needs unit of a school.

TYPE OF GRANT Usually one-off.

SAMPLE GRANTS Previous beneficiaries have included Barnardo's Dundee Family Support Team, Children's Hospice Association Scotland, Lady Hoare Trust for Physically Disabled Children, Hopscotch Holidays, Over the Wall Gang Group, Peak Holidays, React, Scotland Yard Adventure Centre, Sense Scotland, Special Needs Adventure Play Ground and Scottish Spina Bifida Association.

FINANCES *Year* 2011–12 *Income* £71,816 *Grants* £75,000

TRUSTEE Information not available.

OTHER INFORMATION Around £75,000 is given in grants each year.

HOW TO APPLY In writing to the correspondent. A copy of the latest audited accounts should be included together with details of the organisation, the number of children who would benefit and the proposed holiday.

WHO TO APPLY TO Edward Elworthy, Administrator, PO Box 26334, Crieff, Perthshire PH7 9AB *email* edward@elworthy.net

■ The Victor Adda Foundation

CC NO 291456 **ESTABLISHED** 1984

WHERE FUNDING CAN BE GIVEN UK, but in practice Greenwich.

WHO CAN BENEFIT Charitable organisations.

WHAT IS FUNDED This trust mainly supports the Fan Museum in Greenwich.

SAMPLE GRANTS Previous beneficiaries have included the Child Trust, Fan Museum Greenwich, Jewish Museum and St Christopher Hospice.

FINANCES *Year* 2011–12 *Income* £21,500 *Grants* £62,203

TRUSTEES Helene Alexander; Susannah Alexander; Jeremy Hawes; Linda Estelle.

HOW TO APPLY In writing to the correspondent. Only successful applications are notified of a decision.

WHO TO APPLY TO The Trustees, c/o Kleinwort Benson Trustees, 14 St George Street, London W1S 1FE *Tel.* 020 3207 7091

■ Adenfirst Ltd

CC NO 291647 **ESTABLISHED** 1984

WHERE FUNDING CAN BE GIVEN Worldwide.

WHO CAN BENEFIT Jewish organisations only.

WHAT IS FUNDED Jewish causes related to education, medical care, relief of poverty and the advancement of religion.

RANGE OF GRANTS £0–£35,000

SAMPLE GRANTS Previously: Beis Aaron Trust (£30,000); Ezer Vehatzolo and Kahal Chassidim

Wiznitz (£20,000 each); and Beis Rochel D'Satmar, Lolev Charitable Trust and Mercaz Hatorah Belz Machnovke (£10,000 each).

FINANCES *Year* 2011 *Income* £518,058 *Grants* £112,030 *Assets* £1,480,832

TRUSTEES H. F. Bondi; Leonard Bondi; R. Cymerman; Sylvia Cymerman; Ian Heitner; Michael Cymerman; Sarah Heitner.

OTHER INFORMATION Latest accounts available from the Charity Commission were for 2011.

HOW TO APPLY In writing to the correspondent.

WHO TO APPLY TO Leonard Bondi, Trustee, c/o 479 Holloway Road, London N7 6LE *Tel.* 020 7272 2255

■ The Adint Charitable Trust

CC NO 265290 **ESTABLISHED** 1973

WHERE FUNDING CAN BE GIVEN Worldwide, in practice UK.

WHO CAN BENEFIT Registered charities.

WHAT IS FUNDED Health and social welfare.

WHAT IS NOT FUNDED Individuals.

TYPE OF GRANT One-off grants and recurrent grants for more than three years are considered, for capital costs (including buildings) and core costs.

RANGE OF GRANTS £50–£15,000. Grants are usually for £10,000 and £5,000.

SAMPLE GRANTS Aldis Trust, BLISS, Dementia Relief Trust, KIDS, Meningitis Trust, Salvation Army and Springboard (£10,000 each); Acorn Children's Hospice, British Epilepsy Association, Cruse Bereavement Care, Help the Hospices, Listening Books, Prostate Cancer Charity, The Firefighters Charity and Thomas Coram Foundation (£5,000 each); Norwood Ravenswood (£1,000); and Noah's Ark Children's Hospice (£500).

FINANCES *Year* 2012–13 *Income* £250,365 *Grants* £302,500 *Assets* £6,819,162

TRUSTEES Anthony J. Edwards; Margaret Edwards; Douglas R. Oram; Brian Pate.

HOW TO APPLY In writing to the correspondent. Each applicant should make its own case in the way it considers best, but the application should include full details of the applicant charity. The trust states that it cannot enter into correspondence and unsuccessful applicants will not be notified.

WHO TO APPLY TO Douglas R. Oram, Trustee, Suite 42, 571 Finchley Road, London NW3 7BN *email* adintct@gmail.com

■ The Adnams Charity

CC NO 1000203 **ESTABLISHED** 1990

WHERE FUNDING CAN BE GIVEN Within a 25-mile radius of St Edmund's Church, Southwold.

WHO CAN BENEFIT Small local projects.

WHAT IS FUNDED General charitable purposes. The charity gives support to a wide variety of organisations including those involved with health and social welfare, education, recreation, the arts, environment and conservation and historic buildings.

WHAT IS NOT FUNDED The charity does not normally make grants to religious organisations or private clubs unless they can demonstrate that the purpose of the grant is for something of clear public benefit, accessible to all. It does not provide raffle prizes or sponsorship of any kind. No grants are made to individuals. However, public bodies and charities may apply on behalf of individuals. Grants are not made in successive years.

TYPE OF GRANT The trustees prefer applications for specific items. Grants are generally of a one-off nature. The trustees are reluctant to give grants to cover ongoing running costs, although in very exceptional circumstances they may do so.

RANGE OF GRANTS Normally £100–£2,500.

SAMPLE GRANTS NWES World of Work and Peer Support (£2,500 each); Friends of John Turner House Day Centre, Prisoners' Education Trust, Suffolk Social Services and The Thirst Youth Cafe (£1,000 each); Alpington and Bergh Apton CE VA Primary School, Anglia Care Trust, Jubilee Opera, Mettingham Village Hall, New Cut Arts and Wacton Village Hall (£500 each); and Lowestoft Shopmobility (£400).

FINANCES *Year* 2011–12 *Income* £33,801 *Grants* £59,940 *Assets* £6,808

TRUSTEES Jonathan Adnams, Chair; Lizzy Cantwell; Guy Heald; Emma Hibbert; Melvyn Horn; Simon Loftus; Andy Wood; Alison Kibble; Ann Cross.

HOW TO APPLY Application forms are available on request to the Charity Administrator. Grants are considered at quarterly meetings, in January, April, July and October. Application deadlines usually fall in the previous month and are listed on the charity's website.

WHO TO APPLY TO Rebecca Abrahall, Charity Administrator, c/o The Street, Brockdish, Norfolk IP21 4JY *Tel.* 01502 727200 *email* rebecca.abrahall@adnams.co.uk *Website* www.adnams.co.uk/charity

....

■ AF Trust Company

CC NO 1060319   ESTABLISHED 1996
WHERE FUNDING CAN BE GIVEN England.
WHO CAN BENEFIT Higher education institutions.
WHAT IS FUNDED Charitable purposes connected with the provision of higher education.
WHAT IS NOT FUNDED No grants to individuals.
RANGE OF GRANTS Up to £18,000.
SAMPLE GRANTS Imperial College (£36,000); University of Nottingham, Samworthy Academy (£34,500); University of Reading (£33,500); University of Canterbury Christ Church (£17,000); and other institutions (£9,000).
FINANCES *Year* 2011–12 *Income* £2,430,308 *Grants* £130,000 *Assets* £451,153
TRUSTEES Martin Wynne-Jones; Andrew Connolly; David Leah; Carol Wright.
OTHER INFORMATION The income figure also relates to funds used to lease buildings from educational establishments and then enter into lease-back arrangements rather than indicating the size of funds available.
HOW TO APPLY In writing to the correspondent. However, unsolicited applications are only accepted from higher education institutions within England.
WHO TO APPLY TO Paul Welch, Secretary, 34 Chapel Street, Thatcham, Reading, Berkshire RG18 4QL *Tel.* 01635 867222

....

■ Age Scotland

SC NO SC010100   ESTABLISHED 2009
WHERE FUNDING CAN BE GIVEN Scotland.
WHO CAN BENEFIT Groups for the benefit and welfare of older people
WHAT IS FUNDED Organising special outings or event, purchasing equipment, producing and distributing information, attending/running and event which will benefit older people, start-up costs for new groups, training costs, developing a substantial new project.

WHAT IS NOT FUNDED No grants to statutory authorities, commercial organisations and individuals.

TYPE OF GRANT Capital; one-off; running costs; salaries; and start-up costs.

RANGE OF GRANTS Up to £10,000.

SAMPLE GRANTS 8th World Congress on Active Ageing and Dumfries and Galloway Seniors Forum (£10,000 each); Jura Care Centre Group (£8,000); Moray Handyperson Service (£5,000); Highland Rainbow Folk (£3,000); Cowal Elderly Befriending Scheme (£2,500); Dalbeattie Floral Club (£2,300); Age Concern Glenrothes (£2,000) and Barmhill Jolly Beggars (£1,000).

FINANCES *Year* 2011–12 *Income* £3,031,450 *Grants* £168,610 *Assets* £1,014,444

TRUSTEES James Wright; Primrose Scott; Hamilton Smillie; James Fry; Paul Adams; Prof. John Williams; William Martin; Diana Findlay; Anne Glencorse; Susanne Munday; Brenda Nicolson; Glenda Watt.

PUBLICATIONS A wide range of fact sheets are available on money matters, health and wellbeing, travel and lifestyle, home and care and work and learning. Research reports are also published on a number of topics. See the website for full details.

OTHER INFORMATION In 2011–12 grants were given to 118 organisations.

HOW TO APPLY Applicants are requested to call the freephone telephone number or visit the website for details of current grant programmes.

WHO TO APPLY TO Katie Docherty, Head of Charity Services, Causewayside House, 160 Causewayside, Edinburgh EH9 1PR *Tel.* 0800 169 8787 *Website* www.ageuk.org. uk/scotland

....

■ Age UK

CC NO 1128267   ESTABLISHED 1977
WHERE FUNDING CAN BE GIVEN UK and overseas.
WHO CAN BENEFIT Independently constituted, not-for-profit organisations that are accessible to all people in later life. Research organisations.
WHAT IS FUNDED The charity administers a variety of grant programmes aimed at organisations working to make life better for older people by addressing people's immediate needs or tackling the root causes of problems they are experiencing. Research grants, designed to increase understanding of the ageing process, of what it means to grow old and the implications for society and the economy, are also made.
WHAT IS NOT FUNDED No grants to individuals.
TYPE OF GRANT Capital; one-off; running costs; salaries; and start-up costs. Funding is available for up to three years.
RANGE OF GRANTS About £200–£50,000.
FINANCES *Year* 2011–12 *Income* £167,655,000 *Grants* £16,317,000 *Assets* £34,166,000
TRUSTEES Dianne Jeffrey, Chair; Patrick Cusack; Dr Bernadette Fuge; Jeremy Greenhalgh; Timothy Hammond; Chris Hughes; Glyn Kyle; Prof. Brendan McCormack; Jane Newell; Michael Vincent; Lucy Bracken; Timothy Hunter; Prof. John Williams; Prof. James Wright.
PUBLICATIONS A wide range of fact sheets are available on *money matters, health and wellbeing, travel and lifestyle, home and care and work and learning.* Research reports are also published on a number of topics. See the website for full details.
OTHER INFORMATION Total grants figure relates to UK charities. A significant proportion of the grant

total is given to local Age Concern and Age UK branches.

HOW TO APPLY For further information on general grant programmes currently open to applications, contact the Grants Team. Applicants interested in research funding should contact the Research Department at Tavis House, 1–6 Tavistock Square, London WC1H 9NA or email research@ageuk.org.uk.

WHO TO APPLY TO Grants Unit, Tavis House, 1–6 Tavistock Square, London WC1H 9NA *Tel.* 0800 169 8787 *email* contact@ageuk.org. uk *Website* www.ageuk.org.uk

■ The Agger Foundation

CC NO 1145302   **ESTABLISHED** 2012
WHERE FUNDING CAN BE GIVEN UK and Denmark.
WHO CAN BENEFIT Charities and community groups.
WHAT IS FUNDED Social welfare and children and young people.
TRUSTEES Morten Christensen; Daniel Agger; Tommy Paulsen; Niels Frederiksen; Claus Christensen.
HOW TO APPLY In writing to the correspondent.
WHO TO APPLY TO Morten Christensen, Trustee, Aeblehaven 3, Valby, 2500, Denmark *Tel.* 004526298563 *email* theaggerfoundation@liverpoolfc.dk *Website* www.theaggerfoundation.org

■ Aid to the Church in Need (UK)

CC NO 1097984   **ESTABLISHED** 1947
WHERE FUNDING CAN BE GIVEN Eastern Europe, Africa, Russia, Asia and South America.
WHO CAN BENEFIT Persecuted and suffering Christians, especially Roman Catholics, Russian Orthodox and refugees.
WHAT IS FUNDED Religion and pastoral projects.
WHAT IS NOT FUNDED Private individuals with schooling, medical or living expenses.
TYPE OF GRANT Buildings, capital, core costs, endowment, one-off, project, running costs, salaries and start-up costs.
FINANCES *Year* 2012 *Income* £6,875,597 *Grants* £5,500,000
TRUSTEES Fr Ronald Creighton-Jobe; Philipp Habsburg-Lothringen; Graham Hutton; Lisa Sanchez-Corea Simpson; Father Paul Morton.
PUBLICATIONS 'Persecuted and Forgotten – A Report on Christians Oppressed for their Faith'
OTHER INFORMATION Note: the focus of this charity is the church overseas and that individuals without the backing as required may not apply for funding.
In 2012 grants were given to 713 projects worldwide.
HOW TO APPLY The trust has an informative website where the criteria, guidelines and application process are posted. All applications by individuals must have the backing of a Catholic Bishop or religious superior.
WHO TO APPLY TO Neville Kyrke-Smith, National Director, 12–14 Benhill Avenue, Sutton, Surrey SM1 4DA *Tel.* 020 8642 8668 *email* acn@acnuk.org *Website* www.acnuk.org

■ The AIM Foundation

CC NO 263294   **ESTABLISHED** 1971
WHERE FUNDING CAN BE GIVEN Worldwide. In practice, UK with a preference for Essex.
WHO CAN BENEFIT Charitable organisations.
WHAT IS FUNDED Healthcare, community development, youth, environmental matters and

other charitable activities particularly related to influencing long-term social change
WHAT IS NOT FUNDED No grants to individuals.
TYPE OF GRANT Revenue grants: core costs and salaries.
RANGE OF GRANTS Up to £100,000.
SAMPLE GRANTS New Economics Foundation (£110,000); The Impetus Trust (£50,000); ChildLine NSPCC (£35,000); Health Empowerment Through Nutrition (£20,000); Friends of the Earth and the Children's Society (£15,000 each); ASHOKA (£10,000); Families in Focus, Wells for India, Freedom from Torture and Chance to Shine (£5,000 each); and Amnesty International (£3,000).
FINANCES *Year* 2011–12 *Income* £300,213 *Grants* £418,900 *Assets* £9,316,914
TRUSTEES Ian Roy Marks; Angela D. Marks; Nicolas Marks; Joanna Pritchard-Barrett; Caroline Marks; Philippa Bailey.
HOW TO APPLY It cannot be stressed enough that this foundation 'is proactive in its approach' and does not wish to receive applications. Unsolicited requests for assistance will not be responded to under any circumstance.
WHO TO APPLY TO Louisa Tippett, Whittle and Co, 15 High Street, West Mersea, Colchester, Essex CO5 8QA *Tel.* 01206 385049 *email* louisa@whittles.co.uk

■ Aim to Zero Foundation

CC NO 1145228   **ESTABLISHED** 2011
WHERE FUNDING CAN BE GIVEN UK and India.
WHO CAN BENEFIT Charities and community groups.
WHAT IS FUNDED General charitable purposes.
TRUSTEES Sudhir Maheshwari; Sangeeta Maheshwari; Rajan Tandon.
HOW TO APPLY In writing to the correspondent.
WHO TO APPLY TO Mr Sudhir Maheshwari, 85 Platts Lane, London NW3 7NL *Tel.* 020 7543 1177

■ The Green and Lilian F. M. Ainsworth and Family Benevolent Fund

CC NO 267577   **ESTABLISHED** 1974
WHERE FUNDING CAN BE GIVEN UK, with some preference for northwest England.
WHO CAN BENEFIT Charities benefiting young, elderly and people with disabilities.
WHAT IS FUNDED Registered charities with some preference for the NW of England.
WHAT IS NOT FUNDED No grants to individuals or non-registered charities.
TYPE OF GRANT Prefers specific projects.
RANGE OF GRANTS Up to £1,000.
SAMPLE GRANTS British Wireless for the Blind (£560); and Autism Initiatives UK, Bat Conservation Trust, Cross Roads Care, Donna Louise Children's Hospice, Ipswich Community Playbus, Kinship Care, Make A Wish, Martha Trust, Anthony Nolan Trust, Seashell Trust, Lee Smith Foundation, Wherever the Need and The Wildlife Trust (£500 each).
FINANCES *Year* 2011–12 *Income* £22,516 *Grants* £24,060 *Assets* £859,632
TRUSTEE The Royal Bank of Scotland plc.
HOW TO APPLY In writing to the trustees, there is no application form.
WHO TO APPLY TO The Trust Section Manager, RBS Trust Services, Eden Building, Lakeside, Chester Business Park, Wrexham Road, Chester CH4 9QT *Tel.* 01244 625810

■ The Sylvia Aitken Charitable Trust

SC NO SC010556 **ESTABLISHED** 1985
WHERE FUNDING CAN BE GIVEN UK, with a preference for Scotland.
WHO CAN BENEFIT Registered medical research and welfare charities, and any small local groups – particularly in Scotland.
WHAT IS FUNDED General charitable purposes, with a preference for medical and welfare organisations.
WHAT IS NOT FUNDED No grants to individuals: the trust can only support UK registered charities.
SAMPLE GRANTS Previous grant beneficiaries have included: Association for International Cancer Research, Barn Owl Trust, British Lung Foundation, British Stammering Association, the Roy Castle Lung Cancer Foundation, Disabled Living Foundation, Epilepsy Research Trust, Friends of the Lake District, Motor Neurone Disease Association, Network for Surviving Stalking, Royal Scots Dragoon Guards Museum Trust, Sense Scotland, Scottish Child Psychotherapy Trust, Tall Ships Youth Trust, Tenovus Scotland, Wood Green Animal Shelters and Young Minds.
FINANCES *Year* 2011–12 *Income* £98,489 *Grants* £396,422
TRUSTEES S. M. Aitken; M. Harkis; J. Ferguson.
HOW TO APPLY In writing to the correspondent. Applicants should outline the charity's objectives and current projects for which funding may be required. The trustees meet at least twice a year, usually in March/April and September/October.
WHO TO APPLY TO The Administrator, Fergusons Chartered Accountants, 24 Woodside, Houston, Renfrewshire PA6 7DD *Tel.* 01505 610412

■ The Ajahma Charitable Trust

CC NO 273823 **ESTABLISHED** 1977
WHERE FUNDING CAN BE GIVEN Unrestricted.
WHO CAN BENEFIT Registered charities.
WHAT IS FUNDED Development, health, disability, poverty, women's issues, family planning, human rights and social need.
WHAT IS NOT FUNDED Large organisations with a turnover above £4 million will not normally be considered, nor will applications with any sort of religious bias or those which support animal rights/welfare, arts, medical research, buildings, equipment, local groups or overseas projects where the charity income is less than £500,000 a year. Applications for grants or sponsorship for individuals will not be supported.
TYPE OF GRANT Core and running costs, projects and salaries. Funding is available for up to three years.
SAMPLE GRANTS CAMFED, Global Witness and Microloan Foundation (£50,000 each); Womankind Worldwide (£40,000); and Age Concern Ealing, Ashiana Network, Beat Bullying and Tower Hamlets Friends and Neighbours (£4,500 each).
FINANCES *Year* 2011–12 *Income* £84,947 *Grants* £261,436 *Assets* £2,780,768
TRUSTEES Jennifer Sheridan; Elizabeth Simpson; James Sinclair Taylor; Carole Pound; Roger Paffard.
OTHER INFORMATION In addition to the total grants figure, Headway groups have received awards totalling £36,000 (7 grants).
HOW TO APPLY The trust has reviewed their grantmaking criteria and will now pro-actively seek and select organisations to which they wish to award grants. They will no longer consider unsolicited applications.
WHO TO APPLY TO Suzanne Hunt, Administrator, 275 Dover House Road, London SW15 5BP *Tel.* 020 8788 5388

■ The Al Fayed Charitable Foundation

CC NO 297114 **ESTABLISHED** 1987
WHERE FUNDING CAN BE GIVEN Mainly UK.
WHO CAN BENEFIT Mainly children and young people and health.
WHAT IS FUNDED General charitable purposes.
TYPE OF GRANT 'One off' and recurring.
RANGE OF GRANTS £1,000–£850,000
SAMPLE GRANTS Shooting Star (Chase) (£390,000); West Heath (£328,000); Zoe's Place (£180,000); Francis House (£175,000); Lotus Children's Centre (£77,000); WSPA (£40,000); The New School at West heath (£30,000); Spring Films (£8,400); Fauna and Flora International (£5,000); Harrods Limited (£3,700); Opera Rara (£2,000); Thando Art (£1,400); and Bespoke Food (£1,100).
FINANCES *Year* 2012 *Income* £1,395,965 *Grants* £1,380,000 *Assets* £81,251
TRUSTEES Mohammed Al-Fayed; A. Fayed; S. Fayed.
OTHER INFORMATION The grant total includes £8,300 given in grants to individuals.
HOW TO APPLY In writing to the correspondent including the following: name and contact details; an overview of why you are seeking funding; a breakdown of funds sought and a stamped addressed envelope.
WHO TO APPLY TO Susie Mathis, 60 Park Lane, London W1K 1QE *Tel.* 07717 652316 *email* mathissusie@aol.com *Website* www.alfayed.com/philanthropy

■ The Alabaster Trust

CC NO 1050568 **ESTABLISHED** 1995
WHERE FUNDING CAN BE GIVEN UK and overseas.
WHO CAN BENEFIT Organisations benefiting evangelical Christian organisations.
WHAT IS FUNDED General charitable purposes, particularly the advancement of the Christian faith.
WHAT IS NOT FUNDED No grants to individuals.
FINANCES *Year* 2011–12 *Income* £66,516 *Grants* £59,136 *Assets* £51,235
TRUSTEES Jill Kendrick; Graham Kendrick; Abigail Sheldrake; Amy Waterman; Miriam Kendrick; Tamsin Kendrick.
HOW TO APPLY In writing to the correspondent. The trustees meet to consider grants quarterly, usually in March, June, September and December.
WHO TO APPLY TO John Caladine, Trust Administrator, Chantry House, 22 Upperton Road, Eastbourne, East Sussex BN21 1BF *Tel.* 01323 644579 *email* john@caladine.co.uk

■ The Alborada Trust

CC NO 1091660 **ESTABLISHED** 2001
WHERE FUNDING CAN BE GIVEN Worldwide.
WHO CAN BENEFIT Charitable organisations.
WHAT IS FUNDED Veterinary causes in the United Kingdom and Ireland with activities primarily devoted to the welfare of animals and/or in their associated research. Projects throughout

the world associated with the relief of poverty, human suffering, sickness or ill health.
RANGE OF GRANTS £20,000–£245,000
SAMPLE GRANTS Home of Horseracing Trust (£250,000); The Langford Trust for Animal Health and Welfare (£200,000); Alzheimer's Society (£139,000); Médecins Sans Frontières (£85,000); and Greatwood Charity (£14,000).
FINANCES *Year* 2012 *Income* £120,586 *Grants* £1,073,569 *Assets* £13,282,014
TRUSTEES Eva Rausing; David Way; Roland Lerner; James Nicholson.
HOW TO APPLY The 2012 annual report states that funds are fully committed. The trust does not accept unsolicited applications.
WHO TO APPLY TO Jamie Matheson, Administrator, Fladgate Fielder LLP, 16 Great Queen Street, London WC2 5DG *Tel.* 020 3036 7308 *Website* www.alboradatrust.com

■ D. G. Albright Charitable Trust
CC NO 277367   **ESTABLISHED** 1978
WHERE FUNDING CAN BE GIVEN UK, with a preference for Gloucestershire.
WHO CAN BENEFIT Registered charities.
WHAT IS FUNDED General charitable purposes.
WHAT IS NOT FUNDED Grants are not usually made to individuals.
TYPE OF GRANT One-off and recurrent.
RANGE OF GRANTS £300–£4,000.
SAMPLE GRANTS Bromesberrow Church of England School (£6,500); Bromesberrow Parochial Church Council (£3,500); Independent Age (£2,500); Shelter – Gloucestershire Advice Service (£2,000); The Children's Society, Butterfly Conservation and Abbeyfield (Reading) Society (£1,000 each) and War Memorials Trust (£500).
FINANCES *Year* 2011–12 *Income* £44,879 *Grants* £36,500 *Assets* £1,022,945
TRUSTEES Hon. Dr Gilbert Greenall; Richard Wood.
HOW TO APPLY In writing to the correspondent.
WHO TO APPLY TO Richard Wood, Trustee, Old Church School, Hollow Street, Great Somerford, Chippenham, Wiltshire SN15 5JD *Tel.* 01249 720760

■ The Alchemy Foundation
CC NO 292500   **ESTABLISHED** 1985
WHERE FUNDING CAN BE GIVEN UK and overseas.
WHO CAN BENEFIT Community projects, voluntary organisations and registered charities.
WHAT IS FUNDED The foundation's 2011/12 accounts state that its objects are, 'particularly focused on the Orpheus Centre, water projects in the developing world, disability (particularly mobility, access, helplines and communications), social welfare (inner city community projects, disaffected youth, family mediation, homelessness), personal reform, penal reform (work with prisoners, especially young prisoners, and their families), medical research and aid (especially in areas of blindness and disfigurement), individual enterprise (by helping Raleigh International and similar organisations to give opportunities to young people according to need) and respite for carers.'
WHAT IS NOT FUNDED No grants for organisations exclusive to one faith or political belief.
TYPE OF GRANT Capital; revenue; one-off; salaries.
SAMPLE GRANTS A list of beneficiaries was not available.

FINANCES *Year* 2011–12 *Income* £352,316 *Grants* £263,829 *Assets* £2,437,547
TRUSTEES Dr Jemima Stilgoe; Holly Stilgoe; Jack Stilgoe; Rufus Stilgoe; Richard Stilgoe; Alex Armitage; Andrew Murison; Annabel Stilgoe; Esther Rantzen; Joseph Stilgoe; Tony Elias.
HOW TO APPLY In writing to the correspondent.
WHO TO APPLY TO Richard Stilgoe, Trustee, Trevereux Manor, Limpsfield Chart, Oxted, Surrey RH8 0TL *Tel.* 01883 730600

■ Aldgate and All Hallows' Foundation (formerly Aldgate and All Hallows' Barking Exhibition Foundation)
CC NO 312500   **ESTABLISHED** 1893
WHERE FUNDING CAN BE GIVEN City of London and the London borough of Tower Hamlets.
WHO CAN BENEFIT Children or young people under the age of 25.
WHAT IS FUNDED The foundation is particularly keen to encourage and support: (i) projects initiated by schools that enhance the National Curriculum; (ii) projects aimed at improving literacy and numeracy; (iii) projects aimed at promoting the study of science, mathematics and the arts; (iv) projects which attract match funding; (v) projects which test out new ideas. Priority will be given to projects that are not yet part of a school's or organisation's regular activities; to developments that are strategic, such as practical initiatives seeking to address the root causes of problems, and those that have the potential to influence policy and practice more widely. The foundation may also from time to time initiate new projects that do not fall into the priority areas for grantmaking to enable governors to explore ground-breaking or emergent fields of educational practice.
WHAT IS NOT FUNDED Note that the foundation does not give grants for: equipment or teachers' salaries that are the responsibility of education authorities; youth groups or community projects; supplementary schools or mother tongue teaching; the purchase, repair or furnishing of buildings; conferences or seminars; university or medical research; trips abroad; stage, film, publication or video production costs; performances, exhibitions or festivals; retrospective requests (i.e. any activity that has already taken place); requests to substitute for the withdrawal or reduction of statutory funding; general fundraising campaigns or appeals.
RANGE OF GRANTS Up to £45,000
SAMPLE GRANTS School Funding Network Ltd. (£45,000); Centre of the Cell (£30,000); Rich Mix (£28,000); Box Clever Theatre Company (£18,000) and Ben Johnson Primary School (£11,000).
FINANCES *Year* 2012 *Income* £80,870 *Grants* £271,839 *Assets* £7,084,742
TRUSTEES D. Ross; Robin Hazlewood; Cllr Denise Jones; David Mash; Revd Bertrand Olivier; John Hall; Graham Forbes; William Hamilton-Hinds; Marianne Fredericks; Billy Whitbread; Paul James; Susan Knowles; Cllr Sirajul Islam; Revd Laura Burgess; Kevin Everett.
OTHER INFORMATION The 2012 grant total includes £39,000 given in grants to individuals.
HOW TO APPLY Initial enquiries should be sent to the foundation. These must include the following information: (i) Information about your school or organisation; including an outline of its current activities, its legal status, aims, brief history, details of staffing levels, management structure

and composition of the management committee. (ii) An outline description of, and timetable for, the project for which funding is being sought, including information about who will be involved in and/or benefit from the project. (iii) Details of the aims and outcomes for the project, including information about how you will monitor and evaluate the project. (iv) A detailed budget for the project. (v) Information about any other sources of income and partnership funding for the project.

who to apply to Richard Foley, Clerk and Chief Executive, 31 Jewry Street, London EC3N 2EY *Tel.* 020 7488 2518 *Fax* 020 7488 2519 *email* aldgateandallhallows@sirjohncass.org *Website* www.aldgateallhallows.org.uk

■ The Aldgate Freedom Foundation

cc no 207046   **established** 1962
where funding can be given Freedom part of the parish of St Botolph-without-Aldgate.
who can benefit Organisations benefiting older people and people who are homeless or otherwise in need.
what is funded Hospitals and voluntary organisations.
range of grants Up to £3,500.
sample grants Portsoken Ward Club for Three Score Club, Wingate Golden Oldies (£3,500 each); St Botolph's Maintenance (£3,000); Chiropody Clinic (£2,500); St Botolph's Churchyard Maintenance (£1,500); Aldgate Estate Residents Association and Middlesex Estate Residents' Association (£1,000 each); St Botolph's Rectors Discretionary Fund (£300).
finances *Year* 2012 *Income* £60,619 *Grants* £16,300 *Assets* £1,397,752
trustees Revd L. Jorgensen; M. D. Bear; S. J. Borton; G. Caughey; H. L. M. Jones; I. Priest; C. Jones; C. Knowles.
how to apply In writing to the correspondent.
who to apply to M. Pierce, Clerk to the Trustees, St Botolph-without-Aldgate, Aldgate, London EC3N 1AB *Tel.* 01708 222482

■ The Alexis Trust

cc no 262861   **established** 1971
where funding can be given UK and overseas.
who can benefit Individuals and organisations.
what is funded Support for a variety of causes, principally Christian missionary projects.
what is not funded No grants for building appeals, or to individuals for education.
type of grant One-off, project and some recurring costs will be considered.
sample grants Barnabas Fund and Mission Aviation Fellowship (£2,000 each); UCCF (£1,200); and Epping Forest Youth for Christ and Tower Hamlets Mission (£1,000 each).
finances *Year* 2011–12 *Income* £37,221 *Grants* £37,711 *Assets* £449,140
trustees Prof. Duncan Vere; Chris Harwood; Elisabeth Harwood; Vera Vere.
how to apply In writing to the correspondent, although the trust states that most of the funds are regularly committed.
who to apply to Prof. Duncan Vere, Trustee, 14 Broadfield Way, Buckhurst Hill, Essex IG9 5AG

■ All Saints Educational Trust

cc no 312934   **established** 1978
where funding can be given UK and overseas.
who can benefit Ultimately, persons who are or intend to become engaged as teachers or in other capacities connected with education, in particular home economics and religious subjects, and those who teach or intend to teach in multicultural areas.
what is funded Primarily, the training of Christian teachers. Its main purposes is to: help increase the number of new teachers with Qualified Teacher Status; improve the skills and qualifications of experienced teachers; encourage research that can assist teachers in their work; support specifically the teaching of religious studies and home economics and related areas – such as the promotion of public health and nutrition, both at home and in the Commonwealth.
what is not funded Note that the trust will not support: general or core funds of any organisation; public appeals; school buildings, equipment or supplies (except library resources); the establishment of new departments in universities and colleges; general bursary funds of other organisations.
type of grant One-off, project or annual grants for a limited period. Funding may be given for more than three years. Preference will be given to 'pump-priming' projects.
sample grants Previously: National Association of Teachers in Home Economics, Southwark Cathedral Education Centre, British Nutrition Foundation, Design and Technology Association, Sheffield Hallam University, Wulugu – Ghana, Scripture Union, Christian Education Movement and the Soil Association.
finances *Year* 2011–12 *Income* £427,878 *Grants* £447,600 *Assets* £9,066,264
trustees Diane McCrea; Revd Canon Peter Hartley; Revd Dr Keith Riglin; David J. Trillo; Dorothy Garland; Barbara E. Harvey; Dr Augur Pearce; Prof. Anthony R. Leeds; Ven. Stephan J. Welch; Stephanie Valentine; Joanna Moriarty; Frances M. Smith; Anna E. Cumbers; Michael C. Jacob; Stephen Brooker.
other information 1n 2011–12 grants to organisations (Corporate Awards) totalled £260,000, with £187,000 going to individuals in scholarships and bursaries.
how to apply For applications from organisations (not individuals): applicants are invited to discuss their ideas informally with the clerk before making an application. In some cases, a 'link trustee' is appointed to assist the organisation in preparing the application and who will act in a liaison role with the trust. Completed applications are put before the awards committee in April/May, with final decisions made in June. Application forms are available on the trust's website, either in interactive or printable form.
who to apply to The Clerk, Suite 8C, First Floor, VSC Charity Centre, Royal London House, 22–25 Finsbury Square, London EC2A 1DX *Tel.* 02072488380. *email* aset@aset.org.uk *Website* www.aset.org.uk

■ The Derrill Allatt Foundation

cc no 1148440   **established** 2012
where funding can be given UK.
who can benefit Charities and community groups.
what is funded General charitable purposes.

TRUSTEES Alexandra Rhodes; Diana Hargreaves; Payne Hicks Beach Trust Corporation Limited (Frank Airey; James Bacon; Peter Black; Graham Brown; M. R. T. Kinross; Elisabeth Lyle; Alastair Murdie; Alice Palmer; Christopher Sly; Neil Wingerath).

HOW TO APPLY No grants to unsolicited applications.

WHO TO APPLY TO Alexander Jones-Davies, Administrator, Payne Hicks Beach (Ref. ECL/AJD), 10 New Square, Lincoln's Inn, London WC2A 3QG *Tel.* 020 7465 4300

■ Allchurches Trust Ltd

CC NO 263960   **ESTABLISHED** 1972
WHERE FUNDING CAN BE GIVEN UK.
WHO CAN BENEFIT Churches, church establishments, religious charities and charities preserving UK heritage.
WHAT IS FUNDED Promotion of the Christian religion and contributions to the funds of other charitable institutions.
WHAT IS NOT FUNDED The trust is unable to support: charities with political associations; national charities; individuals; appeals for running costs and salaries. Applications cannot be considered from the same recipient twice in one year or in two consecutive years.
TYPE OF GRANT Primarily one-off.
RANGE OF GRANTS Usually £100–£5,000.
SAMPLE GRANTS Butterwick Hospice Care – Stockton-on-Tees, Cleveland: A grant was given towards the construction of a new Family Support and Complementary Therapy Centre at the Hospice; Dobwalls United Church – Liskeard, Cornwall: A donation was given towards the re-rendering of the outside of the church, to replace the wooden porch doors with glass ones, and to install kitchen and toilet facilities; Hope Corner Community Church and Kids First – Runcorn, Merseyside: A grant was made towards furnishing and equipping a new church and community centre specifically with the needs of young people and their families in mind; and Trinity Methodist Church – East Grinstead, West Sussex: Financial assistance was given towards the building of a new multi-functional church for a growing congregation.
FINANCES *Year* 2012 *Income* £5,334,000 *Grants* £9,465,000 *Assets* £376,490,000
TRUSTEES Michael Chamberlain; Rt Revd Nigel Stock; Fraser Hart; Nick J. E. Sealy; The Ven. Annette Cooper; Philip Mawer; Christopher Smith; Denise Wilson.
HOW TO APPLY Applications should be submitted in writing using the form available on the trust's website.
WHO TO APPLY TO The Relationship and Grants Manager, Beaufort House, Brunswick Road, Gloucester GL1 1JZ *Tel.* 01452 873189 *Fax* 01452 423557 *email* atl@ecclesiastical.com *Website* www.allchurches.co.uk

■ The H. B. Allen Charitable Trust

CC NO 802306   **ESTABLISHED** 1985
WHERE FUNDING CAN BE GIVEN Worldwide.
WHO CAN BENEFIT Registered charities in the UK.
WHAT IS FUNDED General charitable purposes including: blindness; children and young people; churches; people with disabilities; education/schools; environment, wildlife and animals; general community, hospices; housing/homeless; mental health; museums/galleries/heritage and overseas/international.

WHAT IS NOT FUNDED No grants to individuals, organisations which are not UK-registered charities or gap-year students (even if payable to a registered charity). No initial funding to newly established charities.
TYPE OF GRANT One-off and recurrent up to three years, revenue and capital including core costs.
RANGE OF GRANTS Mainly £5,000–£25,000.
SAMPLE GRANTS Libraries and Archives (£250,000); St Michael and All Angels Church Bedford Park (£150,000); Friends of Butser Ancient Farm (£72,000); RN Submarine Museum (£50,000); Wildlife Conservation Research Unit (£40,000); Deafness Research UK and St Botolph's – Boston Stump (£35,000 only); National Eye Research Centre (£30,000); Bowel Disease Research Foundation (£20,000); The Sobriety Project – Young Offenders Scheme (£15,000); Fauna and Flora International, Little Ouse Headwaters Project, St Wilfrid's Hospice and The Orton Trust (£10,000 each); Birmingham Pen Trade Heritage Association, Books Abroad, The Gurkha Welfare Trust and Wheelpower – British Wheelchair Sport (£5,000 each); Rural Youth Trust (£3,000); and Frontier Youth Trust and Small Woods Association (£2,500 each).
FINANCES *Year* 2012 *Income* £1,401,809 *Grants* £1,078,000 *Assets* £32,411,586
TRUSTEES Helen Ratcliffe; Peter Shone.
HOW TO APPLY In writing to the correspondent: including a copy of the organisation's latest annual report and accounts. Read the application guidelines available from the trust's helpful and concise website. Applications should be submitted by post, not email, although enquiries prior to any application can be made by email. Note the following comments from the trust. 'Applicants should note that, at their main annual meeting (usually in January or February), the trustees consider applications received up to 31 December each year but do not carry them forward. Having regard for the time of year when this meeting takes place, it makes sense for applications to be made as late as possible in the calendar year so that the information they contain is most up to date when the trustees meet. It would be preferable, from all points of view, if applications were made only in the last quarter of the calendar year. Although, preferably not in December. The trustees receive a very substantial number of appeals each year. It is not their practice to acknowledge appeals, and they prefer not to enter into correspondence with applicants other than those to whom grants are being made or from whom further information is required. Only successful applicants are notified of the outcome of their application.'
WHO TO APPLY TO Peter Shone, Trustee, Homefield, Chidden Holt, Hambledon, Waterlooville, Hampshire PO7 4TG *Tel.* 02392 632406 *email* mail@hballenct.org.uk *Website* www.hballenct.org.uk

■ The Allen Lane Trust

CC NO 1149044   **ESTABLISHED** 2012
WHERE FUNDING CAN BE GIVEN UK.
WHO CAN BENEFIT Charities and community groups.
WHAT IS FUNDED Health, disability, relief of poverty, children and young people and older people.
TRUSTEES Gayle Davenport; Ben Lane; James Allen.
HOW TO APPLY In writing to the correspondent.
WHO TO APPLY TO Gayle Davenport, Trustee, Allen Lane Ltd, 50 Pall Mall, London SW1Y 5JH *Tel.* 020 7101 8804

■ The Allen Trust

CC NO 1146388 **ESTABLISHED** 2012
WHERE FUNDING CAN BE GIVEN UK and Africa, with a preference for Sudan, Tanzania and Uganda.
WHO CAN BENEFIT Registered charities.
WHAT IS FUNDED General, religion, economic development and children and young people.
TRUSTEES Tony Allen; Paige Allen; Richard Gough.
HOW TO APPLY In writing to the correspondent.
WHO TO APPLY TO Tony Allen, Trustee, Copsem Manor, 50 Copsem Lane, Esher, Surrey KT10 9HJ *Tel.* 020 8939 3977

■ The Alliance Family Foundation

CC NO 258721 **ESTABLISHED** 1968
WHERE FUNDING CAN BE GIVEN UK and Israel.
WHO CAN BENEFIT Organisations, particularly Jewish causes, benefiting young people and people disadvantaged by poverty.
WHAT IS FUNDED The relief of poverty and advancement of religion, education and medical knowledge.
RANGE OF GRANTS Up to £50,000.
SAMPLE GRANTS Jewish Community Secondary School Trust (£50,000); University of Manchester (£47,500); Prince Ali Reza Pahlavi Foundation Fellowship (£32,000); and the Weizmann Institute – Israel (£30,000).
FINANCES *Year* 2011–12 *Income* £641,733 *Grants* £660,830 *Assets* £13,684,817
TRUSTEES Lord David Alliance; Graham Alliance; Sara Esterkin; Joshua Alliance.
OTHER INFORMATION £313,000 was given to organisations and £238,000 was distributed to individuals. The remaining £110,000 was classified as 'sundry general charitable donations'.
HOW TO APPLY 'The trustees review requests for financial support and make donations periodically and will continue to do so over the forthcoming twelve months.'
WHO TO APPLY TO The Trustees, Spencer House, 27 St James's Place, London SW1A 1NR

■ Angus Allnatt Charitable Foundation

CC NO 1019793 **ESTABLISHED** 1993
WHERE FUNDING CAN BE GIVEN UK.
WHO CAN BENEFIT Young people.
WHAT IS FUNDED This trust makes grants to organisations which offer opportunities for young musicians aged 13 to 25 or which provide water-based activities for those up to the age of 20.
WHAT IS NOT FUNDED No grants to individuals, and none to organisations which use music primarily for therapeutic or social purposes.
TYPE OF GRANT One-off for specific needs or start-up costs. Funding is available for up to one year.
RANGE OF GRANTS £250–£1,000 with a maximum of £2,000.
FINANCES *Year* 2011–12 *Income* £15,924 *Grants* £48,000
TRUSTEES David Briggs; Rodney Dartnall; Marian Durban; Andrew Hutchison, Shahareen Hilmy.
HOW TO APPLY In writing to the correspondent. Trustees meet three times a year to consider applications. The trust has no staff and no telephone. Appeals falling outside the guidelines will not be considered.

WHO TO APPLY TO Marian Durban, Trustee, 62 Westfield Way, Charlton Heights, Wantage, Oxfordshire OX12 7EP *Tel.* 01235 223250 *email* m.durban1@ntlworld.com

■ The Pat Allsop Charitable Trust

CC NO 1030950 **ESTABLISHED** 1973
WHERE FUNDING CAN BE GIVEN UK.
WHO CAN BENEFIT UK organisations benefiting: children; people in property management; people disadvantaged by poverty; people living in urban areas; refugees; and the victims of famine.
WHAT IS FUNDED Medicine and health; welfare; and education. Particularly concerned with: almshouses; housing associations; hospices; medical studies and research; schools and colleges; special needs education; and emergency care for refugees and people affected by famine. The founder of the trust was a partner in Allsop and Co. Chartered Surveyors, Auctioneers and Property Managers, therefore the trust favours supporting those educational projects and charities which have connections with surveying and property management professions.
WHAT IS NOT FUNDED No grants to individuals.
TYPE OF GRANT One-off, project, research and recurring costs.
RANGE OF GRANTS £100–£7,500. The trustees have a policy of making a small number of major donations (over £2,500) and a larger number of smaller donations.
SAMPLE GRANTS Jewish Care (£7,500); The Duke of Edinburgh's Award (£5,000); The Annington Trust (£3,000); Kids Company (£1,500); CORAM Children's Charity, Land Aid Charitable Trust and National Autistic Society (£500 each); and Maasai Heritage Foundation, Save the Children and Walk the Walk Worldwide (£250 each).
FINANCES *Year* 2011–12 *Income* £36,232 *Grants* £28,831 *Assets* £908,036
TRUSTEES John Randel; Patrick Kerr; Wayne Taylor; Neil MacKilligin.
HOW TO APPLY The trust does not accept unsolicited applications.
WHO TO APPLY TO John Randel, Trustee, Lee Bolton Monier-Williams solicitors, 1 The Sanctuary, London SW1P 3JT *Tel.* 020 7222 5381 *email* jrandel@lbmw.com

■ The Almond Trust

CC NO 328583 **ESTABLISHED** 1990
WHERE FUNDING CAN BE GIVEN UK and worldwide.
WHO CAN BENEFIT Mostly individuals or organisations of which the trustees have personal knowledge, particularly those benefiting Christians and evangelists.
WHAT IS FUNDED Support of evangelical Christian projects, Christian evangelism, and advancement of Scripture.
TYPE OF GRANT Largely recurrent.
RANGE OF GRANTS Up to £12,000. The average grant in 2009–10 was £4,586.
SAMPLE GRANTS Lawyers' Christian Fellowship (£12,000 in two grants); St Mary's Warbleton Parochial Church Council (£10,000); Agape, Haggai Institute, Jews for Jesus and Titus Trust (£5,000 each); Friends International (£3,000); and CVM (£1,500).
FINANCES *Year* 2011–12 *Income* £67,210 *Grants* £50,100 *Assets* £356,492

Does the trust you have chosen match your needs? Haphazard applications waste postage and time

TRUSTEES Sir Jeremy Cooke; Jonathan Cooke; Lady Cooke.

OTHER INFORMATION The grant total includes five payments totalling £8,800, which were given to individuals.

HOW TO APPLY In writing to the correspondent, but note that the trust states it rarely responds to uninvited applications.

WHO TO APPLY TO Sir Jeremy Cooke, Trustee, 19 West Square, London SE11 4SN *Tel.* 020 7587 5167

....

■ Almondsbury Charity

CC NO 202263   **ESTABLISHED** 1963

WHERE FUNDING CAN BE GIVEN The parish of Almondsbury as it existed in 1892, i.e. Almondsbury, Patchway, Easter Compton and parts of Pilning and Bradley Stoke North.

WHO CAN BENEFIT Church of England; residents and organisations in the beneficial area.

WHAT IS FUNDED Grants are made to maintain and repair churches, to further the religious and charitable work of the Church of England and to support educational requirements and sick and needy residents and organisations within the old parish of Almondsbury.

RANGE OF GRANTS Between £500 and £5,000.

SAMPLE GRANTS St Chads Church (£5,000); Southern Brooks Community Partnership (£2,700); Patchway Community College (£2,300); Holy Trinity Primary School (£2,000); Wheatfield Primary School (£1,600); 1st Almonsbury Scout Group (£1,500); St Peters Hospice (£850) and Patchway Festival (£500).

FINANCES *Year* 2011–12 *Income* £63,351 *Grants* £33,478 *Assets* £2,043,617

TRUSTEES Alan Gaydon; Ivor Humphries; Revd Howard Jameson; Lewis Gray; Alan Bamforth; Diane Wilson; Revd Philip Rowe; Sheila Futon; Jane Jones; Lucy Hamid; Revd Roger Ducker; Ben Walker.

OTHER INFORMATION The grant total for 2011–12 includes the total of £4,500 which was distributed in grants to individuals.

HOW TO APPLY On a form available to download from the website.

WHO TO APPLY TO Peter Orford, Wayside, Shepperdine Road, Oldbury Naite, Bristol BS35 1RJ *Tel.* 01454 415346 *email* peter.orford@gmail.com *Website* www.almondsburycharity.org.uk/almondsbury

....

■ The Altajir Trust

CC NO 284116   **ESTABLISHED** 1982

WHERE FUNDING CAN BE GIVEN UK and Arab or Islamic states.

WHO CAN BENEFIT Individuals and organisations.

WHAT IS FUNDED Support for exhibitions, publications, educational activities and other programmes related to Islamic culture and Muslim-Christian relations. The trust provides scholarships for undergraduates and graduates, mainly from the Arab world, to undertake further studies at approved colleges of higher education within the United Kingdom. Funding may also be given towards the cost of conservation of Islamic artefacts and manuscripts in the United Kingdom, assisting conservation in Muslim countries, and to charitable and academic institutions assisting in rebuilding societies in the Islamic world after conflict.

RANGE OF GRANTS Up to £55,000.

SAMPLE GRANTS University of York – Lectureship (£53,000); British Council – Chevening

Scholarships (£19,000); St John of Jerusalem Eye Hospital (£14,000); Council for British Research in the Levant (£5,500); Chatham House – MENA programme (£5,000); and University of Sterling – Scholarships (£2,500).

FINANCES *Year* 2012 *Income* £567,151 *Grants* £79,570 *Assets* £209,963

TRUSTEES Prof. Alan Jones, Chair; Prof. Roger Williams; Dr Charles Tripp; Dr Noel Brehony.

OTHER INFORMATION The trust also gave a further £201,070 in student support and £67,791 in support for events and publications.

HOW TO APPLY On a form available from the trust's website. The trustees meet about four times a year. Applications can be submitted at any time but may have to await the next trustees' meeting for a decision. However, they will all be acknowledged when received and an indication of the time frame for a decision will be given. Note: applications should be printed and signed before being sent to the trust.

WHO TO APPLY TO The Trustees, 11 Elvaston Place, London SW7 5QG *Tel.* 020 7581 3522 *Fax* 020 7584 1977 *email* awitrust@tiscali.co.uk *Website* www.altajirtrust.org.uk

....

■ Altamont Ltd

CC NO 273971   **ESTABLISHED** 1977

WHERE FUNDING CAN BE GIVEN Worldwide.

WHO CAN BENEFIT Organisations benefiting Jewish people.

WHAT IS FUNDED Jewish charitable purposes.

FINANCES *Year* 2011–12 *Income* £16,236 *Grants* £101,761

TRUSTEES David Last; Henry Last; H. Kon; S. Adler; Gina Wiesenfeld.

HOW TO APPLY In writing to the correspondent.

WHO TO APPLY TO David Last, Trustee, 18 Green Walk, London NW4 2AJ *Tel.* 020 8457 8760

....

■ Alvor Charitable Trust

CC NO 1093890   **ESTABLISHED** 2002

WHERE FUNDING CAN BE GIVEN UK, with a preference for Sussex, Norfolk and north east Scotland.

WHO CAN BENEFIT Charitable organisations.

WHAT IS FUNDED Christian social change and general charitable purposes on a local basis.

WHAT IS NOT FUNDED The trust does not look to support animal charities or medical charities outside of the geographic areas mentioned above.

TYPE OF GRANT The trust tends to support smaller projects where the grant will meet a specific need.

RANGE OF GRANTS £500 upwards. The trust typically makes a few larger donations each year and a number of smaller grants.

SAMPLE GRANTS Previously: Kenward Trust (£50,000 in two grants); Salt Sussex Trading Ltd (£40,000 in four grants); Anne Marie School, Ghana (£35,000); Urban Saints (£33,000); Hymns Ancient and Modern (£30,000 in two grants); Romance Academy (£25,000) World In Need (£20,000); Trussell Trust (£15,000); Release International (£10,000); Brighton FareShare (£5,000 each); Chestnut Tree House (£2,000); and Impact Initiatives (£500).

FINANCES *Year* 2011–12 *Income* £0 *Grants* £47,172

TRUSTEES Clive Wills; Shaena Wills; Mark Atherton; Fiona Atherton; Ian Wilkins; Julie Wilkins.

OTHER INFORMATION Despite the trust having no income for this accounting year, we have retained the entry as the charity remains on the

Central Register of Charities and as far as we know, has not been dissolved.

HOW TO APPLY In writing to the correspondent.

WHO TO APPLY TO Ian Wilkins, Trustee, Stone End, Fox Hill Close, Haywards Heath, West Sussex RH16 4RA *Tel.* 01444 473347

■ AM Charitable Trust

CC NO 256283   **ESTABLISHED** 1968

WHERE FUNDING CAN BE GIVEN UK and overseas.

WHO CAN BENEFIT Registered charities; Jewish organisations.

WHAT IS FUNDED General charitable purposes, including medical, welfare, arts and conservation causes.

WHAT IS NOT FUNDED No grants to individuals.

TYPE OF GRANT Certain charities are supported for more than one year, although no commitment is usually given to the recipients.

RANGE OF GRANTS £100–£15,000. Mainly smaller amounts under £500 each to non–Jewish organisations.

SAMPLE GRANTS The Wallace Collection (£75,000); Youth Aliyah – Child Rescue and British ORT (£15,000 each); Friends of the Hebrew University of Jerusalem and Jerusalem Foundation (£10,000 each); Cancer Research Campaign (£3,000) and British Heart Foundation (£2,000); Blond McIndoe Research Foundation (£1,500); Royal Academy of Music (£1,000); Alzheimer's Research Trust (£500) and Crimestoppers Trust (£200).

FINANCES *Year* 2011–12 *Income* £128,529 *Grants* £145,250 *Assets* £2,012,878

TRUSTEE Kleinwort Benson Trustees Ltd.

HOW TO APPLY 'Donations are decided periodically by the Trustee having regard to the wishes of the Settlor, and unsolicited appeals are considered as well as causes which have already been supported. Only successful applicants are notified of the trustee's decision.'

WHO TO APPLY TO The Administrator, Kleinwort Benson Trustees Ltd, 14 St George Street, London W1S 1FE *Tel.* 020 3207 7091

■ Amabrill Limited

CC NO 1078968   **ESTABLISHED** 2000

WHERE FUNDING CAN BE GIVEN UK, with a preference for north west London.

WHO CAN BENEFIT Jewish charities.

WHAT IS FUNDED The advancement of education and religious practice in accordance with the teachings of the Orthodox Jewish faith.

SAMPLE GRANTS Previous beneficiaries include: Kahal Chassidim Bobov; YMER; BFON Trust; Beth Hamedrash Elyon Golders Green Ltd; Friends of Shekel Hakodesh Ltd; Friends of Mir and Parsha Ltd; Cosmon Bels Ltd; United Talmudical Academy; British Friends of Mosdos Tchernobel; Mayfair Charities Ltd; Friends of Toldos Avrohom Yitzchok; Achisomoch Aid Company; the Gertner Charitable Trust; and Higher Talmudical Education Ltd.

FINANCES *Year* 2011–12 *Income* £2,557,596 *Grants* £2,734,550 *Assets* £3,784,207

TRUSTEES Charles Lerner; Frances R. Lerner; Salamon Noe; Israel Grossnass.

OTHER INFORMATION A list of grants was not included in the most recent accounts.

HOW TO APPLY Appeal letters are received from, and personal visits made by representatives of Jewish charitable, religious and educational institutions. These requests are then considered

by the trustees and grants are made in accordance with the trustees' decisions.

WHO TO APPLY TO Charles Lerner, Trustee, 1 Golder's Manor Drive, London NW11 9HU *Tel.* 020 8455 6785

■ The Amalur Foundation Limited

CC NO 1090476   **ESTABLISHED** 2002

WHERE FUNDING CAN BE GIVEN Worldwide.

WHO CAN BENEFIT Charitable organisations.

WHAT IS FUNDED General charitable purposes.

SAMPLE GRANTS Previously: Absolute Return for Kids (£110,000); St Patrick's Catholic Church (£50,000); Prostate Research Campaign UK (£10,000); Brain Tumour Research Campaign (£5,500); Breakthrough Breast Cancer (£3,000); and the Extra Care Charitable Trust (£2,000).

FINANCES *Year* 2011–12 *Income* £0 *Grants* £162,000

TRUSTEES Claudia Garuti; David Way; Helen Mellor.

HOW TO APPLY We were informed (September 2011) by the correspondent that the charity's income is diminishing and that it does not have a long-term future. While the trustees have funds available, they are pleased to consider applications. Applications should be made to the correspondent in writing please.

WHO TO APPLY TO David Way, Trustee, Fladgate LLP, 16 Great Queen Street, London WC2B 5DG

■ The Ammco Trust

CC NO 327962   **ESTABLISHED** 1988

WHERE FUNDING CAN BE GIVEN Oxfordshire and adjoining counties.

WHO CAN BENEFIT Small local charities and charitable projects based in the area of benefit.

WHAT IS FUNDED Disability, health, medical, special needs education, ex-services, sport and arts/heritage.

WHAT IS NOT FUNDED No grants to individuals, students or for research.

TYPE OF GRANT One-off.

RANGE OF GRANTS Usually up to £2,000, except in exceptional circumstances.

SAMPLE GRANTS Previous beneficiaries have included BEWSA, Contact a Family Oxford, DEBRA Berkshire, Dorothy House Hospice Care Wiltshire, Live Music Now!, Oxford Children's Hospital Campaign, Pathway Workshop Oxford, Riding for the Disabled Association Abingdon Group and Wellbeing of Women.

FINANCES *Year* 2011–12 *Income* £58,162 *Grants* £54,235 *Assets* £1,347,561

TRUSTEES Esther Lewis; Rowena Vickers; Nicholas Cobbold.

HOW TO APPLY In writing to the correspondent; there are no application forms. Applications are considered at any time. An sae is appreciated.

WHO TO APPLY TO Esther Lewis, Glebe Farm, Hinton Waldrist, Faringdon, Oxfordshire SN7 8RX *Tel.* 01865 820269

■ Sir John and Lady Amory's Charitable Trust

CC NO 203970   **ESTABLISHED** 1961

WHERE FUNDING CAN BE GIVEN UK, with a preference for Devon and the South West.

WHO CAN BENEFIT Local organisations, plus a few UK-wide charities.

WHAT IS FUNDED General charitable purposes, including education, health and welfare.

TYPE OF GRANT One-off grants for capital expenditure.

RANGE OF GRANTS Up to £8,500. Generally for smaller amounts.

SAMPLE GRANTS National Trust (£8,500).

FINANCES *Year* 2011–12 *Income* £305,746 *Grants* £47,151 *Assets* £1,935,640

TRUSTEES Sir Ian Heathcoat Amory; Lady Heathcoat Amory; William Heathcoat Amory.

OTHER INFORMATION A further £2,000 was given to individuals.

HOW TO APPLY In writing to the correspondent.

WHO TO APPLY TO Lady Heathcoat Amory, Trustee, The Island, Lowman Green, Tiverton, Devon EX16 4LA *Tel.* 01884 254899

■ Viscount Amory's Charitable Trust

CC NO 204958   **ESTABLISHED** 1962

WHERE FUNDING CAN BE GIVEN UK, primarily in Devon.

WHO CAN BENEFIT Particular favour is given to young adults and older people. Charities benefiting people from different family situations, clergy, ex-service and service people, people with disabilities, people disadvantaged by poverty, homeless people and people living in rural areas are also considered.

WHAT IS FUNDED The income is employed mostly in the field of youth service and elderly people particularly to help a number of charitable objects with which the trust has been associated for a number of years, mostly within the county of Devon, including education and training for children and young people. Conservation and heritage causes are also considered.

WHAT IS NOT FUNDED No grants to individuals from outside South West England.

TYPE OF GRANT Usually one-off including capital (including building) costs. Grants for up to three years will be considered.

RANGE OF GRANTS £1,000–£95,000; typically for £5,000 or less.

SAMPLE GRANTS Rona Sailing Trust (£94,000); Blundells School (£25,500); Exeter Cathedral School (£16,500); Churches Housing Action Team (£6,500); Magdalen Court School (£5,500); and Calvert Trust Exmoor and Creative Cow (£5,000 each).

FINANCES *Year* 2011–12 *Income* £388,183 *Grants* £276,918 *Assets* £11,817,584

TRUSTEES Sir Ian Heathcoat Amory; Catherine Cavender.

HOW TO APPLY In writing to the correspondent, giving general background information, total costs involved, amount raised so far and details of applications to other organisations.

WHO TO APPLY TO The Trust Secretary, The Island, Lowman Green, Tiverton, Devon EX16 4LA *Tel.* 01884 254899

■ The Bryan and June Amos Foundation

CC NO 1148785   **ESTABLISHED** 2012

WHERE FUNDING CAN BE GIVEN UK, with a preference for Reigate and Banstead in Surrey.

WHO CAN BENEFIT Charities, community groups and individuals.

WHAT IS FUNDED Relief of poverty, social welfare, older people.

TRUSTEES Jeremy Stacey; Paul Bradley.

HOW TO APPLY In writing to the correspondent.

WHO TO APPLY TO Paul Bradley, Trustee, c/o T. W. M. Solicitors LLP, 40 West Street, Reigate, Surrey RH2 9BT *Tel.* 01737 221212 *email* paul.bradley@twmsolicitors.com

■ The Ampelos Trust

CC NO 1048778   **ESTABLISHED** 1995

WHERE FUNDING CAN BE GIVEN UK.

WHO CAN BENEFIT Registered charities.

WHAT IS FUNDED General charitable purposes.

TYPE OF GRANT Usually one-off.

SAMPLE GRANTS Handel House Trust and Shelter (£20,000 each); Little Hearts Matter (£15,000); National Clinical Group (£12,000); CLIC Sargent (£10,000); and Prostate Cancer Charity and Little Angels Theatre (£5,000 each).

FINANCES *Year* 2011–12 *Income* £242,834 *Grants* £111,000 *Assets* £464,333

TRUSTEES Baroness of Babergh Ruth Rendell; Ann Marie Witt; MMH. Trustees Limited.

HOW TO APPLY The 2011/12 annual report states: 'Since the trustees anticipate being able to identify sufficient potential recipients to whom to distribute the income of the trust, the trustees do not wish to receive unsolicited applications for grants.'

WHO TO APPLY TO Philip Hitchinson, Secretary, c/o Menzies LLP, Ashcombe House, 5 The Crescent, Leatherhead, Surrey KT22 8DY *Tel.* 01372 360130 *email* leatherhead@menzies.co.uk

■ The AMW Charitable Trust

SC NO SC006959   **ESTABLISHED** 1974

WHERE FUNDING CAN BE GIVEN Scotland only, with a priority for the West of Scotland.

WHO CAN BENEFIT Charitable organisations.

WHAT IS FUNDED A broad range of activity is supported including those connected with religion, education, culture, poverty, sickness, disability, social welfare and young adults.

WHAT IS NOT FUNDED No grants for individuals, or to organisations outside Scotland.

SAMPLE GRANTS Previous beneficiaries have included: The Dixon Community, Girl Guiding School, Kelvingrove Refurb Appeal, Lifeboats of the Cycle Appeal, Friends of Glasgow Humane Society, MND Scotland, Maryhill Parish Church, Aberlour Child Care Trust, Dystonia Society, Glasgow School of Arts, Momentum, Hansel Foundation and Muscular Dystrophy Campaign.

FINANCES *Year* 2011–12 *Income* £146,734

TRUSTEE M. McColl.

HOW TO APPLY In writing to the correspondent. Appeals are not acknowledged and the trust only advises successful applicants.

WHO TO APPLY TO M. McCol, c/o KPMG, 191 West George Street, Glasgow G2 2LJ

■ The Anchor Foundation

CC NO 1082485   **ESTABLISHED** 2000

WHERE FUNDING CAN BE GIVEN UK and occasionally overseas.

WHO CAN BENEFIT Christian charities.

WHAT IS FUNDED Social inclusion, particularly through ministries of healing and the arts. Organisations with a number of projects operating are advised to choose a single project for their application.

WHAT IS NOT FUNDED No grants to individuals.

TYPE OF GRANT Applications for capital and revenue funding are considered. Only in very exceptional circumstances will grants be given for building

Think carefully about every application. Is it justified?

345

work. It is not the normal practice of the charity to support the same project for more than three years (projects which have had three years funding may apply again two years from the payment of the last grant).

RANGE OF GRANTS Up to £10,000. Mostly for £5,000 or less.

SAMPLE GRANTS Al Massira, Oasis Cardiff and Fountain of Life (£7,500 each); Crisis Centre Ministries, Greenbelt, Hebrides Alpha Project and The Restorer Trust (£5,000 each); Tron Kirk (£4,000); and Coffee Craft, Derby City Church, Footprint Theatre, Genesis Trust, Living Well Trust, Streetlytes and Zephaniah Music (£3,000 each).

FINANCES *Year* 2011–12 *Income* £305,946 *Grants* £205,300 *Assets* £5,853,765

TRUSTEES Revd Michael Mitton; Revd Robin Anker-Petersen; Nina Anker-Petersen.

HOW TO APPLY An initial application form can be completed online at the Anchor Foundation website. Full guidelines for applicants are also available online. If the trustees decide they are interested in your application you will be contacted and asked to send further relevant information such as a project budget and your annual accounts. **Do not send these with your application form.** Also note that applications should not be sent to the registered office in Nottingham. Applications are considered at twice yearly trustee meetings in April and November and need to be received by 31 January and 31 July each year. The foundation regrets that applications cannot be acknowledged. Successful applicants will be notified as soon as possible after trustees' meetings – usually before the end of May or the end of November. Unsuccessful applicants may reapply after twelve months.

WHO TO APPLY TO Catherine Middleton, Company Secretary, PO Box 21107, Alloa FK12 5WA *Tel.* 01159 500055 *email* secretary@theanchorfoundation.org.uk *Website* www.theanchorfoundation.org.uk

■ The Andrew Anderson Trust

CC NO 212170   **ESTABLISHED** 1954

WHERE FUNDING CAN BE GIVEN UK and overseas.

WHO CAN BENEFIT Organisations benefiting: Christians and evangelists; at risk groups; carers; people with disabilities; people disadvantaged by poverty; socially isolated people; and victims of abuse, crime and domestic violence.

WHAT IS FUNDED Grants to evangelical organisations and churches, small grants to health, disability and social welfare causes.

WHAT IS NOT FUNDED Individuals should not apply for travel or education.

RANGE OF GRANTS Usually under £1,000

SAMPLE GRANTS Aycliffe Evangelical Church, Christian Medical Fellowship, Concern Worldwide, Emmanuel Baptist Church – Sidmouth, Fellowship of Independent Evangelical Churches, Good Shepherd Mission, Kenward Trust, Latin Link, Proclamation Trust, Rehoboth Christian Centre – Blackpool, Scientific Exploration Society, St Ebbe's Parochial Church Council – Oxford, St Helen's Church – Bishopsgate, TNT Ministries, Trinity Baptist Church – Gloucester, Whitefield Christian Trust, Weald Trust and Worldshare.

FINANCES *Year* 2011–12 *Income* £269,217 *Grants* £253,750 *Assets* £10,159,389

TRUSTEES Revd Andrew Robertson Anderson; Anne Alexander Anderson; Margaret Lillian Anderson.

HOW TO APPLY The trust has previously stated that 'we prefer to honour existing commitments and initiate new ones through our own contacts rather than respond to applications'.

WHO TO APPLY TO Revd Andrew Robertson Anderson, Trustee, 1 Cote House Lane, Bristol BS9 3UW *Tel.* 01179 621588

■ Andor Charitable Trust

CC NO 1083572   **ESTABLISHED** 2000

WHERE FUNDING CAN BE GIVEN UK and overseas.

WHO CAN BENEFIT Charitable organisations.

WHAT IS FUNDED Health, arts, Jewish and general charitable purposes.

RANGE OF GRANTS Mostly £2,000–£5,000.

SAMPLE GRANTS The Chicken Shed Theatre Trust (£7,500 in two payments); Pavilion Opera Educational Trust and The Wiener Library Institute of Contemporary History (£5,000 each); The Prostate Cancer Charity (£4,000); The British Refugee Council (£2,500); London Mozart Players, Lupus UK and Riders for Health (£2,000 each) and Music in Hospitals and The Blond McIndoe Research Foundation (£1,000 each).

FINANCES *Year* 2011–12 *Income* £75,637 *Grants* £86,500 *Assets* £3,048,972

TRUSTEES David Rothenberg; Nicholas Lederer; Dr Donald Dean; Jeanne Szego.

HOW TO APPLY In writing to the correspondent.

WHO TO APPLY TO David Rothenberg, Trustee, c/o Blick Rothenberg Chartered Accountants, 16 Great Queen Street, Covent Garden, London WC2B 5AH *Tel.* 020 7486 0111

■ The André Christian Trust

CC NO 248466   **ESTABLISHED** 1950

WHERE FUNDING CAN BE GIVEN UK.

WHO CAN BENEFIT Christian organisations.

WHAT IS FUNDED Charities specified in the trust deed; advancement of the Christian religion.

SAMPLE GRANTS SIFT (£13,000); ECFT (£6,000); Care for the Family, Entheos Trust, Open Air Campaigners and Strangers' Rest Mission (£3,000 each); Choices Pregnancy Centre (£2,000); and Bible Society and Overseas Missionary Fellowship (£1,000 each).

FINANCES *Year* 2012 *Income* £51,173 *Grants* £41,000 *Assets* £1,195,314

TRUSTEES Andrew K. Mowll; Stephen Daykin.

HOW TO APPLY In writing to the correspondent. However, the trust states: 'Applications are discouraged since grants are principally made to those organisations which are listed in the trust deed.' Funds are therefore fully committed and unsolicited requests cannot be supported.

WHO TO APPLY TO Andrew K. Mowll, Trustee, 2 Clevedon Close, Exeter EX4 6HQ *Tel.* 01392 258681

■ Andrews Charitable Trust

CC NO 243509   **ESTABLISHED** 1965

WHERE FUNDING CAN BE GIVEN UK and overseas.

WHO CAN BENEFIT Charities and community groups.

WHAT IS FUNDED Social welfare and Christian causes.

WHAT IS NOT FUNDED 'Do not apply if: you are an individual seeking support for educational expenses (academic or vocational); you are an individual undertaking charitable works in their own or another country on a project/'gap' year/work experience/exchange basis; you are an organisation solely based outside of the UK; you are seeking funding for ongoing work of any organisation; your project is a satellite aspect of an existing organisation; you are looking to cover the costs of building, renovating or other capital works; you offer something that is already done by other organisations; you are not in a position to make your vision a reality; you want funding for an event or project with a time limited span e.g. appeals; you are not open to sharing learning, resources and materials with others working your field; the work is NOT innovative, replicable and sustainable. Applications with any of the above characteristics will not be considered for funding and we urge you not to waste your time working on an application that will not be successful.'

SAMPLE GRANTS Carers Worldwide; Restored; Excellent Development; The Bristol Housing Partnership; Kainos Community; Advantage Africa; BasicNeeds; Digital Links; Catch Up; Credit Action and Opportunity International.

FINANCES *Year* 2012 *Income* £459,783 *Grants* £95,000 *Assets* £9,054,238

TRUSTEES Andrew Radford, Chair; Michael Robson; David Saint; David Westgate; Nicholas Wright; Tony Jackson; Helen Battrick; Paul Heal; Alastair Page; Nicholas Colloff; Elisabeth Hughes; Chris Chapman.

HOW TO APPLY The following information is provided by the foundation:
'We don't have an application form or pack. If you are in doubt about whether or not you 'fit' our criteria, then you can email us with a short introduction to your work and the initiative for which you were thinking of applying. We suggest this is done before writing a full application, if you are unsure of the suitability of your work to the interests of this trust. Written applications can be in any format, but should aim to briefly answer the following questions in not more than three pages: what it is you want to do – explain the idea/work and its value. Are you looking to start a new initiative or is it a step change that you are looking to make; why it should be done – present evidence of the need for it and why it is innovative/better than what is currently offered; where do you want to work and how will this impact on the people/communities you will work with; how many people are expected to benefit and who are they; how do you plan to deliver the change that you are seeking to make; how much will it cost and over what time frame are you looking for funding? (include both the human and financial input you are looking for). As part of this explain how you will sustain the work beyond the support requested; who are the key individuals that will lead the initiative? What experience do you, your organisation and its Trustees/Board have which will give us confidence that you will be able to undertake the proposed work?'

WHO TO APPLY TO Sian Edwards, Director, The Clockhouse, Bath Hill, Keynsham, Bristol BS31 1HL *Tel.* 01179 461834 *email* info@andrewscharitabletrust.org.uk *Website* www.andrewscharitabletrust.org.uk

■ Anglo American Group Foundation

CC NO 1111719   **ESTABLISHED** 2005
WHERE FUNDING CAN BE GIVEN United Kingdom and overseas (priority countries include Brazil, Peru, Chile, Colombia, China, UK, Zimbabwe, Botswana, Namibia and the Democratic Republic of Congo amongst others).

WHO CAN BENEFIT Charitable organisations.
WHAT IS FUNDED Education, international development, health/HIV, environment and London-based community development.
WHAT IS NOT FUNDED Organisations which are not registered charities.
TYPE OF GRANT Support to ongoing projects by organisations.
RANGE OF GRANTS £23,000–£197,000 plus £75,000 in grants under £20,000.
SAMPLE GRANTS Care International (£197,000); pro Mujer Inc (£170,000); The Royal Academy of Engineering (£150,000); International Women's Health Coalition and The Cambridge Foundation (£100,000 each); The Prince's Trust (£71,000); Habitat for Humanity (£63,000); Children of the Andes (£55,000); Sentebale (£30,000); Action far Brazil's Children, The National AIDS Trust and St Andrew's Club (£25,000 each); and Samaritans (£23,000).
FINANCES *Year* 2012 *Income* £1,999,105 *Grants* £1,926,463 *Assets* £526,866
TRUSTEES Nick Jordan; Angela Bromfield; Ian Botha; Duncan Wanblad; Jonathan Samuel; Mervyn Walker.
OTHER INFORMATION Established by Anglo American plc who make donations to the foundation from its annual pre-tax profits.
HOW TO APPLY Applicants are invited to contact the trust directly. The trustees meet quarterly.
WHO TO APPLY TO Charlotte Edgeworth, 20 Carlton House Terrace, London SW1Y 5AN *Tel.* 020 7968 8951 *email* aagf@angloamerican.com *Website* www.angloamericangroupfoundation.org

■ Anguish's Educational Foundation

CC NO 311288   **ESTABLISHED** 1605
WHERE FUNDING CAN BE GIVEN Norwich and the parishes of Costessey, Hellesdon, Catton, Sprowston, Thorpe St Andrews and Corpusty.
WHO CAN BENEFIT Residents of the area of benefit under the age of 25.
WHAT IS FUNDED School clothing, school trips, books/equipment, sports and musical training, grants for fees/maintenance at university/ tertiary education.
SAMPLE GRANTS Community Action Norwich and Mancroft Advice Project (£8,000); BUILD (£5,000); Norwich International Youth Project (£3,000); The Chermond Trust (£700).
FINANCES *Year* 2011–12 *Income* £667,542 *Grants* £433,735 *Assets* £17,487,492
TRUSTEES Roy Blower; Philip Blanchflower; Iain Brooksby; Brenda Ferris; David Fullman; Heather Tyrrell; Geoffrey Loades; Pamela Scutter; Jeanne Southgate; Brenda Ferris; Jeffrey Hooke; Amy Stammers; Peter Shields.
OTHER INFORMATION In 2011–12 grants were given mainly to individuals (£378,000). A total of £56,000 was given to organisations.
HOW TO APPLY In writing to the correspondent. Applications from other charities are considered at two meetings in a year. Applications from individuals are considered at seven meetings throughout the year. Individuals are usually invited to the office for an informal interview.
WHO TO APPLY TO David Walker, Clerk to the Trustees, 1 Woolgate Court, St Benedict's Street, Norwich NR2 4AP *Tel.* 01603 621023 *email* david.walker@norwichcharitabletrusts.org.uk

■ The Animal Defence Trust

cc no 263095   **ESTABLISHED** 1971
WHERE FUNDING CAN BE GIVEN UK.
WHO CAN BENEFIT UK organisations benefiting animals.
WHAT IS FUNDED Capital projects for animal welfare/ protection.
WHAT IS NOT FUNDED No grants to individuals.
TYPE OF GRANT Usually one-off payments.
SAMPLE GRANTS Brooke Hospital for Animals, Ferne Animal Sanctuary, Woodside Animal Welfare Trust and Worldwide Veterinary Service (£4,000 each); International Otter Survival Fund (£3,000); Greek Cat Welfare Society and Himalayan Animal Treatment Centre (£2,000 each); and Care4cats, Cat Register and Rescue, Fox Project, Greyhound Rescue, Rotherham Dog Rescue and Safe Haven for Donkeys in Holy Land (£1,000 each).
FINANCES *Year* 2011–12 *Income* £56,515 *Grants* £78,000 *Assets* £1,317,878
TRUSTEES Marion Saunders; Carole Bowles; Richard J. Vines; Jenny Wheadon.
HOW TO APPLY On a form which together with guidelines can be downloaded from the trust's website.
WHO TO APPLY TO Alan A. Meyer, Secretary, Horsey Lightly Fynn, Devon House, 12–15 Dartmouth Street, Queen Anne's Gate, London SW1H 9BL *Tel.* 020 7222 8844 *email* ameyer@ horseylightly.com *Website* www. animaldefencetrust.org

■ Philip Anker Trust

cc no 1149163   **ESTABLISHED** 2012
WHERE FUNDING CAN BE GIVEN UK.
WHO CAN BENEFIT Charities and community groups. Individuals are also supported.
WHAT IS FUNDED General, education, social welfare, children and young people.
TRUSTEES Paul Haley; Vivien Haley; Natasha Evans.
HOW TO APPLY In writing to the correspondent.
WHO TO APPLY TO Paul Haley, Trustee, 14 Knights Orchard, Hemel Hempstead, Hertfordshire HP1 3QA *Tel.* 01442 219468 *email* paul. haley@virgin.net

■ The Eric Anker-Petersen Charity

cc no 1061428   **ESTABLISHED** 1997
WHERE FUNDING CAN BE GIVEN UK.
WHO CAN BENEFIT Charitable causes in the fields of screen and stage.
WHAT IS FUNDED Grants are made towards the conservation of classic films.
WHAT IS NOT FUNDED No grants to individuals or for non-charitable purposes.
SAMPLE GRANTS Theatrical Ladies Guild, and Imperial War Museum for the following films: *The British Atomic Trials at Maralinga*, *Everybody's Business*, *The Women's Portion* and for the book: *This Film is Dangerous.*
FINANCES *Year* 2011–12 *Income* £12,363
TRUSTEES George Duncan; Shan Warnock-Smith; David Long.
OTHER INFORMATION Grants usually total about £35,000 a year.
HOW TO APPLY In writing to the correspondent. The trust has previously wished to emphasise that it is always looking for projects to support which meet its criteria, outlined above.

WHO TO APPLY TO David Long, Trustee, 8–10 New Fetter Lane, London EC4A 1RS *Tel.* 020 7203 5096 *email* grainne.feeney@charlesrussell.co. uk

■ The Annandale Charitable Trust

cc no 1049193   **ESTABLISHED** 1995
WHERE FUNDING CAN BE GIVEN UK.
WHO CAN BENEFIT Major charities.
WHAT IS FUNDED General charitable purposes.
SAMPLE GRANTS Unicef East Africa Children's Appeal (£10,000); Age NI, Battersea Dogs and Cats Home, Dogs Trust, Just 42, Medequip4kids, Southampton Hospital Charity, The Horse Trust and Unicef Ivory Coast Emergency Appeal (£5,000 each); Breakthrough Breast Cancer, Cherished Memories, icandance, Marine Conservation Society and Talking with Hands (£3,000 each); and Unicef Libya Crisis Appeal (£2,000).
FINANCES *Year* 2011–12 *Income* £259,415 *Grants* £298,758 *Assets* £10,665,586
TRUSTEES Carole Duggan; HSBC. Trust Company (UK) Ltd.
HOW TO APPLY The trust has previously stated that it has an ongoing programme of funding for specific charities and all its funds are fully committed.
WHO TO APPLY TO The Trust Manager, HSBC Trust Services, 10th Floor, Norwich House, Nelson Gate, Commercial Road, Southampton SO15 1GX *Tel.* 02380 722248

■ Anpride Ltd

cc no 288978   **ESTABLISHED** 1984
WHERE FUNDING CAN BE GIVEN London and Israel.
WHO CAN BENEFIT Registered charities.
WHAT IS FUNDED Advancement of the Jewish faith and the relief of poverty.
WHAT IS NOT FUNDED Grants to state-aided institutions will generally not be considered and no grants to individuals.
FINANCES *Year* 2011–12 *Income* £152,463 *Grants* £50,890 *Assets* £93,173
TRUSTEES Chaim Benedikt; Golda Benedikt; Israel Benedikt.
HOW TO APPLY In writing to the correspondent.
WHO TO APPLY TO Golda Benedikt, Trustee and Secretary, 99 Geldeston Road, London E5 8RS *Tel.* 020 8806 1011

■ The Anson Charitable Trust

cc no 1111010   **ESTABLISHED** 2005
WHERE FUNDING CAN BE GIVEN UK.
WHO CAN BENEFIT Charitable organisations and individuals.
WHAT IS FUNDED General charitable purposes, there is a preference for work with children and older people. Health and medical research causes are also widely supported.
RANGE OF GRANTS £200–£16,000.
SAMPLE GRANTS The Pace Centre (£12,000); Royal Shakespeare Society and Tate Gallery (£10,000 each); Royal Opera House Foundation (£9,000); ABF The Soldiers' Charity and Weedon Methodist Church Trust (£6,000 each); Buckinghamshire Agricultural Association and Project Trust (£5,000 each); British Stammering Association, Listening Books and Queen Alexandra Hospital Home (£3,000 each); Prince's Regeneration Trust (£2,500); Braille Chess Association and Oundle School

Foundation (£2,000 each); Anthony Nolan Trust and The Woodland Trust (£1,000 each); WaterAid (£600); and WNAA (£250).
FINANCES *Year* 2011–12 *Income* £833,654 *Grants* £214,756 *Assets* £646,390
TRUSTEES George Anson; Kirsty Anson; Peter Nichols.
HOW TO APPLY In writing to the correspondent.
WHO TO APPLY TO George Anson, Trustee, The Lilies, High Street, Weedon, Aylesbury, Buckinghamshire HP22 4NS *Tel.* 01296 640331 *email* ansonctrust@btinternet.com

■ The Apax Foundation

CC NO 1112845   **ESTABLISHED** 2006
WHERE FUNDING CAN BE GIVEN UK, USA, Asia, Africa, Europe.
WHO CAN BENEFIT Charitable organisations.
WHAT IS FUNDED Relief in need and education.
RANGE OF GRANTS Up to £200,000. In 2011/12, donations of £10,000 or less totalled £188,000.
SAMPLE GRANTS Private Equity Foundation (£204,00); INSEAD Social Entrepreneurship Initiative (£100,000); Mosaic Business in the Community (£99,000); International Bridges to Justice (£62,000); Shivia and Trickle Up (£50,000 each); Joblinge (£33,000); PilotLight (£28.000); Ascension Eagles Cheer, Bromley by Bow Centre and Casa Do Zezinho (£25,000 each).
FINANCES *Year* 2011–12 *Income* £1,593,981 *Grants* £966,056 *Assets* £17,879,195
TRUSTEES Sir Ronald Cohen, Chair; Peter Englander; Martin Halusa; David Marks; John Megrue; Michael Phillips; Irina Hemmers; Simon Cresswell; Mitch Truwit; Shashank Singh.
OTHER INFORMATION 'The Apax Foundation is the formal channel for Apax Partners' charitable giving and receives a percentage of the firm's profits and carried interest.'
HOW TO APPLY 'Organisations which the trustees identify as potentially suitable recipients of grants are invited to submit funding proposals, which are reviewed by the trustees.' The trustees meet quarterly to review donations and grants.
'Before deciding on a significant grant to a recipient, the trustees will spend time with a potential recipient organisation to assess its effectiveness and agree how our grant will be deployed. In this way, we are reasonably confident that our major grants will be spent wisely.'
'As a private foundation, we are principally concerned that we will be able to operate into the foreseeable future without relying on the continuation of receiving substantial annual donations and therefore we intend to maintain our current level of giving rather than seek to expand it.'
WHO TO APPLY TO David Marks, Trustee, 33 Jermyn Street, London SW1Y 6DN *Tel.* 020 7872 6300 *email* foundation@apax.com

■ Ambrose and Ann Appelbe Trust

CC NO 208658   **ESTABLISHED** 1944
WHERE FUNDING CAN BE GIVEN UK.
WHO CAN BENEFIT Organisations benefiting students and research workers and individuals.
WHAT IS FUNDED Education and training, especially postgraduate education (bursaries and fees), literacy, professional or specialist training; general charitable purposes.

WHAT IS NOT FUNDED Buildings are not funded. No funding to for sponsorship with Operation Raleigh, the Project Trust or similar establishments, for medical electives, for schoolchildren or for theatrical training.
RANGE OF GRANTS Up to £3,000.
SAMPLE GRANTS Previous beneficiaries have included: Anatomical Donors Association (£7,000); the Firbank Charitable Trust (£5,500); Orchestra of the Age of Enlightenment (£3,000); Godshill Trust (£2,800); Soil Association (£2,500); WPF (£1,500); National Youth Orchestra, Peterhouse Development Fund, St Gabriel's School Foundation, Tommy's and Zanzibar Aid Project (£1,000 each); Camphill St Albans, the Project Trust and RNLI (£500 each); Southbank Sinfonia (£500 each); and Wednesday's Child (£250).
FINANCES *Year* 2011–12 *Income* £29,002 *Grants* £32,000
TRUSTEES Valentine Thomas; Felix Appelbe; Dr Lucinda Hobby.
HOW TO APPLY In writing to the correspondent, enclosing an sae. Individuals should apply through their college/university.
WHO TO APPLY TO Felix Appelbe, Trustee, c/o Ambrose Appelbe Solicitors, Lincoln's Inn, 7 New Square, London WC2A 3RA

■ The Appletree Trust

SC NO SC004851   **ESTABLISHED** 1982
WHERE FUNDING CAN BE GIVEN UK and overseas, with a preference for Scotland and the North East Fife district.
WHO CAN BENEFIT Charitable organisations.
WHAT IS FUNDED Disability, sickness and poverty causes.
WHAT IS NOT FUNDED No grants to individuals.
TYPE OF GRANT Capital, buildings, project, research. Grants can be for up to two years.
SAMPLE GRANTS Previous grant beneficiaries included: 1st St Andrews Boys Brigade, Alzheimer Scotland, Arthritis Care In Scotland, the Broomhouse Centre, Children's Hospice Association, Discovery Camps Trust, Home Start East Fife, Marie Curie Cancer Care, PDSA, Prince and Princess of Wales Hospice, RNID, the Salvation Army, Scottish Motor Neurone Disease Association and Scottish Spina Bifida Association.
FINANCES *Year* 2011–12 *Income* £35,292 *Grants* £40,000
TRUSTEE The Royal Bank of Scotland plc.
HOW TO APPLY In writing to the correspondent. Trustees meet to consider grants in April.
WHO TO APPLY TO Administrator, The Royal Bank of Scotland plc, Trust and Estate Services, Eden Lakeside, Chester Business Park, Wrexham Road, Chester, CH4 9QT

■ The John Apthorp Charity (formerly Summary Limited)

CC NO 1102472   **ESTABLISHED** 2004
WHERE FUNDING CAN BE GIVEN UK, with a preference for Hertfordshire.
WHO CAN BENEFIT Charitable organisations.
WHAT IS FUNDED Education, religion and social welfare.
RANGE OF GRANTS Up to £50,000.
SAMPLE GRANTS Radlett Lawn and Tennis Club (£35,000); Tools for Self Reliance (£25,000); John Clements Centre (£20,000); Reach Out Plus (£15,000); The Living Room, Home Start

Welwyn and Teens Unite Fighting Cancer (£10,000 each); Radlett Art Society (£7,000); Alzheimer's Society (£5,000); and the Tall Ships Youth Trust (£1,500).

FINANCES *Year* 2012 *Income* £422,699 *Grants* £480,119 *Assets* £9,536,185

TRUSTEES John Apthorp; Duncan Apthorp; Justin Apthorp; Kate Arnold.

HOW TO APPLY In writing to the correspondent.

WHO TO APPLY TO John Apthorp, Trustee, The Field House Farm, 29 Newlands Avenue, Radlett, Hertfordshire WD7 8EJ *Tel.* 01923 855727

■ The Arbib Foundation

CC NO 296358   **ESTABLISHED** 1987

WHERE FUNDING CAN BE GIVEN Unrestricted.

WHO CAN BENEFIT Registered charities and local organisations with charitable purposes.

WHAT IS FUNDED Social welfare, medical, education and children's welfare In particular to maintain the River and Rowing Museum in the Thames Valley for the education of the general public in the history, geography and ecology of the Thames Valley and the River Thames, with some donations for general purposes.

WHAT IS NOT FUNDED No grants to individuals.

TYPE OF GRANT Recurrent and single donations.

RANGE OF GRANTS £100–£125,000.

SAMPLE GRANTS Langley Academy (£86,000 in total – Annabel Nichol is the sponsor and chair of governors at the academy); Institute of Cancer Research and the River and Rowing Museum Foundation (£50,000 each); Row to Recovery (£30,000 in total); Alfred Dunhill Foundation and the Barbados Community Foundation (£25,000 each); Ramsbury Recreation Centre (£15,000); RNIB (£11,500 in total); CLIC Sargent (£10,000 in total); Community Security Trust (£5,000); and Bowel Cancer Research Fund and Movember (£1,000 each).

FINANCES *Year* 2011–12 *Income* £747,853 *Grants* £366,709 *Assets* £408,054

TRUSTEES Sir Martyn Arbib; Lady Arbib; Annabel Nicoll.

HOW TO APPLY Note: the trust has previously stated that unsolicited applications are not being considered as funds are fully committed for the 'foreseeable future'.

WHO TO APPLY TO Paula Doraisamy, 61 Grosvenor Street, London W1K 3JE *Tel.* 020 3011 1100

■ Archbishop of Wales' Fund for Children

CC NO 1102236   **ESTABLISHED** 2004

WHERE FUNDING CAN BE GIVEN Wales.

WHO CAN BENEFIT Children in need and their families and local communities.

WHAT IS FUNDED The work of organisations in this order of priority: (1) those in the Dioceses of the Church in Wales; (2) those associated with other Christian bodies which are members of Cytun – Churches Together in Wales; (3) other organisations working with children in Wales.

SAMPLE GRANTS Previous beneficiaries have included: the Bridge Mentoring Plus Scheme; Cardiff People First; Family Awareness Drug and Support; MENFA; Pontllanfraith, Brecon, Aberdare and Merthyr Tydfil Contact Centres; and Valley Kids. A number of church-based projects were also supported.

FINANCES *Year* 2012 *Income* £32,551 *Grants* £50,648 *Assets* £99,424

TRUSTEES Revd J. Michael Williams, Chair; Cheryl Beach; Ruth Forrester; Caroline Owen; James Tovey.

HOW TO APPLY Application forms are available from the correspondent. Telephone calls are welcome before application submitted.

WHO TO APPLY TO Karen Phillips, Administrator, Church in Wales, 39 Cathedral Road, Cardiff CF11 9WH *Tel.* 02920 348234 *email* awfc@churchinwales.org.uk

■ The John M. Archer Charitable Trust

SC NO SC010583   **ESTABLISHED** 1969

WHERE FUNDING CAN BE GIVEN UK and overseas.

WHO CAN BENEFIT Registered charities.

WHAT IS FUNDED General charitable purposes, including: the prevention or relief of individuals in need; welfare of people who are sick or distressed; alleviation of need; advancement of education; advancement of religious or missionary work; advancement of scientific research and discovery; and preservation of Scottish heritage and the advancement of associated cultural activities.

SAMPLE GRANTS Previous beneficiaries have included Angkor Hospital For Children (Cambodia), the Canonmills Baptist Church, Castlebrae School Tutoring Programme, Erskine Stewarts Melville College – Arts Centre, Mercy Corps Scotland, the Bobby Moore Fund, Red Cross – Aberdeen Guest House and Royal Liverpool University Hospital – Macular Degeneration Research.

FINANCES *Year* 2011–12 *Income* £40,715 *Grants* £22,000

TRUSTEE E. Grant.

OTHER INFORMATION The grant total is an approximate figure.

HOW TO APPLY In writing to the correspondent.

WHO TO APPLY TO E. Grant, Secretary, 10 Broughton Place Lane, Edinburgh EH1 3RS

■ The Archer Trust

CC NO 1033534   **ESTABLISHED** 1994

WHERE FUNDING CAN BE GIVEN Worldwide.

WHO CAN BENEFIT Voluntary organisations, especially those which make good use of volunteers or are located in areas of high unemployment or disadvantage. Preference is given to smaller organisations. Support is given to projects both in the UK and overseas, but for overseas projects only via UK charities.

WHAT IS FUNDED Provision of aid and support to a defined group of needy or deserving people, such as people with mental or physical disabilities or people who are otherwise disadvantaged; Christian causes.

WHAT IS NOT FUNDED No grants are made for the benefit of: Individuals (including for gap years), conservation or heritage projects, environmental causes, conversion for disability access, animal charities or research.

RANGE OF GRANTS Usually £250–£3,000

SAMPLE GRANTS International Refugee Trust, Lilias Graham Trust, Sheltered Work Opportunities Programme, The Sycamore Project and Hertford Regional College (£3,000 each); Christian International Peace Service, The Community of Camden Churches Cold Weather Scheme, Cricklewood Homeless Concern, Disability Recreation Unity Movement, The Esther Benjamins Trust, The Hailer Foundation, The

Maxie Richards Foundation, The Respite Association and Support Line (£2,000 each).

FINANCES *Year* 2011–12 *Income* £110,421 *Grants* £72,995 *Assets* £1,705,233

TRUSTEES C. M. Archer; M. F. Baker; J. N. Archer; L. Packman.

HOW TO APPLY In writing to the correspondent. Unsuccessful applicants will not receive a response, even if an sae is enclosed. Applications are considered twice a year, usually in March and September.

WHO TO APPLY TO The Secretary, Bourne House, Wadesmill, Ware, Hertfordshire SG12 0TT *Tel.* 01920 462312 *Website* www.archertrust. org.uk

■ The Architectural Heritage Fund

CC NO 266780   **ESTABLISHED** 1973

WHERE FUNDING CAN BE GIVEN UK (excluding the Channel Islands and the Isle of Man).

WHO CAN BENEFIT Registered charities, social enterprises, and charitable incorporated organisations. Organisations must have charitable status.

WHAT IS FUNDED Support is given in the form of grants, loans, advice and information for the preservation and sustainable re-use of historic buildings.

WHAT IS NOT FUNDED Applications from private individuals and non-charitable organisations. Applications for projects not involving a change of ownership or of use, or for a building not on a statutory list or in a conservation area.

TYPE OF GRANT Loans; feasibility study grants; project administration grants; project organiser grants; refundable project development grants.

RANGE OF GRANTS Grants up to £20,000; loans up to £500,000 (more in exceptional circumstances).

FINANCES *Year* 2011–12 *Income* £4,150,992 *Grants* £808,743 *Assets* £15,796,000

TRUSTEES Colin Amery; Malcolm Crowder; Roy Dantzic; Rita Harkin; George McNeill; Philip Kirby; Merlin Waterson; Thomas Lloyd; Liz Davidson; John Townsend; Michael Hoare; John Duggan.

OTHER INFORMATION In addition to the amount given in grants, £69,500 was given in loans.

HOW TO APPLY Detailed notes for applicants for loans and feasibility studies are supplied with the application forms, all of which are available from the fund's website. The trustees meet in March, June, September and December; applications must be received six weeks before meetings.

WHO TO APPLY TO Barbara Wright, Loans and Grants Manager, Alhambra House, 27–31 Charing Cross Road, London WC2H 0AU *Tel.* 020 7925 0199 *Fax* 020 7930 0295 *email* ahf@ahfund. org.uk *Website* www.ahfund.org.uk

■ The Ardeola Charitable Trust

CC NO 1124380   **ESTABLISHED** 2008

WHERE FUNDING CAN BE GIVEN Worldwide.

WHO CAN BENEFIT Registered charities.

WHAT IS FUNDED General charitable purposes, although the main beneficiary each year is Target Ovarian Cancer.

SAMPLE GRANTS Target Ovarian Cancer (£600,000); Durham University (£75,000); and Non-Profit Enterprise and Self-Sustainability Team (NESST Inc) (£71,000).

FINANCES *Year* 2011–12 *Income* £565,346 *Grants* £746,205 *Assets* £2,558,867

TRUSTEES Graham Barker; Joanna Barker; Coutts and Co.

HOW TO APPLY In writing to the correspondent, although potential applicants should note that the trust's main beneficiary is connected with the trustees.

WHO TO APPLY TO The Trustees, Coutts and Co, Trustee Dept., 440 Strand, London WC2R 0QS *Tel.* 020 7753 1000

■ The Ardwick Trust

CC NO 266981   **ESTABLISHED** 1975

WHERE FUNDING CAN BE GIVEN UK, Israel and the developing world.

WHO CAN BENEFIT Institutions and registered charities (mainly UK charities) benefiting people of all ages, students and Jews.

WHAT IS FUNDED To support Jewish welfare, along with a wide range of non-Jewish causes to include social welfare, health, education (especially special schools), elderly people, conservation and the environment, child welfare, disability and medical research. In general most of the largest grants go to Jewish organisations, with most of the smaller grants to non-Jewish organisations.

WHAT IS NOT FUNDED No grants to individuals.

TYPE OF GRANT One-off or recurrent grants up to two years. Capital, including buildings, research and start-up costs.

RANGE OF GRANTS Mostly under £1,000.

SAMPLE GRANTS Nightingale Hammerson and Pinhas Rutenberg Educational Trust (£5,000 each); British Friends of the Hebrew University, Jewish Care and Technion UK (£3,000); World Jewish Relief (£1,500); and British ORT, Langdon Foundation, Norwood and UJIA (£1,000 each). Remaining beneficiaries were all for £700, £500, £200 or £100 each. Beneficiaries included: Cancer Research UK, Cheltenham Ladies' College, Friends of Israel Educational Foundation, Great Ormond Street Hospital Charity, Jewish Deaf Association, North London Hospice, Pancreatic Cancer UK, Scope, Shelter, Shine, Springboard for Children, Stroke Association, Target Ovarian Cancer, Target Tuberculosis, Womankind Worldwide, World 4 Girls, WWF-UK, Y Care International YMCA England, WaterAid and Whizz-Kidz.

FINANCES *Year* 2012–13 *Income* £88,439 *Grants* £82,200 *Assets* £1,163,129

TRUSTEES Janet Bloch; Dominic Flynn; Judith Portrait.

HOW TO APPLY In writing to the correspondent.

WHO TO APPLY TO Janet Bloch, Trustee, c/o Knox Cropper, 24 Petworth Road, Haslemere, Surrey GU27 2HR *Tel.* 01428 652788

■ The Argentarius Foundation

CC NO 1079980   **ESTABLISHED** 2000

WHERE FUNDING CAN BE GIVEN UK.

WHO CAN BENEFIT Charitable organisations.

WHAT IS FUNDED General charitable purposes.

SAMPLE GRANTS No details available.

FINANCES *Year* 2011–12 *Income* £2,738 *Grants* £95,131

TRUSTEES Emily Marbach; Judy Jackson; Anna Josse.

OTHER INFORMATION Basic information taken from the Charity Commission website. Accounting documents had been received but were not published due to the foundation's low income.

HOW TO APPLY In writing to the correspondent.

WHO TO APPLY TO Philip Goodman, Goodman and Co, 14 Basing Hill, London NW11 8TH *Tel.* 020 8458 0955 *email* philip@goodmanandco.com

----

■ The Argus Appeal

CC NO 1013647   ESTABLISHED 1992
WHERE FUNDING CAN BE GIVEN Sussex.
WHO CAN BENEFIT Registered charities.
WHAT IS FUNDED Relief-in-need and older people.
SAMPLE GRANTS Friends of Downs View School (£7,000); and the Dame Vera Lynn Trust (£5,000).
FINANCES *Year* 2012 *Income* £158,298 *Grants* £63,727 *Assets* £323,935
TRUSTEES Ian Hunter; Sue Meheux; Elsa Gillio; David Goldin; Roger French; Michael Beard; Sue Addis.
OTHER INFORMATION The grant total in includes £42,500 to 34 organisations and £21,000 to individuals.
HOW TO APPLY In writing to the correspondent.
WHO TO APPLY TO Elsa Gillio, Trustee, Argus House, Crowhurst Road, Hollingbury, Brighton BN1 8AR *Tel.* 01273 544465 *email* elsa.gillio@theargus.co.uk

----

■ Armenian General Benevolent Union London Trust

CC NO 282070   ESTABLISHED 1981
WHERE FUNDING CAN BE GIVEN UK and overseas.
WHO CAN BENEFIT Armenian individuals and organisations.
WHAT IS FUNDED The purpose of the trust is to advance education among Armenians, particularly those in the UK, and to promote the study of Armenian history, literature, language, culture and religion.
WHAT IS NOT FUNDED No support for projects of a commercial nature.
SAMPLE GRANTS The Armenian Church Trust (£5,000) and the RP Musical for Remembrance Concert (£1,500). A further £4,000 was given under the grant category 'Education' to K Tahta Armenian Sunday School.
FINANCES *Year* 2011 *Income* £142,832 *Grants* £73,404 *Assets* £3,732,954
TRUSTEES Dr Berge Azadian; Berge Setrakian; Aris Atamian; Noushig Yakoubian Setrakian; Assadour Guzelian; Tro Manoukian; Arline Medazoumian; Armine Afrikian.
OTHER INFORMATION The grant total in 2011 included £59,500 given in 29 student loans and grants.
HOW TO APPLY In writing to the correspondent. Applications are considered all year around.
WHO TO APPLY TO Dr Berge Azadian, Trustee, 51c Parkside, Wimbledon Common, London SW19 5NE

■ The Armenian Relief Society of Great Britain Trust

CC NO 327389   ESTABLISHED 1987
WHERE FUNDING CAN BE GIVEN Worldwide.
WHO CAN BENEFIT Individuals and organisations.
WHAT IS FUNDED Welfare of Armenians.
SAMPLE GRANTS Armenian Relief Society Inc USA (£12,000); Armenian Scouting Association (£3,000); Hamazkayin (£2,500); Armenian Community Church Council (£1,500); Armenian National Committee (£500); K Tahta Armenian Community School (£200) and Armenian Medical Association (£100).

FINANCES *Year* 2011–12 *Income* £53,704 *Grants* £20,105 *Assets* £55,326
TRUSTEES Arshalouys Babayan; Zovig Haladjian; Sonia Bablanian; Jacqueline Karanfilian; Janet Khachatourian; Estela Tarverdi; Juliet Simonian.
HOW TO APPLY In writing to the correspondent.
WHO TO APPLY TO The Trustees, 19 Somervell Road, Middlesex HA2 8TY

■ The John Armitage Charitable Trust

CC NO 1079688   ESTABLISHED 2000
WHERE FUNDING CAN BE GIVEN England and Wales.
WHO CAN BENEFIT Institutions and registered charities.
WHAT IS FUNDED Medical, relief-in-need, education, religion, environment, general.
SAMPLE GRANTS The Thames Diamond Jubilee Foundation and Westminster Abbey Foundation (£100,000 each); Marie Curie Cancer Care (£72,000); National Churches Trust and Russian Revival Project (£60,000 each); Sir John Soanes Museum Trust (£50,000); Independence at Home, Miracles, Redress and Youth Sport Trust (£36,000 each); Bibury School (£27,000); Fishmongers Company Charitable Trust and New Horizon Youth (£24,000 each); Only Connect (£17,000); Barnsley Parochial Church Council (£10,000); and Aspire (£5,000).
FINANCES *Year* 2011–12 *Income* £1,518,261 *Grants* £1,453,000 *Assets* £39,537,291
TRUSTEES John Armitage; Catherine Armitage; William Francklin; Celina Francklin.
HOW TO APPLY Applications received by the trust are 'reviewed by the trustees and grants awarded at their discretion'.
WHO TO APPLY TO John C. Armitage, Trustee, c/o Sampson West, 34 Ely Place, London EC1N 6TD *Tel.* 020 7404 5040 *Fax* 020 7831 1098 *email* finance@sampsonwest.co.uk

----

■ The Armourers' and Brasiers' Gauntlet Trust

CC NO 279204   ESTABLISHED 1979
WHERE FUNDING CAN BE GIVEN UK, with some preference for London.
WHO CAN BENEFIT Charitable organisations.
WHAT IS FUNDED The objectives of the trust are: support for education and research in materials science and technology and for basic science in schools; encouragement of the understanding and preservation of historic armour; encouragement of the armourers' trade in the armed services; encouragement of professional excellence in the training of young officers in the Royal Armoured Corps. It also considers appeals in the following overall categories: (i) community, social care and armed forces; (ii) children, youth and general education; medical and health; (iii) art, arms and armour; and (iv) Christian mission.
WHAT IS NOT FUNDED In general grants are not made: to organisation or groups which are not registered charities; in response to applications for the benefit of individuals; to organisations or groups whose main object is to fund or support other charitable bodies; which are in direct relief of, or will lead to, a reduction of financial support from public funds; to charities with a turnover in excess of £1 million; to charities which spend over 10% of their income on fundraising activities; towards general

maintenance, repair or restoration of buildings, including ecclesiastical buildings, unless there is a connection with the Armourers and Brasiers' Company, or unless of outstanding importance to the national heritage; to appeals for charitable sponsorship from individuals.

TYPE OF GRANT 'Regular annual grants are not a policy of the trust at present, but charities can still apply for grants on an annual basis.'

RANGE OF GRANTS The trustees prefer to make grants to smaller and less well known charitable organisations rather than to those with a high public profile. Over 100 such charities receive grants each year.

SAMPLE GRANTS Royal Opera House and The Richard House Hospice (£2,000 each); Combat Stress, Just Different, Lumos Foundation, Medical Engineering Unit, Morning Star Trust, National Life Story Collection, and Spitalfields Festival Limited (£1,000 each); and 4 Cancer Group, Cricklewood Homeless Concern, Hope UK, Local Employment Access Projects, My Voice London, Open Door Young People's Consultation Service, Siblings Together, Target Ovarian Cancer, The Eyeless Trust, The Migraine Trust, The National Tremor Foundation and Toucan Employment (£500 each).

FINANCES *Year* 2011–12 *Income* £396,824 *Grants* £267,390 *Assets* £6,040,803

TRUSTEES Prof. William Bonfield; Ven. C. J. H. Wagstaff; Jonathan Stopford Haw; David Chapman; Simon Archer; David Davies.

OTHER INFORMATION Grants of £62,350 were made to 108 individuals and grants of £205,040 were made to organisations.

HOW TO APPLY In writing to the correspondent, with a copy of the latest annual report and audited accounts. Applications are considered quarterly. For full guidelines, visit the trust's website.

WHO TO APPLY TO Christopher Waite, Secretary, Armourers' Hall, 81 Coleman Street, London EC2R 5BJ *Tel.* 020 7374 4000 *Fax* 020 7606 7481 *email* info@armourersandbrasiers.co.uk *Website* www.armourersandbrasiers.co.uk

■ The Arsenal Foundation Limited

CC NO 1145668   **ESTABLISHED** 2012

WHERE FUNDING CAN BE GIVEN Mainly Greater London.

WHO CAN BENEFIT Organisations and individuals.

WHAT IS FUNDED Youth projects; the provision of recreational facilities; education; the relief of poverty; and the relief of sickness and distress, including (but not exclusive to) people who are injured through sport and assist dependants of people who are killed through participating in sport. Also for any charitable purpose for the inhabitants of Islington and Hackney.

TRUSTEES Kenneth Friar; David Miles; Alan Sefton; Ivan Gazidis; Svenja Geissmar.

OTHER INFORMATION The Arsenal Foundation was re-established as The Arsenal Foundation Limited with a new Charity Commission number in January 2012.
No accounts are available for the new foundation. Previously, in 2010/11, grants to organisations totalled £83,000.

HOW TO APPLY In writing to the correspondent.

WHO TO APPLY TO The Trustees, Highbury House, 75 Drayton Park, London N5 1BU *Tel.* 020 7704 4406

■ The Artemis Charitable Trust

CC NO 291328   **ESTABLISHED** 1985

WHERE FUNDING CAN BE GIVEN UK.

WHO CAN BENEFIT Registered charities benefiting parents, counsellors and psychotherapists.

WHAT IS FUNDED Counselling, psychotherapy, parenting, and human relationship training.

WHAT IS NOT FUNDED We cannot entertain applications either from individuals or from organisations which are not registered charities.'

TYPE OF GRANT Recurring.

SAMPLE GRANTS Voluntary Sector Mental Health Providers Forum (£49,000); Relate (£7,000); Royal African Society (£4,000); and Core System Trust (£560).

FINANCES *Year* 2012 *Income* £49,868 *Grants* £146,996 *Assets* £1,550,220

TRUSTEES Primary Care Psychological Services (£124,000); Chichester Festival Theatre (£17,000); The Expeditionary Trust (£5,000); Mental Health Informatics (£720); and Relate (£500).

HOW TO APPLY 'Applicants should [. . .] be aware that most of the trust's funds are committed to a number of major ongoing projects and that spare funds available to meet new applications are very limited.'

WHO TO APPLY TO Richard Evans, Trustee, Brook House, Quay Meadow, Bosham, West Sussex PO18 8LY *Tel.* 01243 573475

■ Arthritis Research UK

CC NO 207711   **ESTABLISHED** 1936

WHERE FUNDING CAN BE GIVEN Mainly UK.

WHO CAN BENEFIT Mostly universities.

WHAT IS FUNDED Research into the cause and cure of arthritis and related musculoskeletal diseases.

WHAT IS NOT FUNDED Applications for welfare and social matters will not be considered.

TYPE OF GRANT One-off, project, recurring, running costs, and salaries. Programme support is for five years; project grants are usually for three years.

FINANCES *Year* 2011–12 *Income* £40,224,000 *Grants* £25,925,000 *Assets* £108,759,000

TRUSTEES Charles Maisey, Chair; Joe Carlebach; Dr Josh Dixey; Dr Sylvie Jackson; Lord Lewis of Newnham; Prof. Sir Patrick Sissons; Peter Henderson; Richard Raworth; Prof. Mike Pringle; Chris Cowpe; Prof. Sir Alex Markham; Paul Rowen; Tom Hayhoe.

HOW TO APPLY Application forms and guidelines are available from the Arthritis Research UK website.

WHO TO APPLY TO Grants Team, Copeman House, St Mary's Court, St Mary's Gate, Chesterfield, Derbyshire S41 7TD *Tel.* 0300 790 0400 *Fax* 0300 790 0401 *email* enquiries@arthritisresearchuk.org *Website* www.arthritisresearchuk.org

■ The Arthur Ronald Dyer Charitable Trust

CC NO 1134181   **ESTABLISHED** 2010

WHERE FUNDING CAN BE GIVEN Undefined, in practice the UK.

WHO CAN BENEFIT Registered charities.

WHAT IS FUNDED Supports other charitable organisations in the following areas: the advancement of health or saving of lives;

disability; animals; environment/conservation/ heritage.

SAMPLE GRANTS 'The Trustees will take into account the Letter of Wishes which requests that consideration be given to benefit the following charities: British Heart Foundation, Parkinson's Disease Society UK, First Air Ambulance Trust, Devon Air Ambulance Trust, RSPB, WWF, League of Friends Torbay Hospital, League of Friends Musgrove Hospital, NSPCC and Age Concern Devon.'

FINANCES *Year* 2012–13 *Income* £40,255 *Grants* £15,588

TRUSTEE NatWest Trust Services

HOW TO APPLY In writing to the correspondent.

WHO TO APPLY TO The Administrator, NatWest Trust Services, 5th Floor, Trinity Quay 2, Avon Street, Bristol BS2 0PT *Tel.* 05516577371

■ The Arts and Entertainment Charitable Trust

CC NO 1031027   **ESTABLISHED** 1994

WHERE FUNDING CAN BE GIVEN UK.

WHO CAN BENEFIT Charitable organisations.

WHAT IS FUNDED Welfare, medical, disability, including those causes relating to children.

SAMPLE GRANTS Previous beneficiaries have included Cancer Treatment and Research, the Children's Leukaemia Ward, ChildLine, the Metropolitan Police Peel Ski Club, the Phoenix Garden Charity, the Royal Grammar School and SOS Children Tsunami Disaster.

FINANCES *Year* 2011–12 *Income* £1,454 *Grants* £1,737

TRUSTEES D. A. Graham; P. D. C. Collins; C. N. Parsons; Sir W. Blackburn; Hon S. Nicholls; D. R. King; I. Stokes.

OTHER INFORMATION The trust distributes funds raised by The Heritage Foundation.

HOW TO APPLY In writing to the correspondent. Trustees meet every three months.

WHO TO APPLY TO David A. Graham, Administrator, 30 Highcroft, North Hill, London N6 4RD *Tel.* 020 8342 9953 *email* david@ theheritagefoundation.co.uk *Website* www. theheritagefoundation.co.uk

■ Arts Council England

CC NO 1036733   **ESTABLISHED** 1994

WHERE FUNDING CAN BE GIVEN England.

WHO CAN BENEFIT Organisations and individuals.

WHAT IS FUNDED Developing, sustaining and promoting the arts. The majority of funding is provided to organisations that are regularly funded by the Arts Council.

WHAT IS NOT FUNDED Grants below £1,000

FINANCES *Year* 2011–12 *Income* £613,359,000 *Grants* £604,000,000

TRUSTEES Alice Rawsthorn; Alastair Spalding; Anil Ruia; Ekow Eshun; Francois Matarasso; Janet Barnes; Keith Khan; Prof. Jon Cook; Rosemary Squire; Sir Nicholas Kenyon; Liz Forgan; Sheila Healy; Peter Phillips; Joe Docherty; Caroline Collier; Veronica Wadley.

PUBLICATIONS The Council produces various publications and information sheets concerning the arts. These are available on the Arts Council website.

HOW TO APPLY 'Grants for the Arts' forms are available to download, together with criteria and guidance notes and information about other sources of funding, from the website. If you are unable to complete the application online

contact the Arts Council England by phone, email or post at Arts Council England, Grants for the Arts, PO Box 4353, Manchester, M61 0DQ.

WHO TO APPLY TO Enquiries Team, The Hive, 49 Lever Street, Manchester M1 1FN *Tel.* 0845 300 6200 *email* enquiries@artscouncil.org.uk *Website* www.artscouncil.org.uk

■ Arts Council of Northern Ireland

ESTABLISHED 1995

WHERE FUNDING CAN BE GIVEN UK and Ireland (but projects must benefit people of Northern Ireland).

WHO CAN BENEFIT Artists and arts organisations and individuals.

WHAT IS FUNDED 'The Arts Council is the lead development agency for the arts in Northern Ireland. We are the main support for artists and arts organisations, offering a broad range of funding opportunities through our Exchequer and National Lottery funds.'

SAMPLE GRANTS BEAM Creative Network (£31,000); Ulster Orchestra Society (£15,000); Waterside Theatre Company Ltd (£12,000); Arts Care (£10,000); Play Resource Warehouse (£8,000) and In Your Space (NI) Ltd (£4,000).

FINANCES *Year* 2012–13 *Grants* £13,381,472 *Assets* £1,802,841

TRUSTEES Damien Coyle; William Montgomery; Prof. Ian Montgomery; Prof. Paul Seawright; Janine Walker; Brian Sore; Bob Collins; David Alderdice; Anna Carragher; Noelle McAlinden; Katherine McCloskey; Paul Mullan.

HOW TO APPLY Guidelines and full details of how to apply can be found at the Arts Council of Northern Ireland website.

WHO TO APPLY TO The Arts Development Department, MacNeice House, 77 Malone Road, Belfast BT9 6AQ *Tel.* 02890 385200 *email* info@ artscouncil-ni.org *Website* www.artscouncil-ni.org

■ Arts Council of Wales (also known as Cyngor Celfyddydau Cymru)

CC NO 1034245   **ESTABLISHED** 1994

WHERE FUNDING CAN BE GIVEN Wales.

WHO CAN BENEFIT Arts organisations and individuals based in Wales.

WHAT IS FUNDED Arts activities and projects based in or mainly in Wales.

WHAT IS NOT FUNDED Individuals and organisations not meeting the eligibility criteria.

TYPE OF GRANT Both recurrent and one-off grants.

RANGE OF GRANTS £380–£4.8 million.

SAMPLE GRANTS Welsh National Opera (£4.8 million); Wales Millennium Centre (£4 million); National Theatre Wales and Clwyd Theatr Cymru (£1.6 million each); Sherman Cymru (1.2 million); Theatr Genedlaethol Cymru (£1.1 million); Literature Wales (£892,000) and BBC National Orchestra of Wales (£844,000); Galeri Caernarfon Cyf (£325,000); Ballet Cymru (£200,000); Pontardawe Arts Centre (£63,000); Hafren (£15,000); The Republic of Imagination (£10,000); Institute of Welsh Affairs (£6,000) and Jukebox Studios (£1,500).

FINANCES *Year* 2011–12 *Income* £36,561,000 *Grants* £29,228,764 *Assets* £2,903,000

TRUSTEES Prof. Dai Smith; Emma Evans; Dr John Geraint; Margaret Jervis; Osi Rhys Osmond; Alan Watkin; Prof. Gerwyn Wiliams; John Williams; Dr Kate Woodward; Marian Jones; Richard Turner; Dr Lesley Hodgson; Michael Griffiths; Melanie Hawthorne; Andrew Miller.

354

Does the trust you have chosen match your needs? Haphazard applications waste postage and time

HOW TO APPLY By applying online on council's website www.artscouncilofwales.org.uk. The council offers assistance to those without access to a computer or having any other difficulties in completing the application online. Any enquiries should be communicated via email, telephone, SMS (07797800504) or by post to the correspondent.

The council's website provide requirements for eligible individuals looking to apply, these are as follows: live in Wales; be a professional artist or practitioner whose work is mainly based in Wales; be over 18; not be in full-time education (either at school, college or university); be able to provide evidence of track record of creating artistic work for presentation to audiences; have an awareness and understanding of equal opportunities and be able to provide evidence of how equality and diversity are reflected in applicant's creative work; and not be in default on any financial agreement with the Arts Council of Wales.

Eligibility criteria for applications from organisations state that applicants must: be based in Wales, another part of the UK or another European Union country; be a charitable or not-for-profit organisation, or an educational institution seeking to provide arts activity that will clearly benefit the wider community or artists, or a private or public company seeking to deliver a self-contained arts project that will clearly benefit the public and not your private interests; be able to provide evidence of track record of delivering arts activity for audiences or participants; have an equal opportunities policy that has been reviewed by applicants' board or management committee within the last three years and complies with current legislation and provide evidence of equality and diversity being reflected in applicants' artistic programming and their day to day planning and operations; not be in default on any financial agreement with the Arts Council of Wales.

In addition to that, the requirements for a fundable project for both individuals and organisations include: project needs to take place mainly in Wales; must be additional to applicant's usual professional practice; have to be time-limited, i.e. have definite start and end dates; have a start date that allows enough time for a thorough planning and preparation period if funding is awarded; must consist entirely of activity that hasn't started yet, so that the funding will not be used retrospectively; must not include prizes, catering, gifts, fireworks, competitive events or purely promotional activity; must not have partnership or match funding; applicants will also be asked to confirm that they understand and accept that a range of supporting information needs to be included with their application form. Application for creative Wales and Major Creative Wales Awards for individuals can only be pursued after a discussion with Arts Council of Wales officer. Organisations are invited to apply for Lottery Capital Programme for funding of projects requiring over £50,000 at any time.

WHO TO APPLY TO Hywel Tudor, Director of Finance and Resources, Bute Place, Cardiff CF10 5AL *Tel.* 0845 873 4900 *email* info@ artscouncilofwales.org.uk *Website* www. artscouncilofwales.org.uk

■ The Ove Arup Foundation

CC NO 328138   **ESTABLISHED** 1989
WHERE FUNDING CAN BE GIVEN Unrestricted.
WHO CAN BENEFIT Organisations benefiting research workers and designers.
WHAT IS FUNDED Education and research in matters related to the built environment, particularly if related to multi-disciplinary design, through educational institutions and charities.
WHAT IS NOT FUNDED No grants to individuals, including students.
TYPE OF GRANT Research and project, including start-up and feasibility costs. They can be one-off or recurrent.
RANGE OF GRANTS Up to £50,000.
SAMPLE GRANTS The Royal Academy of Engineering (£50,000); The University of Edinburgh (£40,000); The London School of Economics (£35,000); The Industrial Trust (£13,500); Institution of Civil Engineers (£12,500) and The Royal Academy of Arts (£5,000).
FINANCES *Year* 2011–12 *Income* £197,435 *Grants* £156,000 *Assets* £2,807,914
TRUSTEES R. B. Haryott, Chair; A. Chan; F. Cousins; J. Kennedy; M. Shears; D. Michael; R. T. M. Hill; C. Cole; R. Hough; P. Dilley.
HOW TO APPLY On a form available to download from the foundation's website.
WHO TO APPLY TO Peter Klyhn, Ove Arup and Partners, 13 Fitzroy Street, London W1T 4BQ *email* ovarfound@arup.com *Website* www. theovearupfoundation.com

■ The AS Charitable Trust

CC NO 242190   **ESTABLISHED** 1965
WHERE FUNDING CAN BE GIVEN UK and developing countries.
WHO CAN BENEFIT Preference for charities in which the trust has special interest, knowledge of or association with. Christian organisations will benefit. Support may go to victims of famine, man-made or natural disasters, and war.
WHAT IS FUNDED The trust is sympathetic to projects which combine the advancement of the Christian religion with Christian lay leadership, third world development, peacemaking and reconciliation, or other areas of social concern.
WHAT IS NOT FUNDED Grants to individuals or large charities are very rare. Such applications are discouraged.
RANGE OF GRANTS Up to £16,000, often in multiple gifts to the one charity.
SAMPLE GRANTS GRACE (£25,000 in two gifts); The De Laszlo Foundation (£10,000); Lambeth Partnership (£4,000 in two gifts); and The Message Trust and Vision 2025 (£1,000 each).
FINANCES *Year* 2009–10 *Income* £241,805 *Grants* £55,576 *Assets* £8,168,194
TRUSTEES Caroline Eady; George Calvocoressi; Simon Sampson.
OTHER INFORMATION The most recent accounts available from the Charity Commission at the time of writing were for 2009/10. 2010/11 accounts were 633 days late.
HOW TO APPLY In writing to the correspondent.
WHO TO APPLY TO George Calvocoressi, Trustee, Bix Bottom Farm, Henley-on-Thames, Oxfordshire RG9 6BH

■ ASCB Charitable Fund

CC NO 1123854   **ESTABLISHED** 2008
WHERE FUNDING CAN BE GIVEN UK
WHO CAN BENEFIT Individual sports people, sports unions and associations and garrisons/units of the army.
WHAT IS FUNDED Annual grants to sports unions and associations; capital project grants for sports equipment/infrastructure; Army Sports Lottery Grants.
TYPE OF GRANT Annual grants and capital grants.
RANGE OF GRANTS Up to £270,000, Mostly £20,000 or less.
SAMPLE GRANTS Army Football Association (£264,000); Army Rowing Club Association (£58,000); HQ 2 Division (£25,000); Motor Sports Association (£22,000); Angling Association (£16,000); Golf Association (£14,000); Football association (£9,000); Squash Rackets Association (£6,500); Army Rugby Union (£5,400); Water-skiing and Wakeboarding Association (£3,500); Army Hockey Association (£2,000) and 3 Para (£800).
FINANCES *Year* 2011–12 *Income* £3,526,886 *Grants* £883,256 *Assets* £6,157,830
TRUSTEES Nicky Murdoch; Thomas O'Brien; Mark Noel; William Pacter; David Rowe; Gerald Berragan; Miles Wade; James Bowden; David Cullen; Benjamin Bathurst.
HOW TO APPLY In writing to the organisation. Applications for annual grants to sports unions and associations should be made in January/February, for capital projects in March and September and at any time for Army Sports Lottery grants.
WHO TO APPLY TO Maj Gen Christopher Elliott, Army Sport Control Board, Clayton Barracks, Thornhill Road, Aldershot GU11 2BG *Tel.* 01252 348569 *email* accountant@ascb.uk.com *Website* www.army.mod.uk/events/23325.aspx

■ Ashburnham Thanksgiving Trust

CC NO 249109   **ESTABLISHED** 1965
WHERE FUNDING CAN BE GIVEN UK and worldwide.
WHO CAN BENEFIT Individuals and organisations benefiting Christians and evangelists.
WHAT IS FUNDED Only Christian work already known to the trustees is supported, particularly evangelical overseas missionary work.
WHAT IS NOT FUNDED No grants for buildings.
RANGE OF GRANTS Under £5,000.
SAMPLE GRANTS Genesis Arts Trust (£4,000); St Stephen's Society – Hong Kong (£3,800); Prison Fellowship (£2,900); Wycliffe Bible Translators (£2,800); Youth with a mission (£2,200); Interserve (£2,200); Care Trust (£1,100) and Advantage Africa (£1,000). The majority of beneficiaries received a small grant of £1,000 or less, including: Wonersh and Blackheath Parochial Church Council, Servants with Jesus, Movember, Lee Abbey Fellowship, Hebron Trust and Cherith Trust.
FINANCES *Year* 2011–12 *Income* £186,767 *Grants* £108,000 *Assets* £6,187,921
TRUSTEES E. R. Bickersteth; R. D. Bickersteth; R. F. Dowdy.
OTHER INFORMATION Grants totalled £108,000, of which £72,000 was distributed in grants to 93 organisations. Further monies were distributed in restricted grants and grants to individuals.
HOW TO APPLY Grants are typically made to organisations known to the trustees.

WHO TO APPLY TO The Charity Secretary, Brooke Oast, Jarvis Lane, Goudhurst, Cranbrook, Kent TN17 1LP *email* att@lookingforward.biz

■ A. J. H. Ashby Will Trust

CC NO 803291   **ESTABLISHED** 1990
WHERE FUNDING CAN BE GIVEN UK, especially Lea Valley area of Hertfordshire.
WHO CAN BENEFIT Charitable organisations, sports clubs and schools.
WHAT IS FUNDED Wildlife, particularly birds; heritage; education projects; and children.
WHAT IS NOT FUNDED No grants to individuals or students.
TYPE OF GRANT One-off and recurrent.
SAMPLE GRANTS RSPB (£26,000 in four grants); Woodland Trust (£10,000); The Hertfordshire Groundwork Trust (£6,000); Wheelyboat Trust (£5,000); Harpenden Lions Club (£3,000) and Birchanger Wood Trust (£2,000).
FINANCES *Year* 2011–12 *Income* £27,253 *Grants* £51,014 *Assets* £1,195,307
TRUSTEE HSBC Trust Company (UK) Ltd.
HOW TO APPLY In writing to the correspondent.
WHO TO APPLY TO Sandra Hill, Trust Manager, HSBC Trust Company (UK) Ltd, Trust Services, Norwich House, Nelson Gate, Commercial Road, Southampton SO15 1GX *Tel.* 02380 722243

■ The Ashden Trust

CC NO 802623   **ESTABLISHED** 1989
WHERE FUNDING CAN BE GIVEN UK and overseas.
WHO CAN BENEFIT Registered charities.
WHAT IS FUNDED Programme areas: Sustainable Development – International and UK; Sustainable Regeneration; People at Risk; Arts and Sustainability; Social Investment Fund; Low Carbon Fund. These include the natural environment and wildlife.
WHAT IS NOT FUNDED The trustees generally do not make grants in response to unsolicited applications. However, see 'How to Apply'.
TYPE OF GRANT Primarily project.
SAMPLE GRANTS World Wildlife Fund UK (£60,000); Julie's Bicycle (£45,000); ACE Africa (£15,000); Manna Society and Sustainable Food Trust (£5,000 each); Culture and Climate Change (£1,000).
FINANCES *Year* 2011–12 *Income* £1,422,929 *Grants* £1,323,499 *Assets* £28,557,079
TRUSTEES Sarah Butler-Sloss; Robert Butler-Sloss; Judith Portrait.
OTHER INFORMATION The trust is one of the Sainsbury Family Charitable Trusts which share a common administration. An application to one is taken as an application to all.
HOW TO APPLY **Who should apply?** If your organisation has a proven track record in supplying local, sustainable energy solutions in the UK or in the developing world then you should read the guidelines for the 'Ashden Awards for Sustainable Energy'. The Ashden Trust is one of the Sainsbury Family Charitable Trusts. Before applying read the guidelines below. For further, more detailed information visit: Ashden Trust – How to Apply.
'We primarily support programmes which have a focus on climate change, sustainable development or on improving the quality of life in poorer communities. Generally, we do not accept unsolicited approaches, unless they are exceptional proposals which closely fit our specific areas of interest. The trustees take a proactive approach to the work they wish to

support, employing a range of specialist staff and advisers to research their areas of interest and bring forward suitable proposals. It should therefore be understood that the majority of unsolicited proposals we receive will be unsuccessful. The trust does not normally fund individuals for projects, educational fees or to join expeditions; support for general appeal or circular; work that is routine or well-proven elsewhere or with a low impact; or work that is the responsibility of central or local government, health trusts or health authorities, or which are substantially funded by them. We never support retrospective funding, that is, work that has already been completed. Do not apply to more than one of the Sainsbury Family Charitable Trusts. Each application will be considered by each trust which may have an interest in this field. If you would like to apply to the trust you should send a brief description of the proposed project, by post, to the director, or email your application to ashdentrust@sfct.org.uk. The proposed project needs to cover: the aims and objectives of the project; why the project is needed; how, where, when the project will be delivered; who will benefit and in what way; how the project will continue once your funding has come to an end; income and expenditure budget; details of funding – secured, applied for; description of the organisation.'

WHO TO APPLY TO Alan Bookbinder, Director, The Peak, 5 Wilton Road, London SW1V 1AP *Tel.* 020 7410 0330 *Fax* 020 7410 0332 *email* ashdentrust@sfct.org.uk *Website* www. ashdentrust.org.uk

■ The Ashendene Trust

CC NO 270749   **ESTABLISHED** 1975
WHERE FUNDING CAN BE GIVEN Unrestricted, in practice mainly London, Oxfordshire and Berkshire.
WHO CAN BENEFIT Registered charities.
WHAT IS FUNDED Small organisations including those assisting ex-offenders, people who are socially deprived, horticulture, the arts and churches. This is a small trust that gives to organisations where the grant will really make an impact.
WHAT IS NOT FUNDED No support for large organisations, education or health. No scholarships or individual grants.
TYPE OF GRANT Capital, core costs and project. Funding available for up to three years.
RANGE OF GRANTS £250–£5,000
SAMPLE GRANTS Downe House 21st Century Appeal (£5,000); Portobeilo Rugby Trust (£3,000); Deptford Action Group for the Elderly and Save the Children (£2,500 each); Relate Brighton, Hove, Eastbourne, Worthing and Districts (£2,000); Ambitious About Autism and Chipping Norton Theatre (£1,000 each).
FINANCES *Year* 2011–12 *Income* £46,369 *Grants* £20,850 *Assets* £1,040,442
TRUSTEES Camilla Pugh; Nicholas Hornby; James Spence.
HOW TO APPLY In writing to the correspondent. Replies are only made to those who enclose an sae.

   'While we will endeavour to contact those who have sent in applications, note that The Ashendene Trust is run by part-time volunteers. Therefore be patient for our response.'
WHO TO APPLY TO The Trustees, 34 Sackville Street, London W1S 3ED *Tel.* 020 7382 4110 *Website* www.ashendenetrust.com

■ The Ashley Family Foundation

CC NO 288099   **ESTABLISHED** 1985
WHERE FUNDING CAN BE GIVEN Mostly Wales, other areas considered.
WHO CAN BENEFIT Charitable organisations. In recent years focus has been on the advancement of education particularly in fine and applied arts and projects supporting communities in Wales, particularly Mid-Wales.
WHAT IS FUNDED The foundation has a strong commitment to art and design and also to Wales, particularly Powys, where the Ashley business was first established. As a guide the foundation, for the past few years, has had a policy of giving half its funds to Welsh projects. Support is given in areas in which the family have a connection such as helping the communities of Mid-Wales that supported the growth of the Laura Ashley business. The trustees focus on the following priorities: support of charitable textiles projects, including small scale community textiles initiatives; support for the arts; support for projects which seek to strengthen rural communities in Wales, especially in Mid-Wales.
WHAT IS NOT FUNDED The foundation does not generally fund individuals, business ventures, overseas projects, projects falling within the field of religion or retrospective work.
TYPE OF GRANT One-off up to a period of three years
RANGE OF GRANTS £500–£35,000
SAMPLE GRANTS Charleston Trust (£35,000); Royal College of Art (£18,000); London College of Communication and Music in Hospitals (£12,000 each); Phoenix Community Furniture, Quilt Association, Textprint and Wilderness Trust (£10,000 only); Bipolar UK (£5,000); Poems in the Waiting Room and Welsh National Sheepdog Trials (£3,000 each); A Voice for You (£2,000); Carno Bowling Club (£1,000); and Builth Wells Hand Bells, Volunteer Reading Help and Welsh Football Trust (£500 each).

FINANCES *Year* 2011–12 *Income* £204,605 *Grants* £533,965 *Assets* £10,396,076
TRUSTEES Jane Ashley, Chair; Martyn C. Gowar; Emma Shuckburgh; Oriana Baddeley; Sue Timney; Mike Hodgson; Jeremy McIlroy.
HOW TO APPLY There is a two stage application process. Applications can be made throughout the year and are assessed in line with the guidelines available from the foundation's website. The final decision is made by the trustees during meetings held three times a year. The website states: 'Due to the economic downturn we are receiving an unprecedented increase in requests. We are therefore changing our long held policy of replying to all requests. If you have submitted a stage one proposal and have not heard within eight weeks assume you have been unsuccessful.'
WHO TO APPLY TO Mia Duddridge, Administrator, 6 Trull Farm Buildings, Trull, Tetbury, Gloucestershire GL8 8SQ *Tel.* 03030401005 *email* info@ashleyfamilyfoundation.org.uk *Website* www.ashleyfamilyfoundation.org.uk

■ The Ashworth Charitable Trust

CC NO 1045492   **ESTABLISHED** 1995
WHERE FUNDING CAN BE GIVEN UK and worldwide, with some preference for certain specific needs in Honiton, Ottery St Mary, Sidmouth and Wonford Green surgery, Exeter.
WHO CAN BENEFIT Individuals (living in the areas covered by the medical practices in Ottery St

Mary, Honiton and Sidmouth only) and organisations.

WHAT IS FUNDED General charitable purposes. Particular emphasis is given to support for the Ironbridge Gorge Museum Trust and to humanitarian projects.

WHAT IS NOT FUNDED No grants for research-based charities; animal charities; 'heritage charities' such as National Trust or other organisations whose aim is the preservation of a building, museum, library and so on (with the exception of the Ironbridge Gorge Museum).; 'faith-based' charities, unless the project is for primarily humanitarian purposes and is neither exclusive to those of that particular faith or evangelical in its purpose. Grants to individuals are strictly limited to the geographical area and purpose specified in the general section.

RANGE OF GRANTS Usually £500–£3,000.

SAMPLE GRANTS Ironbridge Gorge Museum Trust (£10,000); Appropriate Technology Asia, Excellent Development Limited, Find Your Feet and Hospiscare Exeter (£5,000 each); Livingstone Tanzania Trust, Medical Assistance Sierra Leone and Wherever the Need (£3,000 each); Balloons, Exeter CAB, The Dignity Project and World Child Cancer (£2,000 each); and Accessible Coach Holidays, Devon Link-Up, Exeter Gateway Centre and Hope (£1,000 each).

FINANCES *Year* 2011–12 *Income* £135,637 *Grants* £121,818 *Assets* £4,013,721

TRUSTEES Shahin Saebnoori; Sharareh Rouhipour; Katherine Gray; Hoshmand Rouhipour; Kian Golestani; Wendi Cunningham Momen.

OTHER INFORMATION Of the grants total £5,000 was given to 21 individuals from the Doctors' and Social Services Fund.

HOW TO APPLY In writing to the correspondent. There is no application form but applications should include: registered charity number; an email address; a recent set of accounts; a brief (not more than two pages) analysis of the main objectives of your organisation and any particular project for which funding is required. Incomplete applications will not be considered. Do not send brochures, DVDs, books, annual reviews or any other bulky promotional material. If more information is needed, you will be contacted. The trustees meet twice a year in May and November. Applications should be submitted by the middle of March or the middle of September respectively. Note that the trustees are unable to enter into any discussions regarding funding, successful or otherwise, as there are no funds designated for this purpose.

WHO TO APPLY TO Glenys Towner, Foot Anstey, Senate Court, Southernhay Gardens, Exeter EX1 1NT *Tel.* 01392 411221 *Fax* 01392 685220 *email* ashworthtrust@btinternet.com *Website* www.ashworthtrust.org

....
■ The Ian Askew Charitable Trust

CC NO 264515   **ESTABLISHED** 1972
WHERE FUNDING CAN BE GIVEN UK, with a preference for Sussex.

WHO CAN BENEFIT Charitable organisations.

WHAT IS FUNDED General charitable purposes; education; health research; particularly mental health; preservation of ancient buildings; and the maintenance and conservation of woodlands belonging to the trust.

WHAT IS NOT FUNDED None known.

RANGE OF GRANTS Most grants are for £500 or less.

SAMPLE GRANTS Ditchling Museum, Friends of East Sussex Records Office and Ringmer Community College (£2,000 each); Commonwealth Housing Trust CPRE Sussex, Forces Support, The Georgian Group and The Victorian Society Appeal (£1,000 each).

FINANCES *Year* 2011–12 *Income* £370,905 *Grants* £151,392 *Assets* £15,782,555

TRUSTEES John Hecks; Cleone Pengelley; Richard Lewis; Rory Askew; James Rank.

OTHER INFORMATION Grants to 215 charitable organisations totalled £129,000, excluding all support costs. Grants of £18,500 were made from the Conservation fund and £4,200 from the Educational sub fund.

HOW TO APPLY In writing to the correspondent. Applications are considered every other month.

WHO TO APPLY TO The Trustees, c/o Baker Tilly, 18 Mount Ephraim Road, Tunbridge Wells, Kent TN1 1ED *Tel.* 01892 511944 *email* bill.owen@ bakertilly.co.uk

....
■ The Associated Country Women of the World

CC NO 290367   **ESTABLISHED** 1933
WHERE FUNDING CAN BE GIVEN Overseas.

WHO CAN BENEFIT Local projects and established organisations benefiting women and /or children in rural communities.

WHAT IS FUNDED Projects that are mainly ran by women and directly benefit women and/or children in connection with: literacy, health education, nutrition and home economics, agricultural training and development, income generating activities, water and sanitation, civic consciousness/community involvement.

WHAT IS NOT FUNDED The organisation does not provide funding to individuals, NGOs/SHGs not registered or registered for less than two years, emergency relief work, motor vehicles, items of large mechanical equipment, the purchase of land and capital infrastructure projects. Funding only available for projects taking place in the same country where the organisation is registered and directly benefit women and children in those countries.

TYPE OF GRANT One-off grants for projects for organisations.

RANGE OF GRANTS £5,001–£10,000.

SAMPLE GRANTS Integrated Prevention of Female Infanticide and HIV/AIDS Project (Phase 3) – India (£84,000); My Name is Woman – South Africa (£6,000); Vocational Skills Development Tailoring – Uganda and Rain Water Harvesting – Sri Lanka (£5,000 each); and Facilities of Water Supply and Sanitation to End Disease and Poverty – Bangladesh and Rural Women Livelihood Development Project – Cambodia (£4,000 each).

FINANCES *Year* 2011–12 *Income* £555,701 *Grants* £125,568 *Assets* £2,254,136

TRUSTEES Jo Almond; Alison Bumett; May Kidd; Anphia Grobler.

PUBLICATIONS *Working with Women Worldwide.* (Visit the trusts website for a full list of publications.)

OTHER INFORMATION Processing of the application and the approval of a grant usually takes around ten months.

HOW TO APPLY Application forms can be downloaded from the organisation's website. In addition to the application form, it is necessary to provide a copy of a valid registration certificate for the applicant's organisation and an itemised budget.

WHO TO APPLY TO Jo Almond, Secretary, 24 Tufton Street, London SW1P 3RB *Tel.* 020 7799 3875 *email* info@acww.org.uk *Website* www.acww.org.uk

■ The Association of Colleges Charitable Trust

CC NO 1040631 **ESTABLISHED** 1994
WHERE FUNDING CAN BE GIVEN UK.
WHO CAN BENEFIT Further education establishments
WHAT IS FUNDED Further education. The charitable trust is responsible for administering two programmes. The largest of these is the Beacon Awards, which provide monetary grants to award-winning initiatives within further education colleges. The other scheme is the AoC Gold Awards for Further Education Alumni, which reward former members of further education colleges who have since excelled in their chosen field or profession.
WHAT IS NOT FUNDED Grants are not made to individuals.
SAMPLE GRANTS Cardiff and Vale College (£5,000 for the Welsh Assembly Government – Overcoming Deprivation Award); West Cheshire College (£5,000 for the AoC – Inclusive Learning Award) and Fareham College (£3,500 for the Jardine Lloyd Thompson – Health and Community Care Award).
FINANCES *Year* 2011–12 *Income* £232,798 *Grants* £68,500 *Assets* £148,022
TRUSTEES Alice Thiagaraj; Peter Brophy; David Forrester; John Bingham; Martin Doel; Carole Stott; Wesley Streeting; Jane Samuels; Simon Francis; Shahida Aslam.
HOW TO APPLY See the trust's website for further information.
WHO TO APPLY TO Alice Thiagaraj, Managing Trustee, 2–5 Stedham Place, London WC1A 1HU *Tel.* 020 7034 9917 *email* alice_thiagaraj@aoc.co.uk *Website* www.aoc.co.uk

■ Astellas European Foundation

CC NO 1036344 **ESTABLISHED** 1993
WHERE FUNDING CAN BE GIVEN Worldwide.
WHO CAN BENEFIT Scientific research institutes, universities, research workers and medical professionals.
WHAT IS FUNDED The objects of the foundation are: committing long-term support to basic medical and related scientific programmes through organisations such as the Société Internationale D'Urologie; supporting selected short, medium and long-term projects, aimed at integrating basic science and clinical research through interdisciplinary projects; providing facilities, promoting or sponsoring the exchange of ideas and views through lectures and discussions of an educational or cultural nature; promoting, assisting or otherwise supporting charitable institutions aimed at serving good causes.
FINANCES *Year* 2011–12 *Income* £39,248 *Grants* £117,000 *Assets* £7,324,013
TRUSTEES Yasuo Ishii, Chair; Dr Toichi Takenaka; Kenneth Jones; Masafumi Nogimori; Dr Patrick Errard; Yoshirou Miyokawa; Dr Ayad Abdulahad; Naoki Okamura.
HOW TO APPLY In writing to the correspondent.
WHO TO APPLY TO The Trustees, 2000 Hillswood Drive, Chertsey, Surrey KT16 0RS *Tel.* 020 3379 8000

■ Asthma UK

CC NO 802364 **ESTABLISHED** 1990
WHERE FUNDING CAN BE GIVEN UK.
WHO CAN BENEFIT Organisations benefiting scientists, clinicians, general practitioners, research workers and people with asthma.
WHAT IS FUNDED Research into and the provision of information and education on asthma and allied respiratory disorders. 'Through our 2011–2016 Research Strategy, we have a number of different funding schemes available. We plan to fund research through three main mechanisms over the next five years: Research Projects, Fellowships and Studentships, and Professors and Research Centres.'
WHAT IS NOT FUNDED 'Researchers work across a variety of disciplines within hospitals, universities, GP surgeries and clinics throughout the UK. Asthma UK is therefore able to fund researchers who work directly with people with asthma as well as those who are undertaking basic science research in the laboratory.'
TYPE OF GRANT Project grants and fellowships.
FINANCES *Year* 2011–12 *Income* £7,503,000 *Grants* £5,141,000 *Assets* £6,363,000
TRUSTEES Jane Tozer; June Coppel; Barbara Herts; David Steeds; John Lelliott; Dr Anne Thomson; Dr Iain Small; Martin Sinclair; Dr Robert Wilson; Sarah Walter; Prof. Jurgen Schwarze; Paulette Graham; Mary Leadbetter; Simon Tilley; Mathew Smith; Kate Clarke.
HOW TO APPLY 'Each year Asthma UK invites proposals for research projects through its website and through the research professional press. All applications for funding are assessed for scientific quality and relevance to asthma by our research committee, which is comprised of an independent panel of scientists, clinicians and lay representatives. Research proposals are also subjected to further scrutiny by international experts through our external review process, who have experience closely related to the subject area. Asthma UK's Council of Trustees then decides how many of the recommended research proposals can be funded, based on the projected income of the charity.'
WHO TO APPLY TO Kessington Ijegbai, Summit House, 70 Wilson Street, London EC2A 2DB *Tel.* 020 7786 4900 *Fax* 020 7256 6075 *email* info@asthma.org.uk *Website* www.asthma.org.uk

■ Aston–Mansfield Charitable Trust

CC NO 208155 **ESTABLISHED** 1930
WHERE FUNDING CAN BE GIVEN The borough of Newham.
WHO CAN BENEFIT Organisations.
WHAT IS FUNDED 'The objects of the charity are to develop the community wealth of East London and promote a diverse and inclusive society in which all are free to participate.'
'Aston-Mansfield's Seed Grants, a small funding programme aimed at newly formed or completely unfunded groups, is a new initiative launched in April 2011. Groups can apply for up to a maximum of £400.'
WHAT IS NOT FUNDED Revenue funding for salaries and maintenance is unlikely to be given. No national appeals and no grants to individuals.
TYPE OF GRANT Capital (including buildings), feasibility studies, one-off, project and research. Funding of one year or less will be considered.
FINANCES *Year* 2011–12 *Income* £488,570 *Grants* £653,008 *Assets* £12,832,362

TRUSTEES Christopher C. Keen, Chair; Dharam B. Lall; Andrew F. West; Bernard A. Taylor; Stephen M. Wright.

HOW TO APPLY For Seed Grants applicants should see the trust's website where all information is posted. Applicants for all other grants should apply in writing to the correspondent.

WHO TO APPLY TO Geoffrey Wheeler, Company Secretary, Durning Hall, Earlham Grove, Forest Gate, London E7 9AB *Tel.* 020 8536 3812 *email* geoffrey.wheeler@aston-mansfield.org.uk *Website* www.aston-mansfield.org.uk

■ The Astor Foundation

CC NO 225708   **ESTABLISHED** 1963
WHERE FUNDING CAN BE GIVEN UK.
WHO CAN BENEFIT Medical research organisations. Children and youth groups, people who are disabled, the countryside, the arts, sport, carers groups and animal welfare.

WHAT IS FUNDED Medical research in its widest sense, favouring research on a broad front rather than in specialised fields. In addition to its medical connection, the foundation has also supported initiatives for children and youth groups, people with disabilities, the countryside, the arts, sport, carers groups and animal welfare.

WHAT IS NOT FUNDED No grants to individuals or towards salaries. Grants are given to registered charities only.

TYPE OF GRANT Preference for assistance with the launching and initial stages of new projects and filling in gaps/shortfalls.

RANGE OF GRANTS £500–£45,000; generally £500–£2,500.

SAMPLE GRANTS The single biggest beneficiary was University College London Medical School (£16,000). Other beneficiaries include: University College London Hospitals Charitable Foundation (£5,000); Independence at Home (£4,500); Autistica (£3,000); Royal College of Music (£2,500); Meningitis Trust (£2,000); Royal Air Force Cadets and Penrith and District Red Squirrel Group (£1,500 each) and The Anaphylaxis Campaign and Parkinson's UK (£1,000 each).

FINANCES *Year* 2011–12 *Income* £135,585 *Grants* £119,870 *Assets* £3,404,636

TRUSTEES Robert Astor, Chair; the Hon. Tania Astor; Lord Latymer; Charles Astor; Dr Howard Swanton; Prof. John Cunningham.

HOW TO APPLY There are no deadline dates or application forms. Applications should be in writing to the correspondent and must include accounts and an annual report if available. The trustees meet twice yearly, usually in October and April. If the appeal arrives too late for one meeting it will automatically be carried over for consideration at the following meeting. An acknowledgement will be sent on receipt of an appeal. No further communication will be entered into unless the trustees raise any queries regarding the appeal, or unless the appeal is subsequently successful.

WHO TO APPLY TO Lisa Rothwell-Orr, Secretary, PO Box 3096, Marlborough, Wiltshire SN8 3WP *email* astor.foundation@gmail.com

■ The Astor of Hever Trust

CC NO 264134   **ESTABLISHED** 1955
WHERE FUNDING CAN BE GIVEN UK and worldwide, with a preference for Kent and the Grampian region of Scotland.

WHO CAN BENEFIT Both headquarters and local branches of charities, mainly established organisations with particular emphasis on Kent.

WHAT IS FUNDED Charitable bodies in the fields of the arts, medicine, religion, education, conservation, youth and sport.

WHAT IS NOT FUNDED No grants to individuals.

TYPE OF GRANT Unrestricted.

RANGE OF GRANTS £20–£1,000.

SAMPLE GRANTS Columbia Memorial Hospital, Combat Stress, Fields in Trust, Fifth Trust and Rochester Cathedral Trust (£1,000 each); Ambitious about Autism and Sound (£750 each); Buildings of Scotland Trust, Cage Green Autism Centre, Deafblind UK, Mercy Ships and National Memorial Arboretum (£500 each); Aberlour Child Care Trust, Books Abroad, Independence at Home and Street Pastors (£250 each); Chiddington Causeway Village Hall and Fund for Refugees in Slovenia (£100 each); and Tarland Agricultural Show (£50).

FINANCES *Year* 2011–12 *Income* £33,774 *Grants* £27,575 *Assets* £1,002,322

TRUSTEES John Jacob, Third Baron Astor of Hever; Hon. Philip D. P. Astor; Hon Camilla Astor.

HOW TO APPLY In writing to the correspondent. Trustees meet twice each year. Unsuccessful applications are not acknowledged.

WHO TO APPLY TO Gill Willis, Administrator, Frenchstreet House, Westerham, Kent TN16 1PW *Tel.* 01959 565070 *email* astorofhevertrust@btinternet.com

■ The Aurelius Charitable Trust

CC NO 271333   **ESTABLISHED** 1975
WHERE FUNDING CAN BE GIVEN UK.
WHO CAN BENEFIT Registered charities, historic societies, museums/galleries and academic institutions.

WHAT IS FUNDED Conservation/preservation of culture inherited from the past; the dissemination of knowledge, particularly in the humanities field; research or publications.

WHAT IS NOT FUNDED No grants to individuals.

TYPE OF GRANT Seed-corn or completion funding not otherwise available, usually one-off.

RANGE OF GRANTS Generally £500–£3,000.

SAMPLE GRANTS British School at Athens (£6,000); University of Westminster (£5,000); Bethel Chapel – Lye, Stourbridge (£4,000); British Exploring Society and Clophill Heritage Trust (£3,000 each); Lauderdale House Society and Society of Antiquaries of London (£2,000 each); Faversham Society (£1,000); and Christ Church Brockham Parochial Church Council (£500).

FINANCES *Year* 2012–13 *Income* £83,062 *Grants* £73,312 *Assets* £2,374,209

TRUSTEES William Wallis; Philip Haynes.

HOW TO APPLY In writing to the correspondent. Donations are generally made on the recommendation of the trust's board of advisors. Unsolicited applications will only be responded to if an sae is included. Trustees meet twice a year.

WHO TO APPLY TO Philip Haynes, Trustee, Briarsmead, Old Road, Buckland, Betchworth, Surrey RH3 7DU *Tel.* 01737 842186 *email* philip.haynes@tiscali.co.uk

■ The Lord Austin Trust

cc no 208394 **established** 1937

where funding can be given Birmingham and its immediate area.

who can benefit Charitable institutions or projects in England, restricted to: local charities based in Birmingham and West Midlands; and national organisations (but not their provincial branches).

what is funded Emphasis on the welfare of children, the care of older people, medical institutions and research.

what is not funded No support for appeals from, or on behalf of, individual applicants.

type of grant One-off.

range of grants Up to £10,000.

sample grants Birmingham St Mary's Hospice (£5,000); City of Birmingham Symphony Orchestra (£4,500); Acorns Children's Hospice Trust (£3,000); Tamworth Nursery (Special Needs) (£2,500); Saltley Neighbourhood Pensioner's Centre and Queen Elizabeth Hospital Birmingham (£2,000 each); Children's Heart Foundation (£1,500) and All Saints Youth Project, Army Benevolent Fund, Avoncroft Museum, Broadening Choices for Older People and St Martins Centre for Health and Healing (£1,000 each).

finances *Year* 2011–12 *Income* £118,698 *Grants* £132,000 *Assets* £3,338,373

trustees James Fea; Rodney Kettel; Anthony Andrews.

other information In 2011–12 grants were given to 108 organisations.

how to apply In writing to the correspondent, including a set of recent accounts. Trustees meet twice a year in or around May and November to consider grants.

who to apply to Chrissy Norgrove, c/o Martineau Johnson, 1 Colmore Square, Birmingham B4 6AA *Tel.* 0800 763 1000 *email* christine.norgrove@sghmartineau.com

■ Autonomous Research Charitable Trust

cc no 1137503 **established** 2010

where funding can be given UK, mainly London, and Africa.

who can benefit Registered charities.

what is funded 'To help disadvantaged people get a step up in life; to empower people to improve the quality of their lives; to focus our resources upon a small number of key partner charities – both in London and abroad – where we feel we can make a difference and establish long-term relationships.'

sample grants One Degree – The Adnan Jaffery Educational Trust (£95,000); Plan UK and Tusk (£63,000); Macmillan Cancer UK (£6,000); Group B Strep Support and Hakuna Matata (£2,000 each); and Cardiac Risk in the Young and Get Kids Going (£1,500 each).

finances *Year* 2011–12 *Income* £278,514 *Grants* £244,299 *Assets* £163,852

trustees Graham Stuart; Britta Schmidt; Nathalie Garner; Neeta Atkar.

how to apply In writing to the correspondent.

who to apply to Keith Lawrence, Administrator, Moore Stephens, 150 Aldersgate Street, London EC1A 4AB *Tel.* 020 7334 9191 *email* keith.lawrence@moorestephens.com

■ The Avenue Charitable Trust

cc no 264804 **established** 1972

where funding can be given Worldwide.

who can benefit Registered charities and individuals.

what is funded General charitable purposes.

type of grant One-off and recurrent.

range of grants Generally £25–£50,000, although occasionally larger grants are given.

sample grants Previous beneficiaries included: Delta Trust (£225,000); Neuro-psychoanalysis Fund (£65,000); David Astor Journalism Award Trust (£50,000); Adonis Mosat Project (£25,000); Living Landscape Project (£10,000); Adam von Trott Memorial Appeal (£5,000); Amnesty International, Cheek By Jowl and Koestler Trust (£1,000 each); and Prisoners Abroad (£500).

finances *Year* 2011–12 *Income* £1,416 *Grants* £3,000

trustees Richard Astor; Bonny Astor; Alfred Astor; Geoffrey Todd.

other information Estimated grant total – accounts received at the Charity Commission but not published due to low income.

how to apply The trust has previously stated that all available income is now committed to existing beneficiaries.

who to apply to Susan Simmons, Administrator, Sayers Butterworth LLP, 3rd Floor, 12 Gough Square, London EC4A 3DW *Tel.* 020 7936 1910

■ The John Avins Trustees

cc no 217301 **established** 1931

where funding can be given Birmingham and district.

who can benefit Medical charities. Support may be given to medical professionals and research workers.

what is funded Medical charities in Birmingham and neighbourhood, and the following charities mentioned in the will of John Avins: Birmingham Blue Coat School; Birmingham Royal Institution for the Blind; and Middlemore Homes, Birmingham.

what is not funded No grants to individuals, non-medical charities or for purposes outside the beneficial area.

type of grant One-off.

range of grants Up to £5,000.

sample grants Focus Birmingham and The Blue Coat School (£2,500 each); Birmingham Centre for Arts Therapies, Live Music Now, Macmillan Cancer Support and Spinal Injuries Association (£2,000 each) and Tiny Tim's Children's Centre, Action Medical Research and Troop Aid (£1,000 each).

finances *Year* 2011–12 *Income* £50,953 *Grants* £40,100 *Assets* £1,320,393

trustees Hon Alderman Ian McArdle; Colin Smith; J. Millward; Vimal Sharma; Prof. David Cox; Fiona Collins.

other information In 2011–12 a further £6,500 was given in scholarships.

how to apply On a form available from the correspondent. Trustees meet in April and November.

who to apply to H. M. B. Carslake, Secretary, c/o SGH Martineau LLP, 1 Colmore Square, Birmingham B4 6AA *Tel.* 0870 763 2000 *email* christine.norgrove@sghmartineau.com

Think carefully about every application. Is it justified?

361

■ The Avon and Somerset Police Community Trust

CC NO 1076770   ESTABLISHED 1999

WHERE FUNDING CAN BE GIVEN The Avon and Somerset Constabulary area.

WHO CAN BENEFIT Organisations.

WHAT IS FUNDED The trustees favour projects that: promote safety and quality of life in the Avon and Somerset Constabulary area; through the prevention of crime and disorder, protect young people, people who are vulnerable and older people from criminal acts; advance education, including that related to alcohol, drugs, solvent abuse, community relations and responsible citizenship.

WHAT IS NOT FUNDED The trust does not support: individuals, including students; expeditions; bursaries or scholarships; replacement of statutory funding; building works; projects that fall outside the constabulary's geographical area.

RANGE OF GRANTS Usually up to £3,000

SAMPLE GRANTS Bobby Van Scheme (£54,500); Hartcliffe and Withywood Angling Club, Stand Against Violence, The National Smelting Co Amateur Boxing Club, Henbury Football Club and Priory Community Association (£1,000 each); Sandford Scouts (£880); Wolverhampton Playing Fields and Thornbury Sea Cadets (£600 each); Oasis Community Club (£500) and Clevedon YMCA and Bath and North East Somerset Youth Offending Team (£250 each).

FINANCES Year 2011–12 Income £114,244 Grants £99,728 Assets £514,495

TRUSTEES Colin Port; Mary Prior; Lady Gass; Ian Hoddell; Roger James; Paul Upham; Paul Hooper; Beatrice Selter; Dr Peter Heffer; Dame Janet Trotter; Sean Connelly; Allen Bell.

OTHER INFORMATION The grant total includes funds used to run the trust's own projects and initiatives.

HOW TO APPLY On a form available to download, together with criteria and guidelines, on the website. For further information about the trust or advice on obtaining or completing the trust's application form contact the Trust Manager. The trustees meet quarterly to consider the business of the trust and approve grants in accordance with the trust's aims and objectives. Grants in support of major projects are routinely reviewed and awarded by the trustees at the commencement of each financial year at their April meeting. All other grants are considered on their merit, having met the criteria for a grant as set out in the trust's aims and objectives.

WHO TO APPLY TO Tracey Clegg, Trust Manager, PO Box 37, Valley Road, Portishead, Bristol BS20 8QJ Tel. 01275 816240 Fax 01275 816129 email tracey.clegg@avonandsomerset. police.uk Website www.avonandsomerset. police.uk

■ Awards for All (see also the Big Lottery Fund)

WHERE FUNDING CAN BE GIVEN UK.

WHO CAN BENEFIT Community groups/clubs/ societies; registered charity or exempt or excepted charities registered with the Inland Revenue in England; parish or town councils; schools; health bodies; companies limited by guarantee; non-registered not for profit group.

WHAT IS NOT FUNDED Generally, organisations with an income more than £20,000 a year (though there are exceptions to this, particularly for projects coming through schools and similar bodies). Also: costs related to existing projects, activities or resources currently provided by your group, for example, ongoing staff costs and utility bills, regular rent payments, maintenance (including maintenance equipment) and annual events; items which only benefit an individual, for example, scholarships or bursaries; activities promoting religious beliefs; activities that are part of statutory obligations or replace statutory funding, including curricular activity in schools; endowments; loan payments; second hand road vehicles; projects with high ongoing maintenance costs – unless your group can show that you have the funds/skills to maintain them once your Awards for All grant runs out.

TYPE OF GRANT Here are some of the things that a grant could be spent on: publicity materials; venue hire; computers; research costs; transport costs; volunteers' expenses; updating equipment for health and safety reasons; refurbishment; training; sessional staff; fees to hire equipment; educational toys and games.

RANGE OF GRANTS £300–£10,000

FINANCES Year 2012–13 Grants £73,700,000

HOW TO APPLY All information is in the application pack available from the number below. The application form is simple, but the applicant organisation must be organised to the extent of having a constitution, a bank account and a set of accounts (unless a new organisation). If you have a general enquiry or want an application form to be sent to you, contact Awards for All on one of the following: Tel: 0845 600 20 40; Textphone: 0845 755 66 56; Email: general.enquiries@awardsforall.org.uk. The application form and guidance notes may also be downloaded from the Awards for All website.

WHO TO APPLY TO England: 1 Plough Place, London EC4A 1DE; Northern Ireland: 1 Cromac Quay, Cromac Wood, Ormeau Road, Belfast BT7 2JD; Scotland: 1 Atlantic Quay, 1 Robertson Street, Glasgow G2 8JB; Wales: 10th Floor, Helmont House, Churchill Way, Cardiff CF10 2DY Tel BIG Advice Line: 0845 410 2030 Website www. awardsforall.org.uk

■ The Aylesford Family Charitable Trust

CC NO 328299   ESTABLISHED 1989

WHERE FUNDING CAN BE GIVEN West Midlands and Warwickshire.

WHO CAN BENEFIT Registered charities.

WHAT IS FUNDED General charitable purposes.

WHAT IS NOT FUNDED Grants are not normally given to individuals.

RANGE OF GRANTS Usually £100 to £5,000.

SAMPLE GRANTS Lady K Leveson Fund (£5,000); Prince's Trust and Starlight Foundation (£2,000 each); Oundle School, Countryside Foundation, University of Birmingham and County Air Ambulance (£1,000 each); Bowel Disease Foundation, Adoption Support, Canine Partners and Radio Lollipop (£500 each); Young at Heart Club and Solihull Church (£300 each); Breast Cancer Care and British Blind Support (£250 each) and Alzheimer's Society (£100).

FINANCES Year 2011–12 Income £48,514 Grants £35,665 Assets £1,559,234

TRUSTEES Lord Charles Aylesford; Lady Aylesford.

OTHER INFORMATION In 2011–12 grants were given to 80 organisations.

HOW TO APPLY In writing to the correspondent at any time.

WHO TO APPLY TO The Trustees, Packington Hall, Meriden, Warwickshire CV7 7HF Tel. 01676 522020

■ B. W. Charitable Trust

cc no 1134407   **established** 2010
where funding can be given Undefined, in practice local.
who can benefit Registered charities.
what is funded General charitable purposes.
finances *Year* 2011–12 *Income* £28,500 *Grants* £27,550 *Assets* £1,325
trustees David Breuer-Weil; Samantha Breuer-Weil.
other information In 2011–12 grants were categorised as follows: Religious Activities (£11,500); Education (£11,000); Medical Care (£4,800); Care and Welfare (£260).
how to apply In writing to the correspondent.
who to apply to Pinnick Lewis Chartered Accountants, c/o Pinnick Lewis Chartered Accountants, Handel House, 95 High Street, Edgware HA8 7DB

■ The BAA Communities Trust

cc no 1058617   **established** 1996
where funding can be given Communities local to Heathrow Airport Holdings Group's four UK airports; Aberdeen, Glasgow, Heathrow and Southampton.
who can benefit National/international charities, delivering projects in or involving people from the communities local to Heathrow Airport Holdings Group's airports, locally-based charitable organisations, schools and local authorities delivering community projects, grassroots community groups and organisations, local grant makers, national/international charities in support of staff fundraising activity.
what is funded The trust was established to help communities, primarily those around BAA Limited airports, meet the challenges of the 21st Century. Through their grants they aim to create learning opportunities for young people and so raise their aspirations, break down barriers to employment through skills development, help protect the environment and support airport staff active in the community.
what is not funded Applications which benefit individuals only, whether or not they meet the other criteria, will fail. No support for religious or political projects. Grants will not be made to nationally based organisations unless the direct benefit will be felt locally and the other criteria are satisfied. The trust does not support general running costs or staff costs.
range of grants Up to £50,000.
sample grants Inchgarth Community Centre, Southampton City Council and Groundwork Trust Thames Valley (£50,000 each); Scottish Business in the Community (£40,000); Celtic Football Club Ltd (£25,000); Colnbrook C of E Primary School and Friends of the Fitch Way and Associated Woodlands (£10,000 each); Glasgow Film Theatre (£7,500); Macmillan Cancer Support and Barnardo's (£4,000 each); Essex Boys and Girls Clubs (£2,600); Walden Wanderers Football Club and Essex Wildlife Trust (£2,000 each); Wye Valley School Zambia Project (£1,000) and William Hobbayne Community Gardens Association (£100).

finances *Year* 2012 *Income* £750,000 *Grants* £678,801 *Assets* £901,887
trustees Mary Francis; Alison Moore; David Macmillan; Alan Coates; Matthew Gorman; Clare Harbord; Punam Kharbanda; Steve Ronald.
other information In 2012 grants were given to 308 organisations.
how to apply Each airport runs its own community fund. Application forms, criteria and guidelines, for the four funds, are available to download on the website. Before making a formal grant application, email a summary of your proposal to your local community fund representative, or the correspondent, so that they can give guidance. The trustees meet four times a year to assess applications over £5,000. Each local panel meets at least three times a year to consider applications under £5,000.
who to apply to Caroline Nicholls, Director, The Compass Centre, Nelson Road, Hounslow, Middlesex TW6 2GW *Tel.* 07836 342495 *email* communitiestrust@heathrow.com *Website* www.baacommunitiestrust.com

■ The Bacit Foundation

cc no 1149202   **established** 2012
where funding can be given UK.
who can benefit Charities and research institutes.
what is funded Research into cancer and related diseases.
trustees Martin Thomas; Arabella Cecil; Catherine Scivier; John McDonald; Jorge Villon; Thomas Henderson; Fenella Dernie.
how to apply In writing to the correspondent.
who to apply to Martin Thomas, Trustee, 9th Floor, 1 Knightsbridge Green, London SW1X 7QA *Tel.* 020 7968 6460

■ Backstage Trust

cc no 1145887   **established** 2012
where funding can be given UK.
who can benefit Small scale arts organisations, particularly those benefiting the young and disadvantaged.
what is funded Theatre and the performing arts.
trustees Lady Susan Sainsbury; Dominic Flynn; David Wood.
other information The trust was established in February 2012 by Lady Susan Sainsbury for general charitable purposes. In practice, the trust's priorities are likely to be focused on the arts, particularly theatre and the performing arts. Lady Sainsbury is the deputy chair of both the Royal Shakespeare Company and the Royal Academy of Music, and she and her husband, Lord David Sainsbury of Turville, are high profile patrons of the arts.
how to apply In writing to the correspondent.
who to apply to Lady Susan Sainsbury, Trustee, North House, 27 Great Peter Street, London SW1P 3LN *Tel.* 020 7072 4590 *email* info@backstagetrust.org.uk

■ Harry Bacon Foundation

cc no 1056500   **established** 1996
where funding can be given UK.
who can benefit Registered charities.
what is funded Particularly medical charities and animal welfare. The same charities are generally supported every year.
range of grants Around £6,000.

SAMPLE GRANTS RNLI, Imperial Cancer Research, British Heart Foundation, PDSA, Parkinson's Disease Society, the Arthritis and Rheumatism Council for Research, Donkey Sanctuary and World Horse Welfare.

FINANCES *Year* 2011–12 *Income* £464,851 *Grants* £46,400 *Assets* £132,889

TRUSTEE NatWest Bank plc.

HOW TO APPLY In writing to the correspondent. The trustees meet regularly to consider applications.

WHO TO APPLY TO The Trust Manager, NatWest Bank plc, Trustee Department, 5th Floor, Trinity Quay 2, Avon Street, Bristol BS2 0PT *Tel.* 01179 403283

....

■ The BACTA Charitable Trust

CC NO 328668   **ESTABLISHED** 1991

WHERE FUNDING CAN BE GIVEN UK.

WHO CAN BENEFIT UK registered charities.

WHAT IS FUNDED Generally to support causes recommended to it by members of the British Amusement Catering Trade Association (BACTA).

WHAT IS NOT FUNDED No grants for overseas charities or religious purposes.

TYPE OF GRANT Long-term support (usually two to three years) to a specific project or charity and one-off donations.

RANGE OF GRANTS £1,000 upwards.

SAMPLE GRANTS Macmillan (£42,000); and Rays of Sunshine (£30,000); Helen Rollason Cancer Charity (£3,000); Birmingham Children's Hospital (£3,000); Meningitis UK and The National Brain Appeal (£1,000 each); and Breast Cancer Campaign (£500).

FINANCES *Year* 2011–12 *Income* £36,355 *Grants* £80,063 *Assets* £52,037

TRUSTEES John Stergides; Mark Horwood; Jimmy Thomas; Stephen Hawkins; John Oversby-Powell; Anthony Boulton; Peter Weir; James Godden; Derek Petrie; Gabino Stergides; Michael Green; Neil Chinn.

HOW TO APPLY 'BACTA have just entered into a three-year partnership with Rays of Sunshine Children's Charity [up to early 2015], so unfortunately no other financial donations can be made at this time.'

WHO TO APPLY TO Pru Kemball, Administration Assistant, 134–136 Buckingham Palace Road, London SW1W 9SA *Tel.* 020 7730 6444 *email* pru@bacta.org.uk *Website* www.bacta.org.uk

....

■ The Scott Bader Commonwealth Ltd

CC NO 206391   **ESTABLISHED** 1951

WHERE FUNDING CAN BE GIVEN UK, Eire, Canada, France, South Africa, Croatia, Dubai, USA, Czech Republic, Sweden, Spain, China.

WHO CAN BENEFIT Projects, activities or charities which: find difficulty raising funds; are innovative, imaginative and pioneering; or are initiated and/or supported by local people. Each year there is a particular area of focus, so applicants should check current focus before applying.

WHAT IS FUNDED Assistance of distressed and needy people of all nationalities. The commonwealth looks for projects, activities or charities which respond to the needs of those who are most underprivileged, disadvantaged, poor or excluded e.g. poor, homeless, vulnerable children, women and minority communities and people affected by poverty, hunger and disease.

Also those who encourage the careful use and protection of the earth's resources (those which assist poor rural people to become self-reliant are particularly encouraged); or promote peace-building and democratic participation. The commonwealth also supports the research, development and advancement of education and advancement of education in industrial participation of a nature beneficial to the community.

WHAT IS NOT FUNDED No support for charities concerned with the well-being of animals, individuals in need or organisations sending volunteers abroad. It does not respond to general appeals or support the larger well-established national charities. It does not provide grants for medical research. It does not make up deficits already incurred, or support the arts, museums, travel/adventure, sports clubs or the construction, renovation or maintenance of buildings.

TYPE OF GRANT One-off and funding over a period (3–5 years).

RANGE OF GRANTS Local Fund: £1,000–£5,000. Central Fund: Up to £25,000.

SAMPLE GRANTS In the UK Small donations to support small local charities in their fundraising activities Donations ranging £500–£5,000 to support the projects of nine charities –Tall Ships Youth Trust, The Prince's Trust, Ro-Ro Sailing Projects, Children Aid's Team, Wollaston Baptist Church, Volunteer Reading Help, Nene Valley Care Trust, Mad Scientist, The Northampton Hope Centre. Other funds were made available worldwide to organisations in the Scott Bader Group.

FINANCES *Year* 2011–12 *Income* £178,000 *Grants* £142,800 *Assets* £42,000,000

TRUSTEES Andrew Radford; Syed Omar Hayat; Richard Stillwell; Julie Rogers; Anne Atkinson-Clark; Les Norwood; Jacquie Findlay; Barry Mansfield; Christian Caulier; Richard Hirst.

OTHER INFORMATION There are two categories of grants as follows: Local Funds and Central Funds. Currently the Central Fund supports two large community based environmental/educational projects to the value of £25,000 each.

HOW TO APPLY In writing or by e-mail to the correspondent. Trustees meet quarterly in February, May, September and November.

WHO TO APPLY TO Sue Carter, Commonwealth Secretary, Scott Bader, Wollaston Hall, Wellingborough, Northamptonshire NN29 7RL *Tel.* 01933 666755 *Fax* 01933 666608 *email* commonwealth_office@scottbader.com *Website* www.scottbader.com

....

■ Bag4Sport Foundation

CC NO 1146920   **ESTABLISHED** 2012

WHERE FUNDING CAN BE GIVEN UK

WHO CAN BENEFIT Sports clubs, schools, youth organisations, and individuals who have already participated in fundraising through Bag4Sport textile recycling (see website).

WHAT IS FUNDED Sport

RANGE OF GRANTS Up to £500

TRUSTEES Rishi Ladwa; Andrew Trusler; Jide Ihenacho; Paul Baker; Scott Sartin; Stuart Wright; Steven Taylor; Straker John.

OTHER INFORMATION Since its inception, the foundation has distributed around £50,000 annually.

HOW TO APPLY On a form available to download, together with guidelines, from the website.

WHO TO APPLY TO Andrew Trusler, Trustee, Unit 2a Roundway Business Park, Hopton Industrial Estate, Devizes, Wiltshire SN10 2HU *Tel.* 01380 728880 *email* andy@bag4sport.co. uk *Website* www.bag4sport.co.uk

■ The Bagri Foundation

CC NO 1000219   **ESTABLISHED** 1990
WHERE FUNDING CAN BE GIVEN Worldwide.
WHO CAN BENEFIT Organisations and individuals.
WHAT IS FUNDED General charitable purposes.
SAMPLE GRANTS London Business School (£200,000).
FINANCES *Year* 2011–12 *Income* £12,602,578 *Grants* £277,829 *Assets* £14,455,696
TRUSTEES Lord Bagri; Hon. A. Bagri; Lady Bagri; Hon. A. Bagri.
OTHER INFORMATION No breakdown of the total grants figure was available from the accounts.
HOW TO APPLY In writing to the correspondent.
WHO TO APPLY TO D. M. Beaumont, Administrator, 80 Cannon Street, London EC4N 6EJ *Tel.* 020 7280 0000 *email* enquiries@bagrifoundation. org *Website* bagrifoundation.org

■ Veta Bailey Charitable Trust

CC NO 1007411   **ESTABLISHED** 1981
WHERE FUNDING CAN BE GIVEN Developing countries (generally those with GNP less than US$1,000 a head), or UK for work in developing countries.
WHO CAN BENEFIT Organisations (UK or overseas based) training medical personnel in developing countries.
WHAT IS FUNDED Training of doctors and other medical personnel and the development of good healthcare practices in third world and developing countries.
WHAT IS NOT FUNDED No grants to individuals.
TYPE OF GRANT One-off grants.
RANGE OF GRANTS Up to £10,000.
SAMPLE GRANTS Cambodia Trust, International Medical Corps (UK) and Maternal and Childhealth Advocacy International (£5,000 each); Christian Blind Mission (£4,250); Gurkha Welfare Trust (£3,000) and International Centre for Eye Health (£1,000).
FINANCES *Year* 2011–12 *Income* £39,371 *Grants* £23,250
TRUSTEES Brian Worth; John Humphreys; Sue Yates; Dr Madura Gupta; David Trim.
HOW TO APPLY In writing to the correspondent by June, for consideration at a trustees' meeting in August.
WHO TO APPLY TO Brian Worth, Trustee, The Cottage, Tiltups End, Horsley, Stroud, Gloucestershire GL6 0QE *Tel.* 01453 833399

■ The Austin Bailey Foundation

CC NO 514912   **ESTABLISHED** 1984
WHERE FUNDING CAN BE GIVEN Swansea and worldwide.
WHO CAN BENEFIT Churches, overseas aid organisations and local organisations.
WHAT IS FUNDED The foundation was set up to give approximately 25% of its income towards the advancement of religion by supporting the activities of local churches, 25% to relief agencies in poorer nations and 50% to local charities or branches of national charities to help older people, people with disabilities and families or children who are otherwise in need.
WHAT IS NOT FUNDED No payments to individuals.

TYPE OF GRANT Core costs; salaries; start-up costs. One-off, up to three years.
RANGE OF GRANTS Up to £10,000.
SAMPLE GRANTS Y-Care International – reconciliation and development work in Northern Sri Lanka following the civil war (£4,000); Mandimba Alliances in Mozambique – ongoing work with the poor (£3,000); Friends of Ibba Girls School, South Sudan – help with building costs, Send a Cow – Uganda Women's Project for women farmers, Hope and Homes for Children – giving orphans a loving home (£500 each).
St Teilo's Church, Caereithin, Swansea – outreach development programme (£1,000); Christchurch School, Swansea – continued support for their good work (£600).
The Family Centre, Bonymaen, Swansea – contribution towards salaries (£2,000); Cyrenians Cymru – employment support project (£1,000); Whizz-Kidz – mobility equipment for disabled children (£750); Swansea Centre for Deaf People – support for their ongoing work and Asthma Relief at Work in Swansea – nebulising machines (£600).
FINANCES *Year* 2011–12 *Income* £189,896 *Grants* £50,765 *Assets* £678,931
TRUSTEES Clive Bailey; Sandra Morton; The Venerable Robert Williams; Penny Ryan; Revd Jonathan Davies.
OTHER INFORMATION Because of the fewer applications received within the Local Churches category, the trustees at their discretion allocated additional funds to overseas charities
HOW TO APPLY In writing to the correspondent. Applications are considered in May, September and December. Applications under the local charity or church category from groups based outside the local area will only be considered if they demonstrate a strong local involvement. Applications under the overseas category must be from a UK based charity. An application form is available at the Trust's website: www.austinbaileyfoundation.org/grants/applying-for-a-grant
WHO TO APPLY TO Clive Bailey, Chair, 64 Bosworth Road, Barnet EN5 5LP *Tel.* 020 8449 4327 *Website* www.austinbaileyfoundation.org

■ The Baily Thomas Charitable Fund

CC NO 262334   **ESTABLISHED** 1970
WHERE FUNDING CAN BE GIVEN UK.
WHO CAN BENEFIT Community groups, support groups and organisations benefiting people affected by learning disability. Applications will only be considered from voluntary organisations which are registered charities or are associated with a registered charity. Schools and Parent Teachers Associations and Industrial and Provident Societies can also apply. The fund does not currently accept appeals from Community Interest Companies.
WHAT IS FUNDED The trustees restrict their remit to learning disability. This can include residential facilities; respite; sheltered accommodation; crafts and music; support to volunteers; special schools and special needs education; care in the community; day centres; holidays and outings; play schemes; and research.
WHAT IS NOT FUNDED Grants are not normally awarded to individuals. The following areas are unlikely to receive funding: hospices; minibuses except those for residential and/or day care services for people who have learning disabilities; conductive education projects;

Think carefully about every application. Is it justified?

365

swimming and hydro-therapy pools; advocacy projects; arts and theatre projects; physical disabilities unless accompanied by significant learning disabilities.

TYPE OF GRANT Capital and revenue. Loans may be made in certain circumstances. Grants are usually one-off.

RANGE OF GRANTS £250 to £130,000.

SAMPLE GRANTS Kings College London – Institute of Psychiatry (£187,000 in two grants); University of Edinburgh (£131,000); Autistica (£100,000); Rix-Thompson-Rothenberg Foundation (£70,000); Berwickshire Housing Association (£50,000); Papworth Trust (£40,000); and Grace Eyre Foundation, Hextol Foundation, National Family Carer Network and Young Epilepsy (£25,000 each).

FINANCES *Year* 2011–12 *Income* £1,770,848 *Grants* £2,664,480 *Assets* £77,866,625

TRUSTEES Prof. Sally-Ann Cooper; Prof. Anne Farmer; Suzanne Jane Marriott; Kenneth Young.

OTHER INFORMATION Beneficiaries receiving £25,000 or more were listed in the accounts. There were 288 grants made in total in 2011–12.

HOW TO APPLY Meetings of the trustees are usually held in April and October each year and applicants are advised to visit the charity's website for details of current deadlines. The website states that late applications will not be considered. If your application is considered under the Small Grants procedure then this will be reviewed by the trustees ahead of the usual meetings. Following the meeting all applicants are contacted formally to advise on the status of their application. Feel free to submit your application whenever you are ready, rather than waiting for the deadline.

Applications must be made online via the charity's website from which the following information is taken:

'**General applications:** Funding is normally considered for capital and revenue costs and for both specific projects and for general running/core costs. Grants are awarded for amounts from £250 and depend on a number of factors including the purpose, the total funding requirement and the potential sources of other funds including, in some cases, matching funding. Normally one-off grants are awarded but exceptionally a new project may be funded over two or three years, subject to satisfactory reports of progress. Grants should normally be taken up within one year of the issue of the grant offer letter which will include conditions relating to the release of the grant. The following areas of work normally fall within the fund's policy: capital building/renovation/refurbishment works for residential, nursing and respite care, and schools; employment schemes including woodwork, crafts, printing and horticulture; play schemes and play therapy schemes; day and social activities centres including building costs and running costs; support for families, including respite schemes; independent living schemes; support in the community schemes; snoezelen rooms.'

'**Research applications:** We generally direct our limited funds towards the initiation of research so that it can progress to the point at which there is sufficient data to support an application to one of the major funding bodies. Applications will only be considered from established research workers and will be subject to normal professional peer review procedures. Applications, limited to five pages with the type no smaller than Times New Roman 12, should be in the form of a scientific summary with a research plan to include a brief background and a short account of the design of

the study and number of subjects, the methods of assessment and analysis, timetable, main outcomes and some indication of other opportunities arising from the support of such research. A detailed budget of costs should be submitted together with a justification for the support requested. Details should be included of any other applications for funding which have been made to other funders and their outcomes, if known. The fund does not contribute towards university overheads. A one page curriculum vitae will be required for each of the personnel actually carrying out the study and for their supervisor together with a note of the total number of their peer reviewed publications and details of the ten most significant publications. Evidence may be submitted of the approval of the ethics committee of the applicant to the study and approval of the university for the application to the fund. An 80 word lay summary should also be submitted with the scientific summary. Any papers submitted in excess of those stipulated above will not be passed to the research committee for consideration. Before submitting a full application, researchers may submit a one page summary of the proposed study so that the trustees may indicate whether they are prepared to consider a full application.'

WHO TO APPLY TO Ann Cooper, Secretary to the Trustees, c/o TMF Management (UK) Ltd, 400 Capability Green, Luton LU1 3AE *Tel.* 01582 439225 *Fax* 01582 439206 *email* info@bailythomas.org.uk *Website* www.bailythomas.org.uk

··

■ The Baird Trust

SC NO SC016549   **ESTABLISHED** 1873

WHERE FUNDING CAN BE GIVEN Scotland.

WHO CAN BENEFIT Generally, the Church of Scotland.

WHAT IS FUNDED The trust is chiefly concerned with supporting the repair and refurbishment of the churches and halls belonging to the Church of Scotland. It also endows parishes and gives help to the Church of Scotland in its work.

TYPE OF GRANT One-off for capital and revenue.

SAMPLE GRANTS Airth Parish Church, Bellshill West Parish Church, Canisbay Church of Scotland, Church of Scotland Board Ministry, Coltness Memorial Church – Newmains, Kinross Parish Church, Kinnaird Church – Dundee, Lodging House Mission, London Road Church – Edinburgh, Newmachar Parish Church, St Andrew's Erskine Parish Church, St Michael's Parish Church – Edinburgh, Scottish Churches House and South Parish Church – East Kilbride.

FINANCES *Year* 2012 *Income* £342,271 *Grants* £250,000

TRUSTEES Marianne Baird; Hon. Mary Coltman; Maj. J. Erskine; Revd Dr Johnston McKay; Alan Borthwick; Dr Alison Elliot; Luke Borwick; Walter Barbour; Lieut. Col. Richard Callander.

HOW TO APPLY An application form can be completed online or by paper copy and submitted to the secretary.

WHO TO APPLY TO Iain Mowat, Secretary, 182 Bath Street, Glasgow G2 4HG *Tel.* 01413 320476 *Fax* 01413 310874 *email* info@bairdtrust.org.uk *Website* www.bairdtrust.org.uk

········

366   *Does the trust you have chosen match your needs? Haphazard applications waste postage and time*

■ The Baker Charitable Trust

CC NO 273629   **ESTABLISHED** 1977

WHERE FUNDING CAN BE GIVEN The North East of England.

WHO CAN BENEFIT Registered charities including the headquarters of national organisations.

WHAT IS FUNDED Priority is given to charities concerned with the welfare of Jewish, elderly and disabled people; neurological research; and people with diabetes and epilepsy. Preference is given to charities in which the trust has special interest, knowledge or association.

WHAT IS NOT FUNDED No grants to individuals or non-registered charities.

TYPE OF GRANT Core costs.

RANGE OF GRANTS £250–£10,000; typical grant £500–£3,000.

SAMPLE GRANTS Previous beneficiaries have included: British Council Shaare Zedek Medical Centre, Chai Cancer Care, Community Security Trust, Disabled Living Foundation, Friends of Magen David Adom in Great Britain, Hillel Foundation, Institute of Jewish Policy Research, Jewish Care; Jewish Women's Aid, Marie Curie Cancer Care, National Society for Epilepsy, Norwood; United Jewish Israel Appeal, St John's Hospice, United Synagogue, Winged Fellowship and World Jewish Relief.

FINANCES *Year* 2011–12 *Income* £81,857 *Grants* £70,000 *Assets* £2,864,816

TRUSTEES Dr Harvey Baker; Dr Adrienne Baker.

HOW TO APPLY In writing to the correspondent. The trustees meet to consider applications in January, April, July and October.

WHO TO APPLY TO Dr Harvey Baker, Trustee, 16 Sheldon Avenue, Highgate, London N6 4JT *Tel.* 020 8340 5970

■ The Roy and Pixie Baker Charitable Trust

CC NO 1101988   **ESTABLISHED** 1995

WHERE FUNDING CAN BE GIVEN UK and overseas.

WHO CAN BENEFIT Charitable organisations.

WHAT IS FUNDED Medical research, education, heritage, relief-in-need.

TYPE OF GRANT One-off and recurrent.

RANGE OF GRANTS Up to £10,000.

SAMPLE GRANTS Daft as a Brush (£10,000); Literary and Philosophical Society, Cathedral Church of St Nicholas and Holy Island Parochial School Trust (£5,000 each); Nunnykirk Centre for Dyslexia (£4,000); Groundwork North East (£3,500); Washington Riding Centre for the Disabled (£2,500); The North of England Cadet Forces Trust (£2,000) and Evening Chronicle Sunshine Fund (£500).

FINANCES *Year* 2011–12 *Income* £58,354 *Grants* £55,980 *Assets* £1,193,989

TRUSTEES Tony Glenton; George Straker; Lesley Caisley; David Irvin; Bill Dryden.

HOW TO APPLY In writing to the correspondent, providing full back up information. Trustees' meetings are held half yearly. The trustees require a receipt from the donee in respect of each grant.

WHO TO APPLY TO The Trustees, c/o Ryecroft Glenton, 32 Portland Terrace, Newcastle upon Tyne NE2 1QP *Tel.* 01912 811292 *email* bakercharitabletrust@ryecroft-glenton.co.uk

■ The C. Alma Baker Trust

CC NO 1113864   **ESTABLISHED** 1981

WHERE FUNDING CAN BE GIVEN UK and overseas, particularly New Zealand.

WHO CAN BENEFIT Individuals or scientific research institutions benefiting young adults, farmers, academics, research workers and students.

WHAT IS FUNDED The Trust makes grants for agricultural research and scholarships for students of agriculture wishing to attend a University or Technical Institute. The Trust also supports travel likely to benefit agriculture and, in particular, travel between the UK and New Zealand, together with grants for educational purposes and general charitable donations.

WHAT IS NOT FUNDED No general education grants.

TYPE OF GRANT Range of grants, though normally one-off annual grants.

SAMPLE GRANTS Royal Smithfield Club (£5,000); Worshipful Company of Farmers (£2,000) and East of England Agricultural Society (£1,000).

FINANCES *Year* 2011–12 *Income* £1,287,139 *Grants* £123,089 *Assets* £10,897,755

TRUSTEES Charles Boyes; Roger Moore; Simon Taylor.

PUBLICATIONS Limestone Downs Annual Report in New Zealand.

OTHER INFORMATION The trust's main asset is Limestone Downs, a sheep and beef property in the North Island, New Zealand utilised for new ideas and development in agriculture to be explored and debated in a working farm environment.

HOW TO APPLY In writing to the correspondent.

WHO TO APPLY TO Jane O'Beirne, Company Secretary, 20 Hartford Road, Huntingdon, Cambridgeshire PE29 3QH *Tel.* 01480 411331 *email* admin@calmabakertrust.co.uk *Website* www.calmabakertrust.co.uk

■ The Balcombe Charitable Trust

CC NO 267172   **ESTABLISHED** 1975

WHERE FUNDING CAN BE GIVEN UK and overseas.

WHO CAN BENEFIT Registered charities benefiting children and young adults, students, at risk groups, disabled people, people disadvantaged by poverty, socially isolated people, and people who are sick.

WHAT IS FUNDED Education; the environment; health and welfare.

WHAT IS NOT FUNDED No grants to individuals or non-registered charities.

TYPE OF GRANT One-off and recurrent grants.

RANGE OF GRANTS £5,000–£100,000

SAMPLE GRANTS Durrell Wildlife Conservation Trust (£114,500); Samaritans (£38,000); Brook Advisory Centres Limited (£30,000); Oxfam (£25,000); Who Cares Trust and Christian Aid (£20,000 each); Beating Bowel Cancer (£15,000); Platform 51 (£12,500); Tel Aviv University Trust (£8,500); and the 999 Club Trust (£5,000).

FINANCES *Year* 2011–12 *Income* £721,909 *Grants* £422,713 *Assets* £25,660,403

TRUSTEES R. A. Kreitman; Patricia M. Kreitman; Nicholas Brown.

HOW TO APPLY In writing to the correspondent.

WHO TO APPLY TO Jonathan W. Prevezer, Administrator, c/o Citroen Wells, Devonshire House, 1 Devonshire Street, London W1W 5DR *Tel.* 020 7304 2000 *email* jonathan.prevezer@citroenwells.co.uk

■ The Andrew Balint Charitable Trust

CC NO 273691   **ESTABLISHED** 1961
WHERE FUNDING CAN BE GIVEN UK, Israel, Hungary.
WHO CAN BENEFIT Charitable organisations; Jewish organisations.
WHAT IS FUNDED General charitable causes; health, elderly, ex-service people, Jewish faith, and disability organisations.
TYPE OF GRANT One off and recurring.
RANGE OF GRANTS £50–£20,000.
SAMPLE GRANTS Nightingale House (£20,000); Hungarian Senior Citizens (£6,000); Former Employee Trust (£6,000); Jewish Care and United Jewish Israel Appeal £5,000 each); The Board of Deputies of British Jews (£500); and British Friends of Children's Town (£250).
FINANCES *Year* 2012–13 *Income* £46,892 *Grants* £55,133 *Assets* £1,654,938
TRUSTEES Dr Gabriel Balint-Kurti; Angela Balint; Roy Balint-Kurti; Daniel Balint-Kurti.
OTHER INFORMATION The Andrew Balint Charitable Trust, The George Balint Charitable Trust, The Paul Charitable Trust and the Trust for Former Employees of Balint Companies are jointly administered. They have some trustees in common and are independent in other matters.
HOW TO APPLY In writing to the correspondent.
WHO TO APPLY TO David Kramer, Administrator, Carter Backer Winter, Enterprise House, 21 Buckle Street, London E1 8NN *Tel.* 020 7309 3800 *email* david.kramer@cbw.co.uk

■ The George Balint Charitable Trust

CC NO 267482   **ESTABLISHED** 1961
WHERE FUNDING CAN BE GIVEN UK, Israel, Hungary.
WHO CAN BENEFIT Charitable organisations; individuals.
WHAT IS FUNDED General; education; medical care and research; Jewish.
RANGE OF GRANTS £150–£15,000
SAMPLE GRANTS Previous beneficiaries include: United Jewish Israel Appeal (£15,000); Hungarian Senior Citizens (£10,200); Former Employees Trust (£8,500); Neviot Olam Institution and British Friends of Bar-Ilan University (£2,000 each); Imperial College London (£1,000); Norwood: Children and Families First (£750); and Marie Curie Cancer Care (£200).
FINANCES *Year* 2011–12 *Income* £21,407 *Grants* £56,000
TRUSTEES Dr Andrew Balint; George Rothschild; Dr Marc Balint.
OTHER INFORMATION 'The George Balint Charitable Trust, the Paul Balint Charitable Trust and The Charitable Trust for Former Employees of Balint Companies operate from the same premises and are jointly administered. They have some trustees in common and are independent in all other matters.'
HOW TO APPLY In writing to the correspondent.
WHO TO APPLY TO David Kramer, Administrator, Carter Backer Winter, Enterprise House, 21 Buckle Street, London E1 8NN *Tel.* 020 7309 3800 *email* david.kramer@cbw.co.uk

■ The Paul Balint Charitable Trust

CC NO 273690   **ESTABLISHED** 1977
WHERE FUNDING CAN BE GIVEN UK; Hungary; Israel.
WHO CAN BENEFIT Charitable organisations.
WHAT IS FUNDED General charitable purposes; medical research; education; elderly assistance; relief of poverty.
FINANCES *Year* 2011–12 *Income* £1,963 *Grants* £43,905
TRUSTEES Dr Andrew Balint; Dr Gabriel Balint-Kurti; Dr Marc Balint; Paul Balint.
OTHER INFORMATION The Andrew Balint Charitable Trust, The George Balint Charitable Trust, The Paul Balint Charitable Trust and the Trust for Former Employees of Balint Companies are jointly administered. They have some trustees in common and are independent in other matters.
HOW TO APPLY In writing to the correspondent.
WHO TO APPLY TO Dr Andrew Balint, Trustee, 15 Portland Court, 101 Hendon Lane, London N3 3SH *Tel.* 020 8346 1266

■ The Albert Casanova Ballard Deceased Trust

CC NO 201759   **ESTABLISHED** 1962
WHERE FUNDING CAN BE GIVEN Within a 7-mile radius of Plymouth (but within the city of Plymouth boundary).
WHO CAN BENEFIT Local charities, local branches of national organisations and individuals.
WHAT IS FUNDED General charitable purposes, health, welfare and young people. Grants are made to schoolchildren towards uniforms and other costs.
WHAT IS NOT FUNDED The trust cannot fund anyone or any charity organisation outside of Plymouth (a seven mile radius from the city centre, within the city of Plymouth boundary, is the trust's limit).
RANGE OF GRANTS Charities: £150–£2,500. Individuals: £100–£200.
SAMPLE GRANTS YMCA (£2,750); Ford Youth and Community Centre (£1,750); Macmillan Cancer Support (£1,500); St Luke's Hospice (£1,250); and PLIMS (£1,200); Mutley Baptist Youth and YWCA (£900 each); Marjon Basketball (£800); Highbury Trust (£600); Parkinson's Disease Society (£500); Lifeline Resources (£400); and Pregnancy Crisis Centre (£300).
FINANCES *Year* 2011–12 *Income* £47,805 *Grants* £37,580 *Assets* £954,120
TRUSTEES Kenneth Banfield, Chair; Audrey Houston; Margaret Pengelly; Joy Rendle; Nigel Norris; Frances Norris; Lynn Smith.
OTHER INFORMATION The 2011–12 grant total includes the sum of £20,000 donated to 135 individuals.
HOW TO APPLY In writing to the correspondent. Applications from local charities are considered in November and notices appear in the Evening Herald and The Plymouth Extra around that time. There are no application forms available. Grants for individuals are made once a year in June. Grants will NOT be entertained outside these periods.
WHO TO APPLY TO The Trustees, 6 Victory Street, Keyham, Plymouth PL2 2BY *Tel.* 01752 569258

■ The Ballinger Charitable Trust

cc no 1121739   **established** 1994

where funding can be given North east England, Tyne and Wear.

who can benefit Registered charities only.

what is funded 'The focus of the Ballinger Charitable Trust is currently to support projects in the North East of England, principally by providing funds that: support the health, development and well being of young people; support the elderly; to improve the quality of life for people and communities; promote cultural/arts projects based in the North East of England.'

what is not funded No grants to individuals or sponsorships.

sample grants Bath Institute of Medical Engineering Limited, Durham Association of Clubs for Young People, the Lady Hoare Trust and St Mary's Cathedral.

finances *Year* 2012 *Income* £2,796,609 *Grants* £1,728,000

trustees Diana Ballinger; John Flynn; Andrew Ballinger; Nicola Crowther.

how to apply For amounts over £5,000 an online application form can be completed at the trust's website. The trust may then make contact at a later date for additional documentation. Alternatively, the application form can be downloaded with the completed application retuned by post. For amounts up to £5,000, the trust is happy to receive a written request in the form of a letter. There is no annual deadline. The larger the fund applied for, the greater the amount of detail will be required in the application form. A decision may take up to six months depending on the size of fund applied for.

who to apply to Nicola Crowther, Trustee, P. O. Box 245, Morpeth, Northumberland NE61 3DA *Tel.* 01914 880520 *email* info@ballingercharitabletrust.org.uk *Website* www.ballingercharitabletrust.org.uk

■ Balmain Charitable Trust

cc no 1079972   **established** 1998

where funding can be given UK.

who can benefit Charitable organisations.

what is funded General charitable purposes.

range of grants Mostly £1,000–£2,000.

sample grants The Light Dragoons Regimental Charity (£10,000); British Red Cross Society and Oxfam (£8,000 each); Second Chance (£6,000); The Suzy Lamplugh Trust (£5,000); Wilderness Foundation UK, Unlock (National Association of Ex-Offenders) and RNLI (£2,000 each); The Wildfowl and Wetlands Trust (£1,500) and National Art Collections Fund, Cerebra and Age UK (£1,000 each).

finances *Year* 2011–12 *Income* £116,884 *Grants* £105,800 *Assets* £2,605,522

trustees Andrew B. Tappin; Iain D. Balmain; Leonora D. Balmain; Charles A. G. Wells; Stewart Balmain; Penntrust Ltd.

other information Many of the beneficiaries are supported year after year.

how to apply In writing to the correspondent.

who to apply to Trust Administrator, c/o Rutter and Alhusen, 2 Longmead, Shaftesbury, Dorset SP7 8PL

■ The Balmore Trust

sc no SC008930   **established** 1980

where funding can be given Developing countries and UK, with a preference for Strathclyde.

who can benefit Organisations.

what is funded Two-thirds of grants are given to overseas projects and the remainder to local projects in the UK, working in the areas of education, health, alleviation of poverty and community development. Grant giving in the UK is concentrated mainly in the Glasgow area and favours families, teenagers, and women's aid groups. Overseas, the trust has close connections with community development programmes in India (Kolkata, Rajasthan and Kerala), Burma and Africa (Kenya, South Africa, Swaziland, Lesotho and Namibia).

what is not funded No grants to individuals.

range of grants £50–£7,000.

sample grants Previous beneficiaries have included Church House – Bridgeton, Daynes Education Fund – South Africa, East Dunbartonshire Women's Aid, Family Action in Rogerfield and Easterhouse, Friends of CINI – India, Glasgow Children's Holiday Scheme, Humura Child Care Family – Uganda, Inverclyde Youth for Christ Reality at Work, Mission Aviation Fellowship, the Village Storytelling Centre – Pollok and Wells for India – Rajasthan.

finances *Year* 2011–12 *Income* £112,831 *Grants* £100,000

trustees J. Riches; G. Burns; J. Eldridge; B. Holman; Ms R. Jarvis; Ms R. Riches.

publications Newsletter available on website

other information The Balmore Trust distributes the profits of the Coach House charity craft shop as well as other donations. The trust's policy in grantmaking is increasingly to build on partnerships already established. In 2011–12 the trust had a total expenditure of £123,000.

how to apply The trust is run entirely voluntarily and the trust states that it is unlikely that money will be available for new applicants, unless they have a personal link with the trust or its shop, the Coach House charity craft shop.

who to apply to The Secretary, Viewfield, Balmore, Torrance, Glasgow G64 4AE *Tel.* 01360 620742 *email* mailto@balmoretrust.org.uk *Website* www.balmoretrust.org.uk

■ The Balney Charitable Trust

cc no 288575   **established** 1983

where funding can be given UK, with a preference for north Buckinghamshire and north Bedfordshire.

who can benefit Individuals and registered charities.

what is funded The furtherance of any religious and charitable purposes in connection with the parishes of Chicheley, North Crawley and the SCAN Group i.e. Sherington, Astwood, Hardmead and churches with a Chester family connection; the provision of housing for persons in needy circumstances; agriculture, forestry and armed service charities; care of older people and people who are sick and disabled.

what is not funded Local community organisations and individuals outside north Buckinghamshire and north Bedfordshire.

type of grant Start-up costs, capital grants (including contributions to building projects, e.g. local churches) and research. Funding for up to three years will be considered.

range of grants £25–£5,000.

SAMPLE GRANTS Previously: St Lawrence Church – Chicheley (£7,500); National Trust – Montecute House (£7,000 in two grants); Queen Alexandra Hospital Home (£5,000); CHIT, Combat Stress, Motor Neurone Disease Association and St Luke's Hospital for the Clergy (£2,000 each); Emmaus Village – Carlton, Help for Heroes, MS Therapy Centre and Tree Aid – Ghana Village Tree Enterprise (£1,000 each); and Fun 4 Young People (£500).
FINANCES *Year* 2011–12 *Income* £105,029 *Grants* £46,176 *Assets* £804,195
TRUSTEES Ian Townsend; Robert Ruck-Keene; Jill Heaton.
HOW TO APPLY In writing to the correspondent. Applications are acknowledged if an sae is enclosed, otherwise if the charity has not received a reply within six weeks the application has not been successful.
WHO TO APPLY TO Helen Chapman, Administrator, Hill Farm, North Crawley Road, Newport Pagnell, Buckinghamshire MK16 9HQ

■ The Baltic Charitable Fund

CC NO 279194   **ESTABLISHED** 1979
WHERE FUNDING CAN BE GIVEN UK, with a preference for the City of London.
WHO CAN BENEFIT Registered charities benefiting residents of the City of London, seafarers, fishermen, and ex-service and service people.
WHAT IS FUNDED Registered charities only which must be connected with the City of London, shipping or the military forces.
WHAT IS NOT FUNDED No support for advertising or charity dinners, and so on.
TYPE OF GRANT One-off.
RANGE OF GRANTS £300–£36,000.
SAMPLE GRANTS London Nautical School (£30,000); Lord Mayor's Appeal (£7,500); Jubilee Sailing Trust (£5,000); Sailor's Society (£3,300); South Georgia Heritage Trust (£1,000) and Cancer Research and Sustrans (£300 each).
FINANCES *Year* 2011–12 *Income* £82,591 *Grants* £52,850 *Assets* £1,950,425
TRUSTEE The directors of the Baltic Exchange Limited.
HOW TO APPLY Unsolicited applications are not considered.
WHO TO APPLY TO The Company Secretary, The Baltic Exchange, 38 St Mary Axe, London EC3A 8BH *Tel.* 020 7623 5501

■ The Bamford Charitable Foundation

CC NO 279848   **ESTABLISHED** 1979
WHERE FUNDING CAN BE GIVEN Within a 40-mile radius of Rocester.
WHO CAN BENEFIT Mainly local organisations.
WHAT IS FUNDED General charitable purposes.
TYPE OF GRANT One-off.
RANGE OF GRANTS Typically up to £15,000, with larger grants occasionally considered.
SAMPLE GRANTS Denstone Foundation (£60,000); The Litchfield Festival (£22,500); Racing Welfare (£20,000); Farms not Factories (£10,000); Central Indian Christian Mission (£6,000); Alton Castle and The Great Britons Foundation (£5,000 each); Society for the Welfare of Horses and Ponies (£2,500); Royal National Institute of Blind People (£2,000) and Childreach International and Rhinology and Laryngology Fund and Air Ambulance (£1,000 each).

FINANCES *Year* 2011–12 *Income* £35,844 *Grants* £146,182 *Assets* £1,078,834
TRUSTEES Sir Anthony Bamford; Lady C. Bamford.
OTHER INFORMATION In 2011–12 fourteen further small grants were made totalling £4,000.
HOW TO APPLY In writing to the correspondent. 'Successful applicants are required to demonstrate to the trustees that the receipt of the grant is wholly necessary to enable them to fulfil their own objectives.'
WHO TO APPLY TO D. G. Garnett, Administrator, c/o J. C. Bamford Excavators Ltd, Lakeside Works, Denstone Road, Rocester, Uttoxeter ST14 5JP *Tel.* 01889 593140

■ The Banbury Charities

CC NO 201418   **ESTABLISHED** 1961
WHERE FUNDING CAN BE GIVEN Banbury or its immediate environs.
WHO CAN BENEFIT Individuals and groups.
WHAT IS FUNDED General charitable purposes.
WHAT IS NOT FUNDED No grants for debts or ongoing expenses.
TYPE OF GRANT One-off grants.
RANGE OF GRANTS Up to £35,000.
SAMPLE GRANTS Banbury Welfare Trust (£35,000); Lady Arran (£28,000); Katherine House Hospice (£10,000); The Glebe Recreational Charity (£9,000); Marlborough Road Methodist Church (£8,000); Balscote Village Hall and Samaritans (£5,000 each); Life Education Centres (£4,000); Azad Football Club (£2,000) and Focus Counselling Service Banbury and Rotary Club of Banbury (£1,000 each).
FINANCES *Year* 2011–12 *Income* £400,873 *Grants* £340,000
TRUSTEES Fred Blackwell; Valerie Fisher; Helen Madeiros; Judy May; Julia Colegrave; Keiron Mallon; Martin Humphris; Nigel Morris; Angela Heritage; Jamie Briggs; Janet Justice; Colin Clarke.
OTHER INFORMATION The Banbury Charities are The Bridge Estate, Lady Arran's Charity, Banbury Arts and Educational Charity, Banbury Sick Poor Fund, Banbury Almshouse Charity, and the Banbury Welfare Trust. About one-third of the grant total is given to individuals.
HOW TO APPLY In writing to the correspondent.
WHO TO APPLY TO Nigel Yeadon, Clerk to the Trustees, 36 West Bar, Banbury, Oxfordshire OX16 9RU *Tel.* 01295 251234

■ William P. Bancroft (No 2) Charitable Trust and Jenepher Gillett Trust

CC NO 288968   **ESTABLISHED** 1984
WHERE FUNDING CAN BE GIVEN UK and overseas.
WHO CAN BENEFIT Mainly charities benefiting Quakers.
WHAT IS FUNDED Mainly Quaker charities or projects including education; peace and reconciliation work; homeless charities.
WHAT IS NOT FUNDED No appeals unconnected with Quakers. No support for individual or student grant applications.
TYPE OF GRANT Buildings, core costs, endowment, one-off and start-up costs. Funding of up to three years will be considered.
SAMPLE GRANTS Charney Manor Quake Course (£14,000); BYM (£5,000); Woodbrooke College (£2,000); Quaker Social Action (£2,500); Bootham School and Quaker Voluntary Action

(£1,000 each); West Midland Quaker Peace Education, and Leaveners (£500 each).

FINANCES *Year* 2011 *Income* £43,238 *Grants* £42,000 *Assets* £734,678

TRUSTEES Dr Godfrey Gillett; Martin B. Gillett; Dr D. S. Gillett; Jenepher Moseley; Dr Christopher Bancroft Wolff; Marion McNaughton.

HOW TO APPLY In writing to the correspondent. Trustees meet in May, applications must be received no later than April.

WHO TO APPLY TO Dr D. S. Gillett, Trustee, 13 Woodbury Park Road, Tunbridge Wells, Kent TN4 9NQ *Tel.* 01892 528150

■ The Band Trust

CC NO 279802   **ESTABLISHED** 1976
WHERE FUNDING CAN BE GIVEN UK.
WHO CAN BENEFIT Registered UK charities.
WHAT IS FUNDED People with disabilities, children and young people, scholarships, hospices and hospitals, education, older people and people who are disadvantaged.
WHAT IS NOT FUNDED Individuals directly; political activities; commercial ventures or publications; retrospective grants or loans; direct replacement of statutory funding or activities that are primarily the responsibility of central or local government.
TYPE OF GRANT One-off and recurring.
RANGE OF GRANTS Up to £50,000.
SAMPLE GRANTS NSPCC (£45,000); National Memorial Arboretum (£35,000); U Can Do It (£30,000); Victim Support (£15,000); Stanley Spencer Gallery, Norfolk Hospice and Cancer Research UK (£10,000 each); Church Housing Trust (£7,500); and the Barristers Benevolent Fund (£2,000). Scholarship funds were awarded to the Florence Nightingale Foundation and the Honourable Society of Gray's Inn (£25,000 each).
FINANCES *Year* 2011–12 *Income* £783,044 *Grants* £648,731 *Assets* £23,316,446
TRUSTEES The Hon. Nicholas Wallop; The Hon. Nicholas Wallop; Richard J. S. Mason; Bruce G. Streather.
HOW TO APPLY The trust's accounts state that 'the trustees do not wish to receive unsolicited applications for grants'. The trustees identify potential recipients themselves, although their method of doing this is not known. One would assume that they need to be made aware of organisations that fit in with their objectives. The trustees' meetings are held three times a year.
WHO TO APPLY TO Richard J. S. Mason, Trustee, Moore Stephens, 150 Aldersgate Street, London EC1A 4AB *Tel.* 020 7334 9191 *Fax* 020 7248 3408 *email* richard.mason@ moorestephens.com *Website* www.bandtrust.co. uk

---

■ The Bank of Scotland Foundation (formerly The HBOS Foundation)

SC NO SC032942   **ESTABLISHED** 2002
WHERE FUNDING CAN BE GIVEN Scotland.
WHO CAN BENEFIT Registered charities and community groups.
WHAT IS FUNDED Social welfare, relief of poverty.
WHAT IS NOT FUNDED The foundation: does not make donations to discriminatory, political or religious organisations; does not support animal charities

or medical research; does not make donations to individuals or for advertising or sponsorship.
RANGE OF GRANTS Up to £20,000.
SAMPLE GRANTS North United Communities Limited (£20,000); Maryhill Citizens Advice (£19,000); Rape and Abuse Line (£15,000); Upward Mobility Limited (£12,500); Marie Curie Cancer Care and Muirhouse Youth Development Group (£10,000 each); Scottish Youth Theatre Limited (£9,000); Befriend a Child (£8,000); MND Scotland (£7,000); North Glasgow Community Food Initiative (£6,000); Fostering Network Scotland and Getting Better Together (£5,000 each); Lung Ha's Theatre Company (£3,000); and Active Seniors and Samaritans of Dunfermline (£2,000 each).
FINANCES *Year* 2012 *Income* £1,276,308 *Grants* £918,773 *Assets* £237,172
TRUSTEES Kate Guthrie; Jim Coyle; Alasdair Gardner; Sarah Deas; Paul Grice; Peter Navin.
OTHER INFORMATION From 2014, Lloyds Banking Group's annual donation to the foundation will increase to £2 million.
HOW TO APPLY On a form available to download on the foundation's website, where criteria and guidelines are also posted. All applicants will be informed in writing of the trustees' decisions approximately eight weeks from the closing date for applications (see website for current deadlines). Applicants are required to leave one year between applications whether they are successful or unsuccessful.
WHO TO APPLY TO Scott James, Finance and Grants Manager, The Mound, Edinburgh EH1 1YZ *Tel.* 01316 552599 *email* enquiries@ bankofscotlandfoundation.co.uk *Website* www. bankofscotlandfoundation.org

---

■ The Barbers' Company General Charities

CC NO 265579   **ESTABLISHED** 1973
WHERE FUNDING CAN BE GIVEN UK.
WHO CAN BENEFIT Organisations and individuals.
WHAT IS FUNDED General charitable purposes, including medical education and nursing.
WHAT IS NOT FUNDED No grants to unsolicited applications.
RANGE OF GRANTS £1,000–£50,000.
SAMPLE GRANTS Royal College of Surgeons (£40,000); Phyliss Tuckwell Hospice (£22,000); The Guildhall School Trust (£6,500); City of London School for Girls, Epsom College and Reeds School (£5,000 each); City of London Freemen's School (£4,000) and ABF – The Big Curry, Treloars and The Barbican Centre Trust (£1,000 each).
FINANCES *Year* 2011–12 *Income* £191,243 *Grants* £164,815 *Assets* £1,414,921
TRUSTEE The Barbers Company.
OTHER INFORMATION The trust no longer has direct contact with the hairdressing fraternity. However, a small amount is given each year to satisfy its historical links. The grants total includes £159,581 was given to organisations.
HOW TO APPLY The trustees do not welcome unsolicited applications.
WHO TO APPLY TO The Clerk, Barber-Surgeons' Hall, Monkwell Square, Wood Street, London EC2Y 5BL *Tel.* 020 7606 0741 *email* clerk@ barberscompany.org *Website* barberscompany. org.uk

■ The Barbour Foundation

cc no 328081   established 1988

where funding can be given England with a preference for Tyne and Wear, Northumberland and South Tyneside. Overseas aid.

who can benefit The trust likes to support local activities, and also supports local branches of national charities.

what is funded Relief of patients suffering from any form of illness or disease, promotion of research into causes of such illnesses; furtherance of education; preservation of buildings and countryside of environmental, historical or architectural interest; relief of people in need; disaster relief whether in England or not. Charities working in the fields of infrastructure development, religious umbrella bodies and animal welfare will also be considered.

what is not funded No support for: requests from outside the geographical area; individual applications, unless backed by a particular charitable organisation; capital grants for building projects.

type of grant Capital, core costs, one-off, project, research, running costs, recurring costs, salaries, and start-up costs. Funding for up to one year will be considered.

sample grants Newcastle School for Boys (£100,000); Hexham Abbey Project Appeal (£30,000); Prince's Countryside Fund (£27,000); Marie Curie (£25,000); Duke of Edinburgh Award (£20,000); Barnardo's, British Red Cross and Calvert Trust (£5,000 each); East Africa Food Crisis, Revive Furniture Recycling and Sunnybank Centre (£3,000 each); Bubble Foundation, Contact (Morpeth Mental Health Group), Cedarwood Trust, Child Care Action Trust, Sailors' Families Society and YMCA (£2,000 each); and Arthritis Research UK, Bipolar Association, Brinkburn Music Festival and Target Ovarian Cancer (£1,000 each).

finances *Year* 2011–12 *Income* £444,758 *Grants* £509,975 *Assets* £9,199,361

trustees Dame Margaret Barbour, Chair; Helen Barbour; Helen Tavroges.

other information Grant total includes £4,346 paid in goods to the foundation by J Barbour and Sons Ltd.

how to apply Applications should be made in writing to the following address: PO Box 21, Guisborough, Cleveland, TS14 8YH. The application should include full back-up information, a statement of accounts and the official charity number of the applicant. A main grants meeting is held every three to four months to consider grants of £500 plus. Applications are processed and researched by the administrator and secretary and further information may be requested. A small grants meeting is held monthly to consider grants up to £500. The trust always receives more applications than it can support. Even if a project fits its policy priority areas, it may not be possible to make a grant.

who to apply to Helen Tavroges, Trustee, J. Barbour and Sons Ltd, Simonside, South Shields, Tyne and Wear NE34 9PD *Tel.* 01914 554444 *Website* www.barbour.com

■ The Barcapel Foundation

sc no SC009211   established 1964

where funding can be given Scotland and other parts of the UK.

who can benefit Charitable organisations.

what is funded The three priority areas of interest for funding are:

'Health – the foundation supports all aspects of health, a wide ranging remit acknowledging that health is a state of complete physical, mental and social well-being and not merely the absence of disease or infirmity; Heritage – the original financiers of the foundation had a keen interest in our heritage, specifying that one of the foundation's aims was the preservation and beautification of historic properties. The foundation continues to support the built environment and will support our literary and artistic heritage as well as architectural; Youth – the development of people is one of the principal objectives of the Foundation. Whilst charitable giving can be used to alleviate problems it can also be used to empower people and this is particularly true of the young.'

what is not funded No support for: individual applications for travel or similar; organisations or individuals engaged in promoting religious or political beliefs; applications for funding costs of feasibility studies or similar. Support is unlikely to be given for local charities whose work takes place outside the British Isles.

range of grants Up to £50,000.

sample grants Great Ormond Street Hospital (£60,000); Macmillan Cancer Support (£44,500); Innerpeffray Library (£42,500); St Mark's Hospital (£40,000); National Youth Theatre, Prince's Trust Scotland and PRIME (£25,000 each); Place2Be (£20,000); and Edinburgh Art Festival and The Beacon Centre (£15,000).

finances *Year* 2012 *Income* £201,302 *Grants* £833,086

trustees Robert Wilson; Amanda Richards; Jed Wilson; Clement Wilson; Niall Scott.

how to apply A preliminary application form can be downloaded from the foundation's website. Ensure that interests, aims and objectives are compatible with those of the foundation. Applications are not accepted by email.

who to apply to Mia McCartney, The Mews, Skelmorlie Castle, Skelmorlie, Ayrshire PA17 5EY *Tel.* 01475 521616 *email* admin@barcapelfoundation.org *Website* www.barcapelfoundation.org

■ Barchester Healthcare Foundation

cc no 1083272   established 2000

where funding can be given England, Scotland and Wales.

who can benefit Individuals and organisations.

what is funded Older people and other adults (18 plus) with a physical or mental disability whose health and/or social care needs cannot be met by the statutory public sector or by the individual. 'Our mission is to make a difference to the lives of older people and other adults with a physical or mental disability, supporting practical solutions that lead to increased personal independence, self-sufficiency and dignity.'

what is not funded Grants will not be made to community groups and small charities for: core/running costs or salaries or financial support to general projects; indirect services such as help lines, newsletters, leaflets or research; major building projects or large capital projects; training of staff and volunteers. The trustees reserve the right to put a cap on grants to a single charity (including all of its branches) in any one year.

RANGE OF GRANTS Up to £5,000

SAMPLE GRANTS Sefton Opera (£2,000); South Liverpool Voluntary Inclusion Programme (£1,500); and Barchester White Lodge, Canterbury Shopmobility, PHAB, Brandwood Community Centre, Galloping Grannies Community Riding Group, SERVE and Walsall Leisure Ramblers (£1,000 each).

FINANCES *Year* 2012 *Income* £167,000 *Grants* £162,000 *Assets* £60

TRUSTEES Chris Vellenoweth; Mike Parsons; Janice Robinson; Lesley Flory; Pauline Houchin; David Walden; Dr Jackie Morris; Andrew Cozens.

OTHER INFORMATION Grants for 2012 totalled £162,000 of which £59,000 went to small charities/community groups and the remaining funds to individuals. 25 grants to organisations were over £1,000 and totalled £43,000 and 32 grants of under £1,000 were made to organisations and totalled £16,000.

HOW TO APPLY Application can be made via the foundation's website. A decision usually takes approximately ten weeks from the date of application. All applications supported by Barchester Healthcare staff will be given priority.

WHO TO APPLY TO Jon Hather, Administrator, Suite 201, The Chambers, 2nd Floor, Design Centre East, Chelsea Harbour, London SW10 0XF *Tel.* 0800 328 3328 *email* info@bhcfoundation. org.uk *Website* www.bhcfoundation.org.uk

■ The Barclay Foundation

CC NO 803696   **ESTABLISHED** 1990

WHERE FUNDING CAN BE GIVEN Not defined, in practice, UK.

WHO CAN BENEFIT Registered charities, hospitals and universities.

WHAT IS FUNDED Medical research; young people; the elderly; advancement of religion; people with disabilities; the sick; and the disadvantaged.

TYPE OF GRANT Projects and one-off grants.

RANGE OF GRANTS £1,000–£1.2 million.

SAMPLE GRANTS Great Ormond Street Children's Hospital (£1 million); the Prince's Foundation (£250,000 in two grants); University of Oxford (£147,500); the Healing Foundation (£100,000); Elton John AIDS Foundation (£50,000); and the Make-A-Wish Foundation (£18,000).

FINANCES *Year* 2012 *Income* £1,635,173 *Grants* £1,565,500 *Assets* £42,569

TRUSTEES Sir David Barclay; Sir Frederick Barclay; Aidan Barclay; Howard Barclay.

OTHER INFORMATION Two individuals received grants totalling £12,000

HOW TO APPLY Applications should be in writing, clearly outlining the details of the proposed project, (for medical research, as far as possible in lay terms). The total cost and duration should be stated, also the amount, if any, which has already been raised. Following an initial screening, applications are selected according to their merits, suitability and funds available. Visits are usually made to projects where substantial funds are involved. The foundation welcomes reports as to progress and requires these on completion of a project.

WHO TO APPLY TO Michael Seal, Administrator, 3rd Floor, 20 St James's Street, London SW1A 1ES *Tel.* 020 7915 0915 *email* mseal@ellerman.co. uk

■ The Barham Charitable Trust

CC NO 1129728   **ESTABLISHED** 2009

WHERE FUNDING CAN BE GIVEN UK.

WHO CAN BENEFIT Charitable organisations.

WHAT IS FUNDED General charitable purposes.

RANGE OF GRANTS Up to £10,000

SAMPLE GRANTS Medical Aid for Palestinians; The British Shalom Salaam Trust; War on Want; National Schizophrenia; Galilee Foundation; The Cambridge Foundation and IMET2000.

FINANCES *Year* 2012–13 *Income* £60,676 *Grants* £57,000 *Assets* £39,466

TRUSTEES Dr John Barham; Dr Eugenia Metaxa-Barham; Coutts and Co.

HOW TO APPLY In writing to the correspondent.

WHO TO APPLY TO The Trustees, Coutts and Co, 440 Strand, London WC2R 0QS *Tel.* 020 7663 6838

■ The Baring Foundation

CC NO 258583   **ESTABLISHED** 1969

WHERE FUNDING CAN BE GIVEN England and Wales, with a special interest in London, Merseyside, Cornwall and Devon; also UK charities working with NGO partners in developing countries.

WHO CAN BENEFIT Varies from programme to programme; refer to the foundation's guidelines.

WHAT IS FUNDED 'Arts and Older People 2014: we will continue to fund under the theme of arts and older people. We are supporting the Arts and Older People programme run by the Arts Council Northern Ireland and details of this can be found at: www.artscouncil-ni.org. Other decisions for 2014 have not yet been made but we may be in a position to announce a limited open programme in April [2014]; International Development Programme 2014: no grants will be made under this programme in 2014. A full review will take place and a new programme will be announced in 2015; Strengthening the Voluntary Sector programme 2014: this will continue to fund under the theme of Future Advice. We will review this programme with several under partners in the first quarter of 2014 and it likely that we will announce a new funding round in late April [2014].' Check the foundation's website for the current status of these programmes.

WHAT IS NOT FUNDED See guidelines for specific programmes. More generally: appeals or charities set up to support statutory organisations; animal welfare charities; grant maintained, private, or local education authority schools or their parent teachers associations; individuals.

SAMPLE GRANTS Conciliation Resources (£166,500); Trust for Africa's Orphans (£166,000); Fauna and Flora International (£152,000); Citizens UK, Community Links Trust Limited and Coventry Law Centre (£75,000 each); AIRE Centre and Disability Law Service (£73,000); Creative Scotland and Legal Action Group (£50,000); Cheshire Dance and Gallery Oldham (£30,000 each); Serpentine Trust (£15,000); Arts 4 Dementia (£12,000); and African Diaspora Academic Network (UK) (£4,000).

FINANCES *Year* 2012 *Income* £2,165,832 *Grants* £2,558,073 *Assets* £59,039,728

TRUSTEES Amanda Jordan, Chair; Mark Baring; Geoffrey Barnett; Prof. Ann Buchanan; David Elliott; Katherine Garrett-Cox; Janet Morrison; Andrew Hind; Ranjit Sondhi; Dr Danny Sriskandarajah; Christopher Steane; Prof. Myles Wickstead.

PUBLICATIONS Various reports connected with its work are available from the foundation's website.

HOW TO APPLY On application forms available via the foundation's website. Potential applicants should check the foundation's website for current guidelines and application deadlines.

WHO TO APPLY TO David Cutler, Director, 60 London Wall, London EC2M 5TQ *Tel.* 020 7767 1348 *Fax* 020 7767 7121 *email* baring.foundation@uk.ing.com *Website* www.baringfoundation.org.uk

■ Peter Barker-Mill Memorial Charity

CC NO 1045479   **ESTABLISHED** 1995

WHERE FUNDING CAN BE GIVEN UK, with a preference for Hampshire, including Southampton.

WHO CAN BENEFIT Charitable organisations.

WHAT IS FUNDED General charitable purposes, arts and culture, community facilities and conservation.

RANGE OF GRANTS Usually £250–£20,000.

SAMPLE GRANTS New Forest Ninth Centenary Trust and QK Southampton Football Club (£30,000 each); 4th New Forest Sea Scouts and Home-Start New Forest (£10,000 each); The Furzey Gardens Charitable Trust (£7,500); Redbridge Community School and Romsey Rugby Club (£5,000 each); Music at Beaulieu Trust and 10th Romsey Scout Group (£3,000 each); The Elizabeth Foundation and The Southern Spinal Injuries Trust (£2,000 each); New Forest CAB and Waterside Heritage (£1,000 each); and CLIC Sargent Cancer Care for Children (£350).

FINANCES *Year* 2011–12 *Income* £140,040 *Grants* £248,565 *Assets* £3,680,732

TRUSTEES Christopher Gwyn-Evans; Tim Jobling; Richard Moyse.

OTHER INFORMATION We do not have a breakdown of the amount given to organisations and the number of grants given to individuals.

HOW TO APPLY In writing to the correspondent.

WHO TO APPLY TO Christopher Gwyn-Evans, Trustee, c/o Longdown Management Ltd, The Estate Office, Longdown, Marchwood, Southampton SO40 4UH *Tel.* 02380 292107 *email* info@barkermillfoundation.com *Website* www.barkermillfoundation.com

■ The Barleycorn Trust

CC NO 296386   **ESTABLISHED** 1987

WHERE FUNDING CAN BE GIVEN Worldwide.

WHO CAN BENEFIT Christian; relief of poverty; ill-health; older people; young people.

WHAT IS FUNDED The advancement of the Christian faith, furtherance of religious or secular education, the encouragement of missionary activity, relief-in-need and welfare.

WHAT IS NOT FUNDED No grants for building projects or gap year projects.

RANGE OF GRANTS £500–£15,000.

SAMPLE GRANTS Pathway (£15,000); Off the Fence (£10,000); Giving Insight (£6,000); Mustard Seed (£4,000); Romanian Aid Fund (£2,200); Hurn Zambia (£1,500); Yeldall Christian Centres, Sudbury Neighbourhood Centre, The Bridge and Kidz Club Leeds (£500 each).

FINANCES *Year* 2012 *Income* £39,027 *Grants* £47,200 *Assets* £1,114,736

TRUSTEES Helen Hazelwood; Sally Beckwith.

HOW TO APPLY In writing to the correspondent, on no more than two sides of A4 including financial details of the proposed project.

WHO TO APPLY TO Helen Hazelwood, Trustee, 32 Arundel Road, Sutton, Surrey SM2 6EU *email* partners@tudorjohn.co.uk

■ Lord Barnby's Foundation

CC NO 251016   **ESTABLISHED** 1966

WHERE FUNDING CAN BE GIVEN UK

WHO CAN BENEFIT Registered charities.

WHAT IS FUNDED The preservation of the environment; medical; heritage; the countryside and ancient buildings, particularly the 'great Anglican cathedrals' ex-service and service people; Polish people and refugees; welfare of horses and those who look after them; youth and other local organisations in Ashtead – Surrey, Blyth – Nottinghamshire and Bradford – Yorkshire.

WHAT IS NOT FUNDED No grants to individuals.

TYPE OF GRANT One-off, capital (including buildings), project, research. Funding is up to two years.

RANGE OF GRANTS Grants range from £500–£10,000; but are generally for £1,000–£2,000.

SAMPLE GRANTS Winston Churchill Memorial Trust (£8,000); The Joshua Project (£7,500); Canine Partners (£5,300); Christchurch Cathedral (£5,000); Cystic Fibrosis Trust and the Atlantic Salmon Trust (£2,000 each); Dame Vera Lynn Trust and Gloucester Cathedral (£1,000); RAF Wings Appeal, Leeds Templar and District Scouts and Plymouth Foyer (£500 each); and Anna Freud Centre (£200).

FINANCES *Year* 2011–12 *Income* £212,200 *Grants* £157,500 *Assets* £4,223,642

TRUSTEES Hon. George Lopes; Countess Peel; Sir Michael Farquhar; Algy Smith-Maxwell; Laura Greenall.

HOW TO APPLY Applications will only be considered if received in writing accompanied by a set of the latest accounts. Applicants do not need to send an sae. Appeals are considered three times a year, in February, June and November.

WHO TO APPLY TO Jane Lethbridge, Secretary, PO Box 71, Plymstock, Plymouth PL8 2YP

■ Barnes Workhouse Fund

CC NO 200103   **ESTABLISHED** 1970

WHERE FUNDING CAN BE GIVEN Ancient parish of Barnes only (SW13 postal district in London).

WHO CAN BENEFIT Charitable organisations and individuals.

WHAT IS FUNDED The fund makes grants to organisations who can demonstrate that their activities will benefit some of the inhabitants of its area of benefit.

TYPE OF GRANT Capital (including buildings), core costs, feasibility studies, one-off, project, research, running costs, recurring costs, salaries and start-up costs.

SAMPLE GRANTS Castelnau Centre Project (£42,000); Richmond Citizens Advice (£35,000); Barn Elms Sport Trust (£30,000); Homestart – Richmond upon Thames and Richmond Crossroads Care (£6,000 each); Age Concern – Handyperson Scheme (£5,000); Brentford F.C. Community Sports Trust (£4,000); Barnes Baptists (£3,000); Barnes Music Society (£1,000) and Diana House Jubilee Party (£100).

FINANCES *Year* 2012 *Income* £561,465 *Grants* £229,312 *Assets* £8,060,898

TRUSTEES Caroline Kelsall; Nicolas Phillips; Philip Conrath; John Brocklebank; K. Pengelley; Prof. Tim Besley; Lucy Hine; Paul Hodgins

OTHER INFORMATION The grant total in 2012 includes £27,500 given to individuals.

HOW TO APPLY In writing to the Clerk to the Trustees. Application forms and guidelines are available from the clerk or downloaded from the website. Applications must state clearly the extent to which any project will benefit residents of Barnes (postal district SW13) and include details of other sources of funding. Trustees meet to consider grants every two months in January, March, May, July, September and November each year. For consideration at a meeting, applications must be received by the 13th of the preceding month. The trust states the following: 'we feel that the application process is important and cannot be streamlined to any great degree, as the better the fund knows its applicants, the more likely it is to make appropriate, meaningful grants in the local community.'

WHO TO APPLY TO Miranda Ibbetson, Clerk to the Trustees, PO Box 665, Richmond, London TW10 6YL *Tel.* 020 8241 3994 *email* mibbetson@barnesworkhousefund.org.uk *Website* www.barnesworkhousefund.org.uk

■ The Barnsbury Charitable Trust

CC NO 241383   **ESTABLISHED** 1964

WHERE FUNDING CAN BE GIVEN UK, but no local charities outside Oxfordshire.

WHO CAN BENEFIT Charitable organisations.

WHAT IS FUNDED General charitable purposes.

WHAT IS NOT FUNDED No grants to individuals.

RANGE OF GRANTS £15–£10,000.

SAMPLE GRANTS Oxford Chamber Music Festival (£10,000); National Trust (£8,000); Victoria History of Oxfordshire Trust (£7,500); Oxfordshire Family Mediation and Friends of Dorchester Abbey (£5,000 each); Age UK – Oxfordshire and Parochial Church Council of St John of Jerusalem, South Hackney (£2,500 each); St Margaret's War Memorial Appeal, Bookfeast and Disasters Emergency Committee (£1,000 each) and Music in Country Churches (£500).

FINANCES *Year* 2011–12 *Income* £86,442 *Grants* £80,740 *Assets* £2,877,488

TRUSTEES H. L. J. Brunner; M. R. Brunner; T. E. Yates.

HOW TO APPLY In writing to the correspondent.

WHO TO APPLY TO H. L. J. Brunner, Trustee, 26 Norham Road, Oxford OX2 6SF *Tel.* 01865 316431

■ The Barnstaple Bridge Trust

CC NO 201288   **ESTABLISHED** 1961

WHERE FUNDING CAN BE GIVEN Barnstaple and surrounding area.

WHO CAN BENEFIT Local organisations.

WHAT IS FUNDED General, grants are made to a wide range of causes, including welfare, older people and young people, health and medical, schools and sport.

WHAT IS NOT FUNDED No grants to individuals, other than on referral through a caring agency.

TYPE OF GRANT Capital including buildings, core costs, one-off, project, research, running costs, recurring costs and start-up costs will be considered. Funding may be given for up to one year.

RANGE OF GRANTS Up to £9,000.

SAMPLE GRANTS Previous beneficiaries include: North Devon Hospice Care (£9,000); Go North Devon and Westcountry Projects (£6,000 each); North Devon Citizens Advice and Children's Hospice (£4,000 each); Relate and Barnstaple Poverty Action Group (£3,000 each); Vivian Moon Foundation and North Devon Music Centre (£2,500 each); Pilton House, St Peter's Church and North Devon All Starz (£1,500 each); North Devon Samaritans, Braunton CC, Pilton CC, Barnstaple Tennis Club, St Francis Chichester, Barnstaple RFC Juniors, Hamish Thompson, North Devon Scouts and Guides Gang Show, Alfie Huxtable, Torridge Home Start, Learning Difficulties, Two Moors Festival and Motor Neurone disease (£1,000 each).

FINANCES *Year* 2012 *Income* £337,863 *Grants* £131,945 *Assets* £4,935,937

TRUSTEES D. Trueman; G. K. Lofthouse; J. W. Waldron; S. P. Upcott; D. C. Burgess; A. J. Bradbury; S. G. Haywood; J. Lynch; I. E. A. Scott; A. J. Isaac; J. Hunt; K. Trigger; E. Davies; R. Knight; V. Elkins; L. Brown.

HOW TO APPLY In writing to the correspondent. The trustees meet quarterly on the first Tuesday of March, June, September and December.

WHO TO APPLY TO C. J. Bartlett, Clerk, 7 Bridge Chambers, The Strand, Barnstaple, Devon EX31 1HB *Tel.* 01271 343995

■ The Barnwood House Trust

CC NO 218401   **ESTABLISHED** 1972

WHERE FUNDING CAN BE GIVEN Gloucestershire.

WHO CAN BENEFIT Gloucestershire-based charitable and voluntary organisations whose services seek to improve the quality of life of local people with long-term disabilities. Individuals who are sick, convalescent, disabled, infirm or in need, hardship or distress.

WHAT IS FUNDED The relief of sickness, poverty and distress affecting people with mental or nervous disorders or with serious physical infirmity or disability. The relief of persons in need by providing housing or other accommodation, care nursing and attention.

WHAT IS NOT FUNDED Grants are not normally made in the following circumstances: people or organisations outside Gloucestershire; people with problems relating to drugs or alcohol – unless they also have physical disabilities or a diagnosed mental illness; To pay for funeral costs; medical equipment; private healthcare; counselling or psychotherapy; top-up nursing home fees; council tax; court fines; house purchase or rent; regular income supplements; needs of non-disabled dependants or carers. Grants will not be awarded retrospectively.

TYPE OF GRANT Small grants and grants to individuals.

RANGE OF GRANTS up to £750.

SAMPLE GRANTS Consortium of Mental Health Day Support Providers (£305,000); Crossroads Care – Cheltenham and Tewkesbury, Independence Trust and People and Places in Gloucestershire (£30,000 each); Whitefriars Sailing Club (£27,500); Stroke Association (£25,000); Forest of Dean Citizen's Advice Bureau and Hop, Skip and Jump (Cotswold) (£18,000 each); Art Shape LTD, Barnwood Residents Association and Watershed Riding for the Disabled (£10,000 each).

FINANCES *Year* 2011–12 *Income* £2,475,403 *Grants* £31,531 *Assets* £72,218,829

TRUSTEES John Colquhoun; James Davidson; Anne Cadbury; David A. Acland; Clare de Haan;

Annabella Scott; Jonathan Carr; Prof. Clair Chilvers; Andrew North; Jonathan Harvie.

PUBLICATIONS *Strategic Framework 2011–2021; ten-year investment plan; five work programmes* available on the trust's website or request them by post.

OTHER INFORMATION The trust has undergone a strategic review which means they will be phasing out services and have terminated the grants over £750 scheme. Instead the trust is running the community animation programme which aims to work in partnership with people living with disabilities and mental health problems, the voluntary and community and public sectors, and employers to strengthen capacity.

HOW TO APPLY If you would like more information or to talk through your idea before applying, contact Gail Rodway, Grants Manager, on 01452 611292 or email gail.rodway@barnwoodtrust.org.

WHO TO APPLY TO Gail Rodway, Grants Manager, Ullenwood Manor Farm, Ullenwood, Cheltenham GL53 9QT *Tel.* 01452 614429 *email* gail. rodway@barnwoodtrust.org *Website* www. barnwoodtrust.org

■ The Misses Barrie Charitable Trust

CC NO 279459 **ESTABLISHED** 1979
WHERE FUNDING CAN BE GIVEN UK
WHO CAN BENEFIT Registered charities.
WHAT IS FUNDED General charitable purposes.
WHAT IS NOT FUNDED No grants to individuals.
TYPE OF GRANT Mainly one-off.
RANGE OF GRANTS Average £1,000–£5,000.
SAMPLE GRANTS Scottish Chamber Orchestra and University of Oxford Institute of Molecular Medicine (£10,000 each); East Neuk Festival (£5,000); Highlanders Museum (£3,000); Action for Blind people, Age Concern Dundee, Beating Bowel Cancer, Brighton and Hove Parents and Children Group, Croydon Voluntary Association for the Blind, Fairbridge, Hearts and Minds, I Can, Let's Face It, Lupus UK, Operation New World, Regain, Scottish Veterans' Residences, Sense, The Jennifer Trust, The Shakespeare Hospice and The Willow Trust (£2,000 each); React and Strongbones Children's Charitable Trust (£1,500 each); Addiscombe Boys and Girls Club, Ambitious About Autism, Baginton Village Hall, Braille Chess Association, CHICKS, Cued Speech, London Air Ambulance, Marine Conservation Society, Mid-Surrey Mencap, Parkinson's UK, RAFT, Raynaud's and Scleroderma Association, REHAB, RNLI, Seeing Ear, South Croydon Centre Trust, Steer Right and Wellbeing of Women (£1,000 each); and Over the Wall and The Encephalitis Society (£500 each).

FINANCES *Year* 2011–12 *Income* £213,395 *Grants* £181,800 *Assets* £5,647,924
TRUSTEES John A. Carter; Robin Stuart Ogg; Rachel Fraser.
HOW TO APPLY In writing to the correspondent accompanied by up to date accounts or financial information. Trustees meet three times a year, in April, August and December. 'The trustees regret that due to the large number of unsolicited applications for grants received each week they are not able to notify those which are unsuccessful.'
WHO TO APPLY TO John A. Carter, Trustee, Raymond Carter and Co, 1b Haling Road, South Croydon CR2 6HS *Tel.* 020 8686 1686

■ Barrington Family Charitable Trust

CC NO 1078702 **ESTABLISHED** 1999
WHERE FUNDING CAN BE GIVEN UK.
WHO CAN BENEFIT Registered charities.
WHAT IS FUNDED Mainly arts and culture
FINANCES *Year* 2011–12 *Income* £26,836 *Grants* £27,000
TRUSTEES Jessica Watkins; Jill Barrington; Michael Barrington; Saul Barrington; Amanda Thompson.
HOW TO APPLY In writing to the correspondent.
WHO TO APPLY TO Michael Barrington, Trustee, Suite 1, First Floor, 1 Duchess Street, London W1W 6AN *Tel.* 020 7323 0896

■ Bartholomew Charitable Trust

CC NO 1063797 **ESTABLISHED** 1997
WHERE FUNDING CAN BE GIVEN UK.
WHO CAN BENEFIT Registered charities only, for the benefit of people who are sick, disabled or terminally ill.
WHAT IS FUNDED Particularly respite care, hospices, rehabilitation centres and cancer research. Hospices are supported in preference to nursing homes.
WHAT IS NOT FUNDED No grants are made to individuals. Normally grants are not made in response to general appeals from large national charities.
RANGE OF GRANTS £75–£3,500.
SAMPLE GRANTS Marie Curie Memorial Trust (£26,000); St Christopher's Hospice (£25,000); League of the Helping Hand (£500); and Springfield Boy's Club, The Quaker Tapestry, REMAP, Royal Marsden Cancer Campaign and Diabetes UK (£250).
FINANCES *Year* 2011–12 *Income* £28,000 *Grants* £53,000
TRUSTEES Julian Berry; Simon Berry; Rita Berry; Charlotte Irwin.
HOW TO APPLY In writing to the correspondent, or via email. No telephone calls will be accepted.
WHO TO APPLY TO Julian Berry, Trustee, Goddards Farm, Ardingly Road, Lindfield, Haywards Heath, West Sussex RH16 2QX *email* charity@ bartholomew.co.uk

■ The Bartlett Taylor Charitable Trust

CC NO 285249 **ESTABLISHED** 1982
WHERE FUNDING CAN BE GIVEN Preference for Oxfordshire.
WHO CAN BENEFIT Registered charities.
WHAT IS FUNDED General charitable purposes, with grants given in the following categories: (a) international charities; (b) UK national charities – medical; UK national charities – educational; (c) local organisations – community projects; local organisations – medical; local organisations – other; (d) individuals – educational; individuals – relief.
RANGE OF GRANTS £100–£1,000.
SAMPLE GRANTS There was no list of beneficiaries available.
FINANCES *Year* 2011–12 *Income* £177,615 *Grants* £47,467 *Assets* £1,834,040
TRUSTEES Richard Bartlett; Gareth Alty; Katherine Bradley; Brenda Cook; James W. Dingle; Rosemary Warner; Ms S. Boyd.
HOW TO APPLY In writing to the correspondent. Trustees meet bi-monthly.

WHO TO APPLY TO Gareth Alty, Trustee, John Welch and Stammers, 24 Church Green, Witney, Oxfordshire OX28 4AT *Tel.* 01993 703941 *email* galty@johnwelchandstammers.co.uk

---

■ Baruch Family Charitable Trust

CC NO 1146647   **ESTABLISHED** 2012
WHERE FUNDING CAN BE GIVEN Worldwide.
WHO CAN BENEFIT People on low incomes and organisations that support them.
WHAT IS FUNDED General, relief of poverty and education and training.
TRUSTEES Emil Baruch; Robert Baruch.
HOW TO APPLY In writing to the correspondent.
WHO TO APPLY TO Emil Baruch, Trustee, c/o Baruch Enterprises Ltd, Watkins House, Pegamoid Road, London N18 2NG *Tel.* 020 8803 8899 *Fax* 020 8803 8939

■ The Paul Bassham Charitable Trust

CC NO 266842   **ESTABLISHED** 1973
WHERE FUNDING CAN BE GIVEN UK, mainly Norwich and Norfolk.
WHO CAN BENEFIT UK registered charities.
WHAT IS FUNDED General charitable purposes. Preference given to Norfolk charitable causes; if funds permit, other charities with national coverage will be considered.
WHAT IS NOT FUNDED Grants are not made directly to individuals, nor to unregistered organisations.
RANGE OF GRANTS £1,000–£20,000. Average grant between £1,000–£5,000.
SAMPLE GRANTS Norfolk Community Foundation, Norwich Historic Churches and Norfolk Archaeological Trust (£10,000 each); Community Action Norwich (£7,000); MAP, Solo Housing and British Wireless for the Blind (£5,000 each); Norfolk County Council (Castle Museum) (£3,000); The Friends of Norfolk and Norwich University Hospital, RSPB, Norwich Cathedral and Norfolk Eating Disorder Association (£2,000 each) and Motor Neurone Disease Association, Costessey Baptist Church, Whizz-Kidz and Bliss (£1,000 each).
FINANCES *Year* 2011–12 *Income* £362,033 *Grants* £444,300 *Assets* £10,623,523
TRUSTEES Alexander Munro; Richard Lovett; Graham Tuttle; Patrick Harris.
HOW TO APPLY Only in writing to the correspondent – no formal application forms issued. Telephone enquiries are not invited because of administrative costs. The trustees meet quarterly to consider general applications.
WHO TO APPLY TO Richard Lovett, Trustee, c/o Howes Percival, The Guildyard, 51 Colegate, Norwich NR3 1DD *Tel.* 01603 762103

■ The Batchworth Trust

CC NO 245061   **ESTABLISHED** 1965
WHERE FUNDING CAN BE GIVEN Worldwide.
WHO CAN BENEFIT Major UK and international charities.
WHAT IS FUNDED General charitable purposes, medical, humanitarian aid, social welfare. 'The trustees have a policy of mainly distributing to nationally recognised charities but consider other charities where it felt a grant would be of significant benefit when matched with other funds to launch a new enterprise or initiative.'
WHAT IS NOT FUNDED No grants to individuals.

RANGE OF GRANTS £1,000–£25,000.
SAMPLE GRANTS The Francis Crick Institute (£30,000); Roger Feneley Project (£20,000); MOSS (£13,000); Blue Elephant Theatre, Copenhagen Youth Project, Crisis UK Re Oxford, International Red Cross – Syria, Oxfordshire Relate, Practical Action and The Archie Foundation (£10,000 each); Action Aid – Malawi (£5,000); Royal Highland Educational Trust (£3,000); and Dumfries and Galloway Arts Festival (£1,000).
FINANCES *Year* 2012–13 *Income* £393,684 *Grants* £362,000 *Assets* £12,389,051
TRUSTEE Lockwell Trustees Limited.
HOW TO APPLY In writing to the correspondent. An sae should be included if a reply is required.
WHO TO APPLY TO Martin R. Neve, Administrative Executive, Haines Watts LLP, 3rd Floor, Consort House, Consort Way, Horley, Surrey RH6 7AF *Tel.* 01293 776411 *email* mneve@hwca.com

---

■ The Bates Charitable Trust

CC NO 280602   **ESTABLISHED** 1980
WHERE FUNDING CAN BE GIVEN UK.
WHO CAN BENEFIT Registered charities benefiting the Church of England, at risk groups, people disadvantaged by poverty and socially isolated people.
WHAT IS FUNDED A wide range of humanitarian causes, with particular regard to work which stands within the evangelical tradition of the Church of England.
WHAT IS NOT FUNDED No donations to individuals.
RANGE OF GRANTS £100–£2,500.
SAMPLE GRANTS St Nicholas Parochial Church Council – Allestree (£10,000); Manna Mozambique and Angola Anglican Association, Good News Family Care, Medical Foundation, TEAR Fund and Christian Aid (£2,000 each); YMCA Derbyshire (£1,500); St Peter's City Centre Church Derby and Christian Solidarity Worldwide (£1,000 each); and Derby Kids Camp (£500).
FINANCES *Year* 2011–12 *Income* £29,000 *Grants* £30,000 *Assets* £745,000
TRUSTEES N. Waldron; Revd William Bates; John Bates; Joy Bates.
HOW TO APPLY In writing to the correspondent.
WHO TO APPLY TO The Trustees, 4 Lawn Avenue, Allestree, Derby, Derbyshire DE22 2PE

■ Bay Charitable Trust

CC NO 1060537   **ESTABLISHED** 1997
WHERE FUNDING CAN BE GIVEN UK and overseas.
WHO CAN BENEFIT Jewish organisations.
WHAT IS FUNDED 'The objectives of the charity are to give charity for the relief of poverty and the advancement of traditions of the Orthodox Jewish Religion and the study of Torah.'
SAMPLE GRANTS No list available.
FINANCES *Year* 2012 *Income* £1,190,000 *Grants* £582,685 *Assets* £1,060,769
TRUSTEES Ian M. Kreditor; Michael Lisser.
HOW TO APPLY In writing to the correspondent.
WHO TO APPLY TO Ian Kreditor, Trustee, Hermolis House, Abbeydale Road, Wembley, Middlesex HA0 1AY *Tel.* 020 8810 4321

■ The Bay Tree Charitable Trust

cc no 1044091   **established** 1994
where funding can be given UK and overseas.
who can benefit Charitable organisations.
what is funded Development work.
what is not funded No grants to individuals.
range of grants Up to £30,000.
sample grants Age UK (£20,000); Combat Stress, Samaritans and Shelter (£10,000 each); and Bipolar UK, FareShare, Greenfingers and Support Dogs (£5,000 each).
finances *Year* 2012 *Income* £121,693 *Grants* £130,000 *Assets* £3,582,126
trustees Ian Benton; Emma Benton; Paul Benton.
how to apply All appeals should be by letter containing the following: aims and objectives of the charity; nature of appeal; total target if for a specific project; contributions received against target; registered charity number; any other relevant factors. Letters should be accompanied by a set of the charitable organisation's latest report and full accounts.
who to apply to The Trustees, PO Box 53983, London SW15 1VT

■ The Louis Baylis (Maidenhead Advertiser) Charitable Trust

cc no 210533   **established** 1962
where funding can be given UK, but mainly Berkshire, Buckinghamshire and Oxfordshire with a preference for Maidenhead.
who can benefit General charitable purposes.
what is funded The trust states that it was 'established to safeguard the newspaper, The Maidenhead Advertiser, from all outside influence and provide for the newspaper's continuance as part of the civic and social life of the community it serves'. Grants can be given towards any charitable purpose.
what is not funded No grants to individuals.
range of grants £500–£25,000.
sample grants Maidenhead Citizens Advice (£25,000); People to Places (£25,000); Maidenhead at the Movies (£11,000); Maidenhead Carnival (£6,000); Norden Farm Centre for the Arts and Thames Valley, British Forces Foundation and Chiltern Air Ambulance Service (£2,000 each) and Sue Ryder Homes and Great Ormond Street Hospital for Children (£1,000 each).
finances *Year* 2011–12 *Income* £376,973 *Grants* £259,584 *Assets* £12,947,884
trustees John Robertson; Peter Sands; Peter Murcott; Patricia Lattimer.
other information In 2011–12 grants were made totalling £259,500, of which £20,500 was distributed to 14 national charities, £14,000 to 11 regional charities and a total of £225,000 was donated to local charities and organisations.
how to apply On forms available to download on the website and returned, by email or post, to the correspondent. The trustees meet twice a year.
who to apply to Andrew Chitty, Administrator, 78 Queen Street, Maidenhead, Berkshire SL6 l. HY *Tel.* 01628 678290 *email* lbctrust@baylismedia.co.uk *Website* baylis-trust.org.uk

■ BBC Children in Need

cc no 802052   **established** 1989
where funding can be given UK
who can benefit Registered charities and not-for-profit organisations.
what is funded Children and young people of 18 years and under experiencing disadvantage through: illness, distress, abuse or neglect; any kind of disability; behavioural or psychological difficulties; living in poverty or situations of deprivation.
what is not funded Grants will not be given for: relief of statutory responsibility; applications from local government or NHS bodies; building projects which are applying for more than £20,000; the promotion of religion; trips or projects abroad; medical treatment/research; projects for pregnancy testing or advice, information or counselling on pregnancy choices; general awareness-raising work; bursaries, sponsored places, fees or equivalent; individuals (unless an eligible organisation is applying on their behalf); distribution to another/other organisation/s, for example, PTAs applying on behalf of schools; general appeals or endowment funds; deficit funding or repayment of loans; retrospective funding (projects taking place before the grant award date); projects unable to start within 12 months of the grant award date; unspecified expenditure; for organisational overheads or running costs which the organisation would incur whether the project was running or not. (Although the trustees will consider funding support costs incurred as a direct result of running the project).
range of grants Up to £100,000.
sample grants Buttle UK (Emergency Essentials Programme) (£2 million); Zinc Arts – Essex (£286,000); Llamau – Wales (£164,000); Headway – Devon (£83,000); Women's Aid – Cheltenham (£82,000); Positive Action on Cancer – Somerset (£47,000); Bookbug – Leith (£26,000); and Meningitis Trust – Northern Ireland (£3,000).
finances *Year* 2011–12 *Income* £50,541,000 *Grants* £31,292,000 *Assets* £45,189,000
trustees Daniel Cohen; Susan Elizabeth; Beverley Tew; Phil Hodkinson; Luke Mayhew; Peter McBride; Robert Shennan; Ralph Rivera; Stevie Spring; Donalda Mackinnon; Gillian Sheldon.
how to apply Straightforward and excellent application forms and guidelines are available from the charity's website. Application forms must be completed online. Note: incomplete or late application forms will not be assessed. If you have a general enquiry, are unsure about anything you have read or are looking for support regarding your application contact the helpdesk on 0345 609 0015 or at pudsey@bbc.co.uk. The helpdesk is open from 9am-5pm Monday to Friday. You can also contact your local regional or national office.
who to apply to Sheila Jane Malley, Director of Grants and Policy, PO Box 1000, London W12 7WJ *Tel.* 03456090015 *email* pudsey@bbc.co.uk *Website* www.bbc.co.uk/pudsey

■ BC Partners Foundation

cc no 1136956   **established** 2010
where funding can be given UK.
who can benefit Registered charities in the UK and worldwide.
what is funded General charitable purposes.

SAMPLE GRANTS Private Equity Foundation (£102,000); Royal Opera House (£25,000); Over The Wall and the Fondation Philanthropique (£16,000); The Dolphin Society (£5,000); Opportunity International (£3,000); WaterAid (£2,000); and Feedback Madagascar (£1,000).
FINANCES *Year* 2012 *Income* £355,497 *Grants* £368,395 *Assets* £168,532
TRUSTEES Nikos Stathopolous; Joseph Cronley; Lorna Parker; Michael Pritchard; Richard Kunzer.
HOW TO APPLY In writing to the correspondent.
WHO TO APPLY TO The Trustees, BC Partners Limited, 40 Portman Square, London W1H 6DA *Tel.* 020 7009 4800 *email* bcpfoundation@bcpartners.com

■ The B-CH Charitable Trust

CC NO 263241   **ESTABLISHED** 1971
WHERE FUNDING CAN BE GIVEN UK, with preference for Cornwall and Devon.
WHO CAN BENEFIT Registered charities only, benefiting children and sick people. Support may be given to medical professionals and research workers.
WHAT IS FUNDED Children's and medical charities.
WHAT IS NOT FUNDED No grants to individuals.
RANGE OF GRANTS Up to £1,000.
SAMPLE GRANTS Carers UK, British Red Cross Disaster Fund and ShelterBox (£1,000 each); Macmillan Cancer Support, Cornwall Hospice Care, Blue Cross (£750 each); Act, Aspire, Challey Heritage School, Cornwall Air Ambulance, East Anglian Sailing Trust, Independence at Home and Young Minds (£500 each).
FINANCES *Year* 2011–12 *Income* £31,275 *Grants* £29,500 *Assets* £883,087
TRUSTEES Miss J. Holman; Edward N. Reed.
HOW TO APPLY In writing to the correspondent. The trustees meet twice a year to consider applications.
WHO TO APPLY TO Edward N. Reed, c/o Macfarlanes, 20 Cursitor Street, London EC4A 1LT *Tel.* 020 7831 9222

■ BCH Trust

CC NO 1138652   **ESTABLISHED** 2010
WHERE FUNDING CAN BE GIVEN UK.
WHO CAN BENEFIT Jewish organisations.
WHAT IS FUNDED General charitable purposes with a stated interest in education, social welfare, the Jewish faith and disability.
FINANCES *Year* 2011–12 *Income* £66,117 *Grants* £46,650 *Assets* £58,807
TRUSTEES Benny Stone; Charles Bernstein; Yossef Bowden.
HOW TO APPLY In writing to the correspondent.
WHO TO APPLY TO Benny Stone, Trustee, 59 Kings Road, Prestwich, Manchester M25 0LQ *Tel.* 01617 412543 *email* mail@bchtrust.org

■ The Beacon Trust

CC NO 230087   **ESTABLISHED** 1963
WHERE FUNDING CAN BE GIVEN Mainly UK, but also some overseas (usually in the British Commonwealth) and Spain and Portugal.
WHO CAN BENEFIT Organisations benefiting evangelical Protestants, including Baptists, Anglican and Methodists. Funding is usually given to headquarters organisations.
WHAT IS FUNDED The emphasis of the trust's support is on Christian work overseas, particularly

amongst students, although the trust does not support individuals.
WHAT IS NOT FUNDED Applications from individuals are not considered.
TYPE OF GRANT One-off grants for development funding. Longer-term grants may be considered.
SAMPLE GRANTS Latin Link (£5,000); Bible Society and Arocha (£4,000 each); Arbon Markland Project (£3,000); Alan Palister (£2,000); FEBA and Fegan's Homes (£1,500 each); L'Abri (£600) and David Cotton (£500).
FINANCES *Year* 2011–12 *Income* £51,687 *Grants* £22,148 *Assets* £2,466,779
TRUSTEES Jillian Spink; Martin Spink; Joanna Benson.
HOW TO APPLY In writing to the correspondent.
WHO TO APPLY TO Grahame Scofield, 3 Newhouse Business Centre, Old Crawley Road, Horsham, West Sussex RH12 4RU *Tel.* 01293 851715

■ Bear Mordechai Ltd

CC NO 286806   **ESTABLISHED** 1982
WHERE FUNDING CAN BE GIVEN Worldwide.
WHO CAN BENEFIT Individuals, small local projects and national organisations benefiting Jewish people.
WHAT IS FUNDED Jewish charities.
TYPE OF GRANT One-off and recurrent costs.
SAMPLE GRANTS Previous beneficiaries have included: Agudat Yad Yemin Jerusalem, Almat, Chevras Mo'oz Ladol, Craven Walk Charities Trust, Havenpoint, Keren Tzedaka Vachesed, Lolev, UTA and Yetev Lev Yerusholaim.
FINANCES *Year* 2011–12 *Income* £188,196 *Grants* £200,836 *Assets* £1,508,644
TRUSTEES Chaim Benedikt; Eliezer Benedikt; Yechiel Benedikt.
HOW TO APPLY In writing to the correspondent.
WHO TO APPLY TO Yechiel Benedikt, Trustee, 40 Fountayne Road, London N16 7DT

■ The Bearder Charity

CC NO 1010529   **ESTABLISHED** 1992
WHERE FUNDING CAN BE GIVEN Calderdale.
WHO CAN BENEFIT Registered charities and individuals.
WHAT IS FUNDED General charitable purposes, particularly the arts, infrastructure support and development, education and training and community facilities and services.
RANGE OF GRANTS Up to £5,000.
SAMPLE GRANTS Poetry Workshops (£3,700); Noel Singers (£3,000); Sure Start (£2,500); Halifax Junior Cricket (£1,500); Eureka Children's Museum, Alzheimer's Society and St Michael's Church, Rastrick (£1,000 each); and Halifax Boys' Brigade, Asthma Relief, Halifax Table Tennis Club, Southgate Methodist Church and Prison After Care (£500 each).
FINANCES *Year* 2011–12 *Income* £119,119 *Grants* £108,762 *Assets* £3,288,241
TRUSTEES Richard Smithies; David Normanton; Trevor Simpson; Leyland Smith; Brendan Mowforth.
OTHER INFORMATION The grant total includes £76,300 that was given to individuals.
HOW TO APPLY In writing to the correspondent, detailing requirements and costings. Trustee board meetings are held six times a year.
WHO TO APPLY TO R. D. Smithies, Trustee, 5 King Street, Brighouse, West Yorkshire HD6 1NX *Tel.* 01484 710571 *email* bearders@btinternet.com *Website* www.bearder-charity.org.uk

■ The James Beattie Charitable Trust

CC NO 265654 **ESTABLISHED** 1961

WHERE FUNDING CAN BE GIVEN Wolverhampton area.

WHO CAN BENEFIT Local projects and organisations benefiting the people of Wolverhampton.

WHAT IS FUNDED General charitable purposes including accommodation and housing; community development, support to voluntary and community organisations; and social care professional bodies. Also health; conservation and the environment; education; community facilities and services; dance groups and orchestras; volunteer bureaux; Christian education and churches; schools; and youth projects such as scouts and air training corps may be considered.

WHAT IS NOT FUNDED No grants to individuals, organisations outside the West Midlands, or exclusive organisations (e.g. all-white or all-Asian groups).

TYPE OF GRANT Grants awarded for capital including buildings, core costs, project research, running costs, salaries and start-up costs. Grants may be one-off or recurring and funding for a single project may be available for less than one year to more than three.

SAMPLE GRANTS Barnardo's, James Beattie House, Cottage Homes, Marie Curie Cancer Care, St Chad's – Pattingham, St Martin's School, Whizz-Kidz, Wolverhampton Grammar School and YMCA.

FINANCES *Year* 2011–12 *Income* £47,543 *Grants* £158,259 *Assets* £3,250,431

TRUSTEES Jane Redshaw; Michael Redshaw; Kenneth Dolman; Susannah Norbury.

OTHER INFORMATION In 2011–12 grants were made to 82 organisations. Donations made ranged between £250 and £17,500 and were made largely to local charities or local branches of national charities.

HOW TO APPLY In writing to the correspondent, including accounts.

WHO TO APPLY TO The Trustees, PO Box 12, Bridgnorth, Shropshire WV15 5LQ *Tel*. 01215 516021

■ The Jack and Ada Beattie Foundation

CC NO 1142892 **ESTABLISHED** 2011

WHERE FUNDING CAN BE GIVEN The Midlands and London.

WHO CAN BENEFIT Registered charities and individuals.

WHAT IS FUNDED Social welfare, injustice and equality. The foundation's initial funding priorities are: dignity; freedom; and sanctuary.

TYPE OF GRANT One-off project grants.

RANGE OF GRANTS The size of the average grant is between £5,000–£10,000.

SAMPLE GRANTS Contact the Elderly, Coventry Foodbank, Richard House Children's Hospice, Sense, SIFA Fireside, St Mungo's and Thrive.

FINANCES *Year* 2012–13 *Income* £108,747 *Grants* £23,289 *Assets* £52,735

TRUSTEES Trevor Beattie; Peter Beattie; Paul Beattie.

OTHER INFORMATION The foundation was established in July 2011 by Trevor Beattie, a marketing executive for the advertising company Beattie McGuinness Bungay. 'Charitable activities' were listed as £83,000 and this figure included administration and support costs such as salaries of £42,000.

HOW TO APPLY Initial proposals should be emailed to the foundation. Eligible applicants will then be notified if the foundation is interested in receiving a full application, which is made using a form available on the foundation's website. If your application is successful you will be required to monitor and evaluate the project and report back to the foundation. Details will be sent with the grant. Application forms will only be accepted by email unless there are exceptional circumstances. Contact the Foundation Director if you have any queries. The foundation endeavours to acknowledge each stage of the application process. Decisions will be reached within two months of each stage.

WHO TO APPLY TO Alexandra Taliadoros, Director, 203 Larna House, 116 Commercial Street, London E1 6NF *Tel*. 020 3287 8427 *email* info@beattiefoundation.com *Website* www.beattiefoundation.com

■ Beauland Ltd

CC NO 511374 **ESTABLISHED** 1981

WHERE FUNDING CAN BE GIVEN Worldwide, with some preference for the Manchester area.

WHO CAN BENEFIT To benefit Jewish people and those in need.

WHAT IS FUNDED Educational institutions (including adult education) and institutions for the relief of poverty.

SAMPLE GRANTS Previous beneficiaries have included: Asos Chesed, Cosmon Belz, Famos Charity Trust, Radford Education Trust, Sunderland Yeshiva and Yetev Lev.

FINANCES *Year* 2012–13 *Income* £488,648 *Grants* £317,788 *Assets* £3,536,455

TRUSTEES Fanny Neumann; Henry Neumann; Miriam Friedlander; Hannah Rosemann; Janet Bleier; Rebecca Delange; Maurice Neumann; Pinchas Neumann; E. Neumann; Esther Henry.

HOW TO APPLY In writing to the correspondent.

WHO TO APPLY TO Maurice Neumann, Trustee, 32 Stanley Road, Salford M7 4ES

■ The Beaverbrook Foundation

CC NO 310003 **ESTABLISHED** 1954

WHERE FUNDING CAN BE GIVEN UK and Canada.

WHO CAN BENEFIT Registered charities, mainly headquarters organisations or national charities.

WHAT IS FUNDED 'The object of this foundation include: (i) the erection or improvement of the fabric of any church building; (ii) the purchase of books, papers, manuscripts or works of art; (iii) care of the aged or infirm in the UK. One of the areas that the foundation has concentrated on over the past twenty years has been supporting small charitable projects. We recognise that it is often more difficult to raise a few thousand to refurbish a church hall than it is to raise millions for a major public building. In the past twenty years, the foundation has donated to more than 400 charities.'

WHAT IS NOT FUNDED Only registered charities are supported.

TYPE OF GRANT One-off capital grants.

RANGE OF GRANTS Up to £10,000. Generally between £1,000–£5,000.

SAMPLE GRANTS Battle of Britain Memorial Trust (£80,000); RNLI (£12,000); Bright Ideas Trust (£10,000); Saints and Sinners Trust (£5,000); London Air Ambulance and Starlight Children's Foundation (£2,000 each)

FINANCES *Year* 2011–12 *Income* £58,533 *Grants* £145,280 *Assets* £11,394,340

TRUSTEES Lord Beaverbrook; Lady Beaverbrook; Lady Aitken; Hon. Laura Levi; John Kidd; Hon. Maxwell Aitken.

HOW TO APPLY There is an online application form at the foundation's website.

WHO TO APPLY TO Ms Ford, Administrator, Third Floor, 11/12 Dover Street, London W1S 4LJ *Tel.* 020 7042 9435 *email* jane@beaverbrookfoundation.org *Website* www.beaverbrookfoundation.org

■ The Beccles Town Lands Charity

CC NO 210714   ESTABLISHED 1963

WHERE FUNDING CAN BE GIVEN Beccles only.

WHO CAN BENEFIT Organisations and individuals in Beccles.

WHAT IS FUNDED General charitable purposes.

WHAT IS NOT FUNDED Applications from outside of, or not to the benefit of, Beccles and its inhabitants will not be considered.

SAMPLE GRANTS Beccles Museum; Beccles Carnival; Beccles Music Festival; Beccles Lido; Beccles Cycle Trails; Waveney Stardust – Boat trips for the disabled; Waveney Enterprises; Beccles Blind Association; New Year Suppers; Variety Show; St Raphael Club; St Luke's Lunch Club – for wheelchairs and The Dell – Home for Senior Citizens.

FINANCES *Year* 2011–12 *Income* £124,825 *Grants* £40,000

TRUSTEES James Hartley; Dennis Hipperson; Montagu Pitkin; Kenneth Leggett; Gillian Campbell; Gordon Hickman; Jennifer Langeskov; Keith Gregory; Jane Seppings; Robert Seppings.

HOW TO APPLY In writing to the correspondent.

WHO TO APPLY TO Robert Peck, Secretary, 6 Cherry Hill Close, Worlingham, Beccles, Suffolk NR34 7EG

■ The Becker Family Charitable Trust

CC NO 1047968   ESTABLISHED 1995

WHERE FUNDING CAN BE GIVEN UK and overseas.

WHO CAN BENEFIT Registered charities.

WHAT IS FUNDED General charitable purposes, particularly Orthodox Jewish organisations.

SAMPLE GRANTS Previous beneficiaries have included Keren Shabbas, Lolev CT, Menora Grammar School, Torah Temima and WST.

FINANCES *Year* 2011–12 *Income* £41,772 *Grants* £51,000 *Assets* £328,911

TRUSTEES Allan Becker; Ruth Becker; Deanna Fried.

HOW TO APPLY In writing to the correspondent. However, note that the trust has previously stated that its funds are fully committed.

WHO TO APPLY TO Allan Becker, Trustee, 33 Sinclair Grove, London NW11 9JH

■ The Becketts and Sargeants Educational Foundation

CC NO 309766   ESTABLISHED 1986

WHERE FUNDING CAN BE GIVEN The borough of Northampton.

WHO CAN BENEFIT Church schools, and individuals under 25 years of age and in need of financial assistance, and either a resident in the borough or attending schools or full-time courses of education at any further education establishment in the borough, or a former pupil of All Saints' Middle School for at least two years.

WHAT IS FUNDED Education.

WHAT IS NOT FUNDED No grants are given for part-time courses.

RANGE OF GRANTS Up to £40,000.

SAMPLE GRANTS All Saints CEVA Primary School (£18,000); Collingtree Primary School (£15,000); Friends of All Saints' Music (£3,000); St Andrew's CEVA Primary School (£2,300) and St John the Baptist (£500).

FINANCES *Year* 2012 *Income* £219,071 *Grants* £126,968 *Assets* £2,985,981

TRUSTEES Philip Richard Saunderson; Richard Pestell; Eileen Beeby; Linda Ann Mayne; Ven. Christine Allsopp; David Smith; Hilary Spenceley; Margaret Pickard; Andrew Cowling; Christopher Davidge.

OTHER INFORMATION The 2012 grant total includes £88,000 that was given to 134 individuals.

HOW TO APPLY On a form available from the correspondent. Applications are considered four times a year, usually in February/March, May, September and December.

WHO TO APPLY TO Angela Moon, Grants Sub-Committee Clerk, Hewitsons LLP, 7 Spencer Parade, Northampton NN1 5AB *Tel.* 01604 233233 *email* angelamoon@hewitsons.com

■ The Victoria and David Beckham Children's Charity

CC NO 1091838   ESTABLISHED 2002

WHERE FUNDING CAN BE GIVEN UK and overseas.

WHO CAN BENEFIT Organisations and individuals.

WHAT IS FUNDED Work benefiting children and general charitable purposes.

SAMPLE GRANTS Previous beneficiaries include UNICEF, Action for Kids, Motability, Demand, Theraplay, Wheelchair Centre, St Joseph's in the Park Parent Fellowship, Gerald Symonds Healthcare Limited and Helping Hand Company.

FINANCES *Year* 2011–12

TRUSTEES Victoria Beckham; David Beckham; Jacqueline Adams.

OTHER INFORMATION The charity's basic accounts provide no information on its achievements during the year or who its beneficiaries were.

HOW TO APPLY In writing to the correspondent; however, a letter requesting information from the charity received a standard reply stating that the charity has 'limited funds', and that our request was 'outside the objectives and criteria set and therefore we are unable to help you'. This indicates that correspondence to the charity are not read.

WHO TO APPLY TO Jacqueline Adams, Old School House, St James Road, Goffs Oak, Waltham Cross EN7 6TP

■ The John Beckwith Charitable Trust

CC NO 800276   ESTABLISHED 1987

WHERE FUNDING CAN BE GIVEN UK and overseas.

WHO CAN BENEFIT Registered charities.

WHAT IS FUNDED General charitable purposes with a preference for: sports programmes for young people; education; children's charities; medical research; the arts; and charities involved with overseas aid.

TYPE OF GRANT Capital, one-off and recurring.

SAMPLE GRANTS Wycombe Abbey School (£46,000); RNIB (£20,500); Great Ormond Street Children's Charity (£14,000); Rekindle (£5,000); Crisis (£2,000); New Ways (£1,500); and British Red Cross, Changing Faces, Dogs Trust, Parkinson's Disease Society, Shining

Faces in India and Vision for Africa (£1,000 each).

FINANCES *Year* 2011–12 *Income* £322,271 *Grants* £556,001 *Assets* £1,267,381

TRUSTEES Sir John Beckwith; Heather Beckwith; Christopher Meech.

HOW TO APPLY In writing to the correspondent.

WHO TO APPLY TO Sally Holder, Administrator, 124 Sloane Street, London SW1X 9BW *Tel.* 020 7225 2250

■ The Peter Beckwith Charitable Trust

CC NO 802113   **ESTABLISHED** 1989

WHERE FUNDING CAN BE GIVEN UK.

WHO CAN BENEFIT Institutions and registered charities benefiting at risk groups, people disadvantaged by poverty and socially isolated people.

WHAT IS FUNDED A broad range of medical and welfare charities. General charitable purposes.

SAMPLE GRANTS Previous beneficiaries included: Wimbledon and Putney Common Conservators (£10,000); Richmond Theatre (£5,000); Imperial War Museum (£2,000); and BAAF, ORCHID and Starlight Children's Foundation (£1,000 each).

FINANCES *Year* 2011–12 *Income* £21,250 *Grants* £29,926

TRUSTEES Peter Beckwith; Clare Van Dam; Tamara Veroni.

OTHER INFORMATION Accounts received but not published at the Charity Commission due to the charity's low income.

HOW TO APPLY In writing to the correspondent.

WHO TO APPLY TO Peter Beckwith, Trustee, Hill Place House, 55a High Street, Wimbledon Village, London SW19 5BA *Tel.* 020 8944 1288

■ The Bedfordshire and Hertfordshire Historic Churches Trust

CC NO 1005697   **ESTABLISHED** 1991

WHERE FUNDING CAN BE GIVEN Bedfordshire, Hertfordshire and that part of Barnet within the Diocese of St Albans.

WHO CAN BENEFIT Those entrusted with the upkeep of places of active Christian worship.

WHAT IS FUNDED Work to ensure that places of active Christian worship are maintained in a structurally sound and weatherproof condition.

WHAT IS NOT FUNDED No grants to individuals.

TYPE OF GRANT One-off and buildings. Funding may be given for one year or less.

RANGE OF GRANTS £1,000–£15,000.

SAMPLE GRANTS St Peter – Arlesey, St Lawrence – Ayot, St Mary – Haynes, St Catherine – Sacombe, All Saints – Sandon, All Saints – Shillington, St George – Toddington, St Mary – Westmill and St Michael and All Angels – Woolmer.

FINANCES *Year* 2011–12 *Income* £206,421 *Grants* £169,500 *Assets* £220,428

TRUSTEES Stuart Russell; Aymeric Jenkins; Richard Genochio; Peter Griffiths; Jim May; Terry Warburton; Dr Christopher Green; P. Lepper; William Masterson.

OTHER INFORMATION Annual income comes from member subscription and from the annual 'Bike 'n Hike' event. The trust also acts as a distributive agent for church grants made by the Wixamtree Trust and Waste Recycling Environmental Ltd.

HOW TO APPLY Initial enquiries should be made to the Grants Secretary. Applications can only be made by members of the trust.

WHO TO APPLY TO Archie Russell, Grants Secretary, Wychbrook, 31 Ivel Gardens, Biggleswade, Bedfordshire SG18 0AN *Tel.* 01767 312966 *email* grants@yahoo.co.uk *Website* www. bedshertshct.org.uk

■ The Bedfordshire and Luton Community Foundation

CC NO 1086516   **ESTABLISHED** 2001

WHERE FUNDING CAN BE GIVEN The county of Bedfordshire and the borough of Luton.

WHO CAN BENEFIT The grant schemes aim to assist community voluntary organisations and groups in Bedfordshire and Luton in new or exciting projects that can help make a positive difference in the local community.

WHAT IS FUNDED The foundation is dedicated to improving the quality of community life of those in Bedfordshire and Luton and in particular those in special need by reason of disability, age, financial or other disadvantage.

WHAT IS NOT FUNDED No grants are made: to profit-making organisations; for the furtherance of any one religion; to fund political activities; to private business (other than social enterprises); to projects that would otherwise be funded from statutory sources.

FINANCES *Year* 2011–12 *Income* £528,881 *Grants* £291,925 *Assets* £849,008

TRUSTEES Janet Ridge; Malcolm Newman; Clifton Ibbett; Wendi Momen; Geoff Lambert; Andy Rayment; Keith Rawlings; Matthew Willson.

OTHER INFORMATION The foundation manages a number of schemes that change regularly, therefore check its website for details of up to date schemes.

HOW TO APPLY Application forms for the various funds are available from the website, ensure you use the correct one and do not apply for more than one fund at the same time without contacting the foundation first. The panel meets six times a year and applicants should ensure their application is submitted at least three months before the funds are needed.

WHO TO APPLY TO Mark West, Chief Executive, The Old School, Southill Road, Cardington MK44 3SX *Tel.* 01234 834930 *Fax* 07006 006800 *email* administrator@blcf.org.uk *Website* www.blcf.org.uk

■ The David and Ruth Behrend Fund

CC NO 261567   **ESTABLISHED** 1969

WHERE FUNDING CAN BE GIVEN UK, with a preference for Merseyside.

WHO CAN BENEFIT Registered charities.

WHAT IS FUNDED General charitable purposes. The fund only gives funding to charities known to the settlors.

RANGE OF GRANTS Up to £8,000

SAMPLE GRANTS Merseyside Development Foundation (£6,000); Digital Production for Disabled People, Merseyside Somali Community Association, Porchfield Community Association, Top Spin Table Tennis Club, Tuebrook Community Centre Group and Wavertree Garden Suburb Institute (£2,000 each); and Bethlehem Community, British Red Cross, LGBT Choir Liverpool, Merseyside Holiday Service, Save the Children, Sheila Kay Fund, Support for Asylum

Seekers and WAM Friendship Centre (£1,000 each).

FINANCES *Year* 2011–12 *Income* £86,051 *Grants* £66,657 *Assets* £1,395,595

TRUSTEE Liverpool Charity and Voluntary Services.

HOW TO APPLY This fund states that it does not respond to unsolicited applications. 'The charity only makes grants to charities already known to the settlors as this is a personal charitable trust.'

WHO TO APPLY TO The Secretary, 151 Dale Street, Liverpool L2 2AH *Tel.* 01512 275177 *Website* www.merseytrusts.org.uk

....

■ The Beit Trust

CC NO 232478   **ESTABLISHED** 1906

WHERE FUNDING CAN BE GIVEN Zimbabwe, Zambia and Malawi.

WHO CAN BENEFIT Individuals and charities benefiting young adults, students, teachers and academics, at-risk groups, people disadvantaged by poverty, and homeless and socially isolated people.

WHAT IS FUNDED Post-primary education; health and welfare. Most grants are for buildings and infrastructure, with occasional grants made for environmental projects.

WHAT IS NOT FUNDED Grants are only given to charities in the areas above and the trust is reluctant to give grants to other grantmaking charities. The trust stated in 2004 that it does not provide support for gap year students, undergraduates, individual schoolchildren or vehicles.

TYPE OF GRANT Recurring, one-off, capital, bursaries, postgraduate fellowships.

RANGE OF GRANTS Not normally in excess of £30,000.

FINANCES *Year* 2012 *Income* £2,188,914 *Grants* £1,708,941 *Assets* £78,370,740

TRUSTEES C. J. Driver; Prof. C. B. D. Lavy; R. P. Lander; Sir K. Prendergast; Sir A. Munro; A. Duncan.

HOW TO APPLY Applications for infrastructure grants to Beit Trust Representative, P.O. Box CH 76, Chisipite, Harare, Zimbabwe. General enquiries to UK office. Contact the trust by telephone or in writing for an application form. Grants are approved by trustees at their six-monthly meetings.

WHO TO APPLY TO Maj. Gen A. I. Ramsey, Secretary, Beit House, Grove Road, Woking, Surrey GU21 5JB *Tel.* 01483 772575 *email* enquiries@beittrust.org *Website* www.beittrust.org.uk

....

■ The Bellahouston Bequest Fund

SC NO SC011781   **ESTABLISHED** 1888

WHERE FUNDING CAN BE GIVEN Glasgow and district, but not more than five miles beyond the Glasgow city boundary (churches only).

WHO CAN BENEFIT Churches and registered charities in Glasgow or within five miles especially those benefiting Protestant evangelical denominations and clergy of such churches, as well as people disadvantaged by poverty.

WHAT IS FUNDED The trust supports a wide variety of causes. Its main priority is to help build, expand and repair Protestant evangelical churches or places of religious worship, as well as supporting the clergy of these churches. It further states that it is set up to give grants to charities for the relief of poverty or disease and to organisations concerned with promotion of

the Protestant religion, education, and conservation of places of historical and artistic significance. It will consider social welfare causes generally and also animal welfare and sport and recreation.

WHAT IS NOT FUNDED No grants to organisations or churches whose work does not fall within the geographical remit of the fund. Overseas projects and political appeals are not supported.

RANGE OF GRANTS Usually between £1,000 and £5,000.

SAMPLE GRANTS Previous beneficiaries have included 119th Glasgow Boys Brigade, Airborne Initiative, Ballieston Community Care, Bellahouston Academy, Calvay Social Action Group, Citizens' Theatre, Church of Scotland, Colquhoun Trust, Crosshill Evangelical Church, Dalmarnock After School Care, Erskine Hospital, Girlguiding Scotland, Glasgow School of Art, Glasgow Old People's Welfare Association, Glasgow YMCA, Govanhill Youth Project, House for an Art Lover, Kelvingrove Refurbishment Appeal, Maryhill Parish Church, William McCunn's Trust, Northwest Women's Centre, Pearce Institute, Prince and Princess of Wales Hospice, Shawlands United Reformed Church, St Paul's Parish Council, Strathclyde Youth Club Association, University of Strathclyde and Williamwood Parish Church.

FINANCES *Year* 2011–12 *Income* £171,648 *Grants* £142,389

TRUSTEES Peter C. Paisley; Peter L. Fairley; Andrew Primrose; Donald Blair; Graeme Kidd.

HOW TO APPLY On a form available from the trust for church applications only. Other charitable organisations can apply in writing to the correspondent. The trustees meet to consider grants in March, July, October and December.

WHO TO APPLY TO Edward Barry, Mitchells Roberton Solicitors, George House, 36 North Hanover Street, Glasgow G1 2AD

....

■ Bellasis Trust

CC NO 1085972   **ESTABLISHED** 2000

WHERE FUNDING CAN BE GIVEN UK.

WHO CAN BENEFIT Mainly local charities.

WHAT IS FUNDED General charitable purposes.

RANGE OF GRANTS Up to £10,000.

SAMPLE GRANTS Royal Horticultural Society and Wheelpower (£5,000 each); Institute of Economic Affairs (£4,000); Foundation for Social and Economic Thinking (£2,000); and Disability Sport and Walk the Walk (£1,000 each).

FINANCES *Year* 2011–12 *Income* £36,329 *Grants* £31,470 *Assets* £935,945

TRUSTEES Paul Wates; Annette Wates; Annabelle Elliott.

HOW TO APPLY 'The trustees research and consider applicants for grants.'

WHO TO APPLY TO Paul Wates, Trustee, Bellasis House, Headley Heath Approach, Mickleham, Dorking, Surrey RH5 6DH *Tel.* 01372 861058

....

■ The Bellhouse Foundation

CC NO 1076698   **ESTABLISHED** 1999

WHERE FUNDING CAN BE GIVEN UK.

WHO CAN BENEFIT Organisations working in the fields of engineering and pharmacology.

WHAT IS FUNDED The advancement of education through the promotion of medical research in the field of engineering and pharmacology.

SAMPLE GRANTS Previous beneficiaries have included: Oxford University Development Trust

(£400,000); Magdalen College Development Trust (£150,000); Medical Foundation (£10,000); and the Woodland Trust (£1,000).
FINANCES *Year* 2011–12 *Income* £2,457 *Grants* £14,000
TRUSTEES Prof. Brian Bellhouse; Elisabeth Bellhouse; Clare Maurice.
OTHER INFORMATION The foundation's income and total expenditure have reduced significantly in recent years.
HOW TO APPLY In writing to the correspondent.
WHO TO APPLY TO The Trustees, 2 Friars Road, Winchelsea TN36 4ED

■ The Bellinger Donnay Trust

CC NO 289462   **ESTABLISHED** 1984
WHERE FUNDING CAN BE GIVEN Unrestricted, in practice, London, Wiltshire and the south east of England.
WHO CAN BENEFIT Small, independent charities.
WHAT IS FUNDED General charitable causes, in particular, those concerned with youth, older people, people with disabilities and the relief of poverty and deprivation.
WHAT IS NOT FUNDED The trustees do not usually support: animal organisations; travel overseas for individuals; medical research; or building projects. The trust does not solicit applications from large, well established, national charities.
RANGE OF GRANTS Usually up to £1,000; occasionally up to £5,000 or higher.
SAMPLE GRANTS Broderers Charity Trust and European Youth Orchestra (£5,000 each); Richmond Theatre and Haiti Earthquake Appeal (£2,500 each); Kew Foundation and Polka Theatre (£1,500 each); Age Concern, Macmillan Cancer Care and Centrepoint (£1,000 each); UK Sailing Academy and Combat Stress (£500 each); Backup Trust and Action for Children (£250 each); George Bailey Trust and Motor Neurone Disease (£100 each); and Council for Assisting Academic Refugees (£50).
FINANCES *Year* 2011–12 *Income* £39,873 *Grants* £29,847 *Assets* £2,156,757
TRUSTEES Lady C. M. L. Bellinger; L. E. Spackman; Ian Bellinger.
OTHER INFORMATION The trust also provides an advocacy service.
HOW TO APPLY 'PLEASE NOTE: In view of the fact that our income will be severely affected by the current economic climate, our grants programme will be substantially reduced. In the circumstances, until further notice, we do not wish to receive unsolicited grant applications from charities that we do not already support.' Potential applicants are advised to check the trust's website for up-to-date information.
WHO TO APPLY TO I. A. Bellinger, Byways, Coombe Hill Road, Kingston upon Thames, Surrey KT2 7DY *email* bdct@ianbellinger.co.uk *Website* www.bellingerdonnay.btck.co.uk

■ The Benfield Motors Charitable Trust

CC NO 328149   **ESTABLISHED** 1989
WHERE FUNDING CAN BE GIVEN North east England, Leeds and Edinburgh.
WHO CAN BENEFIT Neighbourhood-based community projects and national schemes.
WHAT IS FUNDED Grants are given in the areas of social welfare; community development; work which supports children, young people and the

elderly, local hospitals and hospices; Christian activities and the arts.
TYPE OF GRANT One-off or recurrent.
RANGE OF GRANTS Mostly under £1,000, with some larger grants reaching between £5,000 and £40,000.
SAMPLE GRANTS Live Theatre (£20,000); Metro Kids Africa (£16,000); Carlisle Youth Zone (£15,000); Traidcraft (£10,000); Newcastle Royal Grammar School (£9,327); Keyfund (£7,425); Great North Air Ambulance (£6,500); The People's Kitchen (£6,000); Strongbones Children's Charitable Trust (£2,601); Sixty Eighty Thirty, Samaritans of Northumbria, Contagious, Christian Aid Re East Africa Food Crisis and Metro Kids Africa Charity Drive (£2,000 each).
FINANCES *Year* 2011–12 *Income* £245,649 *Grants* £145,156 *Assets* £330,622
TRUSTEES John Squires, Chair; Malcolm Squires; Stephen Squires.
OTHER INFORMATION 71 grants were made, 50 of which were made for £1,000 or less.
HOW TO APPLY In writing to the correspondent. The trustees' meet twice a year, this is usually in May and November with applications needing to be received by the beginning of April or October respectively.
WHO TO APPLY TO Lynn Squires, Hon. Secretary, c/o Benfield Motor Group, Asama Court, Newcastle Business Park, Newcastle upon Tyne NE4 7YD *Tel.* 01912 261700 *email* charitabletrust@benfieldmotorgroup.com

■ The Benham Charitable Settlement

CC NO 239371   **ESTABLISHED** 1964
WHERE FUNDING CAN BE GIVEN UK, with very strong emphasis on Northamptonshire.
WHO CAN BENEFIT Registered charities.
WHAT IS FUNDED The trust's policy is to make a large number of relatively small grants to groups working in many charitable fields, including charities involved in medical research, disability, elderly people, children and young people, disadvantaged people, overseas aid, missions to seamen, the welfare of ex-servicemen, wildlife, the environment, and the arts. The trust also supports the Church of England, and the work of Christian mission throughout the world. Special emphasis is placed upon those churches and charitable organisations within the county of Northamptonshire [especially as far as new applicants are concerned].
WHAT IS NOT FUNDED No grants to individuals.
TYPE OF GRANT One-off and recurring grants will be considered.
RANGE OF GRANTS Mostly between £200–£700, with some larger grants up to £30,000.
SAMPLE GRANTS Northamptonshire Association of Youth Clubs (£30,000); William Wilberforce Trust (£6,000); Zimbabwe A National Emergency (£3,000); LifeCentre (£2,000); British Red Cross (£1,000); Anglo Peruvian Child Care Mission (£600); Action on Poverty, Tall Ships Youth Trust and Willen Hospice (£500 each); and Y Care International (£400).
FINANCES *Year* 2011–12 *Income* £206,720 *Grants* £140,100 *Assets* £5,186,498
TRUSTEES M. M. Tittle; Lady Hutton; E. N. Langley; D. A. H. Tittle; Revd J. A. Nickols.
OTHER INFORMATION The majority of grants range from £200–£700.
HOW TO APPLY In recent years the trust has not been considering new applications.

WHO TO APPLY TO The Secretary, Hurstbourne, Portnall Drive, Virginia Water, Surrey GU25 4NR

■ The Hervey Benham Charitable Trust

CC NO 277578   **ESTABLISHED** 1978

WHERE FUNDING CAN BE GIVEN Colchester and North East Essex.

WHO CAN BENEFIT Individuals or self-help organisations from Colchester and North East Essex.

WHAT IS FUNDED Artistic (particularly musical) activities which benefit the people of Colchester and district and which would benefit from pump-priming by the trust and/or a contribution which enables self-help to function more effectively; individuals with potential artistic (especially musical) talent who are held back by physical, environmental or financial disability; preservation of Colchester and district's heritage with particular emphasis on industrial heritage and the maritime traditions of the Essex/Suffolk coast; local history and conservation affecting the heritage and environment of the area.

WHAT IS NOT FUNDED Capital including buildings, feasibility studies, interest-free loans, one-off, and pump-priming costs. Funding is available for up to three years. Tuition fees are normally paid direct to educational institutions.

TYPE OF GRANT Capital including buildings, feasibility studies, interest-free loans, one-off, and pump-priming costs. Funding is available for up to three years. Tuition fees are normally paid direct to educational institutions.

RANGE OF GRANTS Up to £20,000.

SAMPLE GRANTS Kingsway Hall Arts and Community Trust (£20,000); Cuckoo Farm Studios (£3,500); Greenstead Community Centre (£3,000); ACE Youth Musical Theatre (£1,700); the Mad About Theatre Company, Brightlingsea Free Music Festival, Hamilton Lodge Trust and Colchester Scout Gang Show (£1,000 each); Hervey Benham Young Soloists Concert (£500); and Slackspace, Colchester (£300).

FINANCES *Year* 2012–13 *Income* £26,500 *Grants* £10,000

TRUSTEES M. Ellis; A. B. Phillips; M. R. Carr; K. E. Mirams.

PUBLICATIONS Brochure.

HOW TO APPLY In writing to the correspondent by the normal quarterly dates.

WHO TO APPLY TO John Woodman, 18 Wren Close, Stanway, Colchester, Essex CO3 8ZB *email* admin@herveybenhamtrust.org.uk

---

■ Maurice and Jacqueline Bennett Charitable Trust

CC NO 1047566   **ESTABLISHED** 1995

WHERE FUNDING CAN BE GIVEN Throughout England and Wales

WHO CAN BENEFIT Charitable organisations; Jewish charities.

WHAT IS FUNDED General charitable purposes; support of Jewish charitable organisations.

RANGE OF GRANTS Up to £26,000. Usually between £100 and £300.

SAMPLE GRANTS Previous beneficiaries included; Iron Fell Consult (£26,000); Starlight Child (£3,000); Jewish Care and KOL NIDRE (£2,000 each); and Global Enduro (£1,000). A further 15 small donations totalling £3,100.

FINANCES *Year* 2011–12 *Income* £12,514 *Grants* £33,000

TRUSTEES Maurice Bennett; M. Jacqueline Bennett.

HOW TO APPLY In writing to the correspondent.

WHO TO APPLY TO Mai Brown, Administrator, Blick Rothenberg, 16 Great Queen Street, Covent Garden, London WC2B 5AH *Tel.* 020 7544 8862

■ Michael and Leslie Bennett Charitable Trust

CC NO 1047611   **ESTABLISHED** 1995

WHERE FUNDING CAN BE GIVEN UK.

WHO CAN BENEFIT Mostly Jewish organisations.

WHAT IS FUNDED The trust supports a range of causes, but the largest donations were to Jewish organisations.

RANGE OF GRANTS Up to £18,000.

SAMPLE GRANTS World Jewish Relief (£10,000); Jewish Care (£8,500); Community Security Trust (£5,000); Chai Cancer Care and Norwood Ravensworth (£3,000 each); Magen David Adom and Nightingale Hammerson (£2,500 each) and Anglo Israel Association (£1,400). There were also 18 grants of less than £1,000, totalling £3,200.

FINANCES *Year* 2011–12 *Income* £33,522 *Grants* £39,030 *Assets* £290,570

TRUSTEES Michael Bennett; Lesley V. Bennett.

HOW TO APPLY In writing to the correspondent.

WHO TO APPLY TO Michael Bennett, Trustee, Bedegars Lea, Kenwood Close, London NW3 7JL *Tel.* 020 8458 4945

■ Bennett Lowell Limited

CC NO 1149726   **ESTABLISHED** 2012

WHERE FUNDING CAN BE GIVEN UK and overseas, with a possible preference for California.

WHO CAN BENEFIT Registered charities.

WHAT IS FUNDED General charitable purposes.

TRUSTEES David Borthwick; John Attree; Molly Borthwick; William Borthwick.

HOW TO APPLY In writing to the correspondent.

WHO TO APPLY TO John Ward, Administrator, CGW/345049, Speechly Bircham LLP, 6 New Street Square, London EC4A 3LX *Tel.* 020 7427 6400 *Fax* 020 7427 6600 *email* information@speechlys.com

---

■ The Gerald Bentall Charitable Trust

CC NO 271993   **ESTABLISHED** 1976

WHERE FUNDING CAN BE GIVEN Mainly southern England including London.

WHO CAN BENEFIT The elderly, people with disability, youth

WHAT IS FUNDED Hospitals, churches, youth organisations, education

WHAT IS NOT FUNDED No grants to individuals.

RANGE OF GRANTS £69–£1,000.

SAMPLE GRANTS Old Bentallians Association and Steadfast Sea Cadets (£1,000 each); Friends of Penshurst Church (£500); Kent/Surrey/Sussex Air Ambulance Fund (£450); Alzheimer's Research Trust, Hospice in the Weald and Normandy Veterans Association (£300 each); Rushmoor Healthy Living (£250); Royal Air Forces Association, Royal National Institute for Deaf People, Ro-Ro Sailing Project, National Association of Swimming Clubs for the

Handicapped and Friends of Chichester Harbour (£225) and RSPB (£69).

FINANCES *Year* 2011–12 *Income* £38,862 *Grants* £27,066 *Assets* £1,134,910

TRUSTEES Anthony Anstee; Caroline Thorp; Emma Purcell; Clare Jackson.

OTHER INFORMATION Grants were given to 107 organisations. The average grant was £225.

HOW TO APPLY In writing to the correspondent, however note that 'the trustees have a list of charities which receive annual donations – very few charities are added each year'.

WHO TO APPLY TO Zoe Peters, 24 Stoudes Close, Worcester Park, Surrey KT4 7RB *Tel.* 020 8330 4586

....

■ Bergqvist Charitable Trust

CC NO 1015707   **ESTABLISHED** 1992

WHERE FUNDING CAN BE GIVEN Buckinghamshire and neighbouring counties.

WHO CAN BENEFIT Registered charities and community organisations.

WHAT IS FUNDED Education; medical health; environment; and disaster and famine relief.

WHAT IS NOT FUNDED Grants are not made to individuals, non-registered charities or for animal causes.

TYPE OF GRANT One-off and recurrent grants.

SAMPLE GRANTS Generation Trust for medical research, Abracadabra – Royal Surrey Hospital Paediatric Unit, Stoke Mandeville Hospital for MRI scanner appeal, British Epilepsy Association for general purposes, Cancer Care and Haematology at Stoke Mandeville Hospital, PACE school for children with cerebral palsy, British Heart Foundation for research, Church Urban Fund for diocese expenses and Sight Savers International for eyesight research.

FINANCES *Year* 2012 *Income* £37,100 *Grants* £33,000

TRUSTEES Patricia Bergqvist; Philip Bergqvist; Sophia Bergqvist.

HOW TO APPLY In writing to the correspondent.

WHO TO APPLY TO Patricia Bergqvist, Trustee, Moat Farm, Water Lane, Ford, Aylesbury, Buckinghamshire HP17 8XD *Tel.* 01296 748560

....

■ The Ruth Berkowitz Charitable Trust

CC NO 1111673   **ESTABLISHED** 2005

WHERE FUNDING CAN BE GIVEN UK and overseas.

WHO CAN BENEFIT Charitable organisations.

WHAT IS FUNDED Youth; medical research; education; Jewish causes, including education and community.

RANGE OF GRANTS £2,500–£50,000.

SAMPLE GRANTS Community Security Trust (£55,000); World Jewish Relief (£47,000); B'nai B'rith Hillel Foundation/Union of Jewish Students (£46,000); The Institute of Jewish Studies (£43,000); Magen David Adom UK (£35,000); Lord Ashdown Charitable Settlement (£32,000); Marie Curie cancer Care (£30,000); World ORT (£20,000); Nightingale House (£18,000); Jewish Women's Aid (£15,000); Simon Marks Jewish Primary School Trust (£10,000); British Friends of United Hatzalah Israel (£5,000) and One to One Children's Fund (£2,000).

FINANCES *Year* 2011–12 *Income* £76,488 *Grants* £677,450 *Assets* £3,881,582

TRUSTEES Philip Beckman; Brian Beckman.

HOW TO APPLY The trustees stated in their annual report that as the trust is not reactive they will 'generally only make grants to charities that are known to them and will not normally respond to unsolicited requests for assistance. There is no application form.'

WHO TO APPLY TO The Trustees, 39 Farm Avenue, London NW2 2BJ

....

■ The Berkshire Community Foundation

CC NO 294220   **ESTABLISHED** 1985

WHERE FUNDING CAN BE GIVEN Berkshire, i.e. the unitary authorities of Bracknell, Reading, Slough, Windsor and Maidenhead, West Berkshire and Wokingham.

WHO CAN BENEFIT Voluntary organisations or groups established for charitable purposes and individual children. Grants are directed to: older people; children and young people; people with a long-term illness or disability and their carers; people with mental health needs; minority ethnic communities; those suffering from addiction.

WHAT IS FUNDED Grants are made through various funds to support groups addressing need in the county. Up-to-date details can be found at the foundation's website.

WHAT IS NOT FUNDED 'We do not fund medical research or equipment, sponsored events, animal welfare, overseas travel/expeditions, promotion of religious or political causes, statutory work (in educational institutions or replacing statutory obligation/public funding) or groups with more than one year's unrestricted reserves... Grants are not intended to support major capital appeals and cannot be made retrospectively.'

RANGE OF GRANTS Up to £113,000

SAMPLE GRANTS Local Giving (£113,000); Mars (£72,000); Three Windsor and Maidenhead (£50,000); Give a Child a Chance (£47,000); Blagrave Small Grants (£36,000); Comic Relief (£16,000); Slough Social (£15,000); Sport Relief (£14,800); Sage (£13,000); Prudential (£10,000); Herongate and Kaye Family (£7,000 each); Osborne Clark and Peter King (£5,000 each).

FINANCES *Year* 2011–12 *Income* £1,611,925 *Grants* £502,375 *Assets* £7,612,638

TRUSTEES Chris Barrett; Ramesh Kukar; Sue Ormiston; Gordon West; Dick Taylor; Susie Tremlett; Emma van Zeller; Revd Allen Walker; Christine Weston; Peter Mason; David Seward; Catherine Stephenson; Jane Wates; Gordon Storey; Torquil Montague-Johnstone; Richard Griffiths-Jones.

OTHER INFORMATION Donations from individuals, companies and charitable trusts are pooled in the foundation's Community Capital Fund from which the foundation draws income to make its grants.

HOW TO APPLY Full details of how to apply to the various funding streams can be found at the foundation's website.

WHO TO APPLY TO Andrew Middleton, Arlington Business Park, Theale, Reading, Berkshire RG7 4SA *Tel.* 01189 303021 *email* info@berkshirecf.org *Website* www.berkshirecf.org

■ The Bertarelli UK Foundation

CC NO 1140189 **ESTABLISHED** 2011
WHERE FUNDING CAN BE GIVEN UK.
WHO CAN BENEFIT Charities and community groups.
WHAT IS FUNDED General charitable purposes.
SAMPLE GRANTS Stoke-On-Trent Theatres Trust (£55,000).
FINANCES *Year* 2012 *Income* £61,286 *Grants* £54,700
TRUSTEES Ernesto Bertarelli; Donata Bertarelli; Maria Bertarelli; Kirsty Bertarelli.
OTHER INFORMATION This is the charitable foundation of the Bertarelli family and the vehicle for their philanthropy in the UK. The family has a number of business interests, most notably in the pharmaceutical industry and property investments. Waypoint Corporate Services Ltd is also one of their companies. The family's wealth is estimated at around £7.4 billion.
HOW TO APPLY In writing to the correspondent.
WHO TO APPLY TO Jeremy Arnold, c/o Waypoint Corporate Services Ltd, 1 Curzon Street, London W1J 5HD *Tel.* 020 7016 4000

■ The Bestway Foundation

CC NO 297178 **ESTABLISHED** 1987
WHERE FUNDING CAN BE GIVEN UK and overseas.
WHO CAN BENEFIT Individuals, UK registered charities, non-registered charities and overseas charities.
WHAT IS FUNDED Advancement of education by grants to schoolchildren and students who are of Indian, Pakistani, Bangladeshi or Sri Lankan origin; relief of sickness, and preservation and protection of health in the UK and overseas, especially in India, Pakistan, Bangladesh and Sri Lanka.
WHAT IS NOT FUNDED No grants for trips/travel abroad.
RANGE OF GRANTS £1,000–£200,000.
SAMPLE GRANTS Bestway Foundation Pakistan (£200,000); Imran Khan Cancer Appeal (£100,000); Crimestoppers (£34,000); Duke of Edinburgh Awards (£15,000); SOS Children's Villages (£5,000); British Pakistan Foundation (£4,000); The Priory School and John Ferneley College (£3,000 each); The Coexistence Trust and Silver Star Appeal (£2,000 each) and The Royal Commonwealth Society (£1,000).
FINANCES *Year* 2011–12 *Income* £821,577 *Grants* £681,258 *Assets* £5,766,492
TRUSTEES A. K. Bhatti; A. K. Chaudhary; M. Y. Sheikh; Z. M. Choudrey; M. A. Pervez.
OTHER INFORMATION All trustees of this foundation are directors and shareholders of Bestway (Holdings) Limited, the parent company of Bestway Cash and Carry Limited.
The grant total for 2011–12 includes awards to individuals and foreign charities totalling £184,000.
HOW TO APPLY In writing to the correspondent, enclosing an sae. Applications are considered in March/April. Telephone calls are not welcome.
WHO TO APPLY TO M. Y. Sheikh, Trustee, Bestway Cash and Carry Ltd, Abbey Road, Park Royal, London NW10 7BW *Tel.* 020 8453 1234 *email* zulfikaur.wajid-hasan@bestway.co.uk *Website* www.bestwaygroup.co.uk/page/bestway-foundation

■ Bet365 Foundation

CC NO 1149110 **ESTABLISHED** 2012
WHERE FUNDING CAN BE GIVEN UK and overseas.
WHO CAN BENEFIT Charities and community groups.
WHAT IS FUNDED General, children and young people, older people and people with a disability, with a preference for 'community participation in health recreation'.
TRUSTEES Simon Adlington; Denise Coates; John Coates; Peter Coates.
HOW TO APPLY In writing to the correspondent.
WHO TO APPLY TO Simon Adlington, Trustee, c/o Baker Tilly, Festival Way, Festival Park, Stoke-on-Trent, Staffordshire ST1 5BB *Tel.* 01782 216000

■ BHST

CC NO 1004327 **ESTABLISHED** 1991
WHERE FUNDING CAN BE GIVEN UK and Israel.
WHO CAN BENEFIT Jewish organisations.
WHAT IS FUNDED Jewish charitable purposes.
RANGE OF GRANTS Usually £300–£7,400.
SAMPLE GRANTS Adath Yisroel Burial Society (£64,000); Easy Chasnea (£7,000); Shulum Berger Association (£3,000); United Talmudical Association (£2,500); and Beis Rochel (£1,600).
FINANCES *Year* 2011–12 *Income* £345,780 *Grants* £126,957 *Assets* £107,472
TRUSTEES Solomon Laufer; Pinchas Ostreicher; Joshua Sternlicht.
OTHER INFORMATION A total of £103,500 was given in student grants.
HOW TO APPLY In writing to the correspondent.
WHO TO APPLY TO Solomon Laufer, Secretary, c/o Cohen Arnold and Co., New Burlington House, 1075 Finchley Road, London NW11 0PU *Tel.* 020 8731 0777 *Fax* 020 8731 0778 *email* mail@cohenarnold.com

■ The Mason Bibby 1981 Trust

CC NO 283231 **ESTABLISHED** 1981
WHERE FUNDING CAN BE GIVEN Merseyside and other areas where the company has or had a presence.
WHO CAN BENEFIT Priority to elderly people and employees and ex-employees of J Bibby and Sons plc (since renamed Barloworld plc).
WHAT IS FUNDED Main area of interest is elderly people but applications are considered from other groups, particularly from areas in which the company has a presence.
WHAT IS NOT FUNDED Apart from employees and ex-employees of J Bibby and Sons plc, applications are considered from registered charities only.
RANGE OF GRANTS £250–£3,500.
SAMPLE GRANTS Liverpool Personal Service Society (£3,300); Age Concern Liverpool (£2,800); Liverpool Charity and Voluntary Services (£1,600); Macmillan Cancer Support (£1,400); Royal School for the Blind, Liverpool (£1,200); The Shakespeare Hospice, Hoylake Cottage Hospital and Hospice of the Good Shepherd (£1,000 each); Talking Newspapers for the Blind and West Lancashire Community Hospice Association (£500 each).
FINANCES *Year* 2011–12 *Income* £88,044 *Grants* £50,000
TRUSTEES John Bibby; John Wood; Dorothy Fairclough; Stephen Bowman; John McPheat; Alan Gresty; Peter Blocksidge; Lindsey Stead.

OTHER INFORMATION Donations are also made to employees and ex-employees. These have previously totalled around £20,000.

HOW TO APPLY In writing to the correspondent. Trustees meet half yearly. Applications are only acknowledged if a grant is agreed.

WHO TO APPLY TO Dorothy Fairclough, Trustee, c/o Rathbone Brothers and Co. Ltd, Port of Liverpool Building, Pier head, Liverpool L3 1NW

....

■ The Bideford Bridge Trust

CC NO 204536   **ESTABLISHED** 1973

WHERE FUNDING CAN BE GIVEN The parish of Bideford, Devon and the immediate neighbourhood.

WHO CAN BENEFIT Charities and individuals.

WHAT IS FUNDED Grants are dictated by the scheme of the trust, which maintains that the following grants should be made: (i) to encourage education; (ii) to encourage poor people to become more self-sufficient by assisting them in business start-up schemes (iii); to individual applications for charitable assistance (such as on the grounds of poverty or ill health); (iv) to clubs, organisations and charities (v); to assist people with disabilities living in the Parish of Bideford.

WHAT IS NOT FUNDED Computer purchases for individuals. Political donations.

TYPE OF GRANT Core and recurring costs.

RANGE OF GRANTS Up to £100,000

SAMPLE GRANTS Business Start-Ups (M Lillis/ Torridge Training Service) (£97,000); Devon County Council Bideford Railway Path (£40,000); School Swimming Lessons (1610 Limited/Parkwood Leisure) (£28,000); Bideford Amateur Athletic Club (£15,000); Bideford Amateur Boxing Club and Bideford Amateur Rowing Club (£10,000 each); Grow @ Jigsaw Project (Westcountry Housing Association Limited) (£8,000); Home-Start Torridge and North Devon, Jigsaw Furniture Project (Westcountry Housing Association Limited) and Lavington United Reformed Church (£5,000 each).

FINANCES *Year* 2012 *Income* £1,058,860 *Grants* £475,938 *Assets* £14,951,978

TRUSTEES P. Christie; William Isaac; E. Junkison; E. Hubber; Oliver Chope; Angus Harper; Trevor Johns; David Dark; Philip Pester, S. Ellis; M. Langmead.

HOW TO APPLY In writing to the correspondent.

WHO TO APPLY TO P. R. Sims, Steward, 24 Bridgeland Street, Bideford, Devon EX39 2QB *Tel.* 01237 473122

....

■ The Big Lottery Fund (see also Awards for All)

ESTABLISHED 2004

WHERE FUNDING CAN BE GIVEN UK and overseas

WHO CAN BENEFIT Charities, statutory bodies.

WHAT IS FUNDED BIG runs many different programmes, some UK-wide and others specific to England, Northern Ireland, Scotland and Wales. New programmes are introduced from time to time, and others close. Potential applicants are advised to check the fund's website for up-to-date information on current and upcoming programmes.

FINANCES *Year* 2012–13 *Income* £838,688,000 *Grants* £778,700,000 *Assets* £440,371,000

TRUSTEES Peter Ainsworth, Chair; Anna Southall; Nat Sloane; Frank Hewitt; Rajay Naik; Sir Adrian

Webb; Maureen McGinn; Dr Astrid Bonfield; Tony Burton.

OTHER INFORMATION There are a number of regional offices. Call 0845 410 2030 for details.

HOW TO APPLY All application forms and guidance are available via the website or by calling 0845 410 2030.

WHO TO APPLY TO England: 1 Plough Place, London EC4A 1DE; Northern Ireland: 1 Cromac Quay, Cromac Wood, Ormeau Road, Belfast BT7 2JD; Scotland: 1 Atlantic Quay, 1 Robertson Street, Glasgow G2 8JB; Wales: 10th Floor, Helmont House, Churchill Way, Cardiff CF10 2DY *Tel.* 0845 410 2030 *email* enquiries@ biglotteryfund.org.uk *Website* www. biglotteryfund.org.uk

....

■ The Billmeir Charitable Trust

CC NO 208561   **ESTABLISHED** 1956

WHERE FUNDING CAN BE GIVEN UK, with a preference for the Surrey area, specifically Elstead, Tilford, Farnham and Frensham.

WHO CAN BENEFIT Charitable organisations.

WHAT IS FUNDED General charitable purposes. About a quarter of the grants are for health and medical causes and many are given to charities in Surrey.

RANGE OF GRANTS £2,000–£10,000.

SAMPLE GRANTS Reed's School – Cobham (£10,000); Marlborough College (£8,000); Arundel Castle Cricket Foundation and Old Kiln Museum Trust (£7,000 each); RNIB and Woodlarks Campsite Trust (£5,000 each); Elstead Pavilion (£3,000); and Cancer Vaccine and Broomwood Hall School (£2,000 each).

FINANCES *Year* 2011–12 *Income* £190,810 *Grants* £116,500 *Assets* £4,074,582

TRUSTEES M. Whitaker; S. Marriott; J. Whitaker.

HOW TO APPLY The trust states that it does not request applications and they are very rarely successful.

WHO TO APPLY TO Keith Lawrence, Secretary, Moore Stephens, 150 Aldersgate Street, London EC1A 4AB *Tel.* 020 7334 9191

....

■ Percy Bilton Charity

CC NO 1094720   **ESTABLISHED** 1962

WHERE FUNDING CAN BE GIVEN UK.

WHO CAN BENEFIT Large grants are only available to registered charities. Unregistered organisations can apply for a small grant but a reference from another charity, Council for Voluntary Service or the local authority youth service will be required.

WHAT IS FUNDED Projects working with disadvantaged and underprivileged young people (under 25), people with disabilities (physical or learning disabilities or mental health problems) and/or older people (aged over 60).

WHAT IS NOT FUNDED The charity will not consider the following (the list is not exhaustive): running expenses for the organisation or individual projects; salaries, training costs or office equipment/furniture; projects for general community use e.g. community centre and church halls; disabled access to community buildings; publication costs e.g. printing/ distributing promotional and information leaflets; projects that have been completed; items that have already been purchased; provision of disabled facilities in schemes mainly for the able-bodied; general funding/circularised appeals; pre-schools or playgroups (other than predominantly for disabled children); play schemes/summer schemes; holidays or expeditions for individuals or groups; trips, activities or events; community sports/play area facilities; consumables (e.g. stationery, arts and crafts materials); refurbishment or repair of places of worship/church halls; research projects; mainstream pre-schools, schools, colleges and universities (other than special schools); welfare funds for individuals; hospital/medical equipment; and works to premises not used primarily by the eligible groups.

TYPE OF GRANT One-off.

RANGE OF GRANTS Grants to individuals: up to £200; small grants to organisations: up to £500 towards furnishing and equipment for small projects; main funding single grants for capital expenditure: in excess of £2,000.

SAMPLE GRANTS Albert Kennedy Trust – London (£11,000); Jumbulance Trust – Hertfordshire (£10,000); Home Farm Trust – Oxfordshire (£9,500); St Raphael's Hospice – Surrey (£7,500); Age UK – Hull (£6,000); Children's Trust – Surrey, Reigate and Redhill YMCA and Sunfield – West Midlands (£5,000 each); Cumbria Cerebral Palsy, Carlisle and Greenwich and Bexley Community Hospice – London (£2,000 each); Barons Court Project – London, Grenfell Club – Redcar, Music Space – Bristol, Making a Difference – Tameside, STEPS – Devon, Wellspring Family Centre – Norfolk and Where Next Association – Worcester (£500 each); Eyres Monsell Club for Young People – Leicester, Phoenix Stroke Club – West Sussex and Oxfordshire Family Mediation – Oxford (£400 each); and North Somerset Crossroads (£300).

FINANCES *Year* 2011–12 *Income* £711,061 *Grants* £419,689 *Assets* £19,292,276

TRUSTEES Miles A. Bilton, Chair; James R. Lee; Stefan J. Paciorek; Kim Lansdown; Hayley Bilton.

OTHER INFORMATION Assistance is also given on a one-off basis to individuals and families who fall within the following categories: older people on a low income and people with physical or learning disabilities or mental health problems. All applications for individuals to be sent in by the relevant social worker on local or health authority headed notepaper. In 2011–12 individuals received grants totalling £143,500 (not included in the grant total).

HOW TO APPLY The charity's website gives the following guidance on making an application: '*Large grants (£2,000 and over)* Apply on your organisation's headed notepaper giving or attaching the following information. 1–6 must be provided in all cases and 7 as applicable to your appeal: 1. A summary outlining the amount you are requesting and what the funding is for. 2. A brief history of your Charity, its objectives and work. 3. Description of the project and what you intend to achieve. 4. A copy of your most recent Annual Report and audited accounts. 5. Details of funds already raised and other sources that you have approached. 6. Proposals to monitor and evaluate the project. 7. Any other relevant information that will help to explain your application. The following additional information that applies to your appeal: *Building/Refurbishment appeals:* A statement of all costs involved. Itemise major items and professional fees; confirmation that the project has ongoing revenue funding; confirmation that all planning and other consents and building regulations approvals have been obtained; details of ownership of the premises and if leased, the length of the unexpired term; timetable of construction/refurbishment and anticipated date of completion.'

'*Equipment appeals:* An itemised list of all equipment with estimate of costs. Obtain at least two competitive estimates except where this is not practicable e.g. specialised equipment; when you plan to purchase the equipment.'

'*Contribution towards purchase of minibuses:* Note that minibuses can only be considered if used to transport older and/or disabled people with mobility problems. Give details of provision made for insurance, tax and maintenance etc. We require confirmation that your organisation can meet future running costs.'

'*Small grants (up to £500)* Apply on your organisation's headed notepaper with the following information: brief details about your organisation and its work; a copy of your most recent annual accounts; outline of the project and its principal aims; breakdown of the cost of item/s required; the organisation's bank account name to which the cheque should be made payable if a grant is approved. (We cannot make cheques payable to individuals); if your organisation is not a registered charity, supply a reference from a registered charity with whom you work or from the local Voluntary Service Council.'

WHO TO APPLY TO Tara Smith, Charity Administrator, Bilton House, 7 Culmington Road, Ealing, London W13 9NB *Tel.* 020 8579 2829 *Fax* 020 8579 3650 *Website* www.percybiltoncharity.org.uk

··

■ The Bingham Trust

CC NO 287636   **ESTABLISHED** 1977

WHERE FUNDING CAN BE GIVEN Buxton and district.

WHO CAN BENEFIT Organisations and individuals.

WHAT IS FUNDED Community needs, churches, arts and educational needs.

WHAT IS NOT FUNDED Generally, limited to the town of Buxton and district.

TYPE OF GRANT One-off, capital including buildings, project, running costs, salaries and start-up costs. Funding is for up to three years.

RANGE OF GRANTS Up to £5,000.

SAMPLE GRANTS Peaks and Dales Advocacy (£5,400); Blythe House Hospice, Kinder Choir and Marie Curie Cancer Care (£5,000 each); St John's Church and Buxton Festival (£3,000 each); Buxton Mountain Rescue Team and Buxton Cricket Club (£2,000 each); Volunteer Centre Buxton, Friends of Buxton Museum and Art Gallery and Action Medical Research (£1,500 each); Fairfield Older Persons Group (£1,000); Harpur Hill Youth Club (£800); High Peak Gymnastics (£500); Yoga Group (£250) and Strines Youth Club (£50).

FINANCES *Year* 2011–12 *Income* £148,573 *Grants* £116,647 *Assets* £3,960,826

TRUSTEES Dr Geoffrey Willis; Roger Horne; Helen Mirtle; Alexandra Hurst.

OTHER INFORMATION In 2011–12 the trust distributed around 100 grants to individuals and organisations. Grants to organisations totalled £103,000, while approximately £14,000 was distributed to individuals.

HOW TO APPLY On a form available to download on the trust's website, or in writing to the correspondent on no more than two pages of A4, stating the total cost of the project and sources of other funding. Applications should arrive before the end of March, June, September and December each year.

WHO TO APPLY TO Roger Horne, Trustee, Blinder House, Flagg, Buxton, Derbyshire SK17 9QG *email* binghamtrust@aol.com *Website* www.binghamtrust.org.uk

■ The Bintaub Charitable Trust

CC NO 1003915   **ESTABLISHED** 1991

WHERE FUNDING CAN BE GIVEN Greater London, worldwide.

WHO CAN BENEFIT Jewish, health, education, children.

WHAT IS FUNDED Mainly London organisations, towards 'the advancement of education in and the religion of the Orthodox Jewish faith'. Grants are also given for other charitable causes, mainly towards medical and children's work.

SAMPLE GRANTS Gateshead Jewish Academy (£6,400); Yeshiva Be'er Hatorah (£6,000); Gateshead Jewish Primary School (£3,000); JTTC (£2,900); Menorah Foundation School (£2,600); Kupat Ha'ir (£2,500); Friends of Yeshivat Lomdei Torah, Friends of Mir and Va'ad Harabbanim L'inyanei Tzedaka (£2,000 each); and Sunderland Kollel (£700).

FINANCES *Year* 2011–12 *Income* £38,076 *Grants* £33,319 *Assets* £9,035

TRUSTEES James Frohwein; Tonia Frohwein; Ra; Rabbi E. Stefansky.

HOW TO APPLY The trust has previously stated that new applications are not being accepted.

WHO TO APPLY TO J. Wahnon, Secretary, Ki Tob Chartered Accountants, 125 Wolmer Gardens, Edgware HA8 8QF

■ The Birmingham and Black Country Community Foundation

CC NO 1048162   **ESTABLISHED** 1995

WHERE FUNDING CAN BE GIVEN Greater Birmingham.

WHO CAN BENEFIT Small community-based groups and organisations involved in activities that regenerate and rebuild communities.

WHAT IS FUNDED Small grants are generally given to community based groups involved in activities that regenerate and build communities, however priority is given to those projects which: encourage community responsibility; develop community capacity; are unable to access other forms of funding; and do not duplicate other work being done within the area.

WHAT IS NOT FUNDED No funding is available: for individuals, for whatever purpose; to statutory organisations, including PCT's and *schools; for groups which are not constituted or do not have a set of rules; to fund trips abroad or overseas activities; to fund buses, mini buses or other community transport schemes (not including transport costs forming part of a project) to fund building costs, including access adaptations to buildings; for projects operating outside Birmingham, Dudley, Sandwell, Walsall and Wolverhampton; for donations towards general appeals or for an application from a large national charity; for organisations and individuals in the promotion of political or purely religious ideology – although some faith group activities can be supported. *Note – whilst schools are not currently eligible to apply, independent groups within schools such as PTA's and before/after school clubs can apply. Note: These are general exclusions to BBCCF and you are advised to read specific grant guidelines associated with funding programmes being administered by BBCCF at any one time.

RANGE OF GRANTS Mostly under £2,000.

SAMPLE GRANTS Jerico Enterprises CIC (£50,000); Kingshurst Development Trust (£22,000); Alexandra High School and Sixth Form Centre (£20,000); The Big Clean Up (£17,500); City United (£15,000); Birmingham Friends of the Earth (£12,000); Aspire4U (£11,000); The Dean Foundation (£4,500); and Banners Gate Coffee Club (£3,000).

FINANCES *Year* 2011–12 *Income* £2,783,173 *Grants* £1,558,222 *Assets* £789,983

TRUSTEES David Bucknall; John Andrews; Kay Cadman; Angela Henry; Richard Harris; John Matthews.

HOW TO APPLY Refer to the foundation's website for full details of how to apply to the various programmes currently being administered.

WHO TO APPLY TO Karen Argyle, Programmes Manager, Nechells Baths, Nechells Park Road, Nechells, Birmingham B7 5PD *Tel.* 01213 225560 *Fax* 01213 225579 *email* team@ bbccf.org.uk *Website* www.bhamfoundation.co. uk

■ The Birmingham District Nursing Charitable Trust

CC NO 215652   **ESTABLISHED** 1960

WHERE FUNDING CAN BE GIVEN Within a 20-mile radius of the Council House in Birmingham.

WHO CAN BENEFIT Local organisations benefiting medical professionals. Grants may be made to local branches of national organisations.

WHAT IS FUNDED Medical or nursing organisations; convalescent homes; convalescent homes or rest homes for nurses or other medical or nursing institution; amenities for patients or nursing staff of Birmingham Domiciliary Nursing Service; amenities for patients or nursing staff of any state hospital.

WHAT IS NOT FUNDED No grants are given to individuals.

TYPE OF GRANT One-off and recurrent

RANGE OF GRANTS £500–£6,000

SAMPLE GRANTS Birmingham PHAB Camps (£6,000); Acorns Children's Hospice, Birmingham St Mary's Hospice, St Giles Hospice (£5,000 each); Age UK, BLAT, Careers Advice and Resources Establishment Sandwell, Focus Birmingham, Medical Foundation for the Victims of Torture, Mobility Trust, Motor Neurone Disease Association, Primrose Hospice Cancer Help, Shakespeare Hospice, Vitalise Skylarks and Walsall Carers Centre (£2,000 each); Better Understanding of Dementia in Sandwell and Ex Cathedra (£500 each).

FINANCES *Year* 2011–12 *Income* £81,339 *Grants* £56,168 *Assets* £1,655,981

TRUSTEES H. W. Tuckey; T. Cull; Prof. C. M. Clifford; Dr P. Mayer; S. Reynolds; A. H. Jones; Dr M. Honeyman.

HOW TO APPLY In writing to the correspondent with a copy of the latest accounts. Applications should be sent in August/September. Trustees meet to consider grants in the first week of November.

WHO TO APPLY TO Prof. C. M. Clifford, c/o Shakespeare Putsman, Somerset House, Temple Street, Birmingham B2 5DJ *Tel.* 01212 373000 *email* hannah.tait@shakespeares.co.uk

■ The Birmingham Hospital Saturday Fund Medical Charity and Welfare Trust

CC NO 502428   **ESTABLISHED** 1972

WHERE FUNDING CAN BE GIVEN UK, but mostly centred around the West Midlands and Birmingham area.

WHO CAN BENEFIT Hospitals and other medical and welfare organisations and charities.

WHAT IS FUNDED To improve the quality of life for those disadvantaged in society; provide comforts and amenities for patients in hospital and medical charities, assist medical research, education and science, and support charitable organisations concerned with people who are sick. The trust will consider funding: health; speech therapy; scholarships; building services; information technology and computers; publishing and printing; and health professional bodies.

WHAT IS NOT FUNDED The trust will not generally fund: direct appeals from individuals or students; administration expenditure including salaries; bank loans/deficits/mortgages; items or services which should normally be publicly funded; large general appeals; vehicle operating costs; or motor vehicles for infrequent use and where subsidised vehicle share schemes are available to charitable organisations.

TYPE OF GRANT One-off grants, capital, project and research, all funded for up to one year.

RANGE OF GRANTS Usually up to £2,000.

SAMPLE GRANTS Previous beneficiaries included: Friends of Victoria School – Northfield (£3,800); NHS West Midlands (£3,400); Birmingham Centre for Arts Therapies and Starlight Children's Foundation (£2,500 each); Vascular Department, Selly Oak Hospital (£2,000); Dream Holidays, Isle of Wight (£1,900); the Mary Stevens Hospice, Stourbridge, West Midlands (£1,600); Institute of Ageing and Health, Birmingham (£1,500); Contact the Elderly, Birmingham (£1,200); Christian Lewis Trust – Cardiff (£1,100); Action Medical Research – Horsham, Children's Heart Foundation and REACT Surrey (£1,000); Katherine House – Stafford (£900); St Martin's Centre for Health and Healing (£750); Deep Impact Theatre Company and Birmingham Heart Care – Walsall (£500 each); and Acorns Children's Hospice – Birmingham (£315).

FINANCES *Year* 2012 *Income* £549 *Grants* £27,153

TRUSTEES Dr Paul Kanas; Stephen Hall; Eric Hickman; Michael Malone; David Read; James Salmons.

OTHER INFORMATION Income has been below £5,000 for the fourth year running (2008: £22,000) but expenditure has increased from last year (2011: £17,000). Full accounts were not required at the Charity Commission due to the low income this year; therefore, further details on grants and beneficiaries were not available.

HOW TO APPLY On a form available from the correspondent. The form requires basic information and should be submitted with financial details. Evidence should be provided that the project has been adequately considered through the provision of quotes or supporting documents, although the trust dislikes applications which provide too much general information or have long-winded descriptions of projects. Applicants should take great care to read the guidance notes on the application form. The trustees meet four times a year and deadlines are given when application forms are sent out.

WHO TO APPLY TO Philip Ashbourne, Administrator, Gamgee House, 2 Darnley Road, Birmingham B16 8TE *Tel.* 01214 543601 *email* charitabletrust@bhsf.co.uk

··
■ Birmingham International Airport Community Trust

CC NO 1071176   **ESTABLISHED** 1998

WHERE FUNDING CAN BE GIVEN The areas affected by the airport's operation (East Birmingham, Solihull and parts of north Warwickshire).

WHO CAN BENEFIT Established local charities.

WHAT IS FUNDED Areas of work the trust supports are: environment improvement and heritage conservation; bringing the community closer together through facilities for sport, recreation and other leisure-time activities; improving awareness of environmental issues or environmental education and training activities; encouraging and protecting wildlife. It describes the types of projects it wishes to support as including community centres, community groups, sports, playgroups, schools, youth clubs, scouts, gardens/parks, environment, music and churches. Work should benefit a substantial section of the community rather than less inclusive groups, although work with older people or people with special needs is positively encouraged.

WHAT IS NOT FUNDED The following are not eligible for grants: individuals; projects which have already been carried out or paid for; organisations which have statutory responsibilities e.g. hospitals, surgeries, clinics, schools etc. unless the project is clearly not a statutory responsibility. Grants are not normally recurrent, or given towards the purchase of land or buildings.

TYPE OF GRANT Grants may be for capital or revenue projects, although the trust will not commit to recurrent or running costs, such as salaries.

RANGE OF GRANTS Generally up to £3,000.

SAMPLE GRANTS Previous beneficiaries have included: 298th Birmingham Brownies/Rangers Pack, Age Concern – Castle Bromwich, Blakenhale Infant School, Chelmsley Town Football Club, Coleshill Bell Ringers, Coleshill Town Football Club, George Fentham Endowed School, Hatchford Brook Youth and Community Centre and Land Lane Baptist Free Church.

FINANCES *Year* 2012–13 *Income* £51,977 *Grants* £55,165 *Assets* £1,396

TRUSTEE The trust acts independently of the airport management, with nine representatives of the following bodies making up the trustees: The Airport Consultative Committee (3), Birmingham City Council (2), Birmingham International Airport (2) and Solihull Council (2).

HOW TO APPLY On a form available from the correspondent. Full guidelines can be downloaded from the trust's website.

WHO TO APPLY TO The Administrator, Birmingham International Airport Ltd, Birmingham B26 3QJ *Tel.* 01217 677448 *email* commtrust@bhx.co.uk *Website* www.bhx.co.uk

··
■ The Lord Mayor of Birmingham's Charity

CC NO 1036968   **ESTABLISHED** 1994

WHERE FUNDING CAN BE GIVEN Birmingham

WHO CAN BENEFIT Charities determined by the Lord Mayor at the commencement of term of office.

WHAT IS FUNDED Beneficiaries are determined by the Lord Mayor prior to taking up office. Three or four charities/voluntary organisations are usually selected at the beginning of the year. No other donations are made.

WHAT IS NOT FUNDED Charities working outside the area of Birmingham.

TYPE OF GRANT One-off.

FINANCES *Year* 2011–12 *Income* £109,308 *Grants* £76,266 *Assets* £140,295

TRUSTEES Lord Mayor of Birmingham; Deputy Lord Mayor of Birmingham; Cllr Sue Anderson; Jim Whorwood; John Alden; Michael Wilkes; John Cotton.

HOW TO APPLY In writing to the correspondent. Although the beneficiaries are often predetermined, applications can be sent in January/February for the new Lord Mayor to consider.

WHO TO APPLY TO Leigh Nash, Administrator, Development Section, Room 403, 4th Floor, Council House, Birmingham B1 1BB *Tel.* 01213 032691 *email* leigh_nash@birmingham.gov.uk *Website* www.birmingham.gov.uk

....

■ Birthday House Trust

CC NO 248028   **ESTABLISHED** 1966

WHERE FUNDING CAN BE GIVEN England and Wales.

WHO CAN BENEFIT Charitable organisations and individuals.

WHAT IS FUNDED General charitable purposes.

WHAT IS NOT FUNDED No applications will be considered from individuals or non-charitable organisations.

TYPE OF GRANT One-off and recurrent.

RANGE OF GRANTS Mostly up to £10,000.

SAMPLE GRANTS Druk White Loftus School (£20,000); Climate Parliament and Merton Road Scouts (£10,000 each); Soil Association and The Ecology Trust (£2,500 each); Chichester Cathedral Trust (£2,000); Smile Support and Care (£1,000); Chichester Area Mind, Eastbourne Scout and Guide Hut Committee and Fire Services National Benevolent Fund (£500 each); and Murray Downland Trust (£50).

FINANCES *Year* 2011 *Income* £211,636 *Grants* £49,800 *Assets* £6,389,098

TRUSTEE The Dickinson Trust Limited and Rathbone Trust Company Limited.

OTHER INFORMATION The main work of this trust is engaged with the running of a residential home for people who are elderly in Midhurst, West Sussex. In 2011 a further £49,685 was distributed to pensioners.

HOW TO APPLY In writing to the correspondent, including an sae. No application forms are issued and there is no deadline. Only successful applicants are acknowledged.

WHO TO APPLY TO Laura Gosling, Trust Administrator, Millbank Financial Services Limited, 4th Floor, Swan House, 17–19 Stratford Place, London W1C 1BQ *Tel.* 020 7907 2100 *email* charity@mfs.co.uk

....

■ Miss Jeanne Bisgood's Charitable Trust

CC NO 208714   **ESTABLISHED** 1963

WHERE FUNDING CAN BE GIVEN UK, overseas and locally in Bournemouth and Dorset, especially Poole.

WHO CAN BENEFIT Registered charities.

WHAT IS FUNDED General charitable purposes. Main grants have been and will be concentrated on the following categories: (a) operating under Roman Catholic auspices; (b) operating in Poole, Bournemouth and the county of Dorset; (c) national (not local) charities concerned with older people.

WHAT IS NOT FUNDED Grants are not given to local charities which do not fit categories 1 or 2

listed above. Individuals and non-registered charities are not supported.

TYPE OF GRANT One-off, capital and recurring.

RANGE OF GRANTS £25–£2,500.

FINANCES *Year* 2011–12 *Income* £160,843 *Grants* £199,000 *Assets* £5,363,670

TRUSTEES Jeanne Bisgood; Patrick Bisgood; Paula Schulte.

OTHER INFORMATION The trust operates a sub-fund – the Bertram Fund from which grants are usually made anonymously.

HOW TO APPLY In writing to the correspondent, quoting the UK registration number and registered name of the charity. Accounts no longer need to be submitted along with the application as the trust can obtain them from the Charity Commission. Applications should NOT be made directly to the Bertram Fund. Applications for capital projects 'should provide brief details of the main purposes, the total target and the current state of the appeal'. The trustees regret that they are unable to acknowledge appeals. The trustees normally meet in late February/early March and September.

WHO TO APPLY TO Jeanne Bisgood, Trustee, 12 Waters Edge, Brudenell Road, Poole BH13 7NN *Tel.* 01202 708460

....

■ The Michael Bishop Foundation

CC NO 297627   **ESTABLISHED** 1987

WHERE FUNDING CAN BE GIVEN Worldwide with a preference for Birmingham and the Midlands.

WHO CAN BENEFIT Registered charities.

WHAT IS FUNDED Arts, health, child welfare, education and religion.

SAMPLE GRANTS Loughborough University Development Trust (£1 million); Mill Hill School Foundation (£300,000); Glendonbrook Foundation (£231,000); Future Directions International (£189,000); Commonwealth Youth Orchestra (£75,000); The Terrence Higgins Trust and Vipingo Village Fund (£25,000 each); the Student Entrepreneurial Fund (£15,000); Barry and Martin's Trust and Christchurch Earthquake Appeal (£2,500 each); and Autistica (£500).

FINANCES *Year* 2011–12 *Income* £429,894 *Grants* £2,629,881 *Assets* £18,602,713

TRUSTEES Grahame N. Elliott; Baron Glendonbrook of Bowdon; John S. Coulson.

OTHER INFORMATION The trustees in their annual report of 2011–12 state that given the increase in the size of the funds at their disposal, they will in due course establish more formal guidelines as to the types of charitable activities they favour in order to assist those seeking support.

HOW TO APPLY In writing to the correspondent.

WHO TO APPLY TO Charlotte Newall, Administrator, Staunton House, Ashby-de-la-Zouch, Leicestershire LE65 1RW *Tel.* 01530 564388

....

■ The Bishop's Development Fund

CC NO 700588   **ESTABLISHED** 1988

WHERE FUNDING CAN BE GIVEN Yorkshire

WHO CAN BENEFIT Church of England organisations.

WHAT IS FUNDED The objects of the trust are 'to promote any charitable purposes within the areas of the diocese of Wakefield which are in need of spiritual and material assistance by reason of social or economic changes with a view to reinforcing the work of the Church of England among the people of those areas' and 'to promote and assist the charitable work of the Church Urban Fund'.

WHAT IS NOT FUNDED Any application which does not meet the criteria outlined here.

RANGE OF GRANTS £190–£4,000

SAMPLE GRANTS St Mary's Todmorden (£4,000); St John's Golcar (£3,000); Trinity, Ossett (£2,500); St Saviour's Brownhill (£1,500); St John the Baptist Dodworth (£500); Love Huddersfield (£190).

FINANCES *Year* 2011–12 *Income* £32,595 *Grants* £11,690 *Assets* £675,102

TRUSTEES The Right Revd Anthony Robinson; Mary Judkins; David Buckingham; Alison Dean; The Ven. Peter Townley; Bishop of Wakefield; Brian Pearson; Dr Anne Dawtry; David Smethurst; Elizabeth Morton and Ian Pinder-Packard.

HOW TO APPLY In writing to the correspondent. Only applications formally approved by the parochial church councils of Church of England churches in the diocese of Wakefield will be considered. The trustees meet four times a year.

WHO TO APPLY TO Susan Parker, Church House, 1 South Parade, Wakefield, West Yorkshire WF1 1LP *Tel.* 01924 371802

■ The Sydney Black Charitable Trust

CC NO 219855   **ESTABLISHED** 1949

WHO CAN BENEFIT Charitable organisations.

WHAT IS FUNDED Youth organisations, religious, medical and other institutions, such as those helping people who are disadvantaged.

TYPE OF GRANT One-off grants for core support, equipment and vehicles.

RANGE OF GRANTS Generally under £1,000.

SAMPLE GRANTS A previous beneficiary was Endeavour with an unusually large grant of £20,000.

FINANCES *Year* 2011–12 *Income* £70,867 *Grants* £58,400 *Assets* £3,057,431

TRUSTEES Jennifer Crabtree; Hilary Dickenson; Stephen Crabtree; Philip Crabtree.

OTHER INFORMATION In 2001 The Edna Black Charitable Trust and The Cyril Black Charitable Trust were incorporated into this trust. Grants are generally in the region of £125 and £250 each.

HOW TO APPLY Applications should be made in writing to the correspondent.

WHO TO APPLY TO Jennifer Crabtree, Trustee, 30 Welford Place, London SW19 5AJ

■ The Bertie Black Foundation

CC NO 245207   **ESTABLISHED** 1965

WHERE FUNDING CAN BE GIVEN UK, Israel.

WHO CAN BENEFIT Registered charities.

WHAT IS FUNDED The relief and assistance of people who are in need, the advancement of education and religion, and other charitable purposes.

SAMPLE GRANTS Previously: I Rescue (£50,000); Magen David Adom (£47,000 in three grants); Alyn Hospital (£49,000 in two grants); Emunah (£38,000); Laniardo Hospital and Shaare Zedek (£25,000 each); Friends of Israel Sports Centre for Disabled (£20,000); Child Resettlement Trust (£10,000 in four grants); Norwood (£7,600 in four grants); and Hope (£5,200 in four grants).

FINANCES *Year* 2011–12 *Income* £102,896 *Grants* £220,000

TRUSTEES Isabelle Seddon; Doris Black; Carolyn Black; Harry Black; Ivor Seddon.

OTHER INFORMATION Accounts and annual report for 2011–12 received at the Charity Commission but, in error, only the independent examiner's statement page published online.

HOW TO APPLY The trust states it 'supports causes known to the trustees' and that they 'do not respond to unsolicited requests'.

WHO TO APPLY TO Harry Black, Trustee, Abbots House, 13 Beaumont Gate, Shenley Hill, Radlett, Hertfordshire WD7 7AR *Tel.* 01923 850096 *email* sonneborn@btconnect.com

■ Sir Alec Black's Charity

CC NO 220295   **ESTABLISHED** 1942

WHERE FUNDING CAN BE GIVEN UK, with a preference for Grimsby.

WHO CAN BENEFIT Ex-employees of Sir Alec Black, charitable institutions benefiting the sick and infirm including hospices, and poor fishermen and dockworkers of Grimsby.

WHAT IS FUNDED Primarily to benefit former employees of Sir Alec Black and to provide bed linen and pillows to hospitals. Secondarily to benefit sick poor fishermen and dockworkers of Grimsby.

TYPE OF GRANT One-off.

RANGE OF GRANTS Generally under £1,000.

FINANCES *Year* 2011–12 *Income* £551,751 *Grants* £26,474 *Assets* £1,657,196

TRUSTEES Stewart Wilson; Dr Diana F. Wilson; Michael Parker; Philip A. Mounfield; John N. Harrison.

OTHER INFORMATION In 2011–12 grants to former employees of the settlor totalled £11,392. A further £14,551 went in grants for bed linen to organisations, with £531 given to fishermen and dockworkers.

HOW TO APPLY In writing to the correspondent. Trustees meet in May and November; applications need to be received in March or September.

WHO TO APPLY TO Stewart Wilson, Trustee, Wilson Sharpe and Co., 27 Osborne Street, Grimsby, North East Lincolnshire DN31 1NU *email* sc@wilsonsharpe.co.uk

■ Blackheart Foundation (UK) Limited

CC NO 1136813   **ESTABLISHED** 2010

WHERE FUNDING CAN BE GIVEN UK

WHO CAN BENEFIT Individuals and organisations.

WHAT IS FUNDED Primarily the areas of health, education and sport.

FINANCES *Year* 2011–12 *Income* £120,000

TRUSTEES Richard Lewis; Ilina Singh; Claire Heath.

OTHER INFORMATION The foundation was established in 2010 by Richard Lewis, chief executive of Tristan Capital Partners. Richard Lewis also serves on the board of several other charitable ventures, including the I I Foundation, Teach First and Eastside Young Leaders Academy. 'No grants were made in the year as donations were only received in April 2012'.

HOW TO APPLY In writing to the correspondent.

WHO TO APPLY TO Claire Heath, Trustee, c/o Tristan Capital Partners, Berkeley Square House, 8th Floor, Berkeley Square, London W1J 6DB *Tel.* 0204638900

Think carefully about every application. Is it justified?

393

■ Isabel Blackman Foundation

CC NO 313577 **ESTABLISHED** 1966
WHERE FUNDING CAN BE GIVEN Hastings and St Leonards-on-sea.
WHO CAN BENEFIT Organisations benefiting children, young adults, older people, retired people, people with disabilities, Christians and people with sight loss or blindness.
WHAT IS FUNDED People who are elderly, blind or disabled, hospitals, churches, voluntary charitable bodies, youth organisations, education.
WHAT IS NOT FUNDED Note only applications from Hastings and district are considered.
RANGE OF GRANTS Up to £50,000.
SAMPLE GRANTS Kent Surrey Sussex Air Ambulance (£10,000); Halton Baptist Church (£5,000); Alzheimer's Society (£3,500); Citizens Advice 1066 and Silverdale School (£3,000 each); Myasthenia Gravis Association and Listening Books (£2,500); Fire Fighters Charity (£2,000); Broomgrove Playscheme (£1,500); Hastings, Rye and District Cub Scouts (£1,000); Association of Carers (£500) and PDSA (£150).
FINANCES *Year* 2012–13 *Income* £299,564 *Grants* £158,103 *Assets* £5,260,896
TRUSTEES Denis Jukes; Patricia Connolly; Margaret Haley; John Lamplugh; Evelyn Williams; Christine Deacon.
HOW TO APPLY In writing to the correspondent. The trustees meet bi-monthly to consider applications.
WHO TO APPLY TO D. J. Jukes, Secretary, Stonehenge, 13 Laton Road, Hastings, East Sussex TN34 2ES *Tel.* 01424 431756

■ The BlackRock (UK) Charitable Trust

CC NO 1065447 **ESTABLISHED** 1999
WHERE FUNDING CAN BE GIVEN UK.
WHO CAN BENEFIT Charitable organisations.
WHAT IS FUNDED General charitable purposes.
FINANCES *Year* 2012 *Income* £1,754
TRUSTEES Richard Royds; Andrew Johnston; Elizabeth Tracey; Peter Walker; BlackRock Group Limited.
HOW TO APPLY 'The trustees invite staff, clients and business associates of BlackRock Investment Management (UK) Limited to submit applications for grants to a registered charity of their choice.' Other appeals would usually be declined.
WHO TO APPLY TO Agnieszka Caban, Administrator, 12 Throgmorton Avenue, London EC2N 2DL

■ The Blagrave Trust (formerly The Herbert and Peter Blagrave Charitable Trust)

CC NO 277074 **ESTABLISHED** 1978
WHERE FUNDING CAN BE GIVEN South of England with a preference for Hampshire, Wiltshire and Berkshire.
WHO CAN BENEFIT Registered charities only working in the geographical areas stated.
WHAT IS FUNDED The focus for grants is primarily charities that work with children and young people, including those with special needs and disabilities, and their families and carers. Occasional consideration will be given to applications from organisations working with adult disabled people.

WHAT IS NOT FUNDED No grants are given for medical research, insured sportspeople (except where they fall under work of disability charities), older people (The only limited exception to this is where a proposal supporting adult disability is recommended for funding), general appeals, individuals, sponsored events, campaigning activities or party political activities. A three year interval is normally required before further applications from the same organisation can be accepted.
TYPE OF GRANT One-off and recurrent.
RANGE OF GRANTS Between £5,000 and £50,000.
SAMPLE GRANTS Winchester Cathedral Trust (£100,000); Skillforce (£34,000); KIDS (£30,000); Brainwave (£26,000); Disability Challengers (£22,000); Bath Institute of Medical Engineering (£21,000); Country Trust for Hampshire Country Learning (£19,000); Listening Books (£10,000) and Rainbow Trust Children's Charity (£7,000).
FINANCES *Year* 2011–12 *Income* £1,326,753 *Grants* £967,000 *Assets* £32,742,083
TRUSTEES Julian Whately; Timothy Jackson-Stops; Sir Paul Neave.
OTHER INFORMATION For full funding guidelines and criteria visit the trust's website: www.blagravetrust.org
HOW TO APPLY In the first instance complete the online 'Grant Checklist and Outline Proposal' form on the website (www.blagravetrust.org) which asks you to outline your project in no more than 200 words. The trust will then either contact you to indicate your application is not of interest, or to discuss in more detail by phone.
WHO TO APPLY TO Executive Director, c/o Rathbone Trust Company Limited, 1 Curzon Street, London W1J 5FB *Tel.* 020 7399 0370 *email* grants@blagravetrust.org *Website* www.blagravetrust.org

■ The Blair Foundation

CC NO 801755 **ESTABLISHED** 1989
WHERE FUNDING CAN BE GIVEN UK, particularly southern England and Scotland; overseas.
WHO CAN BENEFIT Organisations, particularly disability and wildlife groups.
WHAT IS FUNDED General, especially conservation and protection of the environment; improving disabled access to wildlife areas; and medical charities.
WHAT IS NOT FUNDED Charities that have objectives which the trustees consider harmful to the environment are not supported.
RANGE OF GRANTS Up to £12,000.
SAMPLE GRANTS Previous beneficiaries included: Ayrshire Wildlife Services (£12,000); King's School – Canterbury and Ayrshire Fiddler Orchestra (£10,000 each); Scottish National Trust (£7,000); Home Farm Trust (£5,000); CHAS (£2,000); Handicapped Children's Action Group and Penny Brohn Cancer Care (£1,500); Ro-Ro Sailing Project and Sustrans (£1,000 each).
FINANCES *Year* 2011–12 *Income* £17,379 *Grants* £78,452
TRUSTEES Robert Thornton; Jennifer Thornton; Graham Healy; Alan Thornton.
OTHER INFORMATION Accounts were received at the Charity Commission but due to the charity's low income, were not published online.
HOW TO APPLY In writing to the correspondent, for consideration at trustees' meetings held at least once a year. A receipt for donations is requested from all donees.
WHO TO APPLY TO The Trustees, Smith and Williamson, 1 Bishops Wharf, Walnut Tree

Close, Guildford, Surrey GU1 4RA *Tel.* 01483 407100

■ Blakemore Foundation

cc no 1015938   **established** 1992
where funding can be given England and Wales.
who can benefit The trust supports local and national charitable organisations.
what is funded General charitable purposes.
what is not funded No grants for: salaries; national charities (unless there is a direct request from an employee of A. F. Blakemore); grants to individuals, including students; charities/ organisations outside of England and Wales; overseas appeals; expeditions or overseas travel; sponsorship and marketing promotions; endowment funds; political donations.
type of grant One-off.
range of grants Up to £200.
sample grants Foundation for Conductive Education; St Andrew's Church – Biggleswade and Wenlock Poetry Festival.
finances *Year* 2011–12 *Income* £91,376 *Grants* £135,639 *Assets* £28,499
trustees Peter Blakemore; Gwendoline Blakemore; Julian Tonks.
how to apply On a form available to download from the trust's website, where the trust's criteria, guidelines and application process are also posted.
who to apply to Kate Senter, Community Affairs Officer, Unit 401, Bentley Road South, Darlaston, Wednesbury WV10 8LQ *Tel.* 01215 682910 *email* ksenter@afblakemore.com *Website* www.afblakemore.com

■ The Blanchminster Trust

cc no 202118   **established** 1421
where funding can be given The parishes of Bude, Stratton and Poughill (i.e. the former urban district of Bude-Stratton on 31 March 1974).
who can benefit Organisations or individuals residing in the area of benefit and showing proof of financial need. Organisations benefiting children; young adults; older people; academics; students; actors and entertainment professionals; and musicians may be considered.
what is funded Charities working in the fields of education, social welfare and community aid.
what is not funded Applications from Bude-Stratton only will be considered, or in respect of educational applications from people who have at least one parent so residing.
type of grant Cash or equipment. Cash may be grant or loan, equipment normally 'permanent loan'. Capital including buildings, core costs, feasibility studies, interest free loans, one-off, project, running costs and start-up costs. Funding will be considered for one year or less.
sample grants League of Friends of Stratton Hospital (£50,000); Friends of Bude Sea Pool and Stratton Play Area Regeneration Committee (£10,000 each); St Michael and All Angels Church (£5,000); Poughill Village Hall (£1,800); Bude Infant School (£1,500); St Andrew's Church (£1,300); Cornwall Blind (£1,000); Bude Youth Theatre and Neetside Community Centre (£500 each) and Bude Toy Library (£350).
finances *Year* 2012 *Income* £485,547 *Grants* £301,465 *Assets* £10,434,265
trustees Christopher Cornish; John Gardiner; Wilfred Keat; Valerie Newman; Chris Nichols; Gordon Rogers; Byron Rowlands; Julia

Shepherd; Leonard Tozer; Owen May; Ian Whitfield; Michael Worden; Christine Bilsland
how to apply In writing to the correspondent. Applicants may be called for an informal interview by the relevant committee. Following this a recommendation is made to the full board of trustees who make the final decision. Applications are considered at monthly meetings. All applications are acknowledged. Guidelines and criteria are available to view on the trust's website.
who to apply to J. E. Bunning, The Clerk to the Trustees, Blanchminster Building, 38 Lansdown Road, Bude, Cornwall EX23 8EE *Tel.* 01288 352851 *email* office@blanchminster.plus.com *Website* www.blanchminster.org.uk

■ The Blandford Lake Trust

cc no 1069630   **established** 1998
where funding can be given North Wales and overseas.
who can benefit Registered charities.
what is funded Overseas development, church outreach work, Christian youth work, educational resources.
what is not funded All projects outside the criteria are excluded. Grants are not given to churches for building work.
sample grants Operation Smile (£37,000); Send a Cow (£10,500); Responding to Conflict (£10,000); Traidcraft (£8,000); Mission Aviation Fellowship (£5,000); and Christian Solidarity Worldwide (£2,000).
finances *Year* 2012 *Income* £107,116 *Grants* £129,995 *Assets* £442,845
trustees Lucy Lake; Richard Lake; Jonathan Lake; Mathew Lake.
how to apply In writing to the correspondent including budgets and accounts. Only applications from eligible bodies will be acknowledged.
who to apply to Lucy Lake, Chair, The Courts, Park Street, Denbigh, Denbighshire LL16 3DE *Tel.* 01745 813174

■ The Sir Victor Blank Charitable Settlement

cc no 1084187   **established** 2000
where funding can be given Worldwide.
who can benefit Jewish organisations and other registered charities.
what is funded Jewish causes and general charitable purposes.
sample grants United Jewish Israel Appeal (£31,000); Jewish Care (£30,000); Community Security Trust and Norwood Ravenswood (£15,000 each); Global Leadership Foundation and JLGB (£10,000 each); Jewish Deaf Association and Limmud (£5,000 each); University of Nottingham (£2,500); Ellenor Lions Hospice (£2,000); and Deafblind UK, Listening Books and Teenage Cancer Trust (£1,000 each).
finances *Year* 2011–12 *Income* £43,412 *Grants* £232,050 *Assets* £2,106,238
trustees Sir Maurice Blank; Lady Sylvia Blank; Ronald Gulliver.
other information Other grants of less than £1,000 each totalled over £11,000.
how to apply In writing to the correspondent.
who to apply to Ronald Gulliver, Trustee, c/o Wilkins Kennedy, Bridge House, London Bridge, London SE1 9QR *Tel.* 020 7403 1877

■ Blatchington Court Trust

CC NO 306350   **ESTABLISHED** 1966
WHERE FUNDING CAN BE GIVEN UK, preference for Sussex.
WHO CAN BENEFIT Charities and other bodies in the field of education for the under 30 age group who are visually impaired.
WHAT IS FUNDED To provide funding for the education of children and young people under 30 years of age with visual impairment. The trust's grants programme awards funding for: (i) the provision of recreational and leisure facilities (or contributions towards such facilities), which enable vision impaired people to develop their physical, mental and moral capacities; (ii) any voluntary or charitable organisation approved by the trustees, the objects of which include the promotion of education, training and/or employment of vision impaired young people and their general well-being in pursuance of all the foregoing.
TYPE OF GRANT One-off capital grants.
FINANCES *Year* 2011–12 *Income* £496,201 *Grants* £132,716 *Assets* £10,912,680
TRUSTEES Richard Martin, Chair; Alison Acason; Daniel Ellman-Brown; Georgina James; Roger Jones; Stephen Pavey; Anna Hunter; Jonathan Wilson; Martin Reith Murdoch.
OTHER INFORMATION The grant total in 2011–12 included £87,000 payable in 189 grants to individuals.
HOW TO APPLY On a form available from the correspondent. Applications can be considered at any time. An application on behalf of a registered charity should include audited accounts and up-to-date information on the charity and its commitments.
WHO TO APPLY TO The Executive Manager, Ridgeland House, 165 Dyke Road, Hove, East Sussex BN3 1TL *Tel.* 01273 727222 *Fax* 01273 722244 *email* info@blatchingtoncourt.org.uk *Website* www.blatchingtoncourt.org.uk

■ The Neville and Elaine Blond Charitable Trust

CC NO 206319   **ESTABLISHED** 1953
WHERE FUNDING CAN BE GIVEN Worldwide.
WHO CAN BENEFIT Particularly Jewish charities.
WHAT IS FUNDED Jewish causes and general charitable purposes.
WHAT IS NOT FUNDED Only registered charities are supported.
RANGE OF GRANTS Up to £50,000.
SAMPLE GRANTS Previous beneficiaries included: Beth Shalom Holocaust Memorial Centre (£30,000); United Jewish Israel Appeal (£30,000); and British WIZO and Community Security Trust (£10,000 each); Holocaust Educational Trust (£5,000); Halle Orchestra (£4,000); Nordoff Robbins Music Therapy Centre (£2,000); Chicken Shed Theatre (£1,000); and Walk the Walk (£200).
FINANCES *Year* 2011–12 *Income* £43,442 *Grants* £103,300 *Assets* £1,158,546
TRUSTEES Dame Simone Prendergast; Peter Blond; Ann Susman; Simon Susman; Jennifer Skidmore.
OTHER INFORMATION Previous beneficiaries included: Beth Shalom Holocaust Memorial Centre (£30,000); United Jewish Israel Appeal (£30,000); and British WIZO and Community Security Trust (£10,000 each); Holocaust Educational Trust (£5,000); Halle Orchestra (£4,000); Nordoff Robbins Music Therapy

Centre (£2,000); Chicken Shed Theatre (£1,000); and Walk the Walk (£200).
HOW TO APPLY In writing to the correspondent. Applications should arrive by 31 January for consideration in late spring.
WHO TO APPLY TO The Trustees, c/o H. W. Fisher and Co, Chartered Accountants, Acre House, 11–15 William Road, London NW1 3ER *Tel.* 020 7388 7000

■ The Bluston Charitable Settlement

CC NO 256691   **ESTABLISHED** 1968
WHERE FUNDING CAN BE GIVEN Mostly UK.
WHO CAN BENEFIT Registered charities, particularly Jewish organisations.
WHAT IS FUNDED General charitable purposes, particularly education, welfare and medical.
WHAT IS NOT FUNDED No grants to individuals.
RANGE OF GRANTS £5,000 to £100,000.
SAMPLE GRANTS Norwood (£75,000); British Friends of Bet Medrash Gevoha, Gateshead Talmudical College, Jewish Care and Ohel Sarah (£50,000 each); Weizmann Institute Foundation (£40,000); Jaffa Institute (£31,000); Langdon Foundation and Prisoners Abroad (£25,000 each); Holocaust Educational Trust (£20,000); Golders Green Beth Hamedrash and Keren Hatorah Trust (£10,000 each); and Kisharon (£5,000).
FINANCES *Year* 2011–12 *Income* £465,257 *Grants* £699,385 *Assets* £8,524,886
TRUSTEES Daniel Dover; Martin D. Paisner.
OTHER INFORMATION The trust has a list of regular beneficiaries.
HOW TO APPLY In writing to the correspondent. The trustees meet annually in the spring.
WHO TO APPLY TO Martin D. Paisner, c/o Prism Gift Fund, 20 Gloucester Place, London W1U 8HA *Tel.* 020 7486 7760

■ The Nicholas Boas Charitable Trust

CC NO 1073359   **ESTABLISHED** 1998
WHERE FUNDING CAN BE GIVEN Worldwide.
WHO CAN BENEFIT Educational institutions, charities and other organisations connected with the arts.
WHAT IS FUNDED Education, performing and visual arts.
TYPE OF GRANT One-off
SAMPLE GRANTS IMS Prussia Cove, Guildhall School of Music and Drama, English National Opera, Wye Valley Festival, English Music Festival, Mayor of London's Fund for Young Musicians, Midsummer Music, Music in Winchester, Wigmore Hall, St George's Bristol, Opera East, Barefoot Opera, Vocal Futures, Consort Foundation, Jericho House and a variety of young musicians.
FINANCES *Year* 2011–12 *Income* £32,855 *Grants* £51,553 *Assets* £353,577
TRUSTEES Robert Boas; Christopher Boas; Helena Boas; Elizabeth Boas.
OTHER INFORMATION Grants include travel scholarships for students of architecture
HOW TO APPLY In writing to the correspondent.
WHO TO APPLY TO Robert Boas, Trustee, 22 Mansfield Street, London W1G 9NR *Tel.* 020 7436 0344 *email* boas22 million@btinternet.com *Website* www.nicholasboastrust.org.uk

■ The Marjory Boddy Charitable Trust

CC NO 1091356   **ESTABLISHED** 2002

WHERE FUNDING CAN BE GIVEN UK, with a preference for North West England.

WHO CAN BENEFIT Organisations and individuals.

WHAT IS FUNDED General charitable purposes.

SAMPLE GRANTS Brathay Trust, Motability, Nightingale House Hospice – Wrexham, Chance to Shine, the Christie Charitable Fund and Chester Mystery Plays.

FINANCES *Year* 2011–12 *Income* £91,641 *Grants* £80,000 *Assets* £2,747,082

TRUSTEES Revd Canon Christopher Samuels; Edward Walton; Randal Hibbert; Richard Raymond.

HOW TO APPLY In writing to the correspondent.

WHO TO APPLY TO Adele Bebbington-Plant, Administrator, c/o Cullimore Dutton Solicitors, 20 White Friars, Chester CH1 1XS *Tel.* 01244 356789 *Fax* 01244 312582 *email* info@cullimoredutton.co.uk

■ The Body Shop Foundation

CC NO 802757   **ESTABLISHED** 1990

WHERE FUNDING CAN BE GIVEN UK and overseas.

WHO CAN BENEFIT Organisations at the forefront of social and environmental change; groups with little hope of conventional funding; projects working to increase public awareness.

WHAT IS FUNDED Grants are given to innovative, grassroots organisations working in the field of human and civil rights, and environmental and animal protection.

WHAT IS NOT FUNDED As the majority of applications come from projects nominated by staff, the foundation does not ask for public applications or nominations. Nor does it: sponsor individuals; fund sporting activities or the arts; sponsor or support fundraising events, receptions or conferences.

TYPE OF GRANT One-off and recurring grants.

RANGE OF GRANTS £5,000–£45,000.

SAMPLE GRANTS Village Water, Zambia (£45,000); Changing Faces, UK (£44,000); Kidscape, UK (£33,000); National Association for People Abused in Childhood (NAPAC), UK (£30,000); Born Free Foundation/Last Great Ape Alliance (LAGA), Cameroon (£22,500); The British Union for the Abolition of Vivisection Charitable Trust (BUAV), UK (£20,000); Environmental Investigation Agency (EIA), UK (£15,000); Girls Educational and Mentoring Services (GEMS), USA (£13,000) and Brooke Hospital For Animals, Afghanistan (£6,000).

FINANCES *Year* 2012–13 *Income* £1,392,783 *Grants* £582,889 *Assets* £646,157

TRUSTEES Paul Sanderson; Paul McGreevy; Rita Godfrey; Andrew Radford; Bhupendra Mistry; Alastair Kerr; Andrew Wade; Jason Mathews; Jill Cochrane; Fabiola Williams; Guy Culquhoun; Mark Davis

OTHER INFORMATION Grants were given to 92 organisations.

HOW TO APPLY The foundation does not accept unsolicited applications. The trustees research projects which meet their funding criteria and only then invite organisations to make an application.

WHO TO APPLY TO Philippa Gautrey, Senior Grants Administrator, Watersmead Business Park, Littlehampton, West Sussex BN17 6LS *Tel.* 01903 844039 *email* bodyshopfoundation@thebodyshop.com *Website* thebodyshopfoundation.org

■ The Boltini Trust

CC NO 1123129   **ESTABLISHED** 2008

WHERE FUNDING CAN BE GIVEN UK, with a particular focus on Surrey and West Sussex. Some international support to developing world.

WHO CAN BENEFIT Charitable organisations and community foundations.

WHAT IS FUNDED General including education, medical, disaster relief, international development, music and the disadvantaged.

WHAT IS NOT FUNDED No grants to individuals.

SAMPLE GRANTS Royal Opera House, Breakthrough Breast Cancer and Médecins Sans Frontières (£25,000 each); Island Academy (Antigua) (£16,000); St Barnabas Hospices (Sussex) Limited – Chestnut Tree House and Music Theatre Wales (£15,000 each); Hong Kong Academy of Performing Arts (£14,000); The Prince's Trust (£11,400); The Challenge Network and Rother Valley Together (£10,000 each); The Mary Howe Trust for Cancer Prevention (£7,500); International Spinal Research Trust, British Association for Adoption and Fostering and Drop-for-Drop (India) (£5,000 each); and Missing People Limited and National Opera Studio (£2,500 each).

FINANCES *Year* 2012–13 *Income* £411,736 *Grants* £425,899 *Assets* £9,522,707

TRUSTEES Anthony Bolton; Sarah Bolton; James Nelson; Emma Nelson; Oliver Bolton; Benjamin Bolton.

HOW TO APPLY Initial enquiries should be made in writing to the correspondent. Trustees meet twice a year to consider applications. Successful applicants may be visited.

WHO TO APPLY TO Anthony Bolton, Trustee, Woolbeding Glebe, Woolbeding, Midhurst, West Sussex GU29 9RR *email* boltinitrust@gmail.com

■ The Boltons Trust

CC NO 257951   **ESTABLISHED** 1967

WHERE FUNDING CAN BE GIVEN Unrestricted.

WHO CAN BENEFIT Charitable organisations.

WHAT IS FUNDED Relief of suffering; Jewish causes; cultural and religious teaching; international rights of the individual; other charitable purposes.

TYPE OF GRANT Generally single grants for core costs, project, recurring costs and running costs. Funding is available for one year or less.

SAMPLE GRANTS Heifer International (£5,000) and Movember Europe (£1,000).

FINANCES *Year* 2011–12 *Income* £33,985 *Grants* £6,000 *Assets* £1,182,352

TRUSTEES C. Albuquerque; R. M. Baldock; S. D. Albuquerque.

HOW TO APPLY In writing to the correspondent. The trustees meet on a regular basis to consider applications.

WHO TO APPLY TO Mai Brown, Blick Rothenberg, 12 York Gate, Regent's Park, London NW1 4QS *Tel.* 020 7544 8862

■ The Bonamy Charitable Trust

CC NO 326424   **ESTABLISHED** 1983

WHERE FUNDING CAN BE GIVEN UK and overseas, with a preference for North-West England.

WHO CAN BENEFIT Charitable organisations.

WHAT IS FUNDED Jewish causes and general charitable purposes.

RANGE OF GRANTS Up to £17,000

SAMPLE GRANTS South Manchester Synagogue (£17,000); Agudat Ahavat Israel Synagogue

(£13,000); King David School (£8,000); Langdon Foundation (£5,000).

FINANCES *Year* 2012 *Income* £87,327 *Grants* £77,277 *Assets* £352,106

TRUSTEES M. Moryoussef; J. Moryoussef; R. Moryoussef.

HOW TO APPLY In writing to the correspondent.

WHO TO APPLY TO M. Moryoussef, Trustees, Flat 2, Forest Hills, South Downs Road, Bowdon, Altrincham, Cheshire *Tel.* 01706 345868

■ **The John and Celia Bonham Christie Charitable Trust**

CC NO 326296   **ESTABLISHED** 1983

WHERE FUNDING CAN BE GIVEN UK, with some preference for the former county of Avon.

WHO CAN BENEFIT Local and national organisations.

WHAT IS FUNDED Medical charities and organisations, though smaller grants are made to a wide range of other organisations.

WHAT IS NOT FUNDED No grants to individuals.

TYPE OF GRANT Recurrent, over three to five years.

RANGE OF GRANTS £200–£2,000.

SAMPLE GRANTS Previous beneficiaries have included: BIBIC, Butterwick Hospice, Cancer Research Campaign, Derby TOC, Digestive Disorder Foundation, Dorothy House, Elizabeth Finn Trust, Foundation for the Study of Infant Cot Deaths, Frome Festival, Home Start South Wiltshire, Inspire Foundation, Kings Medical Trust, Royal Society for the Blind Winsley, Sea Cadet Association, St John Ambulance and Ten of Us.

FINANCES *Year* 2011–12 *Income* £47,285 *Grants* £33,130

TRUSTEES Richard Bonham Christie; Robert Bonham Christie; Rosemary Ker.

OTHER INFORMATION Accounts had been received at the Commission but were unavailable to view.

HOW TO APPLY In writing to the correspondent. Only a small number of new applications are supported each year.

WHO TO APPLY TO Rosemary Ker, Trustee, PO Box 9081, Taynton, Gloucester GL19 3WX

■ **The Charlotte Bonham-Carter Charitable Trust**

CC NO 292839   **ESTABLISHED** 1985

WHERE FUNDING CAN BE GIVEN UK, with some preference for Hampshire.

WHO CAN BENEFIT Registered charities.

WHAT IS FUNDED General charitable purposes which were of particular concern to Lady Charlotte Bonham-Carter during her lifetime or are within the county of Hampshire. 'The trustees continue to support a core number of charities to whom they have made grants in the past as well as reviewing all applications received and making grants to new charities within their grant-giving criteria.'

WHAT IS NOT FUNDED No grants to individuals or non-registered charities.

TYPE OF GRANT One-off grants.

RANGE OF GRANTS £500–£10,000.

SAMPLE GRANTS Previous beneficiaries included: National Trust (£10,000); Florence Nightingale Museum (£5,000); City and London Guilds Bursary Fund (£4,000); British Museum – Friends of the Ancient Near East (£3,500); British Institute for the Study of Iraq (£3,000); Chelsea Physic Garden (£2,000); British Schools Exploring Society, Enterprise Education Trust and Firefly International (£1,000 each);

Fields in Trust, National Council for the Conservation of Plants and Gardens and Sir Joseph Banks Archive Project (£500 each).

FINANCES *Year* 2011–12 *Income* £123,655 *Grants* £103,349

TRUSTEES Sir Matthew Farrer; David Bonham-Carter; Eliza Bonham-Carter; Georgina Nayler.

OTHER INFORMATION Although the trust's annual report and accounts had been received at the Commission, they were not published online.

HOW TO APPLY In writing to the correspondent. There are no application forms. The application should include details of the funds required, funds raised so far and the timescale involved. The trust states that: 'unsolicited general applications are unlikely to be successful and only increase the cost of administration. Trustees meet in January and July; applications need to be received by May or November.'

WHO TO APPLY TO Jenny Cannon, Administrator, Chelwood, Rectory Road, East Carleton, Norwich NR14 8HT *Tel.* 01508 571230

■ **Bonhomie United Charity Society**

CC NO 247816   **ESTABLISHED** 1966

WHERE FUNDING CAN BE GIVEN Southampton and district.

WHO CAN BENEFIT Local organisations.

WHAT IS FUNDED Disability causes.

WHAT IS NOT FUNDED Individual applications are not eligible, except those made by voluntary organisations and social services on the individual's behalf.

TYPE OF GRANT One-off for buildings and capital.

SAMPLE GRANTS Previous beneficiaries include Wessex Heart – Cardiac Trust, Salvation Army – Southampton, Southampton Mayor's Appeal, Thorner's Homes Southampton, British Red Cross, Southampton Care Association, Hampshire and Isle of Wight Outward Bound Association and Hampshire Autistic Society.

FINANCES *Year* 2011–12 *Income* £36,119 *Grants* £35,000 *Assets* £1,434,835

TRUSTEES Bernard John Davies; Sally Davies; John Davies; Robin Davies.

HOW TO APPLY The trust states that funds are fully committed, but will consider all applications from within the Southampton and district area only.

WHO TO APPLY TO Bernard John Davies, Trustee, 48 Lingwood Close, Southampton SO16 7GJ *Tel.* 02380 769000

■ **The Linda and Gordon Bonnyman Charitable Trust**

CC NO 1123441   **ESTABLISHED** 2008

WHERE FUNDING CAN BE GIVEN Unrestricted.

WHO CAN BENEFIT Unrestricted.

WHAT IS FUNDED General charitable purposes.

SAMPLE GRANTS No information available.

FINANCES *Year* 2011–12 *Income* £7,998 *Grants* £1,071,646

TRUSTEES James Gordon Bonnyman; Linda Bonnyman; James Wallace Taylor Bonnyman.

OTHER INFORMATION Accounts were received at the Charity Commission but not published online due to the charity's low income.

HOW TO APPLY In writing to the correspondent.

WHO TO APPLY TO Linda Bonnyman, Trustee, Ely Grange, Bells Yew Green Road, Frant, Tunbridge Wells, East Sussex TN3 9DY

■ BOOST Charitable Trust

CC NO 1111961   **ESTABLISHED** 2005

WHERE FUNDING CAN BE GIVEN Principal focus is in the UK but is extended to other countries where there are areas of significant disadvantage.

WHO CAN BENEFIT Organisations involved in sport, individuals with disabilities, socially, economically disadvantaged people.

WHAT IS FUNDED Advancement of health, sports and physical education.

WHAT IS NOT FUNDED Only charities or non-profit making organisations with a focus on sport can be supported.

TYPE OF GRANT One off grants to organisations and individuals.

RANGE OF GRANTS £19,000–£2,000.

SAMPLE GRANTS CP Sport (£19,000); Westminster Befriend A Family (Swimming) (£18,000); GBWRA and GBWBA (£15,000 each); Southwark City Tennis Club and Swaziland (£10,000 each); Wheelpower, Cowplain Judo and Cumbria Youth Alliance (£5,000 each); Plymouth College and Sport In Mind (£4,000 each); Sitting Volleyball and Amputee Games/Limbpower (£3,000 each) and Disability Snowsport UK (£2,000).

FINANCES *Year* 2011–12 *Income* £128,643 *Grants* £119,021 *Assets* £1,120,214

TRUSTEES Robert Houston; Rachel Booth; Alurie Dutton; Oliver Bartrum.

OTHER INFORMATION The trust aims to **B**uild **O**n **O**verlooked **S**porting **T**alent. All of its activities, are designed to 'champion the disabled and disadvantaged and to inspire them to overcome their challenges through the power of sport'.

HOW TO APPLY Applicants should send or email a letter, no more than two sides of A4. The letter should contain the following details: the name of their organisation, what they do and who their beneficiaries are, why they need funding, details of the project and approximate funding requirements. The trustees meet quarterly to consider what grants they will make and to review the existing awards. Additional information can be found on the trust's website.

WHO TO APPLY TO Lucy Till, Administrator, Boost Charitable Trust, 5 St Bride Street, London EC4A 4AS *Tel.* 020 7078 1955 *email* lucy.till@boostct.org *Website* www.boostct.org

■ The Booth Charities

CC NO 221800   **ESTABLISHED** 1963

WHERE FUNDING CAN BE GIVEN Salford.

WHO CAN BENEFIT Organisations supporting the inhabitants of the City of Salford, especially those over 60 years of age.

WHAT IS FUNDED Relief of elderly people and people in need, including payments of pensions and provision of almshouses; relief of distress and sickness; provision and support of facilities for recreation and other leisure-time occupation; provision and support of educational facilities; any other charitable purpose.

TYPE OF GRANT Capital and revenue funding; up to three years.

SAMPLE GRANTS RECLAIM Project (£30,000); Macmillan Cancer Support (£20,000); Wood Street Mission (£10,000); Eccles Community Hall Organisation (£8,000); Together Trust and Salford Mayoral Appeal (£5,000 each); Live Music Now (£3,000); PDSA and Start in Salford (£1,500); and Manchester University Guild of Change Ringers (£100).

FINANCES *Year* 2012–13 *Income* £964,000 *Grants* £358,496 *Assets* £31,783,000

TRUSTEES William Whittle, Chair; David Tully; Philip Webb; Richard Kershaw; Edward Wilson Hunt; Roger Weston; Michael Prior; John Willis; Alan Dewhurst; Richard Fildes; Jonathan Shelmerdine.

HOW TO APPLY In writing to the correspondent.

WHO TO APPLY TO Jonathan Aldersley, Clerk to the Trustees, Butcher and Barlow, 34 Railway Road, Leigh, Greater Manchester WN7 4AU *Tel.* 01942 674144 *email* enquiries@butcher-barlow.co.uk

■ The Boots Charitable Trust

CC NO 1045927   **ESTABLISHED** 1971

WHERE FUNDING CAN BE GIVEN Nottinghamshire.

WHO CAN BENEFIT Registered charities benefiting people who live in Nottinghamshire. Also small voluntary organisations whose income and expenditure are both less than £5,000 per year, who are not yet therefore required to register with the Charity Commission.

WHAT IS FUNDED (1) Health: community healthcare such as community healthcare services, home care, after care, relief of people who are disabled or have a medical condition and continuing care; and health education and prevention by promoting knowledge and awareness of specific diseases and medical conditions. (2) Lifelong learning: Helping people of any age to achieve their educational potential, supporting supplementary schools, literacy and numeracy projects, community education, vocational/restart education for the unemployed and alternative education for excluded school pupils. (3) Community development: Helping groups to organise and respond to problems and needs in their communities or networks. This could include groups such as Councils for Voluntary Services and self-help groups. (4) Social care including: personal social services – organisations assisting individuals or families to overcome social deprivation, such as people who are homeless or disabled and their carers, lone parent and childcare groups and other family support groups; social preventive schemes – activities preventing crime, dropping out and general delinquency and providing other social care outreach work, social health and safety awareness schemes and so on; and community social activity – activities to promote social engagement for vulnerable people, mitigating against isolation and loneliness. ['We are especially interested in projects with the capacity to deliver significant impact and which reach the greatest number of people.']

WHAT IS NOT FUNDED The trust does not provide funding for: projects benefiting people outside Nottinghamshire; individuals; organisations which are not registered charities and which have income or expenditure of more than £5,000 per year; charities seeking funds to redistribute to other charities; projects for which there is a legal statutory obligation or which replace statutory funding.

RANGE OF GRANTS Up to £10,000.

SAMPLE GRANTS Bassetlaw MIND (£9,000); Platform 51 (£7,000); CASY (£6,000); Jericho Road Project and Phoenix Farm Open Door Project (£5,000 each); Russell Youth Club and Voluntary Action Broxtowe (£10,000 each); Rumbles Catering Project (£7,500); The Lenton Centre (£6,000); Rev and Go (£5,500); Netherfield Forum (£5,000); Community CentrePoint (£9,000); Homestart Nottingham and Homestart Newark (£10,000 each); 36

Nottinghamshire Brownie Guides and Trefoil, Fundays in Nottinghamshire and Nottingham Cares for Kids (£5,000 each).

FINANCES *Year* 2011–12 *Income* £272,515 *Grants* £180,161 *Assets* £92,901

TRUSTEES Kay Croot; Sandra Rose; Oonagh Turnbull; Colin Reid; Judith Lyons; Elizabeth Fagen.

HOW TO APPLY By post or on a form available, with guidelines, from the website: www.boots-uk.com/Corporate_Social_Responsibility/Community/Charitable_giving.aspx Completed forms should be sent to the correspondent with the latest annual report and accounts.

For applications over £2,000 the deadlines are on 7th of February, April, June, August, October and December. These applications take between two and four months to process.

There is no deadline for applications under £2,000, and these applications take between one and two months.

WHO TO APPLY TO Caroline Ward, 1698 Melton Road, Rearsby, Leicester LE7 4YR *Tel.* 01159 492185 *email* rachel.mcguire@boots.co.uk *Website* www.boots-uk.com/csr

■ Salo Bordon Charitable Trust

CC NO 266439   **ESTABLISHED** 1973

WHERE FUNDING CAN BE GIVEN UK and worldwide.

WHO CAN BENEFIT Organisations, primarily Jewish.

WHAT IS FUNDED Religious education and social welfare.

SAMPLE GRANTS Previous beneficiaries have included Agudas Israel Housing Association Ltd, Baer Hatorah, Beth Jacob Grammar School, Brisk Yeshivas, Golders Green Beth Hamedrash Congregation Jaffa Institute, Jewish Learning Exchange, London Academy of Jewish Studies, Society of Friends of Torah and WST Charity.

FINANCES *Year* 2011–12 *Income* £594,242 *Grants* £477,567 *Assets* £7,599,581

TRUSTEES Marcel Bordon; Salo Bordon; Lilly Bordon.

HOW TO APPLY In writing to the correspondent.

WHO TO APPLY TO Marcel Bordon, Trustee, 39 Gresham Gardens, London NW11 8PA

■ The Bordon Liphook Haslemere Charity (formerly The Bordon and Liphook Charity)

CC NO 1032428   **ESTABLISHED** 1994

WHERE FUNDING CAN BE GIVEN In practice Bordon, Liphook, Haslemere and surrounding areas, Hampshire.

WHO CAN BENEFIT Organisations and Individuals.

WHAT IS FUNDED General charitable purposes.

WHAT IS NOT FUNDED Non-priority loans.

TYPE OF GRANT Cash or loan.

SAMPLE GRANTS British Kidney Patient Association; Breast Cancer Campaign; British Red Cross; Bordon Day Care Unit; Bordon Infants School; Cranstoun Drug Services Crossways Counselling; East Hants Advocacy Scheme (EHAS); Senior Luncheon Club Liphook (SCLC); St Francis Church; St John Ambulance; Stroke Association and Weyford County Junior School.

FINANCES *Year* 2012 *Income* £129,861 *Grants* £88,000

TRUSTEES Toni Shaw; Gerard Alexander; Jennie Vernon-Smith; Mandy Batten; Michael Gallagher; Vanessa Moss.

HOW TO APPLY On a form available to download, together with criteria and guidelines, from the website. Alternatively, applicants can request forms to be sent out by post.

WHO TO APPLY TO Sue Nicholson, Administrator, Room 29, The Forest Centre, Bordon, Hampshire GU35 0TN *Tel.* 01420 477787 *email* info@blhcharity.co.uk *Website* www.blhcharity.co.uk

■ The Oliver Borthwick Memorial Trust

CC NO 256206   **ESTABLISHED** 1968

WHERE FUNDING CAN BE GIVEN UK.

WHO CAN BENEFIT Registered charities benefiting homeless people and people disadvantaged by poverty. In particular the trustees welcome applications from small but viable charities in disadvantaged inner-city areas.

WHAT IS FUNDED Currently the main areas of interest are to provide shelter and help for homeless people.

WHAT IS NOT FUNDED No grants to individuals, including people working temporarily overseas for a charity where the request is for living expenses, together with applications relating to health, disability and those from non-registered charitable organisations.

TYPE OF GRANT Mainly one-off.

RANGE OF GRANTS Usually £5,000.

SAMPLE GRANTS Christian Action and Response in Society, Clock Tower Sanctuary – Brighton, Notting Hill Churches – Homeless Concern and Vine Drop-In Centre; (£5,000 each); and Slough Homeless Our Concern and Winchester Churches Night Shelter (£3,000 each).

FINANCES *Year* 2011–12 *Income* £54,500 *Grants* £35,000 *Assets* £1,098,375

TRUSTEES Michael Bretherton; David Scott; The Earl Bathurst; James MacDonald; John Toth; Andrew Impey; Virginia Buckley; Sebastian Cresswell-Turner.

HOW TO APPLY Letters should be set out on a maximum of two sides of A4, giving full details of the project with costs, who the project will serve and the anticipated outcome of the project. Meetings take place once a year in May. Applications should be received no later than April.

WHO TO APPLY TO Anthony Blake, Administrator, c/o Donor Grants Department, Charities Aid Foundation, Kings Hill, West Malling, Kent ME19 4TA *Tel.* 01732 520107 *email* tblake@charaplus.co.uk

■ The Boshier-Hinton Foundation

CC NO 1108886   **ESTABLISHED** 2005

WHERE FUNDING CAN BE GIVEN England and Wales.

WHO CAN BENEFIT Charitable organisations.

WHAT IS FUNDED Work with children and adults with special educational or other needs.

WHAT IS NOT FUNDED No repeat grants are made within two years.

TYPE OF GRANT One-off grants.

RANGE OF GRANTS £250–£20,000. Generally around £1,000–£2,000.

SAMPLE GRANTS Paralympics GB (£20,000); Starlight Children's Foundation (£5,000); Disability Partnership (£2,500); Afasic, Asperger East Anglia, Asthma UK, Barnardo's, Communications for Blind People, Hearing Dogs for Deaf People, Treehouse Trust and Us in a Bus (£2,000 each); Green Light Trust, Just Different and Wheelyboat Trust (£1,000 each);

Movement Foundation (£750); and Tyneside
Challenge (£500).

FINANCES *Year* 2011–12 *Income* £239,186
Grants £164,919 *Assets* £962,316

TRUSTEES Thea Boshier, Chair; Dr Peter Boshier;
Colin Flint; Janet Beale.

HOW TO APPLY The application form can be
downloaded from the website. The foundation
welcomes informal email enquiries prior to the
submission of a formal application.

WHO TO APPLY TO Dr Peter Boshier, Trustee,
Yeomans, Aythorpe Roding, Great Dunmow,
Essex CM6 1PD *Tel.* 01245 231032
email boshierhinton@yahoo.co.uk *Website* www.
boshierhintonfoundation.org.uk

■ The Bosson Family Charitable Trust

CC NO 1146096 **ESTABLISHED** 2012
WHERE FUNDING CAN BE GIVEN UK.
WHO CAN BENEFIT Registered charities and churches.
WHAT IS FUNDED Education and training and religious
activities.
TYPE OF GRANT Capital costs.
TRUSTEES Paul Bosson; Alison Bosson; George
Bosson.
OTHER INFORMATION Registered in February 2012,
the trust's objects are education, training and
religious activities, with capital grants being
given to registered charities and churches. The
settlors of the trust are Paul Bosson, chief
financial officer at Sophis, and his wife.
HOW TO APPLY Unsolicited applications are not
considered.
WHO TO APPLY TO Paul Bosson, Trustee, 7 Seer
Mead, Seer Green, Beaconsfield,
Buckinghamshire HP9 2QL *Tel.* 01494 680148

■ The Bothwell Charitable Trust

CC NO 299056 **ESTABLISHED** 1987
WHERE FUNDING CAN BE GIVEN England, particularly
the South East.
WHO CAN BENEFIT Registered charities benefiting
carers, people with disabilities and people
disadvantaged by poverty.
WHAT IS FUNDED Health, disability and research.
WHAT IS NOT FUNDED No grants for animal charities,
overseas causes, individuals, or charities not
registered with the Charity Commission.
TYPE OF GRANT Core costs, running costs and
research grants, for one year or less.
RANGE OF GRANTS £1,000 or £2,000.
SAMPLE GRANTS Previous beneficiaries included:
Arthritis Research UK, Blackthorn Trust, British
Heart Foundation, ECHO International Health
Services Ltd, Friends of the Elderly, Invalid
Children's Aid Nationwide, Leukaemia Research
Fund (£2,000 each); and Brain Research Trust,
British Trust for Conservation Volunteers,
Childlink Adoption Society, Multiple Sclerosis
Society and Riding for the Disabled Association
(£1,000 each).
FINANCES *Year* 2011–12 *Income* £206,430
Grants £186,300 *Assets* £4,434,309
TRUSTEES Paul L. James; Crispian M. P. Howard;
Theresa McGregor.
HOW TO APPLY In writing to the correspondent.
Distributions are usually made in February or
March each year.
WHO TO APPLY TO Paul Leonard James, Trustee,
25 Ellenbridge Way, South Croydon CR2 0EW
Tel. 020 8657 6884

■ H. E. and E. L. Botteley Charitable Trust

CC NO 1036927 **ESTABLISHED** 1994
WHERE FUNDING CAN BE GIVEN England and Wales,
with some preference for Birmingham area.
WHO CAN BENEFIT Children, young people, older
people, people with disabilities.
WHAT IS FUNDED General, overseas aid, Christian
welfare.
RANGE OF GRANTS £7,000 to £250.
SAMPLE GRANTS REACH for Rwanda (£7,000); Rema
UK (£6,000); Action for Blind People, Prison
Fellowship, SOAR and Mission Aviation
Fellowship (£1,000 each); African Steps,
Birmingham City Mission and Deafblind UK
(£500 each); Motivation (£400); and Chaplaincy
Plus and Narthex (£250 each).
FINANCES *Year* 2011–12 *Income* £25,898
Grants £23,400 *Assets* £635,321
TRUSTEES Sally Botteley; Rosalind Barney.
OTHER INFORMATION Grants were made to 18
organisations totalling around £24,000.
HOW TO APPLY In writing to the correspondent. The
trustees normally meet biannually to consider
applications for funding.
The trust has stated that most of its funds have
been allocated to organisations of personal
interest to the trustees and that it is rare for
unsolicited applications to receive funding.
WHO TO APPLY TO Sally Botteley, Trustee, c/o
10 Oaklands Road, Sutton Coldfield B74 2TB

■ The Harry Bottom Charitable Trust

CC NO 204675 **ESTABLISHED** 1960
WHERE FUNDING CAN BE GIVEN UK, with a preference
for Yorkshire and Derbyshire.
WHO CAN BENEFIT Registered charities.
WHAT IS FUNDED The trust states that support is
divided roughly equally between religion,
education and medical causes. Within these
categories grants are given to: religion – small
local appeals and cathedral appeals; education
– universities and schools; and medical –
equipment for hospitals and charities concerned
with disability.
WHAT IS NOT FUNDED No grants to individuals.
RANGE OF GRANTS £250–£35,000.
SAMPLE GRANTS Yorkshire Baptist Association
(£35,000); St Luke's Hospice (£5,000); and
Cherry Tree Children's Home and Sheffield
Mencap (£3,000 each).
FINANCES *Year* 2011–12 *Income* £226,675
Grants £93,734 *Assets* £5,321,987
TRUSTEES Revd James Kilner; Prof. Terence Lilley;
Prof. Andrew Rawlinson.
HOW TO APPLY In writing to the correspondent at any
time enclosing your most recent set of annual
accounts.
WHO TO APPLY TO John Hinsley, c/o Westons,
Chartered Accountants, Queen's Buildings,
55 Queen Street, Sheffield S1 2DX *Tel.* 01142
738341

■ The A. H. and E. Boulton Trust

CC NO 225328 **ESTABLISHED** 1935
WHERE FUNDING CAN BE GIVEN Worldwide, with some
preference for Merseyside.
WHO CAN BENEFIT Christian charities and individuals.
WHAT IS FUNDED The trust mainly supports the
erection and maintenance of buildings to be
used for preaching the Christian gospel and for

Think carefully about every application. Is it justified?

401

relieving the sick or needy. The trustees can also support other Christian institutions, especially missions in the UK and developing world.

TYPE OF GRANT Mostly recurrent.

SAMPLE GRANTS Boulton's Cottage Homes Trust (£45,000); Holy Trinity Church (£21,000); Pioneer People Wirral (£15,000); Peel Beech Mission (£10,500); Bethesda Church (£10,000).

FINANCES *Year* 2011–12 *Income* £75,915 *Grants* £103,780 *Assets* £2,780,935

TRUSTEES Dr Frank Gopsill; Jennifer Gopsill; Michael Gopsill; Peter Gopsill.

OTHER INFORMATION The grant total includes sundry small grants to individual ministers totalling £2,000.

HOW TO APPLY In writing to the correspondent. The trust tends to support a set list of charities and applications are very unlikely to be successful.

WHO TO APPLY TO Brian McGain, Administrator, c/o Moore Stephens LLP, 110–114 Duke Street, Liverpool L1 5AG *Tel.* 01517 031080

■ P. G. and N. J. Boulton Trust

CC NO 272525   **ESTABLISHED** 1976

WHERE FUNDING CAN BE GIVEN Worldwide.

WHO CAN BENEFIT Organisations with whom the trustees have existing commitments/special interest.

WHAT IS FUNDED Christian missionary work; disaster and poverty relief; medical research and healthcare; disability relief and care of elderly.

WHAT IS NOT FUNDED No grants for: individuals; environment and conservation; culture and heritage; sport and leisure; animal welfare; church building repairs.

SAMPLE GRANTS Vision for China (£23,000); New Life Centre (£10,000); Shalom Christian Trust (£6,000); Longcroft Christian Trust (£5,000); Children Alone (£4,500); Just Care (£4,000); International Mission Project (£2,250); Barnabas Fund (£2,000); and Christian Institute, Creation Research Trust and Shepherd's Purse Trust (£1,500 each).

FINANCES *Year* 2011–12 *Income* £128,918 *Grants* £64,250 *Assets* £3,450,203

TRUSTEES Andrew L. Perry; Shirley Perry; Peter H. Stafford; Margaret Jardine-Smith.

HOW TO APPLY Note the following statement from the trust's website: 'We are currently undergoing a long term review of our policies and this means that in practice, we are currently only making donations to organisations to whom we have an existing commitment. This unfortunately means that any new requests for funding at the present time will almost certainly be unsuccessful.'

WHO TO APPLY TO Andrew L. Perry, Trustee, PO Box 72, Wirral CH28 9AE *Website* www.boultontrust. org.uk

---

■ Sir Clive Bourne Family Trust

CC NO 290620   **ESTABLISHED** 1984

WHERE FUNDING CAN BE GIVEN UK.

WHO CAN BENEFIT Individuals and institutions benefiting Jewish people.

WHAT IS FUNDED The trustees favour Jewish causes. A number of health and medical charities (particularly relating to cancer) have also benefited.

SAMPLE GRANTS Prostate Action (£13,500); Jewish Care (£12,500); Norwood Ravenswood (£8,000); WIZO UK (£6,000); One Family UK (£5,000); Magen David Adom and Community

Security Trust (£2,000 each); World Jewish Relief (£1,000); and Jewish Museum and Zionist Federation (£500 each).

FINANCES *Year* 2012–13 *Income* £82,909 *Grants* £87,109 *Assets* £4,149,903

TRUSTEES Lady Joy Bourne; Katie Cohen; Lucy Furman; Claire Lefton; Merryl Flitterman.

HOW TO APPLY In writing to the correspondent.

WHO TO APPLY TO Janet Bater, Administrator, Gardiner House, 6B Hemnall Street, Epping, Essex CM16 4LW *Tel.* 01992 560500

■ The Anthony Bourne Foundation

CC NO 1015759   **ESTABLISHED** 1992

WHERE FUNDING CAN BE GIVEN UK, especially Warwickshire.

WHO CAN BENEFIT Primarily organisations benefiting children and young people.

WHAT IS FUNDED 'Through supporting a wide range of charitable organisations, the trustees have resolved to give support to charities which seek to promote the wellbeing of young people and to foster their active positive engagement in their local communities.'

WHAT IS NOT FUNDED No grants to individuals.

TYPE OF GRANT One-off grants for capital (including buildings), core costs and start-up costs. Funding of up to three years will be considered.

RANGE OF GRANTS £350–£3,000

SAMPLE GRANTS Previous beneficiaries included: Kids 'n' Action, Lancaster and District YMCA – YZUP Young Offender Project, Life Church, Maximum Life Youth Project and Tiverton Market Drop-In-Centre (£3,000 each); Living Hope Charity, St Margaret's Hospice Somerset and Straight Talking (£1,000); and Warwickshire Association of Youth Clubs – Dream Catcher Appeal (£350).

FINANCES *Year* 2011–12 *Income* £21,808 *Grants* £19,920

TRUSTEES V. A. Bourne; Celia Louise Jeune; M. A. Hunter-Craig.

OTHER INFORMATION All enquiries should be made through the Foundation's website.

HOW TO APPLY All applicants are directed to the Foundation's website (www.anthonybournefoundation.org/home) where criteria, guidelines and application process are posted.

WHO TO APPLY TO PO Box 5334, Rugby CV21 9JY *Website* www.anthonybournefoundation.org

---

■ Bourneheights Limited

CC NO 298359   **ESTABLISHED** 1984

WHERE FUNDING CAN BE GIVEN UK.

WHO CAN BENEFIT Orthodox Jews.

WHAT IS FUNDED Orthodox Jewish organisations.

SAMPLE GRANTS Previous beneficiaries include: Moreshet Hatorah, Mercaz Torah Vahesed Ltd, BFOT, Belz Synagogue, Telz Academy Trust, Gevurath Ari Academy, UTA, Toreth Emeth, Olam Chesed Yiboneh, Before Trust, Heaven Point, Yeshivas Avas Torah and Lubavitch Mechina.

FINANCES *Year* 2011–12 *Income* £1,269,812 *Grants* £518,641 *Assets* £6,229,725

TRUSTEES Chaskel Rand; Esther Rand; Erno Berger; Yechiel Chersky; Schloime Rand.

HOW TO APPLY In writing to the correspondent.

WHO TO APPLY TO Schloime Rand, Trustee, Flat 10, Palm Court, Queen Elizabeth's Walk, London N16 5XA *Tel.* 020 8809 7398

402

Does the trust you have chosen match your needs? Haphazard applications waste postage and time

■ The Bower Trust

cc no 283025　　　**established** 1981
where funding can be given Wales and developing countries, mainly in Africa.
who can benefit Generally, registered charities.
what is funded Charities connected activities in the 'third world', particularly in Africa, and Wales.
what is not funded No personal sponsorships. Generally the trustees are not interested in regional requests from charities.
range of grants Less than £1,000
sample grants Llanilltyd Fawr in Flower and South Sudan School (£3,000 each); Wildlife Trust Skomer (£2,000); Bees Abroad Zambia, St Catherine's College Oxford (£1,000 each); Marine Theatre Lyme Regis (£800); WaterAid Mozambique, Red Cross Syria and Fair Trade International (£500 each); National Trust (£200); World Land Trust (£150) and Norfolk Wildlife Trust (£32).
finances *Year* 2011–12 *Income* £33,220 *Grants* £44,156 *Assets* £742,467
trustees Tina Benfield; Jack Benfield; Robert Benfield; Graham Benfield.
other information In 2011–12 grants were given to 57 organisations.
how to apply In writing to the correspondent. Trustees meet quarterly to consider grants.
who to apply to Graham Benfield, Trust Administrator, Old Rosedew House, Colhugh Street, Llantwit Major CF61 1RF

■ The Bowerman Charitable Trust

cc no 289446　　　**established** 1984
where funding can be given UK, with a preference for West Sussex.
who can benefit Registered charities.
what is funded Church activities, the arts, medical charities, youth work and other charitable activities.
type of grant One-off.
range of grants Usually up to £20,000.
sample grants St Paul's Hammersmith (£100,000); St Margaret's Trust (£12,000); British Youth Opera (£10,000) and Royal Academy of Music (£8,000).
finances *Year* 2011–12 *Income* £168,406 *Grants* £217,554 *Assets* £10,882,965
trustees D. W. Bowerman; C. M. Bowerman; J. M. Taylor; K. E. Bowerman; A. M. Downham; J. M. Capper; M. Follis.
how to apply In writing to the correspondent. The trustees have previously stated that they are bombarded with applications and unsolicited applications will not be considered.
who to apply to D. W. Bowerman, Trustee, Champs Hill, Coldwatham, Pulborough, West Sussex RH20 1LY *Tel.* 01798 831205

■ John and Susan Bowers Fund

cc no 266616　　　**established** 1973
where funding can be given Worldwide.
who can benefit Registered charities.
what is funded Social justice, health and welfare, arts, environment, religion, emergency appeals and development.
range of grants Up to £1,000.
sample grants Médecins Sans Frontières and Quaker Social Action (£1,000 each); Impact Foundation and Peace Direct (£800 each); Heathrow Special Needs Farm and Benslow Musical Instrument Loan (£600 each); International Childcare Trust and Anti-Slavery International (£500 each); Streetchild Africa (£400) and World Film Collective and Just Different (£300 each).
finances *Year* 2011–12 *Income* £32,864 *Grants* £22,500 *Assets* £278,598
trustees Chris Bowers; John Bowers; Sue Bowers; Louise Gorst; Jenny Johns, Stephen Johns; Jennifer Armistead.
other information Grants were given to 40 organisations.
how to apply In writing to the correspondent; most new appeals are acknowledged, generally by email. The charity tends to make recurrent grants – 'our reluctance to drop charities we have supported in the past and spread ourselves more thinly, invariably means that only a very small number of new applications receive a positive response.' The charity informed us: 'we ask for a letter summarising what a £300–£800 grant could achieve and shortlist based on this information'. Funding decisions are made in November.
who to apply to Sue Bowers, Trustee5 Greenacres Drive, Ringmer, Lewes, East Sussex BN8 5LZ *Tel.* 01273 813331 *email* jsbf@gn.apc.org

■ The Bowland Charitable Trust

cc no 292027　　　**established** 1985
where funding can be given North west England.
who can benefit Individuals, institutions and registered charities benefiting, in general, children and young adults.
what is funded Young people, education and general charitable purposes.
sample grants Institute for Effective Education – York (£1.4 million); The Church School Company (£1.1 million); Success for All Foundation (£644,000); National Maths Case Studies Project (£241,000); Gaskell House Restoration Project and Grindleton Recreation Ground Charity (£100,000 each); Blackburn Youth Zone (£75,000); Blackburn Cathedral (£50,000); Nazareth Unitarian Chapel (£14,000 each); Age UK (£10,000); and Cumbria Country History Trust (£2,000).
finances *Year* 2011 *Income* £5,911,871 *Grants* £4,571,988 *Assets* £10,649,491
trustees Tony Cann; Ruth A. Cann; Carole Fahy; Hugh D. Turner.
other information At the time of writing (December 2013) the trust's 2012 accounts were overdue with the Charity Commission.
how to apply 'The charity invites applications for funding of projects from individuals, institutions and charitable organisations. The applications are made directly to the trustees, who meet regularly to assess the applications.'
who to apply to Carole Fahy, Trustee, Activhouse, Philips Road, Blackburn, Lancashire BB1 5TH *Tel.* 01254 290433

■ The Frank Brake Charitable Trust

cc no 1023245　　　**established** 1993
where funding can be given Kent.
who can benefit Registered charities.
what is funded General charitable purposes.
sample grants Canterbury Diocesan Board of Finance and NSPCC (£10,000 each); Wyvern School Foundation (£3,500); Spring Grove School (£3,000); Kent College Canterbury and Papplewick Education Trust Ltd (£2,000 each) and the Brittle Bone Society (£1,000).
finances *Year* 2011–12 *Income* £55,987 *Grants* £95,500 *Assets* £5,550,989

TRUSTEES Philip Wilson; Michael Trigg; Michelle Leveridge; Richard Brake.

HOW TO APPLY In writing to the correspondent.

WHO TO APPLY TO Michael Trigg, Trustee, c/o Gill Turner Tucker, Colman House, King Street, Maidstone, Kent ME14 1JE *Tel.* 01622 759051

■ The William Brake Charitable Trust

CC NO 1023244   **ESTABLISHED** 1984

WHERE FUNDING CAN BE GIVEN UK, with a preference for Kent.

WHO CAN BENEFIT Registered charities.

WHAT IS FUNDED General charitable purposes.

TYPE OF GRANT £1,000–£50,000.

RANGE OF GRANTS £1,000–£50,000.

SAMPLE GRANTS Previous beneficiaries included: Whitely Fund for Nature; the Royal Masonic Benevolent Institution; NSPCC; the Duke of Edinburgh's Award; the Ecology Trust; Wooden Spoon Society; Aurora Tsunami Orphanage; Mike Collingwood Memorial Fund; League of Remembrance; Friends of St Peter's Hospital Chertsey; Canterbury Cathedral Development; Cancer Research UK; Elimination of Leukaemia Fund; Maidstone Mencap Charitable Trust; RNLI; Alzheimer's Society; Breast Cancer Care; Courtyard – Petersfield; Dorothy Grinstead Memorial Fund; Macmillan and Portland College.

FINANCES *Year* 2011–12 *Income* £94,669 *Grants* £324,000 *Assets* £9,387,584

TRUSTEES Philip Wilson; Deborah Isaac; Penelope Lang; Michael Trigg.

HOW TO APPLY The 2011–12 accounts note that, 'the charity invites applications from the William Brake family for funding of worthy registered charities each year, with a particular emphasis on local charities where the family know the charity's representative'.

WHO TO APPLY TO Michael Trigg, Trustee, c/o Gill Turner Tucker, Colman House King St, Maidstone, Kent ME14 1JE *Tel.* 01622 759051

■ The Tony Bramall Charitable Trust

CC NO 1001522   **ESTABLISHED** 1990

WHERE FUNDING CAN BE GIVEN UK, with some preference for Yorkshire.

WHO CAN BENEFIT Local charities within Yorkshire and national medical institutions.

WHAT IS FUNDED Medical research, ill health and social welfare.

RANGE OF GRANTS Usually £1,000–£5,000.

SAMPLE GRANTS Tree of Hope (£10,000); BEN, Help Harry Help Others, St Luke's and Saint Gemma's Hospice (£5,000 each); Children Heart Surgery Fund (£3,000); Helen's Trust and Well-being of Women (£2,500 each); Toy Libraries Association (£500); and Caring Hands Skydive (£250).

FINANCES *Year* 2012–13 *Income* £156,707 *Grants* £75,786 *Assets* £4,443,341

TRUSTEES Tony Bramall; Karen Bramall Odgen; Melanie Foody; Geoffrey Tate; Anna Bramall.

HOW TO APPLY In writing to the correspondent.

WHO TO APPLY TO The Trustees, 12 Cardale Court, Beckwith Head Road, Harrogate, North Yorkshire HG3 1RY *Tel.* 01423 535300 *email* alison. lockwood@bramallproperties.co.uk

■ The Liz and Terry Bramall Foundation

CC NO 1121670   **ESTABLISHED** 2007

WHERE FUNDING CAN BE GIVEN UK, in practice mainly Yorkshire.

WHO CAN BENEFIT Churches and charitable organisations.

WHAT IS FUNDED Support for the Christian faith; promotion of urban or rural regeneration, in areas of social and economic deprivation; relief of sickness and the advancement of health; education; and arts and culture.

RANGE OF GRANTS Mostly up to £500,000.

SAMPLE GRANTS The Prince's Trust (£1 million); Horizon Life Coaching (£527,000); St Peter's Church Building Fund (£450,000); Neuroblastoma and Yorkshire Air Ambulance (£200,000 each); Royal College of Church Music (£140,000); Martin House Children's Hospice, St Michael's Hospice and Yorkshire Sculpture (£100,000 each); Yorkshire Historic Churches Trust (£50,000); Wakefield Cathedral (£42,000); Harrogate Theatre (£40,000); Christians Against Poverty and Ripon Cathedral Choristers (£20,000 each); Cyclone Technology (£16,500); Bowel and Cancer Research, Chrissy's Quest, Hospital Heartbeat Appeal and Magic Breakfast (£10,000 each); and Cerebra and Listening Books (£1,000 each).

FINANCES *Year* 2011–12 *Income* £2,272,416 *Grants* £4,347,571 *Assets* £105,853,291

TRUSTEES Terry Bramall; Liz Bramall; Suzannah Allard; Rebecca Bletcher; Rachel Tunnicliffe; Anthony Sharp.

OTHER INFORMATION The trustees' annual report for 2011–12 states that the grantmaking policy of the charity is being developed but it will include small donations (on application) to causes within the objectives and also larger long term projects. In the short term, additional spend, over and above the current level of income, will be employed to bring the free reserves down to £500,000.

HOW TO APPLY In writing to the correspondent. The trust also states that 'unsolicited requests from national charities will generally only be considered if there is some public benefit to the Yorkshire region'.

WHO TO APPLY TO Terry Bramall, Trustee, c/o Gordons LLP, Riverside West, Whitehall Road, Leeds, West Yorkshire LS1 4AW *Tel.* 01132 270100 *Fax* 01132 270113

■ The Bransford Trust

CC NO 1106554   **ESTABLISHED** 2004

WHERE FUNDING CAN BE GIVEN Preference for the West Midlands.

WHO CAN BENEFIT Registered charities.

WHAT IS FUNDED General charitable purposes.

SAMPLE GRANTS University of Worcester (£200,000); the Leys School (£150,000); St Richard Hospice (£110,000); Sing (UK) (£37,000); Acorns Children's Trust (£35,000); Worcester Porcelain Museum (£20,000); English Symphony, Vitalise Trust and Worcester Live (£10,000 each); Noah's Ark Trust (£7,500); and County Air Ambulance (£6,000).

FINANCES *Year* 2011–12 *Income* £5,083,880 *Grants* £746,635 *Assets* £12,611,543

TRUSTEES Arthur Neil; Colin Kinnear; Brenda Kinnear; John Carver.

HOW TO APPLY In writing to the correspondent.

WHO TO APPLY TO Julia Kirkham, Administrator, Bransford Facilities Management, 6 Edgar Street, Worcester WR1 2LR *Tel.* 0870 066 2446 *email* julia@bransford-facilities.co.uk

■ The Breadsticks Foundation

CC NO 1125396   ESTABLISHED 2008
WHERE FUNDING CAN BE GIVEN UK, Africa and Asia.
WHO CAN BENEFIT Charities and community groups.
WHAT IS FUNDED Healthcare and education, particularly young people and disadvantaged adults.
WHAT IS NOT FUNDED The foundation will not sponsor individuals or fund animals, medical research or capital and building projects. It will not fund faith-based programmes unless they work with beneficiaries from all faiths and none.
TYPE OF GRANT Core funding; project funding.
SAMPLE GRANTS Hope and Homes for Children (£240,000); The Medical Foundation (£153,000); Class Act Educational Services – Johannesburg (£139,500); Kids in Need of Education – Mumbai (£85,000); St Mungo's (£70,000); International Childcare Trust (£40,000); Hanley Crouch Community Centre – London (£25,000); Christine Revell Children's Home (£15,500); and the International Children's Trust (£5,000).
FINANCES *Year* 2011–12 *Income* £1,688,307 *Grants* £1,193,723 *Assets* £491,640
TRUSTEES Beatrix Payne, Chair; Dr Yolande Knight; Dr Paul Ballantyne; Beatrice Roberts; Trevor Macy.
HOW TO APPLY Applications are by invitation only, and unsolicited applications will not be considered. The foundation does, however, welcome communication via email.
WHO TO APPLY TO Beatrix Payne, Trustee, 35 Canonbury Square, London N1 2AN *Tel.* 020 7288 0667 *email* info@breadsticksfoundation. org *Website* www.breadsticksfoundation.org

■ The Breast Cancer Research Trust

CC NO 272214   ESTABLISHED 1961
WHERE FUNDING CAN BE GIVEN UK.
WHO CAN BENEFIT Recognised cancer centres or research institutions.
WHAT IS FUNDED Clinical and translational research into the prevention, early diagnosis and treatment of breast cancer.
WHAT IS NOT FUNDED No grants to students.
TYPE OF GRANT Limited grants available up to a term of three years. Grants reviewed annually.
SAMPLE GRANTS Southampton University (£50,000); Southampton General Hospital (20,000); University of Leets (£19,000); and CBC Research (£10,000).
FINANCES *Year* 2011–12 *Income* £104,775 *Grants* £103,854 *Assets* £527,411
TRUSTEES Dame Vera Lynn; Prof. Charles Coombes; Virginia Lewis-Jones; Bob Potter; Prof. Trevor J. Powles; R. M. Rainsbury; Dr Margaret Spittle.
HOW TO APPLY Application forms available only from the trust's website. The trust has stated that they are not open for new applications until 2015.
WHO TO APPLY TO Rosemary Sutcliffe, Executive Administrator, PO BOX 861, Bognor Regis PO21 9HW *Tel.* 01243 583143 *email* bcrtrust@bt.internet.com *Website* www. breastcancerresearchtrust.org.uk

■ The Brendish Family Foundation

CC NO 1079065   ESTABLISHED 2000
WHERE FUNDING CAN BE GIVEN UK and overseas, with a preference for India.
WHO CAN BENEFIT The trust was established in 2000 for general charitable purposes. The trust's recent accounts state that in the future the trustees would like to support projects including those that involved children, education, health care and access to food and water.
WHAT IS FUNDED General, children, education, health care and access to food and water.
SAMPLE GRANTS Beneficiaries in previous years have included: Brendish Foundation (£30,000); Child in Need Institute – India (£10,000); the Children with Special Needs Foundation (£5,000); the Busoga Trust (£3,000); Marie Curie Cancer Care (£2,500); Digital Himalayan Project – Cambridge University (£1,500); and Haiti Earthquake Appeal (£1,000).
FINANCES *Year* 2011–12 *Income* £24,406 *Grants* £41,803
TRUSTEES Graham Chambers; Susan Brendish; Clayton Brendish; Nathan Brendish; Natalie Brendish.
HOW TO APPLY In writing to the correspondent.
WHO TO APPLY TO Graham Chambers, Trustee, Dixon Wilson Chartered Accountants, 22 Chancery Lane, London WC2A 1LS *Tel.* 020 7680 8100

■ Bridgepoint Charitable Trust (formerly Bridgepoint Inspire)

CC NO 1134525   ESTABLISHED 2010
WHERE FUNDING CAN BE GIVEN UK and overseas
WHO CAN BENEFIT Registered charities.
WHAT IS FUNDED General charitable purposes.
SAMPLE GRANTS Leaders' Quest (£75,000); Fryshuset and Teens and Toddlers (£50,000 each) and Orchestre à l'école (£49,000). Donations below £25,000 totalled £52,000.
FINANCES *Year* 2012 *Income* £303,997 *Grants* £280,420 *Assets* £654,064
TRUSTEES Michael Walton; James Murray; Ruth McIntosh; Gibbons; Gunner; Jamie Wyatt; David Hankin; Emma Watford; Xavier Robert; Stefanie Arensmann; Mathew Legg.
OTHER INFORMATION This trust is linked to the international private equity firm, Bridgepoint.
HOW TO APPLY In writing to the correspondent.
WHO TO APPLY TO David Hankin, Secretary, Bridgepoint, 30 Warwick Street, London W1B 5AL *Tel.* 020 7432 3500 *Website* www. bridgepoint.eu

■ The Harold and Alice Bridges Charity

CC NO 236654   ESTABLISHED 1963
WHERE FUNDING CAN BE GIVEN South Cumbria and North Lancashire (as far south as Preston)
WHO CAN BENEFIT Particular favour is given to children, young adults, older people and village activities.
WHAT IS FUNDED General charitable purposes, particularly young people, elderly people and supporting village capital projects.
WHAT IS NOT FUNDED No grants to individuals.
TYPE OF GRANT The trustees prefer mainly capital projects which have an element of self-help.
RANGE OF GRANTS Usually £500–£5,000.
SAMPLE GRANTS Previous beneficiaries included: Stainton Institute and Rosemere Cancer Foundation – Preston (£5,000 each); St John's

Churchyard – Tunstall (£4,000); Emmanuel Parish Church – Southport (£2,500); British Wireless for the Blind Fund (£2,000); Rainbow Trust Children's Charity (£1,000); and Dolly Mops and Springfield Bowling Club – High Bentham (£500 each).

FINANCES *Year* 2011–12 *Income* £560,296 *Grants* £100,900 *Assets* £3,016,847

TRUSTEES Richard N. Hardy; Irene Greenwood.

HOW TO APPLY Refer to the charity's website for full application details including a downloadable form. The trustees meet three times a year to discuss and approve grant applications and review finances. Cheques are sent out to those successful applicants within days of each meeting.

WHO TO APPLY TO Richard N. Hardy, Trustee, Linder Myers, 21–23 Park Street, Lytham FY8 5LU *Tel.* 0844 984 6001 *email* richard.hardy@lindermyers.co.uk *Website* www.haroldandalicebridgescharity.co.uk

■ The Bridging Fund Charitable Trust

CC NO 1119171 **ESTABLISHED** 2007

WHERE FUNDING CAN BE GIVEN UK

WHO CAN BENEFIT Charitable organisations that help individuals in need.

WHAT IS FUNDED Social welfare and the relief of poverty.

WHAT IS NOT FUNDED No grants for running costs or directly to individuals.

FINANCES *Year* 2012 *Income* £20,811 *Grants* £200,000

TRUSTEES Debbie Cockrill; David Reeds; Mike Richardson; Rosemary Mackay; Gordon Hayes.

HOW TO APPLY In writing to the correspondent.

WHO TO APPLY TO Debbie Cockrill, Trustee, PO Box 3106, Lancing, West Sussex BN15 5BL *Tel.* 01903 750008 *email* info@bridgingfund.org

■ Briggs Animal Welfare Trust

CC NO 276459 **ESTABLISHED** 1978

WHERE FUNDING CAN BE GIVEN UK and overseas.

WHO CAN BENEFIT Charities concerned with animal welfare, particularly animals in distress caused by man including wildlife.

WHAT IS FUNDED Although the original objects of the trust were general, but with particular support for animal welfare, the trust's policy is to support only animal welfare causes.

TYPE OF GRANT Ongoing grants.

RANGE OF GRANTS £1,000–£2,000.

SAMPLE GRANTS There are five named beneficiaries in the trust deed: RSPCA, Reystede Animal Sanctuary Ringmer, Brooke Hospital for Animals Cairo, Care of British Columbia House and the Society for the Protection of Animals in North Africa.

FINANCES *Year* 2011–12 *Income* £600 *Grants* £284,140

TRUSTEES Louise Hartnett; Adrian Schouten.

OTHER INFORMATION Accounts were received by the Charity Commission but were not available to view.

HOW TO APPLY In writing to the correspondent.

WHO TO APPLY TO Louise Hartnett, Trustee, Little Champions Farm, Maplehurst Road, West Grinstead, Horsham, West Sussex RH13 6RN

■ Bristol Archdeaconry Charity

CC NO 1058853 **ESTABLISHED** 1996

WHERE FUNDING CAN BE GIVEN Archdeaconry of Bristol.

WHO CAN BENEFIT Charities and individuals for advancement of the Church of England.

WHAT IS FUNDED Religious and other charitable purposes of the Church of England in the area of benefit. Grants should generally be associated with church-based ministry and community projects in UPA parishes and made wherever possible by way of start-up funding'.

TYPE OF GRANT Recurrent

RANGE OF GRANTS £500–£142,000

SAMPLE GRANTS Bristol Diocesan Board of finance (£142,000); Parish of Bishopston and St Andrew's (£25,000); Kingswood Street Pastors (£10,000); Community of Sisters of the Church (£5,000); St Aidan with St George (£3,000); Redland Education Centre and Sea Mills Community Initiatives (£1,500 each) and St Stephen's, Soundwell (£1,000).

FINANCES *Year* 2012 *Income* £148,455 *Grants* £214,595 *Assets* £3,218,285

TRUSTEES Roger Metcalfe; Peter Woolf; Hugh Wares; Simon Baughen; L. Farrall; Canon Tim Higgins; Timothy Thom; Anthony Brown; David Worthington.

OTHER INFORMATION In 2012 grants were given to 20 institutions.

HOW TO APPLY In writing to the correspondent. Trustees meet three times a year.

WHO TO APPLY TO Philippa Drewett, Clerk, All Saints' Church, 1 All Saints Court, Bristol BS1 1JN *Tel.* 01179 292709

■ The Bristol Charities

CC NO 1109141 **ESTABLISHED** 1960

WHERE FUNDING CAN BE GIVEN Within a 10-mile radius of Bristol city centre.

WHO CAN BENEFIT Individuals and organisations.

WHAT IS FUNDED Education; relief of sickness; and relief of need.

FINANCES *Year* 2011–12 *Income* £1,501,988 *Grants* £185,510 *Assets* £25,018,718

TRUSTEES Barry England; Dudley Lewis; Kamala Das; Helen Moss; Susan Hampton; Andrew Hillman; The Very Revd Dr David Hoyle; Alfred Morris; Vanessa Stevenson; David Watts; Laura Claydon; Tony Harris; John Webster; Richard Gore; Dr Ros Kennedy.

OTHER INFORMATION The 2011–12 grant total includes £159,000 that was donated to individuals and £26,600 that was given to local organisations.

HOW TO APPLY On a form available to download, together with criteria and guidelines, from the website.

WHO TO APPLY TO Sarah Davies, Chief Executive, 17 St Augustine's Parade, Bristol BS1 4UL *Tel.* 01179 300301 *email* info@bristolcharities.org.uk *Website* www.bristolcharities.org.uk

■ John Bristow and Thomas Mason Trust

CC NO 1075971 **ESTABLISHED** 1999

WHERE FUNDING CAN BE GIVEN Parish of Charlwood (as the boundaries stood in 1926).

WHO CAN BENEFIT Children, people with disabilities and people in need.

WHAT IS FUNDED Churches, community amenities, disability, and education.

WHAT IS NOT FUNDED Any application that will not benefit the residents of the Parish of Charlwood (as the boundaries stood in 1926) will not be considered.

RANGE OF GRANTS Usually up to £3,000.

SAMPLE GRANTS St Nicholas Parochial Church Council £3,500); Parish Venture Week (£3,000); Hello Hookwood (£2,500); 8th Horley (Charlwood) Scouts (£1,000); Charlwood Evening Women's Institute (£850); and Charlwood Day Centre (£350).

FINANCES *Year* 2011–12 *Income* £64,673 *Grants* £41,569 *Assets* £2,398,756

TRUSTEES Martin James; Revd Bill Campen; Feargal Hogan; Alison Martin; Howard Pearson; Julie King; Carole Jordan; Richard Parker.

HOW TO APPLY Applications should be made on a form available from the correspondent upon written request, and should include an estimate of the total cost of the project, with three quotations where applicable.

WHO TO APPLY TO M. Singleton, Secretary, 3 Grayrigg Road, Maidenbower, Crawley RH10 7AB *Tel.* 01293 883950 *email* trust.secretary@jbtmt.org.uk *Website* www.jbtmt.org.uk

■ The British Council for Prevention of Blindness

CC NO 270941   **ESTABLISHED** 1976

WHERE FUNDING CAN BE GIVEN Worldwide.

WHO CAN BENEFIT Organisations benefiting people with sight loss, and medical professionals, research workers and scientists in the field.

WHAT IS FUNDED Funding research, including fellowships, which has the potential to make breakthroughs in understanding and treating currently incurable eye diseases; and operational research to determine the best methods of preventing blindness.

WHAT IS NOT FUNDED this trust does not deal with the individual welfare of blind people in the UK.

RANGE OF GRANTS Usually for a maximum of £40,000.

SAMPLE GRANTS International Centre for Eye Health, London School of Hygiene and Tropical Medicine (£60,000); Southampton University (£59,000); and Aberdeen University (£45,000).

FINANCES *Year* 2011–12 *Income* £192,831 *Grants* £239,699 *Assets* £352,507

TRUSTEES Stephen Brooker; Arvind Chandna; Prof. James Morgan; Prof. Paul Foster; Dr Jeffrey Jay; Dr Clare O'Neill.

HOW TO APPLY Applications can be made throughout the year.

WHO TO APPLY TO Stephen Silverton, Administrator, 4 Bloomsbury Square, London WC1A 2RP *Tel.* 020 7404 7114 *email* info@bcpb.org *Website* www.bcpb.org

■ The British Dietetic Association General and Education Trust Fund

CC NO 282553   **ESTABLISHED** 1981

WHERE FUNDING CAN BE GIVEN UK.

WHO CAN BENEFIT Individuals and to recognised associations or groups of people engaged in dietetic research and associated activities.

WHAT IS FUNDED Education, research and other purposes related to the science of dietetics.

WHAT IS NOT FUNDED No direct support of dietetic students in training or postgraduate qualifications for individuals, i.e. the trust will

not pay postgraduate fees/expenses, or elective/MSc study for doctors.

TYPE OF GRANT Project, one-off, research, recurring costs, salaries, start-up costs, interest-free loans and running costs. Funding can be given for up to three years.

FINANCES *Year* 2011–12 *Income* £46,764 *Grants* £84,167 *Assets* £1,420,414

TRUSTEES P. Brindley; E. Elliot; W. T. Seddon; M. Mackintosh H. Davidson.

HOW TO APPLY Application forms can be downloaded from the trust's website.

WHO TO APPLY TO The Secretary to the Trustees, 5th Floor, Charles House, 148–149 Great Charles Street, Queensway, Birmingham B3 3HT *Tel.* 01212 008080 *email* info@bda.uk.com *Website* www.bda.uk.com

■ The British Gas (Scottish Gas) Energy Trust

CC NO 1106218   **ESTABLISHED** 2004

WHERE FUNDING CAN BE GIVEN England, Scotland and Wales.

WHO CAN BENEFIT Voluntary sector organisations and current domestic customers of British Gas or Scottish Gas.

WHAT IS FUNDED Relief-in-need; the provision of money and debt prevention advice and education, often with a particular fuel poverty emphasis.

WHAT IS NOT FUNDED No grants for: fines for criminal offences; educational or training needs; debts to central government departments; medical equipment, aids and adaptations; holidays; business debts; catalogues; credit cards; personal loans; deposits for secure accommodation; or overpayment of benefits.

TYPE OF GRANT One-off grants for individuals; one-off and recurrent capital and revenue grants for organisations.

SAMPLE GRANTS Five Lamps (Sunderland), Manchester CAB and Money Matters (Glasgow) (£36,000 each); Coventry Law Centre (£35,000); Community Links Trust (London) (£34,000); Preston CAB (£18,000); Riverside Advice (Cardiff) (£17,500) and Money Advice Scotland (£7,000).

FINANCES *Year* 2012 *Income* £12,765,432 *Grants* £10,000,000

TRUSTEES Stephen Harrap; Gillian Tishler; Maria Wardrobe; Imelda Redmond; Andrew Brown; Michelle Mitchell.

OTHER INFORMATION The majority of grants are given to individuals and families. In 2012 organisations received a total of around £500,000.

HOW TO APPLY Grants for organisations: funding rounds are publicised on the trust's website and in its newsletter. Grants for individuals: applications should be made by post using a form available from the trust's website.

WHO TO APPLY TO The Trustees, 3rd Floor, Midgate House, Midgate, Peterborough PE1 1TN *Tel.* 01733 421021 *email* bget@charisgrants.com *Website* www.britishgasenergytrust.org.uk

■ British Heart Foundation

CC NO 225971   **ESTABLISHED** 1961

WHERE FUNDING CAN BE GIVEN UK.

WHO CAN BENEFIT Organisations that benefit people of all ages; academics; medical professionals; students; and people with heart disease.

WHAT IS FUNDED Medical research into all aspects of heart disease.

WHAT IS NOT FUNDED Applications are accepted only from appropriately qualified individuals.

TYPE OF GRANT Project, programme and fellowship grants.

RANGE OF GRANTS No limit.

FINANCES *Year* 2011–12 *Income* £249,893,000 *Grants* £124,200,000 *Assets* £15,479,000

TRUSTEE The Council.

OTHER INFORMATION In 2011–12 a total of 262 research grants were awarded. For a complete list of all grants see the website.

HOW TO APPLY Criteria, guidelines, forms and application process are available on the Foundation's website.

WHO TO APPLY TO Jennifer Christie, The Research Funds Manager, Greater London House, 180 Hampstead Road, London NW1 7AW *Tel.* 020 7554 0434 *email* research@bhf.org.uk *Website* www.bhf.org.uk

■ British Humane Association

CC NO 207120   **ESTABLISHED** 1922

WHERE FUNDING CAN BE GIVEN UK.

WHO CAN BENEFIT (a) Charities directly involved in humanitarian activities; (b) charities distributing grants to individuals; (c) charities providing relief of poverty or sickness, or benefit to the community.

TYPE OF GRANT One-off, capital and recurring grants will be considered.

SAMPLE GRANTS St John Wales (£20,000); St John of Jerusalem Eye Hospital (£12,000); Karabuni Trust and GARAS (£6,000 each); Close House Hereford (£5,000); and Ardent Hare and MERU (£2,000 each).

FINANCES *Year* 2012 *Income* £128,634 *Grants* £71,000 *Assets* £3,960,432

TRUSTEES Dr John Breen: David Eldridge; Benedict Campbell-Johnston; Rachel Campbell-Johnston; Duncan Cantlay; Philip Gee; John Huntington-Whiteley; Anthony Chignell; Michael Nemko.

HOW TO APPLY Applications not considered – see 'General' section.

WHO TO APPLY TO Henry Grant, Company Secretary, The Cottage, New Road, Cutnall Green, Droitwich WR9 0PQ *Tel.* 01299 851588

■ British Institute at Ankara

CC NO 313940   **ESTABLISHED** 1948

WHERE FUNDING CAN BE GIVEN UK, Turkey and the Black Sea region.

WHO CAN BENEFIT British and UK-resident students and academics of archaeology and associated fields.

WHAT IS FUNDED Research focused on Turkey and the Black Sea littoral in all academic disciplines within the arts, humanities and social sciences.

SAMPLE GRANTS University College London (£24,000); University of Oxford (£17,000); University of Manchester (£14,500); University of Cambridge (£3,500); SOAS and University of Liverpool (£2,500 each); University of Exeter (£1,300) and LSE (£1,000).

FINANCES *Year* 2011–12 *Income* £659,235 *Grants* £141,519 *Assets* £398,259

TRUSTEES Sir David Logan; Dr Aylin Orbasli; Prof. Stephen Mitchell; Dr Simon Corcoran; Dr Neil Macdonald; Anthony Sheppard; Dr Ulf Schoop; William Park; Prof. John Haldon; Shahina Farid; Dr Claire Norton; Dr Gulnur Aybet; Dr Peter Sarris.

PUBLICATIONS *Anatolian Studies and Anatolian Archaeology*. Both annual publications.

OTHER INFORMATION The grant total includes £60,500 that was given to individuals.

HOW TO APPLY Initial inquiries regarding potential applications are welcomed. Full details can be found on the institute's website.

WHO TO APPLY TO Claire McCafferty, The British Academy, 10 Carlton House Terrace, London SW1Y 5AH *Tel.* 020 7969 5204 *email* biaa@britac.ac.uk *Website* www.biaa.ac.uk

■ British Olympic Foundation

CC NO 1122080   **ESTABLISHED** 2007

WHERE FUNDING CAN BE GIVEN UK

WHO CAN BENEFIT Organisations benefiting children and young people.

WHAT IS FUNDED Sport and recreation.

SAMPLE GRANTS Youth education projects (£964,000); Olympic academy seminars (£45,000); Museum costs (£37,500).

FINANCES *Year* 2012 *Income* £901,458 *Grants* £1,046,493 *Assets* £670,412

TRUSTEES Neil Townshend; John James.

HOW TO APPLY In the first instance, contact the correspondent.

WHO TO APPLY TO Jan Paterson, Chief Executive, 60 Charlotte Street, London W1T 2NU *Tel.* 020 7842 5700 *email* boa@boa.org.uk

■ British Ornithologists' Union

CC NO 249877   **ESTABLISHED** 1966

WHERE FUNDING CAN BE GIVEN Worldwide, with a preference for Eastern Europe and northern Asia.

WHO CAN BENEFIT 'The BOU tries to support as wide a range of research projects as is possible, including applications from both amateurs and professionals.'

WHAT IS FUNDED Financial support for research and expeditions. Applications may be on any aspect of ornithology but the BOU will look especially favourably on areas where there are particular difficulties in funding research from national or local sources.

WHAT IS NOT FUNDED UK-based applicants seeking funding for overseas projects should note that the funds being sought should only be used towards defined project requirements outside the UK.

TYPE OF GRANT To individuals for research

RANGE OF GRANTS £800–£2,000

SAMPLE GRANTS Projects supported included: Research into the conservation of the critically endangered Spoon-billed Sandpiper in Bangladesh (£19,000); research into climatic impacts on productivity of Arctic Terms in Iceland (£800); Researching the effectiveness of White-shouldered Ibis nest protection in the UK (£2,000).

FINANCES *Year* 2012 *Income* £171,862

TRUSTEES Jenny Gill; Graham Martin; Tom Pizzari; Dr Gavin Siriwardena; Dr Ken Smith; Claire Spottiswoode; Dr Niall Burton; Dr Stuart Butchart; Dr Paul Dolman; Julianne Evans; Hugh Wright; Dr J. Collinson.

PUBLICATIONS The BOU's international journal 'Ibis' is published quarterly.

OTHER INFORMATION The trust has also set up a website (www.birdgrants.org) to provide information on grants and awards available for bird conservation and ornithological projects.

HOW TO APPLY Further information and application forms can be obtained from the BOU website.

Applications are only accepted via e-mail to the following address: grants@bou.org.uk.The deadline for applications is 30 November.

WHO TO APPLY TO Steve Dudley, Senior Administrator, PO Box 417, Peterborough PE7 3FX *Tel.* 01733 844820 *email* bou@bou. org.uk *Website* www.bou.org.uk

....

■ British Record Industry Trust

CC NO 1000413   **ESTABLISHED** 1989

WHERE FUNDING CAN BE GIVEN Worldwide, in practice UK.

WHO CAN BENEFIT Registered charities benefiting young people involved in the arts, particularly music.

WHAT IS FUNDED The mission of the British Record Industry Trust (BRIT) is to encourage young people in the exploration and pursuit of educational, cultural or therapeutic benefits emanating from music. The trust has an ongoing commitment to the BRIT School for Performing Arts and Technology and Nordoff-Robbins Music Therapy but will also give to other appropriate good causes.

WHAT IS NOT FUNDED No scholarships or grants to individuals. No capital funding projects are considered. Only registered charities in the UK are supported.

TYPE OF GRANT One-off and recurring grants.

RANGE OF GRANTS £1,000–£350,000

SAMPLE GRANTS The BRIT School for the Performing Arts and Technology (£735,000); and Nordoff-Robbins Music Therapy (£300,000); Drugscope (£60,000); Chickenshed Theatre, Heart n Soul and Bigga Fish (£5,000 each); and the Paul Walter Award (£1,000).

FINANCES *Year* 2012 *Income* £1,227,360 *Grants* £1,145,666 *Assets* £7,342,061

TRUSTEES John Craig, Andy Cleary; Derek Green; Paul Burger; David Kassner; Rob Dickins; Tony Wadsworth; Jonathan Morrish; Geoff Taylor; Korda Marshall; David Sharpe; John Deacon; Simon Robson; Emma Pike.

HOW TO APPLY Taken from the trust's website: 'Note that The BRIT Trust is only able to consider applications from fellow organisations with a charitable status. Unfortunately it is unable to consider individual grants, scholarships or capital grants or grant donations outside of the UK. For details of other organisations that may be able to assist, check-out our Contacts page. To apply for funding from The BRIT Trust, complete the application form [on its website]. (Note that applications are only considered annually at a trust meeting in September. All applications should be received by the trust no later than August and should be for projects planned for the following year).'

WHO TO APPLY TO Jenny Clarke, Riverside Building, County Hall, Westminster Bridge Road, London SE1 7JA *Tel.* 020 7803 1351 *email* jenny. clarke@bpi.co.uk *Website* www.brittrust.co.uk

....

■ The Britten-Pears Foundation

CC NO 295595   **ESTABLISHED** 1986

WHERE FUNDING CAN BE GIVEN UK.

WHO CAN BENEFIT Registered charities organisations or individuals whose aims and objectives are of charitable intent. UK-based commissioning bodies such as festivals, concert halls or professional performers, ranging from solo instrumentalist to symphony orchestra and/or chorus.

WHAT IS FUNDED The commissioning of new music. The Grants Panel will look more favourably on applications that can demonstrate that the work will receive more than one performance and will be looking to support composers who have demonstrated a real gift for their craft or a recognised potential and for a partnership of composer and performer/s that impresses them as a significant project. There is also a 'Local Grants' programme that supports grassroots projects (that need not relate to music or the other arts) within 20 miles of Aldeburgh.

WHAT IS NOT FUNDED The Britten-Pears Foundation does not invite applications for grants of a capital nature (including those for instrumental purchase or restoration), for tuition fees, performance costs, recordings, educational or non-musical projects. The foundation does not consider applications for support for performances or recordings of the works of Benjamin Britten, of whose estate it is the beneficiary. Subsidy for works by Britten which, in the Estate's view, need further promotion can be sought from the Britten Estate Limited.

TYPE OF GRANT One-off, some recurring and project. Funding may be given for one year or less, or more than three years. Partnership funding will be considered, though it will wish to be a major contributor in all cases. Matching funding will not be a condition of grant.

SAMPLE GRANTS Aldeburgh Music (£205,000); Royal Philharmonic Society–Britten-Pears Foundation 2013 commissions (£80,000); Isango Ensemble, *Noye's Fludde* film (£30,000); Juventus Lyrica, *The Turn of the Screw* (£15,000); Choir of London, *Albert Herring*; Glyndebourne, *Billy Budd/Rape of Lucretia/ Canticles* (£10,000 each); Stanislavsky Music Theatre, *A Midsummer Night's Dream* (£7,500); Composers Edition Distribution Service (£5,000); Birmingham University students – *Paul Bunyan* (£2,000) and Bramfield Primary School (£1,200).

FINANCES *Year* 2012 *Income* £2,215,791 *Grants* £597,670 *Assets* £21,502,239

TRUSTEES Nicholas Prettejohn; Caroline Brazier; Edward Blakeman; Andrew Fane; Penelope Heath; Lady Sally Irvine; Lady Ghislaine Kenyon; Dr Colin Matthews; Philip Ramsbottom; Sybella Zisman; Janis Susskind.

HOW TO APPLY Full details of how to apply, including application forms, guidelines, criteria and deadlines, can be found on the foundation's website.

WHO TO APPLY TO Amanda Arnold, Company Secretary, The Red House, Golf Lane, Aldeburgh, Suffolk IP15 5PZ *Tel.* 01728 451700 *email* grants@brittenpears.org *Website* www.brittenpears.org

....

■ The J. and M. Britton Charitable Trust

CC NO 1081979   **ESTABLISHED** 1996

WHERE FUNDING CAN BE GIVEN Mainly Bristol and the former county of Avon.

WHO CAN BENEFIT General, education.

WHAT IS FUNDED Local charities such as hospital appeals and other charities that the trustees are involved in.

WHAT IS NOT FUNDED No grants to individuals or to non-registered charities.

RANGE OF GRANTS Up to £20,000.

SAMPLE GRANTS Cancer Research (£20,000); University of Bristol Centenary Appeal (£10,000); Temple Church Organ Fund

(£8,000); St Mary's Church Olveston, Ex-Service Personnel Self Build, Catherine Grace Foundation and Merchants Academy Withywood (£5,000 each); Clifton College (£2,500); and Colston's Girls' School (£1,400).

FINANCES *Year* 2011–12 *Income* £71,273 *Grants* £70,000

TRUSTEES Robert Bernays; R. Bernays; Lady Merrison; Alison Bernays.

HOW TO APPLY In writing to the correspondent enclosing an sae. Charities can apply at any time, but the trust makes distributions twice a year, usually in May and November.

WHO TO APPLY TO R. E. J. Bernays, Trustee, Kilcot House, Lower Kilcot, Hillesley, Wotton-Under-Edge, Gloucestershire GL12 7RL *Tel.* 01454 238571

■ The Charles and Edna Broadhurst Charitable Trust

CC NO 702543   **ESTABLISHED** 1988

WHERE FUNDING CAN BE GIVEN Southport area.

WHO CAN BENEFIT Academics; research workers; Christians; at risk groups; people disadvantaged by poverty; socially isolated people; people with arthritis/rheumatism or cancer.

WHAT IS FUNDED Grants are mainly given to social welfare organisations, and medical academic research, arts and Christian causes.

WHAT IS NOT FUNDED No grants to individuals.

RANGE OF GRANTS £200–£3,000.

SAMPLE GRANTS St Philip's and St Paul's with Wesley Church (£3,000); British Red Cross, Derian House (£2,000 each); MedEquip 4 Kidz (£1,000 each); Autism Initiatives UK (£500); Christ Church YCC (£250) and Southport Blind Aid Society (£200).

FINANCES *Year* 2011–12 *Income* £25,302 *Grants* £20,200 *Assets* £595,561

TRUSTEES Janet Carver; Gillian Edmondson; Kathleen Griffith; David Wood; Guy Wigmore.

HOW TO APPLY In writing to the correspondent. Applications are considered twice a year, usually in July and November.

WHO TO APPLY TO David Wood, Trustee, 13 Melling Road, Southport PR9 9DU *Tel.* 01704 540438 *email* woodypowr@hotmail.com

---

■ The Bromley Trust

CC NO 801875   **ESTABLISHED** 1989

WHERE FUNDING CAN BE GIVEN Worldwide.

WHO CAN BENEFIT UK registered charities only.

WHAT IS FUNDED The trust supports charities concerned with human rights, prison reform and conservation and sustainability. This well organised and focused trust also offers other organisations with similar interests and objectives the chance to participate in a network of like-minded groups.

WHAT IS NOT FUNDED Grants are only given to UK registered charities. The following are not supported: individuals; expeditions; scholarships, although in certain cases the trust supports research that falls within its aims (but always through a registered charity); statutory authorities, or charities whose main source of funding is via statutory agencies; overseas development or disaster relief; local conservation projects or charities that work with single species; drug rehabilitation programmes.

TYPE OF GRANT Often recurrent, unrestricted grants. One-off grants are occasionally made, but these are infrequent. It is the trust's policy to give

larger amounts to fewer charities rather than to spread income over a large number of small grants.

RANGE OF GRANTS Up to £25,000.

SAMPLE GRANTS The Clink (£30,000); Prison Reform Trust (£25,000); Ashden Awards and Redress Trust (£20,000 each); Anti-Slavery International, Landlife and World Pheasant Association (£15,000 each); Cape Farewell, Gatwick Detainees Welfare Group and Wave Trust (£10,000 each); Koestler Award Trust (£8,000); Birdlife Human Rights, Detention Forum and National Working Group for Sexually Exploited Children and Young People (£5,000 each); and PRT – Women's Justice Taskforce (£2,000).

FINANCES *Year* 2011–12 *Income* £619,920 *Grants* £684,500 *Assets* £15,421,675

TRUSTEES Bryan Blamey; Dr Judith Brett; Peter Alan Edwards; Jean Ritchie; Anthony John Roberts; Anne-Marie Edgell; Nigel Dyson.

HOW TO APPLY New applicants are directed, where possible, to the trust's website where the trust's criteria, guidelines and application process are posted. An application form can be accessed from the website for charities that fit the trust's remit, and should be completed and returned via email to applicant@thebromleytrust.org.uk. There is no strict page limit on completed application forms but the average length is approximately eight to ten pages. Applicants are asked not to return applications which are significantly larger than this. The trust aims to notify applicants within four to six weeks as to whether or not they are eligible for the next stage of the process, although this may vary. No feedback is given to unsuccessful applicants. All charities are visited before a grant is made. Note: the trust asks that organisations who have previously submitted an application do not submit any further requests for funding. Applicant details are held on the trust's database and if any assistance can be provided in the future, they will make contact.

WHO TO APPLY TO Teresa Elwes, Grants Executive, Studio 7, 2 Pinchin Street, Whitechapel, London E1 1SA *Tel.* 020 7481 4899 *email* info@thebromleytrust.org.uk *Website* www.thebromleytrust.org.uk

---

■ The Roger Brooke Charitable Trust

CC NO 1071250   **ESTABLISHED** 1998

WHERE FUNDING CAN BE GIVEN UK, with a preference for Hampshire.

WHO CAN BENEFIT Registered charities.

WHAT IS FUNDED General charitable purposes, especially medical research, support for carers and social action.

WHAT IS NOT FUNDED In general, individuals are not supported.

SAMPLE GRANTS Previous beneficiary: The Southampton University Development Fund (£100,000).

FINANCES *Year* 2011–12 *Income* £5,959 *Grants* £25,840

TRUSTEES Nancy Brooke; Stephen Brooke.

HOW TO APPLY In writing to the correspondent. Applications will only be acknowledged if successful.

WHO TO APPLY TO The Trustees, Withers LLP, 16 Old Bailey, London EC4M 7EG *Tel.* 020 7597 6123

Does the trust you have chosen match your needs? Haphazard applications waste postage and time

■ The David Brooke Charity

CC NO 283658   **ESTABLISHED** 1961
WHERE FUNDING CAN BE GIVEN UK.
WHO CAN BENEFIT Voluntary and community-based groups, especially those concerned with disadvantaged young people.
WHAT IS FUNDED Preference is given to organisations which provide opportunities for self-help programmes and outdoor activity training. Medical charities are also supported.
TYPE OF GRANT Long-term support.
RANGE OF GRANTS Up to £6,000.
SAMPLE GRANTS Great Ormond Street Hospital (£3,000); Arthritis Research Campaign and ASTO (£2,500 each); British Stammering Association and YMCA (£2,000 each); Independence at Home, Kennet and Avon Canal Trust and the Mission to Seafarers (£1,000 each).
FINANCES *Year* 2011–12 *Income* £35,635 *Grants* £45,000 *Assets* £2,071,101
TRUSTEES David Rusman; Peter Hutt; Nigel Brooke.
HOW TO APPLY The correspondent stated that the trust's annual income is not for general distribution as it is committed to a limited number of charities on a long-term basis.
WHO TO APPLY TO David Rusman, Trustee, Cook Sutton, Tay Court, Blounts Court Road, Sonning Common, Oxfordshire RG4 9RS *Tel.* 01491 573411

■ The Rory and Elizabeth Brooks Foundation

CC NO 1111587   **ESTABLISHED** 2005
WHERE FUNDING CAN BE GIVEN Worldwide.
WHO CAN BENEFIT Charitable organisations.
WHAT IS FUNDED The main objects of the charity are to promote and advance education, medical research, healthcare, community care and arts and culture.
FINANCES *Year* 2011–12 *Income* £284,347 *Grants* £505,850 *Assets* £177,667
TRUSTEES Elizabeth Brooks; Roderick Brooks; David Way.
OTHER INFORMATION A list of beneficiaries was unavailable, but the total amount was shared between 20 organisations.
HOW TO APPLY In writing to the correspondent.
WHO TO APPLY TO Josie Lawrence, Grand Buildings, 1–3 Strand, London WC2N 5HR *Tel.* 020 7024 2200

■ The Charles Brotherton Trust

CC NO 227067   **ESTABLISHED** 1940
WHERE FUNDING CAN BE GIVEN The cities of Birmingham, Leeds, Liverpool, Wakefield, York and Bebington in the borough of Wirral.
WHO CAN BENEFIT Charitable organisations.
WHAT IS FUNDED 'The charity is principally directed to encourage young people to improve their own lives by taking advantage of educational opportunities and organised recreational activities. The charity is also empowered to help improve the standard of living of the elderly and disabled people and relieve the suffering caused by illness.'
WHAT IS NOT FUNDED Grants to registered charities and recognised bodies only. No grants to individuals.
TYPE OF GRANT Recurrent
RANGE OF GRANTS Mostly £250 or less.
SAMPLE GRANTS Salvation Army, Shaftesbury Youth Club (£250 each) Wirral Christian Centre Trust

Ltd (£120) Birmingham City Mission, Cerebral Palsy Midlands, Voluntary Action – Leeds (all £200); Liverpool Diocesan Board for Social Responsibility, Marie Curie Cancer Care (£175 each); Merseyside Society for the Deaf (£150); Sailors' Families' Society (£100).
FINANCES *Year* 2011–12 *Income* £68,937 *Grants* £62,500 *Assets* £1,741,704
TRUSTEES C. Brotherton-Ratcliffe; D. Ratcliffe-Brotherton.
HOW TO APPLY In writing to the correspondent. The application should clearly show the organisation's activities, geographical area of operations, and for what the funds are required. Applications should be accompanied by the organisation's most recent set of accounts. There is no formal application form and applications are not acknowledged. Grants are considered by the trustees at the start of the trust's accounting year in April, and a single payment made to successful applicants in October. (Scholarships are available to students on scientific courses at the universities of Leeds, Liverpool, Birmingham and York, but applications for these must be made to the university in question, not to the above correspondent.)
WHO TO APPLY TO The Secretary, PO Box 374, Harrogate, North Yorkshire HG1 4YW *Website* www.charlesbrothertontrust.com

■ Joseph Brough Charitable Trust

CC NO 227332   **ESTABLISHED** 1940
WHERE FUNDING CAN BE GIVEN The historic counties of Northumberland and Tyne and Wear and some areas of Durham.
WHO CAN BENEFIT Small community groups with a special interest in Methodist courses.
WHAT IS FUNDED Social and community work.
WHAT IS NOT FUNDED Major appeals are not supported unless they are very close to their target.
RANGE OF GRANTS Up to £11,000.
SAMPLE GRANTS Depaul UK (£11,000); Greggs Foundation (£7,000); Millin Centre (£5,000) and County Durham Community Foundation (£3,000).
FINANCES *Year* 2011–12 *Income* £33,623 *Grants* £26,090 *Assets* £1,293,917
TRUSTEE Community Foundation (serving Tyne and Wear and Northumberland).
HOW TO APPLY On a form available to download, together with criteria and guidelines, on the website.
WHO TO APPLY TO Sue Legg, 9th Floor, Cale Cross House, 156 Pilgrim Street, Newcastle upon Tyne NE1 6SU *Tel.* 01912 220945 *email* general@communityfoundation.org.uk *Website* www.communityfoundation.org.uk

■ The Swinfen Broun Charitable Trust

CC NO 503515   **ESTABLISHED** 1973
WHERE FUNDING CAN BE GIVEN City of Lichfield.
WHO CAN BENEFIT City of Lichfield, residents/organisations.
WHAT IS FUNDED Support for public buildings and facilities, and general charitable purposes.
WHAT IS NOT FUNDED No grants for the benefit of ecclesiastical or relief of poverty charities.
RANGE OF GRANTS £300–£4,000.
SAMPLE GRANTS Beneficiaries that had received grants in previous years have included: Lichfield

Table Tennis Club £980, Staffordshire Pre School Learning Alliance £3,117, Lichfield Mysteries £1,000, Lichfield District Council – Proms in the Park 2012 £1,000, and City of Lichfield Band Trusts £450.

FINANCES *Year* 2011–12 *Income* £25,471 *Grants* £18,227 *Assets* £586,115

TRUSTEES J. N. Wilks, Chair; D. English; A. D. Thompson; B. D. Diggle; Cllr T. V. Finn; J. M. Eagland; J. A. Allsopp; Cllr Norma Bacon; C. Lamb; C. J. Spruce; D. Smedley; B. W. Derrick.

OTHER INFORMATION Grants to seven individuals totalled £1,775.

HOW TO APPLY Application forms are available from the trust website. Completed application forms may be emailed or posted to the correspondent.

WHO TO APPLY TO A. G. Birch, Clerk, 42 Lincoln Close, Lichfield, Staffordshire WS13 7SW *Tel.* 01543 304948 *email* clerk@swinfenbroun.org.uk *Website* www.swinfenbroun.org.uk

----

■ Bill Brown 1989 Charitable Trust

CC NO 801756　　　　**ESTABLISHED** 1989
WHERE FUNDING CAN BE GIVEN UK, preference for South England.
WHO CAN BENEFIT Charities registered in the UK.
WHAT IS FUNDED Research into blindness, medical research, deaf and blind people, elderly, people with disabilities, general welfare and hospices.
WHAT IS NOT FUNDED No grants to individuals. No grants for animal welfare; small/local charitable causes; wildlife or environmental charities; building maintenance; regional branches of national charitable organisations or religious charities.
TYPE OF GRANT Mainly recurrent.
RANGE OF GRANTS Mostly £1,000–£10,000.
SAMPLE GRANTS Charities Aid Foundation Trust (£65,000 in two grants); Macmillan Cancer Support and Salvation Army (£13,000 each); Scout Council – Greater London Middlesex West County, Contact the Elderly and Alzheimer's Society (£6,500 each) and Richmond Borough Association for Mental Health (£3,250).
FINANCES *Year* 2011–12 *Income* £364,208 *Grants* £172,250 *Assets* £11,789,481
TRUSTEES G. S. Brown; A. J. Barnett.
HOW TO APPLY In writing containing the following: aims and objectives of the charity; nature of appeal; total target if for a specific project; contributions received against target; registered charity number; any other relevant factors. Appeals should be accompanied by a set of the organisation's latest report and full accounts. Trustees meet to consider applications in mid-June and December; applications should be received by the end of May and October to be considered at the respective meeting. Only successful applicants will be notified.
WHO TO APPLY TO The Trustees, BM BOX 4567, London WC1N 3XX *Website* www.billbrowncharity.org

----

■ Edna Brown Charitable Settlement (Mrs E. E. Brown Charitable Settlement)

CC NO 261397　　　　**ESTABLISHED** 1970
WHO CAN BENEFIT Registered charities; local, regional and international organisations.
WHAT IS FUNDED General charitable purposes and Jewish causes.

WHAT IS NOT FUNDED No grants to individuals or activities involving medical research.
TYPE OF GRANT Recurring and one-off.
RANGE OF GRANTS Up to £2,000.
SAMPLE GRANTS Friends of Israel Education Academic Study Group; Jewish Historical Society; Oxfam – Horn of Africa; and SCOPE (£1,000 each).
FINANCES *Year* 2011–12 *Income* £28,557 *Grants* £25,650 *Assets* £749,601
TRUSTEES Malcolm Brown; Lord Brown of Eaton-under-Heywood.
HOW TO APPLY In writing to the correspondent. However in the accounts for 2011/12, the trust states that it is not currently considering appeals for assistance, preferring to concentrate on organisations already supported.
WHO TO APPLY TO Chris Hardwick, Administrator, Barber Harrison and Platt, 2 Rutland Park, Sheffield S10 2PD *Tel.* 01142 667171

■ R. S. Brownless Charitable Trust

CC NO 1000320　　　　**ESTABLISHED** 1990
WHERE FUNDING CAN BE GIVEN Mainly UK and occasionally overseas.
WHO CAN BENEFIT Organisations working with children, young adults and people with disabilities.
WHAT IS FUNDED Accommodation and housing, education, job creation and voluntary work.
WHAT IS NOT FUNDED Grants are rarely given to individuals for educational projects or to education or conservation causes or overseas aid.
TYPE OF GRANT Usually one-off; sometimes annual.
RANGE OF GRANTS Up to £2,000 (occasionally more); usually £100–£500.
SAMPLE GRANTS Previous beneficiaries have included: Alzheimer's Society, Camp Mohawk, Casa Allianza UK, Crisis, Foundation for Study of Infant Deaths, Prader-Willi Foundation, St Andrew's Hall, UNICEF, Wargrave Parochial Church Council and Witham on the Hill Parochial Church Council.
FINANCES *Year* 2011–12 *Income* £60,689 *Grants* £62,799 *Assets* £1,253,075
TRUSTEES Frances Plummer; Philippa Nicolai.
HOW TO APPLY In writing to the correspondent. The trustees meet twice a year, but in special circumstances will meet at other times. The trust is unable to acknowledge all requests.
WHO TO APPLY TO Philippa Nicolai, Trustee, Hennerton Holt, Hennerton, Wargrave, Reading RG10 8PD *Tel.* 01189 404029

■ Brown-Mellows Trust

CC NO 1135821　　　　**ESTABLISHED** 2010
WHERE FUNDING CAN BE GIVEN UK.
WHO CAN BENEFIT Registered charities.
WHAT IS FUNDED General charitable purposes, with an apparent preference for education, social welfare, the arts and the environment.
FINANCES *Year* 2011–12 *Income* £27,261 *Grants* £42,000 *Assets* £16,544
TRUSTEES Janet Newman; Alexander Newman; Hannah Newman; David Newman.
HOW TO APPLY In writing to the correspondent. However, the trust states that it 'does not normally respond to unsolicited requests for funding.'
WHO TO APPLY TO The Trustees, c/o Goodman Jones LLP, 29–30 Fitzroy Square, London W1T 6LQ *Tel.* 020 7388 2444 *email* info@goodmanjones.com

■ The Brownsword Charitable Foundation

CC NO 1012615 **ESTABLISHED** 1992
WHERE FUNDING CAN BE GIVEN The city of Bath, principally but not exclusively.
WHO CAN BENEFIT Charitable organisations, preferably in the city of Bath.
WHAT IS FUNDED General charitable purposes, with particular focus on children and young people, the elderly, arts, community and neighbourhood work, physical and learning disabilities, educational projects and medical projects.
TYPE OF GRANT One – off grants to organisations.
RANGE OF GRANTS £100–£75,000.
SAMPLE GRANTS Exeter Cathedral Third Millennium (£75,000); Bath Institute for Medical Research and Iford Arts (£5,000 each); Merchant Venturers, Friends of the RUH and Teenage Cancer Trust (£1,000 each); RNLI (£250) and Fight for Sight and Sarcoma UK (£100 each).
FINANCES *Year* 2012 *Income* £274,255 *Grants* £88,450 *Assets* £9,266,499
TRUSTEES Christina Brownsword; Andrew Brownsword; George Goodall; Robert Calleja.
HOW TO APPLY In writing to the correspondent.
WHO TO APPLY TO Nicholas Burrows, Administrator, 4 Queen Square, Bath BA1 2HA *Tel*. 01225 339661

■ The T. B. H. Brunner Charitable Settlement

CC NO 260604 **ESTABLISHED** 1969
WHERE FUNDING CAN BE GIVEN UK with some preference for Oxfordshire.
WHO CAN BENEFIT Registered charities and individuals.
WHAT IS FUNDED Church of England preservation projects and other charities dealing with historical preservation, both local to Oxfordshire and nationally; the arts; music; and general charitable purposes.
RANGE OF GRANTS £100–£4,100.
SAMPLE GRANTS Rotherfield Greys Parochial Church Council (£7,000); Institute of Economic Affairs (£2,500); Care International, King Edward Hospital, the London Library and Opera Holland Park (£1,000 each); the Children's Society and the Pearl Harris Trust (£500 each); and Friends of Dorchester Abbey (£250).
FINANCES *Year* 2011–12 *Income* £51,218 *Grants* £37,650 *Assets* £1,734,004
TRUSTEES Timothy Brunner; Helen Brunner; Dr Imogen Brunner.
HOW TO APPLY In writing to the correspondent.
WHO TO APPLY TO Timothy Brunner, Trustee, Flat 4, 2 Inverness Gardens, London W8 4RN *Tel*. 020 7727 6277

■ The Jack Brunton Charitable Trust

CC NO 518407 **ESTABLISHED** 1986
WHERE FUNDING CAN BE GIVEN Old North Riding area of Yorkshire.
WHO CAN BENEFIT Registered charities for the benefit of the population of the rural villages and towns within the beneficial area.
WHAT IS FUNDED General charitable purposes.
WHAT IS NOT FUNDED 'Grants to individuals or out of area applicants are only made in very rare and exceptional circumstances.'
TYPE OF GRANT One-off for capital costs.
RANGE OF GRANTS Between £100 and £40,000.

SAMPLE GRANTS York Minster (£40,000); Captain Cook Schoolroom Museum, Great Ayton and St Eloy's Church, Great Smeaton (£5,000 each); Multiple Sclerosis Society, Middlesbrough (£4,000); Masham Town Hall (£3,000); Asthma Relief, North Yorkshire, Safe and Sound Homes, North Yorkshire and Scout and Guide Headquarters, Bedale (£2,000 each); Northallerton Silver Band (£1,500) and Cleveland Search and Rescue Team, Narconon Drug Education Services, York and The Blue Cross Pet Charity, Thirsk (£1,000 each).
FINANCES *Year* 2011–12 *Income* £118,043 *Grants* £115,850 *Assets* £4,081,884
TRUSTEES Joan Brunton; Jonathan Brunton; Edward Marquis; Derek Noble; James Lumb; Dr Clair Hurst.
OTHER INFORMATION In 2011–12 grants were given to 47 organisations.
HOW TO APPLY In writing to the correspondent including full details of costings if relevant.
WHO TO APPLY TO David Swallow, Administrator, Commercial House, 10 Bridge Road, Stokesley, North Yorkshire TS9 5AA *Tel*. 01642 711407

■ The Bruntwood Charity

CC NO 1135777 **ESTABLISHED** 2010
WHERE FUNDING CAN BE GIVEN UK
WHO CAN BENEFIT Registered charities.
WHAT IS FUNDED General charitable purposes.
SAMPLE GRANTS From 2011–13 the charity focused on fundraising for five charities; they were: Onside and the Factory Youth Zone (Manchester); St Gemma's Hospice (Leeds); Claire House Children's Hospice (Liverpool); The Prince's Trust (Birmingham). St Gemma's Hospice is being supported through to March 2015.
FINANCES *Year* 2011–12 *Income* £104,968 *Grants* £120,000 *Assets* £52,445
TRUSTEES Katharine Vokes; Andy Allan; Rob Yates; Sally Hill; Kathryn Graham; Jane Williams.
OTHER INFORMATION This is the charity of Bruntwood Ltd, a company which owns and manages commercial property and offices space in Birmingham, Leeds, Manchester and Liverpool.
HOW TO APPLY In writing to the correspondent, although potential applicants should be aware that the relationships with the nominated charities may continue.
WHO TO APPLY TO Sally Hill, Trustee, Bruntwood Ltd, City Tower, Piccadilly Plaza, Manchester M1 4BT *Tel*. 01612 373883

■ Brushmill Ltd

CC NO 285420 **ESTABLISHED** 1982
WHERE FUNDING CAN BE GIVEN Worldwide.
WHO CAN BENEFIT Organisations benefiting Jewish people.
WHAT IS FUNDED Jewish charitable purposes, education and social welfare.
SAMPLE GRANTS Previous beneficiaries have included Bais Rochel, Friends of Yeshivas Shaar Hashomaim and Holmleigh Trust.
FINANCES *Year* 2011–12 *Income* £403,929 *Grants* £442,146 *Assets* -£19,613
TRUSTEES C. Getter, Chair; J. Weinberger; E. Weinberger.
OTHER INFORMATION A list of beneficiaries was not available.
HOW TO APPLY In writing to the correspondent.
WHO TO APPLY TO M. Getter, Secretary, 76 Fairholt Road, London N16 5HN

Think carefully about every application. Is it justified?

413

■ Buckingham Trust

CC NO 237350   **ESTABLISHED** 1962
WHERE FUNDING CAN BE GIVEN UK and worldwide.
WHO CAN BENEFIT Charitable organisations and churches.
WHAT IS FUNDED Advancement of religion (including missionary activities); relief of people disadvantaged by poverty and older people or those who are ill.
TYPE OF GRANT One-off and recurrent grants.
RANGE OF GRANTS Up to £18,000.
SAMPLE GRANTS Tear Fund (£38,000); Barnabas Fund (£37,000); OMF International (£33,000); Church Mission Society (£32,000); All Saints – Crowborough (£30,000); Battle Methodist Church (£29,000); Cure International (£7,400); World in Need (£6,000); Christchurch Claypath Durham (£3,000); Giddeons (£1,400) and The Manor Preparatory School (£1,200).
FINANCES *Year* 2011–12 *Income* £243,994 *Grants* £492,854 *Assets* £619,408
TRUSTEES Richard Foot; Tina Clay.
OTHER INFORMATION Preference is given to charities of which the trustees have personal interest, knowledge, or association. The trust acts mainly as an agency charity acting on behalf of other donors. The grant total also includes £5,800 in grants to individuals.
HOW TO APPLY Unsolicited applicants are not considered. As an agency charity, the trustees allow the donors to choose for the funds which they have donated, which registered charities or churches the funds are given to.
WHO TO APPLY TO The Trustees, Foot Davson, 17 Church Road, Tunbridge Wells, Kent TN1 1LG *Tel.* 01892 774774

■ Buckinghamshire Community Foundation

CC NO 1073861   **ESTABLISHED** 1998
WHERE FUNDING CAN BE GIVEN The administrative County of Buckinghamshire, excluding Milton Keynes.
WHO CAN BENEFIT Voluntary and community groups.
WHAT IS FUNDED Community development. Visit the foundation's website for details of up-to-date schemes.
WHAT IS NOT FUNDED No grants to organisations outside of the beneficial area, to individuals, religious or political organisations, animal welfare or to statutory organisations (with the exception of Parish Councils).
RANGE OF GRANTS £200–£25,000.
SAMPLE GRANTS Work Aid (£25,000); Talkback UK (£24,000); Think Local, Give Local Project (£23,000); Lane End Oasis Centre (£15,000); Horses Helping People (£10,000); Dorney Youth Club (£6,000); Bucks Play Association and Trinity United Reformed Church (£5,000 each); Bedgrove Dynamos Football Club (£4,000); Queens Park Art Centre (£3,500); Chesham Over 50's Positive (£1,500); Beaconsfield Festival of Lights (£1,000); Aylesbury Youth Motor Project (£500) and Beachview School (£230).
FINANCES *Year* 2011–12 *Income* £822,474 *Grants* £383,926 *Assets* £3,140,957
TRUSTEES Peter Keen; Guy Birkby; Graham Peart; Alexander Shephard; David Sumpter; Roy Collis; Cherry Aston; Simon Deans; Colin Hayfield; Munir Hussain; The Countess Howe; Graham Corney.
HOW TO APPLY In the first instance, an 'expression of interest' form available from the Foundation's website, where criteria and guidelines are also posted.
WHO TO APPLY TO The Grants Panel, Foundation House, 119A Bicester Road, Aylesbury, Buckinghamshire HP19 9BA *Tel.* 01296 330134 *Fax* 01296 330158 *email* info@buckscf.org.uk *Website* www.buckscf.org.uk

■ The Buckinghamshire Historic Churches Trust

CC NO 206471   **ESTABLISHED** 1957
WHERE FUNDING CAN BE GIVEN The county or archdeaconry of Buckingham.
WHO CAN BENEFIT Parochial church councils or trustees of Christian churches and chapels, including Baptist, Anglican, Methodist and Catholic.
WHAT IS FUNDED The preservation, repair, maintenance and upkeep of the fabric of churches or chapels in Buckinghamshire. Grants are made to churches and chapels embarking upon restoration.
WHAT IS NOT FUNDED Grants cannot be given for repairs to bells, bell frames, bell chambers, window glass, organs, furnishings and work on heating, lighting, decoration or churchyard maintenance. Churches and chapels not in use for public worship are not supported.
TYPE OF GRANT One-off.
RANGE OF GRANTS £1,000–£5,000
SAMPLE GRANTS Kingsey, St Nicholas (£8,000); Great Missenden, St Peter and St Paul (£6,000); Horsenden, St Michael and All Angels (£4,500); Ickford, St Nicholas (£3,000) and Princes Risborough, St Mary (£1,000).
FINANCES *Year* 2011–12 *Income* £77,219 *Grants* £57,000 *Assets* £731,329
TRUSTEES Sir Henry Aubrey-Fletcher; Caroline Abel-Smith; Cherry Aston; Rupert Carington; Revd Canon Herbert Cavell-Northam; Ann Cutcliffe; Roger Evans; Hon Jenefer Farncombe; Andrew Finn-Kelcey; Jennifer Moss; Timothy Oliver; Francis Robinson; Mary Villiers; Rt Revd Alan Wilson; Mary Saunders; Marilynne Morgan.
OTHER INFORMATION In 2011–12 grants were given to ten churches.
HOW TO APPLY An application form is available from the correspondent.
WHO TO APPLY TO Penny Keens, Hon. Secretary, 377 Japonica Lane, Willen Park, Milton Keynes MK15 9EG *Tel.* 01908 242632 *email* penny@pkeens.plus.com *Website* www.bucks-historic-churches.org

■ The Buckinghamshire Masonic Centenary Fund

CC NO 1007193   **ESTABLISHED** 1991
WHERE FUNDING CAN BE GIVEN Buckinghamshire.
WHO CAN BENEFIT Registered charities and individuals.
WHAT IS FUNDED The fund will normally only give consideration to: non-Masonic charitable causes within Buckinghamshire; specific projects or facilities, rather than general appeals or requests to fund routine activities; Buckinghamshire charities that deal solely with cases in Buckinghamshire, and Buckinghamshire charities that also have connections in adjacent areas; individual cases within Buckinghamshire, or outside Buckinghamshire if there is a strong Buckinghamshire connection, only if referred through, or supported by, community welfare or

health agencies because of the implications for State and other welfare benefit provisions.

WHAT IS NOT FUNDED No grants to individuals for expeditions or for youth work overseas, no sponsorship of events or individuals. No grants to heritage, wildlife or conservation projects. No grants towards routine expenditure and activities, including staff costs.

TYPE OF GRANT The focus is normally on specific projects or facilities, complete in themselves, rather than general appeals or requests to fund activities.

RANGE OF GRANTS Up to £15,000

SAMPLE GRANTS Chilterns MS Centre (£14,800); Maya (£9,500); Kirton Healthcare Centre (£4,000); Carers Milton Keynes (£4,000); National Autistic Society (£1,400); Waddesdon Methodist Church (£1,200); Horsewyse and Milton Keynes Mayoral Charity Appeal (£1,000 each).

FINANCES *Year* 2011–12 *Income* £36,377 *Grants* £36,490 *Assets* £646,673

TRUSTEES Clifford Drake; Michael Stimson; Robert Wharton.

HOW TO APPLY In writing to the correspondent, setting out aims and objectives on one page of A4 with a copy of the latest audited annual report and accounts if available. Details should be supplied of the specific facilities or projects for which funding is sought. The trustees meet three or four times a year to consider applications. The trust states that some grants are made after the organisation has been visited by a committee member.

WHO TO APPLY TO Peter Carey, Administrator, 46 Parklands, Great Linford, Milton Keynes, Buckinghamshire MK14 5DZ *Tel.* 01908 605997 *email* prc@mkcareys.co.uk *Website* www.buckspgl.org

---

■ **Buckland Charitable Trust**

CC NO 273679   **ESTABLISHED** 1977

WHERE FUNDING CAN BE GIVEN UK and overseas.

WHO CAN BENEFIT Charitable organisations.

WHAT IS FUNDED General, health, international development and welfare.

RANGE OF GRANTS Up to £4,000.

SAMPLE GRANTS Macmillan (£3,000); Médecins Sans Frontières, Eden Valley Hospice and Cancer Research (£2,000 each); East Cumbria Family Support and Scope (£1,000 each); Camphill Village Trust, Kids in Action and RNLI (£500 each) and The Smile Train (£200).

FINANCES *Year* 2011–12 *Income* £832,939 *Grants* £31,250 *Assets* £1,579,065

TRUSTEES Paul Bannister; Ali Afsari; Anna Bannister.

HOW TO APPLY In writing to the correspondent.

WHO TO APPLY TO The Trustees, c/o Smith and Williamson Limited, 1 Bishops Wharf, Walnut Tree Close, Guildford, Surrey GU1 4RA *Tel.* 01483 407100

■ **The Buffini Chao Foundation**

CC NO 1111022   **ESTABLISHED** 2005

WHERE FUNDING CAN BE GIVEN England and Wales.

WHO CAN BENEFIT Charitable organisations.

WHAT IS FUNDED General charitable purposes, especially organisations working in the field of education and with children.

RANGE OF GRANTS Up to £50,000.

SAMPLE GRANTS Foundation and Friends of the Royal Botanic Gardens Kew and Royal Shakespeare Company (£50,000 each); Notre Dame School (£30,000); National Youth Orchestra (£28,000);

EYLA – education co-ordinator (£15,000); Build Africa (£11,000); London Children's Ballet – Dancer sponsorship (£1,000).

FINANCES *Year* 2011–12 *Income* £66,260 *Grants* £185,281 *Assets* £3,197,139

TRUSTEES Ms D. Buffini; D. M. Buffini; M. G. Hindmarsh.

HOW TO APPLY In writing to the correspondent.

WHO TO APPLY TO D. Buffini, Trustee, 12 Mount Ephraim Road, Tunbridge Wells, Kent TN1 1EG *Tel.* 01892 515121

■ **The Rosemary Bugden Charitable Trust**

CC NO 327626   **ESTABLISHED** 1987

WHERE FUNDING CAN BE GIVEN UK, with a preference for the former county of Avon (in practice Bath and North East Somerset, Bristol, North Somerset and South Gloucestershire).

WHO CAN BENEFIT Arts, education, general charitable causes.

WHAT IS FUNDED Local schools for the purchase musical instruments.

SAMPLE GRANTS Previously: £25,000 to 113 state schools; £10,000 to the Royal College of Music.

FINANCES *Year* 2011–12 *Income* £12,913

TRUSTEES John Sharpe; Elizabeth Frimston.

OTHER INFORMATION In 2011–12 the trust had a total expenditure of £33,112.

HOW TO APPLY In writing to the correspondent.

WHO TO APPLY TO John Sharpe, Trustee, c/o Osborne Clarke, 2 Temple Back East, Temple Quay, Bristol BS1 6EG *Tel.* 01179 173022

■ **The Bulldog Trust Limited**

CC NO 1123081   **ESTABLISHED** 1983

WHERE FUNDING CAN BE GIVEN Worldwide, with a preference for the South of England.

WHO CAN BENEFIT Charitable organisations.

WHAT IS FUNDED General charitable purposes.

WHAT IS NOT FUNDED No grants are given to individuals or to unsolicited applications.

SAMPLE GRANTS University of Winchester (£22,500); Public Catalogue Foundation (£16,500); English Heritage Foundation, Park and Gardens Data Service and Special Boat Service Association (£10,000 each).

FINANCES *Year* 2011–12 *Income* £594,801 *Grants* £179,800 *Assets* £9,907,805

TRUSTEES Martin Riley; Brian Smouha; Charles Hoare; Hamish McPherson; Kim Hoare; Alex Williams.

HOW TO APPLY The trust regrets that unsolicited applications cannot be accepted.

WHO TO APPLY TO Mary Gunn, Administrator, 2 Temple Place, London WC2R 3BD *Tel.* 0207246044 *email* info@bulldogtrust.org *Website* www.bulldogtrust.org

---

■ **The E. F. Bulmer Benevolent Fund**

CC NO 214831   **ESTABLISHED** 1938

WHERE FUNDING CAN BE GIVEN Herefordshire.

WHO CAN BENEFIT Organisations, former employees of H P Bulmer Holdings plc or its subsidiaries and individuals.

WHAT IS FUNDED Organisations benefiting people who are sick or disadvantaged by poverty. Former employees of H P Bulmer Holdings plc and individuals who are in need.

WHAT IS NOT FUNDED Large UK charities and those from outside Herefordshire are unlikely to be supported.

TYPE OF GRANT One-off for capital (including buildings), core costs, feasibility studies, project, research, running costs, salaries and start-up costs. Funding may be given for up to three years.

RANGE OF GRANTS Up to £25,000.

SAMPLE GRANTS Martha Trust (£25,000); Leominster Shopmobility (£10,000); Yeleni Support Centre For Cancer and Chronic Illness (£5,250); Herefordshire Riding For The Disabled and Age Concern Ross-On-Wye and District (£4,000 each) and Family Drug Support, Acorns Children's Hospice, Women4Women and Newton Farm Community Centre (£3,000 each).

FINANCES *Year* 2011–12 *Income* £352,260 *Grants* £235,327 *Assets* £11,287,872

TRUSTEES Richard Bulmer; Edward Bulmer; Jocelyn Wood; Andrew Patten; Hannah Lort-Phillips.

OTHER INFORMATION The grant total includes £53,000 to pensioners of H P Bulmer Holdings plc or its subsidiaries and £15,000 to other individuals.

HOW TO APPLY In writing to the correspondent, although a voluntary application form is available and will be sent if requested. Applications should be accompanied by a copy of the latest report and accounts. The administrator is very happy to discuss applications by e-mail or telephone prior to the application being submitted. The trustees usually meet four times a year. Smaller groups who may have difficulty in receiving support from large national trusts are normally given priority.

WHO TO APPLY TO James Greenfield, Administrator, Fred Bulmer Centre, Wall Street, Hereford, Herefordshire HR4 9HP *Tel.* 01432 271293 *email* efbulmer@gmail.com *Website* www.efbulmer.co.uk

■ Bumba Foundation

CC NO 1145624 **ESTABLISHED** 2012

WHERE FUNDING CAN BE GIVEN North West England and Uganda.

WHO CAN BENEFIT Children and young people.

WHAT IS FUNDED Education and the relief of poverty.

TRUSTEES Martin Tilbury; Jane Hanson; Nancy Elkins; Judith Boyce; Stephen Rouch; Anthony Hegarty.

HOW TO APPLY Unsolicited application are not considered.

WHO TO APPLY TO Martin Tilbury, Trustee, 40 Dane Road, Sale, Cheshire M33 7AR *Tel.* 01619 732786 *email* bumbafoundation@yahoo.co.uk

■ The Burden Trust

CC NO 235859 **ESTABLISHED** 1913

WHERE FUNDING CAN BE GIVEN UK and overseas.

WHO CAN BENEFIT Charitable organisations and institutions; hospitals; retirement homes; schools and training institutions

WHAT IS FUNDED Medical research, the priority is to support research in neurosciences; education and training; the care of older people, children, people who are sick and people in need. There is an overall adherence to the tenets and principles of the Church of England.

WHAT IS NOT FUNDED No grants to individuals.

TYPE OF GRANT Recurring and one-off. Grants are not automatic and must be applied for annually.

SAMPLE GRANTS Langham Research Scholarships (£18,000); Oxford Centre for Mission Studies

(£16,000); Easton Families Project (£17,500); Crisis Centre Ministries and Trinity College Bristol (£10,000 each); Changing Tunes (£7,800); Barton Camp and Wheels Project (£4,000); Urban Saints (£3,000); The Seed Project and Frontier Youth Trust (£2,500); Avon Riding Camp (£2,000) and BCAN (£1,000).

FINANCES *Year* 2011–12 *Income* £84,602 *Grants* £125,800 *Assets* £3,754,317

TRUSTEES A. C. Miles, Chair; Dr Joanna Bacon; R. E. J. Bernays; Dr M. G. Barker; Prof. A. Halestrap.

HOW TO APPLY Via the online form available on the trusts website by 31 March each year in preparation for the trustee meeting in June. Once an online application is submitted the trustees will make further contact before the June meeting if they want a full application.

WHO TO APPLY TO Patrick O'Conor, Secretary, 51 Downs Park West, Westbury Park, Bristol BS6 7QL *Tel.* 01179 628611 *email* p.oconor@netgates.co.uk *Website* www.burdentrustbristol.co.uk

■ Burdens Charitable Foundation

CC NO 273535 **ESTABLISHED** 1977

WHERE FUNDING CAN BE GIVEN UK, but mostly overseas, with special interest in Sub-Saharan Africa.

WHO CAN BENEFIT Registered charities only.

WHAT IS FUNDED 'There are no formal restrictions on the charitable activities that can be supported, but the trustees' main activities currently embrace the prevention and relief of acute poverty, substantially through the medium of education and healthcare and most especially in countries such as those of sub-Saharan Africa.'

WHAT IS NOT FUNDED Causes which rarely or never benefit include animal welfare (except in less developed countries), the arts and museums, political activities, most medical research, preservation etc. of historic buildings and monuments, individual educational grants and sport, except sport for people with disabilities. No grants are made to individuals.

TYPE OF GRANT Generally one-off grants, exceptionally more than one-year. Capital, project, research, running and recurring costs, salaries and start-up costs will also be considered. No loans are made.

SAMPLE GRANTS Build-it (£49,000); The Message Trust (£20,000); REAP (£11,000); Kings World Trust India and Wuluga (£10,000 each); and Zagalona Workshop (£3,000).

FINANCES *Year* 2011 *Income* £587,375 *Grants* £254,418 *Assets* £20,848,909

TRUSTEES Arthur James Burden; Godfrey Wilfred Burden; Hilary Margaret Perkins; Sally Anne Schofield; Anthony David Burden; Professor Burden.

HOW TO APPLY In writing to the correspondent, accompanied by recent, audited accounts and statutory reports, coupled with at least an outline business plan where relevant. Trustees usually meet in March, June, September and December.

WHO TO APPLY TO Arthur James Burden, Trustee, St George's House, 215–219 Chester Road, Manchester M15 4JE *Tel.* 01618 324901

■ The Burdett Trust for Nursing

CC NO 1089849   **ESTABLISHED** 2001

WHERE FUNDING CAN BE GIVEN Mostly UK.

WHO CAN BENEFIT Nurses and other healthcare professionals involved in innovative projects.

WHAT IS FUNDED The trust makes grants to support the nursing contribution to health care within three key priority areas: 1. *Building Nursing Research Capacity:* to support clinical nursing research and research addressing policy, leadership development and delivery of nursing care. 2. *Building Nurse Leadership Capacity:* supporting nurses in their professional development to create a cadre of excellent nursing and allied health professionals who will become leaders of the future and foster excellence and capacity-building in advancing the nursing profession. 3. *Supporting Local Nurse-led Initiatives:* to support nurse-led initiatives that make a difference at local level and are focused explicitly on improving care for patients and users of services. Details on the current grant programmes can be found on the trust's website.

WHAT IS NOT FUNDED Consult the relevant programme guidance for information on the funding criteria.

TYPE OF GRANT Usually one-off, although up to three years will be considered.

RANGE OF GRANTS Up to £200,000.

SAMPLE GRANTS Tenovus (£188,500); Terrence Higgins Trust (£180,000); Pennine Care NHS Foundation Trust (£116,500); Age Cymru (£168,000); QNIS (£87,000); Hospices of Hope (£50,000); University of Hull (£40,000).

FINANCES *Year* 2012 *Income* £1,498,450 *Grants* £1,544,836 *Assets* £67,556,428

TRUSTEES Alan Gibbs, Chair; Dame Christine Beasley; Jack Gibbs; Bill Gordon; Andrew Martin-Smith; Lady Henrietta St George; Eileen Sills; Jo Webber; Evy Hambro.

OTHER INFORMATION The grant total represents the amount of grants committed during the year and includes £307,000 given to individuals.

HOW TO APPLY See the trust's website for information on the current grant programmes and details on how to apply.

WHO TO APPLY TO Rachel Iles, Administrator, SG Hambros Trust Company, Norfolk House, 31 St James's Square, London SW1Y 4JR *Tel.* 020 7597 3065 *email* administrator@btfn.org.uk *Website* www.btfn.org.uk

■ The Clara E. Burgess Charity

CC NO 1072546   **ESTABLISHED** 1998

WHERE FUNDING CAN BE GIVEN UK and worldwide.

WHO CAN BENEFIT Registered charities benefiting children.

WHAT IS FUNDED Provision of facilities and assistance to enhance the education, health and physical well-being of children, particularly (but not exclusively) those under the age of ten who have lost one or both parents.

WHAT IS NOT FUNDED No grants to non-registered charities.

TYPE OF GRANT One-off and recurrent grants (up to three years) for capital costs, core costs, salaries, projects, research, and start-up costs.

RANGE OF GRANTS Mostly up to £15,000.

SAMPLE GRANTS Operation Orphan, Positive Action on Cancer and Rucksack (£10,000); Smile Train (£7,500); Autism Initiatives (£5,500); Douglas Bader Foundation, Play Train, Richard House and Sign Post (£5,000 each); Nelson's Journey and Toybox (£3,000 each); Dove Service and

Royal Horticultural Society (£2,000 each); and Human Farleigh Hospice (£500).

FINANCES *Year* 2011–12 *Income* £281,705 *Grants* £274,700 *Assets* £10,432,504

TRUSTEE The Royal Bank of Scotland

HOW TO APPLY In writing to the correspondent. Applications are considered in January and July.

WHO TO APPLY TO The Trust Section Manager, RBS Trust Services, Eden, Lakeside, Chester Business Park, Wrexham Road, Chester CH4 9QT *Tel.* 01244 625810

■ The Burry Charitable Trust

CC NO 281045   **ESTABLISHED** 1961

WHERE FUNDING CAN BE GIVEN UK, with a preference for Highcliffe and the surrounding and further areas.

WHO CAN BENEFIT Charities, voluntary groups and other not for profit organisations.

WHAT IS FUNDED Medicine, health, disability and welfare.

WHAT IS NOT FUNDED No grants to individuals or students.

SAMPLE GRANTS Oakhaven Hospital Trust (£15,000; Canine Partners and Salvation Army (£5,000 each); British Red Cross and Isle of Wight Air Ambulance (£2,500 each); St John Ambulance (£2,000); Wessex Autistic Society, Christchurch Music Centre and Parkinson's Disease Society (£1,500 each); Myeloma UK, New Milton Guides and 3rd Ringwood Scout Group £1,000 each) and Sway Welfare Aid Group (£250).

FINANCES *Year* 2011–12 *Income* £80,817 *Grants* £57,000 *Assets* £930,074

TRUSTEES Robert Burry; Adrian Osman; Judith Knight; James Lapage.

HOW TO APPLY **This trust states that it does not respond to unsolicited applications.**

WHO TO APPLY TO Robert J. Burry, Trustee, 261 Lymington Road, Highcliffe, Christchurch, Dorset BH23 5EE *Tel.* 01425 277661

■ The Arnold Burton 1998 Charitable Trust

CC NO 1074633   **ESTABLISHED** 1998

WHERE FUNDING CAN BE GIVEN Worldwide.

WHO CAN BENEFIT Jewish charities.

WHAT IS FUNDED Medical research, education, social welfare and heritage.

WHAT IS NOT FUNDED No grants to individuals.

SAMPLE GRANTS Hillel Foundation B'nai B'rith (£10,000); JNF Charitable Trust and Lubavitch Foundation (£5,000 each); Berkshire School, Clothing Solutions, NSPCC, Pain Relief Foundation and Paperworks (£1,000 each); Apex Challenge, Macular Disease Society and Sign Health (£500 each); Scope (£250); and Cued Speech Association (£30).

FINANCES *Year* 2011–12 *Income* £139,643 *Grants* £132,420 *Assets* £5,393,449

TRUSTEES Arnold Burton; Mark Burton; Jeremy Burton; Nicholas Burton.

HOW TO APPLY In writing to the trust managers. Unsuccessful appeals will not necessarily be acknowledged.

WHO TO APPLY TO The Trust Managers, c/o Trustee Management Ltd, 19 Cookridge Street, Leeds LS2 3AG *Tel.* 01132 436466

Think carefully about every application. Is it justified?

417

■ The Burton Breweries Charitable Trust

cc no 1068847 **established** 1998

where funding can be given Burton, East Staffordshire and South Derbyshire district (including a small area of north west Leicestershire).

who can benefit Young people (11–25 years), education and training for individuals of any age who assist young people and youth/community organisations.

what is funded Young people and youth organisations. Funding is given in areas such as equipment facilities and services, and extra-curricular education and training.

what is not funded Beneficiaries must be aged between 11 and 25 – other age groups are excluded. Organisations and individuals living, or in full-time education, outside the beneficial area are not supported. No support for education where there is provision by the state.

type of grant Capital including buildings, core costs, one-off, project, recurring costs, running costs and start-up costs. Funding is available for up to two years.

range of grants Usually up to £5,000

sample grants Grants of £1,000 or more included those to: Barton Under Needwond Parish Council, Burton Bike Club and Burton Performing Arts Centre (£2,500 each); Extreme Support and Hillon Cricket Club (£2,000 each); and Alrewas Cricket Club, the Able Too Forum, and Winshill Youth Forum (£1,000 each).

finances *Year* 2011–12 *Income* £35,116 *Grants* £29,161 *Assets* £767,836

trustees Stephen Oliver; Keith Norris; Emma Gilleland; Jeremy Derbyshire; Jackie Burn; Debbie Moore.

how to apply Application form available online at www.burtonbctrust.co.uk

who to apply to Brian E. Keates, Secretary to the Trustees, Gretton House, Studio 3, Third Avenue, Centrum 100, Burton on Trent DE14 2WQ *Tel.* 01283 740600 *email* info@ burtonbctrust.co.uk *Website* www.burtonbctrust. co.uk

■ Consolidated Charity of Burton upon Trent

cc no 239072 **established** 1981

where funding can be given The former county borough of Burton upon Trent and the parishes of Branston, Stretton and Outwoods.

who can benefit Individuals, and organisations that benefit people in need, who live in the beneficial area.

what is funded General charitable purposes.

what is not funded No grants for salaries.

range of grants Up to £10,000.

sample grants Burton and District Operatic Society (£8,700); Winshill Parish Youth Council and St Peter's Church Stapenhill Parish Council (£5,000 each); ESBC Sports Development and Pulse for Music Staffordshire (£3,000 each); Able Too Forum (£2,000); Burton and District Arts Council (£1,000); Waterside Youth Project (£900) and Harvey Girls (£500).

finances *Year* 2012 *Income* £483,978 *Grants* £134,793 *Assets* £11,140,669

trustees Valerie Burton; Gwendoline Foster; Patricia Phyllis Hill; Cllr Beryl Toon; John Peach; Marie Lorain Nash; Peter Davies; Margaret Heather; Cllr Dennis Fletcher; Patricia Ackroyd; Gerald Hamilton; Cllr Elizabeth Staples; Ben Robinson; Cllr David Clegg Leese; Revd Robert Styles; Cllr Leonard Milner; George Faragher; Geoffrey Brown.

other information £77,000 of the grant total was distributed to individuals.

how to apply On a form which can be downloaded from the trust's website. Applications for grants from organisations are considered by the main committee which meets three times a year. Meeting dates and deadlines are available published along with the application form and guidelines.

who to apply to T. J. Bramall, Clerk to the Trustees, Talbot and Co, 148 High Street, Burton upon Trent, Staffordshire DE14 1JY *Tel.* 01283 564716 *email* clerk@ consolidatedcharityburton.org.uk *Website* www. consolidatedcharityburton.org.uk

■ The Paul Bush Foundation Trust

cc no 1147536 **established** 2012

where funding can be given UK.

who can benefit Registered charities and community groups.

what is funded General, disability

what is not funded The trust does not give funding to: organisations that are not a registered charity or expert charity; projects where there is a legal statutory obligation or which replace statutory funding; organisations where the beneficiaries are not based in the UK.

trustees Paul H. Bush; Karen Burgin; Rachel Brodie; Sally Sinclair Bush.

how to apply On an application form available from the foundation's website. Applicants must also submit their latest annual report and accounts. The trustees meet twice yearly in April and October with successful applicants being advised by 1 November and 1 May each year.

who to apply to Paul H. Bush, Trustee, March House, Long March, Daventry, Northamptonshire NN11 4NR *Tel.* 01327 876210 *Website* www. bushco.co.uk

■ The Worshipful Company of Butchers General Charities

cc no 257928 **established** 1969

where funding can be given City of London or its adjacent boroughs

who can benefit Organisations benefiting people in need.

what is funded The charities aim to: provide relief to persons who are in conditions of need, hardship, or distress; further its broad remit of charitable giving through grants to appropriate groups and organisations.

what is not funded The committee does not fund groups which it considers have large financial reserves. No grants to individuals.

range of grants Up to £22,000.

sample grants Farms for City Children (£22,000); Barts and the London Trust (£21,000); Farm Africa, ABF Soldiers Charity and National Federation of Meat and Food Traders (£1,000 each); Service Fund RAF Northolt (£500); United Guilds (£250) and Smithfield Trust (£50).

finances *Year* 2011–12 *Income* £95,293 *Grants* £46,486 *Assets* £1,498,686

trustee The members of the court of the Worshipful Company of Butchers.

other information 'The principal purpose of the Charities Committee is to provide ongoing financial support to TWO chosen charities for a

418

Does the trust you have chosen match your needs? Haphazard applications waste postage and time

period of three years.' The Charities currently support Farms for City Children and Barts Hospital. This support will come to an end on 31 December 2017. Note: other organisations are also supported, albeit on a lesser scale.

HOW TO APPLY In writing to the correspondent. 'Whilst there is an annual review, it is anticipated that applications from other groups/ organisations will not be considered during the fixed three year period. Applications for the next three year period will be invited from new organisations from 1 July 2016.'

WHO TO APPLY TO The Chair of the Charities Committee, Butchers Hall, 87 Bartholomew Close, London EC1A 7EB *Tel.* 020 7600 4106 *email* clerk@butchershall.com *Website* www. butchershall.com

....

■ The Derek Butler Trust

CC NO 1081995   **ESTABLISHED** 2000
WHERE FUNDING CAN BE GIVEN Worldwide, in practice UK.
WHO CAN BENEFIT Institutions and charitable organisations.
WHAT IS FUNDED Medical research, health, music and music education. The charity is particularly interested in supporting research into the study of oesophageal and related cancers of the digestive tract, projects for public education in respect of HIV/AIDS and relief of sufferers from HIV/AIDS.
RANGE OF GRANTS Usually up to £10,000.
SAMPLE GRANTS Awards for Young Musicians (£100,000); The Digestive Disorders Foundation (£68,500); St Luke's Hospice Plymouth (£45,000); The International Organ Festival Society (£18,000); Kensington and Chelsea Cruse (£20,000); Anglican Centre in Rome and Seventy4 Foundation (£15,000 each); Akamba Aid Fund Charity (£2,000); Royal College of Music (£1,500); and St Martin-in-the-Fields (£1,000).
FINANCES *Year* 2011–12 *Income* £343,444 *Grants* £402,257 *Assets* £12,259,359
TRUSTEES Bernard W. Dawson; Donald F. Freeman; Revd Michael Fuller; Hilary A. E. Guest.
OTHER INFORMATION Grants were made during the year totalling £402,000, which included £58,000 in awards through the Derek Butler London Prize.
HOW TO APPLY In writing to the correspondent. 'The trustees continue to seek new charities to which they can make suitable donations.'
WHO TO APPLY TO James McLean, Trustee, c/o Underwood Solicitors LLP, 40 Welbeck Street, London W1G 8LN *Tel.* 020 7526 6000 *email* info@thederekbutlertrust.org.uk *Website* www.thederekbutlertrust.org.uk

....

■ The Noel Buxton Trust

CC NO 220881   **ESTABLISHED** 1919
WHERE FUNDING CAN BE GIVEN UK, eastern and southern Africa.
WHO CAN BENEFIT Registered charities, although grants are not made to large popular national charities or in response to general appeals. Smaller local bodies and less popular causes are preferred, which benefit: children under 12 in disadvantaged families; prisoners and their families and young people at risk of offending; and education and development in eastern and southern Africa.
WHAT IS FUNDED Welfare of children in disadvantaged families and children in care;

prevention of crime, especially among young people; the rehabilitation of prisoners and the welfare of their families; education and development in eastern and southern Africa.
WHAT IS NOT FUNDED In addition to the specific exclusions of each programme, grants are not made for: academic research; advice centres; animal charities including those running sanctuaries, rescue or adoption services; the arts for their own sake; buildings; conferences; counselling for individuals; expeditions, exchanges, holidays, study tours, visits; housing and homelessness; human rights; HIV/AIDS programmes; grants are not made to INDIVIDUALS for any purpose; Northern Ireland; organisations set up primarily to treat medical conditions, physical disabilities or mental health issues; playgrounds; prizes; race relations; contribution to a specific salaried post; schools, including school infrastructure and teaching equipment; vehicles; victims of crime (except those affected by domestic violence and victims involved with restorative justice projects); videos and IT.
TYPE OF GRANT One-off or recurrent. Not for buildings or salaries.
RANGE OF GRANTS £500–£5,000. Most grants are for £1,000 or less.
SAMPLE GRANTS Family Rights Group, Fatherhood and Vida (£5,000 each); Exeter Ethiopia Link, Microloan Foundation and Renewable World (£4,000 each); International Childcare Trust (£3,500); African Children's Fund and Find Your Feet (£3,000 each); Fair Shares, Forest of Mercia and Prison Fellowship (£2,000 each); The Forgiveness Project and Women Acting in Today's Society (£1,500 each); Daylight, Mentoring Plus and Prison Advice and Care Trust (£1,000 each); and Cumbria Reducing Offending Partnership Trust (£500).
FINANCES *Year* 2012 *Income* £111,902 *Grants* £93,718 *Assets* £2,383,814
TRUSTEES Simon Buxton; Jon Snow; Jo Tunnard; John Littlewood; Brendan Gormley; Emma Compton-Burnett; Katie Aston; Katie Buxton.
HOW TO APPLY Visit the trust's website for guidance on how to apply to each programme.
WHO TO APPLY TO The Trustees, PO Box 520, Fleet, Hampshire GU51 9GX *Website* www. noelbuxtontrust.org.uk

■ C. and F. Charitable Trust

cc no 274529   **established** 1977
WHERE FUNDING CAN BE GIVEN UK and overseas.
WHO CAN BENEFIT Orthodox Jewish charities.
WHAT IS FUNDED Relief of poverty amongst the
Jewish Community; the furtherance of the
Jewish education and religion.
WHAT IS NOT FUNDED Registered charities only.
SAMPLE GRANTS Previous beneficiaries have included
Community Council of Gateshead, Ezras
Nitrochim, Gur Trust, Kollel Shaarei Shlomo,
SOFT and Yetev Lev Jerusalem Trust.
FINANCES *Year* 2011–12 *Income* £175,855
Grants £85,120 *Assets* £1,190,629
TRUSTEES Fradel Kaufman; Simon Kaufman.
PUBLICATIONS An analysis of charitable donations is
published separately in a document entitled 'C
and F Charitable Trust – Schedule of Charitable
Donations'. Copies are available on written
request to the correspondent.
HOW TO APPLY In writing to the correspondent.
WHO TO APPLY TO The Trustees, 50 Keswick Street,
Gateshead, Tyne and Wear NE8 1TQ

■ C. M. L. Family Foundation

cc no 1151765   **established** 2013
WHERE FUNDING CAN BE GIVEN UK.
WHO CAN BENEFIT Registered charities.
WHAT IS FUNDED General charitable purposes.
TRUSTEES Alexander Lemos; Constantine Lemos;
Michael Lemos.
OTHER INFORMATION Registered in April 2013, the
foundation's objects are general charitable
purposes. The Lemos family are involved in
shipping and maritime insurance.
HOW TO APPLY In writing to the correspondent.
WHO TO APPLY TO Martin Pollock, Administrator, c/o
Moore Stephens, 150 Aldersgate Street,
London EC1A 4AB *Tel.* 020 7651 1707

■ The James Caan Foundation

cc no 1136617   **established** 2010
WHERE FUNDING CAN BE GIVEN UK and Pakistan.
WHO CAN BENEFIT Organisations and individuals.
WHAT IS FUNDED The objects of the foundation are
broadly social welfare and education in the UK
and Caan's native Pakistan.
SAMPLE GRANTS Previously, Caan, either personally
or through the foundation, has supported
organisations in the UK and Pakistan including:
Prince's Trust; NSPCC; Care Foundation; BBC
Children in Need; Big Issue; Comic Relief; Sport
Relief; vInspired; Marie Curie Cancer Care;
Mosaic; and the British Asian Trust.
FINANCES *Year* 2011–12 *Income* £142,221
Grants £192,694 *Assets* £350,161
TRUSTEES James Caan; Deepak Jalan; Hanah Caan.
HOW TO APPLY In writing to the correspondent.
WHO TO APPLY TO Hanah Caan, Trustee, Hamilton
Bradshaw, 60 Grosvenor Street, London
W1K 3HZ *Tel.* 020 7399 6700 *email* hanah@
thejcf.co.uk *Website* www.thejcf.co.uk

■ The Christopher Cadbury Charitable Trust

cc no 231859   **established** 1922
WHERE FUNDING CAN BE GIVEN UK, with a preference
for the Midlands.
WHO CAN BENEFIT Registered charities.
WHAT IS FUNDED To support approved charities by
annual contribution. The trustees have drawn up
a schedule of commitments covering charities
which they have chosen to support.
WHAT IS NOT FUNDED No support for individuals.
SAMPLE GRANTS Fircroft College and Island
Conservation Society UK (£10,500 each);
Playthings Past Museum Trust (£7,500); Devon
Wildlife Trust (£6,000); Bower Trust, R V J
Cadbury Charitable Trust, Norfolk Wildlife Trust,
R A and V B Reekie Charitable Trust and Sarnia
Charitable Trust (£2,000 each); Survival
International (£1,000); and Avoncroft Arts
Society and Selly Oak Nursery School (£500
each).
FINANCES *Year* 2011–12 *Income* £87,418
Grants £60,450 *Assets* £1,867,789
TRUSTEES Roger Cadbury; Tim Peet; Dr James
Cadbury; Tina Benfield; Virginia Reekie; Peter
Cadbury.
HOW TO APPLY Unsolicited applications are unlikely
to be successful.
WHO TO APPLY TO The Trust Administrator, PKF (UK)
LLP, New Guild House, 45 Great Charles Street,
Queensway, Birmingham B3 2LX *Tel.* 01212
122222

■ C. J. Cadbury Charitable Trust

cc no 270609   **established** 1969
WHERE FUNDING CAN BE GIVEN UK
WHO CAN BENEFIT Registered charities.
WHAT IS FUNDED General, preference for wildlife
conservation and music projects.
TYPE OF GRANT Unrestricted.
SAMPLE GRANTS Island Conservation Society UK
(£8,000) and Devon Wildlife Trust (£1,000).
FINANCES *Year* 2011–12 *Income* £36,468
Grants £12,847 *Assets* £700,366
TRUSTEES Hugh Carslake; Joy Cadbury; Thomas
Cadbury; Lucy Cadbury.
HOW TO APPLY The trust does not generally support
unsolicited applications.
WHO TO APPLY TO Deborah Ashbourne, Martineau
LLP, No. 1 Colmore Square, Birmingham
B4 6AA *Tel.* 0870 763 2000 *Fax* 0870 763
2001

■ Edward Cadbury Charitable Trust

cc no 227384   **established** 1945
WHERE FUNDING CAN BE GIVEN Worldwide, in practice
mainly UK with a preference for the Midlands
region.
WHO CAN BENEFIT Registered charities only.
WHAT IS FUNDED General, including: conservation
and the environment; arts and culture;
community projects and integration;
compassionate support; ecumenical mission
and interfaith relations; education and training;
research.
WHAT IS NOT FUNDED No student grants or support
for individuals.
TYPE OF GRANT Usually one-off grants for a specific
purpose or part of a project.
RANGE OF GRANTS £250–£1 million. Generally
£500–£5,000.
SAMPLE GRANTS Birmingham Royal Ballet and
Woodbrooke Quaker Study Centre (£250,000

each); Birmingham Museum and Art Gallery (£35,000); Aston University's Woodcock Sports Centre (£25,000); Fircroft College of Adult Education (£20,000); Arthritis Research UK and Youth Hostel Association's centre at Wilderhope Manor (£10,000 each); Action Centres UK, Birmingham Museum and Art Gallery – Soho House, Samaritans – Birmingham and Sunfield Children's Home (£5,000 each); Cruse Bereavement Care – Birmingham and Black Country Living Museum (£2,500 each); and Birmingham City Mission, Carrs Lane Counselling Centre, Home from Hospital Care, Marine Conservation, No Panic and St John Ambulance, (£1,000 each).

FINANCES *Year* 2011–12 *Income* £880,909 *Grants* £728,030 *Assets* £30,313,915

TRUSTEES Andrew Littleboy; Charles R. Gillett; Nigel Cadbury; Hugh Marriott; Dr William Southall.

HOW TO APPLY The Edward Cadbury Charitable Trust (Inc.) only makes grants to registered charities and not to individuals. An application for funding may be made at any time and should be submitted in writing to the Trust Manager either by post or email. Trustees request that the letter of application should provide a clear and concise description of the project for which the funding is required as well as the outcomes and benefits that it is intended to achieve. They also require an outline budget and explanation of how the project is to be funded initially and in the future together with the latest annual report and accounts for the charity. Applications for funding are generally considered within a three month timescale. Note that applications which fall outside the trust's stated areas of interest may not be considered or acknowledged. Before awarding a grant, trustees assess applications against the trust's objectives and the Charity Commission's public benefit guidelines to check that public benefit criteria are met.

WHO TO APPLY TO Sue Anderson, Trust Manager, Rokesley, University of Birmingham, Bristol Road, Selly Oak, Birmingham B29 6QF *Tel.* 01214 721838 *Fax* 01214 721838 *email* ecadburytrust@btconnect.com *Website* www.edwardcadburytrust.org.uk

■ The G. W. Cadbury Charitable Trust

CC NO 231861   **ESTABLISHED** 1922

WHERE FUNDING CAN BE GIVEN Worldwide.

WHO CAN BENEFIT Organisations benefiting at-risk groups, people disadvantaged by poverty, and socially isolated people.

WHAT IS FUNDED General charitable purposes.

WHAT IS NOT FUNDED No grants to individuals or non-registered charities, or for scholarships.

SAMPLE GRANTS Colston's Primary School (£35,000); Pacific Northwest Ballet – USA (£30,000); Gender and Development Network (£10,000); British Pregnancy Advisory Service (£6,000); Compassion in Dying (£5,000); Brook (£4,000); Birmingham Royal Ballet (£2,000); and Swaledale Friends (£1,000).

FINANCES *Year* 2011–12 *Income* £244,895 *Grants* £181,942 *Assets* £5,724,071

TRUSTEES Jennifer Boal; Jessica Woodroffe; Peter Boal; Lyndall Boal; Nick Woodroffe; Caroline Woodroffe.

HOW TO APPLY In writing to the correspondent.

WHO TO APPLY TO The Trust Administrator, PFK (UK) LLP, GW Cadbury Charitable Trust, New Guild House, 45 Great Charles Street, Queensway, Birmingham B3 2LX

■ Henry T. and Lucy B. Cadbury Charitable Trust

CC NO 280314   **ESTABLISHED** 1924

WHERE FUNDING CAN BE GIVEN Mainly UK, but also the Third World.

WHO CAN BENEFIT Registered charities only.

WHAT IS FUNDED Quaker causes and institutions, health, homelessness and support groups.

WHAT IS NOT FUNDED No grants to non-registered charities.

TYPE OF GRANT One-off.

SAMPLE GRANTS Previously: Quaker United Nations Office (£5,000); Battle Against Tranquillizers, British Pugwash Trust, the People's Kitchen and Slower Speeds Trust (£2,000 each); Action for ME, Money for Madagascar and Tools for Self Reliance (£1,500 each); and Calcutta Rescue Fund, Quaker Opportunity Playgroup and Youth Education Service Midnapore (£1,000 each).

FINANCES *Year* 2012 *Income* £22,449 *Grants* £31,224

TRUSTEES Candia Carolan; Ruth Charity; Bevis Gillett; Elizabeth Rawlins; Tamsin Yates; Dr Emma Hambly.

OTHER INFORMATION Accounts received at the Charity Commission but not available online due to the charity's low income.

HOW TO APPLY The trust's income is committed each year and so unsolicited applications are not normally accepted. The trustees meet in March to consider applications.

WHO TO APPLY TO The Secretary, c/o B. C. M, Box 2024, London WC1N 3XX

■ Peter Cadbury Charitable Trust

CC NO 327174   **ESTABLISHED** 1986

WHERE FUNDING CAN BE GIVEN UK and overseas.

WHO CAN BENEFIT Registered charities.

WHAT IS FUNDED General charitable purposes, particularly the arts; conservation and cancer-related charities also considered.

RANGE OF GRANTS Up to £2,500.

SAMPLE GRANTS The Royal Ballet School (£3,000 in two grants); Tate Gallery (£2,000); Garsington Opera, Trinity Hospice and The Wallace Collection (£1,500 each); The Reliance Trust (£1,300) and Natural History Museum (£1,000).

FINANCES *Year* 2011–12 *Income* £31,494 *Grants* £28,300 *Assets* £539,708

TRUSTEES Derek Larder; Peter Cadbury; Sally Cadbury.

HOW TO APPLY The trust does not usually respond to unsolicited applications.

WHO TO APPLY TO Derek Larder, Trustee, KS Carmichael Accountants, PO Box 4UD, London W1A 4UD *Tel.* 020 7258 1577 *email* dlarder@kscarmichael.com

■ The Richard Cadbury Charitable Trust

CC NO 224348   **ESTABLISHED** 1948

WHERE FUNDING CAN BE GIVEN UK, but mainly Birmingham, Coventry and Worcester.

WHO CAN BENEFIT Organisations with charitable status.

WHAT IS FUNDED Community centres and village halls; libraries and museums; counselling; crime prevention; play schemes; gay and lesbian rights; racial equality, discrimination and relations; social advocacy; health care; hospices and rehabilitation centres; cancer and prenatal research; health promotion; and health-related volunteer schemes. Grants also for accommodation and housing; infrastructure support and development; conservation and environment; and religion.

WHAT IS NOT FUNDED No grants for running costs or core funding.

TYPE OF GRANT One-off and capital costs.

RANGE OF GRANTS £250–£1,000.

SAMPLE GRANTS Barnardo's, Centrepoint, Marie Curie Cancer Centre and RNLI (£1,000 each); Birmingham Settlement, Dodford Children's Holiday Farm and NSPCC (£750 each); LEPRA and VSO (£500 each); ESO (£400); Worcester Live and Youth at Risk – Nottingham (£300 each); and Sandwell Asian Development Association and St David's Church – Selly Oak (£250 each).

FINANCES *Year* 2011–12 *Income* £21,606 *Grants* £45,000

TRUSTEES Richard Cadbury; Margaret Eardley; David Slora; Jacqueline Slora; Lucy Cadbury-Hamood.

OTHER INFORMATION In 2011–12 the trust had a total expenditure of £47,686.

HOW TO APPLY In writing to the correspondent giving reasons why a grant is needed and including a copy of the latest accounts if possible. Meetings are held in February, June and October. Unsolicited applications are not accepted.

WHO TO APPLY TO Margaret Eardley, Trustee, 26 Randall Road, Kenilworth, Warwickshire CV8 1JY *Tel.* 01926 857793

....

■ The William A. Cadbury Charitable Trust

CC NO 213629   **ESTABLISHED** 1923

WHERE FUNDING CAN BE GIVEN West Midlands, especially Birmingham and, to a lesser extent, UK, Ireland and overseas.

WHO CAN BENEFIT Organisations serving Birmingham and the West Midlands; organisations whose work has a national significance; organisations outside the West Midlands where the trust has well-established links; organisations in Northern Ireland, and UK-based charities working overseas.

WHAT IS FUNDED Birmingham and the West Midlands: *community action* – community based and organised schemes (which may be centred on a place of worship) aimed at solving local problems and improving the quality of life of community members; *vulnerable groups* – vulnerable groups include the elderly, children and young people, the disabled, asylum seekers and similar minorities; *advice, mediation and counselling* – applicants must be able to point to the rigorous selection, training and monitoring of front line staff (particularly in the absence of formal qualifications) as well as to the overall need for the service provided; *education and training* – trustees are particularly interested in schemes that help people of working age develop new skills in order to re-enter the jobs market; *environment and conservation* – projects which address the impact of climate change and projects to preserve buildings and installations of historic importance and local interest; *medical and healthcare* – covers hospices, self-help groups and some medical research which must be based in and be of potential benefit to the West Midlands; *the arts* – music, drama and the visual arts, museums and art galleries. United Kingdom: *the Religious Society of Friends* – support for groups with a clear Quaker connection and support for the work of the Religious Society of Friends in the UK; *penal affairs* – restorative justice, prison based projects and work with ex-offenders aimed at reducing re-offending. Ireland: *peace and reconciliation.* International development: *Africa* – the international development programme is concentrated on West Africa and work to reduce poverty on a sustainable basis in both rural and urban communities – schemes that help children access education are also supported; *Asia and Eastern Europe; South America.'* Note: The international development programme is heavily oversubscribed and unsolicited applications are unlikely to be successful.

WHAT IS NOT FUNDED The trust does not fund: individuals (whether for research, expeditions, educational purposes or medical treatment); projects concerned with travel, adventure, sports or recreation; organisations which do not have UK charity registration, except those which are legally exempt. Though, small grants may be made to unregistered groups in the West Midlands (as long as they have a constitution, an elected committee and a bank account controlled by two or more committee members).

TYPE OF GRANT Specific grant applications are favoured. Grants are generally one-off or for projects of one year or less. The trust will consider applications for core costs as well as for development/project funding. Grants are not usually awarded on an annual basis, except to a small number of charities for revenue costs.

RANGE OF GRANTS Small grants up to £2,000; large grants usually range from £10,000–£20,000 with an occasional maximum of £50,000.

SAMPLE GRANTS Concern Universal (£90,000); Youth Hostel Association – Wilderhope Manor (£50,000); Birmingham Royal Ballet Trust (£24,000 each); Ideal for All and The Patients Association (£15,000 each); Age Concern and Royal Birmingham Society of Artists (£10,000 each); Castle Gates Family Trust (£8,000); Britain Yearly Meeting (£5,000); and Birmingham Settlement (£3,000).

FINANCES *Year* 2011–12 *Income* £902,188 *Grants* £674,750 *Assets* £25,322,495

TRUSTEES Victoria Salmon; Rupert Cadbury; Katherine van Hagen Cadbury; Margaret Salmon; Sarah Stafford; Adrian Thomas; John Penny; Sophy Blandy; Janine Cobain.

PUBLICATIONS Policy statement and guidelines for applicants.

HOW TO APPLY Applications can be submitted via the trust's online application form. Alternatively, they can be made in writing to the correspondent, including the following information: charity registration number; a description of the charity's aims and achievements; the grant programme being applied to; an outline and budget for the project for which funding is sought; details of funds raised and the current shortfall; if the organisation has received funding from the trust before, provide brief details of the outcome of this project. There is no requirement to send your charity's annual report and accounts as the trust will refer to the accounts held online by the Charity Commission. Applications are considered on a continuing basis throughout the year. Small grants are assessed each month. Large grants are awarded at the trustees' meetings held twice annually, normally in May and November. Applicants whose appeals are to be considered at one of the meetings will be notified in advance.

WHO TO APPLY TO Carolyn Bettis, Trust Administrator, Rokesley, University of Birmingham, Bristol Road, Selly Oak, Birmingham B29 6QF *Tel.* 01214 721464 *email* info@wa-cadbury.org.uk *Website* www.wa-cadbury.org.uk

....

■ The Cadbury Foundation

CC NO 1050482   **ESTABLISHED** 1994
WHERE FUNDING CAN BE GIVEN UK and Africa, particularly in areas where the company has operations.
WHO CAN BENEFIT Registered charities.
WHAT IS FUNDED Cadbury Foundation projects must fall within one of the key focus areas: education and enterprise, poverty and homelessness, the environment and Africa Aid.
WHAT IS NOT FUNDED Individuals looking for funding for education, training (or help with an expedition, travel or leisure project); groups looking for help with an expedition, travel or leisure projects; charities looking for funds for building or refurbishment projects; projects based outside of the UK or Africa; programmes looking for funding for arts projects, unless as part of an education theme; charities looking for support for entertainment (e.g. fundraising dinners and raffles).
RANGE OF GRANTS Up to £120,000, but usually between £10,000 and £25,000.
SAMPLE GRANTS Tembisa Child Welfare (£120,000); Sheffield Academy of Young Leaders, Hold it Down and SARVAM (£10,000 each); Crisis at Christmas (£9,000) and Crisis UK (£500).
FINANCES *Year* 2012 *Income* £792,111 *Grants* £234,500 *Assets* £123,161
TRUSTEES Jonathan Horrell; Diane Tomlinson; Neil Chapman; David Oliver; Sonia Jane Chhatwal; Maurizio Brusadelli; Vinzenz Gruber; Kieran Conway; Michael Huggins; Sonia Farrell.
HOW TO APPLY In writing to the correspondent.
WHO TO APPLY TO Louise Ayling, c/o Kraft Foods, Unit 3, Sanderson Road, Uxbridge Business Park, Uxbridge UB8 1DH *Tel.* 01895 615131

....

■ The George Cadbury Trust

CC NO 1040999   **ESTABLISHED** 1924
WHERE FUNDING CAN BE GIVEN Preference for the West Midlands, Hampshire and Gloucestershire.
WHO CAN BENEFIT UK-based charities.
WHAT IS FUNDED General charitable purposes.
WHAT IS NOT FUNDED No support for individuals for projects, courses of study, expeditions or sporting tours. No support for overseas appeals.
RANGE OF GRANTS £1,000–£50,000.
SAMPLE GRANTS Birmingham Royal Ballet (£33,000); Dean and Chapters Gloucester Cathedral (£20,000); Cheltenham College Charity Fund (£15,000); ForceSelect Foundation (£12,000); Gloucestershire Community Foundation and Green Oasis Appeal (£10,000 each); Peter H G Cadbury Trust (£6,000); Fircroft College, Soil Association and Sydney Children's Hospital Foundation (£5,000 each); Hackwood Festival (£4,000); Friends of Bournville Carillon Limited (£3,600); Help for Heroes (£3,000); Second Chance (£2,000 and St Luke's Hospice, Hillside Animal Sanctuary and Gosford Forest Guide House Co Armagh (£1,000 each).
FINANCES *Year* 2011–12 *Income* £411,581 *Grants* £379,052 *Assets* £10,426,966
TRUSTEES Anne L. K. Cadbury; Robin N. Cadbury; Sir Adrian Cadbury; Roger V. J. Cadbury; A. Jane Cadbury.

HOW TO APPLY In writing to the correspondent to be considered quarterly. Note that very few new applications are supported due to ongoing and alternative commitments.
WHO TO APPLY TO Sarah Moss, PKF Accountants, New Guild House, 45 Great Charles Street, Queensway, Birmingham B3 2LX *Tel.* 01216 093282

....

■ The Edward and Dorothy Cadbury Trust

CC NO 1107327   **ESTABLISHED** 1928
WHERE FUNDING CAN BE GIVEN Preference for the West Midlands area.
WHO CAN BENEFIT Registered charities.
WHAT IS FUNDED The trust continues to support, where appropriate, the interests of the founders and the particular charitable interests of the trustees. Grants are grouped under six main headings: arts and culture; community projects and integration; compassionate support; education and training; conservation and environment; and research.
'As a matter of good practice, trustees undertake a programme of visits to organisations where a grant of high value has been made or the activity is of particular interest to the trust in terms of future development. This has proved helpful in building up positive relationships with grantees and providing networking opportunities.'
WHAT IS NOT FUNDED No grants to individuals.
TYPE OF GRANT Ongoing funding commitments rarely considered.
RANGE OF GRANTS Usually £500–£2,500, with occasional larger grants made.
SAMPLE GRANTS Birmingham Royal Ballet (£15,000); Acorns Children's Hospice, Quaker Memorial Service Trust and RSPB (£5,000 each); Bromsgrove Festival (£4,000); Birmingham Settlement, Camphill Village Trust, Motability and RNIB (£1,000 each); Foundation for Conductive Education and SENSE (£750 each); Association for Rehabilitation of Communication and Oral Skills, British Wireless for the Blind Forum, Contact a Family, Orchestra of the Swan, Send a Cow and Worcestershire Wildlife Trust (£500 each).
FINANCES *Year* 2011–12 *Income* £172,021 *Grants* £124,435 *Assets* £5,518,988
TRUSTEES Dr Cathleen Elliott; Philippa Ward; Susan Anfilogoff; Julia Gillett; Julie Cadbury.
HOW TO APPLY The following is taken from the trust's helpful website: 'An application for funding may be made at any time and should be submitted in writing to the Trust Manager either by post or email. Trustees request that the letter of application should provide a clear and concise description of the project for which the funding is required as well as the outcomes and benefits that it is intended to achieve. They also require an outline budget and explanation of how the project is to be funded initially and in the future together with the latest annual report and accounts for the charity. Applications for funding are generally considered within a three month timescale. Note that applications which fall outside the Trust's stated areas of interest may not be considered or acknowledged.'
WHO TO APPLY TO Susan Anderson, Company Secretary/Trust Manager, Rokesley, University of Birmingham Selly Oak, Bristol Road, Selly Oak, Birmingham B29 6QF *Tel.* 01214 721838 *email* e-dcadburytrust@btconnect.com *Website* www.e-dcadburytrust.org.uk

■ The Barrow Cadbury Trust and the Barrow Cadbury Fund

CC NO 1115476   **ESTABLISHED** 1920

WHERE FUNDING CAN BE GIVEN Unrestricted, with a preference for Birmingham and the Black Country (Wolverhampton, Dudley, West Bromwich, Smethwick or Sandwell).

WHO CAN BENEFIT Charities and voluntary organisations which benefit causes within the trust's programmes. Organisations working on grassroots, user-led projects are preferred. Groups do not have to be a registered charity but should have a formal structure and governing documents.

WHAT IS FUNDED The trust promotes social justice through grantmaking, research, influencing public policy and supporting local communities. There are three main programme areas: criminal justice; migration; and poverty and inclusion. Detailed guidelines are available on the trust's website.

WHAT IS NOT FUNDED The trust does not fund: activities that central or local government is responsible for; animal welfare; arts and cultural projects; capital costs for building, refurbishment and outfitting; endowment funds; fundraising events or activities; general appeals; general health; individuals; housing; learning disability; medical research or equipment; mental health; children under 16 and older people; physical disability; the promotion of religion or belief systems; schools; sponsorship or marketing appeals; unsolicited international projects. The trust will not consider funding the following areas unless they are part of a broader project: *counselling drug and alcohol services* – will only be considered under the trust's criminal justice programme, and must be part of a broader project that meets the aims of the programme; *environmental projects* – will only be considered under the poverty and inclusion programme, and must be as part of a broader project that meets the aims of the programme; *homelessness and destitution* – will only be considered for those leaving the criminal justice system or in relation to the trust's migration programme; *IT training; sporting activities*. The trust asks that organisations submitting a proposal that includes one of these services should contact the grants team first. Colleges and universities can only apply under the policy and research funding streams.

TYPE OF GRANT Project funding, recurring costs, running costs and start-up costs.

RANGE OF GRANTS Average grassroots grant is £15,000–£50,000 per year. The maximum grant is £50,000 per year for two years (£100,000 in total).

SAMPLE GRANTS Detailed examples of previously funded projects are available on the trust's website.

FINANCES *Year* 2011–12 *Income* £2,656,000 *Grants* £3,067,000 *Assets* £63,509,000

TRUSTEES Ruth Cadbury, Chair; Anna Southall; Erica Cadbury; Nicola Cadbury; Tamsin Rupprechter; Gordon Mitchell; Harry Serle; Helen Cadbury.

PUBLICATIONS A number of publications and reports are published on the trust's website.

HOW TO APPLY The trust asks that potential applicants first contact the grants team, either by calling 020 7632 9068 or completing the online enquiry form available through the trust's website. Note: applicants for policy and research grants under the Criminal Justice and Migration categories are asked to email general@barrowcadbury.org.uk with their proposal or call 020 7632 9068. If the trust is not able to support the project, it will notify the applicant within one month. It can take three to six months for proposals that the trust wishes to take forward to be assessed and presented to trustees, but the trust will be in contact during this period. Grants are approved by trustees at quarterly meetings throughout the year.

WHO TO APPLY TO Mark O'Kelly, Company Secretary, Kean House, 6 Kean Street, London WC2B 4AS *Tel.* 020 7632 9075 *email* info@barrowcadbury. org.uk *Website* www.barrowcadbury.org.uk

■ The Cadogan Charity

CC NO 247773   **ESTABLISHED** 1966

WHERE FUNDING CAN BE GIVEN Worldwide. In practice, UK with a preference for London and Scotland.

WHO CAN BENEFIT Registered charities.

WHAT IS FUNDED General, in particular social welfare, medical research, services charities, animal welfare, education and conservation and the environment.

WHAT IS NOT FUNDED No grants to individuals.

TYPE OF GRANT Support is usually given over one to two years, although some one-off grants may be made.

RANGE OF GRANTS Up to £300,000.

SAMPLE GRANTS Holy Trinity Church – Sloane Street (£800,000); St George's Cathedral – Perth (£390,000); Royal Horticultural Society (£250,000); Historic Royal Palaces (£200,000); In-Pensioners Mobility Fund (£100,000); Eton College (£50,000); Home of Horseracing Trust (£25,000); Blue Cross and Priors Court Fountain £20,000 each); Alzheimer's Research Trust, Meningitis Research Foundation Oatridge Agricultural College, Scottish Countryside Alliance Educational Trust and Scottish Uplands Appeal (£10,000 each); Guild of Air Pilots (£9,000); Haven, New Astley Club, Royal Hospital for Neuro-disability, Samaritans and Skin Treatment and Research Trust(£5,000 each); Action for Blind People and Songbird Revival (£2,000 each); and Atlantic Salmon Trust and Epilepsy Research Foundation (£1,000 each).

FINANCES *Year* 2011–12 *Income* £2,174,964 *Grants* £2,467,344 *Assets* £37,603,223

TRUSTEES Earl Cadogan; Countess Cadogan; Viscount Chelsea; Lady Anna Thomson; The Hon. William Cadogan.

HOW TO APPLY In writing to the correspondent. However, note that we have received information stating that the trust's funds are fully committed until 2016.

WHO TO APPLY TO P. M. Loutit, Secretary, 18 Cadogan Gardens, London SW3 2RP *Tel.* 020 7730 4567

■ CAF (Charities Aid Foundation)

CC NO 268369   **ESTABLISHED** 1974

WHERE FUNDING CAN BE GIVEN Worldwide, in practice mainly UK.

WHO CAN BENEFIT Charitable organisations.

WHAT IS FUNDED General funding programmes are run on a periodic basis with each programme having its own theme. Usually, the foundation researches suitable organisations and invites them to apply.

Loans and investment support is available through the Venturesome scheme for charitable organisations which need finance but whose requirements may be too risky for a bank loan or outside the criteria of a grantmaker. This support might take the form of underwriting, unsecured loans or equity type investments and it is anticipated that the money loaned will be repaid over time.

TYPE OF GRANT One-off grants, loans and investment support.

RANGE OF GRANTS Loans from £25,000–£250,000.

SAMPLE GRANTS Previous beneficiaries include: London Business School, City Centre for Charity Effectiveness Trust – CASS Business School, Nottingham Law Centre, Kairos in Soho, UK Youth Parliament, People in Action, Northern Ireland Childminding Association, Scottish Adult Learning Partnership and African and Caribbean Voices Association.

FINANCES *Year* 2011–12 *Income* £399,946,000 *Assets* £865,399,000

TRUSTEES Dominic Casserley, Chair; Saphy Ashtiany; Robin Creswell; Philip Hardaker; Alison Hutchinson; Martyn Lewis; David Locke; Stephen Lovegrove; Iain Mackinnon; Matthew Hammerstein; Tina Lee.

HOW TO APPLY In the first instance, applicants to the Venturesome programme should contact the trust directly to discuss their requirements.

WHO TO APPLY TO Ann Doan, Administrator, 25 Kings Hill Avenue, Kings Hill, West Malling, Kent ME19 4TA *Tel.* 0300 012 3000 *Fax* 0300 012 3001 *email* companysecretary@cafonline.org *Website* www.cafonline.org

....

■ **CAFOD (Catholic Agency for Overseas Development)**

CC NO 285776   **ESTABLISHED** 1962

WHERE FUNDING CAN BE GIVEN Predominantly overseas, with some funding to partners in the England and Wales.

WHO CAN BENEFIT Poorer communities overseas and victims of famine, disasters or war.

WHAT IS FUNDED Long-term development work with some of the world's poorest communities. In almost all cases work overseas is planned and run by local people. Programmes include education and skills training, human rights promotion, healthcare, HIV/AIDS, safe water, agriculture and small businesses. Immediate help for people affected by emergencies such as wars and natural disasters is also funded, as is the analysis of the causes of underdevelopment and campaigns on behalf of the world's poor. All programmes seek to promote gender equality. In England and Wales CAFOD's Development Education Fund makes small grants to local or national groups with young people and adults for projects developing education and action on local/global poverty and injustice issues.

WHAT IS NOT FUNDED CAFOD does not make grants to individuals or to organisations whose aims are primarily political.

TYPE OF GRANT Partnership, programme and project.

FINANCES *Year* 2012–13 *Income* £48,803,000 *Grants* £27,481,000 *Assets* £31,300,000

TRUSTEES Rt Revd Keiran Conry; Mary Ney; Dr Hugo Slim; Revd Jim O'Keefe; Leslie Ferrar; Charles Reeve-Tucker; Dominic Jermey; Revd Dr Timothy Radcliffe; Margaret Mwaniki; Bishop John Arnold; Catherine Newman; Chris Knowles; Joanne Rule; John Darley.

HOW TO APPLY UK applicants are advised to contact the Education Fund Coordinator for further details. Criteria, guidelines and application process for Development Education Fund grants can be found on the CAFOD website.

WHO TO APPLY TO Education Fund Coordinator, Romero House, 55 Westminster Bridge Road, London SE1 7JB *Tel.* 020 7733 7900 *Fax* 020 7274 9630 *email* cafod@cafod.org.uk *Website* www.cafod.org.uk

....

■ **Community Foundation for Calderdale**

CC NO 1002722   **ESTABLISHED** 1991

WHERE FUNDING CAN BE GIVEN Calderdale, with ability to manage funds outside of this area.

WHO CAN BENEFIT Constituted voluntary, community and faith groups, run for and by local people and registered charities working in Calderdale.

WHAT IS FUNDED General. Each scheme has different criteria but priority tends to be given to projects which: achieve outstanding community impact; help people living in communities identified as being particularly disadvantaged; benefit people from black and minority ethnic communities; help people with special needs; benefit older people; and/or benefit young people under the age of 19.

WHAT IS NOT FUNDED The foundation will not fund any of the following: general appeals; projects which have already taken place or for retrospective funding; projects which would normally be funded from statutory sources, i.e., Calderdale MBC, the local education authority, social services or central government; projects for the advancement of religion; projects where the main beneficiaries are animals; projects that do not directly benefit people living in Calderdale; political activities; applications made up entirely of core and/or running costs (exceptions may be made in extraordinary circumstances).

TYPE OF GRANT Revenue, capital, one-off.

RANGE OF GRANTS £100– £40,000 dependent upon scheme.

SAMPLE GRANTS Mirfield Community Trust (£37,000); Healthy Minds (£29,000); Noah's Ark Centre and Relate Pennine Keighley and Craven (£11,000 each); Pavilion in the Park and St Andrew's Youth Centre (£5,000 each); British School Trust (£2,500); Make A Dream £1,000); Rastrick Local History Group (£850) and Halifax Irish JFC and Handmade Parade CIC (£300 each).

FINANCES *Year* 2011–12 *Income* £1,317,286 *Grants* £681,500 *Assets* £8,148,763

TRUSTEES Leigh-Anne Stradeski; Rod Hodgson; Russell Earnshaw; Juliet Chambers; Roger Moore; Clare Townley; Stuart Rumney; Wim Batist; Susanna Hammond; Spencer Lord; John Mitchell.

HOW TO APPLY The foundation's website has details of the grant schemes currently being administered. Application packs for all of the programmes are available to download from the website. Alternatively, contact the foundation directly and they will send a pack in the post. If you wish to discuss your project before applying, the grants team are always happy to answer any queries. The foundation also runs a monthly drop-in, where groups can go for advice and support on their applications.

WHO TO APPLY TO Danni Bailey, Senior Grants Administrator, The 1855 Building (first floor), Discovery Road, Halifax HX1 2NG *Tel.* 01422 438738 *Fax* 01422 350017 *email* enquiries@cffc.co.uk *Website* www.cffc.co.uk

■ The Callander Charitable Trust

SC NO SC016609   **ESTABLISHED** 1972

WHERE FUNDING CAN BE GIVEN Scotland and other parts of the UK.

WHO CAN BENEFIT Charitable organisations.

WHAT IS FUNDED General charitable purposes.

WHAT IS NOT FUNDED No grants to individuals and non-registered charities.

FINANCES *Year* 2011–12 *Income* £73,125 *Grants* £60,000

OTHER INFORMATION Total expenditure in 2011–12 was £67,000.

HOW TO APPLY In writing to the correspondent.

WHO TO APPLY TO The Secretary, Morrisons, 53 Bothwell Street, Glasgow G2 6TS

■ Calleva Foundation

CC NO 1078808   **ESTABLISHED** 1999

WHERE FUNDING CAN BE GIVEN UK and worldwide.

WHO CAN BENEFIT Charitable organisations.

WHAT IS FUNDED Grants were categorised as follows: social services; children's holidays; overseas/international relief; education; arts and culture; medical research; and animal welfare.

SAMPLE GRANTS No sample available.

FINANCES *Year* 2011–12 *Income* £394,913 *Grants* £263,180 *Assets* £168,322

TRUSTEES Stephen Butt; Caroline Butt.

HOW TO APPLY This trust does not accept unsolicited applications.

WHO TO APPLY TO The Trustees, PO Box 22554, London W8 5GN *email* contactcalleva@btopenworld.com

■ Calouste Gulbenkian Foundation – UK Branch

ESTABLISHED 1956

WHERE FUNDING CAN BE GIVEN UK and the Republic of Ireland.

WHO CAN BENEFIT Registered charities or tax exempt organisations concerned with the arts, education, social change or Anglo-Portuguese cultural relations.

WHAT IS FUNDED The foundation is organised around programmes in three areas: cultural understanding; fulfiling potential; environment. The foundation develops its own work, initiatives and partnerships, and is not generally open to applications, with the exception of its Open Fund.

WHAT IS NOT FUNDED Work that does not have a direct benefit in the UK or the Republic of Ireland; individuals; curriculum based activities in statutory education; student grants or scholarships for tuition and maintenance; vocational training; teaching or research posts or visiting fellowships; educational resources and equipment; gap year activities; group or individual visits abroad, including to Portugal; core services and standard provisions; routine information and advice services; capital costs for housing or the purchase, construction, repair or furnishing of buildings; equipment, including vehicles, IT, or musical instruments; scientific or medical research; medicine or related therapies such as complementary medicine, hospices, counselling and therapy; promoting religion or belief system; publications; website development; sports; holidays of any sort; animal welfare.

TYPE OF GRANT Generally one-off grants, occasionally recurring for a maximum of three years.

SAMPLE GRANTS Homeless Link (£250,000); Independent Age (£100,000); Battersea Arts Centre and Manchester International Festival (£75,000 each); Climate Outreach and Information Network (COIN) (£50,000); The Geffrye – Museum of the Home (£35,000); British Trust for Conservation Volunteers (£30,000); Capacity Global (£25,000); And Other Stories and Norwood School (£15,000 each); and Planning Aid for Scotland and WWF – UK (£10,000 each).

FINANCES *Year* 2011–12 *Grants* £1,915,515

TRUSTEE The foundation's board of administration in Lisbon. UK resident trustee: Martin Essayan.

PUBLICATIONS Advice to Applicants for Grants; publications catalogue. The UK Branch commissions and publishes a number of reports and books connected with its programmes of work in the arts, education and social change.

HOW TO APPLY **Open Fund** *only*

How and when to apply: Outline ideas should be submitted by email using the Initial Enquiry Form which is available from the foundation's website. Initial Enquiries can be sent in at any time of the year, but you should allow at least three months between this and the proposed starting date of your research period. Initial enquiries will be assessed in the context of other applications and, if short-listed, fuller information will be requested and applicants invited to discuss their project with foundation staff. After completion of this stage, final applications will be considered at one of the three annual trustee meetings. Email the completed Initial Enquiry Form to info@gulbenkian.org.uk

WHO TO APPLY TO Barbara Karch, Grants Administrator, 50 Hoxton Square, London N1 6PB *Tel.* 020 7012 1400 *Fax* 020 7739 1961 *email* bkarch@gulbenkian.org.uk *Website* www.gulbenkian.org.uk

■ The Calpe Trust

CC NO 1004193   **ESTABLISHED** 1990

WHERE FUNDING CAN BE GIVEN Worldwide.

WHO CAN BENEFIT Registered charities benefiting people in need including refugees, homeless people, people who are socially disadvantaged, victims of war, victims of disasters and so on.

WHAT IS FUNDED Grants towards human rights, health and welfare, emergencies and so on.

WHAT IS NOT FUNDED No grants towards animal welfare or to individuals.

TYPE OF GRANT One-off and ongoing up to three years.

RANGE OF GRANTS £1,000–£5,000.

SAMPLE GRANTS Ecumenical Project for International Cooperation Inc (£8,000); New Israel Fund and Salt of the Earth (£5,000 each); Womankind for Nepal (£1,000); and Peace Trails through London (£500).

FINANCES *Year* 2011–12 *Income* £32,407 *Grants* £26,588 *Assets* £1,095,492

TRUSTEES Reggie Norton; Beatrice Norton; Edward Perks.

HOW TO APPLY In writing to the correspondent. Applicants must contact the trust before making an application.

WHO TO APPLY TO Reggie Norton, Trustee, The Hideaway, Sandy Lane, Hatford Down, Faringdon, Oxfordshire SN7 8JH *Tel.* 01367 870665 *email* reggienorton@talktalk.net

■ Calypso Browning Trust

CC NO 281986   **ESTABLISHED** 1979
WHERE FUNDING CAN BE GIVEN UK.
WHO CAN BENEFIT Organisations benefiting homeless people and animals.
WHAT IS FUNDED Regular grants made to some chosen charities but very occasionally to new charities in line with the trust's objects.
WHAT IS NOT FUNDED No grants to individuals.
RANGE OF GRANTS Up to £5,000
SAMPLE GRANTS Notting Hill Housing Trust and Kensington Housing Trust (£5,000 each); SHELTER (£4,500); Brighton Housing Trust (£3,500); SPEAR (£1,600); People's Dispensary for Sick Animals and RSPCA (£1,250 each) and Dogs Trust and The Donkey Sanctuary (£800 each).
FINANCES *Year* 2011–12 *Income* £33,437 *Grants* £28,100 *Assets* £809,823
TRUSTEES Arthur Weir; Annabel Kapp.
HOW TO APPLY In writing to the correspondent. Note that most of the donations/grants are ongoing, as specified in the trust's deed.
WHO TO APPLY TO The Trustees, c/o Veale Wasbrough Vizards, Barnards Inn, 86 Fetter Lane, London EC4A 1AD

■ The Cambridgeshire Community Foundation

CC NO 1103314   **ESTABLISHED** 2003
WHERE FUNDING CAN BE GIVEN Cambridgeshire.
WHO CAN BENEFIT Voluntary and charitable groups.
WHAT IS FUNDED Community projects seeking to tackle a need or disadvantage. The foundation administers a number of funds. For up-to-date details, see its website.
WHAT IS NOT FUNDED Groups that have more than one year's running costs held as unrestricted reserves; registered charities whose submissions to the Charity Commission are not up to date; statutory responsibilities (i.e. projects which should be funded by a statutory body); sponsored events; improvements to land that is not open to the general public at convenient hours; projects promoting political activities; deficit or retrospective funding (i.e. grants for activities which have already taken place); faith groups promoting religious, non-community based activities. Projects outside Cambridgeshire.
In addition, the foundation does 'not normally' fund national or regional charities with no independent office in Cambridgeshire; animal welfare; general contributions to large appeals (though specific items can be funded); medical research and equipment; grants for more than one year; projects lobbying for a particular cause or action; school projects; building or buying premises and freehold or leasehold land rights; minibuses or other vehicles and overseas travel.
TYPE OF GRANT One-off.
RANGE OF GRANTS The majority of the grants awarded are for small amounts of between £500–£5,000.
SAMPLE GRANTS All Saints Church, Broughton; Cambridge Family Mediation Service; Doddington Parish Council; Linton Allotments Association; Waterbeach Day Centre for the Elderly (funding amounts not listed).
FINANCES *Year* 2011–12 *Income* £1,520,192 *Grants* £848,959 *Assets* £2,975,830
TRUSTEES John Bridge; Allyson Broadhurst; Anthony Clay; Jerry Turner; William Dastur; Richard Symond Gyles Barnwell; Peter Gutteridge; Sam

Weller; Mick Leggett; Neil McKittrick; Christopher Belcher.
OTHER INFORMATION 'We award grants from the funds that local individuals, companies, and local and national government set up with us. The funds have different criteria (including the amounts they give out) and on receiving your application we will match your request to the most appropriate fund (unfortunately we will not be able to find a match for all requests received).'
HOW TO APPLY Guidelines and application forms can be downloaded from the foundation's website. Organisations with an income of £30,000 or less can apply for up to £1,000. Direct applications may be made to a specific fund (as listed on the site) or applicants can complete an expression of interest form and the foundation team will advise on whether your request fits with the objects of any of their funds.
WHO TO APPLY TO Jane Darlington, Chief Executive, The Quorum, Barnwell Road, Cambridge CB5 8RE *Tel.* 01223 410535 *email* info@cambscf.org.uk *Website* www.cambscf.org.uk

■ The Cambridgeshire Historic Churches Trust

CC NO 287486   **ESTABLISHED** 1983
WHERE FUNDING CAN BE GIVEN Cambridgeshire.
WHO CAN BENEFIT Bodies responsible for the upkeep, repair and maintenance of a church, chapel or other building used for public worship.
WHAT IS FUNDED The preservation, repair, significant maintenance, improvement, upkeep and reconstruction of churches in the county of Cambridgeshire and the monuments, fittings, fixtures, stained glass, furniture, ornaments and chattels in such churches and the churchyards belonging to any such churches.
WHAT IS NOT FUNDED Grants are not usually available for additional building work, re-ordering, re-decoration or minor programmes of maintenance.
RANGE OF GRANTS From £1,000–£5,000 primarily for urgent repairs to fabric or renewal of essential services in churches and chapels.
SAMPLE GRANTS Holy Trinity Church, Great Paxton (£5,000); St Andrew's Church, Kimbolton (£4,000) All Saints Church, Paston (£2,500) and St John The Baptist Church – Somersham (£135).
FINANCES *Year* 2011–12 *Income* £41,540 *Grants* £30,000
TRUSTEES Richard Halsey; Alison Taylor; Canon Christopher Barber; Ven. Richard Sledge; Julian Limentani; Dr John Maddison; Revd; Bishop David.
PUBLICATIONS Newsletter.
OTHER INFORMATION In 2011–12 a further £80,500 was given in interest free loans.
HOW TO APPLY In the first instance, contact the correspondent. Application forms, criteria and guidelines are available to download from the trust's website.
WHO TO APPLY TO Andrew Clarke, Grants Officer, PO Box 1112, Balsham, Cambridge CB21 4WP *Tel.* 01223 861314 *email* grants@cambshistoricchurchestrust.co.uk *Website* www.cambshistoricchurchestrust.co.uk

■ The Camelia Trust

CC NO 1081074   **ESTABLISHED** 2000
WHERE FUNDING CAN BE GIVEN Liverpool and Manchester.
WHO CAN BENEFIT Charitable organisations.
WHAT IS FUNDED General charitable purposes.
RANGE OF GRANTS Up to £6,000.
SAMPLE GRANTS Clatterbridge Cancer Charity (£5,200); Action on Addiction (£3,000); the Salvation Army (£2,000) and the Tall Ships Youth Trust (£1,200).
FINANCES *Year* 2011–12 *Income* £43,938 *Grants* £42,108 *Assets* £752,193
TRUSTEES Jennifer Sykes, Prudence Gillett; David Sykes; Michael Taxman.
HOW TO APPLY In writing to the correspondent.
WHO TO APPLY TO Jennifer Sykes, Trustee, Hillside, 9 Wainwright Road, Altrincham, Cheshire WA1 4 4BW *Tel.* 01619 280731

■ The Campden Charities Trustee

CC NO 1104616   **ESTABLISHED** 1629
WHERE FUNDING CAN BE GIVEN The former parish of Kensington, London; a north-south corridor, roughly from north of the Fulham Road to the north of Ladbroke Grove (a map can be viewed on the website).
WHO CAN BENEFIT Individuals and non-statutory not for profit organisations which refer and support individuals.
WHAT IS FUNDED Supporting outcomes for disadvantaged people, particularly young people and adults who have experienced a long period of unemployment.
WHAT IS NOT FUNDED UK charities or charities outside Kensington, unless they are of significant benefit to Kensington residents; schemes or activities which are generally regarded as the responsibility of the statutory authorities; UK fundraising appeals; environmental projects unless connected with education or social need; medical research or equipment; animal welfare; advancement of religion or religious groups, unless they offer non-religious services to the community; commercial and business activities; endowment appeals; projects of a political nature; retrospective capital grants.
TYPE OF GRANT One-off and recurrent funding for buildings, capital, core costs, feasibility studies and full project costs. Pensions to older people, grants in cash or in kind to relieve need, bursaries and all kinds of grants to Kensington-based organisations.
RANGE OF GRANTS £1,000–£119,000.
SAMPLE GRANTS NOVA and Westway Community Transport (£72,000 each); Nucleus Legal Advice Centre (£68,000); Volunteer Centre (£50,000); Blenheim Project (£30,000); Earls Court YMCA (£23,000); St Mungo's Housing (£10,000); Age UK (£8,000); North Kensington Women's Textile Workshop (£6,000); Notting Hill Housing Trust (£3,000); and Harrison Housing, London Cyrenians, St Christopher's Fellowship and St Clements (£1,000 each).
FINANCES *Year* 2011–12 *Income* £3,083,089 *Grants* £387,800 *Assets* £124,687,130
TRUSTEES Revd Gillean Craig, Chair; David Banks; Elisabeth Brockmann; Dr Chris Calman; Dr Kit Davis; Robert Atkinson; Susan Lockhart; Tim Martin; Terry Myers; Ben Pilling; Michael Finney; Richard Walker-Arnott; Ms M. Rodkina; Sam Berwick.
OTHER INFORMATION An additional £1.2 million was given in grants to individuals.

HOW TO APPLY The charity's website provides the following information: 'We are trying to target our resources where they can be of the most direct benefit to financially disadvantaged individuals. **We therefore do not receive unsolicited applications from organisations.** However, the Charities' officers are eager to meet with colleagues from other not-for-profit organisations to explore ways in which we can work together to help individuals to end dependency on benefits or improve a low wage. We make incentive payments to any not-for-profit non-statutory organisations that successfully refer individuals and families to us. The best way to show us that you are working with the people that we want to help is to refer individuals to us and at the same time you will benefit your organisation.'
'**Referrals:** Non-statutory not-for-profit organisations that are working directly with low-income residents of Kensington are eligible to receive £1,000 for each individual or family that they refer successfully (i.e. each individual or family that is awarded a grant or pension).' If you have contact with individuals whom you would like to refer, telephone the correspondent: working age and students: 020 7313 3797; older people: 020 7313 3794 or 020 7313 3796
WHO TO APPLY TO Chris Stannard, Clerk to the Trustees, 27a Pembridge Villas, London W11 3EP *Tel.* 020 7243 0551 *Fax* 020 7229 4920 *Website* www.campdencharities.org.uk

■ The Frederick and Phyllis Cann Trust

CC NO 1087863   **ESTABLISHED** 1998
WHERE FUNDING CAN BE GIVEN Northamptonshire.
WHO CAN BENEFIT The Trust Deed names seven charities, but trustees are prepared to consider other charities that fall within the charitable objects of the trust.
WHAT IS FUNDED The main objects of the trust are animal welfare, welfare of children and safety at sea.
RANGE OF GRANTS Up to £5,000.
SAMPLE GRANTS PDSA (£5,000); The Donkey Sanctuary (£4,600); RNLI (£4,500); Frontier Centre, Pitsford Sports Field, Starlight Children's Foundation and Dogs for the Disabled (£3,000 each); Boys Brigade (£2,500); Red Cross and Brainwave (£2,000 each); Children's Aid Team and Pavilion Pre School (£1,000 each) and Handicapped Children (£800).
FINANCES *Year* 2011–12 *Income* £72,133 *Grants* £68,315 *Assets* £2,008,527
TRUSTEES Michael Percival; David Sharp; Keith Panter; Philip Saunderson; Christopher Toller; Laura Steedman.
OTHER INFORMATION Grants were made to 28 organisations.
HOW TO APPLY In writing to the correspondent.
WHO TO APPLY TO Angela Moon, c/o Hewitsons, 7 Spencer Parade, Northampton NN1 5AB *Tel.* 01604 233233

■ The Canning Trust

CC NO 292675   **ESTABLISHED** 1985
WHERE FUNDING CAN BE GIVEN UK and the developing world.
WHO CAN BENEFIT Small concerns.
WHAT IS FUNDED Only donations proposed internally by staff members.

WHAT IS NOT FUNDED Unsolicited applications are not considered. The trust states that it generally only makes grants to charities which staff; ex-staff and friends are directly involved with.

RANGE OF GRANTS Up to £10,000.

SAMPLE GRANTS Village Water (£10,000); Tushar Project – Herbertpur Christian Hospital (£4,000); Dogodogo Centre, Softpower and TESFA (£3,000 each); Alive and Kicking (£2,100); Kafue Fisheries (£2,000); St Mary's National School (£1,600); and Loldia (£1,000).

FINANCES *Year* 2011–12 *Income* £9,001

TRUSTEES Richard Griffiths; Krystina Mecner; Andrew Ure; Cressida Hulme; Nigel White.

OTHER INFORMATION In 2011–12 the trust had a total expenditure of £27,851.

HOW TO APPLY Note that the trust only makes grants to charities which staff, ex-staff and friends are involved with.

WHO TO APPLY TO The Trustees, 593–599 Fulham Road, London SW6 5UA *Tel.* 020 7381 7410

■ M. R. Cannon 1998 Charitable Trust

CC NO 1072769   **ESTABLISHED** 1998

WHERE FUNDING CAN BE GIVEN Preference for North Devon, Dorset, Bristol, North Yorkshire and County Durham.

WHO CAN BENEFIT Charities and community groups.

WHAT IS FUNDED 'The objectives of the charity are general charitable purposes to the benefit of the general public. The trustees have no specific grantmaking criteria but are interested in supporting medical/health charities and conservation and countryside related initiatives, as well as small local projects in North Devon, Dorset, Bristol, North Yorkshire and County Durham. The trustees also support young people who wish to carry out vocational training or studies.'

RANGE OF GRANTS Up to £10,000.

SAMPLE GRANTS Killing Cancer (£10,000); Game and Wildlife Conservation Trust (£3,000); Middleton in Teesside Community Gym (£2,700); Calvert Trust Exmoor (£2,500); North Devon Hospice (£1,250); Families For Children (£500); North Devon Athletics Club (£300); Encephalitis Society (£250); Starlight Children's Foundation (£200) and St Helen's Church and Macmillan Cancer Support (£100 each).

FINANCES *Year* 2011–12 *Income* £2,234,257 *Grants* £58,125 *Assets* £3,568,139

TRUSTEES Michael Cannon; Sally Cannon; Chris Mitchell.

OTHER INFORMATION The grant total includes £35,700 that was given to individuals.

HOW TO APPLY In writing to the correspondent.

WHO TO APPLY TO The Trustees, 53 Stoke Lane, Westbury-on-Trym, Bristol BS9 3DW *Tel.* 01173 776540

■ H. and L. Cantor Trust

CC NO 220300   **ESTABLISHED** 1959

WHERE FUNDING CAN BE GIVEN UK, with some preference for Sheffield.

WHO CAN BENEFIT Registered charities, with particular consideration to be given to Jewish charities.

WHAT IS FUNDED Jewish causes and general charitable purposes.

RANGE OF GRANTS Up to £15,000.

SAMPLE GRANTS Previous beneficiaries include: Delamere Forest School Ltd, Sheffield Jewish Congregation and Centre, Sheffield Jewish Welfare Organisation, I Rescue, Jewish Childs Day, Sense, Share Zadek UK, Brain Research Trust, PDSA – Sheffield and World Cancer Research.

FINANCES *Year* 2011–12 *Income* £465 *Grants* £314,932

TRUSTEES Lily Cantor; Nicholas Jeffrey.

OTHER INFORMATION Due to the trust's low income in 2011–12, only basic financial information was available from the Charity Commission.

HOW TO APPLY Unsolicited applications are not invited.

WHO TO APPLY TO Lilly Cantor, Trustee, 3 Ivy Park Court, 35 Ivy Park Road, Sheffield S10 3LA *Tel.* 01142 306354

■ Cardy Beaver Foundation

CC NO 265763   **ESTABLISHED** 1973

WHERE FUNDING CAN BE GIVEN UK with preference for Berkshire.

WHO CAN BENEFIT National and local registered charities.

WHAT IS FUNDED General charitable purposes.

WHAT IS NOT FUNDED Registered charities only.

RANGE OF GRANTS Usually under £5,000.

SAMPLE GRANTS Previous beneficiaries have included: Cancer Research UK, Watermill Theatre Appeal, Wallingford Museum, NSPCC, Berkshire Blind Society, Adventure Dolphin, St Peter's Parochial Church Council, Church House Trust, RNLI and Asthma Relief, Julia's House, Elizabeth Foundation, Com Exchange – Newbury and Pangbourne Fete.

FINANCES *Year* 2012–13 *Income* £158,688 *Grants* £110,500 *Assets* £2,414,475

TRUSTEES John James; Mary Cardy; Sandra Rice.

HOW TO APPLY In writing to the correspondent.

WHO TO APPLY TO John James, Trustee, Clifton House, 17 Reading Road, Pangbourne, Berkshire RG8 7LU *Tel.* 01189 614260

■ The Carew Pole Charitable Trust

CC NO 255375   **ESTABLISHED** 1968

WHERE FUNDING CAN BE GIVEN UK, in practice mainly Cornwall.

WHO CAN BENEFIT Donations normally made only to registered charities, but applications will be considered from individuals for non-full-time education purposes.

WHAT IS FUNDED General charitable purposes principally in Cornwall. In the case of support to churches and village halls, donations are in practice only made to those in the immediate vicinity to Antony House, Torpoint or to those with connections to the Carew Pole Family.

WHAT IS NOT FUNDED The trustees do not support applications from individuals for full-time education.

RANGE OF GRANTS Up to £15,000.

SAMPLE GRANTS Antony Parish Church (£6,750); Eton College (£2,500); The Eden Project (£2,000); Cornwall Community Foundation (£1,000); Professional Gardeners Guild Trust (£500) and St Stephen's Church (£100).

FINANCES *Year* 2011–12 *Income* £72,884 *Grants* £49,096 *Assets* £2,046,775

TRUSTEES Tremayne Pole; James Kitson; James Williams.

OTHER INFORMATION In 2011–12 grants were given to 29 organisations.

HOW TO APPLY On an application form available from the trust. The trustees consider and approve major donations in November each year, while other smaller appeals are considered, and donations made, throughout the year.

WHO TO APPLY TO Thomas Rattray, The Antony Estate Office, Antony, Torpoint, Cornwall PL11 3AB *Tel.* 01752 815303

■ The D. W. T. Cargill Fund

SC NO SC012703 **ESTABLISHED** 1939
WHERE FUNDING CAN BE GIVEN UK, with a preference for the West of Scotland.
WHO CAN BENEFIT Registered charities.
WHAT IS FUNDED General charitable purposes, particularly religious causes, medical charities and help for older people.
WHAT IS NOT FUNDED No grants are made to individuals.
TYPE OF GRANT One-off and recurrent.
SAMPLE GRANTS Previous beneficiaries have included: City of Glasgow Society of Social Service, Colquhoun Bequest Fund for Incurables, Crathie Opportunity Holidays, Glasgow and West of Scotland Society for the Blind, Glasgow City Mission, Greenock Medical Aid Society, North Glasgow Community Forum, Scottish Maritime Museum – Irvine, Scottish Episcopal Church, Scottish Motor Neurone Disease Association, Lead Scotland and Three Towns Blind Bowling/Social Club.
FINANCES *Year* 2011–12 *Income* £285,504 *Grants* £255,656
TRUSTEES A. C. Fyfe; W. G. Peacock; N. A. Fyfe; Mirren Elizabeth Graham.
HOW TO APPLY In writing to the correspondent, supported by up-to-date accounts. Trustees meet quarterly.
WHO TO APPLY TO Norman A. Fyfe, Trustee, Miller Beckett and Jackson Solicitors, 190 St Vincent Street, Glasgow G2 5SP

■ Carlee Ltd

CC NO 282873 **ESTABLISHED** 1981
WHERE FUNDING CAN BE GIVEN Worldwide.
WHO CAN BENEFIT Talmudic scholars and Jewish people.
WHAT IS FUNDED The advancement of religion in accordance with the Orthodox Jewish faith; the relief of poverty; general charitable purposes.
SAMPLE GRANTS Previous beneficiaries have included Antryvale Ltd, Asos Chesed, Egerton Road Building Fund, Glasgow Kollel, HTVC, Rav Chesed Trust, Tevini, Union of Hebrew Congregations, YHS and YHTC.
FINANCES *Year* 2012–13 *Income* £231,241 *Grants* £237,931 *Assets* £756,557
TRUSTEES Hershel Grunhut; Pearl Grunhut; Bernard Dor Stroh; Blima Stroh.
HOW TO APPLY In writing to the correspondent.
WHO TO APPLY TO The Secretary, 32 Pagent Road, London N16 5NQ

■ The Carlton House Charitable Trust

CC NO 296791 **ESTABLISHED** 1986
WHERE FUNDING CAN BE GIVEN UK and overseas.
WHO CAN BENEFIT Charitable organisations and Jewish organisations.
WHAT IS FUNDED The advancement of education, research work and fellowships. Most funds are committed to various charitable institutions in the UK and abroad; a limited number of

bursaries are given, mainly connected with the professional interests of the trustees.
TYPE OF GRANT One-off.
RANGE OF GRANTS £35–£9,000.
SAMPLE GRANTS Western Marble Arch Synagogue (£3,000); Community Security Trust and B'nai B'rith Hillel Foundation, National Trust (£2,000 each); Royal Academy of Music and Board of Deputies Charitable Foundation (£1,000 each); Beit Halochem and London Philharmonic Orchestra (£500); Nightingale House and Ovarian Cancer Action (£250 each) and B'nai B'rith First Lodge of England (£170).
FINANCES *Year* 2012–13 *Income* £173,098 *Grants* £31,767 *Assets* £1,271,970
TRUSTEES Stewart Cohen; Pearl Cohen; Fiona Stein.
OTHER INFORMATION Grants for £100 or less were given to 124 organisations.
HOW TO APPLY In writing to the correspondent.
WHO TO APPLY TO Stewart Cohen, Trustee, Craven House, 121 Kingsway, London WC2B 6PA *Tel.* 020 7242 5283

■ The Carmelite Monastery Ware Trust

CC NO 298379 **ESTABLISHED** 1987
WHERE FUNDING CAN BE GIVEN UK with preference for Ware, and overseas.
WHO CAN BENEFIT Registered charities and churches.
WHAT IS FUNDED Religious and other charitable work carried out in Ware for the benefit of the public.
SAMPLE GRANTS Previous beneficiaries have included: Association of British Carmels, Cardinal Hume Centre Trust, Catholic Aid Fund for Overseas Development, Catholic Housing Aid Society, Emmaus UK, Hertfordshire Community Trust, Medical Foundation for the Care of Victims of Torture, Passage Day Centre, Shelter, and Sion Evangelisation Centre for National Training.
FINANCES *Year* 2011–12 *Income* £51,163 *Grants* £47,200 *Assets* £286,429
TRUSTEES Patricia E. McGee; Theresa M. Linforth; Margaret Prickett; Mary Bosworth-Smith.
HOW TO APPLY In writing to the correspondent.
WHO TO APPLY TO Sister Mary Bosworth-Smith, Bursar, Carmelite Monastery, Ware, Hertfordshire SG12 0DT

■ The Worshipful Company of Carmen Benevolent Trust

CC NO 1050893 **ESTABLISHED** 1995
WHERE FUNDING CAN BE GIVEN City of London and UK.
WHO CAN BENEFIT People connected with transport.
WHAT IS FUNDED Objects of relieving necessitous past or present Liverymen or Freemen of the Company, its employees and servants, or those connected with transport in the UK. The trust is also allowed to made grants to any charitable fund in the City of London or elsewhere.
RANGE OF GRANTS £100–£6,000.
SAMPLE GRANTS Lord and Lady Taverners' Minibus Appeal (£30,000); City of London Freeman's School (Bursary) (£25,000); Breast Cancer Campaign (£20,000); King Edward's School (£3,000); Hackney Carriage Drivers (£2,500); Wallace School of Motoring (£2,000); London's Air Ambulance and Family Holiday Association (£1,200 each); Whizz-Kidz (£1,000); City of London Police Orphans' Fund (£500); Clapton Common Boys Club (£350) and 19 Tank Transporter Squadron RLC (£250).

FINANCES *Year* 2011–12 *Income* £117,066 *Grants* £127,324 *Assets* £1,133,765

TRUSTEES Telfer Saywell; Michael Power; Brig. Mike Turner; John Older; Mary Bonar; M. Simpkin; Robert Russett.

OTHER INFORMATION In 2011–12 five individuals received a total of £2,000.

HOW TO APPLY In writing to the correspondent.

WHO TO APPLY TO Michael Breeze, The. Hon. Secretary, Five Kings House, 1 Queen Street Place, London EC4R 1QS *Tel.* 020 7489 8289 *email* bentrust@thecarmen.co.uk *Website* www.thecarmen.co.uk

---

■ The Richard Carne Trust

CC NO 1115903   **ESTABLISHED** 2006

WHERE FUNDING CAN BE GIVEN UK.

WHO CAN BENEFIT Young people.

WHAT IS FUNDED The performing arts.

RANGE OF GRANTS Up to £50,000 to organisations.

SAMPLE GRANTS Royal College of Music (£30,000); Trinity Laban Conservatoire of Dance and Music (£16,000); Royal Welsh College of Music and Drama (£15,000); Classical Opera Company and Theatre 503 (£5,000 each); Red Handed Theatre Company (£3,000); and British Isles Music Festival (£2,000).

FINANCES *Year* 2011–12 *Income* £218,600 *Grants* £146,300 *Assets* £977,841

TRUSTEES Kleinwort Benson Trustees Ltd; Philip Edward Carne; Marjorie Christine Carne.

HOW TO APPLY 'The trustees' current policy is to consider all written appeals received, but only successful applications are notified of the trustees' decision. [. . .] The trustees review the selected charities, and consider new appeals received at their annual trustee meeting, normally held in June.

WHO TO APPLY TO Christopher Gilbert, Administrator, Kleinwort Benson Trustees Ltd, 14 St George Street, London W1S 1FE *Tel.* 020 3207 7356

■ The Carnegie Dunfermline Trust

SC NO SC015710   **ESTABLISHED** 1903

WHERE FUNDING CAN BE GIVEN Dunfermline and Rosyth.

WHO CAN BENEFIT Registered charities and schools.

WHAT IS FUNDED Projects, activities and schemes with social, community, educational, cultural, sport and recreational purposes for the benefit of those within the defined geographic area of the operation of the Trust. We look for proposals that are innovative and far reaching together with those that particularly impact on young people. We are also interested in active partnerships where organisations decide to work together and adopt a joint approach. Start-up funding is offered on a one-off basis. Additional guidelines are available for schools.

WHAT IS NOT FUNDED Individuals; closed groups (with the exception of those catering for specialist needs); political, military or sectarian bodies; activities out of the geographic scope of the trust; medical organisations; routine running or salary costs; costs which are the responsibility of a government body.

TYPE OF GRANT Principally single grants and capital funding. Pump priming and start-up funding is offered on a one off basis.

RANGE OF GRANTS Typical grant between £300 and £10,000.

SAMPLE GRANTS Dunfermline Reign Basketball Club (£7,000); Dunfermline Rugby Football Club (£5,000); Gillespie Memorial Church (£3,000);

Queen Anne High School (£2,500); Zodiak Gymnastic Club, Edinburgh International Book Festival and 2nd Fife (Dunfermline) Scout Group (£1,000 each); and Pitcorthie Nursery (£700).

FINANCES *Year* 2012 *Income* £447,790 *Grants* £1,000,000

TRUSTEES Andrew Croxford; Dr David Fraser; Claire Gemmell; Angus Hogg; Jane Livingstone; William Livingstone; Janet McCauslin; Keith Punler; Dr Ruth Ray; Fiona Robertson; J. Douglas Scott; David Walker; Robin Watson; Ian M. Wilson; David Fleetwood; Cllr Alice Callaghan; Cllr Willie Campbell; Cllr Mike Shirkie; Nora Rundell.

HOW TO APPLY On a form which can be downloaded from the trust's website. The trust provides the following additional information: 'Trustees meet every two months and applications can be submitted at any time. Application forms are available from the website or from the office and initial discussion with the Grants Officer is encouraged. Where possible applications will be acknowledged and further information may be sought. Once all the necessary background is available the application will be considered by the appropriate assessing trustee in the first instance who will decide if a grant under delegated powers is applicable, if it should go to the board, or if it is not suitable to progress. When a grant is awarded the recipient will be notified in writing with any related terms and conditions which will include the take up of the grant within a twenty four month period. If an application is unsuccessful, the trust is unlikely to consider a further application within twelve months.'

WHO TO APPLY TO Elaine Stewart, Grants Officer, Andrew Carnegie House, Pittencrieff Street, Dunfermline KY12 8AW *Tel.* 01383 749789 *Fax* 01383 749799 *email* grants@carnegietrust.com *Website* www.andrewcarnegie.co.uk

---

■ The Carnegie Trust for the Universities of Scotland

SC NO SC015600   **ESTABLISHED** 1901

WHERE FUNDING CAN BE GIVEN Scotland.

WHO CAN BENEFIT Undergraduates of Scottish birth, Scottish parentage or Scottish schooling; graduates and members of staff of the Scottish universities.

WHAT IS FUNDED Universities in Scotland through the improvement of facilities and support of research. Graduates and members of staff of Scottish universities, and undergraduates of Scottish birth or extraction for fees for first degrees at Scottish universities.

WHAT IS NOT FUNDED Those applications with no relation to Scotland, those living Scotland or those of Scottish extraction.

TYPE OF GRANT Capital for projects of value to the Scottish universities, with wide discretion on what is allowable. Core costs.

SAMPLE GRANTS University of St Andrews; University of Edinburgh, University of Aberdeen (funding amounts unspecified).

FINANCES *Year* 2011–12 *Income* £2,524,552 *Grants* £1,868,029

TRUSTEE 12 nominated trustees and 14 ex officio trustees.

OTHER INFORMATION All of the trust's schemes are described in detail on its website.

HOW TO APPLY Regulations and application forms can be obtained from the secretary and from the website. Preliminary telephone enquiries are welcome.

Alphabetical register of grant making charitable trusts

....

■ The Carpenter Charitable Trust

cc no 280692   ESTABLISHED 1980
WHERE FUNDING CAN BE GIVEN UK and overseas.
WHO CAN BENEFIT Humanitarian and Christian outreach charities are preferred.
WHAT IS FUNDED General charitable objects with a Christian bias. 'The charity is established on wide grant giving terms. The trustees continue to pursue their 'preferred' list approach – a list of charities with which the trustees have developed a good relationship over the years.'
WHAT IS NOT FUNDED 'The trustees do not consider applications for church repairs (other than in respect of Kimpton Church) nor applications from individuals nor any applications received from abroad unless clearly 'sponsored' by an established charity based in England and Wales.'
TYPE OF GRANT One-off (but some are in practice repeated).
RANGE OF GRANTS £250–£2,500.
SAMPLE GRANTS Previously: Mission Aviation Fellowship Europe (£7,500); ORBIS Charitable Trust (£6,000); Andrew Christian Trust, Barnabas Fund, Help in Suffering UK and Relationships Foundation (£5,000 each); DEC Bangladesh (£2,500); Brooke Hospital for Animals, Crisis UK, Merlin and Salvation Army (£1,000 each); Blue Cross, Fight for Sight, Mercy Ships, Prison Fellowship, RSPB, Send a Cow and Tibet Relief (£500 each); and Cats Protection League (£250).
FINANCES *Year* 2011–12 *Income* £14,466 *Grants* £64,991
TRUSTEES Michael Carpenter; Gabriel Carpenter.
OTHER INFORMATION Accounts were received at the Commission but unavailable to view.
HOW TO APPLY In writing to the correspondent including sufficient details to enable a decision to be made. However, as about half the donations made are repeat grants, the amount available for unsolicited applications remains small.
WHO TO APPLY TO Michael Carpenter, Trustee, 1 Codicote Road, Welwyn, Hertfordshire AL6 9LY *Tel.* 01438 718439

....

■ The Carpenters' Company Charitable Trust

cc no 276996   ESTABLISHED 1978
WHERE FUNDING CAN BE GIVEN UK.
WHO CAN BENEFIT Individuals and schools, colleges, universities and other charitable organisations promoting the craft of carpentry.
WHAT IS FUNDED Charitable causes benefiting from grants include organisations supporting the elderly, disabled, homeless, youth and children, education, medical and museums. Craft causes receive a high priority when awards are considered.
WHAT IS NOT FUNDED Grants are not normally made to individual churches or cathedrals, or to educational establishments having no association to the Carpenters' Company. No grants (except educational grants) are made to individual applicants. Funds are usually only available to charities registered with the Charity Commission or exempt from registration.
SAMPLE GRANTS Carpenters and Docklands Centre (£25,000); Carpenters Road School (£15,000); Wood Awards (£13,000); and Institute of Carpenters (£6,000).
FINANCES *Year* 2011–12 *Income* £1,047,633 *Grants* £1,044,764 *Assets* £20,140,199
TRUSTEES Peter A. Luton; Michael Matthews; Michael I. Montague-Smith; Guy Morton-Smith.
OTHER INFORMATION The Building Crafts College received a grant of over £880,000.
HOW TO APPLY The consideration of grans is delegated to the Charitable Grants Committee which meets three times each year. Day to day management is the responsibility of the Clerk to whom applications should usually be addressed. However, the trust's website states: 'In normal years the Carpenters' Company Charitable Trust disburses grants to a wide range of charitable causes but all funds for 2013 and 2014 are already committed. We will not be considering new applications until 2015 at the earliest.'
WHO TO APPLY TO The Clerk, Carpenters' Hall, 1 Throgmorton Avenue, London EC2N 2JJ *Tel.* 020 7588 7001 *email* info@carpentersco. com *Website* www.carpentersco.com/ charitable_ccct.php

....

■ The Carr-Gregory Trust

cc no 1085580   ESTABLISHED 2001
WHERE FUNDING CAN BE GIVEN UK.
WHO CAN BENEFIT Charitable organisations.
WHAT IS FUNDED Arts, social welfare, health and education.
RANGE OF GRANTS Up to £11,000.
SAMPLE GRANTS the Royal National Theatre (£25,000); The Royal Academy of Music (£7,500); Quartet Charitable Foundation (£2,500); Alzheimer's Society, Diana Award and Penny Brohn Cancer Care (£2,000 each); Beating Bowel Cancer and Shakespeare at the Tobacco Factory (£1,000 each); and Centrepoint and St Mungo's (£500 each).
FINANCES *Year* 2012 *Income* £61,249 *Grants* £73,450 *Assets* £432,333
TRUSTEES Russ Carr; Heather Wheelhouse; Linda Carr; Hannah Nicholls.
OTHER INFORMATION The grant total includes one award to an individual of £7,000.
HOW TO APPLY In writing to the correspondent.
WHO TO APPLY TO Russ Carr, Trustee, 56 Pembroke Road, Clifton, Bristol BS8 3DT

....

■ The Carrington Charitable Trust

cc no 265824   ESTABLISHED 1973
WHERE FUNDING CAN BE GIVEN UK with a preference for Buckinghamshire.
WHO CAN BENEFIT Local branches of a wide range of charities, and local charities.
WHAT IS FUNDED General charitable purposes.
WHAT IS NOT FUNDED Registered charities only – no grants to individuals.
RANGE OF GRANTS Up to £21,000, mostly for smaller amounts.
SAMPLE GRANTS Grenadier Guards – Colonel's Fund (£15,000); Hope and Homes for Children (£2,500); Bledlow Parochial Church Council Holy Trinity Church (£5,500); Combat Stress (£5,000); Garsington Opera (£4,000); Help for Heroes, Aylesbury Grammar School Foundation, Coombe Hill Monument Appeal and Hospice of St Francis (£500 each); Friends of Kew Gardens

Every application represents a cost to you and to the trust

(£85); Chiltern Open Air Museum (£50); and Bucks Archaeological Society (£12).
FINANCES *Year* 2011–12 *Income* £98,644 *Grants* £54,696 *Assets* £4,839,847
TRUSTEES Rt Hon. Lord Carrington; J. A. Cloke; Rt Hon. V. Carrington.
HOW TO APPLY In writing to the correspondent.
WHO TO APPLY TO Jeffrey Cloke, Trustee, c/o JA Cloke, Cloke and Co, 475 Salisbury House, London Wall, London EC2M 5QQ *Tel.* 020 7638 8992

■ The Carron Charitable Settlement

CC NO 289164   **ESTABLISHED** 1984
WHERE FUNDING CAN BE GIVEN UK and overseas.
WHO CAN BENEFIT Charitable organisations.
WHAT IS FUNDED 'The trust was created for charitable purposes in connection with wildlife, education, medicine, the countryside and the printing and publishing trade.' Ongoing support is given to the St Bride's Church – Fleet Street.
WHAT IS NOT FUNDED No grants to individuals.
TYPE OF GRANT Project, research, running costs and salaries.
SAMPLE GRANTS Previous beneficiaries included: St Bride's Church Appeal (£20,000); INTBAU (£10,000); Academy of Aviation and Space Medicine (£3,000); and Curwen Print Study Centre (£1,500).
FINANCES *Year* 2011–12 *Income* £0 *Grants* £3,100
TRUSTEES Peter Fowler; David Morgan.
OTHER INFORMATION Income for this charity has been steadily declining, however, it is still on the Central Register of Charities and while it remains on the register will be included here in case it should come to life again.
HOW TO APPLY The trust does not invite applications from the general public.
WHO TO APPLY TO Amanda Dorman, Administrator, c/o Rothman Panthall and Co., 10 Romsey Road, Eastleigh, Hampshire SO50 9AL *Tel.* 02380 614555

■ The Leslie Mary Carter Charitable Trust

CC NO 284782   **ESTABLISHED** 1982
WHERE FUNDING CAN BE GIVEN UK, with a preference for Norfolk, Suffolk and North Essex.
WHO CAN BENEFIT Registered charities.
WHAT IS FUNDED The preferred areas for grant giving are conservation/environment and welfare causes. Other applications will be considered but acknowledgements may not always be sent. Trustees prefer well thought-out applications for larger gifts, than many applications for smaller grants.
WHAT IS NOT FUNDED No grants to individuals.
TYPE OF GRANT Capital including buildings, core costs, one-off, project, research, running costs and recurring costs will be considered.
RANGE OF GRANTS Grants generally range from £500–£5,000, but larger grants are sometimes considered.
SAMPLE GRANTS Animal Health Trust (£50,000); Action Medical Research, Essex Wildlife Trust, RNIB, St Nicholas Hospice Care and The Long Shop Project Trust (£5,000 each); National Search and Rescue Dog Association and Shelter (£3,000 each); Excelsior Trust and Suffolk Accident Rescue Service (£2,000 each); and RSPB and Suffolk Preservation Society (£1,000 each).

FINANCES *Year* 2012 *Income* £116,848 *Grants* £157,000 *Assets* £3,089,952
TRUSTEES Sam Wilson; Leslie Carter; Martyn Carr.
HOW TO APPLY In writing to the correspondent. Telephone calls are not welcome. There is no need to enclose an sae unless applicants wish to have materials returned. Applications made outside the preferred areas for grant giving will be considered, but acknowledgements may not always be sent.
WHO TO APPLY TO Sam Wilson, Trustee, c/o Birketts, 24–26 Museum Street, Ipswich IP1 1HZ *Tel.* 01473 232300

■ Carter's Educational Foundation

CC NO 528161   **ESTABLISHED** 1888
WHERE FUNDING CAN BE GIVEN The ancient parish of Wilford.
WHO CAN BENEFIT The trust supports the South Wilford Endowed Church of England School. It may also give grants to individuals under 25 living in the ancient parish and organisations for such people, with a broadly educational nature, operating within the beneficial area of the ancient parish of Wilford, Nottingham, including Wilford Village, Silverdale, Compton Acres, part of West Bridgford mainly west of Loughborough Road, and parts of the south of the Meadows.
WHAT IS FUNDED Education.
WHAT IS NOT FUNDED No grants to anyone living outside the ancient parish of Wilford, Nottingham or any organisation based outside of that area.
SAMPLE GRANTS School of the Foundation (£75,000); St Saviour's Children's Pioneer and Youth Pioneer (£7,000); Carter Hall (£1,500); Nottingham Hoods Basketball Club (£750); Kidz United (£250); and Wilford Lions Football Club (£70).
FINANCES *Year* 2012 *Income* £291,411 *Grants* £119,708 *Assets* £6,096,538
TRUSTEES Paula Hammond; Robert Stanley; Madeleine Cox; Roy Nettleship; Raymond Hutchins; Robert Baxter; Roger Steel.
OTHER INFORMATION Grants to individuals totalled £32,000.
HOW TO APPLY The following information is provided by the foundation: 'Subject to the availability of funds, grants to voluntary charitable organisations in the ancient parish are normally considered at the same time as educational grants for individuals and awarded on the basis of the school year. Trustees meet four times a year however letters of application should be with the clerk to the foundation before 31 May. Letters should identify the base for the organisation's work, outline the nature of the activities involved and the approximate number of young people participating from the ancient parish. If this is the first application from your organisation, give full details and include a copy of your latest accounts. Applications must be made in writing.'
WHO TO APPLY TO Sally Morrant, The Clerk to the Trustees, Pennine House, 8 Stanford Street, Nottingham NG1 7BQ *Tel.* 01159 586262 *Website* www.wilford-carters-education.org.uk

■ The Casey Trust

CC NO 1055726   **ESTABLISHED** 1996
WHERE FUNDING CAN BE GIVEN UK and developing countries.
WHO CAN BENEFIT Charities benefiting children.

WHAT IS FUNDED Children and young people in the UK and developing countries by supporting new projects.

WHAT IS NOT FUNDED Grants are not given to 'individual applicants requesting funds to continue studies or travel'.

TYPE OF GRANT Three years ongoing.

RANGE OF GRANTS £750–£13,000. Average grant between £1,000–£5,000.

SAMPLE GRANTS WMF (World Monuments Fund) (£12,500); Norwood (£10,000); Youth Aliyah (£7,000); Save the Children (£5,000); Princess Royal Trust Carers and Hope (£3,000 each); Kisharon and Barnstondale Centre (£2,000 each); Trinity Hospice (£1,500); Lothians Autistic Society and Dame Vera Lynn Trust (£1,000 each) and Yes Outdoors (£900).

FINANCES *Year* 2011–12 *Income* £193,744 *Grants* £111,700 *Assets* £2,830,607

TRUSTEES Kenneth Howard; Edwin Green; Leonard Krikler.

HOW TO APPLY Not being a reactive trust, it is regretted that the trustees will be unable to respond to the majority of requests for assistance. In order to both reduce costs and administration the trustees will respond mainly to those charitable institutions known to them. There is no application form. Trustees meet four times a year. The trustees will only notify unsuccessful applicants if a self-addressed envelope is enclosed.

WHO TO APPLY TO Kenneth Howard, Trustee, 27 Arkwright Road, London NW3 6BJ *Tel.* 020 7435 9601 *Website* www.caseytrust.org

----

■ Cash for Kids – Radio Clyde

SC NO SC003334   **ESTABLISHED** 1984

WHERE FUNDING CAN BE GIVEN Radio Clyde transmission area, i.e. west central Scotland.

WHO CAN BENEFIT Children and young adults up to the age of 16 disadvantaged through: illness, distress, abuse or neglect; any kind of disability; behavioural or psychological difficulties; living in poverty or situations of deprivation. Organisations benefiting this group.

WHAT IS FUNDED Grants, Christmas presents, food, pantomime trips, clothing and other support is given to children via social work departments and through community and voluntary groups.

WHAT IS NOT FUNDED The trust does not fund: trips or projects abroad; medical treatment/research; unspecified expenditure; deficit funding or repayment of loans; retrospective funding (projects taking place before the grant award date); projects unable to start within six months of the grant award date; distribution to another/ other organisation/s; general appeals or endowment funds; relief of statutory responsibility; the promotion of religion. No funding for capital expenditure except in very special circumstances that must be made clear at the time of applying. Organisations whose administration costs exceed 15% of total expenditure will not be supported.

SAMPLE GRANTS Previous beneficiaries include: Aberlour Bridges Project – Royston: supporting children affected by addiction; and Centre for Under 5s Toy Library: supporting children with physical disabilities through a novel 'Toys on the Road' mobile library.

FINANCES *Year* 2012 *Income* £1,414,175 *Grants* £1,000,000

TRUSTEES J. Brown; Ewan Hunter; Ian Grabiner; Lord Jack McConnell; Sir Tom Hunter; Brenda Ritchie.

HOW TO APPLY Application forms and guidelines are available from the charity's website.

WHO TO APPLY TO Trust Administrator, Radio Clyde, 3 South Avenue, Clydebank Business Park, Glasgow G81 2RX *Tel.* 01412 041025 *Fax* 01415 652370 *email* lesley.cashforkids@radioclyde.com *Website* www.clydecashforkids.com

----

■ The Cass Foundation

CC NO 1146296   **ESTABLISHED** 2012

WHERE FUNDING CAN BE GIVEN UK, with a preference for Merseyside.

WHAT IS FUNDED 'To advance the education of the public in the techniques and practices of creating, managing and conserving places, both urban and rural, including buildings, open spaces and landscapes which promote and aim to promote good health.'

TRUSTEES Dr Simon Abrams; Judy Cass; Richard Cass; Rachael Gosling.

HOW TO APPLY In writing to the correspondent.

WHO TO APPLY TO Richard Cass, Trustee, Cass Associates, Studio 104, The Tea Factory, 82 Wood Street, Liverpool L1 4DQ *Tel.* 01517 070110 *email* foundation@cassassociates.co.uk

----

■ Sir John Cass's Foundation

CC NO 312425   **ESTABLISHED** 1748

WHERE FUNDING CAN BE GIVEN The inner London boroughs – Camden, Greenwich, Hackney, Hammersmith and Fulham, Islington, Kensington and Chelsea, Lambeth, Lewisham, Newham, Southwark, Tower Hamlets, Wandsworth, Westminster and the City of London.

WHO CAN BENEFIT Individuals; schools and organisations. The foundation will only consider proposals from schools and organisations that benefit: children or young people under the age of 25, who are permanent residents of named *inner* London boroughs (Camden, Greenwich, Hackney, Hammersmith and Fulham, Islington, Kensington and Chelsea, Lambeth, Lewisham, Newham, Southwark, Tower Hamlets, Wandsworth, Westminster and the City of London), and from disadvantaged backgrounds or areas of high deprivation.

WHAT IS FUNDED Education, especially of people in financial need. The foundation has four areas of focus for grant giving: widening participation in further and higher education; truancy, exclusion and behaviour management; prisoner education; new initiatives.

WHAT IS NOT FUNDED There are many activities and costs that the foundation will not fund. The following list gives an idea of the type the foundation cannot support: projects that do not meet a foundation priority; conferences, seminars and academic research; holiday projects, school journeys, trips abroad or exchange visits; supplementary schools or mother tongue teaching; independent schools; youth and community groups, or projects taking place in these settings; pre-school and nursery education; general fundraising campaigns or appeals; costs for equipment or salaries that are the statutory responsibility of education authorities; costs to substitute for the withdrawal or reduction of statutory funding; costs for work or activities that have already taken place prior to the grant application; costs already covered by core funding or other grants; curriculum enhancing projects; capital costs, that are exclusively for the purchase, repair or furnishing of buildings, purchase of vehicles, computers, sports equipment or improvements to school grounds.

TYPE OF GRANT Recurrent for individuals; project, recurrent or one-off support for groups, organisations and schools. Funding may be given for up to three years.

RANGE OF GRANTS Usually £5,000–£50,000.

SAMPLE GRANTS British Schools Exploring Society (£50,000); Music First (£44,000); Pitch Perfect (£30,000); East London Business Alliance (£22,000); University of the Arts (£16,500); New Bridge (£10,000); and the Specialist Schools and Academies Trust (£5,000).

FINANCES *Year* 2011–12 *Income* £5,979,407 *Grants* £1,121,703 *Assets* £119,387,755

TRUSTEES Michael Bear; Kevin Everett; Mark Boleat; HH. Judge Brian Barker; Revd Christopher Burke; Barbara Lane; Graham Forbes; David Turner; Mervyn Streatfeild; Helen Meixner; Dr Ray Ellis; Revd Nigel Kirkup; Sarah Dalgarno; David Hogben; Prof. Michael Thorne; Inigo Woolf; Revd Laura Burgess.

OTHER INFORMATION Grants include £153,500 to individuals.

HOW TO APPLY The foundation operates a two stage application process – an initial enquiry and a full application stage. At stage 1, applicants are required to complete and submit the initial enquiry form which is available from the foundation's website and on request from the correspondent. The form asks for outline information about your proposed project; information about how the project meets the foundation's priorities; a summary of the project that includes the following information: the aims of the project including outputs and outcomes, how the project will be delivered; the duration of the project, including when and where it will take place; and a budget covering project costs. Enquiries will then be considered and applicants informed of the decision taken within three weeks. Successful stage 1 applicants will be invited to proceed to Stage 2 and submit a full application. A copy of the stage 2 guidelines will be sent to you at that time. This form should be completed and submitted with copies of the memorandum and articles of association (or constitution) of your organisation, together with the latest annual report and accounts. On receipt of your application foundation staff may meet with you as part of the assessment process. The grants committee meets in March, June and November each year. It normally takes between two and four months from receipt of a full application until a decision is made. All applicants will be sent formal notification of the outcome of their applications within two weeks of the committee decision. Those who are offered a grant will be sent a formal offer letter and copies of the foundation's standard terms and conditions of grant. Copies of the standard terms and conditions of grant are available on the foundation's website. Additional conditions are sometimes included depending on the nature of the grant. All applications are assessed on merit. If your application is refused you can apply again twelve months after the date you submitted your last application.

WHO TO APPLY TO Tony Mullee, Clerk/Chief Executive, 31 Jewry Street, London EC3N 2EY *Tel.* 020 7480 5884 *Fax* 020 7488 2519 *email* contactus@sirjohncass.org *Website* www.sirjohncass.org

■ The Elizabeth Casson Trust

CC NO 227166   **ESTABLISHED** 1930

WHERE FUNDING CAN BE GIVEN Worldwide.

WHO CAN BENEFIT Occupational therapy schools/ departments and individual occupational therapists.

WHAT IS FUNDED The training and development of occupational therapists. Ongoing support is given to Oxford Brookes University.

WHAT IS NOT FUNDED No support for anything other than occupational therapy education and training.

TYPE OF GRANT Research projects and courses/ travel bursaries that will benefit the profession as well as the individual.

SAMPLE GRANTS United Kingdom Occupational Therapy Research Foundation (£10,000) and Ugandan Association of Occupational Therapists (£1,000)

FINANCES *Year* 2011–12 *Income* £210,769 *Grants* £48,567 *Assets* £6,361,162

TRUSTEES Carolyn Rutland; Juliet Croft; Dr Peter Agulnik; Geoffrey Paine; Rosemary Hallam; Bernard Davies; Sally Townsend; Dr David Parker; Mark Drasdo; Prof. Elizabeth Turner.

HOW TO APPLY On the trust's application form which can be obtained from the website.

WHO TO APPLY TO Caroline Gray, Secretary to the Trustees, Corner House, Cote, Bampton, Oxfordshire OX18 2EG *Tel.* 01993 850716 *email* ec.trust@btinternet.com *Website* www.elizabethcassontrust.org.uk

■ The Castang Foundation

CC NO 1003867   **ESTABLISHED** 1991

WHERE FUNDING CAN BE GIVEN UK.

WHO CAN BENEFIT Registered charities.

WHAT IS FUNDED Research into neurodevelopmental disorders in children.

SAMPLE GRANTS Royal United Hospital NHS Trust (£70,000); Imperial College (£19,000); Oxford University (£13,000); and the European Academy of Childhood Disability (£600).

FINANCES *Year* 2011–12 *Income* £94,863

TRUSTEES I. A. Burman; M. B. Glynn, M. Bax.

OTHER INFORMATION In 2011–12 the foundation had a total expenditure of £163,622.

HOW TO APPLY In writing to the correspondent.

WHO TO APPLY TO Ian Burman, Administrator, 2 More London Riverside, London SE1 2AP *Tel.* 020 7842 8000 *email* ian.burnham@laytons.com *Website* www.castangfoundation.net

■ The Catalyst Charitable Trust

CC NO 1001962   **ESTABLISHED** 1990

WHERE FUNDING CAN BE GIVEN Mainly Suffolk and Essex.

WHO CAN BENEFIT Charitable causes.

WHAT IS FUNDED This trust has an interest in supporting small charities in the Suffolk/Essex area, particularly churches, schools and hospitals.

SAMPLE GRANTS The Suffolk Foundation, Hadleigh High School, The Oundle Schools Foundation, The Iceni Project, Livability (John Grooms), The Tree House Appeal and Macmillan Cancer Support.

FINANCES *Year* 2011–12 *Income* £25,000 *Grants* £47,000

TRUSTEES Gillian Buckle; James Buckle; Louise Somerset; Charles Course.

HOW TO APPLY In writing to the correspondent although beneficiaries are normally selected through personal contact.

WHO TO APPLY TO Penny Andrews, Buckle Farms, Dairy Farm Office, Dairy Road, Semer, Ipswich IP7 6RA

■ **The Catholic Charitable Trust**

CC NO 215553   **ESTABLISHED** 1935
WHERE FUNDING CAN BE GIVEN America and Europe.
WHO CAN BENEFIT Traditional Catholic organisations.
WHAT IS FUNDED The traditional teachings of the Roman Catholic faith. The trust's income is usually fully committed.
WHAT IS NOT FUNDED The trust does not normally support a charity unless it is known to the trustees. Grants are not made to individuals.
RANGE OF GRANTS £1,500–£15,000.
SAMPLE GRANTS Society of Saint Pius X – England (£16,000); White Fathers (£5,000); Little Sisters of the Poor (£4,000); California Friends of the Society of St Pius X and Holy Cross Parish Fulham (£2,000 each); and Carmelite Monastery Carmel California (£1,000).
FINANCES *Year* 2012 *Income* £71,037 *Grants* £53,656 *Assets* £1,979,658
TRUSTEES John C. Vernor-Miles; Wilfrid E. Vernor-Miles; David P. Orr.
HOW TO APPLY Applications can only be accepted from registered charities and should be in writing to the correspondent. The trust does not normally support a charity unless it is known to the trustees. In order to save administration costs replies are not sent to unsuccessful applicants. For the most part funds are fully committed.
WHO TO APPLY TO Wilfrid Miles, Trustee, c/o Hunters, 9 New Square, London WC2A 3QN *Tel.* 020 7412 0050

■ **Catholic Foreign Missions**

CC NO 249252   **ESTABLISHED** 1941
WHERE FUNDING CAN BE GIVEN UK and overseas.
WHO CAN BENEFIT Catholic Foreign Missions.
WHAT IS FUNDED Grants are made in support of Catholic Foreign Missions in any part of the world.
SAMPLE GRANTS Congregation of the Mission – Province of Paris (£269,000); Congregation of the Mission Province of Toulouse (£196,000); Congregation of the Mission – General Curia-Rome (£183,000); Oeuvre du Bienheureux Perboyre (£30,000); Congregation of the Mission – Province of Ireland (£25,000) and Prelazia De Cameta (£4,000).
FINANCES *Year* 2011–12 *Income* £640,417 *Grants* £707,533 *Assets* £16,987,219
TRUSTEES Revd Desmond Beirne; Revd Jean Marie Lesbats; Revd Eric Ravoux; Revd Bernard Meade; Revd Eric Saint-Sevin; Revd Philip Walshe; Revd Philipe Lamblin; Revd Kieran Magovern.
HOW TO APPLY No external applications are considered. The funds are fully committed.
WHO TO APPLY TO Revd Bernard Meade, The Secretary, c/o Pothecary Witham Weld, 70 St George's Square, London SW1V 3RD

■ **The Catholic Trust for England and Wales**

CC NO 1097482   **ESTABLISHED** 1968
WHERE FUNDING CAN BE GIVEN England and Wales.
WHO CAN BENEFIT Roman Catholic organisations.
WHAT IS FUNDED The advancement of the Roman Catholic religion in England and Wales.
WHAT IS NOT FUNDED No grants to individuals, local projects or projects not immediately advancing the Roman Catholic religion in England and Wales.
SAMPLE GRANTS CARITAS Social Action Network (£119,500); Catholic Voices (£60,000); Churches Legislation Advisory Service (£18,000); National Board of Catholic Women (£10,000); International Eucharistic Congress (£8,000); Diocese of Menevia (£3,500); and MACSAS (£2,000).
FINANCES *Year* 2012 *Income* £4,163,069 *Grants* £271,500 *Assets* £12,520,256
TRUSTEES Rt Revd Malcolm McMahon; Ben Andradi; Richard King; Revd John Nelson; Michael Prior; Dr Elizabeth Walmsley; William Moyes; Nigel Newton.
HOW TO APPLY In writing to the correspondent. The trust has stated previously that it does not respond to unsolicited applications.
WHO TO APPLY TO Revd Marcus Stock, Secretary, 39 Eccleston Square, London SW1V 1BX *Tel.* 020 7901 4810 *email* secretariat@cbcew.org.uk *Website* www.catholicchurch.org.uk

■ **The Cattanach Charitable Trust**

SC NO SC020902   **ESTABLISHED** 1992
WHERE FUNDING CAN BE GIVEN Scotland.
WHO CAN BENEFIT The trust will fund charities registered either in Scotland or in England for work done exclusively in Scotland. 'Organisations should be registered with the Office of the Scottish Charity Regulator, or, if registered with the Charity Commission, should be in the process of registering with OSCR.'
WHAT IS FUNDED 'The Cattanach Trust seeks applications for projects which support children from pre-birth to three years old, who are affected by levels of relative deprivation. There is good evidence that supporting children during the first years of a child's life has the greatest positive impact on their developmental progress. Good quality services improve not only a child's life during these years, but also have substantial benefits into adolescence and adulthood. Projects should be working from a strengths based model; the existing and potential strengths of the child, the family and the community should be recognised and should form the basis of the work. Projects must actively involve the parent(s)/main carers of the children. The trust's view is that prioritising this age group values children in Scotland appropriately, and will make a significant contribution to Scotland's National Outcome.'
WHAT IS NOT FUNDED The trust will not fund individuals, hospices and palliative care, appliances for illness or disability, organisations concerned with specific diseases, or animal charities.
TYPE OF GRANT The trust prefers to make grants which contribute substantially to smaller-scale projects.
RANGE OF GRANTS Mostly £3,000–£20,000.
SAMPLE GRANTS Dumfries Toy Library (£14,500); Saheliya, Edinburgh (£14,000); Relationships Scotland Family Mediation South Lanarkshire and Home-Start, Stirling (£10,000 each); and

Pennyburn Regeneration Youth Development Enterprise (PRYDE), and Langholm Playcare (£4,000 each).

FINANCES *Year* 2012 *Income* £514,431 *Grants* £400,000

TRUSTEES Malcolm Borthwick; Anne Houston; Euan Davidson; Michael Gotz; Duncan McEachran; Alastair Wilson; Rachel Lewis; Janet Barr; Steven Murray; Colin Mackenzie; Andrew Millington.

HOW TO APPLY On a form which can be completed online or downloaded from the trust's website. The trust does not normally accept hand-written applications – phone if you do not have access to a computer. The trust no longer has application deadlines, but works on a rolling programme. Trust meetings are listed on its website and you should allow around ten weeks for your application to reach a meeting.

WHO TO APPLY TO Alison Campbell, 15 Warriston Crescent, Edinburgh EH3 5LA *Tel.* 01315 572052 *email* alison@cattanach.org.uk *Website* www.cattanach.org.uk

....

■ The Joseph and Annie Cattle Trust

CC NO 262011 **ESTABLISHED** 1970

WHERE FUNDING CAN BE GIVEN Worldwide, with a preference for Hull and East Yorkshire.

WHO CAN BENEFIT Organisations and individuals. "The aged, disabled and underprivileged are assisted wherever possible as are children suffering from dyslexia. Financial assistance is provided as far as possible by supporting institutions specialising in these areas.'

WHAT IS FUNDED General charitable purposes.

WHAT IS NOT FUNDED The trust **only** works with charitable bodies or statutory authorities and we do not provide grants directly to individuals.

TYPE OF GRANT One-off, capital, recurring and interest-free loans are considered.

RANGE OF GRANTS Up to £15,000.

SAMPLE GRANTS Sobriety Project (£15,000); Dyslexia Action (£14,000); Anlaby Park Methodist Church and Prince's Trust (£5,000 each); Hull and East Riding Institution for the Blind (£3,000); Bath Institute of Medical Engineering and Ocean Youth Trust (£2,000 each); and Age UK East Riding, Longhill Primary School and Prison Fellowship (£1,000 each).

FINANCES *Year* 2011–12 *Income* £364,839 *Grants* £288,699 *Assets* £7,391,236

TRUSTEES Paul Edwards; Michael Gyte; Christopher Munday; S. C. Jowers.

OTHER INFORMATION Included in the grants total is £24,000 awarded to individuals.

HOW TO APPLY The following information is taken from the trust's website:

'There are two main types of application that we are looking to support: Firstly, there are applications by charitable or statutory bodies on behalf of individuals or families. The application form available through this web page must be completed by the charitable organisation/ statutory body concerned and not the individual/ family. Supporting papers should be attached where necessary. Secondly, there are applications for projects and work with the groups of people who are outlined in our key objective above. Submit full details to the address shown below including the following: the charitable organisation including contact details and the latest financial statements; projects/work successfully completed to date that support the current application. Outline work already carried

out in the Hull and East Riding area. Because we will request that our grants are used exclusively in the Hull and East Riding area identify how your organisation will guarantee this is achieved; the project/work together with detailed costings and supporting information. (e.g. estimates/planning permission etc.); identify other grants received or currently being considered by other bodies; how the grant is to be spent. In considering applications the trustees may require further information so remember it is in your interests to give as much detail as possible. Application forms should be printed, **completed in handwriting** and sent to the correspondent by post or fax.'

WHO TO APPLY TO Roger Waudby, Administrator, PO Box 23, Hull HU12 0WF *Tel.* 01964 671742 *Fax* 01964 671742 *Website* www.jacattletrust. co.uk

....

■ The Thomas Sivewright Catto Charitable Settlement

CC NO 279549 **ESTABLISHED** 1979

WHERE FUNDING CAN BE GIVEN Unrestricted (for UK-based registered charities).

WHO CAN BENEFIT Registered charities only.

WHAT IS FUNDED General charitable purposes.

WHAT IS NOT FUNDED The trust does not support non-registered charities, expeditions, travel bursaries and so on, or unsolicited applications from churches of any denomination. Grants are unlikely to be considered in the areas of community care, playschemes and drug abuse, or for local branches of national organisations.

RANGE OF GRANTS Up to £14,000.

SAMPLE GRANTS Previously: Royal College of Music (£14,000) Royal Scottish Academy of Music and Drama (£12,000); Bowel Cancer Research and King VII's Hospital for Officers (£10,000 each); Haddo House Choral and Operatic Society and World YWCA (£5,000 each); Aviation for Paraplegics and Tetraplegics Trust (£2,000); NACRO (£1,500); Refugee Council, St Mungo's, Shelter and Charlie Waller Memorial Trust (£1,000 each); Crisis (£750); and Sportability (£500).

FINANCES *Year* 2011–12 *Income* £74,125 *Grants* £80,312 *Assets* £7,260,817

TRUSTEES Lord Catto; Olivia Marchant; Zoe Richmond-Watson.

HOW TO APPLY In writing to the correspondent, including an sae.

WHO TO APPLY TO The Secretary to the Trustees, PO Box 47408, London N21 1YW

....

■ The Wilfrid and Constance Cave Foundation

CC NO 241900 **ESTABLISHED** 1965

WHERE FUNDING CAN BE GIVEN UK, with preference for Berkshire, Cornwall, Devon, Dorset, Hampshire, Oxfordshire, Somerset, Warwickshire and Wiltshire.

WHO CAN BENEFIT Registered charities. Mainly local charities or charities which the trustees have personal knowledge of, interest in, or association with are considered.

WHAT IS FUNDED General charitable purposes including conservation, animal welfare, health and social welfare.

WHAT IS NOT FUNDED No grants to individuals.

TYPE OF GRANT Buildings, core costs, one-off, project, research, and running costs. Grants may be given for up to three years.

Think carefully about every application. Is it justified?

437

RANGE OF GRANTS £500–£50,000.

SAMPLE GRANTS Oxford Museum of Children's Literature (£40,000); Royal Academy of Music (£10,000); Farmers' Club Pinnacle Award (£7,000); East Berkshire Women's Aid and Moorland Mousie Trust (£5,000 each); Twitchen Parish Hall (£3,000); Two Moors Festival (£2,000); and Himalayan Children and Shooting Star Children's Hospice (£1,000 each).

FINANCES *Year* 2011–12 *Income* £247,778 *Grants* £135,000 *Assets* £4,168,836

TRUSTEES Toni Jones; Jacqueline Archer; Mark Pickin; Nicola Thompson; Glyn Howells; Francois Jones; Janet Pickin; Melanie Waterworth; Roy Walker; William Howells.

HOW TO APPLY In writing to the correspondent a month before the trustees' meetings held twice each year, in May and October.

WHO TO APPLY TO The Secretary, New Lodge Farm, Drift Road, Winkfield, Windsor SL4 4QQ *email* tcf@eamo.co.uk

■ The Cayo Foundation

CC NO 1080607   **ESTABLISHED** 1999

WHERE FUNDING CAN BE GIVEN UK.

WHO CAN BENEFIT Charitable organisations.

WHAT IS FUNDED Medical research, the fight against crime, children and youth charities and general charitable purposes.

SAMPLE GRANTS Previous beneficiaries included: NSPCC (£125,000); the Disability Foundation, PACT, the Royal Opera House (£25,000 each); the Prince's Foundation (£20,000); Wessex Youth Trust (£10,000); Christian Blind Mission (£6,000); Wellbeing of Women (£3,000); Institute for Policy Research and Royal Humane Society (£2,500 each); and Sue Ryder Care – St John's Hospice (£1,000).

FINANCES *Year* 2011–12 *Income* £751,108 *Grants* £555,580 *Assets* £1,750,908

TRUSTEES Angela E. McCarville; Stewart A. Harris.

HOW TO APPLY In writing to the correspondent.

WHO TO APPLY TO Angela E. McCarville, Trustee, 7 Cowley Street, London SW1P 3NB *Tel.* 020 7248 6700

■ The B. G. S. Cayzer Charitable Trust

CC NO 286063   **ESTABLISHED** 1982

WHERE FUNDING CAN BE GIVEN UK.

WHO CAN BENEFIT Registered charities.

WHAT IS FUNDED General charitable purposes.

WHAT IS NOT FUNDED No grants to organisations outside the UK.

RANGE OF GRANTS Up to £25,000.

SAMPLE GRANTS Limited information on beneficiaries was available although grants to the Feathers Association (£3,000), The Patricia Baines Trust (£2,500) and the Westerkirk Parish Trust (£300) were published in the accounts. Previous beneficiaries have included: Friends of the National Maritime Museum, Hike for Hope, Marie Curie Cancer Care, RAFT, St Paul's Cathedral Foundation, Scottish Countryside Alliance Education Trust and Worshipful Company of Shipwrights Charitable Fund.

FINANCES *Year* 2011–12 *Income* £101,169 *Grants* £67,800 *Assets* £2,795,712

TRUSTEES P. R. Davies; M. Buckley; A. M. Hunter; R. N. Leslie.

HOW TO APPLY Note the following statement taken from the charity's 2011/12 accounts: 'The trustees identify the projects and organisations

they wish to support and so do not consider grants to people or organisations who apply speculatively. The trust also has a policy of not responding to any correspondence unless it relates to grants it has agreed to make or to the general management of the trust.'

WHO TO APPLY TO Sonia Barry, Trust Administrator, The Cayzer Trust Company Limited, Cayzer House, 30 Buckingham Gate, London SW1E 6NN *Tel.* 020 7802 8439

■ Elizabeth Cayzer Charitable Trust

CC NO 1059265   **ESTABLISHED** 1996

WHERE FUNDING CAN BE GIVEN UK.

WHO CAN BENEFIT Museums, galleries and other arts organisations and projects.

WHAT IS FUNDED Funds are used in promoting activities related to art, including education, restoration, research, conservation and conferences and exhibitions.

SAMPLE GRANTS Previous beneficiaries have included Elias Ashmole Trust, Dulwich Picture Gallery, the National Gallery and Sir John Soane's Museum.

FINANCES *Year* 2011–12 *Income* £821,757 *Grants* £38,500 *Assets* £3,393,531

TRUSTEES The Hon. Elizabeth Gilmour; Diana Lloyd; Dominic Gibbs.

OTHER INFORMATION This charity was established by The Honourable Elizabeth Gilmour, who has made significant donations to the charity since 1996. In formulating policy the trustees have taken into account the wishes of the Settlor, which are that the assets of the charity should be used in supporting and promoting activities relating to art.

HOW TO APPLY The trust tends to support only people/projects known to the Cayzer family or the trustees. Unsolicited appeals will not be supported.

WHO TO APPLY TO The Hon. Elizabeth Gilmour, Trustee, The Cayzer Trust Company Limited, Cayzer House, 30 Buckingham Gate, London SW1E 6NN *Tel.* 020 7802 8080

■ The Cazenove Charitable Trust

CC NO 1086899   **ESTABLISHED** 1969

WHERE FUNDING CAN BE GIVEN UK.

WHO CAN BENEFIT Charitable organisations. This Trust primarily supports the charitable activities sponsored by current and ex Cazenove employees.

WHAT IS FUNDED General charitable purposes.

SAMPLE GRANTS Starlight Children's Foundation (£9,000); Disability Snowsport, NCC Foundation and Wheelpower (£2,500); Essex Community Foundation (£2,000); and Mayor of Havering Appeal (£1,000 each).

FINANCES *Year* 2012 *Income* £70,020 *Grants* £34,578 *Assets* £2,396,584

TRUSTEES David Mayhew; Edward M. Harley; Michael Wentworth-Stanley; Michael Power.

HOW TO APPLY This trust does not respond to unsolicited applications.

WHO TO APPLY TO Edward Harley, Trustee, Cazenove, 12 Moorgate, London EC2R 6DA *Tel.* 020 3479 0102

■ The CBD Charitable Trust

cc no 1136702   **established** 2010
where funding can be given Worldwide.
who can benefit Children and young people.
what is funded General charitable purposes.
sample grants Earthway, Hope Community Village, Martlets Hospice, Self Help Africa, Unity Church New York.
finances *Year* 2011–12 *Income* £149,370 *Grants* £237,652 *Assets* £40,722
trustees Coutts and Co; Ingrid Scott.
how to apply In writing to the correspondent.
who to apply to Trustee Dept, Coutts and Co, 440 Strand, London WC2R 0QS *Tel.* 020 7663 6825

■ CBRE Charitable Trust (formerly CB Richard Ellis Charitable Trust)

cc no 299026   **established** 1987
where funding can be given Unrestricted
who can benefit Registered charities or recognised charitable causes, which have a strong link to C B Richard Ellis Ltd, for example, through client requests for support or staff fundraising activities.
what is funded General charitable causes.
what is not funded No grants to third parties, such as fundraising organisations or publication companies producing charity awareness materials.
range of grants £20–£1,100.
sample grants Cancer Research UK (£2,500); Breast Cancer Campaign (£2,000); UNICEF (£1,200); ME Research UK (£1,000); Age UK (£750); Sparks (£500); Deafblind, London Legal Support Trust, Footprints and Different Strokes (£250 each) and Meningitis Research Foundation (£200).
finances *Year* 2011–12 *Income* £78,098 *Grants* £34,105 *Assets* £105,751
trustees Matthew D. Black; Nicholas E. Compton; Guy Gregory; Lena Ubhi; David Hitchcock; Miles Skinner.
how to apply In writing to the correspondent. The trust stated that in recent years they have received as many as two hundred unsolicited requests for support that do not meet with the above donations criteria. Given the size of the trust, a response to such requests is not always possible.
who to apply to A. C. Naftis, Secretary to the Trustees, St Martin's Court, 10 Paternoster Row, London EC4M 7HP *Tel.* 020 7182 3452

■ Celtic Charity Fund

sc no SC024648   **established** 1995
where funding can be given Worldwide but with a preference for Scotland and Ireland.
who can benefit Charitable organisations.
what is funded Health, education, homelessness, employability and social welfare.
range of grants Up to £3,000.
finances *Year* 2011–12 *Income* £1,064,442
trustees Chris Traynor; Peter Lawwell; Neil Lennon; Craig Paterson; Gavin Kelly; Eric Riley; Adrian Filby.
other information There is approximately £100,000 available on an annual basis.
how to apply On a form available to download from the website. Closing dates for applications are 30 June and 31 December.

who to apply to Jane Maguire, Celtic Football Club, Celtic Park, Glasgow G40 3RE *Tel.* 01415 514262 *email* janemaguire@celticfc.co.uk *Website* www.celticfc.net

■ The Gaynor Cemlyn-Jones Trust

cc no 1039164   **established** 1994
where funding can be given North Wales and Anglesey.
who can benefit Registered charities.
what is funded Conservation and protection of general public amenities, historic or public interests in Wales; medical research; protection and welfare of animals and birds; study and promotion of music; activities and requirements of religious and educational bodies.
what is not funded No grants to individuals or non-charitable organisations.
type of grant One-off.
range of grants £100 upwards.
sample grants Bangor University (£33,000 in four grants); Music in Hospitals Wales (£2,000); Beaumaris Festival, All Saints Church – Deganwy and Snowdonia Society (£1,000 each); and Llandudno Youth Music Theatre (£500).
finances *Year* 2011–12 *Income* £377,259 *Grants* £74,725 *Assets* £1,002,566
trustees Philip G. Brown; Janet Lea; Eryl G. Jones; Colin Wickens.
other information Four grants went to Bangor University towards the following funds, schools and departments: Stewardship (£12,000); C J Fellowship fund (£8,000); Outreach (£6,000); School of Ocean Sciences (£4,000); and Royal Society (£3,000).
how to apply In writing to the correspondent.
who to apply to Philip G. Brown, Trustee, Park Cottage, Gannock Park, Deganwy, Conwy LL31 9PZ *Tel.* 01492 596360 *email* philip.brown@brewin.co.uk

■ The CH (1980) Charitable Trust

cc no 279481   **established** 1980
where funding can be given UK and Israel.
who can benefit Jewish organisations.
what is funded Jewish causes.
sample grants Oxford Centre for Hebrew and Jewish Studies (£100,000); Traditional Alternatives Foundation (£25,000); Jerusalem Foundation (£18,000); Israel Diaspora Trust and Anglo Israel Foundation (£8,000 each); West London Synagogue Charitable Fund (£3,000); B'nai B'rith Hillel Foundation (£1,000); and British Friends of the Israel Guide Dog Centre for the Blind (£500).
finances *Year* 2011–12 *Income* £40,228 *Grants* £179,500 *Assets* £1,370,623
trustee Kleinwort Benson Trustees Limited.
how to apply In writing to the correspondent.
who to apply to The Administrator, Kleinwort Benson Trustees Ltd, 14 St George Street, London W1S 1FE *Tel.* 020 3207 7000

■ R. E. Chadwick Charitable Trust

cc no 1104805   **established** 2004
where funding can be given UK.
who can benefit Registered charities.
what is funded General charitable purposes.
what is not funded No grants for individuals.
sample grants Action Aid, British Refugee Council, Henshaws College, Leeds Community Foundation and Unicef (£1,000 each); Age UK,

British Heart Foundation, Claro Enterprises, Martin House Children's Hospice, Save the Children Fund and Sightsavers International (£500 each); and Donna's Dream House (£200).

FINANCES *Year* 2011–12 *Income* £34,895 *Grants* £28,500 *Assets* £867,025

TRUSTEES Peter Chadwick; Esme Knowles; Paul Knowles; Ann Chadwick.

HOW TO APPLY In writing to the correspondent.

WHO TO APPLY TO Peter Chadwick, Trustee, Hathenshaw Farm, Hathenshaw Lane, Denton, Ilkley, West Yorkshire LS29 0HR *Tel.* 01132 446100

■ The Amelia Chadwick Trust

CC NO 213795   **ESTABLISHED** 1960

WHERE FUNDING CAN BE GIVEN UK, especially Merseyside.

WHO CAN BENEFIT Neighbourhood-based community projects, some UK organisations.

WHAT IS FUNDED General charitable purposes including education, health, the arts, social welfare and the environment.

WHAT IS NOT FUNDED No grants to individuals.

TYPE OF GRANT Mostly recurring.

RANGE OF GRANTS £100–£25,000.

FINANCES *Year* 2011–12 *Income* £144,887 *Grants* £91,859 *Assets* £3,614,226

TRUSTEES Liverpool Charity and Voluntary Services; Ruth Behrend; Caroline Dawson; Christopher Bibby.

HOW TO APPLY All donations are made through Liverpool Charity and Voluntary Services. Grants are only made to charities known to the trustees, and unsolicited applications are not considered.

WHO TO APPLY TO The Trustees, c/o Liverpool Charity and Voluntary Services, 151 Dale Street, Liverpool L2 2AH *Tel.* 01512 275177

■ The Pamela Champion Foundation

CC NO 268819   **ESTABLISHED** 1974

WHERE FUNDING CAN BE GIVEN UK, with a preference for Kent.

WHO CAN BENEFIT Registered charities.

WHAT IS FUNDED General charitable purposes.

WHAT IS NOT FUNDED No grants to non-registered charities.

RANGE OF GRANTS Up to £2,500.

SAMPLE GRANTS Heart of Kent Hospice, Kent Community Foundation and Macmillan (£2,000 each); Afghanistan Trust and Carers UK (£1,000 each); Beacon Church, Cancer Research UK, Odyssey Project and Phyllis Tuckwell Hospice (£500 each).

FINANCES *Year* 2012 *Income* £29,581 *Grants* £26,500 *Assets* £748,089

TRUSTEES Caroline Winser; Elizabeth Bell; Peter Williams.

HOW TO APPLY In writing to the correspondent.

WHO TO APPLY TO Elizabeth Bell, Trustee, Wiltons, Newnham Lane, Eastling, Faversham, Kent ME13 0AS *Tel.* 01795 890233

■ Champneys Charitable Foundation

CC NO 1114429   **ESTABLISHED** 2006

WHERE FUNDING CAN BE GIVEN UK.

WHO CAN BENEFIT Charitable organisations.

WHAT IS FUNDED Health, medical and disability causes.

RANGE OF GRANTS Up to £20,000.

SAMPLE GRANTS Variety Club (£14,000); Dogs for the Disabled (£9,000); Standing Start (£6,600); Rainbow Hospice (£5,600) and New Life Foundation (£2,000).

FINANCES *Year* 2011–12 *Income* £70,362 *Grants* £50,000

TRUSTEES Dorothy Purdew; Stephen Purdew; Michael Hawkins.

OTHER INFORMATION Grants are also given to individuals.

HOW TO APPLY In writing to the correspondent.

WHO TO APPLY TO Bev Strong, Charity Administrator, Henlow Grange, Henlow, Bedfordshire SG16 6DB *Tel.* 01462 810712 *email* charity@ champneys.co.uk *Website* www.champneys.com

■ The Chapman Charitable Trust

CC NO 232791   **ESTABLISHED** 1963

WHERE FUNDING CAN BE GIVEN UK, with preference for North Wales, London and South East England.

WHO CAN BENEFIT Any recognised charity, but mainly those charities in which the late settlor had, or the trustees have, a personal interest or concern.

WHAT IS FUNDED General charitable purposes. Main areas supported are social services, culture and recreation, education and research, health, environment and heritage.

WHAT IS NOT FUNDED No grants to or for the benefit of individuals, local branches of national charities, animal welfare, sports tours, research expeditions or sponsored adventure holidays.

RANGE OF GRANTS Mostly £1,000–£2,000.

SAMPLE GRANTS Pesticide Action Network UK (£20,000); Action for Children, Aldeburgh Music and Methodist Homes for the Aged (£12,000 each); A Rocha UK and TreeHouse Trust (£6,000 each) and Yateley Industries for the Disabled, Global Rescue Services, Mind, The National Police Community Trust and Working Families (£2,000 each).

FINANCES *Year* 2011–12 *Income* £249,132 *Grants* £245,000 *Assets* £6,517,598

TRUSTEES Roger Chapman; Richard Chapman; Bruce Chapman; Guy Chapman; Bryony Chapman.

OTHER INFORMATION There were 91 grants of £1,000 each made to organisations.

HOW TO APPLY In writing at any time. The trustees currently meet to consider grants twice a year at the end of September and in March. They receive a large number of applications and regret that they cannot acknowledge receipt of them. The absence of any communication for six months would mean that an application must have been unsuccessful.

WHO TO APPLY TO Roger S. Chapman, Trustee, Crouch Chapman, 62 Wilson Street, London EC2A 2BU *Tel.* 020 7782 0007 *email* cct@ rpgcrouchchapman.co.uk *Website* www. chapmancharitabletrust.org.uk

■ John William Chapman's Charitable Trust

CC NO 223002   **ESTABLISHED** 1942

WHERE FUNDING CAN BE GIVEN The borough of Doncaster.

WHO CAN BENEFIT Individuals or other bodies assisting individuals in need.

WHAT IS FUNDED Relief-in-need.

WHAT IS NOT FUNDED The trust funds are to be used for the relief of hardship and distress but will not be given for payments in respect of council tax, income tax or where public funds are available for the relief of that hardship. Grants are not given for large, national appeals.

RANGE OF GRANTS Up to £6,000.

SAMPLE GRANTS Doncaster Women's Aid and Safe@last (£6,000 each); Doncaster Conversation Club and William Nuttall Cottage Homes (£5,000 each); Barnardo's Young Carers Project (£3,000); Cavendish Cancer Care (£2,500); Platform 51 (£2,000) and The Sequal Trust (£1,000).

FINANCES *Year* 2011–12 *Income* £189,101 *Grants* £60,521 *Assets* £3,666,275

TRUSTEES Lady Neill; Miss V. R. Ferres; M. Hunter; M. Gornall; D. Kirk.

OTHER INFORMATION The 2011–12 grant total includes £30,000 that was given to individuals.

HOW TO APPLY On an application form available to download, together with criteria and guidelines, on the website.

WHO TO APPLY TO Rosemarie Sharp, Secretary, c/o Jordans Solicitors, 4 Priory Place, Doncaster DN1 1BP *email* info@chapmantrust.org *Website* chapmantrust.org

■ The Charities Advisory Trust

CC NO 1040487   **ESTABLISHED** 1994

WHERE FUNDING CAN BE GIVEN UK and overseas.

WHO CAN BENEFIT Any charitable purpose is considered, but generally the trust is proactive.

WHAT IS FUNDED General charitable purposes, particularly: income generation projects; homelessness; museums; cancer research and treatment; peace and reconciliation; and refugees.

WHAT IS NOT FUNDED The trustees rarely respond to unsolicited applications for projects of which they have no knowledge. In such cases where support is given, the amounts are usually £200 or less. No support for individuals, large fundraising charities or missionary work.

TYPE OF GRANT Buildings, capital, core costs, endowments, interest-free loans; one-off, project, research, running costs, recurring costs, salaries and start-up costs. Funding is available for up to and over three years.

SAMPLE GRANTS Survivors Fund (£112,000); Africa Education Trust (£50,000); Ashwini (£14,000); Ikamva Labantu (£79,000); Shuhada Organisation (£27,000); and Life for African Mothers (£18,000).

FINANCES *Year* 2011–12 *Income* £1,473,672 *Grants* £1,420,949 *Assets* £2,530,911

TRUSTEES Prof. Cornelia Navari; Dr Carolyne Dennis; Brij Bhasin; Dawn Penso.

HOW TO APPLY The trustees are pro-active in looking for causes to support. They are though 'happy for charities to keep us informed of developments, as we do change our support as new solutions to needs emerge.' **Unsolicited applications for projects of which the trust know nothing are rarely responded to.** 'To apply, simply send details of your proposal (no more than two pages in length) in the form of a letter. You might try to include the following information: the aims and objectives of your organisation; the project for which you need money; who benefits from the project and how; breakdown of the costs and total estimated costs; how much money you need from us; other funding secured for the project a summary of your latest annual accounts. If we refuse you it is not because your project is not worthwhile – it is because we do not have sufficient funds, or it is simply outside our current area of interest.'

WHO TO APPLY TO Dame Hilary Blume, Director, Radius Works, Back Lane, London NW3 1HL *Tel.* 020 7794 9835 *Fax* 020 7431 3739 *email* people@charitiesadvisorytrust.org.uk *Website* www.charitiesadvisorytrust.org.uk

■ Charitworth Limited

CC NO 286908   **ESTABLISHED** 1983

WHERE FUNDING CAN BE GIVEN Worldwide, mainly UK and Israel.

WHO CAN BENEFIT Charitable organisations.

WHAT IS FUNDED Religious, educational and charitable purposes. In practice, mainly Jewish causes.

TYPE OF GRANT One-off and recurring.

RANGE OF GRANTS Up to around £150,000.

SAMPLE GRANTS Previous beneficiaries include: Zichron Nahum; British Friends of Tshernobil; Cosmon Belz; Chevras Maoz Ladal; Dushinsky Trust; Centre for Torah Education Trust; Finchley Road Synagogue; Friends of Viznitz; Beer Yaakov; and Beis Soroh Schneirer.

FINANCES *Year* 2011–12 *Income* £782,185 *Grants* £904,230 *Assets* £25,259,790

TRUSTEES David Halpern; Reilly Halpern; Sidney Halpern; Samuel J. Halpern.

HOW TO APPLY In writing to the correspondent.

WHO TO APPLY TO David Halpern, Trustee, Cohen Arnold and Co., New Burlington House, 1075 Finchley Road, London NW11 0PU *Tel.* 020 8731 0777 *Fax* 020 8731 0778

■ The Charter 600 Charity

CC NO 1051146   **ESTABLISHED** 1994

WHERE FUNDING CAN BE GIVEN UK.

WHO CAN BENEFIT Registered charities. Community-based, grass-roots organisations

WHAT IS FUNDED General charitable purposes, with particular emphasis on education, social and medical welfare support for young people and communities.

WHAT IS NOT FUNDED Applications for charitable grants will only be accepted when put forward by a member of the Mercers' Company.

RANGE OF GRANTS Up to £2,500.

SAMPLE GRANTS Claire House Children's Hospice, Howbury Friends and Meadow Orchard Project (£1,500 each); Emma's Bubble Trust, Headway, Musical Moving and West Lavington Youth Club (£1,000 each); Addis Yimer, Samuel Lithgow Youth Centre and Student Volunteers Abroad (£500 each); and Federation of London Youth Clubs, Friends of Workholt Park and Salmon Youth Centre in Bermondsey (£250 each).

FINANCES *Year* 2011–12 *Income* £136,524 *Grants* £44,000 *Assets* £920,137

TRUSTEE The Mercers Company.

HOW TO APPLY The charity does not consider unsolicited applications.

WHO TO APPLY TO M. McGregor, The Clerk, Mercers' Hall, Ironmongers Lane, London EC2V 8HE *Website* www.mercers.co.uk

■ The Worshipful Company of Chartered Accountants General Charitable Trust (also known as CALC)

CC NO 327681   **ESTABLISHED** 1988
WHERE FUNDING CAN BE GIVEN UK.
WHO CAN BENEFIT Registered charities and voluntary organisations.
WHAT IS FUNDED At least one theme directly or indirectly of relevance to the work of the profession (chosen by the master on their appointment in October of each year). Other recommendations and proposals put to the trustees by members of the Livery.
SAMPLE GRANTS The Master's project (£30,000); Institute of Chartered Accountants bursary (£18,000); MANGO and St Paul's Cathedral Foundation (£5,000 each); and The Lord Mayor's Appeal 2012 (£2,500).
FINANCES *Year* 2011–12 *Income* £119,160 *Grants* £99,168 *Assets* £1,294,728
TRUSTEES Richard Dyson; Richard Green; Adam Vere Broke; Nigel Turnbull; Richard Battersby; Peter Wyman; Andrew Popham.
OTHER INFORMATION £36,000 was distributed between 30 Primary Schools to promote numeracy and literacy.
HOW TO APPLY Applications must be sponsored by a liveryman of the company.
WHO TO APPLY TO Peter Lusty, Clerk, Hampton City Services, Hampton House, High Street, East Grinstead, West Sussex RH19 3AW *Tel*. 01342 319038 *email* peterlusty@btconnect.com

■ The Chasah Trust

CC NO 294898   **ESTABLISHED** 1986
WHERE FUNDING CAN BE GIVEN Greater London and UK.
WHO CAN BENEFIT Evangelists and Christians.
WHAT IS FUNDED The encouragement of poverty relief and missionary activity as well as the advancement of the evangelical tenets of Christianity.
WHAT IS NOT FUNDED Buildings or general appeals are not funded.
RANGE OF GRANTS Up to £15,000.
FINANCES *Year* 2011–12 *Income* £39,456 *Grants* £48,583 *Assets* £18,814
TRUSTEES Karen Collier-Keywood; Richard Collier-Keywood. Laura Collier-Keywood.
OTHER INFORMATION The grant total in 2011–12 includes £35,000 donated to individuals.
HOW TO APPLY In writing to the correspondent.
WHO TO APPLY TO Richard Collier-Keywood, Glydwish Hall, Fontridge Lane, Etchingham, East Sussex TN19 7DG *Tel*. 01435 882768

■ The Chelsea Square 1994 Trust

CC NO 1040479   **ESTABLISHED** 1994
WHERE FUNDING CAN BE GIVEN Southern England, and to a limited extent, overseas.
WHO CAN BENEFIT Charitable organisations.
WHAT IS FUNDED Chiefly projects related to animals and people who are older or underprivileged.
WHAT IS NOT FUNDED No grants to individuals.
TYPE OF GRANT One-off grants.
RANGE OF GRANTS £1,500–£2,000.
SAMPLE GRANTS Macmillan Cancer Support, WaterAid, British Red Cross Libya and Region Appeal, Médecins Sans Frontières and RSPCA (£2,000 each) and A Rocha International, Tazamia Foundation and RSPB (£1,500 each).

FINANCES *Year* 2011–12 *Income* £26,204 *Grants* £32,000 *Assets* £177,606
TRUSTEES Patrick Talbot; Jonathan Woods; John Woods; Evans.
HOW TO APPLY In writing to the correspondent with report and accounts. Unsuccessful applicants will not receive a reply; send an sae if you wish documents to be returned.
WHO TO APPLY TO Paul Shiels, c/o Moon Beaver Solicitors, 21a John Street, London WC1N 2BF *Tel*. 020 7400 7799

■ Cherry Grove Charitable Trust

CC NO 1147640   **ESTABLISHED** 2012
WHERE FUNDING CAN BE GIVEN UK.
WHO CAN BENEFIT Charities and community groups.
WHAT IS FUNDED General charitable purposes.
TRUSTEES Peter Scott; Joan Rowe.
HOW TO APPLY In writing to the correspondent.
WHO TO APPLY TO Peter Scott, Trustee, c/o Cripps Harries Hall, Wallside House, 12 Mount Ephraim Road, Tunbridge Wells, Kent TN1 1EG *Tel*. 01892 506004 *email* peter.scott@crippslaw.com

■ The Cheruby Trust

CC NO 327069   **ESTABLISHED** 1986
WHERE FUNDING CAN BE GIVEN UK and worldwide.
WHO CAN BENEFIT Registered charities.
WHAT IS FUNDED Welfare, education and general charitable purposes.
RANGE OF GRANTS £100–£6,000.
SAMPLE GRANTS World Jewish Relief (£6,000); Alzheimer's Society and Save the Children (£5,000 each); Family Action (£3,500); APT Enterprise Development and Indian Rural Health Trust (£3,000 each); Breadline Africa and National Autistic Society (£2,000 each); Cruse Bereavement Care (£1,000) and London Wildlife Trust (£100).
FINANCES *Year* 2011–12 *Income* £115,392 *Grants* £88,150 *Assets* £42,161
TRUSTEES A. L. Corob; L. E. Corob; T. Corob; C. J. Cook: S. A. Wechsler.
HOW TO APPLY In writing to the correspondent.
WHO TO APPLY TO S. Wechsler, Trustee, 62 Grosvenor Street, London W1K 3JF *Tel*. 020 7499 4301

■ Cheshire Freemason's Charity (formerly Cheshire Provincial Fund of Benevolence)

CC NO 219177   **ESTABLISHED** 1963
WHERE FUNDING CAN BE GIVEN Cheshire and parts of Greater Manchester and Merseyside.
WHO CAN BENEFIT Individuals and organisations benefiting Masons and their families.
WHAT IS FUNDED The relief of Masons and their dependants, Masonic charities and other charities, especially medical.
SAMPLE GRANTS Previous beneficiaries have included Children's Cancer Support Group, Mencap, Wirral Autistic Society, Bollington and Macclesfield Sea Cadets and Cathedral Road Kids Project.
FINANCES *Year* 2011–12 *Income* £403,986 *Grants* £117,559 *Assets* £3,857,370
TRUSTEES Alan Glazier; Peter Carroll; Stephen Kinsey; Eric McConnell; Ivor Henry; Leyland Preston; David Littlewood.

OTHER INFORMATION In 2011–12 the grant total was split between masonic institutions (£68,000) and charities and individuals (£42,000).

HOW TO APPLY In writing to the correspondent.

WHO TO APPLY Peter Carroll, Provincial Grand Secretary, 92 Nuttall Lane, Ramsbottom, Bury, Lancashire BL0 9JZ *Tel.* 01706 823850 *email* enquiries@cheshiremasons.co.uk

■ Chest, Heart and Stroke Scotland

SC NO SC018761   ESTABLISHED 1990

WHERE FUNDING CAN BE GIVEN Scotland.

WHO CAN BENEFIT Academics, research workers and medical professionals living and working in Scotland.

WHAT IS FUNDED Medical research into all aspects of the aetiology, diagnosis, prevention, treatment and social impact of chest, heart and stroke illness. Applications directly relating to improvements in patient care, quality of life and health promotion are particularly welcomed.

WHAT IS NOT FUNDED Research projects involving animals are not funded or research studies whose primary focus is lung or other cancers.

TYPE OF GRANT Research fellowships, project grants, travel and equipment grants, career development awards, research secondments, and student electives. Funding may be given for up to three years.

RANGE OF GRANTS Research grants up to £120,000.

FINANCES *Year* 2011–12 *Income* £7,761,777

HOW TO APPLY Contact the correspondent for further details of how to apply or visit the website where criteria, guidelines and application process are posted.

WHO TO APPLY Research Manager, Third Floor, Roseberry House, 9 Haymarket Terrace, Edinburgh EH12 5EZ *Tel.* 01312 256963 *email* research@chss.org.uk *Website* www.chss.org.uk

■ Chesterhill Charitable Trust

CC NO 1147108   ESTABLISHED 2012

WHERE FUNDING CAN BE GIVEN UK.

WHO CAN BENEFIT Children and young people, young offenders and carers.

WHAT IS FUNDED Social welfare, education and health.

FINANCES *Year* 2012–13 *Income* £100,022 *Grants* £19,000

TRUSTEES Brian Binstock; Pauline Binstock; Roy Peter.

HOW TO APPLY In writing to the correspondent.

WHO TO APPLY Brian Binstock, Trustee, c/o Chesterhill Investments Ltd, Albany House, 10 Wood Street, Barnet, London EN5 4BW *Tel.* 020 8449 9192 *email* info@chesterhill-ct.org.uk

■ The Chetwode Foundation

CC NO 265950   ESTABLISHED 1973

WHERE FUNDING CAN BE GIVEN UK, with a preference for Nottinghamshire, Leicestershire and Derby.

WHO CAN BENEFIT Registered charities only.

WHAT IS FUNDED General charitable purposes with a preference for the disadvantaged and young people.

WHAT IS NOT FUNDED No grants to individuals, national charities or organisations outside the UK.

RANGE OF GRANTS Up to £15,000.

SAMPLE GRANTS The Vineyard Arches Trust and Hope for the Homeless (£15,000 each); The Canaan Trust (£6,200); The Rotary Club of Nottingham Trust Fund (£5,000); Tythby and Cropwell Butler Parochial Church Council (£3,000); Radcliffe on Trent Advice Centre (£1,300) and The Prostate Cancer Charity, Remar Association and Derby Toc-H Children's Camp (£1,000 each).

FINANCES *Year* 2011–12 *Income* £76,704 *Grants* £70,665 *Assets* £1,605,204

TRUSTEES J. G. Ellis; R. N. J. S. Price.

HOW TO APPLY On an application form available to download from the website or by contacting the trust via email or post. The application form is basic, with the majority of detail to be included in a written statement outlining the project on no more than two sides of A4. Consult the application guidelines for an idea of what the trustees want to see. Applications can be submitted at any time and the trust aims to acknowledge all relevant applications within four weeks. If you are unsuccessful at the initial assessment you will be informed within eight weeks of receipt of your application. Multiple grants over successive years will only be considered in exceptional circumstances.

WHO TO APPLY Grants Administrator, Samworth Brothers (Holdings) Ltd, Chetwode House, 1 Samworth Way, Leicester Road, Melton Mowbray LE13 1GA *Tel.* 01664 414500 *email* info@thechetwodefoundation.co.uk *Website* www.thechetwodefoundation.co.uk

■ Cheviot Asset Management Charitable Trust

CC NO 265596   ESTABLISHED 1973

WHERE FUNDING CAN BE GIVEN UK

WHO CAN BENEFIT Charitable organisations.

WHAT IS FUNDED General charitable purposes.

RANGE OF GRANTS £100–£4,000.

SAMPLE GRANTS TBA Tour de Racing and Leukaemia Research (£3,000 each); Colonels Fund Grenadier Guards, Interhealth, Nicholls Spinal Injury Foundation and the Prostate Cancer Charity (£2,000 each), The Watermill Theatre (£1,000); and NSPCC (£250).

FINANCES *Year* 2011–12 *Income* £21,777 *Grants* £21,500

TRUSTEES David Malpas; Gerald Rothwell; Michael Kerr-Dineen; James Mann; Thomas Lahaise.

OTHER INFORMATION The grant total is generally between £20,000 and £30,000 per year.

HOW TO APPLY No unsolicited applications.

WHO TO APPLY James Mann, Trustee, c/o Cheviot Asset Management, 90 Long Acre, London WC2E 9RA *Tel.* 020 7438 5600

■ Child Growth Foundation

CC NO 274325   ESTABLISHED 1977

WHERE FUNDING CAN BE GIVEN UK.

WHO CAN BENEFIT Institutions researching child/adult growth disorders, and people with such diseases.

WHAT IS FUNDED Research into the causes and cure of growth disorders in children within the area of benefit and to publish the results of such research. The conditions covered by the foundation are: Turner syndrome; Russell Silver syndrome/intrauterine growth retardation; bone dysplasia; Sotos syndrome; premature sexual maturity; growth/multiple pituitary hormone deficiency.

TYPE OF GRANT Research.

RANGE OF GRANTS Up to £96,000.

SAMPLE GRANTS Bradford Hospitals NHS Trust (£47,000); University of Birmingham (£20,000); Institute of Child Health (£5,000); and King's College Hospital (£2,000).

FINANCES *Year* 2011–12 *Income* £189,135 *Grants* £99,197 *Assets* £436,391

TRUSTEES Tam Fry; Nick Child; Russell Chaplin; Rachel Pidcock; Linda Washington; Mark Coyle; Sue Davies; Nikos Tzvadis; Kevin Kirk; Simon Lane.

HOW TO APPLY In writing to the correspondent.

WHO TO APPLY TO Tam Fry, Trustee, 2 Mayfield Avenue, Chiswick W4 1PY *Tel.* 020 8995 0257 *email* tamfry@childgrowthfoundation.org *Website* www.childgrowthfoundation.org

---

■ Children's Liver Disease Foundation

CC NO 1067331   **ESTABLISHED** 1998

WHERE FUNDING CAN BE GIVEN UK.

WHO CAN BENEFIT Organisations benefiting children (up to the age of 18) with liver disease.

WHAT IS FUNDED Clinical and laboratory-based research and social research which looks at topics such as how to improve quality of life.

WHAT IS NOT FUNDED The charity does not accept applications from organisations whose work is not associated with paediatric liver disease. No grants to individuals, whether medical professionals or patients. No grants for travel or personal education. No grants for general appeals.

TYPE OF GRANT Research and project (maximum three years). Occasionally medical equipment.

RANGE OF GRANTS Small grant programme: up to £5,000.

SAMPLE GRANTS King's College Hospital; University of Birmingham; University College Medical School.

FINANCES *Year* 2011–12 *Income* £649,156 *Grants* £169,591 *Assets* £487,845

TRUSTEES Thomas Ross; David Tildesley; Mairi Everard; Kellie Charge; Nicholas Budd; Georgina Sugden.

PUBLICATIONS Research priorities for 2011–14 are available to download from the website.

HOW TO APPLY Applicants are strongly advised to look at the relevant pages on the Children's Liver Disease Foundation website where further information and application forms are available.

WHO TO APPLY TO Alison Taylor, Administrator, 36 Great Charles Street, Queensway, Birmingham B3 3JY *Tel.* 01212 123839 *Fax* 01212 124300 *email* info@ childliverdisease.org *Website* www. childliverdisease.org

---

■ The Children's Research Fund

CC NO 226128   **ESTABLISHED** 1962

WHERE FUNDING CAN BE GIVEN UK.

WHO CAN BENEFIT Institutes of child health and university child health departments.

WHAT IS FUNDED Promoting, encouraging and fostering research into all aspects of diseases in children, child health and prevention of illness in children. Support of research centres and research units by grants to academic institutions, hospitals and other bodies with similar aims and objects to the fund. Support after the first year is dependent on receipt of a satisfactory report.

WHAT IS NOT FUNDED No grants for capital projects.

TYPE OF GRANT Research.

SAMPLE GRANTS The British Association of Paediatric Surgeons and The Peninsula Foundation (£30,000 each); Dubai – War Damaged Children (£9,600); The Not Forgotten Association (£3,000); Alder Hey Children's Hospital (£2,100) and Coming Home (£2,000).

FINANCES *Year* 2011–12 *Income* £53,229 *Grants* £82,722 *Assets* £1,366,923

TRUSTEES Hugo Greenwood; Gerald Inkin; Hugo Greenwood; Elizabeth Theobald; David Lloyd.

HOW TO APPLY Applicants from child health research units and university departments are invited to send in an initial outline of their proposal; if it is eligible they will then be sent an application form. Applications are considered in March and November.

WHO TO APPLY TO The Trustees, 6 Scarthill Property, New Lane, Aughton, Ormskirk L39 4UD *Tel.* 01695 420928 *email* children'sresearchfund@btinternet.com *Website* www.children'sresearchfund.org.uk

---

■ The Childs Charitable Trust

CC NO 234618   **ESTABLISHED** 1962

WHERE FUNDING CAN BE GIVEN Worldwide.

WHO CAN BENEFIT Churches or Christian organisations.

WHAT IS FUNDED Christian activity at home and overseas, especially the furtherance of the Christian Gospel.

TYPE OF GRANT One-off and recurrent. Preference for large-scale project grants.

SAMPLE GRANTS Amano Christian School (£67,000); Redcliffe College (£58,000); Mission Aviation Fellowship (£38,000); Memralife Group (£33,000); LAMA Ministries (£27,000); Institute for Bible Translation and Outreach UK – Home Evangelism (£25,000 each); Cross Teach (£21,000); Slavic Gospel Association (£14,000); Scripture Gift Mission (£13,000); Moorlands College (£10,000); Operation Mobilisation (£9,000); People Matter (£7,000); Christian Institute, Elam Ministries, Frontiers, Hope FM, London City Mission and Shared Hope (£5,000 each); and Sports Reach (£2,000).

FINANCES *Year* 2011–12 *Income* £409,038 *Grants* £740,000 *Assets* £9,155,557

TRUSTEES Derek N. Martin; John Harris; Chris Large; Andrew B. Griffiths; Steve Puttock.

OTHER INFORMATION Grants were made totalling over £740,000 which included £70,000 to organisations outside the UK and £750 to individuals.

HOW TO APPLY In writing to the correspondent. The trust states that all applications are considered but it is impossible to respond positively to them all.

WHO TO APPLY TO Melanie Churchyard, Secretary, 3 Cornfield Terrace, Eastbourne, East Sussex BN21 4NN *Tel.* 01323 417944 *email* info@ childstrust.org *Website* childscharitabletrust.org

---

■ The Childwick Trust

CC NO 326853   **ESTABLISHED** 1985

WHERE FUNDING CAN BE GIVEN UK; South Africa.

WHO CAN BENEFIT Registered charities only.

WHAT IS FUNDED In the UK, health, people with disabilities and older people, welfare and research in connection with the (horses) bloodstock industry and Jewish charities; in South Africa, education.

WHAT IS NOT FUNDED Grants to registered charities only. No funding for: complementary health and therapy projects; charities offering legal advice; charities offering counselling; hospices outside the South East of England; NHS Hospitals and other statutory bodies; universities – academic research, scholarships and bursaries; homeless charities; projects related to drugs or alcohol addiction; HIV/Aids related projects; charities which are part of a wider network i.e. Age UK, Mind, Mencap etc., only those who are based within the South East can apply; individuals or organisations applying on behalf of an individual (other than in relation to South African educational grants); students seeking sponsorship for educational or gap year projects; animal charities unless they are connected to thoroughbred racehorses; larger charities with widespread support are less likely to be considered unless they support local causes in Hertfordshire/ Bedfordshire; national appeals; conferences, Seminars and workshops; organisations that have received a grant within the previous two years; apart from South Africa, funding outside the UK.

TYPE OF GRANT Mainly one-off, project and capital for research and medical equipment.

SAMPLE GRANTS UK: Racing Welfare – Newmarket (£200,000); British Racing School – Newmarket (£100,000); Early Learning Resource Unit (£40,000); Iain Rennie Grove House Hospice – St Albans (£30,000); Deafblind UK – Peterborough and St Elizabeth's Centre – Hertfordshire (£20,000 each); J's Hospice – Chelmsford (£18,000); and Hop, Skip and Jump – Gloucestershire and Not Forgotten Association – London (£15,000 each). South Africa: Ntataise Trust (£65,500); Tree – South Africa (£41,000); Little Elephant Training Centre (£29,000); Sekhukhune Educare Project (£21,000); Thusanang Association (£20,000); and Sego Monene and Sunshine Centre Association (£16,000 each).

FINANCES *Year* 2011–12 *Income* £1,994,831 *Grants* £2,395,176 *Assets* £70,416,373

TRUSTEES John Wood, Chair; Anthony Cane; Peter Glossop; Sarah Frost; Peter Anwyl-Harris.

OTHER INFORMATION The total grants figure includes £9,000 in welfare payments to pensioners.

HOW TO APPLY In writing to the correspondent. Note: the trust welcomes initial enquiries by email or telephone, but asks that formal applications are sent by post. There is no official application form but the trust does provide the following guidelines for potential applicants: applications should be written, with a fully completed cover sheet (available from the trust's website); applications should be no longer than two pages of A4; applications must clearly and concisely describe the project for which funding is being sought; applications should include breakdown of costings for the project; applications *should not* include charity accounts; applications *should not* include DVDs, newsletters or bulky reports. Applications that do not meet these requirements will not be considered for funding – should the trust require any further documentation, staff will request it. Send to Karen Groom after following the guidelines given in the PDF document 'Guidelines for Applicants' available from the trust's website. The trustees meet in January and July to consider applications which can be submitted between the months of April – May and October – November. Applications are assessed before each meeting to check that they meet the trust's objectives. Applicants will be informed of the outcome within six weeks following the meeting.

Applications for funding in South Africa should be made to Mrs G. Bland (Fund Director) at jimjoel@iafrica.com.

WHO TO APPLY TO Karen Groom, Trust Administrator, 9 The Green, Childwick Bury, St Albans, Hertfordshire AL3 6JJ *Tel.* 01727 844666 *email* karen@childwicktrust.org *Website* www.childwicktrust.org

....

■ The Chippenham Borough Lands Charity

CC NO 270062   **ESTABLISHED** 1990

WHERE FUNDING CAN BE GIVEN Chippenham parish.

WHO CAN BENEFIT Individuals or community/ charitable organisations which benefit the people of the Parish of Chippenham. Individuals must be living within the Parish of Chippenham at the date of application, and for a minimum of two years immediately prior to applying.

WHAT IS FUNDED The charity's income can be used by, or for the benefit of, the inhabitants of the Parish of Chippenham for: (i) relief of the aged, sick, disabled or poor; (ii) provision of facilities for recreation or other leisure time occupation; (iii) the advancement of education; (iv) the promotion of any other charitable purpose.

WHAT IS NOT FUNDED No help can be given for the following: individual adult sportsmen/woman; direct subsidy to local authorities; religious organisations (except for projects involving substantial non-denominational use for community benefit); retrospective applications; first degrees.

RANGE OF GRANTS Usually £100–£20,000

SAMPLE GRANTS Relate, Mid-Wiltshire (£17,000); The Rise Trust (£12,000); Wiltshire CAB (£10,000); Chippenham Folk Festival (£7,000); North Wiltshire Holiday Club (£6,000); Abbeyfield School (£5,000); St Andrew's Parish Church (£3,000); Monkton Park School (£2,500); The Golden Oldies Charity (£1,500) and Chippenham Town Bowls Club and Chippenham Gateway Club (£1,000 each).

FINANCES *Year* 2011–12 *Income* £426,704 *Grants* £205,294 *Assets* £12,140,769

TRUSTEES Chris Dawe; Mike Braun; Jack Konynenburg; Desna Allen; Graham Bone; Jenny Budgell; Stuart Anglin; Jan Morgan; Sue Hollands; Ian Humphrey.

OTHER INFORMATION In 2011–12 a total of £168,000 was given to 74 organisations. The remainder went to individuals.

HOW TO APPLY On a form available from the correspondent, either via an agency or self-referral.

WHO TO APPLY TO Catherine Flynn, Jubilee Building, 32 Market Place, Chippenham, Wiltshire SN15 3HP *Tel.* 01249 658180 *Fax* 01249 446048 *email* pam@cblc.org.uk *Website* www.cblc.org.uk

....

■ The Chipping Sodbury Town Lands Charity

CC NO 236364   **ESTABLISHED** 1977

WHERE FUNDING CAN BE GIVEN The parishes of Chipping Sodbury and Old Sodbury.

WHO CAN BENEFIT Individuals and organisations.

WHAT IS FUNDED The trust gives grants for relief-in-need and educational purposes, and also other purposes within Sodbury, including the provision of leisure facilities.

Think carefully about every application. Is it justified?

445

TYPE OF GRANT Buildings, capital, one-off and recurring costs will be considered.

RANGE OF GRANTS £350–£20,000

SAMPLE GRANTS Chipping Sodbury Endowed School (£20,000); Sodbury Town Council Playscheme (£4,000 each); Old Sodbury School (£3,000); St John the Baptist Nativity Celebration (£1,000).

FINANCES *Year* 2012 *Income* £356,858 *Grants* £72,910 *Assets* £8,277,716

TRUSTEES Paul Tily; David Shipp; Bill Ainsley; Michelle Cook; Wendy Whittle; Colin Hatfield; Jim Elsworth; Bryan Seymour; Paul Robins.

OTHER INFORMATION In 2012 £24,309 was made in grants to individuals.

HOW TO APPLY In writing to the correspondent. The trustees meet on the third week of each month except August.

WHO TO APPLY TO Nicola Gideon, Clerk, Town Hall, 57–59 Broad Street, Chipping Sodbury, Bristol, South Gloucestershire BS37 6AD *Tel.* 01454 852223 *email* nicola.gideon@chippingsodburytownhall.co.uk

··

■ CHK Charities Limited

CC NO 1050900   **ESTABLISHED** 1995

WHERE FUNDING CAN BE GIVEN UK, with a special interest in national charities and the West Midlands.

WHO CAN BENEFIT Registered charities.

WHAT IS FUNDED Charities working in countryside matters, drug prevention, education, job creation, population control, culture, conservation, deafness, blindness, and the provision of treatment and care for people with disabilities.

WHAT IS NOT FUNDED The following will not normally be considered for funding: organisations not registered as charities or those that have been registered for less than a year; pre-school groups; out of school play schemes including pre-school and holiday schemes; 'bottomless pits' and unfocussed causes; very small and narrowly specialised activities; community centres; local authorities; umbrella or grantmaking organisations; universities and colleges and grant maintained private or local education authority schools or their Parent Teachers Associations, except if these schools are for students with special needs; individuals or charities applying on behalf of individuals; general requests for donations; professional associations and training of professionals; projects which are abroad even though the charity is based in the UK; expeditions or overseas travel; 'campaigning organisations' or Citizens Advice projects providing legal advice; community transport projects; general counselling projects, except those in areas of considerable deprivation and with a clearly defined client group.

TYPE OF GRANT One-off, conditionally renewable and large grants.

RANGE OF GRANTS Mostly £3,000–£5,000. Can be over £100,000.

SAMPLE GRANTS Charities Aid Foundation and Marie Curie Cancer Centre (£105,000 each); Home-Start UK (£75,000); Margaret Pyke Trust (£60,000); Calvert Trust, Skill Force Development and St Clement and St James' Community Development Project (£50,000 each); Reeds School (£20,000); Academy of Ancient Music, Beechen Cliff School, Chipping Norton Theatre Trust, Hospital of St Cross and Almshouse of Noble Poverty, House of Illustration, Interact Worldwide, Support Parents Autistic Children Everywhere, Royal National College for the Blind, Well Child and Winston's Wish (£10,000 each); Almshouse Association, Chaos Theory, Great Oaks Dean Forest Hospice, Listening Post, Motobility, Nordoff-Robbins Music Therapy, Peach, Royal Opera House, Sportsaid South West and YMCA (£5,000 each); Volunteer Reading Help (£4,000); Children's Country Holidays Fund and Woodland Heritage Limited (£3,000 each); Leys Youth Programme (£2,000); and Garsington Opera Limited (£1,000).

FINANCES *Year* 2011–12 *Income* £2,225,608 *Grants* £1,650,458 *Assets* £77,630,780

TRUSTEES David Peake; Charlotte Percy; David Acland; Joanna Prest; Katharine Loyd; Lucy Morris; Rupert Prest; Serena Acland; Susanna Peake.

OTHER INFORMATION This trust has a very useful website that should be referred to when considering making an application.

HOW TO APPLY The following information is taken from the trust's website:
'Preference is given to National or West Midlands charities, and the organisation will normally be based within the United Kingdom. The trust does not have an application form, but suggests that the following guidelines be used when making an application which should be in writing to the secretary: applications should be no longer than four A4 sides, and should incorporate a short (half page) summary; applications should also include a detailed budget for the project and the applicant's most recent audited accounts. If those accounts show a significant surplus or deficit of income, explain how this has arisen. Applicants should: state clearly who they are, what they do and whom they seek to help; give the applicant's status, e.g., registered charity; confirm that the organisation has a Child Protection Policy (where appropriate) and that Criminal Record Bureau checks are carried out on all staff working with children; describe clearly the project for which the grant is sought answering the following questions: What is the aim of the project and why is it needed? What practical results will it produce? How many people will benefit from it? What stage has the project reached so far? How will you ensure that it is cost-effective?; if the request is for a salary, enclose a job description; explain how the project will be monitored, evaluated and how its results will be disseminated; state what funds have already been raised for the project, and name any other sources of funding applied for; explain where ongoing funding (if required) will be obtained when the Charity's grant has been used; if the request is for revenue funding for a specific item, state the amount needed.'
'Keep the application as simple as possible and avoid the use of technical terms, acronyms and jargon. If you are sending videos or CD-ROMs, provide a stamped address envelope so that they may be returned.'

WHO TO APPLY TO Nick R. Kerr-Sheppard, Administrator, Kleinwort Benson Trustees Ltd, 14 St George Street, London W1S 1FE *Tel.* 020 3207 7338 *Fax* 020 3207 7655 *Website* www.chkcharities.co.uk

··

■ The Jimmy Choo Foundation

CC NO 1146842   **ESTABLISHED** 2012

WHERE FUNDING CAN BE GIVEN Worldwide.

WHO CAN BENEFIT Charities and community groups.

WHAT IS FUNDED Women, social welfare and human rights.

········

446   *Does the trust you have chosen match your needs? Haphazard applications waste postage and time*

FINANCES *Year* 2012 *Income* £98,650 *Grants* £0 *Assets* £98,650

TRUSTEES Hannah Merritt; Pierre Denis; Sandra Yuk-San Choi.

HOW TO APPLY In writing to the correspondent.

WHO TO APPLY TO The Trustees, c/o Jimmy Choo Ltd, Interfocus House, 4 Lancer Square, London W8 4EH *Tel.* 020 7368 5000 *email* jimmychoofoundation@jimmychoo.com *Website* www.jimmychoo.com/icons/jimmy-choo-the-foundation/page/foundations

■ The Chownes Foundation

CC NO 327451 **ESTABLISHED** 1987

WHERE FUNDING CAN BE GIVEN UK, priority is given to charities based in Sussex, particularly in mid-Sussex.

WHO CAN BENEFIT Organisations and individuals.

WHAT IS FUNDED The advancement of religion, the advancement of education among the young, the amelioration of social problems, and the relief of poverty amongst older people and the former members of Sound Diffusion plc who lost their pensions when the company went into receivership. Preference will be given to projects where a donation may have some meaningful impact on an identified need rather than simply being absorbed into a larger funding requirement. Applications from smaller charities whose aims mirror those of the founder, Paul Stonor, will be favoured.

TYPE OF GRANT One-off, recurrent, buildings, capital, core costs, research and running costs. Funding is available for up to and over three years.

RANGE OF GRANTS Up to £10,000.

SAMPLE GRANTS Age Unlimited (£10,000 in two grants); Worth Abbey (£3,500); CamFed and FareShare Brighton and Hove (£3,000 each); Amnesty International (£2,500) and the Howard League for Penal Reform and Mencap (£1,000 each).

FINANCES *Year* 2011–12 *Income* £30,750 *Grants* £72,586 *Assets* £1,566,006

TRUSTEES U. Hazeel; The Rt Revd S. Ortiger; M. Woolley.

OTHER INFORMATION £27,000 of the grant total was given to individuals.

HOW TO APPLY In writing to the correspondent.

WHO TO APPLY TO Sylvia Spencer, Secretary, The Courtyard, Beeding Court, Shoreham Road, Steyning, West Sussex BN44 3TN *Tel.* 01903 816699 *email* chownes@russellnew.com

■ The Chrimes Family Charitable Trust

CC NO 210199 **ESTABLISHED** 1955

WHERE FUNDING CAN BE GIVEN Merseyside, Wirral and North Wales.

WHO CAN BENEFIT Registered charities.

WHAT IS FUNDED The relief of poverty and distress and in the provision of funds towards projects for community welfare and the improvement of health and education with a preference for the support of community welfare in Merseyside and North Wales.

WHAT IS NOT FUNDED No grants to individuals, arts, or conservation.

RANGE OF GRANTS Up to £1,000.

FINANCES *Year* 2012–13 *Income* £36,223 *Grants* £31,398 *Assets* £882,466

TRUSTEES Anne Williams; Helen Prosser.

HOW TO APPLY In writing to the correspondent.

WHO TO APPLY TO Anne Williams, Trustee, Northfield, Upper Raby Road, Neston, Wirral CH64 7TZ

■ The Christabella Charitable Trust

CC NO 800610 **ESTABLISHED** 1988

WHERE FUNDING CAN BE GIVEN General, mainly Essex and the surrounding areas.

WHO CAN BENEFIT Registered charities, local organisations and individuals.

WHAT IS FUNDED Christian causes are much favoured and there are several local organisations regularly supported including St Francis Church in West Horndon and Viz-a-Viz's evangelical work. The trustees prefer 'seed corn' funding of projects involving volunteers. Normally only one or two additional projects of special interest to the trust are supported each year.

WHAT IS NOT FUNDED No support for UK-wide or international charities. Applications for grants towards general running costs or building refurbishment are very unlikely to be supported.

TYPE OF GRANT The trust prefer 'seed corn' funding of projects involving volunteers.

RANGE OF GRANTS Up to £20,000.

SAMPLE GRANTS National Garden Scheme and St Francis Church (£10,000 each); LDF Charitable Trust (£9,000); Viz-a-Viz (£7,500); and the Nippon Sei Kokai (5,200).

FINANCES *Year* 2011–12 *Income* £284,911 *Grants* £54,796 *Assets* £5,134,453

TRUSTEES Ernest Munroe; Christine Turner; Richard Hilburn; Ian Elliot; Robert Folwell.

OTHER INFORMATION This trust's primary objective is to maintain the charity's property at Barnards Farm in West Horndon as the house of the National Malus Collection, to allow the general public access on various published dates each year and for use by other charitable organisations.

HOW TO APPLY In writing to the correspondent, from whom an application form is available.

WHO TO APPLY TO Robert Folwell, Trustee, 24 Leasway, Rayleigh, Essex SS6 7DW *Tel.* 01268 906593 *Fax* 01268 776400 *email* bobfolwell@hotmail.com *Website* www.barnardsfarm.eu/christabella.htm

■ Christadelphian Samaritan Fund

CC NO 1004457 **ESTABLISHED** 1991

WHERE FUNDING CAN BE GIVEN UK and overseas.

WHO CAN BENEFIT Registered charities.

WHAT IS FUNDED Preference is given to human causes and aid to third world.

WHAT IS NOT FUNDED Individuals and non-registered charities are not eligible for support.

TYPE OF GRANT Single donations.

SAMPLE GRANTS MSF – Sudan Appeal (£6,400); British Red Cross – Hurricane Sandy Appeal and UNICEF – West Africa and Syria (£5,000 each) and British Red Cross – Turkey Earthquake Appeal (£2,000).

FINANCES *Year* 2012 *Income* £67,305 *Grants* £85,128 *Assets* £47,998

TRUSTEES K. H. A. Smith; David Ensell; Judith Norcross; William Moss; Dr John Hellawell; John Buckler; Roger Miles; Pauline Bromage; Elizabeth Briley.

HOW TO APPLY In writing to the correspondent.

WHO TO APPLY TO K. H. A. Smith, Treasurer, Westhaven House, Arleston Way, Shirley, Solihull, West Midlands B90 4LH *Tel.* 01217 137100

■ Christian Aid

cc no 1105851 ESTABLISHED 1945
WHERE FUNDING CAN BE GIVEN Mainly Third World. Limited assistance for development education projects in the UK.
WHO CAN BENEFIT Councils of Churches; other ecumenical bodies, development and relief groups; UN agencies which benefit at risk groups; people disadvantaged by poverty; homeless people; refugees; immigrants; socially isolated people; victims of famine, man-made or natural disasters, and war.
WHAT IS FUNDED Organisations which work with the world's poorest people and communities. Funding is given to partner organisations only.
WHAT IS NOT FUNDED Individuals, political causes or organisations whose aims are primarily political are not eligible for grants.
TYPE OF GRANT Project.
FINANCES Year 2011–12 Income £95,453,000 Grants £45,700,000
TRUSTEES Revd John Davies; Bob Fyfe; Carolyn Gray; Tom Hinton; Kumar Jacob; Gillian Kingston; Morag Mylne; Bishop Wilton Powell; Revd Alastair Redfern; Brian Ridsdale; Charlotte Seymour-Smith; Paul Spray; Bishop Trevor Williams; Dr Rowan Williams; Alan McDonald; Victoria Hardman; Mervyn McCullach.
HOW TO APPLY Initial approaches by potential partner organisations should be made in writing.
WHO TO APPLY TO Martin Birch, Director of Finance and Operations, 35–41 Lower Marsh, London SE1 7RL Tel. 020 7620 4444 email info@christian-aid.org Website www.christianaid.org.uk

■ Christian Response to Eastern Europe

cc no 1062623 ESTABLISHED 1997
WHERE FUNDING CAN BE GIVEN Eastern Europe (in practice Romania and Moldova).
WHO CAN BENEFIT Christian organisations working in Eastern Europe.
WHAT IS FUNDED The objects of the charity are to provide relief to disadvantages and vulnerable people living in Eastern Europe. Help is given by supporting families, churches and medical organisations.
SAMPLE GRANTS Gura Bicului Centre (£20,000); Gura Bicului VW Transporter (£8,000); Soup Kitchen (£4,000); Orhei Church and Soup Kitchen (£3,000); and Children's Parties (£500).
FINANCES Year 2012 Income £143,177 Grants £136,963 Assets £40,948
TRUSTEES David Northcote Passmore, Chair; Timothy Mason; Hugh Scudder.
OTHER INFORMATION The 2012 grant total includes £87,500 given to individuals and families.
HOW TO APPLY In writing to the correspondent.
WHO TO APPLY TO David Northcote-Passmore, Trustee, Cherith, 130 Honiton Road, Exeter EX1 3EW Tel. 01392 367692 email davidnpass@aol.com Website www.cr2ee.org.uk

■ Christie Foundation

cc no 1151063 ESTABLISHED 2013
WHERE FUNDING CAN BE GIVEN Worldwide.
WHO CAN BENEFIT Registered charities
WHAT IS FUNDED General, education, health, social welfare.

TRUSTEES Iain Abrahams; Alexandra Christie Abrahams; Richard Stern.
HOW TO APPLY In writing to the correspondent.
WHO TO APPLY TO Iain Abrahams, Trustee, 27 Queensdale Place, London W11 4SQ Tel. 020 3586 8041

■ Chrysalis Trust

cc no 1133525 ESTABLISHED 2010
WHERE FUNDING CAN BE GIVEN North East of England, UK national organisations providing benefit across the UK, overseas.
WHO CAN BENEFIT Charities, community groups and educational projects.
WHAT IS FUNDED General, education, social welfare
WHAT IS NOT FUNDED Grants are not made for: research – academic or medical; holidays or outings; arts or entertainment activities; animal welfare; general appeals.
TYPE OF GRANT One-off grants to support capital costs and core funding.
RANGE OF GRANTS Up to £20,000.
SAMPLE GRANTS Cry in the Dark (£20,000); Greggs Foundation (£10,000); Huntington's Association (£4,000); Wamba Community Trust (£2,000); and Sunshine Fund (£1,000).
FINANCES Year 2011–12 Income £37,490 Grants £63,084 Assets £1,364,549
TRUSTEES Mark Price Evans; Sarah Evans; Andrew Playle; Alba Lewis.
HOW TO APPLY The trust provides the following helpful information on its website:
'**Application Checklist:** There is no application form. Outline your project on no more than 4 A4 sides using the following checklist: what is the name of your organisation and what is your charitable registration number if you have one?; what does your organisation do?; who are you helping, how many and how?; how many staff and volunteers do you have?; which statutory and voluntary organisations do you have links with, if any?; how much money do you need? [e.g., a contribution of £X towards a total budget of £Y]. Where will the balance of the funds required come from? what do you need the money for?; when do you need the money?; have you applied to other sources? If so, give details and outcomes; who is your key contact regarding this application and what are their contact details (including telephone, email and mailing address)? Attach: a 250 word summary of your proposal; the contact details of two organisations or individuals able to provide a reference on your behalf; a copy of your latest audited annual report and accounts or a copy of your most recent bank statement if you do not have accounts; a budget for the project for which the application is made; a do not attach any unnecessary documentation. Applications should then be submitted preferably by email; if necessary, applications may be sent by post. **What will happen next?** You will receive an acknowledgement that your application has been received. Applications are considered by the Trustees twice a year – usually in June and December, however, applications for amounts less than £1,001 may be considered sooner. We may contact you by telephone or email to discuss your application or to arrange a visit. We aim to let applicants know whether or not their application has been successful within two weeks of the trustees meeting at which the application is being considered.
What are the terms and conditions of a grant? Successful applicants will be asked to sign a simple grant agreement setting out their obligations in relation to the grant. Grants must

be used for the purposes outlined in the application. If the project is unable to go ahead as planned we are happy to consider variations as to how the money is to be spent, however, the money must not be used for any other purposes without our agreement. It must be returned if the project does not go ahead. Recipients of a grant will be required to provide a report on the funded project to the trustees within six months of receiving the grant.'

WHO TO APPLY TO Sarah Evans, Trustee, Piper Close House, Aydon Road, Corbridge, Northumberland NE45 5PW *email* info@chrysalis-trust.co.uk *Website* www.chrysalis-trust.co.uk

■ The Church and Community Fund

CC NO 1074857   **ESTABLISHED** 1915
WHERE FUNDING CAN BE GIVEN England and Wales.
WHO CAN BENEFIT Parish, deanery or diocesan projects.
WHAT IS FUNDED Church and community projects.
WHAT IS NOT FUNDED No funding is given towards: projects that are essentially insular and inward looking; projects which are primarily about maintaining the nation's architectural heritage; projects which are primarily about liturgical reordering; restoration works to bells or organs; research projects or personal grants; the repayment of debts or overdrafts; projects which are not directly connected with the Church of England, ecumenical or other faith; partnerships in which the Church of England element is small and projects which are predominantly secular in nature; anything for which the Church Commissioners' funds or diocesan core funding are normally available, including stipend support; feasibility studies (the fund is able to offer limited support towards the preliminary costs of projects, for example professional fees, but where a grants is awarded at this stage, no further funding will be available for the main body of the work).
TYPE OF GRANT One-off and reoccurring.
RANGE OF GRANTS Usually less than £5,000.
SAMPLE GRANTS Chapel Street Community Arts – Salford and Luton Roma Church – St Albans (£15,000 each); CHAT Trust – Newcastle (£13,000); Three Spires Tots – Coventry (£12,000); and Narthex Centre – Sparkhill and YeovilNET – Bath and Wells (£10,000 each).
FINANCES *Year* 2012 *Income* £90,000 *Grants* £506,000 *Assets* £17,373,000
TRUSTEE The Archbishop's Council.
OTHER INFORMATION This fund is an excepted charity but its trustee, the Archbishop's Council, is registered under the above number. Brief accounting details for the fund were included in the notes to the accounts for the Archbishops' Council, of which the fund is a subsidiary.
HOW TO APPLY Full details of how to apply can be found on the fund's website and applicants are advised to refer to these before applying. If you feel that your project meets the aims of the funding themes and match the criteria detailed in the guidelines, then complete the eligibility quiz and online application.
WHO TO APPLY TO Andrew Hawkings, Grants Manager, Church House, Great Smith Street, London SW1P 3AZ *Tel.* 020 7898 1541 *email* ccf@churchofengland.org *Website* www.centralchurchfund.org.uk

■ The Church Burgesses Educational Foundation

CC NO 529357   **ESTABLISHED** 1963
WHERE FUNDING CAN BE GIVEN Sheffield.
WHO CAN BENEFIT Individuals and schools benefiting children and young adults.
WHAT IS FUNDED Church schools, independent schools, junior schools, language schools, primary and secondary schools, special schools, tertiary and higher education, and youth organisations. Also funded are bursaries, fees, scholarships, and the purchase of books.
TYPE OF GRANT Core costs, one-off and running costs. Funding may be given for up to three years.
RANGE OF GRANTS Up to £10,000.
SAMPLE GRANTS Previous beneficiaries have included Dyslexia Institute, the Flower Estate Community Association, Pitstop, Sheffield County Guide Association, Sheffield YMCA, South Yorkshire and Hallam Clubs for Young People, Whirlow Hall Farm Trust and Wybourn Youth Trust.
FINANCES *Year* 2012 *Income* £283,008 *Grants* £343,278 *Assets* £282,019
TRUSTEES Prof. G. D. Sims; Revd S. A. P. Hunter; B. R. Hickman; D. Stanley; D. Heslop; W. Thomas; Prof. D. Luscombe.
OTHER INFORMATION In 2012 grants were made in the following categories: Church Schools Grant (£24,400); Donations to Youth Organisations (£14,500); Individual Grants for Education (£98,000); Special Individual Grants (£19,000); Special Grants (£36,000); Church-based youth work (£89,000); Music in the City (£62,500).
HOW TO APPLY On forms available to download, together with criteria and guidelines, from the website. Trustees meet four times a year. Initial telephone calls are welcome.
WHO TO APPLY TO Godfrey Smallman, Law Clerk, Sheffield Church Burgesses Trust, 3rd Floor, Fountain Precinct, Balm Green, Sheffield S1 2JA *Tel.* 01142 675594 *Fax* 01142 763176 *email* sheffieldchurchburgesses@wrigleys.co.uk *Website* www.sheffieldchurchburgesses.org.uk

■ Church Burgesses Trust

CC NO 221284   **ESTABLISHED** 1554
WHERE FUNDING CAN BE GIVEN Sheffield.
WHO CAN BENEFIT Voluntary organisations, registered charities and churches.
WHAT IS FUNDED Ecclesiastical purposes, education, and other charitable purposes.
TYPE OF GRANT One-off and recurring.
SAMPLE GRANTS St Luke's Hospice (£35,000); University of Sheffield Chaplaincy (£16,000); Attercliffe Deanery (£12,500); Families Action Support – Sheffield (£7,000); Macmillan Cancer Relief and Whirlow Grange Limited (£5,000 each); Share Psychotherapy (£4,000); Shine (£2,500); Action for Children, Action for Stannington, FareShare South Yorkshire, Grenoside Community Association, Sheffield Mencap and Gateway and Trinity Day Care Trust (£2,000 each); and Whizz-Kidz (£1,500).
FINANCES *Year* 2012 *Income* £2,257,230 *Grants* £1,089,066 *Assets* £39,462,318
TRUSTEES D. F. Booker; Revd S. A. P. Hunter; Nicholas J. A. Hutton; Julie Banham; Peter W. Lee; J. F. W. Peters; Prof. G. D. Sims; Ian G. Walker; Mike R. Woffenden; D. Stanley; B. R. Hickman; S. Bain.
PUBLICATIONS *We of Our Bounty* – a history of the Sheffield Church Burgesses.
HOW TO APPLY In writing to the correspondent. The trustees meet in January, April, July and October

Think carefully about every application. Is it justified?

449

and at other times during the year through its various committees. The day to day administration of the trust, work in connection with its assets, liaison with outside bodies such as the Diocese of Sheffield, the administration of its grant programmes and the processing and handling of applications prior to their consideration by relevant committees is delegated to the Law Clerk. Completed application forms and all supporting papers need to be received by the Law Clerk before the beginning of the second week of December, March, June and September. The trust invites applications from Anglican parishes, from individuals involved in Christian work of a wide variety of types and from charities both national and local, involved in general charitable work within the trust's geographical area of remit. Further information, guidelines for applying and application forms are available on the trust's website.

WHO TO APPLY TO Godfrey Smallman, Law Clerk, Sheffield Church Burgesses Trust, 3rd Floor, Fountain Precinct, Balm Green, Sheffield S1 2JA *Tel.* 01142 675594 *Fax* 01142 763176 *email* godfrey.smallman@wrigleys.co.uk *Website* www.sheffieldchurchburgesses.org.uk

■ Church of Ireland Priorities Fund

ESTABLISHED 1980
WHERE FUNDING CAN BE GIVEN Ireland.
WHO CAN BENEFIT Charitable organisations.
WHAT IS FUNDED Church of Ireland projects. Areas currently supported by the fund are: ministry; retirement; education; community; areas of need; outreach initiatives.
WHAT IS NOT FUNDED The committee make the following choices whilst considering applications: people not buildings; new projects rather than recurrent expenditure; mission and outreach rather than maintenance; projects and programmes rather than structure.
RANGE OF GRANTS €500–€25,000
FINANCES *Year* 2012 *Grants* £498,149
PUBLICATIONS Priorities News – Published each year in May
OTHER INFORMATION All the financial information is in euros.
HOW TO APPLY On a form available, together with criteria and guidelines, from the fund's website. Applications must be made by 31 October each year. Applications are considered in February and approved in March.
WHO TO APPLY TO Sylvia Simpson, Organiser, Church of Ireland House, Church Avenue, Rathmines, Dublin 6 *Tel* 00353 (0) 1 4125607 *email* priorities@ireland.anglican.org *Website* www.priorities.ireland.anglican.org

■ Church Urban Fund

CC NO 297483   **ESTABLISHED** 1988
WHERE FUNDING CAN BE GIVEN The most deprived areas of England.
WHO CAN BENEFIT Local faith-based groups and activists working to help individuals, families and communities of people living in deprived neighbourhoods in England.
WHAT IS FUNDED The fund will support projects that: tackle major problems in their area, such as poverty, unemployment, disaffected youth, lack of community facilities, loneliness and isolation, or housing and homelessness; equip local communities to address local needs and issues and encourage people to take control of their

lives; empower the faith community to take an active role in wider community development, particularly through interfaith and ecumenical developments; are innovative, will make a practical impact and can develop partnerships with other agencies.
WHAT IS NOT FUNDED The fund's website states that it will not fund the following: 'projects outside England; individuals; projects not directly tackling profound poverty; projects without faith links; organisations with an annual turnover of over £150,000; salary costs, except where there is a significant increase in hours in order to expand an existing project or begin new work; core costs; repeated activities; work that has already been completed or started; campaigning and fundraising activity; revenue and capital for national voluntary/community organisations and public and private sector organisations; activities open only to church members; evangelistic activity not part of a response to poverty; clergy stipends including church army posts; general repairs and refurbishment; and general appeals.'
Those that fall outside of the priority groups, which are: offenders/ex-offenders; refugees and asylum seekers; deprived young people aged 14–19 years; homelessness; and substance misuse are unlikely to be funded. The fund is also unable to fund health and wellbeing projects, general family work, or work addressing shorter term aspects of poverty such as food banks.
TYPE OF GRANT Capital, project and revenue funding for up to three years.
RANGE OF GRANTS £100–£5,000.
SAMPLE GRANTS Project Freedom Trust; Sussex Pathways; Faith Drama Productions; Housing Justice; Community Money Advice; Reading Refugee Support Group; The Bridge Pregnancy Crisis Centre; All Saints Hanley (£5,000 each); (£4,900 each); Church Action on Poverty; Bristol Inter Faith Group Keeping Health in Mind (£4,500) Youth Project @ Apostles and Cuthbert's (£4,200); St Andrew's Community Network (£4,000).
FINANCES *Year* 2012 *Income* £4,540,000 *Grants* £1,655,000 *Assets* £3,101,000
TRUSTEES Andrew Dorton; Revd Canon Denise Poole; Revd Christopher Chessun; Derek Twine; Patrick Coldstream; Canon Paul Hackwood; Revd David Walker; Brian Carroll; Marnie Woodward.
PUBLICATIONS The trust has produced a detailed and helpful grants policy and procedure manual and applicants are advised to read this before making an application. The manual is available from the trust's website. The trust also publishes excellent reports on a wide range of issues related to poverty and deprivation. These are also available on the website.
HOW TO APPLY The trust has produced a detailed and helpful grants policy and procedure manual and applicants are advised to read this before making an application. The manual is available from the trust's website, as is detailed guidance on application procedures and guidelines.
WHO TO APPLY TO Revd Canon Paul Hackwood, Trustee, Church House, 27 Great Smith Street, Westminster, London SW1P 3AZ *Tel.* 020 7898 1090 *email* enquiries@cuf.org.uk *Website* www.cuf.org.uk

■ City and County of Swansea Welsh Church Act Fund

CC NO 1071913 **ESTABLISHED** 1997
WHERE FUNDING CAN BE GIVEN Swansea.
WHO CAN BENEFIT Registered charities.
WHAT IS FUNDED General charitable purposes.
WHAT IS NOT FUNDED No grants to individuals.
'Applications will not be considered for grants, which would normally be dealt with out of the annual budgets of the council's service departments or by public agencies or that would commit the fund to regular payments for a particular purpose.'
TYPE OF GRANT Revenue projects, up to a maximum of £5,000. For capital costs, only churches are eligible, up to a maximum of £1,000.
RANGE OF GRANTS Up to £5,000.
SAMPLE GRANTS St Vincent de Paul Society, Clydach and Christian Lewis Trust (£5,000 each); Victim Support and Swansea Music Art Dance Community Interest Co. (£2,000 each); St Stephen's Mother and Toddler Group (£1,600) and Brain Tumour UK and Pitton Methodist Church (£1,000 each).
FINANCES *Year* 2011–12 *Income* £36,261 *Grants* £27,720 *Assets* £975,873
TRUSTEE City and County of Swansea.
HOW TO APPLY On a form available from the correspondent. Trustees meet twice a year to consider grants. 'Applications should be sent by April or the end of September. Successful applicants cannot re-apply for three years.
WHO TO APPLY TO The Clerk, Financial Department, City and County of Swansea, County Hall, Oystermouth Road, Swansea SA1 3SN *Tel.* 01792 636421

■ The City Bridge Trust

CC NO 1035628 **ESTABLISHED** 1995
WHERE FUNDING CAN BE GIVEN Greater London.
WHO CAN BENEFIT Third sector organisations, mainly registered charities whose activities benefit the people of Greater London.
WHAT IS FUNDED Arts, culture, recreation and sports; community development; mental health; environment; older people; disability; voluntary sector.
WHAT IS NOT FUNDED The trust cannot fund: political parties; political lobbying; non-charitable activities; and work which does not benefit the inhabitants of Greater London. The trust does not fund: individuals; grantmaking bodies to make grants on its behalf; schools, PTAs, universities or other educational establishments (except where they are undertaking ancillary charitable activities specifically directed towards one of the agreed priority areas); medical or academic research; churches or other religious bodies where the monies will be used for religious purposes; hospitals; projects which have already taken place or building work which has already been completed; statutory bodies; profit making organisations (except social enterprises); and charities established outside the UK. Grants will not usually be given to: work where there is statutory responsibility to provide funding; organisations seeking funding to replace cuts by statutory authorities, except where that funding was explicitly time-limited and for a discretionary (non-statutory) purpose; organisations seeking funding to top up on under-priced contracts; and work where there is significant public funding available (including funding from sports governing bodies).

TYPE OF GRANT Grants for either running costs or capital costs. Grants for running costs are made for one to three years. Projects of an exceptionally strategic nature may make an application for a further two years, a maximum of five years in all.
RANGE OF GRANTS No minimum amount but applications over £55,000 need to be accompanied by a detailed proposal. Large grants to small organisations are unlikely to be made.
SAMPLE GRANTS Hampstead Heath Charitable Trust (£3 million); London Wildlife Trust (£169,000); Campaign Against Living Miserably – CALM and Thames 21 Ltd (£150,000 each); Bromley by Bow Centre (£149,000); Learn English at Home (£132,000); Refugee Action Kingston (£126,000); Haringey Shed (£107,000); Heart n Soul and Fashion Awareness Direct (£90,000 each); City of London Sinfonia (£86,000); Westway Community Transport (£80,000); East European Advice Centre and Mayhew Animal Home (£75,000 each); Art in Perpetuity Trust, Charles Dickens Museum and Thrive (£50,000 each); Jewish Community Centre (£46,000); All Saints Church – Ealing Common (£37,000); Afghanistan and Central Asian Association (£33,000); Alternatives to Violence Project and JAN Trust (£25,000 each); Russian Immigrants Association (£21,000); Vocaleyes, Creekside Education Trust, Kisharon and Beyond Youth (£20,000 each); Artangel (£15,000); St Christopher's Hospice (£11,000); In-Deep Community Task Force (£5,000); and Battersea Arts Centre (£3,500).
FINANCES *Year* 2011–12 *Income* £44,700,000 *Grants* £18,900,000 *Assets* £870,000,000
TRUSTEE The Corporation of the City of London.
OTHER INFORMATION The City Bridge Trust is the grantmaking arm of the Bridge House Estates charity whose prime objective is the provision and maintenance of the four bridges across the Thames into the City of London.
HOW TO APPLY Application forms are available from the trust or downloadable from its website, along with full and up-to-date guidelines. Applications are assessed by a member of the grants team and then considered by the grants committee. Most programmes do not have deadlines. Applications aim to be processed within four months. Applications are encouraged to contact the trust for initial guidance before making an application. Applications for grants of £5,000 and over must be accompanied by a detailed proposal. The trust expects applicants to work to its principles of good practice. These include: involving beneficiaries in the planning, delivery and management of services; valuing diversity; supporting volunteers; and taking steps to reduce the organisation's carbon footprint. The trust requires all grants to be monitored and evaluated. Details of the trust's monitoring and evaluation policy can be found on the website.
WHO TO APPLY TO Steven Reynolds, Administrator, c/o Corporation of London, PO Box 270, Guildhall, London EC2P 2EJ *Tel.* 020 7332 3710 *email* citybridgetrust@cityoflondon.gov.uk *Website* www.citybridgetrust.org.uk/cbt

■ The City Educational Trust Fund

CC NO 290840 **ESTABLISHED** 1967
WHERE FUNDING CAN BE GIVEN Greater London.
WHO CAN BENEFIT Institutions in London benefiting young adults, research workers, students and teachers.

WHAT IS FUNDED A variety of educational groups and institutions to promote study, teaching and training in areas such as science, technology, business management, commerce, biology, ecology and the cultural arts.

WHAT IS NOT FUNDED No grants to individuals.

TYPE OF GRANT One-off, ongoing and fixed period grants.

RANGE OF GRANTS Up to £75,000.

SAMPLE GRANTS £40,000 to the Spitalfields Festival towards the running costs of the festival; £15,000 to St Paul's Cathedral School Foundation towards the cost of choristers boarding costs; £10,000 to The Prisoners of Conscience Appeal Fund towards the cost of bursaries; £10,000 to Dr Johnson's House towards revenue running costs and £4,000 to Clio's Company towards the costs of replica costumes and Tudor artefacts for drama education workshops.

FINANCES *Year* 2011–12 *Income* £106,213 *Grants* £79,000 *Assets* £2,887,311

TRUSTEE The Corporation of London.

HOW TO APPLY In writing to the correspondent. Guidelines are available from the trust.

WHO TO APPLY TO Steven Reynolds, Administrator, c/o Corporation of London, PO Box 270, Guildhall, London EC2P 2EJ *Tel.* 020 7332 1382

■ CLA Charitable Trust

CC NO 280264   **ESTABLISHED** 1980

WHERE FUNDING CAN BE GIVEN England and Wales only.

WHO CAN BENEFIT Small local projects, innovative projects and newly established projects, where a grant can make a 'real contribution to the success of the project'.

WHAT IS FUNDED (i) To encourage education about the countryside for those who are disabled or disadvantaged, particularly youngsters from urban areas. (ii) To provide facilities for those with disabilities to have access to recreation in the countryside. (iii) To promote education in agriculture, horticulture and conservation for those who are disabled or disadvantaged.

WHAT IS NOT FUNDED No grants to individuals.

TYPE OF GRANT Specific projects or items rather than for ongoing running costs.

RANGE OF GRANTS Rarely more than £2,000.

SAMPLE GRANTS Farms for City Children (£10,000); Harper Adams College (£6,000); East Kent Sports Club and Wirral Swallows and Amazons (£2,000 each); British Red Squirrel (£1,500); and Calvert Trust (£1,100).

FINANCES *Year* 2012 *Income* £58,710 *Grants* £40,250 *Assets* £313,212

TRUSTEES Sir Henry Aubrey-Fletcher; Gordon Lee Steere; Anthony Duckworth-Chad; Hugh Duberly; Neil Mainwaring.

OTHER INFORMATION The CLA Charitable Trust was founded by CLA members in 1980.

HOW TO APPLY In writing to the correspondent. Trustees meet four times a year.

WHO TO APPLY TO Peter Geldart, Director, Hopbine Farm, Main Street, Ossington, Newark NG23 6LJ *Tel.* 01636 823835 *Website* www.cla.org.uk

■ Stephen Clark 1957 Charitable Trust

CC NO 258690   **ESTABLISHED** 1969

WHERE FUNDING CAN BE GIVEN Some preference for Bath and Somerset.

WHO CAN BENEFIT Registered charities.

WHAT IS FUNDED The trust's priorities are 'to make donations to charities in respect of the preservation, embellishment, maintenance, improvement or development of any monuments, churches or other buildings', but also general charitable purposes. The trust prefers local charities to national ones.

WHAT IS NOT FUNDED No grants to animal charities or to individuals.

TYPE OF GRANT One-off

RANGE OF GRANTS Up to £27,000, but usually under £3,000.

SAMPLE GRANTS Bath Industrial Heritage Trust (£27,000); Holbume Museum and Lennox Children's Cancer Fund (£3,000); St John's, Glastonbury, National Holiday Fund, Iford Arts and The Parochial Church Council of Kilsby Parish – Water Project (£1,000 each); St Philip and St James, Burtle (£800); Médecins Sans Frontières and PEACH (Autism) (£500 each); Target Tuberculosis and Send a Cow (£300 each); Somerset Wildlife Trust and Music Alive (£100 each) and Crossroads Care Wessex (£50).

FINANCES *Year* 2012 *Income* £89,835 *Grants* £78,120 *Assets* £2,159,053

TRUSTEES Dr Marianna Clark; Mary Lovell; Alice Clark.

HOW TO APPLY In writing to the correspondent. Note, replies are not usually made to unsuccessful applications. Include sae for reply.

WHO TO APPLY TO Dr Marianna Clark, Trustee, 16 Lansdown Place East, Bath BA1 5ET

■ Clark Bradbury Charitable Trust

CC NO 1129841   **ESTABLISHED** 2009

WHERE FUNDING CAN BE GIVEN UK and overseas with a preference for Cambridgeshire.

WHO CAN BENEFIT Registered charities.

WHAT IS FUNDED To provide support to charities involved in environmental conservation and in educating the public about the environment; to provide support to charities helping people with disabilities to experience the outdoors; to respond to specific world crises.

TYPE OF GRANT Usually one-off.

RANGE OF GRANTS Generally less than £2,000.

SAMPLE GRANTS Jubilee Sailing Trust (£3,000); Disability Snowsport UK (£2,500); Nancy Oldfield Trust (£2,000); Tall Ships Youth Trust (£1,500) and Garden Science Trust (£1,200).

FINANCES *Year* 2012–13 *Income* £60,093 *Grants* £56,606 *Assets* £56,011

TRUSTEES Dr Mike Clark; Dr Jane Bradbury; Prof. Elizabeth Morris; Robin Hodgkinson.

HOW TO APPLY In writing to the correspondent, via email.

WHO TO APPLY TO Dr Mike Clark, Trustee, 124 Richmond Road, Cambridge CB4 3PT *Tel.* 01223 740237 *email* contact@cbct.org.uk

■ The Hilda and Alice Clark Charitable Trust

CC NO 290916   **ESTABLISHED** 1953
WHERE FUNDING CAN BE GIVEN Street, Somerset.
WHO CAN BENEFIT There is a preference given to the Society of Friends (Quakers) and to children and young adults.
WHAT IS FUNDED General charitable purposes and Quaker causes.
WHAT IS NOT FUNDED Only registered charities are considered.
SAMPLE GRANTS Britain Yearly Meeting (£22,000 in total); Greenbank Swimming Pool (£15,000); UK Friends of Hope Flowers (£10,000); Ulster Quaker Social Committee (£9,000); Medical Aid for Palestinians (£6,000); Crispin Hall and Mid Somerset Area Meeting (£3,000 each); Red Brick Building Centre Ltd (£2,000); and Sightsavers International and Warwick Quaker Meeting (£1,000 each).
FINANCES *Year* 2012 *Income* £76,227 *Grants* £72,000 *Assets* £1,911,782
TRUSTEES Richard Clark; Thomas Clark; Martin Lovell; Alice Clark; Susannah Clark.
HOW TO APPLY In writing to the correspondent by 30 September. Trustees meet in December each year.
WHO TO APPLY TO The Secretary, c/o KPMG, 100 Temple Street, Bristol BS1 1AG *Tel.* 01179 054000

■ The Roger and Sarah Bancroft Clark Charitable Trust

CC NO 211513   **ESTABLISHED** 1960
WHERE FUNDING CAN BE GIVEN UK and overseas, with preference for Somerset.
WHO CAN BENEFIT Religious Society of Friends, registered charities and individuals. Preference is given to local appeals.
WHAT IS FUNDED General charitable purposes with particular reference to: Religious Society of Friends and associated bodies; charities connected with Somerset; education.
WHAT IS NOT FUNDED Students.
TYPE OF GRANT Recurrent grants.
RANGE OF GRANTS Mostly £200–£5,000.
SAMPLE GRANTS Hindhayes School (£40,000); Street Quaker Meeting House (£15,000); Britain Yearly Meeting (£14,000); Oxfam (£10,000); Barts and London School of Medicine and Dentistry and the Society for the Protection of Ancient Buildings (£5,000 each); Arthritis Research UK (£4,000); Retreat Grants Fund and Royal Academy of Music (£2,000 each); Alfred Hillett Trust (£1,900); Amnesty International and Alzheimer's Society (£1,000 each); Age UK and Womankind Worldwide (£500 each); African Initiatives (£300); Ziyaret Tepe Archaeological Trust (£250); and Penicuik and district YMCA (£200).
FINANCES *Year* 2012 *Income* £251,864 *Grants* £264,233 *Assets* £5,776,998
TRUSTEES Mary Lovell; Alice Clark; Martin Lovell; Caroline Gould; Roger Goldby; Robert Robertson.
HOW TO APPLY In writing to the correspondent.
WHO TO APPLY TO Lynette Cooper, Administrator, 40 High Street, Somerset BA16 0EQ *email* lynette.cooper@clarks.com

■ J. A. Clark Charitable Trust

CC NO 1010520   **ESTABLISHED** 1992
WHERE FUNDING CAN BE GIVEN UK, with a preference for South West England.
WHO CAN BENEFIT Charitable organisations.
WHAT IS FUNDED Health, education, peace, preservation of the earth and the arts
SAMPLE GRANTS Eucalyptus Charitable Foundation (£99,000); SHIN (£55,000); Khwendo Kor Pakistan (£50,000); Conflicts Forum and Innercity Scholarship (£20,000 each); Oval House (£18,000); Ground Work (£13,000); Combatants for Peace (£9,000); Peacock Gym (£7,500); and Hamlin Fistula (£5,000).
FINANCES *Year* 2012 *Income* £649,973 *Grants* £487,664 *Assets* £16,650,013
TRUSTEE William Pym.
HOW TO APPLY This trust does not respond to unsolicited applications.
WHO TO APPLY TO Jackie Morgan, Secretary, PO Box 1704, Glastonbury, Somerset BA16 0YB

■ The Clarke Charitable Settlement

CC NO 702980   **ESTABLISHED** 1990
WHERE FUNDING CAN BE GIVEN Staffordshire and Derbyshire.
WHO CAN BENEFIT Funding may be considered for Christians, research workers and medical professionals.
WHAT IS FUNDED The advancement of Christian religion, medical research and hospices.
RANGE OF GRANTS Most grants are for under £5,000, although they can be for much more.
SAMPLE GRANTS M. A. Future Foundations Appeal (£50,000); The Lichfield Festival (£20,000); St Giles Hospice (£5,000); The Needwood Singers (£3,000); The Prince's Trust (£1,000) The Christie Charitable Fund (£500); The Children's Society (£200); The Gurkha Welfare Trust (£100).
FINANCES *Year* 2011–12 *Income* £173,999 *Grants* £155,950 *Assets* £1,761,077
TRUSTEES Lady Hilda Clarke; Sally Hayward; Mary MacGregor; Jane Gerard-Pearse.
HOW TO APPLY In writing to the correspondent, although the trust has previously stated that support is only given to charities known to the trustees or the Clarke family.
WHO TO APPLY TO Lady H. J. Clarke, Trustee, The Knoll, Main Street, Barton-under-Needwood, Burton-on-Trent, Staffordshire DE13 8AB *Tel.* 01283 712294

■ The Clear Light Trust

CC NO 1147567   **ESTABLISHED** 2012
WHERE FUNDING CAN BE GIVEN UK, India, Papua New Guinea, USA.
WHO CAN BENEFIT Organisations and institutions.
WHAT IS FUNDED General charitable purposes.
TRUSTEES Brian Wright; Helena Weaver; Jonathan Pickard.
HOW TO APPLY No grants to unsolicited applications. The trust states that it has been overwhelmed by applications since registering, none of which it is able to support.
WHO TO APPLY TO Brian Wright, Trustee, Green Dragon House, Burwash Common, Etchingham, East Sussex TN19 7LX *Tel.* 01435 883135

Think carefully about every application. Is it justified?

453

■ The Cleevely Family Charitable Trust

CC NO 1137902   ESTABLISHED 2010
WHERE FUNDING CAN BE GIVEN Worldwide.
WHO CAN BENEFIT Registered charities.
WHAT IS FUNDED General, children and young people, health.
SAMPLE GRANTS Cambridge Science Centre; Teenage Cancer Trust and The Prince's Trust.
FINANCES *Year* 2011–12 *Income* £7,213 *Grants* £90,000 *Assets* £530,152
TRUSTEES Dr David Cleevely; Rosalind Cleevely; Olivia Florence.
OTHER INFORMATION As Dr Cleevely and his wife Rosalind are patrons of the Prince's Trust, it is likely that the trust has a preference for organisations working with children and young people. There may also be a preference for education and the Cambridge area.
HOW TO APPLY Applications for grants must be in writing to the correspondent. The trustees meet regularly. Recipients of grants are required to provide copies of receipts for expenditure and the grant may be subject to an ongoing monitoring programme – further instalments of grants only released subject to timescales being reached.
WHO TO APPLY TO Coutts and Co, Trustee Dept, 440 Strand, London WC2R 0QS *Tel.* 020 7753 1000

■ The Cleopatra Trust

CC NO 1004551   ESTABLISHED 1990
WHERE FUNDING CAN BE GIVEN Mainly UK.
WHO CAN BENEFIT Registered charities with a national focus.
WHAT IS FUNDED General charitable purposes; health and disability.
WHAT IS NOT FUNDED Organisations only.
RANGE OF GRANTS £500–£16,000.
SAMPLE GRANTS Environmental Vision, Maggie Keswick Jencks Cancer Caring Centres Trust and PSP Association (£10,000 each); Relate Brighton (£3,500); and St Barnabas Hospice, Southern Spinal Injuries Unit and Casa Alianza Charitable Co. (£1,000 each).
FINANCES *Year* 2012 *Income* £31,972 *Grants* £45,084 *Assets* £3,226,407
TRUSTEES Bettine Bond; Charles Peacock; Dr Clare Peacock.
OTHER INFORMATION Grants were made totalling £45,000. 11 grants were made to organisations in 2012.
HOW TO APPLY In writing to the correspondent.
WHO TO APPLY TO Charles Peacock, Trustee, Charities Aid Foundation, 25 Kings Hill Avenue, Kings Hill, West Malling ME19 4TA *Tel.* 01732 520028

■ Lord Clinton's Charitable Trust

CC NO 268061   ESTABLISHED 1974
WHERE FUNDING CAN BE GIVEN North and East Devon.
WHO CAN BENEFIT Registered charities benefiting people of all ages, ex-service and service people, seafarers and fishermen, sportsmen and women, volunteers, parents and children, people with disabilities, victims of man-made or natural disasters, people with cancer, paediatric diseases, or sight loss, and people who are terminally ill.
WHAT IS FUNDED Young people and the encouragement of youth activities, people who have disabilities, support for older people, medical aid and research, maritime charities. Respite and sheltered accommodation; churches; information technology and computers; personnel and human resources; support to voluntary and community organisations and volunteers; professional bodies; community centres; village halls and clubs.
WHAT IS NOT FUNDED No support for animal charities. No grants made in response to general appeals from large UK organisations or to smaller bodies working in areas other than those set out above.
TYPE OF GRANT For projects, recurring costs and start-up costs. Funding is available for one year or less.
RANGE OF GRANTS Up to £10,000.
SAMPLE GRANTS Previous beneficiaries have included: University of Exeter Sponsorship x two grants (£4,600 each); Vicar's Christmas Fund (£1,400); Kingfisher Award Scheme (£1,200); North Devon Cancer Care (£1,000); Exmouth Lifeboat Station Appeal and Families for Children (£500 each); Brixington Pre-School and the Countryside Foundation (£200 each); and Charity Golf Day (£50).
FINANCES *Year* 2011–12 *Income* £21,188 *Grants* £18,000
TRUSTEES Hon. Charles Fane Trefusis; John C. Varley.
HOW TO APPLY In writing to the correspondent. Applications not falling within the trust's objects and funding priorities will not be considered or acknowledged.
WHO TO APPLY TO John C. Varley, Trustee, Rolle Estate Office, East Budleigh, Budleigh Salterton, Devon EX9 7BL *Tel.* 01395 443881 *email* mail@clintondevon.co.uk

■ The Clore Duffield Foundation

CC NO 1084412   ESTABLISHED 2000
WHERE FUNDING CAN BE GIVEN UK, the larger grants go to London-based institutions.
WHO CAN BENEFIT Institutions and registered charities, particular emphasis on supporting children, young people and society's more vulnerable individuals.
WHAT IS FUNDED Main grants programme, mainly in the fields of museums, galleries and heritage sites (particularly for learning spaces), the arts, education, health, social care and disability and Jewish charities with interests in any of these areas.
WHAT IS NOT FUNDED Potential applicants should note that their organisation must be a registered charity to be eligible. Unfortunately, the foundation does not fund projects retrospectively and will not support applications from the following: individuals; general appeals and circulars. It should also be noted that the following are funded only very rarely: projects outside the UK; staff posts; local branches of national charities; academic or project research; conference costs.
TYPE OF GRANT Capital.
SAMPLE GRANTS Jewish Community Centre (£13 million); Royal Shakespeare Company (£275,000); University Church of St Mary the Virgin – Oxford (£215,000); Holburne Museum and Turner Contemporary Art (£125,000 each); BalletBoyz and Historic Royal Palaces (£100,000 each); Aldeburgh Foundation, Jewish Museum and NSPCC (£50,000 each); Maggie Keswick Jencks Cancer Caring Centre and Motivation Charitable Trust (£25,000 each); Afghan Connection, Amber Foundation, Anglo-

Israeli Association, the Art Room, Grange Park Opera, Hampstead Theatre and Whitworth Gallery (£10,000 each); and Apples and Snakes and Quintessentially Foundation (£5,000 each).

FINANCES *Year* 2012 *Income* £14,050,397
Grants £16,975,837 *Assets* £77,322,825

TRUSTEES Dame Vivien Duffield, Chair; Caroline Deletra; David Harrel; Michael Trask; Sir Mark Weinberg; James Harding; Melanie Clore.

HOW TO APPLY Refer to the foundation's guidance leaflet which can be downloaded from its website. You are invited to contact the foundation, before making application if you have any queries regarding criteria set or the process itself.

WHO TO APPLY TO Sally Bacon, Executive Director, The Clore Foundation, Unit 3, Chelsea Manor Studios, Flood Street, London SW3 5SR *Tel.* 020 7351 6061 *Fax* 020 7351 5308 *email* info@cloreduffield.org.uk *Website* www.cloreduffield.org.uk

■ Miss V. L. Clore's 1967 Charitable Trust

CC NO 253660   **ESTABLISHED** 1967
WHERE FUNDING CAN BE GIVEN UK.
WHO CAN BENEFIT Registered charities and social enterprise.

WHAT IS FUNDED General charitable purposes, especially performing arts, education, social welfare, health and disability. Jewish causes are also supported.

WHAT IS NOT FUNDED No grants are given to individuals.

TYPE OF GRANT Grants of up to one year are usually made.

RANGE OF GRANTS Usually £1,000–£5,000.

SAMPLE GRANTS Bloomsbury Art Fair, Chickenshed Theatre and Blond McIndoe Foundation (£5,000 each); and European Union Youth Orchestra and Lady Joseph Trust (£1,000 each).

FINANCES *Year* 2011–12 *Income* £39,635
Grants £28,871 *Assets* £1,204,939

TRUSTEES Dame Vivien Duffield; Caroline Deletra; David Digby Harrel.

OTHER INFORMATION An anonymous grant of £10,000 was made to an organisation within the arts, heritage and education sector.

HOW TO APPLY In writing to the correspondent on one to two sides of A4, enclosing an sae.

WHO TO APPLY TO Sally Bacon, Executive Director, The Clore Foundation, Unit 3, Chelsea Manor Studios, Flood Street, London SW3 5SR *Tel.* 020 7351 6061 *Fax* 020 7351 5308 *email* info@cloreduffield.org.uk *Website* www.cloreduffield.org.uk

■ Closehelm Limited

CC NO 291296   **ESTABLISHED** 1983
WHERE FUNDING CAN BE GIVEN UK and Israel.
WHO CAN BENEFIT Individuals and institutions benefiting Jewish people and people disadvantaged by poverty.

WHAT IS FUNDED The advancement of religion in accordance with the Jewish faith; the relief of poverty; and general charitable purposes.

SAMPLE GRANTS Zaks (£111,200); the Mutual Trust (£5,000); Beenstock Home (£1,700); Yeshivat and Kol Torah (£1,000); Hayomi Trust (£800); Friends of Mir (£500); and Friends of Karlin-Stolin (£200).

FINANCES *Year* 2011–12 *Income* £349,391
Grants £206,483 *Assets* £3,550,213

TRUSTEES A. Van Praagh; Hanna Grosberg; Henrietta Van Praagh.

OTHER INFORMATION Grants totalling £73,000 were given to individuals and £134,000 to organisations in 2011–12.

HOW TO APPLY In writing to the correspondent.

WHO TO APPLY TO A. Van Praagh, Trustee, 30 Armitage Road, London NW11 8RD *Tel.* 020 8201 8688

■ The Clothworkers' Foundation

CC NO 274100   **ESTABLISHED** 1977
WHERE FUNDING CAN BE GIVEN UK.
WHO CAN BENEFIT UK registered charities only.
WHAT IS FUNDED Homelessness, alcohol and substance misuse, domestic and sexual violence, prisoners and ex-offenders, integration of minorities, disadvantaged young people, disability, elderly, visual impairment and textiles.

WHAT IS NOT FUNDED The foundation does not fund: salaries; overheads; training; rent; lease of equipment; volunteer expenses; professional fees; websites; databases; software; any other running costs; in the Main Grants programme: IT equipment which will only be used by staff/volunteers and not by service users; hospices; arts and education projects, unless they are focused on disadvantaged young people, elderly people, or disabled people; educational establishments, other than schools specifically for disabled children/children with learning difficulties or special educational needs; emergency response appeals; environmental organisations or projects; events (including exhibitions); general or mass appeals; grantmaking organisations; heritage projects; individuals (other than CPD Bursaries for conservators); medical research or equipment; non UK-registered charities; organisations that have received a grant from the foundation in the last five years; organisations with an annual operating income of more than £15 million (read the FAQ for more information); overseas work/projects; political, industrial, or commercial projects; projects that do not fall within the programme areas; projects where the item(s) funded will be used for religious purposes, or projects or organisations which promote a particular religion; work which is needed to meet the requirements of the Disability Discrimination Act; projects that we have already declined to fund.

TYPE OF GRANT Capital; one-off; occasionally recurring for more than three years.

RANGE OF GRANTS *Main grants*: grants of up to £100,000 (larger grants awarded on very rare occasions). Average grant size of £20,000, grants size is relative to project size–smaller projects usually receive smaller grants and vice versa. *Small grants*: grants of between £500 and £10,000 for capital costs.

SAMPLE GRANTS Vision Aid Overseas (£366,000); North of England Refugee Service (£60,000); Ashley Foundation (£65,000); Julian House (£45,000); Blind Aid, Fine Cell Work, Hope for Tomorrow, LifeLine Community Projects and South Tyneside Churches' KEY Project (£40,000 each); Wester Hailes Youth Agency (£33,000); Bury Hospice, Exodus Project, RedR (Register of Engineers for Disaster Relief), UCL Medical School (£30,000 each); Preshal Trust (£25,000); Age UK Lancashire, Caldecott Foundation and Citizens Advice West Lothian (£20,000); It's Your Choice, Ray's Playhouse and Young Devon (£15,000 each); Oxfordshire Motor Project (£13,000); Parkinson's Self Help

Group and Survive South Gloucestershire and Bristol (£12,000 each).

FINANCES *Year* 2011–12 *Income* £5,123,962 *Grants* £4,339,625 *Assets* £89,237,062

TRUSTEES Michael Howell; Joanna Dodd; Alexander Nelson; Andrew Clarke; Robin Booth; Thomas Clark; Philip Portal; Michael Jarvis; Richard Jonas; Michael Maylon; Christopher McLean May; Dr Carolyn Boulter; Melville Haggard.

HOW TO APPLY Refer to the foundation's very helpful and detailed guidelines on how to apply for either main or small grants, which can be downloaded from the foundation's website.

WHO TO APPLY TO Andrew Blessley, Chief Executive, Clothworkers' Hall, Dunster Court, Mincing Lane, London EC3R 7AH *Tel.* 020 7623 7041 *Fax* 020 7397 0107 *email* foundation@clothworkers.co.uk *Website* www.clothworkers.co.uk

■ Richard Cloudesley's Charity

CC NO 205959 **ESTABLISHED** 1517

WHERE FUNDING CAN BE GIVEN North Islington, London.

WHO CAN BENEFIT Voluntary and charitable organisations. Individuals are assisted through the trust's welfare fund.

WHAT IS FUNDED Church of England churches, health and welfare.

TYPE OF GRANT One-off grants are preferred; the vast majority of grants are free of restrictions. Grants for capital, core, recurring, running and start-up costs will be considered, as will grants for buildings, feasibility studies, project, research and salaries.

RANGE OF GRANTS £100–£40,000.

SAMPLE GRANTS St David's – Lough Road (£50,000); St Mary's – Islington (£29,000); St Jude and St Paul – Mildmay Park (£23,500); Claremont Park, Maya Centre and St Andrew Whitehall Park (£10,000 each); Angel Shed Theatre Company, CARIS – Islington and Community Language Support Services (£6,000 each); Islington Bangladesh Association (£3,000); and EAGLE Recovery Project (£1,000).

FINANCES *Year* 2011–12 *Income* £1,240,301 *Grants* £488,000 *Assets* £23,425,435

TRUSTEE Richard Cloudesley Trustee Limited

OTHER INFORMATION The grants total figure includes an amount of £147,000 paid to individuals.

HOW TO APPLY Applicants should write to the correspondent requesting an application form. Applications should be in time for the trustees' meetings in April and November and should be accompanied by the organisation's accounts. The following information should be supplied: details of the work your organisation undertakes; how it falls within the geographical area of the trust; and details what the grant will fund. If you would like acknowledgement of receipt of your application send an sae. Block grants are considered twice a year, around late April, and early November at a grants committee meeting. Recommendations are made by the grants committee at these meetings and are reviewed and authorised by the trustees two weeks later. The trust will give brief reasons with any application that is not successful.

WHO TO APPLY TO Melanie Griffiths, Director, Reed Smith LLP, 26th Floor, Broadgate Tower, 20 Primrose Street, London EC2A 2RS *Tel.* 020 3116 3624 *email* kwallace@reedsmith.com *Website* www.richardcloudsleyscharity.org.uk

■ The Clover Trust

CC NO 213578 **ESTABLISHED** 1961

WHERE FUNDING CAN BE GIVEN UK, and occasionally overseas, with a slight preference for West Dorset.

WHO CAN BENEFIT Registered charities.

WHAT IS FUNDED Older people, young people, Catholicism, health, disability.

TYPE OF GRANT Up to three years.

RANGE OF GRANTS £2,000–£35,000.

SAMPLE GRANTS Friends of Children in Romania (£35,000); Action Medical Research, CAFOD, Childhood First and Downside Fisher Youth Club (£8,000 each); West London Action, JOLT and 999 Club (£6,500 each); Orchard Vale Trust, Brainwave and Bridport Stroke Club (£4,000 each); and Disability Snowsport UK, The Car Care Support Group and W4B Wavelength (£2,000 each).

FINANCES *Year* 2012 *Income* £208,583 *Grants* £190,500 *Assets* £4,327,503

TRUSTEES Sara Woodhouse; Nicholas Haydon; Benedict Woodhouse; Charlotte Morrison.

HOW TO APPLY In writing to the correspondent. Replies are not given to unsuccessful applications.

WHO TO APPLY TO George Wright, Administrator, DTE Herbert Pepper, Park House, 26 North End Road, London NW11 7PT *Tel.* 020 8458 4384

■ The Robert Clutterbuck Charitable Trust

CC NO 1010559 **ESTABLISHED** 1992

WHERE FUNDING CAN BE GIVEN UK, with preference for Cheshire and Hertfordshire.

WHO CAN BENEFIT Registered charities and other organisations with a charitable focus.

WHAT IS FUNDED Personnel within the armed forces and ex-servicemen and women; sport and recreational facilities for young people benefiting Cheshire and Hertfordshire; the welfare, protection and preservation of domestic animal life benefiting Cheshire and Hertfordshire; natural history and wildlife; other charities associated with the counties of Cheshire and Hertfordshire; charities which have particular appeal to the founder, Major Robert Clutterbuck.

WHAT IS NOT FUNDED No grants to individuals.

TYPE OF GRANT Specific items and projects rather than running costs. One-off.

RANGE OF GRANTS £1,000–£3,000.

SAMPLE GRANTS Wood Green Animal Charity (£2,800); Churches Housing Trust, 9 Lives Furniture and North West Air Ambulance (£2,000 each); Leonard Cheshire Disability and Cheshire MS Support (£1,500 each); Wheathampstead Cricket Club, National Deaf Children's Society, MedEquip4Kids and Barnstonedale Centre (£1,000 each); Buxton Sea Cadets, Walton Lea Project and Seal and Bird Rescue (£750 each); Penrith Red Squirrel Group, PDSA, Evergreen and Harpenden Lions Club (£500 each) and Honeypot (£400).

FINANCES *Year* 2011–12 *Income* £40,747 *Grants* £41,903 *Assets* £1,230,578

TRUSTEES Roger Pincham; Ian Pearson; Lucy Pitman.

HOW TO APPLY In writing to the correspondent. There are no application forms. Applicants should write to the secretary giving details of what they propose to do with any grant made and of their current financial position. The deadlines for the rounds of applications are 30 June and 31 December in each year. The trustees generally meet in March and September. The trustees will not normally consider appeals from charities within two years of a previous grant being approved.

WHO TO APPLY TO George Wolfe, Secretary, 28 Brookfields, Calver, Hope Valley, Derbyshire S32 3XB *Tel.* 01433 631308 *email* secretary@ clutterbucktrust.org.uk *Website* www. clutterbucktrust.org.uk

■ Clydpride Ltd

CC NO 295393　　**ESTABLISHED** 1982

WHO CAN BENEFIT Individuals and institutions benefiting Jewish people and people disadvantaged by poverty.

WHAT IS FUNDED Advancement of the Orthodox Jewish faith; relief of poverty; general charitable purposes. The main focus is to support the 'renaissance of religious study and to alleviate the plight of poor scholars'.

SAMPLE GRANTS Previously: Achiezer; Achisomoch Aid Company; Beis Chinuch Lebonos; Beis Soroh Scheneirer Seminary; Bnei Braq Hospital; Comet Charities Limited; EM Shasha Foundation; Friends of Mir; Gevurath Ari Torah Academy Trust; Mosdos Tchernobil; Notzar Chesed; Seed; Society of Friends of Torah; and Telz Talmudical Academy Trust.

FINANCES *Year* 2012 *Income* £4,893,768 *Grants* £246,710 *Assets* £19,641,118

TRUSTEES L. Faust; M. H. Linton; A. Faust.

OTHER INFORMATION A list of grant beneficiaries was not included in the trust's accounts. However, we know that the grants total comprised: £106,000 to educational institutions to support the advancement of religion through education; £99,500 for the relief of poverty; £31,000 which was donated to institutions that benefit the Jewish community in ways such as through medical facilities; and £9,700 was given to individuals.

HOW TO APPLY The trust states that unsolicited applications are not considered.

WHO TO APPLY TO L. Faust, Trustee, c/o Rayner Essex Accountants, Tavistock House South, Tavistock Square, London WC1H 9LG *Tel.* 020 8731 7744

■ The Francis Coales Charitable Foundation

CC NO 270718　　**ESTABLISHED** 1975

WHERE FUNDING CAN BE GIVEN UK, with a preference for Bedfordshire, Buckinghamshire, Hertfordshire and Northamptonshire.

WHO CAN BENEFIT Old buildings open to the public, usually churches. Organisations involved in archaeological research and related causes.

WHAT IS FUNDED Repair and restoration of buildings, monuments, etc.; archaeological research with preference to Buckinghamshire, Bedfordshire, Northamptonshire and Hertfordshire.

WHAT IS NOT FUNDED In respect of buildings, assistance is only given towards fabric repairs, but not to 'domestic' items such as heating, lighting, wiring, installation of facilities etc.

TYPE OF GRANT Largely one-off.

SAMPLE GRANTS Paulerspury – Northants, Upton – Bucks and Ivinghoe – Beds (£2,500 each); Wingrave – Bucks and Hockliffe – Beds (£2,000 each); Alpheton – Suffolk and Cransley – Northants (£1,000 each); Tibenham – Norfolk and Laindon – Essex (£750 each); Harlaxton Series (£500); and Church Monuments Soc. (£250).

FINANCES *Year* 2012 *Income* £123,362 *Grants* £67,803 *Assets* £3,588,758

TRUSTEES Martin Stuchfield; Guy Harding; Revd Brian Wilcox; Ian Barnett; Matthew Saunders.

OTHER INFORMATION 44 grants were made totalling £68,000.

HOW TO APPLY On a form which can be downloaded from the foundation's website. Trustees normally meet three times a year to consider grants. 'In respect of a building or contents, include a copy of the relevant portion only of the architect's (or conservator's) specification showing the actual work proposed. Photographs illustrating this are a necessity, and only in exceptional circumstances will an application be considered without supporting photographs here. It is of help if six copies of any supporting documentation are submitted in order that each trustee may have a copy in advance of the meeting.'

WHO TO APPLY TO Trevor Parker, Administrator, The Bays, Hillcote, Bleadon Hill, Weston-super-Mare, Somerset BS24 9JS *Tel.* 01934 814009 *email* fccf45@hotmail.com *Website* franciscoales.co.uk

■ The Coalfields Regeneration Trust

CC NO 1074930　　**ESTABLISHED** 1999

WHERE FUNDING CAN BE GIVEN Coalfield and former coalfield communities in England (North West and North East, Yorkshire, West Midlands and East Midlands, Kent), Scotland (West and East) and Wales.

WHO CAN BENEFIT Community and voluntary organisations who are working to tackle problems at grass-roots level within coalfield communities.

WHAT IS FUNDED Welfare of coalfield communities.

WHAT IS NOT FUNDED The following are not eligible to receive support: individuals; private businesses; statutory bodies; national organisations; parish, town and community councils; organisations with total annual income (from all sources) above £100,000; organisations that we believe are in a poor financial position or whose financial management systems are not in good order; friends of groups where the end beneficiary will clearly be a statutory body; pigeon (flying) clubs; organisations not established in the UK.

TYPE OF GRANT Usually one-off grants.

RANGE OF GRANTS Up to £100,000

SAMPLE GRANTS Previous beneficiaries included: Aylesham Neighbourhood Project (£210,000); Haswell and District Mencap Society – The Community Anchor (£98,000); Derbyside Rural Community Council – Wheels to Work (£89,000); The Cornforth Partnership – The Reach project (£75,000); Nottinghamshire Independent Domestic Abuse Link Workers (£66,000); Stoke On Trent and District Gingerbread Centre Ltd – Peer Mentoring (£37,000); St John's Church – A Building in Which to Serve Our Community (£10,000); Mansfield and Dukeries Irish Association – Luncheon Club (£5,000); City of Durham Air Cadets – Achieving Duke of Edinburgh's Awards (£3,800); Thornycroft Art Club – Christmas Tree Exhibition (£520).

FINANCES *Year* 2011–12 *Income* £22,323,000 *Grants* £15,643,000 *Assets* £9,191,000

TRUSTEES Peter McNestry, Chair; Jim Crewdson; Prof. Anthony Crook; Dawn Davies; John Edwards; Vernon Jones; Wayne Thomas; Fran

Think carefully about every application. Is it justified?

457

Walker; Sylvia Wileman; Nicholas Wilson; Michael Clapham; Bill Skilki; Roger Owen; Thomas McAughtrie.

OTHER INFORMATION The trust provides advice, support and financial assistance to community and voluntary organisations who are working to tackle problems at grass-roots level within coalfield communities. It is closely connected with the areas it serves, operating through a network of staff based at offices located within coalfield regions themselves.

HOW TO APPLY Application details are different for each programme. The trust has produced very comprehensive information booklets that should be read before applying to any fund. Applicants are advised to contact their regional manager before making an application, details of which are also on the trust's website. The staff will be able to advise on the trust's application process and an appointment can be made with a member of the development team to discuss the application in more detail.

WHO TO APPLY TO Louise Dyson, Head of Finance and Corporate Services, 1 Waterside Park, Valley Way, Wombwell, Barnsley S73 0BB *Tel.* 01226 270800 *Fax* 01226 272899 *email* info@coalfields-regen.org.uk *Website* www.coalfields-regen.org.uk

■ The John Coates Charitable Trust

CC NO 262057   **ESTABLISHED** 1969
WHERE FUNDING CAN BE GIVEN UK, mainly southern England.
WHO CAN BENEFIT Institutions either national or of personal or local interest to one or more of the trustees.
WHAT IS FUNDED Preference is given to education, arts and culture, children, environment and health.
WHAT IS NOT FUNDED Grants are given to individuals only in exceptional circumstances.
TYPE OF GRANT Capital and recurring.
RANGE OF GRANTS £500–£10,000.
SAMPLE GRANTS National Trust (£10,000); Action for Addiction, Campaign to Protect Rural England, Age UK and National Ankylosing Spondylitis Association – NASS (£5,000 each); British Association for Adoption and Fostering and the National Literacy Trust (£4,000 each); Amberley Museum and Heritage Centre, Calibre Audio Library and Fine Cell Work (£3,000 each); Breast Cancer Haven, Hampshire and Wight Trust for Maritime Archaeology and Kidscape (£2,000 each); and the Barn Owl Trust and Lifelites (£1,000 each).
FINANCES *Year* 2011–12 *Income* £381,031 *Grants* £291,000 *Assets* £10,380,150
TRUSTEES Gillian McGregor; Rebecca Lawes; Phyllida Youngman; Catharine Kesley; Claire Cartledge.
OTHER INFORMATION The trust made grants totalling £291,000 to 76 organisations in 2011–12.
HOW TO APPLY In writing to the correspondent. Small local charities are visited by the trust. It is the trust's policy to request a post-grant report detailing how a donation has been spent for any single donation over £15,000.
WHO TO APPLY TO Rebecca Lawes, Trustee, 3 Grange Road, Cambridge CB3 9AS

■ The Cobalt Trust

CC NO 1096342   **ESTABLISHED** 2002
WHERE FUNDING CAN BE GIVEN UK and overseas.
WHO CAN BENEFIT Registered charities known to the trustees,
WHAT IS FUNDED General charitable purposes.
TYPE OF GRANT Capital and revenue grants over three years.
SAMPLE GRANTS Previous beneficiaries included: Impetus Trust (£169,000); EVPA (£26,000); Streets Limited (£14,000); Enable Ethiopia and Tree Aid (£12,000 each); Rose trees Trust and Money for Madagascar (£10,000 each); Beat – Eating Disorders Association (£5,000); Wherever the Need (£1,000); Red Squirrel Survival Trust (£500); Wessex MS Therapy Centre (£100); and Bath RSPB (£50). Many of the beneficiaries were supported on a recurrent basis.
FINANCES *Year* 2011–12 *Income* £15,680 *Grants* £125,000
TRUSTEES Stephen Dawson; Brigitte Dawson.
HOW TO APPLY The trustees do not respond to unsolicited applications
WHO TO APPLY TO Stephen Dawson, Trustee, 17 New Row, London WC2N 4LA

■ The Cobtree Charity Trust Ltd

CC NO 208455   **ESTABLISHED** 1951
WHERE FUNDING CAN BE GIVEN Maidstone and district.
WHO CAN BENEFIT Registered charities.
WHAT IS FUNDED The maintenance and development of Cobtree Manor Estate, and other general charitable purposes by other charities in the Maidstone and district area.
WHAT IS NOT FUNDED No support for individuals, non-registered charities and charities outside Maidstone and district.
TYPE OF GRANT Largely recurrent.
RANGE OF GRANTS Average £1,000–£5,000
SAMPLE GRANTS Dandelion Time (£10,000); The Peggy Wood Foundation (£4,000); Kent Youth Trust (£3,800) Samaritans (£3,500); Maidstone Choral Union (£2,000) Maidstone Girl Guides (£1,300) Relate, Kent (£1,100) The Symbol Trust (£850); and The Winfield Trust (£500).
FINANCES *Year* 2011–12 *Income* £143,697 *Grants* £95,900 *Assets* £5,047,833
TRUSTEES R. J. Corben; J. Fletcher; L. J. Martin; R. N. Hext; D. T. B. Wigg; M. W. Hardcastle; S. W. L. Brice; M. Lawrence.
HOW TO APPLY In writing to the correspondent. The trustees meet quarterly.
WHO TO APPLY TO Colin Mills, c/o Larkings (S.E.) LLP, Cornwallis House, Pudding Lane, Maidstone, Kent ME14 1NH *Tel.* 01622 754033 *Website* thecobtreecharitytrust.co.uk

■ The Vivienne and Samuel Cohen Charitable Trust

CC NO 255496   **ESTABLISHED** 1965
WHERE FUNDING CAN BE GIVEN UK and Israel.
WHO CAN BENEFIT Charitable organisations.
WHAT IS FUNDED Jewish, education, health, medical, culture, general charitable purposes.
WHAT IS NOT FUNDED No grants to individuals.
RANGE OF GRANTS £7,000–£500 or less.
SAMPLE GRANTS The Spiro Ark, Ariel, Yeshivat Har Hamor and Mishkan David (£7,000 each); Nidrash Shmuel and Friends of Tiferet Shlomo (£6,500 each); Friends of S H Hospital and World Jewish Relief (£5,000 each); Glazer Institute of Jewish Studies (£4,000); East

London NHS Foundation Trust (£3,500); Friends of the Israel Opera, University Jewish Chaplaincy Board and Society for the Protection of Nature in Israel (£2,000 each); Israel Free Loan Association, Friends of Jerusalem College of Technology and National Osteoporosis Society (£1,000 each); and Home for Aged Jews and Bridge Lane Beth Hamedrash (£500 each).

FINANCES *Year* 2011–12 *Income* £130,885 *Grants* £147,442 *Assets* £2,974,974

TRUSTEES Jonathan Lauffer; Gershon Cohen; Michael Ben-Gershon; Dr Vivienne Cohen; Gideon Lauffer.

OTHER INFORMATION 214 of the 278 grants made were under £1,000. These totalled £38,000.

HOW TO APPLY In writing only, to the correspondent.

WHO TO APPLY TO Dr Vivienne Cohen, Trustee, Clayton Start and Co, 5th Floor, Charles House, 108–110 Finchley Road, London NW3 5JJ *Tel.* 020 7431 4200

■ The Denise Cohen Charitable Trust

CC NO 276439   **ESTABLISHED** 1977

WHERE FUNDING CAN BE GIVEN UK.

WHO CAN BENEFIT Registered charities.

WHAT IS FUNDED Jewish; education; health and welfare of older people, infirm people and children; humanities; arts and culture.

RANGE OF GRANTS Between £9,000 and £100.

SAMPLE GRANTS Chai Cancer Charity (£7,000); Nightingale (£6,000); Jewish Woman's Aid (£3,500); Community Security Trust (£3,000); Lewis W Hammerson Memorial Home (£2,500); Ben Uri Gallery (£2,000); British Friends of Herzog Hospitality and Royal British Legion (£1,000 each); The Shalom Foundation (£750); Jewish Child's Day and Royal Star and Garter Home (£500 each); Youth Aliyah Child Rescue (£250); and Institute for Jewish Policy Research (£100).

FINANCES *Year* 2011–12 *Income* £57,664 *Grants* £70,794 *Assets* £1,416,802

TRUSTEES Denise Cohen; Martin Paisner; Sara Cohen.

HOW TO APPLY In writing to the correspondent incorporating full details of the charity for which funding is requested. No acknowledgements will be sent out to unsuccessful applicants.

WHO TO APPLY TO Martin Paisner, Trustee, Berwin Leighton and Paisner, Adelaide House, London Bridge, London EC4R 9HA *Tel.* 020 3400 1000

■ The John S. Cohen Foundation

CC NO 241598   **ESTABLISHED** 1965

WHERE FUNDING CAN BE GIVEN Worldwide, in practice mainly UK.

WHO CAN BENEFIT Registered charities.

WHAT IS FUNDED General charitable purposes but particularly supporting education, music and the arts and the environment, both built and natural.

TYPE OF GRANT One-off and recurring.

RANGE OF GRANTS Typically £5,000 or less; larger grants around £25,000.

SAMPLE GRANTS Royal Opera House (£25,000); the National Gallery (£20,000); British Museum and Public Catalogue Foundation (£10,000 each); Wigmore Hall Trust (£7,000); Chatham House, Garsington Opera and Poetry Book Society (£5,000 each); Mayor of London's Fund and Truro Cathedral (£4,000 each); Eden Trust and The Sixteen (£3,000 each); British Film Institute

and Jewish Museum (£2,000 each); 45' Aid Society, Alzheimer's Society, Birmingham Repertory Theatre and World Jewish Relief (£1,000 each); Musical Brain (£500); and Tait Memorial Trust (£100).

FINANCES *Year* 2011–12 *Income* £442,429 *Grants* £316,298 *Assets* £6,999,308

TRUSTEES Dr David Cohen; Imogen Cohen; Olivia Cohen; Veronica Cohen.

HOW TO APPLY In writing to the correspondent.

WHO TO APPLY TO Diana Helme, Foundation Administrator, PO Box 21277, London W9 2YH *Tel.* 020 7286 6921

■ The R. and S. Cohen Foundation

CC NO 1078225   **ESTABLISHED** 1999

WHERE FUNDING CAN BE GIVEN Worldwide.

WHO CAN BENEFIT Educational, theatrical, operatic, medical and Jewish charitable organisations.

WHAT IS FUNDED Education and relief-in-need.

TYPE OF GRANT One-off and recurrent.

SAMPLE GRANTS Previously: UJIA (£50,000); Design Museum (£40,000); Muscular Dystrophy, Royal National Institute for the Blind (£25,000 each); Jewish Care (£20,000); Tel-Aviv University Trust (£15,000); British Museum (£13,000); New Israel Fund (£8,000); Tate Foundation (£5,000); Royal Academy of the Arts (£4,500); WLS Charitable Fund (£1,200).

FINANCES *Year* 2012 *Income* £15,503 *Grants* £1,000,000

TRUSTEES Lady Sharon Harel-Cohen; Sir Ronald Cohen; Tamara Harel-Cohen; David Marks; Jonathan Harel-Cohen.

OTHER INFORMATION Basic details taken from the Charity Commission website. Accounts for 2012 were not available to view at the Commission due to the charity's low income.

HOW TO APPLY In writing to the correspondent.

WHO TO APPLY TO Martin Dodd, Administrator, 42 Portland Place, London W1B 1NB

■ The Colchester Catalyst Charity

CC NO 228352   **ESTABLISHED** 1959

WHERE FUNDING CAN BE GIVEN North-east Essex.

WHO CAN BENEFIT Health organisations.

WHAT IS FUNDED Provision of support by direct contributions to health organisations for specific and well-designed projects in order to improve healthcare.

WHAT IS NOT FUNDED No support for general funding, staff or running costs (usually). Retrospective funding is not considered. The charity is unable to consider applications for any item where there is an obligation for provision by a statutory authority.

TYPE OF GRANT One-off.

SAMPLE GRANTS Essex University (£28,000); Opportunities through Technology (19,452) SCANS (£10,000); Chariot Community Buses (£7,000) The Ark Centre, TCVS, Halstead Day Centre (£5,000 each); Leonard Cheshire Homes (£3,000); St Helena Hospice (£2,500); Colchester Hospital Unit (£1,000).

FINANCES *Year* 2011–12 *Income* £287,927 *Grants* £256,545 *Assets* £8,682,132

TRUSTEES P. Fitt, Chair; C. Hayward; Dr E. Hall; Dr M. P. Hickman; A. W. Livesley; M. F. Pertwee; Dr T. P. Rudra; Dr N. J. Busfield.

HOW TO APPLY The application procedure varies for the different grants, full instructions can be obtained on the trust's website. Alternatively applicants may call or email the trust for further information on the application procedure.

WHO TO APPLY TO Peter Fitt, Company Secretary, 7 Coast Road, West Mersea, Colchester CO5 8QE *Tel.* 01206 752545 *email* info@colchestercatalyst.co.uk *Website* www.colchestercatalyst.co.uk

....

■ John Coldman Charitable Trust

CC NO 1050110   ESTABLISHED 1995
WHERE FUNDING CAN BE GIVEN UK, with a preference for Edenbridge in Kent.
WHO CAN BENEFIT Registered charities.
WHAT IS FUNDED General charitable purposes, particularly community and Christian groups and UK organisations whose work benefits the community, such as children's and medical charities and schools.
RANGE OF GRANTS £250 upwards.
SAMPLE GRANTS Hever Primary School (£50,000); St Luke's Parochial Church Council (£30,000); Oasis International (£27,000); Prince's Trust and Tonbridge School Foundation (£20,000 each); Citizen's Advice Bureau, Edenbridge and Westerham Branch (£15,000); St Mary's Church, Chiddingstone (£9,000); Domestic Abuse Volunteer Support Service (£5,000); Prostate Cancer Charity (£2,500); Age UK Sevenoaks and Tonbridge (£1,300) and CARE International (£250).
FINANCES *Year* 2011–12 *Income* £25,231 *Grants* £251,911 *Assets* £1,269,080
TRUSTEES John Coldman; Graham Coldman; Charles Warner.
OTHER INFORMATION During 2011–12 an additional £35,000 went towards the running of the Holcot Residential Centre, which operates as a hostel, holiday centre and community centre for the use of young people and others.
HOW TO APPLY In writing to the correspondent.
WHO TO APPLY TO Charles Warner, Trustee, Warners Solicitors, Bank House, Bank Street, Tonbridge, Kent TN9 1BL *Tel.* 01732 770660 *Fax* 01732 362452 *email* charles.warner@warners-solicitors.co.uk

....

■ The Cole Charitable Trust

CC NO 264033   ESTABLISHED 1972
WHERE FUNDING CAN BE GIVEN Greater Birmingham, Kent and Cambridge.
WHO CAN BENEFIT Local community projects.
WHAT IS FUNDED General charitable purposes, including: social welfare, housing/homelessness, health, community and environmental development, opportunities for young people, promotion of improved quality of life and personal or community empowerment.
WHAT IS NOT FUNDED No grants for large national organisations, religion, further education, animal welfare or individuals.
TYPE OF GRANT Small capital or project grants; normally one-off; core costs.
RANGE OF GRANTS £300–£1,000, occasionally more.
SAMPLE GRANTS Swale Youth Fund (£2,000); Daneford Trust (£1,600); Asylum Aid, Books Abroad and Spade Work (£1,000 each); Carr Lane Counselling Centre Limited (£800) and Big Brum Theatre in Education, Cross Roads Care, Sport4Life and Albrighton Trust (£500 each).
FINANCES *Year* 2011–12 *Income* £54,126 *Grants* £35,750 *Assets* £1,305,426
TRUSTEES Prof. T. J. Cole; G. N. Cole; Dr J. G. L. Cole; T. E. C. Cole; Dr J. N. Cole; A. Frewin; K. Hebron; A. J. L. Cole.
HOW TO APPLY On an application form available to download from the website. Application forms

should be returned with a one page letter outlining your project and how a grant can help you. You should also attach a copy of your latest accounts if these are not already available to view on the Charity Commission website. The trust prefers to receive applications electronically. Trustees meet to consider applications twice a year usually in April/May and October/November, applications should be received six weeks before the meeting and precise deadlines are available on the website. Applicants will be notified of the outcome in writing within six weeks of the meeting.
WHO TO APPLY TO Lise Jackson, PO Box 955, Haslingfield, Cambridge CB23 1WX *Tel.* 01223 871676 *email* thecoletrust@gmail.com *Website* www.colecharitabletrust.org.uk

....

■ The Colefax Charitable Trust

CC NO 1017285   ESTABLISHED 1993
WHERE FUNDING CAN BE GIVEN Berkshire and Hampshire.
WHO CAN BENEFIT Registered charities.
WHAT IS FUNDED General charitable purposes.
WHAT IS NOT FUNDED No grants to individuals.
SAMPLE GRANTS Previous beneficiaries have included: Church on the Heath, Homestart, Jumbulance, Living Paintings Trust, Newbury District OAP Association, Newbury Spring Festival, Prospect Educational Trust, Reading Voluntary Action, Reliance Cancer Foundation, Southend Residents' Association and Watership Brass.
FINANCES *Year* 2011–12 *Income* £247,969 *Grants* £89,110 *Assets* £10,794,769
TRUSTEES J. E. Heath; H. J. Krohn.
HOW TO APPLY 'The trustees decide jointly which charitable institutions are to receive donations from the trust. No invitations are sought from eligible institutions.'
WHO TO APPLY TO Hans J. Krohn, Trustee, Westbrook House, St Helens Gardens, The Pitchens, Wroughton, Wiltshire SN4 0RU *Tel.* 01635 200415

....

■ The John and Freda Coleman Charitable Trust

CC NO 278223   ESTABLISHED 1979
WHERE FUNDING CAN BE GIVEN Hampshire and Surrey and surrounding areas.
WHO CAN BENEFIT Education and training centres.
WHAT IS FUNDED The trust aims to provide: 'an alternative to an essentially academic education, to encourage and further the aspirations of young people with talents to develop manual skills and relevant technical knowledge to fit them for satisfying careers and useful employment. The aim is to develop the self-confidence of individuals to succeed within established organisations or on their own account and to impress upon them the importance of service to the community, honesty, good manners and self-discipline.'
WHAT IS NOT FUNDED No grants are made to students.
TYPE OF GRANT Loans not given. Grants to 'kick start' relevant projects, capital costs other than buildings and core costs are all considered. Recurrent grants are given.
RANGE OF GRANTS Up to £20,000.
SAMPLE GRANTS Surrey Care Trust (£11,000); Surrey SATRO (£10,000); Transform (£8,000);

Guildford YMCA (£5,500); Second Chance (£3,000); the Yvonne Arnaud Theatre Youth Drama Training (£2,500); Step by Step (£1,500); and Leonard Cheshire (£500).

FINANCES *Year* 2011–12 *Income* £36,593 *Grants* £50,200 *Assets* £833,842

TRUSTEES Paul Coleman; Jeanette Bird; Brian Coleman.

HOW TO APPLY In writing to the correspondent. Telephone calls are not welcome.

WHO TO APPLY TO Jeanette Bird, Trustee, 3 Gasden Drive, Witley, Godalming, Surrey GU8 5QQ *Tel.* 01428 681333 *email* questrum.holdings@ gmail.com

■ The Bernard Coleman Trust

CC NO 1075731   **ESTABLISHED** 1999

WHERE FUNDING CAN BE GIVEN England and Wales.

WHO CAN BENEFIT Charitable organisations.

WHAT IS FUNDED 'The objects of the charity are to provide coaching facilities to young sportsmen and sportswomen and to give donations to other similar sporting charities and grants to sporting clubs and associations. It also makes grants to medical services and to youth projects.'

RANGE OF GRANTS £500–£10,000.

SAMPLE GRANTS Previous beneficiaries include: Chance to Shine and Royal Hospital for Neurodisability (£10,000 each); Surrey Care Trust, the Hornsby Trust and Arundel Castle Cricket Foundation (£5,000 each); National Rheumatoid Arthritis Society and UCL Hospital Charitable Foundation (£3,000 each).

FINANCES *Year* 2011–12 *Income* £22,600 *Grants* £65,000

TRUSTEES Bernard Coleman; Derek Newton; James Fairclough; Michael Courtness; Joyce Coleman.

HOW TO APPLY In writing to the correspondent.

WHO TO APPLY TO Sheila Stewart, The Secretary, 5 Ravenswood Close, Cobham, Surrey KT11 3AQ *Tel.* 01932 866508 *email* sheilastew@live.co.uk

■ The George Henry Collins Charity

CC NO 212268   **ESTABLISHED** 1959

WHERE FUNDING CAN BE GIVEN Within a 50-mile radius of Birmingham, or overseas.

WHO CAN BENEFIT Local charities and local branches of registered national charities in Birmingham benefiting older people, the socially isolated, or people who are ill.

WHAT IS FUNDED Wide, but the relief of illness, infirmity, old age or loneliness take preference. Trustees will consider donating one-tenth of annual income to charities for use overseas.

WHAT IS NOT FUNDED No grants to individuals.

TYPE OF GRANT One-off project funding.

RANGE OF GRANTS Between £250–£1,000

SAMPLE GRANTS ABF The Soldiers Charity, Birmingham City Mission and Spinal Injuries Association (£1,000 each); Adoption Support, The Birmingham Pen Trade Heritage Association, Medical Foundation for the Care of Victims of Torture, Whizz-Kidz, Yemeni Day Centre, Birmingham Children's Hospital, City of Birmingham Symphony Orchestra, Cyclists Fighting Cancer and Deafblind UK (£500 each) and Birmingham Music Festival, Black Country Living Museum Trust, Home from Hospital Care, Solihull Bereavement Counselling Service and 1st Bilston Scout Group (£250 each).

FINANCES *Year* 2011–12 *Income* £51,583 *Grants* £41,400 *Assets* £1,525,348

TRUSTEES Anthony Collins; Sally Botteley; Andrew Waters; Roger Otto; Peter Coggan.

OTHER INFORMATION In 2011–12 grants were given to 77 organisations.

HOW TO APPLY In writing to the correspondent. The trustees usually meet in March, July and November.

WHO TO APPLY TO Chrissy Norgrove, c/o SGH Martineau LLP, 1 Colmore Square, Birmingham B4 6AA *Tel.* 0870 763 1000

■ The Sir Jeremiah Colman Gift Trust

CC NO 229553   **ESTABLISHED** 1920

WHERE FUNDING CAN BE GIVEN UK, with a preference for Hampshire, especially Basingstoke.

WHO CAN BENEFIT Projects with well-established needs for support; the trust has already established priority beneficiaries.

WHAT IS FUNDED Advancement of education and literary scientific knowledge; moral and social improvement of people; maintenance of churches of the Church of England and gifts and offerings to the churches; financial assistance to past and present employees/members of Sir Jeremiah Colman at Gatton Park or other institutions associated with Sir Jeremiah Colman.

WHAT IS NOT FUNDED Grants are not made to individuals requiring support for personal education, or to individual families for welfare purposes.

SAMPLE GRANTS The Bucke Collins Charitable Trust (£5,000); The Nehemiah Project (£3,000); The Art Fund (£2,000); Basingstoke and North Hants Medical Trust, Royal Horticultural Society and Oakley Parochial Church Council (£1,500 each); Hackney Academy, National Trust, The Hunting office, Royal Alexandra and Albert School, Spinal Injuries Association, Wessex Counselling Service, St Michael's Hospice and Youth for Christ (£1,000 each).

FINANCES *Year* 2011–12 *Income* £144,608 *Grants* £105,965 *Assets* £4,839,147

TRUSTEES Michael Colman; Judith Colman; Oliver Colman; Cynthia Colman; Jeremiah Colman; Sue Colman.

OTHER INFORMATION The grants total is comprised of £57,000 in 'annual donations' and £49,000 in 'special donations'.

HOW TO APPLY The trust states the unsolicited applications are unwelcome.

WHO TO APPLY TO V. R. Persson, Secretary to the Trustees, Malshanger, Basingstoke, Hampshire RG23 7EY *Tel.* 01256 780252

■ Col-Reno Ltd

CC NO 274896   **ESTABLISHED** 1977

WHERE FUNDING CAN BE GIVEN UK, USA and Israel.

WHO CAN BENEFIT Religious and educational institutions benefiting children, young adults, students and Jewish people.

WHAT IS FUNDED Jewish religion and education.

RANGE OF GRANTS Mostly under £2,000.

SAMPLE GRANTS Society of Friends of the Torah (£17,000); Chabad of Hendon and Lubavitch of Liverpool (£8,500 each); Hasmonean High School (£2,000); Friends of Small Communities (£1,600); Yad Eliezer Trust (£1,250); Zionist Federation (£1,150); Ohel Torah Trust (£800) and Jerusalem College for Girls (£400).

FINANCES *Year* 2011–12 *Income* £110,528
Grants £53,260 *Assets* £1,116,761
TRUSTEES Martin Stern; Alan Stern; Keith Davis;
Rhona Davis; Chaim Stern; Libbie Goldstein.
HOW TO APPLY In writing to the correspondent.
WHO TO APPLY TO The Trustees, 10 Hampshire
Court, 9 Brent Street, London NW4 2EW
Tel. 020 8202 7013

■ The Colt Foundation

CC NO 277189   **ESTABLISHED** 1978
WHERE FUNDING CAN BE GIVEN UK.
WHO CAN BENEFIT Universities and research
establishments benefiting research workers and
students taking higher degrees.
WHAT IS FUNDED Research projects at universities
and other independent research institutions into
occupational and environmental health.
WHAT IS NOT FUNDED Grants are not made for the
general funds of another charity, directly to
individuals or projects overseas.
TYPE OF GRANT Research, project.
RANGE OF GRANTS £20,000–£100,000.
SAMPLE GRANTS University of Oxford (£75,000);
Heriot-Watt University (£59,500); Edinburgh
University (£56,500 in total); City University
(£27,000); Imperial College (£14,000); and Colt
Foundation Day 2012 (£8,000).
FINANCES *Year* 2012 *Income* £559,581
Grants £582,977 *Assets* £15,041,145
TRUSTEES Prof. David Coggon; Clare Gilchrist; Prof.
Sir Anthony J. Newman Taylor; Peter O'Hea; Alan
O'Hea; Jerome O'Hea; Natasha Heydon; Patricia
Lebus.
OTHER INFORMATION £161,000 was awarded to an
unspecified number of students.
HOW TO APPLY The foundation provided the following
information on its website:
'The trustees meet twice a year to review
applications, in the spring and in the autumn, and
applications normally need to be received at the
beginning of April and October to be considered at
the meetings. Applicants can submit a single
sheet lay summary at any time during the year
prior to working on a full application, so that
advice can be given on whether the work is likely
to fall within the remit of the foundation. The
trustees are particularly keen to fund research
that is likely to make a difference to government
policy or working practices.'
'**What needs to be in an application**'
'Applications should contain sufficient
information for the Scientific Advisers to be able
to comment, and should include a lay summary
for the trustees' first appraisal. This lay summary
is essential as the majority of the trustees do not
have a medical or scientific background. This
summary will help them in their decision between
the different applications under consideration.
Applications are not expected to exceed 3,000
words, excluding references, the lay summary and
justification of resources. Brief CVs, not
exceeding two sides of A4 paper, should be
attached for each of the major applicants. Read
the following questions carefully and bear them in
mind when preparing your application: what is the
work you would like to do? Explain the background
and its relevance for occupational health; explain
the specific research question and why it is
important; what are you proposing to do to
answer the research question? Why do you think
this is the right approach? How will it answer the
research question? What potential problem (e.g.
biases) do you see with this study design, and
how will they be addressed?; what do you think
will be the potential ultimately to influence policy

or practice for the benefit of workers or the wider
public? Who else is doing or has done work in the
same area, and how will your work complement
theirs?; what resources will you need to do the
work, and to what extent are these resources
already available? How much money do you need
to complete the work? You will need to
demonstrate that the study is good value for
money; who will do the work, and how much time
will each of the people, including yourself as PI,
involved devote to it?; how long will the work take
and when do you plan to start?'
'Applications involving research on people and/or
on human tissues must receive the approval of an
ethics committee. As a charity, the Colt
Foundation will only pay the Directly Incurred
Costs of a project, together with some categories
of necessary Directly Attributable Costs.
Universities are reimbursed by HEFCE for the
majority of Directly Attributable and Indirect
Costs. In addition to funding, the foundation
takes a continuing interest in its research
projects and holds annual review meetings. The
trustees may appoint an external assessor to
report on project progress. Grants are not made
to the general funds of other charities, or directly
to individuals, or to projects based outside the
UK. Details of recent projects supported are
shown on the website under 'Projects'.
Applicants are advised to visit the foundation's
helpful website.
WHO TO APPLY TO Jacqueline Douglas, Director, New
Lane, Havant, Hampshire PO9 2LY *Tel.* 02392
491400 *Fax* 02392 491363 *email* jackie.
douglas@uk.coltgroup.com *Website* www.
coltfoundation.org.uk

■ The Coltstaple Trust

CC NO 1085500   **ESTABLISHED** 2001
WHERE FUNDING CAN BE GIVEN Worldwide.
WHO CAN BENEFIT Charitable organisations.
WHAT IS FUNDED The relief of persons in need,
poverty or distress in third world countries and
the relief of persons who are homeless or in
housing need in the UK or any other part of the
world.
TYPE OF GRANT Recurrent.
SAMPLE GRANTS Oxfam (£140,000); St Mungo's and
Opportunity International (£40,000 each); Sport
for Life (£20,000) and The Connection at St
Martin's (£10,000).
FINANCES *Year* 2011–12 *Income* £218,048
Grants £250,000 *Assets* £4,514,438
TRUSTEES Lord Oakeshott of Seagrove Bay; Lord
Stoneham of Droxford; Elaine Colville; Dr
Philippa Oakeshott.
HOW TO APPLY Unfortunately the trust's funds are
fully committed. The trustees intend to continue
providing grants in a similar way to the recent
past while retaining flexibility as to the timing
and scale of grants.
WHO TO APPLY TO Lord Oakeshott of Seagrove Bay,
Trustee, Pollen House, 10–12 Cork Street,
London W1S 3NP *Tel.* 020 7439 4400

■ Colwinston Charitable Trust

CC NO 1049189   **ESTABLISHED** 1995
WHERE FUNDING CAN BE GIVEN Mostly Wales.
WHO CAN BENEFIT UK registered charities.
WHAT IS FUNDED The trustees seek to support
charitable organisations working in the fields of
opera/music theatre, classical music, and the
visual arts. They will also consider specific
project proposals for the assistance of libraries

and archives. Opera/music theatre – the trust aims to widen the opportunities to enjoy and appreciate performances of opera and music theatre, especially by assisting organisations to develop new audiences for performances of the highest quality; classical music – the trust aims to widen the opportunities to enjoy and to appreciate traditional classical music, and is especially interested to support projects that deliver high quality performances to areas where provision is limited; visual arts – the trust aims to widen the opportunities to enjoy and to be stimulated by the visual arts, to foster creative endeavour and to help develop new audiences; and libraries and archives – the trust will consider applications for specific projects but are unlikely to support capital projects. 'The trust is especially interested in *exceptional* projects that demonstrate *excellence* in terms of the creative ambition of the project, the quality of the artistic product, the calibre of the participating artists, and the value of the artistic experience for audiences and/or participants.'

WHAT IS NOT FUNDED The trust will not consider applications for capital building projects, for general appeals, for retrospective funding, for conferences and seminars, websites, publications, or from individuals.

RANGE OF GRANTS Up to £77,000.

SAMPLE GRANTS Agatha Christie Trust for Children (£77,000); Welsh National Opera (£75,000); Contemporary Galleries (£50,000); Artes Mundi (£32,000); Sinfonia Cymru (£25,000); Streetwise Opera and Three Choirs Festival (£20,000 each); Gregynog Festival (£15,000); Presteigne Festival of Music and the Arts (£9,000); Longborough Opera (£5,000) and Cardiff Ardwyn Singers (£1,000).

FINANCES *Year* 2011–12 *Income* £310,206 *Grants* £508,400 *Assets* £902,588

TRUSTEES Martin Paisner; Mathew Prichard; Robert Maskrey; Martin Tinney.

OTHER INFORMATION The trust derives its income from the royalties from the West End production of *The Mousetrap*, the Agatha Christie play, which opened in 1952.

HOW TO APPLY Full and detailed guidelines and an application form are available on the trust's website. 'In the first instance, and prior to sending any application to the trust, organisations should make contact with the Consultant Director, preferably by email, supplying a brief summary of the project and indicating the grant level being sought.' The trustees meet twice yearly (usually March and October) to consider applications and to make decisions on grants.

WHO TO APPLY TO Amanda McMurray, Consultant Director, c/o Rawlinson and Hunter, 8th Floor, 6 New Street Square, New Fetter Lane, London EC4A 3AQ *email* colwinston.trust@ntlworld.com *Website* www.colwinston.org.uk

----

■ Colyer-Fergusson Charitable Trust

CC NO 258958　　　**ESTABLISHED** 1969
WHERE FUNDING CAN BE GIVEN Kent.
WHO CAN BENEFIT Registered charities
WHAT IS FUNDED Social welfare and education of young people.
WHAT IS NOT FUNDED No grants to the following: animal welfare charities; individuals directly; research (except practical research designed to benefit the local community directly); hospitals or schools; political activities; commercial

ventures or publications; the purchase of vehicles including minibuses; overseas travel or holidays; retrospective grants or loans; direct replacement of statutory funding or activities that are primarily the responsibility of central or local government; large capital, endowment or widely distributed appeals; applications from churches and charities outside Kent.

TYPE OF GRANT One-off, recurring, capital, core, running and start-up costs will all be considered, as will salaries, buildings, project and research costs. Funding may be given for up to three years.

RANGE OF GRANTS £500–£75,000

SAMPLE GRANTS The Caldecott Foundation (£75,000); Kings Church Medway (£30,000); Herne Bay Sea Cadets and Special Needs Advisory and Activities Project (£20,000 each); Caring All Together on Romney Marsh and Cerebral Palsy Care – Kent (£15,000 each); Listening Books (£12,000); Eastbridge Hospital (£10,000); and Cliffe Memorial Hall (£5,000).

FINANCES *Year* 2011–12 *Income* £596,283 *Grants* £514,585 *Assets* £17,171,576

TRUSTEES Jonathan Monckton, Chair; Nicholas Fisher; Robert North; Ruth Murphy.

HOW TO APPLY Full guidance and application forms are available on the trust's website.

WHO TO APPLY TO Jacqueline Rae, Director, Hogarth House, 34 Paradise Road, Richmond, Surrey TW9 1SE *Tel.* 020 8948 3388 *email* grantadmin@cfct.org.uk *Website* www.cfct.org.uk

----

■ Comic Relief

CC NO 326568　　　**ESTABLISHED** 1985
WHERE FUNDING CAN BE GIVEN UK and overseas.
WHO CAN BENEFIT UK registered charities; voluntary organisations; and self-help groups.
WHAT IS FUNDED The charity's UK and international grantmaking strategy is based on five themes. Better Futures: improving the lives of vulnerable young people in the UK, and enabling some of the world's poorest people to gain access to vital services such as health and education; Healthier Finances: tackling financial poverty, and enabling economic resilience in families and communities, as well as supporting enterprise and employment; Safer Lives: reducing violence, abuse and exploitation; Stronger Communities: empowering people, organisations and networks to play an effective role in their communities and society, as well as nurturing talent and leadership; Fairer Society: helping people overcome inequality and have a say in decisions that affect their lives, whoever and wherever they are.

WHAT IS NOT FUNDED There are certain types of work and organisations that Comic Relief does not fund. If your proposal falls into one of these categories, do not apply: grants to individuals; medical research or hospitals; churches or other religious bodies where the monies will be used for religious purposes; work where there is statutory responsibility to provide funding; projects where the work has already taken place; statutory bodies, such as local authorities or Primary Care Trusts or organisations seeking funding to replace cuts by statutory bodies; profit-making organisations, except social enterprises; organisations who hold free reserves equivalent to the amount applied for may be turned down. The charity is also unable to fund minibuses.

TYPE OF GRANT Capital or revenue. One-off or spread over up to three years.

RANGE OF GRANTS Grants average between £25,000 and £40,000, and rarely exceed this upper limit.

FINANCES *Year* 2011–12 *Income* £89,465,000 *Grants* £76,838,000 *Assets* £134,457,000

TRUSTEES Tim Davie, chair; Richard Curtis; Lenny Henry; Suzi Aplin; Peter Salmon; Cilla Snowball; Colin Howes; Diana Barran; Harry Cayton; Imelda Walsh; Joe Cerrell; Mike Harris; Robert S. Webb; Theo Sowa; Tristia Clarke; Danny Cohen.

PUBLICATIONS Essential Information for applicants; Grants Strategy.

OTHER INFORMATION The grant total includes £32.3 million in UK grants and £45.7 million in international grants.

HOW TO APPLY Applications are made online via the charity's website, where full guidance is also provided. Potential applicants must register and complete Stage 1 of the process, an initial proposal. Applicants are shortlisted from those successfully completing Stage 1.

WHO TO APPLY TO Judith McNeill, Grants Director, 5th Floor, 89 Albert Embankment, London SE1 7TP *Tel.* 020 7820 2000 *Fax* 020 7820 2222 *Minicom* 020 7820 2005 *email* ukgrants@ comicrelief.com *Website* www.comicrelief.com

■ The Comino Foundation

CC NO 312875   **ESTABLISHED** 1971
WHERE FUNDING CAN BE GIVEN UK.

WHO CAN BENEFIT Organisations benefiting young adults and academics.

WHAT IS FUNDED Support of educational activities which encourage and enable individuals and groups to motivate and empower themselves; progressively develop their potential for the benefit of themselves and others; and encourage a culture which affirms and celebrates both achievement and responsible practice in industry and commerce.

WHAT IS NOT FUNDED No grants to individuals or for or research projects.

TYPE OF GRANT One-off.

RANGE OF GRANTS Typically up to around £50,000.

SAMPLE GRANTS Ideas Foundation (56,248); RSA Tipton Academy, Sheffield Hallam University (50,000 each); University of Winchester (£45,000); PAL Laboratories (£29,925); Local Solutions, Liverpool (29,401); Potential Trust (£12,000); Foundation for Science and Technology (3,000); and Association for Science Education (£2,500).

FINANCES *Year* 2011–12 *Income* £203,474 *Grants* £2,878,074 *Assets* £4,045,764

TRUSTEES A. Comino-James; David Perry; James Westhead.

OTHER INFORMATION The trust meets these aims through its patented GRASP approach, which offers a structure for thinking in a results-driven manner through a greater pattern, design and method of thinking. Most of the funds are given towards centres which promote the GRASP approach. Further information on this can be gathered from a leaflet prepared from the trust or on their extensive website.

HOW TO APPLY 'As a small charity, the foundation prefers to fund projects referred by the trustees and the Development Fellow. It does not run a small grant programme.'

WHO TO APPLY TO Anthony Darbyshire, Administrator, c/o Firs House, Bilby, Retford, Nottinghamshire DN22 8JB *Tel.* 01777 711141 *email* anthony. darbyshire@cominofoundation.org.uk *Website* www.cominofoundation.org.uk

■ Community First (Landfill Communities Fund)

CC NO 288117   **ESTABLISHED** 1983
WHERE FUNDING CAN BE GIVEN Wiltshire and Swindon

WHO CAN BENEFIT Charities, community organisations, parish or town councils.

WHAT IS FUNDED Community, built heritage and environmental projects in the vicinity of landfill sites and / or landfill operator depots.

WHAT IS NOT FUNDED Individuals and private companies.

TYPE OF GRANT Project costs.

RANGE OF GRANTS £3,000 to £20,000, occasionally more.

SAMPLE GRANTS Crickdale Jenner Hall (£52,000); Albdbourne Youth Council (£45,000); Forest Community Centre Group, Melksham (£30,000); Warminster Athenaeum Trust (£24,000); Leigh Park Community Association (£18,000); Alton Barnes Coronation Hall (£15,000) and Cholderton Village Hall and Codford Village Hall (£10,000 each.)

FINANCES *Year* 2012–13 *Grants* £482,455

TRUSTEES Alison Irving; Arthur Benjamin; Su Thorpe; Jane James; Dr Hoshang Barucha; Piers Dibbin; Dr Martin Hamer; Brian Clake; A. Fox.

HOW TO APPLY In the first instance download and complete the expression of interest form from the trust's website then email to: grants@communityfirst.org.uk. If you have been advised that your project is eligible for LCF funding, then download and complete the application form on the website, and submit with supporting documents as specified in the form.

WHO TO APPLY TO 41 Victoria Park, Great Cheverell, Devizes, Wiltshire SN10 5TS *Tel.* 01380 722475 *email* grants@communityfirst.org.uk *Website* www.communityfirst.org.uk

■ The Compton Charitable Trust

CC NO 280404   **ESTABLISHED** 1980
WHERE FUNDING CAN BE GIVEN Northamptonshire.

WHO CAN BENEFIT Charitable organisations, with a preference for those with a connection to the family estates of the Marquess of Northampton as well as those which the Marquess is a patron of.

WHAT IS FUNDED General charitable purposes.

SAMPLE GRANTS Shared Presence Foundation (£315,500); Northampton Community Foundation (£100,000); Feldon Church Trust (£5,000) and KIDS and Canonbury Masonic Research Centre (£4,000 each).

FINANCES *Year* 2011–12 *Income* £431,333 *Grants* £428,188 *Assets* £637,416

TRUSTEES Marquess of Northampton; Lady Pamela Northampton; Earl Daniel Compton.

HOW TO APPLY In writing to the correspondent. Unsolicited applications are considered, but are usually unsuccessful.

WHO TO APPLY TO The Trustees, Moore Stephens LLP, 150 Aldersgate Street, London EC1A 4AB

■ The Douglas Compton James Charitable Trust

CC NO 1091125   **ESTABLISHED** 2002
WHERE FUNDING CAN BE GIVEN Northamptonshire.

WHO CAN BENEFIT Registered charities.

WHAT IS FUNDED General, education and social welfare. Some preference is given for Masonic charities.

TYPE OF GRANT One-off and recurrent.

RANGE OF GRANTS Up to £30,000.

SAMPLE GRANTS Grand Charity (£27,000); NHS Bedford Hospital (£12,000); Corby Women's Centre (£9,100); Lakeland Day Care Hospice and Cransley Hospital (£5,000 each); Kettering General Hospital Charity Fund and Newton in the Willows (£3,000 each); and Life Education Northamptonshire Limited, Wellingborough All Saints Scouts, Lakeland Day Care Hospice and Deafblind UK (£2,000 each).

FINANCES *Year* 2011–12 *Income* £128,067 *Grants* £100,000

TRUSTEES Ian Clarke; John Humphrey; Richard Ongley; Brian Huckle.

HOW TO APPLY In writing to the correspondent.

WHO TO APPLY TO Louise Davies, Montague House, Chancery Lane, Thrapston, Northamptonshire NN14 4LN *Tel.* 01832 732161

■ The Congleton Inclosure Trust

CC NO 244136   **ESTABLISHED** 1795

WHERE FUNDING CAN BE GIVEN The town of Congleton and the parishes of Hulme Walfield and Newbold with Astbury.

WHO CAN BENEFIT Local organisations; UK organisations with projects in the area.

WHAT IS FUNDED The relief of people who are older, impotent and poor; the relief of distress and sickness; the provision and support of facilities for recreation or other leisure-time activities; the provision and support of educational facilities; and any other charitable purpose.

WHAT IS NOT FUNDED No grants to individuals outside the beneficial area or to organisations not benefiting exclusively the people in the area of benefit.

TYPE OF GRANT Buildings, capital, core costs, feasibility studies, salaries and start-up costs will be considered. Funding may be given for up to one year.

RANGE OF GRANTS Up to £5,000.

SAMPLE GRANTS Grant beneficiaries included: Visyon (5,000) New Life Church (£2,500); Age UK, Beartwon FM, Fol Hollow Club (£2,000 each); Congleton Choral Society (£1,500); Congleton High School (£1,200) and Electric Picture House (£250).

FINANCES *Year* 2012 *Income* £63,764 *Grants* £45,927 *Assets* £1,916,827

TRUSTEES KS. Wainwright, Chair; JW. Beardmore; J. Goodier; Revd Canon D. Taylor; KP. Boon; Revd JDM. Sharples; WB. Ball; JS. Davies; DL. Boon; D. Gibbons; JR. Hulse; D. Newman; J. Hollins.

OTHER INFORMATION The trust is willing to provide funding for core costs and capital costs with grants averaging £1,000–£5,000.

HOW TO APPLY On a form available from the correspondent. The trustees meet in January, April, July and October. Applications should be submitted by the first day of the month in which the trustees meet.

WHO TO APPLY TO D. A. Daniel, Clerk, PO Box 138, Congleton, Cheshire CW12 3SZ *Tel.* 01260 273180 *email* daviddaniel@uwclub.net

---

■ The Congregational and General Charitable Trust

CC NO 297013   **ESTABLISHED** 1987

WHERE FUNDING CAN BE GIVEN UK.

WHO CAN BENEFIT Protestant churches and community projects, in particular those associated with United Reformed and Congregational denominations.

WHAT IS FUNDED (i) Funds for building or property projects to churches and charities of the United Reformed and Congregational denominations or other Protestant churches. (ii) Church community projects seeking funding towards their capital costs.

TYPE OF GRANT One-off for property projects and capital costs.

FINANCES *Year* 2011–12 *Income* £3,758,000 *Grants* £169,000 *Assets* £13,615,000

TRUSTEES Robert B. Copleton; Revd Michael Heaney; Robert Wade; Margaret Atkinson; Revd Anthony G. Burnham; Stephen Wood; Stuart Young.

HOW TO APPLY In a form which can be downloaded from the trust's website. 'When sending your application attach any supporting documentation – such as your church's or organisation's accounts, the project's accounts, appeal leaflets or project literature – along with your signed application form.' The closing dates for applications are 31 January and 31 July each year.

WHO TO APPLY TO Robert B. Copleton, c/o 24 Hawkhead Road, Paisley, Renfrewshire PA1 3NA *Tel.* 01418 890402 *email* trust@congregational.co.uk *Website* www.congregational.co.uk

---

■ The Conscience Trust

CC NO 1044136   **ESTABLISHED** 1995

WHERE FUNDING CAN BE GIVEN UK.

WHO CAN BENEFIT Charitable organisations.

WHAT IS FUNDED 'The charity provides grants to other registered charities and organisations, primarily to assist with projects of a horticultural and eco-friendly nature.'

WHAT IS NOT FUNDED 'The trustees do not make grants in response to unsolicited applications not to individuals.'

SAMPLE GRANTS The sole beneficiary during the year was Torbay Coast and Countryside Trust (£29,555). Previous beneficiaries include: Fauna and Flora International; Garden Organic; The Miracle Trust; National Farmer Network; Organic Research Centre; Oxfam, St Christopher's Hospice; Sightsavers International; The Soil Association; The Woodland Trust and Worldwide Life Foundation.

FINANCES *Year* 2011–12 *Income* £41,618 *Grants* £29,555 *Assets* £588,115

TRUSTEES Adrian Miller; Will Michelmore; Simon Whewell; Prof. Jonathan Anderson.

HOW TO APPLY The trustees have stated that they do not make grants in response to unsolicited applications.

WHO TO APPLY TO Miller, c/o Michelmores LLP, Woodwater House, Pynes Hill, Exeter EX2 5WR

■ The Conservation Foundation

CC NO 284656   **ESTABLISHED** 1982

WHERE FUNDING CAN BE GIVEN Throughout the UK and overseas projects.

WHO CAN BENEFIT Individuals and organisations involved in environmental and conservation projects throughout the UK and overseas.

WHAT IS FUNDED Creation, management and support towards environmental and conservation orientated projects.

RANGE OF GRANTS £100–£1,500.

FINANCES *Year* 2012 *Income* £181,208 *Grants* £82,403 *Assets* £248,281

TRUSTEES David Shreeve; William Moloney; Prof. David Bellamy; Libby Kinmonth; Lindsay Dunn; Dorothy Harris.

OTHER INFORMATION Information about the foundation's current projects can be found on its website.

HOW TO APPLY Application details for specific awards are outlined on the foundation's website. General enquiries can also be directed to the correspondent.

WHO TO APPLY TO William Moloney, Trustee, 1 Kensington Gore, London SW7 2AR *Tel.* 020 7591 3111 *Fax* 020 7591 3110 *email* info@conservationfoundation.co.uk *Website* www.conservationfoundation.co.uk

■ The Consolidated Charities for the Infirm – Merchant Taylors' Company

CC NO 214266　　　**ESTABLISHED** 1960

WHERE FUNDING CAN BE GIVEN Lewisham, Southwark, Tower Hamlets, Hackney and environs; occasionally Greater London.

WHO CAN BENEFIT Charitable organisations.

WHAT IS FUNDED Relief of need, people with disabilities, infirm, older people and children, sheltered housing and residential care homes.

WHAT IS NOT FUNDED As a matter of policy, the Trustees do not usually contribute to: 'Bricks and mortar', although they will consider contributing to the fitting out or refurbishment of new or existing buildings; medical research; funds for 'on-granting' to third-party charities or individuals; generalised appeals; very large charities, except occasionally in support of localised work in the trustees' geographical area of interest; individual applicants.

RANGE OF GRANTS £250 to £32,000.

SAMPLE GRANTS Crossroads Greenwich and Lewisham (£31,500) St John's at Hackney (£26,000); Crisis Recovery UK (£20,000); Deptford Methodist Mission – Disabled People's Contact (£17,500); Queen Elizabeth's Foundation for Disabled People and Volunteer Centre Southwark (£15,000 each); St Mary-Le-Bow Young Homeless Charity (£10,000); Tall Ships Youth Trust (£8,000); Calibre Audio Library and Clapton Common Boys' Club (£5,000 each); Half Moon Theatre (£3,000); Connaught Opera (£1,000) and Childreach International (£250).

FINANCES *Year* 2012 *Income* £474,039 *Grants* £485,082 *Assets* £10,195,401

TRUSTEES Rupert Bull; Peter Magill; Judge Hugh Stubbs; Duncan Eggar.

HOW TO APPLY On a form available to download, together with criteria and guidelines, from the website. The charity states that emailed enquiries are preferred and responded to quickest.

WHO TO APPLY TO Nick Harris, Merchant Taylors' Hall, 30 Threadneedle Street, London EC2R 8JB *Tel.* 020 7450 4440 *email* charities@merchant-taylors.co.uk *Website* www.merchant-taylors.co.uk

■ Gordon Cook Foundation

SC NO SC017455　　　**ESTABLISHED** 1974

WHERE FUNDING CAN BE GIVEN UK

WHO CAN BENEFIT National curriculum agencies in the four home nations, Local Education Authorities, universities, colleges, schools and clusters of schools and the voluntary sector.

WHAT IS FUNDED The foundation is dedicated to the advancement of all aspects of education and training which are likely to promote character development and citizenship. In recent years the foundation has adopted the term 'values education' to denote the wide range of activity it seeks to support.

WHAT IS NOT FUNDED Individuals are unlikely to be funded.

TYPE OF GRANT One-off and recurring for projects and research. Funding may be given for more than three years.

RANGE OF GRANTS £5,000–£15,000.

SAMPLE GRANTS Tan Dance (£15,000); Five Nations (£9,000); and R.H.E.T and Association of Directors Education in Scotland (£5,000 each).

FINANCES *Year* 2011–12 *Income* £311,871 *Grants* £33,690 *Assets* £9,327,972

TRUSTEES Anne Harper; David Adams; Gavin Ross; Dr D. Sutherland; James Anderson.

OTHER INFORMATION Grants of £34,000 were made during 2011–12.

HOW TO APPLY Applications not accepted unless recommended through a trustee. The foundation has stated (November 2013) the following: 'the Gordon Cook Foundation operates a proactive policy in making grants to other bodies which means that the foundation itself identifies areas of work in values education which would benefit from further work and development and does not normally invite or respond to unsolicited applications for grant aid.'

WHO TO APPLY TO Sharon Hauxwell, Foundation Secretary, 15 Golden Square, Aberdeen AB10 1WF *Tel.* 01224 571010 *email* gordoncook@btconnect.com *Website* www.gordoncook.org

■ The Ernest Cook Trust

CC NO 313497　　　**ESTABLISHED** 1952

WHERE FUNDING CAN BE GIVEN UK.

WHO CAN BENEFIT Charitable or not for profit organisations working through education or training in three main areas of activity, being the environment and the countryside, the arts, crafts and architecture and literacy and numeracy.

WHAT IS FUNDED Grants are given for educational work only, focusing on children and young people in the fields of countryside and environment, arts and crafts, architecture, literary and numeracy, research and other educational projects.

WHAT IS NOT FUNDED Applicants must represent either registered charities or not-for-profit organisations. Grants are normally awarded on an annual basis and will not be awarded retrospectively. Grants are not made to pre-school groups, individuals, agricultural colleges, independent schools or local authorities; for building work, infrastructure or refurbishment work; for youth work, social support, therapy and medical treatment, including projects using the arts, environment or literacy and numeracy for these purposes; for projects related to sports, outward bound type activities or recreation; for overseas projects; for wildlife trusts and for farming and wildlife advisory groups other than those which are based in counties in which the ECT owns land (Buckinghamshire, Dorset, Gloucestershire, Leicestershire and Oxfordshire).

TYPE OF GRANT Conditional; annual; one-off. Project; research; salaries; and start-up costs. Funding may be given for up to three years.

466

Does the trust you have chosen match your needs? Haphazard applications waste postage and time

SAMPLE GRANTS Canterbury Cathedral and Opera North (£10,000 each); Watts Gallery (£8,000); Conservation Volunteers Northern Ireland (£7,000); Edward Peake Middle School (£5,000); Read for Life CIC (£4,000); and Making Places (£2,000).

FINANCES *Year* 2011–12 *Income* £3,433,460 *Grants* £1,523,732 *Assets* £112,741,609

TRUSTEES Anthony Bosanquet, Chair; Harry Henderson; Andrew Christie-Miller; Patrick Maclure; Miles C. Tuely; Victoria Edwards.

HOW TO APPLY The ECT aims to have a 'light-touch' application process with a view to enabling small regional or local organisations to apply for support. All applicant organisations must be based and working in the UK and should be either state schools, registered charities or other recognised not-for-profit organisations. It is very important however to read the exclusions before applying. Grants are normally awarded for one year only. There are no application forms. All applicants are asked to post a covering letter on the official headed paper of the applicant organisation and also include: up to two additional sheets of A4 describing the organisation, outlining the project and specifying its educational elements and the way in which it fits in with the interests of the ECT; a simple budget for the project, outlining the way in which the grant would be spent; a list of any other funding applications; the latest annual report and accounts for the organisation (schools are not required to send one). Do not send further supporting material or email applications, which are not accepted. It is advisable to read the examples of projects supported before making an application. **Questions** (not applications) can be addressed to the Grants Administrator. Applications must be posted.

'Applicants who have been successful previously are asked to wait for **three years** before re-applying.'

'**Large Grants programme:** The full board of trustees meets twice a year, in April and September, to consider grants in excess of £4,000. At the spring meeting only projects related to the arts, crafts and architecture and literacy and numeracy are considered while at the autumn meeting only projects covering environment and countryside and literacy and numeracy are considered. Apart from a few larger awards to projects especially close to the interests of the trustees, most awards are in the range of £4,000 – £10,000. Applications for the spring meeting (which usually takes place in mid-April) must be received by the trust by 31 January of that year. Applications for the autumn meeting (which takes place in September) must be received by the trust by 31 July of that year.'

'**Small Grants Programme:** Meetings to consider applications for the small grants programme take place bi-monthly throughout the year. This programme deals mainly, but not exclusively, with requests for support from state schools and small charitable organisations. There is no specific closing date; suitable applications are allocated to the next available meeting though it is always wise to think well ahead of the start date of your project. Although the full range of the small grants programme is up to £4,000, due to the huge pressure on the available resources most awards are in the region of £1,000 to £1,500.

WHO TO APPLY TO The Grants Administrator, Fairford Park, Fairford, Gloucestershire GL7 4JH *Tel.* 01285 712492 *Fax* 01285 713417 *email* grants@ernestcooktrust.org.uk *Website* www.ernestcooktrust.org.uk

■ The Cooks Charity

CC NO 297913   **ESTABLISHED** 1987

WHERE FUNDING CAN BE GIVEN UK, especially City of London.

WHO CAN BENEFIT Charities and individuals.

WHAT IS FUNDED Projects concerned with catering.

WHAT IS NOT FUNDED No individuals.

SAMPLE GRANTS Academy of Culinary Arts (£65,000); Springboard and FareShare (£25,000 each); Treloar Trust, Jamie Oliver Foundation and Bridge Project (£15,000 each); City University (£10,500); and Christ's Hospital (£5,000).

FINANCES *Year* 2011–12 *Income* £178,298 *Grants* £221,956 *Assets* £4,356,234

TRUSTEES Hugh Thornton; George Rees; Bev Puxley; Oliver Goodinge.

HOW TO APPLY In writing to the correspondent. Applications are considered in spring and autumn.

WHO TO APPLY TO Peter Wilkinson, Administrator, 18 Solent Drive, Warsash, Southampton SO31 9HB *email* clerk@cookslivery.org.uk

■ The Cookson Charitable Trust

CC NO 265207   **ESTABLISHED** 1972

WHERE FUNDING CAN BE GIVEN UK.

WHO CAN BENEFIT Charitable organisations.

WHAT IS FUNDED General charitable purposes.

RANGE OF GRANTS Up to £20,000.

SAMPLE GRANTS Amber Foundation (£20,000); The Landmark Trust (£5,000); Besom Foundation (£1,000); New College Oxford (£750); Bishopstone Parochial Church Council (£600) and Help for Heroes (£250).

FINANCES *Year* 2011–12 *Income* £26,209 *Grants* £47,000

TRUSTEES Hugh Cookson; Clive Cookson.

HOW TO APPLY In writing to the correspondent.

WHO TO APPLY TO Hugh Cookson, Trustee, Manor Farm, Stratford Tony, Salisbury SP5 4AT *Tel.* 01722 718496

■ The Catherine Cookson Charitable Trust

CC NO 272895   **ESTABLISHED** 1977

WHERE FUNDING CAN BE GIVEN UK, with some preference for the North East of England.

WHO CAN BENEFIT Charitable organisations.

WHAT IS FUNDED General charitable purposes.

RANGE OF GRANTS Mostly £1,000 or less. A few large grants are made.

SAMPLE GRANTS The British Library (£250,000); RNIB and Cancer Research (£100,000 each); Newcastle Dioceses Education Board (£50,000); Newcastle Royal Grammar School (£35,000); Clore Leadership Programme (£30,000); South West Tyneside Methodist Church (£25,000); Bedes World (£20,000) and Cystic Fibrosis (£10,000). Smaller grants were made to: Willow Burn Hospice (£1,000); Moorview Percy Hedley School, Lupus UK, 23rd South Shields Scout Group, Tall Ships Youth Trust, St Mary's Church – Horden and The Wheelyboat Trust (£500 each); Listening Books (£300) and Whizz-Kidz London, Sedgefield Players and Family Action (£250 each).

FINANCES *Year* 2011–12 *Income* £929,418 *Grants* £695,025 *Assets* £24,074,122

TRUSTEES David S. S. Hawkins; Peter Magnay; Hugo F. Marshall; Daniel E. Sallows; Jack E. Ravenscroft.

HOW TO APPLY In writing to the correspondent.

WHO TO APPLY TO Peter Magnay, Trustee, Thomas Magnay and Co, 13 Regent Terrace, Gateshead, Tyne and Wear NE8 1LU *Tel.* 01914 887459

WHO TO APPLY TO Ian Harbottle, Trustee, Middle Manor, Lascot Hill, Wedmore BS28 4AF *Tel.* 01934 712102

■ The Keith Coombs Trust

CC NO 1149791   ESTABLISHED 2012
WHERE FUNDING CAN BE GIVEN UK, with a preference for the West Midlands.
WHO CAN BENEFIT Registered charities.
WHAT IS FUNDED General, children and young people, disability.
TRUSTEES Anthony Coombs; Graham Coombs; Demetrios Markou; Christine Ingram; John Hanson.
HOW TO APPLY In writing to the correspondent.
WHO TO APPLY TO Anthony Coombs, Trustee, c/o S. & U. plc, Princes Gate Buildings, 2–6 Homer Road, Solihull, West Midlands B91 3QQ *Tel.* 01217 057777

■ Harold and Daphne Cooper Charitable Trust

CC NO 206772   ESTABLISHED 1962
WHERE FUNDING CAN BE GIVEN UK.
WHO CAN BENEFIT National charities.
WHAT IS FUNDED Medical research, health and Jewish charities.
WHAT IS NOT FUNDED No grants to individuals.
TYPE OF GRANT Small one-off grants and ongoing support for capital (buildings considered), project and research. Core costs and running costs are considered.
RANGE OF GRANTS One large grant; the remainder for smaller amounts.
SAMPLE GRANTS Jewish Care (£45,000); Action Against Cancer (£20,000) and Macmillan Cancer Support (£5,000).
FINANCES *Year* 2011–12 *Income* £93,651 *Grants* £70,000 *Assets* £2,834,901
TRUSTEES Judith Portrait; Timothy Roter; Abigail Roter; Dominic Roter.
HOW TO APPLY In writing to the correspondent; applications are not acknowledged.
WHO TO APPLY TO Alison Burton, Trust Administrator, c/o Portrait Solicitors, 21 Whitefriars Street, London EC4Y 8JJ *Tel.* 020 7092 6984

■ Mabel Cooper Charity

CC NO 264621   ESTABLISHED 1972
WHERE FUNDING CAN BE GIVEN UK, with a possible interest in South Devon.
WHO CAN BENEFIT Registered charities.
WHAT IS FUNDED General charitable purposes. Preference is given to projects with low overheads.
WHAT IS NOT FUNDED No grants to individuals.
RANGE OF GRANTS up to £10,000
SAMPLE GRANTS Crisis (£5,000); Devon Air Ambulance (£10,000); Force Devon (£5,000); Salvation Army (£2,500); Shelter (£2,500); Cancer Research (£5,000); Alzheimer's Research UK (£5,000); St Luke's Hospice (£5,000); Macmillian Cancer Support (£5,000); Clic Sargent (£1,000) and St Peter's Hospice (£5,000).
FINANCES *Year* 2011–12 *Income* £54,833 *Grants* £53,700 *Assets* £3,346,681
TRUSTEES Alison Barrett; Joan Harbottle; Ian Harbottle; David John Harbottle.
HOW TO APPLY The trust states that it does not welcome, or reply to, unsolicited applications.

■ The Alice Ellen Cooper Dean Charitable Foundation

CC NO 273298   ESTABLISHED 1977
WHERE FUNDING CAN BE GIVEN Mainly local organisations in Dorset and west Hampshire as a top priority.
WHO CAN BENEFIT Registered charities.
WHAT IS FUNDED Registered charities supporting health, humanitarian causes, social disadvantage, education, religion, community, arts and culture, amateur sport and disability.
WHAT IS NOT FUNDED No grants to individuals.
TYPE OF GRANT One-off and recurring.
RANGE OF GRANTS Mostly £1,000–£10,000
SAMPLE GRANTS Sheltered Work Opportunities (£30,000); The Crumbs Project, Dorset Archives Trust, Marie Curie Cancer Care, Shelter and Youth Resources Services Limited (£10,000 each); Eventide Homes Bournemouth (£8,000); Families for Children Trust Inspire Foundation and Listening Books (£5,000 each); Forest Forge Theatre Company and Motivation Charitable Trust (£3,000 each); British Liver Trust and Talking Newspapers Association (£2,000 each); and Moving On and Samaritans – Hampshire Projects (£1,000 each).
FINANCES *Year* 2011–12 *Income* £1,065,933 *Grants* £543,700 *Assets* £24,338,894
TRUSTEES John Bowditch; Linda Bowditch; Rupert Edwards; Douglas Neville-Jones; Emma Blackburn.
HOW TO APPLY In writing to the correspondent. Each application should include: name and address of organisation; charity registration number; details of the project; details of the community, including area covered and numbers who will benefit from the project; details of fundraising activities and other anticipated source of grants; a copy of the latest financial accounts.
WHO TO APPLY TO Rupert Edwards, Trustee, Edwards and Keeping, Unity Chambers, 34 High East Street, Dorchester, Dorset DT1 1HA *Tel.* 01305 251333 *Fax* 01305 251465 *email* office@ edwardsandkeeping.co.uk

■ The Co-operative Charitable Foundation

CC NO 1080834   ESTABLISHED 2000
WHERE FUNDING CAN BE GIVEN The trading area of the Co-operative Group 's United Region which has interests within the North West, south Cumbria, Yorkshire, north Midlands, Northern Ireland and North Wales.
WHO CAN BENEFIT Local groups and organisations. 'It is particularly interested in locally led and run groups which can demonstrate evidence of co-operative values and principles: self-help, equality, democracy, concern for the community.'
WHAT IS FUNDED 'Supporting community groups to find co-operative solutions to community challenges.' In support of its community-led approach the foundation has one focussed grantmaking programme, the *Community Support Programme*. This programme was developed to help groups who want to 'make a difference' in their own communities, through grass roots community activity. The community can be geographically-based, such as a village,

town or housing estate, or could be a community of people brought together to address a specific issue. Examples of work we may fund under the programme include: activities that encourage people to work with others who have similar needs or face similar challenges, including the development of community groups; work that aims to resolve or reduce conflict, such as community mediation or the reduction of harassment; the setting up or development of community safety schemes; provision and improvement of community facilities that allow premises and equipment to be shared between organisations; work to assist people, who would not otherwise have the opportunity, to gain access to IT equipment, training or support; development of out-reach work to offer services to the most vulnerable in society; improvement of access to information, advice and advocacy services that enable people to make informed choices about their lives or lifestyle; work which supports that undertaken by volunteers; work with communities with significant needs such as minority groups, people with disabilities and their carers, or those with special needs, mental health problems and learning disabilities.

WHAT IS NOT FUNDED No funding for: applications from outside the Co-operative Group – United Region area, including overseas applications; organisations whose activities are not recognised as charitable or philanthropic; charities that have large unrestricted reserves; national charities (unless there is a specific local project, which has been initiated by the local community benefiting from the grant); applications for salaries; replacement of statutory funding; applications from local authorities; applications from health authorities; activities that are the responsibility of local or central government; organisations that promote political parties; applications for projects which are deemed to promote a particular religious group or activity; applications to help animals; the Scout movement, including Guides, Cubs, Brownies, Beavers and Rainbows; groundwork; YMCA and YWCA; schools, including PTAs; residential homes which are the responsibility of the local authority; retrospective grants; groups not demonstrating self-help; applications benefiting individuals; grants for outstanding debts or down payments for loans; groups that have received a grant from the foundation in the last twelve months; groups which are applying for more than one year's worth of funding; applications where the questions on the form have been amended or altered.

TYPE OF GRANT One-year projects – for either part or total funding, capital costs and revenue costs (but not salaries).

SAMPLE GRANTS Envision (£140,000); YWCA (£105,000); Regional Youth Work Unity North East (£93,000); Young Scot (£70,000); Changemakers (£4,000); the Prince's Trust and UnLtd (£2,000 each); and Community Arts North West, Contact, Groundwork London, Young Bristol and ICA: UK (£1,000 each).

FINANCES *Year* 2011–12 *Income* £156,858 *Grants* £135,500 *Assets* £11,563,113

TRUSTEES Tom Maddison; Roger Berry; Eleanor Stitt; John Crouch; Marilynne Burbage; Maria Cearns; Robert Moore; William Sadler; Dorothy Miller; Edward Powell; Ms Katherine Savage.

HOW TO APPLY Full guidelines, application details and application forms can be downloaded from the foundation's website. The trustees meet four times a year to approve grants, deadline dates can be found on the website.

WHO TO APPLY TO Clare Oakley, Charity Manager, New Century House, 6th Floor, Corporation Street, Manchester M60 4ES *Tel.* 01612 463044 *email* foundation@coop.co.uk *Website* www.co-operative.coop/join-the-revolution/our-plan/keeping-communities-thriving/funds-and-foundations

....

■ The Marjorie Coote Animal Charity Trust

CC NO 208493   **ESTABLISHED** 1954
WHERE FUNDING CAN BE GIVEN Worldwide.
WHO CAN BENEFIT Registered charities for the benefit of animals.
WHAT IS FUNDED The care and protection of horses, dogs and other animals and birds. It is the policy of the trustees to concentrate on research into animal health problems and on the protection of species, whilst continuing to apply a small proportion of the income to general animal welfare, including sanctuaries.
WHAT IS NOT FUNDED No grants to individuals.
TYPE OF GRANT One-off and recurrent.
RANGE OF GRANTS Grants are usually in the range of £500–£10,000.
SAMPLE GRANTS Recurrent grants: Animal Health Trust (£20,000); Pet Aid Hospital Sheffield (£8,000); RSPCA Sheffield (£5,000); Friends of Conservation and Brooke Hospital for Animals (£3,000 each); Wildfowl and Wetlands Trust and Devon Wildlife Trust (£2,000 each) and Sheffield Wildlife Trust (£1,000). One-off grants: PSDA (New Sheffield Centre (£50,000); The David Shepherd Wildlife Foundation, Save the Rhino International and Elephant Family (£1,000 each); Cat Abuse Treatment Society, Nowzad Dogs Charity and South West Equine Protection (£500) and World Society for the Protection of Animals (£250).
FINANCES *Year* 2011–12 *Income* £105,780 *Grants* £132,700 *Assets* £3,265,458
TRUSTEES Sir Hugh Neill; Jill P. Holah; Lady Neill; S. E. Browne; N. C. Baguley.
HOW TO APPLY In writing to the correspondent. Applications should reach the correspondent during September for consideration in October/ November. Appeals received at other times of the year are deferred until the following Autumn unless they require consideration for an urgent 'one-off' grant for a specific project.
WHO TO APPLY TO Jill P. Holah, Trustee, End Cottage, Terrington, York YO60 6PU *email* info@ mcacharity.org.uk

....

■ The Marjorie Coote Old People's Charity

CC NO 226747   **ESTABLISHED** 1958
WHERE FUNDING CAN BE GIVEN South Yorkshire.
WHO CAN BENEFIT Old people of small means.
WHAT IS FUNDED The established charitable organisations which work actively for the benefit of old people in the area of jurisdiction.
WHAT IS NOT FUNDED No grants to individuals.
RANGE OF GRANTS Usually up to £15,000.
SAMPLE GRANTS St Luke's Capital Appeal Project (£75,000); Cavendish Cancer Care and Age UK Sheffield (£15,000 each); Sheffield Dial-A-Ride (£10,000); The University of Sheffield (SISA)(for dementia information) and South Yorkshire Community Foundation (£5,000 each); British Red Cross (£2,000); Lost Chord (£1,000); Deafblind UK (£500) and The Almshouse Association (£200).

Think carefully about every application. Is it justified?

469

FINANCES *Year* 2011–12 *Income* £101,623
Grants £168,700 *Assets* £2,878,137
TRUSTEES Sir Hugh Neill; J. A. Lee; Lady Neill;
N. Hutton.
HOW TO APPLY In writing to the correspondent during
May. Appeals received at other times of the year
are deferred unless for an urgent grant for a
specific one-off project.
WHO TO APPLY TO Lady Neill, Trustee, Barn Cottage,
Lindrick Common, Worksop, Nottinghamshire
S81 8BA *Tel.* 01909 562806
email neillcharities@me.com

■ The Helen Jean Cope Trust

CC NO 1125937   ESTABLISHED 1998
WHERE FUNDING CAN BE GIVEN Mostly Leicestershire,
but also Derbyshire and Nottinghamshire.
WHO CAN BENEFIT Registered charities only.
WHAT IS FUNDED General charitable purposes,
supporting single projects.
WHAT IS NOT FUNDED No grants to individuals or
unregistered charities.
TYPE OF GRANT Generally single projects. Capital and
core costs. Unrestricted funding. Replacement
of statutory funding.
RANGE OF GRANTS £500 to £5,000
SAMPLE GRANTS Hearing Dogs for Deaf People,
Derbyshire Wildlife Trust and The Salvation Army
(£5,000 each); Coping with Cancer (£3,000); St
John the Baptist Church Belton and Epilepsy
Society (£2,000 each); Good News Family Care
and John's Lee Wood Scout Campsite (£1,500
each); Music in Hospitals (£1,000); Orchard
Primary School (£800) and Stoney Stanton War
Memorial Playing Fields (£500).
FINANCES *Year* 2012 *Income* £104,291
Grants £96,940 *Assets* £3,091,698
TRUSTEES J. M. Carrington; Lindsay Brydson;
Graham Freckelton; Alan Roberts
HOW TO APPLY An online application is available from
the trust's website. For details of what
information should be included in the
application see the website.
WHO TO APPLY TO J. M. Carrington, Secretary,
1 Woodgate, Loughborough, Leicestershire
LE11 2TY *Tel.* 01509 218298 *email* info@
thehelenjeancopecharity.co.uk *Website* www.
thehelenjeancopecharity.co.uk

■ The J. Reginald Corah Foundation Fund

CC NO 220792   ESTABLISHED 1953
WHERE FUNDING CAN BE GIVEN Leicestershire and
Rutland.
WHO CAN BENEFIT Charitable organisations. However,
particular favour is given to hosiery firms
carrying out their business in the city or county
of Leicester and Rutland.
WHAT IS FUNDED General charitable purposes,
particularly for the benefit of employees and ex-
employees of hosiery firms carrying on business
in the city or county of Leicester and Rutland
WHAT IS NOT FUNDED Applications from individuals
are not considered unless made by, or
supported by, a recognised charitable
organisation.
TYPE OF GRANT One-off and recurrent
RANGE OF GRANTS Up to £10,000.
SAMPLE GRANTS Leicester Children's Holiday Centre
and Leicester Grammar School (£5,000 each);
LOROS and In Kind (£2,000 each); SSAFA
(£1,700); Family Action Leicester and Army

Benevolent Fund (£1,600) and Leicester Scouts
Council (£1,500).
FINANCES *Year* 2011–12 *Income* £112,570
Grants £77,434 *Assets* £4,064,892
TRUSTEES David Corah; Roger Bowder; Geoffrey
Makings.
OTHER INFORMATION In 2011–12 grants were given
to 104 organisations.
HOW TO APPLY In writing to the correspondent.
Trustees meet about every two months.
WHO TO APPLY TO The Trustees, c/o Harvey Ingram
Shakespeares LLP, 20 New Walk, Leicester
LE1 6TX *Tel.* 01162 545454

■ The Gershon Coren Charitable Foundation (also known as The Muriel and Gus Coren Charitable Foundation)

CC NO 257615   ESTABLISHED 1968
WHERE FUNDING CAN BE GIVEN UK and the developing
world.
WHO CAN BENEFIT Charitable organisations,
particularly Jewish organisations.
WHAT IS FUNDED General charitable purposes, social
welfare and Jewish causes.
RANGE OF GRANTS £500–£40,000.
SAMPLE GRANTS Gategi Village Self Help Group
(£75,000); Friends of the United Institute of
Arad (£30,000); Laniado UK (£9,000); Aish UK
(£7,000); Jewish Care, Hobrifa and Spiro Ark
(£5,000 each); Manchester Balfour Trust and
UKLFI (£3,000 each); Jewish Renaissance and
Kisharon (£2,000 each); Prostate Cancer
Research Fund and Macmillan Cancer Support
(£1,000 each); and Royal British Legion, Crisis
and CPRE (£500 each).
FINANCES *Year* 2011–12 *Income* £232,691
Grants £225,000 *Assets* £2,563,684
TRUSTEES Walter Stanton; Anthony Coren; Muriel
Coren.
HOW TO APPLY In writing to the correspondent.
WHO TO APPLY TO Muriel Cohen, Trustee, 5 Golders
Park Close, London NW11 7QR

■ Michael Cornish Charitable Trust

CC NO 1107890   ESTABLISHED 2005
WHERE FUNDING CAN BE GIVEN Nationwide and
overseas, however Lincolnshire area is
preferred.
WHO CAN BENEFIT Registered charities, individual
supported only in exceptional circumstances.
Preference for charities in the Lincolnshire area
and charities involving children.
WHAT IS FUNDED General charitable purposes,
involving advancement of health, education,
community and youth support, overseas aid.
TYPE OF GRANT Most grants are awarded to
registered charities, but grants to individuals for
worthy causes or in exceptional circumstances
may be considered. Capital grants. Unrestricted
funding.
RANGE OF GRANTS Average grant between £1,000
–£5,000.
SAMPLE GRANTS Christian Partners in Africa
(£13,500); Hill Holt Wood (£10,000); Off the
Bench, Pelican Trust and RNLI (£5,000 each);
Operation Smile and Wells for India (£2,500
each); Fenside Umbrella Group and the
Salvation Army (£2,000 each); Lincolnshire
Chaplaincy Services, Alternatives – Pregnancy
Advice Centre, Tall Ships Youth Trust and the
Crosby Community Association (£1,000 each)
and Raleigh Foundation for an individual (£200).

FINANCES *Year* 2012 *Income* £168,884 *Grants* £109,450 *Assets* £13,606,004
TRUSTEES Michael Cornish; Susan Cornish; Richard Vigar.
OTHER INFORMATION The trustees meet quarterly.
HOW TO APPLY In writing to the correspondent.
WHO TO APPLY TO Richard Vigar, Trustee, 15 Newland, Lincoln, Lincolnshire LN1 1XG *Tel.* 01522 531341

■ The Evan Cornish Foundation

CC NO 1112703   **ESTABLISHED** 2005
WHERE FUNDING CAN BE GIVEN UK and overseas.
WHO CAN BENEFIT Charitable organisations.
WHAT IS FUNDED Education, older people, health, human rights, social and economic inequality, prisons.
WHAT IS NOT FUNDED The foundation is unable to support the following activities: religious activities; animal welfare; individuals/gap year students; political activities; medical research; and holiday club providers.
TYPE OF GRANT One-off.
RANGE OF GRANTS £200–£13,000.
SAMPLE GRANTS Unicef – City of Joy (£13,000); Christ Church Armley, Sheffield Together Women and Angels International (£10,000 each); Artlink (£8,500); Ambitious About Autism, Everychild and Lippy People (£7,500 each); Emmaus (£6,500); Hope Foundation, CAFOD and Kickstart (£5,000 each); Find Your Feet, Hope and Homes for Children and NOEL (£3,000 each); Sheffield Conversation Club and Notting Hill Churches Homeless Concern (£2,000 each); and Friends of the Elderly (£1,000).
FINANCES *Year* 2011–12 *Income* £7,091,264 *Grants* £714,554 *Assets* £12,934,334
TRUSTEES Rachel Cornish; Barbara Ward; Sally Cornish.
HOW TO APPLY The trustees will consider applications as well as seeking out causes to support. They have a three step application process which can be found on the foundation's website. First time applicants should complete the standard application form. Applicants who wish to apply again should complete the re-application form, which can also be found on the foundation's website. The trustees have two meetings per application deadline. One for UK based projects and one for overseas projects. This allows trustees to compare applications which are focused in similar areas. Applicants can re-apply for additional funding one year from the date of the last grant, however a one year progress report must be provided. Recipients of support are expected to provide feedback on the use of any grant and the achievements from it, through a six month update and a one year progress report.
WHO TO APPLY TO Rachel Cornish, Trustee, The Innovation Centre, 217 Portobello, Sheffield S1 4DP *email* contactus@evancornishfoundation.org.uk *Website* www.evancornishfoundation.org.uk

■ Cornwall Community Foundation

CC NO 1099977   **ESTABLISHED** 2003
WHERE FUNDING CAN BE GIVEN Cornwall and the Isles of Scilly.
WHO CAN BENEFIT Local projects in Cornwall and the Isles of Scilly that engage local people in making their communities better places to live. This includes groups, projects and individuals.
WHAT IS FUNDED Community-based causes.

RANGE OF GRANTS Usually up to £10,000.
SAMPLE GRANTS Goonhilly Wind Farm Community Fund (£65,000); Magic Porridge Pot (£48,000); The Lord and Lady St Levan Fund (£40,000); Adult Social Care (£37,000); Cornwall 100 Club (£14,500); Short Breaks for Carers Organisations (£13,000); China Clay Community Fund (£10,000); Cornwall Emergency Fund (£5,000); Youth Academy Fund (£2,000) and Gilbert McCabe Fund (£275).
FINANCES *Year* 2012 *Income* £838,131 *Grants* £457,533 *Assets* £2,460,421
TRUSTEES Tony Hogg; Oliver Baines; The Hon Evelyn Boscawen; The Lady Mary Holborow; Jane Hartley; James Williams; Margaret Bickford-Smith; Daphne Skinnard; John Ede; Bishop Tim Thornton; Lady George; Tim Smith; Elaine Hunt; Mark Mitchell; Thomas Varcoe; Charles Reynolds; Nicola Marquis.
HOW TO APPLY On a form available from the foundation. For general information about grants contact the grants team (tel.: 01566 779333 or e-mail: grants@cornwallfoundation.com). Criteria, guidelines and application process are also posted on the Foundation's website.
WHO TO APPLY TO Carolyn Boyce, Suite 1, Sheers Barton Barns, Lawhitton, Launceston, Cornwall PL15 9NJ *Tel.* 01566 779333 *email* office@cornwallfoundation.com *Website* www.cornwallfoundation.com

■ The Cornwall Historic Churches Trust

CC NO 218340   **ESTABLISHED** 1955
WHERE FUNDING CAN BE GIVEN Cornwall.
WHO CAN BENEFIT Places of Christian worship.
WHAT IS FUNDED The repair and restoration of churches, with particular regard to those of architectural or historical merit.
WHAT IS NOT FUNDED The trust is unlikely to consider the following: routine maintenance and repair work which the church community could be expected to deal with themselves; re-decoration – other than when it follows from a major restoration scheme; introduction of domestic or similar facilities within the church building; schemes which damage or adversely affect the basic building, especially its external appearance; replacement or installation of heating systems required for the comfort of the congregations; redesign and layout of the churchyard and work on tombstones – other than the restoration of specific tombstones with some significant historic connections; repair and/or maintenance of associated buildings (e.g. school rooms and church halls).
TYPE OF GRANT One-off grants.
RANGE OF GRANTS Up to £5,000. When determining the level of grant support, the trust operates a points system which takes the following factors into account: the age of the church or chapel; the merit of the building; the church's effort in two respects–(i) its participation in the CHCT's annual sponsored event and (ii) other church efforts to raise funds for the project; financial need; the church's own financial resources.
FINANCES *Year* 2012 *Income* £45,843
TRUSTEES Helen Briggs; Charles Hall; Vanessa Leslie; Dr Joanna Mattingly; Alice Boyd.
PUBLICATIONS Leaflet on Cornish church conservation.
OTHER INFORMATION Donations were approved to 23 churches and chapels.
HOW TO APPLY On an application form available from the trust's website or from the correspondent.

WHO TO APPLY TO Simon Coy, Hon. Secretary, Dipper Bridge, Ruthernbridge, Bodmin PL30 5LU *Tel.* 01208 831906 *email* mail@chct.info *Website* www.chct.info

■ The Duke of Cornwall's Benevolent Fund

CC NO 269183   ESTABLISHED 1975
WHERE FUNDING CAN BE GIVEN UK, with a number of grants made in the Cornwall area.
WHO CAN BENEFIT Charitable organisations.
WHAT IS FUNDED The relief of people in need of assistance because of sickness, poverty or age; the provision of alms-houses, homes of rest, hospitals and convalescent homes; the advancement of education; the advancement of the arts and religion; and the preservation for the benefit of the public of lands and buildings.
WHAT IS NOT FUNDED No grants to individuals.
TYPE OF GRANT One-off.
RANGE OF GRANTS Typically under £5,000 each.
SAMPLE GRANTS Business in the Community (£20,000); Strata Florida and Gordonstown School (£5,000 each); St Mary's Pilot Gig and Dorchester Festival (£2,000 each); and Phoenix Stroke Appeal, Friends of the Countryside, Soil Association and Echo Cornwall (£1,000 each).
FINANCES *Year* 2011–12 *Income* £540,772 *Grants* £100,010 *Assets* £3,330,033
TRUSTEES Bertie Ross; The Hon. James Leigh-Pemberton.
HOW TO APPLY In writing to the correspondent.
WHO TO APPLY TO Robert Mitchell, 10 Buckingham Gate, London SW1E 6LA *Tel.* 020 7834 7346

■ The Cornwell Charitable Trust

CC NO 1012467   ESTABLISHED 1992
WHERE FUNDING CAN BE GIVEN The south west of England, with a preference for Cornwall.
WHO CAN BENEFIT Registered charities.
WHAT IS FUNDED General charitable purposes, funding projects and individuals specifically and primarily in the Cornwall area.
WHAT IS NOT FUNDED No support for travel, expeditions or university grants.
TYPE OF GRANT Project and capital.
RANGE OF GRANTS Up to £10,000.
SAMPLE GRANTS Reprieve (£10,000); St Buryan Church (£5,000); George Orwell Memorial Trust (£3,000); Cornwall Hospice Care (£1,500) and Prostate Action Appeal, BBC Children in Need, Phoenix Stroke Appeal and Truro Cathedral Inspire Appeal (£1,000 each).
FINANCES *Year* 2011–12 *Income* £43,976 *Grants* £42,904 *Assets* £1,093,584
TRUSTEES David Cornwell; Valerie Cornwell; Matthew Bennett; Mark Bailey.
OTHER INFORMATION In 2011–12 grants were given to 63 organisations, the majority of which were for under £1,000.
HOW TO APPLY In writing to the correspondent.
WHO TO APPLY TO Mark Bailey, Trustee, Devonshire House, 1 Devonshire Street, London W1W 5DR *Tel.* 020 7304 2000

■ The Sidney and Elizabeth Corob Charitable Trust

CC NO 266606   ESTABLISHED 1973
WHERE FUNDING CAN BE GIVEN UK.
WHO CAN BENEFIT Charitable organisations.
WHAT IS FUNDED General charitable purposes, supporting a range of causes including education, arts, welfare and Jewish charities.
WHAT IS NOT FUNDED No grants to individuals or non-registered charities.
RANGE OF GRANTS Up to £90,000.
SAMPLE GRANTS Oxford Centre for Hebrew and Jewish Studies (£50,000); University College London (£40,000); British Friends of Feuerstein and London Jewish Cultural Centre (£10,000 each); The Council of Christians and Jews and Ohel Torah Beth David (£5,000 each); JNF – Jewish Botanical Gardens (£3,000); Ben-Gurion University Foundation and Community Security Trust (£2,500 each) and Israel Educational Foundation, Royal National Theatre and World Jewish Relief (£2,000 each).
FINANCES *Year* 2011–12 *Income* £535,805 *Grants* £245,353 *Assets* £364,196
TRUSTEES A. L. Corob; E. Corob; C. J. Cook; J. V. Hajnal; S. A. Wechsler; S. Wiseman.
HOW TO APPLY In writing to the correspondent. The trustees meet at regular intervals.
WHO TO APPLY TO The Trustees, c/o Corob Holdings, 62 Grosvenor Street, London W1K 3JF *Tel.* 020 7499 4301

■ The Corona Charitable Trust

CC NO 1064320   ESTABLISHED 1997
WHERE FUNDING CAN BE GIVEN UK and overseas.
WHO CAN BENEFIT Jewish people, particularly the aged and the young.
WHAT IS FUNDED Jewish religious education and relief-in-need.
SAMPLE GRANTS Previous beneficiaries have included: Menorah Foundation School, the ZSV Trust, Ahavas Shalom Charity Fund, WST Charity Limited, and Edgware Jewish Primary School.
FINANCES *Year* 2011–12 *Income* £21,269 *Grants* £45,000
TRUSTEES Abraham Levy; Alison Levy; Ben Levy.
HOW TO APPLY In writing to the correspondent.
WHO TO APPLY TO The Trustees, 16 Mayfield Gardens, Hendon, London NW4 2QA

■ The Bryan Christopher Corrigan Charitable Trust

CC NO 1147872   ESTABLISHED 2012
WHERE FUNDING CAN BE GIVEN UK.
WHO CAN BENEFIT Registered charities.
WHAT IS FUNDED Health and religious activities.
TRUSTEE NatWest Trust Services.
HOW TO APPLY In writing to the correspondent.
WHO TO APPLY TO NatWest Trust Services, 5th Floor, Trinity Quay 2, Avon Street, Bristol BS2 0PT *Tel.* 05516577371

■ The Costa Family Charitable Trust (formerly the Morgan Williams Charitable Trust)

CC NO 221604   ESTABLISHED 1964
WHERE FUNDING CAN BE GIVEN UK.
WHO CAN BENEFIT Christian organisations.
WHAT IS FUNDED Charities with which the trustees have some connection.

SAMPLE GRANTS Previously: Alpha International (£250,000); VSO (£12,000); Pentecost Festival (£10,000); the Chase Trust and the Philo Trust (£5,000 each); British Museum (£2,000); and the Wallace Collection (£1,000).

FINANCES *Year* 2011–12 *Income* £322,241 *Grants* £300,000

TRUSTEES Kenneth Costa; Ann Costa.

HOW TO APPLY NB The trust states that only charities personally connected with the trustees are supported and absolutely no applications are either solicited or acknowledged.

WHO TO APPLY TO Kenneth Costa, Trustee, 43 Chelsea Square, London SW3 6LH *Tel.* 07785 467441

■ The John and Barbara Cotton Charitable Foundation

CC NO 1145865   **ESTABLISHED** 2012

WHERE FUNDING CAN BE GIVEN UK, with a preference for West Yorkshire.

WHO CAN BENEFIT Registered charities.

WHAT IS FUNDED General charitable purposes

TRUSTEES John Cotton; Barbara Cotton.

OTHER INFORMATION The foundation was registered in February 2012 and has general charitable purposes. The settlors and trustees of the foundation are directors of John Cotton Group Limited, which includes 'Europe's leading manufacturer of pillows, duvets and mattress protectors'.

HOW TO APPLY In writing to the correspondent.

WHO TO APPLY TO John Cotton, Trustee, c/o John Cotton Group Limited, Nunbrook Mils, Huddersfield Road, Mirfield, West Yorkshire WF14 0EH *Tel.* 01924 496571 *email* saraha@johncotton.co.uk

■ The Cotton Industry War Memorial Trust

CC NO 242721   **ESTABLISHED** 1947

WHERE FUNDING CAN BE GIVEN UK.

WHO CAN BENEFIT Individuals and organisations.

WHAT IS FUNDED This trust makes grants to all aspects of aid and assistance to employees, former employees and students of the textile industry.

SAMPLE GRANTS Children's Adventure Farm Trust (£30,000); Samuel Crompton Fellowship Award (£12,000); the Society of Dyers and Colourists (£10,000); Participation Works (£6,600); Bradford Textile Society (£1,500); and Salford Children Holiday Camp (£130).

FINANCES *Year* 2012 *Income* £305,065 *Grants* £60,730 *Assets* £5,989,036

TRUSTEES Peter Booth; Christopher Trotter; Prof. Albert Lockett; Keith Lloyd; Keith Garbett; Peter Reid; Philip Roberts; John Reed.

OTHER INFORMATION The grants figure includes one grant to an individual of £500.

HOW TO APPLY In writing to the correspondent. The trust meets at least four times a year to consider requests for funds and grants.

WHO TO APPLY TO Hilda Ball, Secretary, 42 Boot Lane, Heaton, Bolton BL1 5SS *Tel.* 01204 491810

■ The Cotton Trust

CC NO 1094776   **ESTABLISHED** 1956

WHERE FUNDING CAN BE GIVEN UK and overseas.

WHO CAN BENEFIT UK-registered charities.

WHAT IS FUNDED Relief of suffering; elimination and control of disease; people who have disabilities and disadvantaged people.

WHAT IS NOT FUNDED Grants are only given to UK-registered charities that have been registered for at least one year.

TYPE OF GRANT Grants are primarily awarded for capital expenditure for specific projects or items of specialist equipment. A limited number of grants are awarded for running costs where the grant will provide direct support for a clearly identifiable charitable project.

RANGE OF GRANTS Usually £250–£2,000.

SAMPLE GRANTS Leicester Charity Link (£30,500); Merlin (£25,000); Camfed (£15,000); Earl Shilton Social Institute, British Red Cross, Save The Children and Concern Worldwide (£5,000 each); Cecily's Fund and the Queen Alexandra Hospital Home (£2,000 each); Computer Aid International, Health Poverty Action and Resolve International (£1,000 each); Special Toys Educational Postal Service, Strongbones Children's Charitable Trust and Inter Care (£500 each); Orcadia Creative Learning Centre (£250); and the Leysian Mission (£10).

FINANCES *Year* 2011–12 *Income* £158,353 *Grants* £162,935 *Assets* £5,887,485

TRUSTEES Joanne Congdon; Erica Cotton; Tenney Cotton.

OTHER INFORMATION A total of £163,000 was made in grants to 78 organisations in 2011–12.

HOW TO APPLY In writing to the correspondent. According to the trustees' report for 2011/12, trustees reach decisions on applications by taking into accounts the following: 'how effective the grant is expected to be towards fulfiling a charity's stated objective; the size of the grant requested in relation to the stated overall project and/or capital costs; and the financial standing of the charity as presented in its latest report and accounts with respect to: the extent of the applicant's exclusively charitable expenditure in relation to its annual income; the extent of expenditure on fundraising and management as a proportion of the charity's annual income; and the level of a charity's free and restricted reserves against its annual spending on charitable activities.'

WHO TO APPLY TO Joanne Congdon, Trustee, PO Box 6895, Earl Shilton, Leicester LE9 8ZE *Tel.* 01455 440917

■ Country Houses Foundation

CC NO 1111049   **ESTABLISHED** 2005

WHERE FUNDING CAN BE GIVEN England.

WHO CAN BENEFIT Registered charities, building preservation trusts and private owners.

WHAT IS FUNDED The preservation of buildings of historic or architectural significance together with their gardens and grounds, for the public benefit. 'We aim to give grants for repairs and restoration work required to prevent loss or damage to historic buildings located in England, their gardens, grounds and any outbuildings. We would normally expect your building to be listed, scheduled, or in the case of a garden included in the English Heritage Register of Parks and Gardens. However, we may also make grants to projects which involve an unlisted building of sufficient historic or architectural significance or importance if it is within a conservation area.'

WHAT IS NOT FUNDED 'As a general rule we do not offer grants for the following: buildings and structures which have been the subject of recent purchase and where the cost of works for which grant is sought should have been recognized in the purchase price paid; projects which do not principally involve the repair or conservation of a historic building or structure; churches and chapels unless now or previously linked to a country house or estate; alterations and improvements, and repairs to non-historic fabric or services; routine maintenance and minor repairs; general running costs; demolition unless agreed as part of a repair and conservation programme; rent, loan or mortgage payments; conservation of furniture, fittings and equipment except where they are themselves of historic or architectural significance, have a historic relationship with the site, are relevant to the project, and can be secured long term from sale or disposal; work carried out before a grant offer has been made in writing and accepted.'

SAMPLE GRANTS Beneficiaries included: Hadlow Tower (£75,000); Godolphin House (£70,000); Wolfeton (£56,000); Duncombe Park, Llanthony Secunda and Wellbrook (£50,000 each); Astley Castle (£42,000); Eastnor Castle (£40,000); Compton Verney (£25,000); Cockle Park Tower and Harrowden Hall (£20,000 each); Faringdon Folly (£11,000); Sinai Park (£10,000); New Hall Farm (£6,000); and Heritage Alliance (£2,000).

FINANCES *Year* 2011–12 *Income* £396,729 *Grants* £941,958 *Assets* £12,134,576

TRUSTEES Oliver Pearcey; Nicholas Barber; Michael Clifton; Norman Hudson; Christopher Taylor; Sir John Parsons; Mary King.

HOW TO APPLY Refer to the foundation's very helpful website for full information on how to make an application. *Pre-Application Forms* can be completed online, or in a hard copy and returned by post. The foundation tries to respond to within 28 days of receipt. If a project fits the criteria then a unique reference number will be issued which must be quoted on the *Full Application Form*. Applications can be made at any time.

WHO TO APPLY TO David Price, Company Secretary, The Manor, Sheephouse Farm, Uley Road, Dursley, Gloucestershire GL11 5AD *Tel.* 0845 402 4102 *Fax* 0845 402 4103 *email* david@countryhousesfoundation.org.uk *Website* www.countryhousesfoundation.org.uk

....

■ County Durham Community Foundation

CC NO 1047625   **ESTABLISHED** 1995

WHERE FUNDING CAN BE GIVEN County Durham, Darlington and surrounding areas.

WHO CAN BENEFIT Community groups and grassroots organisations seeking to improve the quality of life in their local area, particularly those aiming to combat poverty and disadvantage or promote a more equitable and just society. Applications from branches of UK organisations will only be considered if they are able to demonstrate financial independence.

WHAT IS FUNDED The foundation encourages applications from groups working in the following areas: children and young people – groups and projects that help children and young people access activities and services where they play a key role in the decision making; vulnerable people – groups and projects working with disadvantaged people, in particular providing increased access to services and

facilities for people with disabilities, the homeless and the elderly; community regeneration – local partnerships plus residents' and tenants' associations that aim to improve health, education, reduce crime levels (and improve community safety) and to regenerate employment, housing and the physical environment with the support of their local community; self-help groups – community based, small self-help groups who deliver basic services; environmental improvements – small-scale environmental projects particularly improvements to community held land; education, capacity and skills development – group and community-based training and education programmes, particularly for those who have had no previous access to training opportunities; health – groups and community based projects providing access to healthy eating, increased physical activity and self-help services, which aim to improve the health and well-being of communities; and in particular applications from groups working in rural areas.

WHAT IS NOT FUNDED The foundation will not fund: projects outside County Durham and Darlington; national or regional charities with no independent office in County Durham or Darlington; groups that have more than one year's running costs held as free reserves; projects which should be funded by a statutory body; sponsored events; improvements to land that is not open to the general public at convenient hours; projects promoting political activities; deficit or retrospective funding; faith groups promoting religious, community based activities. Funding is not normally given for: medical research and equipment; school projects; animal welfare; general contributions to large appeals (but specific items can be funded); building or buying premises and freehold or leasehold land rights; minibuses or other vehicles; overseas travel; grants for more than one year. Some of the programmes have other exclusions. If your project is at all unusual contact the foundation to discuss your application before submitting it.

TYPE OF GRANT Various depending on funding criteria.

RANGE OF GRANTS £1,000–£5,000

FINANCES *Year* 2011–12 *Income* £2,885,664 *Grants* £2,184,970 *Assets* £8,539,808

TRUSTEES Mark I'Anson, Chair; David Watson; Michele Armstrong; Ada Burns; George Garlick; Christopher Lendrum; Andrew Martell; David Martin; Lady Sarah Nicholson; Gerry Osborne; Kate Welch; Ruth Thompson.

PUBLICATIONS Newsletter, information leaflets, grant guidelines and application forms.

OTHER INFORMATION An additional £166,000 was awarded to individuals.

HOW TO APPLY 'Community groups, non-registered charities and registered charities are all able to apply to our many funds using just one main application form. We mix-and-match applications to the most appropriate fund behind the scenes, so you don't need to worry about which fund is right for you. With the exception of the Banks Community Fund, ESF Community Grants and Surviving Winter, which have their own bespoke application forms, all our funds can be accessed using our standard application form. Choose one of the options below to be taken to the application form. To apply for a grant you need to read our general guidelines before filling in an application form.' The full guidelines are available from the foundation's website.

WHO TO APPLY TO Barbara Gubbins, Chief Executive, Victoria House, Whitfield Court, St John's Road,

Meadowfield Industrial Estate, Durham DH7 8XL
Tel. 01913 786340 *Fax* 01913 782409
email info@cdcf.org.uk *Website* www.cdcf.org.uk

■ The Augustine Courtauld Trust

cc no 226217   **ESTABLISHED** 1956
WHERE FUNDING CAN BE GIVEN UK, with a preference
for Essex.
WHO CAN BENEFIT Registered charities benefiting
people in Essex, conservation work and Arctic
and Antarctic explorers.
WHAT IS FUNDED General charitable purposes, but
mostly organisations in Essex working with
young people who are disadvantaged and
conservation. Exploration of the Arctic and
Antarctic regions are also supported. Preference
is given to charities which the trust has a
special interest in, knowledge of, or, association
with.
WHAT IS NOT FUNDED No grants to individuals. No
grants to individual churches for fabric repairs or
maintenance.
TYPE OF GRANT One-off grants for projects and core
costs, which may be made for multiple years if
an application is submitted for each year.
RANGE OF GRANTS £500–£9,000. Normally in the
range of £500–£2,000
SAMPLE GRANTS The largest grants went to: Gino
Watkins Memorial Trust (£9,000) and Cirdan
Sailing Trust and Essex Boys and Girls Clubs
(£5,000 each). Other beneficiaries included:
Stubbers Adventure Centre (£2,500); Rural
Community Council of Essex (£2,350); Marie
Curie Cancer Care (£2,000); Stanley Hall Opera
and The Peaceful Place Ltd (£1,000 each);
Country Holidays for Inner City Kids (£800) and
SOS Domestic Abuse Projects, Crossroads Care
Essex and St Andrew's Church – Great Yeldham
(£500 each).
FINANCES *Year* 2011–12 *Income* £53,567
Grants £45,900 *Assets* £1,238,194
TRUSTEES Revd A. C. Courtauld, Chair; Lord John
P. Petre; Julien Courtauld; Derek Fordham; Sir
Anthony Denison-Smith; Thomas J. R. Courtauld;
Bruce R. Ballard.
OTHER INFORMATION This trust was founded in 1956
by Augustine Courtauld, an Arctic explorer who
was proud of his Essex roots. His charitable
purpose was simple: 'my idea is to make
available something that will do some good.'
HOW TO APPLY Applications must be submitted via
the online form on the trust's website. Written
applications will not be accepted.
WHO TO APPLY TO Bruce Ballard, Clerk, Birkett Long
Solicitors, Essex House, 42 Crouch Street,
Colchester, Essex CO3 3HH *Tel.* 01206
217300 *Fax* 01206 572393 *email* julienc@
summershall.com *Website* www.
augustinecourtauldtrust.org

■ Coutts Charitable Foundation

cc no 1150784   **ESTABLISHED** 2014
WHERE FUNDING CAN BE GIVEN UK and overseas.
WHO CAN BENEFIT Registered charities.
WHAT IS FUNDED Social welfare and the relief of
poverty.
TRUSTEES Nicholas Rory Tapner, Chair; Sir
Christopher Geidt; Ian Ewart; Lord Waldegrave of
North Hill; Alexander Classen; Leslie Gent;
Shirley Tang; Michael Morley; Shivaashish
Gupta; Andrew Sumner.
OTHER INFORMATION Registered in February 2014,
the foundation was established by Coutts to
help to address poverty in the UK and overseas.

The following information is taken from a
statement on the company's website (March
2014): 'The foundation's aim is to support
sustainable approaches to tackle the causes
and consequences of poverty, focusing on the
communities where Coutts has a presence.
Coutts has a long history of supporting
philanthropic causes and the foundation will
extend and amplify these values. The new
Coutts foundation will fund work both in the UK
and internationally. In 2014, it will proactively
award grants to a small number of organisations
that are delivering sustainable approaches to
ensure basic human needs are met. These
include energy, food, water, housing, and
access to education or health care. It will
especially focus on organisations that are
developing innovative solutions as well as those
whose successful work has the potential to be
scaled-up. The foundation believes that building
the resilience of vulnerable communities so they
are better able to tackle current and future
challenges is essential. The foundation will draw
inspiration from the work of Angela Burdett-
Coutts, granddaughter of Thomas Coutts. A
progressive 19th century philanthropist, Angela
was concerned with breaking cycles of poverty
and the provision of basic human needs. She
worked closely with Charles Dickens and
supported many of the organisations that are
still in existence today. To date, the Coutts
foundation has approved four grants. These are
to: The Ashden Trust, to help fund the Ashden
Award for Reducing Fuel Poverty; City Gateway,
to support their Apprenticeship Scheme for
disadvantaged young people in East End of
London; Lien AID to help fund the Gift of Water
project in China; and the Ranthambhore
Foundation, to support their sanitation
programme for schools in India. Others will be
announced in due course.'
'The foundation's board, chaired by Rory Tapner,
Chief Executive of Coutts, includes a number of
highly experienced individuals who strongly
identify with the foundation's mission and
approach. The foundation will be governed by a
board comprising of both Coutts staff and
independent trustees, including: Lord Waldegrave
of North Hill, Chair, Coutts and Co; The Rt Hon Sir
Christopher Geidt; and Dr Andrew Sumner, co-
Director of the King's International Development
Institute at King's College London, an interdisciplinary development economist with research
interests in the structural causes of poverty.'
HOW TO APPLY In writing to the correspondent,
although potential applicants should note that
the foundation aims to adopt a proactive
approach which may mean that unsolicited
applications may not be accepted.
WHO TO APPLY TO Kay Boland, Administrator, Coutts
& Co, 440 Strand, London WC2R 0QS *Tel.* 020
7957 2822

■ General Charity of Coventry

cc no 216235   **ESTABLISHED** 1983
WHERE FUNDING CAN BE GIVEN The Midlands.
WHO CAN BENEFIT People in need, children, young
and older people, disabled (physically or
mentally), people in need of social or health
care and organisations that would benefit such
people in the City of Coventry.
WHAT IS FUNDED Welfare; general charitable
purposes; health; education and training.
WHAT IS NOT FUNDED No grants to organisations
outside Coventry, or for holidays unless of a
recuperative nature.

RANGE OF GRANTS Up to £50,000.

SAMPLE GRANTS Warwickshire and Northampton Air Ambulance (£50,000); David Scott's Coventry Jubilee Community Care Trust (£40,000); Coventry Boys' Club, Tiny Tim's Children's Centre and Midland Sports Centre for the Disabled (£30,000 each); Alzheimer's Society (£15,000); Myton Hospice (£10,000); Coventry CAB (£5,500); Coventry City Mission and 3rd Coventry Scout Group (£5,000 each); Coventry Godiva Harriers (£3,000); Crow Recycling (£2,500); Hillfields Evangelical Baptist Church (£1,500); Kidz Klub Coventry (£750) and The British Retinitis Pigmentosa Society (£120).

FINANCES *Year* 2012 *Income* £60,164 *Grants* £26,890 *Assets* £5,216

TRUSTEES Richard Smith; David Mason; Michael Harris; Edna Eaves; Margaret Lancaster; Terence McDonnell; William Thomson; Cllr Nigel Lee; David Evans; Terry Proctor; Dr Caroline Rhodes; Cllr Marcus Lapsa; Edward Curtis; Cllr Catherine Miks; Vivian Kershaw; Cllr Ram Lakha; Julia McNaney; Cllr Gary Crookes.

HOW TO APPLY In writing to the correspondent. Applications are not accepted directly from the general public for relief in need (individuals).

WHO TO APPLY TO V. A. Tosh, Clerk to the Trustees, General Charities Office, Old Bablake, Hill Street, Coventry CV1 4AN *Tel.* 02476 222769 *email* cov.genchar@virgin.net

■ Coventry Building Society Charitable Foundation

CC NO 1072244 **ESTABLISHED** 1998

WHERE FUNDING CAN BE GIVEN Within the boundary of the City of Coventry.

WHO CAN BENEFIT Registered charities.

WHAT IS FUNDED A wide range of causes based, or active, in the Midlands, with a preference for smaller local charities.

WHAT IS NOT FUNDED No grants can be given outside of the Midlands area. The following are not eligible for support: large charities which enjoy national coverage; charities with no base within the branch area; charities with an annual donated income in excess of £250,000; charities with assets over £500,000; projects requiring ongoing commitment; large capital projects; maintenance or building works for buildings, gardens or playgrounds; major fundraising; projects which are normally the responsibility of other organisations such as NHS and local authorities; sponsorship of individuals; requests from individuals; replacing funds which were the responsibility of another body; educational institutions, unless for the relief of disadvantage; promotion of religious, political or military causes; sporting clubs or organisations, unless for the relief of disadvantage; medical research or equipment; more than one donation to the same organisation in a year – further applications will be considered after a period of three years; animal welfare.

TYPE OF GRANT One-off.

RANGE OF GRANTS Up to £3,000, but, generally £500–£2,000.

SAMPLE GRANTS Volunteer Centre Daventry, Arty Folks and Family Support Link (£2,000 each); Refugee Advice Group, Deaf World and Walsall Street Teams (£1,500 each) and Fallings Park Methodist Church and Community Centre, Coventry Artspace Ltd, West Orchard United Reform Church and Swindon Scrapstore (£1,000 each).

FINANCES *Year* 2012 *Income* £852,083 *Grants* £840,000

TRUSTEES Emma Brodie; Anna Cuskin.

HOW TO APPLY The foundation's applications are administered by the Heart of England Community Foundation. An application form is available to download from their website (www.heartofenglandcf.co.uk). Initial telephone calls are welcome: Telephone Kat on 02476 883262.

WHO TO APPLY TO Anna Cuskin, Secretary, Oak Tree Court, Binley Business Park, Harry Weston Road, Coventry CV3 2UN *Website* www.coventrybuildingsociety.co.uk

■ The John Cowan Foundation

CC NO 327613 **ESTABLISHED** 1987

WHERE FUNDING CAN BE GIVEN UK, specifically local to Surrey.

WHO CAN BENEFIT Charitable organisations.

WHAT IS FUNDED The foundation makes grants to purely local causes apart from national established charities. Charitable support will be considered for: oncology, hospices, hospices at home, medical transport, youth work, almshouses, community and social centres, Alzheimer's disease, arthritis and rheumatism, cancers, heart disease, motor neurone disease, terminal illness and sight loss.

WHAT IS NOT FUNDED No support for individuals, community projects outside Surrey area, or overseas projects.

RANGE OF GRANTS Usually up to £5,000.

SAMPLE GRANTS Royal Marsden Cancer Campaign (£2,300); South East Cancer Help Centre, The Children's Trust, Macmillan Cancer Support, Alzheimer's Society and British Forces Foundation (£2,000 each); Rainbow Children's Trust Charity and RNLI (£1,500 each); Surrey Community Development Trust, Dreams Come True Charity and Teenage Cancer Trust (£1,000 each); and the Friends of White Lodge Centre, Sense and Changing Faces (£500 each).

FINANCES *Year* 2011–12 *Income* £34,374 *Grants* £30,000

TRUSTEES Christine Foster; Susan Arkoulis; Kate Arkoulis; James Arkoulis.

HOW TO APPLY In writing to the correspondent.

WHO TO APPLY TO Christine Foster, Trustee, 12 Kingswood Place, 119 Croydon Road, Caterham, Surrey CR3 6DJ *Tel.* 01883 344930 *email* joram@freenet.co.uk

■ The Sir Tom Cowie Charitable Trust

CC NO 1096936 **ESTABLISHED** 2003

WHERE FUNDING CAN BE GIVEN City of Sunderland and County Durham.

WHO CAN BENEFIT Young people, older people, the infirm and disabled, poor or needy people due to social and/or economic circumstances.

WHAT IS FUNDED General charitable purposes.

RANGE OF GRANTS Usually up to £20,000.

SAMPLE GRANTS Wolsingham Community College (£64,000); Consett Churches Youth Project and Bowes Museum Schools Project (£18,000 each); Beechdale Nursery School Building Project (£15,000); Shield Row Primary School (£13,000); Centrepoint Dundas Street Kitchen (£7,500); Wolsingham Youth Club (£5,500); Dogs for the Disabled (£5,000); Durham Wildlife Trust Adder Monitoring Project (£3,000) and Blind Veterans UK (£1,000).

FINANCES *Year* 2011–12 *Income* £138,939
Grants £194,234 *Assets* £4,433,100
TRUSTEES Peter Blackett; David Gray; Lady Diana
Cowie.
HOW TO APPLY In writing to the correspondent.
WHO TO APPLY TO Loraine Maddison, Estate Office,
Broadwood Hall, Lanchester, Durham DH7 0TN
Tel. 01207 529663 *email* lorraine@
sirtomcowie.com

....

■ Cowley Charitable Foundation

CC NO 270682 **ESTABLISHED** 1973
WHERE FUNDING CAN BE GIVEN Worldwide, with some
preference for south Buckinghamshire and the
Aylesbury area.
WHO CAN BENEFIT Registered charities.
WHAT IS FUNDED General charitable purposes.
WHAT IS NOT FUNDED No grants to non-registered
charities. No grants to individuals, or for causes
supposed to be serviced by public funds or with
a scope considered to be too narrow.
TYPE OF GRANT One-off donations for development,
capital projects and project funding.
RANGE OF GRANTS Usually £1,000–£2,000.
SAMPLE GRANTS Tau Zero Foundation (£5,000);
MAST (£4,000); Underwater Archaeology
Research Centre – University of Nottingham
(£3,500); Age UK (£2,200); Children with
Cancer UK and John Soane Museum (£1,000
each) and Camphill Village Trust, Save the
Children and Shelter (£500 each).
FINANCES *Year* 2011–12 *Income* £36,001
Grants £36,250 *Assets* £914,711
TRUSTEES 140 Trustee Co. Ltd; Harriet
M. M. Cullen.
HOW TO APPLY The trust states that unsolicited
applications are not invited, and that the
trustees carry out their own research into
charities.
WHO TO APPLY TO The Secretary, 140 Trustee Co.
Ltd, 2nd Floor, 17 Grosvenor Gardens, London
SW1W 0BD *Tel.* 020 7834 9797

....

■ Dudley and Geoffrey Cox Charitable Trust

CC NO 277761 **ESTABLISHED** 1979
WHERE FUNDING CAN BE GIVEN UK.
WHO CAN BENEFIT Organisations benefiting children
and young adults; former employees of
Haymills; at-risk groups; people who are
disadvantaged by poverty and socially isolated
people.
WHAT IS FUNDED The trust seeks to support projects
which are not widely known, and therefore likely
to be inadequately funded. Grants fall into four
main categories: education – schools, colleges
and universities; medicine – hospitals,
associated institutions and medical research;
welfare – primarily to include former Haymills
staff, people in need, or who are otherwise
distressed or disadvantaged; and youth –
support for schemes to assist in the education,
welfare and training of young people.
WHAT IS NOT FUNDED No personal applications will be
considered unless endorsed by a university,
college or other appropriate authority.
SAMPLE GRANTS Merchant Taylor's School – Geoffrey
Cox scholarships (£32,500); and British Red
Cross, RAFT, Royal College of Physicians,
Independent Age and Workaid (£5,000 each).
FINANCES *Year* 2011–12 *Income* £222,389
Grants £267,000 *Assets* £6,633,911

TRUSTEES Ian Ferres; Bill Underwood; Ted Drake;
John Sharpe; John Wosner; Michael Boyle.
HOW TO APPLY In writing to the correspondent.
Trustees meet at least twice a year.
WHO TO APPLY TO Matthew Dear, Charities Officer,
c/o Merchant Taylors' Company,
30 Threadneedle Street, London EC2R 8JB
Tel. 020 7450 4440 *email* mdear@merchant-
taylors.co.uk

....

■ The Sir William Coxen Trust Fund

CC NO 206936 **ESTABLISHED** 1940
WHERE FUNDING CAN BE GIVEN England.
WHO CAN BENEFIT Hospitals or charitable institutions
carrying out orthopaedic work.
WHAT IS FUNDED Hospitals and other charitable
institutions in England carrying out orthopaedic
work, particularly in respect of children.
WHAT IS NOT FUNDED No grants to individuals or non-
charitable institutions.
TYPE OF GRANT One-off grants and research
fellowships.
SAMPLE GRANTS Fire Fighters Charity (£4,500); Child
Care Action Trust (£4,100); British School of
Osteopathy (£4,000); Action Medical Research
Council, Association for Spina Bifida and
Hydrocephalus, Conductive Education,
Motability, Royal Manchester Children's
Hospital, Strongbones and Therapy Centre
(£3,500 each).
FINANCES *Year* 2011–12 *Income* £103,597
Grants £69,050 *Assets* £2,005,639
TRUSTEES John Stuttard; Neil Redcliffe; Michael
Savory; Michael Bear; John Garbutt; Andrew
Parmley.
OTHER INFORMATION Grants were made to 19
organisations.
HOW TO APPLY In writing to the correspondent.
WHO TO APPLY TO Caroline Webb, Administrator, The
Town Clerk's Office, City of London, PO Box
270, Guildhall, London EC2P 2EJ *Tel.* 020
7332 1416 *Website* www.cityoflondon.gov.uk/
about-the-city/what-we-do/Pages/trusts-
charities-awards.aspx

....

■ The Lord Cozens-Hardy Trust

CC NO 264237 **ESTABLISHED** 1972
WHERE FUNDING CAN BE GIVEN Merseyside and
Norfolk.
WHO CAN BENEFIT Registered charities.
WHAT IS FUNDED General charitable purposes with a
particular interest in supporting medical, health,
education and welfare causes.
WHAT IS NOT FUNDED No grants to individuals.
TYPE OF GRANT One-off and recurrent.
RANGE OF GRANTS Up to £20,000, mostly for smaller
amounts of £5,000 or less.
SAMPLE GRANTS Cancer Research UK (£11,000);
Waveney Stardust (£10,000); Action for Children
– Warrington, Help and Woodlands Hospice
Charitable Trust (£5,000 each); St John
Ambulance (£3,000) and Norfolk and Norwich
Association for the Blind, World Association of
Girl Guides and Girl Scouts and Liverpool School
of Tropical Medicine (£1,000 each).
FINANCES *Year* 2011–12 *Income* £103,621
Grants £91,150 *Assets* £2,709,421
TRUSTEES J. E. V. Phelps; L. F. Phelps; J. Ripman.
HOW TO APPLY In writing to the correspondent.
Applications are reviewed quarterly.
WHO TO APPLY TO The Trustees, PO Box 28, Holt,
Norfolk NR25 7WH

....

■ The Craignish Trust

SC NO SC016882   **ESTABLISHED** 1961
WHERE FUNDING CAN BE GIVEN UK, with a preference for Scotland.
WHO CAN BENEFIT Charitable organisations.
WHAT IS FUNDED Education, the arts, heritage, culture, science and environmental protection and improvement
WHAT IS NOT FUNDED Running costs are not normally supported.
TYPE OF GRANT Project grants.
RANGE OF GRANTS £500–£7,500.
SAMPLE GRANTS Previous beneficiaries have included Art in Healthcare, Boilerhouse Theatre Company Ltd, Butterfly Conservation – Scotland, Cairndow Arts Promotions, Centre for Alternative Technology, Edinburgh International Book Festival, Edinburgh Royal Choral Union, Friends of the Earth Scotland, Human Rights Watch Charitable Trust and Soil Association Scotland.
FINANCES Year 2012–13 Income £134,421 Grants £150,000
TRUSTEES M. Matheson; J. Roberts; C. Younger.
HOW TO APPLY There is no formal application form; applicants should write to the correspondent. Details of the project should be included together with a copy of the most recent audited accounts.
WHO TO APPLY TO The Trustees, c/o Geoghegan and Co, 6 St Colme Street, Edinburgh EH3 6AD

■ The Craps Charitable Trust

CC NO 271492   **ESTABLISHED** 1976
WHERE FUNDING CAN BE GIVEN UK, Israel.
WHO CAN BENEFIT Charitable organisations.
WHAT IS FUNDED General charitable purposes, particularly Jewish organisations.
RANGE OF GRANTS Up to £25,000.
SAMPLE GRANTS British Technion Society (£25,000); Jewish Care (£20,000); WIZO.UK and Nightingale – Home for Aged Jews (£16,000 each); Jerusalem Foundation and Friends of the Hebrew University (£14,000 each); CBF World Jewish Relief (£5,000); Ravenswood Foundation, British Friends of Herzog Hospital and British Friends of Haifa University (£4,000 each); the United Jewish Israel Appeal and Medical Foundation for Care of Victims of Torture (£3,000 each); and Shelter and National Theatre (£1,000 each).
FINANCES Year 2011–12 Income £177,060 Grants £182,000 Assets £3,814,730
TRUSTEES Caroline Dent; Jonathan Dent; Louisa Dent.
WHO TO APPLY TO The Trustees, Grant Thornton, Chartered Accountants, 202 Silbury Boulevard, Milton Keynes MK9 1LW

■ Michael Crawford Children's Charity

CC NO 1042211   **ESTABLISHED** 1994
WHERE FUNDING CAN BE GIVEN Throughout England and Wales.
WHO CAN BENEFIT Children and young people especially those disadvantaged by poverty and/or illness, organisations benefiting such people.
WHAT IS FUNDED Relief of sickness, prevention/relief of poverty.
TYPE OF GRANT Grants to individuals and institutions.
SAMPLE GRANTS The Sick Children's Trust (£50,000).

FINANCES Year 2011–12 Income £192,238 Grants £108,319 Assets £4,129,494
TRUSTEES Alan Clark; Michael Crawford; Kenneth Dias.
OTHER INFORMATION £102,000 of grants allocated to relief of sickness and £6,000 to other charitable activities.
HOW TO APPLY In writing to the correspondent.
WHO TO APPLY TO Kenneth Dias, Trustee, Regina House, 124 Finchley Road, London NW3 5JS Tel. 020 7433 2400

■ The Cray Trust

SC NO SC005592   **ESTABLISHED** 1976
WHERE FUNDING CAN BE GIVEN Mainly the east of Scotland.
WHO CAN BENEFIT Charitable organisations.
WHAT IS FUNDED General charitable purposes.
WHAT IS NOT FUNDED No support for political appeals and large UK or international charities. No grants to individuals.
SAMPLE GRANTS Charitable Assets Trust; Canine Partners; Equibuddy; Equine Grass Sickness Fund; Princess Royal Trust for Carers; Alzheimer's Scotland; Cherish India; Backup Trust; Barnardo's Scotland; the Priory Church; and Rainbow RDA.
FINANCES Year 2011–12 Income £52,780 Grants £40,000 Assets £1,000,000
TRUSTEES P. R. Gammell; J. E. B. Gammell.
HOW TO APPLY This trust does not accept unsolicited applications.
WHO TO APPLY TO The Trustees, c/o Springfords Accountants, Dundas House, Westfield Park, Eskbank, Midlothian EH22 3FB

■ Creative Scotland

ESTABLISHED 2010
WHERE FUNDING CAN BE GIVEN Scotland
WHO CAN BENEFIT The arts.
WHAT IS FUNDED 'Creative Scotland is the national agency for the arts, screen and creative industries. We distribute money from Scottish Government and the National Lottery through a series of Funding Programmes which allow artists, practitioners and organisations to apply for financial support to develop talent, create new work, and support widening access and participation.'
FINANCES Year 2011–12 Grants £66,335,996
TRUSTEES Sir Sandy Crombie; Steve Grimond; Prof. Robin Macpherson; Dr Gary West; Ruth Wishart; Barclay Price; Fergus Muir; May Miller; Richard Scott; Sandra Gunn; Peter Caprelli.
OTHER INFORMATION Creative Scotland assumed the responsibilities and function of the Scottish Arts Council in 2010. For a complete list and details of each funding programme that Creative Scotland operates visit the website.
HOW TO APPLY For all information regarding grant applications visit the Creative Scotland website.
WHO TO APPLY TO Janine Hunt, Director of Operations, 249 West George Street, Glasgow G2 4QE Tel. 0845 603 6000 email enquiries@creativesciotland.com Website www.creativescotland.com

■ The Crerar Hotels Trust (formerly the North British Hotel Trust)

CC NO 221335 **ESTABLISHED** 1903
WHERE FUNDING CAN BE GIVEN Scotland.
WHO CAN BENEFIT Mainly registered charities.
WHAT IS FUNDED General, mainly welfare, health, older people, people with disabilities.
WHAT IS NOT FUNDED No grants to individuals.
TYPE OF GRANT Capital, revenue and project funding.
SAMPLE GRANTS Euan MacDonald Microscope (£61,000 in total); Hospitality Industry Trust (£25,000); Autistica and the Scottish Book Trust (£15,000 each); Music in Hospitals and the Wellchild Trust (£10,000 each); Action Medical Research (£7,000); Happy Days (£6,000); Argyll Piping Trust and Motability (£5,000 each); Guide Dogs for the Blind (£4,000); Rape and Abuse Scotland (£3,000); Moray Arts Centre and Pain Association Scotland (£2,000 each).
FINANCES *Year* 2011–12 *Income* £390,002 *Grants* £360,186 *Assets* £9,825,453
TRUSTEES Patrick Crerar; Graham Brown; Jeanette Crerar; Mike Still; James Barrack; John Williams; Claire Smith; Tarquin de Burgh.
HOW TO APPLY Application forms are available from the correspondent.
WHO TO APPLY TO Claire Smith, Clerk, c/o Crerar Management Limited, 1 Queen Charlotte Lane, Edinburgh EH6 6BL *Tel.* 08430502020 *email* crerarhotelstrust@samuelston.com

■ The Crescent Trust

CC NO 327644 **ESTABLISHED** 1987
WHERE FUNDING CAN BE GIVEN UK.
WHO CAN BENEFIT Charitable organisations.
WHAT IS FUNDED The arts, heritage and ecology.
TYPE OF GRANT One-off and recurrent.
RANGE OF GRANTS £250–£43,000
SAMPLE GRANTS Hertford House Trust and University of Oxford (£10,000 each); the Attingham Trust (£8,500); Fairbridge London (£5,000); Courtauld Institute of Art, Impetus Trust and Sea the Future (£2,500 each); Countryside Alliance (£500); Galapagos Conservation Trust and Save the Children (£250 each); and Mondo Challenge Fund (£125).
FINANCES *Year* 2011–12 *Income* £67,210 *Grants* £50,100 *Assets* £356,492
TRUSTEES John Tham; Richard Lascelles.
HOW TO APPLY This trust states that it does not respond to unsolicited applications.
WHO TO APPLY TO Christine Akehurst, Administrator, 9 Queripel House, 1 Duke of York Square, London SW3 4LY *Tel.* 020 7730 5420

■ Criffel Charitable Trust

CC NO 1040680 **ESTABLISHED** 1994
WHERE FUNDING CAN BE GIVEN UK and overseas.
WHO CAN BENEFIT Registered charities, churches and schools.
WHAT IS FUNDED The advancement of Christianity and the relief of poverty, sickness and other needs.
WHAT IS NOT FUNDED Individuals.
TYPE OF GRANT Up to three years.
RANGE OF GRANTS Up to £3,000.
SAMPLE GRANTS The only beneficiary of a grant over £2,000 was Four Oaks Methodist Church (£3,000).

FINANCES *Year* 2011–12 *Income* £47,070 *Grants* £59,560 *Assets* £907,241
TRUSTEES Jim Lees; Joy Harvey; Juliet Lees.
HOW TO APPLY The trust states that 'unsolicited applications are declined on each of two applications and shredded on a third application.'
WHO TO APPLY TO The Trustees, Ravenswood Lodge, 1a Wentworth Road, Sutton Coldfield B74 2SG *Tel.* 01213 081575

■ Cripplegate Foundation

CC NO 207499 **ESTABLISHED** 1891
WHERE FUNDING CAN BE GIVEN London borough of Islington and part of the City of London.
WHO CAN BENEFIT Charitable organisations, schools and organisations working with schools and individuals.
WHAT IS FUNDED Grants which aim to improve the quality of life in the area of benefit and provide opportunities for local residents. There are three main themes: social cohesion, reducing poverty and inequality and increasing access to opportunities and making connections.
WHAT IS NOT FUNDED In the main grants programme no funding is given for: national charities or organisations outside the area of benefit; schemes or activities which would relieve central or local government of their statutory responsibilities; grants to replace cuts in funding made by the local authority or others; medical research or equipment; national fundraising appeals; advancement of religion unless the applicant also offers non-religious services to the community; animal welfare; retrospective grants; commercial or business activities; grants for events held in the church of St Giles-without-Cripplegate; grants to organisations recruiting volunteers in south Islington for work overseas.
TYPE OF GRANT Grants for core costs, project funding, salary costs and capital costs, often over more than one year.
RANGE OF GRANTS Up to £150,000.
SAMPLE GRANTS Islington Giving (£100,000); Friendship Works (£60,000); The New Economics Foundation and The Women's Therapy Centre (£50,000 each); Children Our Ultimate Investment (UK) (£44,000); Angel Shed Theatre Company and CASA Social Care (£30,000 each); Freightliners Farms Limited (£20,000); and CARIS – Islington (£15,000).
FINANCES *Year* 2011–12 *Income* £2,687,195 *Grants* £2,053,793 *Assets* £30,992,256
TRUSTEE Cripplegate Foundation Limited – Sole Corporate Trustee
OTHER INFORMATION The grant total includes £327,000 given to individuals.
HOW TO APPLY Each programme has a different application form and deadline dates. Applicants are encouraged to telephone or email the foundation to discuss their project before making a full application. Full details of the application process are available on the foundation's helpful website.
WHO TO APPLY TO Kristina Glenn, Director, 13 Elliott's Place, Islington, London N1 8HX *Tel.* 020 7288 6940 *email* grants@cripplegate.org.uk *Website* www.cripplegate.org

■ The Violet and Milo Cripps Charitable Trust

CC NO 289404   ESTABLISHED 1984
WHERE FUNDING CAN BE GIVEN UK.
WHO CAN BENEFIT Charitable organisations.
WHAT IS FUNDED Prison and human rights organisations.
SAMPLE GRANTS Previous beneficiaries have included: Lancaster University, the Prison Advice and Care Trust, Dorothy House Hospice Care, Frank Langford Charitable Trust and Trinity Hospice.
FINANCES Year 2011–12 Income £3,117 Grants £100,000
TRUSTEES Richard Linenthal; Anthony Newhouse; Jennifer Beattie.
HOW TO APPLY The trust states that unsolicited applications will not receive a response.
WHO TO APPLY TO The Trustees, Wedlake Bell, 52 Bedford Row, London WC1R 4LR

■ The Harry Crook Foundation

CC NO 231470   ESTABLISHED 1963
WHERE FUNDING CAN BE GIVEN Bristol.
WHO CAN BENEFIT Registered charities.
WHAT IS FUNDED In 2007 the trust informed us that it had decided to 'close' the fund to external application until further notice, with all available funds directed towards a single identified charity [Redland High School].
WHAT IS NOT FUNDED Medical research charities and charities serving need outside the boundaries of the City of Bristol. No grants to individuals.
SAMPLE GRANTS Redland High School (£31,000).
FINANCES Year 2011–12 Income £24,974 Grants £47,000
TRUSTEES Richard West; D. J. Bellew; Michael Manisty.
HOW TO APPLY In light of the foundation's 2007 resolution to 'close' the trust to external applications until further notice, any future applications to the trust will be ignored, 'no acknowledgement will be given, and, in particular, no consideration will be given to them.' In 2013 the trust stated that this situation has not changed.
WHO TO APPLY TO Helen Robertson, Administrator, c/o Veale Wasbrough Lawyers, Orchard Court, Orchard Lane, Bristol BS1 5WS Tel. 01179 252020

■ The Cross Trust

SC NO SC008620   ESTABLISHED 1943
WHERE FUNDING CAN BE GIVEN Scotland, with a preference for Perth.
WHO CAN BENEFIT Individuals and organisations.
WHAT IS FUNDED About 80% of the grants are given to individuals for educational purposes (including travel for their courses). Grants to organisations are normally made for music, drama or outdoor activities to benefit young people.
WHAT IS NOT FUNDED No retrospective applications will be considered.
TYPE OF GRANT Normally one-off, occasionally for longer periods.
RANGE OF GRANTS £500–£10,000
SAMPLE GRANTS Perth Festival of Fine Arts (£10,000); Perth Theatre and Concert Hall, Out of the Blue Arts and Education Trust (£5,000 each); Byre Theatre (£2,000).
FINANCES Year 2011–12 Income £195,458 Grants £104,666 Assets £4,736,180

TRUSTEES Beppo Buchanan-Smith; Hannah Buchanan-Smith; Dr R. H. MacDougall; Clair Orr; Dougal Philip; Mark Webster.
HOW TO APPLY Application forms and guidance notes are available from the correspondent. Deadlines for applications as follows:
University and college courses and other studies: 1 Feb, 7 June and 30 Aug
Vacation studies in the arts: 1 April
Medical elective studies abroad: 1 April, 30 Sept and 31 Dec
John Fife travel awards: 1st
Organisations: 1 Feb and 16 Aug
WHO TO APPLY TO Kathleen Carnegie, McCash and Hunter Solicitors, 25 South Methven Street, Perth PH1 5ES Tel. 01738 620451 email kathleencarnegie@mccash.co.uk Website www.thecrosstrust.org.uk

■ The Croydon Relief in Need Charities

CC NO 810114   ESTABLISHED 1962
WHERE FUNDING CAN BE GIVEN The borough of Croydon.
WHO CAN BENEFIT Local charities and individuals.
WHAT IS FUNDED General, health and welfare.
TYPE OF GRANT Recurrent.
RANGE OF GRANTS Up to £50,000.
SAMPLE GRANTS Croydon Parish Church (£50,000); St Christopher's Hospice (£39,000); Marie Curie Cancer Care (£19,000); Mencap (£12,000); Croydon Carers Centre (£10,000); Nightwatch (£9,000); Wheels for Wellbeing and Macmillan Cancer Support (£5,000 each); Theodora's Children's Trust (£4,000); Whitgift Special Needs Activity Project (£3,000); Listening Books (£1,000); and Croydon Pet PDSA Hospital (£500).
FINANCES Year 2012 Income £200,922 Grants £200,000
TRUSTEES Noel Hepworth; Beryl Cripps; Lynda Talbot; C. Trower; Alan Galer; Diana Harries; Diana Hemmings; Caroline Melrose; Christopher Clementi; Revd Canon Colin Boswell; John Tough; John Tough; Gail Winter; Cllr Margaret Mead; Cllr Donald Speakman; Patricia Galer; Deborah Knight.
HOW TO APPLY In writing to the correspondent. Guidelines and criteria are available to view on the website.
WHO TO APPLY TO W. B. Rymer, Clerk, Elis David Almshouses, Duppas Hill Terrace, Croydon CR0 4BT Tel. 020 8774 9382 email billrymer@croydonalmshousecharities.org.uk Website www.croydonalmshousecharities.org.uk

■ The Peter Cruddas Foundation

CC NO 1117323   ESTABLISHED 2006
WHERE FUNDING CAN BE GIVEN UK, with a particular interest in London.
WHO CAN BENEFIT Registered charities.
WHAT IS FUNDED The foundation gives priority to programmes calculated to help disadvantaged young people to pursue their education (including vocational) and more generally develop their potential whether through sport or recreation, voluntary programmes or otherwise. Preference is given to the support of projects undertaken by charitable organisations for the benefit of those young people, but consideration will also be given in appropriate circumstances to applications for individual support.

The foundation adopts a priority funding programme scheme that is available to be scrutinised on the web site. The programmes are subject to trustee review at any time.

In addition to financial funding given by the foundation, it also provides mentoring support to many organisations through the foundation administrator's experience in the third sector.

TYPE OF GRANT One-off and recurrent grants for capital and revenue costs.

SAMPLE GRANTS Royal Opera House Foundation (£105,000); The White Ensign Association (£50,000); Jewish Care and The Institute for Policy Research (£25,000 each); The Prince's Trust (£20,000); ARK, Mayor's Fund for London, Guildhall School Development Fund and British Cardiac Research Trust (£10,000 each); English National Opera and Royal Ballet School (£5,000 each); and WaterAid (£1,000).

FINANCES *Year* 2011–12 *Income* £5,966 *Grants* £715,705 *Assets* £274,323

TRUSTEES Lord David Young, Chair; Peter Cruddas; Martin Paisner.

HOW TO APPLY On an application form available to download from the foundation's website. The foundation provides guidance on how to complete the application form, also available on the website.

WHO TO APPLY TO Stephen D. Cox, Administrator, 133 Houndsditch, London EC3A 7BX *Tel.* 020 3003 8360 *Fax* 020 3003 8580 *email* s.cox@pcfoundation.org.uk *Website* www.petercruddasfoundation.org.uk

■ Cruden Foundation Ltd

SC NO SC004987   **ESTABLISHED** 1956
WHERE FUNDING CAN BE GIVEN Mainly Scotland.
WHO CAN BENEFIT Registered charities.
WHAT IS FUNDED General charitable purposes.
WHAT IS NOT FUNDED No grants to individuals.
TYPE OF GRANT Recurrent and one-off.
RANGE OF GRANTS Up to £15,000.
SAMPLE GRANTS Edinburgh International Festival (£17,500); St Columba's Hospice (£11,000); Marie Curie Cancer Care (£10,000); Festival City Theatres Trust (£7,500); Scottish Cancer Foundation (£3,000); Scottish Seabird Centre (£2,500); Gurkha Welfare Trust (£2,000); Open Door (£1,500); and the Factory Skatepark, Bobath Scotland, Corstorphine Trust, NSPCC Scotland and Dyslexia Action (£1,000 each).
FINANCES *Year* 2011–12 *Income* £314,772 *Grants* £229,350 *Assets* £5,795,383
TRUSTEES J. C. Rafferty, Chair; M. R. A. Matthews; J. G. Mitchell; A. Johnston; M. J. Rowley; D. D. Walker; K. D. Reid.
HOW TO APPLY In writing to the correspondent, accompanied by most recent accounts.
WHO TO APPLY TO M. J. Rowley, Secretary, Baberton House, Juniper Green, Edinburgh EH14 3HN

■ The Ronald Cruickshanks Foundation

CC NO 296075   **ESTABLISHED** 1987
WHERE FUNDING CAN BE GIVEN UK, with some preference for Folkestone, Faversham and the surrounding area.
WHO CAN BENEFIT Individuals and organisations, including various local churches.
WHAT IS FUNDED General charitable purposes, but particularly for the benefit of people in financial and other need within the stated beneficial area.

TYPE OF GRANT Recurrent.
RANGE OF GRANTS £250–£9,000.
SAMPLE GRANTS The Pilgrims Hospice (The Hospice on the Hill) (£9,000); The Pilgrims Hospice (Canterbury) and Demelza House Children's Hospice (£8,500); Parish Church of St Mary and St Eanswythe – Fabric Fund (£6,000); Kent Air Ambulance (£5,500); Operation Sunshine (£4,000); Jesuit Missions (3,500); Marie Curie Cancer Centre (£2,000); Disasters Emergency Committee – East African drought/starvation crisis, St Stephen's Church, Lympne, The Fire Fighters Charity and PDSA (£1,000 each); Kent Autistic Trust, Action for Kids and Volunteer Reading Help (£500 each) and The Folkestone Pipes and Drums and Shelter (£250 each).
FINANCES *Year* 2011–12 *Income* £256,501 *Grants* £163,850 *Assets* £1,787,149
TRUSTEES I. F. Cloke, Chair; J. S. Schilder; S. E. Cloke.
HOW TO APPLY In writing to the correspondent. Applications should be received by the end of September for consideration on a date coinciding closely with the anniversary of the death of the founder, which was 7 December.
WHO TO APPLY TO I. F. Cloke, Trustee, 34 Cheriton Gardens, Folkestone, Kent CT20 2AX *Tel.* 01303 251742

■ The Cuby Charitable Trust

CC NO 328585   **ESTABLISHED** 1990
WHERE FUNDING CAN BE GIVEN UK, overseas.
WHO CAN BENEFIT Registered charities.
WHAT IS FUNDED Jewish causes.
FINANCES *Year* 2011–12 *Income* £75,100 *Grants* £47,855 *Assets* £350,115
TRUSTEES C. Cuby; Sidney Cuby; Jonathan Cuby; Raquel Talmor.
OTHER INFORMATION No list of grant beneficiaries was included with the accounts.
HOW TO APPLY In writing to the correspondent.
WHO TO APPLY TO Sidney Cuby, Trustee, 16 Mowbray Road, Edgware HA8 8JQ *Tel.* 020 7563 6868

■ Cullum Family Trust

CC NO 1117056   **ESTABLISHED** 2006
WHERE FUNDING CAN BE GIVEN UK.
WHO CAN BENEFIT Registered charities and institutions.
WHAT IS FUNDED Social welfare, education and general charitable purposes.
TYPE OF GRANT One off and up to two years funding.
RANGE OF GRANTS £1,000–£5,000.
SAMPLE GRANTS City University (£337,000); the Sussex Community Foundation (£25,000); and Kids Company (£10,000).
FINANCES *Year* 2011–12 *Income* £660,222 *Grants* £380,700 *Assets* £21,175,184
TRUSTEES Ann Cullum; Claire Cullum; Peter Cullum; Simon Cullum.
OTHER INFORMATION The trust offers full project funding and will fund core and capital costs.
HOW TO APPLY In writing to the correspondent.
WHO TO APPLY TO Peter Cullum, Trustee, Wealden Hall, Parkfield, Sevenoaks TN15 0HX

■ The Culra Charitable Trust

CC NO 274612   **ESTABLISHED** 1977
WHERE FUNDING CAN BE GIVEN UK.
WHO CAN BENEFIT Registered charities only.
WHAT IS FUNDED General charitable purposes.

WHAT IS NOT FUNDED Grants are not given to non-registered charities or individuals. The trust does not tend to support large national charities.

TYPE OF GRANT One-off grants.

RANGE OF GRANTS Usually between £200 and £500.

FINANCES *Year* 2011–12 *Income* £23,110 *Grants* £25,000

TRUSTEES Charles Cook; Guy Needham; George Francis; Henry Byam-Cook.

HOW TO APPLY The trust tends to support organisations known to the trustees, rather than responding to unsolicited applications. The trustees meet twice a year.

WHO TO APPLY TO Mary Kitto, Administrator, Victoria House, 1–3 College Hill, London Ec4R 2RA *Tel.* 020 7489 8076

■ The Cumber Family Charitable Trust

CC NO 291009   **ESTABLISHED** 1985

WHERE FUNDING CAN BE GIVEN Worldwide, with a preference for the developing world and Berkshire and Oxfordshire.

WHO CAN BENEFIT Charitable organisations.

WHAT IS FUNDED General, with preference being given to overseas projects, housing and welfare, children, youth and education, medical and disability and environment.

WHAT IS NOT FUNDED Individuals are not usually supported. Individuals with local connections and who are personally known to the trustees are occasionally supported.

TYPE OF GRANT One-off grants.

RANGE OF GRANTS £200–£8,000.

SAMPLE GRANTS Thames Valley and Chiltern Ambulance (£8,000); Helen and Douglas House (£4,000); Shelter, Nuffield Orthopaedic Centre and Bradfield Primary Project (£2,000 each); Marcham Village Shop (£1,500); Vale and Downland Museum, Riders for Health and Mission Aviation Fellowship – MAF (£1,000 each); Tools for Self Reliance and Rushmoor Healthy Living (£500 each); and Rakome School Education Day (£200).

FINANCES *Year* 2011–12 *Income* £38,112 *Grants* £48,820 *Assets* £765,970

TRUSTEES William Cumber; Mary Tearney; Alec Davey; Margaret Freeman; Marian Cumber; Julia Mearns.

HOW TO APPLY Applications must be sent in paper format and not via email. There is no formal application; however the trust has provided guidelines which can be found on the trust's website. Applications must be sent to the secretary. Trustees meet twice a year to consider applications, usually in March and October. Applications need to be made at least a month before the meeting date. First time applicant must provide a copy of the latest annual report and accounts.

WHO TO APPLY TO Mary Tearney, Secretary, Manor Farm, Mill Road, Marcham, Abingdon OX13 6NZ *Tel.* 01865 391327 *email* mary.tearney@hotmail.co.uk *Website* www.cumberfamilycharitabletrust.org.uk

■ Cumberland Building Society Charitable Foundation

CC NO 1072435   **ESTABLISHED** 1998

WHERE FUNDING CAN BE GIVEN Cumbria, Dumfries and Galloway, Lancashire (Preston area) and Northumberland (Haltwhistle area).

WHO CAN BENEFIT Registered charities.

WHAT IS FUNDED General charitable purposes in areas where the trustees determine Cumberland Building Society operates.

WHAT IS NOT FUNDED Examples of those areas the foundation does not support are: requests for administration equipment, such as computers, for a charity's own use or general expenses such as salaries; overseas travel, expeditions; events mainly for the general public such as village fetes/carnivals/concerts; organisations supporting other charities; fabric appeals for places of worship unless principally for the benefit of the community as a whole; activities which are mainly/normally the responsibility of central or local government or some other responsible body; hospitals, medical centres and medical research; animal welfare.

RANGE OF GRANTS Up to £1,000.

SAMPLE GRANTS Bootle and District Swimming Club (£750) and Portinscale Village Hall (£500). Previous beneficiaries have included Children's Heart Federation, Community Action Furness, Community Transport South Lakeland, Currock House Association, DEBRA, the Food Train, the Genesis Appeal, Hospice at Home, L'Arche Preston and St John Ambulance.

FINANCES *Year* 2011–12 *Income* £28,102 *Grants* £33,353 *Assets* £3,864

TRUSTEES Linda Jackson; Carol Graham; J. Carr; Brian Edmundson; Janet Booth; Nick Utting; Michael Pearson.

OTHER INFORMATION Grants were made to 75 organisations. A full list of donations was not available, however the accounts stated that grants were made across all geographical areas in the foundation's remit, ranging from £100 to £1,000 and were given to small community groups encompassing children's activities, disability support and a variety of other activities.

HOW TO APPLY Applicants are directed, where possible, to the foundation's website where the foundation's criteria, guidelines and application process are posted.

WHO TO APPLY TO The Secretary, Cumberland House, Castle Street, Carlisle CA3 8RX *Tel.* 01228 541341 *email* charitablefoundation@cumberland.co.uk *Website* www.cumberland.co.uk

■ Cumbria Community Foundation

CC NO 1075120   **ESTABLISHED** 1999

WHERE FUNDING CAN BE GIVEN Cumbria.

WHO CAN BENEFIT Organisations and individuals under several different programmes.

WHAT IS FUNDED Improving the quality of the community life of people in Cumbria, and in particular those in need by reason of disability, age, low-income or other disadvantage.

WHAT IS NOT FUNDED The following are not supported: animal welfare; deficit funding; general large appeals; boxing clubs; medical research and equipment; non-Cumbrian projects; sponsored events; replacement of statutory funding; projects that have already happened; applications where you have had a grant from that fund within the last year (except Grassroots Grants); and individuals (except for specific funds). Contact the foundation for information on any individual restrictions on any of the grant programmes.

TYPE OF GRANT One off and recurring.

RANGE OF GRANTS Generally under £10,000

SAMPLE GRANTS Warm Homes Healthy People (£234,000); Bridging the Gap (£61,500); Robin

Rigg West Cumbria Fund (£40,500); High Sheriff's Crimebeat Fund (£16,000); BNFL Live the Dream Fund (£11,000); John Winder Fund (£10,000); Youth Work Aid Fund (£9,000); Barrow Community Trust (£7,500); High Pow Community Fund (£3,000); Kipling Fund for Older People (£2,000); Cumbria Cultural Fund £1,250); and AMW Environment Fund (£750).

FINANCES *Year* 2011–12 *Income* £2,622,709 *Grants* £1,377,527 *Assets* £7,050,970

TRUSTEES W. Slavin; S. Snyder; C. Tomlinson; J. Whittle; Ian Brown; June Chapman; David Brown; James Carr; Rob Cairns; Robin Burgess; Catherine Alexander; Mike Casson; James Airey; T. Knowles; Dawn Roberts; Dr A. Naylor; J. Humphries; T. Foster; C. Giel; Lyndsay Aspin.

OTHER INFORMATION The total grant figure includes £115,000 paid to individuals; £102 spent in distributing flood bags to households and £174,000 was distributed from funds managed for other organisations.

HOW TO APPLY Application forms and clear and full guidelines for each of the foundation's programmes are available to download on the foundation's website or by contacting the correspondent directly. The foundation prefers to receive applications via email, even if supporting documents have to be sent by post. Applicants are encouraged to contact the foundation prior to making an application in order to confirm their eligibility. Applications are accepted throughout the year and decisions are usually taken within two months. Some programmes offer a faster process for small urgent projects.

WHO TO APPLY TO Andrew Beeforth, Director, Dovenby Hall, Dovenby, Cockermouth, Cumbria CA13 0PN *Tel.* 01900 825760 *Fax* 01900 826527 *email* enquiries@cumbriafoundation.org *Website* www.cumbriafoundation.org

■ The Cunningham Trust

SC NO SC013499   **ESTABLISHED** 1984

WHERE FUNDING CAN BE GIVEN Scotland.

WHO CAN BENEFIT Mostly universities, also individuals.

WHAT IS FUNDED Grants are made to university departments which are carrying out academic research in the field of medicine and zoology.

WHAT IS NOT FUNDED Grants are unlikely to be made available to non-regular beneficiaries.

TYPE OF GRANT Revenue and project funding for up to two years.

SAMPLE GRANTS Aberdeen University – Department of Zoology, Aberdeen University – Department of Ophthalmology, Department of Biomedical Sciences, Edinburgh University's Centre of Tropical Veterinary Medicine and St Andrew's University – School of Biomedical Sciences.

FINANCES *Year* 2011–12 *Income* £254,272 *Grants* £295,108

TRUSTEES Dr D. Corner; A. C. Caithness; Dr D. M. Greenhough.

HOW TO APPLY All applications must be submitted on the standard form.

WHO TO APPLY TO Kim Falconer, Administrator, Murray Donald Drummond Cook LLP, Kinburn Castle, St Andrews, Fife KY16 9DR *email* kfalconer@murraydonald.co.uk

■ The Harry Cureton Charitable Trust

CC NO 1106206   **ESTABLISHED** 2005

WHERE FUNDING CAN BE GIVEN The area covered by Peterborough and Stamford hospitals.

WHO CAN BENEFIT Individuals and organisations.

WHAT IS FUNDED Medical, Health and Sickness

SAMPLE GRANTS Peterborough and Stamford Hospitals NHS Foundation (£31,000); Sue Ryder Care (£22,000); Breast Cancer Care (£7,500); Bretton Medical Practice (£3,000); Dream Holidays (£1,400) and The New Queen Street Surgery (£1,000).

FINANCES *Year* 2011–12 *Income* £82,750 *Grants* £124,041 *Assets* £2,920,895

TRUSTEES Tony Bhullar; Nick Monsell; Nick Plumb; Simon Richards.

OTHER INFORMATION £23,000 was also given to individuals with chronic illness towards new equipment.

HOW TO APPLY Grant applications are administered by the Cambridgeshire Community Foundation. Forms are available to download via the website.

WHO TO APPLY TO Jane Darlington, c/o Cambridgeshire Community Foundation, The Quorum, Barnwell Road, Cambridge CB5 8RE *Tel.* 01223 410535 *email* hcct@cambscf.org.uk *Website* www.harrycureton.org.uk

■ The D. J. H. Currie Memorial Trust

CC NO 802971   **ESTABLISHED** 1990

WHERE FUNDING CAN BE GIVEN Essex.

WHO CAN BENEFIT Registered charities.

WHAT IS FUNDED General charitable purposes. The trust continues to support causes which the founder had an interest in including charities supporting people with disabilities (particularly children), conservation of the countryside, homes for older people and sporting activities in Essex.

WHAT IS NOT FUNDED No grants to individuals.

SAMPLE GRANTS Little Heath School, Live Music Now, Colchester Carers Centre, Braintree Women's Aid, SOS Domestic Abuse Projects, Maldon (Essex) Mind, Saint Francis Hospice, The Wheelyboat Trust, Caring Hearts, Tabor Centre, Barnardo's, Autism Anglia, Support 4 Sight, The Boys' Brigade, Transplant Sport UK and St John's Church Colchester.

FINANCES *Year* 2011–12 *Income* £35,839 *Grants* £37,000 *Assets* £94,249

TRUSTEE National Westminster Bank plc.

HOW TO APPLY In writing to the correspondent. The trustees consider applications in June each year and all applications should be submitted by the end of May. Annual accounts/last annual report to be enclosed with application. No recipient may benefit more than once every four years.

WHO TO APPLY TO The Trust Secretary, NatWest Trust Services, 5th Floor, Trinity Quay 2, Avon Street, Bristol BS2 0PT *Tel.* 05516577371

■ The Dennis Curry Charitable Trust

CC NO 263952   **ESTABLISHED** 1971

WHERE FUNDING CAN BE GIVEN UK.

WHO CAN BENEFIT Charitable organisations.

WHAT IS FUNDED General, particular interest in conservation/environment and education.

Occasional support is given to churches and cathedrals.

RANGE OF GRANTS £500–£20,000.

SAMPLE GRANTS University of Oxford – Dept. of Zoology, Wildlife Conservation Research Unit (£15,000); The British Museum Friends, The Frozen Ark Project and Friends of Little Chalfont Library (£10,000 each); Galapagos Conservation Trust (£5,000); University of Glasgow Trinidad Expedition (£3,000); Project Trust (£1,000); and Médecins Sans Frontières and The Open Spaces Society (£500 each).

FINANCES *Year* 2011–12 *Income* £74,461 *Grants* £55,000 *Assets* £3,106,360

TRUSTEES Michael Curry; Anabel Sylvia Curry; Margaret Curry-Jones; Patricia Rosemary Edmund.

HOW TO APPLY In writing to the correspondent.

WHO TO APPLY TO Nigel Armstrong, Secretary to the Trust, Alliotts, Imperial House, 15 Kingsway, London WC2B 6UN *Tel.* 020 7240 9971 *email* denniscurryscharity@alliotts.com

··

■ The Manny Cussins Foundation

CC NO 219661   **ESTABLISHED** 1962

WHERE FUNDING CAN BE GIVEN Mainly UK, with some emphasis on Yorkshire.

WHO CAN BENEFIT Organisations.

WHAT IS FUNDED Welfare and care of older people and children at risk; Jewish causes; healthcare in Yorkshire and overseas; general in Yorkshire and the former county of Humberside.

WHAT IS NOT FUNDED No grants to individuals.

SAMPLE GRANTS Previous beneficiaries have included Angels International, Christie Hospital – Children Against Cancer, Forgiveness Project, Hadassah Lodge, Leeds International Piano Competition, Leeds Jewish Education Authority, Leeds Jewish Welfare Board (where a family project is named after the settlor), Lifeline for the Old Jerusalem, Martin House Hospice, United Jewish Israel Appeal, Wheatfields Hospice and Women's International Zionist Organisation.

FINANCES *Year* 2011–12 *Income* £56,082 *Grants* £36,247 *Assets* £746,288

TRUSTEES A. Reuben; A. Cussins; A. J. Cussins; B. Cussins; A. Zucker.

HOW TO APPLY The correspondent states that applications are not sought as the trustees carry out their own research.

WHO TO APPLY TO The Trustees, Rotherhill, Lower Street, Fittleworth, Pullborough RH20 1EJ

··

■ The Cutler Trust (the Worshipful Company of Makers of Playing Cards)

CC NO 232876   **ESTABLISHED** 1943

WHERE FUNDING CAN BE GIVEN England and Wales.

WHO CAN BENEFIT Organisations and individuals.

WHAT IS FUNDED 'The aims and objectives of the trust are: to support the City of London ('civic') charities/connected charities and City of London schools and colleges and, where relevant, inner London schools; to assist specific deserving students in their education; to support relevant, smaller charities in which Liverymen are actively involved and which they support; to support smaller charities where the trustees are able to establish an ongoing relationship.'

FINANCES *Year* 2011–12 *Income* £52,597 *Grants* £31,298 *Assets* £627,716

TRUSTEES D. M. Ladd; P. M. Cregeen; R. A. Howells; D. C. Warner; A. J. Carter; N. P. Nicholson; M. J. Winston; L. E. Whitehouse.

OTHER INFORMATION The grant total in 2011–12 included £1,000 given in annuities. 'The Cutler Trust was set up on 25 October 1943 by two card manufacturers, John Waddington Limited and De La Rue Company Limited and named after the then Master, Lindsay Cutler, (whose grandsons have been apprenticed to the Livery and are now Liverymen). Consistent to the original Livery concept, it was initially for beneficiaries and dependants of those who were or had been employed in the manufacture of Playing Cards.'

HOW TO APPLY 'The trust invites applications for funding of grants from members of the Worshipful Company of Makers of Playing Cards, from educational bodies connected with the City of London, and from members of the public. The Marshall of Appeals considers the merits of the applications and seeks further information before submitting recommendations to the trustees' meeting.' Trustees meet at least twice a year to review applications.

WHO TO APPLY TO David A. Barrett, 256 St Davids Square, London E14 3WE *Tel.* 020 7531 5990 *email* clerk@makersofplayingcards.co.uk *Website* www.makersofplayingcards.co.uk

··

■ The Cwmbran Trust

CC NO 505855   **ESTABLISHED** 1976

WHERE FUNDING CAN BE GIVEN Cwmbran and surrounding area.

WHO CAN BENEFIT Local groups.

WHAT IS FUNDED Grants are made to provide social amenities, for the advancement of education and the relief of poverty and sickness in the urban area of Cwmbran town. Particular support is given to local groups for older people and people who are disabled.

WHAT IS NOT FUNDED No grants are made outside of Cwmbran or to organisational running costs.

SAMPLE GRANTS St Anne's Hospice (£10,000); Congress Theatre (£7,500); Ty Hafon Children's Hospice and Medecinema (£5,000 each); Victory Outreach UK (£2,900); Torfean People's First (£2,500); Torfaen Sea Cadets (£2,000); and All Creatures Great and Small and Blaen Bran Woodland (£1,000 each).

FINANCES *Year* 2012 *Income* £86,500 *Grants* £90,000 *Assets* £2,000,000

TRUSTEE Ken Maddox, John Cunningham, Anthony Rippon, David Bassett, Anna Price and C Thomas.

OTHER INFORMATION The grant total in 2010 includes £2,500 donated to 14 individuals.

HOW TO APPLY In writing to the correspondent. Trustees usually meet five times a year in March, May, July, October and December. Where appropriate, applications are investigated by the grants research officer. When the trustees judge it would be helpful, applicants are invited to put their case to the trustees in person. Where an application has to be dealt with urgently, for example, because of the pressure of time or of need, trustees may be contacted by letter or telephone in order that an early decision may be made.

WHO TO APPLY TO K. L. Maddox, Arvin Meritor HVBS (UK) Ltd, H. V. B. S. (UK) Ltd, Grange Road, Cwmbran, Gwent NP44 3XU *Tel.* 01633 834040 *email* cwmbrantrust@arvinmeritor.com

··

■ Itzchok Meyer Cymerman Trust Ltd

CC NO 265090   **ESTABLISHED** 1972

WHERE FUNDING CAN BE GIVEN UK and Israel.

WHO CAN BENEFIT Registered charities and occasional small grants to individuals – both mainly of the Jewish faith.

WHAT IS FUNDED Advancement of the Orthodox Jewish faith, education, social welfare, relief of sickness, medical research and general.

TYPE OF GRANT Mostly recurrent.

RANGE OF GRANTS Up to £125,000.

SAMPLE GRANTS M D and S Charitable Trust (£125,000); Dencommon Limited (£105,000); Russian Immigrant Aid Fund (£104,000); and Trumart Limited (£84,000).

FINANCES *Year* 2011–12 *Income* £2,124,184 *Grants* £661,430 *Assets* £11,498,508

TRUSTEES H. F. Bondi; M. D. Cymerman; S. Cymerman; S. Heitner; L. H. Bondi; Ian Heitner; R. Cymerman.

HOW TO APPLY In writing to the correspondent.

WHO TO APPLY TO Ian Heitner, Trustee, 497 Holloway Road, London N7 6LE *Tel.* 020 7272 2255

Think carefully about every application. Is it justified?

········

485

■ D. C. R. Allen Charitable Trust

CC NO 277293   **ESTABLISHED** 1979
WHERE FUNDING CAN BE GIVEN England and Wales.
WHO CAN BENEFIT Charitable organisations.
WHAT IS FUNDED General charitable purposes.
WHAT IS NOT FUNDED No individuals.
FINANCES *Year* 2012–13 *Income* £298,529
Grants £116,900 *Assets* £335,924
TRUSTEES Julie Frusher; Martin Allen; Colin Allen.
OTHER INFORMATION A list of beneficiaries was
unavailable.
HOW TO APPLY In writing to the correspondent.
WHO TO APPLY TO Julie Frusher, Trustee, Estate
Office, Edgcote House, Edgcote, Banbury,
Oxfordshire OX17 1AG

■ The D. G. Charitable Settlement

CC NO 1040778   **ESTABLISHED** 1994
WHERE FUNDING CAN BE GIVEN UK.
WHO CAN BENEFIT Registered charities.
WHAT IS FUNDED General charitable purposes to a
mainly fixed list of charities.
RANGE OF GRANTS £500–£200,000.
SAMPLE GRANTS Oxfam (£100,000); Crisis
(£40,000); Great Ormond Street Hospital and
Shelter (£25,000 each); Cancer Research UK,
Environmental Investigation Agency Charitable
Trust, Friends of the Earth and Reprieve UK
(£10,000 each); Defend the Right to Protest,
Media Standards Trust – Hacked Off and
University of St Andrews (£5,000 each); and
Terrence Higgins Trust (£2,000).
FINANCES *Year* 2011–12 *Income* £3,585
Grants £344,200 *Assets* £1,088,158
TRUSTEES David Gilmour; Patrick Grafton-Green;
Polly Samson.
HOW TO APPLY This trust does not consider
unsolicited applications.
WHO TO APPLY TO Joanna Nelson, Secretary, PO Box
62, Heathfield, East Sussex TN21 8ZF
Tel. 01435 867604 *email* joanna.nelson@
btconnect.com

■ The D'Oyly Carte Charitable Trust

CC NO 1112457   **ESTABLISHED** 1972
WHERE FUNDING CAN BE GIVEN UK.
WHO CAN BENEFIT Registered charities only, or where
it is clear the objects of the appeal are for
charitable purposes.
WHAT IS FUNDED Mainly the arts, medical/welfare
charities and the environment.
WHAT IS NOT FUNDED The trust is unlikely to support
the following: animal welfare; campaigning or
lobbying projects; community transport
organisations or services; conferences and
seminars; exhibitions; expeditions and overseas
travel; friend/Parent Teacher Associations;
general appeals; individuals or applications for
the benefit of one individual; large national
charities enjoying wide support; local authorities
and areas of work considered a statutory
requirement; medical research; NHS hospitals
for operational and building costs; projects
taking place or benefiting people outside the

UK; recordings and commissioning of new
works; religious causes and activities; routine
maintenance of religious buildings; salaries and
positions, though the trustees will consider
contributing to core operating costs of which
they recognise general salary costs will be a
part; support and rehabilitation from drug abuse
or alcoholism; universities, colleges, schools,
nurseries, playgroups (other than those for
special needs children). The trustees do not
consider requests from charities that have had
an application turned down until two years have
elapsed after the date of rejection.
TYPE OF GRANT Mainly one-off.
RANGE OF GRANTS Up to £20,000 but mostly under
£5,000.
SAMPLE GRANTS Royal Academy of Dramatic Art
(£20,000); Anthony Nolan Trust, Ashgate
Hospice, BREAK, Cahoots NI, Grasslands Trust,
Leicestershire Chorale, Polka Theatre for
Children, SignHealth and Whale and Dolphin
Conservation Society (£5,000 each); Bach
Choir, Bournemouth Symphony Orchestra,
British Stammering Association, CHICKS,
Gabriele, Live Music Now, Spinal Injuries
Association, Two Moors Festival and Wirral
Society for the Blind and Partially Sighted
(£4,000 each); Action Transport Theatre, Artlink
Central, Buglife, Children's Aid Team, Sickle Cell
Society, St John's Hospice and Wigmore Hall
Trust (£3,000 each); Leicester Theatre Trust,
New English Ballet Theatre and YMCA Sutton
Coldfield (£2,000 each); and Swaledale Festival
and Young Dementia UK (£1,000 each).
FINANCES *Year* 2011–12 *Income* £1,126,310
Grants £929,718 *Assets* £41,707,443
TRUSTEES Jeremy Leigh Pemberton, Chair;
Francesca Radcliffe; Julia Sibley; Henry
Freeland; Andrew Jackson; Michael O'Brien.
HOW TO APPLY Potential applicants should write to
the correspondent with an outline proposal of
no more than two A4 pages. This should cover
the work of the charity, its beneficiaries and the
need for funding. Applicants qualifying for
consideration will then be required to complete
the trust's application form. The form should be
returned with a copy of the latest annual report
and accounts. Applications for specific projects
should also include clear details of the need the
intended project is designed to meet and an
outline budget.
WHO TO APPLY TO Jane Thorne, Secretary, 1 Savoy
Hill, London WC2R 0BP *Tel.* 020 7420 2600

■ Roald Dahl's Marvellous Children's Charity

CC NO 1137409   **ESTABLISHED** 1991
WHERE FUNDING CAN BE GIVEN UK.
WHO CAN BENEFIT Registered charities and
individuals. In general, the charity aims to
provide help to organisations where funds are
not readily available. Preference for small or
new organisations rather than long-established,
large or national organisations.
WHAT IS FUNDED 'The charity makes grants to benefit
children who have the following conditions.
Neurology: acquired brain injury as the result of
benign brain tumour, encephalitis, head injury,
hydrocephalus, meningitis, stroke, neurodegenerative conditions, defined as conditions
in which there is progressive intellectual and/or
neurological deterioration and rare and/or
severe forms of epilepsy; Haematology: chronic
debilitating blood diseases of childhood,
excluding leukaemia and related disorders;

conditions include: sickle cell anaemia, thalassaemia, haemolytic anaemia, bone marrow failure syndrome, haemophilia, thrombophilia and Von Willebrand's Disease. The charity primarily makes grants to benefit children (i.e. up to the 18th birthday). However, we may consider supporting young people between the ages of 18 and 25 (i.e. up to the 26th birthday) where a case can be made that they have specific needs associated with their medical condition. We are looking for applications that will clearly tackle the needs and challenges children face as a result of living with the conditions listed above. We are particularly interested in: pump-priming of new specialist Paediatric nursing posts, where there is an emphasis on community care, for a maximum of two years. We will only consider funding posts where the applicant organisation commits to taking over funding of the post for a minimum of three years after our grant ends; the provision of information and/or support to children and their families; specific projects within residential and day centres to benefit children within the above-mentioned criteria; small items of medical equipment, not available from statutory sources, to enable children to be cared for in their own homes; activities to disseminate good practice in support of children living with our priority conditions; other projects which specifically benefit children and young people within the above mentioned medical criteria may be considered. Although we prefer to fund specific projects, posts and activities, we will consider providing core funding particularly in the case of very small organisations.'

WHAT IS NOT FUNDED The charity will not fund: general appeals from large, well-established charities; national appeals for large building projects; arts projects; any organisations which do not have charitable status or exclusively charitable aims (other than NHS organisations under the charity's specialist nurses programme); statutory bodies (other than NHS organisations under the charity's specialist nurses programme); school or higher education fees; organisations outside the UK; organisations for people with blood disorders which are cancer related due to the relatively large number of charities helping in the oncological field.

TYPE OF GRANT One-off, start-up costs, salaries, projects for up to two years; the range is wide.

RANGE OF GRANTS Individual: £50–£500. Organisations: up to £50,000.

SAMPLE GRANTS Child Brain Injury Trust NI (£50,000); Sickle Cell and Young Stroke Survivors (£38,000); OSCAR – Sandwell (£15,000); Batten Disease Family Association (£12,500); Meningitis Trust NI (£11,000); Cerebra and Sickle Cell Society (£10,000 each); and Huntington's Disease Association and Matthew's Friends (£9,000).

FINANCES *Year* 2011–12 *Income* £638,866 *Grants* £216,636 *Assets* £1,494,140

TRUSTEES Felicity Dahl, Chair; Martin Goodwin; Roger Hills; Georgina Howson; Virginia Fisher; Graham Faulkner.

OTHER INFORMATION The charity was established in 2010 to supersede the Roald Dahl Foundation following a strategic review, although the focus of the charity remains the same.
The grant total figure includes £106,909 given to organisations.

HOW TO APPLY Visit the charity's website for full and current information on how to apply.

WHO TO APPLY TO Dr Richard Piper, Chief Executive, 81a High Street, Great Missenden, Buckinghamshire HP16 0AL *Tel.* 01494 890465 *Fax* 01494 890459 *email* grants@ marvellouschildren'scharity.org *Website* www. marvellouschildren'scharity.org

■ Daily Prayer Union Charitable Trust Limited

CC NO 284857   **ESTABLISHED** 1983

WHERE FUNDING CAN BE GIVEN UK.

WHO CAN BENEFIT Christians and evangelists.

WHAT IS FUNDED Evangelical Christian purposes.

RANGE OF GRANTS £1,000–£7,000.

SAMPLE GRANTS Monkton Combe School (£7,000); Jesus Lane Trust (£3,000); London City Mission and People International (£2,000 each); Interserve (£1,500); and AIM International (£1,000).

FINANCES *Year* 2011–12 *Income* £32,969 *Grants* £96,350 *Assets* £41,584

TRUSTEES Revd David Jackman; Revd Timothy Sterry; Anne Tompson; Elizabeth Bridger; Fiona Ashton; Dr Joanna Sudell; Giles Rawlinson; Revd Raymond Porter; Carolyn Ash.

OTHER INFORMATION £67,000 to 50 individuals (2011–12)

HOW TO APPLY The trustees meet regularly to review applications for new grants and grants which are due for renewal.

WHO TO APPLY TO Clare Palmer, Secretary, 12 Weymouth Street, London W1W 5BY

■ The Daisy Trust

CC NO 283890   **ESTABLISHED** 1981

WHERE FUNDING CAN BE GIVEN The borough of Hammersmith and Fulham.

WHO CAN BENEFIT Local organisations in Hammersmith and Fulham

WHAT IS FUNDED General charitable purposes

WHAT IS NOT FUNDED The trust only makes grants to those residing inside the area of benefit. No grants to individuals. No grants for general running costs, salaries or long term projects.

TYPE OF GRANT One-off.

RANGE OF GRANTS £80–£1,000

SAMPLE GRANTS Fulham Good Neighbour Service, Sulivan Primary School and Upper Room (£1,000 each); Craven Cottage Senior Citizens Club and Royal Hospital for Neuro-disability (£500 each); Farm Lane Luncheon Club and Play Association (£250 each); and Sands End After School Childcare (£150).

FINANCES *Year* 2012 *Income* £42,111 *Grants* £25,000

TRUSTEES Patrick Ground; Caroline Ground; Pepita Stonor; Frances Stainton; Peter Stonor; Caroline MacKenzie; Richard Cormack

HOW TO APPLY An application form is available to download, together with criteria and guidelines, from the trust's website. Applicants are welcomed to include a one page covering letter and any leaflets or brochures about their organisation. The trust will acknowledge receipt of an application and inform as to whether or not it has been successful.

WHO TO APPLY TO The Secretary, 25 Felden Street, London SW6 5AE *Tel.* 020 7736 0131 *email* secretary@daisytrust.org *Website* www. daisytrust.org

■ The Daiwa Anglo-Japanese Foundation

CC NO 299955 **ESTABLISHED** 1988
WHERE FUNDING CAN BE GIVEN UK, Japan.
WHO CAN BENEFIT Individuals and organisations (UK or Japanese) benefiting young adults, students and Japanese people – including schools, universities, grass roots and professional groups.
WHAT IS FUNDED The education of citizens of the UK and Japan in each other's culture, institutions, arts, and so on. Scholarships, bursaries and awards to enable students and academics in the UK and Japan to pursue their education abroad. Grants to charitable organisations and institutions promoting education in the UK or Japan, and research.
WHAT IS NOT FUNDED Daiwa Foundation Small Grants cannot be used for: general appeals; capital expenditure (e.g., building refurbishment, equipment acquisition, etc.); consumables (e.g., stationery, scientific supplies, etc.); school, college or university fees; research or study by an individual school/college/university student; salary costs or professional fees; commissions for works of art; retrospective grants; replacement of statutory funding; commercial activities.
Daiwa Foundation Awards cannot be used for: any project that does not involve both a British and a Japanese partner; general appeals; capital expenditure (e.g., building refurbishment, equipment acquisition, etc.); salary costs or professional fees; commissions for works of art; retrospective grants; commercial activities.
TYPE OF GRANT Outright or partnership grants, paid in sterling or Japanese yen. One year funding.
RANGE OF GRANTS £5,000–£15,000 for collaborative projects; £1,000–£5,000 for small grants.
SAMPLE GRANTS De Montfort University (£13,000); Clifton Scientific Trust and Tokyo College of Music (£10,000 each); Ruthin Craft Centre (£7,500); Sadler's Wells (£7,000); Shakespeare's Globe (£5,000); and Barbican Centre Trust, Bridgewater Hall, and English Speaking Union of Japan (£3,000 each).
FINANCES *Year* 2011–12 *Grants* £828,032
TRUSTEES Sir Michael Perry; Hiroaki Fujii; Takafumi Sato; Mami Mizutori; Masahiro Dozen; Christopher Everett; Merryn Somerset Webb; Lord Brittan; Sir Peter Williams; Andrew Smithers; Akira Kyota.
OTHER INFORMATION The total grants figure for 2011–12 includes £486,000 awarded as scholarships.
HOW TO APPLY Application forms are available from the foundation's website. Details of deadlines and criteria for grants, awards and prizes, together with the relevant application forms and guidelines are available on the foundation's website.
WHO TO APPLY TO Jason James, Director General and Secretary, Daiwa Foundation, Japan House, 13/14 Cornwall Terrace, London NW1 4QP *Tel.* 020 7486 4348 *Fax* 020 7486 2914 *email* office@dajf.org.uk *Website* www.dajf.org.uk

■ Oizer Dalim Trust

CC NO 1045296 **ESTABLISHED** 1994
WHERE FUNDING CAN BE GIVEN UK and overseas.
WHO CAN BENEFIT Registered charities.
WHAT IS FUNDED To alleviate poverty and further education within the Orthodox Jewish community.

FINANCES *Year* 2011–12 *Income* £93,571 *Grants* £102,015 *Assets* £16,059
TRUSTEES Mordechai Cik; Maurice Freund; Moshe Cohen.
HOW TO APPLY In writing to the correspondent.
WHO TO APPLY TO Mordechai Cik, Trustee, 68 Osbaldeston Road, London N16 7DR

■ The Danego Charitable Trust

CC NO 1118123 **ESTABLISHED** 2007
WHERE FUNDING CAN BE GIVEN UK and overseas.
WHO CAN BENEFIT Registered, national charities.
WHAT IS FUNDED General charitable purposes including humanitarian appeals and charities related to the film production trade.
RANGE OF GRANTS £5,000–£30,000.
SAMPLE GRANTS First Story Limited, Hands On and Cinema TV Fund
FINANCES *Year* 2012–13 *Income* £116,684 *Grants* £50,000 *Assets* £17,189
TRUSTEES Timothy Bevan; Amy Gadney; Coutts and Co.
HOW TO APPLY In writing to the correspondent. 'Recipients of grants are required to sign a formal receipt. Where relevant, the trustees also ask to be provided with copies of receipts for expenditure and the grant may be subject to an ongoing monitoring programme and further instalments of grants only released subject to timescales being reached.'
WHO TO APPLY TO The Trustees, Coutts and Co, Trustee Department, 440 The Strand, London WC2R 0QS *Tel.* 020 7663 6825

■ The Dr and Mrs A. Darlington Charitable Trust

CC NO 283308 **ESTABLISHED** 1981
WHERE FUNDING CAN BE GIVEN Devon, in particular Sidmouth and east Devon.
WHO CAN BENEFIT Only registered charities.
WHAT IS FUNDED The trust mainly supports medical causes; people who are disabled; older people; and socially isolated people. Grants also given in the fields of nature conservation and preservation.
WHAT IS NOT FUNDED Applications from individuals, including students, are unlikely to be successful. Applications for donations to be used outside Devon (particularly outside Sidmouth and East Devon) are also unlikely to be successful.
TYPE OF GRANT One-off, some recurring.
SAMPLE GRANTS Peninsula Medical School Foundation, Children's Health and Exercise Research Centre, Salcombe Regis Church, Vitalise, Freedomwheels, Listening Books, Motability, West of England School and College, MS Therapy Centre, Brainwave, SSAFA, St Loyes, UBS and Countryside Foundation.
FINANCES *Year* 2011–12 *Income* £203,362 *Grants* £57,250 *Assets* £34,840
TRUSTEE Lloyds TSB Bank plc.
HOW TO APPLY In writing to the correspondent. The trustees regret that they cannot send replies to unsuccessful applicants. The trustees meet quarterly in March, June, September and December; applications should be received the previous month.
WHO TO APPLY TO The Trust Manager, Lloyds TSB Bank plc, UK Trust Centre, The Clock House, 22–26 Ock Street, Abingdon, Oxfordshire OX14 5SW *Tel.* 01235 232700

■ Baron Davenport's Charity

CC NO 217307 **ESTABLISHED** 1930

WHERE FUNDING CAN BE GIVEN Warwickshire, Worcestershire, Staffordshire, Shropshire and West Midlands.

WHO CAN BENEFIT Individuals and charitable organisations and institutions, benefiting children, young adults, retired people, widows, and people disadvantaged by poverty.

WHAT IS FUNDED Social welfare, children and young people under the age of 25.

WHAT IS NOT FUNDED There are no exclusions, providing the applications come within the charity's objects and the applying organisation is based within the charity's beneficial area, or the organisation's project lies within or benefits people who live in the beneficial area.

TYPE OF GRANT One-off or annual grants, for capital or revenue costs.

RANGE OF GRANTS Mostly £2,500 or less.

SAMPLE GRANTS Marie Curie Hospice (£20,000); Stonehouse Gang (£12,000); Compton Hospice, Donna Louise Trust and St Richard's Hospice (£9,000 each); and Age Concern Birmingham, James and Ada Robb Charity and Laslett's Charities (£8,000 each).

FINANCES *Year* 2011–12 *Income* £1,164,960 *Grants* £986,440 *Assets* £29,988,062

TRUSTEES Christopher Hordern, Chair; Sue M. Ayres; William M. Colacicchi; Paul Dransfield; Lisa Bryan; Rob Prichard.

OTHER INFORMATION The grant total includes £408,049 to 1,671 individuals.

HOW TO APPLY In writing to the correspondent, accompanied by the latest accounts and any project costs. Distributions take place twice a year at the end of May and November and applications should be received at the charity's office by 15 March or 15 September. All applications are acknowledged and those not within the charity's objects are advised.

WHO TO APPLY TO Marlene Keenan, Administrator, Portman House, 5–7 Temple Row West, Birmingham B2 5NY *Tel.* 01212 368004 *Fax* 01212 332500 *email* enquiries@barondavenportscharity.org *Website* www.barondavenportscharity.org

■ The Davidson (Nairn) Charitable Trust

SC NO SC024273 **ESTABLISHED** 1995

WHERE FUNDING CAN BE GIVEN Nairn area.

WHO CAN BENEFIT Social welfare organisations and all charities recognised in Scottish Law.

WHAT IS FUNDED Grants may be made towards the provision of leisure and recreation facilities, relieving poverty, assisting older people and educational concerns.

WHAT IS NOT FUNDED Only registered charities are supported or charities recognised in Scottish law.

FINANCES *Year* 2011–12 *Income* £44,457 *Grants* £30,000

TRUSTEES Iain Bain; John Anderson; William Cowie.

HOW TO APPLY On a form available from the correspondent.

WHO TO APPLY TO The Trustees, c/o R. and R. Urquhart, Incorporating MacGregor and Co Solicitors, Royal Bank of Scotland Buildings, 20 High Street, Nairn IV12 4AX

■ The Davidson Family Charitable Trust

CC NO 262937 **ESTABLISHED** 1971

WHERE FUNDING CAN BE GIVEN UK.

WHO CAN BENEFIT Mainly Jewish organisations.

WHAT IS FUNDED Jewish and charitable purposes.

SAMPLE GRANTS United Synagogue (£351,000); Holburne Museum (£210,000); Jewish Care (£205,000); The Hertford House Trust (£50,000); Emunah Child Resettlement Fund and Treehouse (£20,000 each); Cystic Fibrosis (£15,000); British Ort Foundation, Centre for Jewish Life, Magen David Adom UK and Peterhouse Development Fund (£10,000 each); and Kisharon and UK Branch of Meir Panim (£1,000 each).

FINANCES *Year* 2011–12 *Income* £1,312,533 *Grants* £1,694,565 *Assets* £418,417

TRUSTEES Gerald A. Davidson; Maxine Y. Davidson; Eve Winer.

HOW TO APPLY In writing to the correspondent.

WHO TO APPLY TO Eve Winer, Trustee, c/o Queen Anne Street Capital, 58 Queen Anne Street, London W1G 8HW *Tel.* 020 7224 1030 *email* ewiner@wolfeproperties.co.uk

■ The Alderman Joe Davidson Memorial Trust

CC NO 202591 **ESTABLISHED** 1962

WHERE FUNDING CAN BE GIVEN UK, with a preference for Hampshire.

WHO CAN BENEFIT Local and specific national organisations and individuals benefiting: children; older people, nominated by Age Concern; and Jewish people.

WHAT IS FUNDED Charities that are named in the trust deed, people who are in need and the provision of Christmas parties. The trust also presents watches to schoolchildren for regular attendance.

TYPE OF GRANT Recurring grants given to specific organisations.

SAMPLE GRANTS Jewish Educational Committee (£5,300); Portsmouth Voluntary Association for the Blind, Portsmouth Voluntary Cate Committee for Tuberculosis and Lung Diseases, Dr Barnardo's Homes, Portsmouth Council of Community Service and Hampshire County Council – Children's Cottage Homes (£1,500 each); Nightingale House Home for Aged Jews, Norwood Home for Jewish Children, Jewish Home and Hospital at Tottenham, Jewish Blind Society, Portsmouth and Southsea Hebrew Congregation and Society of Friends of Jewish Refugees (£700 each).

FINANCES *Year* 2011–12 *Income* £41,014 *Grants* £25,310 *Assets* £771,528

TRUSTEES K. Crabbe; J. Stock; C. Davidson; C. Trevellick; J. Woolsgrove; E. Baker.

OTHER INFORMATION The trust was established to provide 'dwellings for persons over 70 years of age in necessitous circumstances preferably resident in Portsmouth for more than 25 years'.

HOW TO APPLY The trustees are only permitted to make grants to individuals or organisations that are specified in the Trust Deed.

WHO TO APPLY TO K. Crabbe, Local Democracy Manager, Democratic Services, Portsmouth City Council, Civic Offices, Guildhall Square, Portsmouth *Tel.* 02392 834056 *email* teresa.deasy@portsmouthcc.gov.uk

Think carefully about every application. Is it justified?

489

■ Michael Davies Charitable Settlement

CC NO 1000574 **ESTABLISHED** 1990
WHERE FUNDING CAN BE GIVEN UK.
WHO CAN BENEFIT Charities.
WHAT IS FUNDED General charitable purposes.
RANGE OF GRANTS Up to £15,000.
SAMPLE GRANTS Marie Curie Cancer Care and The Sorrell Foundation (£20,000 each); Docklands Scout Project and RNLI (£10,000 each); University of Westminster Prize and Scholarship Fund (£3,000); Cycle to Cannes (£2,000); Macmillan Cancer Support (£1,250); Royal Parks Foundation and Super Strings Club (£1,000 each); and NSPCC (£500).
FINANCES *Year* 2011–12 *Income* £118,064 *Grants* £68,933 *Assets* £798,856
TRUSTEES Michael Davies; Kenneth Hawkins.
HOW TO APPLY In writing to the correspondent.
WHO TO APPLY TO Kenneth Hawkins, Trustee, Lee Associates, 5 Southampton Place, London WC1A 2DA *Tel.* 020 7025 4600

■ The Gwendoline and Margaret Davies Charity

CC NO 235589 **ESTABLISHED** 1934
WHERE FUNDING CAN BE GIVEN UK, with particular favour given to Wales.
WHO CAN BENEFIT Registered charities only. Welsh charities are particularly favoured.
WHAT IS FUNDED General charitable purposes, with special consideration given to the arts, health and young people. Organisations in the fields of education, medical research, community care services environment and faith activities may also be considered.
WHAT IS NOT FUNDED Grants are made to registered charities only.
TYPE OF GRANT Mainly one-off, occasionally recurrent for specific capital projects.
RANGE OF GRANTS Up to £28,000
SAMPLE GRANTS David Davies Memorial Institute (£28,000); Welsh National Opera (£10,000); Age Concern Powys (£9,000); Gregynog Festival (£8,000); Autistica and Llandinam Village Hall (£5,000 each); Llwyn-yr-Eos Out of School Club (£3,000); North Powys Youth Orchestra and Ferndale Skate Park Ltd (£2,000 each); Friends of Pedal Power (£1,500) and Machynlleth Tabernacle (£1,000).
FINANCES *Year* 2011–12 *Income* £265,852 *Grants* £103,823 *Assets* £6,637,851
TRUSTEES Lord David Davies; Dr David Lewis; Dr Denis Balsom; Dr Janet Lewis.
HOW TO APPLY The trustees consider appeals on an individual basis. There are no application forms as the trustees prefer to receive letters from applicants setting out the following information: whether the organisation is a registered charity; details of the reason for the application – the type of work and so on; the cost; how much has been raised so far towards the cost; the source of the sums raised; a copy of the last audited accounts if available; and any other information that the applicant may consider would help the application. Unsuccessful appeals are not informed unless an sae is enclosed.
WHO TO APPLY TO Susan Hamer, Secretary, The Offices, Plas Dolerw, Milford Road, Newtown, Powys SY16 2EH *Tel.* 01686 625228 *email* susan@daviescharities.freeserve.co.uk

■ The Hamilton Davies Trust

CC NO 1106123 **ESTABLISHED** 2004
WHERE FUNDING CAN BE GIVEN Irlam and Cadishead (in Salford) and Rixton with Glazebrook (in Warrington).
WHO CAN BENEFIT Community organisations.
WHAT IS FUNDED '(1) Youth – Supporting youth leaders and developing the youth movement with the aim of promoting links to education, sports and community initiatives and encouraging organised activities. (2) Education – Adding value to existing provision and raising children's expectations. (3) Sport – Sport is particularly important in the development of young people and the trust has supported projects by providing funds for equipment and kit, holiday programmes and competitions. (4) Community – Support for the community by way of rebuilding and refurbishment of community buildings, supporting group work, festivals and enhancing communication between local facilities and residents.'
WHAT IS NOT FUNDED Applications for projects outside the beneficial area will not be considered.
SAMPLE GRANTS Irlam and Cadishead Leisure Centre – Improvements to sports facilities (5 grants totalling £350,000); Irlam Steel Recreation and Social Club – Irlam Steel Pavilion Construction (5 grants totalling £87,000); Irlam and Cadishead Community Committee – Christmas lights in Irlam and Cadishead (£20,000); Glazebrook Methodist Church – Refurbishment (3 grants totalling £20,000); Irlam and Cadishead Community Festival Committee – Festival costs (£5,000); Irlam and Cadishead Youth Centre – Equipment for Youth Centre and BMX Park graffiti project (2 grants totalling £4,000); Fiddlers Lane Community Primary School – Outdoor canopy for early years area (£3,000); Irlam Catholic Club FC – Team kit (£500) and Rixton with Glazebrook Community Hall – Diamond Jubilee lights (£72).
FINANCES *Year* 2011–12 *Income* £1,113,478 *Grants* £613,904 *Assets* £4,249,317
TRUSTEES Neil McArthur; Graham Chisnall; Frank Cocker.
HOW TO APPLY In writing to the correspondent. Applications should include a brief outline of the project for which support is requested, the amount of funding required and details of any other funding applications that have been made. The trustees will consider all applications, with applicants being informed of their decision in writing. The trust welcomes initial telephone calls to discuss potential projects.
WHO TO APPLY TO Mandy Coleman, General Manager, Hamilton Davies House, 117c Liverpool Road, Cadishead, Manchester M44 5BG *Tel.* 01612 224003 *email* info@hamiltondavies.org.uk *Website* www.hamiltondavies.org.uk

■ The Wilfrid Bruce Davis Charitable Trust

CC NO 265421 **ESTABLISHED** 1967
WHERE FUNDING CAN BE GIVEN UK, but mainly Cornwall; India.
WHO CAN BENEFIT Voluntary groups and registered charities.
WHAT IS FUNDED The trust presently concentrates on 'improving the quality of life for those who are physically disadvantaged and their carers'. The geographical area covered is almost exclusively Cornwall, however the main thrust of the trust's activities is now focused on India.

WHAT IS NOT FUNDED No applications from individuals are considered.

RANGE OF GRANTS £100–£20,000.

SAMPLE GRANTS Pallium India (£20,000); Merlin Project and Guwahati Pain Clinic (£5,000 each); Cornwall Community Foundation (£2,000) Precious Lives Appeal and Jubilee Sailing Trust (£1,000 each).

FINANCES *Year* 2011–12 *Income* £58,559 *Grants* £45,588 *Assets* £156,676

TRUSTEES W. B. Davis; D. F. Davis; D. S. Dickens; C. A. S. Pierce.

HOW TO APPLY Unsolicited applications are generally not supported.

WHO TO APPLY TO W. B. Davis, Trustee, La Feock Grange, Feock, Truro, Cornwall TR3 6RG *Tel.* 01872 862795

■ Davis-Rubens Charitable Trust

CC NO 263662   **ESTABLISHED** 1971

WHERE FUNDING CAN BE GIVEN UK.

WHO CAN BENEFIT Registered charities with a preference for UK-wide and Jewish charities.

WHAT IS FUNDED General charitable purposes.

WHAT IS NOT FUNDED No grants to individuals.

TYPE OF GRANT Mainly recurrent.

RANGE OF GRANTS £50–£1,000, mostly under £500.

SAMPLE GRANTS Vitalise (£750); Jewish Deaf Association (£600); Diabetes UK (£500); Musician's Benevolent Fund (£400); Trinity Hospice (£350); Greater London Fund for the Blind (£250); British Friends of the Hebrew University of Jerusalem (£200); Butler Trust (£100); and Universal Beneficent Society – UBS (£50).

FINANCES *Year* 2011–12 *Income* £23,016 *Grants* £25,000

TRUSTEES Enid Rubens; Giles Rubens; Edward Checkley.

HOW TO APPLY In writing to the correspondent, however, the trust states that applications from new charities are rarely considered.

WHO TO APPLY TO Geoffrey Easton, c/o G. and W. Tax Consultants, 40 Vellacotts, Chelmsford, Essex CM1 7EB *Tel.* 01245 444081

■ The Dawe Charitable Trust

CC NO 1060314   **ESTABLISHED** 1997

WHERE FUNDING CAN BE GIVEN Cambridgeshire, national, international.

WHO CAN BENEFIT Charitable organisations.

WHAT IS FUNDED Disadvantaged people and homelessness.

RANGE OF GRANTS £1,000–£100,000.

SAMPLE GRANTS Previous beneficiaries included: Prince's Trust (£50,000); St Theresa Charity and Manda Wilderness Agricultural Project (£5,000 each).

FINANCES *Year* 2011–12 *Income* £114,527 *Grants* £322,861 *Assets* £1,831,311

TRUSTEES Dr Peter Dawe; Lindsay Dawe; David Kerr.

HOW TO APPLY In writing to the correspondent, outlining ideas and needs.

WHO TO APPLY TO Dr Peter Dawe, Fen View, 17a Broad Street, Ely, Cambridgeshire CB7 4AJ *Tel.* 0845 345 8999

■ The De Brye Charitable Trust

CC NO 326226   **ESTABLISHED** 1982

WHERE FUNDING CAN BE GIVEN Mostly within the UK, however the trustees have discretion to make grants outside the UK.

WHO CAN BENEFIT Charitable organisations.

WHAT IS FUNDED General charitable purposes, preference may be given to the activities affecting the orphans, neglected children and children with physical disabilities, older people and the blind.

TYPE OF GRANT One-off grants to organisations.

RANGE OF GRANTS £2,000–£35,000.

SAMPLE GRANTS Save the Children Fund (£35,000); Salisbury Cathedral (£20,000); Corton Parochial Church (£12,500); Disability Snowsport UK (£8,000); The William Wilberforce Trust, NSPCC, Amber and British Red Cross (£5,000 each); Chafyn Grove, North Hampshire Medical Fund and UNICEF (£4,000 each); British Wireless for the Blind Fund and Operation Smile (£3,000 each) and Cherry Orchard Surgery and The Blue Cross (£2,000 each).

FINANCES *Year* 2011–12 *Income* £94,806 *Grants* £117,312 *Assets* £2,304,350

TRUSTEES Alexander de Brye; Jennifer de Brye; Phillip Sykes.

HOW TO APPLY In writing to the correspondent.

WHO TO APPLY TO George Georghiou, Mercer and Hole, 72 London Road, St Albans, Hertfordshire AL1 1NS *Tel.* 01727 869141

■ The De Clermont Charitable Company Ltd

CC NO 274191   **ESTABLISHED** 1977

WHERE FUNDING CAN BE GIVEN Generally UK, with a preference for north east England.

WHO CAN BENEFIT Headquarters organisations and local organisations in the north east of England.

WHAT IS FUNDED General charitable purposes, particularly those charities of special interest to the founders of this company, i.e. medical research, children and young people, service organisations and overseas disaster appeals.

WHAT IS NOT FUNDED No grants for organisations concerned with drug or alcohol misuse.

SAMPLE GRANTS Previous beneficiaries have included: Sedburgh School Foundation, Borders Support Group, Alzheimer's Research Trust, Lowick Village Hall and Universal Beneficent Society, Brooke Hospital for Animals and Haydn Bridge High School and CLIC Sargent.

FINANCES *Year* 2011–12 *Income* £29,420 *Grants* £22,329 *Assets* £827,790

TRUSTEES Elizabeth de Clermont; Caroline Orpwood; Herbert Orpwood.

OTHER INFORMATION No grants list was available from the latest accounts.

HOW TO APPLY In writing to the correspondent.

WHO TO APPLY TO Caroline Orpwood, Morris Hall, Norham, Berwick-upon-Tweed TD15 2JY *Tel.* 01890 850266

■ Peter De Haan Charitable Trust

CC NO 1077005   **ESTABLISHED** 1999

WHERE FUNDING CAN BE GIVEN UK.

WHO CAN BENEFIT Charitable organisations.

WHAT IS FUNDED General charitable purposes, including organisations connected with children and young people. The current focus of the trust is social welfare, the environment and the arts.

WHAT IS NOT FUNDED The trust will not accept applications for grants: that directly replace or subsidise statutory funding; from individuals or for the benefit of one individual; for work that has already taken place; which do not have a direct benefit to the UK; for medical research; for adventure and residential courses, expeditions or overseas travel; for holidays and respite care; for endowment funds; for the promotion of a specific religion; that are part of general appeals or circulars; from applicants who have applied to the trust within the last 12 months. In addition to the above, the trust is unlikely to support: large national charities which enjoy widespread support; local organisations which are part of a wider network of others doing similar work; individual pre-schools, schools; out-of-school clubs, supplementary schools, colleges, universities or youth clubs; websites, publications, conferences or seminars.

TYPE OF GRANT Project grants or core costs.

RANGE OF GRANTS Mostly up to £20,000.

SAMPLE GRANTS Chickenshed Theatre; City Hope Church; Cumbria Wildlife Trust; Leicestershire and Rutland Wildlife Trust; Old Vic New Voices; RashDash; South Bank Mosaics; Southwark Sea Cadets; Steam Industry Free Theatre; Ulster Wildlife Trust; and Yorkshire Wildlife Trust.

FINANCES *Year* 2011–12 *Income* £516,000 *Grants* £705,000 *Assets* £13,081,000

TRUSTEES Peter Charles De Haan; Janette McKay; Dr Rob Stoneman; Carol Stone; Opus Corporate Trustees Limited.

OTHER INFORMATION A further £453,000 was awarded in grants to young adults.

HOW TO APPLY The PDHCT website states: 'Historically we made traditional grants in support of social welfare, the environment and the arts. Funding for our arts programme is now channeled through IdeasTap. Our previous grant programmes are now fully assigned. We are not open to unsolicited applications.' For information on IdeasTap funding visit: www.ideastap.com/Funding/our-funding

WHO TO APPLY TO Simon Johnson, Finance Director, Wool Yard, 54 Bermondsey Street, London SE1 3UD *Tel.* 020 7232 5465 *email* sjohnson@pdhct.org.uk *Website* www.pdhct.org.uk

■ The De Laszlo Foundation

CC NO 327383   **ESTABLISHED** 1978

WHERE FUNDING CAN BE GIVEN UK and worldwide.

WHO CAN BENEFIT Arts organisations and registered charities.

WHAT IS FUNDED Promotion of the arts; general charitable purposes.

SAMPLE GRANTS Previous beneficiaries included: the De Laszlo Archive Trust (£188,000); Gordonstoun School Arts Centre (£20,000); Durham University and Royal Marsden (£10,000 each); Foundation for Liver Research (£8,000); Southampton University (£5,000); Federation of British Artists (£3,000); AGORA (£2,500); National Youth Orchestra (£1,500); Tate Foundation (£1,000); Cardboard Citizens (£500); and Chelsea Open Air Nursery School (£250).

FINANCES *Year* 2011–12 *Income* £444,345 *Grants* £305,204 *Assets* £1,874,890

TRUSTEES Damon de Laszlo, Chair; Lucy Birkbeck; Robert de Laszlo; William de Laszlo.

OTHER INFORMATION The foundation was set up to promote the advancement and promotion of education and interest in the visual arts with special reference to encouraging knowledge of the works of contemporary painters, in particular those of the late Philip de Laszlo.

HOW TO APPLY No grants to unsolicited applications.

WHO TO APPLY TO Christabel Wood, 5 Albany Courtyard, London W1J 0HF *Tel.* 020 7437 1982

■ The Deakin Charitable Trust

CC NO 258001   **ESTABLISHED** 1968

WHERE FUNDING CAN BE GIVEN Surrey, with a preference for Woking.

WHO CAN BENEFIT Mainly local charities including hospices and various religious organisations, and students seeking to extend their music education.

WHAT IS FUNDED General charitable purposes.

RANGE OF GRANTS £250–£500

SAMPLE GRANTS Friends of the Elderly and Queen Alexandra Hospital (£500 each); Oakleaf Enterprise, Computer Aid, White Lodge Centre, Radio Lollypop, Over the Wall, Action for the Blind, British Forces, McIndoe Research and Asthma Relief (£400 each); Goldstone Church, Extend Exercise and Sunnybank Trust, Epsom (£250 each).

FINANCES *Year* 2011–12 *Income* £60,999 *Grants* £51,000 *Assets* £971,629

TRUSTEES Geraldine Lawson; Paul Deakin; William Hodgetts.

HOW TO APPLY In writing to the correspondent.

WHO TO APPLY TO William Hodgetts, Station House, Connaught Road, Brookwood, Woking GU24 0ER *Tel.* 01483 485444

■ William Dean Countryside and Educational Trust

CC NO 1044567   **ESTABLISHED** 1995

WHERE FUNDING CAN BE GIVEN Principally Cheshire; also Derbyshire, Lancashire, Staffordshire and the Wirral.

WHO CAN BENEFIT Individuals and organisations.

WHAT IS FUNDED The trust gives grants individuals and organisations in its immediate locality which promote education in natural history, ecology and the conservation of the natural environment. For example, wildlife trusts; schools for ecological and conservation projects; and parks and pleasure grounds for similar purposes.

WHAT IS NOT FUNDED Education is not funded, unless directly associated with one of the stated eligible categories.

TYPE OF GRANT Capital, core costs. One-off grants.

RANGE OF GRANTS £100–£15,000.

SAMPLE GRANTS Cheshire Wildlife Trust (£15,000); St Mary's Church Astbury Conservation (£8,000); Congleton Projects Garden Festival (£3,000); Lower Moss Wood Animal Hospital (£2,000); Riverside Concern, Friends of Sandbach Park and Staffordshire Wildlife Trust (£1,000 each); Centre for Alternative Technology and Garden Organic Schools Program (£700 each); Derbyshire Wildlife Trust, Autism Initiatives UK and National Lobster Hatchery (£500 each); and Songbird Survival (£100).

FINANCES *Year* 2012 *Income* £63,646 *Grants* £67,997 *Assets* £1,277,041

TRUSTEES John Ward; David Daniel; William Crawford; Margaret Williamson; David Crawford.

HOW TO APPLY In writing to the correspondent. The Trustees meet four times each year in March, June, September and December when applications for grants are considered.

WHO TO APPLY TO Brenda Bell, Administrator, St Mary's Cottage, School Lane, Astbury, Congleton CW12 4RG *Tel.* 01260 290194 *email* bellstmarys@hotmail.com

■ The Debmar Benevolent Trust

CC NO 283065 **ESTABLISHED** 1979
WHERE FUNDING CAN BE GIVEN UK and Israel.
WHO CAN BENEFIT Jewish organisations.
WHAT IS FUNDED Jewish charitable purposes.
RANGE OF GRANTS Up to £30,000, but mostly under £1,000.
SAMPLE GRANTS Previous beneficiaries included: Beis Hamedrash Hachodosh, Chasdei Belz, Chevras Mauous Lador, Gevurath Ari, Telz Talmudical Academy, Friends of Assos Chesed, Pardes Chana, ATLIB, Bobov Institutions, Ohr Akiva Institute, Tomchei Shaarei Zion, Ponivitch Institutions, Yeshiva Shaarei Zion, Beis Yoel High School, Format Charity Trust and Manchester Kollel.
FINANCES *Year* 2011–12 *Income* £1,154,464 *Grants* £76,448 *Assets* £6,196,858
TRUSTEES Martin Weisz; Gella Klein; Hilary Olsberg; Rosalind Halpern; Vivienne Lewin.
OTHER INFORMATION The grants total was considerably lower than in previous years due to the fact that the company received fewer donations and was committed to make capital repayments off its bank loan. A list a grants was not provided in the trust's latest accounts.
HOW TO APPLY In writing to the correspondent.
WHO TO APPLY TO Hilary Olsberg, Trustee, 16 Stanley Road, Salford M7 4RW

■ The Delius Trust

CC NO 207324 **ESTABLISHED** 1935
WHERE FUNDING CAN BE GIVEN UK.
WHO CAN BENEFIT Registered charities and individuals.
WHAT IS FUNDED 'The trust promotes the music of Frederick Delius and of British composers born since 1860, by giving help towards the cost of performances, publications and recordings. In addition, assistance is occasionally offered to organisations and institutions active in this field. Priority is always given to the promotion of the works of Delius, especially those that are rarely performed.'
WHAT IS NOT FUNDED The trust will not usually make retrospective grants, nor does it consider support for capital projects. Grants are not generally made for individual performance, recording or publishing projects.
RANGE OF GRANTS £1,000 to £5,000.
FINANCES *Year* 2012 *Income* £93,044 *Grants* £47,056 *Assets* £2,118,372
TRUSTEES Musicians' Benevolent Fund (Representative: John Axon); David Lloyd-Jones; Martin Williams.
HOW TO APPLY In writing for consideration by the trustees and the advisers. See the trust's website for further details. The trust meets three times a year, in February, June and October. Applications should be received early in the month before each meeting. The Trust will not usually make retrospective grants. There is no standard application form.
WHO TO APPLY TO Helen Faulkner, Secretary to the Trust, 7–11 Britannia Street, London WC1X 9JS *Tel.* 020 7239 9143 *email* deliustrust@mbf.org.uk *Website* www.delius.org.uk

■ The Dellal Foundation

CC NO 265506 **ESTABLISHED** 1973
WHERE FUNDING CAN BE GIVEN UK.
WHO CAN BENEFIT Registered charities only.
WHAT IS FUNDED Mostly 'the welfare and benefit of Jewish people'.
WHAT IS NOT FUNDED No grants to individuals.
TYPE OF GRANT One-off.
FINANCES *Year* 2011–12 *Income* £1,223 *Grants* £141,688
TRUSTEES Edward Azouz; Guy Dellal.
HOW TO APPLY In writing to the correspondent.
WHO TO APPLY TO S. Hosier, Administrator, 25 Harley Street, London W1G 9BR *Tel.* 020 7299 1400

■ The Delves Charitable Trust

CC NO 231860 **ESTABLISHED** 1922
WHERE FUNDING CAN BE GIVEN UK and overseas.
WHAT IS FUNDED General charitable purposes. To support approved charities by annual subscriptions and donations.
WHAT IS NOT FUNDED The trust does not give sponsorships or personal educational grants.
SAMPLE GRANTS Action Medical Research (£20,500); SEQUAL Trust (£18,000); British Heart Foundation (£16,000); Macmillan Cancer Support (£15,500); Alzheimer's Society (£15,000); Médecins Sans Frontières (£10,500; Parkinson's UK (£10,000); CRISIS and DEC East Africa – crisis appeal (£5,000 each); William Morris Craft Fellowship Trust and Tree of Life for Animals (£4,000 each); Ghana Education Project and Motivation (£3,000 each); and Big Issue Foundation (£1,500).
FINANCES *Year* 2011–12 *Income* £236,498 *Grants* £191,000 *Assets* £6,701,542
TRUSTEES Elizabeth Breeze; John Breeze; George Breeze; Charles Breeze; William Breeze; Mark Breeze; Catharine Mackey.
HOW TO APPLY In writing to the Trust Administrator 'concisely explaining the objective, activities, intended public benefit and anticipated achievements. Enclosures such as detailed accounts and brochures should not be sent at the initial application stage and are indeed discouraged on environmental grounds. Applications are accepted on a rolling basis and reviewed by the Trustees quarterly, whose decision is final. No response is made to unsuccessful unsolicited applications.'
WHO TO APPLY TO The Trust Administrator, Luminary Finance LLP, PO Box 135, Longfield, Kent DA3 8WF *Tel.* 01732 822114

■ The Demigryphon Trust

CC NO 275821 **ESTABLISHED** 1978
WHERE FUNDING CAN BE GIVEN UK, with a preference for Scotland.
WHO CAN BENEFIT Registered charities only.
WHAT IS FUNDED General charitable purposes. The trust supports a wide range of organisations and appears to have a preference for education, medical, children and Scottish organisations.
WHAT IS NOT FUNDED No grants to individuals; only registered charities are supported.
TYPE OF GRANT Mainly one-off grants.
RANGE OF GRANTS Mostly up to £5,000.
SAMPLE GRANTS Game and Wildlife Conservation Trust (£5,000); Leeds University – Cowdray Legacy Exhibition (£2,000); Friends of St Mary's Petworth (£1,000); The Silver Circle and Tillington Parochial Church Council (£500 each);

and The Amber Foundation, Breakthrough Breast Cancer and Help for Heroes (£250 each).
FINANCES *Year* 2011–12 *Income* £52,171 *Grants* £61,639 *Assets* £2,574,208
TRUSTEE The Cowdray Trust Ltd.
OTHER INFORMATION The grant total includes payments to pensioners totalling £47,639.
HOW TO APPLY No grants to unsolicited applications.
WHO TO APPLY TO Laura Gosling, 4th Floor, Swan House, 17–19 Stratford Place, London W1C 1BQ *Tel.* 020 7907 2100 *email* charity@mfs.co.uk

■ The Denman Charitable Trust

CC NO 326532   ESTABLISHED 1983
WHERE FUNDING CAN BE GIVEN Bath, North-East Somerset, Bristol and Gloucestershire.
WHO CAN BENEFIT Organisations benefiting research workers, at-risk groups, people disadvantaged by poverty, and socially isolated people.
WHAT IS FUNDED Medical research, health, welfare and the arts.
WHAT IS NOT FUNDED No grants to individuals or non-charitable organisations.
TYPE OF GRANT Pump priming rather than running costs.
RANGE OF GRANTS £100–£25,000. Mostly under £5,000.
SAMPLE GRANTS RWA (£25,000); Meningitis UK (£10,000); Rework (£5,000); Friends of Claremont School, Gloucestershire Society, Tobacco Factory (Summer School), The Jessie May Trust and Golden-Oldies Charity (£2,000 each); Bristol Children's Help Society, Hammer Out, Clover House, Young and Free, Chas Bristol, Heart Research UK, Bristol and district Tranquiliser Project and Alive (£1,000 each).
FINANCES *Year* 2011–12 *Income* £90,574 *Grants* £82,939 *Assets* £35,752
TRUSTEES Arnold Denman; Dorothy Denman; David Marsh; Sue Blatchford; Joanna Denman.
HOW TO APPLY In writing to the correspondent.
WHO TO APPLY TO Dorothy Denman, c/o Steeple Group, PO Box 1881, Old Sodbury, Bristol BS37 6WS *email* dorothydenman@camers.org

■ The Dentons UKMEA LLP Charitable Trust

CC NO 1041204   ESTABLISHED 1994
WHERE FUNDING CAN BE GIVEN England and Wales.
WHO CAN BENEFIT Normally registered charities.
WHAT IS FUNDED General charitable purposes with a preference for organisations with a legal connection, such as community law centres, or children's charities, medical charities or the arts. Preference is also given to organisations which have a connection with Denton Wilde Sapte LLP or are local to the company's offices.
WHAT IS NOT FUNDED No grants to individuals. Education and scholarships will not be funded.
TYPE OF GRANT One-off and recurrent.
RANGE OF GRANTS Previously between £75 and £6,000, usually up to £2,000.
SAMPLE GRANTS DWS Social Committee (£6,000); London Legal Support Trust and WaterAid (£2,000 each); Birkbeck College and Red Lion Boys Club (£1,500 each); St Francis Hospice and the Whitechapel Mission (£1,000 each); Macmillan Cancer Support (£750); Action for Kids, Cyclists Fighting Cancer and Human Relief (£500 each); Children with Leukaemia and Breast Cancer Hope (£250 each); and British Heart Foundation (£100).

FINANCES *Year* 2011–12 *Income* £64,183 *Grants* £134,000
TRUSTEES Mark Andrews; Virginia Glastonbury; Matthew Harvey and Brandon Ransley.
HOW TO APPLY In writing to the correspondent. Trustees meet quarterly.
WHO TO APPLY TO Bernadette O'Sullivan, 1 One Fleet Place, London EC4M 7WS *Tel.* 020 7246 4843

■ The Earl of Derby's Charitable Trust

CC NO 515783   ESTABLISHED 1984
WHERE FUNDING CAN BE GIVEN Merseyside.
WHO CAN BENEFIT Local charitable organisations, predominantly within the beneficial area.
WHAT IS FUNDED Grant giving is categorised as follows: age, disablement and sickness; education and youth; religion; racing charities; and general.
WHAT IS NOT FUNDED No grants to individuals.
RANGE OF GRANTS £100–£1,000; generally £750.
SAMPLE GRANTS The Colonel's Fund and Liverpool University Equine Appeal (£10,000 each); Royal National Institute for the Blind – Liverpool (£5,000); Cameron House School Foundation (£2,500); Local Solutions (£1,000); St Michael's Church – Huyton, Anfield Youth Club, British Racing School and Willowbrook Hospice (£750 each); and Liver Research Trust (£500).
FINANCES *Year* 2011–12 *Income* £23,860 *Grants* £23,000
TRUSTEE Christopher Allen.
HOW TO APPLY In writing to the correspondent, although potential applicants should note that almost all grants goes to organisations with whom the charity is already involved. Trustees meet twice a year in January and July; applicants should apply two months before the meetings.
WHO TO APPLY TO A. Burton, Administrator, c/o Knowsley Ltd, The Estate Office, Prescot, Merseyside L34 4AF *email* charity@knowsley.com

■ The Derbyshire Churches and Chapels Preservation Trust

CC NO 1010953   ESTABLISHED 1992
WHERE FUNDING CAN BE GIVEN Derbyshire.
WHO CAN BENEFIT Churches and chapels of any Christian denomination.
WHAT IS FUNDED The preservation, repair and improvement of churches and chapels in Derbyshire.
SAMPLE GRANTS St Andrew, Langley Mill (£10,000); St Mary Mappleton (£8,000); St Katherine, Rowsley (£5,000); Tissington Methodist Chapel and St Peter, Derby (£2,000 each); St Mary the Virgin, Denby (£750) and Westhouses Methodist Chapel (£500).
FINANCES *Year* 2011–12 *Income* £20,007 *Grants* £41,172 *Assets* £33,551
TRUSTEES David Garnett; Canon M. A. B. Mallender; Dr Patrick Strange; Christopher Cunliffe; Sir Richard FitzHerbert; G. Roper.
HOW TO APPLY On a form available from the correspondent. The grants panel meets quarterly.
WHO TO APPLY TO Andrea Hambleton, 1 Greenhill, Wirksworth, Derbyshire DE4 4EN *Tel.* 01629 824904

■ Derbyshire Community Foundation

CC NO 1039485   **ESTABLISHED** 1996

WHERE FUNDING CAN BE GIVEN Derbyshire and the city of Derby.

WHO CAN BENEFIT Voluntary groups and volunteers and the people they work with in Derbyshire across a wide spectrum of activity tackling disadvantage and promoting quality of life.

WHAT IS FUNDED Community groups and voluntary organisations working to tackle disadvantage and improve quality of life. Likely priority themes are as follows: supporting families; getting back to work; health and wellbeing; young people; helping groups work; and creative community.

WHAT IS NOT FUNDED The foundation's general exclusions are: profit making organisations; medical equipment; animal charities; any project which promotes faith or involves the refurbishment/building of a place of worship; statutory bodies including schools, hospitals, police etc.; any project which directly replaces statutory obligations; any project which promotes a political party; projects which benefit people outside of Derbyshire; retrospective funding (grants for activities which have already taken place); sponsored events.

TYPE OF GRANT Usually one-off, though depending on the programme and donor's wishes, the trust may give more than one grant to the same group for different projects or items. Capital, core costs, feasibility studies, research, running costs, salaries and start-up costs. Funding for up to one year will be considered.

RANGE OF GRANTS Mainly between £100 to £5,000; possibly more for managed programmes depending on their criteria.

SAMPLE GRANTS SNAP (Project Fairshare) (£34,000); Fairshare Derby Community Safety Officers (£12,000); The Laura Centre – Derby, Repton Foundation Bursary and Sinfonia Viva (£10,000 each); and Derby Academy of Performing Arts (£7,500).

FINANCES *Year* 2011–12 *Income* £461,860 *Grants* £454,000 *Assets* £6,348,638

TRUSTEES Dr Ranjit Virma; Michael Hall; Arthur Blackwood; David Coleman; Nicola Phillips; Sir Alan Jones; Nick Mirfin; Matthew Montague; Lucy Palmer; David Walker; Robin Wood; Rt Revd Alastair Redfern; Janet Birkin; Louise Pinder; Simon Ingham; Helen Bishop.

HOW TO APPLY The grants team are always willing to discuss applications before they are formally submitted, this saves both the applicant and the foundation time. Call them on: 01773 514850. The foundation offers several different funds, each with a specific focus or set of criteria. Visit the foundation's website for full details of the current grant programmes and the relevant application documents. Applicants should download and complete the appropriate application form from the website and send it to the correspondent. Applications are passed to a member of the grants team for assessment and to prepare all of the information ready to present to the award making panel. During this time, applicants are likely to be contacted by the grants team for an informal chat about their application and their group, which helps the foundation to understand the background of the project and gives the best chance of a successful bid. Applicants will be informed of the decision date for their application and are invited to call the grants team or check the website to find out the decision two days after the panel date. You will also receive the panel decision in writing within one week of the panel date. The foundation states that it is willing to provide full, honest feedback on all decisions and is happy to discuss any outcome with applicants.

WHO TO APPLY TO The Grants Team, Foundation House, Unicorn Business Park, Wellington Street, Ripley, Derbyshire DE5 3EH *Tel.* 01773 514850 *Fax* 01773 741410 *email* info@derbyshirecommunityfoundation.co.uk *Website* www.derbyshirecommunityfoundation.co.uk

■ The J. N. Derbyshire Trust

CC NO 231907   **ESTABLISHED** 1944

WHERE FUNDING CAN BE GIVEN Mainly Nottingham and Nottinghamshire.

WHO CAN BENEFIT Organisations with charitable status.

WHAT IS FUNDED General charitable purposes, including: the promotion of health; the development of physical improvement; the advancement of education; and the relief of poverty, distress and sickness. Local charities receive preferential consideration.

WHAT IS NOT FUNDED No grants to individuals. Costs of study are not supported.

TYPE OF GRANT Buildings, capital, core costs, project, research, recurring and running costs, salaries, and start-up costs will be considered. Funding may be given for up to three years.

RANGE OF GRANTS Up to £10,000.

SAMPLE GRANTS Rotary Club of Nottingham Trust Fund (£10,000); Emmanuel House (£9,000); Southwell Cathedral Chapter (£8,000); Fields in Trust and Broxtowe Youth Homelessness (£5,000 each); Zone Youth Project (£4,000); Broxtowe Women's Project, Survivors Helping Each other (SHE), Nottinghamshire Club for Young People and The Lords Taverners (£3,000 each); Rutland House School, Victim Support and YMCA (£2,500 each) and 32nd Nottingham Boys Brigade, Pintsize Theatre and Dyslexia Action (£2,000 each).

FINANCES *Year* 2011–12 *Income* £179,793 *Grants* £160,850 *Assets* £4,548,194

TRUSTEES Andora Carver; Sidney Christophers; Peter Moore; Lucy Whittle; Charles George; Belinda Lawrie.

OTHER INFORMATION In 2011–12 grants were broken down into the following categories:

Physical health and disability	£29,000
Youth organisations	£28,500
Miscellaneous	£28,000
Relief of Poverty	£25,000
Educational	£24,000
Protection and welfare of women and children	£19,000
Old age	£6,000
General medical and ambulance	£1,700

HOW TO APPLY On a form available from the correspondent. Applications can be made at any time but trustees usually only meet to consider them twice a year in March and September. Details of the project are required. A reply is only given to unsuccessful applicants if they enclose an sae.

WHO TO APPLY TO Amy Taylor, Secretary, The Poynt, 45 Wollaton Street, Nottingham NG1 5FW *Tel.* 01159 489400 *email* amy.taylor@rsmtenon.com

■ The Desmond Foundation (formerly known as the RD Crusaders Foundation)

CC NO 1014352   **ESTABLISHED** 1992
WHERE FUNDING CAN BE GIVEN Worldwide.
WHO CAN BENEFIT Charitable organisations, with a preference towards Jewish organisations.
WHAT IS FUNDED The relief of poverty and sickness, particularly among children.
TYPE OF GRANT One-off grants.
RANGE OF GRANTS Up to £157,000 (2012).
SAMPLE GRANTS Norwood (£157,000); World Jewish Relief (£61,500); Dalaid and Fight for Sight (£50,000 each); IC Trust (£19,500); Well Being of Women (£15,000); Forward Thinking, University of Nottingham and Community Security Trust (£10,000 each); Creative Access, the Disability Foundation and Caron Keating Foundation (£5,000 each); Tsu'Chu Biz Foundation and Richard House Trust (£2,000 each); and the Holocaust Centre and St Bride's Church (£1,000 each).
FINANCES *Year* 2012 *Income* £617,776 *Grants* £569,896 *Assets* £89,933
TRUSTEES Richard Desmond; Northern and Shell Services Limited; Northern and Shell Media Group Limited.
HOW TO APPLY In
WHO TO APPLY TO Allison Racher, Administrator, The Northern and Shell Building, Number 10 Lower Thames Street, London EC3R 6EN *Tel.* 020 8612 7760 *email* allison.racher@express.co.uk

■ Devon Community Foundation

CC NO 1057923   **ESTABLISHED** 1996
WHERE FUNDING CAN BE GIVEN Devon.
WHO CAN BENEFIT Voluntary and community groups.
WHAT IS FUNDED Support primarily for voluntary and community organisations, particularly those working to relieve the effects of poverty and disadvantage.
WHAT IS NOT FUNDED The foundation does not fund: more than one application to the same fund in a 12 month period; non-constituted organisations; grantmaking organisations; commercial organisations; groups that have funded before but have not returned an evaluation form when requested; no major building works associated costs; organisations that are regional or national charities (unless locally led and run); organisations that have substantial unrestricted funds; activities that promote political or religious beliefs (groups that are based in a religious building can apply, providing the activity/project is open to all people in the community); statutory bodies e.g. schools/colleges, local councils. However, 'Friends of' or Parents' Associations may be eligible to apply; organisations or activities that primarily support animals or plants; 100% of the project costs; retrospective funding – this includes activities that have already taken place or repayment of money that you have already spent; consultancy fees or feasibility studies; sponsorship and/or fundraising events; contributions to an endowment; minibuses or other vehicle purchases; activities or organisations that are for personal profit or are commercial; grants for IT and associated equipment will be limited to no more than £400; overseas travel; never 100% of the project costs; capital purchases over £1,000; projects outside Devon; no funding individuals (except from the Devonian Fund). Individual programmes may have further eligibility criteria. Check the website or contact the foundation directly to confirm that your organisation is eligible to apply.
TYPE OF GRANT Predominantly one-off small grants for projects. Running costs and start-up costs will be considered. Funding may be given for up to one year, and very occasionally for two years.
SAMPLE GRANTS Grow 4 Good South West Limited (£35,000); Exeter YMCA (£23,000); Cornwall Community Foundation (£22,500); Young Devon (£15,000); Plymouth Cricket Club, Shout it Out Learning Project and Time Out For All (£5,000 each); Coast Net and Community Housing Aid (£4,500); Plymouth Foodbank (£2,000); and Devon and Cornwall Refugee Support, Play Torbay and Tavistock Street Pastors (£1,000 each).
FINANCES *Year* 2011–12 *Income* £694,732 *Grants* £605,120 *Assets* £3,384,372
TRUSTEES Dr Katherine Gurney; Steve Hindley; Mike Bull; Arthur Ainslie; Peter Keech; John Glasby; Caroline Marks; Nigel Arnold; James Bullock; James Cross; Steven Pearce; Robin Barlow; Christine Allison.
OTHER INFORMATION There were various grants under £1,000 but these were not listed in the accounts.
HOW TO APPLY The foundation's website has details of the grant schemes currently being administered and how to apply. The website also has a 'grant alert sign-up' which emails information about new grant programmes as they are available.
WHO TO APPLY TO Martha Wilkinson, Chief Executive, The Factory, Leat Street, Tiverton, Devon EX16 5LL *Tel.* 01884 235887 *Fax* 01884 243824 *email* grants@devoncf.com *Website* www.devoncf.com

■ The Devon Educational Trust

CC NO 220921   **ESTABLISHED** 1988
WHERE FUNDING CAN BE GIVEN Devon.
WHO CAN BENEFIT Primarily individuals living in Devon, or whose parents live in Devon. Individuals, and organisations benefiting children, young adults and students.
WHAT IS FUNDED The education of people under the age of 25.
WHAT IS NOT FUNDED No grants for school fees and help is not normally given to people starting a second or higher degree.
TYPE OF GRANT One-off. Capital and unrestricted.
RANGE OF GRANTS Up to £2,500.
SAMPLE GRANTS Sir Francis Chichester Trust (£2,500); Bristol Channel Pilot Cutter Trust, Friends of Victoria Road Primary School and Chicks (£500 each); Friends of Erme Primary School (£400); Inverteign Community Nursery School (Teignmouth), Freefall Youth Group and Life Education Wessex Centres (£250 each).
FINANCES *Year* 2011–12 *Income* £39,423 *Grants* £5,200 *Assets* £1,014,494
TRUSTEES Robin Wakinshaw; Frank Rosamond; Brian Wills-Pope; Bryn Evans; Judith Cook; Dr M. Gillett; P. Freeman.
OTHER INFORMATION In 2011–12, grants were made to 112 individuals totalling £26,800.
HOW TO APPLY In writing to the correspondent for an application form. Two referees will be approached for letters of support for each applicant. The trustees meet three times a year in March, July and November with a closing date four weeks before each meeting.
WHO TO APPLY TO The Clerk, PO Box 86, Teignmouth, Devon TQ14 8ZT *email* devonedtrust@talktalk.net

■ The Devon Historic Churches Trust

CC NO 265594   **ESTABLISHED** 1973
WHERE FUNDING CAN BE GIVEN Devon.
WHO CAN BENEFIT Churches and chapels.
WHAT IS FUNDED The trust gives grants/loans for 'the preservation, repair, maintenance, improvement and upkeep of churches in the County of Devon.'
WHAT IS NOT FUNDED Redundant churches/chapels, bells, plumbing, disabled facilities and routine maintenance.
TYPE OF GRANT Grants and loans.
RANGE OF GRANTS £1,000–£5,000.
SAMPLE GRANTS Chivelstone (St Sylvester) and Atherington (St Mary) (£5.000 each); Kingsbridge (St Edmunds), Beaford (All Saints), Littlehempston (St John) and Thornbury (St John) (£3,000 each); Westleigh (St Peter), Newton Poppleford, Cornworthy (St Peter) and Dawlish (St Gregory) (£2,000 each); Gulworthy (St Paul) and Feniton (£1,000 each).
FINANCES *Year* 2011–12 *Income* £93,010 *Grants* £47,000 *Assets* £1,159,005
TRUSTEES Nicholas Maxwell-Lawford; Lady Anne Boles; Carole May Plumstead; Christopher Barry Tuke; The Earl of Devon; James Duncan Villiers Michie; Judith Mary Kauntze; Rosemary Howell; Lady Burnell-Nugent; Christopher Hewetson; Revd Dr David Keep; Phillip Tuckett; Lt Col Charles Rich; John Mills; Hendrik Vollers.
HOW TO APPLY In writing to the correspondent. The trustees meet quarterly to receive reports from officers and committees and to consider grant applications.
WHO TO APPLY TO John Malleson, Dolphins, Popes Lane, Colyford, Colyton EX24 6QR *Tel.* 01297 553666 *email* stavern@nascr.net *Website* www.devonhistoricchurches.co.uk

■ The Duke of Devonshire's Charitable Trust

CC NO 213519   **ESTABLISHED** 1949
WHERE FUNDING CAN BE GIVEN UK.
WHO CAN BENEFIT Registered charities only.
WHAT IS FUNDED General charitable purposes.
WHAT IS NOT FUNDED The following information is taken from the trust's concise and helpful website: The trust will not normally consider any funding request made within 12 months of the outcome of a previously unsuccessful application or five years of a successful one. This is to ensure that the trust can assist as wide a spread of worthwhile organisations as possible; the trust only considers applications from UK registered charities and your registration number is required (unless you have exempt status as a church, educational establishment, hospital etc.); the trust does not typically fund projects outside the UK, even if the organisation is a registered charity within Britain; the trust is not able to accept applications from individuals or for individual research or study. This includes gap year activities, study trips, fundraising expeditions and sponsorship; the trust does not normally make funding commitments over several years – grants made are typically for a single year with few exceptions; the trust does not normally fund specific salaries and positions. This is primarily because grants are single-year commitments and the trustees would not wish a specific job to become unsustainable; it is unusual for the trust to consider making a grant to organisations who cannot demonstrate significant progress with fundraising, so bear this in mind when considering the timing of your application; applications will not be considered until all the information we have requested has been being provided. Keep your answers concise and avoid including protracted 'Mission Statements', jargon and acronyms. Failure to do so may result in your application being overlooked.
RANGE OF GRANTS Typically up to £10,000, though exceptions are made.
SAMPLE GRANTS St Wilfred's Hospice (£25,000); St Peter's Church (£20,000); Fine Cell Trust (£10,000); Hertford House Trust (£5,000); Sight Support Derbyshire (£4,000); Good News Family Care, Helen's Trust, Help for Heroes and Medway Centre Community Association (£2,000 each); and Northern Racing College, On Side and The School of Artisan Food (£1,000 each).
FINANCES *Year* 2011–12 *Income* £238,363 *Grants* £158,569 *Assets* £11,323,036
TRUSTEES Duke of Devonshire; Duchess of Devonshire; Earl of Burlington; Sir Richard Beckett.
OTHER INFORMATION The donations figure has fallen significantly in this accounting year. According to the latest accounts, this is because in 2009, the trustees received a donation of £5.4 million from the liquidation of funds in the 'Bermuda Settlement'. These funds were used to assist Chatsworth House Trust over a period of two years. Income has now reverted to the more usual figure of between £200,000–£300,000.
HOW TO APPLY In writing to the correspondent. The trust's website gives guidelines and details of current application deadlines.
WHO TO APPLY TO Mollie Moseley, Administrator, Chatsworth, Bakewell, Derbyshire DE45 1PP *Tel.* 01246 565437 *Website* ddct.org.uk

■ The Sandy Dewhirst Charitable Trust

CC NO 279161   **ESTABLISHED** 1979
WHERE FUNDING CAN BE GIVEN UK, with a strong preference for East and North Yorkshire.
WHO CAN BENEFIT Charitable organisations and individuals connected with I J Dewhirst Holdings Limited.
WHAT IS FUNDED General charitable purposes – social welfare and community.
SAMPLE GRANTS Sargent Cancer Care for Children (£10,000); Help for Heroes (£5,000); Salivation Army, the Army Benevolent Fund and Yorkshire Air Ambulance (£3,000 each); Action Medical Research (£2,000); Driffield Town Cricket and Recreation Club (£1,500); St Catherine's Hospice, Hull Sea Cadets and All Saints Church – Nafferton (£500 each).
FINANCES *Year* 2012 *Income* £61,575 *Grants* £46,500 *Assets* £1,593,159
TRUSTEES Paul Howell; Timothy Dewhirst.
OTHER INFORMATION 23 grants totalling £47,000 and of this almost £20,000 was given to local organisations and £17,000 to national organisations.
HOW TO APPLY The trust does not accept unsolicited applications.
WHO TO APPLY TO Louise Cliffe, Administrator, Addleshaw Goddard, 100 Barbirolli Square, Manchester M2 3AB *Tel.* 01619 346373

Think carefully about every application. Is it justified?

497

■ Deymel Charitable Trust

cc no 1145305   ESTABLISHED 2012
WHERE FUNDING CAN BE GIVEN UK.
WHO CAN BENEFIT Registered charities.
WHAT IS FUNDED General charitable purposes.
FINANCES *Year* 2012–13 *Income* £65,346
  Assets £169,060
TRUSTEES W. R. Morgan; T. Morgan.
OTHER INFORMATION The trust was registered in
January 2012 for general charitable purposes.
The trustees are descendants of David Morgan,
founder of the David Morgan department store
in Cardiff which closed in 2005 after 125 years.
The store was operated by the Morgan family
through the holding company, Deymel
Investments Ltd, which also went into
liquidation at the end of 2009. The trust's first
set of accounts, for the financial year 2012–13,
show an income of £65,500 and a total
expenditure of £2,000. The trust's first set of
accounts, for the financial year 2012–13, show
an income of £65,500 and a total expenditure
of £2,000. No grants were made during the year
and the trust has expressed its intention to
build up its funds.
HOW TO APPLY In writing to the correspondent.
WHO TO APPLY TO The Trustees, Rathbone Trust
Company Limited, 4th Floor, Port of Liverpool
Building, Pier Head, Liverpool L3 1NW
Tel. 01512 366666

■ The Laduma Dhamecha Charitable Trust

cc no 328678   ESTABLISHED 1990
WHERE FUNDING CAN BE GIVEN UK and overseas.
WHO CAN BENEFIT Organisations only.
WHAT IS FUNDED General charitable purposes
including the relief of sickness and education in
rural areas.
FINANCES *Year* 2011–12 *Income* £366,643
  Grants £123,142 *Assets* £1,580,964
TRUSTEES K. R. Dhamecha; S. R. Dhamecha;
P. K. Dhamecha.
HOW TO APPLY In writing to the correspondent.
WHO TO APPLY TO Pradip Dhamecha, Trustee,
2 Hathaway Close, Stanmore, Middlesex
HA7 3NR *Tel.* 020 8903 8181

■ Diabetes UK

cc no 215199   ESTABLISHED 1934
WHERE FUNDING CAN BE GIVEN UK.
WHO CAN BENEFIT Organisations which benefit people
with diabetes.
WHAT IS FUNDED To promote and fund research into
the causes and effects of diabetes, and the
treatment and alleviation of the effects of
diabetes to minimise the potential serious
complications that can arise.
TYPE OF GRANT Equipment, fellowships, research
grants, small grants, and studentships will be
considered.
RANGE OF GRANTS £5,000–£40,000
SAMPLE GRANTS Grants to institutions were broken
down as follows: cause and prevention –
£2.3 million; care, treatment and cure –
£3 million.
FINANCES *Year* 2012 *Income* £27,834,000
  Grants £5,850,000 *Assets* £11,834,000
TRUSTEES Dr Robert Young; David McCance; Helene
Brenchley-King; Noah Franklin; Julian Baust; Gill
Fine; Susan Browell; Gerard Tosh; Halima Khan;
Gavin Cookman; Sir Peter Dixon.

HOW TO APPLY Potential applicants are first advised
to read the 'General guidelines for research
grant applicants' on the charity's website.
Information on the application process and
deadlines for each specific scheme is also
available on the website or by contacting the
trust directly.
WHO TO APPLY TO Research Committee, 10 Parkway,
London NW1 7AA *Tel.* 020 7424 1000 *Fax* 020
7424 1001 *email* info@diabetes.org.uk
Website www.diabetes.org.uk

■ Alan and Sheila Diamond Charitable Trust

cc no 274312   ESTABLISHED 1977
WHERE FUNDING CAN BE GIVEN UK.
WHO CAN BENEFIT Registered charities only,
particularly Jewish charities.
WHAT IS FUNDED Jewish causes and general
charitable purposes.
WHAT IS NOT FUNDED No grants to individuals.
SAMPLE GRANTS British School of Osteopathy
(£10,000); Norwood (£8,000); Youth Aliyah
Child Rescue (£7,800); Anglo Israel Association
(£6,000); The Royal Navy and Royal Marines
(£5,000); Community Security Trust (£4,000);
and Sidney Sussex College (£2,000).
FINANCES *Year* 2011–12 *Income* £70,497
  Grants £60,344 *Assets* £1,471,922
TRUSTEES Alan Diamond, Chair; Sheila Diamond;
Jonathan Kropman; Kate Goldberg.
HOW TO APPLY The trust states that it will not
consider unsolicited applications. No preliminary
telephone calls. There are no regular trustees'
meetings. The trustees frequently decide how
the funds should be allocated. The trustees
have their own guidelines, which are not
published.
WHO TO APPLY TO The Trustees, Mazars LLP, 8 New
Fields, 2 Stinsford Road, Nuffield, Poole, Dorset
BH17 0NF *Tel.* 01202 680777

■ The Dibden Allotments Fund

cc no 255778   ESTABLISHED 1995
WHERE FUNDING CAN BE GIVEN Hythe, Fawley and
Marchwood in Hampshire.
WHO CAN BENEFIT Grants can be made to individuals
as well as organisations, including students and
unemployed people.
WHAT IS FUNDED To relieve need, hardship or
distress, and to invest in the community's
future. Grants are awarded to individuals in
need, to voluntary and charitable organisations,
and to schemes benefiting children, particularly
under-fives, older people and young people.
WHAT IS NOT FUNDED Scholarships to 'Schools of
Excellence', such as those for the performing
arts.
RANGE OF GRANTS Up to £22,500.
SAMPLE GRANTS Handy Trust (£22,500); Solent
Dolphin (£15,000); Waterside Ecumenical
Project (£6,000); Hythe Library and Fawley
Parish Council (£5,000 each); Waterside
Primary (£3,500); St Anne's Neighbourhood
Centre (£3,000); Hythe Sailing Club (£2,000);
and League of Volunteers (£500).
FINANCES *Year* 2011–12 *Income* £360,329
  Grants £251,781 *Assets* £8,189,649
TRUSTEES Rosemary Dash; Malcolm Fidler; Chris
Harrison; Pat Hedges; Maureen McLean; Peter
Parrott; Judy Saxby; Jill Tomlin; Declan English

OTHER INFORMATION The grants total includes £161,000 that was given to individuals for general and educational purposes.

HOW TO APPLY On an application form available to download, together with criteria and guidelines, from the website. A third party, such as social services, teachers, and so on, must support applications from individuals.

WHO TO APPLY TO Harvey Mansfield, Clerk, 7 Drummond Court, Prospect Place, Hythe, Hampshire SO45 6HD *Tel.* 02380 841305 *email* dibdenallotments@btconnect.com *Website* www.daf-hythe.org.uk

■ Diced Cap Charity (formerly Grampian Police Diced Cap Charitable Fund)

SC NO SC017901   **ESTABLISHED** 1991

WHERE FUNDING CAN BE GIVEN Within the Grampian police force area only.

WHO CAN BENEFIT Charitable organisations.

WHAT IS FUNDED General charitable purposes.

WHAT IS NOT FUNDED National charities and those outside the beneficial area cannot be supported.

FINANCES *Year* 2011–12 *Income* £73,190

TRUSTEES Susan Barclay; Betty Bates; Alan Findlay; Colin Menzies; Pauline Adam; Colin Gray; Simon Lewis-Dalby; Craig Menzies.

HOW TO APPLY In writing to the correspondent.

WHO TO APPLY TO Robbie Ross, The Secretary, Grampian Police Headquarters, Queen Street, Aberdeen AB10 1ZA *email* secretary@dicedcap. org *Website* www.dicedcap.org

■ The Gillian Dickinson Trust

CC NO 1094362   **ESTABLISHED** 2002

WHERE FUNDING CAN BE GIVEN County Durham, Northumberland and Tyne and Wear.

WHO CAN BENEFIT Registered charities, museums, arts and theatre groups.

WHAT IS FUNDED Arts and general charitable purposes.

WHAT IS NOT FUNDED No grants to individuals.

TYPE OF GRANT One-off or capital grants.

RANGE OF GRANTS Up to £37,000.

SAMPLE GRANTS The Samling Foundation (£37,000); Hexham Book Festival and Durham University – Library Project (£20,000 each); Live Theatre and Tyneside Cinema – Northern Stars (£15,000 each); Little Big Mouth (£12,000); Sunderland AFC Foundation and Pianoforte North Foundation – Young Pianist of the North (£10,000 each); Northern Stage and Durham Army Cadets Force – Borneo Band (£5,000 each); Live Music Now (£3,000); Northumbrian Association Writers Award (£1,500); Youth Opera in the North East and Palace Green Pavilion Trust (£1,000) and Allendale First School (£500).

FINANCES *Year* 2011–12 *Income* £73,620 *Grants* £156,000 *Assets* £2,155,199

TRUSTEES Alexander Dickinson; Piers Dickinson; Adrian Gifford; James Ramsbotham.

HOW TO APPLY On a form available to download from the website, where criteria and guidelines are also posted. Applications should be kept short (less than 500 words) and should only include attachments where the applicant considers them absolutely necessary for the purposes of the application. If the trustees need to see any documents (for example financial statements) they will request them.

WHO TO APPLY TO The Trustees, c/o Dickinson Dees LLP, St Ann's Wharf, 112 Quayside, Newcastle upon Tyne NE1 3DX *email* grants@gilliantrust. org.uk *Website* www.gilliandickinsontrust.org.uk

■ The Dickon Trust

CC NO 327202   **ESTABLISHED** 1986

WHERE FUNDING CAN BE GIVEN North East England and Scotland.

WHO CAN BENEFIT Registered charities.

WHAT IS FUNDED General charitable purposes with some preference for children and young people.

WHAT IS NOT FUNDED No support for individuals, unregistered charities or churches.

TYPE OF GRANT One-off.

RANGE OF GRANTS £500–£2,000.

SAMPLE GRANTS B.U.G.S. and Kids' Company (£2,000 each); Age Concern Gateshead, Bobath Scotland, Butterwick House Children's Hospice, Esh Winning Residents Group, Fairbridge Tyne and Wear, Heel and Toe, Mental Health Matters, Partners in Advocacy, Pathfinder Guide Dogs, Samaritans of Kirkcaldy and District, Spinal Injuries Association, Tweed Valley Mountain Rescue Team (£1,000 each).

FINANCES *Year* 2011–12 *Income* £55,227 *Grants* £50,000 *Assets* £1,294,497

TRUSTEES Diana Linda Barrett; Maj.-General Robin Brims; Richard Younger Barrett; M. L. Robson; A. Copeman.

HOW TO APPLY Applications can be made online at the trust's website. The trustees meet twice a year in summer and winter to consider appeals. Any applications received by the end of October will be considered at the winter meeting and any applications made after that time, up to the end of May, will be considered at the summer meeting.

WHO TO APPLY TO Helen Tavroges, Dickinson Dees, St Anne's Wharf, 112 Quayside, Newcastle NE99 1SB *Tel.* 01912 799698 *Website* www. dickontrust.org.uk

■ The Peter Alan Dickson Foundation

CC NO 1129310   **ESTABLISHED** 2009

WHERE FUNDING CAN BE GIVEN UK and overseas.

WHO CAN BENEFIT Organisations and individuals.

WHAT IS FUNDED Education, children and young people, natural disasters.

WHAT IS NOT FUNDED The foundation will not give grants for the following purposes: 'a general appeal or circular; the promotion of religion – note we will not make grants which promote a particular religious belief but will consider applications from faith-based organisations where the work is not for religious purposes and clearly fits our funding guidelines; work that is routine or well-proven elsewhere or with a low impact; work that is primarily the responsibility of central, local or national government – our general preference is to fund independent voluntary organisations and individuals but not to replace or subsidise statutory funding; projects that primarily benefit the independent education sector; individual energy efficiency or waste reduction schemes, such as recycling, composting, or renewable energy schemes. We will only consider this work if the social benefits are exceptionally strong or there is something groundbreaking about what is proposed; retrospective funding meaning support for work that has already taken place; any project which promotes a political party.'

FINANCES *Year* 2011–12 *Income* £5,747 *Grants* £11,250

TRUSTEES Pauline Broomhead; Charles Dickson; James Dickson; Al Brierley.

HOW TO APPLY On an application form available from the foundation's website along with guidelines.

WHO TO APPLY TO Conchita Garcia, Administrator, c/o The FSI, Ingestre Court, Ingestre Place, London W1F 0JL *email* info@padfoundation.org *Website* www.tarncourt.com/the-pad-foundation

■ Grace Dieu Charitable Trust

CC NO 1148838   **ESTABLISHED** 2012

WHERE FUNDING CAN BE GIVEN UK.

WHO CAN BENEFIT Charities and community groups.

WHAT IS FUNDED General charitable purposes, arts, culture and heritage and Christian causes. There is a preference for organisations working with children and young people, older people and people with a disability.

TRUSTEES Stephan Jenkins; Margaret Jenkins.

HOW TO APPLY In writing to the correspondent.

WHO TO APPLY TO Stephan Jenkins, Trustee, 67 Haig Avenue, Rochester, Kent ME1 2RY *Tel.* 01634 846862

■ The Digbeth Trust Limited

CC NO 517343   **ESTABLISHED** 1984

WHERE FUNDING CAN BE GIVEN West Midlands, principally Birmingham.

WHO CAN BENEFIT Smaller local, new and emerging voluntary and community groups, particularly those addressing exclusion and disadvantage.

WHAT IS FUNDED The trust manages a number of grant programmes that are generally targeted by area or theme, or both. See its website for current schemes.

WHAT IS NOT FUNDED General appeals, capital core costs, medical research, project running costs and grants for individuals.

TYPE OF GRANT One-off grants to enable groups to access specialist advice and services.

SAMPLE GRANTS Basis 2 (£81,000); the Mental Health Grants Programme (£30,500) and Future Jobs Fund (£12,500).

FINANCES *Year* 2011–12 *Income* £293,303 *Grants* £318,555 *Assets* £27,251

TRUSTEES Eddie Currall, Chair; Christopher Burrows; David Williams-Masinda; Graham Mitchell; Daina Anderson; Ben Cunningham; Mark Lynes and Mark Peters.

OTHER INFORMATION The grant total includes all support costs such as salaries (£141,000).

HOW TO APPLY The trust welcomes direct contact with groups. Application forms and guidance notes are available for the programmes it manages (this changes from time to time). Development worker support is offered to eligible groups.

WHO TO APPLY TO Guy Kibbler, Operations Manager, Unit F1 The Arch 48–52, Floodgate Street, Birmingham B5 5SL *Tel.* 01217 530706 *email* info@digbethtrust.org.uk *Website* www. digbethtrust.org.uk

■ The Dinwoodie Settlement

CC NO 255495   **ESTABLISHED** 1968

WHERE FUNDING CAN BE GIVEN UK.

WHO CAN BENEFIT Organisations benefiting academics and postgraduate research workers.

WHAT IS FUNDED Postgraduate medical education centres (PMCs) and research fellowships for suitably qualified medical practitioners of registrar status in general medicine or general surgery.

WHAT IS NOT FUNDED Anything falling outside the main areas of work referred to above. The trustees do not expect to fund consumable or equipment costs or relieve the NHS of its financial responsibilities.

TYPE OF GRANT Building projects will be considered. The trust's funds can be committed for three years when supporting major projects.

RANGE OF GRANTS Maximum of £1 million towards no more than one postgraduate medical centre project in an area. No more than the salary of two research workers in any one year.

SAMPLE GRANTS Blackpool Victoria Hospital (£133,000); Pembury Hospital, Tunbridge Wells (£121,000); Royal Wolverhampton Hospital (£100,000); N W Kent Postgraduate Medical Association (£50,000); Imperial College London (£15,000); and Royal Free Hospital, Hampstead (£12,500).

FINANCES *Year* 2011–12 *Income* £278,130 *Grants* £433,225 *Assets* £4,250,792

TRUSTEES William A. Fairbairn; John Black; Christian Webster; Rodney B. N. Fisher; John A. Gibson.

OTHER INFORMATION Annual figures for grants versus income may vary substantially as payments towards building costs of each project usually absorb more than one year's available income.

HOW TO APPLY The trustees state they are proactive rather than reactive in their grant-giving. Negotiating for new PMCs and monitoring their construction invariably takes a number of years.

WHO TO APPLY TO The Clerk to the Trustees, c/o Thomas Eggar, The Corn Exchange, Baffins Lane, Chichester, West Sussex PO19 1GE

■ Disability Aid Fund (The Roger and Jean Jefcoate Trust)

CC NO 1096211   **ESTABLISHED** 2002

WHERE FUNDING CAN BE GIVEN UK.

WHO CAN BENEFIT People with physical, mental or multiple disabilities or hearing or visual impairment.

WHAT IS FUNDED The following statement from the trust's 2011/12 accounts explains its grantmaking strategy: 'We support a few carefully selected local, regional and small national healthcare and disability charities for older people in Buckinghamshire and Milton Keynes and adjacent counties, especially charities which promote health and wellbeing through information, advice and practical help like developing or providing special needs technology. We look for charities showing strong support from service users and volunteers and only modest expenditure on fundraising and administration.'

TYPE OF GRANT Building and refurbishment, equipment, training and general costs.

RANGE OF GRANTS £2,000–£25,000.

SAMPLE GRANTS Pace – Aylesbury – refurbishment of local centre and Canine Partners – Midhurst – launch a Midlands training centre (£25,000 each); L'Arche Community – Bognor – appeal for Jericho community house (£15,000); Friends of Bedford House – Pinner – wheelchair vehicle (£10,000); SHARE Community – Wadsworth – general needs (£5,000) and Carers Milton Keynes – new communications system (£3,600).

FINANCES *Year* 2011–12 *Income* £162,994 *Grants* £125,800 *Assets* £3,327,523
TRUSTEES Vivien Dinning, Chair; Roger Jefcoate; Valerie Henchoz; Rosemary McCloskey; Carol Wemyss.
HOW TO APPLY Information provided by the trust: 'if you think that your charity might fit our remit telephone Roger Jefcoate on 01296 715466 weekdays before 7pm to discuss your proposal. You may then be invited to submit a written application summarising your request on just one side of paper, with minimal supporting information like a single sheet general leaflet or a magazine article; do not send your annual review, we would ask for that if we need it. We would normally only consider a further request after two years, and then only by invitation.'
WHO TO APPLY TO Roger Jefcoate, Trustee, 2 Copse Gate, Winslow, Buckingham MK18 3HX *Tel.* 01296 715466

■ Dischma Charitable Trust
CC NO 1077501   **ESTABLISHED** 1999
WHERE FUNDING CAN BE GIVEN Worldwide, with a strong preference for London and the south east of England.
WHO CAN BENEFIT Charitable organisations.
WHAT IS FUNDED General charitable purposes, with a preference for education, arts and culture, conservation and human and animal welfare.
WHAT IS NOT FUNDED Medical research charities.
RANGE OF GRANTS £500–£5,000.
SAMPLE GRANTS Trinity Hospice (£5,000); International Animal Rescue (£4,300); Guide Dogs (£3,400); Epic Arts (£3,000); Fields in Trust, Forces Support, Camden Arts Centre, Contact the Elderly and West London Churches Homeless Concern (£2,000 each); the Gorilla Organisation and Theatre for a Change (£1,000 each); and Tall Ships Youth Trust (£500).
FINANCES *Year* 2012 *Income* £113,305 *Grants* £77,282 *Assets* £4,857,347
TRUSTEES Simon Robertson; Edward Robertson; Lorna Robertson Timmis; Virginia Robertson; Selina Robertson; Arabella Brooke.
OTHER INFORMATION Grants were made to 52 organisations totalling £77,000 in 2012.
HOW TO APPLY The trustees meet half-yearly to review applications for funding. Only successful applicants are notified of the trustees' decision. Certain charities are supported annually, although no commitment is given.
WHO TO APPLY TO Linda Cousins, Secretary, Rathbones, 1 Curzon Street, London W1J 5FB *Tel.* 020 7399 0820 *email* linda.cousins@ rathbones.com

■ The Djanogly Foundation
CC NO 280500   **ESTABLISHED** 1980
WHERE FUNDING CAN BE GIVEN UK and overseas, mainly Israel.
WHO CAN BENEFIT Registered charities, schools and universities.
WHAT IS FUNDED Developments in medicine, education, social welfare and the arts. Welfare of older and younger people. Jewish charities.
RANGE OF GRANTS £15–£250,000.
SAMPLE GRANTS University of Nottingham (£211,500); Jerusalem Foundation (£203,500); Victoria and Albert Museum (£125,000); Great Ormond Street Children's Hospital and Nottingham Trent University (£100,000 each); Mencap (£25,000); Nottingham City Academy – (now called Djanogly City Academy) (£12,000);

Israel Philharmonic Orchestra and the Oxford Centre for Hebrew and Jewish Studies (£10,000 each); Churchill Centre and Tate Foundation (£5,000 each); Institute of Jewish Policy Research and Southwell Minster (£2,000 each); and Chicken Shed Theatre Trust and Wellington Hospital (£1,000 each).
FINANCES *Year* 2011–12 *Income* £55,044 *Grants* £867,874 *Assets* £6,407,254
TRUSTEES Sir Harry Djanogly; Michael S. Djanogly; Lady Carol Djanogly.
HOW TO APPLY In writing to the correspondent. 'The charity achieves its objectives receiving and evaluating grant applications.'
WHO TO APPLY TO Christopher Sills, Secretary, 3 Angel Court, London SW1Y 6QF *Tel.* 020 7930 9845

■ The Novak Djokovic Foundation (UK) Limited
CC NO 1147341   **ESTABLISHED** 2012
WHERE FUNDING CAN BE GIVEN UK and Serbia.
WHO CAN BENEFIT Charities, community groups and individuals.
WHAT IS FUNDED General, education, social welfare, relief of poverty.
TRUSTEES David Lumley; Novak Djokovic; Jelena Ristic.
HOW TO APPLY Unsolicited applications are not considered.
WHO TO APPLY TO David Lumley, Trustee, c/o Arena Wealth Management, 3rd Floor, Chiswick Gate, 598–608 Chiswick High Road, London W4 5RT *Tel.* 020 8104 1000 *Fax* 020 8994 0993 *Website* novakdjokovicfoundation.org

■ The DLM Charitable Trust
CC NO 328520   **ESTABLISHED** 1990
WHERE FUNDING CAN BE GIVEN UK, especially the Oxford area.
WHO CAN BENEFIT Organisations benefiting: children; young adults; older people; medical professionals, nurses and doctors; and people with head and other injuries, heart disease or blindness.
WHAT IS FUNDED Charities operating in Oxford and the surrounding areas, particularly charities working in the fields of: arts, culture and recreation; religious buildings; self-help groups; the conservation of historic buildings; memorials; monuments and waterways; schools; community centres and village halls; parks; various community services and other charitable purposes.
WHAT IS NOT FUNDED No grants to individuals.
TYPE OF GRANT Feasibility studies, one-off, research, recurring costs, running costs and start-up costs. Funding of up to three years will be considered.
SAMPLE GRANTS Ley Community (£20,000); See Saw (£15,000); Stillbirth and Neonatal Death Charity and Wildlife Conservation Research Unit (£10,000 each); Brainwave and Home Farm Trust (£5,000 each); Action for Blind People and Cecily's Fund (£3,000 each); and OXRAD and Prison Phoenix Trust and (£2,000 each).
FINANCES *Year* 2011–12 *Income* £136,344 *Grants* £111,500 *Assets* £5,227,289
TRUSTEES Jeffrey Alan Cloke; Dr Eric Anthony de la Mare; Jennifer Elizabeth Pyper; Philippa Sawyer.
HOW TO APPLY In writing to the correspondent. Trustees meet in February, July and November to consider applications.

WHO TO APPLY TO Jeffrey Alan Cloke, Trustee, c/o Cloke and Co, 475 Salisbury House, London Wall, London EC2M 5QQ *Tel.* 020 7638 8992

■ The DM Charitable Trust

CC NO 1110419   **ESTABLISHED** 2005
WHERE FUNDING CAN BE GIVEN UK and Israel.
WHO CAN BENEFIT Jewish registered charities.
WHAT IS FUNDED Social welfare and education.
FINANCES *Year* 2011–12 *Income* £985,953 *Grants* £1,352,690 *Assets* £6,128,221
TRUSTEES Stephen J. Goldberg, Chair; David Cohen; Patrice Klein.
OTHER INFORMATION Previous attempts to obtain a list of grants have been unsuccessful.
HOW TO APPLY In writing to the correspondent.
WHO TO APPLY TO Stephen J. Goldberg, Trustee, Sutherland House, 70–78 West Hendon Broadway, London NW9 7BT *Tel.* 020 8457 3258

■ Louise Dobson Charitable Trust

CC NO 1022659   **ESTABLISHED** 1986
WHERE FUNDING CAN BE GIVEN Some preference for West Sussex.
WHO CAN BENEFIT Children, people with mental disabilities, religious groups and general poverty relief.
WHAT IS FUNDED General charitable purposes with some preference for causes local to the trust.
SAMPLE GRANTS Previous beneficiaries have included: £1,000 to CAFOD; £700 to Worth Abbey Lay Community; £650 to HCPT; £500 to Worth Abbey Parish; £450 to A and B Lourdes Fund; £350 to Inside Trust; £300 St Catherine's Hospice; £200 each to Catherington School, Catenian Association and SASBA.
FINANCES *Year* 2012–13 *Income* £4,301 *Grants* £4,310
TRUSTEES Christopher Dobson, Chair; Stephen Leach.
HOW TO APPLY In writing to the correspondent.
WHO TO APPLY TO C. N. Y. Dobson, Flat 1 Hapstead House, Hett Close, Ardingly, Haywards Heath, West Sussex, RH176TE

■ The Derek and Eileen Dodgson Foundation

CC NO 1018776   **ESTABLISHED** 1993
WHERE FUNDING CAN BE GIVEN Brighton and Hove.
WHO CAN BENEFIT Individuals and organisations.
WHAT IS FUNDED Welfare of older people.
SAMPLE GRANTS Age Concern; Grace Eyre Foundation; Brighton, Hove and Adur Social Services; Hove YMCA; and Sussex Probation Services.
FINANCES *Year* 2011–12 *Income* £114,367 *Grants* £80,368 *Assets* £2,035,379
TRUSTEES Christopher Butler; Peter Goldsmith; Roy Prater; Ed Squires; Natasha Glover; Georgina Reed.
HOW TO APPLY In writing to the correspondent. Trustees meet quarterly, or more frequently if necessary to assess grant applications.
WHO TO APPLY TO Ian Dodd, Clerk, 8 Locks Hill, Portslade, Brighton and Hove, East Sussex BN41 2LB *Tel.* 01273 419802 *email* ianwdodd@gmail.com

■ The Dollond Charitable Trust

CC NO 293459   **ESTABLISHED** 1986
WHERE FUNDING CAN BE GIVEN UK and Israel.
WHO CAN BENEFIT Jewish organisations.
WHAT IS FUNDED Jewish communities; general charitable purposes.
TYPE OF GRANT One-off and recurrent.
RANGE OF GRANTS Typically £5,000–£10,000.
SAMPLE GRANTS Organisations grants made during the year were broken down as: 34 grants for education and training (£616,000); 45 grants for religious education (£420,000); 33 grants in support of medical, health and sickness charities (£390,500); 44 grants to relieve poverty (£362,000); 12 grants for organisations supporting people with disabilities; and 12 grants for religious activities (£120,000). A list of specific beneficiary organisations was not published within the annual report and accounts.
FINANCES *Year* 2011–12 *Income* £1,131,753 *Grants* £2,129,239 *Assets* £35,959,146
TRUSTEES Adrian Dollond; Jeffrey Milston; Melissa Dollond; Brian Dollond; Rina Dollond.
OTHER INFORMATION 'Although the constitution of the charity is broadly based, the trustees have adopted a policy of principally assisting the Jewish communities in Britain and Israel. The trustees aim to maximise the grants that it pays taking into account the return on its investments and likely infrastructure projects.'
HOW TO APPLY In writing to the correspondent.
WHO TO APPLY TO Jeffrey Milston, Trustee, c/o FMCB, Hathaway House, Popes Drive, Finchley, London N3 1QF *Tel.* 020 8346 6446 *email* gwz@fmcb.co.uk

■ Domepride Ltd

CC NO 289426   **ESTABLISHED** 1983
WHERE FUNDING CAN BE GIVEN UK and overseas.
WHO CAN BENEFIT To benefit Jewish people, at risk groups, and people who are disadvantaged by poverty or socially isolated.
WHAT IS FUNDED Jewish causes, especially those in the welfare field. General charitable purposes.
RANGE OF GRANTS About £500– £5,000.
SAMPLE GRANTS Chesed L'Yisroel, Beis Ruchel, TTT, Heichal Hatorah, Amud Manchester, Bikur Cholim Trust, Beis Medrash d'Nitra and Ahavas Chesed.
FINANCES *Year* 2011–12 *Income* £35,792 *Grants* £41,000
TRUSTEES Joshua Padwa; Gita Padwa; Abraham Cohen; Elieza Padwa.
OTHER INFORMATION No grants list was available from the latest accounts.
HOW TO APPLY In writing to the correspondent.
WHO TO APPLY TO Gita Padwa, Trustee and Secretary, 3rd Floor, Manchester House, 86 Princess Street, Manchester M1 6NP

■ The Dorcas Trust

CC NO 275494   **ESTABLISHED** 1978
WHERE FUNDING CAN BE GIVEN UK.
WHO CAN BENEFIT Designated charities specified by the trustees, benefiting children, young adults, students, Christians, and people disadvantaged by poverty.
WHAT IS FUNDED Advancement of the Christian religion, relief of poverty and advancement of education.
SAMPLE GRANTS Navigators (£16,000); British Youth for Christ (£3,000); Tear Fund (£2,500);

Chippenham Cricket Club and Coach House Riding for the Disabled (£1,000 each); New Hope Ministries (£750); Salvation Army (£500); New Market Day Centre (£100); and Movember (£50).

FINANCES *Year* 2011–12 *Income* £41,189 *Grants* £28,910 *Assets* £1,560,969

TRUSTEES James Cecil Lionel Broad; Jan Broad; Peter Butler.

OTHER INFORMATION The trustees will also consider making loans to organisations and individuals

HOW TO APPLY In writing to the correspondent, although the trustees have stated that applications cannot be considered as funds are already committee.

WHO TO APPLY TO I. Taylor, Administrator, c/o Rathbone Trust Co Ltd, Port of Liverpool Building, Pier Head, Liverpool L3 1NW *Tel.* 01512 366666

■ Dorfred Charitable Trust

CC NO 1092347   **ESTABLISHED** 2001
WHERE FUNDING CAN BE GIVEN Worldwide.
WHO CAN BENEFIT Small UK-registered charities working in Africa, Asia and South America.
WHAT IS FUNDED Projects working to alleviate the many problems of peoples in 'poorer' countries and emergency aid in response to, for example, natural disasters or war.
TYPE OF GRANT Mainly small one-off grants.
RANGE OF GRANTS Up to £2,000.
SAMPLE GRANTS Mercury Corp (£2,000) and Health Unlimited, Lepra and CIWI (£1,500 each).
FINANCES *Year* 2011–12 *Income* £13,146 *Grants* £25,000 *Assets* £350,000
TRUSTEES Roger E. Dean; Philip G. Gardam; Revd Father Wood.
HOW TO APPLY In writing to the correspondent.
WHO TO APPLY TO Philip Gardam, Trustee, 9 Bailey Mews, Auckland Road, Cambridge CB5 8DR *Tel.* 01233 510914 *email* info@dorfred-trust.org.uk *Website* www.dorfred-trust.org.uk

■ Dorset Community Foundation (formerly known as Community Foundation for Bournemouth, Dorset and Poole)

CC NO 1122113   **ESTABLISHED** 2007
WHERE FUNDING CAN BE GIVEN The county of Dorset, including the authorities of Bournemouth and Poole.
WHO CAN BENEFIT Local organisations.
WHAT IS FUNDED Community; social welfare; education; health; the relief of poverty.
WHAT IS NOT FUNDED Each fund has different criteria, consult the website for up to date eligibility.
TYPE OF GRANT Longer than three years.
RANGE OF GRANTS £50–£40,500. Average grant range is between £1,000 and £5,000.
SAMPLE GRANTS West Howe Neighbourhood Worker (£40,500); Action for Children (£12,500); Youth Resources Services – the Rendezvous Sherborne (£10,000); Victim Support, Corfe Mullen Sports Association and Shaftesbury Town Council (£7,500 each); Frampton Village Hall and Age Concern – Christchurch (£6,000 each); Moving On and Diverse Abilities Plus (£5,000 each); Club Bournemouth and Poole, Bournemouth Fellowship of Clubs and Active Games for All (£2,000 each); Age Concern – North Dorset, Match Patch and Bourne Spring Trust (£1,000 each); Dorset Blind Association, Dorset Fire and Rescue Service and Beaminster

Festival (£500 each); Walkford Youth Club (£250); and St Luke's Church Hall (£50).

FINANCES *Year* 2011–12 *Income* £404,839 *Grants* £284,261 *Assets* £1,287,787

TRUSTEES Christopher Beale; Ashley Rowlands; Gwyn Bates; Christopher Morle; Gordon Page; Richard Cossey; Christopher Mills; Jeffrey Hart; Henry Digby.

OTHER INFORMATION Just over £4,500 was granted to individuals.

HOW TO APPLY Contact the foundation for details of up-to-date programmes. An online contact form is available on the site. Information regarding criteria and eligibility for each individual fund can be found on the foundation's website. For any further advice and guidance contact the grants team on 01202 292255 or email: grants@dorsetcf.org. According to the foundation's website, most of the grant schemes, unless otherwise stated, require the completion of an online application form. This is a two stage application, which should then be posted to the grants team along with the following documentation: 'a signed copy of your organisation's rules/constitution/governing document; a copy of your last year's accounts (or any other years accounts this will be specified on the application); a copy of your safeguarding: child protection/vulnerable persons policy (if appropriate); quotes (as appropriate); a list of your management committee/trustee names with any relationships to one another and cheque signatories identified; and any other material you consider relevant to your application (do not send material you want returned) e.g. leaflets, flyers, press cuttings.'

WHO TO APPLY TO Ashley Rowlands, Trustee, Abchurch Chambers, Dorset, Bournemouth BH1 2LN *Tel.* 01202 292255 *email* Philanthropy@dorsetcf.org *Website* www. dorsetcommunityfoundation.org

■ The Dorset Historic Churches Trust

CC NO 282790   **ESTABLISHED** 1960
WHERE FUNDING CAN BE GIVEN Dorset.
WHO CAN BENEFIT Churches.
WHAT IS FUNDED Grants or Loans towards the cost of restoring Dorset Church buildings are made in order to maintain the structure, and on some occasions other items of significant historical and architectural interest, in good repair.
WHAT IS NOT FUNDED Grants or Loans will normally NOT be made for works of modernisation, alteration, improvement, or demolition except where a pre-requisite to make the building more suitable for community use or where rebuilding is necessary in cases of structural instability.
TYPE OF GRANT One-off grants, mainly, but also interest-free loans for up to four years will be considered.
RANGE OF GRANTS Governed by funds available and by need.
SAMPLE GRANTS Milton Abbey (£20,000); Shroton St Mary (£10,000); Tolpuddle St John (£5,000); Ashmore St Nicholas (£4,000) and Fontmell Magna (£1,000).
FINANCES *Year* 2012 *Income* £97,771 *Grants* £101,000 *Assets* £469,461
TRUSTEES Capt. Nigel Thimbleby; Simon Pomeroy; Anthony Yeatman; Robin Adeney; Elizabeth Ashmead; Peter Hodgkins; Barry De Morgan; Susan Bruce-Payne; James Sabben-Clare;

Andrew Boggis; Patrick Moule; Revd Canon Eric Woods; Col Jeremy Selfe.

HOW TO APPLY Applications are to be made to the Deanery Representative of the Trust in the area in which the Church is located, on a form available to download, together with criteria and guidelines, from the website.

WHO TO APPLY TO R. Fox, Hon. Secretary, Kingsley Cottage, Kingsley Paddock, Maiden Newton, Dorchester, Dorset DT2 0DR *Website* www.dorsethistoricchurchestrust.co.uk

■ The Dorus Trust

CC NO 328724   **ESTABLISHED** 1990

WHERE FUNDING CAN BE GIVEN Mainly UK but sometimes overseas.

WHO CAN BENEFIT Registered UK charities.

WHAT IS FUNDED General charitable purposes.

WHAT IS NOT FUNDED No grants to individuals.

TYPE OF GRANT Projects and one-off grants. Funding for one year or less.

RANGE OF GRANTS £500–£15,000.

SAMPLE GRANTS St Raphael's Hospice (£8,000); Practical Action and Home-Start Merton (£7,000 each); Volunteer Centre Merton and Switchback (£5,000 each); and St Catherine's – Oxford (£3,000).

FINANCES *Year* 2012 *Income* £31,756 *Grants* £58,000 *Assets* £3,073,445

TRUSTEES Bettine Bond; Charles Peacock; Sarah Peacock.

HOW TO APPLY This trust no longer accepts applications.

WHO TO APPLY TO Charles Peacock, Trustee, c/o Charities Aid Foundation, 25 Kings Hill Avenue, Kings Hill, West Malling ME19 4TA *Tel.* 01732 520028

■ The Double 'O' Charity Ltd

CC NO 271681   **ESTABLISHED** 1976

WHERE FUNDING CAN BE GIVEN UK and overseas.

WHO CAN BENEFIT Registered charities and individuals.

WHAT IS FUNDED Primarily, grants towards the relief of poverty, preservation of health and the advancement of education. However, the charity considers all requests for aid.

WHAT IS NOT FUNDED No grants to individuals towards education or for their involvement in overseas charity work.

TYPE OF GRANT Preferably one-off.

RANGE OF GRANTS Up to £50,000

SAMPLE GRANTS Spirit of Recovery (£38,000); Refuge (£30,000); NAPAC (£27,000); Promise Clinic and Richmond Bridge Friendship Club (£25,000 each); Livewire Youth Music Project (£10,000); The Wroxham Trust (£1,000); and The William Donkin Memorial Fund (£200).

FINANCES *Year* 2011–12 *Income* £178,664 *Grants* £178,132 *Assets* £33,765

TRUSTEES Peter Townshend; Karen Townshend.

OTHER INFORMATION The grant total includes grants to individuals – £2,750.

HOW TO APPLY In writing to the correspondent.

WHO TO APPLY TO The Trustees, c/o 4 Friars Lane, Richmond, Surrey TW9 1NL *Tel.* 020 8940 8171

■ The Doughty Charity Trust

CC NO 274977   **ESTABLISHED** 1977

WHERE FUNDING CAN BE GIVEN England, Israel.

WHO CAN BENEFIT Jewish organisations benefiting people who are disadvantaged by poverty or who are sick.

WHAT IS FUNDED Orthodox Jewish, religious education, relief of poverty.

TYPE OF GRANT Usually £5,000 or less.

RANGE OF GRANTS £250–£24,000

SAMPLE GRANTS FKHS (£24,000); Ezras Nitrochim (£17,500); Kerren Shabbos (£13,500); Torah Vodaas and Torah Emes (£10,000 each); Zichron Menachem (£8,500); and Mir and Yad Elizer (£6,000 each).

FINANCES *Year* 2012 *Income* £325,445 *Grants* £266,634 *Assets* £115,310

TRUSTEES G. Halibard; M. Halibard.

OTHER INFORMATION Various donations of £5,000 and under amounted to £89,500.

HOW TO APPLY In writing to the correspondent. The trustees are experiencing increasing demands upon the charities resources. They have decided to not add to the list of present donees.

WHO TO APPLY TO Gerald Halibard, Trustee, 22 Ravenscroft Avenue, London NW11 0RY *Tel.* 020 8209 0500

■ Douglas Arter Foundation

CC NO 201794   **ESTABLISHED** 1960

WHERE FUNDING CAN BE GIVEN UK, with preference for Bristol, Somerset and Gloucestershire.

WHO CAN BENEFIT Registered charities whose principal activity is to assist people with physical or mental disabilities.

WHAT IS FUNDED Principally in respect of specific projects on behalf of people who are mentally or physically disabled.

WHAT IS NOT FUNDED Support is not given for overseas projects; general community projects*; individuals; general education projects*; religious and ethnic projects*; projects for unemployment and related training schemes*; projects on behalf of offenders and ex-offenders; projects concerned with the abuse of drugs and/or alcohol; wildlife and conservation schemes*; and general restoration and preservation of buildings, purely for historical and/or architectural. (*If these projects are mainly or wholly for the benefit of people who have disabilities then they may be considered.) Ongoing support is not given, and grants are not usually given for running costs, salaries, research and items requiring major funding. Loans are not given.

TYPE OF GRANT One-off for specific projects. Ongoing, research, core funding and major funding appeals are not supported.

RANGE OF GRANTS Usually between £250–£2,500.

SAMPLE GRANTS SCOPE (£10,000); Amber Trust, Macmillan Cancer Support – Somerset, Marches Family Network, British Wireless for the Blind Fund and Music Alive (£1,000 each); Penny Brohn Cancer Care – Bristol, North Devon Voluntary Services, Where Next Association and Weston Hospicecare – Weston-super-Mare (£500 each); and Prostate Cancer Support Group, Rainbow Centre – Bristol and Merseyside Thursday Club (£250 each).

FINANCES *Year* 2012 *Income* £105,901 *Grants* £80,750 *Assets* £2,554,988

TRUSTEES Geoffrey Arter; John Gurney; Peter Broderick; John Hudd.

HOW TO APPLY The trust does not have an official application form. Appeals should be made in writing to the secretary. Telephone calls are not welcome. The trust asks that the following is carefully considered before submitting an application – appeals must: be from registered charities; include a copy of the latest audited accounts available (for newly registered charities a copy of provisional accounts showing estimated income and expenditure for the current financial year); show that the project is 'both feasible and viable' and, if relevant, give the starting date of the project and the anticipated date of completion; include the estimated cost of the project, together with the appeal's target-figure and details of what funds have already been raised and any fundraising schemes for the project. The trustees state that 'where applicable, due consideration will be given to evidence of voluntary and self-help (both in practical and fundraising terms) and to the number of people expected to benefit from the project'. They also comment that their decision is final and 'no reason for a decision, whether favourable or otherwise, need be given' and that 'the award and acceptance of a grant will not involve the trustees in any other commitment'. Appeals are dealt with on an ongoing basis, but the trustees meet formally four times per year usually in March, June, September and December.

WHO TO APPLY TO Peter Broderick, Trustee, 16 Westway, Nailsea, Bristol BS48 2NA *Tel.* 01275 851051 *email* gntbristol@aol.com

---

■ The R. M. Douglas Charitable Trust

CC NO 248775   **ESTABLISHED** 1966
WHERE FUNDING CAN BE GIVEN UK with a preference for Staffordshire.
WHO CAN BENEFIT Registered charities already in receipt of support from the trust.
WHAT IS FUNDED The relief of poverty (including provision of pensions) especially for present and past employees (and their families) of Robert M Douglas (Contractors) Ltd, and general charitable purposes especially in the parish of St Mary, Dunstall.
TYPE OF GRANT Mostly small grants, including buildings, capital, core costs, one-off, research, and recurring costs.
RANGE OF GRANTS £200–£5,000. Typically £200–£500.
SAMPLE GRANTS Previously: Bible Explorer for Christian outreach, British Red Cross for general purposes, Burton Graduate Medical College to equip a new lecture theatre, Four Oaks Methodist Church for its centenary appeal, Lichfield Diocesan Urban Fund for Christian mission, St Giles Hospice – Lichfield for development, SAT-7 Trust for Christian outreach and John Taylor High School – Barton in Needwood for a performing arts block.
FINANCES *Year* 2011–12 *Income* £40,280 *Grants* £37,000 *Assets* £944,175
TRUSTEES Juliet Lees, Jonathan Douglas; Murray Lees.
OTHER INFORMATION In 2011–12 grants were also given to individuals totalling £6,700.
HOW TO APPLY The trust has previously stated that its funds were fully committed.
WHO TO APPLY TO Juliet Lees, Trustee, c/o Geens, 68 Liverpool Road, Stoke-on-Trent ST4 1BG *Tel.* 01782 847952

■ Downlands Educational Trust

CC NO 270943   **ESTABLISHED** 1973
WHERE FUNDING CAN BE GIVEN South East England (excluding London).
WHO CAN BENEFIT Charities and schools working with children and young people with special needs, with particular reference to dyslexia but not excluding other disabilities.
WHAT IS FUNDED Education and training.
WHAT IS NOT FUNDED Applications for grants outside the trust's policy are unlikely to be successful. In particular the trust does not support: individual children or their parents; projects which are not of direct educational benefit; research projects; organisational development; publicity projects; revenue costs; medical, health or mental health charities; charities that spend more than a reasonable proportion of their income on administration or generating voluntary income; organisations which are not UK-registered charities; fundraising intermediaries, grantmaking trusts, friends' associations or similar.
TYPE OF GRANT Mainly equipment, books and musical instruments etc. but also training courses.
RANGE OF GRANTS Usually £300 to £3,000.
SAMPLE GRANTS Seaford Downs Syndrome and Special Needs Support Group (£3,500); Autism Sussex and Chestnut Tree House (£3,000 each), Frewen College and St Mary's School (£2,500 each); Chailey Heritage (£2,200); Guild Care (£2,100); Children's Trust and Muntham House (£2,000 each); Caldecott Community (£1,600); and Disability Challenges (£1,500).
FINANCES *Year* 2011–12 *Income* £31,000 *Grants* £26,000 *Assets* £670,000
TRUSTEES Phoebe Cameron, Chair; Alison Henderson; Ian Henderson; Samantha Matthews; Stephen Burley; Jack Cookson; Susan Morgan.
HOW TO APPLY On an application form available from the trust's website. The trust gives the following information for potential applicants: 'in the interests of brevity and economy use the form as it stands and do not re-type, modify or expand it. Limit content to the space made available; the trustees will consider limited other papers, if they support specific information cross-referred in the application, such as price quotes for equipment. Do not submit other material, including appeal letters in lieu of properly completing the application form, annual reports/accounts/reviews and general publicity information; they will not be considered; the application should be signed by a senior member of staff or trustee; applications should be submitted in hard copy only. Submit eight copies of the application and any supporting documents, preferably double-sided; applications should be sent by post to arrive by 15 January, 15 May or 15 September for consideration at the following month's trustees' meeting. Applications will be acknowledged, successful applications being announced on [the trust's] website shortly after the meeting and all applicants notified in due course. We may wish to visit a charity or commission a professional assessment before making a final decision. Informal enquiries prior to a formal application are welcome. The trustees intend the application form and guidance notes to assist applicants give all and only the information required in considering awards, and welcome comments on the form and notes in use.'

WHO TO APPLY TO Joe Kirk, Secretary, 15 Trent Close, Sompting, Lancing, West Sussex BN15 0EJ *Tel.* 01903 523206 *email* sec@ downlandsedtrust.org *Website* www. downlandsedtrust.org

■ The Drapers' Charitable Fund

CC NO 251403   **ESTABLISHED** 1959
WHERE FUNDING CAN BE GIVEN UK, with a special interest in the City and adjacent parts of London and County Derry.
WHO CAN BENEFIT Registered or exempt charities.
WHAT IS FUNDED General charitable purposes including social welfare, education, heritage, the arts, prisoner support, Northern Ireland and textile conservation.
WHAT IS NOT FUNDED Grants are not usually made for: individuals; schools, colleges and universities (except in certain circumstances); churches; almshouses; animal welfare; medical research/relief, hospitals or medical centres; children's disabilities, physical disabilities or medical conditions; holidays or general respite care; organisations that are not registered charities, unless exempt from registration; funds that replace or subsidise statutory funding; local branches of national charities, associations or movements; work that has already taken place; general appeals or circulars; loans or business finance.
TYPE OF GRANT Generally, one-off grants for capital and core costs.
RANGE OF GRANTS Mostly for £10,000 or less.
SAMPLE GRANTS Beneficiaries included: Bancroft's School (£75,000); Industrial Trust (£70,000); Kirkham Grammar School (£53,000); Centre of the Cell (£42,000); Pembroke College – Cambridge (£35,000); Poppy Factory, Shannon Trust and St Anne's College – Oxford (£25,000 each); Boxing Academy, Fields in Trust and Futureversity (£15,000 each); Baytree Centre, Fine Cell Work and Shelter from the Storm (£10,000 each); Living Paintings, Somerset Sight and Unicorn Theatre (£8,000 each).
FINANCES *Year* 2011–12 *Income* £10,054,543 *Grants* £997,669 *Assets* £42,917,732
TRUSTEE The Drapers' Company.
OTHER INFORMATION £8,350 was also awarded to individuals.
HOW TO APPLY We would advise that for full details of the application process and the trust's current priorities, applicants refer to the trust's website. The Charities Committee meets five times a year to review all applications which fall within the current priorities for funding. The charity aims to deal with each application within three months of its being received. Applications can be made at any time during the year. Applicants should complete the 'application summary sheet' (available to download from the trust's website) and submit it together with a document on proposed funding. This should include detailed information about the organisation and the project/activity to be funded; full costings and project budget for the proposed work for which the grant is requested, or the organisation's income and expenditure budget for the current year (whichever is appropriate); and the most recent audited financial statements and trustees report. Applications should be submitted by post only.
WHO TO APPLY TO Andy Mellows, Head of Charities, The Drapers' Company, Drapers' Hall,

Throgmorton Avenue, London EC2N 2DQ *Tel.* 020 7588 5001 *Fax* 020 7628 1988 *email* charities@thedrapers.co.uk *Website* www. thedrapers.co.uk

■ The Drayson Foundation

CC NO 1076700   **ESTABLISHED** 1999
WHERE FUNDING CAN BE GIVEN UK.
WHO CAN BENEFIT Children who are sick and in need, including social welfare services and medical welfare and research charities.
WHAT IS FUNDED Relief of sickness, with particular emphasis on children and the advancement of education.
RANGE OF GRANTS up to £33,000
FINANCES *Year* 2011–12 *Income* £88,039 *Assets* £3,865,769
TRUSTEES Clare Maurice; Lord Paul Drayson; Lady Elspeth Drayson.
HOW TO APPLY In writing to the correspondent.
WHO TO APPLY TO Clare Maurice, Trustee, 201 Bishopsgate, London EC2M 3AB *Tel.* 020 7456 8610 *email* clare.maurice@MTGLLP.com

■ Dromintee Trust

CC NO 1053956   **ESTABLISHED** 1996
WHERE FUNDING CAN BE GIVEN UK and developing countries
WHO CAN BENEFIT Charitable organisations.
WHAT IS FUNDED People in need by reason of age, illness, disability or socio-economic circumstances; for charitable purposes connected with children's welfare; the advancement of health and education; research into rare diseases and disorders, in particular metabolic disorders; and for general charitable purposes.
TYPE OF GRANT One-off and recurrent.
RANGE OF GRANTS Up to £151,000.
SAMPLE GRANTS Great Ormond Street Hospital Charity (£250,000); CAFOD – Assumption Sisters of Nairobi (£35,000); Consolata Fathers – Ikonda Hospital (£25,000); Intercare (£20,000); Let the Children Live and Belinda Stanford Memorial Fund (£5,000 each); African Mission (£3,000) and UCL – two professors' trip to Namibia (£1,500).
FINANCES *Year* 2011–12 *Income* £312,255 *Grants* £375,500 *Assets* £1,178,851
TRUSTEES Hugh Murphy; Margaret Murphy; Mary Murphy; Patrick Hugh Murphy; Robert Smith; Paul Tiernan; Joseph Murphy.
HOW TO APPLY In writing to the correspondent.
WHO TO APPLY TO Hugh Murphy, Trustee, The Manor House, Main Street, Thurnby, Leicester LE7 9PN *Tel.* 01162 415100

■ The Duis Charitable Trust

CC NO 800487   **ESTABLISHED** 1987
WHERE FUNDING CAN BE GIVEN Worldwide.
WHO CAN BENEFIT Children, medical, general.
WHAT IS FUNDED The trust makes grants benefiting groups largely concerned with children and Jewish causes, although this incorporates support of social welfare, education, capital library and hospital appeals.
WHAT IS NOT FUNDED No grants to individuals.
SAMPLE GRANTS Norwood Ravenswood, Great Ormond Street Hospital, BINOH Norwood Childcare, Dulwich Picture Gallery, National Playing Fields, Down's Syndrome Association, Joint Jewish Charitable Trust, Hillel Special

Purposes Fund, Breakaway Charity Committee, Children's Wish Foundation and Jewish Care.

FINANCES *Year* 2011–12 *Income* £14,180 *Grants* £62,583

TRUSTEE Jayne Steiner and Cheryl Davis

HOW TO APPLY In writing to the correspondent.

WHO TO APPLY TO Jayne Steiner, 16 Ranulf Road, London NW2 2DE

■ The Royal Foundation of the Duke and Duchess of Cambridge and Prince Harry

CC NO 1132048   **ESTABLISHED** 2009

WHERE FUNDING CAN BE GIVEN UK and overseas.

WHO CAN BENEFIT Registered charities.

WHAT IS FUNDED Currently: veterans and military families; disadvantaged children and young people; conservation and sustainable development.

SAMPLE GRANTS PEAS (£830,000); ARK UK Programmes (£400,000); Fields in Trust (£330,000); Race 2 Recovery (£100,000); Greenhouse Charity (£97,000); Skillforce (£51,000); The Zoological Society of London (£50,000); Sentebale (£35,000); Together for Short Lives (£22,000); Help for Heroes (£20,000) and Army Widows Association (£7,000).

FINANCES *Year* 2011–12 *Income* £3,843,390 *Grants* £1,941,414 *Assets* £4,801,471

TRUSTEES Anthony James Lowther-Pinkerton; Guy Monson; Sir David Manning; Edward Harley; Lord Janvrin; Fiona Shackleton.

HOW TO APPLY To apply for an Endeavour Fund grant email a proposal no longer than four sides of A4 with the following criteria in mind: For distributing any size of grant: The applicants and/or beneficiaries should be wounded, injured or sick (including psychological illness) servicemen or women. They may or may not have been injured or become ill whilst on active duty but must have been in service at the time; The activity must be either a sporting or adventurous challenge and must represent a significant challenge for the applicant; Applicants should be able to demonstrate clear outcomes from the activity and should have the formal backing of their medical or rehabilitation team. For the Development and Venture grants: The activity must contribute to personal recovery and must contribute to a successful transition to civilian life; The activity must contribute to raising awareness of wounded, injured and sick servicemen and women; The activity must contribute to inspiring others, either other wounded, injured or sick servicemen and women, or members of the community, such as schoolchildren; There must be a clear and credible plan both for raising awareness and inspiring others; The applicant must demonstrate an ability to secure additional funding for the activity. **Currently the foundation is unable to accept unsolicited requests for support apart from through this fund.**

WHO TO APPLY TO Victoria Hornby, St James's Palace, London SW1A 1BS *Tel.* 020 7101 2963 *email* info@royalfoundation.com *Website* www.royalfoundation.com

■ The Dulverton Trust

CC NO 1146484   **ESTABLISHED** 1949

WHERE FUNDING CAN BE GIVEN Unrestricted. Mainly UK in practice. Limited support to parts of Africa. No grants for work in Greater London or Northern Ireland.

WHO CAN BENEFIT Mainly UK projects, some regional and local projects at a minor level.

WHAT IS FUNDED Youth and education, conservation, general welfare and to a lesser extent activities in preservation and peace and humanitarian support.

WHAT IS NOT FUNDED Grants rarely given for: individuals; museums, galleries, libraries, exhibition centres and heritage attractions; individual churches, cathedrals and other historic buildings; individual schools, colleges, universities or other educational establishments; hospices, hospitals, nursing or residential care homes; expeditions or research projects; activities outside the stated geographical scope. Support is rarely given to charities whose main beneficiaries live within Greater London or Northern Ireland. No support for the following areas of activity: health and medicine, including drug and alcohol addiction, therapy and counselling; support for people with disabilities; the arts, including theatre, music and drama; sport, including sports centres and individual playing field projects; animal welfare or projects concerning the protection of single species; expeditions and research projects; individuals volunteering overseas; conferences, cultural festivals, exhibitions and events; salaries for specific posts; major building projects, including the purchase of property or land; endowments; retrospective funding; appeals which seek to replace statutory funding.

TYPE OF GRANT Project and one-off funding. Also capital and core costs. Funding is rarely given for more than one year.

RANGE OF GRANTS Average grant £20,000–£25,000.

SAMPLE GRANTS Dulverton Scholarships (£450,000); The Community Foundation in Wales, The Cranfield Trust, Home Start UK and The Place2Be (£90,000 each); Rendcomb College (£75,000); Forgiveness Project and MapAction (£60,000 each); Devon Community Foundation (£45,000); Beatbullying and Endeavour Training (£30,000 each); Countryside Learning and Women in Prison (£25,000 each); Peace Direct, Peterhouse Appeal (UK) and West-Eastern Divan Trust UK (£15,000 each); Anna Plowden Trust (£10,000); and The Nelson Trust and Three Choirs Festival (£2,500 each).

FINANCES *Year* 2012–13 *Income* £3,209,443 *Grants* £2,795,715 *Assets* £86,586,187

TRUSTEES Christopher Wills, Chair; Sir John Kemp-Welch; Tara Douglas-Home; Lord Dulverton; Lord Gowrie; Dr Catherine Wills; Richard Fitzalan Howard; Sir Malcolm Rifkind; Dame Mary Richardson.

OTHER INFORMATION Minor grants for smaller charities working in the North East of England, Cornwall, Devon or Wales are no longer administered by the trust. The scheme is now administered by the local community foundations in these areas, namely the Community Foundation Tyne and Wear and Northumberland, Cornwall Community Foundation, Devon Community Foundation and the Community Foundation in Wales respectively. The grants total includes £270,000 distributed in this way.

HOW TO APPLY **Note: The trust has asked us to emphasise that they do not accept applications via post. You should apply only**

through the trust's website. 'Read the guidelines carefully, making sure that none of the exclusions apply to your charity or project. If you believe that your appeal falls within the funding policy of the trust, you are welcome to apply as follows: send your application by post to the Grants Director. The trust reserves the right not to respond to appeals by email from unfamiliar sources; there is no set application form, but you should restrict your application to two pages; make sure you include your organisation's full contact details, together with an email address and telephone number. Also confirm your charitable status, giving the registered charity number; include a brief description of the background, aims and objectives of the charity; details of the specific purpose for which funding is sought together with the funding target; and the balance of funding outstanding at the time of the application; finally, enclose a copy of your most recent annual report and accounts if they are not available on the Charity Commission's website. If you wish to make initial enquiries, establish eligibility, discuss time scales or need to seek further guidance about an application, telephone the trust's office. The trustees meet four times a year to consider major appeals: in February, May, July and October. There are no deadlines or closing dates. The selection procedure can take between three to six months so it is advisable to apply in plenty of time, especially if funding is required by a certain date. Each application is considered on its merits and all will receive a reply as soon as possible, although research and consultation may delay a response from time to time. The trust will usually acknowledge receipt of your application by email, so remember to include a current email address. If you do not have one, we will send you an acknowledgement by post. All rejected applications will receive notification and an outline explanation for the rejection will usually be given. Applications that are listed for consideration for a Major Grant will normally receive a visit from one of the trust's directors who will subsequently report to the trustees. Following the trustees' meeting, successful applicants will be notified of their award in writing. The trustees' decisions are final.'

WHO TO APPLY TO Anna de Pulford, Grants and Administration Manager, 5 St James's Place, London SW1A 1NP *Tel.* 020 7629 9121 *Fax* 020 7495 6201 *email* grants@dulverton.org *Website* www.dulverton.org

■ The P. B. Dumbell Charitable Trust

CC NO 232770   **ESTABLISHED** 1964
WHERE FUNDING CAN BE GIVEN Occasionally worldwide, but mostly the Wolverhampton and Shropshire area.
WHO CAN BENEFIT Institutions and individuals.
WHAT IS FUNDED General charitable purposes.
WHAT IS NOT FUNDED No educational grants are given.
RANGE OF GRANTS Up to £3,000.
SAMPLE GRANTS St Peter's Church Worfield and Clocolan Peace Feeding Scheme (£3,000 each); Ironbridge Gorge Museum Trust, Compton Hospice and Beacon Centre for the Blind (£2,500 each); Ludlow Festival 2011 (£2,000); Macmillan Cancer Relief and Midlands Air Ambulance (£1,500 each); Bishops Castle Community Hospital and South Shropshire

Furniture Appeal (£1,000 each); Wolverhampton M.S. Therapy Centre (£750); South Shropshire Youth Forum (£500) and Multiple Sclerosis Society – Black Country Branch and 1st Bilston Scout Group (£250 each).
FINANCES *Year* 2011–12 *Income* £42,928 *Grants* £29,750 *Assets* £1,009,337
TRUSTEES M. H. Gilbert; C. F. Dumbell.
OTHER INFORMATION In 2011–12 grants were given to 33 organisations and two grants were made to individuals totalling £500.
HOW TO APPLY In writing to the correspondent. The trustees meet annually in June when most grants are considered. Some applications will be considered at other times. Telephone calls are not welcomed.
WHO TO APPLY TO Christopher Dumbell, Trustee, Lower Hall, Worfield, Bridgnorth, Shropshire WV15 5LH *Tel.* 01746 716607

■ The Dumbreck Charity

CC NO 273070   **ESTABLISHED** 1976
WHERE FUNDING CAN BE GIVEN Worldwide, especially the west Midlands.
WHO CAN BENEFIT Charitable organisations. New applications are restricted to Midlands organisations.
WHAT IS FUNDED Animal welfare and conservation; children's welfare; people who are elderly or who have mental or physical disabilities; medical causes; and general charitable purposes.
WHAT IS NOT FUNDED No grants to individuals.
TYPE OF GRANT Recurring and one-off grants.
RANGE OF GRANTS £500–£5,000, but mainly for amounts under £1,000.
SAMPLE GRANTS DEC East Africa Crisis Appeal and CHARMS – Birmingham Children's Hospital (£5,000 each); Shipston Home Nursing (£3,000); Brooke Hospital for Animals Cairo and Macular Disease Support Group Leamington (£2,000 each); Army Benevolent Fund, Taste for Adventure, Greatwood – Horse Power Programme, Hunt Staff Benefit Society and Friends of Pershore Abbey (£1,000 each) and Academy Chamber Orchestra, Kenwood Eagles FC, Mobility Trust and Teenage Cancer Trust (£500 each)
FINANCES *Year* 2011–12 *Income* £133,965 *Grants* £73,750 *Assets* £3,600,335
TRUSTEES Chris Hordern; Hugh Carslake; Jane Uloth; Judith Melling.
HOW TO APPLY In writing to the correspondent. The trustees meet annually in April/May. Unsuccessful applications will not be acknowledged. Organisations operating in the UK outside Worcestershire, Warwickshire or the West Midlands will not be supported.
WHO TO APPLY TO P. M. Spragg, c/o PS Accounting, 41 Sycamore Drive, Hollywood, Birmingham B47 5QX

■ Dunard Fund

CC NO 295790   **ESTABLISHED** 1986
WHERE FUNDING CAN BE GIVEN UK with a particular interest in Scotland.
WHO CAN BENEFIT Arts, environment and humanitarian causes.
WHAT IS FUNDED Principally to the training for and performance of classical music at the highest standard and to education and display of the visual arts, also at international standard. A small percentage of the fund is dedicated to

environmental, humanitarian and architectural projects.

WHAT IS NOT FUNDED Grants are only given to charities recognised in Scotland or charities registered in England and Wales.

TYPE OF GRANT The trustees prefer to engage with recipients to enable long-term development of projects and initiatives which have major and lasting significance; they are therefore less inclined to provide one-off donations.

RANGE OF GRANTS £500–£500,000

SAMPLE GRANTS London Philharmonic Orchestra (£151,000); Edinburgh International Festival (£110,000); Edinburgh Sculpture Workshop and Anglia Ruskin University (£100,000 each); National Galleries Scotland and Refuge (£50,000 each); Ludus Baroque (£40,000); Royal Scottish National Orchestra (£30,000); Rosslyn Chapel (£25,000); The Public Catalogue Foundation (£10,000); Perth Festival of Arts and Pitlochry Festival Theatre (£5,000 each); Maritime Rescue Institute (£3,000); and The Salvation Army (£1,000).

FINANCES *Year* 2011–12 *Income* £2,272,778 *Grants* £2,422,716 *Assets* £4,723,681

TRUSTEES Carol Colburn Grigor; Dr Catherine Colburn Høgel; Erik Colburn Høgel; Colin Liddell.

OTHER INFORMATION The charity is also registered with the Office of the Scottish Charity Regulator.

HOW TO APPLY No grants to unsolicited applications.

WHO TO APPLY TO Carol Colburn Grigor, Trustee, 4 Royal Terrace, Edinburgh EH7 5AB *Tel.* 01315 564043 *Fax* 01315 563969

....

■ The Dunhill Medical Trust

CC NO 1140372 **ESTABLISHED** 1951

WHERE FUNDING CAN BE GIVEN UK

WHO CAN BENEFIT Registered charities particularly those benefiting older people and academic institutions undertaking medical research.

WHAT IS FUNDED The trust's current charitable priorities are: care of older people, including rehabilitation and palliative care; and research into the causes and treatments of disease, disability and frailty associated with ageing. The trust makes grants under four programmes: research grants, general grants, serendipity awards and research training fellowships. Full guidelines are available on the trust's website.

WHAT IS NOT FUNDED The trust will not fund: organisations based outside the UK, or whose work primarily benefits people outside the UK; large national charities, with an income in excess of £10 million, or assets exceeding £100 million; issues that are already well-funded in the UK, such as heart disease, cancer or HIV/AIDS; sponsorship of individuals; sponsorship of conferences or charitable events; services or equipment that would be more appropriately provided by the National Health Service; grants to cover the revenue or capital costs of hospices*; travel or conference fees (except where these items are an integral part of a project); new or replacement vehicles (unless an integral part of a community-based development); general maintenance; institutional overheads associated with research activity (i.e. the trust will not pay the full economic cost of research activities); research via a third party (such as a fundraising charity supporting research); continuation/replacement funding where a project or post has been previously supported from statutory sources or similar.

*Although the trust does not award grants to cover the revenue or capital costs of hospices,

research undertaken within a hospice setting is eligible for consideration.

TYPE OF GRANT Project grants to research groups, as well as some grants for salaries and building or equipment costs for specific projects.

RANGE OF GRANTS Up to £1 million.

SAMPLE GRANTS Beneficiaries included: University of Southampton (£80,000); University of Glasgow (£50,000); University of Leeds (£37,000); Integrated Neurological Services and Lost Chord – South Yorkshire (£30,000 each); Age Concern Halton and St Helens (£29,000) Alzheimer's Support (£23,000); Neighbourly Care Southall (£26,000); Green Candle Dance Company (£18,000); Fair Shares Gloucestershire £13,000); Manor Gardens Welfare Trust – London (£10,000); and RADICLE (£5,000).

FINANCES *Year* 2011–12 *Income* £102,266,309 *Grants* £3,267,580 *Assets* £98,486,584

TRUSTEES Ronald E. Perry, Chair; Prof. Sir Roger M. Boyle; The Rt Revd Christopher T. J. Chessun; Kay Glendinning; Prof. Roderick J. Hay; Prof. James McEwen; Richard A. H. Nunneley; Timothy W. Sanderson; Prof. Martin P. Severs; John Ransford; Peter Lansley.

OTHER INFORMATION £2.6 million going to research and research related awards and £593,000 to non-research/general grants. The Dunhill Medical trust is a member of the Association of Medical Research Charities.

HOW TO APPLY Applicants to the Research, Research-related and Serendipity funding programmes should complete the appropriate online *outline application form* available in the 'policies and documents' section of the trust's website. Applicants to the General Grants programme are asked to provide an initial outline (approximately two sides of A4) by post or email, including the following information: a brief description of the organisation and its status (e.g. whether it is a registered charity); who you are and what you do within the organisation; a description of the project for which funding is being sought, where it will take place and who it will involve; an outline of who will benefit from the work and why; the key outcomes and timescales; the total cost of the project/work and the specific amount being applied for from the trust. Outline applications for all programmes can be submitted at any time and those which are eligible will be invited to submit a formal application.

The formal application requirements differ depending upon the type of grant being applied for and applicants are strongly advised to visit the trust's website before making an application to ensure that they have all the relevant information. Full applications are considered by the Grants and Research Committee which meets quarterly (normally in February, May, July and November). The committee makes recommendations on whether applications should be supported and decisions are then referred to the board of trustees for approval at their quarterly meetings (normally held in March, June, September and December). Successful applicants are normally notified within two weeks of the meeting. Generally, decisions are made within three to four months.

WHO TO APPLY TO Claire Large, Administrative Director, 3rd Floor, 16–18 Marshalsea Road, London SE1 1HL *Tel.* 020 7403 3299 *Fax* 020 7403 3277 *email* info@dunhillmedical.org.uk *Website* www.dunhillmedical.org.uk

■ The Dunn Family Charitable Trust

CC NO 297389   **ESTABLISHED** 1987
WHERE FUNDING CAN BE GIVEN UK, with a strong preference for Nottinghamshire.
WHO CAN BENEFIT Organisations benefiting people with multiple sclerosis; environmental charities, medical charities.
WHAT IS FUNDED Charities working in the fields of health facilities and buildings; support to voluntary and community organisations; MS research; conservation; bird sanctuaries and ecology.
WHAT IS NOT FUNDED Only organisations known to the trustees are supported. No grants to individuals.
TYPE OF GRANT Core costs and one-off; funding for one year or less will be considered.
RANGE OF GRANTS £100–£5,000
SAMPLE GRANTS The Oakes Trust (Sheffield) (£4,500); Nottingham Multiple Sclerosis Therapy Centre Limited (£4,000); Treetops Hospice (£3,500); Support Dogs (£3,000); Nottinghamshire Historic Churches Trust (£2,500); Seafarers UK and West Bridgeford Shopmobility (£2,000 each); Age UK and Rainbow Children's Hospice (£1,500 each); RNLI (Wells-next-the-sea) and Nottinghamshire Wildlife Trust (£1,000 each) and Dolly Parton Imagination Library (£500).
FINANCES *Year* 2011–12 *Income* £68,830 *Grants* £59,500 *Assets* £1,815,521
TRUSTEES A. H. Dunn; N. A. Dunn; R. M. Dunn.
HOW TO APPLY In writing to the correspondent.
WHO TO APPLY TO Jacky Chester, Rushcliffe Estates Ltd, Tudor House, 13–15 Rectory Road, West Bridgford, Nottingham NG2 6BE *Tel.* 01159 455300 *email* jrc@rushcliffe.co.uk

■ The W. E. Dunn Trust

CC NO 219418   **ESTABLISHED** 1958
WHERE FUNDING CAN BE GIVEN Midlands.
WHO CAN BENEFIT Charitable organisations and individuals.
WHAT IS FUNDED The general policy of the trust is to benefit people who are sick or in need and live in the Midlands, particularly Warwickshire, Staffordshire, Shropshire or Worcestershire and surrounding areas.
It is the policy of the trustees to determine at the first meeting of the trustees for the year beginning 5 April how much will be available for grants. When the amount available for grants for the coming year has been calculated the trustees determine how this total shall be divided between: needy individuals for purposes other than further education; students for further educational purposes; and to charitable organisations.
WHAT IS NOT FUNDED No grants to settle or reduce debts already incurred.
TYPE OF GRANT Buildings, capital, core costs, one-off, project and start-up costs. All funding is for up to three years.
RANGE OF GRANTS Up to £1,000.
SAMPLE GRANTS University of Birmingham (£7,000); YMCA Birmingham, Compton Hospice, Midlands Air Ambulance and Grove Residential Home (£2,000 each); Acorns (£1,500) and Birmingham Royal Ballet, Bowel Disease Research Foundation, 1st Bilston Guide Company, St Michael's Church Budbrooke and National Youth Orchestra (£1,000 each).
FINANCES *Year* 2011–12 *Income* £142,559 *Grants* £148,207 *Assets* £3,993,167

TRUSTEES David Corney; Leita Smethurst; Christopher King; Jennifer Warbrick.
OTHER INFORMATION The grant total in 2011–12 includes 358 grants to individuals totalling £56,000 and £92,000 given to 139 organisations.
HOW TO APPLY There is a detailed policy statement on the making of grants and guidance notes and model application for sponsoring bodies making application for a grant for an individual.
Potential applicants are advised to contact the correspondent for copies of these documents in order to make an appropriate and relevant application.
Generally, applications should be in writing to the correspondent giving the name and address, some idea of the income/outgoings and any other necessary particulars of the grantee.
Organisations should always enclose accounts. Grants to individuals are considered every week; grants to organisations, every three or four months.
WHO TO APPLY TO Alan Smith, Secretary to the Trustees, The Trust Office, 30 Bentley Heath Cottages, Tilehouse Green Lane, Knowle, Solihull B93 9EL *Tel.* 01564 773407

■ The Charles Dunstone Charitable Trust

CC NO 1085955   **ESTABLISHED** 2001
WHERE FUNDING CAN BE GIVEN UK.
WHO CAN BENEFIT Registered charities.
WHAT IS FUNDED General charitable purposes. 'The trustees will continue to make a small number of grants in the following areas: making lasting improvements to the lives of children with disabilities and their families; improving the prospects of prisoners on release, especially through the provision of better opportunities and services whilst in prison; making lasting improvements to the education and wellbeing of those living in disadvantaged communities, particularly young people; improving the availability of support and service for young carers.'
WHAT IS NOT FUNDED The trustees do not normally make grants to individuals.
SAMPLE GRANTS Community Links and the Family Fund (£100,000 each); Fulwood Academy (£75,000); Prince's Trust (£80,000 for the Fairbridge merger; a further £70,000 was given for the enterprise fellowship); Dance United and Churches Conservation (£50,000 each); Kingwood Trust (£30,000); and Royal Marsden Cancer Research (£25,000).
FINANCES *Year* 2011–12 *Income* £1,608,533 *Grants* £1,249,970 *Assets* £2,346,280
TRUSTEES Denis Dunstone; Adrian Bott; Nicholas Folland; John Gordon.
OTHER INFORMATION 'In September 2009 the trustees began funding the development and improvement of the Fulwood Academy in Preston, Lancashire. This represents a substantial commitment of time and funds over the coming five years at least and is likely to be the focus for much of the trust's work.'
HOW TO APPLY 'Proposals are generally invited by the trustees or initiated at their request. Unsolicited applications are not encouraged and are unlikely to be successful. The trustees prefer to support innovative schemes that can be successfully replicated or become self-sustaining.'
WHO TO APPLY TO The Trustees, H. W. Fisher and Company, Acre House, 11–15 William Road, London NW1 3ER *Tel.* 020 7388 7000

■ Dushinsky Trust Ltd

CC NO 1020301　　**ESTABLISHED** 1992
WHERE FUNDING CAN BE GIVEN Mainly Israel.
WHO CAN BENEFIT Jewish and Israeli charities.
WHAT IS FUNDED Alleviation of poverty and the furtherance of Orthodox Jewish education.
SAMPLE GRANTS Previous beneficiaries have included: United Institutes of Dushinsky, Minchat Yitzchok Institutions and Ish Lerehu Fund.
FINANCES *Year* 2012 *Income* £495,750 *Grants* £504,695 *Assets* £2,324
TRUSTEES S. Reisner; Z. Levine; M. Schischa.
HOW TO APPLY The trust does not accept unsolicited applications.
WHO TO APPLY TO Simon Reisner, Secretary, 23 Braydon Road, London N16 6QL *Tel.* 020 8802 7144

■ Mildred Duveen Charitable Trust

CC NO 1059355　　**ESTABLISHED** 1996
WHERE FUNDING CAN BE GIVEN Worldwide.
WHO CAN BENEFIT Charitable organisations.
WHAT IS FUNDED General charitable purposes.
RANGE OF GRANTS £500–£10,000
SAMPLE GRANTS Missing People (£10,000); Almeida Theatre and Masterclass Trust (£5,000 each); Charlie Waller Memorial Trust (£3,300); Whittington Babies (£2,500); Three Wings Trust, St John's College and Hearing Dogs for Deaf People (£2,000 each); Combat Stress, Lingfield and District RDA, Old Meeting URC Bedworth and The Firefighters Charity (£1,000 each); Centrepoint (£750) and ACT (Prostate Cancer Charity), Cruse Bereavement Care, Shooting Start and The Rainbow Centre for Children (£500 each).
FINANCES *Year* 2011–12 *Income* £26,538 *Grants* £61,500 *Assets* £1,053,223
TRUSTEES Peter Holgate; Adrian Houstoun; Peter Loose; John Shelford.
OTHER INFORMATION Grants were made to 37 organisations.
HOW TO APPLY In writing to the correspondent.
WHO TO APPLY TO Peter Holgate, Trustee, Devonshire House, 60 Goswell Road, London EC1M 7AD *Tel.* 020 7566 4000

■ The Annette Duvollet Charitable Trust

CC NO 326505　　**ESTABLISHED** 1984
WHERE FUNDING CAN BE GIVEN UK.
WHO CAN BENEFIT Registered charities supporting young people aged 14–25.
WHAT IS FUNDED General charitable purposes.
RANGE OF GRANTS Usually up to £5,000.
SAMPLE GRANTS DePaul Trust and Pathway Workshop (£5,000); NMC Charity (£3,000); Island Trust Ltd, Support Line and Tiverton Market Centre (£2,000 each); Sense (£1,500); and Sayers Croft Environmental Educational Trust (£1,000).
FINANCES *Year* 2011–12 *Income* £28,854 *Grants* £23,601 *Assets* £676,751
TRUSTEES Peter Clarke; Richard Shuttleworth; Caroline Dawes.
HOW TO APPLY In writing to the correspondent.
WHO TO APPLY TO Peter Clarke, Trustee, 18 Nassau Road, London SW13 9QE *Tel.* 020 8748 5401 *email* peteaclarke@yahoo.com

■ The Dwek Family Charitable Trust

CC NO 1001456　　**ESTABLISHED** 1989
WHERE FUNDING CAN BE GIVEN UK, with a preference for the Greater Manchester area.
WHO CAN BENEFIT Individuals and small charities without a large fundraising profile. In previous years mainly Jewish charities have been supported.
WHAT IS FUNDED People who are in need, disabled or disadvantaged.
SAMPLE GRANTS Previously: Manchester International Festival; The Wilbraham Road Manchester Trust and The Royal Society.
FINANCES *Year* 2011–12 *Income* £22,670 *Grants* £30,000
TRUSTEES Anthony Jack Leon; Jonathan Victor Dwek; Joseph Claude Dwek.
OTHER INFORMATION In 2011–12 the trust had a total expenditure of £35,000. No further information was available.
HOW TO APPLY In writing to the correspondent.
WHO TO APPLY TO Joseph Claude Dwek, Trustee, Suite One, Courthill House, 66 Water Lane, Wilmslow, Cheshire SK9 5AP *Tel.* 01625 549081

■ The Dyers' Company Charitable Trust

CC NO 289547　　**ESTABLISHED** 1984
WHERE FUNDING CAN BE GIVEN UK.
WHO CAN BENEFIT Registered charities only.
WHAT IS FUNDED General charitable purposes.
WHAT IS NOT FUNDED No grants to individuals or international charities.
TYPE OF GRANT One-off and long-standing.
RANGE OF GRANTS Up to £25,000, in practice around £500–£5,000
SAMPLE GRANTS Boutcher C. of E. Primary School and Archbishop Tenison's School (£25,000 each); Society of Dyers and Colourists (£20,000); University of Manchester (£17,000); Cirdan Sailing Trust (£4,000); HANDS (£3,000); Combat Stress (£2,500); Orchid Cancer Appeal and National Memorial Arboretum (£2,000 each); Oakhaven Hospice and River Thames Boat Project (£1,000 each); Fashion and Textile Children's Trust and Fairbridge West (£500 each); and Association of Weavers (£200).
FINANCES *Year* 2011–12 *Income* £855,736 *Grants* £429,695 *Assets* £10,014,330
TRUSTEE The Dyers Company.
OTHER INFORMATION The trust also funds a bursary for a school in Norwich, for which it gave £63,500 in 2011–12.
HOW TO APPLY The company's website provides information regarding applications and is as follows: 'Note that the company does not accept unsolicited applications as a matter of policy unless supported/endorsed by a member of the company. Nevertheless, the charitable activities of our company continue to be as flexible as we can manage to accommodate requests for funds.'
WHO TO APPLY TO The Clerk of the Dyers, Dyer's Hall, Dowgate Hill, London EC4R 2ST *Tel.* 020 7236 7197 *Website* www.dyerscompany.co.uk

■ The James Dyson Foundation

CC NO 1099709 **ESTABLISHED** 2003

WHERE FUNDING CAN BE GIVEN Mainly UK, local
community around the Dyson company's UK
headquarters, in Malmesbury, Wiltshire.

WHO CAN BENEFIT Registered charities and
educational institutions.

WHAT IS FUNDED Educational institutions working in
the field of design, technology and engineering;
charities carrying out medical or scientific
research; and projects which aid the local
community around Dyson, in Malmesbury,
Wiltshire.

TYPE OF GRANT One-off and recurrent.

RANGE OF GRANTS Up to £350,000.

SAMPLE GRANTS James Dyson Award (£106,000);
Japan Education Programme (£26,000);
Malmesbury Schools Project (£22,000); Dyson
Centre for Neonatal Care (£16,500); Sparks
(£7,000).

FINANCES *Year* 2011 *Income* £2,180,432
Grants £888,556 *Assets* £2,114,737

TRUSTEES Sir James Dyson; Lady Deirdre Dyson;
Valerie West; Prof. Sir Christopher Frayling.

PUBLICATIONS A number of engineering and design
related resources are available to download
from the foundation's website.

OTHER INFORMATION At the time of writing (November
2013) the foundation's 2012 accounts were
overdue with the Charity Commission.

HOW TO APPLY Applications in writing on headed
paper to the correspondent. Organisations can
also apply through the 'get in touch' section of
the foundation's website.

WHO TO APPLY TO Lydia Beaton, Foundation
Manager, Tetbury Hill, Malmesbury, Wiltshire
SN16 0RP *Tel.* 01666 828001
email jamesdysonfoundation@dyson.com
Website www.jamesdysonfoundation.com

■ eaga Charitable Trust

CC NO 1088361   **ESTABLISHED** 2001

WHERE FUNDING CAN BE GIVEN UK and European Union.

WHO CAN BENEFIT Organisations and institutions benefiting research workers, academics and medical professionals.

WHAT IS FUNDED The trust currently provides grants to fund research and other projects within the following programme: Understanding and combating fuel poverty – ensuring energy services are fair and accessible for all groups in society. Grant applications should consist of one or more of the following elements: rigorous academic or policy-related research; robustly evaluated action projects that can offer new models for use on a wider scale; and wider promotion of good practice (for example through toolkits and workshops). The main focus of support is to promote a better understanding of fuel poverty and more effective means of tackling it. This includes understanding the causes of fuel poverty, how to prevent it and which groups are most likely to suffer fuel poverty. It also includes how best to target assistance to those in fuel poverty or at risk of it. Essential to this is improving energy efficiency and comfort in homes.

WHAT IS NOT FUNDED No grants for: general fundraising appeals; projects that comprise solely of capital works; retrospective funding; energy advice provision materials; maintenance of websites; or local energy efficiency/warm homes initiatives. No grants to individuals.

TYPE OF GRANT One-off for projects and research, including reasonable overhead costs. Funding is available for up three years.

RANGE OF GRANTS The trust does not have minimum or maximum grant levels but it does encourage the co–funding of projects where appropriate. Average grant can go up to ££25,000–£30,000.

SAMPLE GRANTS Association for the Conservation of Energy (ACE); Centre for Consumers and Essential Services, University of Leicester; Centre for Sustainable Energy; Department of Social Policy and Social Work, University of York; and Joanne Wade and Impetus Consulting Limited.

FINANCES *Year* 2011–12 *Income* £83,085 *Grants* £48,618 *Assets* £765,014

TRUSTEES William Baker; Anne Toms; Prof. Dave Gordon; Elizabeth Gore; Virginia Graham; Pedro Guertler; Jack Harrison.

HOW TO APPLY Application forms and detailed guidance on the application process are available on the trust's website. Meetings are held three times a year to consider submissions.

WHO TO APPLY TO Dr Naomi Brown, Trust Manager, PO Box 225, Kendal LA9 9DR *Tel.* 01539 736477 *email* eagact@aol.com *Website* www.eagacharitabletrust.org

■ The Eagle Charity Trust

CC NO 802134   **ESTABLISHED** 1989

WHERE FUNDING CAN BE GIVEN UK, in particular Manchester, and overseas.

WHO CAN BENEFIT UK, international and local charities.

WHAT IS FUNDED The trust stated it supports a wide variety of charities, especially those concerned with welfare.

TYPE OF GRANT One-off, with no commitment to providing ongoing funding.

RANGE OF GRANTS Around £500–£3,000

SAMPLE GRANTS Previously: Oxfam – Darfur and Chad (£2,500); Médecins Sans Frontières, UNICEF and Shelter (£2,000 each); British Red Cross – Bangladesh and Macmillan Cancer Support (£1,500 each); Amnesty International, Sight Savers International and Samaritans (£1,000 each); and Turning Point, Claire House and WaterAid (£500 each).

FINANCES *Year* 2012 *Income* £44,184 *Grants* £43,000 *Assets* £1,071,080

TRUSTEES Laura Gifford; Daphne Gifford; Elizabeth Williams; Sarah Nowakowski; Robert Gifford.

OTHER INFORMATION The trustees opted not to publicise a list of beneficiaries in 2012. The majority of grants were for either £500 or £1,000.

HOW TO APPLY In writing to the correspondent. However, note that unsolicited applications are not invited.

WHO TO APPLY TO The Trustees, c/o Nairne Son and Green, 477 Chester Road, Cornbrook, Manchester M16 9HF *Tel.* 01618 721701

■ Audrey Earle Charitable Trust

CC NO 290028   **ESTABLISHED** 1984

WHERE FUNDING CAN BE GIVEN UK.

WHO CAN BENEFIT Registered charities.

WHAT IS FUNDED General charitable purposes with some preference for animal welfare and conservation charities.

TYPE OF GRANT Mostly recurrent.

RANGE OF GRANTS Up to £10,000, in practice, £500–£4,000.

SAMPLE GRANTS Previous beneficiaries have included: Wells Hospital and Hospice Trust (£7,000); Animal Health Trust, British Red Cross Society, Royal British Legion, People's Dispensary for Sick Animals – PDSA, Age Concern England, Redwings Horse Sanctuary, Salvation Army and Oxfam (£4,000 each); Burnham Market and Norton Village Hall (£3,000); Burnham Overy Parochial Church Council (£1,000) and Farming and Wildlife Advisory Group (£500).

FINANCES *Year* 2011–12 *Income* £80,099 *Grants* £31,500 *Assets* £4,994,400

TRUSTEES Paul Andrew Sheils; Roger James Weetch.

HOW TO APPLY In writing to the correspondent.

WHO TO APPLY TO Paul Sheils, Trustee, 24–25 Bloomsbury Square, London WC1A 2PJ *Tel.* 020 7359 4135 *email* psheils@mail.com

■ The Earley Charity

CC NO 244823   **ESTABLISHED** 1820

WHERE FUNDING CAN BE GIVEN The Ancient Liberty of Earley (i.e. the central eastern and southern part of Reading, Earley and Lower Earley, northern Shinfield, Winnersh, Sonning and Lower Caversham).

WHO CAN BENEFIT Individuals in need and charitable and community organisations.

WHAT IS FUNDED To give aid to: the relief of distress and sickness; the relief of people who are elderly, disabled or living in poverty; the provision and support (with the object of improving the conditions of life in the interests of social welfare) of facilities for recreation and other leisure time occupation; the provision and support of educational facilities; and any other charitable purpose for the benefit of the community.

WHAT IS NOT FUNDED No nationwide appeals are considered. The trust has previously stated that it would prefer applications from local offices of national organisations.

TYPE OF GRANT One-off, project and start-up costs. Funding is available for up to one year.

RANGE OF GRANTS Usually up to £5,000.

SAMPLE GRANTS Age UK Reading (£47,000); Reading Voluntary Action (£42,000); Reading International Solidarity Centre (£39,000); Reading Community Welfare Rights Unit (£27,000); Christian Community Action (£8,000); Age UK Berkshire (£7,500); Whitley Arts Festival and Reading Repertory Theatre (£5,000 each); Reading Fairtrade Steering Committee (£3,000); Coley Park High Rise Picnic Area (£2,000); Snowhounds Disability Ski Club (£1,000); Shinfield OAP Club (£800) and The Dementia Forum (£50).

FINANCES *Year* 2012 *Income* £1,167,239 *Grants* £385,478 *Assets* £12,258,892

TRUSTEES Robert Ames; Leslie Owen; Miryam Eastwell; Phillip Hooper; Dr Deborah Jenkins; Bobby Richardson; Richard Rodway; Dr David Sutton.

OTHER INFORMATION The grant total includes £11,500 that was paid in grants individuals.

HOW TO APPLY On a form available from the correspondent or to download, together with criteria and guidelines, on the website; applications are considered at any time. No response is given to applicants from outside the beneficial area. Telephone calls or emails are welcome from applicants who wish to check their eligibility.

WHO TO APPLY TO Jane Wittig, Clerk to the Trustees, The Liberty of Earley House, Strand Way, Earley, Reading, Berkshire RG6 4EA *Tel.* 01189 755663 *Fax* 01189 752263 *email* enquiries@earleycharity.org.uk *Website* www.earleycharity.org.uk

....

■ Earls Colne and Halstead Educational Charity

CC NO 310859   **ESTABLISHED** 1975

WHERE FUNDING CAN BE GIVEN The catchment area of the former Earls Colne and Halstead grammar schools.

WHO CAN BENEFIT Organisations for the furtherance of education, individuals and local schools.

WHAT IS FUNDED Furtherance of the education of local children and young adults.

RANGE OF GRANTS Up to £6,000.

SAMPLE GRANTS Hedingham School (£5,000); Honywood School (£4,000); Richard De Clare School (£2,600); Ramsey School (£2,500); Richard De Clare School (£1,700) and Earls Colne (£1,200).

FINANCES *Year* 2011–12 *Income* £52,305 *Grants* £40,812 *Assets* £1,198,592

TRUSTEES Patricia Taylor; Susan Thurgate; Margarita James; Cllr Joe Pike; Oliver Forder; Angela Paramor; John Panayi; Mike Murray; Cllr David

Finch; Cllr Chris Siddall; Frank Williams; Cllr David Hume; Fiona Lee-Allan; Julie Winstanley.

OTHER INFORMATION In 2011–12 individuals received £11,000.

HOW TO APPLY In writing to the correspondent.

WHO TO APPLY TO Martyn Woodward, Clerk to the Trustees, St Andrew's House, 2 Mallows Field, Halstead, Essex C09 2LN *Tel.* 01787 479960 *email* earlscolnehalstead.edcharity@yahoo.co.uk

....

■ The Earmark Trust

CC NO 267176   **ESTABLISHED** 1974

WHERE FUNDING CAN BE GIVEN UK, with a preference for charities based in Kent.

WHO CAN BENEFIT Charitable organisations, usually those personally known to the trustees.

WHAT IS FUNDED People with disabilities, children, cancer research, the arts, Christian causes and general charitable purposes.

WHAT IS NOT FUNDED Applications from individuals are seldom considered. Applications from large-scale charities, church/cathedral restoration schemes or organ rebuilding projects are also not considered.

RANGE OF GRANTS £500–£5,000.

SAMPLE GRANTS Royal Ballet School (£5,000); Royal Opera House Trust (£2,500); Cardinal Hume Centre, CLIC Sargent Cancer Care, Deafblind UK, Listening Books, Macmillan Cancer Relief, The Martha Trust and Youth Cancer Trust (£1,000 each); 3H Fund, Action for Blind People, Anthony Nolan Trust, Bibles for Children, British Blind Sport, Compaid Trust, Dogs Trust, Help for Heroes and National Autistic Society (£500 each).

FINANCES *Year* 2011–12 *Income* £29,640 *Grants* £24,500 *Assets* £951,929

TRUSTEES F. C. Raven; A. C. M. Raven.

HOW TO APPLY In writing to the correspondent.

WHO TO APPLY TO The Trustees, 8 Bidborough Court, Penshurst Road, Bidborough, Tunbridge Wells, Kent TN3 0XJ

....

■ East End Community Foundation (formerly the St Katharine and Shadwell Trust)

CC NO 1147789   **ESTABLISHED** 1990

WHO CAN BENEFIT Grants are available to voluntary and community organisations. Some grants may be made to statutory organisations such as schools.

WHAT IS FUNDED 'We give grants and run projects to improve the quality of life in the local area. We work in the London Boroughs of Tower Hamlets Hackney and the City of London.'

WHAT IS NOT FUNDED Individuals.

TYPE OF GRANT Capital, revenue and full project funding.

RANGE OF GRANTS £250–£10,000.

SAMPLE GRANTS Previous beneficiaries (of Isle of Dogs Community Foundation and St Katharine and Shadwell Trust) include: Common Ground East, Futureversity, Shadwell Basin Outdoor Activity Centre and Tower Hamlets Education Business Partnership (£10,000 each); London Borough of Tower Hamlets (summer holiday programme) (£8,500); Summer Holiday Programme for Pensioners (£7,000); Wellington Way Sports Project, Somali Development Association, Kudu Arts Project and Banglatown Association (£5,000 each); ADEEG Community Centre (£4,000); Providence Row (£2,000); Vital Arts (£1,500) and Science in Schools –

Hermitage Primary School and Mulberry School for Girls (£1,000 each).
FINANCES *Year* 2012 *Grants* £1,400,000
TRUSTEES Eric Sorensen; Revd P. David Paton; Denise Jones; Angela Orphanou; Dan Jones; David Hardy; Mark Gibson; Rosemary Ryde; Ian Fisher; Dr Tobias Jung; Christopher Martin; Jonathan Norbury.
OTHER INFORMATION This is a newly formed community foundation. In October 2012 the St Katharine and Shadwell Trust ceased to operate as an independent charity and merged with a neighbouring charity, the Isle of Dogs Community Foundation (IDCF) to form East End Community Foundation (EECF). The area of benefit remains the same and all trustees of both charities have joined the board of the new charity for its first year of operation.
HOW TO APPLY See the foundation's website for details of up-to-date schemes.
WHO TO APPLY TO Tracey Walsh, Director, Jack Dash House, 2 Lawn House Close, London E14 9YQ *Tel.* 020 7345 4444 *email* grants@eastendcf.org *Website* www.eastendcf.org

■ Eastern Counties Educational Trust Limited

CC NO 310038   **ESTABLISHED** 1922
WHERE FUNDING CAN BE GIVEN Preference for Essex, Suffolk, Norfolk, Cambridgeshire and Hertfordshire.
WHO CAN BENEFIT Those with special educational needs, particularly those under 25 who have emotional and behavioural difficulties.
WHAT IS FUNDED Activities, projects or equipment which will assist the above.
WHAT IS NOT FUNDED No grants to individuals. Normally no grants are given for recurring costs.
TYPE OF GRANT One-off and recurring.
RANGE OF GRANTS Up to £20,000.
SAMPLE GRANTS The College of West Anglia (£20,500); Woodlands School (£18,500); St Clement's High School (£14,000); Listening Books (£6,000); Just 42, Woodbridge and Romsey Mill (£4,000 each); Loughton Youth Project and Cambridge University disability resource centre (£2,500 each) and Graeae Theatre Company (£1,300).
FINANCES *Year* 2011–12 *Income* £136,901 *Grants* £97,796 *Assets* £3,029,673
TRUSTEES H. Anderson; D. Boyle; B. Salmon; L. M. Lepper; Deborah Reed; Lady Singleton; Joanna Clark.
HOW TO APPLY An application form should be obtained from the correspondent. This provides details of information to be submitted with it. Unsuccessful applicants will not be informed unless an sae is provided.
WHO TO APPLY TO A. H. Corin, Company Secretary, Brook Farm, Wet Lane, Boxted, Colchester CO4 5TN *Tel.* 01206 273295

■ The Sir John Eastwood Foundation

CC NO 235389   **ESTABLISHED** 1964
WHERE FUNDING CAN BE GIVEN UK, but mainly Nottinghamshire in practice.
WHO CAN BENEFIT Local organisations, particularly those concerned with disabled and older people and children with special needs.
WHAT IS FUNDED General charitable purposes.
WHAT IS NOT FUNDED No grants to individuals.

TYPE OF GRANT One-off projects and longer term funding.
RANGE OF GRANTS Mostly £3,000 to £100.
SAMPLE GRANTS Nottingham Hospice (£24,000); Newark and Nottinghamshire Agricultural Society, the Oaklands and Sherwood Forest Hospital Voluntary Services (£10,000 each); Nottingham University (£9,000); Macmillan Cancer Support, Disability Living Centre and Southwell Minster (£5,000 each); and British Wireless for the Blind (£3,000).
FINANCES *Year* 2011–12 *Income* £415,665 *Grants* £230,250 *Assets* £7,589,253
TRUSTEES Diana Cottingham; Constance Mudford; Gordon Raymond; Valerie Hardingham; David Marriott.
OTHER INFORMATION The foundation's income has reduced significantly following the cessation of trading of Adam Eastwood and Sons Limited, a company which is wholly owned by the foundation and from where income was derived.
HOW TO APPLY In writing to the correspondent.
WHO TO APPLY TO David Marriott, Trustee, PO Box 9803, Mansfield NG18 9FT *Fax* 01623 847955

■ The Ebenezer Trust

CC NO 272574   **ESTABLISHED** 1976
WHERE FUNDING CAN BE GIVEN UK and overseas.
WHO CAN BENEFIT Registered charities.
WHAT IS FUNDED Advancement of the evangelical tenets of the Christian faith.
WHAT IS NOT FUNDED No grants to individuals.
TYPE OF GRANT Occasionally interest-free loans. One-off grants. Core costs, capital costs and unrestricted funding.
RANGE OF GRANTS Up to around £10,000, in practice, between £500 and £5,000.
SAMPLE GRANTS Christ Church – Stock (£5,000); Barnabas Fund and TEAR Fund (£4,000 each); Stepping Stones Trust (£3,000); Gideons International (£2,500); Alpha Partners (£2,000); Brentwood Christian Schools Worker Trust (£1,500); Wheels for the World and Christians Against Poverty (£1,000 each); Spurgeon's Child Care and Scripture Union (£500 each); London Institute of Contemporary Christianity and Sierra Leone Mission (£250 each); and Arsenal Charitable Trust (£50).
FINANCES *Year* 2011–12 *Income* £76,557 *Grants* £53,939 *Assets* £716,260
TRUSTEES Nigel Davey; Ruth Davey.
HOW TO APPLY The trust states that they 'are most unlikely to consider unsolicited requests for grants'.
WHO TO APPLY TO Nigel Davey, Trustee, Longwood Lodge, Whites Hill, Stock, Ingatestone CM4 9QB *Tel.* 01277 829893

■ The EBM Charitable Trust

CC NO 326186   **ESTABLISHED** 1982
WHERE FUNDING CAN BE GIVEN UK.
WHO CAN BENEFIT Charitable organisations.
WHAT IS FUNDED General charitable purposes, especially animal welfare and research, youth development and the relief of poverty.
TYPE OF GRANT Recurring and one-off.
RANGE OF GRANTS £3,500–£200,000.
SAMPLE GRANTS The Prostate Cancer Charity (£100,000); Fairbridge (£70,000); Animal Health Trust (£50,000); Prior's Court Foundation (£40,000); Cardinal Hume Centre (£35,000); Marie Curie Cancer Care, Worshipful Company of Shipwrights Charitable Fund and Youth at Risk (£20,000 each); Ingwood,

Macmillan Cancer Support, Royal Veterinary College and Seeability (£10,000 each); The Cirdan Sailing Trust and I Can (£5,000 each); and New Astley Club (£3,500).

FINANCES *Year* 2011–12 *Income* £1,195,881 *Grants* £668,500 *Assets* £44,742,189

TRUSTEES Richard Moore; Michael Macfadyen; Stephen Hogg; Francis Moore.

OTHER INFORMATION The trust manages two funds, the general fund and the Fitz' fund. The Fitz' fund was established following the death of Cyril Fitzgerald, one of the original trustees of the charity who left the residue of his estate to the trust. The money is held as a designated fund for animal charities.

HOW TO APPLY The trustees have previously stated: 'Unsolicited applications are not requested as the trustees prefer to support donations to charities whose work they have researched and which is in accordance with the wishes of the settlor. The trustees do not tend to support research projects as research is not a core priority but there are exceptions. The trustees' funds are fully committed. The trustees receive a very high number of grant applications which are mostly unsuccessful.'

WHO TO APPLY TO Keith Lawrence, Secretary, Moore Stephens, 150 Aldersgate Street, London EC1A 4AB *Tel.* 020 7334 9191 *Fax* 020 7651 1953

······································

■ The Ecology Trust

CC NO 1099222 **ESTABLISHED** 2003

WHERE FUNDING CAN BE GIVEN Mainly UK.

WHO CAN BENEFIT Registered charities working on ecological and environmental initiatives, particularly, in the areas of agriculture, energy, and climate change.

WHAT IS FUNDED Support is given to projects that prevent environmental degradation and that change values and attitudes, both amongst the public and with people in positions of power. In general the trust seeks to address the causes of the environmental crisis that we face, and to tackle these, rather than to make the consequences of this crisis easier to live with.

WHAT IS NOT FUNDED The trust is unlikely to make grants to the following kinds of projects: work that has already taken place; part of general appeals or circulars; outward-bound courses, expeditions and overseas travel; capital projects (i.e. buildings and refurbishment costs); conservation of already well-supported species or of non-native species; and furniture, white goods, computer, paint, timber and scrap recycling projects.

TYPE OF GRANT One-off and recurring grants for project and core costs.

RANGE OF GRANTS Up to £30,000.

SAMPLE GRANTS ChemSec and Pesticide Action Network UK (£30,000 each); UK Without Incineration Network (£24,500); Campaign For Better Transport Trust (£20,000); CPRE (£15,000); Gen-GOB Eivissa (£13,000); Federacion Pitiusa de Razas Autoctonas (£9,000); Food Ethics Council (£7,000); Amics de la Terra Eivissa and 'Other grants' (£500).

FINANCES *Year* 2011–12 *Income* £342,164 *Grants* £155,590 *Assets* £291,306

TRUSTEES Benjamin Goldsmith; Charles Filmer; Alexander Goldsmith.

HOW TO APPLY In writing to the correspondent.

WHO TO APPLY TO Jon Cracknell, Hon. Secretary, Unicorn Administration Ltd, 30–36 King Street, Maidenhead SL6 1NA *Tel.* 01797 222773

······································

■ Eden Arts Trust

CC NO 1000476 **ESTABLISHED** 1990

WHERE FUNDING CAN BE GIVEN The Eden district of Cumbria.

WHO CAN BENEFIT Individuals and organisations benefiting: young adults and older people; artists; actors and entertainment professionals; musicians; textile workers and designers; volunteers; and writers and poets.

WHAT IS FUNDED To promote and develop the arts and art projects involving the community, and to encourage new groups.

WHAT IS NOT FUNDED Only projects/groups in the Eden district can be funded.

TYPE OF GRANT Local arts and crafts projects, days and events, feasibility studies.

RANGE OF GRANTS Up to £5,000.

SAMPLE GRANTS Highlights and Blue Jam (£2,000 each). Small grants paid totalled £4,250. A further £5,000 was spent on project costs.

FINANCES *Year* 2011–12 *Income* £120,996

TRUSTEES Keith Morgan; Terry Smith; Elizabeth Halliday.

OTHER INFORMATION Grants made during the year totalled £8,250 including £4,250 for 'small grants'. A further £5,000 was spent on project costs.

HOW TO APPLY Contact the trust by telephone or e-mail for further information.

WHO TO APPLY TO Adrian Lockhead, Chief Executive Officer, 1 Sandgate, Penrith, Cumbria CA11 7TP *Tel.* 01768 899444 *Fax* 01768 895920 *email* enquiries@edenarts.co.uk *Website* www. edenarts.co.uk

······································

■ EDF Energy Trust (EDFET)

CC NO 1099446 **ESTABLISHED** 1996

WHERE FUNDING CAN BE GIVEN UK.

WHO CAN BENEFIT Individuals and families and voluntary and not-for-profit organisations.

WHAT IS FUNDED The trust offers two types of grants: *individual grants* – to cover the payment of gas and electricity debts and other essential household debts or costs (applicants must be EDF Energy account holders); and *organisational grants* – for organisations working in the field of money advice, debt counselling or energy efficiency advice.

WHAT IS NOT FUNDED No grants for: fines for criminal offences; educational or training needs; debts to central government departments; medical equipment, aids and adaptations; holidays; business debts; catalogues; credit cards; personal loans; deposits for secure accommodation; or overpayment of benefits.

TYPE OF GRANT Contracts and full project funding for up to three years.

SAMPLE GRANTS Bristol Debt Advice Centre, East London Financial Inclusion (£20,000 each); Brixton Advice Centre (£18,300); Money Advice Plus – East Sussex (£18,100); Thanet District CAB (£17,000); Brighton and Hove CAB (£13,800)

FINANCES *Year* 2012 *Income* £2,095,843 *Grants* £2,500,000

TRUSTEES Denice Fennell; Tim Cole; Steve Meakin; Brian Cross; Bob Richardson; Richard Sykes

OTHER INFORMATION The grant total includes around £2 million that was given to individuals.

HOW TO APPLY Organisational grants: It is advisable to contact the foundation for further information on future grant programmes and deadlines. Individual grants: applications can be submitted throughout the year. Applications must be made on a standard application form, which can be downloaded from the website, obtained from local advice centres such as citizen's advice bureau or by writing to the trust. The trust also has an online application form, accessible via the website.

WHO TO APPLY TO The Trustees, PO Box 42, Peterborough PE3 8XH *Tel.* 01733 421060 *Fax* 01733 421020 *email* edfet@charisgrants. com *Website* www.edfenergytrust.org.uk

....

■ The Gilbert and Eileen Edgar Foundation

CC NO 241736   **ESTABLISHED** 1965
WHERE FUNDING CAN BE GIVEN UK (and a few international appeals).
WHO CAN BENEFIT Charitable organisations.
WHAT IS FUNDED General charitable purposes with preference towards medical research; care and support; fine arts; education in the fine arts; religion; and recreation.
WHAT IS NOT FUNDED Grants for education in the fine arts are made by way of scholarships awarded by academies.
TYPE OF GRANT One-off and longer term projects.
RANGE OF GRANTS Usually £250–£9,000.
SAMPLE GRANTS Royal College of Music (£9,000); Royal Academy of Arts (£6,000); Royal Academy of Dramatic Art (£5,000); English National Ballet (£2,000); Worshipful Company of Clockmakers, Gurkha Welfare Trust, Coram Life Education and Atlantic Salmon Trust (£1,000 each); Action for Elder Abuse, Child Brain Injury Trust and National Eye Research Centre (£500 each); and Hambledon Surgery Medical Fund (£250).
FINANCES *Year* 2012–13 *Income* £82,547 *Grants* £71,874 *Assets* £1,848,214
TRUSTEES Simon Gentilli; Adam Gentilli.
OTHER INFORMATION 87 organisations were given grants totalling £72,000.
HOW TO APPLY In writing to the correspondent. There are no application forms.
WHO TO APPLY TO Adam Gentilli, Trustee, Greville Mount, Milcote, Stratford-upon-Avon, Warwickshire CV37 8AB *Tel.* 01491 848500 *email* info@jamescowper.co.uk

....

■ Gilbert Edgar Trust

CC NO 213630   **ESTABLISHED** 1955
WHERE FUNDING CAN BE GIVEN Predominantly UK, limited overseas.
WHO CAN BENEFIT Registered charities, educational or cultural bodies benefiting children, medical professionals and research workers.
WHAT IS FUNDED Only charities which the trustees find worthwhile will be supported. Grants are given in the following categories: children, deaf/blind, disabled, drug abuse, handicapped, homeless, hospice, medical, overseas, research, social, youth and other.
WHAT IS NOT FUNDED No grants to individuals or non-registered charities.
RANGE OF GRANTS Mostly £500–£1,500.
SAMPLE GRANTS British Red Cross, Samaritans, Shelter and Simon Community (£1,500 each); Echo, Impact Foundation, Macmillan Cancer Support, Notting Hill Foundation and Prostate Cancer Charity (£1,000 each); Broadreach House, East Anglia's Children's Hospices, Pain Relief Foundation, Prisoners Abroad, Re-Solv, Saint John's Ambulance and Spinal Injuries Foundation, (£500 each); and Worshipful Company of Clockmakers (£100).

FINANCES *Year* 2011–12 *Income* £42,178 *Grants* £36,600 *Assets* £900,509
TRUSTEES Simon Gentilli; Adam Gentilli; Dr Richard Solomons.
HOW TO APPLY In writing to the correspondent, with a copy of a brochure/flyer describing your work.
WHO TO APPLY TO Simon Gentilli, Trustee, Barnwell House, Skirmett Road, Fingest, Oxon RG9 6TH

....

■ Edge Fund

ESTABLISHED 2012
WHERE FUNDING CAN BE GIVEN UK.
WHO CAN BENEFIT Registered charities; CICs, social enterprises and community groups.
WHAT IS FUNDED Social, economic and environmental justice.
FINANCES *Year* 2012–13 *Grants* £150,000
OTHER INFORMATION Edge Fund was established in April 2012 by a group of philanthropists aiming to achieve a different funding model from traditional donor-led philanthropy. The fund is not a registered charity, but in September 2012 decided on the Community Benefit Society legal form.
HOW TO APPLY Check the fund's website for current information on open rounds and deadlines.
WHO TO APPLY TO Sophie Pritchard, Co-ordinator, *Tel.* 07767 126915 *email* edgefund@riseup.net *Website* edgefund.org.uk

....

■ Edinburgh Children's Holiday Fund

SC NO SC010312   **ESTABLISHED** 1912
WHERE FUNDING CAN BE GIVEN Edinburgh and the Lothians.
WHO CAN BENEFIT Children.
WHAT IS FUNDED Grants are awarded to charitable and voluntary organisations that are concerned with children's welfare and provide holidays for children who are disadvantaged.
WHAT IS NOT FUNDED No grants directly to individuals.
TYPE OF GRANT One-off grants.
SAMPLE GRANTS Previous beneficiaries have included: Acorn Christian Centre, Castleview Primary School, Children 1st, Drug Prevention Group, Forthview Primary School, Mother's Union Holiday Scheme, the Roses Charitable Trust, Scottish Spina Bifida Association, Stepping Stones and Uphill Ski Club.
FINANCES *Year* 2011–12 *Income* £63,924 *Grants* £50,000
HOW TO APPLY On a form available from the correspondent. Trustees meet to consider grants in January and May. Applications should be sent in mid-December and mid-April respectively.
WHO TO APPLY TO The Secretaries, c/o Bryce Wilson and Co., Granite House, 18 Alva Street, Edinburgh EH2 4QG *Tel.* 01312 255111 *Fax* 01312 200283

....

■ Edinburgh Trust No 2 Account

CC NO 227897   **ESTABLISHED** 1959
WHERE FUNDING CAN BE GIVEN UK and worldwide.
WHO CAN BENEFIT Registered charities only.
WHAT IS FUNDED Education, armed services, scientific expeditions.
WHAT IS NOT FUNDED No grants to individuals and non-registered charities.
TYPE OF GRANT Unrestricted funding.
RANGE OF GRANTS Usually £500–£3,000

Think carefully about every application. Is it justified?

....

517

SAMPLE GRANTS Edwina Mountbatten Trust (£2,800); the Federation of London Youth Clubs, Royal Marines General Fund and the Game and Wildlife Conservancy Trust (£2,000 each); Burma Star Association, the Cutty Sark Trust and British Trust for Conservation Volunteers (£1,500 each); and the Countryside Foundation for Education and Royal Air Force Benevolent Fund (£1,000 each).

FINANCES *Year* 2011–12 *Income* £96,596 *Grants* £82,853 *Assets* £2,374,821

TRUSTEES Charles Woodhouse; Sir Brian McGrath; Brigadier Archie Miller-Bakewell.

OTHER INFORMATION 82 grants were given in 2011–12 totalling £83,000.

HOW TO APPLY In writing to the correspondent.

WHO TO APPLY TO The Secretary, The Duke of Edinburgh's Household, Buckingham Palace, London SW1A 1AA *Tel.* 020 7024 4107

······································

■ Edinburgh Voluntary Organisations' Trust Funds (EVOT)

SC NO SC031561   **ESTABLISHED** 1868

WHERE FUNDING CAN BE GIVEN Edinburgh and the Lothians.

WHO CAN BENEFIT Organisations and individuals. Organisations should have an annual turnover of under £200,000. Priority is given to local charitable organisations so that a national organisation will be required to indicate need and a local presence in Edinburgh and the Lothians according to the agreed policy.

WHAT IS FUNDED The Edinburgh Voluntary Organisations Council (EVOC) helps to support, develop and promote the interests and work of voluntary and community organisations in Edinburgh that operate in the area of social welfare.

WHAT IS NOT FUNDED The Trust does not normally provide grants for the following: Salaries or similar; All core property costs, such as new buildings, property repairs, extensions, alterations, property rental, rates, etc. Educational and adventure type projects, holidays or day visits; Arts, environmental or sports activities, except where a significant social service or therapeutic intent is the main aim; Travel and transport (except as part of core volunteer expenses); Disbursement to other agencies; General appeals.

TYPE OF GRANT One-off and recurrent for a maximum of three years.

RANGE OF GRANTS Organisations: up to £2,000 annually.

SAMPLE GRANTS Multiple Sclerosis Therapy, Link Up Women's Group, SANDS (Stillbirth and Neo-natal Death Society) and The Prop Stress Centre (£2,000 each); Edinburgh Gardeners Partnership (£1,800); Thornton Rose Rideability Group (£1,500); Complementary Foundation for Planetary Healing (£1,000) and Midlothian Association of Play (£650).

FINANCES *Year* 2011–12 *Income* £164,711 *Grants* £123,947 *Assets* £3,782,490

TRUSTEES Sandra Blake; Geoffrey Lord; David Bennett; Mike Gilbert; Madeleine Allen.

OTHER INFORMATION The 2011–12 grant total includes £90,000 that was given to 1193 individuals.

HOW TO APPLY On forms available to download, together with guidelines and criteria, on the website.

WHO TO APPLY TO Janette Scappaticcio, Trust Administrator, 14 Ashley Place, Edinburgh

EH6 5PX *Tel.* 01315 559100 *Fax* 01315 559101 *email* janettescappaticco@evoc.org.uk *Website* www.evoc.org.uk

······································

■ Educational Foundation of Alderman John Norman

CC NO 313105   **ESTABLISHED** 1962

WHERE FUNDING CAN BE GIVEN Norwich and Old Catton.

WHO CAN BENEFIT Individuals who are descendants of Alderman Norman, and organisations benefiting children, young adults and students.

WHAT IS FUNDED Primarily supports the education of the descendants of Alderman Norman, but also supports young people, local schools and educational establishments in the area.

WHAT IS NOT FUNDED No applications from outside Norwich and Old Catton will be considered.

RANGE OF GRANTS £300–£3,000.

SAMPLE GRANTS 1st Norwich Sea Scouts (£7,000); the Matthew Project and How Hill Trust (£5,000 each); East Norwich Youth Project, Norfolk Eating Disorders Association and Norfolk Archaeological Trust – St Benet's Abbey (£3,000 each); West Norwich Partnership and Your Future (£2,000 each); Norwich Cycle Speedway and Eaton Vale Scouts and Guides Activity Centre (£1,000 each); and Sewell Toy Library (£500).

FINANCES *Year* 2011–12 *Income* £225,484 *Grants* £215,108 *Assets* £6,270,831

TRUSTEES Revd Jonathan Boston; Roger Sandall; Dr Julia Leach; Revd Canon Martin Smith; Derek Armes; Tracey Hughes; Stephen Slack; Christopher Brown; Francis Whymark; James Hawkins; Roy Hughes.

OTHER INFORMATION In 2011–12, grants were given to descendants, Old Catton residents (£166,000) and organisations (£49,000).

HOW TO APPLY In writing to the correspondent. Grants to organisations are considered at the trustees meeting in May/June. All applications should be made through the clerk.

WHO TO APPLY TO N. F. Saffell, Clerk, The Atrium, St George's Street, Norwich NR3 1AB *Tel.* 01603 629871

······································

■ Edupoor Limited

CC NO 1113785   **ESTABLISHED** 2006

WHERE FUNDING CAN BE GIVEN Worldwide.

WHO CAN BENEFIT Registered charities.

WHAT IS FUNDED Projects in line with the trust's objects of, 'the advancement in education and training through the world, the relief of poverty, old age, illness, both mental and physical and the relief of persons suffering from any disability, and such other charitable purpose as the association may time to time authorise'.

FINANCES *Year* 2011–12 *Income* £240,427 *Grants* £240,005 *Assets* £3,050

TRUSTEES Shmuel Amitay; Richard Fraser.

OTHER INFORMATION Accounts were on file at the Charity Commission, without a list of grants.

HOW TO APPLY In writing to the correspondent.

WHO TO APPLY TO Meir Amitay, Secretary, 50 Craven Park Road, South Tottenham, London N15 6AB

········

■ Dr Edwards Bishop King's Fulham Endowment Fund

CC NO 1113490   **ESTABLISHED** 1981

WHERE FUNDING CAN BE GIVEN Fulham: specifically the postcode areas of SW6, part of W14 and part of W6.

WHO CAN BENEFIT Organisations or local groups that help people on low incomes who live in Fulham. Grants are also made to individuals in need.

WHAT IS FUNDED One-off projects and summer schemes.

WHAT IS NOT FUNDED 'The charity does not respond to general funding appeals but will consider matching funding raised from other sources, but not for any purpose for which statutory funding is available.'

TYPE OF GRANT Running costs, one off project grants.

RANGE OF GRANTS Up to £7,000.

SAMPLE GRANTS Hammersmith and Fulham Mind (£7,000); Counselling Pastoral Trust and The Doorstep Library Network (£4,500 each); London Sports Trust (£4,000); Hammersmith and Fulham Action on Disability and Maggie's Cancer Care Centre (£3,000 each); Sir John Lillie Playcentre and Sands End Adventure project SEAPIA (£2,500 each) and New Youth Generation (£1,500).

FINANCES *Year* 2012–13 *Income* £384,121 *Grants* £293,069 *Assets* £9,039,455

TRUSTEES Michael Clein; Carol Bailey; Lindsey Brock; Ronald Lawrence; Susan O'Neill; Revd Mark Osborne; Allen Smith; Cllr Adronie Alford; Charles Treloggan; B. Richards; Michael Waymouth.

OTHER INFORMATION The 2012–13 grant total includes £178,500 that was given to individuals. The majority of these grants were made for relief in need purposes.

HOW TO APPLY On an application form available, together with criteria and guidelines, from the correspondent or the trust's website.

WHO TO APPLY TO Jonathan Martin, Clerk to the Trustees, Percy Barton House, 33–35 Dawes Road, Fulham, London SW6 7DT *Tel.* 020 7386 9387 *Fax* 020 7610 2856 *email* clerk@debk. org.uk *Website* www.debk.org.uk

■ The W. G. Edwards Charitable Foundation

CC NO 293312   **ESTABLISHED** 1985

WHERE FUNDING CAN BE GIVEN UK.

WHO CAN BENEFIT Projects benefiting older people.

WHAT IS FUNDED The provision of care for older people through existing charities.

WHAT IS NOT FUNDED No grants to individuals. According to the trustees' report for 2012/13, 'beneficiaries must be established registered charities that assist with the care of old people...the trustees consider than an older person is generally assumed to be over 60 years of age, but they will also look at projects for over 50s.'

TYPE OF GRANT Principally one-off capital projects. Trustees currently prefer to give towards a named item rather than into a pool building fund.

RANGE OF GRANTS £1,000 to £5,000.

SAMPLE GRANTS Family Support Clacton and Garvald Glenesk (£5,000 each); Aspire Living Ltd and Age UK Lewisham and Southwark (£4,000 each); West Herts Against Crime (£3,500); Independent Age (£3,000); NBFA Assisting the Elderly and Newent Association for the Disabled

(£2,000 each); Vine Community Trust and Alive Activities Ltd (£1,000 each); AM Arts Ltd (£500).

FINANCES *Year* 2012–13 *Income* £125,517 *Grants* £98,290 *Assets* £3,054,843

TRUSTEES Gillian Shepherd Coates; Wendy Savage; Yewande Savage; William Mackie.

HOW TO APPLY The trust's website states that applications should be in writing to the correspondent, including: confirmation of charitable status (charity number on letterhead will suffice); brief details of the project; budget statement for the project; current fundraising achievements and proposals for future fundraising; items of expenditure within project costing approx. £1,000 to £5,000 – trustees currently prefer to give towards a named item rather than into a pool building fund; copy of latest accounts if available. There are no forms or deadlines for applications. If your project fulfils the foundation's policy criteria, your details will be passed on to the trustees for consideration at their next meeting. According to the trustees' report for 2012/13, 'beneficiaries must be established registered charities that assist with the care of old people...the trustees consider than an older person is generally assumed to be over 60 years of age, but they will also look at projects for over 50s.'

WHO TO APPLY TO Janet Brown, Clerk, 123A Station Road East, Oxted, Surrey RH8 0QE *Tel.* 01883 714412 *email* janetbrown@ wgedwardscharitablefoundation.org.uk *Website* www.wgedwardscharitablefoundation. org.uk

■ The William Edwards Educational Charity

CC NO 528714   **ESTABLISHED** 1981

WHERE FUNDING CAN BE GIVEN Kenilworth.

WHO CAN BENEFIT Schools and colleges benefiting children, young adults, academics and students under the age of 25.

WHAT IS FUNDED The education of young people.

TYPE OF GRANT One-off and recurrent grants.

RANGE OF GRANTS Generally around £500 to £10,000.

SAMPLE GRANTS Kenilworth School and Sports College (£42,000); Abbotsford School (£8,600); Clinton Primary School (£7,000); Kenilworth School (£2,250) and Thorns Community Infant School (£1,000).

FINANCES *Year* 2011–12 *Income* £242,645 *Grants* £75,000

TRUSTEES John Cooke; Cllr Pauline Edwards; Cllr Michael Coker; Cllr Norman Vincett; Joanne Richmond; Dr George Raper; Cllr Patrick Ryan; Dr Roger Davies.

OTHER INFORMATION The 2011–12 grant total includes grants to schools and grants to individuals.

HOW TO APPLY In writing to the correspondent. Trustees meet four times a year.

WHO TO APPLY TO John Hathaway, Clerk to the Trustees, Heath and Blenkinsop, 42 Brook Street, Warwick CV34 4BL *Tel.* 01926 492407 *email* heath.blenkinsop@btopenworld.com

■ The Eighty Eight Foundation

CC NO 1149797   **ESTABLISHED** 2012

WHERE FUNDING CAN BE GIVEN UK.

WHO CAN BENEFIT Registered charities.

WHAT IS FUNDED General charitable purposes.

TRUSTEES Anna Jaworski; Ann Fitzmaurice; Edward Fitzmaurice.

HOW TO APPLY In writing to the correspondent.

WHO TO APPLY TO The Trustees, c/o Rawlinson and Hunter, 6 New Street Square, London EC4A 3AQ *Tel.* 020 7842 2000 *Fax* 020 7842 2080

■ The Elephant Trust

CC NO 269615   **ESTABLISHED** 1975

WHERE FUNDING CAN BE GIVEN England and Wales.

WHO CAN BENEFIT Individual artists, arts organisations and publications concerned with the visual arts.

WHAT IS FUNDED Visual arts; advancement of public education in all aspects of arts; development of artistic taste and knowledge; understanding and appreciation of the fine arts.

WHAT IS NOT FUNDED The following categories are not supported: arts festivals; group exhibitions; charities organising community projects; students; educational or other studies; residencies or research; symposia or conferences; publications or catalogues and projects taking place outside the UK.

TYPE OF GRANT One-off contributions to specific projects by individuals or organisations.

RANGE OF GRANTS Usually £2,000, but up to £5,000 may be considered.

SAMPLE GRANTS Transmission Gallery, University of Dundee, Artists Collective Gallery, Cubbits Artist Ltd, Chisenhale Gallery, Barts and the London Charity, North Devon Theatres Trust, Electra and Redmond Entwistle (£2,000 each); Sierra Metro Ltd and Salisbury Artists Centre (£1,500 each) and the Pavillion, Spike Island Artspace, Lido Projects and RGAP (£1,000 each).

FINANCES *Year* 2011–12 *Income* £1,354,135 *Grants* £58,794 *Assets* £2,857,957

TRUSTEES Prof. Dawn Ades; Antony Forwood; Rob Tufnell; Benjamin Cook; Jeremy Deller; Elizabeth Carey-Thomas; Melissa Gronlund; Elizabeth Price; Antony Penrose.

OTHER INFORMATION The Elephant Trust also administers both the George Melhuish Bequest and the Shelagh Wakely Bequest.
A total of 37 grants were made, 20 of which were given to individuals.

HOW TO APPLY Only postal applications will be accepted. Applications should include: synopsis of the project – single side of A4, 300 words maximum; budget – single side of A4, including total cost of the project, amount requested, details of other funding applications made and name and address of the recipient of grant if awarded; brief CV – one sheet of A4; visual material – still images, maximum of 8; DVDs are only accepted when artists are working with film/video; other material(e.g. catalogues, press cuttings, etc.) only if relevant and might help trustees in their consideration of application. *Note that no materials will be returned.* The trust's website states that 'priority is given to artists and small organisations and galleries who should submit well argued, imaginative proposals for making or producing new work or exhibitions.' If not contacted within six months, application has been unsuccessful.

WHO TO APPLY TO Ruth Rattenbury, Administrator, Bridge House, 4 Borough High Street, London SE1 9QR *Tel.* 020 7403 1877 *email* ruth@elephanttrust.org.uk *Website* www.elephanttrust.org.uk

■ The George Elias Charitable Trust

CC NO 273993   **ESTABLISHED** 1977

WHERE FUNDING CAN BE GIVEN Some preference for Manchester.

WHO CAN BENEFIT Mostly Jewish organisations.

WHAT IS FUNDED Mainly Jewish causes, some smaller donations to more general charitable causes, including educational needs, healthcare and the fight against poverty.

SAMPLE GRANTS Previous beneficiaries included: UK Friends of Nadar Deiah (£50,000); Ahavat Shalom (£45,000); UJIA (£30,000); Hale and District Hebrew Congregation (£24,000); JEM (£5,000); South Manchester Mikva Trust (£4,000); British Friends of Rinat Aharon (£2,500); Moracha LTD (£1,000); Chai Lifeline Cancer Trust (£300); and Friends of the Sick (£100).

FINANCES *Year* 2011–12 *Income* £257,024 *Grants* £409,579 *Assets* £729,056

TRUSTEES Ernest Elias; Stephen Elias.

OTHER INFORMATION A list of beneficiaries was not included.

HOW TO APPLY In writing to the correspondent. Trustees meet monthly.

WHO TO APPLY TO Stephen Elias, Trustee, Shaws Fabrics Ltd, 1 Ashley Road, Altrincham, Cheshire WA14 2DT *Tel.* 01619 287171 *email* textiles@kshaw.com

■ The Gerald Palmer Eling Trust Company

CC NO 1100869   **ESTABLISHED** 2003

WHERE FUNDING CAN BE GIVEN Berkshire.

WHO CAN BENEFIT Charitable organisations.

WHAT IS FUNDED Christian religion, particularly the Orthodox Church; medical research and the study of medicine; and relief of sickness and poverty.

WHAT IS NOT FUNDED No grants to individuals.

TYPE OF GRANT One-off.

RANGE OF GRANTS Up to £20,000

SAMPLE GRANTS The Mary Hare Foundation (£20,000); Convent of the Annunciation (£10,000); Brainwave (£5,000); Bede House Association (£3,000); Fledglings Family Services (£2,000); The Bishop of Winches (£1,500); Berks' Healthcare Foundation NHS Trust (£500) and Hermitage Village Hall (£250).

FINANCES *Year* 2011–12 *Income* £1,227,002 *Grants* £243,870 *Assets* £63,803,503

TRUSTEES Desmond Harrison; Robin Broadhurst; James Gardiner; Kenneth McDiarmid.

OTHER INFORMATION The trust is responsible for the long term maintenance of the character and qualities of the Eling Estate, which is the principal asset of the original endowment, and the protection and sustenance of its environment. The sum of £721,000 went towards running the estate during the year.

HOW TO APPLY In writing to the correspondent.

WHO TO APPLY TO A. J. Blackwell, Company Secretary, Englefield Estate Office, Englefield Road, Theale, Reading RG7 5DU *Tel.* 01189 302504 *email* mcd@englefield.co.uk

■ The Wilfred and Elsie Elkes Charity Fund

CC NO 326573　　**ESTABLISHED** 1984
WHERE FUNDING CAN BE GIVEN Staffordshire and especially Uttoxeter, including UK-wide charities benefiting the area.
WHO CAN BENEFIT Organisations benefiting children and elderly people.
WHAT IS FUNDED The trustees have a particular interest in child welfare, the welfare of older people, organisations working with deaf people, and medical charities involved with deafness, Alzheimer's disease, Parkinson's disease and a range of other diseases. Animal welfare; infrastructure development; charity or voluntary umbrella bodies; accommodation and housing; and community facilities and services, are also considered.
WHAT IS NOT FUNDED Grants are normally made to organisations rather than to individuals.
TYPE OF GRANT Recurrent grants are given in a number of cases but more normally the grant is a one-off payment. Grants can be made for buildings, capital, core costs, project, research, running costs, salaries and start-up costs. Funding is available for up to and over three years.
RANGE OF GRANTS £500–£1,600.
SAMPLE GRANTS Childhood Eye Cancer Trust; Father Hudson's Society; Breath of Life; Juvenile Diabetes Research and Somerset Rural Music School (£1,600 each); Stafford Churches Audio Magazine (£1,000); Rays of Sunshine Children's Charity, Cerebra and MedEquip4Kids (£800 each); Uttoxeter Methodist Church and Mad Hatter's Tea Party (£500 each).
FINANCES *Year* 2011–12 *Income* £107,563 *Grants* £80,000
TRUSTEE Royal Bank of Scotland plc.
HOW TO APPLY In writing to the correspondent.
WHO TO APPLY TO The Trust Section Manager, RBS Trust and Estate Services, Eden Building, Lakeside, Chester Business Park, Wrexham Road, Chester CH4 9QT *Tel.* 01244 625810

■ The Maud Elkington Charitable Trust

CC NO 263929　　**ESTABLISHED** 1972
WHERE FUNDING CAN BE GIVEN Mainly Desborough, Northamptonshire and Leicestershire.
WHO CAN BENEFIT Registered charities, particularly local, and local branches of UK charities and individuals through established bodies such as NHS trusts.
WHAT IS FUNDED General charitable purposes including health and welfare, especially of older people, youth and community.
WHAT IS NOT FUNDED No grants directly to individuals.
TYPE OF GRANT One-off and recurrent.
SAMPLE GRANTS Previous beneficiaries include: Nottinghamshire County Council; Leicester Grammar School – Bursary; Bromford Housing Association; Cynthia Spencer Hospice; Launde Abbey; Cancer Research UK; CARE Shangton; Multiple Sclerosis Society; Elizabeth Finn Care; Voluntary Action Northants; and Phoenix Furniture.
FINANCES *Year* 2011–12 *Income* £577,533 *Grants* £478,140 *Assets* £21,530,345
TRUSTEES Roger Bowder, Chair; Michael Jones; Katherine Hall.
OTHER INFORMATION Unfortunately, unlike previous accounts, a list of beneficiaries was not included.

HOW TO APPLY In writing to the correspondent. There is no application form or guidelines. The trustees meet every seven or eight weeks.
WHO TO APPLY TO Paula Fowle, Administrator, c/o Shakespeares LLP, Two Colton Square, Leicester LE1 1QH *Tel.* 01162 545454 *Fax* 01162 554559 *email* paula.fowle@ shakespeares.co.uk

■ Ellador Ltd

CC NO 283202　　**ESTABLISHED** 1981
WHERE FUNDING CAN BE GIVEN UK and overseas
WHO CAN BENEFIT Jewish people.
WHAT IS FUNDED The trust supports organisations benefiting Jewish people and also Jewish individuals.
FINANCES *Year* 2011–12 *Income* £66,683 *Grants* £75,992 *Assets* £523,770
TRUSTEES Joel Schreiber; Helen Schreiber; Rivka Schreiber; J. Schreiber; Y. Schreiber; S. Reisner; C. Hamburger; R. Benedikt.
HOW TO APPLY In writing to the correspondent.
WHO TO APPLY TO Helen Schreiber, Trustee, 20 Ashtead Road, London E5 9BH *Tel.* 020 7242 3580

■ The Ellerdale Trust

CC NO 1073376　　**ESTABLISHED** 1998
WHERE FUNDING CAN BE GIVEN Norfolk.
WHO CAN BENEFIT Local charitable organisations and some national charities which work with Norfolk children.
SAMPLE GRANTS The Atrium Project (£35,000); Action for Kids (£30,000); Rainbow Centre (£20,000); The Nancy Oldfield Trust (£16,000); Mind (£15,000); Break and Autism Anglia (£10,000 each); British Blind Sport (£8,000); Africa Equipment for Schools and BLISS (£6,000 each); Inspire and Musical Keys (£5,000 each); Nelson's Journey and NORCAS (£4,000 each); Home Start Norwich (£3,000); Norwich MIND (£2,000); and Whatever the Need (£1,500).
FINANCES *Year* 2011–12 *Income* £1,414,114 *Grants* £291,000 *Assets* £4,334,564
TRUSTEES Alistair Macfarlane; P. C. Kurthausen; S. P. Moores.
HOW TO APPLY In writing to the correspondent.
WHO TO APPLY TO Mary Adlard, Director of Grantmaking, The Parlour, The High Street, Ketteringham, Wymondham, Norfolk NR18 9RU *Tel.* 01603 813340 *email* mary.adlard@ btconnect.com

■ The John Ellerman Foundation

CC NO 263207　　**ESTABLISHED** 1971
WHERE FUNDING CAN BE GIVEN Mainly UK; East and Southern Africa.
WHO CAN BENEFIT UK registered charities which operate nationally or across England; local/ regional charities should not apply.
WHAT IS FUNDED Welfare, environment and the arts.
WHAT IS NOT FUNDED 'Grants are not made for the following purposes: for or on behalf of individuals; individual hospitals and hospices; local branches of national organisations; mainstream education/establishments; purchase of vehicles; direct replacement of public funding, or deficit funding; drug or alcohol abuse; charities with an annual income less than £100,000; religious causes; friends of groups; medical research; conferences and

seminars; sports and leisure facilities; domestic animal welfare; prisons and offenders; military museums at regimental/arm/corps level. The foundation will only consider applications from registered and exempt charities with a UK office. Most of our grants are for one and two years, but we will give grants for three years if a very strong case is made. Our minimum grant is £10,000. We aim to develop relationships with funded charities. We will only support charities that work – or have reach and impact – across England/UK. Those operating within a single locality, city, borough, county or region will not be considered. We believe other trusts and funders are better placed to help individuals and local or regional charities. For this reason also, applications operating exclusively in Wales, Scotland or Northern Ireland will NOT be considered.'

TYPE OF GRANT One-off and multi-year. Core costs, project, running costs, salaries, and start-up costs. Funding may be given for up to three years.

RANGE OF GRANTS £10,000–£40,000.

SAMPLE GRANTS British Liver Trust (£35,000) – towards core costs; Counsel and Care (£35,000) – towards the merger with Independent Age and to sustain the Advice Service; Freedom From Torture (£32,000) – towards the work of one of the Adult Therapy and Assessment team members who helps survivors of torture; British Film Institute (£30,000) – towards the salary of a conservation specialist; FoodCycle (£30,000) – towards the Hubs Programme, combining volunteers, surplus food and under-utilised kitchen space to create nutritious meals; Friends of the Earth Trust (£30,000) – towards the Get Serious About CO2 project; Leap Confronting Conflict (£30,000) – towards the 'Improving Prospects' project which aims to work with 150 NEET and vulnerable young people; KIDS (£28,000) – towards KIDS Direct Short Breaks service, for disabled children and their families; Derwent Initiative (£20,000) – towards core costs, helping to reduce the risk and incidence of sexual offending; Mid Wales Opera (£20,000) – towards core costs; Spike Island (£20,000) – towards core costs, in particular to support marketing and audience development; AfriKids (£16,000) – towards capacity building of AfriKids Ghana and local partners to prevent north-south migration in Ghana, including direct resettlement and rehabilitation of displaced children and Pallant House Gallery (£10,000) – towards core costs enabling the continuation of the Gallery's exhibitions and community programmes.

FINANCES *Year* 2011–12 *Income* £1,573,000 *Grants* £4,456,000 *Assets* £115,638,000

TRUSTEES Sarah Riddell, chair; Dominic Caldecott; Tim Glass; Brian Hurwitz; Hugh Raven; Diana Whitworth; Vivien Gould.

HOW TO APPLY Information taken from the foundation's website: 'If you are unsuccessful, we will ask you to wait for one year before you reapply. It is therefore important to make the best case you can at the first stage. The foundation encourages informal phone calls to discuss projects and eligibility before applications are submitted. Only one application per organisation can be considered at any one time. **Stage 1** – Your first-stage application should include: 1. A description of what you are seeking funding for, on no more than two sides of A4. Include: a brief summary of your organisation and relevant track record; where your work takes place, as we only support work with a national footprint; what you would like us to fund and why you are well placed to do this work and how your proposal fits our guidelines for this category. 2. A copy of your most recent annual accounts. If your accounts show a significant surplus or deficit, high or low reserves, explain this briefly. If the year-end date of your accounts is more than ten months old, include your latest management accounts. First stage applications can be submitted by post or email. Applications can be submitted at any time, unless you are applying for the museums and galleries fund. Applications are acknowledged and decisions made within ten weeks. **Stage 2** – If we invite you to the second stage, we will ask for a more detailed application. Then we will arrange to meet you to find out more about your work. At this second stage we aim to make a decision within three months. If your application takes longer we will be in touch.'

WHO TO APPLY TO Barbra Mazur, Head of Grants, Aria House, 23 Craven Street, London WC2N 5NS *Tel.* 020 7930 8566 *Fax* 020 7839 3654 *email* enquiries@ellerman.org.uk *Website* www.ellerman.org.uk

■ The Ellinson Foundation Ltd

CC NO 252018   **ESTABLISHED** 1967

WHERE FUNDING CAN BE GIVEN Worldwide.

WHO CAN BENEFIT Jewish organisations, especially boarding schools teaching the Torah. The trust usually supports the same organisations each year.

WHAT IS FUNDED Hospitals, education and homelessness, usually with a Jewish teaching aspect.

WHAT IS NOT FUNDED No grants to individuals.

TYPE OF GRANT Capital and recurring grants.

RANGE OF GRANTS Usually up to £35,000.

SAMPLE GRANTS Kesser Yeshua Refua – Israel (£150,000); Friends of Yeshivas Brisk (£35,000); Three Pillars (£20,000); Mifaley Tzedoka Vochesed (£13,000); Yad Eliezer (Jerusalem) (£12,000); Kollel Ohel Torah (Jerusalem) (£9,000); Tomchei Yotzei Anglia (£5,000); British Friends of Rinat Aharon (£4,000); Vaani Sfolosi Kitat Tzanz (£3,000); The Bridge Lane Beth Hamedrash (£2,000); Kollel America (£1,500) and Darcey Miriam (Jerusalem) (£1,000).

FINANCES *Year* 2011–12 *Income* £309,716 *Grants* £267,000 *Assets* £3,466,397

TRUSTEES A. Ellinson; A. Z. Ellinson; U. Ellinson.

OTHER INFORMATION Grants of less than £1,000 totalled £6,200.

HOW TO APPLY In writing to the correspondent. However, the trust generally supports the same organisations each year and unsolicited applications are not welcome.

WHO TO APPLY TO The Trustees, c/o Robson Laidler and Co, Fernwood House, Fernwood Road, Jesmond, Newcastle upon Tyne NE2 1TJ *Tel.* 01912 818191

■ The Edith Maud Ellis 1985 Charitable Trust

CC NO 292835   **ESTABLISHED** 1985

WHERE FUNDING CAN BE GIVEN UK and overseas.

WHO CAN BENEFIT UK registered charities or non-governmental organisations.

WHAT IS FUNDED Grants are made to organisations that fall within following categories: UK registered charities, NGOs and social enterprises with a turnover of less than £250,000; those who can demonstrate other sources of funding for their project; and innovative charities/projects not normally able to attract regular funding.

WHAT IS NOT FUNDED In general the trust does not support the following: core funding for organisations; individuals; infrastructure organisations; conferences or seminars; ongoing work; general appeals; educational bursaries; humanitarian relief appeals; and medical research and services.

TYPE OF GRANT Grants tend to be either: one-off; time limited in support; or; are given in the form of seed money for start-up projects. Usually small grants of up to £3,000 (in exceptional circumstances larger grants may be given) or interest free loans of up to £5,000 repayable over five years.

RANGE OF GRANTS Up to £10,000.

SAMPLE GRANTS Barmoor 1982 Trust Appeal and Quaker Council for European Affairs (£3,000 each); Association of Visitors to Immigration Detainees and Glenthorne Bursary Fund (£2,000 each); UNHCR (£1,500); Off the Fence, Jubilee Debt Campaign and Pathway Project (£1,000 each); Build Africa and Afrinspire (£750 each); and Fairtrade Foundation (£500).

FINANCES *Year* 2011–12 *Income* £410,268 *Grants* £49,800 *Assets* £227,274

TRUSTEES Michael Phipps; Jane Dawson; Elizabeth Cave; Nicholas Sims.

HOW TO APPLY According to the trust's website, 'applications should be received by the end of January, May and September, in order to be considered at one of the trustee meetings. It is sensible to get applications in well ahead of these dates. Late applicants will be considered in the next funding round. Successful applicants will be informed as soon as possible of the trustees' decisions. If you have not heard within one calendar month of the relevant closing date you should assume you have been unsuccessful. Successful applicants will be encouraged to contribute to our website in a variety of ways and may be approached to showcase the work of the trust.'

WHO TO APPLY TO Jacqueline Baily, Administrator, Virtuosity Executive Support, 6 Westgate, Thirsk, North Yorkshire YO7 1QS *Tel.* 01845 574882 *email* jackie@virtuosity-uk.com *Website* www.theedithmellischaritabletrust.org

■ The Ellis Campbell Foundation

CC NO 802717   **ESTABLISHED** 1989

WHERE FUNDING CAN BE GIVEN London, Hampshire and Perthshire.

WHO CAN BENEFIT Organisations benefiting young disadvantaged people. Maintenance and preservation of buildings is also considered.

WHAT IS FUNDED Education of disadvantaged people under 25; preservation/protection/improvement of items of architectural/structural/horticultural/mechanical heritage; encouragement of community based projects.

WHAT IS NOT FUNDED No grants to individuals. Other than the grants made annually over a period, no grants will be made more regularly than every other year. No funding for annual running costs.

TYPE OF GRANT Usually one-off funding, though grants may be given for over three to five years.

RANGE OF GRANTS Average grants of £2,000

SAMPLE GRANTS Grants have been given previously to: Anvil Trust; Scottish Community Foundation; Prince's Trust; Bhutan Society; Meridian Trust

Association; Hampshire Scouting; Hampshire Country Learning; Martin Sailing Project; Ro-Ro Sailing Project; and Wheatsheaf Trust.

FINANCES *Year* 2012 *Income* £44,990 *Grants* £108,416 *Assets* £1,842,958

TRUSTEES Michael Campbell, Chair; Linda Campbell; Jamie Campbell; Alexandra Andrews; Laura Montgomery.

OTHER INFORMATION In 2012 the foundation made 54 grants. The average donation was for £2,008.

HOW TO APPLY In writing to the correspondent. Trustees meet in April and November. Applications should be submitted before the preceding month and will only be acknowledged if they fall strictly within the trust's eligibility guidelines.

WHO TO APPLY TO Laura Montgomery, Trustee, c/o The Ellis Campbell Group, 10–12 Blandford Street, London W1U 4AZ *email* office@elliscampbell.co.uk

■ James Ellis Charitable Trust

CC NO 1055617   **ESTABLISHED** 1996

WHERE FUNDING CAN BE GIVEN UK.

WHO CAN BENEFIT Registered medical research charities and organisations involved with health issues.

WHAT IS FUNDED The trust gives in the areas of medical research and the relief of serious illness.

TYPE OF GRANT One-off.

RANGE OF GRANTS £500–£5,000.

SAMPLE GRANTS Alzheimer's Research Trust, Down's Syndrome Research Association, Deafness Research UK, Arthritis Research Campaign, Association for Spina Bifida and Hydrocephalus, British Lung Foundation, Children's Liver Disease Foundation, Motor Neurone Disease Association and the Brain Research Trust.

FINANCES *Year* 2011–12 *Income* £19,433 *Grants* £25,000

TRUSTEES Stephen Ellis; John Sheard; Eric Lord.

HOW TO APPLY In writing to the correspondent between November and January, for consideration in February.

WHO TO APPLY TO Stephen Ellis, Trustee, Barn Cottage, Botany Lane, Lepton, Huddersfield HD8 0NE *Tel.* 01484 602066

■ The Elm House Trust

CC NO 1109073   **ESTABLISHED** 2005

WHERE FUNDING CAN BE GIVEN North Yorkshire and the north east of England.

WHO CAN BENEFIT Organisations and educational establishments in Durham and N E Yorkshire

WHAT IS FUNDED Education and general charitable purposes

SAMPLE GRANTS Soundbyte (£5,000) and Ripon Vacation Chamber Orchestra and North Country Theatre (£1,000 each).

FINANCES *Year* 2012 *Income* £30,118 *Grants* £13,563 *Assets* £1,454,354

TRUSTEES Jane Ritchie; John Ritchie; Richard Whiteley.

OTHER INFORMATION The charity's current priority is the maintenance of a vocational learning centre in Durham. The grant total was considerably down on previous years.

HOW TO APPLY In writing to the correspondent.

WHO TO APPLY TO Richard Whiteley, Trustee, 2 Greengate, Cardale Park, Harrogate HG3 1GY *Tel.* 01423 534100

■ The Elmgrant Trust

CC NO 313398   **ESTABLISHED** 1936

WHERE FUNDING CAN BE GIVEN South West of England (Cornwall, Devon, Somerset, Dorset, Wiltshire and Gloucestershire).

WHO CAN BENEFIT Individuals and organisations.

WHAT IS FUNDED Encouragement of local life through education, the arts and the social sciences.

WHAT IS NOT FUNDED The following are not supported: large scale UK organisations; postgraduate study, overseas student grants, expeditions and travel and study projects overseas; counselling courses; renewed requests from the same (successful) applicant within a two-year period.

TYPE OF GRANT Primarily one-off, occasionally recurring (but not within a two-year period); core funding; no loans.

RANGE OF GRANTS £50–£5,000 (very occasionally over this). Typically £150 to £1,500.

SAMPLE GRANTS Previously: Dartington International Summer School; Kinergy; Prison Phoenix Trust; Centre for the Spoken Word; Dawlish Gardens Trust; the Towersey Foundation; and the Daisy Garland and Guild of St Lawrence.

FINANCES *Year* 2011–12 *Income* £59,944 *Grants* £57,563 *Assets* £1,905,218

TRUSTEES Marian Ash; Sophie Young; Paul Elmhirst; Mark Sharman; David Young.

OTHER INFORMATION In 2011–12 there were 11 grants to individuals totalling £4,800.

HOW TO APPLY In writing to the correspondent, giving full financial details and dates, and where possible, a letter of support or acceptance onto a course. Applications from organisations should include the previous year's accounts. Initial telephone calls are welcome if advice is needed.
Trustee meeting are three times a year on the last Saturday in February, June and October and the deadlines are one month before the meetings. All applications are acknowledged and applicants will be informed if they are shortlisted for presentation at the trustee meeting.

WHO TO APPLY TO Amanda Horning, Secretary, The Elmhirst Centre, Dartington Hall, Totnes, Devon TQ9 6EL *Tel.* 01803 863160 *email* info@elmgrant.org.uk *Website* www.elmgrant.org.uk

■ The Elmley Foundation

CC NO 1004043   **ESTABLISHED** 1991

WHERE FUNDING CAN BE GIVEN Herefordshire and Worcestershire.

WHO CAN BENEFIT Individuals and organisations benefiting: actors and entertainment professionals; musicians; writers and poets; and textile workers and designers; students of the arts.

WHAT IS FUNDED Arts activity.

WHAT IS NOT FUNDED No grants for endowments, loans or general appeals.

TYPE OF GRANT Capital, core costs, contracts and full project funding. Funding of up to, and over, three years will be considered.

RANGE OF GRANTS £500–£30,000.

SAMPLE GRANTS The Three Choirs Festival (£26,000); Meadow Arts (£25,000); Penyard Singers, Ross-on-Wye (£18,000); The Courtyard Centre for the Arts, Hereford (£14,000); Worcester Live Limited (£12,000); Rural Media Company, Festivals of Literature Charitable Trust Ltd and Ledbury Poetry Festival (£10,000 each); Presteigne Festival (£8,000); Bromsgrove Concerts (£5,500); DanceFest (£2,000); Arts Alive (£1,000) and Redditch Music Society (£500).

FINANCES *Year* 2011–12 *Income* £291,149 *Grants* £211,366 *Assets* £3,796,243

TRUSTEES Deborah Swallow; Diana Johnson; Sam White.

OTHER INFORMATION The grants total includes £21,000 given to nine individuals.

HOW TO APPLY Application forms, criteria and guidelines, for both the Small Grants Scheme and the Main Grants Scheme, are available to download on the website. Applicants for the Main Grants Scheme are strongly advised to contact the foundation before making a formal application. Applicants for the Small Grants Scheme should contact Cheryl Cooney at Community First on 01684 312739, or email cherylc@comfirst.org.uk

WHO TO APPLY TO Samuel Driver White, Secretary, West Aish, Morchard Bishop, Crediton, Devon EX17 6RX *Tel.* 01363 877433 *email* foundation@elmley.org.uk *Website* www.elmley.org.uk

■ Elshore Ltd

CC NO 287469   **ESTABLISHED** 1983

WHERE FUNDING CAN BE GIVEN Worldwide.

WHO CAN BENEFIT Jewish organisations.

WHAT IS FUNDED Advancement of religion and relief of poverty.

SAMPLE GRANTS Previous beneficiaries included: Eminor Educational Centre (£26,000); Cosmon Belz (£20,000); Gur Trust and Marbe Torah Trust (£10,000 each).

FINANCES *Year* 2011–12 *Income* £100,181 *Grants* £131,299 *Assets* £78,076

TRUSTEES Hersz M. Lerner; Susan Yanofsky; Ahuva Ann Lerner.

HOW TO APPLY In writing to the correspondent.

WHO TO APPLY TO Hersz M. Lerner, Trustee, c/o Michael Pasha and Co., 220 The Vale, Golders Green, London NW11 8SR *Tel.* 020 8209 9880

■ The Vernon N. Ely Charitable Trust

CC NO 230033   **ESTABLISHED** 1962

WHERE FUNDING CAN BE GIVEN Worldwide, with a preference for London borough of Merton.

WHO CAN BENEFIT Charitable organisations.

WHAT IS FUNDED General charitable purposes, with a preference to the London borough of Merton and sports charities.

WHAT IS NOT FUNDED No grants to individuals.

RANGE OF GRANTS Around £4,000.

SAMPLE GRANTS Previous beneficiaries included: Age Concern, Cardiac Risk in the Young, Samaritans, London Sports Forum for Disabled People, Christchurch URC, Polka Children's Theatre and Community Housing Therapy (£4,000 each); British Tennis Foundation (£1,750); and West Barnes Singers and Sobell Hospice (£500 each).

FINANCES *Year* 2011–12 *Income* £63,521 *Grants* £73,750 *Assets* £1,652,704

TRUSTEES Derek Howorth; John Moyle; Richard Main.

HOW TO APPLY In writing to the correspondent.

WHO TO APPLY TO Derek Howorth, Trustee, Grosvenor Gardens House, 35–37 Grosvenor Gardens, London SW1W 0BY *Tel.* 020 7828 3156 *email* dph@helmores.co.uk

■ The Embleton Trust

CC NO 285274 **ESTABLISHED** 1982
WHERE FUNDING CAN BE GIVEN UK and abroad.
WHO CAN BENEFIT Organisations.
WHAT IS FUNDED Nearly all of the funds are committed to long-term projects relating to legal education and free legal advice centres.
TYPE OF GRANT One off and recurrent.
RANGE OF GRANTS £100–£10,000.
SAMPLE GRANTS British institute of International and Comparative Law (£10,000); The Social Mobility Foundation (£5,000); BLESMA (£3,653); British and Irish Legal Information institute and St Christopher's Hospice (£1,000 each); Breast Cancer Campaign (£750); Frank Water Projects (£500); Army Benevolent Fund (£188).
FINANCES *Year* 2011–12 *Income* £59,776 *Grants* £26,671 *Assets* £40,057
TRUSTEES Simon Martin; Charles Martin, Julian Howard.
OTHER INFORMATION The trust is associated with and funded by partners in Macfarlanes, a firm of solicitors.
The majority of the trust's income came from Gift Aid donations.
HOW TO APPLY Unsolicited applications are not accepted.
WHO TO APPLY TO Simon Martin, Macfarlanes Solicitors, 20 Cursitor Street, London EC4A 1LT *Tel.* 020 7831 9607

■ Embrace the Middle East (formerly Bible Lands)

CC NO 1076329 **ESTABLISHED** 1854
WHERE FUNDING CAN BE GIVEN Lands of the Bible, especially Lebanon, the Holy Land and Egypt.
WHO CAN BENEFIT Local organisations working in the beneficial area that benefits people of all ages, faiths and nationalities in the region especially those who are marginalised or vulnerable. Support is given to areas including education, special needs, vocational training, care and support of refugees, medical, social care.
WHAT IS FUNDED Embrace the Middle East (formerly Bible Lands) exists to support and encourage local Christians in the lands of the Bible, who are dedicated to fulfiling the compassionate ministry of Christ.
WHAT IS NOT FUNDED Individuals and UK bodies are not eligible. Grants are confined to Christian-led work, but beneficiaries are helped regardless of faith or nationality.
TYPE OF GRANT Capital including buildings, recurring, core costs, one-off, running costs and start-up costs. Funding is for up to or more than three years. Child sponsorship schemes and ongoing grants to specific projects are also in place.
RANGE OF GRANTS £1,000–£200,000
SAMPLE GRANTS Al-Kafaart Foundation (£244,000); Coptic Evangelical Organisation for Social Services and Habitat for Humanity, Egypt (£50,000 each); Salaam Centre for Medico Social Services (£30,000); Cedar Home Orphanage (£16,000); Armenian Evangelical School, Beirut (£11,000); Learning Centre for the Deaf (£3,000) and Armenian Evangelical College (£1,300).
FINANCES *Year* 2012 *Income* £4,216,922 *Grants* £1,554,000 *Assets* £5,232,000
TRUSTEES Joanna Robertson; Revd Andrew Ashdown; Douglas Callander; Judy Hackney; Vicky Smith; Revd Brian Jolly; Hugh Bradley; Dr Brian McGucken; Lisa Toner; Tanas Alqassis; Revd Anthony Ball; Miriam Tadras.

PUBLICATIONS *The Star in the East*, quarterly magazine.
HOW TO APPLY Apply in writing for an application form, giving brief outline of the support being sought.
WHO TO APPLY TO Jeremy Moodey, 24 London Road West, Amersham, Buckinghamshire HP7 0EZ *Tel.* 01494 897950 *Fax* 01494 897951 *email* info@embraceme.org *Website* www.embraceme.org

■ The Emerton-Christie Charity

CC NO 262837 **ESTABLISHED** 1971
WHERE FUNDING CAN BE GIVEN UK.
WHO CAN BENEFIT Registered charities only.
WHAT IS FUNDED General charitable purposes. Preference is given to assist older and younger people, particularly those with disabilities or who are disadvantaged. Arts and health charities are also supported.
WHAT IS NOT FUNDED Generally no grants to individuals; religious organisations; restoration or extension of buildings; start-up costs; animal welfare and research; cultural heritage; or environmental projects.
TYPE OF GRANT Donations for capital projects and/or income requirements.
RANGE OF GRANTS Usually up to £5,000.
SAMPLE GRANTS Trinity Laban Conservatoire of Music and Dance (£4,600); Action Medical Research, Centre for Sustainable Health, Disability North, Médecins Sans Frontières, Music in Detention, The Calvert Trust, The Life Centre and Trinity Hospice (£3,000 each); Papworth Trust (£2,400); Whizz-Kidz (£1,000) and BBACT (£500).
FINANCES *Year* 2011–12 *Income* £69,857 *Grants* £56,490 *Assets* £2,350,622
TRUSTEES Norman Walker; William Niekirk; Claire Mera-Nelson; Sally Walker.
HOW TO APPLY In writing to the correspondent. A demonstration of need based on budgetary principles is required and applications will not be acknowledged unless accompanied by an sae. Trustees normally meet once a year in the autumn to select charities to benefit.
WHO TO APPLY TO The Trustees, c/o Cartmell Shepherd, Viaduct House, Victoria Viaduct, Carlisle CA3 8EZ *Tel.* 01228 516666 *email* joanna.jeeves@cartmells.co.uk

■ EMI Music Sound Foundation

CC NO 1104027 **ESTABLISHED** 1996
WHERE FUNDING CAN BE GIVEN UK and Ireland.
WHO CAN BENEFIT Individuals and organisations benefiting: children and young adults; musicians; music students; and music teachers.
WHAT IS FUNDED Non-specialist schools to fund music education; music students in full time education to fund instrument purchase; music teachers to fund courses and training. Every year EMI Music Sound Foundation awards bursaries to students at seven music colleges in the UK and Ireland. These bursaries are distributed at each college's discretion, based on criteria provided by the foundation.
WHAT IS NOT FUNDED The foundation does not support: applications from applicants based outside the United Kingdom and Ireland; non-school based community groups; applications for tuition fees and living expenses other than as described under the bursary awards section on the foundation's website; applications over £2,000; independent music teachers; payment

Think carefully about every application. Is it justified?

525

of staffing costs to cover the teaching of the national curriculum or peripatetic teaching costs; and retrospective grants.

RANGE OF GRANTS Maximum award £2,500 (for schools, individuals and music teachers).

SAMPLE GRANTS Royal Welsh College of Music and Drama (£10,000); and Royal Conservatoire of Scotland, National Children's Orchestra and Brighton Institute of Modern Music (£5,000 each).

FINANCES *Year* 2011–12 *Income* £298,391 *Grants* £500,931 *Assets* £7,172,408

TRUSTEES David Hughes; Charles Ashcroft; Jim Beach; John Deacon; Paul Gambaccini; Jo Hibbit; Leslie Hill; Max Hole; Richard Lyttleton; Rupert Perry; Tony Wadsworth; Christine Walter.

OTHER INFORMATION During the year £167,000 was awarded to individuals and £334,000 to organisations.

HOW TO APPLY On a form which can be downloaded from the foundation's website. Guidance notes are also available regarding applications.

WHO TO APPLY TO Janie Orr, Chief Executive, Beaumont House, Avonmore Road, Kensington Village, London W14 8TS *Tel.* 020 7550 7898 *Fax* 020 7550 7809 *email* enquiries@musicsoundfoundation.com *Website* www.emimusicsoundfoundation.com

■ The Emilienne Charitable Trust

CC NO 327849   **ESTABLISHED** 1988

WHERE FUNDING CAN BE GIVEN Hampshire.

WHO CAN BENEFIT Charitable organisations.

WHAT IS FUNDED The trustees are particularly interested in support for charities involved in the treatment of addiction and in promoting education.

SAMPLE GRANTS Streetscene (£7,300); SCRATCH (£5,000); Wessex Medical Trust (£2,000); and Myositis Support Group (£1,500).

FINANCES *Year* 2011–12 *Income* £30,531 *Grants* £46,990 *Assets* £575,121

TRUSTEES Michael Howson-Green; B. M. Baxendale; M. A. Howson-Green; David Hoare.

OTHER INFORMATION During the year a further 50 grants of less than £1,000 were made totalling £31,000.

HOW TO APPLY In writing to the correspondent.

WHO TO APPLY TO Michael Howson-Green, Trustee, Ashton House, 12 The Central Precinct, Chandler's Ford, Eastleigh, Hampshire SC53 2GB *Tel.* 02380 274555

■ The Endure Foundation

CC NO 1149455   **ESTABLISHED** 2012

WHERE FUNDING CAN BE GIVEN UK and overseas.

WHO CAN BENEFIT Registered charities and community groups.

WHAT IS FUNDED General charitable purposes. 'The Endure Foundation is [. . .] a member of the Institute of Fundraising. The purpose of the foundation is to award grants to projects both in the UK and in developing countries, supporting all charities large and small across a variety of different causes.'

TRUSTEES Gareth Sym; Nicola Plant; Phillip Hayday Brown; Conrad Dickinson.

HOW TO APPLY In writing to the correspondent.

WHO TO APPLY TO Nicola Plant, Trustee, Pemberton Greenish Solicitors, 45 Cadogan Gardens, London SW3 2AQ *Tel.* 020 7591 3314 *email* n.plant@pglaw.co.uk

■ The Worshipful Company of Engineers Charitable Trust Fund

CC NO 289819   **ESTABLISHED** 1984

WHERE FUNDING CAN BE GIVEN UK.

WHO CAN BENEFIT Individuals and registered charities.

WHAT IS FUNDED The trust's main aim is to support professional engineers who are in need and in the final stages of their educational qualification. Grants are also made to organisations, especially those with an engineering bias for educational purposes.

RANGE OF GRANTS £250–£5,000.

SAMPLE GRANTS Ironbridge Gorge Museum Trust (£1,000); Imperial College London (£500); Tools for Self Reliance and Queen Elizabeth's Foundation for Disabled People (£250 each); and The Royal British Legion Poppy Appeal (£125).

FINANCES *Year* 2012 *Income* £521,102 *Grants* £27,830 *Assets* £1,167,057

TRUSTEES John Robinson; Christopher Price; Air Vice Marshall Graham Skinner; Revd Peter Hartley; Prof. David Johnson; Malcolm Vincent; David Scahill.

HOW TO APPLY In writing to the correspondent.

WHO TO APPLY TO Wing Commander Anthony Willenbruch, Clerk, Wax Chandlers Hall, 6 Gresham Street, London EC2V 7AD *Tel.* 020 7726 4830 *Fax* 020 7726 4820 *email* clerk@engineerscompany.org.uk *Website* www.engineerscompany.org.uk

■ The Englefield Charitable Trust

CC NO 258123   **ESTABLISHED** 1968

WHERE FUNDING CAN BE GIVEN Worldwide. In practice, UK with a special interest in Berkshire.

WHO CAN BENEFIT Mainly registered charities; some local schools and churches are supported.

WHAT IS FUNDED General charitable purposes but particularly charities working in the fields of: infrastructure development; religion; residential facilities and services; arts, culture and recreation; health; conservation; education and training; and various community facilities and services.

WHAT IS NOT FUNDED Individual applications for study or travel are not considered.

TYPE OF GRANT Buildings, capital, interest-free loans, research, running costs, salaries and start-up costs. Funding for one year or less will be considered.

RANGE OF GRANTS Mainly £5,000 or less.

SAMPLE GRANTS Ufton Court Educational Trust (£100,000); Englefield Parochial Church Council (£36,500); Thames Valley Chiltern Air Ambulance (£5,500); Trooper Potts VC Memorial Trust and Watermill Theatre (£5,000 each); Thrive and Corn Exchange Newbury (£3,000 each); 14–21 Time to Talk, Children's Trust and Church Housing Trust (£2,000 each); Christians Against Poverty, Andover MIND and British Horseracing Education (£1,000 each); Aldermaston Parish Hall (£500); and Volunteer Centre West Berks (£350).

FINANCES *Year* 2011–12 *Income* £448,278 *Grants* £358,414 *Assets* £13,605,313

TRUSTEES Catherine Haig; James Shelley; Lady Elizabeth Benyon; Richard Benyon; Sir William Benyon; Zoe Benyon; Melissa Owston; Richard Bampfylde.

OTHER INFORMATION 700 applications were made for the year. 122 donations were made, varying in size from £200 to £100,000.

HOW TO APPLY In writing to the correspondent enclosing the latest accounts, stating the charity's registered number and the purpose for which the money is to be used. Applications are considered in March and September. Only applications going before the trustees will be acknowledged.

WHO TO APPLY TO Alexander Reid, Secretary, The Quantocks, North Street, Theale, Reading RG7 5EX *Tel.* 01189 323582 *email* charity@ englefield.co.uk

....

■ The English Schools' Football Association

CC NO 306003   **ESTABLISHED** 1904
WHERE FUNDING CAN BE GIVEN England.
WHO CAN BENEFIT Members of the association, and organisations benefiting children and young adults, sportspersons and teachers.
WHAT IS FUNDED Mental, moral and physical development of schoolchildren through association football. Assistance to teacher charities.
WHAT IS NOT FUNDED Grants are restricted to membership and teacher charities.
FINANCES *Year* 2012 *Income* £1,004,350 *Grants* £853,199 *Assets* £1,394,926
TRUSTEES Philip Harding; Nigel Brown; Michael Coyne.
HOW TO APPLY In writing to the correspondent.
WHO TO APPLY TO John Read, Chief Executive, 4 Parker Court, Staffordshire Technology Park, Stafford ST18 0WP *Tel.* 01785 785970 *email* office@efsa.co.uk *Website* www.esfa.co. uk

....

■ The Enkalon Foundation

IR NO XN62210   **ESTABLISHED** 1985
WHERE FUNDING CAN BE GIVEN Northern Ireland.
WHO CAN BENEFIT Grants made only to organisations for projects inside Northern Ireland.
WHAT IS FUNDED Improving the quality of life in Northern Ireland. Funding is given to cross-community groups, self-help, assistance to unemployed people and groups helping people who are disadvantaged.
WHAT IS NOT FUNDED No grants to individuals unless ex-employees. No grants are given outside Northern Ireland or for travel outside Northern Ireland. Normally grants are not made to playgroups or sporting groups outside the Antrim borough area or for medical research.
TYPE OF GRANT Mainly for starter finance, single projects or capital projects.
RANGE OF GRANTS Up to £6,000 maximum but usually between £500 and £1,000.
SAMPLE GRANTS Beneficiaries include: Antrim Borough Council – Old Courthouse Auditorium Seating (£88,000); Lyric Theatre – Belfast (£15,000); Macmillan Cancer Support – Antrim Area Hospital Palliative Care Unit Project (£10,000); Elisabeth Svendsen Trust for Children and Donkeys (£5,000); Antrim Citizens Advice (£4,000); Ulster Association of Youth Drama and Newlife Foundation for Disabled Children in NI (£2,000 each); Disability Action (NI) (£1,500); Art Ability (NI) Ltd (£1,000); Family Holiday Association – NI Project and Race Against Multiple Sclerosis – NI Ltd (£500 each) and The Crafts Class St Swithin's Church – Magherafelt (£200).
FINANCES *Year* 2010–11 *Grants* £280,000

TRUSTEES Raymond Milnes; Peter Dalton; Mark Patterson; Stephen Montgomery; John Wallace.
OTHER INFORMATION The grant total was shared between 305 beneficiaries.
HOW TO APPLY In writing to the correspondent. There are no closing dates or application forms. Guidance notes are available from the foundation's website. Applications, by letter, should provide the following information: description of the organisation and a copy of the constitution and rules; proposed budget and details of the project; audited accounts (if available) or statement of accounts for the most recent; completed financial year and a copy of the latest annual report; details of charitable status; other sources of finance for the organisation at present and for the proposed project; experience and/or qualifications of staff and committee members; a list of officers and committee members; contact address and telephone number. Trustees meet four times a year and applicants will be advised as soon as practical after a meeting has taken place. All applicants, successful or unsuccessful, will be advised of the trustees' decision. Applications will not be acknowledged unless accompanied by an sae.
WHO TO APPLY TO Claire Cawley, Administrator, 25 Randalstown Road, Antrim, Northern Ireland BT41 4LJ *Tel.* 02894 463535 *Fax* 02894 465733 *email* info@enkalonfoundation.org *Website* www.enkalonfoundation.org

....

■ Entindale Ltd

CC NO 277052   **ESTABLISHED** 1978
WHERE FUNDING CAN BE GIVEN Unrestricted.
WHO CAN BENEFIT Organisations benefiting Orthodox Jews.
WHAT IS FUNDED Orthodox Jewish charitable organisations.
TYPE OF GRANT Capital.
RANGE OF GRANTS Up to £100,000; typically less than £10,000.
SAMPLE GRANTS Yesamach Levav Trust (£80,000); Rachel Charitable Trust (£50,000); Doughty Charitable Trust (£37,000); Chevrat Maoz LaDol (£34,000); Beis Yaacov Primary School Foundation (£25,000); British Friends of Nadvorne (£15,000); Baer Avrohom UK Trust (£10,000); Project Seed (£8,000); Tora Ernes Primary School (£6,000); British Friends of Igud Hakolelim B'Yerushalayim (£5,000); William and Iboja Carrant Charitable Trust (£4,000); Whitefield Community Kollel (£2,500); and Golders Charitable Trust (£1,000).
FINANCES *Year* 2011–12 *Income* £1,647,792 *Grants* £1,503,497 *Assets* £14,059,138
TRUSTEES Allan Becker; Barbara Bridgeman; Dov Harris; Jonathan Hager.
HOW TO APPLY In writing to the correspondent.
WHO TO APPLY TO Barbara Bridgeman, Secretary, 8 Highfield Gardens, London NW11 9HB *Tel.* 020 8458 9266 *Fax* 020 8458 8529

....

■ The Epigoni Trust

CC NO 328700   **ESTABLISHED** 1990
WHERE FUNDING CAN BE GIVEN UK.
WHO CAN BENEFIT Registered UK charities.
WHAT IS FUNDED General charitable purposes.
WHAT IS NOT FUNDED No grants to individuals.
TYPE OF GRANT Project and one-off. Funding for one year or less.
RANGE OF GRANTS £3,000–£17,000

SAMPLE GRANTS Pallant House Gallery (£20,000); Chichester Festival Theatre and Mondo Challenge Foundation (£10,000 each); and St Richard of Chichester Christian Care Association (£5,000).

FINANCES *Year* 2012 *Income* £31,928 *Grants* £60,000 *Assets* £3,167,336

TRUSTEES Bettine Bond; Charles Peacock; Andrew Bond.

HOW TO APPLY This trust no longer accepts applications.

WHO TO APPLY TO Charles Peacock, Trustee, c/o Charities Aid Foundation, 25 Kings Hill Avenue, Kings Hill, West Malling ME19 4TA *Tel.* 01732 520028

■ Epilepsy Research UK

CC NO 1100394 **ESTABLISHED** 1985

WHERE FUNDING CAN BE GIVEN UK.

WHO CAN BENEFIT Researchers conducting studies that will benefit people with epilepsy.

WHAT IS FUNDED 'Epilepsy Research UK annually invites applications for grants to support basic, clinical and scientific research work in the UK into the causes, treatment and prevention of epilepsy. We encourage applications on all aspects of epilepsy including basic and social science, clinical management and holistic management of patients.'

TYPE OF GRANT Projects, fellowship, research and equipment. Funding is for up to three years.

RANGE OF GRANTS Up to £150,000.

FINANCES *Year* 2012–13 *Income* £1,141,339 *Grants* £687,346 *Assets* £736,295

TRUSTEES Barrie Akin; Prof. Helen Cross; Rt Hon David Cameron; John Hirst; Prof. Mark Rees; Dr Lina Nashef; Prof. Brian Neville; Dr Joylon Oxley; H. Salmon; Martin Stevens; Prof. Mathew Walker; Dr Graeme Sills; Prof. Michael Kerr; Simon Lanyon; Mary Manning.

OTHER INFORMATION In 2012–13 a total of eight research grants were awarded.

HOW TO APPLY Application forms, together with criteria and guidelines, are available to download on the charity's website.

WHO TO APPLY TO Delphine van der Pauw, Research and Information Executive, PO Box 3004, London W4 4XT *Tel.* 020 8995 4781 *email* info@eruk.org.uk *Website* www.epilepsyresearch.org.uk

■ The Equilibrium Foundation

CC NO 1136933 **ESTABLISHED** 2010

WHERE FUNDING CAN BE GIVEN Undefined, in practice throughout the UK.

WHO CAN BENEFIT Older people; children and young people.

WHAT IS FUNDED General charitable purposes; education and training; health; relief of poverty.

FINANCES *Year* 2011–12 *Income* £25,000 *Grants* £18,500

TRUSTEES Colin Lawson; Debbie Jukes; Mark Milton-Edwards; Helen Besant-Roberts.

OTHER INFORMATION There is another charity known as Equilibrium – The Bipolar Foundation, (Charity Commission no. 1117177), dedicated to improving treatment and understanding of the causes and effects of bipolar disorder ('manic-depression'). There would appear to be no connection between the two organisations.

HOW TO APPLY In writing to the correspondent.

WHO TO APPLY TO The Trustees, The Equilibrium Foundation, Equilibrium Foundation, Equilibrium

Asset, Brooke Court, Lower Meadow Road, Handforth, Wilmslow *Tel.* 01614 862250

■ The Equitable Charitable Trust

CC NO 289548 **ESTABLISHED** 1984

WHERE FUNDING CAN BE GIVEN Mainly UK: overseas projects can sometimes be supported.

WHO CAN BENEFIT Schools and other organisations benefiting disabled or disadvantaged children. Priority to organisations and charities with an annual income of less than £5 million.

WHAT IS FUNDED Specific projects for the educational needs of disabled or disadvantaged young people. The trust has three specific priorities: education projects or services that support the learning and development of disabled children and young people in the UK; formal education projects for disadvantaged children and young people in the UK that support delivery of the National Curriculum (i.e. curriculum enrichment projects) or that deliver accredited vocational learning that will increase employability; education projects that will help increase participation in, or improve the quality of, education for disadvantaged or disabled children and young people in developing countries.

WHAT IS NOT FUNDED The trust does not make grants towards the following: 'general appeals or mail shot requests for donations; informal education projects and those that are only loosely educational (we include projects in youth work settings such as money management, drug and alcohol awareness and healthy eating in our definition of informal education, whether or not the activities are accredited); projects felt to be more akin to social work than education; therapeutic treatments (including music and play therapy); supplementary schooling and homework clubs; mother tongue language classes; local authorities; sports education, facilities or activities (e.g. playing fields, sports clubs, or projects that are delivered through the medium of sport); salaries for posts that are not directly related to service delivery (we would not make a grant towards the salary of a fundraiser or book-keeper, for instance) or that will benefit only a single child (we would not fund the cost of an additional worker to support a disable child attending a mainstream or integrated nursery, for instance); minibuses or vehicles; pre-school education projects (unless these are solely for the benefit of children with disabilities or special needs); individuals; bursary schemes; projects that promote religious belief or practice; holidays, recreational activities or overseas trips; capital applications for equipment or facilities that will be only partly used for education or by under 25s from disadvantaged or disabled backgrounds (e.g. outdoor education centres that also deliver recreational activities, or that are not exclusively for the use of disadvantaged or disabled children and young people); retrospective requests for work that has already taken place; sole traders or organisations such as companies limited by shares such as companies limited by shares whose constitutions allow the distribution of profits (whether or not this happens in practice); grassroots projects without a strategic element, such as those which support students by paying their school fees or purchasing school uniforms, are also unlikely to be funded; projects in the UK that are primarily to deliver training to adults, staff or teachers (even if children and young people will be the ultimate beneficiaries of this work); projects which relate to PSHE and Citizenship subjects are unlikely to be funded as they are a low priority; the only schools eligible to apply to us are independent special schools with registered charity status. State-maintained or voluntary aided schools, academies, public schools, independent schools that are not exclusively for disabled children or young people, colleges and universities are not eligible to apply, either directly or via a related charity (e.g. Friends, PTAs). We are also unable to fund groups of schools (whether set up via a partnership agreement or as a registered charity) which are seeking funding for services that were previously provided by their local authorities.'

TYPE OF GRANT Project costs, capital expenditure, equipment and the salary costs of a post.

RANGE OF GRANTS £2,000–£30,000

SAMPLE GRANTS Mary Hare Foundation, St John's Catholic School for the Deaf and Prior's Court Foundation (£30,000 each); National Literacy Trust (£25,000); Futureversity (£20,000); Area 51 Education and Care International UK (£18,000 each); Afghan Connection (£15,000); Unitas, Young Vic Theatre Company, Tir Coed, Prior's Court Foundation, Living Paintings Trust, Gwent Wildlife Trust, Construction Youth Trust and British Stammering Association (£10,000 each); AfriKids (£9,600); Artburst (£8,000); Dhaka Ahsania Mission (£6,000); Camden Arts Centre and London Philharmonic Orchestra (£5,000 each) and Stick 'n' Step (£4,300).

FINANCES *Year* 2012 *Income* £179,753 *Grants* £992,641 *Assets* £4,041,054

TRUSTEES Brian McGeough; Roy Ranson; Peter Goddard.

OTHER INFORMATION The trust website notes that they are in the process of spending out and expects to wind up having spent all available funds during 2015. Therefore the grants programme is likely to close at the end of 2014.

HOW TO APPLY There is no form but there are very comprehensive application guidelines available on the trust's website. Audited or independently inspected accounts must be included. If your organisation is new and does not yet have accounts, we will not be able to consider your application. Trustees meet monthly. Decisions are usually made within eight weeks. The website states that demand is high and the success rate for applications is around one in six. If you are unsure of whether your project meets the requirements the trust welcomes informal contact prior to the submission of a formal application.

WHO TO APPLY TO Jennie Long, Grants Officer, Sixth Floor, 65 Leadenhall Street, London EC3A 2AD *Tel.* 020 7264 4993 *Fax* 020 7488 9097 *email* jennielong@equitablecharitabletrust.org.uk *Website* www.equitablecharitabletrust.org.uk

■ The Equity Trust Fund

CC NO 328103   **ESTABLISHED** 1989

WHERE FUNDING CAN BE GIVEN UK.

WHO CAN BENEFIT Theatres, theatre companies and professional theatre performers in genuine need, with special reference to members, past and present, of the union Equity.

WHAT IS FUNDED Welfare and educational grants to individuals and work performed by theatres and theatre companies.

WHAT IS NOT FUNDED No grants to non-professional performers, drama students, non-professional theatre companies, multi-arts venues,

community projects or projects with no connection to the professional theatre.

TYPE OF GRANT Grants and loans.

RANGE OF GRANTS Up to £50,000.

SAMPLE GRANTS Interact Reading Services (£45,000); Dancers' Career Development (£40,000); Birmingham Repertory Theatre, Chickenshed Theatre and Tricycle Theatre (£3,000 each); Soho Theatre (£1,000) and Stone Crabs Theatre (£950).

FINANCES *Year* 2011–12 *Income* £394,358 *Grants* £95,950 *Assets* £8,653,461

TRUSTEE The Trustees.

OTHER INFORMATION A further £173,000 was given in 121 grants to individuals for welfare and education.

HOW TO APPLY In the first instance call the office to ascertain if the application is relevant. Failing that, submit a brief letter outlining the application. A meeting takes place about every six to eight weeks. Ring for precise dates. Applications are required at least two weeks beforehand.

WHO TO APPLY TO Kaethe Cherney, Secretary, Plouviez House, 19–20 Hatton Place, London EC1N 8RU *Tel.* 020 7831 1926 *Fax* 020 7242 7995 *email* kaethe@equitycharitabletrust.org.uk *Website* www.equitycharitabletrust.org.uk

■ The Eranda Foundation

CC NO 255650   **ESTABLISHED** 1967

WHERE FUNDING CAN BE GIVEN UK and overseas.

WHO CAN BENEFIT Registered charities, schools, hospitals and universities.

WHAT IS FUNDED The promotion of original research, and the continuation of existing research into medicine and education, fostering of the arts, and promotion of social welfare.

WHAT IS NOT FUNDED No grants to individuals.

TYPE OF GRANT Capital, project, running costs and recurring costs for up to three years.

RANGE OF GRANTS About £5,000–£150,000.

SAMPLE GRANTS Franklin D Roosevelt Four Freedoms Park – New York (£158,000); Peterson Institute for International Economics (£154,500); Forum for Jewish Leadership, Cancer Research UK and the Eden Project (£100,000 each); Exploring the Arts (£94,500); Fund for Refugees (£75,000); Prince's Foundation for Children and the Arts (£65,000); Young Vic (£50,000); Alzheimer's Drug Discovery Foundation (£31,000); St John of Jerusalem Eye Hospital (£30,000); Arabian School of Gymnastics (£20,000); National Association for Gifted Children (£16,000); London School of Economics (£10,000); and Friends of Africa Foundation (£5,000).

FINANCES *Year* 2011–12 *Income* £3,930,069 *Grants* £2,232,868 *Assets* £84,997,992

TRUSTEES Sir Evelyn de Rothschild; Renée Robeson; Jessica de Rothschild; Anthony de Rothschild; Sir Graham Hearne; Lady Lynn de Rothschild; Sir John Peace.

HOW TO APPLY In writing to the correspondent. Trustees usually meet in March, July and November and applications should be received two months in advance.

WHO TO APPLY TO Gail Devlin-Jones, Secretary, PO Box 6226, Wing, Leighton Buzzard, Bedfordshire LU7 0XF *Tel.* 01296 689157 *email* eranda@btconnect.com

Think carefully about every application. Is it justified?

529

■ The Ericson Trust

cc no 219762 established 1962
where funding can be given UK, developing
countries, Eastern and Central Europe.
who can benefit Registered charities only,
benefiting: middle-aged and older people;
researchers; people disadvantaged by poverty;
ex-offenders and those at risk of offending;
homeless people; immigrants and refugees.
what is funded Older people; community projects/
local interest groups, including arts; prisons,
prison reform, mentoring projects, and research
in this area; refugees; mental health;
environmental projects and research; aid to
developing countries only if supported and
represented or initiated and administered by a
UK registered charity.
what is not funded No grants to individuals or to
non-registered charities. Applications from the
following areas are generally not considered
unless closely connected with one of the above:
children's and young people's clubs, centres
and so on; schools; charities dealing with
illness or disability (except psychiatric); or
religious institutions, except in their social
projects.
type of grant Project.
range of grants Up to £6,000, with average grants
ranging from £1,000–£5,000.
sample grants Previous beneficiaries have
included: Action on Elder Abuse, Anti-Slavery
International, Ashram International, Bhopal
Medical Appeal, Headway East London, Howard
League for Penal Reform, the Koestler Trust,
Minority Rights Group, Psychiatric Rehabilitation
Association, Quaker Social Action, the
Rainforest Foundation, the Relatives and
Residents Association, Tools for Self Reliance
and the Umalini Mary Brahma Charitable Trust.
finances Year 2011–12 Income £23,672
Grants £40,000
trustees Miss R. C. Cotton; V. J. Barrow;
A. M. C. Cotton.
other information In 2011–12 the trust had an
expenditure of £50,009. No further information
was available but based upon previous years
grants probably totalled about £40,000.
how to apply Unsolicited applications cannot be
considered as the trust has no funds available.
The correspondent stated: 'We are increasing
worried by the waste of applicants' resources
when they send expensive brochures at a time
when we are unable to consider any new
appeals and have, indeed, reduced some of our
long standing grants due to the bad economic
situation. It is particularly sad when we receive
requests from small charities in Africa and
Asia.'
who to apply to Claudia Cotton, Flat 2, 53 Carleton
Road, London N7 0ET email claudia.cotton@
googlemail.com

■ The Ernest Hecht Charitable Foundation

cc no 1095850 established 2002
where funding can be given England and Wales.
who can benefit Registered charities.
what is funded Support is given for: the
advancement of education; relief of poverty; and
advancement of religion.
finances Year 2012 Income £49,793
Grants £88,970 Assets £512,335
trustees Ernest Hecht; Eddie Bell.
other information 'The Foundation aims to
support the work of other charitable

organisations in helping the disadvantaged and
promoting the advancement of the arts and
education by making grants, with the aim of
making a difference in a particular field.'
how to apply In writing to the correspondent.
who to apply to Graham Manfield, Administrator,
c/o Michelmores LLP, Woodwater House, Pynes
Hill, Exeter, Devon EX2 5WR Tel. 01392
688688

■ The Erskine Cunningham Hill Trust

sc no SC001853 established 1955
where funding can be given Scotland.
who can benefit Organisations registered in
Scotland benefiting older people, young people,
ex-service men and women, seamen, and the
Church of Scotland.
what is funded The Church of Scotland is the
largest single focus of the trust's interest (50%
of annual income). Other grants are restricted to
charitable work in Scotland with older people;
young people; ex-servicemen and women;
seamen; Scottish interests; with priority given to
charities administered by voluntary or honorary
officials.
what is not funded No grants to individuals.
type of grant Recurring grants to the Church of
Scotland; one-off grants to individual Scottish
charities.
range of grants Approximately £1,000 each to
individual charities.
sample grants Beneficiaries have included:
ChildLine and Cruse Bereavement Care, The
Sailors' Family Society and Venture Trust.
finances Year 2012 Income £54,355
Grants £50,000
trustees R. M. Maiden; Very Revd Dr A. McDonald;
I. W. Grimmond; Very Revd J. Cairns; Very Revd
A. McLellan; Dr A. Elliot; The Church of Scotland
Trust.
how to apply In writing to the correspondent at the
above address. An application form is available
via email from the correspondent. There is a
two-year time bar on repeat grants. The trustees
do not consider applications from outside
Scotland.
who to apply to Nicola Laing, Secretary,
Stewardship and Finance Department, Church of
Scotland Offices, 121 George Street, Edinburgh
EH2 4YN Tel. 01312 255722 email nlaing@
cofscotland.org.uk

■ The Esfandi Charitable Foundation

cc no 1103095 established 2004
where funding can be given UK and overseas.
who can benefit Charitable organisations.
what is funded Jewish causes.
range of grants Up to £250,000.
sample grants Schlomo High School (£250,000);
British Friends of Migdal Or (£60,000); Jewish
Care and Jewish Community Secondary School
Trust (£12,500); Naima Jewish Preparatory
School (£8,000); Royal National Theatre and
Chief Rabbinate Trust (£5,000 each); British
Friends of Gesher (£2,000); Western Marble
Arch Synagogue (£1,500); and Norwood (£750).
finances Year 2011–12 Income £461,620
Grants £416,040 Assets £140,438
trustees Joseph Esfandi; Denise Esfandi.
how to apply In writing to the correspondent.

WHO TO APPLY TO Joseph Esfandi, Trustee, 36 Park Street, London W1K 2JE *Tel.* 020 7629 6666

■ The Essendon Charitable Trust

CC NO 1146733   **ESTABLISHED** 2012
WHERE FUNDING CAN BE GIVEN UK.
WHO CAN BENEFIT Children and young people.
WHAT IS FUNDED The relief of suffering and poverty and health. The trust also supports hospices and organisations that work with carers.
FINANCES *Grants* £50,000
TRUSTEES Lesley Reith; Catherine Kilhams; Jane Hughes-Jones.
HOW TO APPLY In writing to the trustees via email.
WHO TO APPLY TO Lesley Reith, Trustee, Essendon House, Church Street, Essendon, Hatfield, Hertfordshire AL9 6AR *email* trustees@essendontrust.co.uk *Website* www.essendontrust.co.uk

■ The Essex and Southend Sports Trust

CC NO 1092238   **ESTABLISHED** 2002
WHERE FUNDING CAN BE GIVEN Essex, Southend-on-Sea.
WHO CAN BENEFIT Charities, other not for profit organisations and individuals.
WHAT IS FUNDED Sports facilities, equipment, coaching and training.
RANGE OF GRANTS Usually up to £3,000.
SAMPLE GRANTS Southend Rugby Club (£3,000); Orsett Cricket Club (£2,885); Old Southendian and Southchurch Cricket Club (£2,500); YMCA Southend (£2,000) and Star Shooting Club Hockley (£1,000).
FINANCES *Year* 2011–12 *Income* £145,217 *Grants* £81,780 *Assets* £3,436,669
TRUSTEES Joseph Sims; Linley Butler; Peter Butler.
HOW TO APPLY Contact the correspondent to enquire about making an application.
WHO TO APPLY TO Joe Sims, Red House, Larks Lane, Great Waltham, Chelmsford CM3 1AD *Tel.* 01245 360385 *Fax* 01245 360303 *email* jwh_sims@hotmail.co.uk *Website* www.easst.org.uk

■ Essex Community Foundation

CC NO 1052061   **ESTABLISHED** 1996
WHERE FUNDING CAN BE GIVEN Essex, Southend and Thurrock
WHO CAN BENEFIT Any voluntary and community organisations, or any non-profit making organisation working for the benefit of people living in Essex, Southend and Thurrock. The foundation is particularly interested in small grass-roots groups.
WHAT IS FUNDED Support generally falls under the broad heading of social welfare. The foundation distributes grants through various funds. Information on current funds and their criteria is available on the foundation's website.
WHAT IS NOT FUNDED The foundation does not support the following: political activities; statutory bodies undertaking their statutory obligations, including schools; general appeals; activities which support animal welfare; projects that operate outside of Essex, or benefit non-Essex residents; retrospective funding.
TYPE OF GRANT Core costs/revenue costs, new or continuing projects, one-off initiatives and capital costs.

RANGE OF GRANTS £50–£100,000.
SAMPLE GRANTS 2nd Witham Boys' Brigade (£117,000); Basildon Women's Aid (£20,000); Tendring CVS (£12,000); Opportunities Through Technology and Victim Support (£10,000 each); Support 4 Sight (£6,000); Uttlesford Carers (£5,000); Colchester Furniture Project (£4,000); Dedham Youth Club and Saffron Walden Youth Outreach Project (£3,500 each); Essex Wildlife Trust (£3,400); Essex Young Peoples Drug and Alcohol Service (£1,300); Colchester MIND (£1,000); ASD Support (£500).
FINANCES *Year* 2011–12 *Income* £4,450,048 *Grants* £1,516,709 *Assets* £19,586,955
TRUSTEES John Spence; Peter Blanc; Jason Bartella; John Barnes; Carole Golbourn; Peter Heap; Rhianneld Pratley; Martin Hopkins; Jonny Minter; Owen Richards; Jackie Sully; Kate Barker.
OTHER INFORMATION The foundation administers a variety of funds which are subject to change and are likely to open and close throughout the year. Potential applicants are therefore advised to check the foundation's website for exact information on funds.
HOW TO APPLY Essex Community Foundation manages a number of funds, many of which are tailored to the individual wishes of the donors. Applicants should use the general applications forms (for either under or over £1,000), along with application guidelines. Applicants for Comic Relief, High Sherriff's Award or funding for individuals should use the specific application forms, also available from the foundation. Application forms are available from the foundation's office or can be downloaded from its website; they can be submitted at any time throughout the year. The foundation welcomes initial enquires to discuss an application.
WHO TO APPLY TO Grants Team, 121 New London Road, Chelmsford, Essex CM2 0QT *Tel.* 01245 355947 *email* general@essexcf.org.uk *Website* www.essexcommunityfoundation.org.uk

■ The Essex Fairway Charitable Trust

CC NO 1066858   **ESTABLISHED** 1997
WHERE FUNDING CAN BE GIVEN South east England, with a preference for Essex.
WHO CAN BENEFIT Registered charities, particularly those directly benefiting people in need. Small charities in south east England, particularly Essex, will be favoured.
WHAT IS FUNDED General charitable purposes.
WHAT IS NOT FUNDED No grants for medical research, animal welfare, the environment and political and religious purposes. No grants to large UK charities. No grants to individuals.
TYPE OF GRANT One-off grants for capital and revenue costs and full project funding. Replacement of statutory funding also available.
SAMPLE GRANTS Awareness of Down's Syndrome; CHESS; East Essex District Scouts Council; Fair Haven Hospice; Farleigh Hospice; Felixstowe Youth Development Group; Hamelin Trust; Headway Essex; Anne Lloyd Memorial Trust; Macmillan Cancer Relief; Martha Trust; St Christopher's School; Stepney Children's Fund and St Patrick's Trust.
FINANCES *Year* 2012 *Income* £1,761 *Grants* £200,000
TRUSTEES P. W. George; Bruce Ballard.
PUBLICATIONS A full grants list is available on request to the trust.

OTHER INFORMATION The grant total is an estimate based on previous research.

HOW TO APPLY Note the following statement from the trust: 'The trust very rarely gives donations in response to applications from charities that it has not previously supported and will not reply to such applications'.

WHO TO APPLY TO Bruce Ballard, c/o Birkett Long, Essex House, 42 Crouch Street, Colchester, Essex CO3 3HH *Tel.* 01206 217327

■ The Essex Heritage Trust

CC NO 802317   **ESTABLISHED** 1989

WHERE FUNDING CAN BE GIVEN Essex.

WHO CAN BENEFIT Any organisation, body or individual whose project will be to the benefit of the people of Essex.

WHAT IS FUNDED Grants to bodies or individuals undertaking specific work in accord with the objects of the trust, including publication or preservation of Essex history and restoration of monuments, significant structures, artefacts and church decorations and equipment.

WHAT IS NOT FUNDED No grants involving private property.

TYPE OF GRANT Mostly one-off grants for revenue and capital costs.

RANGE OF GRANTS Up to £10,000.

SAMPLE GRANTS Museum of Power – New collection building (£10,000); St Mary the Virgin, Peldon – New disabled facilities, All Saints Church, Middleton – Improvement of public facilities, All Saints Church, Theydon Garnon – Restoration of William Eyre Archer monument and Colchester and Ipswich Museum Service – Purchase of display case at Colchester Castle (£5,000 each); North Road Burial Ground, Westcliff-on-Sea – Heritage boards (£4,200); St Barnabas Church, Great Tey – Overhaul of church bells and Moot Hall, Malden – Restoration of oil painting (£2,000 each) and St Thomas of Canterbury Church, Brentwood – Organ restoration, Abbey Lane and Newport United Reformed Church – Brass parapet rail, Christ Church, Latchingdon – William Morris window restoration, St Mary's Church, Bockin – Restoration of indoor War Memorial and Publication by David Starling – Nice Looking (Essex) Girls Afloat (£1,000 each).

FINANCES *Year* 2011–12 *Income* £44,588 *Grants* £43,200 *Assets* £1,300,714

TRUSTEES Lord John Petre; Richard Wollaston; Mark Pertwee; Peter Mamelok; Dr James Bettley; Brian Moody; Susan Brice; Cllr Kay Twitchen; Jonathan Douglas-Hughes.

PUBLICATIONS Annual newsletter.

OTHER INFORMATION The trust has been able to keep its governance costs low due to the continuing sponsorship of the salary and payroll costs of the trust's administrator by Essex County Council.

HOW TO APPLY In writing to the correspondent in the first instance. An application form will be returned for detailed completion with estimates if it is considered that the project falls within the trust's objectives. The trustees meet three times a year in March, July and November, when grant awards will be made.

WHO TO APPLY TO Sharon Hill, Administrator, Cressing Temple, Witham Road, Braintree, Essex CM77 8PD *Tel.* 01376 585794 *email* eht@dsl.pipex.com *Website* www.essexheritagetrust.co.uk

■ Essex Provincial Charity Fund

CC NO 215349   **ESTABLISHED** 1932

WHERE FUNDING CAN BE GIVEN Essex.

WHO CAN BENEFIT Essex Freemasons; their dependants; central masonic charities, and other charities.

WHAT IS FUNDED Preference for charities with a medical bias and, primarily in Essex, that assist the community in general.

WHAT IS NOT FUNDED No grants to individuals, other than those who are dependants of freemasons.

SAMPLE GRANTS Essex 2011 Festival (£100,000); (Freemasons' Grand Charity) Friends of Hamilton Court (£51,000); (Freemasons' Grand Charity) Cambridgeshire 2012 Festival (£50,000) and Grants to brethren and dependants (£24,000).

FINANCES *Year* 2011–12 *Income* £292,231 *Grants* £225,167 *Assets* £839,931

TRUSTEES Peter Holland; Frederick Harris; Allan Kemp; Christopher Williams; Andrew Bishop; Paul Cohen; Kenneth Keenes; Laurie Justice.

OTHER INFORMATION In addition to the above figure, grants totalling £259,000 were administered by the trust on behalf of the Freemasons' Grand Charity.

HOW TO APPLY In writing to the correspondent.

WHO TO APPLY TO Kenneth Keenes, Trustee, 113 The Sorrells, Stanford-le-Hope, Essex SS17 7ES *Tel.* 01375 643404

■ The Essex Youth Trust

CC NO 225768   **ESTABLISHED** 1963

WHERE FUNDING CAN BE GIVEN Essex.

WHO CAN BENEFIT Beneficiaries include schools, youth clubs and organisations giving advice, help and information.

WHAT IS FUNDED The advancement of education for people under the age of 25 who are in need of assistance. Preference is given to those who are in need owing to 'being temporarily or permanently deprived of normal parental care or who are otherwise disadvantaged'. 'The trustees favour organisations which develop young people's physical, mental and spiritual capacities through active participation in sports and indoor and outdoor activities. As a result they are particularly supportive of youth clubs and other organisations which provide facilities for young people to take active part in an assortment of activities as well as single activity organisations.'

WHAT IS NOT FUNDED No grants to individuals.

RANGE OF GRANTS Up to £25,000.

SAMPLE GRANTS Summer Action Programme (£45,000); Cirdan Sailing Trust (£50,000 in two grants); Essex Boys and Girls Club (£28,000 in two grants); The College of St Mark (£10,000); Chain Reaction Theatre Company (£8,000); Maldon Essex Mind (£7,000); Barking and Dagenham Training Centre (£5,000); Market Field School (£3,000); Dream Holidays (£1,500) and Harp Acorn Project (£400).

FINANCES *Year* 2011–12 *Income* £426,858 *Grants* £359,517 *Assets* £7,229,027

TRUSTEES Richard Wenley; Julien Courtauld; Michael Dyer; Revd Duncan Green; William David Robson; Lady Julia Denison-Smith; Claire Coltwell; Michael Biegel; Julie Rogers.

HOW TO APPLY On a form available from the correspondent. The trustees meet on a quarterly basis.

WHO TO APPLY TO J. P. Douglas-Hughes, Clerk, Gepp and Sons, 58 New London Road, Chelmsford, Essex CM2 0PA *Tel.* 01245 493939 *Fax* 01245 493940 *email* douglas-hughesj@gepp.co.uk

....

■ The Estelle Trust

CC NO 1101299   **ESTABLISHED** 2003
WHERE FUNDING CAN BE GIVEN Not defined, but in practice Zambia.
WHO CAN BENEFIT Organisations mostly in Zambia.
WHAT IS FUNDED Overseas aid and general charitable purposes.
RANGE OF GRANTS Usually up to £10,000.
SAMPLE GRANTS Project Luangwa and University of Bradford (£15,000 each); Nagwaza (£13,000); Microloan Foundation (£10,000); Arulussa School Development (£9,000); Queens College Cambridge (£7,000); Baynards Zambia Trust (£6,300); Zambia Orphans of AIDS (£6,600); International Rescue Committee (£5,000); Suntech Solar Pump (£4,500); Twavwane Home Based Care (£3,400); Kachele Village (£2,800); St Catherine's Hospice (£1,000); ABF The Soldiers Charity and Prostate Action (£500 each) and Assist Sheffield (£200).
FINANCES *Year* 2011–12 *Income* £102,840 *Grants* £130,122 *Assets* £1,332,093
TRUSTEES Nigel Farrow; G. R. Ornstein; D. Wise; Rachel Lynch; Katherine Farrow; Imogen Abed; Sarah Davies.
HOW TO APPLY In writing to the correspondent.
WHO TO APPLY TO Caroline Harvey, Fisher Phillips, 170 Finchley Road, London NW3 6BP *Tel.* 020 7483 6100

....

■ Joseph Ettedgui Charitable Foundation

CC NO 1139615   **ESTABLISHED** 2010
WHERE FUNDING CAN BE GIVEN UK and overseas.
WHO CAN BENEFIT Registered charities.
WHAT IS FUNDED General charitable purposes, with a preference for organisations working with children and young people, older people and people with disabilities.
RANGE OF GRANTS Up to £40,000
SAMPLE GRANTS Imperial College Trust; In Harmony and My Voice.
FINANCES *Year* 2011–12 *Income* £60,432 *Grants* £43,040 *Assets* £337,288
TRUSTEES Isabel Ettedgui; Peter Ettedgui; Paul Ettedgui; Genevieve Ettedgui; Coutts and Co.
HOW TO APPLY In writing to the correspondent.
WHO TO APPLY TO Steve Harvey, Administrator, c/o Trustee Dept, Coutts and Co, 440 Strand, London WC2R 0QS *Tel.* 020 7663 6814 *email* steve.harvey@coutts.com

....

■ Euro Charity Trust

CC NO 1058460   **ESTABLISHED** 1996
WHERE FUNDING CAN BE GIVEN Worldwide, mainly India, Africa, Bangladesh and the UK.
WHO CAN BENEFIT Registered charities.
WHAT IS FUNDED The relief of poverty; to assist the vulnerable; and to assist in the advancement of education in the UK and the rest of the world.
SAMPLE GRANTS Nathani Charitable Trust (£1.4 million); Maulana Hussain Ahmad Madani Charitable Trust and Charitable Society (£464,500); and Imdadul Muslimeen (£140,000).

FINANCES *Year* 2012 *Income* £2,870,957 *Grants* £2,426,004 *Assets* £751,474
TRUSTEES Nasir Awan; Abdul Malik; Abdul Alimahomed.
OTHER INFORMATION Over two thirds of the trust's grantmaking is concentrated in India.
HOW TO APPLY In writing to the correspondent.
WHO TO APPLY TO Nasir Awan, Trustee, 51a Church Road, Edgbaston, Birmingham B15 3SJ *email* info@eurocharity.org.uk

....

■ The Patrick Evans Foundation

CC NO 1134412   **ESTABLISHED** 2010
WHERE FUNDING CAN BE GIVEN Undefined, in practice the UK.
WHO CAN BENEFIT Organisations and individuals.
WHAT IS FUNDED The foundation was set up to help those suffering from any illness and disease, support those dealing with bereavement and loss, create healthy sporting opportunities for young people and promote awareness of safety in sporting activities.
SAMPLE GRANTS Grants include those awarded for a practice mat for the Sovereign Gymnastics Club, a sports pitch for underprivileged children in Tanzania and a new machine for Prostate Cancer research.
FINANCES *Year* 2011–12 *Income* £57,602
TRUSTEES Mike Dennis; Alun Evans; Catherine Evans; Louise Evans; Matt Lloyd; Rory Evans.
OTHER INFORMATION In 2011–12 the foundation had a total expenditure of £38,500.
HOW TO APPLY In writing to the correspondent.
WHO TO APPLY TO Alun Evans, Trustee, 31 Cronks Hill Road, Redhill RH1 6LY *email* info@patrickevansfoundation.co.uk *Website* www.patrickevansfoundation.co.uk

....

■ The Alan Evans Memorial Trust

CC NO 326263   **ESTABLISHED** 1979
WHERE FUNDING CAN BE GIVEN UK.
WHO CAN BENEFIT Registered charities only.
WHAT IS FUNDED Preservation of lands and tenements, of beauty or historic interest the natural aspect of features and animal and plant life.
WHAT IS NOT FUNDED Grants are given to registered charities only. General appeals will not be acknowledged.
RANGE OF GRANTS £400–£1,500.
SAMPLE GRANTS Previous beneficiaries include: English Hedgerow Trust, Landmark Trust, Zoological Society of London, St Wilfrid's Church – Leeds, Thatcham Charity, Cathedral Church of the Holy Spirit – Guildford, Peterborough Cathedral Development and Preservation Trust, Wells Cathedral – Somerset, Lincoln Cathedral and the Church of Our Lord, St Mary and St Germaine – Selby Abbey.
FINANCES *Year* 2011–12 *Income* £33,455 *Grants* £149,003 *Assets* £455,855
TRUSTEES David Halfhead; Deirdre Moss.
OTHER INFORMATION Grants ranged from £400 to £1,500 and were given to 123 organisations totalling £149,000.
HOW TO APPLY There is no formal application form, but appeals should be made in writing to the correspondent, stating why the funds are required, what funds have been promised from other sources (for example, English Heritage) and the amount outstanding. The trust has also stated previously that it would be helpful when making applications to provide a photograph of the project. The trustees normally meet four

times a year, although in urgent cases decisions can be made between meetings. The trustees may wish to see the work undertaken out of the proceeds of the grant. Grant recipients might be asked to provide copies of receipts for expenditure.

WHO TO APPLY TO The Trustees, Lemon and Co, 34 Regent Circus, Swindon SN1 1PY *Tel.* 0800 135 7917 *email* aevans@lemon-co.co.uk

■ Sir John Evelyn's Charity

CC NO 225707 **ESTABLISHED** 1974
WHERE FUNDING CAN BE GIVEN Ancient parishes of St Nicholas Deptford and St Luke Deptford.
WHO CAN BENEFIT Registered charities benefiting the parishes of St Nicholas and St Luke's in Deptford, which relieve poverty, as well as advance education and community development.
WHAT IS FUNDED Pensions and grants to organisations working to relieve poverty, as well as advance education and community development.
WHAT IS NOT FUNDED Exclusively for the area specified.
TYPE OF GRANT One-off grants and longer term grants.
SAMPLE GRANTS Armada Community Project (£48,000); Henrietta and Hughes Field Young People's Project (£10,000); Partworks (£9,000); Creekside Forum (£3,000); Evelyn 190 Centre (£500); and St Nicholas and St Luke's (£400).
FINANCES *Year* 2012 *Income* £74,903 *Grants* £70,953 *Assets* £2,537,037
TRUSTEES Kay Ingledew; Bridget Perry; Revd Jack Lucas; Janet Miller; Cllr Maureen O'Mara; Margaret Mythen; Revd Louise Cordington-Marshall.
OTHER INFORMATION Grants to individuals totalled £1,100.
HOW TO APPLY In writing to the correspondent.
WHO TO APPLY TO Colette Saunders, Administrator, Clerk's Office, Armada Court Hall, 21 Macmillan Street, Deptford, London SE8 3EZ *Tel.* 020 8694 8953

■ The Eventhall Family Charitable Trust

CC NO 803178 **ESTABLISHED** 1989
WHERE FUNDING CAN BE GIVEN UK with a preference for the north west of England.
WHO CAN BENEFIT Charitable organisations and individuals.
WHAT IS FUNDED General charitable purposes.
SAMPLE GRANTS Previous beneficiaries have included Aish Hatorah, ChildLine, Clitheroe Wolves Football Club, Community Security Trust, Greibach Memorial, Guide Dogs for the Blind, Heathlands Village, International Wildlife Coalition, JJCT, MB Foundation Charity, Only Foals and Horses Sanctuary, Red Nose Day, RNLI, Sale Ladies Society, Shelter and South Manchester Synagogue.
FINANCES *Year* 2012–13 *Income* £98,864 *Grants* £252,666 *Assets* £3,567,007
TRUSTEES Julia Eventhall; David Eventhall.
HOW TO APPLY In writing to the correspondent. Note, however, previous research highlighted that the trust stated it only has a very limited amount of funds available.
WHO TO APPLY TO The Trustees, PO Box 490, Altrincham WA14 2ZT

■ The Everard Foundation

CC NO 272248 **ESTABLISHED** 1976
WHERE FUNDING CAN BE GIVEN Leicestershire.
WHO CAN BENEFIT Local organisations of all sizes. Grants to UK-wide organisations must be to fund something tangibly local.
WHAT IS FUNDED General charitable purposes.
WHAT IS NOT FUNDED No grants to individuals.
TYPE OF GRANT Capital costs.
RANGE OF GRANTS From £200.
SAMPLE GRANTS Leicestershire and Rutland Crimebeat Ltd (£215,500); Age Concern Leicestershire and Rutland and Tennis Leicester Charitable Trust (£10,000 each); Prostaid (£7,000); Leicester Theatre Trust, The John Merricks Sailing Trust and Boost (£5,000 each); De Montfort University and help for Heroes (£2,000 each); Young Enterprise and Royal College of Music (£1,000 each); Combat Stress and County Air Ambulance (£500 each); The British Red Cross Society and The Naseby Battlefield Project (£250 each); and Grange Park Opera (£200).
FINANCES *Year* 2011–12 *Income* £61,214 *Grants* £275,261 *Assets* £2,899,325
TRUSTEES Richard Everard; Serena Richards; Simon Aitkinson.
HOW TO APPLY In writing to the correspondent.
WHO TO APPLY TO Richard Everard, Trustee, C/o Everards Brewery Ltd., Castle Acres, Everard Way, Enderby, Leicester LE19 1BY *Tel.* 01162 014307

■ The Eveson Charitable Trust

CC NO 1032204 **ESTABLISHED** 1994
WHERE FUNDING CAN BE GIVEN Herefordshire, Worcestershire and the county of West Midlands (covering Birmingham, Coventry, Dudley, Sandwell, Solihull, Walsall and Wolverhampton).
WHO CAN BENEFIT Registered charities.
WHAT IS FUNDED People with physical disabilities, (including those who are blind or deaf); people with mental disabilities; hospitals and hospices; children who are in need, whether disadvantaged or with physical or mental disabilities; older people; homeless people; medical research into problems associated with any of these conditions.
WHAT IS NOT FUNDED Grants are not made to individuals, even if such a request is submitted by a charitable organisation.
TYPE OF GRANT Capital and revenue, recurring and one-off.
RANGE OF GRANTS From a few hundred pounds to £150,000; average grant around £8,000.
SAMPLE GRANTS Birmingham Children's Hospital Charities (£100,000), towards a major improvement in facilities at the Hospital's Children's Cancer Unit; Age UK Hereford and Localities (£75,000), towards running costs; Acorns Children's Hospice Trust (£55,000), towards running costs of their hospices in Birmingham, Walsall and Worcester that provide support to life limited or life threatened children; St Paul's Hostel – Worcester (£40,000 in total), towards care farm project and counselling service to benefit homeless people; Martha Trust Hereford Limited (£25,000), towards new furniture and equipment for Sophie House which provides specialised care for people with profound disabilities; Birmingham City Mission (£15,000), towards cost of renovating care centre that will benefit homeless people; British Heart Foundation (£10,000), towards medical research being carried out at the University of

Birmingham; Basement Youth Trust (£8,000), towards running costs; and Dorothy Parkes Centre (£7,000), towards running costs.

FINANCES *Year* 2012–13 *Income* £1,417,268 *Grants* £1,969,383 *Assets* £67,944,181

TRUSTEES David Pearson, Chair; Bruce Maughfling; Rt. Revd Anthony Priddis, Bishop of Hereford; Martin Davies; Louise Woodhead; Bill Wiggin; Richard Mainwaring.

HOW TO APPLY The trustees meet quarterly, usually at the end of March and June and the beginning of October and January. Applications can only be considered if they are on the trust's standard, but very simple, 'application for support' form which can be obtained from the administrator at the offices of the trust in Gloucester. The form must be completed and returned (together with a copy of the latest accounts and annual report of the organisation) to the trust's offices at least six weeks before the meeting of trustees at which the application is to be considered, in order to give time for necessary assessment procedures, often including visits to applicants. Before providing support to statutory bodies (such as hospitals and schools for people with learning difficulties), the trust requires written confirmation that no statutory funds are available to meet the need for which funds are being requested. In the case of larger grants to hospitals, the trust asks the district health authority to confirm that no statutory funding is available. Where applications are submitted that clearly fall outside the grantmaking parameters of the trust, the applicant is advised that the application cannot be considered and reasons are given. All applications that are going to be considered by the trustees are acknowledged in writing. Applicants are advised of the reference number of their application and of the quarterly meeting at which their application is going to be considered. The decisions are advised to applicants in writing soon after these meetings. Funded projects are monitored.

WHO TO APPLY TO Alex D. Gay, Administrator, 45 Park Road, Gloucester GL1 1LP *Tel.* 01452 501352 *Fax* 01452 302195

■ The Beryl Evetts and Robert Luff Animal Welfare Trust Limited

CC NO 283944   **ESTABLISHED** 1981

WHERE FUNDING CAN BE GIVEN UK.

WHO CAN BENEFIT Animal charities. The trust supports the same beneficiaries each year.

WHAT IS FUNDED Veterinary research and the care and welfare of animals.

RANGE OF GRANTS Up to £65,000.

SAMPLE GRANTS Animal Health Trust (£65,000); Royal Veterinary College (£60,000); Blue Cross (£8,000); Brooke Hospitals for Animals, St Tiggywinkles and Kent Wildlife Trust (£1,000 each); and the Cats Protection League and the National Fox Welfare Society (£500 each).

FINANCES *Year* 2011–12 *Income* £259,328 *Grants* £140,000 *Assets* £4,088,467

TRUSTEES Jean Tomlinson; Sir Robert Johnson; Brian Nicholson; Revd Matthew Tomlinson; Richard Price; Melanie Lydiate Condon; Lady Ruth Bodey.

HOW TO APPLY Applications from organisations that the trust has never previously funded are considered, however the trust has stated that it is very unlikely that grants of any higher than £5,000 are likely to be considered. Grants are made annually and administered in June.

Applications should be submitted by the 31 March and should be longer than 3 A4 pages.

WHO TO APPLY TO Richard Price, Trustee, Waters Edge, Ferry Lane, Moulsford, Wallingford, Oxfordshire OX10 9JF *email* rpjprice@gmail.com

---

■ The Exilarch's Foundation

CC NO 275919   **ESTABLISHED** 1978

WHERE FUNDING CAN BE GIVEN Mainly UK, occasionally overseas.

WHO CAN BENEFIT Jewish organisations and educational institutions.

WHAT IS FUNDED Education; medical; social welfare.

RANGE OF GRANTS Up to £1 million.

SAMPLE GRANTS Open University (£1 million); Gateshead Talmudical College and Memorah Grammar School Charitable Trust (£50,000 each); Spanish and Portuguese Jews' Congregation (£34,000); Jewish Chronicle (£21,000); Sephardi Voices and Council of Christians and Jews (£15,000 each); Jewish Association for Business Ethics (£10,000); Westminster Academy (£5,000); and Weizmann UK (£3,000).

FINANCES *Year* 2012 *Income* £5,366,473 *Grants* £1,432,295 *Assets* £60,368,353

TRUSTEES Naim Dangoor; David Dangoor; Elie Dangoor; Robert Dangoor; Michael Dangoor.

OTHER INFORMATION The trustees have built up a designated reserve of £10 million for the specific purpose of assisting the setting up of educational and religious institutions in a future re-established Jewish community in Iraq.

HOW TO APPLY In writing to the correspondent.

WHO TO APPLY TO Dr Naim Dangoor, Trustee, 4 Carlos Place, Mayfair, London W1K 3AW

■ The Expat Foundation

CC NO 1094041   **ESTABLISHED** 2002

WHERE FUNDING CAN BE GIVEN UK and overseas.

WHO CAN BENEFIT Charitable organisations.

WHAT IS FUNDED Education; social welfare; health; community development; young people; elderly people.

WHAT IS NOT FUNDED No grants to individuals or animal welfare charities.

TYPE OF GRANT Capital, core and start-up costs. One-off and up to four years.

RANGE OF GRANTS £5,000–£75,000.

SAMPLE GRANTS Kids Company (£75,000); Impact Foundation and Leap Confronting Conflict (£50,000 each); Notting Hill Housing Trust (£28,000); Build It International (£20,000); Read International and Open Age (£10,000 each); Magic Me (£7,500); and Science Museum (£5,500).

FINANCES *Year* 2012–13 *Income* £210,342 *Grants* £312,748 *Assets* £983,360

TRUSTEES Ann Jacobs; John Barnsley; Patricia Wolfston; Paul Tuckwell; Janet Cummins; Gill Weavers.

OTHER INFORMATION Grants were given to 12 organisations in 2012–13 and totalled nearly £313,000.

HOW TO APPLY In writing to the correspondent. Grant recipients must report on how the funds were spent.

WHO TO APPLY TO Patricia Wolfston, Chair, Flat 9, Rutland Gate House, 43–44 Rutland Gate, London SW7 1PB

■ Extonglen Limited

CC NO 286230   **ESTABLISHED** 1982

WHERE FUNDING CAN BE GIVEN UK.

WHO CAN BENEFIT Orthodox Jewish organisations.

WHAT IS FUNDED Orthodox Jewish causes; education; and the relief of poverty.

RANGE OF GRANTS £0–£500,000

SAMPLE GRANTS Previous beneficiaries have included: Kol Halashon Education Programme (£470,000); Ahavas Chesed (£95,000); Pikuach Nefesh (£50,000); Kupath Gemach Chaim Bechesed Viznitz Trust (£40,000); British Friends of Nishmat Yisrael (£12,000); and Children's Town Charity (£3,600).

FINANCES *Year* 2011 *Income* £805,022 *Grants* £527,706 *Assets* £13,012,923

TRUSTEES Meir Levine; C. Levine; Isaac Katzenberg.

OTHER INFORMATION Investment management costs were £286,000 and governance costs were £24,000. The trustees annual report for 2011 states that the charitable donations have been detailed in a separate publication 'Extonglen Limited – Schedule of Charitable Donations', copies of which are available from the trustees 'on payment of the appropriate fee'.

HOW TO APPLY In writing to the correspondent.

WHO TO APPLY TO C. Levine, Trustee, New Burlington House, 1075 Finchley Road, London NW11 0PU *Tel.* 020 8731 0777 *email* ml@rowdeal.com

■ The William and Christine Eynon Charity

CC NO 1134334   **ESTABLISHED** 2010

WHERE FUNDING CAN BE GIVEN Worldwide, in practice the UK.

WHO CAN BENEFIT Registered charities.

WHAT IS FUNDED General charitable purposes.

FINANCES *Year* 2011–12 *Income* £11,252 *Grants* £40,000

TRUSTEES William Eynon; Christine Eynon; Sophie Eynon; James Eynon.

HOW TO APPLY In writing to the correspondent.

WHO TO APPLY TO William Eynon, Tusker House, Newton, Porthcawl CF36 5ST *Tel.* 01656 782312

■ The Matthew Eyton Animal Welfare Trust

CC NO 1003575   **ESTABLISHED** 1991

WHERE FUNDING CAN BE GIVEN England and Wales

WHO CAN BENEFIT Animal charities, mainly farm animal charities as opposed to wild or companion animals; vegetarians; and vegans

WHAT IS FUNDED Animal charities, vegetarian/vegan

TYPE OF GRANT One-off

RANGE OF GRANTS £10– £78,000

SAMPLE GRANTS PETA's Research and Education Foundation (£78,000); The Vegetarians Campaign Group (£9,000); The Vegetarians and Vegans Foundation (£2,000); The Soil Association (£500); Support Payments to Animal Sanctuaries (£345); The Dogs Trust (£230); The Uncaged Campaign (£150); Sea Shepherd UK (£50); Caring for the Animals Trust (£40) and The Anglican Society for the Welfare of Animals Trust (£10).

FINANCES *Year* 2011–12 *Income* £100,072 *Grants* £91,515 *Assets* £69,162

TRUSTEES Audrey Eyton; Paul Flood.

HOW TO APPLY In writing to the correspondent.

WHO TO APPLY TO The Trustees, 7 Blackfriars Street, Canterbury, Kent CT1 2AP

■ F. C. Charitable Trust

cc no 277686   **established** 1978
where funding can be given Worldwide, but mainly the UK.
who can benefit Christian and welfare organisations.
what is funded The trust gives support in the areas of Christian churches, missionary societies, ministers, missionaries and welfare.
what is not funded Individuals are not eligible for grants and the trust does not normally support a charity unless it is known to the trustees.
sample grants Emmanuel Church Wimbledon (£28,000 in nine grants); Stowe School Foundation and Friends of St Ebbe's (£1,000 each); Bowerman Charitable Trust (£720); Christchurch Durham and The Gaines Christian Centre (£500 each); Fellowship of Confessing Anglicans (£180); Iwerne Holidays (£80); and RNIB (£50).
finances *Year* 2011–12 *Income* £26,056 *Grants* £35,762 *Assets* £500,821
trustees John Vernor-Miles; The Revd Jonathan Fletcher.
how to apply Applications can only be accepted from registered charities and should be in writing to the correspondent. In order to save administration costs, replies are not sent to unsuccessful applicants. For the most part, funds are fully committed.
who to apply to John Vernor-Miles, Trustee, c/o Hunters, 9 New Square, Lincoln's Inn, London WC2A 3QN *Tel.* 020 7412 0050

■ The F. P. Limited Charitable Trust

cc no 328737   **established** 1990
where funding can be given UK, with a possible preference for Greater Manchester.
who can benefit Registered charities.
what is funded This trust supports educational causes, schools, religious bodies and medical appeals, giving most of its funds to regular beneficiaries.
sample grants Donations were made to a variety of schools, religious institutions and medical appeals. Unfortunately a detailed list of beneficiaries was not available.
finances *Year* 2011–12 *Income* £257,500 *Grants* £46,146 *Assets* £226,812
trustees Joshua Pine; Eli Pine.
how to apply In writing to the correspondent.
who to apply to Eli Pine, Trustee, Crown Mill, 1 Crown Street, Salford, Manchester M3 7DH *Tel.* 01618 340456 *Fax* 01618 320385 *email* ABURNETT@RPG.CO.UK

■ The Faber Charitable Trust

cc no 294820   **established** 1986
where funding can be given UK.
who can benefit Jewish causes.
what is funded General charitable purposes.
finances *Year* 2011–12 *Income* £5,799 *Grants* £35,000

trustees Bernard Faber; Fay Faber; Benjamin Rosefelder; Jeremy Golker.
how to apply In writing to the correspondent.
who to apply to David Marks, Devonshire House, 1 Devonshire Street, London W1W 5DR *Tel.* 020 7304 2000

■ Esmée Fairbairn Foundation

cc no 200051   **established** 1961
where funding can be given UK.
who can benefit Organisations with charitable purposes.
what is funded **The Main Fund**: the cultural life of the UK, education and learning, the natural environment and enabling disadvantaged people to participate more fully in society. The foundation prioritises work that: addresses a *significant* gap in provision; develops or strengthens good practice; challenges convention or takes a risk in order to address a difficult issue; tests out new ideas or practices; takes an enterprising approach to achieving its aims; sets out to influence policy or change behaviour more widely.
Strands: the foundation also makes grants under the following strands:
Food– This strand supports work that demonstrates the important role food plays in wellbeing and that connects people to the food that they eat. As part of this primary aim the strand seeks to bring about more sustainable food production and consumption policies and practices. The strand is open to both large-scale strategic interventions and innovative local work. Its budget is £5 million over three years, from January 2013 although it may be extended.
Esmée Fairbairn Collections Fund – This fund is run by the Museums Association. It focuses on time-limited collections work outside the scope of an organisation's core resources. Through this fund the MA will award approximately £800,000 per year to museums, galleries and heritage organisations with two grant rounds per year. Organisations can apply for sums between £20,000 and £100,000. They are keen to fund projects at an early stage of development where it may be difficult to guarantee tangible outcomes. We want organisations that are funded to become part of a network to develop ideas, share knowledge and build a legacy. Projects that are eligible to apply include research into collections, conservation, collections review and initiatives to develop the use of collections.
Merger Fund – to support organisations in the early phases of thinking about a merger. The fund is not intended to meet any costs association with a merger once a firm decision is made to proceed. It is for organisations uncertain about what the decision might involve or those who need reassurance that a proposed merger makes sense. Feasibility work may cover consultation with relevant parties; facilitation of discussions with potential merger partner/s or governance, planning, financial, legal, HR or communications advice.
what is not funded The foundation will not support the following: individuals or causes that will benefit only one person, including student grants or bursaries; support for a general appeal or circular; work that does not have a direct benefit in the UK; the promotion of religion; capital costs, including building work, renovations, and equipment; work that is routine or well-proven elsewhere or with a low impact; healthcare or related work such as medical research, complementary medicine, counselling

and therapy, education and treatment for substance misuse; work that is primarily the responsibility of central or local government, health trusts or health authorities, or which benefits from their funding. This includes residential and day care, housing, individual schools, nurseries and colleges, supplementary schools and vocational training; projects that primarily benefit the independent education sector; environmental projects related to animal welfare, zoos, captive breeding and animal rescue centres; individual energy efficiency or waste reduction schemes; recreational activities including outward bound courses and adventure experiences; we will not normally replace or subsidise statutory income although we will make rare exceptions where the level of performance has been exceptional and where the potential impact of the work is substantial; retrospective funding or general appeals.

TYPE OF GRANT Primarily core and project grants. Funding can be given for up to or over three years.

RANGE OF GRANTS The average grant from the Main Fund was £90,000.

SAMPLE GRANTS Main Fund: Teach First (£568,000), to develop a programme of tailored leadership and development support for social entrepreneurs amongst Teach First's ambassadors; Aldeburgh Music (£500,000), to support a new initiative aimed at nurturing artistic development; Federation of London Youth Clubs (£298,000), towards core costs to support members to strengthen their evidence-base, embed conflict resolution in their practices and build the capacity of disadvantaged young people; SHINE: Support and Help in Education (£284,000), towards the Let Teachers Shine campaign, which will support local and collaborative solutions to raising attainment in literacy and numeracy; Coalition for the Removal of Pimping (£275,000), to provide one-to-one support, information and advocacy to parents whose children are sexually exploited by pimps and organised criminal gangs; London Wildlife Trust (£167,000), towards the salary of a volunteer officer and other related project costs to create a new infrastructure that effectively supports and nurtures local action and advocacy; 20 Stories High (£120,000), towards arts projects particularly for BME and socially-excluded young people in the Liverpool and across the UK; Africans Unite Against Child Abuse (£102,000), towards the cost of safeguarding African children and young people from trafficking and ritual abuse; Incredible Edible Growing Ltd (£90,000), towards core costs for work reconnecting young people to the land and creating training and opportunities in business, food-growing and preparation; Spark and Mettle (£50,000), towards a programme that improves the well-being, employment skills and network disadvantaged young people through social media and Greenwich and Docklands Festivals (£25,000), towards a large-scale performance by deaf and disabled artists which aims to contribute to the development of high-quality disability arts in the UK.

FINANCES *Year* 2012 *Income* £11,952,000 *Grants* £32,423,000 *Assets* £779,602,000

TRUSTEES James Hughes-Hallett, Chair; Tom Chandos; Beatrice Hollond; Thomas Hughes-Hallett; Kate Lampard; Baroness Linklater; William Sieghart; John Fairbairn; Jonathan Phillips; Joe Docherty.

OTHER INFORMATION The fund also makes grants through a TASK Fund for organisations known to the trustees. The trust also runs a loan finance and social investment programme, see the trust website for more details.

HOW TO APPLY **Main Fund** – follow these three steps: 1. Carefully read through the guidance notes, supported areas and exclusions. 2. You may find it useful to take the online eligibility quiz before applying. 3. If you are eligible you must create an account on the site and complete the online application form.

'If your application is successful at first stage we will contact you to invite you to make a second stage application and inform you of what further information is required. If your first stage application is unsuccessful we will notify you by email. We make funding decisions throughout the year so you can apply at any time, but we only consider one application per organisation at a time. We usually only make one Main Fund grant to an organisation at a time. You do not need to have matched funding in place before applying but where the total cost of the work you propose for funding is high, you should indicate other sources of funding or specific plans to apply elsewhere. Our final decisions are based on an assessment of the quality of the work proposed, the importance of the issue, the strength of your idea, the difference the work is likely to make and the match to at least one of our priorities.'

The first stage application form and full guidance notes is available from the foundation's website. There is a different application process for the funding strands. To learn more about the strands and how to apply, visit the foundation's website.

WHO TO APPLY TO Caroline Mason, Chief Executive, Kings Place, 90 York Way, London N1 9AG *Tel.* 020 7812 3700 *Fax* 020 7812 3701 *email* info@esmeefairbairn.org.uk *Website* www.esmeefairbairn.org.uk

----

■ The Fairstead Trust

CC NO 1096359   **ESTABLISHED** 2003
WHERE FUNDING CAN BE GIVEN Worldwide.
WHO CAN BENEFIT UK registered charities.
WHAT IS FUNDED General charitable purposes.
RANGE OF GRANTS £1,000–£30,000
SAMPLE GRANTS East Anglian Children's Hospices (£30,000); Grove House (£20,000); Paul's Cancer Centre and Family Links (£15,000 each); St Albans Cathedral Education Centre (£14,000); Afghan Connection, Castlehaven Community Association, The Archway Project, Hertfordshire Community Foundation and DEC East Africa Appeal (£10,000 each); Cley Memorial Hall Fund, Hillside Animal Sanctuary and Chance to Shine (£5,000 each); Hopefield Animal Sanctuary (£3,000); Smile Train (£1,500) and NNDRA (£1,000).

FINANCES *Year* 2011–12 *Income* £31,405 *Grants* £184,500 *Assets* £2,210,293

TRUSTEES Edward Cox; Wendy Cox; Lucinda Cox; Claire Mitchell.

HOW TO APPLY In writing to the correspondent containing the following: aims and objectives of the charity; nature of appeal; total target if for a specific project; contributions received against target; registered charity number; any other relevant factors.

WHO TO APPLY TO Simon Rees, Administrator 22 Chancery Lane, London WC2A 1LS

■ The Fairway Trust

CC NO 272227   **ESTABLISHED** 1976
WHERE FUNDING CAN BE GIVEN UK and worldwide.
WHO CAN BENEFIT Charities, universities, colleges and schools.
WHAT IS FUNDED Support of universities, colleges, and schools in UK and abroad; scholarships, grants and loans to postgraduates and undergraduates; grants to help religious purposes; support of clubs and recreational facilities for children and young people; preservation and maintenance of buildings of particular interest; and social welfare.
WHAT IS NOT FUNDED No grants to medical charities.
RANGE OF GRANTS £100–£20,000.
SAMPLE GRANTS Family Education Trust (£20,000); Textile Conservation (£6,000); Clubs for Young People Northern Ireland and Welsh National Opera (£2,000); CIVITA's, Fan Museum, Lucy Cavendish and Prayer Book Society (£1,000 each); Grantchester Parochial Church Council (£750) and 4th Ormskirk Guides (£200).
FINANCES *Year* 2011–12 *Income* £41,648 *Grants* £40,401 *Assets* £50,205
TRUSTEES Janet Gudrun Grimstone; Kirsten Suenson-Taylor.
HOW TO APPLY In writing to the correspondent, although the trust has previously stated 'as funds and office resources are limited it cannot be guaranteed that unsolicited applications will be answered'.
WHO TO APPLY TO J. Gudrun Grimstone, Trustee, The Gate House, Coombe Wood Road, Kingston upon Thames, Surrey KT2 7JY

■ The Family Rich Charities Trust

CC NO 264192   **ESTABLISHED** 1972
WHERE FUNDING CAN BE GIVEN UK and developing countries.
WHO CAN BENEFIT Medical, welfare, arts and music charities.
WHAT IS FUNDED Beneficiaries include hospitals; organisations specialising in disease research such as epilepsy, leukaemia, cancer, Parkinson's disease and diabetes; care of people with disabilities; and disaster relief.
WHAT IS NOT FUNDED No grants to individuals.
SAMPLE GRANTS British Heart Foundation; Colon Cancer Concern; the British Epilepsy Association; Computer Aid International; the Diabetes Trust Research Fund; the Leprosy Relief Association; Marie Curie Cancer Care; Médecins Sans Frontières and Scannappeal; the Multiple Sclerosis Society and the Royal Star and Garter Home.
FINANCES *Year* 2011–12 *Income* £46,126 *Grants* £32,000 *Assets* £157,481
TRUSTEES Barbara Anderman; Margaret Fruchter; Tessa Goldstein; Simon Fruchter.
OTHER INFORMATION In 2011–12 grants were given to 33 organisations.
HOW TO APPLY In writing to the correspondent.
WHO TO APPLY TO Margaret Ann Fruchter, Trustee, 6 Forge Lane, Petersham Road, Richmond upon Thames, Surrey TW10 7BF *Tel.* 020 8948 7982

■ Famos Foundation Trust

CC NO 271211   **ESTABLISHED** 1976
WHO CAN BENEFIT Small local projects and established organisations benefiting children, young adults, clergy and Jewish people.
WHAT IS FUNDED Education, religion, international organisations, and general charitable purposes.

The trust will consider funding: the advancement of the Jewish religion; synagogues; Jewish umbrella bodies; church schools; cultural and religious teaching and religious studies.
TYPE OF GRANT One-off, core costs and running costs. Funding is given for one year or less.
RANGE OF GRANTS Up to £5,000.
SAMPLE GRANTS Relief of poverty (£50,000); education (£30,000); Places of Worship (£17,500); medical (£9,500).
FINANCES *Year* 2011–12 *Income* £327,305 *Grants* £107,119 *Assets* £1,637,683
TRUSTEES Rabbi S. M. Kupetz; Fay Kupetz; Isaac Kupetz; Joseph Kupetz.
OTHER INFORMATION No list of beneficiaries available.
HOW TO APPLY In writing to the correspondent, at any time. The trust does not accept telephone enquiries.
WHO TO APPLY TO Rabbi S. M. Kupetz, Trustee, 4 Hanover Gardens, Salford, Greater Manchester M7 4FQ *Tel.* 01617 405735

■ The Lord Faringdon Charitable Trust

CC NO 1084690   **ESTABLISHED** 2000
WHERE FUNDING CAN BE GIVEN UK.
WHO CAN BENEFIT Registered charities only.
WHAT IS FUNDED Educational grants and scholarships; hospitals and the provision of medical treatment for people who are ill; purchase of antiques and artistic objects for museums and collections which have public access; care and assistance of people who are elderly or infirm; community and economic development and housing; development and assistance of arts and sciences, physical recreation and drama; research into matters of public interest; relief of poverty; support of matters of public interest; animal care and conservation; maintaining and improving the Faringdon Collection.
WHAT IS NOT FUNDED No grants to individuals, just to registered charities.
SAMPLE GRANTS Faringdon Collection (£30,000); Buscot Centenary and Millennium Fund (£20,000); the National Trust and the Gordon Palmer Memorial Trust (£10,000 each); the Royal Horticultural Society, Royal Opera House and Royal Choral Society (£5,000 each); Root and Branch and Taunton and Somerset Spinal Unity (£2,000 each); Salvation Army, the Woodland Trust and Prospect Hospice (£1,000 each); and Living Memorial Historical Association, Historical Chapels Trust and Red Squirrel Survival Trust (£500 each).
FINANCES *Year* 2011–12 *Income* £170,822 *Grants* £177,000 *Assets* £6,860,076
TRUSTEES A. Forbes; The Hon J. Henderson; S. Maitland Robinson; Bernard Cazenove.
HOW TO APPLY In writing to the correspondent. According to the trustees' report for 2011/12, 'grant applications are accepted from registered charities and other recognised bodies. All grant applications are required to provide information on the specific purpose and expected beneficiaries of the grants. This information helps the charity assess how its programme of discretionary grantmaking achieves a spread of benefit.'
WHO TO APPLY TO S. L. Lander, Secretary to the Trustees, The Estate Office, Buscot Park, Faringdon SN7 8BU *Tel.* 01367 240786 *email* estbuscot@aol.com

■ Samuel William Farmer's Trust

CC NO 258459   **ESTABLISHED** 1929
WHERE FUNDING CAN BE GIVEN Mainly Wiltshire.
WHO CAN BENEFIT Registered charities benefiting children and older people.
WHAT IS FUNDED Charities working in the fields of residential facilities and services, infrastructure development, churches, hospices, healthcare, medical studies and research, conservation, environmental and animal sciences, education and various community facilities and services.
TYPE OF GRANT One-off and recurrent. Capital and core costs. Funding is given for up to three years.
RANGE OF GRANTS £250–£15,000. Average grants range from £1,000–£5,000.
SAMPLE GRANTS Field in Trust (£10,000); the Crown Centre (£6,000); Sevington Victorian School Appeal (£4,000); SWIFT Medics and Hop, Skip and Jump – Wiltshire (£3,000 each); Wiltshire Blind Association, Epilepsy Society and Wiltshire Scout Council (£2,000 each); and Wiltshire Air Ambulance Appeal, Bath Institute of Medical Engineering and Swindon Therapy Centre for Multiple Sclerosis (£1,000 each).
FINANCES *Year* 2012 *Income* £84,654 *Grants* £82,834 *Assets* £2,246,878
TRUSTEES Bruce Waight; Jennifer Liddiard; Peter Fox-Andrews; Charles Brockis; Jean Simpson.
OTHER INFORMATION Grant total includes £1,200 to individuals.
HOW TO APPLY In writing to the correspondent. Trustees meet half-yearly. Trustees bring suggestions and applications for grants to their half yearly meetings. Grants must be formally approved before they are made. There must be at least three trustees present at a meeting for decisions to be made.
WHO TO APPLY TO Melanie Linden-Fermor, Administrator, 71 High Street, Market Lavington, Devizes SN10 4AG *Tel.* 01380 813299

■ The Farmers' Company Charitable Fund

CC NO 258712   **ESTABLISHED** 1969
WHERE FUNDING CAN BE GIVEN UK.
WHO CAN BENEFIT Individuals and organisations benefiting students, and members of the Farmers' Company who are disadvantaged by poverty or in distress, socially isolated or at risk.
WHAT IS FUNDED Promotion of agriculture research and education, including scholarships; providing relief to members of the Farmers' Company in hardship or distress; providing funds for UK students travelling abroad to study agriculture; environmental issues.
RANGE OF GRANTS Usually up to £2,000.
SAMPLE GRANTS Wye College for the agricultural management course; Seale Hayne College for the agricultural-management course; the Royal Agricultural Benevolent Institution to assist farmers in need and the Lord Mayor's Appeal for various city charities.
FINANCES *Year* 2011–12 *Income* £114,901 *Grants* £34,148 *Assets* £2,056,318
TRUSTEE The Worshipful Company of Farmers.
OTHER INFORMATION The grant total includes nearly £10,000 that was given to individuals.
HOW TO APPLY In writing to the correspondent. The trust has various funds through which it administers different grants and awards – see the trust's websites for details.
WHO TO APPLY TO Col. David King, Clerk, Red Copse End, Red Copse Lane, Boars Hill, Oxford

OX1 5ER *Tel.* 01865 321580 *email* clerk@farmerslivery.org.uk *Website* www.farmerslivery.org.uk

■ The Thomas Farr Charity

CC NO 328394   **ESTABLISHED** 1989
WHERE FUNDING CAN BE GIVEN UK, especially Nottinghamshire.
WHO CAN BENEFIT Registered charities only.
WHAT IS FUNDED General charitable purposes.
WHAT IS NOT FUNDED No grants to individuals.
TYPE OF GRANT Capital costs; core costs; start-up costs. Unrestricted.
RANGE OF GRANTS Up to £25,000; usually for £5,000 or less.
SAMPLE GRANTS Carlton Academy, Nottingham University Hospital Charity and Redhill Academy (£25,000 each); Framework Housing Association (£15,000); Life Education Centres Nottinghamshire (£12,000); FunDays in Nottinghamshire (£10,000); Bromley House Library, Marie Curie Cancer Care and Mansfield Family Life Center (£5,000 each); Zone Youth Project and Carlton Digby School (£3,000 each); Viva Chamber Orchestra (£2,500); Countryside Foundation for Education (£2,000); Literacy Volunteers in Nottinghamshire and Incest and Sexual Abuse Survivors (£1,000 each) and Lowdham Women's Institute (£500).
FINANCES *Year* 2011–12 *Income* £307,480 *Grants* £308,430 *Assets* £7,407,812
TRUSTEES Rathbone Trust Company Ltd; Henry Farr; Amanda Farr; Barry Davys; P. K. Myles.
OTHER INFORMATION In 2011–12 grants were given to 109 organisations.
HOW TO APPLY In writing to the correspondent. Applications are considered in March and September/November.
WHO TO APPLY TO John Thompson, 6A The Almhouses, Mansfield Road, Daybrook, Nottingham NG5 6BW *Tel.* 01159 661222 *email* thomasfarrch@btconnect.com

■ Walter Farthing (Trust) Limited

CC NO 220114   **ESTABLISHED** 1957
WHERE FUNDING CAN BE GIVEN Mid Essex.
WHO CAN BENEFIT Organisations enlarging the range (including innovative projects) and/or volume of charitable services provided in the locality.
WHAT IS FUNDED Initiation or assistance of the development of projects by undertaking or grant aiding the acquisition, erection or adaptation of buildings and the provision of initial equipment.
WHAT IS NOT FUNDED The trust does not ordinarily support the headquarters of national charities, services which public authorities are empowered to provide, individuals or current expenditure of any nature or description.
TYPE OF GRANT Capital grants.
RANGE OF GRANTS £250–£2,500.
SAMPLE GRANTS Little Haven's Hospice (£2,000); Mid Essex Mind (£1,500); Mencap Chelmsford, Marie Curie Cancer Care, Brainwave, J's Hospice, Helping Hands Essex, Vauxhall Christian Trust, and Essex Respite Association (£1,000 each); Colne Engaine Memorial Hall (£750); Handicapped Children's Action Group, Chelmsford Rugby Club, The Eyeless Trust, and Essex Boys' and Girls' Clubs (£500 each); and National Search and Rescue Dog Association and Prospect Trust (£250 each).
FINANCES *Year* 2011–12 *Income* £46,312 *Grants* £46,000

TRUSTEES Geoffrey Chivas; Christine Sands; Michael Vandome; Francis Whitbread; Anthea Tilsley; D. J. Wisbey; Jennifer Black; James Copsey.

HOW TO APPLY In writing to the correspondent. Note that the trust states that it receives many applications that fall outside its area of interest, which cannot be considered.

WHO TO APPLY TO Michael Vandome, Trustee, Fir Tree Lane, Little Baddow, Chelmsford CM3 4SS *Tel.* 01245 223465

■ The Farthing Trust

CC NO 268066   **ESTABLISHED** 1974

WHERE FUNDING CAN BE GIVEN UK and overseas.

WHO CAN BENEFIT Individuals and charitable organisations, most of which are personally known to the trustees.

WHAT IS FUNDED General charitable purposes, with a focus on the advancement of religion, education, health and human rights and the reconciliation and promotion of religious and racial harmony, equality and diversity.

TYPE OF GRANT One-off and recurring grants.

SAMPLE GRANTS During the year grants were broken down into the following categories: overseas Christian causes (£38,000); education – UK and overseas (£37,000); UK churches (£35,000); UK Christian causes (£32,000); Christ's servants (£25,000); individuals in need – UK and overseas (£16,000); overseas general charities (£4,000); local grants (£3,700); and UK general charities (£2,500).

FINANCES *Year* 2011–12 *Income* £118,074 *Grants* £146,325 *Assets* £2,944,295

TRUSTEES C. H. Martin; E. Martin; J. Martin; A. White.

HOW TO APPLY Applications and enquiries should be made in writing to the correspondent. Applicants, and any others requesting information, will only receive a response if an sae is enclosed. Most beneficiaries are known to the trustees personally or through their acquaintances, though applications from other organisations are considered.

WHO TO APPLY TO Heber Martin, Administrator, PO Box 277, Cambridge CB7 9DE

■ The Fassnidge Memorial Trust

CC NO 303078   **ESTABLISHED** 1963

WHERE FUNDING CAN BE GIVEN London borough of Hillingdon, especially the former urban district of Uxbridge.

WHO CAN BENEFIT Individuals and organisations benefiting children, older people, parents and children, carers, people with disabilities, people disadvantaged by poverty, and victims of domestic violence.

WHAT IS FUNDED Welfare of older people and families, particularly charities working in the fields of care in the community, day centres and meals provision.

WHAT IS NOT FUNDED Applications from people or organisations outside the London borough of Hillingdon are not considered.

TYPE OF GRANT Small one-off grants and start-up costs. Funding of one year or less will be considered.

SAMPLE GRANTS Previous beneficiaries include: 60+Fair; Sipson Community Association; and Hillingdon Homelessness Comfort Fund.

FINANCES *Year* 2011–12 *Income* £39,145 *Grants* £38,000

TRUSTEES Brian Fredericks; David Horne; Andrew Retter; David Routledge; David Herriott; Richard Walker; Peter Curling; Peter Ryerson; David Yarrow; George Cooper; Judith Cooper; Tony Burles; John Morgan.

HOW TO APPLY In writing to the correspondent.

WHO TO APPLY TO Paul Cowan, 119 Cannonbury Avenue, Pinner, Middlesex HA5 1TR *Tel.* 0202483372

■ Joseph Fattorini Charitable Trust

CC NO 200032   **ESTABLISHED** 1960

WHERE FUNDING CAN BE GIVEN Throughout the UK.

WHO CAN BENEFIT Charitable organisations, particularly those benefiting the Roman Catholic, older people and children, terminally ill.

WHAT IS FUNDED General charitable purposes, with a particular preference to the Roman Catholic faith and activities benefiting the elderly, children and terminally ill.

WHAT IS NOT FUNDED Grants are never given to organisations concerning animal welfare and to individual students for educational support or 'gap year' projects.

TYPE OF GRANT One – off grants to organisations and an annual grant towards the Stonyhurst College scholarship fund.

RANGE OF GRANTS Generally under £1,000.

SAMPLE GRANTS Previous beneficiaries have included: Rose Charitable Trust (£2,000); Guernsey Art Community, D Day Centre, Community of Holy Fire and St Joseph Catholic Church (£1,000 each); and Sunny Days Children's Fund and Fountaine Hospital Trust (£500 each).

FINANCES *Year* 2011–12 *Income* £26,754 *Grants* £18,015 *Assets* £571,978

TRUSTEES Joseph Fattorini; Peter Fattorini.

HOW TO APPLY In writing to the correspondent. The response will only be provided if a self-addressed envelope is enclosed.

WHO TO APPLY TO Peter Fattorini, Trustee, White Abbey, Linton, Skipton, North Yorkshire BD23 5HQ

■ The February Foundation

CC NO 1113064   **ESTABLISHED** 2006

WHERE FUNDING CAN BE GIVEN UK.

WHO CAN BENEFIT Charitable organisations and institutions.

WHAT IS FUNDED The foundation will consider the following organisations for the receipt of grants, equity investment or loans: charities for the benefit of persons who are making an effort to improve their lives; charities for the benefit of persons no longer physically or mentally able to help themselves; charities which protect the environment; charities offering formal education resulting in recognised qualifications; small or minority charities where small grants will have a significant impact; companies where the acquisition of equity would be in line with the foundation's investment policy.

WHAT IS NOT FUNDED The foundation will not consider applications from the following: child care, Citizens Advice, community centres, higher education, housing associations, individuals, medical research, minibuses, NHS trusts, non-departmental government bodies, overseas projects, primary or secondary education; Scouts, Guides, Brownies, Cubs, and similar organisations; secondary education, single-faith organisations, sports clubs, unless for the mentally or physically disabled, village halls or youth centres.

TYPE OF GRANT One-off grants for capital and revenue costs. Loans are also considered.

FINANCES *Year* 2011–12 *Income* £13,974,744 *Grants* £2,087,032 *Assets* £25,522,798

TRUSTEES Richard Pierce-Saunderson; The February Foundation (Cayman).

OTHER INFORMATION The foundation made 17 grants to 12 organisations. A list of beneficiaries was not available.

HOW TO APPLY 'The February Foundation makes grants to selected charities. It monitors and supports the effective management of grants made. The foundation is focussed on managing its current commitments, although applications from some charities are still being accepted.' The accounts also note that: 'the trustees will normally award grants to registered charities. Exceptions to this policy will be reviewed on a case-by-case basis in the light of the status of the applicant, its organisational structure (for example, was it established for philanthropic and benevolent purposes), and the requested purpose of the grant.'

'Email applications are preferred. Send details and budget of the proposed project, how many people would benefit, how those benefits might be measured (not just financially), and what the estimated cost of raising funds for the project is. It is important to include in your email application full accounts for your most recent completed financial year, and, if your accounts do not contain it, what your total fundraising costs annually are. Note that hardcopy applications take significantly longer to process than email applications. Do not send DVDs, CDs, glossy brochures or other additional information. It normally takes 12 weeks from application to applicants being informed of the trustees' decision. There are no application deadlines as trustees make grant decisions on a monthly basis. **Note that less than 5% of all applications are successful.'**

WHO TO APPLY TO Richard Pierce-Saunderson, Trustee, Spring Cottage, Church Street, Stradbroke, Suffolk IP21 5HT *email* rps@thefebruaryfoundation.org *Website* www.thefebruaryfoundation.org

■ **Federation of Jewish Relief Organisations**

CC NO 250006　　　**ESTABLISHED** 1919

WHERE FUNDING CAN BE GIVEN Mainly Israel.

WHO CAN BENEFIT Jewish people, particularly those disadvantaged by poverty, socially isolated or in at risk groups, and those who are victims of war.

WHAT IS FUNDED Relief of Jewish victims of war and persecution; help wherever Jewish need exists.

SAMPLE GRANTS Israel Charity (£16,500); Children at Risk (£8,000) and Norwood (£5,500).

FINANCES *Year* 2011–12 *Income* £41,132 *Grants* £49,837 *Assets* £205,621

TRUSTEES Alfred Garfield; Angela Lando.

OTHER INFORMATION Founded in 1919 to assist victims of war and persecution in Europe and the Eastern Bloc. Since 1948 it has been concerned mainly in Israel with the rehabilitation, clothing, feeding and education of children of immigrant families.

HOW TO APPLY In writing to the correspondent.

WHO TO APPLY TO Angela Lando, Honorary Secretary and Trustee, HRS Danescroft Avenue, Hendon, London NW4 2NA *Tel.* 020 8457 9169 *email* fjro@btinternet.com

■ **The John Feeney Charitable Bequest**

CC NO 214486　　　**ESTABLISHED** 1906

WHERE FUNDING CAN BE GIVEN Birmingham.

WHO CAN BENEFIT Charitable organisations benefiting the Birmingham area.

WHAT IS FUNDED Benefit of public charities in Birmingham only; promotion of art in Birmingham only; acquisition and maintenance of open spaces near Birmingham.

WHAT IS NOT FUNDED Applications will not be accepted: from, or on behalf of, individuals; which do not directly benefit the Birmingham area or Birmingham charitable organisations; which could be considered as political or denominational.

TYPE OF GRANT One-off.

RANGE OF GRANTS Generally £500–£2,000.

SAMPLE GRANTS Birmingham Bach Choir, the City of Birmingham Museums and Art Gallery Development Trust and MSC Birmingham (£5,000 each); Performances Birmingham Limited (£3,000); Warley Woods Community Trust Limited, Castle Bromwich Hall Gardens Trust and Royal Birmingham Society of Artists (£2,000 each); Orchestra of the Swan and Ackers Adventure (£1,500 each); Birmingham Pen Trade Heritage Association, Black Country Living Museum Trust and Stage 2 Youth Theatre Company (£1,000 each); and Moby Duck Theatre Company (£500).

FINANCES *Year* 2012 *Income* £82,023 *Grants* £36,500 *Assets* £1,583,028

TRUSTEES John Smith; Hugh Carslake; James Lloyd; Michael Darby; Charles King-Farlow; Geoffrey Oakley; Merryn Ford Lloyd; Anouk Perinpanayagam; William Southall; Sally Luton; Lucy Reid.

HOW TO APPLY Priority will be given to applications from charitable organisations operating in the fields of the arts, music, heritage and open spaces. Trustees will seek to give grants to organisations where they feel that the grants, whatever size, will have a significant impact. Applications will only normally be considered from registered charities.

Application forms are available from the trust's website. When the form is completed post or email it with a supporting letter and other documents to the correspondent.

WHO TO APPLY TO Amanda Cadman, Secretary, 55 Wychall Lane, Birmingham B38 8TB *Tel.* 01216 243865 *email* secretary@feeneytrust.org.uk *Website* www.feeneytrust.org.uk

■ **The George Fentham Birmingham Charity**

CC NO 214487　　　**ESTABLISHED** 1907

WHERE FUNDING CAN BE GIVEN City of Birmingham.

WHO CAN BENEFIT Individuals and organisations benefiting young adults and people disadvantaged by poverty.

WHAT IS FUNDED Educational grants to bona fide residents of Birmingham (three-year minimum) aged 16 to 25 years of age. Particularly charities working in the fields of tertiary and higher education, and various community services and facilities, will be considered.

WHAT IS NOT FUNDED Only registered charities are supported. No grants towards salary costs. West Midlands organisations outside the city of Birmingham are not eligible.

RANGE OF GRANTS Up to £10,000.

542

Does the trust you have chosen match your needs? Haphazard applications waste postage and time

SAMPLE GRANTS Birmingham Settlement (£12,000); St Basils (£7,000); Birmingham Crisis Centre, Marie Curie Cancer Care and Birmingham Law Centre (£5,000 each); Happy Days Children's Charity (£4,000); Children with Cystic Fibrosis Dream Holidays (£3,600); Friends of Priestley Smith School (£3,000); Acorns Children's Hospice (£2,500); Lodge Road Church Centre (£2,250); Orchestra of the Swan (£2,000); Interact Reading Services, Craftspace and South Sudanese East Bank Community Centre (£1,500 each) and Cerebral Palsy Midlands (£1,000).

FINANCES *Year* 2012 *Income* £197,664 *Grants* £171,897 *Assets* £5,336,405

TRUSTEES John Bower, Chair; Barry Earp; Diana Duggan; Derek Ridgway; Martin Holcombe; Jean Turner; Margaret Martin.

OTHER INFORMATION In 2012 grants were made to 57 organisations totalling £144,000 and to 13 individuals totalling £28,000.

HOW TO APPLY On a form available from the correspondent or to download from the website, where criteria and guidelines are also posted. General grants are made in April and October, while education grants are made from September to April.

WHO TO APPLY TO Anne Holmes, c/o Veale Wasbrough Vizards LLP, Second Floor, 3 Bindley Place, Birmingham B1 2JB *Tel.* 01212 273705 *email* george.fentham@vwv.co.uk *Website* www.georgefenthamcharity.org.uk

---

■ The A. M. Fenton Trust

CC NO 270353　　　**ESTABLISHED** 1975
WHERE FUNDING CAN BE GIVEN UK, preference for North Yorkshire, and overseas.
WHO CAN BENEFIT Registered charities.
WHAT IS FUNDED General charitable purposes with preference towards health, medical, disability and young people.
WHAT IS NOT FUNDED The trust is unlikely to support local appeals, unless they are close to where the trust is based.
TYPE OF GRANT Mostly one-off.
RANGE OF GRANTS £100–£20,000.
SAMPLE GRANTS Yorkshire County Cricket Club Charitable Youth Trust (£20,000); Hipperholme Grammar School (£10,000); the Tweed Foundation and Dewsbury League of Friendship (£8,000 each); Horticap, Arthritis Research Council and Police Treatment Centres (£4,000 each); Marie Curie Cancer Care and Epilepsy Research UK (£3,000 each); Every Child and Institute of Medical Engineering (£2,000 each); Crimestoppers Trust, Abandoned Animals Charity and Ability Beyond Disability (£1,000 each); Macmillan Centre Fund and Girl Guides Brighouse (£500 each); and Checkheaton Boxing Academy (£200).
FINANCES *Year* 2012 *Income* £142,656 *Grants* £172,785 *Assets* £4,273,415
TRUSTEES James Fenton; C. Fenton.
OTHER INFORMATION Grants were made to over 65 organisations and totalled £173,000.
HOW TO APPLY In writing to the correspondent.
WHO TO APPLY TO James Fenton, Trustee, 14 Beech Grove, Harrogate HG2 0EX *Tel.* 01423 504442

■ The Allan and Nesta Ferguson Charitable Settlement

CC NO 275487　　　**ESTABLISHED** 1977
WHERE FUNDING CAN BE GIVEN UK and overseas.
WHO CAN BENEFIT Registered charities and individuals.
WHAT IS FUNDED Educational and development initiatives, including the promotion of world peace and development.
SAMPLE GRANTS Open University (£1 million); University of Manchester and the School of Oriental and African Studies, University of London (£150,000 each); London School of Hygiene and Tropical Medicine (£110,000); Homeless International (£45,000); Mission Aviation Fellowship and Farm Africa (£30,000 each); The Baynards Zambia Trust (£20,000); and the Latin American Mining Monitoring Programme and Third Hope (£15,000 each).
FINANCES *Year* 2012 *Income* £869,336 *Grants* £3,995,532 *Assets* £24,457,896
TRUSTEES Elizabeth Banister; Prof. David Banister; James Richard Tee; Letitia Glaister.
OTHER INFORMATION Grants are also made towards the fees of postgraduate students who are in their final year of a postgraduate course, subject to evidence of financial hardship.
HOW TO APPLY On an application form available from the trust's website. The following guidance is given by the foundation:
'**When to apply:** Applications by charities for small to medium grants (up to a maximum of £50,000) may be submitted at any time and will be considered on a regular basis. Applications for larger grants will be considered at bi-annual meetings held in March and October and applications should be submitted at the very latest in the previous months i.e. February or September. **Note:** No repeat applications will be considered within three years of the conclusion of the grant term.'
'**How to apply:** We prefer where possible that you complete and submit the on-line application form on [the trust's] website and email it to us. Alternatively you may download and print out the application form, complete it and send it by letter post. Do not extend the length of the forms, or add any attachments. Applications **MUST NOT** exceed three pages. Use text size 12. Do not apply for more than one project. All applications by email will be acknowledged and considered by the trustees within six to eight weeks. If you do not hear further, after the acknowledgement, then unfortunately your application has not been successful. If the trustees do decide to award you a grant then they will contact you. No progress reports will be given and no correspondence will be entered into in the meantime.'
WHO TO APPLY TO James Richard Tee, Trustee, Stanley Tee Solicitors, High Street, Bishops Stortford, Hertfordshire CM23 2LU *Tel.* 01279 755200 *email* jrt@stanleytee.co.uk *Website* www.fergusontrust.co.uk

---

■ Elizabeth Ferguson Charitable Trust Fund

SC NO SC026240　　　**ESTABLISHED** 1988
WHERE FUNDING CAN BE GIVEN UK, with some interest in Scotland.
WHO CAN BENEFIT Organisations benefiting children and young people, particularly those who are sick.
WHAT IS FUNDED The welfare and wellbeing of children and young people. Also charities

involved in medical research and hospitals where special medical equipment is needed.

WHAT IS NOT FUNDED Non-registered charities are not supported. The trust does not make grants overseas.

RANGE OF GRANTS £250–£10,000.

SAMPLE GRANTS Previous beneficiaries have included the Govan Initiative and Harmony Row Boys' Club.

FINANCES *Year* 2011–12 *Income* £821,659 *Grants* £250,500

TRUSTEES Sir Alex Ferguson; Cathy Ferguson; Huw Roberts; Ted Way; Les Dalgarno; Paul Hardman; Jason Ferguson.

HOW TO APPLY An application form and guidelines should be requested in writing from the correspondent. The committee meets to consider grants at the end of January and July. Applications should be received by December and June respectively.

WHO TO APPLY TO The Trustees, c/o 27 Peregrine Crescent, Droylsden, Manchester M43 7TA

....

■ The Fidelity UK Foundation

CC NO 327899   **ESTABLISHED** 1988

WHERE FUNDING CAN BE GIVEN Particular preference is given to projects in Kent, Surrey, London and continental Europe.

WHO CAN BENEFIT Not for profit organisations, charities.

WHAT IS FUNDED General, giving is primarily allocated for charitable purposes in the following areas: community development, health, arts and culture and education. The trust seeks to support projects undertaken by organisations to increase proficiency, achieve goals and reach long-term self-sufficiency. Most often, funding is given for projects such as capital improvements, technology upgrades, organisational development and planning initiatives.

WHAT IS NOT FUNDED Grants are not generally made to: charities that have been in existence for less than three years; sectarian or political organisations; schools, colleges, universities or playgroups; individuals; community centres; sports clubs or general appeals and circulars. Grants are not made for: salaries or general running/core costs; training projects; the replacement of dated or out-of-warranty IT equipment; marketing costs; the promotion of religion; sponsorships or benefit events; university/college fees, research projects or gap year expeditions. Grants will not normally cover the entire cost of a project. Grants will not normally be awarded to an organisation in successive years. Grants are one-off investments; they will not normally be awarded for or across multiple years. Grants are for planned expenditure; they will not normally cover costs incurred prior to application and/or the grant being awarded.

TYPE OF GRANT Buildings, capital, IT development, one-off grants to develop infrastructure. Funding for less than one year is considered.

RANGE OF GRANTS £1,000–£725,000

SAMPLE GRANTS Impetus Trust (Early Years Initiative) and Great Ormond Street Hospital Children's Charity (£500,000 each); English Heritage (Stonehenge) (£400,000); The Design Museum and The Shakespeare Globe Trust (£300,000 each); Royal Opera House Foundation (£270,000); City and Guilds of London Art School Property Trust (£150,000); National Council for Voluntary Organisations and New Philanthropy Capital (£50,000 each); FareShare

(£47,000); Southbank Centre (£40,000) and Greenhouse Schools Project Limited (£31,000).

FINANCES *Year* 2012 *Income* £7,311,423 *Grants* £4,790,262 *Assets* £135,451,012

TRUSTEES Edward Johnson; Barry Bateman; Anthony Bolton; Richard Millar; John Owen; Sally Walden.

HOW TO APPLY In writing to the correspondent. Applicants should enclose a summary form (form can be downloaded from the foundation's website) as well as a separate document outlining: organisation history and key achievements and an overview of the organisations forward strategy and key objectives. It should give the following project details: an indication and evidence of the need for the project that requires funding; an outline of the proposed project, and how it fits into the wider strategic plan; the project's objectives and forecast outcomes; an indication of how the project's success will be monitored and evaluated; an implementation plan/timeline; an itemised budget; the fundraising plan, including a list of other actual/potential funders and the status of each request; an indication of what a grant would allow your organisation to achieve, and how a grant will change or improve the long-term potential and sustainability of your organisation. You should also attach the following: a list of the directors and trustees with their backgrounds; the most recently audited annual financial statements and the most recent monthly management accounts. There are no deadlines for submitting grant proposals. All applications will normally receive an initial response within three months. The review process can take up to six months, which should be factored into the applicant's funding plan. The foundation may request additional information or a site visit to better familiarise themselves with the organisation, its management team and the project. The foundation welcomes informal phone calls prior to the submission of a formal application. Applicants for international grants should not use the application form. Instead you should post a brief outline of your organisation and funding proposal. If appropriate the foundation will respond and advise you whether you should make a full application.

WHO TO APPLY TO Susan Platts-Martin, Chief Executive, Oakhill House, 130 Tonbridge Road, Hildenborough, Tonbridge, Kent TN11 9DZ *Tel.* 01732 777364 *Website* www. fidelityukfoundation.org

....

■ The Doris Field Charitable Trust

CC NO 328687   **ESTABLISHED** 1990

WHERE FUNDING CAN BE GIVEN UK, with a preference for Oxfordshire.

WHO CAN BENEFIT Large UK and small local organisations in Oxfordshire.

WHAT IS FUNDED Medical, welfare, education and general charitable purposes.

WHAT IS NOT FUNDED It is unlikely that grants would be made for salaries, training or higher education costs.

TYPE OF GRANT One-off and recurrent.

RANGE OF GRANTS £50–£40,000, mostly £5,000 or less.

SAMPLE GRANTS Meningitis UK (£40,000); Cancer Research UK (£30,000); Greenpower (£15,000); Medical and Life Sciences Research Fund (£9,000); Vale and Downland Museum, Oxfordshire Historical Churches and Royal British Legion (£5,000 each); the Pegasus School Trust (£3,000); Pathway Workshop

(£2,000); Whizz-Kidz, Wesley Memorial Methodist Church – Oxford and Oxford PHAB Club (£1,000 each); and Blackbirds Leys Adventure Playgroup, the Movement Foundation and the Parasol Project (£500 each).

FINANCES *Year* 2011–12 *Income* £353,206 *Grants* £241,040 *Assets* £7,916,499

TRUSTEES John Cole; N. Harper; Wilhelmina Church.

HOW TO APPLY According to the trustees' report for 2011/12, 'the trustees receive applications from diverse sources. Each applicant is required, except in exceptional cases, to complete a standard application form and to submit information in support of that application.' Applications are considered three times a year or as and when necessary.

WHO TO APPLY TO Helen Fanyinka, Administrator, c/o Morgan Cole, Buxton Court, 3 West Way, Oxford OX2 0SZ *Tel.* 01865 262183

■ Fife Council/Common Good Funds and Trusts

SC NO SC019393 **ESTABLISHED** 1975

WHERE FUNDING CAN BE GIVEN Fife.

WHO CAN BENEFIT Individuals in need and local community groups such as community councils and sports clubs.

WHAT IS FUNDED Arts, buildings, conservation/environment, disability, education/training, heritage, hospitals/hospices, social welfare of people of all ages and sports and recreation.

WHAT IS NOT FUNDED The following causes are not supported: animal welfare; medical/health; medical research; overseas projects; political appeals; and religious appeals.

TYPE OF GRANT One-off grants for capital and revenue costs.

RANGE OF GRANTS Mostly under £1,000.

FINANCES *Year* 2011–12 *Grants* £70,000

OTHER INFORMATION The Office of the Scottish Charity Regulator states that the charity has ceased. The entry is based on the information available on the council website, which states that grants are available.

HOW TO APPLY Contact the correspondent for further details. An application form and guidelines are available for the Common Good Funds but not for the trusts. Applications can be made at any time. Forms can be downloaded from the council's website.

WHO TO APPLY TO Laura MacKean, Policy Officer, Fife Council, Fife House, North Street, Glenrothes, Fife KY7 5LT *Tel* 0845 155 5555 (ext. 460071) *Fax* 01592 583155 *email* laura.mackean@fife.gov.uk *Website* www.fife.gov.uk

■ The Fifty Fund

CC NO 214422 **ESTABLISHED** 1963

WHERE FUNDING CAN BE GIVEN Nottinghamshire and surrounding area.

WHO CAN BENEFIT Individuals and organisations benefiting retired people; unemployed people; those in care, fostered and adopted; parents and children; one-parent families; widows and widowers; carers; disabled people; and people disadvantaged by poverty.

WHAT IS FUNDED Relief of poverty, infrastructure development, charity or voluntary umbrella bodies, advice and information on housing, respite care, and various community services.

WHAT IS NOT FUNDED No grants for education, expeditions or travel.

TYPE OF GRANT Mostly one-off grants for revenue costs and project funding.

RANGE OF GRANTS £500–£18,000.

SAMPLE GRANTS Nottinghamshire Hospice (£18,000); Salvation Army (£6,500); SSAFA (£4,500); Nottingham City Council (£4,000); Dove Cottage Day Hospice (£3,500); Nottingham Winter Shelter, Macmillan Cancer Relief and Council For Family Care (£3,000 each); Dogs for the Disabled and Cotgrave Advice Centre (£2,000 each); Happy Days Children Charity, Nottingham Forresters Access To Football and Missing People (£1,500 each); Nottinghamshire Royal Society For The Blind (£750) and Over the Wall (£500).

FINANCES *Year* 2012 *Income* £280,538 *Grants* £199,332 *Assets* £7,292,792

TRUSTEES E. Whiles; Edward Randall; Revd Canon George Barrodale; Revd Amanda Cartwright.

OTHER INFORMATION The grant total includes £70,000 that was given to 136 individuals and £129,000 that was given to 54 organisations.

HOW TO APPLY In writing to the correspondent.

WHO TO APPLY TO Craig Staten-Spencer, Administrator, c/o Nelsons Solicitors, Pennine House, 8 Stanford Street, Nottingham NG1 7BQ *Tel.* 01159 895251 *email* craig.staten-spencer@nelsonslaw.co.uk

■ Filey Foundation Ltd

CC NO 1148376 **ESTABLISHED** 2012

WHERE FUNDING CAN BE GIVEN UK.

WHO CAN BENEFIT Charities and community groups

WHAT IS FUNDED General, education, social welfare.

FINANCES *Year* 2012–13 *Income* £85,599 *Grants* £49,180 *Assets* £107,687

TRUSTEES Charles Englard; Rachel Englard; Judith Schwarz.

OTHER INFORMATION Unfortunately a list of beneficiaries was not included in the foundation's first set of accounts.

HOW TO APPLY In writing to the correspondent.

WHO TO APPLY TO Charles Englard, Trustee, 73 Bishops Road, Prestwich, Manchester M25 0AS *Tel.* 01617 951999

■ Dixie Rose Findlay Charitable Trust

CC NO 251661 **ESTABLISHED** 1967

WHERE FUNDING CAN BE GIVEN UK.

WHO CAN BENEFIT Charitable organisations.

WHAT IS FUNDED General charitable purposes with preference to children, seafarers, blindness and multiple sclerosis.

TYPE OF GRANT One-off and recurrent.

RANGE OF GRANTS £1,000–£6,000.

SAMPLE GRANTS St John's Wood Church (£6,000); St John's Wood Adventure Playground and Hampshire and Isle of Wight Air Ambulance (£5,000 each); Kent, Surrey and Sussex Air Ambulance Trust (£4,000); Brighton and Hove Parents and Children's Group and Shooting Star CHASE (£3,000 each); Multiple Sclerosis Trust, Pathfinder Guide Dog Programme and Reading Association for the Blind (£2,000 each); and the Legacy Rainbow House and Surrey Association for Visual Impairment (£1,500 each).

FINANCES *Year* 2012–13 *Income* £98,904 *Grants* £100,900 *Assets* £4,496,605

TRUSTEE HSBC Trust Company (UK) Ltd.

HOW TO APPLY In writing to the correspondent.

WHO TO APPLY TO S. Hill, Trust Manager, HSBC Trust Company UK Limited, Trust Services, 10th Floor,

Norwich House, Nelson Gate, Southampton SO15 1GX *Tel.* 02380 722243

....

■ Finnart House School Trust

cc no 220917   **established** 1901
where funding can be given Worldwide.
who can benefit Schools and charitable organisations benefitting Jewish children and young people in need of care and/or education.
what is funded Bursaries and scholarships are given to Jewish secondary school pupils and university entrants who are capable of achieving, but would probably not do so because of family and economic pressures. Jewish school welfare funds and charities concerned with helping Jewish children are also assisted.
type of grant Buildings, capital, one-off and project.
range of grants £1,000–£5,000.
sample grants JFS School (£10,000) and King Solomon High School (£6,000).
finances *Year* 2011–12 *Income* £152,703 *Grants* £16,000 *Assets* £4,463,806
trustees Dame Hilary Blume; Robert Cohen; Linda Paterson; Sue Leifer; Gideon Lyons; Gil Cohen; Mervyn Kaye; Anthony Yadgaroff.
other information A further £171,000 was made in grants to individuals.
how to apply Note the following statement taken from the trust's website: 'If you are a charity (working for Jewish children in need) seeking support, understand that the major part of Finnart's income goes to fund the Finnart Scholars. If you wish to apply, though realising the chances of success are slim, check by telephone, email or letter before doing so. If you are a school seeking a hardship fund, remember that our trust deed restricts our grant giving to Jewish children in need. We may also require evidence of the eligibility of any pupil. We will require a report on how any funds have been dispersed.'
who to apply to Jamie Wood, Administrator, Radius Works, Back Lane, London NW3 1HL *Tel.* 07804 854905 *email* info@finnart.org *Website* www.finnart.org

....

■ Gerald Finzi Charitable Trust

cc no 313047   **established** 1969
where funding can be given UK.
who can benefit Organisations and individuals.
what is funded The trustees aim to reflect the ambitions and philosophy of the composer Gerald Finzi (1901–56), which included the general promotion of 20th century British music through assisting and promoting festivals, recordings and performances of British music. A limited number of modest grants are also offered to young musicians towards musical training.
what is not funded 'We do not fund college or university courses, nor subsistence for students.'
range of grants Up to £1,250
sample grants Three Choirs' Festival (£1,000); Royal Hall Restoration Trust, Harrogate (£750); Celebrating English Song at Tardebigge, National Youth Orchestra and London Song Festival (£500 each); CLIC Sargent Symphony Orchestra (£200); and Abingdon School (£150).
finances *Year* 2011–12 *Income* £57,718 *Grants* £24,645 *Assets* £171,431

trustees Robert Gower, Chair; Andrew Burn; Christian Alexander; Judy Digney; Jean Finzi; Sarah Moule; Stuart Ritchie; Paul Spicer.
other information The grant total includes £5,000 given in grants to organisations.
how to apply In writing to the correspondent.
who to apply to Elizabeth Pooley, Administrator, PO Box 137, Stour Row, Shaftesbury, Dorset SP7 0WX *email* admin@geraldfinzi.org *Website* www.geraldfinzi.org

....

■ Firtree Trust

cc no 282239   **established** 1981
where funding can be given UK and abroad.
who can benefit Christian organisations.
what is funded Religious education and the advancement of the Protestant and Evangelical tenets of the Christian faith.
type of grant One year grants for capital and revenue costs.
range of grants Up to £3,000.
sample grants Harvest Christian Fellowship Trust (£3,000); Open Doors (£2,600); Christians Against Poverty and FEBA (£2,000 each); Sat-7 Trust Ltd (£1,500); Warlingham Methodist Trust (£1,200); Titus Trust (£1,300); Tearfund and United Christian Broadcasters (£1,000 each); and UCCF (£750).
finances *Year* 2011–12 *Income* £49,136 *Grants* £44,330 *Assets* £28,572
trustees Maurice Turner; James Stephen Turner; Paul Turner; Elizabeth Turner; Margaret Turner.
other information The grant total includes £12,500 that was given to individuals.
how to apply In writing to the correspondent.
who to apply to James Turner, Trustee, 12 Purley Bury Avenue, Purley, Surrey CR8 1JB *Tel.* 020 8668 1994

....

■ The Sir John Fisher Foundation

cc no 277844   **established** 1979
where funding can be given UK, with a preference for charities in the Furness peninsula and adjacent area and local branches of national charities.
who can benefit National and local registered charities.
what is funded The foundation has six main areas of interest: maritime; medical and disability; education; music; arts; and community projects in and around Barrow-in-Furness.
what is not funded The trustees will generally not fund: individuals; sponsorship; expeditions; promotion of religion; places of worship; animal welfare; retrospective funding; pressure groups; community projects outside Barrow-in-Furness and surrounding area (except occasional projects in Cumbria or North Lancashire or if they fall within one of the other categories supported by the foundation).
type of grant Capital and revenue funding for up to three years.
range of grants Mostly under £10,000.
sample grants *Local beneficiaries included*: Lancaster University (£185,000 in five grants); Hospice of St Mary of Furness (£25,000); The Wordsworth Trust (£20,000); Blackwell Sailing and Lakeland Arts Trust (£15,000 each); Walney Community Trust (£12,000); Citizens Advice – Barrow (£10,400); Age Concern Barrow and District (£10,000); North West Air Ambulance (£9,000); The Mayor's Relief Fund (£4,000) and West Lakeland Orchestral Society (£1,000). *National beneficiaries included*:

National Maritime Museum (£40,000); Skin Treatment and Research Trust (£37,500); Mary Rose Trust (£25,000); London Handel Society Ltd (£20,000); The English Concert (£15,000); Tall Ships Youth Trust (£8,000); Elizabeth Finn Care (£5,000); Asthma Relief (£3,800); Imperial College (£1,000) and Children in Need (£475).

FINANCES *Year* 2011–12 *Income* £1,304,225 *Grants* £1,055,594 *Assets* £47,206,230

TRUSTEES Daniel P. Tindall, Chair; Diane S. Meacock; Sir David Hardy; Rowland F. Hart Jackson; Michael J. Shields.

HOW TO APPLY Application forms are available from the secretary or to download from the foundation's website. Completed applications should be submitted together with all relevant information (set out on the application form) to the secretary at least six weeks in advance of the next trustees' meeting. The trustees meet at the beginning of May and the beginning of November each year. Urgent grants for small amounts (less than £4,000) can be considered between meetings, but the trustees would expect an explanation as to why the application could not be considered at a normal meeting. Applicants are welcome to contact the secretary for an informal discussion before submitting an application for funding. The trustees expect to receive feedback from the organisations they support, to help in their decision making process. Organisations are asked to provide a brief one page report about nine months after receipt of a grant (or when the specific project assisted has been completed). A feedback form is available from the foundation's website.

WHO TO APPLY TO Dr David Hart Jackson, Trust Secretary, Heaning Wood, Ulverston, Cumbria LA12 7NZ *Tel.* 01229 580349 *email* info@sirjohnfisherfoundation.org.uk *Website* www.sirjohnfisherfoundation.org.uk

■ Fisherbeck Charitable Trust

CC NO 1107287　　**ESTABLISHED** 2004
WHERE FUNDING CAN BE GIVEN Worldwide.
WHO CAN BENEFIT Registered charities worldwide.
WHAT IS FUNDED The advancement of the Christian religion; support for the provision of accommodation for the homeless; the relief of poverty; the advancement of education; conservation of the environment and the preservation of heritage.
WHAT IS NOT FUNDED Grants are only made to individuals known to the trust or in exceptional circumstances.
TYPE OF GRANT One-off and recurrent.
RANGE OF GRANTS Up to £50,000.
SAMPLE GRANTS Christian Viewpoint for Men (£45,000); Tear Fund (£41,000); Urban Saints (£40,000); Worthing Churches Homeless Project (£30,000); Breakout Trust (£22,000); St Paul's Centre (£20,000); Youth for Christ (£10,000) and Alpha International (£8,000).
FINANCES *Year* 2011–12 *Income* £482,937 *Grants* £406,870 *Assets* £313,221
TRUSTEES I. R. Cheal; J. Cheal; M. Cheal.
OTHER INFORMATION £5,300 was also given as a grant to one individual.
HOW TO APPLY In writing to the correspondent, although note: 'This is a family run charitable trust. We have a list of charities supported on an annual basis. There is no money available for new applicants – only occasionally, but not very often.'
WHO TO APPLY TO Ian Cheal, Trustee, Home Farm House, 63 Ferringham Lane, Ferring, Worthing, West Sussex BN12 5LL *Tel.* 01903 241027

■ The Fishmongers' Company's Charitable Trust

CC NO 263690　　**ESTABLISHED** 1972
WHERE FUNDING CAN BE GIVEN UK, however this refers to charities whose objects extend throughout England. Special interest in the City of London and its adjacent boroughs.
WHO CAN BENEFIT Registered charities and individuals (for educational grants only).
WHAT IS FUNDED General. In practice, education, relief of poverty and disability, in particular assistance to almshouses, fishery related bodies, environment and heritage.
WHAT IS NOT FUNDED No grants to individuals except for educational purposes.
RANGE OF GRANTS Up to £300,000.
SAMPLE GRANTS The Gresham's Foundation (£205,000); Gresham's School (£38,000); New Model School (£34,000); Thames Diamond Jubilee Foundation and Redlands Primary School (£10,000 each); Sustainable Eel group (£9,000); London Youth Rowing (£8,400); Countryside Alliance Foundation and Fishermen's' Mission (£5,000 each); Pavilion Opera Educational Trust (£3,000); Corda and The Liver Group (£1,750 each) and Mission to Seafarers, Shadwell Basin Outdoor Activity Centre and Southwark Cathedral Development Trust (£1,000 each).
FINANCES *Year* 2012 *Income* £1,517,114 *Grants* £526,951 *Assets* £19,245,937
TRUSTEES The Worshipful Company of Fishmongers; Peter Woodward.
OTHER INFORMATION £750 was distributed to individuals.
HOW TO APPLY In writing to the correspondent. Meetings take place three times a year, in March, June/July and November, and applications should be received a month in advance. No applications are considered within three years of a previous grant application being successful. Unsuccessful applications are not acknowledged.
WHO TO APPLY TO Peter Woodward, Assistant Clerk, The Fishmongers' Company, Fishmongers' Hall, London Bridge, London EC4R 9EL *Tel.* 020 7626 3531 *Fax* 020 7929 1389 *email* ct@fishhall.org.uk *Website* www.fishhall.org.uk

■ Marc Fitch Fund

CC NO 313303　　**ESTABLISHED** 1956
WHERE FUNDING CAN BE GIVEN UK.
WHO CAN BENEFIT Both individuals and institutions benefiting young adults, research workers and students.
WHAT IS FUNDED Publication and research in archaeology, historical geography, history of art and architecture, heraldry, genealogy, surnames, catalogues of and use of archives (especially ecclesiastical) and other antiquarian, archaeological or historical studies. In many cases, the awards enable work to be undertaken, or the results published either in print or on-line form, which would not otherwise be achieved.
WHAT IS NOT FUNDED No grants are given towards foreign travel or for research outside the British Isles (unless the circumstances are exceptional); building works; mounting exhibitions; or general appeals. No awards are made in connection with vocational or higher education courses or to people reading for higher degrees.
TYPE OF GRANT Mainly publication costs and incidental research expenses.

SAMPLE GRANTS College of Arms and Newcastle University (£25,000 each); Public Catalogue Foundation and Sulgrave Archaeology Group (£10,000 each); Christ Church Oxford (£6,000); North Wales Dendro Project and University of Reading (£5,000 each); University of York (£4,000); London Metropolitan University (£3,000); Royal Cornwall Museum (£2,500); Moothill and Abbey Survey Scone and Romney Society (£2,000 each); Hebden Bridge Society (£1,500); Manchester University Press and Norfolk Heraldry Society (£1,000 each); and Boydell and Brewer (£500).

FINANCES *Year* 2011–12 *Income* £194,291 *Grants* £175,769 *Assets* £5,244,317

TRUSTEES David White; Lindsay Allason-Jones; Andrew Howard Murison; Dr Helen Forde; Prof. John Blair; Prof. David Hey; Dr Michael Hall; David Palliser; Bernard Nurse; Christiana Payne.

OTHER INFORMATION The grant total includes £18,010 given in research grants to individuals.

HOW TO APPLY In writing to the correspondent, providing a brief outline of the project. The Council of Management meets twice a year, in spring and autumn, to consider applications. The deadlines for receipt of completed applications and references are 1 March and 1 August. The fund requests that any application enquiries be made well in advance of these deadlines as the application process is likely to take at least a few weeks to complete.

WHO TO APPLY TO Christopher Catling, Director, 19 The Avenue, Cirencester, Gloucestershire GL7 1EJ *Tel.* 01608 811944 *email* admin@marcfitchfund.org.uk *Website* www.marcfitchfund.org.uk

....

■ The Fitton Trust

CC NO 208758   **ESTABLISHED** 1928
WHERE FUNDING CAN BE GIVEN UK.
WHO CAN BENEFIT Registered charities only.
WHAT IS FUNDED General charitable purposes.
WHAT IS NOT FUNDED No grants to individuals.
RANGE OF GRANTS Usually £100–£250; occasionally £1,000 or more.
SAMPLE GRANTS King's Medical Research Trust.
FINANCES *Year* 2011–12 *Income* £92,246 *Grants* £56,650 *Assets* £1,543,975
TRUSTEES Dr R. P. A. Rivers; D. V. Brand; R. Brand; K. J. Lumsden; E. M. Lumsden; L. P. L. Rivers.
HOW TO APPLY In writing to correspondent. The secretary scrutinises and collates applications in preparation for the trustee meetings. The trustees meet three times each year, usually in April, August and December and they consider all applications.
WHO TO APPLY TO Rosalind Gordon-Cumming, The Secretary, PO Box 661, West Broyle, Chichester PO19 9JS

....

■ The Earl Fitzwilliam Charitable Trust

CC NO 269388   **ESTABLISHED** 1975
WHERE FUNDING CAN BE GIVEN UK, with a preference for areas with historical family connections, chiefly in Cambridgeshire, Northamptonshire and Yorkshire.
WHO CAN BENEFIT Organisations benefiting: children and young adults; clergy; ex-service and service people; volunteers; Christians; Church of England; at risk groups; disabled people; people living in rural areas; victims of abuse and crime; victims of man-made or natural disasters; and

people with cancer, diabetes, head and other injuries, leprosy, mental illness, spina bifida and hydrocephalus. Projects and charities connected in some way with or which will benefit rural life and communities including churches.

WHAT IS FUNDED Preference for charitable projects in areas with historical family connections, chiefly in Cambridgeshire, Northamptonshire and Yorkshire. Particularly charities working in the fields of: accommodation and housing; infrastructure, support and development; Christian outreach; churches; religious umbrella bodies; arts, culture and recreation; health facilities and buildings; cancer research; conservation and environment; schools and colleges; and various community facilities and services.

WHAT IS NOT FUNDED No grants to individuals.

TYPE OF GRANT Buildings, capital, endowments, one-off, project and research.

RANGE OF GRANTS Mostly under £5,000 but occasionally more.

SAMPLE GRANTS Malton Amenity CIFC (£60,000); Peterborough Cathedral Development and Preservation Trust (£25,000); Eton College (New Foundation) (£5,000); I CAN – Million Lost Voices Appeal (£2,500); Break, Hunt Servants Fund, Peterborough Streets and St Margaret's Church – Fletton (£2,000 each); Warwickshire and Northamptonshire Air Ambulance, Safe Haven Children's Trust, National Autistic Society and Mepal Outdoor Centre (£1,000 each); Sheffield Academy of Young Leaders and Support Dogs (£500 each) and Wednesday Phab Club and Movember (£250 each).

FINANCES *Year* 2011–12 *Income* £198,415 *Grants* £177,352 *Assets* £12,928,362

TRUSTEES Sir Philip Naylor-Leyland; Lady Isabella Naylor-Leyland.

HOW TO APPLY In writing to the correspondent. Trustees meet about every three months.

WHO TO APPLY TO R. W. Dalgleish, Secretary to the Trustees, Estate Office, Milton Park, Peterborough PE6 7AH *Tel.* 01733 267740

....

■ The Ian Fleming Charitable Trust

CC NO 263327   **ESTABLISHED** 1971
WHERE FUNDING CAN BE GIVEN UK.
WHO CAN BENEFIT Individual musicians and registered charities benefiting medical professionals, research workers and scientists. Support is also given to at risk groups, and people who are disabled, disadvantaged by poverty or socially isolated.

WHAT IS FUNDED National charities actively operating for the support, relief and welfare of men, women and children who are disabled or otherwise in need of help, care and attention, and charities actively engaged in research on human diseases; and music education awards under a scheme administered by the Musicians Benevolent Fund and advised by a committee of experts in the field of music.

WHAT IS NOT FUNDED No grants to individuals except under the music education award scheme. No grants to purely local charities.

RANGE OF GRANTS £1,000–£3,000.

SAMPLE GRANTS Music in Hospitals, National Blind Children's Society and Edinburgh Young Carers (£1,500 each); and Action Medical Research Child Cataracts Appeal, Army Benevolent Fund, Brain Research Trust, Gurkha Welfare Fund and Mental Health Foundation (£1,000 each).

FINANCES *Year* 2011–12 *Income* £109,130 *Grants* £62,000 *Assets* £1,052,060

TRUSTEES Archibald Fleming; A. Isaacs; Gordon Wyllie.

OTHER INFORMATION Grants were made totalling just over £62,000, of which £20,000 was given in 18 grants to organisations and £42,000 was awarded to the Musicians Benevolent Fund Awards.

HOW TO APPLY In writing to the correspondent.

WHO TO APPLY TO Archibald Fleming, Trustee, Fairfax House, 15 Fulwood Place, London WC1V 6AY *Tel.* 020 7969 5500 *email* dmcgowan@haysmacintyre.com

■ The Joyce Fletcher Charitable Trust

CC NO 297901   **ESTABLISHED** 1987

WHERE FUNDING CAN BE GIVEN England, almost entirely south west.

WHO CAN BENEFIT England/wide and south west charities with a preference towards young people and those with disabilities.

WHAT IS FUNDED Music in the community and in a special needs context; children's welfare; and charities in the south west. Currently main areas of interest are institutions and organisations specialising in music education and performance, special needs education and performance involving music, and charities for children's welfare.

WHAT IS NOT FUNDED Grants to individuals and students are exceptionally rare. No support for areas which are the responsibility of the local authority. No support is given to purely professional music/arts promotions. No support for purely medical research charities.

TYPE OF GRANT One-off and recurring expenses; capital and revenue; or new projects.

RANGE OF GRANTS £500–£5,000.

SAMPLE GRANTS Welsh National Opera (£5,000); Wiltshire Music Centre, RUH Arts Fund and Bath Festivals (£4,000 each); Drake Music, English Touring Opera and Iford Arts (£3,000 each); Bath Area Play Project, International Guitar Festival and National Star College – Cheltenham (£2,000 each); and Beckford Tower Trust, Wessex Foundation and Friends of Music at Wells Cathedral School (£1,000 each).

FINANCES *Year* 2011–12 *Income* £55,664 *Grants* £70,500 *Assets* £2,061,652

TRUSTEES Robert Fletcher; Stephen Fletcher; Susan Sharp; William Reddihough Fletcher.

OTHER INFORMATION Of the 36 organisations receiving support, 25 were based in the south west, ten were national charities, and one was based in another UK region.

HOW TO APPLY In writing to the correspondent before 1 November each year. Applications are considered in the months of October and November. There are no application forms. Letters should include the purpose for the grant, an indication of the history and viability of the organisation and a summary of accounts. Preliminary telephone calls are accepted. Applications via email will not be acknowledged.

WHO TO APPLY TO Robert Fletcher, Trustee, 68 Circus Mews, Bath BA1 2PW *Tel.* 01225 314355 *Website* www.joycefletchercharitabletrust.co.uk

■ Florence's Charitable Trust

CC NO 265754   **ESTABLISHED** 1973

WHERE FUNDING CAN BE GIVEN UK, with preference to Lancashire.

WHO CAN BENEFIT Individuals, registered charities and charitable organisations.

WHAT IS FUNDED General charitable purposes, especially establishment, maintenance and support of places of education; relief of sickness of infirmity for older people; and relief of poverty of anyone employed or formerly employed in the shoe trade.

TYPE OF GRANT One-off grants.

RANGE OF GRANTS £50–£30,000.

SAMPLE GRANTS Previous beneficiaries have included: Pioneer Community Club; Bacup Family Centre; Whitworth Water Ski; Rossendale Search and Rescue; Rossendale United Junior Football Club; North West Air Ambulance; British Heart Foundation; Rochdale Special Needs; Macmillan Cancer Support; Children with AIDS; SENSE; Tenovus; All Black Netball Fund; Sport Relief and Heart of Lancashire appeal. A number of local primary schools and playgroups also benefitted.

FINANCES *Year* 2011–12 *Income* £53,725 *Grants* £69,538 *Assets* £962,244

TRUSTEES Christopher Harrison; Gordon Dewhirst Low; Bob Uttley; Michael Kelly; Simon Holding; Angela Jepson.

HOW TO APPLY In writing only to the correspondent (no telephone calls please).

WHO TO APPLY TO Brian Terry, Secretary, E. Suttons and Sons Ltd, PO Box 2, Bacup OL13 0DT *Tel.* 01706 874961

■ The Flow Foundation

CC NO 328274   **ESTABLISHED** 1989

WHERE FUNDING CAN BE GIVEN UK.

WHO CAN BENEFIT Registered charities.

WHAT IS FUNDED The trust makes grants to support arts and culture, education, environment, Jewish, and medical causes.

RANGE OF GRANTS Usually up to £20,000.

SAMPLE GRANTS Imperial College (£143,000); Westminster School (£15,000); Norwood Ravenswood and The Tate Foundation (£10,000 each); British ORT and Sight Savers (£5,000 each); Families of the Fallen and The British Friends of Haifa University (£2,500 each); and Leuka (£1,000).

FINANCES *Year* 2011–12 *Income* £304,956 *Grants* £208,424 *Assets* £980,704

TRUSTEES Nathalie Shashou; Nita Sowerbutts; Harold Woolf; Josiane Woolf.

HOW TO APPLY In writing to the correspondent on one sheet of paper only.

WHO TO APPLY TO Nita Sowerbutts, Trustee, 22 Old Bond Street, London W1S 4PY *Tel.* 020 7499 9099

■ The Mrs Yvonne Flux Charitable Trust

CC NO 1136459   **ESTABLISHED** 2010

WHERE FUNDING CAN BE GIVEN UK.

WHO CAN BENEFIT Individuals and organisations.

WHAT IS FUNDED General charitable purposes.

FINANCES *Year* 2011–12 *Income* £160,037 *Grants* £161,066 *Assets* £6,744

TRUSTEES Yvonne Flux; Susan Boyle.

OTHER INFORMATION No information on beneficiaries was available.

HOW TO APPLY In writing to the correspondent.

WHO TO APPLY TO The Trustees, c/o Stephenson Smart and Co, 22–26 King Street, King's Lynn, Norfolk PE30 1HJ *Tel.* 01553 774104 *Fax* 01553 692602

....

■ The Gerald Fogel Charitable Trust

CC NO 1004451   **ESTABLISHED** 1991

WHERE FUNDING CAN BE GIVEN UK.

WHO CAN BENEFIT Mainly headquarters organisations benefiting: children and older people, those in care, fostered and adopted, Jewish people and homeless people.

WHAT IS FUNDED Charities working in the fields of: the advancement of the Jewish religion; synagogues; and cultural and religious teaching. The trust may also fund residential facilities, arts activities, care in the community, hospices, hospitals, cancer research and campaigning on health issues.

WHAT IS NOT FUNDED No grants to individuals or non-registered charities.

TYPE OF GRANT One-off and recurrent.

SAMPLE GRANTS Chai Cancer Care (£18,000); World Jewish Relief (£5,500); Norwood (£4,500); Community Security Trust (£2,500); Youth Aliyah (£2,300); United Jewish Israel Appeal (£2,000); Royal National Theatre (£1,300) and Crohn's and Colitis in Childhood – 3C's, Ben-Gurion University Foundation, Magen David Adom and Royal Academy of the Arts (£1,000 each).

FINANCES *Year* 2011–12 *Income* £70,728 *Grants* £58,825 *Assets* £883,755

TRUSTEES David Fogel; Joseph Fogel; Steven Fogel; Benita Fogel.

OTHER INFORMATION Small grants below £1,000 each totalled £5,200.

HOW TO APPLY In writing to the correspondent.

WHO TO APPLY TO David Truman, Accountant, Morley and Scott, Lynton House, 7–12 Tavistock Square, London WC1H 9LT

....

■ The Follett Trust

CC NO 328638   **ESTABLISHED** 1990

WHERE FUNDING CAN BE GIVEN UK and overseas.

WHO CAN BENEFIT Individuals and organisations benefiting children and young adults, actors and entertainment professionals, musicians, textile workers and designers, writers and poets, at risk groups and people disadvantaged by poverty; medical research and hospital projects; people with disabilities.

WHAT IS FUNDED Education; individual students in higher education (including theatre); disability and health; trusts for writers and publishers; and international relief work.

RANGE OF GRANTS Usually up to £20,000.

SAMPLE GRANTS George Orwell (£26,000); Impilo Place of Safety (£20,000); Canon Collins Education Trust (£18,000); Stevenage Citizens Advice (£15,000); UCL Development Fund (£13,000); Rosenhof Ahrensburg (£12,000); APEC and Battersea Arts Centre (£5,000 each); and English Pen, Education for Choice, Piggy Bank Kids, Scope and Turn the Boats Tide (£1,000 each).

FINANCES *Year* 2011–12 *Income* £161,967 *Grants* £195,468 *Assets* £45,788

TRUSTEES Brian Mitchell; Ken Follett; Barbara Follett.

OTHER INFORMATION Grants of less than £1,000 totalled £8,500.

HOW TO APPLY The trust states, 'A high proportion of donees come to the attention of the trustees through personal knowledge and contact rather than by written application. Where the trustees find it impossible to make a donation they rarely respond to the applicant unless a stamped addressed envelope is provided.'

WHO TO APPLY TO Brian Mitchell, Trustee, Po Box 4, Knebworth, Herts SG3 6UT *Tel.* 01438 222908

....

■ The Football Association National Sports Centre Trust

CC NO 265132   **ESTABLISHED** 1972

WHERE FUNDING CAN BE GIVEN UK.

WHO CAN BENEFIT County football associations, football clubs and other sports associations.

WHAT IS FUNDED The provision, maintenance and improvement of facilities for use in recreational and leisure activities.

WHAT IS NOT FUNDED No grants to individuals.

TYPE OF GRANT One-off grants towards community-based projects.

RANGE OF GRANTS £5,000–£25,000.

FINANCES *Year* 2012 *Income* £26,408 *Grants* £224,521 *Assets* £4,542,899

TRUSTEES Geoff Thompson; Barry Bright; Raymond Berridge; William Annable; Jack Perks.

HOW TO APPLY In writing to the correspondent.

WHO TO APPLY TO Richard McDermott, Secretary, Wembley National Stadium Ltd., PO Box 1966, London SW1P 9EQ *Tel* 0844 980 8200 ext. 6575 *email* richard.mcdermott@thefa.com

....

■ The Football Association Youth Trust

CC NO 265131   **ESTABLISHED** 1972

WHERE FUNDING CAN BE GIVEN UK.

WHO CAN BENEFIT County football associations, schools, universities and other sports associations benefiting young people who play football or other sports.

WHAT IS FUNDED The organisation or provision of facilities which will enable young people under the age of 21 in the UK to play association football or other games and sports including the provision of equipment, lectures, training colleges, playing fields or indoor accommodation.

TYPE OF GRANT One-off.

SAMPLE GRANTS Previous categories of expenditure include: Girls Centre of Excellence (£1 million); schools and universities (£204,500); county football associations (£77,500) and 'other' (£1,300).

FINANCES *Year* 2011–12 *Income* £10,408 *Grants* £500,000

TRUSTEES Raymond Berridge; Barry Bright; Geoff Thompson; Mervyn Leggett; Brian Adshead.

HOW TO APPLY In writing to the correspondent. Grants are made throughout the year. There are no application forms, but a copy of the most recent accounts should be sent.

WHO TO APPLY TO Richard McDermott, Secretary, Wembley National Stadium Ltd., PO Box 1966, London SW1P 9EQ *Tel* 0844 980 8200 ext 6575 *email* richard.mcdermott@thefa.com

■ The Football Foundation

CC NO 1079309   **ESTABLISHED** 2000
WHERE FUNDING CAN BE GIVEN England.
WHO CAN BENEFIT Grassroots football. It also occasionally funds educational and community projects.
WHAT IS FUNDED Improving football facilities, using sport to promote healthy lifestyles and build communities, developing children's sporting chances, improving the image of football and establishment of new clubs and teams.
SAMPLE GRANTS Grassroots grants: FC United of Manchester (£500,000); The Abbey School (£390,000); Glenfield Parish Council (£291,000); Telford College of Arts and Technology (£200,000); The London Playing Fields Foundation (£178,000); Norton Cricket Club and Miners Welfare (£51,000) and Gateshead Cleveland Hall Community Football (£26,000). **Premier League Community Facility Fund:** Cardiff City FC Community and Education, Manchester United Football Club and Wigan Athletic Community Trust (£350,000 each) and Tottenham Hotspur Community (£259,000). **Mayor of London: Facility Fund:** London Borough of Richmond upon Thames (£250,000); University of East London (£200,000); Twickenham Rowing Club (£165,000); The Ahoy Centre (£100,000); Homes for Islington (£50,000); Tottenham Community Sports Centre (£36,000) and Kingston Riding School (£24,000). **Barclays Spaces for Sports:** Preston Pirates BMX Club and Silverdale Cricket Club (£25,000) and Coventry City Football Community Scheme and Pompey Sports and Education Foundation (£24,000 each).
FINANCES *Year* 2011–12 *Income* £27,527,000 *Grants* £16,812,000 *Assets* £19,026,000
TRUSTEES Richard Scudamore; Roger Burden; Peter McCormick; Philip Smith; Richard Caborn; Jonathan Hall; Gary Hoffman.
OTHER INFORMATION See the foundation's website for full details of the current schemes.
HOW TO APPLY Detailed guidance notes are available on the website. Applications are submitted online.
WHO TO APPLY TO William Elkerton, Director of Finance, Whittington House, 19–30 Alfred Place, London WC1E 7EA *Tel.* 0845 345 4555 *Fax* 0845 345 7057 *email* enquiries@ footballfoundation.org.uk *Website* www. footballfoundation.org.uk

■ The Forbes Charitable Foundation

CC NO 326476   **ESTABLISHED** 1983
WHERE FUNDING CAN BE GIVEN UK.
WHO CAN BENEFIT Charitable organisations.
WHAT IS FUNDED Welfare causes primarily benefiting people with learning disabilities.
WHAT IS NOT FUNDED Support is only given to charitable organisations whose work primarily benefits people with learning disabilities.
TYPE OF GRANT Capital and some revenue costs.
RANGE OF GRANTS Up to £5,000.
SAMPLE GRANTS Cottage and Rural Enterprises Ltd (£31,500); Acre Housing, Bridge Priory Trust and Down's Syndrome Association (£5,000 each); Sussex Association for Spina Bifida and Hydrocephalus and Calvert Trust (£3,000 each); Camden Society, the Fircroft Trust and the Norman Laud Association (£2,000 each); and Scottish Autism (£1,700).
FINANCES *Year* 2011–12 *Income* £1,404,948 *Grants* £99,265 *Assets* £4,574,374

TRUSTEES John Waite; C. Packham; Nicolas Townsend; Ian Johnson; John Williamson; Robert Bunting.
HOW TO APPLY In writing to the correspondent. Applications should be received close to but no later than the last day of February, June or October. A copy of the latest accounts should be provided along with the application form. Application forms can be obtained from the foundation's website or in writing to the correspondent. Successful applicants will be expected to justify the expenditure of the grant given.
WHO TO APPLY TO John Shepherd, Administrator, PO Box 6256, Nuneaton CV11 9HT *Tel.* 01455 292881 *email* info@ theforbescharitablefoundation.org *Website* www. theforbescharitablefoundation.org

■ The Forces Trust

CC NO 211529   **ESTABLISHED** 1924
WHERE FUNDING CAN BE GIVEN UK.
WHO CAN BENEFIT Registered military or naval charities.
WHAT IS FUNDED Military or naval charities. The trustees prefer to assist people (disabled, injured and disadvantaged) rather than institutions or the preservation of buildings.
WHAT IS NOT FUNDED No grants to any non-naval or military charities, individuals, scholarships or education generally.
TYPE OF GRANT Capital, one-off, project, research and recurring costs. Funding of up to two years.
RANGE OF GRANTS £500–£25,000, typically £2,500.
SAMPLE GRANTS Sir Oswald Stoll Foundation (£20,000); League of Remembrance and Vitalise (£4,000 each) and Queen Alexandra Hospital Home (£2,000).
FINANCES *Year* 2011–12 *Income* £40,663 *Grants* £30,000 *Assets* £1,083,942
TRUSTEES Richard Nugee; Andrew Niekirk; William Niekirk; Brooke Vansittart Bowater.
HOW TO APPLY In writing to the correspondent at any time, preferably on one side of A4.
WHO TO APPLY TO Richard Nugee, Drews Mill, Potterne Road, Devizes, Wiltshire SN10 5LH *email* j.d@gilbert-allen.co.uk

■ Ford Britain Trust

CC NO 269410   **ESTABLISHED** 1975
WHERE FUNDING CAN BE GIVEN Local to the areas in close proximity to Ford Motor Company Limited's locations in the UK. These are Essex (including East London), Bridgend, Southampton and Daventry.
WHO CAN BENEFIT Registered charities; schools; non-profit organisations.
WHAT IS FUNDED Education, the environment, children, disabilities, youth education and projects that benefit the local communities that Ford operates in.
WHAT IS NOT FUNDED Grant applications are not considered if they support the following purposes or activities: major building works; sponsorship or advertising; research; overseas projects; travel; religious projects; political projects; purchase of second hand vehicles; third party fundraising initiatives (exceptions may be made for fundraising initiatives by Ford Motor Company Limited employees and retirees). National charities are assisted rarely and then only when the purpose of their application has specific benefit to communities located in close proximity to Ford locations.

Applications for core funding and major building projects are rarely considered. Grants cannot be provided to individuals.

TYPE OF GRANT Contributions to capital projects (e.g. refurbishments); capital expenditure items (e.g. furniture/equipment/computers); contributions towards the purchase or leasing of new Ford vehicles (up to a maximum of £2,000); and general funds (small grants up to £250 only).

RANGE OF GRANTS Most grants range between £250 and £4,000.

SAMPLE GRANTS St Joseph's Primary School (£3,400); Lllanharan Primary School and Sick Children's Trust (£3,000 each); Leigh Beck Infant School (£2,800); and DACT (£2,600).

FINANCES *Year* 2012–13 *Income* £187,172 *Grants* £134,666 *Assets* £321,661

TRUSTEES Michael Callaghan; David Russell; Michael Brophy; Dr June-Alison Sealy; Mitra Janes; Wendy James; Stephen Evison.

HOW TO APPLY On a form available from the correspondent or to download from the website. Applications for large grants should include a copy of the organisation's most recent report and accounts. Small grant applications are considered in March, June, September and November and should be submitted by the 1st of each month. Applications for large grants are considered in March and September.

WHO TO APPLY TO Gary Smith, 68 Blackheath, Colchester CO2 0AD *Tel.* 01268 404831 *email* fbtrust@ford.com *Website* www.ford.co.uk/fbtrust

....

■ The Oliver Ford Charitable Trust

CC NO 1026551   **ESTABLISHED** 1993

WHERE FUNDING CAN BE GIVEN UK.

WHO CAN BENEFIT Neighbourhood-based community projects, students and institutions. Children, young persons or adults who have learning disabilities or learning difficulties.

WHAT IS FUNDED The trust aims to educate the general public and advance knowledge of the history and techniques of interior decoration, the design of fabrics and other decorative materials and landscape gardening. Charities providing housing, educational or training facilities for children, young persons or adults who have learning disabilities or learning difficulties.

TYPE OF GRANT One-off.

RANGE OF GRANTS Usually up to £10,000.

SAMPLE GRANTS Livability (£10,000); Camphill Devon (£7,000); Autism Sussex Ltd and Enham (£5,000 each); National Star College and Papworth Trust (£4,000 each).

FINANCES *Year* 2011–12 *Income* £102,075 *Grants* £55,000 *Assets* £2,495,149

TRUSTEES Lady Wakeham; Martin Levy.

OTHER INFORMATION In 2011–12 grants were also given to students at the Furniture and History Society (£3,893); the Royal Horticultural Society (£5,000); and the Victoria and Albert Museum (£19,500).

HOW TO APPLY In writing to the correspondent. Trustees meet in March and October.

WHO TO APPLY TO Matthew Pintus, 20 Cursitor Street, London EC4A 1LT *Tel.* 020 7831 9222

....

■ Fordeve Limited

CC NO 1011612   **ESTABLISHED** 1992

WHERE FUNDING CAN BE GIVEN UK

WHO CAN BENEFIT Organisations benefiting Jews, at risk groups and people who are unemployed,

disadvantaged by poverty or socially isolated. Support may also be given to people who are disabled, homeless, immigrants or refugees.

WHAT IS FUNDED Orthodox Jewish causes.

SAMPLE GRANTS Previous beneficiaries include: the Gertner Charitable Trust; Lubavitch Foundation; the Yom Tov Assistance Fund; the Society of Friends of the Torah; Lolev Charitable Trust; Beth Jacob Grammar School for Girls.

FINANCES *Year* 2011–12 *Income* £107,278 *Grants* £108,116 *Assets* £582,482

TRUSTEES Jeremy Kon; Helen Kon.

HOW TO APPLY In writing to the correspondent.

WHO TO APPLY TO Jeremy Kon, Trustee, Hallswelle House, 1 Hallswelle Road, London NW11 0DH *Tel.* 020 8209 1535

....

■ The Forest Hill Charitable Trust

CC NO 1050862   **ESTABLISHED** 1995

WHERE FUNDING CAN BE GIVEN UK and overseas.

WHO CAN BENEFIT Organisations and individuals.

WHAT IS FUNDED Christian causes.

RANGE OF GRANTS Grants usually range between £1,000 and £2,000.

SAMPLE GRANTS LiNX (£21,000) and Great Parks Chapel (£10,000); Marilyn Baker Trust, Caring for Life, Christian Blind Mission, Concern Worldwide, Emmaus, Interserve, Mercy Ships, ROPE and World Emergency Relief (£2,000 each); Christians Against Poverty, Compass Braille, DELTA, Gate Christian Fellowship, Harvest Trust, Prison Fellowship and Time for Families (£1,000 each); and Evangelical Housing Association and Farm Crisis Network (£500 each).

FINANCES *Year* 2011–12 *Income* £179,630 *Grants* £178,800 *Assets* £3,175,584

TRUSTEES Horace Francis Pile; Ronald Stanley Pile; Marianne Sylvia Tapper; Michael Thomas; Patricia Jean Pile.

HOW TO APPLY The trustees have previously stated that their aim was to maintain regular and consistent support to the charities they are currently supporting. New requests for funding are therefore very unlikely to succeed and unsolicited applications are rarely considered.

WHO TO APPLY TO Dr Francis Horace Pile, Trustee, 104 Summercourt Way, Brixham, Devon TQ5 0RB *Tel.* 01803 852857 *email* horacepile@tiscali.co.uk

....

■ The Lady Forester Trust

CC NO 241187   **ESTABLISHED** 1979

WHERE FUNDING CAN BE GIVEN Shropshire

WHO CAN BENEFIT Primarily, the residents of the Parish of Wenlock and then the inhabitants of the County of Shropshire.

WHAT IS FUNDED Residents who are sick, convalescent, disabled or infirm where help is not readily available to them from other sources.

RANGE OF GRANTS Up to £30,000.

SAMPLE GRANTS St Dunstan's, Llandudno (£9,500); Combat Stress (£6,000); County Air Ambulance (£5,000); Marie Curie Cancer Care (£4,000); NSPCC (£2,000) and Surestart's Additional Needs Group (£1,000).

FINANCES *Year* 2012 *Income* £149,144 *Grants* £110,000

TRUSTEES Lady Forester, Chair; Alice Stoker; Libby Collinson; John Dugdale; Henry Carpenter; Lord Forester; The Lady Forester; Janette Stewart.

....

OTHER INFORMATION Previously, grants to organisations totalled £55,000 and grants to 70 individuals amounted to £37,000.

HOW TO APPLY Trustees meet on a quarterly basis to consider applications and will consider unsolicited applications. Grants for individuals are usually recommended by GPs or social workers. Application should be made in writing to the correspondent.

WHO TO APPLY TO Lady Forester, Trustee, Willey Estates, The Estate Office, Willey Park, Broseley, Shropshire TF12 5JJ *Tel.* 01952 884318

■ The Foresters' Fund for Children

CC NO 327449   **ESTABLISHED** 1987
WHERE FUNDING CAN BE GIVEN UK.
WHO CAN BENEFIT Non-profit making organisations, charities and agencies.
WHAT IS FUNDED Projects related to improving the quality of life of children and for specific education needs.
SAMPLE GRANTS The Ipswich Community Playbus; Birmingham Children's Hospital: Cardiac Theatre Appeal; School for Parents and Richard House Children's Hospice.
FINANCES *Year* 2011–12 *Income* £18,000 *Grants* £21,000
TRUSTEES Thomas Ball, Chair; Alex Clark; Darren Hanney; Paul Bayliss; Jason Alexander.
HOW TO APPLY On an application form available from the fund's website. Applications are considered by the trustees at their quarterly meetings.
WHO TO APPLY TO Thomas Ball, 37 Highfield, Penperlleni, Pontypool NP4 0BH *Tel.* 01873 880379 *email* grants@fffc.org.uk *Website* www.forestersfundforchildren.org.uk

---

■ The Foresters' Charity Stewards UK Trust

CC NO 328604   **ESTABLISHED** 1990
WHERE FUNDING CAN BE GIVEN UK.
WHO CAN BENEFIT Individuals and institutions benefiting older people, disabled people and communities as a whole.
WHAT IS FUNDED To improve quality of life and the environment of the community at large.
WHAT IS NOT FUNDED No grants to individuals.
TYPE OF GRANT One-off grants for capital and revenue costs.
SAMPLE GRANTS Previous beneficiaries have included: Abbeyfield, AOF Education Awards Fund, AOF Foresters' Home, AOF Yorkshire Convalescent Home, Mayor of Scarborough's Charity, North Middlesex Hospital, RNLI and Taste for Adventure.
FINANCES *Year* 2012 *Income* £1,901 *Grants* £35,000
TRUSTEES Graham Lloyd; Barbara Lloyd; Carole Shuttle; Derek Shuttle; Richard Biddlecombe; Pat Biddlecombe; Graham Lale; Tim Friend.
HOW TO APPLY In writing to the correspondent.
WHO TO APPLY TO Graham Lloyd, Trustee, Littlecroft, 8 The Marches, Kingsfold, Horsham, West Sussex RH12 3SY *email* CharityStewards@Gmail.com

---

■ Forever Manchester (The Community Foundation for Greater Manchester)

CC NO 1017504   **ESTABLISHED** 1993
WHERE FUNDING CAN BE GIVEN Greater Manchester.
WHO CAN BENEFIT Registered charities and small, locally run community or voluntary groups who seek to improve the circumstances in economically and socially excluded areas in Greater Manchester facing disadvantage.
WHAT IS FUNDED General charitable purposes including health; welfare; education; people with disabilities; older people; youth and children. Improving the quality of life and helping to build stronger communities across Greater Manchester.
WHAT IS NOT FUNDED The foundation will not support: organisations and projects outside the Greater Manchester area; organisations trading for profit or intending to redistribute grant awards; major capital requests, i.e. building and construction work; requests that will replace or enhance statutory provision; academic or medical research and equipment; overseas travel; primary purpose of request is to promote religious or political beliefs; retrospective grants – (projects/activities that have already taken place); projects that fall within statutory sector responsibility; sponsorship or fundraising events; contributions to larger/major appeals. (Where the application sum would not cover at least 75% of the total project cost); holidays and social outings. (Except in cases of specific disablement or proven benefit to a community or group of people); local branches of national charities unless locally managed, financially autonomous and not beneficiaries of national marketing or promotion; more than one application at a time for the same project.
TYPE OF GRANT One-off; project. Start-up costs will be considered.
RANGE OF GRANTS Mostly under £5,000 but can be up to £40,000, dependent upon scheme.
SAMPLE GRANTS Beneficiaries included: Shaw Gas Explosion Disaster Relief fund(£125,000); Mad Hat Hatters, Singing With Dementia, St Willibrord's Primary School Breakfast Club, Great Lever Voice, Lostock Skate Park, MaD Theatre Group and The Life Centre.
FINANCES *Year* 2011–12 *Income* £4,382,324 *Grants* £3,509,103 *Assets* £9,389,943
TRUSTEES John Sandford; Chris Hirst; Richard Hogben; Tony Burns; Simon Webber; Jo Farrell; Han-Son Lee; Sandra Lindsay; Natalie Qureshi.
PUBLICATIONS Guidelines; information packs.
OTHER INFORMATION The grant total includes £76,000 which was distributed in grants to individuals.
HOW TO APPLY The foundation have now changed policies and ask that interested parties contact them via telephone to discuss eligibility and project ideas. They can also send out application packs. Decisions are almost always given within three months but the exact time will often depend on a number of factors and not just when the appropriate committee next meets. One of the grants administrators may contact you for further information or to discuss your application. Contact the foundation directly for up-to-date information on deadlines for programmes and the dates of panel meetings.
WHO TO APPLY TO Nick Massey, Chief Executive Officer, 2nd Floor, 8 Hewitt Street, Manchester M15 4GB *Tel.* 01612 140940 *Fax* 01612 140941 *email* info@forevermanchester.com *Website* www.forevermanchester.com

■ The Forman Hardy Charitable Trust

CC NO 1000687 **ESTABLISHED** 1990

WHERE FUNDING CAN BE GIVEN Mostly Nottinghamshire.

WHO CAN BENEFIT Arts, Christian, medical, and welfare organisations.

WHAT IS FUNDED The trust exists to benefit a wide range of charitable activities but primarily focuses on the charitable needs of the city of Nottingham and the county of Nottinghamshire.

WHAT IS NOT FUNDED No grants are made to individuals.

SAMPLE GRANTS Hint – Base 51 (£10,000); Aysgarth School (£8,000); Hatch – Barnwell Charitable Trust, Sonagachi Sex Workers School Project, NCCL Galleries of Justice and Midlands Appeal for Sri Lanka (£5,000 each); Opera North Limited and The Jennie Marsh Trust (£2,000 each) and National Schools Symphony Orchestra, Relate Nottinghamshire, St Edmund Hall Oxford Boat Club, The British Forces Foundation and The Play Centre (£1,000 each).

FINANCES *Year* 2011–12 *Income* £15,110 *Grants* £68,000

TRUSTEES Nicholas Forman Hardy; Jane Forman Hardy; Charles Bennion; Canon James Neale.

HOW TO APPLY In writing to the correspondent.

WHO TO APPLY TO Rachael Sulley, 64 St James's Street, Nottingham NG1 6FJ *Tel.* 01159 508580

■ The Donald Forrester Trust

CC NO 295833 **ESTABLISHED** 1986

WHERE FUNDING CAN BE GIVEN UK and overseas.

WHO CAN BENEFIT Charities benefiting people who are sick or disabled, particularly older people and children.

WHAT IS FUNDED Medical welfare and relief; overseas; children and youth; old people's welfare; hospitals and hospices, physical and mental disability; blind and deaf; community care and social welfare; medical research; animal and bird welfare; services and ex-services; maritime and culture, heritage, environment and sport.

WHAT IS NOT FUNDED No grants to individuals.

TYPE OF GRANT One off and recurrent.

RANGE OF GRANTS £5,000–£15,000.

SAMPLE GRANTS Most of the beneficiaries received grants for £5,000; however, one significantly large grant of £250,000 was given as a special 25th Anniversary Grant to The Stroke Association for their Life After Stroke Centre near Birmingham. Other beneficiaries across all categories included: Churcher's College 1722 Society (£20,000); Agents of Change (£15,000); The Blue Cross, Hearing Link, Catch 22, Royal Masonic School for Girls, Church Army, FareShare, Peace Hospice, The Music Therapy Charity, Remedi, MIND, Age UK Hillingdon, Mary's Meals, Royal Star and Garter Home and Small Charities Coalition (£5,000 each).

FINANCES *Year* 2011–12 *Income* £807,406 *Grants* £800,000 *Assets* £7,747,971

TRUSTEES Wendy J. Forrester, Anthony J. Smee; Michael B. Jones; Hilary J. Porter; Christopher A. Perkins.

HOW TO APPLY The trust supports a substantial number of charities on a regular basis. We are informed that regrettably, detailed applications, which place 'an intolerable strain' on administrative resources, cannot be considered. It is suggested that very brief details of an application should be submitted to the correspondent on one side of A4. Do not send accounts or other information. The trustees normally meet twice a year to consider and agree on the grants which are paid half yearly. Applications should be submitted before 15 January and 15 August to be considered. There are no specific requirements under the trust deed and over the years the trustees have supported a wide range of national and international charities and endeavoured to achieve a balance between the large institutions and the smaller charities that experience greater difficulty in fundraising. The trustees have developed a fairly substantial list of charities that are supported on a regular basis, but new proposals, both regular and 'one-off' are considered at each meeting.

WHO TO APPLY TO Christopher Perkins, Trustee, Lancaster House, 7 Elmfield Road, Bromley, Kent BR1 1LT *Tel.* 020 8461 8014

■ Gwyneth Forrester Trust

CC NO 1080921 **ESTABLISHED** 2000

WHERE FUNDING CAN BE GIVEN England and Wales.

WHO CAN BENEFIT Charitable organisations.

WHAT IS FUNDED The trustees support a specific charitable sector each year.

WHAT IS NOT FUNDED No grants to individuals.

TYPE OF GRANT One-off.

SAMPLE GRANTS Hearing Dogs for Deaf People, Mary Hare Foundation and Sense (£60,000 each) and Fight for Sight, Royal London Society for the Blind and The Macular Disease Society (£50,000 each).

FINANCES *Year* 2011–12 *Income* £365,665 *Grants* £330,000 *Assets* £21,125,939

TRUSTEES Wendy J. Forrester; Anthony J. Smee; Michael B. Jones; Christopher Perkins.

OTHER INFORMATION No information was available on the future focus of the trust's grantmaking as 'once the charitable sector is chosen, we research that sector and produce a list of possibles and then contact the individual charities to discuss with them their particular needs and any specific projects they have in hand. These are then discussed and the final grant list is decided'.

HOW TO APPLY The trust has previously stated that 'applications for aid cannot be considered'.

WHO TO APPLY TO Christopher Perkins, Trustee, Lancaster House, 7 Elmfield Road, Bromley, Kent BR1 1LT *Tel.* 020 8461 8014

■ The Anna Rosa Forster Charitable Trust

CC NO 1090028 **ESTABLISHED** 1996

WHERE FUNDING CAN BE GIVEN Worldwide.

WHO CAN BENEFIT Charitable organisations.

WHAT IS FUNDED Medical research, animal welfare, famine relief.

RANGE OF GRANTS Usually between £2,500 and £3,500.

SAMPLE GRANTS Previous beneficiaries include: Alzheimer's Research Trust, Cancer Research UK, British Red Cross, Farm Africa, Cats Protection League, CARE International UK, Motor Neurone Disease Association, the Donkey Sanctuary, PDSA, RSPCA, International Spinal Research Trust and the World Medical Fund.

FINANCES *Year* 2011–12 *Income* £88,933 *Grants* £87,095 *Assets* £2,034,028

TRUSTEES R. W. Napier; A. W. Morgan.

554

Does the trust you have chosen match your needs? Haphazard applications waste postage and time

OTHER INFORMATION Grants are split equally between the three areas of work.
HOW TO APPLY In writing to the correspondent.
WHO TO APPLY TO R. W. Napier, Trustee, c/o R. W. Napier Solicitors, Floor E, Milburn House, Dean Street, Newcastle upon Tyne NE1 1LF *Tel.* 01912 301819 *email* rogerw.napier@gmail.com

■ The Fort Foundation

CC NO 1028639   **ESTABLISHED** 1993
WHERE FUNDING CAN BE GIVEN North east Lancashire.
WHO CAN BENEFIT Organisations supporting young people and individuals.
WHAT IS FUNDED Training for industry and life extra curriculum activities.
WHAT IS NOT FUNDED Education fees
TYPE OF GRANT One–off
RANGE OF GRANTS Up to £7,200
SAMPLE GRANTS Royal Yachting Association (£7,200); Marine Society and Sea Cadets (£5,700); Holy Trinity Church, Colne and HMS Portland (£5,000 each); Etchells Cowes Fleet (£4,000); Burwain Sailing Club and DecAid (£3,000 each); Ridgewood Community High School (£2,500); Community Foundation for Lancashire (£2,000); Teenage Cancer Trust and the Charlie Wailer Memorial Trust (£1,500); and Pendle Croquet Club, Lancashire Wildlife Trust and University of Central Lancashire (£1,000 each).
FINANCES *Year* 2011–12 *Income* £153,244 *Grants* £67,912 *Assets* £305,791
TRUSTEES Edward Fort; Ian Wilson; Susan Friedlander.
OTHER INFORMATION £10,000 of the grants total was awarded to individuals.
HOW TO APPLY In writing to the correspondent.
WHO TO APPLY TO Anne Hartley, Administrator, c/o Fort Vale Engineering Ltd, Calder Vale Park, Simonstone Lane, Simonstone, Burnley BB12 7ND *Tel.* 01282 440000 *email* ahartley@fortvale.com

■ The Forte Charitable Trust

CC NO 326038   **ESTABLISHED** 1982
WHERE FUNDING CAN BE GIVEN UK and overseas.
WHO CAN BENEFIT Community-based projects and national organisations and institutions.
WHAT IS FUNDED The Roman Catholic faith, Alzheimer's disease and senile dementia.
FINANCES *Year* 2012–13 *Income* £1,500 *Grants* £40,000
TRUSTEES Sir Rocco Forte; George Proctor; The Hon Olga Polizzi de Sorrentino; Lowndes Trustees Limited.
OTHER INFORMATION Information was provided by the trust.
HOW TO APPLY In writing to the correspondent.
WHO TO APPLY TO Judy Lewendon, Administrator, Rocco Forte Hotels Ltd, 70 Jermyn Street, London SW1Y 6NY *email* jlewendon@roccofortehotels.com

■ The Lord Forte Foundation

CC NO 298100   **ESTABLISHED** 1987
WHERE FUNDING CAN BE GIVEN UK.
WHO CAN BENEFIT Educational establishments.
WHAT IS FUNDED Training courses and research in the field of hotel management, catering and the travel and tourism industries.

WHAT IS NOT FUNDED Grants are given to those organisations which fulfil the objectives of the foundation.
TYPE OF GRANT Up to three years.
RANGE OF GRANTS £1,000–£7,000.
SAMPLE GRANTS British Institute of Innkeeping (£25,500); WCI General Charity Fund (£20,000); Thames Valley University (£11,000); Springboard Charitable Trust and University of Bedfordshire (£7,000 each); Westminster Kingsway College and Jamie Oliver Foundation (£5,000 each); and Cornwall College (£500).
FINANCES *Year* 2011–12 *Income* £65,435 *Grants* £95,291 *Assets* £2,118,451
TRUSTEES Sir Rocco Forte; Lord Janner of Braunstone; George Proctor; The Hon Olga Polizzi di Sorrentino; Nick Scade; Andrew McKenzie.
HOW TO APPLY In writing to the correspondent.
WHO TO APPLY TO Judy Lewendon, Administrator, Rocco Forte Hotels Ltd, 70 Jermyn Street, London SW1Y 6NY *Tel.* 020 7235 6244 *email* jlewendon@roccofortehotels.com

■ The Four Lanes Trust

CC NO 267608   **ESTABLISHED** 1974
WHERE FUNDING CAN BE GIVEN Basingstoke and Deane District Council area.
WHO CAN BENEFIT Organisations benefiting people of all ages; actors and entertainment professionals; musicians; textile workers and designers; writers and poets; at-risk groups; those disadvantaged by poverty; and socially isolated people.
WHAT IS FUNDED Charities working in the fields of information technology and computers; publishing and printing; community development; support to voluntary and community organisations and volunteers; professional bodies; charity or voluntary umbrella bodies; arts, culture and recreation; health facilities and buildings; schools and colleges; community issues; development proposals; various community facilities and services; and other charitable purposes will be considered. Personal and small initiatives are particularly welcomed.
WHAT IS NOT FUNDED No grants to individuals or for general appeals.
TYPE OF GRANT Buildings, capital, core costs, one-off, project, running costs, recurring costs, salaries and start-up costs. Funding for up to three years will be considered.
RANGE OF GRANTS £100–£2,000.
SAMPLE GRANTS £2,000 to Whitchurch Baptist Church; £1,500 to Basingstoke Voluntary Services; £1,300 to Winklebury School; £1,100 to Motor Neurone Disease Association; £1,000 each to The Prince's Trust, Hurst Community College, Cliddesden Village Hall and Create (Arts) Ltd; £850 to Basingstoke Citizen's Advice Bureau; £750 to Basingstoke Youth Service; £600 to The Vyne School.
FINANCES *Year* 2012–13 *Income* £34,063
TRUSTEES Hon. Dwight Makins; Hon. Virginia Shapiro; Edward Roberts; Dr Amanda Britton.
HOW TO APPLY In writing to the correspondent. There is no application form. Initial telephone calls welcome. View the website for criteria and guidelines. The trustees hold three meetings a year, in March, June and November, and all decisions are made at these meetings. The trust actively seeks applications for funds that comply with the objects of the trust.

WHO TO APPLY TO Bob Carr, 5 Ferguson Close, Basingstoke, Hampshire RG21 3JA *Tel.* 01256 477990 *Fax* 01256 477990 *email* applications@fourlanestrust.org.uk *Website* www.fourlanestrust.org.uk

■ The Four Winds Trust

CC NO 262524   ESTABLISHED 1971
WHERE FUNDING CAN BE GIVEN Worldwide.
WHO CAN BENEFIT Registered charities and people working in religion.
WHAT IS FUNDED Christian and overseas aid organisations, but grants are also given to retired evangelists and to missionaries and their dependants.
RANGE OF GRANTS Up to £5,500.
SAMPLE GRANTS Ashbury Free Church (£5,500); Counties Evangelistic Work (£3,000); Forest Hill Community Church (£2,500); South Road Church (£1,500); Swindon Youth for Christ (£1,100) and Edgewell Christian Centre (£1,000).
FINANCES *Year* 2011–12 *Income* £47,860 *Grants* £40,969 *Assets* £793,374
TRUSTEES Philip Charters; Peter John Charters; Simon Charters; Frances Charters.
OTHER INFORMATION The grant total includes grants made to individual evangelists and missionaries totalling £4,500.
HOW TO APPLY The trust was set up for purposes in which the trustees have a personal interest and the funds are earmarked for these purposes. Unsolicited requests are unlikely to be considered.
WHO TO APPLY TO Philip Charters, Trustee, Four Winds, Church Lane, Ashbury, Swindon SN6 8LZ *Tel.* 01793 710431

■ The Foyle Foundation

CC NO 1081766   ESTABLISHED 2000
WHERE FUNDING CAN BE GIVEN UK.
WHO CAN BENEFIT Registered charities and state schools.
WHAT IS FUNDED '**Main Grants Scheme:** *Arts* – The foundation seeks applications that make a strong artistic case for support in either the performing or visual arts. Our Arts programme has a twofold purpose to help sustain the arts and to support projects that particularly help to deliver artistic vision. We look for value for money and sustainability in projects that we support. Typical areas of support include: helping to make the arts more accessible by developing new audiences, supporting tours, festivals and arts educational projects; encouraging new work and supporting young and emerging artists; building projects that improve or re-equip existing arts venues (rather than construction of new facilities, although this will not be excluded); projects that reduce overheads or which help generate additional revenue. Generally, we make grants for specific projects/activities. We will consider applications for core funding (but generally only from smaller organisations or from those not receiving recurrent revenue funding from the Arts Council or local authorities). Note that community arts activity will not generally be supported.
Learning: The foundation will support projects which facilitate the acquisition of knowledge and which have a long-term strategic impact. Key areas for support are: libraries, museums and archives; special educational needs and learning difficulties; projects that reduce overheads or

which help generate additional revenue will also be considered. For state funded schools our main initiative will be The Foyle School Libraries Scheme [special guidance notes are available from the foundation's website]. Dedicated schools catering for those with Special Educational Needs (SEN) may also be supported. Private schools will not generally be supported. Citizenship, esteem-building, training, skills acquisition to aid employment, independent living, early learning projects or playgroups will not generally be considered.
'**Small Grants Scheme:** Our Small Grants Scheme is designed to support smaller charities in the UK, especially those working at grass roots and local community level, in any field, across a wide range of activities. Note we are not able to support individuals. Applications are welcomed from charities that have an annual turnover of less than £100,000 per annum. Larger or national charities will normally not be considered under this scheme. Nor will the Scheme generally support charities that are able consistently to generate operational surpluses or which have been able to build up unrestricted reserves to a level equivalent to three months turnover. If applying on behalf of a state school refer to the state schools webpage [on the foundation's website]. Note that competition for funding is intense and we receive many more applications that we are able to fund.'
WHAT IS NOT FUNDED No grants to individuals, organisations which are not registered charities or for international work. No retrospective funding.
TYPE OF GRANT Capital, revenue and project funding.
RANGE OF GRANTS Up to £300,000.
SAMPLE GRANTS Chichester Festival Theatre (£300,000), towards the theatre's 50th Anniversary capital redevelopment; Battle of Britain Memorial Trust (£200,000), towards the construction and development costs of 'The Wing', a new visitor centre at the national memorial; York Museums Trust (£150,000), towards the redevelopment of York Art Gallery; Square Chapel Trust, Halifax (£100,000), towards the Cornerstone capital development project to expand facilities at the arts venue, including a new 108 seat multi-purpose auditorium; Chichester Harbour Trust (£10,000), towards the ongoing improvement and maintenance of land; National Hospital for Neurology and Neurosurgery Development Foundation (£10,000), towards the National Brain Appeal as part of its participation in the Big Give Christmas Challenge 2011; New Belve Youth and Community Sports Centre Ltd, Liverpool (£8,000), to fund a new part-time Leisure Assistant post for 12 months; Association for Post-Natal Illness (£7,500), towards running costs to support women suffering with Post Natal Depression; Norfolk Concerts (£6,000), towards an expansion of the music programme for young people; Boreland Village Hall (£5,000), towards phase 2 of a refurbishment project; Fairway Fife (£5,000), towards the cost of one of the Activity Coordinators; Purbeck Art Week Festival (£3,500), towards a workshop and performance by Gabrieli Consort and Players as part of the Festival; The Penytrip Project, Porthmadog (£2,000), towards core costs; Westminster Division Guide Association (£1,000), to cover the costs of renting a school premises for two evenings a week.
FINANCES *Year* 2012 *Income* £3,420,799 *Grants* £5,302,050 *Assets* £72,167,252

TRUSTEES Michael Smith; Kathryn Skoyles; Sir Peter Duffell; Roy Amlot; James Korner.

HOW TO APPLY 'Note that competition is intense; we receive many more applications than we are able to fund. Also the foundation only supports charities and is not able to support individuals. Guidelines and application forms are available [from the foundation's website]. Charities wishing to make an application for funding should download and read the appropriate guidelines for applicants before completing and signing the appropriate application form and sending this together with the supporting information requested. Applications are acknowledged by email or by post within two weeks of receipt. If you do not receive this acknowledgement, contact the foundation to confirm safe receipt of your request.

When to Apply: Applications are accepted all year round. We have no deadlines. Except for capital projects, it may take up to four months, occasionally longer, to receive a decision from the trustees, so apply well in advance of your funding requirements.

Capital Projects: Note for capital projects seeking more than £50,000 the foundation will now only consider these twice per year in the spring and autumn. Therefore it could be six months or more before we take a decision on your project.

Small Grants Scheme

How much can you apply for?: We plan to make one year grants of between £1,000 and £10,000 to charities which can demonstrate that such a grant will make a significant difference to their work. If you cannot demonstrate this, your application will be declined. No multi-year funding awards will be made.

Other Information: There are no deadlines for submission. Applications will be received at all times but it may take up to four months to obtain a decision from trustees. Apply well in advance of your requirements. All applications will be acknowledged but in order to reduce administration, usually we will not send declination letters. If you have not heard from the foundation within four months of your application being acknowledged, you should assume that your application has been unsuccessful.'

WHO TO APPLY TO David Hall, Chief Executive, Rugby Chambers, 2 Rugby Street, London WC1N 3QU *Tel.* 020 7430 9119 *Fax* 020 7430 9830 *email* info@foylefoundation.org.uk *Website* www.foylefoundation.org.uk

---

■ The Isaac and Freda Frankel Memorial Charitable Trust

CC NO 1003732　　　**ESTABLISHED** 1991

WHERE FUNDING CAN BE GIVEN UK and overseas, particularly Israel.

WHO CAN BENEFIT Established organisations benefiting children, young adults and people disadvantaged by poverty. People of many different religions and cultures will be funded, but preference is given to Jewish people.

WHAT IS FUNDED Jewish charities, medicine and health, education, religion and the relief of poverty.

WHAT IS NOT FUNDED No grants to individuals or students, for expeditions or scholarships.

TYPE OF GRANT One-off and recurrent grants.

RANGE OF GRANTS £1,000 or less.

FINANCES *Year* 2011–12 *Income* £44,761 *Grants* £63,000 *Assets* £409,216

TRUSTEES M. D. Frankel; Geraldine Frankel; J. Steinhaus; J. Silkin.

HOW TO APPLY In writing to the correspondent.

WHO TO APPLY TO M. D. Frankel, Trustee, 33 Welbeck Street, London W1G 8LX *Tel.* 020 7872 0023

■ The Elizabeth Frankland Moore and Star Foundation

CC NO 257711　　　**ESTABLISHED** 1968

WHERE FUNDING CAN BE GIVEN UK.

WHO CAN BENEFIT Charitable organisations.

WHAT IS FUNDED General charitable purposes.

SAMPLE GRANTS Iceni Project and Kids Company (£20,000 each); Alzheimer's Society (£17,500); Salvation Army (£16,000); Erskine (£15,000); the Not Forgotten Association, Centre Point and Age Scotland (£10,000 each); Eyes for East Africa (£8,500); Prisoners Abroad and Queen Alexandra Hospital Home (£5,000 each); Gardening Leave and RNLI (£1,000 each); and Warminster Food Bank (£500).

FINANCES *Year* 2011–12 *Income* £263,241 *Grants* £230,000 *Assets* £9,362,366

TRUSTEES R. A. Griffiths; Anne Ely; Dr David Spalton; Janine Cameron.

HOW TO APPLY In writing to the correspondent. Trustees meet twice a year.

WHO TO APPLY TO Marianne Neuhoff, Neuhoff and Co, 11 Towcester Road, Whittlebury, Towcester NN12 8XU *Tel.* 01327 858171

■ Sydney E. Franklin Deceased's New Second Charity

CC NO 272047　　　**ESTABLISHED** 1973

WHERE FUNDING CAN BE GIVEN Worldwide. Priority is given to developing world projects.

WHO CAN BENEFIT Small charities with low income (under £300,000).

WHAT IS FUNDED Relief of poverty and disability and the protection of endangered species. Priority is given to projects supporting children in the developing world, education and communities working towards self-sufficiency.

WHAT IS NOT FUNDED Individuals.

TYPE OF GRANT One-off and project grants.

RANGE OF GRANTS Average grant under £1,000.

SAMPLE GRANTS Previous beneficiaries include: Kerala Federation for the Blind, Water for Kids, Narwhal/Niaff, United Charities Fund, Ashram International, Books Abroad, Children of the Andes, Kaloko Trust, Microloan Foundation, Tools for Self Reliance, Tree Aid, Window for Peace UK, Forest Peoples Project, African Initiatives, Lake Malawi Projects, World Medical Fund and Gwalior Children's Hospital.

FINANCES *Year* 2011–12 *Income* £23,721 *Grants* £25,000

TRUSTEES Dr Rodney Franklin; Natasha Franklin; Roxanne Smee; Julia Edwards.

OTHER INFORMATION Limited information was available from the Charity Commission.

HOW TO APPLY Written applications only. Must include most recent audited accounts.

WHO TO APPLY TO Dr Rodney Franklin, Trustee, 39 Westleigh Avenue, London SW15 6RQ

■ The Jill Franklin Trust

CC NO 1000175　　　**ESTABLISHED** 1988

WHERE FUNDING CAN BE GIVEN UK.

WHO CAN BENEFIT Charitable organisations benefiting: disabled people; carers; ex-offenders and those at risk of offending; people with a mental illness; refugees and asylum-seekers.

WHAT IS FUNDED Self-help groups etc. for people with a mental illness or learning difficulties; holidays for carers to provide respite from their caree – this is mainly as a block grant to the Princess Royal Trust for Carers; organisations helping and supporting asylum seekers and refugees coming to the UK; restoration of churches of architectural importance; grants to prisoners for education and training – this is given as a block grant to the Prisoners Education Trust; Camden Bereavement Service, with which Jill Franklin was closely associated.

WHAT IS NOT FUNDED Grants are not given to: appeals for building work; endowment funds; branches of a national organisations, and to the centre itself (unless it is a specific grant, probably for training in the branches); replace the duties of government, local authorities or the NHS; encourage the 'contract culture', particularly where authorities are not funding the contract adequately; religious organisations set up for welfare, education etc. of whatever religion, unless the service is open to and used by people from all denominations; overseas projects; 'heritage schemes' animal charities; students, nor to any individuals nor for overseas travel; and medical research.

TYPE OF GRANT One-off, project, recurring costs, running costs and start-up costs. Funding for up to three years will be considered.

RANGE OF GRANTS £500–£1,000.

SAMPLE GRANTS Prisoners Education Trust and CCIWBS (£12,000 each); Princess Royal Trust for Carers (£7,000); Pevsner Books Trust (£4,000); Camara (£2,500); Devon and Cornwall Refugee Support Council, Hackney Migrant Centre and Respite Association (£1,000 each).

FINANCES *Year* 2011–12 *Income* £69,579 *Grants* £71,613 *Assets* £1,462,923

TRUSTEES Sally Franklin; Norman Franklin; Andrew Franklin; Dr Samuel Franklin; Thomas Franklin.

HOW TO APPLY In writing to the correspondent, enclosing a copy of the latest annual report and accounts and a budget for the project. Organisations based outside the UK should provide the name, address and telephone number of a correspondent or referee in the UK. According to the annual report for 2011/12, 'the trustees tend to look more favourably on an appeal which is simply and economically prepared: glossy, 'prestige' and mail sorted brochures do not impress the trustees.' Unsolicited enquiries are not usually acknowledged.

WHO TO APPLY TO Norman Franklin, Trustee, Flat 5, 17–19 Elsworthy Road, London NW3 3DS *Tel.* 020 7722 4543 *email* jft@jill-franklin-trust. org.uk *Website* www.jill-franklin-trust.org.uk

---

■ **The Gordon Fraser Charitable Trust**

CC NO 260869   **ESTABLISHED** 1966

WHERE FUNDING CAN BE GIVEN UK, with a preference for Scotland.

WHO CAN BENEFIT Registered charities.

WHAT IS FUNDED Children, young people, environment, arts.

WHAT IS NOT FUNDED No grants are made to organisations which are not recognised charities, or to individuals.

RANGE OF GRANTS £100–£13,500, average grant £1,500.

SAMPLE GRANTS The National Galleries of Scotland (£13,500); Hunterian Art Gallery (£10,000); Artlink Central (£6,000); London Children's Flower Society and Royal Scottish National Orchestra (£4,000 each); British Red Cross and the Edinburgh International Festival Society (£2,000 each); Fly Cup Catering Limited, the Glasgow School of Art and John Muir Trust (£1,000 each); Christians Against Poverty and East End Kids and Co (£500 each); and the Council for Music in Hospitals (£300).

FINANCES *Year* 2012–13 *Income* £166,795 *Grants* £140,000 *Assets* £3,230,022

TRUSTEES M. A. Moss; W. F. T. Anderson; Sarah Moss; Susannah Rae; Alexander Moss; Alison Priestley.

HOW TO APPLY In writing to the correspondent. Applications are considered in January, April, July and October.

WHO TO APPLY TO Claire Armstrong, Administrator, Gaidrew Farmhouse, Drymen, Glasgow G63 0DN

■ **The Hugh Fraser Foundation**

SC NO SC009303   **ESTABLISHED** 1960

WHERE FUNDING CAN BE GIVEN UK, especially western or deprived areas of Scotland.

WHO CAN BENEFIT Registered charities working in many different sectors principally hospitals, schools and universities, arts organisations and organisations working with the disabled, the underprivileged and the aged.

WHAT IS FUNDED Medical facilities and research; relief of poverty and assistance for older and infirm people; education and learning; provision of better opportunities for people who are disadvantaged; music and the arts; encouragement of personal development and training of young people.

WHAT IS NOT FUNDED Grants are only awarded to individuals in exceptional circumstances (see 'information').

TYPE OF GRANT Capital and revenue grants for up to three years, sometimes longer. Start-up costs.

RANGE OF GRANTS Up to £250,000.

SAMPLE GRANTS Riverside Museum Appeal (£250,000); Inspiring Scotland (£200,000); University of Strathclyde and Beatson Pebble Appeal (£100,000 each); National Museums Scotland (£50,000) and Miss Margaret Kerr Charitable Trust (£40,000).

FINANCES *Year* 2011–12 *Income* £1,890,640 *Grants* £2,002,250 *Assets* £57,896,147

TRUSTEES Dr Kenneth Chrystie; Patricia Fraser; Belinda Hanson; Gordon Shearer; Heather Thompson.

OTHER INFORMATION Note: In 2007 the Hugh Fraser Foundation merged with the Emily Fraser Trust, a related charity. As a result the trustees will, in exceptional circumstances, also help individuals and the dependents of individuals who were or are engaged in the drapery and allied trades and the printing, publishing, books and stationery, newspaper and allied trades in the UK.

HOW TO APPLY In writing to the correspondent. Applications should also include either a copy of your latest formal accounts if prepared or a copy of your most recent balance sheet, income and expenditure account or bank statement if formal accounts are not prepared. If you are not a registered charity you should also enclose a copy of your constitution or policy statement. The trustees meet quarterly to consider applications in March, June, September and December. Applications should be received early in the preceding month in order to be considered.

WHO TO APPLY TO Katrina Muir, Trust Administrator, Turcan Connell, Princes Exchange, 1 Earl Grey Street, Edinburgh EH3 9EE *Tel.* 01312 288111

■ The Joseph Strong Frazer Trust

CC NO 235311   **ESTABLISHED** 1939

WHERE FUNDING CAN BE GIVEN Unrestricted, in practice, England and Wales only.

WHO CAN BENEFIT Registered charities only.

WHAT IS FUNDED General charitable purposes, with broad interests in the fields of medical and other research, social welfare, people with disabilities, children, hospitals, education, maritime, youth, religion and wildlife.

WHAT IS NOT FUNDED No grants to individuals.

TYPE OF GRANT One-off, capital and recurring costs.

SAMPLE GRANTS Addaction, Archway Project, British Retinitis Pigmentosa Society, Counsel and Care for the Elderly, Iris Fund, Leonard Cheshire Wales and West, Royal School for the Blind Liverpool and Welsh National Opera (£2,000 each).

FINANCES *Year* 2011–12 *Income* £445,725 *Grants* £345,250 *Assets* £12,011,690

TRUSTEES Sir William A. Reardon Smith, Chair; David A. Cook; R. M. H. Read; William N. H. Reardon Smith; William I. Waites.

HOW TO APPLY In writing to the correspondent. Trustees meet twice a year, usually in March and September. Application forms are not necessary. It is helpful if applicants are concise in their appeal letters, which must include an sae if acknowledgement is required.

WHO TO APPLY TO The Trustees, Joseph Miller and Co, Floor A, Milburn House, Dean Street, Newcastle upon Tyne NE1 1LE *Tel.* 01912 328065 *Fax* 01912 221554 *email* uf@joseph-miller.co.uk

---

■ The Louis and Valerie Freedman Charitable Settlement

CC NO 271067   **ESTABLISHED** 1976

WHERE FUNDING CAN BE GIVEN UK, especially Burnham.

WHO CAN BENEFIT National and local (Burnham in Buckinghamshire) charities.

WHAT IS FUNDED Health, welfare, education.

WHAT IS NOT FUNDED No grants to individuals. Only registered charities are considered for support.

RANGE OF GRANTS Usually around £5,000 to £10,000.

SAMPLE GRANTS Burnham Health Promotion Trust (£50,000); Second Chance Children's Society (£15,000); Prostate Cancer Research UK and Cheam School Educational Trust (£10,000 each); and Disability Challenges, Rekindle and SSAFA Forces Help (£5,000 each).

FINANCES *Year* 2011–12 *Income* £142,924 *Grants* £110,960 *Assets* £3,890,730

TRUSTEES Francis Hughes; Michael Ferrier.

OTHER INFORMATION Nine grants totalling £111,000 were provided in 2011–12.

HOW TO APPLY There is no application form. The following information was obtained from the trustees' report 2011/12: 'The trustees meet periodically (and are also in regular contact) to consider what grants they will make and to review any feedback they have received relating to past donations. The trustees receive many applications for assistance but are normally

minded to help those with a link to the Freedman family.'

WHO TO APPLY TO Francis Hughes, Trustee, c/o Bridge House, 11 Creek Road, East Molesey, Surrey KT8 9BE *Tel.* 020 8941 4455

■ The Michael and Clara Freeman Charitable Trust

CC NO 1125083   **ESTABLISHED** 2008

WHERE FUNDING CAN BE GIVEN UK and overseas.

WHAT IS FUNDED General charitable purposes.

SAMPLE GRANTS Previous beneficiaries: Help for Heroes (£23,000); Balliol College – University of Oxford (£7,500); Chipping Norton Theatre (£5,000); Combat Stress and the British Legion (£2,500); Kids Company and St Giles Trust (£2,000 each); and Mary's Meals (£1,000).

FINANCES *Year* 2012–13 *Income* £5,817 *Grants* £500,000

TRUSTEES Michael Freeman; Clara Freeman; Laura Freeman; Edward Freeman.

OTHER INFORMATION The trust was established in 2008 for general charitable purposes with an initial donation of almost £2 million from the settlors, Michael Freeman, co-founder of Argent Property Developers and his wife Clara, a former executive on the board of Marks and Spencer and currently on the University of the Arts London board of governors.

HOW TO APPLY In writing to the correspondent.

WHO TO APPLY TO Michael Freeman, Trustee, 9 Connaught Square, London W2 2HG

■ The Freemasons' Grand Charity

CC NO 281942   **ESTABLISHED** 1980

WHERE FUNDING CAN BE GIVEN England, Wales and overseas.

WHO CAN BENEFIT Charities benefiting freemasons and their dependants; medical research, hospices and other charities concerned with general welfare especially of young and older people and overseas emergency aid.

WHAT IS FUNDED Consideration is only given to charities whose work covers the whole of England and Wales; London charities (no other local charities should apply); freemasons of the United Grand Lodge of England, their widows and certain other dependants; hospices; social welfare organisations, organisations supporting vulnerable people including the young and older people, medical research and emergency aid.

WHAT IS NOT FUNDED Local charities (i.e. serving an individual city or region) should apply to the provincial grand lodge of the region in which they operate, (these are listed in telephone directories, usually under 'freemasons' or 'masons'). Those not eligible for a grant are: individuals (other than for the relief of 'poor and distressed freemasons and their poor and distressed dependants'); charities that serve an individual region or city, for example, a regional hospital, local church, day centre or primary school; organisations not registered with the Charity Commission, except some exempt charities; activities that are primarily the responsibility of central or local government or some other responsible body; organisations or projects outside of England and Wales; animal welfare, the arts or environmental causes; charities with sectarian or political objectives; charities that are deemed to hold funds in excess of their requirements.

RANGE OF GRANTS Up to £250,000.

SAMPLE GRANTS The Prince's Trust (£250,000); Tomorrow's People (£90,000); Diabetes UK (£60,000); Help for Heroes (£50,000); Outward Bound and the Rainbow Trust Children's Charity (£30,000 each); Jubilee Sailing Trust (£25,000); East Anglian Air Ambulance (£16,000); Addington Fund (£15,000); North West Air Ambulance (£12,000); St Christopher's Hospice (£8,000); Earl Mountbatten Hospice and Envision (£3,000 each); Disability Law Service (£2,000); Shelter Cymru (£1,500); and the Dwarf Sports Association (£1,000).

FINANCES *Year* 2011–12 *Income* £15,834,800 *Grants* £2,788,000 *Assets* £61,439,000

TRUSTEES Grahame Elliott; Roderic Mitchell; Peter Griffiths; Sir Stuart Hampson; Ian MacBeth; Charles Assad Akle; Dr Richard Dunstan; Geoff Tuck; Terry Baker; Dr Kevin Williams; Nigel Pett; Anthony Wood; Timothy Dallas-Chapman; Judge Hone; Roger Needham; Alexander Stewart; Christopher Grove; Michael Daws; Ian Johnson; Roy Skinner; Ryland James; Simon Duckworth; Anthony Wood; Ernest Skidmore; Wayne Smith; Guy Elgood; Nigel Buchanan.

PUBLICATIONS Booklet, Information on Masonic Charities.

OTHER INFORMATION The grant total represents awards to non-Masonic organisations. Masonic grants totalled a further £5.6 million.

HOW TO APPLY Application forms are available from the charity's office or from its website. This form must be completed in full accompanied by a copy of the latest annual report and full audited accounts; these must be less than 18 months old. Hospice grant applications are made on a separate form, available from either the appropriate provincial grand lodge or the trust's office. Applications may be submitted at any time throughout the year and are considered at meetings held in January, April and July. Acknowledgement of receipt will be made by post. Applications are not accepted for 'emergency grants' which are made as 'the need arises' and at the trustees' discretion.

WHO TO APPLY TO Laura Chapman, Chief Executive, Freemasons Hall, 60 Great Queen Street, London WC2B 5AZ *Tel.* 020 7395 9261 *Fax* 020 7395 9295 *email* info@the-grand-charity.org *Website* www.grandcharity.org

■ The Thomas Freke and Lady Norton Charity

CC NO 200824   **ESTABLISHED** 1990

WHERE FUNDING CAN BE GIVEN Only within the parishes of Hannington, Inglesham, Highworth, Stanton Fitzwarren, Blunsdon St Leonard's and Castle Eaton.

WHO CAN BENEFIT Local communities and organisations benefiting children, young adults and Christians.

WHAT IS FUNDED Buildings or equipment for churches, schools, youth and community facilities. The trust is willing to consider emergency or unforeseen expenditure. Funding may also be given to community centres, village halls, recreation grounds and sports centres.

WHAT IS NOT FUNDED No grants are given for ordinary running expenses. No applications from outside the beneficial area can be considered.

TYPE OF GRANT Capital.

FINANCES *Year* 2011–12 *Income* £95,713 *Grants* £71,000 *Assets* £1,000,000

TRUSTEES Lorna Wallace; Valerie Davies; Dr Keith Scholes; John Scott; Edwin Cole.

HOW TO APPLY In writing to the correspondent for help with capital projects such as building improvements development or, provision of specialist equipment. Clear outline details of the project and accurate estimated costs are required. Trustees meet four times a year to consider applications. The correspondent has previously stated that: 'There have been many applications from outside the beneficial area that cannot be supported.'

WHO TO APPLY TO Barry T. Compton, Clerk, 23 Chedworth Gate, Broome Manor, Swindon SN3 1NE *email* barry.compton@btinternet.com

■ The Charles S. French Charitable Trust

CC NO 206476   **ESTABLISHED** 1959

WHERE FUNDING CAN BE GIVEN North-east London and south-west Essex.

WHO CAN BENEFIT Registered charities.

WHAT IS FUNDED General charitable purposes, including community services and facilities.

WHAT IS NOT FUNDED Only registered charities are supported.

TYPE OF GRANT Mainly recurrent.

RANGE OF GRANTS Usually £1,000–£10,000.

SAMPLE GRANTS Loughton Youth Project (£20,000); St Luke's Hospice, Baslidon (£14,000); Pioneer Sailing Trust (£6,000); Marie Curie Cancer Care (£2,000); and Asthma Relief at work in SW Essex and British Wireless for Blind (£1,000 each).

FINANCES *Year* 2011–12 *Income* £257,719 *Grants* £168,360 *Assets* £7,444,508

TRUSTEES W. F. Noble; M. P. W. Scarth; J. Thomas; R. Foster.

OTHER INFORMATION In 2011–12 grants were given to 66 organisations.

HOW TO APPLY In writing to the correspondent, including a copy of the latest accounts. The trustees meet four times a year. The trust invites applications for grants and donations from local charities and these applications are reviewed against the trust's objects, with grants and donations being awarded at the trustee's discretion.

'Applicants are encouraged to contact the office and leave telephone or email messages, but, being a low overhead organisation with limited office hours, the response to these may take up to one week.'

WHO TO APPLY TO W. F. Noble, Trustee, c/o 169 High Road, Loughton, Essex IG10 4LF *Tel.* 020 8502 3575 *email* office@csfct.org.uk *Website* www.csfct.org.uk

■ The Anne French Memorial Trust

CC NO 254567   **ESTABLISHED** 1963

WHERE FUNDING CAN BE GIVEN Diocese of Norwich (Norfolk and north Suffolk).

WHO CAN BENEFIT Christians, clergy and local charities.

WHAT IS FUNDED Any charitable purpose in the beneficial area, especially church-related causes.

TYPE OF GRANT One-off, project, research and feasibility.

FINANCES *Year* 2011–12 *Income* £249,905 *Grants* £222,050 *Assets* £6,174,796

TRUSTEE Lord Bishop of Norwich.

HOW TO APPLY The trust states that 'in no circumstances does the Bishop wish to encourage applications for grants.'

WHO TO APPLY TO Christopher Dicker, Hill House, Ranworth, Norwich, Norfolk NR13 6AB *Tel.* 01603 270356 *email* cdicker@hotmail.co. uk

■ The Freshfield Foundation

CC NO 1003316   **ESTABLISHED** 1991
WHERE FUNDING CAN BE GIVEN UK and overseas.
WHO CAN BENEFIT Registered charities.
WHAT IS FUNDED Overseas aid and disaster relief; sustainable development.
SAMPLE GRANTS Disaster Emergency Committee (£500,000); Osteopathic Centre for Children (£40,000); and Afghan Connection (£10,000).
FINANCES *Year* 2011–12 *Income* £1,778,511 *Grants* £630,751 *Assets* £7,299,057
TRUSTEES Paul Kurthausen; Patrick A. Moores; Elizabeth J. Potter.
HOW TO APPLY In writing to the correspondent, although the trust states that 'the process of grantmaking starts with the trustees analysing an area of interest, consistent with the charity's aims and objectives, and then proactively looking for charities that they think can make the greatest contribution'. With this in mind, a letter of introduction to your organisation's work may be more appropriate than a formal application for funding.
WHO TO APPLY TO Paul Kurthausen, Trustee, BWMacfarlane LLP, Castle Chambers, 43 Castle Street L2 9SH *Tel.* 01512 361494 *Fax* 01512 361095 *email* paul.k@bwm.co.uk

■ The Freshgate Trust Foundation

CC NO 221467   **ESTABLISHED** 1962
WHERE FUNDING CAN BE GIVEN Mainly Sheffield and South Yorkshire.
WHO CAN BENEFIT Organisations benefiting: people of all ages; actors and entertainment professionals; musicians; textile workers and designers; writers and poets; at risk groups; people disadvantaged by poverty and socially isolated people. Both innovatory and established bodies may be considered.
WHAT IS FUNDED Local appeals working in the fields of: education (including travel and training); medical (both psychological and physical); recreation; music and arts; welfare and social care; heritage.
WHAT IS NOT FUNDED The trust restricts its grants to UK charitable organisations and does not deal with applications from individuals, national appeals or for church fabric unless used for a wider community purpose. The trust does not fund salaries.
TYPE OF GRANT Start-up costs and capital costs. One-off grants.
SAMPLE GRANTS Museums Sheffield (£13,000); St Wilfred's Drop In Day Centre and St Luke's Hospice (£10,000 each); South Yorkshire and Hallamshire Clubs for Young People and Sheffield Family Holiday Fund (£4,000); Sheffield Dial-A-Ride Club (£2,000); City of Sheffield Youth Orchestra (£1,300); Sheffield Wildlife Trust and University of Sheffield Bursary (£1,000 each); Pro Soccer Pumas JFC (£500) and Dore and Totley Day Centre Luncheon Club (£150).
FINANCES *Year* 2012 *Income* £135,577 *Grants* £105,950 *Assets* £2,893,489
TRUSTEES John Hopkins; John Parkin; Liz Murray; David Stone; Geraldine Russell; Jim Mould; Val Linnemann; Holly Dobson; Perry Else; Usha Fitch; Geoff Marston.

OTHER INFORMATION Grants were given to 61 organisations.
HOW TO APPLY In writing to the correspondent, by early February, June and October each year. Applications are not normally acknowledged.
WHO TO APPLY TO Jonathan Robinson, Secretary, The Hart Shaw Building, Europa Link, Sheffield Business Park, Sheffield S9 1XU *Tel.* 01142 518850 *Fax* 01142 518851

■ The Friarsgate Trust

CC NO 220762   **ESTABLISHED** 1955
WHERE FUNDING CAN BE GIVEN UK, with a strong preference for West Sussex, especially Chichester.
WHO CAN BENEFIT UK and East and West Sussex organisations, especially those already supported by the trust.
WHAT IS FUNDED General charitable purposes, especially education and welfare of children and young people and care of people who are elderly or in need.
WHAT IS NOT FUNDED Local organisations outside Sussex are unlikely to be supported.
RANGE OF GRANTS Up to £20,000, with most grants ranging between £500–£2,000.
SAMPLE GRANTS Chichester District Scouts (£10,000); St Wilfrid's Hospice (£3,200); The Douglas Bader Foundation, Chichester Community Transport and Contact 88 (£2,000 each); The Sussex Snowdrop Trust, Fields in Trust, Shelter, Jubilee Sailing Care and Elizabeth Finn Care (£1,000 each) and Brighton and Hove Unwaged Christmas Appeal (£500).
FINANCES *Year* 2011–12 *Income* £83,293 *Grants* £63,783 *Assets* £2,937,092
TRUSTEES A. C. Colenutt; V. Higgins; N. M. Proctor.
HOW TO APPLY In writing to the correspondent. Applicants are welcome to telephone first to check they fit the trust's criteria.
WHO TO APPLY TO Amanda King-Jones, Thomas Eggar LLP, The Corn Exchange, Baffins Lane, Chichester PO19 1GE *Tel.* 01243 786111

■ Sybilla and Leo Friedler Charitable Trust

CC NO 1150176   **ESTABLISHED** 2012
WHERE FUNDING CAN BE GIVEN Worldwide.
WHO CAN BENEFIT Registered charities.
WHAT IS FUNDED General charitable purposes.
TRUSTEES Michael Friedler; Dr Leo Friedler; Ronald Harris.
HOW TO APPLY In writing to the correspondent.
WHO TO APPLY TO Michael Friedler, Trustee, Heatherby, Beech Drive, Kingswood, Surrey KT20 6PP *Tel.* 020 8681 8611

■ The Friends Hall Farm Street Trust

CC NO 209818   **ESTABLISHED** 1893
WHERE FUNDING CAN BE GIVEN West Midlands
WHO CAN BENEFIT Charitable organisations. Grants are made to organisations and individuals known to the trustees or recommended through the religious Society of Friends.
WHAT IS FUNDED Religion and education, primarily Quaker concerns.
WHAT IS NOT FUNDED Applications from outside the beneficial area cannot be considered.
FINANCES *Year* 2011–12 *Income* £22,000 *Grants* £20,000

TRUSTEES Stuart Morton; Eric Adams; John Bodycote; Roger Gough; Annette Gough; David Taylor.

HOW TO APPLY In writing to the correspondent. Applications should be submitted between March and October for consideration in October/November. Ineligible applications will not receive a reply.

WHO TO APPLY TO Stuart Morton, Trustee, 1 Witherford Way, Selly Oak, Birmingham B29 4AY *Tel.* 01214 725305 *email* stuartm46@gmail.com

■ Friends of Biala Limited

CC NO 271377   **ESTABLISHED** 1964
WHERE FUNDING CAN BE GIVEN UK and overseas.
WHO CAN BENEFIT Jewish organisations and registered charities.
WHAT IS FUNDED Jewish causes, education, relief of poverty.
SAMPLE GRANTS Previous beneficiaries include: Friends of Biala Israel, Aguda Hadadit, Yeshiva Beis Ephraim, Gemach Ezra Hadadit and Freebee Foundation Limited.
FINANCES *Year* 2011–12 *Income* £11,111 *Grants* £100,000
TRUSTEES B. Rabinowitz; T. Weinberg.
OTHER INFORMATION Due to the trust's low income in 2011–12, only basic financial information was available from the Charity Commission.
HOW TO APPLY In writing to the correspondent.
WHO TO APPLY TO The Trustees, Rosenthal and Co, 106 High West Street, Gateshead, Tyne and Wear NE8 1NA *Tel.* 01914 772814

■ Friends of Boyan Trust

CC NO 1114498   **ESTABLISHED** 2006
WHERE FUNDING CAN BE GIVEN Worldwide.
WHO CAN BENEFIT Orthodox Jews.
WHAT IS FUNDED Jewish causes.
SAMPLE GRANTS Previously: Gomlei Chesed of Chasidei Boyan (£84,000); Mosdot Tiferet Yisroel Boyan (£31,000); Kimcha De'Pischa Boyan (£21,000); Kimcha De'Pischa Beitar Ilit (£13,000); Chevras Mo'oz Ladol (£12,000); Kolel Avrechim Boyan, Betar Ilit (£6,000); Ezer Mikoidesh Foundation (£2,000); Beis Rizhin Trust (£1,500); and Yad Vochessed (£1,000).
FINANCES *Year* 2012 *Income* £325,683 *Grants* £258,549 *Assets* £78,062
TRUSTEES Jacob Getter; Mordechai Freund; Nathan Kuflik.
HOW TO APPLY In writing to the correspondent.
WHO TO APPLY TO Jacob Getter, Trustee, 23 Durley Road, London N16 5JW *Tel.* 020 8809 6051

■ Friends of Essex Churches Trust

CC NO 236033   **ESTABLISHED** 1951
WHERE FUNDING CAN BE GIVEN Essex and the boroughs of Waltham Forest, Redbridge, Newham, Barking and Dagenham and Havering.
WHO CAN BENEFIT Places of worship of Christian faith.
WHAT IS FUNDED Preservation and maintenance of churches in Essex and the boroughs of Waltham Forest, Redbridge, Newham, Barking and Havering.
WHAT IS NOT FUNDED Grants are not available for new work or annual maintenance (for example gutter clearance, redecoration) and towards heating systems.

TYPE OF GRANT One-off grants to organisations. Building repairs only.
RANGE OF GRANTS £1,000–£10,000.
SAMPLE GRANTS Previous beneficiaries (2011) included: Leytonstone St Margaret, Great Totham St Peter, Great Waltham St Lawrence, Messing All Saints, Plaistow Baptist Memorial Church and Thaxted St John the Baptist (£10,000 each); Althorne St Andrew (£7,000); Aveley St Michael and Bush End St John the Evangelist (£5,000 each); Wickham Bishops St Bartholomew (£3,500); South Hanningfield St Peter, Leaden Roding St Michael and Great Baddow St Mary the Virgin (£2,000 each) and Little Saling St Peter and St Paul and Ford End St John the Evangelist (£1,000 each).
FINANCES *Year* 2011–12 *Income* £201,914 *Grants* £103,500 *Assets* £222,806
TRUSTEES Dr James Bettley; Keith Gardner; David Lodge; Dr Christopher Starr; Ralph Meloy; Fiona Nelmes; Philip Smith; Catharine Hutley; Jill Cole.
HOW TO APPLY Application forms can be requested by contacting the correspondent. Further details, conditions and application requirements are outlined on the trust's website. The grants committee meets quarterly.
WHO TO APPLY TO Keith Gardner, Hon Secretary, Pink Cottage, Curtis Mill Gree, Stapleford Tawney, Essex RM4 1RT *Tel.* 01708 688576 *Website* www.foect.org.uk

■ The Friends of Kent Churches

CC NO 207021   **ESTABLISHED** 1950
WHERE FUNDING CAN BE GIVEN County of Kent.
WHO CAN BENEFIT Churches of architectural merit and historical interest.
WHAT IS FUNDED The upkeep of their fabric and the preservation of fixtures of importance.
WHAT IS NOT FUNDED No grants for reordering, new extensions, toilets and kitchens; heating, redecorating and rewiring; bells, clocks and organs.
TYPE OF GRANT Building.
RANGE OF GRANTS £250–£20,000.
SAMPLE GRANTS St Mary – Westwell (£15,000); St Mary the Virgin – Chiddingstone and St Nicholas – Wade (£10,000 each); St Augustine – Ramsgate and St Mary of Charity – Faversham (£8,000 each); St Martin of Tours – Ashurst and St Eanswythe – Folkstone (£5,000 each); St John the Baptist – Meopham (£3,000); St Mary the Virgin – Stone in Oxney, St Mary the Virgin – West Malling and St Mary the Virgin – Westerham (£1,000 each); and St John the Baptist – Bredgar (£500).
FINANCES *Year* 2012 *Income* £236,921 *Grants* £141,200 *Assets* £666,574
TRUSTEES Charles Banks; Charles Oliver; Paul Smallwood; Angela Parish; Leslie Smith; Richard Latham; Jane Boucher; Mary Gibbins; Jane Bird.
OTHER INFORMATION 27 grants were made totalling £141,000 in 2012.
HOW TO APPLY In writing to the correspondent. Grants are offered twice a year at meetings in January and July. Applications should be sent to the secretary by 1 May or 1 November. There are no formal architectural or financial requirements, however proposals must be sensible. Applications can also be made for the National Churches Trust Partnership grants, which are available for structural repair projects with a total cost of up to £50,000. Forms and guidance notes can be downloaded from the trust's website. Grants are also distributed on behalf of WREN (Waste Recycling Environmental Limited) for the maintenance, repair and

restoration of places of religious worship. More information can be found on the trust's website.

WHO TO APPLY TO Jane Bird, Parsonage Farm House, Hampstead Lane, Yalding, Maidstone ME18 6HG *Tel.* 01622 815569 *Website* www.friendsofkentchurches.co.uk

....

■ Friends of Muir Group

CC NO 1100471   **ESTABLISHED** 2002
WHERE FUNDING CAN BE GIVEN UK.
WHO CAN BENEFIT Individuals, community groups and charitable organisations benefiting Muir Group residents in areas where they live or work.
WHAT IS FUNDED Priority is given to young people, older people and communities.
WHAT IS NOT FUNDED No grants for: the settling of debts; the promotion of political activities; general public appeals; the ongoing costs for Credit Unions (although start-up grants are considered); the support of individual religions to the exclusion of other religions (however initiatives that promote tolerance and understanding of different faiths and cultures are actively supported).
TYPE OF GRANT Capital grants, revenue costs and full project funding.
RANGE OF GRANTS £500–£16,000
SAMPLE GRANTS Grants made were divided into the following categories: Sport and Play (£14,300); Environment (£12,000); Education and Training (£9,000); Health (£4,000); Equality and Diversity (£2,300); Poverty and Relief of Debt (£1,600); Arts and Sports (£1,200); Crime and Safety (£950); Special Topics (£800).
FINANCES *Year* 2011–12 *Income* £28,500 *Grants* £45,981 *Assets* £27,063
TRUSTEES Richard Hoffman; David Booth; Adrienne Berkson; Martyn Delaney; Leslie Patterson; Robert Robertson; Claire Babbs; Julie Moore.
OTHER INFORMATION A list of beneficiaries was unavailable.
HOW TO APPLY Note the following statement from the trust: 'We receive many applications from organisations that have failed to read our application guidelines and criteria. We also insist that applications are made through our application forms and not in the form of a letter.' Guidance notes and application forms are available on request from the correspondent and can also be downloaded from the trust's website.
WHO TO APPLY TO Andrew Hunt, Secretary, Old Government House, Dee Hills Park, Chester, Cheshire CH3 5AR *Tel.* 01244 313613 *email* andrew.hunt@muir.org.uk *Website* www.muir.org.uk

....

■ Friends of Wiznitz Limited

CC NO 255685   **ESTABLISHED** 1948
WHERE FUNDING CAN BE GIVEN UK and overseas.
WHO CAN BENEFIT Registered charities.
WHAT IS FUNDED Jewish education, relief of poverty, advancement of the Jewish religion.
WHAT IS NOT FUNDED Exclusively Jewish causes.
RANGE OF GRANTS Up to £250,000.
SAMPLE GRANTS Igud Mosdos Wiznitz (£250,000); Zidkat Zadik (£191,500); Lehachzikom Velchachyosom (£56,000); and Ahavat Israel Synagogue (£26,000).
FINANCES *Year* 2011–12 *Income* £1,095,022 *Grants* £665,292 *Assets* £1,453,596
TRUSTEES Heinrich Feldman; Shulom Feldman; Ralph Bergman.

OTHER INFORMATION In 2011–12, £13,000 was provided in grants to individuals.
HOW TO APPLY In writing to the correspondent.
WHO TO APPLY TO E. Gottesfeld, Administrator, 8 Jessam Avenue, London E5 9DU

....

■ Friends Provident Charitable Foundation

CC NO 1087053   **ESTABLISHED** 2002
WHERE FUNDING CAN BE GIVEN UK.
WHO CAN BENEFIT Groups and organisations working with disadvantaged people.
WHAT IS FUNDED The foundation 'currently works to create the conditions throughout the UK for improved access to appropriate financial services for those who are currently excluded, particularly those on low incomes or otherwise vulnerable to market failure'. Friends Provident Tradition – 'The foundation also carries forward a legacy of giving by the Friends Provident Group. Trustees have determined that a proportion (currently up to 15%) of the foundation's funds may be committed in line with previous gifts to charity made by the Group. The current criteria for giving are: medical research aimed at preventative medicine; charities/causes that were related to the regions where Friends Provident operated as an employer, including the City of London; Quaker initiatives.'
TYPE OF GRANT Three years and longer. Full-project funding, capital costs and core costs.
RANGE OF GRANTS £5,000–£150,000.
SAMPLE GRANTS University of Birmingham (CHASM) (£150,000); Lemos and Crane (£73,000); Centre for Economic and Social Inclusion (£50,000); Bangor University (£25,000); New Economics Foundation (£15,000) and Toynbee Hall (£5,000).
FINANCES *Year* 2011–12 *Income* £980,660 *Grants* £584,945 *Assets* £26,009,328
TRUSTEES Nick Perks; Jenny Shellens; Whitni Thomas; Diane Coyle; Jim Gilbourne; Jennifer Barraclough; Joycelin Dawes; Rob Lake; Raj Thamotheram.
HOW TO APPLY Applicants are directed, where possible, to the foundation's website where details of current funding programmes, criteria, guidelines and application process are posted. Reporting requirements, as stated by the foundation, are as follows: 'full formal report at the end of every year (inputs, outputs and any outcomes) and at the end of the grant (to include any impact as well). Brief report (grant spend and activity) when claiming payments.'
WHO TO APPLY TO Andrew Thompson, Grants Manager, Pixham End, Dorking, Surrey RH4 1QA *Tel.* 0845 268 3388 *email* foundation.enquiries@friendsprovident.co.uk *Website* www.friendsprovidentfoundation.org

....

■ The Frognal Trust

CC NO 244444   **ESTABLISHED** 1964
WHERE FUNDING CAN BE GIVEN UK.
WHO CAN BENEFIT Registered charities benefiting older people, children and people with disabilities or sight loss.
WHAT IS FUNDED The trustees' current grantmaking policy is to make relatively small grants to as many qualifying charities as possible. Particularly charities working in the fields of: residential facilities and services; cultural heritage; hospices; nursing homes;

ophthalmological research; conservation; heritage; parks; and community services. Other charitable purposes will be considered.

WHAT IS NOT FUNDED The trust does not support: any animal charities; the advancement of religion; charities for the benefit of people outside the UK; educational or research trips; branches of national charities; general appeals; individuals.

TYPE OF GRANT Buildings, capital, one-off, research and start-up costs will be considered.

RANGE OF GRANTS £200–£3,500.

SAMPLE GRANTS Previous beneficiaries have included: Action Medical Research, Aireborough Voluntary Services to the Elderly, Canniesburn Research Trust, Elderly Accommodation Counsel and Leeds Society for Deaf and Blind People, Friends of the Elderly, Gloucestershire Disabled Afloat Riverboat Trust, National Rheumatoid Arthritis Society, Royal Liverpool and Broad Green University Hospitals, Samantha Dickson Research Trust, Stubbers Adventure Centre, Wireless for the Bedridden Society and Yorkshire Dales Millennium Project.

FINANCES *Year* 2011–12 *Income* £84,415 *Grants* £46,000 *Assets* £2,152,439

TRUSTEES Philippa Blake-Roberts; Jennifer Helen Fraser; Peter Fraser.

HOW TO APPLY In writing to the correspondent. Applications should be received by February, May, August and November, for consideration at the trustees' meeting the following month.

WHO TO APPLY TO Susan Hickley, Administrator, Wilson Solicitors LLP, Alexandra House, St John's Street, Salisbury SP1 2SB *Tel.* 01722 427536

■ T. F. C. Frost Charitable Trust

CC NO 256590   **ESTABLISHED** 1966
WHERE FUNDING CAN BE GIVEN UK and overseas.
WHO CAN BENEFIT Research into the prevention of blindness.
WHAT IS FUNDED Research into the prevention of blindness by establishing research fellowships and supporting specific projects.
WHAT IS NOT FUNDED There are no available resources for the relief of blind people or people suffering from diseases of the eye.
RANGE OF GRANTS Around £5,000–£35,000.
SAMPLE GRANTS University of Southampton (£45,500) and William Beaumont Hospital – Michigan, USA (£25,000).
FINANCES *Year* 2011–12 *Income* £83,407 *Grants* £70,585 *Assets* £2,605,371
TRUSTEES Michael Miller; Thomas Frost; Prof. John Marshall; Dr Elizabeth Graham.
OTHER INFORMATION Funding was given to three individuals via two institutions during 2011–12. Grants totalled £70,500.
HOW TO APPLY In writing to the correspondent. Trustees meet twice a year.
WHO TO APPLY TO John Holmes, 10 Torrington Road, Claygate, Esher, Surrey KT10 0SA *Tel.* 01372 465378 *email* holmes_and_co@hotmail.com

■ The Patrick and Helena Frost Foundation

CC NO 1005505   **ESTABLISHED** 1991
WHERE FUNDING CAN BE GIVEN UK.
WHO CAN BENEFIT Registered charities.
WHAT IS FUNDED The relief and welfare of people of small means and the less fortunate members of society, and assistance for small organisations

where a considerable amount of self-help and voluntary effort is required.

WHAT IS NOT FUNDED No grants to individuals.

TYPE OF GRANT One-off donations.

RANGE OF GRANTS Mainly £7,500 or less.

SAMPLE GRANTS Jubilee Sailing Trust (£7,500); Action for Blind People and Humberside Police Authority (£5,000 each); Practical Action, Tree Aid and Yeldall Christian Centres (£2,500 each); and Bowel and Cancer Research and the Gurkha Welfare Trust (£1,000 each).

FINANCES *Year* 2011–12 *Income* £38,863 *Grants* £93,000 *Assets* £5,022,588

TRUSTEES Luke Valner; Dominic Tayler; Neil Hendriksen.

OTHER INFORMATION 31 grants totalling £93,000 were made during 2011–12.

HOW TO APPLY In writing to the correspondent, accompanied by the last set of audited accounts. The trustees regret that due to the large number of applications they receive, they are unable to acknowledge unsuccessful applications.

WHO TO APPLY TO Allan Twitchett, Administrator, c/o Trowers and Hamlins LLP, 3 Bunhill Row, London EC1Y 8YZ *Tel.* 020 7423 8276 *email* atwitchett@trowers.com

■ Maurice Fry Charitable Trust

CC NO 327934   **ESTABLISHED** 1988
WHERE FUNDING CAN BE GIVEN UK and overseas.
WHO CAN BENEFIT Registered charities.
WHAT IS FUNDED General charitable purposes.
WHAT IS NOT FUNDED No grants to individuals.
RANGE OF GRANTS £500–£2,000.
SAMPLE GRANTS Southbank Centre, British Red Cross, NSPCC and the Maypole Project (£2,000 each); Marie Curie Centre and Special Olympics GB (£1,000 each); and Fairtrade Foundation (£500).
FINANCES *Year* 2011–12 *Income* £36,847 *Grants* £14,500 *Assets* £1,246,747
TRUSTEES L. Fry; Lisa Weaks; Felicity Cooklin; Sam Cooklin-Smith.
HOW TO APPLY The trustees meet twice a year to consider applications from a wide range of sources. It states that it does not respond to unsolicited applications.
WHO TO APPLY TO L. Fry, Trustee, 98 Savernake Road, London NW3 2JR

■ Mejer and Gertrude Miriam Frydman Foundation

CC NO 262806   **ESTABLISHED** 1971
WHERE FUNDING CAN BE GIVEN UK and overseas.
WHO CAN BENEFIT Jewish, general charitable purposes, particular favour is given to Jewish charities.
WHAT IS FUNDED General charitable purposes with particular preference towards Jewish causes and charitable organisations.
WHAT IS NOT FUNDED No grants to individuals for scholarships or any other purpose.
RANGE OF GRANTS Up to £4,000.
SAMPLE GRANTS North West London Jewish Day School (£4,000); Friends of Yeshiva OHR Elchanan (£3,000); Chai Cancer Care and Friends of Eretz Hemdah (£2,500 each); Kesser Torah (£2,000); Achisomoch Aid Co (£1,000); and Talia Trust for Children (£500).
FINANCES *Year* 2011–12 *Income* £41,875 *Grants* £37,250 *Assets* £82,357

TRUSTEES Keith Graham; David Frydman; Gerald Frydman; Louis Frydman.
HOW TO APPLY In writing to the correspondent.
WHO TO APPLY TO David Frydman, Trustee, Westbury, 145–157 St John Street, London EC1V 4PY *Tel.* 020 7253 7272

■ The Fulmer Charitable Trust

CC NO 1070428 **ESTABLISHED** 1998
WHERE FUNDING CAN BE GIVEN Worldwide, especially the developing world and Wiltshire.
WHO CAN BENEFIT Registered charities worldwide, especially in the developing world and Wiltshire.
WHAT IS FUNDED General charitable purposes.
WHAT IS NOT FUNDED No support for gap year requests.
RANGE OF GRANTS Up to £15,000, but mostly for £500–£3,000.
SAMPLE GRANTS The Sequal Trust (£7,000); Save the Children (£4,500); Send a Cow (£4,000); The Leys Youth Programme (£3,000); Micro Loan Foundation (£2,750); Stars Appeal (£2,500); Christian Aid (£2,000); Ashram International, Brooke Hospital for Animals and Cerebral Palsy Africa (£1,000); Aid for the Aged in Distress, Joshua Foundation, Samaritans (£750); Release International and Wiltshire Wildlife Trust (£500 each) and Help Counselling Services (£250).
FINANCES *Year* 2011–12 *Income* £284,084 *Grants* £184,000 *Assets* £7,818,183
TRUSTEES J. S. Reis; S. Reis; C. Mytum.
HOW TO APPLY In writing to the correspondent. Very few unsolicited applications are accepted.
WHO TO APPLY TO The Trustees, Estate Office, Street Farm, Compton Bassett, Calne, Wiltshire SN11 8SW *Tel.* 01249 760410

■ Worshipful Company of Furniture Makers Charitable Fund

CC NO 270483 **ESTABLISHED** 1975
WHERE FUNDING CAN BE GIVEN UK.
WHO CAN BENEFIT Individuals and organisations.
WHAT IS FUNDED Causes directly connected to furniture, funding design competitions, prototypes and visits to exhibitions or factories and offering bursaries to students at colleges.
RANGE OF GRANTS £200–£5,000.
SAMPLE GRANTS Design Student's Industrial Tour (£5,200); The Woods Awards (£5,000); FIT (£4,000); Retails Course (£3,700); Bucks Chilterns University College (£3,000) and Oxford and Cherwell College (£2,000).
FINANCES *Year* 2011–12 *Income* £461,949 *Grants* £126,000
TRUSTEES Margaret Miller; Roger Richardson; Martin Jourdan; David Bubidge.
HOW TO APPLY In writing to the correspondent.
WHO TO APPLY TO Jonny Westbrooke, Clerk, Furniture Makers' Hall, 12 Austin Friars, London EC2N 2HE *Tel.* 020 7256 5558 *Fax* 020 7256 5155 *email* clerk@furnituremakers.org.uk *Website* www.furnituremakers.co.uk

■ The Fuserna Foundation General Charitable Trust

CC NO 1107895 **ESTABLISHED** 2005
WHERE FUNDING CAN BE GIVEN UK and overseas.
WHO CAN BENEFIT Charitable organisations.
WHAT IS FUNDED General charitable purposes, including education and training; the advancement of health; the relief of poverty; accommodation and housing; the arts; the environment; the armed forces; and human rights.
WHAT IS NOT FUNDED The trust will not normally consider making a grant to any charity that has an income over £3 million.
RANGE OF GRANTS £5,000–£15,000.
SAMPLE GRANTS Tandem Befriending Project (£20,000); Immediate Theatre and Lakelands Day Care (£15,000 each); Child Brain Injury Trust (£12,000); Tiverton Market Centre (£10,000); Tuberous Sclerosis Association (£7,000); My Voice London and West Sussex Association for the Blind (£5,000 each); and Support Line and Bag Books (£2,500 each).
FINANCES *Year* 2012 *Income* £250,000 *Grants* £129,900 *Assets* £277,971
TRUSTEES Patrick Maxwell; Ariadne Getty; Louise Creasey.
OTHER INFORMATION 16 grants totalling £130,000 were provided in 2012.
HOW TO APPLY Trustees may approach certain charities and ask them to submit a funding request based on Fuserna's interest in their projects. The trust's website states the following: 'All applications must have a clear sense of objective, how to achieve that objective, and have a very good chance of making a real difference in the field it which it operates. Applications should be submitted in writing and include: a full outline of the project for which funding is needed; the cost of the project; the community affected; the benefits and impact of the project intended; other sources of funding secured in relation to the project; and a full outline of the charity itself, its history, financial position and forecast, as well as its overall strategy. In addition, financial statements, management accounts, tax returns, and any cash-flow statements should also accompany the application. Applications are reviewed on a quarterly basis throughout the calendar year. Certain applications are shortlisted for the trustees and board members. Following an initial review of the shortlist, those applications approved will go through a further stage of assessment before the trustees and board members make a final determination of the successful applications for that quarter and the amount of any grant awarded. If a grant application is successful, the Fuserna team requires regular updates as to the progress of the project funded and the charity itself. This will also benefit the project by giving the charity a way to track its own impact.'
WHO TO APPLY TO Louise Creasey, Trustee, 6th Floor, 6 Chesterfield Gardens, London W1J 5BQ *Tel.* 020 7409 3900 *email* info@fusernafoundation.org *Website* www.fusernafoundation.org

■ The G. D. Charitable Trust

CC NO 1096101   **ESTABLISHED** 2002
WHERE FUNDING CAN BE GIVEN Worldwide.
WHO CAN BENEFIT Registered charities.
WHAT IS FUNDED Animal welfare, the environment, disability, homelessness.
WHAT IS NOT FUNDED No grants to individuals.
RANGE OF GRANTS £50,000–£200.
SAMPLE GRANTS Blue Marine Foundation (£50,000); Whitley Fund for Nature (£25,000); Save the Children UK (£17,000); SWHP, Naomi House and BDFA (£1,000 each); Hart Wildlife Hospital (£500); and Sarah Greene Breakthrough Tribute Fund (£200).
FINANCES Year 2012 Income £93,439 Grants £95,700 Assets £3,500,061
TRUSTEES George Duffield; Alexander Fitzgibbons; Natasha Duffield.
OTHER INFORMATION Grants to eight organisations were made totalling £96,000.
HOW TO APPLY In writing to the correspondent.
WHO TO APPLY TO Jonathan Brinsden, Administrator, Bircham Dyson Bell, 50 Broadway, London SW1H 0BL Tel. 020 7227 7000

■ The G. I. Foundation

CC NO 1148553   **ESTABLISHED** 2012
WHERE FUNDING CAN BE GIVEN UK.
WHO CAN BENEFIT Charities and community groups.
WHAT IS FUNDED Education, health, relief of poverty and Jewish causes.
TRUSTEES Bernard Ost; Gita Ost; Shelley Goldstein.
HOW TO APPLY In writing to the correspondent.
WHO TO APPLY TO Bernard Ost, Trustee, 29 Grosvenor Gardens, London NW11 0HE Tel. 020 8731 6307

■ G. M. C. Trust

CC NO 288418   **ESTABLISHED** 1965
WHERE FUNDING CAN BE GIVEN UK, predominantly West Midlands.
WHO CAN BENEFIT General charitable purposes but organisations benefiting children, young adults and older people are largely supported.
WHAT IS FUNDED Areas in and around the West Midlands, general charitable purposes.
WHAT IS NOT FUNDED No grants to individuals, or to local or regional appeals outside the West Midlands. The trust does not respond to national appeals, except where there are established links.
TYPE OF GRANT One-off.
RANGE OF GRANTS Potentially up to £20,000, but most grants are lower.
SAMPLE GRANTS Ellern Mede School and UN Women UK (£20,000 each); the Salvation Army and ZANE – Zimbabwe A National Emergency (£10,000 each); King's College – Cambridge, Listening Books and London and North Western Railway Society (£5,000 each); King's Lynn Arts Centre Trust (£2,000); Royal Birmingham Society of Artists (£1,500); Institute of Economic Affairs and Oundle Music Trust (£1,000 each); the Society of King's Economists (£500); and Arden School (£200).

FINANCES Year 2011–12 Income £137,849 Grants £103,200 Assets £2,729,412
TRUSTEES Bes Cadbury; Sir Adrian Cadbury; MJ. Cadbury; CE. Fowler-Wright.
OTHER INFORMATION Grants to 19 organisations totalled £103,000 in 2011–12.
HOW TO APPLY In writing to the correspondent. The trust largely supports projects which come to the attention of its trustees through their special interests and knowledge. General applications for grants are not encouraged.
WHO TO APPLY TO Rodney Pitts, Secretary, Flat 4 Fairways, 1240 Warwick Road, Knowle, Solihull B93 9LL Tel. 01564 779971

■ Gableholt Limited

CC NO 276250   **ESTABLISHED** 1978
WHERE FUNDING CAN BE GIVEN Worldwide.
WHO CAN BENEFIT Jewish organisations.
WHAT IS FUNDED Advancement of the Orthodox Jewish faith, education.
FINANCES Year 2011–12 Income £830,939 Grants £8,157 Assets £21,990,653
TRUSTEES Philip Noe; Etelka Noe; Salomon Noe; Aron Bude.
HOW TO APPLY In the past this trust has stated that 'in the governors' view, true charitable giving should always be coupled with virtual anonymity' and for this reason they are most reluctant to be a party to any publicity. Along with suggesting that the listed beneficiaries might also want to remain unidentified, they also state that the nature of the giving (to Orthodox Jewish organisations) means the information is unlikely to be of much interest to anyone else. Potential applicants would be strongly advised to note these comments.
WHO TO APPLY TO Etelka Noe, Trustee, 115 Craven Park Road, London N15 6BL Tel. 0208802478

■ The Galanthus Trust

CC NO 1103538   **ESTABLISHED** 2004
WHERE FUNDING CAN BE GIVEN UK and overseas.
WHO CAN BENEFIT Registered charities and individuals.
WHAT IS FUNDED Medical, developing countries, environment, conservation.
RANGE OF GRANTS UK and overseas.
SAMPLE GRANTS Previously grants had been distributed between three categories: medical and healthcare, projects in the third world and environment and welfare.
FINANCES Year 2011–12 Income £4,538 Grants £97,670
TRUSTEES S. F. Rogers; J. M. Rogers.
OTHER INFORMATION Accounts were received at the Commission but due to the charity's low income, were not published.
HOW TO APPLY In writing to the correspondent. 'All requests for grants are considered carefully by the trustees. The trustees decide whether to donate and the amount to donate.'
WHO TO APPLY TO Juliet Rogers, Trustee, Pile Oak Lodge, Donhead St Andrew, Shaftesbury, Dorset SP7 9EH Tel. 0747829138 email galanthustrust@yahoo.co.uk

■ The Galbraith Trust

CC NO 1086717   **ESTABLISHED** 2001
WHERE FUNDING CAN BE GIVEN The administrative area of Lancaster City Council.
WHO CAN BENEFIT Charitable organisations.

WHAT IS FUNDED General charitable purposes.

RANGE OF GRANTS Usually £100–£3,000

SAMPLE GRANTS Archbishop Hutton After School Fun Club, Bare Necessities Pre-School Playgroup, Bolton-le-Sands Village Hall, Lancashire Outward Bound Association and Night Owls (£1,500 each); Friendship Centre (£1,000); 1st Heysham Guides and Community Learning Network (£800 each); St Barnabas Housebound Club (£600); Lancaster and Garstang Division Girl Guiding and Stage Struck Youth Theatre (£500 each); and Greenfield Court residents Association (£300).

FINANCES *Year* 2011–12 *Income* £19,295 *Grants* £37,000

TRUSTEES Ms K. F. Gordon, Chair; J. W. Wilson; M. V. L. Harris; I. E. Bowker; M. W. Burrow; P. G. Crowther.

HOW TO APPLY Application forms may be obtained from the Lancaster District Council for Voluntary Service at the contact address or are available to download at www.lancastercvs.org.uk (where criteria and guidelines are also posted).
The Trustees meet to agree and distribute grants approximately quarterly. Applicants are asked to complete a simple form and submit their most recent Annual Report and examined/audited accounts. The Council for Voluntary Service (CVS) acts as administrator and also provides support to any organisation needing help with their application.
If you want any clarification or help in completing the form, contact the Funding Officer at CVS, telephone 01524 555900 (ext. 32) or email pennydarby@lancastercvs.org.uk

WHO TO APPLY TO The Trustees, c/o Lancaster District CVS, Trinity Community Centre, Middle Street, Lancaster LA1 1JZ *Tel* 01524 555 900 (ext. 32) *email* pennydarby@lancastercvs.org.uk *Website* www.lancastercvs.org.uk

....

■ **The Gale Family Charity Trust**

CC NO 289212   **ESTABLISHED** 1984

WHERE FUNDING CAN BE GIVEN UK, mainly Bedfordshire.

WHO CAN BENEFIT Registered charities, with a preference for Bedfordshire-based charities.

WHAT IS FUNDED General charitable purposes with preference to churches and church ministries, as well as community life.

WHAT IS NOT FUNDED Grants are rarely given to individuals.

RANGE OF GRANTS Up to £20,000.

SAMPLE GRANTS Bedford Day Care Centre (£20,000); Bedford Modern School (£10,000); Cecil Higgins Arts Gallery, St John's Hospice – Moggerhanger and BECHAR – Prebend Street Day Centre (£5,000 each); Bedford Guild House and Bedford and District Cerebral Palsy Society (£3,000 each); Soundabout and Douglas Bader Foundation (£2,000 each); Action for Sick Children, Dream Holidays and Marie Curie Cancer Care (£1,000 each); and War Memorials Trust (£500).

FINANCES *Year* 2011–12 *Income* £117,394 *Grants* £196,000 *Assets* £5,406,660

TRUSTEES Anthony Ormerod; Gary Payne; John Tyley; Doreen Watson; Warwick Browning; Russell Beard; David Fletcher; Gerry Garner.

OTHER INFORMATION 58 grants were made to organisations in 2011–12 and 20 grants were made to churches. The sum of these was £196,000.

HOW TO APPLY In writing to the correspondent.

WHO TO APPLY TO Alistair Law, Administrator, Northwood House, 138 Bromham Road, Bedford MK40 2QW *Tel.* 01234 354508 *Fax* 01234 349588 *email* alistair.law@garnerassociates.co.uk

....

■ **Gamlen Charitable Trust**

CC NO 327977   **ESTABLISHED** 1988

WHERE FUNDING CAN BE GIVEN UK.

WHO CAN BENEFIT Organisations benefiting law students and trainee solicitors, as well as those looking to relieve poverty and advance education through music and the arts.

WHAT IS FUNDED Legal education, the relief of poverty and the advancement of education through music and the arts.

WHAT IS NOT FUNDED In accordance with charitable objectives, we can surmise that the trust funds exclusively to law students and trainee solicitors, as well as to organisations that aim to relieve poverty and advance education through music and the arts.

TYPE OF GRANT Grants for scholarships, bursaries and prizes. Longer than three years.

RANGE OF GRANTS Up to £30,000.

SAMPLE GRANTS Christ Church – Law Fellowship (£30,000); Newbury Spring Festival and Grange Park Opera (£3,000 each); and Orpheus Foundation (£1,000).

FINANCES *Year* 2012–13 *Income* £46,858 *Grants* £37,000 *Assets* £1,707,962

TRUSTEES Julian Chadwick; Rodney Stubblefield; Paul Eaton.

OTHER INFORMATION Grants to four organisations totalled £37,000.

HOW TO APPLY The trust does not accept unsolicited applications.

WHO TO APPLY TO Julian Chadwick, Trustee, c/o Thomas Eggar LLP, Newbury House, 20 Kings Road West, Newbury, Berkshire RG14 5XR *Tel.* 01635 571000

....

■ **The Gamma Trust**

SC NO SC004330   **ESTABLISHED** 1965

WHERE FUNDING CAN BE GIVEN UK, with preference to Scotland.

WHO CAN BENEFIT Registered charities.

WHAT IS FUNDED General charitable purposes. The advancement of health, the advancement of the arts, heritage, culture or science, the relief of those in need by reason of age, ill health, disability, financial hardship or other disadvantage.

TYPE OF GRANT Project, research and recurring costs.

SAMPLE GRANTS Previous beneficiaries have included British Red Cross, British Heart Foundation, Cancer Research Campaign and Erskine Hospital.

FINANCES *Year* 2011–12 *Income* £86,092 *Grants* £75,687 *Assets* £1,501,134

TRUSTEE Clydesdale Bank plc.

HOW TO APPLY In writing to the correspondent for consideration quarterly.

WHO TO APPLY TO Fiona Tedford, Trust Team Leader, c/o Mazars CYB Services Limited, 90 St Vincent Street, Glasgow G2 5UB *Tel.* 01412 254953 *email* glasgowtrustteam@mazars.co.uk

■ The Gannochy Trust

SC NO SC003133 **ESTABLISHED** 1937

WHERE FUNDING CAN BE GIVEN Scotland, with a preference for the Perth and Kinross area.

WHO CAN BENEFIT Organisations which meet the OSCR Charity Test.

WHAT IS FUNDED The trust's grantmaking mission is: 'to make a positive difference for the benefit of people living in Scotland, with a preference for Perth and Kinross'. It has four grantmaking themes: (1) inspiring young people; (2) improving the quality of life of the disadvantaged and vulnerable; (3) supporting and developing community amenities; (4) care for the natural and man-made environment. NOTE: Themes 3 and 4 are restricted to Perth and Kinross

WHAT IS NOT FUNDED 'General applications for funds will not be considered – applications must be specific, and preferably for a project with a defined outcome, not general running costs; donations will not be made to individuals; donations will only be made to organisations which meet the OSCR Charity Test; projects where the benefit of a donation will be realised outside Scotland; donations will rarely be made to projects that do not demonstrate an element of self or other funding; donations will not be made that contribute to an organisation's healthy reserves or endowments; applications will seldom be considered for more than a 3-year commitment; applications will not be considered for holidays, with the exception of those for the disabled and disadvantaged living in Perth and Kinross where the project has a tangible recreational or educational theme; applications will not be considered for animal welfare projects, with the exception of wildlife projects within Perth and Kinross that meet the sub-themes within theme 4; applications will not be considered from schools for recreational facilities unless there will be a demonstrable and sustained community involvement, preferably for the disadvantaged or vulnerable; applications from pre-school groups, play schemes, after school clubs and parent-teacher associations; applications will not be considered from cancer and other health-related charities unless they demonstrate that their project directly provides tangible relief from suffering and direct patient benefit; applications from places of worship will not be considered unless there is a distinct community benefit through use as a community centre or village hall, and where there is not a similar facility nearby; applications will not be considered from charities re-applying within a year of their previous appeal or award, or instalment thereof; applications will not be considered where funding would normally be provided by central or local government; waste disposal/landfill, pollution control and renewable energy projects will not be considered if they are the sole purpose of the project, and unless they meet the criteria within theme 4; applications will not be considered for political or lobbying purposes; applications will not be considered from higher or further education establishments unless the project has been initiated by the trustees.'

SAMPLE GRANTS Pert and Kinross Heritage Trust and Black Watch Museum Trust (£300,000 each); Perth and Kinross Council Living Communities Project (£247,000); Perth and Kinross Countryside Trust (£200,000); Scottish Opera (£150,000) and Friends of the Birks Cinema (£50,000).

FINANCES *Year* 2011–12 *Income* £5,893,221 *Grants* £1,467,965 *Assets* £128,419,368

TRUSTEES Dr James H. F. Kynaston, Chair; Mark Webster; Ian W. Macmillan; Stewart N. Macleod; Dr John Markland.

OTHER INFORMATION A further £2.3 million was committed for future grants but not paid.

HOW TO APPLY On a form which can be downloaded from the trust's website. The application form also contains detailed guidance notes.

WHO TO APPLY TO Fiona Russell, Secretary, Kincarrathie House Drive, Pitcullen Crescent, Perth PH2 7HX *Tel.* 01738 620653 *email* admin@gannochytrust.org.uk *Website* www.gannochytrust.org.uk

■ The Ganzoni Charitable Trust

CC NO 263583 **ESTABLISHED** 1971

WHERE FUNDING CAN BE GIVEN Suffolk.

WHO CAN BENEFIT Registered charities.

WHAT IS FUNDED General charitable purposes.

WHAT IS NOT FUNDED Grants to individuals will not be considered. Applications from outside Suffolk are not normally considered and will not be acknowledged.

RANGE OF GRANTS £50–£15,000.

SAMPLE GRANTS St Mary's Church, Woodbridge (£15,000); St Edmundsbury Cathedral (£5,000); British Dyslexics (£3,000); Papworth Trust (£2,000); The Ipswich Council for Voluntary Service, The British Forces Foundation, West Suffolk Voluntary Association for the Blind and The No Way Trust (£1,000 each); Guide Dogs for the Blind, Safechild and Girl Guiding Leiston District (£500 each); Suffolk Carers Ltd (£250) and British Red Cross (£50).

FINANCES *Year* 2011–12 *Income* £152,563 *Grants* £72,195 *Assets* £3,270,647

TRUSTEES Hon. Mary Jill Ganzoni; Hon. Charles Boscawen; Nicholas Ridley; John Pickering

OTHER INFORMATION There were 52 grants awarded during 2011–12.

HOW TO APPLY In writing to the correspondent. Telephone calls are not encouraged. There are no application forms, guidelines or deadlines. No sae is required unless material is to be returned.

WHO TO APPLY TO Hon. Charles Boscawen, Trustee, c/o Birketts LLP, 24–26 Museum Street, Ipswich IP1 1HZ

■ The Worshipful Company of Gardeners of London

CC NO 222079 **ESTABLISHED** 1962

WHERE FUNDING CAN BE GIVEN Mainly City of London.

WHO CAN BENEFIT Horticultural organisations.

WHAT IS FUNDED The fund supports charitable activities connected with horticulture in all its forms and within the City of London.

RANGE OF GRANTS £100–£6,000.

SAMPLE GRANTS London Children's Flower Society (£6,000); Gardening for Disabled Trust (£5,000); London Gardens Society (£4,000); Metropolitan Public Gardens Association (£3,500); Flowers in the City Campaign (£2,500); Lord Mayor's Appeal (£1,250); The Queen Alexandra Hospital (£1,000) and Reeds School Foundation Appeal, City of London School for Girls, Central School of Ballet and Newbury Community Resources Centre (£500 each).

FINANCES *Year* 2011–12 *Income* £83,657 *Grants* £61,825 *Assets* £437,604

TRUSTEES Norman Chalmers; Rex Thornborough; Roger Hedgecoe; Louise Robinson; Nicholas

Evans; Stephen Bernhard; Mitch Dowlen; Brian Porter; Daniel Caspi; Dr Stephen Dowbiggin; Rod Petty; Christine Cohen; Trevor Farris.

HOW TO APPLY In writing to the correspondent.

WHO TO APPLY TO Trevor Faris, Clerk, 25 Luke Street, London EC2A 4AR *Tel* 020 7739 6404 (PA to the Clerk) or ext. 6696 (Assistant Clerk) *Fax* 020 7613 3412 *email* paclerk@gardenerscompany.org.uk *Website* www.gardenerscompany.org.uk

■ The Samuel Gardner Memorial Trust

CC NO 261059   **ESTABLISHED** 1970

WHERE FUNDING CAN BE GIVEN Harrow-on-the-Hill.

WHO CAN BENEFIT Organisations and charitable groups.

WHAT IS FUNDED Music and music education; the arts and heritage; preservation of landscaped public spaces. There is an emphasis on the encouragement of young people.

WHAT IS NOT FUNDED No grants to individuals.

SAMPLE GRANTS Streetwise Opera (£3,500)

FINANCES *Year* 2011–12 *Income* £44,931 *Grants* £38,000 *Assets* £1,446,831

TRUSTEES Timothy Brown; Marion Friend; Ursula Jones; Timothy Lines; John Stenhouse; Nicholas Rampley.

HOW TO APPLY In writing to the correspondent.

WHO TO APPLY TO Pauline McAlpine, c/o SBM and Company, 117 Fentman Road, London SW8 1JZ *Tel.* 020 7582 9473 *email* pauline@sbmandco.com

■ The Garennie Charitable Trust

CC NO 1147622   **ESTABLISHED** 2012

WHERE FUNDING CAN BE GIVEN Worldwide.

WHO CAN BENEFIT Charities and community groups.

WHAT IS FUNDED General charitable purposes.

TRUSTEES Rebecca Bannatyne; Thomas Bannatyne; Coutts and Co.

HOW TO APPLY In writing to the correspondent.

WHO TO APPLY TO Coutts and Co, Trustee Department, 440 Strand, London WC2R 0QS *Tel.* 020 7663 6826

■ The Garnett Charitable Trust

CC NO 327847   **ESTABLISHED** 1988

WHERE FUNDING CAN BE GIVEN South west England and Northern Ireland.

WHO CAN BENEFIT Registered charities.

WHAT IS FUNDED Health, hospices, environmental causes and animal welfare groups, arts, culture and recreation.

WHAT IS NOT FUNDED No grants to unsolicited applications. Most funds are earmarked and speculative applications will not be considered.

RANGE OF GRANTS £5–£10,000.

SAMPLE GRANTS All Hallows' School – Cranmore, CARE International, Design Museum, Ireland Fund of Great Britain, National Gallery Trust, St Michael's Parish and Save the Children.

FINANCES *Year* 2011–12 *Income* £4,471 *Grants* £45,000

TRUSTEE Sandra Brown.

HOW TO APPLY No grants to unsolicited applications.

WHO TO APPLY TO Jenny O'Neil, c/o Osbourne Clarke Solicitors, 2 Temple Back East, Temple Quay, Bristol BS1 6EG *Tel.* 01179 173000

■ Garrick Charitable Trust

CC NO 1071279   **ESTABLISHED** 1998

WHERE FUNDING CAN BE GIVEN UK.

WHO CAN BENEFIT Registered charities only.

WHAT IS FUNDED Institutions which are seeking to further theatre (including dance), literature or music.

WHAT IS NOT FUNDED Drama training or academic studies amateur productions projects outside the UK.

TYPE OF GRANT Up to three years.

RANGE OF GRANTS Usually £2,500, exceptionally up to £10,000.

SAMPLE GRANTS Alternative Theatre Company, Africa 95, Birmingham Royal Ballet and Buxton Festival (£5,000 each); Ledbury Petry Festival (£4,000); Arches Theatre, Charleston Trust, Darlington International Summer School and Northern Ballet (£2,500 each); and Brockley Jack Theatre (£1,000).

FINANCES *Year* 2011–12 *Income* £167,507 *Grants* £96,316 *Assets* £4,889,885

TRUSTEES David Sigall; Sir Stephen Waley-Cohen; Roger Braban; Stephen Aris; Ion Trewin.

OTHER INFORMATION Grants were made to 33 organisations totalling £96,500

HOW TO APPLY Initial applications are reviewed by the trustees who decide whether or not to send an application form. Trustees meet quarterly. The trust's website states: 'First, write us a short letter – preferably one, but not more than two, pages, perhaps with a publicity flyer. In your letter tell us: about your organisation and the project you want us to support how much money you are asking for how your organisation will benefit from a grant what will happen if you do not receive a grant. Occasionally we are able to make an immediate grant, but normally we will then send you a form asking for more detailed information about your request and your organisation. The form also asks you for your most recent accounts and income, including earnings and support in kind. You may wish to include CVs of the people involved in the project, reviews of previous productions or publicity flyers.'

WHO TO APPLY TO Fiona Murray, Trust Administrator, Garrick Club, 15 Garrick Street, London WC2E 9AY *Tel.* 020 7395 4136 *email* michaelkb@garrickclub.co.uk *Website* www.garrickclub.co.uk

■ Garthgwynion Charities

CC NO 229334   **ESTABLISHED** 1963

WHERE FUNDING CAN BE GIVEN Primarily the parishes of Isygarreg and Uwchygarreg at Machynlleth, Powys.

WHO CAN BENEFIT Organisations benefiting people who are ill, at-risk groups and people who are disadvantaged by poverty or socially isolated.

WHAT IS FUNDED Main areas of interest are: (a) the leading national charities conducting research into cancer, sight or disorders of the nervous system; (b) community projects or individuals with a Welsh (better still, Mid-Wales) link, having either a social or artistic purpose.

WHAT IS NOT FUNDED Applications by individuals are considered only exceptionally

TYPE OF GRANT Usually one off

SAMPLE GRANTS Machynlleth Tabernacle Trust, Harrow School, Powys Eisteddfod, the Tannery Appeal and Gonville and Caius College, Cambridge.

FINANCES *Year* 2011–12 *Income* £55,749 *Grants* £78,450 *Assets* £1,367,229

Think carefully about every application. Is it justified?

569

TRUSTEES E. R. Lambert; D. H. O. Owen; E. C. O. Owen.
HOW TO APPLY In writing to the correspondent.
WHO TO APPLY TO June Baker, 13 Osborne Close, Feltham, Hounslow, London TW13 6SR *Tel.* 020 8890 0469

....

■ Garvan Limited
CC NO 286110   ESTABLISHED 1980
WHERE FUNDING CAN BE GIVEN UK.
WHO CAN BENEFIT Jewish organisations.
WHAT IS FUNDED The advancement of religion in accordance with the Orthodox Jewish faith and the relief of poverty.
FINANCES *Year* 2011–12 *Income* £183,484 *Grants* £28,022 *Assets* £1,494,705
TRUSTEES Ahron Ebert; Lilly Ebert.
HOW TO APPLY In writing to the correspondent.
WHO TO APPLY TO The Trustees, Flat 9, Windsor Court, Golders Green Road, London NW11 9PP

....

■ The Gatsby Charitable Foundation
CC NO 251988   ESTABLISHED 1967
WHERE FUNDING CAN BE GIVEN Unrestricted.
WHO CAN BENEFIT Registered charities only. Many beneficiary organisations are specialist research institutes.
WHAT IS FUNDED **Plant Science**: to develop basic research in fundamental processes of plant growth and development and molecular plant pathology, to encourage young researchers in the field of plant science in the UK; **Neuroscience**: to support world-class research in the area of neural circuits and behaviour, and in the area of theoretical neuroscience; and to support activities which enhance our understanding in these fields; **Science and Engineering Education** to strengthen science and engineering skills in the UK by developing and enabling innovative programmes and informing national policy; **Africa**: to promote economic development in East Africa that benefits the poor through support to the growth and sustainability of key sectors; **Public Policy** – to support: the Institute for Government as an independent institute available to politicians and the civil service, focused on making government more effective; and the Centre for Cities, which provides practical research and policy advice that helps cities understand how they can succeed economically; **The Arts** – to support the fabric and programming of institutions with which Gatsby's founding family has connections.
WHAT IS NOT FUNDED Generally, the trustees do not make grants in response to unsolicited applications or to individuals.
TYPE OF GRANT One-off and recurring grants.
SAMPLE GRANTS Sainsbury-Wellcome Centre for Brain Circuitry (£7.9 million); University of Cambridge (£6.5 million); Institute for Government (£2.5 million); Aquifier Limited (£1.5 million); Harvard University (£598,000); The Sainsbury Institute for the Study of Japanese Arts and Cultures (£568,000); New Engineering Foundation (£424,000); Rwandan Governance Initiative (£366,000); Society for Neuroscience (£161,000) and the Academy of Ancient Music (£100,000).
FINANCES *Year* 2011–12 *Income* £46,719,000 *Grants* £42,690,000 *Assets* £290,770,000
TRUSTEES Bernard Willis; Sir Andrew Cahn; Judith Portrait.

OTHER INFORMATION The trust is one of the Sainsbury Family Charitable Trusts which share a common administration. An application to one is taken as an application to all.
HOW TO APPLY Proposals are generally invited by the trustees or initiated at their request. Unsolicited applications are not encouraged and are unlikely to be successful.
WHO TO APPLY TO Peter Hesketh, Director, The Peak, 5 Wilton Road, London SW1V 1AP *Tel.* 020 7410 0330 *Fax* 020 7410 0332 *email* contact@gatsby.org.uk *Website* www.gatsby.org.uk

....

■ Gatwick Airport Community Trust
CC NO 1089683   ESTABLISHED 2001
WHERE FUNDING CAN BE GIVEN Parts of East and West Sussex, Surrey and Kent but particularly communities directly affected by operations at Gatwick Airport. A map of the area of benefit can be seen on the website.
WHO CAN BENEFIT Environmental and community projects in the area of benefit.
WHAT IS FUNDED Priority categories for support are: the development of young people; art projects including amateur drama, music and art; sporting facilities; environmental improvement and conservation; improvements to community facilities such as village halls; support for people who are disabled; support for people who are elderly; and the encouragement of additional volunteering or giving in the area.
WHAT IS NOT FUNDED The trustees will not consider projects that involve any of the following categories: projects or beneficiaries that are completely or largely outside the area of benefit (less attention is given to applications from areas not directly affected by the airport); recurrent expenditure or running costs, ongoing maintenance or deficits; salaries or training costs, except start-up costs in relation to an additional amenity or service being established that will be self-sustaining thereafter; costs that should be funded from other sources, e.g. public bodies; applications from organisations that have statutory responsibilities such as local authorities, hospitals, schools, unless it is a project that is over and above their core activities; the purchase of land or buildings. Grants will not be made to organisations that are working to make a profit for shareholders, partners or sole owners, nor to individuals. Grants will not normally be made where it is evident that little or no effort has been made to raise funds elsewhere.
TYPE OF GRANT The trust favours applications that involve one-off capital or project costs, rather than ongoing maintenance, salaries or training costs.
RANGE OF GRANTS £250–£5,000.
FINANCES *Year* 2012 *Income* £192,458 *Grants* £169,065 *Assets* £19,115
TRUSTEES Mike Roberts, Chair; Kay Hammond; Neil Matthewson; John Mortimer; Michael Sander; James Smith; Christopher Hersey; Helyn Clack; Ian Revell.
OTHER INFORMATION The majority of grant applications were successful with 145 out of 161 applications being accepted.
HOW TO APPLY Application forms are available during the period each year when applications are being accepted (see below) by contacting the trust by telephone or writing to: GACT, PO Box 464, Tunbridge Wells, Kent TN2 9PU. Forms can

also be downloaded from the website. Applications are invited once a year, usually between January and March. Grants are paid by the end of May. Further information can be found on the trust's website. Telephone queries are welcomed.

WHO TO APPLY TO Rosamund Quade, Trust Secretary, c/o Public Affairs, 7th Floor, Destinations Place, Gatwick Airport, West Sussex RH6 0NP *Tel.* 01892 826088 *Website* www.gact.org.uk

■ The Robert Gavron Charitable Trust

CC NO 268535   **ESTABLISHED** 1974
WHERE FUNDING CAN BE GIVEN Mainly UK.
WHO CAN BENEFIT Mainly small charities.
WHAT IS FUNDED The principal fields of interest continue to include health and welfare (including charities for people with disabilities), prisons and prison reform, arts and arts education, education and social policy and research.
WHAT IS NOT FUNDED The trust does not give donations to individuals.
TYPE OF GRANT One-off; project; research; recurring cost; and salaries. Funding can be given for up to three years.
RANGE OF GRANTS Up to £60,000.
SAMPLE GRANTS Arab Israel Children's Tennis Charity (£59,500); High Pay Unit and Tricycle Theatre (£50,000 each); Action on Addiction (£30,000); Reprieve (£29,000); House of Illustration (£17,000); Redlands Primary School (£12,500); National Film and TV School (£10,000); Charleston Trust and Mudchute Association (£5,000 each); and Arts for All (£3,000).
FINANCES *Year* 2011–12 *Income* £708,062 *Grants* £528,132 *Assets* £8,049,535
TRUSTEES Sarah Gavron; Charles Corman; Lord Robert Gavron; Jessica Gavron; Lady Katharine Gavron.
OTHER INFORMATION Smaller grants of less than £3,000 totalled £65,000.
HOW TO APPLY The trustees' report for 2011/12 states the following: 'At present the trust is fully committed to its existing areas of interest. Furthermore, the trustees are unlikely to be able to consider further applications for funding in the current financial climate (written in November 2012).'
WHO TO APPLY TO Yvette Dear, Secretary, 44 Eagle Street, London WC1R 4FS *Tel.* 020 7400 4300

■ Jacqueline and Michael Gee Charitable Trust

CC NO 1062566   **ESTABLISHED** 1997
WHERE FUNDING CAN BE GIVEN UK and overseas.
WHO CAN BENEFIT Charitable organisations, with a preference for Jewish groups.
WHAT IS FUNDED Almost exclusively health, arts and educational charities.
RANGE OF GRANTS Usually up to £10,000.
SAMPLE GRANTS Yad Vashem – UK Foundation (£10,000); United Synagogue (£6,800); Youth Aliyah – Child Rescue, SJP Charity Trust Limited, Philharmonia Chorus and Nightingale Hammerson (£5,000 each); Child Resettlement Trust Fund and Garsington Opera Limited (£3,300 each); Israel Philharmonic Orchestra Foundation, Jewish Child's Day and Kisharon (£2,000 each); Lifelites and the Churchill Centre (£1,000 each); Royal Brompton and Harefield Hospital Charitable Fund and Weizmann Institute Foundation (£500 each); and West

London Synagogue Charitable Fund and Musicworks (£200 each).
FINANCES *Year* 2011–12 *Income* £156,321 *Grants* £94,155 *Assets* £119,391
TRUSTEES Michael Gee; Jacqueline Gee.
OTHER INFORMATION Grants were made to 49 organisations totalling £94,000 in 2011–12.
HOW TO APPLY In writing to the correspondent.
WHO TO APPLY TO Michael Gee, Trustee, Flat 27 Berkeley House, 15 Hay Hill, London W1J 8NS *Tel.* 020 7493 1904

■ Sir Robert Geffery's Almshouse Trust

CC NO 219153   **ESTABLISHED** 1973
WHERE FUNDING CAN BE GIVEN UK.
WHO CAN BENEFIT Registered charities only.
WHAT IS FUNDED This charity makes grants for educational activities for children and young people up to the age of 25 from disadvantaged backgrounds. It also gives to specific charitable organisations with which the trustee has an ongoing relationship (e.g. a block grant is made to Housing the Homeless which allocates grants to individuals).
WHAT IS NOT FUNDED Applications for grants to individuals are accepted only from registered social workers or other agencies, not directly from individuals.
RANGE OF GRANTS £1,000–£10,000.
SAMPLE GRANTS MakeBelieve Arts (£21,000); Lyric Hammersmith (£17,000); The Art Room (£14,000); St Vincent's Family Project (£10,000); Royal Academy of Arts (£7,000); North East Theatre Trust (£5,500); and the London Federation of OCA's (£250).
FINANCES *Year* 2011–12 *Income* £932,747 *Grants* £135,761 *Assets* £12,106,019
TRUSTEE The Worshipful Company of Ironmongers.
HOW TO APPLY In writing to the correspondent.
WHO TO APPLY TO The Charities Administrator, Ironmongers' Hall, Barbican, London EC2Y 8AA *Tel.* 020 7776 2311 *email* helen@ironhall.co.uk *Website* www.ironhall.co.uk

■ The General Nursing Council for England and Wales Trust

CC NO 288068   **ESTABLISHED** 1983
WHERE FUNDING CAN BE GIVEN England and Wales
WHO CAN BENEFIT Universities and other public bodies benefiting nurses.
WHAT IS FUNDED Public bodies undertaking research into matters directly affecting nursing or the nursing profession.
WHAT IS NOT FUNDED The Trust will not fund organisational overheads, purchase of equipment, or dissemination costs such as conference attendance.
TYPE OF GRANT One-off or annually towards revenue costs.
RANGE OF GRANTS Up to £20,000
SAMPLE GRANTS London Florence Nightingale Foundation – for promoting research and investigation into matters relating to nursing (£60,000); South Bank University – towards advancing the science and art of nursing (£50,000); University of Swansea – for advancing the science and art of nursing (£35,000); Sacred Space Foundation – for assisting in the furtherance of nurses' welfare (£5,000); and University of Manchester – for advancing the science and art of nursing (£2,800).

FINANCES *Year* 2011–12 *Income* £106,825 *Grants* £0 *Assets* £2,629,763

TRUSTEES Louise Boden; Prof. Dame Betty Kershaw; Dame Jacqueline Docherty; Prof. Kate Gerrish; Carol Rees-Williams; Prof. Judith Ellis MBE.

OTHER INFORMATION In 2011–12 no grant applications were processed due to a strategic review. This has now been completed.

HOW TO APPLY On a form available to download from the website (www.gnct.org.uk), where criteria and guidelines are also posted.

All applications must be submitted in an electronic format (e.g. MS Word or PDF) using the Trust's research grant application form and the review process will be undertaken electronically. A call for grant applications with a specified closing date will be advertised via the website and promoted through other avenues.

WHO TO APPLY TO Dr Sam Koroma, Secretary, 83 Victoria Road, Lower Edmonton, London N9 9SU *Tel.* 020 8345 5379 *email* gnct@koroma5824.fsnet.co.uk *Website* www.gnct.org.uk

---

■ The Generations Foundation

CC NO 1110565   **ESTABLISHED** 2005

WHERE FUNDING CAN BE GIVEN UK, Merton and overseas.

WHO CAN BENEFIT UK based causes; local causes in the Borough of Merton and also in developing countries.

WHAT IS FUNDED Projects helping children who need it the most; those who have disabilities, are disadvantaged, or struggle with ill health. Projects in the areas of environmental protection and conservation are also supported.

TYPE OF GRANT Capital costs, full project and unrestricted funding for up to, and in some cases over, three years.

RANGE OF GRANTS Up to £50,000.

SAMPLE GRANTS Right to Dream (£16,000); Whizz-Kidz (£13,000); Billy Riordan Memorial Trust, Home Start Merton, IT4CH and Mothers to Mothers UK (£10,000 each); Save the Children (£6,000); and Cherished Memories, FoCT (Friends of the Children of Tanzania) and Rosemary Foundation (£5,000 each).

FINANCES *Year* 2011–12 *Income* £437,576 *Grants* £214,073 *Assets* £228,318

TRUSTEES Robert Finch, Stephen Finch; Rohini Finch.

OTHER INFORMATION Further grants of under £5,000 each were made totalling £30,000.

HOW TO APPLY In writing to the correspondent

WHO TO APPLY TO Rohini Finch, Trustee, 36 Marryat Road, Wimbledon, London SW19 5BD *Tel.* 020 8946 7760 *email* rfinch@rfinch.plus.com *Website* www.generationsct.co.uk

---

■ The Steven Gerrard Foundation

CC NO 1140813   **ESTABLISHED** 2011

WHERE FUNDING CAN BE GIVEN UK, with a preference for Merseyside and Cheshire.

WHO CAN BENEFIT Registered charities and community groups.

WHAT IS FUNDED Social welfare and children and young people who are disadvantaged or have a disability, and their families.

SAMPLE GRANTS Wirral Resource Centre and Cheshire Deaf Society (£10,000 each); Split Support Services (£9,500); and the Hugh McAuley Football Academy (£5,000).

FINANCES *Year* 2012 *Income* £182,895 *Grants* £34,116 *Assets* £172,008

TRUSTEES Peter Sterling; Kathryn Taylor; Andrew Sterling; Steven Gerrard.

HOW TO APPLY In writing to the correspondent.

WHO TO APPLY TO The Trustees, c/o Black and Norman Solicitors, 67–71 Coronation Road, Crosby, Liverpool L23 5RE *Tel.* 01519 312777 *email* info@stevengerrardfoundation.org *Website* www.stevengerrardfoundation.org

---

■ Get Kids Going

CC NO 1063471   **ESTABLISHED** 1997

WHERE FUNDING CAN BE GIVEN UK

WHO CAN BENEFIT Registered charities, clubs and societies.

WHAT IS FUNDED Sport for disabled people up to the age of 26.

SAMPLE GRANTS GB Wheelchair Rugby; GB Boccia; Disabled Snow Sport.

FINANCES *Year* 2011–12 *Income* £1,624,543 *Grants* £175,034 *Assets* £8,769,935

TRUSTEES Lesley Tadgell-Foster; Patti Fordyce; Joyce McIntosh.

HOW TO APPLY Email the charity requesting an application form.

WHO TO APPLY TO Jane Emmerson, 10 King Charles Terrace, Sovereign Close, London E1W 3HL *Tel.* 020 7481 8110 *email* info@getkidsgoing.com *Website* www.getkidsgoing.com

---

■ The Gibbons Family Trust

CC NO 290884   **ESTABLISHED** 1985

WHERE FUNDING CAN BE GIVEN Devon, with a preference for East Devon, and the Isle of Thanet in Kent.

SAMPLE GRANTS West of England School for Children with Little or No Sight (£10,000); Oasis Domestic Abuse Service (£4,000); Hartsdown Technology College and Options Pregnancy Crisis Centre (£3,250 each); Exeter YMCA Community (£2,500); EBP Kent, Peninsular Foundation and Exmouth and Budleigh Salterton Explorer Scouts (£2,000 each).

FINANCES *Year* 2012–13 *Income* £100,873 *Grants* £77,910 *Assets* £2,133,803

TRUSTEES Roger Dawe; Dr John Frankish; Dr Miles Joyner; Kerensa Pearson.

OTHER INFORMATION Of the grant total 53 grants were made to organisations totalling £72,000. 14 grants totalling £5,400 were made to individuals.

HOW TO APPLY On an application form which can be downloaded from the foundation's website. Application forms should only be submitted by post. All applications must specify the amount applied for. Organisations should attach a covering letter on your organisation's letter headed paper explaining briefly why you are applying. Additional information may also be attached but the foundation requests no CDs or DVDs. Only send your latest accounts if they are not available on the Charity Commission website.

WHO TO APPLY TO Cathy Houghton, Trusts Manager, 14 Fore Street, Budleigh Salterton, Devon EX9 6NG *Tel.* 01395 445259 *email* Contact via website. *Website* www.gibbonstrusts.org

■ The David Gibbons Foundation

CC NO 1134727   **ESTABLISHED** 2010

WHERE FUNDING CAN BE GIVEN Devon, with a preference for East Devon.

WHO CAN BENEFIT Registered charities and community groups.

WHAT IS FUNDED Health, social welfare and older people.

SAMPLE GRANTS East Devon Volunteer Services Association, Motability and Resthaven (£5,000 each); Age UK Exeter and PATH (£4,000 each); Brixton Community Church and St Loye's Foundation (£3,000 each); Diabetes UK (£2,750); City of Exeter YMCA, Exeter Community Transport Association and Macular Disease Society (£2,500 each) and Chapter 1 Little House Contact Centre, Community Housing Aid and Homestart Exeter and East Devon (£2,000 each).

FINANCES *Year* 2012–13 *Income* £101,718 *Grants* £98,420 *Assets* £2,616,761

TRUSTEES Roger Dawe; Dr Miles Joyner; Dr John Frankish; Kerensa Pearson.

OTHER INFORMATION The grant total is comprised of 48 grants to individuals totalling £85,000 and 25 grants to individuals totalling £14,000.

HOW TO APPLY On an application form which can be downloaded from the foundation's website. Application forms should only be submitted by post. All applications should specify the amount requested. Organisations should attach a covering letter on your organisation's letter headed paper explaining briefly why you are applying. Additional information may also be attached but the foundation requests no CDs or DVDs. Only send your latest accounts if they are not available on the Charity Commission website.

WHO TO APPLY TO Cathy Houghton, Trusts Manager, 14 Fore Street, Budleigh Salterton, Devon EX9 6NG *Tel.* 01395 445259 *Website* www. gibbonstrusts.org

■ The Gibbs Charitable Trust

CC NO 207997   **ESTABLISHED** 1946

WHERE FUNDING CAN BE GIVEN UK with a preference for the south of England and worldwide.

WHO CAN BENEFIT Organisations benefiting Methodists are given particular attention.

WHAT IS FUNDED Primarily to support Methodist charities; also areas of social or educational concern. Grants are normally made to projects of which the trustees have personal knowledge. Also supported are international causes and creative arts, especially those which use the arts for personal development.

WHAT IS NOT FUNDED A large number of requests are received by the trust from churches undertaking improvement, refurbishment and development projects, but only a few of these can be helped. In general, Methodist churches are selected, sometimes those the trustees have particular knowledge of. Individuals and animal charities are not supported.

TYPE OF GRANT Buildings, capital and project grants will be considered.

RANGE OF GRANTS Almost all grants in the range £500–£10,000.

SAMPLE GRANTS Christian Aid and Langley House Trust (£5,000 each); Nixon Memorial Hospital, Sierra Leone, Oxfam, Practical Action and St Paul's Carnival (£3,000 each); Africa Now, Canon Collins Trust, Hope and Homes for Children, Pentecost Festival 2012 and Welsh National Opera (£2,000 each); Brecon and District Contact Association, Fairbridge, Magnet Resources, Splice Productions and Sound Affairs (£1,000 each); and Daylight Christian Prison Trust, Lees Methodist Church and Llangynidr Village Hall (£500 each).

FINANCES *Year* 2011–12 *Income* £88,314 *Grants* £96,950 *Assets* £2,015,213

TRUSTEES John N. Gibbs, Chair; James Gibbs; Andrew Gibbs; Celia Gibbs; Elizabeth Gibbs; Jessica Gibbs; John E. Gibbs; Juliet Gibbs; Patience Gibbs; Rebecca Gibbs; William Gibbs; James D. Gibbs.

HOW TO APPLY The trust has no application forms, although an application cover sheet is available on the trust's website along with a policy and guidelines page. Requests should be made in writing to the correspondent. The trustees meet three times a year, after Christmas, near Easter and late summer. Unsuccessful applicants are not normally notified. The trustees do not encourage telephone enquiries or speculative applications. They also state that they are not impressed by applicants that send a huge amount of paperwork.

WHO TO APPLY TO Dr James M. Gibbs, Trustee, 8 Victoria Square, Clifton, Bristol BS8 4ET *email* jamesgibbs@btinternet.com *Website* www. gibbstrust.org.uk

■ The G. C. Gibson Charitable Trust

CC NO 258710   **ESTABLISHED** 1969

WHERE FUNDING CAN BE GIVEN UK

WHO CAN BENEFIT Registered charities and 'authorities'.

WHAT IS FUNDED General charitable purposes, in practice, mainly art, music and education; health, hospices and medical research; community and other social projects; religion.

WHAT IS NOT FUNDED No grants to individuals.

TYPE OF GRANT Capital, research, running and core costs.

RANGE OF GRANTS £1,000–£10,000; mostly £1,000–£3,000.

SAMPLE GRANTS St Nicholas Hospice – Bury St Edmunds and Leuchie House (£10,000 each); King Edward VII Hospital (£8,000); Marie Curie Cancer Care (£6,000); St David's Cathedral, Campbell Blair Drummond and Riding for the Disabled Midwest Region (£5,000 each); Arts Active Trust and Bristol Old Vic Theatre (£3,000 each); Jo's Cervical Cancer Trust (£2,000) and Worshipful Company of Pattern Makers Educational Fund (£1,000).

FINANCES *Year* 2011–12 *Income* £577,790 *Grants* £470,505 *Assets* £12,982,061

TRUSTEES Simon Gibson; Jane Marson Gibson; Robert D. Taylor; Martin Gibson; Lucy Kelly; Anna Dalrymple.

HOW TO APPLY Online applications open in late summer and stay open for two months, usually August and September. Check in case the criteria have been amended to reflect the new funding round. Initial online applications are assessed and the trustees will contact a shortlist of charities to make a full application via email. Trustees will provide this email address – no postal or telephone applications will be considered. 'Charities that have already received support from the trust do not need to reapply, unless they are specifically invited to, or have a specific appeals they feel we might be interested in supporting. Payments are made in early December in each year and not at any other time of the year. Payments will be made direct to bank accounts.'

WHO TO APPLY TO The Trustees, c/o Deloitte, 5 Callaghan Square, Cardiff CF10 5BT *Tel.* 02920 460000 *email* enquiries@gcgct.org *Website* www.gcgct.org

························

■ Simon Gibson Charitable Trust

CC NO 269501   **ESTABLISHED** 1975
WHERE FUNDING CAN BE GIVEN UK, with a preference for East Anglia, South Wales and Hertfordshire.
WHO CAN BENEFIT Registered or exempt charities.
WHAT IS FUNDED General charitable purposes.
WHAT IS NOT FUNDED No grants to individuals.
TYPE OF GRANT One-off or recurring, core costs, running costs, project, research, buildings and capital. Funding may be given for up to three years.
RANGE OF GRANTS £1,000 to £25,000, but most grants fall in the range £3,000 to £5,000
SAMPLE GRANTS Royal Welsh College of Music and Drama (£25,000); Sherman Cymru (£15,000); Ely Cathedral Appeal Fund (£10,000); New Astley Club Endowment Fund (£6,000); Army Benevolent Fund, Bumblebee Conservation Trust, Papworth Hospital, Welsh National Opera and the Whale and Dolphin Conservation Society (£5,000 each); Bobath Children's Therapy Centre Wales, Dyslexia Action, Listening Books and West Suffolk Association for the Blind (£3,000 each); and Exning Methodist Church Trustees (£1,000).
FINANCES *Year* 2011–12 *Income* £618,521 *Grants* £583,000 *Assets* £13,857,961
TRUSTEES Bryan Marsh; Angela Homfray; George Gibson; Deborah Connor; John Homfray.
HOW TO APPLY 'There are no application forms. Charities applying to the trust should make their application in writing in whatever way they think best presents their cause.' The trust acknowledges all applications but does not enter into correspondence with applicants unless they are awarded a grant. The trustees meet in May and applications should be received by the end of March.
WHO TO APPLY TO Bryan Marsh, Trustee, Wild Rose House, Llancarfan, Vale of Glamorgan CF62 3AD *Tel.* 01446 781459 *email* marsh575@btinternet.com

························

■ Lady Gibson's Charitable Trust

CC NO 261442   **ESTABLISHED** 1970
WHERE FUNDING CAN BE GIVEN Overseas and the UK, with a preference for East Sussex, Kent, Surrey and West Sussex.
WHO CAN BENEFIT Registered charities.
WHAT IS FUNDED General charitable purposes, including arts, culture and recreation.
WHAT IS NOT FUNDED No grants to individuals or non-registered charities.
TYPE OF GRANT One-off capital grants; funding for up to two years are considered.
RANGE OF GRANTS £20–£11,000.
SAMPLE GRANTS Previous beneficiaries included: Withyham Parochial Church Council (£11,000); Royal National Theatre (£1,500); Royal Academy Trust (£1,300); Blond McIndoe Centre (£1,000); Bowles (£500); Chichester Cathedral Restoration and Development Trust (£350); Combat Stress (£250); London Philharmonic Orchestra (£120); Southbank Centre (£45); and Friends of Friendless Churches (£20).
FINANCES *Year* 2011–12 *Income* £21,533 *Grants* £25,246

TRUSTEE The Cowdray Trust Limited.
OTHER INFORMATION Applications for grants will only be acknowledged if a donation is to be sent.
HOW TO APPLY In writing to the correspondent. Acknowledgements will only be sent if a grant is being made.
WHO TO APPLY TO Laura Gosling, Administrator, c/o Millbank Financial Services, 4th Floor, Swan House, 17–19 Stratford Place, London W1C 1BQ *Tel.* 020 7907 2100 *email* charity@mfs.co.uk

························

■ The Harvey and Hilary Gilbert Charitable Trust

CC NO 296293   **ESTABLISHED** 1986
WHERE FUNDING CAN BE GIVEN UK.
WHO CAN BENEFIT Registered charities.
WHAT IS FUNDED General charitable purposes.
RANGE OF GRANTS Up to £25,000
SAMPLE GRANTS Variety Club Children's Charity (£25,000); Jewish Care (£10,000); Prostate Cancer Care and World Jewish Relief (£5,000 each); Friends of the Royal Marsden (£2,000); Jewish Blind and Disabled and Mother's and Daughter's Breast Cancer Campaign (£500 each); Great Ormond Street Hospital Children's Charity (£100) and Upstaged Theatre Company (£50).
FINANCES *Year* 2011–12 *Income* £23 *Grants* £35,420
TRUSTEES Harvey Gilbert; Claire Abrahams.
OTHER INFORMATION Research suggests that all expenditure is accounted for in grants distributed.
HOW TO APPLY In writing to the correspondent.
WHO TO APPLY TO Harvey Gilbert, Trustee, 7 Spaniards Park, Columbas Drive, Hampstead, London NW3 7JD *Tel.* 020 8532 6699

························

■ The Girdlers' Company Charitable Trust

CC NO 328026   **ESTABLISHED** 1988
WHERE FUNDING CAN BE GIVEN UK, with a preference for City and East End of London, and Hammersmith and Peckham.
WHO CAN BENEFIT Registered charities benefiting children, young adults, academics, students and teachers.
WHAT IS FUNDED Medicine and health, education, welfare, youth welfare, heritage, environment, humanities and Christian religion.
WHAT IS NOT FUNDED Applications will only be considered from registered charities.
TYPE OF GRANT One-off and recurrent; core, revenue, salary and capital costs.
RANGE OF GRANTS Mostly up to £10,000.
SAMPLE GRANTS Leyton Orient Community Sports Programme (£60,000); London Youth (£40,000); St Giles Trust (£19,000); Royal School of Needlework (£15,000); Crown and Manor Club – Hoxton, Habitat for Humanity – Southwark and Macmillan Cancer Support (£10,000 each); The Oxford Kilburn Club (£8,000); Disabled Sailors Association (£2,000); The Coldstream Guards Charitable Fund (£1,700); ActionAid – Ethiopia and The Urology Foundation (£1,200 each); Bath Institute of Medical Engineering (£1,100); Vitalise, Institute of Economic Affairs, St Mary's Church – Brook and Lynn Athletic Club (£1,000 each) and Jubilate Choir (£500).
FINANCES *Year* 2011–12 *Income* £1,407,014 *Grants* £802,089 *Assets* £6,605,498

TRUSTEE Court of the Company of Girdlers.

HOW TO APPLY The trust operates an open application process for circa £20,000 of its total grantmaking. Around 20 awards are made, of approximately £1,000, to charities in England and Wales where the charity has an annual income less than £1 million. The guidelines advise that the applicant success rate is around 3% and around half of the general grants are awarded outside London. These general grants can cover core costs, salaries or capital costs. Applicants should write to the correspondent on letter headed paper. Exempt charities must provide audited accounts. To be considered for a donation cover each of the following points: the beneficial area [which trustees support] under which a grant is sought; a brief summary of the organisation's background and aims; the specific nature of the request, highlighting the change you wish to bring about; how you will know if you have achieved these changes; your charity registration number. Each April and November the trustee considers general applications with ten donations of approximately £1,000 being made on each occasion. The closing dates are the last Friday in January and August. Successful applicants are unlikely to be awarded a further donation within the following five years. Successful applicants will be informed in May and December.

WHO TO APPLY TO John Gahan, Charities Manager, Girdlers' Hall, Basinghall Avenue, London EC2V 5DD *Tel.* 020 7638 0488 *Fax* 020 7628 4030 *email* charitiesmanager@girdlers.co.uk *Website* www.girdlers.co.uk/html/charitable-giving

■ The B. and P. Glasser Charitable Trust

CC NO 326571   **ESTABLISHED** 1984

WHERE FUNDING CAN BE GIVEN UK and worldwide.

WHO CAN BENEFIT Registered charities.

WHAT IS FUNDED General charitable purposes, particularly health and disability charities, and Jewish organisations.

WHAT IS NOT FUNDED No grant to individuals or students.

RANGE OF GRANTS £500–£8,000.

SAMPLE GRANTS Practical Action (£8,000); Jewish Care (£6,000); Royal National Institute for the Blind and Sight Savers International (£5,000 each); Ian Rennie Hospice at Home (£2,500); Camphill Village Trust and Jewish Deaf Association (£2,000 each); Help the Aged and Jewish Blind and Disabled (£1,500 each); Action Aid UK, British Red Cross and Fair Trials International (£1,000 each); and Gurkha Welfare Trust and The Samaritans – Chiltern branch (£500 each).

FINANCES *Year* 2011–12 *Income* £87,088 *Grants* £71,550 *Assets* £2,211,782

TRUSTEES James Cullingham; Michael Glasser; John Glasser.

HOW TO APPLY In writing to the correspondent. To keep administrative costs to a minimum the trust is unable to reply to unsuccessful applicants.

WHO TO APPLY TO Julia Strike, Administrator, Chantrey Vellacott DFK, Russell Square House, 10–12 Russell Square, London WC1B 5LF *Tel.* 020 7623 9490

■ The Glass-House Trust

CC NO 1017426   **ESTABLISHED** 1993

WHERE FUNDING CAN BE GIVEN Unrestricted, but UK in practice.

WHO CAN BENEFIT Registered charities and institutions.

WHAT IS FUNDED Housing, the built environment, art and child development.

WHAT IS NOT FUNDED Grants are not normally made to individuals.

RANGE OF GRANTS Up to £200,000.

SAMPLE GRANTS Glass-House Community Led Design (£200,000); Mayday Rooms (£97,000); A Space (£75,000); Money for Madagascar (£37,000); HACT: The Housing Action Charity (£35,000); Transform Drug Policy Foundation and Resonance FM (£30,000 each); Birkbeck College (£18,000) and Birth Companions (£10,000).

FINANCES *Year* 2011–12 *Income* £475,255 *Grants* £438,249 *Assets* £11,143,321

TRUSTEES Alexander Sainsbury; Elinor Sainsbury; Judith Portrait.

OTHER INFORMATION The trust is one of the Sainsbury Family Charitable Trusts which share a common administration. An application to one is taken as an application to all.

HOW TO APPLY See the guidance for applicants in the entry for the Sainsbury Family Charitable Trusts. A single application will be considered for support by all the trusts in the group. However, in the case of this trust, 'proposals are generally invited by the trustees or initiated at their request. The trustees prefer to support innovative schemes that can be successfully replicated or become self-sustaining.'

WHO TO APPLY TO Alan Bookbinder, Director, The Peak, 5 Wilton Road, London SW1V 1AP *Tel.* 020 7410 0330 *Fax* 020 7410 0332 *Website* www.sfct.org.uk

■ The Glastonbury Trust Limited

CC NO 1078170   **ESTABLISHED** 1999

WHERE FUNDING CAN BE GIVEN UK with a preference for Glastonbury.

WHO CAN BENEFIT Individuals, schools and other community groups in providing learning experiences that focus on emotional well-being and spiritual growth.

WHAT IS FUNDED Projects that address the needs of the wider community, particularly those that support family and community cohesion.

WHAT IS NOT FUNDED No funding for individual academic study or gap year projects.

TYPE OF GRANT One-off for start-up or seed funding.

RANGE OF GRANTS Up to about £10,000

SAMPLE GRANTS Previously, donations were made to the following: Isle of Avalon Foundation (£9,600); Avalon Library (£3,900); and Goddess Temple (£3,700). In addition to the above grants, £12,000 was given under the category 'secondary schools', £1,900 to 'primary schools' and a further £1,500 to 'other' causes.

FINANCES *Year* 2012 *Income* £170,394 *Grants* £152,623

TRUSTEES Brian Charlton; Gareth Mills; Mike Jones.

HOW TO APPLY In the first instance contact the correspondent by email or telephone.

WHO TO APPLY TO Mike Jones, Trustee, The Courtyard, 2–4 High Street, Glastonbury BA6 9DU *Tel.* 01458 831399 *email* contact@glastonburytrust.co.uk *Website* www.glastonburytrust.co.uk

■ Global Care

cc no 1054008   established 1996
where funding can be given Overseas.
who can benefit Registered charities.
what is funded Trustees favour children's charities already supported by them working in the poorest countries and the advancement of Christian education. People of many religions, cultures and social circumstances will be supported.
finances *Year* 2012 *Income* £681,407 *Grants* £694,022 *Assets* £670,683
trustees Mark Curran – Chair; Norman Lochhead; Sue Matejtschuk; Margaret Patterson; Raymond Neal; John Scott; Lee Hart.
other information Trustees continue to support projects they seek themselves therefore applications for new grants will not be considered at this time.
how to apply Applications are not recommended. Trustees seek out projects to support, as appropriate, and new grants cannot be considered.
who to apply to John White, Chief Executive Officer, Global Care, 2 Dugdale Road, Coventry CV6 1PB *Tel.* 02476 601800 *Fax* 02476 601444 *email* info@globalcare.org.uk *Website* www.globalcare.org.uk

■ Global Charities

cc no 1091657   established 1978
where funding can be given Greater London; UK.
who can benefit Community organisations and registered charities.
what is funded Projects supporting disadvantaged children and young people; or those with an illness or disability.
what is not funded Each individual branch has specific exclusions, generally however the charities will not fund: individual children or families; retrospective funding; statutory funding – funding for schools or health projects that would otherwise be covered by designated statutory funding from the local authority; salaried posts; deficit funding or repayment of loans; medical research; purchase of a minibus; trips abroad; distribution to other organisations; religious activities; political groups; general structural changes to buildings; projects which are part of a larger charity and are not separately constituted; core funding for a national or regional charity.
type of grant Capital; core costs; one-off; project; running costs.
range of grants Mostly under £10,000. Larger grants are made very occasionally.
sample grants Previous beneficiaries included: Prince's Foundation for Children and the Arts (£100,000); Missing People (£61,000); and Impact Initiatives (£25,000); Sixth Sense Theatre (£7,500); Cambourne Youth Partnership (£5,000); Havens Hospices – Essex (£3,000); Bangladeshi Parents Association (£2,100); Howbury Friends (£1,800); and Centrepoint – Hammersmith and Fulham (£1,600).
finances *Year* 2011–12 *Income* £3,052,112 *Grants* £1,484,913 *Assets* £1,013,203
trustees Martin George, Chair; Nigel Atkinson; Moira Swinbank; Paul Soames; John McGeough; Darren Henley; Gareth Andrewartha; Annabel Sweet.
how to apply The charity provides the following guidance on its website:
'If you have a general enquiry regarding any of our appeals funds contact us (Tel: 020 7054 8391).

We are always glad to answer questions from any organisation, charity or group on our grants process. Help a Capital Child in London has two annual small grants funding rounds. We attempt to fund as many eligible applications as possible, although this is always limited to the funds raised in the year. Details are given on www.capitalfm.com/charity, as well as how to apply for an application form. The form is reviewed and updated by our grants panel in conjunction with the overall Board to ensure the application process is as accessible as possible and to ensure applicants are guided though our funding criteria.'
who to apply to Leah Hayden, Administrator, 30 Leicester Square, London WC2H 7LA *Tel.* 020 7054 8391 *Website* www.thisisglobal. com/charities-and-communities

■ Gloucestershire Community Foundation

cc no 900239   established 1989
where funding can be given Gloucestershire.
who can benefit Charitable organisations and social enterprises.
what is funded Combating disadvantage in Gloucestershire.
type of grant Revenue and full project funding.
range of grants Up to £5,000
sample grants Cirencester Community Group and The Family Haven (£10,000 each); Forest Road Unemployment Community Resource Centre, Forest of Dean Youth Workers Network, Gloucestershire Bike Project and Age UK Gloucestershire (£5,000 each); Frampton on Severn Sailing Club and The Cotswold Downs Syndrome Group (£3,000 each); Milestone School (£2,000) and Horsley Youth Club (£1,200).
finances *Year* 2012 *Income* £516,622 *Grants* £257,000 *Assets* £4,999,066
trustees S. Preston; L. Archer; G. Bruce; I. Brothwood; J. Carr; A. Chambers; G. Cole; C. Evans; R. Graham; R. Head; T. Hitchins; H. Lovatt; T. Standing; B. Thornton; C. J. Wakeman; J. Winstanley.
publications Children in the Community – Making Things Better teachers' pack.
how to apply Information sheets, guidelines and an application forms are available from the website. Staff are pleased to discuss any potential project applications. The foundation operates other funds and administers a number of grantmaking trusts. See its website for up-to-date details.
who to apply to Gail Mattocks, Grants Manager, c/o EDF Energy, Barnett Way, Barnwood, Gloucester GL4 3RS *Tel.* 01452 656386 *email* gail.mattocks@edfenergy.com *Website* www. gloucestershirecommunityfoundation.co.uk

■ The Gloucestershire Historic Churches Trust

cc no 1120266   established 1980
where funding can be given Gloucestershire.
who can benefit Churches and chapels.
what is funded GHCT is a charity which raises funds to help places of Christian worship of all denominations with repairs and improvements to the fabric of the buildings and their contents, as well as to their surrounding churchyards. The trust's aim is to help keep the 500 plus

churches and chapels in the county alive, not only as places of worship and active centres of community life, but also as buildings which make a huge impact on the landscape of Gloucestershire and help to draw visitors to the county.

WHAT IS NOT FUNDED No grants are made for routine maintenance.

TYPE OF GRANT One-off, but repeat applications will be considered.

RANGE OF GRANTS £300–£15,000, typical grants between £1,000 and £4,000.

SAMPLE GRANTS St Peter, Clearwell – Roof and spire repairs; interior paintwork (£15,000); St George, Cam – Stonework repairs to tower (£10,000); St Barnabas, Warmley – Catering facilities; replace gas main (£8,000); Unitarian chapel, Frenchay – Repairs to and replacement of windows (£6,000); All Saints, Turkdean – Interior repairs and redecoration (£3,000); St Bartholomew, Oakridge – Clock overhaul and winding gear (£1,000) and St Michael and A.A., Bussage – Rainwater goods and drainage (£300).

FINANCES *Year* 2012 *Income* £157,508 *Grants* £100,000 *Assets* £1,270,135

TRUSTEES Ian Phillips; Ben Woods; Philip Kendell; Helen Whitbread; Nicholas Rice.

HOW TO APPLY Application forms and full guidelines can be downloaded from the trust's website.

WHO TO APPLY TO Ben Woods, Grants Committee Chair, 2 Shepherds Way, Cirencester, Gloucestershire GL7 2EY *Tel.* 01285 659159 *email* grants@ghct.org.uk *Website* www.ghct.org.uk

■ Worshipful Company of Glovers of London Charity Fund

CC NO 269091   **ESTABLISHED** 1975

WHERE FUNDING CAN BE GIVEN UK with a preference for the City of London.

WHO CAN BENEFIT Glovers and glove-related projects; general charitable purposes.

WHAT IS FUNDED The trust makes grants mainly towards the provision of gloves, or to causes that are related to the City of London.

RANGE OF GRANTS Up to £5,000.

SAMPLE GRANTS **Gloves and Glove Related Projects:** Crisis (£2,000); Christie Charitable Fund and Providence Row (£1,500 each) and The Passage (£1,000). Grants for less than £1,000 each totalled just over £4,000.

Charitable Grants: City of London School for Girls – bursary and King Edwards School, Witley – bursary (£4,500 each); Guildhall School of Music and Drama – bursary (£2,000); Church of St Margaret, Lothbury and 444 Squadron Air Cadets (£1,500 each) and Treloar School and Sheriffs and Recorder's Fund (£1,500 each). Grants for less than £1,000 each totalled just under £7,000.

FINANCES *Year* 2011–12 *Income* £52,054 *Grants* £37,602 *Assets* £627,540

TRUSTEE Worshipful Company of Glovers of London.

HOW TO APPLY In writing to the correspondent.

WHO TO APPLY TO Monique Hood, Clerk, c/o Knox Cropper and Co., 8–9 Well Court, London EC4M 9DN *Fax* 020 7622 0316

■ The GNC Trust

CC NO 211533   **ESTABLISHED** 1960

WHERE FUNDING CAN BE GIVEN UK, with preferences for Birmingham and Cornwall.

WHO CAN BENEFIT Charitable organisations.

WHAT IS FUNDED General charitable purposes.

RANGE OF GRANTS £50,000– £1,000. Generally under £1,000.

SAMPLE GRANTS Everitt Butterfield Foundation (£50,000); Birmingham Royal Ballet (£44,000); St John of Jerusalem Eye Hospital (£10,000); National Youth Ballet and University of Birmingham (£5,000 each); and Elmhurst School for Dance and Alzheimer's Research Trust (£1,000 each).

FINANCES *Year* 2012 *Income* £37,974 *Grants* £134,317 *Assets* £938,877

TRUSTEES G. Cadbury; Jayne Cadbury; P. Richmond-Watson; I. Williamson.

OTHER INFORMATION 77 grants totalling £134,000 were made in 2012.

HOW TO APPLY In writing to the correspondent at any time. There are no application forms and applications are not acknowledged.

WHO TO APPLY TO Paddy Spragg, Administrator, 41 Sycamore Drive, Hollywood, Birmingham B47 5QX *Tel.* 07976 848390

■ The Godinton Charitable Trust

CC NO 268321   **ESTABLISHED** 1974

WHERE FUNDING CAN BE GIVEN Kent

WHO CAN BENEFIT Registered charities.

WHAT IS FUNDED A regular payment to Godinton House Preservation Trust. Local general charitable purposes.

WHAT IS NOT FUNDED No grants to individuals.

TYPE OF GRANT One-off and recurrent.

RANGE OF GRANTS Up to £40,000, usually £2,500 or less.

SAMPLE GRANTS Godinton House Preservation Trust (£40,000); Army Benevolent Fund (£5,000); Friends of Canterbury Museums Trust (£2,500); Rochester cathedral (£2,000) Kent Crime Stoppers (£1,500) and National Arts Collections Fund, Kent Wildlife Trust, Friday People and Soundabout (£1,000 each).

FINANCES *Year* 2012 *Income* £137,683 *Grants* £88,100 *Assets* £4,395,473

TRUSTEES Hon. Wyndham G. Plumptre; Hon. Jon D. Leigh-Pemberton; Michael F. Jennings.

HOW TO APPLY In writing to the correspondent.

WHO TO APPLY TO N. G. Sandford, Godinton House, Godinton Lane, Ashford, Kent TN23 3BP *Tel.* 01233 632652

■ The Sydney and Phyllis Goldberg Memorial Charitable Trust

CC NO 291835   **ESTABLISHED** 1985

WHERE FUNDING CAN BE GIVEN UK.

WHO CAN BENEFIT Organisations benefiting, research workers, at risk groups, and people who are disabled, disadvantaged by poverty or socially isolated.

WHAT IS FUNDED Medical research, welfare and disability.

TYPE OF GRANT One-off, some recurrent.

RANGE OF GRANTS Up to £12,000.

SAMPLE GRANTS Children with Special Needs Foundation, Life Centre, Heart 2 Heart and the British Stammering Association (£12,000 each); and the Isaac Goldberg Charity Trust (£6,000).

FINANCES *Year* 2011–12 *Income* £107,448 *Grants* £102,000 *Assets* £3,253,244

TRUSTEES Christopher Pexton; Howard Vowles; Michael Church.

OTHER INFORMATION In 2011–12, grants were made to nine organisations and totalled £102,000.

HOW TO APPLY In writing to the correspondent. Telephone requests are not appreciated. Applicants are advised to apply towards the end of the calendar year. According to the trustees' report for 2011/12, 'the trust has established its grantmaking policy to achieve its objects for the public benefit by inviting applications from existing and previous donee charities and charitable causes favoured by Sydney and Phyllis Goldberg and by advertising the objectives in the Directory of Grant Making Trusts. The Charity requests a copy of the final reports on all research for which grants are made.'

WHO TO APPLY TO Michael Church, Trustee, Coulthards Mackenzie, 17 Park Street, Camberley, Surrey GU15 3PQ *Tel.* 01276 65470

....

■ The Golden Bottle Trust

CC NO 327026   **ESTABLISHED** 1985
WHERE FUNDING CAN BE GIVEN Worldwide.
WHO CAN BENEFIT Registered charities.
WHAT IS FUNDED General charitable purposes with a preference for charities supporting the environment, health, education, religion, the arts and developing countries.
WHAT IS NOT FUNDED No grants for individuals or organisations that are not registered charities.
TYPE OF GRANT 'One-off' and recurring.
RANGE OF GRANTS Up to £10,000 with larger grants for charities that the Hoare family have a personal relationship with.
SAMPLE GRANTS The Master Charitable Trust (£312,000); The Bulldog Trust (£115,000); Future for Religious Heritage (£93,000); The Henry C Hoare Charitable Trust (£60,000); Leader's Quest Foundation (£25,000); Intermission Youth Theatre and National Literacy Trust (£20,000 each); Migratory Salmon Foundation (£15,000); Wildfowl and Wetlands Trust (£12,000); St Bride's Church (£11,000); Heritage of London Trust (£10,000) and West Country Rivers Trust (£9,000).
FINANCES *Year* 2011–12 *Income* £1,543,031 *Grants* £1,200,764 *Assets* £8,809,587
TRUSTEES Hoare Trustees (H. C. Hoare; Sir D. J. Hoare; R. Q. Hoare; A. S. Hoare; V. E. Hoare; S. M. Hoare; A. S. Hopewell.)
OTHER INFORMATION A further £202,500 of grants were committed, but not paid, in the year.
HOW TO APPLY The trustee does not normally respond to unsolicited approaches.
WHO TO APPLY TO C. Hoare and Co, 37 Fleet Street, London EC4P 4DQ *Tel.* 020 7353 4522 *email* enquiries@hoaresbank.co.uk

....

■ Golden Charitable Trust

CC NO 263916   **ESTABLISHED** 1972
WHERE FUNDING CAN BE GIVEN UK with a preference for West Sussex.
WHO CAN BENEFIT Charitable organisations.
WHAT IS FUNDED Preservation, conservation, medical research.
RANGE OF GRANTS Up to £250,000, usually between £100–£2,500.
SAMPLE GRANTS The London Library (£250,000); the Friends of St Mary's Petworth (£22,000); Westminster Synagogue (£7,000); Friends of Pallant House Gallery and the Langdon Foundation (£2,000 each); the Royal Star and Garter Homes and the Royal School of Needlework (£1,000 each); the Wordsworth Trust, Petworth Film House and the Dermatitis

and Allied Diseases Research Trust (£500 each); the National Trust and the Parachute Regimental Association (£100 each); and St Wilfred's Hospice (£50).
FINANCES *Year* 2012–13 *Income* £34,960 *Grants* £297,971 *Assets* £863,563
TRUSTEES Sara Solnick; Jeremy Solnick.
OTHER INFORMATION Grants totalling £298,000 were made to 20 organisations in 2012–13.
HOW TO APPLY In writing to the correspondent.
WHO TO APPLY TO Lewis Golden, Administrator, Little Leith Gate, Angel Street, Petworth GU28 0BG *Tel.* 01798 342434

....

■ The Jack Goldhill Charitable Trust

CC NO 267018   **ESTABLISHED** 1974
WHERE FUNDING CAN BE GIVEN UK.
WHO CAN BENEFIT Registered charities benefiting those in need.
WHAT IS FUNDED Human need causes and visual arts.
WHAT IS NOT FUNDED No support for individuals or new applications.
SAMPLE GRANTS Previous beneficiaries have included CST, City and Guilds of London School of Art, Jack Goldhill Award Fund, JNF Charitable Trust, Jewish Care, Joint Jewish Charitable Trust, Nightingale House, Royal Academy of Arts, Royal London Hospital, Tate Gallery, Tricycle Theatre Co., West London Synagogue and Atlantic College.
FINANCES *Year* 2011 *Income* £100,416 *Grants* £147,382 *Assets* £967,427
TRUSTEES Grete Goldhill; Michael Louis Goldhill; Anthony Frederick Abrahams.
OTHER INFORMATION A list of grants has not been included with the accounts filed at the Christy Commission in recent years.
HOW TO APPLY The trustees have a restricted list of charities to whom they are committed and no unsolicited applications can be considered.
WHO TO APPLY TO Michael Louis Goldhill, Trustee, 85 Kensington Heights, Campden Hill Road, London W8 7BD *Tel.* 020 7727 4326

....

■ The Goldsmiths' Arts Trust Fund

CC NO 313329   **ESTABLISHED** 1965
WHERE FUNDING CAN BE GIVEN UK.
WHO CAN BENEFIT Registered charities.
WHAT IS FUNDED The arts by the encouragement of the art of design and good craftsmanship.
RANGE OF GRANTS £6,000–£51,000
SAMPLE GRANTS Goldsmiths' Craft and Design Council (£52,000); Royal College of Art (£12,000); University College for the Creative Arts (£10,000); and Contemporary Silversmiths (£6,000). Bursaries and grants to colleges/ students totalled £24,500.
FINANCES *Year* 2011–12 *Income* £1,478,468 *Grants* £104,484 *Assets* £97,014
TRUSTEE The Goldsmiths' Company Trustee.
HOW TO APPLY In writing to the correspondent.
WHO TO APPLY TO The Clerk, The Goldsmiths' Company, Goldsmiths' Hall, Foster Lane, London EC2V 6BN *Tel.* 020 7606 7010 *email* the.clerk@thegoldsmiths.co.uk *Website* www.thegoldsmiths.co.uk

578

Does the trust you have chosen match your needs? Haphazard applications waste postage and time

■ The Goldsmiths' Company Charity

CC NO 1088699 **ESTABLISHED** 1961
WHERE FUNDING CAN BE GIVEN UK, with a special interest in London charities.
WHO CAN BENEFIT Registered charities, schools, individuals connected with the trade of goldsmithing, silversmithing and jewellery, and Londoners in need. Grants are made to London-based or national charities, but not to local provincial charities. Where charities are members, branches or affiliates of an association, appeals are accepted from the governing body or head office of that association only. In the case of church restoration, block grants are made to the Historic Churches Preservation Trust and therefore appeals from individual churches will not normally be considered.
WHAT IS FUNDED Support of the goldsmiths' craft, education, and general charitable purposes (including general welfare, medical welfare, youth, heritage, church, and arts).
WHAT IS NOT FUNDED Applications are not normally considered on behalf of medical research; animal welfare; memorials to individuals; overseas projects; individual housing associations; endowment schemes; charities with a turnover of more than £10 million.
TYPE OF GRANT Buildings, capital, salaries, core, project, start-up and running costs. Funding is occasionally three year, but usually one-off.
RANGE OF GRANTS £500 upwards.
SAMPLE GRANTS University of Cambridge – Department of Material Science and Metallurgy (£173,000); National Churches Trust (£50,000); London Borough of Lambeth – for the support of individuals (£25,000); Refugee Council and School Home Support (£15,000 each); Children's Hospices UK (£10,000); Royal Air Force Disabled Holiday Trust (£6,000); Changing Faces, The Young Vic and Country Holidays for Inner City Kids (£5,000 each); and New Horizon Youth Centre (£3,000).
FINANCES *Year* 2010–12 *Income* £6,679,616 *Grants* £6,899,698 *Assets* £93,797,193
TRUSTEES Goldsmith's Company Trustee: Tim Schroder; Scott Shepherd; Bruno Schroder; Sir John Rose; David Peake; Lord Sutherland; Bryan Toye; Michael Wainwright; Richard Vanderpump; William Parente; Richard Came; Dame Lynne Brindley; The Hon. Mark Bridges; Richard Agutter; Lord Roger Cunliffe; Martin Drury; George MacDonald; Prof. Richard Himsworth; Rupert Hambro; Hector Miller; Arthur Galsworthy; Sir Jerry Wiggin; Sir Anthony Touche; Sir Paul Girolami; Lord Tombs of Brailes; Sir Huntington-Whiteley; C. Aston.
OTHER INFORMATION Income and expenditure are higher than usual as the accounts cover an 18 rather than 12 month period.
HOW TO APPLY Applications should be made by letter, no more than two sides of A4 in length, highlighting the case for the company to give its support. The letter should be accompanied by the completed application form, which can be downloaded from the company's website. The form may be retyped, but should follow the same format and length (three sides of A4). All questions should be answered. Do not cut and paste information on the form. Legible handwritten applications are acceptable. The charity's most recent annual report and audited accounts (or financial report required by the Charities Act) should also be included. Applications are considered monthly, except in August and September, and there is usually a three to four month delay between receipt of an appeal and a decision being made. Applications from any organisation, whether successful or not, are not normally considered more frequently than every three years. Any enquiries should be addressed to the correspondent.
WHO TO APPLY TO R. Melly, Clerk and Administrator, Goldsmiths' Hall, 13 Foster Lane, London EC2V 6BN *Tel.* 020 7606 7010 *Fax* 020 7606 1511 *email* the.clerk@thegoldsmiths.co.uk *Website* www.thegoldsmiths.co.uk/charities

■ The Golf Foundation Limited

CC NO 285917 **ESTABLISHED** 1982
WHERE FUNDING CAN BE GIVEN UK.
WHO CAN BENEFIT Organisations benefiting children and young people.
WHAT IS FUNDED Golf
WHAT IS NOT FUNDED No grants to individuals.
SAMPLE GRANTS Golf Roots Centres (£105,000); Schools Sports Partnerships (£102,000); Special Projects (£38,000); Community Golf Coaches (£37,000); Schools – Special Needs (£13,000); Dragon Golf Centres (£4,000); County and Regional Groups (£1,400) and Schools (£220).
FINANCES *Year* 2012 *Income* £1,740,876 *Grants* £337,374 *Assets* £3,051,258
TRUSTEES Ian Armitage; Norman Fletcher; Duncan Weir; Fredrik Lindgren; Sandy Jones; Sir Robin Miller; Stephen Proctor; Di Horsley; Deborah Allmey; Charles Harrison; Doug Poole.
HOW TO APPLY Although the foundation states that it chooses its beneficiaries each year, there is a suggestion that unsolicited applications from organisations that share its aims and objectives will be considered. Contact the foundation's representative (listed on the website) in your area for further details on applying for funding.
WHO TO APPLY TO Alan Bough, Finance Manager, The Spinning Wheel, High Street, Hoddesdon, Hertfordshire EN11 8BP *Tel.* 01992 449830 *Fax* 01992 449840 *email* admin@golf-foundation.org *Website* www.golf-foundation.org

■ The Golsoncott Foundation

CC NO 1070885 **ESTABLISHED** 1998
WHERE FUNDING CAN BE GIVEN UK.
WHO CAN BENEFIT Arts organisations.
WHAT IS FUNDED The trust states its objects as follows: 'to promote, maintain, improve and advance the education of the public in the arts generally and in particular the fine arts and music. The fostering of the practice and appreciation of the arts, especially amongst young people and new audiences, is a further specific objective.'
WHAT IS NOT FUNDED No grants to individuals.
TYPE OF GRANT One-off and some recurring grants.
RANGE OF GRANTS £200–£5,000.
SAMPLE GRANTS Somerset Museums (£4,500); Rodhuish Parochial Church Council (£4,000); National Children's Orchestra (£3,000); Marian Concert and Poetry Book Society (£2,000 each); National Theatre and Shakespeare Schools (£1,000 each); Oxford Lieder (£750); Arts in Hanworth, Forestage Theatre and Live Music Now (£500 each) and Public Catalogue Foundation (£140).
FINANCES *Year* 2011–12 *Income* £68,914 *Grants* £55,959 *Assets* £1,820,661
TRUSTEES Penelope Lively, Chair; Josephine Lively; Stephen Wick; Dr Harriet Harvey Wood.

OTHER INFORMATION The foundation has a helpful and informative website.

HOW TO APPLY The trustees meet quarterly to consider applications, in February, May, August and November. Applications, made by hard copy with an email contact address, should be sent to the correspondent by the end of the month preceding the month of the trustees meeting. They should include the following: (1) A clear and concise statement of the project, whether the award sought will be for the whole project or a component part. Is the applicant organisation of charitable status? (2) Evidence that there is a clear benefit to the public, i.e. does the project conform with the declared object of the trust. (3) The amount requested should be specified, or a band indicated. Is this the only source of funding being sought? All other sources of funding should be indicated, including those that have refused funding. (4) If the grant requested is part of the match-funding required by the Heritage Lottery Foundation (HLF) following an award, state the amount of that award and the percentage of match-funding required by the HLF and the completion date. (5) Wherever possible an annual report and accounts should accompany the application, as may other supporting information deemed relevant. Second or further applications will not be considered until a minimum of 12 months has elapsed since determination of the previous application, whether successful or not.

WHO TO APPLY TO Hal Cortlandt Bishop, Administrator, 53 St Leonard's Rd, Exeter EX2 4LS *Tel.* 01392 252855 *email* golsoncott@btinternet.com *Website* www.golsoncott.org.uk

■ Golubovich Foundation

CC NO 1113965   **ESTABLISHED** 2006
WHERE FUNDING CAN BE GIVEN UK
WHO CAN BENEFIT UK centres of excellence.
WHAT IS FUNDED The foundation seeks to foster relationships between Russia and the UK in the area of performing arts. This is done mainly through encouraging established UK arts centres to identify and develop the talents of young Russian nationals.
RANGE OF GRANTS Up to £75,000.
SAMPLE GRANTS Previous beneficiaries have included: Trinity College of Music London (£75,000) and University of the Arts London (£65,000).
FINANCES *Year* 2011–12 *Income* £28,100 *Grants* £0 *Assets* £8,310
TRUSTEES Alexei Golubovich; Olga Mirimskaya; Andrey Lisyanski; Arkadiy Golubovich.
OTHER INFORMATION During the year £28,000 was spent on governance costs. Although there were no grants awarded this year, (2011–12), the trustees are actively fundraising and funds could be available again in future years.
HOW TO APPLY In writing to the correspondent.
WHO TO APPLY TO Tim Lewin, c/o MVL Business Services, 15a High Street, Battle, East Sussex TN33 0AE *Tel.* 01424 830723 *email* tim.lewin@btinternet.com

■ Nicholas and Judith Goodison's Charitable Settlement

CC NO 1004124   **ESTABLISHED** 1991
WHERE FUNDING CAN BE GIVEN UK.
WHO CAN BENEFIT Registered charities.
WHAT IS FUNDED Arts and arts education.
WHAT IS NOT FUNDED No grants to individuals.
TYPE OF GRANT Recurrent capital grants. One-off grants.
RANGE OF GRANTS £200–£10,000, although most grants are for £2,000 or less.
SAMPLE GRANTS Victoria and Albert Museum (£10,000); Courtauld Institute (£6,000); English National Opera, Academy of Ancient Music and Handel House (£2,500 each); Crafts Council (£1,500); Attingham Trust and Public Catalogue Foundation (£1,000 each); Royal Society of Arts and Chippendale Society (£500 each); and Venice in Peril (£200).
FINANCES *Year* 2012–13 *Income* £60,713 *Grants* £52,612 *Assets* £1,408,342
TRUSTEES Sir Nicholas Goodison; Judith Goodison; Katharine Goodison.
OTHER INFORMATION Grants were made to 28 organisations totalling £52,500 in 2012–13.
HOW TO APPLY The trust states that it cannot respond to unsolicited applications.
WHO TO APPLY TO Sir Nicholas Goodison, Trustee, PO Box 2512, London W1A 5ZP

■ The Goodman Foundation

CC NO 1097231   **ESTABLISHED** 2003
WHERE FUNDING CAN BE GIVEN UK and overseas.
WHO CAN BENEFIT Registered charities.
WHAT IS FUNDED General, overseas, social welfare, older people, health and disability.
FINANCES *Year* 2011–12 *Income* £10,740,927 *Grants* £255,571 *Assets* £22,169,024
TRUSTEES Laurence Goodman; Catherine Goodman; Richard Cracknell; Lesley Tidd.
OTHER INFORMATION A list of beneficiaries was not included in the accounts. Given the significant increase in the foundation's funds an increase in grantmaking is likely in future years.
HOW TO APPLY In writing to the correspondent.
WHO TO APPLY TO The Trustees, c/o Anglo Beef Processors, Unit 6290, Bishops Court, Solihull Parkway, Birmingham Business Park, Birmingham B37 7YB

■ The Mike Gooley Trailfinders Charity

CC NO 1048993   **ESTABLISHED** 1995
WHERE FUNDING CAN BE GIVEN UK.
WHO CAN BENEFIT Charitable organisations.
WHAT IS FUNDED General charitable purposes, with a special interest in medical research, youth community projects and the armed forces.
WHAT IS NOT FUNDED Grants are not made to overseas charities or to individuals.
RANGE OF GRANTS £100–£100,000.
SAMPLE GRANTS Previous beneficiaries have included: Alzheimer's Society (£400,000); Prostate Cancer Charity (£100,000); and the Second World War Experience Centre (£40,000).
FINANCES *Year* 2011–12 *Income* £1,093,047 *Grants* £285,790 *Assets* £10,282,728
TRUSTEES Mark Bannister; Tristan Gooley; Michael Gooley; Bernadette Gooley; Fiona Gooley; Louise Breton.

OTHER INFORMATION A list of grants was not included in the charity's recent accounts.
HOW TO APPLY In writing to the correspondent.
WHO TO APPLY TO Michael Gooley, Trustee, 9 Abingdon Road, London W8 6AH *Tel.* 020 7938 3143 *email* trailfinders@trailfinders.com *Website* www.trailfinders.com

■ The Gosling Foundation Limited
CC NO 326840   **ESTABLISHED** 1962
WHERE FUNDING CAN BE GIVEN Worldwide. In practice UK.
WHO CAN BENEFIT Registered charities.
WHAT IS FUNDED The relief of poverty, suffering and distress; provision of facilities for recreation and other leisure-time occupation (in the interests of social welfare); naval and service charities; advancement of education; furtherance of other charitable purposes.
WHAT IS NOT FUNDED Grants are made to individuals only in exceptional circumstances.
RANGE OF GRANTS Mainly £100–£10,000, but up to £200,000.
SAMPLE GRANTS HMS Victory Preservation Company (£25 million); Duke of Edinburgh's Award (£1 million); Rowbarge and Thames Diamond Jubilee Foundation (£100,000 each); Food Fortnight ltd (£75,000); Westminster Abbey and SSAFA Forces Help (£50,000 each); Queen Elizabeth Castle of Mey Trust (£20,000); Soldiering on Trust, Centre of the Cell, FAA Memorial Church Fund, Worshipful Company of Shipwrights and HMS Liverpool Central Fund (£10,000 each); Macmillan Cancer Support (£7,000); Smile Support Care (£5,000); Professor Cunningham Research Fund (£2,000) and Turner Syndrome, Young Epilepsy and Variety Club Children's Charity (£1,000).
FINANCES *Year* 2011–12 *Income* £4,531,651 *Grants* £27,490,593 *Assets* £71,152,128
TRUSTEES Sir Donald Gosling; Sir Ronald F. Hobson; Cmdr Gosling.
OTHER INFORMATION Expenditure was swelled in the year by a substantial one-off grant of £25 million to the HMS Victory Preservation Company. Grant expenditure is never usually this high, with total expenditure usually averaging between two and three million each year.
HOW TO APPLY In writing to the correspondent. The grantmaking policies of the foundation are 'regularly reviewed' and currently are: applications should fall within the objects of the charity; there is no minimum limit for any grant; all grants will be approved unanimously. Trustees meet quarterly.
WHO TO APPLY TO Anne Yusof, Secretary, 21 Bryanston Street, Marble Arch, London W1H 7PR *Tel.* 020 7495 5599

■ The Gough Charitable Trust
CC NO 262355   **ESTABLISHED** 1970
WHERE FUNDING CAN BE GIVEN UK.
WHO CAN BENEFIT Registered charities.
WHAT IS FUNDED General charitable purposes.
TYPE OF GRANT One-off.
SAMPLE GRANTS Herbert Old Wellington; the Lifeboat Service Memorial Book Trust; Royal Ballet School Trust; Trinity Hospice; and Irish Guards Lieutenant Colonels Fund.
FINANCES *Year* 2011–12 *Income* £33,668 *Grants* £31,361 *Assets* £33,699
TRUSTEE Lloyds TSB Private Banking.

HOW TO APPLY In writing to the correspondent at any time.
WHO TO APPLY TO The Trustees, Lloyds Private Banking Limited, Trust Centre, The Clock House, 22–26 Ock Street, Abingdon Oxon OX14 5SW *Tel.* 01235 232712

■ The Gould Charitable Trust
CC NO 1035453   **ESTABLISHED** 1993
WHERE FUNDING CAN BE GIVEN Worldwide.
WHO CAN BENEFIT Registered charities only.
WHAT IS FUNDED Education and training, with preference towards Jewish organisations and causes.
WHAT IS NOT FUNDED No grants to individuals.
TYPE OF GRANT Up to three years. Unrestricted funding.
RANGE OF GRANTS Up to £20,000.
SAMPLE GRANTS Kibbutz Eshbal (£20,000); UJIA (£18,000); One to One (£7,000); World Jewish Relief (£3,000); NSPCC and Dignity in Dying (£1,000 each); Youth at Risk and Notting Hill Housing (£200 each); Watford New Hope Trust and Latitude Global Volunteers (£100 each); and Orchestra of Age Enlightenment and National Osteoporosis (£50 each).
FINANCES *Year* 2011–12 *Income* £25,062 *Grants* £66,029 *Assets* £920,822
TRUSTEES Jean Gould; Simon Gould; Sidney Gould; Lawrence Gould; Matthew Gould.
HOW TO APPLY In writing to the correspondent.
WHO TO APPLY TO S. Gould, Trustee, Cervantes, Pinner Hill, Pinner HA5 3XU *Tel.* 020 8868 2700

■ The Hemraj Goyal Foundation
CC NO 1136483   **ESTABLISHED** 2010
WHERE FUNDING CAN BE GIVEN UK and overseas.
WHO CAN BENEFIT Organisations supporting disadvantaged children and young people; promoting women's rights; helping people with disabilities.
WHAT IS FUNDED General charitable purposes, particularly social welfare, women's rights, education and disability.
TYPE OF GRANT One off grants to organisations.
RANGE OF GRANTS Up to £30,000.
SAMPLE GRANTS The Ekal Vidyalaya Foundation (£29,000); Strongbones Children's Charitable Trust (£13,000); The Millennium Tapestry Company (£12,000) and The Rajasthani Foundation (£5,000).
FINANCES *Year* 2012 *Income* £116,533 *Grants* £83,121 *Assets* £1,907
TRUSTEES Mala Ararwal; Vidya Goyal; Avnish Goyal.
HOW TO APPLY In writing to the correspondent.
WHO TO APPLY TO Sarah Bell, Administrator, 2 Kingfisher House, Woodbrook Crescent, Radford Way, Billericay, Essex CM12 0EQ *Tel.* 01277 655655 *email* info@hgf.org.uk *Website* www.hgf.org

■ The Grace Charitable Trust
CC NO 292984   **ESTABLISHED** 1985
WHERE FUNDING CAN BE GIVEN UK.
WHO CAN BENEFIT Registered charities, including Christian organisations.
WHAT IS FUNDED General charitable purposes, Christian, education, medical and social welfare.
RANGE OF GRANTS £1,000–£10,000.
FINANCES *Year* 2011–12 *Income* £299,536 *Grants* £195,389 *Assets* £2,103,372

TRUSTEES G. Payne; E. Payne; G. Snaith; R. Quayle; M. Mitchell.

OTHER INFORMATION Of the total grant figure, £7,700 was distributed in grants to individuals.

HOW TO APPLY The trust states: 'Grants are made only to charities known to the settlors and unsolicited applications are, therefore, not considered.'

WHO TO APPLY TO G. J. R. Payne, Trustee, Swinford House, Nortons Lane, Great Barrow, Chester CH3 7JZ *Tel.* 01928 740773

■ A. B. Grace Trust

CC NO 504332   **ESTABLISHED** 1975
WHERE FUNDING CAN BE GIVEN Garstang and Preston.
WHO CAN BENEFIT Charitable organisations.
WHAT IS FUNDED General charitable purposes.
TYPE OF GRANT Recurrent.
SAMPLE GRANTS St Mary's and St Michael's Church, Bonds; St Helen's Church, Churchtown; United Reformed Church, Garstang; Guide Dogs for the Blind; RSPCA (£4,100 each); St Peter's Parish Church, Scorton; RNLI; RSPB; Christ Church, Over Wyresdale (£5,125 each).
FINANCES *Year* 2011–12 *Income* £41,323
    Grants £43,000
TRUSTEES Anthony Blunt; Thomas Balmain; Valerie Wilson.
HOW TO APPLY 'The charity's trust deed sets out very specifically who are beneficiaries are to be and consequently we are unable to consider any grant applications.'
WHO TO APPLY TO Anthony Blunt, Trustee, 31 Yewlands Drive, Garstang, Preston PR3 1JP *email* abgrace@live.co.uk

----

■ The Graff Foundation

CC NO 1012859   **ESTABLISHED** 1991
WHERE FUNDING CAN BE GIVEN UK and worldwide
WHO CAN BENEFIT Charitable organisations.
WHAT IS FUNDED General charitable purposes.
TYPE OF GRANT One-off and recurrent.
RANGE OF GRANTS £1,000–£100,000
SAMPLE GRANTS Facet Foundation (£93,000); The Museum of Contemporary Art (£47,000); Tate Foundation (£5,000) and Guys and Tikva Organisation (£1,000).
FINANCES *Year* 2012 *Income* £656,369
    Grants £145,821 *Assets* £3,968,898
TRUSTEES Laurence Graff; Francois Graff; Anthony Kerman.
HOW TO APPLY In writing to the correspondent.
WHO TO APPLY TO Anthony Kerman, c/o Kerman and Co. LLP, 200–203 Strand, London WC2R 1DJ *Tel.* 020 7539 7272

■ E. C. Graham Belford Charitable Settlement

CC NO 1014869   **ESTABLISHED** 1991
WHERE FUNDING CAN BE GIVEN Northumberland.
WHO CAN BENEFIT Charitable organisations.
WHAT IS FUNDED General charitable purposes.
RANGE OF GRANTS Up to £15,000.
SAMPLE GRANTS Hexham Youth Initiative (£15,000); Haydon Bridge Youth Drop In and Haltwhistle Swimming and Leisure Centre (£10,000 each); Shaftoe Trust Voluntary Controlled First School (£7,500); National Rheumatoid Arthritis Society, Eden Valley Hospice and Cramlington Voluntary Youth Project (£5,000 each) and Tomorrow's People (£1,000).

FINANCES *Year* 2011–12 *Income* £65,701
    Grants £88,500 *Assets* £6,107,932
TRUSTEES Anthony Thompson; George Hutchinson.
OTHER INFORMATION The trust's main asset is freehold agricultural land and buildings and agricultural dwellings in Northumberland known collectively as the Belford Estate. The trust's income is derived mainly from rents of farms and cottages. A considerable portion of money is spent on the upkeep of these properties.
HOW TO APPLY In writing to the correspondent.
WHO TO APPLY TO Anthony Thompson, Trustee, 4 More London Riverside, London SE1 2AU *Tel.* 020 7379 0000

■ A. and S. Graham Charitable Trust

CC NO 288220   **ESTABLISHED** 1983
WHERE FUNDING CAN BE GIVEN UK
WHO CAN BENEFIT Children and young people.
WHAT IS FUNDED Education, social welfare, the arts, children and young people.
FINANCES *Year* 2011–12 *Income* £23,500
    Grants £28,000
TRUSTEES Andrew Graham; Sandra Graham; Natasha Boucai; Emma Graham; Laura Graham.
OTHER INFORMATION Grants were made to both organisations and individuals totalling around £28,000.
HOW TO APPLY In writing to the correspondent.
WHO TO APPLY TO Keith Hardy, c/o Smith Pearman, Hurst House, Ripley, Surrey GU23 6AY *Tel.* 01483 225457 *Fax* 01483 211023 *email* keithhardy@smithpearman.com

----

■ The Grahame Charitable Foundation Limited

CC NO 1102332   **ESTABLISHED** 1969
WHERE FUNDING CAN BE GIVEN UK and worldwide.
WHO CAN BENEFIT Organisations benefiting: children, young adults, older people and Jewish people.
WHAT IS FUNDED The advancement of the Jewish religion; health facilities and buildings; medical studies and research; special schools; cultural and religious teaching; and community services.
WHAT IS NOT FUNDED No grants to individuals.
TYPE OF GRANT Capital, core costs, interest-free loans, one-off, recurring costs and start-up costs. Funding for up to two years may be considered.
RANGE OF GRANTS £100–£60,000.
SAMPLE GRANTS Avraham Bezalel Foundation and Jerusalem College of Technology (£25,000 each); Child Resettlement Fund (£20,000); Beis Ruzhim Trust, British Friends of the Shaare Zedek Medical Centre, Yad Rachel, Yesodey Hatorah Primary Girl's School and United Jewish Israel Appeal (£10,000 each); and Beit Haknesset Caesarea (£7,500).
FINANCES *Year* 2012 *Income* £230,301
    Grants £212,230 *Assets* £1,066,296
TRUSTEES Alan Grahame; J. M. Greenwood.
HOW TO APPLY The trustees allocate funds on a long-term basis and therefore have none available for other applicants.
WHO TO APPLY TO Miki Shaw, Secretary, 5 Spencer Walk, Hampstead High Street, London NW3 1QZ *Tel.* 020 7794 5281

■ The Granada Foundation

CC NO 241693   **ESTABLISHED** 1965
WHERE FUNDING CAN BE GIVEN North West England.
WHO CAN BENEFIT Organisations.
WHAT IS FUNDED Encouragement and promotion of the study, practice and appreciation of the fine arts and the methods and means of their dissemination; encouragement and promotion of the study and application of the sciences; promotion and advancement of education; promotion and provision of facilities for recreation or other leisure time occupation in the interests of social welfare.
WHAT IS NOT FUNDED No grants will be given for general appeals, individuals (including for courses of study), expeditions, overseas travel or youth clubs/community associations.
RANGE OF GRANTS Up to £100,000.
SAMPLE GRANTS Whitworth Art Gallery (£100,000); Liverpool and Merseyside Theatres Trust (£75,000); Hallé Concerts Society (£50,000); Buxton Festival (£20,000); Greater Manchester Museum of Science and Industry Trust and Manchester City Art Galleries (£5,000 each); Merseyside Dance Initiative (£4,000); Milap Festival Trust (£2,500); Royal Liverpool Philharmonic, XTRAX Arts and Liverpool Lantern Company (£2,000 each); Liverpool and Manchester Design Initiative Ltd and Little Actors Theatre Company (£1,000 each) and Lonsdale Music (£500).
FINANCES *Year* 2011–12 *Income* £125,865 *Grants* £313,960 *Assets* £3,435,496
TRUSTEES Sir Robert Scott; Philip Ramsbottom; Prof. Jennifer Latto.
HOW TO APPLY On an application form, available in writing from the correspondent, giving an outline of the project. Detailed information can be added when the formal application is submitted. Details of the next trustees' meeting will be given when an application form is sent (trustees meet three times a year at irregular intervals). All letters are acknowledged. 'The Advisory Council interprets the guidelines in a flexible way, realising that it cannot hope to achieve a true balance across all the areas of activity. The council does, however, examine the context of each application and tries to make grants in areas where the benefit will be most widely felt.'
WHO TO APPLY TO Irene Langford, Administrator, PO Box 3430, Chester CH1 9BZ *Tel.* 01244 661867 *email* irene.langford@btconnect.com *Website* www.granadafoundation.org

■ Grand Charitable Trust of the Order of Women Freemasons

CC NO 1059151   **ESTABLISHED** 1996
WHERE FUNDING CAN BE GIVEN UK and overseas.
WHO CAN BENEFIT Registered charities.
WHAT IS FUNDED General charitable purposes. This trust donates about half its grant total to causes related to the Order of Women Freemasons, including individual members and their dependants. The remaining half is donated to external charities.
SAMPLE GRANTS £150,000 to Breast Cancer Campaign Tissue Bank Appeal and £53,000 to Adelaide Litten Charitable Trust.
FINANCES *Year* 2011–12 *Income* £233,610 *Grants* £215,047 *Assets* £702,512
TRUSTEES Zuzanka Penn; Jean Masters; Sylvia Major; Ms H. Maldrett; Dr Iris Boggia-Black; Beryl Daniels.
OTHER INFORMATION Specific gifts from members have also enabled the trust to make donations to the Adelaide Litten Charitable Trust which was set up to assist with the running of two properties and also to give general assistance to Order members. These donations totalled £53,000.
HOW TO APPLY In writing to the correspondent. Applications should be submitted by the end of July each year for consideration by the trustees.
WHO TO APPLY TO The Trustees, 27 Pembridge Gardens, London W2 4EF *Tel.* 020 7229 2368 *Website* www.owf.org.uk

■ The Grand Order of Water Rats' Charities Fund

CC NO 292201   **ESTABLISHED** 1889
WHERE FUNDING CAN BE GIVEN Worldwide.
WHO CAN BENEFIT Organisations benefiting: actors and entertainment professionals and their dependents.
WHAT IS FUNDED General charitable purposes with a preference towards drama and theatre, overseas aid and medical and hospital equipment.
WHAT IS NOT FUNDED No grants to students. No grants to cover debts.
TYPE OF GRANT One-off and recurrent.
SAMPLE GRANTS Previous grants included those made to Actors Church Union, British Legion Wales, Bud Flanagan Leukaemia Fund, Cause for Hope, Northwick Park Hospital and Queen Elizabeth Hospital for Children.
FINANCES *Year* 2012 *Income* £104,742 *Grants* £51,275 *Assets* £1,657,995
TRUSTEES Wyn Calvin; Roy Hudd; Kaplan Kaye; Keith Simmons; Chas McDevitt.
HOW TO APPLY In writing to the correspondent. According to the trustees' report for 2012, 'the trustees require written requests for assistance. Grants, both one-off and regular, can be made to members of the theatrical profession and their dependents. To qualify, a professional must have been a performer for a minimum of seven years in the theatrical profession. The trustees do not make grants for student's fees or for education. Nor do they make grants to cover debts incurred by credit card usage, bank loans or overdrafts or for local or national taxes. From time to time the trustees may also grant a one-off payment to organisations or individuals who the trustees feel are in need of assistance.'
WHO TO APPLY TO Mike Martin, Administrator, 328 Gray's Inn Road, London WC1X 8BZ *Tel.* 020 7278 3248 *email* charities@gowr.net *Website* www.gowr.net

■ The Grange Farm Centre Trust

CC NO 285162   **ESTABLISHED** 1984
WHERE FUNDING CAN BE GIVEN The London Metropolitan Police District and Epping Forest.
WHO CAN BENEFIT Charitable organisations, including scout groups etc.
WHAT IS FUNDED Recreation and leisure activities.
WHAT IS NOT FUNDED No grants to individuals and usually no grants to applications received from local authorities.
RANGE OF GRANTS £550–£20,000
SAMPLE GRANTS Over the Wall; Richard House Children's Hospice; Old Parkonians Association; Get Set Girls; Ideal Plus; Ambitions About Autism; Handicapped Children's; Action Group; CCHF All About Children; Chigwell Row Campsite; Buckhurst Hill Junior Sports Club;

Clapton Common Boys Club; Waltham Abbey Youth; Mitcham Rugby Club; Woodford Green Athletics Club; Epping Cricket Club.

FINANCES *Year* 2011–12 *Income* £1,447,725 *Grants* £58,840 *Assets* £11,050,210

TRUSTEES Alex Pelican; Roger Neville; Elizabeth Webster; Michael Tomkin; Robin Flaxman; Audrey Wheeler; Penny Smith; David Johnson; Charles Scrutton.

OTHER INFORMATION In total 15 organisations received grants.

HOW TO APPLY In writing to the correspondent giving a brief outline of what the grant will be used for. After initial consideration that the application falls within both the area of benefit and the objects of the trust, an application form will be sent to the applicant for completion which will then be considered in greater detail by the trustees.

WHO TO APPLY TO Nicholas Gadsby, Clerk, c/o 181 High Street, Epping, Essex CM16 4BQ *Tel.* 01992 578642 *Fax* 01992 572586 *email* info@grangefarmcentre.co.uk *Website* www.grangefarmcentre.co.uk

■ Grantham Yorke Trust

CC NO 228466   **ESTABLISHED** 1975

WHERE FUNDING CAN BE GIVEN The (old) West Midlands metropolitan county area.

WHO CAN BENEFIT People under the age of 25 who are in need and were born within the old West Midlands metropolitan county area, and youth organisations benefiting such people.

WHAT IS FUNDED Education, including providing outfits, clothing, tools, instruments, equipment or books to help such people on leaving school, university and so on, to prepare for, or enter a profession or trade.

WHAT IS NOT FUNDED People aged 25 or over.

RANGE OF GRANTS Generally £50–£5,000.

SAMPLE GRANTS Walsall Street Teams (£5,000), Barnardo's (£5,000), Holy Trinity Community Project (£3,750), E R Mason Youth Centre (£3,500), New Testament Church of God – The Rock (£3,000), Support Help and Advice for Relatives of Prisoners (£3,000), St Francis Youth and Community Centre (£2,500).

FINANCES *Year* 2012 *Income* £216,518 *Grants* £171,534 *Assets* £5,863,211

TRUSTEES Howard Belton; Peter Jones; Tim Clarke; Fred Rattley; Philip Smiglarski, Chair; Barbara Welton; Revd Pamela Ogilvie.

OTHER INFORMATION Grants were made to 77 organisations and 43 individuals totalling £173,000.

HOW TO APPLY In writing to the correspondent. The trustees meet four times a year, in March, June, September and December.

WHO TO APPLY TO Christine Norgrove, Appeals Clerk, C/o Martineau Johnson, No. 1 Colmore Square, Birmingham B4 6AA *Tel.* 0800 763 1000 *email* christine.norgrove@sghmartineau.com

■ GrantScape

CC NO 1102249   **ESTABLISHED** 2004

WHERE FUNDING CAN BE GIVEN UK.

WHO CAN BENEFIT Environmental and community-based projects.

WHAT IS FUNDED Its generic grantmaking policy is as follows: GrantScape will only make grants in line with its charitable objectives; grants will be made on a justifiable and fair basis to projects which provide best value; grants will be made to projects that improve the life of communities and the environment; GrantScape will make available specific criteria for each of the grant programmes that it manages. All grants are subject to meeting the generic grantmaking criteria as well as the specific grant programme criteria.

WHAT IS NOT FUNDED Each programme has slightly different exclusions, consult the fund listing on the website.

SAMPLE GRANTS Oxford Preservation Trust (£73,000); Rushton Parish Council (£70,000); Llannon Community Council (£50,000); Middleton Park Equestrian Centre Riding for the Disabled (£35,000); Leeds City Council – Skateboard/BMX park and Stanwick Pocket Park (£30,000 each); 2nd Otley Scout Group (£25,500); Leeds Rugby Foundation and Llanelli Gymnastics Club (£20,000 each); Amor Baptist Chapel (£10,000); Earith Town Estate (£8,000) and The Wildlife Trust BCN Ltd and Broughton Village Hall Management Committee (£5,000 each).

FINANCES *Year* 2011–12 *Income* £1,036,561 *Grants* £799,553 *Assets* £1,918,359

TRUSTEES Dave Bramley; Alastair Singleton; Michael Clarke; Anthony Cox.

OTHER INFORMATION New grant programmes are introduced from time to time – check the charity's website for up-to-date information.

HOW TO APPLY Applications are made via the charity's website.

WHO TO APPLY TO Grants team, Office E, Whitsundoles, Broughton Road, Salford, Milton Keynes MK17 8BU *Tel.* 01908 247630 *email* helpdesk@grantscape.org.uk *Website* www.grantscape.org.uk

■ The J. G. Graves Charitable Trust

CC NO 207481   **ESTABLISHED** 1930

WHERE FUNDING CAN BE GIVEN Mainly Sheffield.

WHO CAN BENEFIT Registered charities.

WHAT IS FUNDED Charities working in the fields of: provision of parks and open spaces; libraries and art galleries; advancement of education; general benefit of people who are sick or poor; and such other charitable purposes as the trustees see fit. The income is mainly applied to local (Sheffield) charities for capital purposes rather than running costs.

WHAT IS NOT FUNDED Grants are generally not made to or for the benefit of individuals.

TYPE OF GRANT Mainly for capital and one-off for start-ups. Some for running costs.

RANGE OF GRANTS Up to £5,000.

SAMPLE GRANTS The Wildlife Trusts Sheffield and Rotherham (£10,000); Green Estate: Sheffield Manor Lodge (£5,000); Roundabout (£3,000); Heeley Development Trust (£2,000); and Sage Greenfingers (£1,500).

FINANCES *Year* 2012 *Income* £124,679 *Grants* £66,122 *Assets* £4,080,973

TRUSTEES Dona Womack; John Bramah; Gordon Bridge; Dr Derek Cullen; Richard Graves; Peter Price; Peter Clarkson; Cllr Jacqueline Drayton; Liz Frost; Hugh Grayson; Roderick Plews.

HOW TO APPLY In writing to the correspondent, to reach the secretary by 31 March, 30 June, 30 September or 31 December. Applications should indicate whether the applicant is a registered charity, include audited accounts and include a statement giving such up-to-date information as is available with regard to the income and any commitments the organisation has.

WHO TO APPLY TO R. H. M. Plews, Secretary, 2nd Floor, Fountain Precinct, Balm Green, Sheffield S1 2JA *Tel.* 01142 767991 *Fax* 01142 231717

....

■ The Stanley and Lorna Graves Charitable Trust

CC NO 1147769   ESTABLISHED 2012
WHERE FUNDING CAN BE GIVEN UK.
WHO CAN BENEFIT Charities and community groups.
WHAT IS FUNDED General, health, animal welfare.
SAMPLE GRANTS The trust has suggested an interest in Guide Dogs for the Blind, Hearing Dogs for Deaf People and Hospice at Home, West Cumbria.
FINANCES *Year* 2012–13 *Income* £7,560 *Grants* £4,000
TRUSTEE NatWest Trust Services.
HOW TO APPLY In writing to the correspondent.
WHO TO APPLY TO NatWest Trust Services, 5th Floor, Trinity Quay 2, Avon Street, Bristol BS2 0PT *Tel.* 05516577371

....

■ The Gray Trust

CC NO 210914   ESTABLISHED 1962
WHERE FUNDING CAN BE GIVEN Nottinghamshire, especially Linby and Southall.
WHO CAN BENEFIT Organisations benefiting older people, retired people, ex-service and service people, and people who are disadvantaged by poverty or disability.
WHAT IS FUNDED General charitable purposes, primarily for the benefit of older people, charitable purposes in the parishes of Linby and Papplewick and the surrounding area, and to provide sheltered accommodation for older people in Sherwood House and cottages.
WHAT IS NOT FUNDED Grants are not made to individuals and seldom for applications from outside Nottinghamshire.
RANGE OF GRANTS £500–£69,000
SAMPLE GRANTS Friends of the Elderly (£69,000); Age Concern Nottingham (£10,000); Papplewick and Linby Day Centre (£2,000); Family Care, Friary Drop In, Independent Age, NSPCC and Macmillan (£1,000 each); Nottinghamshire Coalition for Disabled People (£800); Myasthenia Gravis Association and Rutland House School for Parents (£500 each).
FINANCES *Year* 2011–12 *Income* £135,997 *Grants* £135,000
TRUSTEES Claire Hardstaff; Bella St Clair Harlow; Richard Pannell; Revd Can. Keith Turner; Kirstin Thompson.
OTHER INFORMATION The majority of grants usually range between £500 and £1,000.
HOW TO APPLY In writing to the correspondent by letter of application together with most recent accounts.
WHO TO APPLY TO Nigel Lindley, Trust Co-ordinator, Smith Cooper LLP, 2 Lace Market Square, Nottingham NG1 1PB *Tel.* 01159 454300 *email* nigel.lindley@smithcooper.co.uk

....

■ The Gordon Gray Trust

CC NO 213935   ESTABLISHED 1967
WHERE FUNDING CAN BE GIVEN England with a preference for Gloucestershire and Worcestershire.
WHO CAN BENEFIT Charitable organisations.

WHAT IS FUNDED General; particularly welfare, disabilities, conservation and the environment.
WHAT IS NOT FUNDED No grants to individuals.
RANGE OF GRANTS £50 to £12,000
SAMPLE GRANTS Avon Navigation Trust (£12,000); British Heart Foundation and Diabetes UK (£3,000 each); Worcestershire Breast Unit Campaign, Royal Medical Benevolent Fund, Keswick Mountain Rescue Team and NSPCC (£2,000 each); Friends of the Lake District (£1,500); Riders for Health, Samaritans (Cheltenham and District) and Great Oaks Dean Forest Hospice (£1,000 each); Tewkesbury and District Choral Society (£750); First Newent Scout Group and Gloucestershire Wildlife Trust (£500 each) and Gloucestershire Historic Churches Trust (£50).
FINANCES *Year* 2011–12 *Income* £46,489 *Grants* £87,400 *Assets* £3,192,091
TRUSTEES Dr B. Gray; S. Watson-Armstrong; C. Wilder; Miss R. Holmes; E. Roberts; M. M. Gray.
OTHER INFORMATION In 2011–12 grants were made to 54 organisations.
HOW TO APPLY In writing to the correspondent.
WHO TO APPLY TO M. A. Gray, Clerk to the Trustees, Grange Farm, Main Road, Bredon, Tewkesbury, Gloucestershire GL20 7EL

....

■ The Great Britain Sasakawa Foundation

CC NO 290766   ESTABLISHED 1985
WHERE FUNDING CAN BE GIVEN UK, Japan.
WHO CAN BENEFIT Voluntary, educational and cultural organisations and registered charities benefiting citizens of UK and Japan. Emphasis on younger people and on projects benefiting groups of people rather than individuals.
WHAT IS FUNDED Advancement of the education of the citizens of the UK and Japan in each other's institutions, people, history, language, culture, and society and in each other's intellectual, artistic and economic life. Research, exchanges, seminars, courses, publications and cultural events may all be funded. The foundation has a special scheme for joint research in medicine and health (the Butterfield Awards).
WHAT IS NOT FUNDED Grants are not made to individuals applying on their own behalf. The foundation will consider proposals from organisations that support the activities of individuals, provided they are citizens of the UK or Japan. No grants are awarded for retrospective funding; the construction, conservation or maintenance of land and buildings, student fees or travel in connection with study for a qualification.
TYPE OF GRANT Mainly one-off; also project and research, maximum term three years. No funding for core-costs.
RANGE OF GRANTS £750–£30,000.
SAMPLE GRANTS The accounts, available on the foundation's website, contain a full list of grants and recipient organisations.
FINANCES *Year* 2012 *Income* £1,173,592 *Grants* £950,559 *Assets* £23,047,985
TRUSTEES Jeremy Brown; Michael French; Prof. Shoichi Watanabe; Sir John Boyd; Hiroaki Fujii; Earl of St Andrews; David Cope; Prof. Nozomu Hayashi; Tatsuya Tanami; Joanna Pitman; Dr Yuichi Hosoya.
OTHER INFORMATION The foundation is rarely able to consider grants for the total cost of any project and encourages applicants to seek additional support from other donors.

Think carefully about every application. Is it justified?

....

585

HOW TO APPLY The foundation expresses a strong preference for emailed applications. A form will be emailed on request, and is also available from the foundation's website, where detailed information is given about the foundation's grant giving and application procedures. Application forms are also available from both the London headquarters or from the Tokyo office at: The Nippon Foundation Bldg. 4F, 1–2–2 Akasaka Minato-ku, Tokyo 107–0052. Telephone enquiries or personal visits are welcomed by the foundation's staff to discuss eligibility in advance of any formal application. The awards committee meets in London in March, May and November. Applications should be received by 15 December, 31 March and 15 September. Awards meetings in Tokyo are held in April and October, with applications to be submitted by the end of February and September.

School applicants are requested to first file an application with Connect Youth International, Japan Exchange Programme, 10 Spring Gardens, London SW1A 2BN (which is part of the British Council), to which the foundation grants external finance, aimed at encouraging exchanges (both ways) for schools in Great Britain and Japan, (their website is: www.connectyouthinternational.com). All applicants are notified shortly after each awards committee meeting of the decisions of the trustees. Those offered grants are asked to sign and return an acceptance form and are given the opportunity to say when they would like to receive their grant. Note: the foundation receives requests for two to three times the amount of money it actually has available for grants. About 75% of applicants receive grants, but often much less than requested.

WHO TO APPLY TO Stephen McEnally, Chief Executive, Dilke House, 1 Malet Street, London WC1E 7JN *Tel.* 020 7436 9042 *email* grants@gbsf.org.uk *Website* www.gbsf.org.uk

··

■ The Great Stone Bridge Trust of Edenbridge

CC NO 224309   **ESTABLISHED** 1964
WHERE FUNDING CAN BE GIVEN The parish of Edenbridge.
WHO CAN BENEFIT Organisations, and individuals under 25 for educational purposes.
WHAT IS FUNDED Education and general charitable purposes in the parish of Edenbridge.
TYPE OF GRANT Some recurrent.
FINANCES *Year* 2011–12 *Income* £121,049 *Grants* £50,000
TRUSTEES A. Russell; R. Davison; R. Cunnington; D. Leigh; G. Jackman; J. Hodson; C. Burges; R. Parsons; M. Elliot; C. Pearman; P. Deans.
HOW TO APPLY In writing to the correspondent.
WHO TO APPLY TO William Ross, Clerk, 8 Church Lane, East Grinstead, West Sussex RH19 3BA *Tel.* 01342 323687

··

■ The Great Torrington Town Lands Charity

CC NO 202801   **ESTABLISHED** 1971
WHERE FUNDING CAN BE GIVEN The former borough of Great Torrington, Devon.
WHO CAN BENEFIT Individuals and organisations, including clubs, societies and churches.
WHAT IS FUNDED People in need and general charitable purposes.

RANGE OF GRANTS Up to £15,000
FINANCES *Year* 2011–12 *Income* £213,144 *Grants* £44,614 *Assets* £6,283,996
TRUSTEES Toni Batty; Steve Blake; Revd Lawrence McLean; Brian Davies; Harold Martin; John Kelly; Sharon Lambert; Geoffrey Lee; Brian Nash; Elaine Norridge; Richard Rumbold; Alan Stacey; Trevor Sutton; Elaine Weeks; Nicola Buckley.
OTHER INFORMATION The 2011–12 accounts categorized the grants as follows: Plough Arts Centre (£15,000); Sick and aged (£9,500); Churches (£8,500); Public purposes (£7,500); North Devon Hospice (£2,500) and Education (£1,500).
HOW TO APPLY In writing to the correspondent.
WHO TO APPLY TO Ian Newman, Town Hall Office, High Street, Torrington, Devon EX38 8HN *Tel.* 01805 623517 *email* greattorringtoncharities@btconnect.com

··

■ The Kenneth and Susan Green Charitable Foundation

CC NO 1147248   **ESTABLISHED** 2012
WHERE FUNDING CAN BE GIVEN UK
WHO CAN BENEFIT Charities and community groups.
WHAT IS FUNDED General, social welfare, education, the arts.
WHAT IS NOT FUNDED No grants to individuals.
FINANCES *Year* 2012 *Income* £540,303 *Grants* £77,200 *Assets* £459,153
TRUSTEES Kenneth Green; Philip Stokes; Susan Green.
HOW TO APPLY In writing to the correspondent.
WHO TO APPLY TO Philip Stokes, Trustee, c/o Kenneth Green Associates, Hill House, Monument Hill, Weybridge, Surrey KT13 8RX *Tel.* 01932 827060

··

■ The Haydn Green Charitable Trust

CC NO 1148099   **ESTABLISHED** 2012
WHERE FUNDING CAN BE GIVEN UK, with a possible preference for Nottinghamshire.
WHO CAN BENEFIT Charities and community groups.
WHAT IS FUNDED General charitable purposes.
TRUSTEES Dennis Green; Maisie Green; Hardev Singh.
HOW TO APPLY In writing to the correspondent.
WHO TO APPLY TO Hardev Singh, Trustee, 16 High Street, Kegworth, Derbyshire DE74 2DA *Tel.* 0845 274 6902

··

■ The Green Hall Foundation (formerly known as the Constance Green Foundation)

CC NO 270775   **ESTABLISHED** 1976
WHERE FUNDING CAN BE GIVEN Mainly England, with some preference for West Yorkshire., overseas.
WHO CAN BENEFIT Social welfare, medicine, health, general.
WHAT IS FUNDED Some preference is given to charities operating in Yorkshire. In previous years grants have been made mainly, but not exclusively, to national organisations in the fields of social welfare and medicine, with special emphasis on support of young people in need and mentally and physically disabled people.
WHAT IS NOT FUNDED Organisations only.

TYPE OF GRANT Capital, special project, buildings and one-off funding of one year or less.

RANGE OF GRANTS Typically up to £10,000.

SAMPLE GRANTS Marie Curie Cancer Care (£10,000); St Martin-in-the-Fields (£7,500); Blond McIndoe Research Foundation, Brathay Trust and Disability Action Yorkshire (£5,000 each); Kidz Club Coventry, Commonwealth Society for the Blind and Cerebra (£2,000 each); and Human Relief, Living Water Satisfies and Malaika Kids UK (£1,000 each).

FINANCES *Year* 2011–12 *Income* £338,211 *Grants* £170,000 *Assets* £7,740,451

TRUSTEES Michael Collinson; Margaret Hall; Sue Collinson; Nigel Hall; Peter Morgan.

HOW TO APPLY At any time in writing to the correspondent (no special form of application required). Applications should include clear details of the need the intended project is designed to meet, plus an outline budget. According to the trustees' report for 2011/12, 'applications for grants should be submitted to the administrator. A grant application form was implemented in the year financial year 2011/12 and all applicants should complete the prescribed application form with clear details of the need the intended project is designed to meet plus an outline budget.'

WHO TO APPLY TO S. Hall, Administrator, Centenary House, La Grande Route de Saint-Pierre, St Peter, Jersey JE3 7AY *Tel.* 01534 487757 *email* greenhallfoundation@fcmtrust.com

■ The Green Room Charitable Trust

CC NO 1134766   ESTABLISHED 2010

WHERE FUNDING CAN BE GIVEN Not defined. In practice, UK.

WHO CAN BENEFIT Social enterprises.

WHAT IS FUNDED General charitable purposes, environmental causes.

FINANCES *Year* 2011–12 *Income* £92,383 *Assets* £102,393

TRUSTEES Tom Prickett; Dino Morra; Andrew Ferry.

OTHER INFORMATION No grants have been given as the trust was building up its reserves. However, the trust's accounts state that from 2013 it hopes to give grants totalling £50,000 a year.

HOW TO APPLY At present the trust is only considering applications for grants from environmental charities and only via email.

WHO TO APPLY TO Tom Prickett, Trustee, 28 Ballingdon Road, London SW11 6AJ *email* thegreenroomct@yahoo.co.uk

■ Philip and Judith Green Trust

CC NO 1109933   ESTABLISHED 2005

WHERE FUNDING CAN BE GIVEN UK and Africa.

WHO CAN BENEFIT Registered charities.

WHAT IS FUNDED Christian and missionary work.

RANGE OF GRANTS £2,000–£100,000

SAMPLE GRANTS Hope Through Action (£51,000); Sentebale (£20,000); Queen Mary's School (£10,000); Greyfriars Church (£8,400); Bible Society (£7,300); Five Talents (£6,200); Rinell Carey Holmquist (£5,300); Alpha International (£5,000); Stewardship Services (£1,700) and Greyfriars Mission (£1,200).

FINANCES *Year* 2011–12 *Income* £78,462 *Grants* £130,454 *Assets* £131,692

TRUSTEES Philip Green; Judith Green.

OTHER INFORMATION Donation of less than £1,000 totalled £7,217, and £15,200 was also given in grants to missionaries.

HOW TO APPLY In writing to the correspondent.

WHO TO APPLY TO Philip Green, Trustee, Marchfield, Flowers Hill, Pangbourne, Berkshire RG8 7BD *Tel.* 01189 845935

■ The Green Woodpecker Trust

CC NO 1150620   ESTABLISHED 2013

WHERE FUNDING CAN BE GIVEN Worldwide.

WHO CAN BENEFIT Registered charities.

WHAT IS FUNDED General, education, religion, disability, children and young people.

TRUSTEES David Christian; Matthew Simkins; Elizabeth Christian; Janie McClean; Joanna Walker; Sally Christian.

HOW TO APPLY Unfortunately, the correspondent informed us in June 2013 that unsolicited applications are not considered.

WHO TO APPLY TO David Christian, Trustee, 25 Park Lane, Maplehurst, Horsham, West Sussex RH13 6LL

■ Mrs H. R. Greene Charitable Settlement

CC NO 1050812   ESTABLISHED 1845

WHERE FUNDING CAN BE GIVEN UK, with a preference for Norfolk and Wistanstow in Shropshire.

WHO CAN BENEFIT Individuals and institutions, particularly those benefiting at risk groups, and people who are disadvantaged by poverty or socially isolated.

WHAT IS FUNDED Welfare and general charitable purposes.

SAMPLE GRANTS Previous beneficiaries included: St Michael's Hospital Bartestree, Norfolk and Norwich Clergymen's Widows' and Children's Charity, Brittle Bone Society, Children's Food Fund, Macmillan Cancer Relief, Muscular Dystrophy Group, Orbis, Beeston Church Organ, Friends of Norwich Cathedral, Horsford and St Faith's Scout Group and Litcham Parochial Church Council.

FINANCES *Year* 2011–12 *Income* £76,825 *Grants* £40,679 *Assets* £2,257,527

TRUSTEES Revd J. B. Boston; C. N. E. Boston; J. R. Boston.

OTHER INFORMATION The grant total includes £4,700 in Christmas gifts.

HOW TO APPLY The trust states that it does not respond to unsolicited applications.

WHO TO APPLY TO N. G. Sparrow, Trust Administrator, Birketts LLP, Kingfisher House, 1 Gilders Way, Norwich, Norfolk NR3 1UB *Tel.* 01603 232300

■ Greenham Common Community Trust Limited

CC NO 1062762   ESTABLISHED 1997

WHERE FUNDING CAN BE GIVEN Newbury and the surrounding areas, northern edges of North Hampshire, West Berkshire.

WHO CAN BENEFIT Charitable organisations and individuals.

WHAT IS FUNDED General charitable purposes, arts, education, economic, social and community development, healthcare, disadvantaged groups, nature and the environment and recreation and leisure with particular emphasis on the next generation.

WHAT IS NOT FUNDED Grants are only made within the trust's geographical area of operation.

TYPE OF GRANT One-off grants and specific projects, but grant delivery on a year-by year basis can be considered. Grants to both individuals and organisations.

RANGE OF GRANTS £100– £33,000.

SAMPLE GRANTS Education Business Partnership West Berkshire (£33,000); Berkshire Association of Club for Young People (£25,000); NHS Berkshire West (£10,000); WBC/Newbury College on behalf of Skills and Enterprise Sub-Partnership (£8,000); Arthritis Matters Reading and Berkshire MS Therapy Centre (£5,000 each); Tadley and District Citizens Advice and Newbury Athletic Club (£3,000 each); The Box Theatre Company (£2,500); West Berkshire Muslim Society and Recreation Centre and Royal Society for the Protection of Birds (RS PB) (£1,000 each); Stockcross and Speen Billiard Club (£400) and Aldermaston Concert Centre (£100).

FINANCES *Year* 2011–12 *Income* £6,207,030 *Grants* £268,651 *Assets* £47,206,330

TRUSTEES Sir Peter Michael; David Bailey; Charles Brims; Dr Paul Bryant; Julian Cazelet; Graham Mather; Malcolm Morris; Orna Ni-Chionna.

OTHER INFORMATION Funds are distributed twice a year – in May and November.

HOW TO APPLY By registering and making an application online at the portal: www.findmeagrant.org. The trust offers help to people without access to a computer or those who find it difficult to operate the system. Hard copy of application form can be requested or any other assistance obtained by either sending an email to: fmaghelp@greenham-common-trust.co.uk, or calling Melissa Elliott on 016 3581 7444.

WHO TO APPLY TO Stuart Tagg, Secretary and Chief Executive, Liberty House, The Enterprise Centre, Greenham Business Park, Newbury, Berkshire RG19 6HS *Tel.* 01635 817444 *email* stuart@greenham-common-trust.co.uk *Website* www.greenham-common-trust.co.uk

....

■ Greggs Foundation (formerly Greggs Trust)

CC NO 296590   **ESTABLISHED** 1987

WHERE FUNDING CAN BE GIVEN UK, with a preference for the North East of England, and in the regions of Greggs plc's Divisional Charity Committees.

WHO CAN BENEFIT The trustees are committed to equal opportunities and anti-discriminatory practice and wish to encourage applications from disadvantaged groups of all kinds including ethnic minorities, people with disabilities and other minorities, without prejudice as to racial origin, religion, age, gender or sexual orientation. Recent grants have included support for work with homeless people, older people, young people, children and women, including unemployed people, for people with disabilities and ethnic and multi-cultural groups.

WHAT IS FUNDED Applications from small community-led organisations and self-help groups are more likely to be successful than those from larger and well-staffed organisations and those that have greater fundraising capacity. Projects in the fields of the arts, the environment, conservation, education and health will be considered so long as they have a social welfare focus and/or are located in areas of deprivation.

WHAT IS NOT FUNDED Major grants are not made for: animal welfare; capital projects including the purchase, construction and refurbishment of buildings; events such as conferences, seminars and exhibitions, expeditions and overseas travel, fee-charging residential homes, nurseries and care facilities; festivals, performance and other entertainment activities; fundraising events; holidays and outings; hospitals, health service trusts, medically related appeals and medical equipment; individuals other than through the Hardship Fund; large, well-staffed organisations with a greater fundraising capacity; loans or repayments of loans; national organisations and their regional branches; mini-buses other than community transport schemes; research – academic and medical; religious promotion; replacement of statutory funds; retrospective grants; schools other than for pre-school and after school clubs and activities promoting parental and community involvement; sponsorship – organisations and individuals; sports kit equipment; uniformed organisations such as Scouts, Guides and Sea Cadets. The following are not supported through the hardship fund: payment of debt; computer equipment; sponsorship; overseas expeditions.

TYPE OF GRANT Core costs, running costs, project, start-up costs, recurring costs, salaries, one-off. Funding may be given for up to three years.

RANGE OF GRANTS Major grant for core costs and salaries between £10,000–£15,000 per year. One off grants to small organisations or low cost budget grants usually up to £2,000. Hardship Fund grants for necessities between £50–£150.

SAMPLE GRANTS Arable MACPI (£43,000 over three years); Owton Fens Community Association (£39,000 over three years); Kids Kabin and About Turn Community Interest Company (£15,000 each); Redcar Development Trust (£8,000); Dementia Forward, Leeds Children's Charity, Woodlawn School, Wheelies Sports Club and The Huddersfield Stroke Club (£2,000 each); and Derby Tock Children's Camp, Louth Seniors Forum and Housebeck Aerobics (£1,000 each).

FINANCES *Year* 2012 *Income* £1,699,531 *Grants* £1,600,000 *Assets* £10,734,953

TRUSTEES Andrew Davison; Richard Hutton; Fiona Nicholson; Annemarie Norman; Kate Welch; Tony Rowson; Nigel Murray; Roisin Currie; Karen Wilkinson-Bell.

OTHER INFORMATION The grant total includes £462,000 that was given in grants to individuals and £186,000 'support costs attributable to grantmaking'

HOW TO APPLY Each grants programme has its own criteria, guidelines and application process, all of which are available to view on the website.

WHO TO APPLY TO Jackie Crombie, Foundation Manager, Fernwood House, Clayton Road, Jesmond, Newcastle upon Tyne NE2 1TL *Tel.* 01912 127626 *email* greggsfoundation@greggs.co.uk *Website* www.greggsfoundation.org.uk

....

■ The Gretna Charitable Trust

CC NO 1020533   **ESTABLISHED** 1993

WHERE FUNDING CAN BE GIVEN UK, with a preference for Hertfordshire and London.

WHO CAN BENEFIT Registered charities.

WHAT IS FUNDED Seedcorn grants or specific needs.

WHAT IS NOT FUNDED The trust will not provide support to fund salaries or administration costs.

TYPE OF GRANT Ongoing and one-off.
RANGE OF GRANTS Usually up to £7,500.
SAMPLE GRANTS Prince William Jubilee Playing Fields (£7,500); St John's Church – Notting Hill (£5,000); Basketmakers' Company (£3,000); Brunel University (£2,000); Age UK (£1,500); British Australia Society, Garden House Hospice, Hertfordshire Scouts and Rosalind Runcie Memorial Fund (£1,000 each); and All Hallows by the Tower, Mensah Recovery Support Agency, St Olave's Church and The Mill Museum (£500 each).
FINANCES *Year* 2011–12 *Income* £99,167 *Grants* £166,500 *Assets* £1,486,178
TRUSTEES Richard Walduck; Susan Walduck; Alexander Walduck; Colin Bowles.
OTHER INFORMATION There was an unusually large grant of £110,000 made to St Alban's Cathedral – Saints Statues.
HOW TO APPLY This trust does not encourage applications.
WHO TO APPLY TO Richard Walduck, Trustee, Imperial London Hotels Limited, Russell Square, London WC1B 5BB

The Greys Charitable Trust

CC NO 1103717   **ESTABLISHED** 2004
WHERE FUNDING CAN BE GIVEN UK and locally in Oxfordshire.
WHO CAN BENEFIT Charitable organisations.
WHAT IS FUNDED Church and historical preservation projects; the arts.
SAMPLE GRANTS The National Trust – two grants (£12,000); Trinity College – Oxford (£10,000); Indo-Myanmar Conservation (£6,000); Sophie Elwes Trust and George Orwell Memorial Trust (£5,000 each); OHCT and the University Church of St Mary – Oxford (£2,000 each); and Ditchling Museum and British Red Cross (£1,000 each).
FINANCES *Year* 2011–12 *Income* £26,267 *Grants* £77,500 *Assets* £979,914
TRUSTEES Jacob Brunner; Timothy Brunner.
HOW TO APPLY In writing to the correspondent, the trustees usually meet twice a year.
WHO TO APPLY TO The Trustees, Flat 4, 2 Inverness Gardens, London W8 4RN *Tel.* 020 7727 6277

The Grimmitt Trust

CC NO 801975   **ESTABLISHED** 1989
WHERE FUNDING CAN BE GIVEN Worldwide, locally Birmingham and the surrounding areas.
WHO CAN BENEFIT Charities, charitable organisations and individuals.
WHAT IS FUNDED Culture and education, community, children and youth, medical and health, overseas, and older people.
WHAT IS NOT FUNDED The trust welcomes applications from charities, charitable organisations and individuals.
TYPE OF GRANT One-off, grants of up to three years.
RANGE OF GRANTS Up to £10,000 but mostly less than £2,500.
SAMPLE GRANTS King Edwards School Birmingham Trust, Methodist Relief and Development Fund and the Ackers (£10,000 each); Aston University and the Ironbridge Gorge Museum (£5,000 each); Allens Croft Project, Dream Makers and the Royal Institution (£3,000 each); and Action Centres UK, Prince's Trust and Wellington Methodist Church Centre (£2,500 each).
FINANCES *Year* 2012–13 *Income* £311,622 *Grants* £272,830 *Assets* £7,630,589

TRUSTEES Patrick Welch; Sue Day; Leon Murray; David Owen; Tim Welch; Jenny Dickins; Sarah Wilkey; Phil Smith.
OTHER INFORMATION In 2012–13, smaller grants of less than £2,500 were made to 208 organisations, totalling £158,500.
HOW TO APPLY Potential applicants should contact the secretary who will advise on the best way to design a grant request and to ensure that all the necessary information is included. The trustees meet three times a year to consider applications. Applicants must demonstrate that their project and the grant received is used in line with the trust's objectives.
WHO TO APPLY TO Vanessa Welch, Administrator, 151B All Saints Road, Kings Heath, Birmingham B14 6AT *Tel.* 01212 512951 *email* admin@grimmitt-trust.org.uk

The Grocers' Charity

CC NO 255230   **ESTABLISHED** 1968
WHERE FUNDING CAN BE GIVEN UK.
WHO CAN BENEFIT Registered charities only.
WHAT IS FUNDED The charity's charitable aims are broad-ranging, encompassing education, the church, the relief of poverty, medicine, support for the arts, heritage, the elderly, young people and those with disabilities. Grants to churches, schools and other educational organisations are given to bodies with close links to the charity. Other categories are open for applications.
WHAT IS NOT FUNDED Only UK-registered charities are supported. Individuals cannot receive grants directly. Support is rarely given to the following unless there is a specific or long-standing connection with the Grocers' Company: cathedrals, churches and other ecclesiastical bodies, hospices, schools and other educational establishments, research projects.
TYPE OF GRANT Both capital and revenue projects. Non-recurring grants of limited size. Core costs, one-off, running costs and salaries will be considered. Funding may be given for up to one year.
RANGE OF GRANTS £1,000–£185,000.
SAMPLE GRANTS Oundle School (£185,000); Motor Neurone Disease (£40,000); Only Connect (£26,000); Peterborough Cathedral Development and Preservation Trust (£10,000); VSO (£7,500); St John the Baptist – Stone (£7,000); Reed's School (£6,600); Royal College of Art (£6,000); St Paul's Cathedral Foundation Fabric Fund (£5,000); National Theatre (£3,000); Ulysses Trust, Bush Theatre and National Osteoporosis Society (£2,000 each); New Forest Disability Information Service (£1,250) and Royal London Society for Blind People (£1,100).
FINANCES *Year* 2011–12 *Income* £662,871 *Grants* £616,026 *Assets* £12,876,764
TRUSTEE The Grocers' Trust Company Limited administers the Charity and the Directors of that company are the Master and Second Warden of the Grocers' Company, together with the Chairmen of the Education and Charities Committee and the Finance Committee. The Master and Second Warden together with eight other Members of the Court of Assistants, all of whom are elected for a fixed term of office, form the Education and Charities Committee which is responsible for grantmaking.
HOW TO APPLY Applications for grants can be considered from UK registered charities only and must comply with current guidelines, including restrictions, as detailed in the Grocers' Charity Annual Review and on the Grocers'

Company website: www.grocershall.co.uk. Applicants should complete the online enquiry form on the charity's website. 'Do not send any further information at this stage. We will review your enquiry and contact you if we wish to take your application further. We regret we are unable to acknowledge receipt of enquiries.' Applications are considered three to four times a year. Unsolicited applications are not accepted for the major grants programme: to apply for a Major Grant you must be supported by a member of the Grocers' Company and fit the criteria decided by the committee each year. Do not contact the Grocers' Charity directly and note the Grocers' Company are unable to provide details of members of the Company.

WHO TO APPLY TO Lucy J. Cummings, Charity Administrator, Grocers' Hall, Princes Street, London EC2R 8AD *Tel.* 020 7606 3113 *Fax* 020 7600 3082 *email* lucy@grocershall.co. uk *Website* www.grocershall.co.uk

■ The M. and R. Gross Charities Limited

CC NO 251888   **ESTABLISHED** 1967
WHERE FUNDING CAN BE GIVEN UK and overseas.
WHO CAN BENEFIT Jewish organisations.
WHAT IS FUNDED Organisations supporting the Orthodox Jewish religion and Jewish education.
SAMPLE GRANTS Atlas Memorial Limited; United Talmudical Associates Limited, a grantmaking organisation which distributes smaller grants made by the trust; Chevras Tsedokoh Limited; Kolel Shomrei Hachomoth; Telz Talmudical Academy; Talmud Torah Trust; Gevurah Ari Torah Academy Trust; Friends of Yeshivas Brisk; Beis Ruchel Building Fund; Beth Hamedresh Satmar Trust; Kehal Chareidim Trust; Daas Sholem; Craven Walk Beis Hamedrash; Union of Orthodox Hebrew Congregations; and Yetev Lev Jerusalem.
FINANCES *Year* 2011–12 *Income* £7,723,521 *Grants* £3,527,700 *Assets* £30,409,071
TRUSTEES Rifka Gross; Sarah Padwa; Michael Saberski; Leonard Lerner.
OTHER INFORMATION A recent list of grants was not available.
HOW TO APPLY In writing to the organisation. Applications are assessed on a weekly basis and many of the smaller grants are dealt with through a grantmaking agency, United Talmudical Associates Limited.
WHO TO APPLY TO Rivka Gross, Secretary, Cohen Arnold and Co., New Burlington House, 1075 Finchley Road, London NW11 0PU *Tel.* 020 8731 0777 *Fax* 020 8731 0778

■ The GRP Charitable Trust

CC NO 255733   **ESTABLISHED** 1968
WHERE FUNDING CAN BE GIVEN UK.
WHO CAN BENEFIT Organisations already known to the trust.
WHAT IS FUNDED Jewish, general.
WHAT IS NOT FUNDED No grants to individuals.
RANGE OF GRANTS Typically up to £80,000.
SAMPLE GRANTS Oxford Centre for Hebrew and Jewish Studies (£102,000); The Wallace Collection (£75,000); Jerusalem Foundation (£31,000); Traditional Alternatives Foundation (£25,000); Magen David Adom – UK and United Jewish Israel Appeal (£10,000 each); Anglo Jewish Association and Trinity College (£5,000 each); Thames Diamond Jubilee (£3,000);

Alexandra Wylie Tower Foundation, Royal British Legion and Simon Marks Jewish Primary School Trust (£1,000 each); Chicken Shed Theatre Company (£500); Spotlight Appeal (£200); and King Edward VII Hospital Sister Agnes (£100).
FINANCES *Year* 2011–12 *Income* £228,808 *Grants* £342,550 *Assets* £5,179,582
TRUSTEE Kleinwort Benson Trustees Ltd.
OTHER INFORMATION The GRP of the title is George Richard Pinto, a London banker who established the trust.
HOW TO APPLY In writing to the correspondent. Trustees meet annually in March.
WHO TO APPLY TO The Secretary, 14 St George Street, London W1S 1FE *Tel.* 020 3207 7000

■ The David and Marie Grumitt Foundation

CC NO 288826   **ESTABLISHED** 1984
WHERE FUNDING CAN BE GIVEN London and Surrey.
WHO CAN BENEFIT Registered charities, with a preference for charities supporting homeless people.
WHAT IS FUNDED Groups with a religious background; people affected by imprisonment.
TYPE OF GRANT Often recurring.
RANGE OF GRANTS £1,000–£6,000.
SAMPLE GRANTS Jesuit Missions (£6,000) and St Ann's Church (£3,000); CAFOD, The Diocese of Arundel and Brighton (£2,000 each); Catholic Children's Society, LIFE, The Manna Society (£1,000 each).
FINANCES *Year* 2011–12 *Income* £22,891 *Grants* £24,000
TRUSTEES The Governor and Company of the Bank of Scotland; Marie Grumitt.
HOW TO APPLY This trust has stated that the income of the foundation is fully committed for the foreseeable future and it does not respond to unsolicited applications.
WHO TO APPLY TO Marion Bisset, Trustee Tax Manager, Lloyds TSB Private Banking, The Clock House, 22–26 Ock Street, Abingdon, Oxfordshire OX14 5SW *Tel.* 01235 232734 *email* marion.bisset@mazars.co.uk

■ N. and R. Grunbaum Charitable Trust

CC NO 1068524   **ESTABLISHED** 1998
WHERE FUNDING CAN BE GIVEN UK and Israel.
WHO CAN BENEFIT Registered charities.
WHAT IS FUNDED Relief of poverty and the advancement of Jewish education and the Jewish religion.
FINANCES *Year* 2012–13 *Income* £38,601 *Grants* £43,525 *Assets* £1,870
TRUSTEES Norman Grunbaum; Rosella Grunbaum; David Grunbaum.
OTHER INFORMATION A list of grants was not available.
HOW TO APPLY In writing to the correspondent.
WHO TO APPLY TO Norman Grunbaum, Trustee, 7 Northdene Gardens, London N15 6LX *Tel.* 020 8800 9974

■ The Bishop of Guildford's Foundation

CC NO 1017385   **ESTABLISHED** 1993
WHERE FUNDING CAN BE GIVEN Diocese of Guildford.
WHO CAN BENEFIT Voluntary and community groups who are linked with a church or faith community,

or engaged in a project working in partnership with a church or faith community. Organisations don't have to be registered charities but do have to have a constitution or set of rules, and a bank account, or be supported by an organisation that has these.

WHAT IS FUNDED Community projects. The purpose of the foundation's grants programme is to support projects and partnerships through which church or faith linked groups meet local needs or get involved in community development and regeneration. Priority will be given to projects and partnerships which build communities' own capacity to meet local needs, especially in relation to those who are excluded or vulnerable.

WHAT IS NOT FUNDED Funding is not normally given to assist individuals directly, or for capital costs, or for projects which have already occurred.

TYPE OF GRANT Small grants, usually up to £2,000 and larger strategic grants, usually up to £10,000. Applications for funding for more than one year can be considered, especially where this enables projects to apply for other funding.

RANGE OF GRANTS £500–£32,000.

SAMPLE GRANTS Previously: Partnership Development Project (£32,000); North East Hampshire Development (£27,000); Faith Communities Capacity (£21,000); Camberley Churches and Lakeview (£10,000 each); South East England Faiths Forum (£7,000); the Vine (£4,200); Watts Gallery (£4,200); Ebbisham Association (£2,000); Emmaus House (£400); and Thames Housing Project (£350).

FINANCES *Year* 2011–12 *Income* £34,203 *Grants* £50,000

TRUSTEES Rt Revd Christopher Hill, Bishop of Guildford; Revd Canon Christopher Rich; Geoffrey Riggs; Revd Carole Bourne; Hugh Bryant.

HOW TO APPLY 'Grantmaking by the Bishop of Guildford's Foundation is done through the Community Foundation for Surrey (CFS), an independent charitable trust which is part of the national network of Community Foundations.' Criteria is available to download on The Bishop of Guildford's Foundation's website. Applicants should contact CFS on 01483 409230 or go to its website: www.cfsurrey.org.uk/

WHO TO APPLY TO Stephen Marriott, Diocesan Secretary, Diocesan House, Quarry Street, Guildford, Surrey GU1 3XG *Tel.* 01483 790300 *email* info@bgf.org.uk *Website* www.bgf.org.uk

---

■ The Guildry Incorporation of Perth

SC NO SC008072   **ESTABLISHED** 1210

WHERE FUNDING CAN BE GIVEN Perth and surrounding area.

WHO CAN BENEFIT Members of the Guildry; residents of Perth and surrounding area who are in need.

WHAT IS FUNDED The main purpose of the trust is to provide support for its members and their families. Charitable donations are also made to local causes at the discretion of the committee. The trust's main aims are to relieve poverty; aid the advancement of education and health, as well as aid the advancement of the arts, sports, environmental protection and recreational activities in the specified area.

WHAT IS NOT FUNDED Any appeals outside Perth.

SAMPLE GRANTS The Diabetes Research Campaign; Guildtown Community Association; Perth Access Cars; Perthshire Rugby Club; and Family Mediation.

FINANCES *Year* 2011–12 *Income* £248,185

TRUSTEES Gordon Bannerman; Michael Norval; Alastair Anderson; Alexander Sneddon; Ian Nicol; Rae Pattillo; Alistair Barn; Louis Flood; Dr Ronald McDougall.

OTHER INFORMATION The total expenditure of the charity in 2011–12 was £200,000.

HOW TO APPLY In writing to the correspondent. 'Requests for charitable donations may be made to the Guildry by members and close members of their family. Additionally, any other individuals living in, or organisations located in, either Perth or Guildtown, may apply for a donation.' The trust meets to consider grants on the last Tuesday of every month.

WHO TO APPLY TO Lorna Peacock, Secretary, 42 George Street, Perth, Perthshire PH1 5JL *Tel.* 01738 623195 *email* guildryperth@ btconnect.com *Website* www.perthguildry.org.uk

---

■ The Walter Guinness Charitable Trust

CC NO 205375   **ESTABLISHED** 1961

WHERE FUNDING CAN BE GIVEN UK with a preference for Wiltshire and overseas.

WHO CAN BENEFIT Charitable organisations only.

WHAT IS FUNDED The trust is unlikely to be able to support anything it is not already in touch with, but would be interested to hear from charities concerned with research, education, communities and ecology.

WHAT IS NOT FUNDED No grants to individuals.

TYPE OF GRANT Normally one-off.

RANGE OF GRANTS Grants from less than £1,000–£10,000.

SAMPLE GRANTS DEC Disaster Emergencies Committee (£5,000); Nursing Cancer Patients (£3,000); Arts Together (£2,500) Inspire Foundation, Prospect Hospice, SCOPE, Shelter, Wiltshire South Girl Guides (£2,000 each); Samaritans (£1,500); Barnardo's, Break Combat Stress and National Deaf Children's Society (£1,000 each).

FINANCES *Year* 2011–12 *Income* £141,046 *Grants* £122,598 *Assets* £6,771,133

TRUSTEES Hon. F. B. Guinness; Hon. R. Mulji; Hon. Catriona Guinness.

HOW TO APPLY In writing to the correspondent. Replies are only sent when there is a positive decision. Initial telephone calls are not possible. There are no application forms, guidelines or deadlines. No sae is required.

WHO TO APPLY TO The Secretary, Biddesden House, Andover, Hampshire SP11 9DN

■ The Gunter Charitable Trust

CC NO 268346   **ESTABLISHED** 1974

WHERE FUNDING CAN BE GIVEN UK and occasionally overseas.

WHO CAN BENEFIT Local and UK organisations.

WHAT IS FUNDED General charitable purposes including medical and wildlife causes in the UK.

WHAT IS NOT FUNDED No support for unsolicited applications.

RANGE OF GRANTS Typically up to £20,000.

SAMPLE GRANTS The Medical Foundation for the Care of Victims of Torture (£6,500); Practical Action (£6,000); Humanitarian Aid Relief Trust (£5,000); Entelechy Arts Ltd (£4,500); St Mary's Church – Fordingbridge, Friends of Dr Pearay Lal Hospital and Liverpool School of Tropical Medicine (£1,000 each); and

Guideposts Trust Ltd and Scottish Wildlife Trust (£400 each).

FINANCES *Year* 2011–12 *Income* £107,707 *Grants* £89,427 *Assets* £2,126,476

TRUSTEES James de Cardonnel Findlay; Geoffrey Worrall.

OTHER INFORMATION In 2011–12 the trust administered £89,500 to 63 organisations.

HOW TO APPLY Applications are considered by the trustees twice a year. No unsolicited applications are accepted.

WHO TO APPLY TO The Trustees, c/o Forsters LLP, 31 Hill Street, London W1J 5LS *Tel.* 020 7863 8333

■ The Gur Trust

CC NO 283423   **ESTABLISHED** 1961

WHERE FUNDING CAN BE GIVEN Worldwide.

WHO CAN BENEFIT Individuals and organisations benefiting children, young adults, students and Jewish people.

WHAT IS FUNDED Advancement of education and the Orthodox Jewish religion.

SAMPLE GRANTS Previous beneficiaries have included Beis Yaacov Casidic Seminary, Beth Yaacov Town, Bnei Emes Institutes, Central Charity Fund, Gur Talmudical College, Kollel Arad, Yeshiva Lezeirim, Pri Gidulim, Maala and Mifal Gevura Shecehessed.

FINANCES *Year* 2011–12 *Income* £45,910 *Grants* £43,136 *Assets* £1,375,044

TRUSTEES Sheldon Morgenstern; David Cymerman; Shaye Traube.

HOW TO APPLY In writing to the correspondent. The trust has previously stated that: 'Funds are raised by the trustees. All calls for help are carefully considered and help is given according to circumstances and funds then available.'

WHO TO APPLY TO Sheldon Morgenstern, Administrator, 206 High Road, London N15 4NP *Tel.* 020 8801 6038

■ The Gurney Charitable Trust

CC NO 1080803   **ESTABLISHED** 2000

WHERE FUNDING CAN BE GIVEN UK with a preference for the south of England.

WHO CAN BENEFIT Charitable organisations.

WHAT IS FUNDED General charitable purposes.

SAMPLE GRANTS National Youth Orchestra, Friends of East Sussex Hospices, Evelina Children's Hospital Appeal, Association of Children's Hospices and Wildfowl and Wetlands Trust (£5,000 each); Brighton and Hove Parents and Children Group, Northern Fells Group, RSPB Broadwater Warren, Seeing Ear, Sussex Air Ambulance, Sussex Wildlife Trust and Thomley Activity Centre (£1,000 each) and Railway Land Wildlife Trust, National Talking Newspapers, Gloucestershire County Association for the Blind and Framfield Memorial Hall (£500 each).

FINANCES *Year* 2011–12 *Income* £24,942 *Grants* £45,000

TRUSTEES Margaret Gurney; Nicola Finney; Mark Finney; Dr Michael Gurney; Adrian Gurney.

HOW TO APPLY In writing to the correspondent.

WHO TO APPLY TO Dr Michael Gurney, Trustee, The Hundred House, Pound Lane, Framfield, Nr Uckfield, East Sussex TN22 5RU *Tel.* 01825 890377

■ Dr Guthrie's Association

SC NO SC009302   **ESTABLISHED** 1986

WHERE FUNDING CAN BE GIVEN Scotland, with a preference for Edinburgh.

WHO CAN BENEFIT Not-for-profit organisations benefiting disadvantaged children and young people under 22 years of age.

WHAT IS FUNDED The care and welfare of young people.

WHAT IS NOT FUNDED No grants to individuals, or in support of: projects of an environmental nature; mainstream activities and statutory requirements of schools, universities and hospitals; large-scale building projects; historic restoration; retrospective funding.

RANGE OF GRANTS £250–£2,000.

SAMPLE GRANTS Abernethy Trust, Citylife Ministries Ltd, City Youth Café, Glasgow City Mission, Happy Days Children's Charity, Reality Adventure Works in Scotland, Riptide Music Studios, Tall Ships Youth Trust, Turning Point Scotland and Visibility (£1,000 each); ChildLine Scotland (£750); Red School Youth Centre (£700); and Bibles for Children (£500).

FINANCES *Year* 2012 *Income* £35,718 *Grants* £60,000

TRUSTEES J. M. P. Galbraith, Chair; S. Crane; R. Derby; P. J. Derby; A. M. G. Hepburn; Ms E. Marquis.

HOW TO APPLY Applications are considered by the trustees three times a year (approximately) in February, June and October.

WHO TO APPLY TO Grant Administrator, PO BOX 28838, Edinburgh EH15 2XZ *Tel.* 07729 018214 *email* drguthrie@tiscali.co.uk *Website* www.scott-moncrieff.com/services/charities/charitable-trusts/dr-guthries-association

■ The H. and J. Spack Charitable Trust

CC NO 1087689   **ESTABLISHED** 2001
WHERE FUNDING CAN BE GIVEN Worldwide.
WHO CAN BENEFIT Charities and organisations working in the worldwide community.
WHAT IS FUNDED Jewish and general charitable purposes.
RANGE OF GRANTS Up to £6,000.
SAMPLE GRANTS The Royal Academy of Arts (£5,600); St John's Wood Synagogue (£5,350); Jewish Care (£5,000); Heart Cells Foundation (£2,200); Jewish Women's Aid (£1,000) and Norwood (£250).
FINANCES *Year* 2012–13 *Income* £44,736 *Grants* £25,150 *Assets* £26,876
TRUSTEES Arvind Shah; Judith Spack.
HOW TO APPLY In writing to the correspondent.
WHO TO APPLY TO Judith Spack, Flat 2, Ellerton House, 10–12 Bryanston Square, London W1H 2DQ

■ The H. and M. Charitable Trust

CC NO 272391   **ESTABLISHED** 1976
WHERE FUNDING CAN BE GIVEN UK, with some preference for Kent.
WHO CAN BENEFIT Charities concerned with the advancement of education and the relief of poverty. Seafaring in the UK, with some preference for Kent.
WHAT IS FUNDED 'Resources are committed on a regular annual basis to organisations who have come to rely upon [the trust] for their funding.'
SAMPLE GRANTS Previous beneficiaries included: Arethusa Venture Centre, Fairbridge – Kent, Guide Dogs for the Blind, Hand in Gillingham, Jubilee Sailing Trust, Kent Air Ambulance, North London Hospice, RSPCA, Royal Engineers Association, Royal National Lifeboat Association and Royal Star and Garter Home.
FINANCES *Year* 2011–12 *Income* £54,102 *Grants* £84,000 *Assets* £2,630,593
TRUSTEES David Harris; Pamela Lister; John Lister.
HOW TO APPLY The trustees said they do not wish their trust to be included in this guide since it leads to disappointment for applicants. Unsolicited applications will not be successful.
WHO TO APPLY TO David Harris, Trustee, Lilac Cottage, Highwood Hill, London NW7 4HD *Tel.* 020 8906 3767 *email* david@brooksgreen. com

■ H. and T. Clients Charitable Trust

CC NO 1104345   **ESTABLISHED** 2004
WHERE FUNDING CAN BE GIVEN England and Wales.
WHO CAN BENEFIT Organisations.
WHAT IS FUNDED General charitable purposes.
FINANCES *Year* 2011–12 *Income* £95,748 *Grants* £79,328 *Assets* £56,909
TRUSTEES Hugh Lask; Ronnie Harris; Neville Newman; Charlotte Harris.
HOW TO APPLY In writing to the correspondent.
WHO TO APPLY TO Hugh Lask, Trustee, 64 New Cavendish Street, London W1G 8TB *Tel.* 020 7467 6300

■ H. C. D. Memorial Fund

CC NO 1044956   **ESTABLISHED** 1995
WHERE FUNDING CAN BE GIVEN Worldwide.
WHO CAN BENEFIT Organisations benefiting the environment and people who are in need. Especially, people disadvantaged by poverty, education or ill-health and people with disabilities.
WHAT IS FUNDED Health, education, community, environment, development aid abroad, and other social and educational work in the UK and the Republic of Ireland.
WHAT IS NOT FUNDED The following are not supported: evangelism or missionary work; individuals; nationwide emergency appeals; animal, cancer and children's' charities. The fund stresses that it receives applications for gap year funding which are always unsuccessful as grants are never made to individuals.
TYPE OF GRANT Can be one-off or recurring, including core costs, buildings and start-up costs. Funding may be given for up to three years.
RANGE OF GRANTS £1,000–£150,000; average grant: £10,000–£20,000.
SAMPLE GRANTS Overseas – 23 grants totalling £458,500. Beneficiaries included: San Carlos Hospital – Mexico (£66,000); Impact Foundation – Cambodia (£40,000); Health Poverty Action (£35,000); Arpana Charitable Trust – India and Lifegate Rehabilitation – Palestine (£20,000 each); Tools for Self-reliance – Africa/UK (£15,000); Tanzania Development Trust (£10,000) and Tigre Trust – Eritrea (£5,000). UK – 12 grants totalling £135,500. Beneficiaries included: Whitehawk Inn (£20,000); Green Light Trust (£17,000); Sussex Pathways (£12,500); People and Planet (£10,000); Resurgo Trust (£5,000) and Friends First (£3,000).
FINANCES *Year* 2011–12 *Income* £711,847 *Grants* £594,000 *Assets* £625,687
TRUSTEES Nicholas Debenham, Chair; Bill Flinn; Harriet Lear; Joanna Lear; Jeremy Debenham; Catherine Debenham; Susannah Drummond.
HOW TO APPLY In writing to the correspondent, although note that the trust has a preference for seeking out its own projects and only very rarely responds to general appeals. 'Unsolicited applications are not encouraged. They are acknowledged, but extremely rarely receive a positive response. No telephone enquiries, please.'
WHO TO APPLY TO Harriet Lear, Secretary and Trustee, Knowlands Farm Granary, Barcombe, Lewes, East Sussex BN8 5EF *Tel.* 01273 400321 *email* hcdmemorialfund@gmail.com

■ H. C. Foundation

CC NO 1148306   **ESTABLISHED** 2012
WHERE FUNDING CAN BE GIVEN UK.
WHO CAN BENEFIT Charities and community groups.
WHAT IS FUNDED General, education, health, social welfare.
TRUSTEES Bernard Groszman; Shelley Groszman; Shirley March.
HOW TO APPLY In writing to the correspondent.
WHO TO APPLY TO John Hamer, Administrator, c/o Hampton Care, 1st Floor, 19 Highfield Road, London NW11 9LS *Tel.* 020 8458 8900

■ The H. P. Charitable Trust

CC NO 278006   **ESTABLISHED** 1979
WHERE FUNDING CAN BE GIVEN UK and overseas.
WHO CAN BENEFIT Jewish charities, especially Orthodox.
WHAT IS FUNDED General charitable purposes; advancement of Orthodox Judaism; poverty relief.
SAMPLE GRANTS Previous beneficiaries included: Craven Walk Charities, Emuno Educational Centre Ltd, Gur Trust, Ponivez, Yad Eliezer, Yeshuas Caim Synagogue and Yetev Lev.
FINANCES *Year* 2011–12 *Income* £205,419 *Grants* £31,341 *Assets* £1,811,368
TRUSTEES Arthur Zonszajn; Aron Piller; Hannah Piller.
HOW TO APPLY In writing to the correspondent.
WHO TO APPLY TO Aron Piller, Trustee, 26 Lingwood Road, London E5 9BN *Tel.* 020 8806 2432

■ The Hackney Parochial Charities

CC NO 219876   **ESTABLISHED** 1904
WHERE FUNDING CAN BE GIVEN The London borough of Hackney.
WHO CAN BENEFIT Organisations benefiting children, young adults and people disadvantaged by poverty may be considered. Community organisations can also benefit.
WHAT IS FUNDED Community and education projects which benefit people in Hackney who are poor.
TYPE OF GRANT One-off and recurrent.
RANGE OF GRANTS Up to £8,000
SAMPLE GRANTS Hackney Quest (£8,000); St Mungo's and Christchurch on the Mead (£5,000 each); Anna Fiorentini Theatre and Film School (£4,000); Chickenshed Theatre, Hackney Joint Estate Charity and Learning Trust (£3,000 each) and Hackney Doorways and North London Muslim Centre (£2,500 each).
FINANCES *Year* 2011–12 *Income* £191,074 *Grants* £102,848 *Assets* £4,908,526
TRUSTEES Father Rob Wickham; Vastiana Belfon; Cllr Geoff Taylor; Peter Cofie; Mary Cannon; Nicola Baboneau; Cllr Chris Kennedy; David Horder.
OTHER INFORMATION Other grants under £2,500 amounted to £52,000.
HOW TO APPLY In writing to the correspondent. The trustees will consider written applications for grants and project funding from individuals and organisations that are in line with the charity's objectives and are within the area of benefit at their discretion.
WHO TO APPLY TO Benjamin Janes, Clerk to the Trustees, c/o The Trust Partnership, 6 Trull Farm Buildings, Trull, Tetbury, Gloucestershire GL8 8SQ *Tel.* 01285 841900 *email* office@thetrustpartnership.com

■ The Hadfield Trust

CC NO 1067491   **ESTABLISHED** 1998
WHERE FUNDING CAN BE GIVEN Unrestricted; in practice, Cumbria.
WHO CAN BENEFIT Organisations benefiting children, young adults and older people; unemployed people; parents and children; one parent families; and widows and widowers.
WHAT IS FUNDED Charities concerned with social needs, youth employment, help for older people, the arts and the environment. Particularly supported are those working in the fields of accommodation and housing; support and development; arts, culture and recreation; health; conservation; education and training; and social care and development.
WHAT IS NOT FUNDED The following would not normally be considered for a grant: applicants from outside the county of Cumbria; individuals; any form of sponsorship; religious bodies; political organisations; pressure groups; feasibility studies; schools seeking specialist status; where funding from statutory bodies is, or should be available.
TYPE OF GRANT Capital projects preferred; buildings will be considered and funding is generally for one year or less.
RANGE OF GRANTS Minimum £50.
SAMPLE GRANTS Rosehill Theatre (£7,000); Whitehaven Harbour Youth Project, Self Injury Support and South Lakeland Hydrotherapy (£4,000 each); Create Arts and Ocean Youth Trust (£3,000 each); Whitehaven Credit Union, Helena Thompson Museum and Barrow and District Scouts (£2,000 each); Dufton Recreation Area (£1,500); Brampton Film Club (£1,000); Lakeland Waste Management (£700); British Horse Society (£500) and Embroiders Guild Kendal (£400).
FINANCES *Year* 2012 *Income* £315,233 *Grants* £285,150 *Assets* £7,156,489
TRUSTEES Roy Morris; William Rathbone; Alan Forsyth; Andrew Morris; Andrew Forsyth; Caroline Addison.
PUBLICATIONS A leaflet setting out the aims and objectives of the trust (available on request).
OTHER INFORMATION In 2012 grants were given to 156 organisations.
HOW TO APPLY A completed application form is always required and is available from the trust's website or offices. The completed application form should be sent to the administrator together with a copy of the applicant's most recent accounts to reach the trust not later than the deadline for the relevant meeting. The deadlines are always the 1st of the month preceding that of the trustees' meeting i.e. 1 February, 1 June and 1 October. If the application form gives insufficient space for your project to be described, up to two sheets of A4 paper can be accepted. The policy of the trust is that capital funding is strongly preferred but some revenue requests will be accepted in particular circumstances. If in any doubt about the best way to complete the application form, including the size of the grant to be requested, applicants are strongly advised to telephone the Administrator who will be glad to advise. In reaching their decision the trustees have the benefit of advice from the Advisory Panel which meets some weeks before them to discuss in detail the applications. The Advisory Panel, under the chairship of Alan Forsyth, is made up of people resident in Cumbria and drawn from all parts of the county who have wide experience and knowledge of the charitable sector.
WHO TO APPLY TO Michael Hope, Administrator, 3 College Path, Formby, Liverpool L37 1LH *Tel.* 01704 834887 *email* admin@hadfieldtrust.org.uk *Website* www.hadfieldtrust.org.uk

■ The Hadley Trust

CC NO 1064823   **ESTABLISHED** 1997
WHERE FUNDING CAN BE GIVEN UK, especially London.
WHO CAN BENEFIT Registered charities.
WHAT IS FUNDED The trust's objects allow it to assist in creating opportunities for people who are disadvantaged as a result of environmental, educational or economic circumstances or physical or other disability to improve their

594

Does the trust you have chosen match your needs? Haphazard applications waste postage and time

situation, either by direct financial assistance, involvement in project and support work, or research into the causes of and means to alleviate hardship.

SAMPLE GRANTS New Economics Foundation, Policy Exchange, Prison Reform Trust and Voice.

FINANCES *Year* 2011–12 *Income* £6,265,387 *Grants* £2,143,604 *Assets* £90,604,289

TRUSTEES Janet Hulme; Philip Hulme; Janet Love; Thomas Hulme; Katherine Prideaux; Sophie Hulme.

HOW TO APPLY In writing to the correspondent. However, note that the trust prefers to work with established partners and therefore 'the trust does not take on many new funding commitments. Nevertheless the trustees will always consider and respond to proposals which might enhance the effectiveness of the trust.'

WHO TO APPLY TO Carol Biggs, Trust Administrator, Gladsmuir, Hadley Common, Barnet, Hertfordshire EN5 5QE *Tel.* 020 8447 4577 *Fax* 020 8447 4571 *email* carol@hadleytrust.org

....

■ The Hadrian Trust

CC NO 272161   **ESTABLISHED** 1976

WHERE FUNDING CAN BE GIVEN Within the boundaries of the old counties of Northumberland and Durham, this includes Tyne and Wear and the former county of Cleveland (north of the Tees).

WHO CAN BENEFIT Organisations benefiting people of all ages; unemployed people; volunteers; people in care, or who are fostered or adopted; one-parent families; and widows and widowers. Typical grants in 2004 were to councils of voluntary service, advice and counselling services, women's projects, youth clubs and schools, charities for people who are disabled, older people, arts and environmental projects, church restoration and block grants for individuals in need.

WHAT IS FUNDED Social welfare and other charitable projects within the boundaries of the old counties of Northumberland and Durham (this includes Tyne and Wear). The main headings under which applications are considered are: social welfare; youth; women; the elderly; the disabled; ethnic minorities; the arts; the environment; education and churches.

WHAT IS NOT FUNDED General appeals from large UK organisations and smaller bodies working outside the beneficial area are not considered.

TYPE OF GRANT Usually one-off for a special project or part of a project. The average grant is £1,000. Buildings, capital, project, research, recurring costs, as well as running costs, salaries and start-up costs will be considered. Funding of up to three years will be considered.

RANGE OF GRANTS £500–£5,000.

SAMPLE GRANTS Young Sinfonia Orchestra (£5,000); Funding Information North East (£4,000); Newcastle CVS (£3,000); Cramlington Voluntary Youth Project and Alnwick Playhouse Trust (£2,000 each); Newburn Sea Cadets, Wooler Young People's Association and Fenham Association of Residents (£1,000 each) and Tees Valley Voices and Student Community Action (£500).

FINANCES *Year* 2011–12 *Income* £180,543 *Grants* £171,700 *Assets* £5,351,555

TRUSTEES Hume Hargreave; John Parker; Pauline Dodgson; Katherine Winskell; Jim Dias.

OTHER INFORMATION A total of 148 grants were made including four grants to individuals.

HOW TO APPLY In writing to the correspondent (there is no application form). Details of what the

application letter must include can be found on the website. Applications are considered at meetings usually held in October, January, April and July each year, or as otherwise required. Eligible applications will be acknowledged and given a date when the application will be considered. Successful applicants will hear within two weeks of the meeting; no further correspondence is sent to unsuccessful applicants. Applications for individuals should be sent to: Greggs Charitable Trust, Fernwood House, Clayton Road, Jesmond, Newcastle upon Tyne NE2 1TL.

WHO TO APPLY TO Pauline Dodgson, Administrator, The Hadrian Trust, PO Box 785, Whitley Bay NE26 9DW *Tel.* 07815 785074 *email* enquiries@hadriantrust.co.uk *Website* www.hadriantrust.co.uk

....

■ The Doris Louise Hailes Charitable Trust

CC NO 1134434   **ESTABLISHED** 2010

WHERE FUNDING CAN BE GIVEN Undefined, in practice in the UK.

WHO CAN BENEFIT Registered charities.

WHAT IS FUNDED The advancement of health and saving of lives, disability, and animals.

SAMPLE GRANTS Under its main clause it is set up to assist the following charities: PDSA – Peoples Dispensary For Sick Animals – Telford; RSPB – Bedfordshire; Royal Society For The Protection Of Birds; Heart Foundation; Arthritis Society; RNIB; RAF Benevolent Fund; and any other like-minded charities.

FINANCES *Year* 2011–12 *Income* £21,216 *Grants* £55,391

TRUSTEE HSBC Trust Co (UK) Ltd.

HOW TO APPLY In writing to the correspondent.

WHO TO APPLY TO HSBC Trust Co (UK) Ltd, c/o HSBC Trust Co (UK) Ltd, Norwich House, 10th Floor, Nelson Gate, Commercial Road Southampton, SO15 1GX *Tel.* 02380 722221

....

■ The Alfred Haines Charitable Trust

CC NO 327166   **ESTABLISHED** 1986

WHERE FUNDING CAN BE GIVEN Birmingham and West Midlands (including Staffordshire and Warwickshire).

WHO CAN BENEFIT Mainly smaller charities.

WHAT IS FUNDED Christian social action. Grants were broken down into the following categories: family support and counselling; youth and children's work; humanitarian and overseas aid; medically disadvantaged; care for older people and people with disabilities; support for homeless people; and holidays for disadvantaged children and teenagers.

WHAT IS NOT FUNDED No support for activities which are primarily the responsibility of central or local government or some other responsible body; animal welfare; church buildings – restoration, improvements, renovations or new ones; environmental – conservation and protection of wildlife and landscape; expeditions and overseas trips; hospitals and health centres; individuals, including students (on the rare occasions that individuals are supported, the person has to be recommended by someone known to the trustees and the funding should be of long-term benefit to others); large national charities; it is unusual for the trust to support large national charities even where there is a local project; loans and business finance; medical research projects; purely evangelistic projects; promotion of any religion other than Christianity; schools, universities and colleges; projects which have been unsuccessful before or projects supported by Quothquan trust. Projects overseas or outside the West Midlands, whether Christian or not, will only be considered where the applicants are known to a trustee or are recommended by someone known to a trustee who has first-hand knowledge of the work.

TYPE OF GRANT Generally one-off. Specific projects rather than general running costs.

SAMPLE GRANTS A list of beneficiaries was not available.

FINANCES *Year* 2011–12 *Income* £31,321 *Grants* £72,405 *Assets* £1,055,383

TRUSTEES A. L. Gilmour; G. L. H. Moss.

HOW TO APPLY In writing to the trustees, quoting ref. CC. Applications should include: a brief description of the activities of the organisation; details of the project and its overall cost; what funds have already been raised and how the remaining funds are to be raised; a copy of the latest accounts including any associated or parent organisation; any other leaflets or supporting documentation. When considering whether to apply for funding, advice (if needed) can be obtained from the administrator prior to writing.
Applicants are advised to consider the exclusion list (available at www.ahct.org.uk/exclusion_list.html) prior to application.
Replies are only sent where further information is required. No telephone calls or correspondence will be entered into for any proposed or declined applications. Successful applicants are required to complete an official receipt and produce a report on the project, usually after ten months. Successful applicants are advised to leave at least ten months before applying for further support.

WHO TO APPLY TO J. A. Gilmour, Administrator, Dale Farm, Worcester Lane, Sutton Coldfield B75 5PR *Tel.* 01213 233236 *Website* www.ahct.org.uk

....

■ The Haley Family Charitable Trust

CC NO 1146603   **ESTABLISHED** 2012
WHERE FUNDING CAN BE GIVEN UK.
WHO CAN BENEFIT Registered charities.
WHAT IS FUNDED General charitable purposes.
TRUSTEES C. Lumsden; H. Lumsden; I. F. Pattison.
HOW TO APPLY In writing to the correspondent.
WHO TO APPLY TO The Trustees, Hollybank, 81 Bramley Lane, Lightcliffe, Halifax, West Yorkshire HX3 8NS *Tel.* 01422 201212

....

■ E. F. and M. G. Hall Charitable Trust

CC NO 256453   **ESTABLISHED** 1968
WHERE FUNDING CAN BE GIVEN South east England.
WHO CAN BENEFIT Charities concerned with children and older people; disability and medical charities; churches; and others.
WHAT IS FUNDED General charitable purposes.
WHAT IS NOT FUNDED No grants to individuals.
TYPE OF GRANT One-off and recurrent.
RANGE OF GRANTS £50– £3,000
SAMPLE GRANTS Guide Dogs for the Blind (£2,550); National Trust (£2,400); Christian Aid (£1,400);

Save The Children (£1,200); Médecins Sans Frontières (£1,000); Gandhi World Hunger (£900); Church Urban Fund (£700); British Legion and Shelter (£600) and Bread and Water for Africa (£550).

FINANCES *Year* 2011–12 *Income* £57,208 *Grants* £46,015 *Assets* £1,028,235

TRUSTEES Anthony Hall; Moira Hall; Ian Hall

OTHER INFORMATION The trust made 172 grants ranging from £50 up to £2,550. The majority of grants made were between £100 and £500.

HOW TO APPLY In writing to the correspondent.

WHO TO APPLY TO Moira Hall, Trustee, Holmsley House, Holtye Common, Cowden, Edenbridge, Kent TN8 7ED *Tel.* 01342 850571

....

■ The Edith Winifred Hall Charitable Trust

CC NO 1057032   **ESTABLISHED** 1996
WHERE FUNDING CAN BE GIVEN UK, with a preference for Northamptonshire.
WHO CAN BENEFIT Registered charities.
WHAT IS FUNDED General charitable purposes, with preference towards young people and social welfare.
SAMPLE GRANTS Youthscape (£450,000); Reachout Plus (£225,000); Northamptonshire Association of Youth Clubs (£150,000); Beds Garden Carers (£80,000); Northampton Community Foundation and St Mary's – Titchmarsh (£20,000 each); Rothwell Parochial Church (£7,000); and Sue Ryder Thorpe Hall Hospital and St Peter's Centre (£1,000 each).
FINANCES *Year* 2011–12 *Grants* £1,023,759
TRUSTEES David Endicott; David Reynolds; Lucie Burgess-Lumsden; Pamela Reynolds.
HOW TO APPLY In writing to the correspondent.
WHO TO APPLY TO David Endicott, Trustee, Spratt Endicott, 52–54 South Bar Street, Banbury OX16 9AB *Tel.* 01295 204000

....

■ Robert Hall Charity

CC NO 1015493   **ESTABLISHED** 1992
WHERE FUNDING CAN BE GIVEN West Walton, Wisbech and Walsoken in Cambridgeshire.
WHO CAN BENEFIT Organisations particularly those benefiting children and young adults.
WHAT IS FUNDED General charitable purposes, including charities working with hospices and hospitals, medical research, conservation and campaigning, education and various community services and facilities.
WHAT IS NOT FUNDED No grants to individuals.
TYPE OF GRANT Range of grants including buildings, capital, recurring costs and start-up costs. Funding for up to three years may be available.
SAMPLE GRANTS West Walton Parish Church (£19,000); Angles Theatre (£10,000); Cancer Research UK and Friends of Wisbech Hospitals (£7,000 each); St Peter's Church of England Junior School (£5,000); West Walton Village Hall (£4,000); Alzheimer's Society (£3,000); Fenland Mencap (£2,000); Downham Market High School (£1,500); and 3rd Wisbech Guides Group (£1,000).
FINANCES *Year* 2011–12 *Income* £34,309 *Grants* £33,000
TRUSTEES David Ball; Eileen Plater; Bernard Lyons; Derek Walker; David Turner.
HOW TO APPLY In writing to the correspondent. Applications are considered at twice yearly trustees' meetings.

WHO TO APPLY TO David Ball, Trustee, c/o Fraser Dawburns, 1–3 York Row, Wisbech, Cambridgeshire PE13 1EA *Tel.* 01945 468727 *Fax* 01945 468709 *email* d.ball@frasers-solicitors.com

■ The Hamamelis Trust

CC NO 280938   ESTABLISHED 1980
WHERE FUNDING CAN BE GIVEN UK, but with a special interest in the Godalming and Surrey areas.
WHO CAN BENEFIT UK charities involved in medical research or conservation projects.
WHAT IS FUNDED Medical research in the UK; and specific projects for conservation of the countryside in the UK.
WHAT IS NOT FUNDED Projects outside the UK are not considered. No grants to individuals.
TYPE OF GRANT Project.
RANGE OF GRANTS Up to £10,000.
SAMPLE GRANTS The Sussex Community Foundation – Slindon Forge Fund (£10,000); Fight for Sight (£3,000); Gwent Wildlife Fund, Surrey Care Trust, The John Muir Trust, Wildlife Aid, The Gatton Trust, Stroke Association, Juvenile Diabetes Research Foundation and The National Trust – Speckled Wood Project (£2,500 each); Deafness Research and Autistica (£2,000 each) and Godalming Museum Trust (£1,600).
FINANCES *Year* 2011–12 *Income* £116,744 *Grants* £43,600 *Assets* £3,262,184
TRUSTEES L. Dadswell; Dr A. F. M. Stone; Mirouze.
HOW TO APPLY In writing to the correspondent. All applicants are asked to include a short summary of the application along with any published material and references. Unsuccessful appeals will not be acknowledged. Dr Adam Stone, one of the trustees, who is medically qualified, assesses medical applications.
WHO TO APPLY TO L. Dadswell, Trustee, c/o Penningtons Solicitors LLP, Highfield, Brighton Road, Godalming, Surrey GU7 1NS *Tel.* 01483 791800

■ Hamilton Wallace Trust

CC NO 1052453   ESTABLISHED 1996
WHERE FUNDING CAN BE GIVEN UK.
WHO CAN BENEFIT Registered charities.
WHAT IS FUNDED General charitable purposes.
RANGE OF GRANTS £500–£1,000.
SAMPLE GRANTS Diabetes UK; Brainwave, Crohn's in Childhood Research Association, Dyslexia Action, Independent Age, Motor Neurone Disease Association and Young Minds; and Disabled Living Foundation, Nightstop UK and Step by Step.
FINANCES *Year* 2011–12 *Income* £22,589 *Grants* £40,000
TRUSTEES Timothy Calder; Peter Phillips.
HOW TO APPLY In writing to the correspondent. Trustees meet twice a year to consider appeals, in November and May of each year, and it would be helpful for any appeals to be received about a month before the meetings.
WHO TO APPLY TO Peter Phillips, Trustee, c/o Rubinstein Phillips Lewis LLP, 13 Craven Street, London WC2N 5PB *Tel.* 020 7925 2244

■ Paul Hamlyn Foundation

CC NO 1102927   ESTABLISHED 1987
WHERE FUNDING CAN BE GIVEN UK and India.
WHO CAN BENEFIT Registered charities and organisations.
WHAT IS FUNDED The foundation aims to address issues of inequality and disadvantage, particularly in relation to children and young people. Its main areas of interest are arts, education and learning in the UK, social justice and local organisations supporting vulnerable groups of people, especially children, in India.
WHAT IS NOT FUNDED In the UK the foundation does not support: individuals or proposals for the benefit of one individual; funding for work that has already started; general circulars/appeals; proposals about property or which are mainly about equipment or other capital items; overseas travel, expeditions, adventure and residential courses; the continuation or expansion of existing provision, unless there are significant elements of innovation and change or applications which primarily benefit the independent education sector.
'We are unlikely to support: endowments; organisations to use our funding to make grants; websites, publications, seminars unless part of a wider proposal.'
In India, the foundation does not support: individuals or proposals for the benefit of one individual; retrospective (funding for work that has already started); general circulars/appeals; proposals that solely concentrate on the purchasing of property, equipment or other capital items; overseas activities, including travel, expeditions, adventure and residential courses.
TYPE OF GRANT Grants are usually one-off, for a specific project or for a specific part of a project, and funding is normally given for one year only.
RANGE OF GRANTS Grants vary significantly, but averaged around £100,000 across the Open programmes in 2011/12.
SAMPLE GRANTS Learning Futures (£393,000) – to complete the development and piloting phase of their student engagement project; Institute for Philanthropy (£154,000) – launch of the Youth and Philanthropy Initiative in Northern Ireland, to pilot in 15 schools over three years, giving young people a 'hands-on' experience of giving whilst developing their communication and presentation skills; User Voice England UK wide (£146,000) – provision of a staff training and support programme to develop the capacity of an ex-offender workforce to develop and promote service-user participation in criminal justice policy and practice; Islington Law Centre (£120,000) – as a service provider in the supported options initiative; Clore Social Leadership Programme UK wide (£105,000) – funding for up to three specialist Paul Hamlyn Foundation Clore Social Fellowships, from 2013. Each fellow will have a particular interest in supporting excluded young people, and/or be drawn from a marginalised community; Philharmonia Limited (£100,000) – core support towards the development of a virtual Philharmonia Orchestra performing Holst's The Planets, enabling the public to explore the orchestra from inside; Carousel Project (£50,000) – for learning-disabled and marginalised artists to create work comprising music, film and visual art elements, to be experienced live, online and as a touring installation; Chaupal Gramin Vikas Prashikshan Evam Shodh Sansthan (£27,000) – to set up health and nutrition surveillance committees to

monitor food and health entitlement in 200 villages and Kielder Partnership Initiative Special Initiative in development (£10,000) – girls and young women in the criminal justice system: looking at addressing the challenges facing girls and young women in the youth justice system or at risk of entering it.

FINANCES *Year* 2011–12 *Income* £14,256,000 *Grants* £17,664,000 *Assets* £559,560,000

TRUSTEES Jane Hamlyn, Chair; Michael Hamlyn; James Lingwood; Baroness Estelle Morris; Lord Claus Moser; Anthony Salz; Peter Wilson-Smith; Tim Bunting; Lord Anthony Hall; Baroness Kidron of Angel; Tom Wylie.

HOW TO APPLY Applications should be completed online.

'We have a two-stage application process. At the first stage, applicants are required to show that the work for which they are seeking funding fits with the themes and priorities of the programme they are applying to. We also require that applicants show how their proposal meets our criteria for Change and Outcomes, Innovation and Participation. If taken forward, at the second stage we ask for more detailed information as we work with you to put together a proposal for decision by the programme committees or board of trustees. The process takes at least four months, so be sure that your work is not due to start imminently when you apply. We do not support applications for work that has already started by the time it reaches the final approval stage. After a short eligibility quiz, if you are eligible, you will be asked to provide details about your organisation, and some specific questions about the nature of the work you would like supported. Alongside details of the proposed activity, we will ask for information on three particular areas that we consider to be important. We are interested in: – The impact of your work: how your work will effect change, and how you propose to measure its outcomes – How innovative your work is: we want to help organisations find new ways of doing things – participation: We believe that the people we are trying to help should have a role in shaping their own destiny by being involved in developing activities that will affect them. We will ask specific questions on each of these areas during the first stage of your application so it is essential that you consider each of them carefully when planning your application. We understand that these issues can be confusing and we want to help all applicants to address them. We have published guidance on each of the areas which you can refer to during your application. We try to respond to all first-stage applications within 28 days. After this, if successful, our grants programme teams will work closely with you to shape your application and make it as strong as possible before putting it to the programme committee or board of trustees for a final decision. We will need you to provide further evidence during this stage of all the areas we ask about during the first stage of the application, as well as going into greater detail about the project budget. We also have processes of due diligence, where we look at your organisation's credentials and the environment you are working in, that we need to carry out. This stage can take several months, and the timings of final decisions will depend on the schedule of our programme committees and board meetings. Not all applications that reach the second stage will definitely progress to being considered by the programme committee or board; many will be declined during this stage.'

India programme

India grants have a separate application form on the website which works differently from the other programmes. Applicants must submit a 'Concept Note' online.

'After you have submitted your 'Concept Note' it will be considered by the India team. If appropriate, one of the programme advisors will be in touch and request more information, or arrange to make an on-site assessment. Before an application is taken forward, the advisors in India will have a discussion with the Foundation's Director in the UK. Note that the applications process takes at least four months from receipt of your Concept Note. Therefore, do not apply for funding for work that is due to commence in less than four months, or for work that has already started.'

WHO TO APPLY TO Grants Team, 5–11 Leeke Street, London WC1X 9HY *Tel.* 020 7812 3300 *Fax* 020 7812 3310 *email* information@phf.org. uk *Website* www.phf.org.uk

....

■ The Helen Hamlyn Trust

CC NO 1084839   **ESTABLISHED** 2000

WHERE FUNDING CAN BE GIVEN Worldwide.

WHO CAN BENEFIT Organisations working in the fields of: medical, the arts and culture, education and welfare, heritage and conservation in India, international humanitarian affairs and healthy ageing. Within these areas of activity the trust also supports a number of projects with a design focus which are undertaken by the Helen Hamlyn Centre for Design at the Royal College of Art, London.

WHAT IS FUNDED Support innovation in the medical arena; increase access to the arts and support the professional development of artists from the fields of music and the performing arts; increase intercultural understanding; provide opportunities for young people to develop new interests and practical skills and to acquire opportunities for young offenders to acquire practical skills which will support their personal development for their future lives and reduce re-offending; conserve heritage in India for public access and cultural activities; support good practice in the humanitarian sector through educational programmes and provide practical support to enable the elderly to maintain their independence for as long as possible.

SAMPLE GRANTS The largest beneficiary was the Hamlyn Centre for Robotic Surgery at Imperial College, London which received £1 million. It has received a similar amount in the last number of years. Other beneficiaries included: London Symphony Orchestra – Panufik (£159,000); Museum of London – FilmIt in Museums (£129,000); The University of York (£92,000 in two grants); Royal Opera House – Paul Hamlyn First Night (£85,000); Reis Magos Fort – INTACH (£79,000); Wells Cathedral School Foundation (£10,000); Volunteer Reading Help (£9,000); St Wilfred's Care Home (£6,800); Hackney Music Development Trust (£500) and Meningitis Trust (£100).

FINANCES *Year* 2011–12 *Income* £2,617,644 *Grants* £2,155,859 *Assets* £2,764,757

TRUSTEES Lady Hamlyn; Dr Kate Gavron; Dr Shobita Punja; Brendan Cahill; Margaret O'Rorke; Dr Deborah Swallow; Mark Bolland.

OTHER INFORMATION £487,000 was paid to Open Futures Trust, a subsidiary trust, to carry out direct educational work.

HOW TO APPLY The trust's website notes: 'our energies are focused on the initiation of projects and we do not accept unsolicited applications for major grants.'

WHO TO APPLY TO John Roche-Kuroda, Trust Administrator and Secretary, 129 Old Church Street, London SW3 6EB *Tel.* 020 7351 5057 *Fax* 020 7352 3284 *email* john.rochekuroda@helenhamlyntrust.org

■ Sue Hammerson Charitable Trust

CC NO 235196   **ESTABLISHED** 1957
WHERE FUNDING CAN BE GIVEN UK, with a preference for London.
WHO CAN BENEFIT Charitable organisations.
WHAT IS FUNDED General charitable purposes. Particular consideration is given to the advancement of medical learning and research and to the relief of sickness and poverty. Substantial support is given to Lewis W Hammerson Memorial Home.
WHAT IS NOT FUNDED No grants to individuals.
RANGE OF GRANTS £100–£151,000, most grants are under £1,000.
SAMPLE GRANTS Painter-Stainers Fine Art Fund (£5,200); and Army Benevolent Fund (£2,000).
FINANCES *Year* 2011–12 *Income* £179,783 *Grants* £157,175 *Assets* £8,077,298
TRUSTEES Sir Gavin Lightman; David Hammerson; Patricia Beecham; Peter Hammerson; Anthony Bernstein; Anthony Thompson; Rory Hammerson.
HOW TO APPLY In writing to the correspondent.
WHO TO APPLY TO Trust Administrator, c/o H. W. Fisher and Company, Acre House, 11–15 William Road, London NW1 3ER *Tel.* 020 7388 7000

■ The Hampshire and Islands Historic Churches Trust

CC NO 299633   **ESTABLISHED** 1988
WHERE FUNDING CAN BE GIVEN Hampshire, Isle of Wight and the Channel Islands.
WHO CAN BENEFIT Churches – interior and exterior.
WHAT IS FUNDED The restoration, preservation, repair, maintenance and improvement of churches, including monuments, fittings and furniture, in the area specified above.
WHAT IS NOT FUNDED No grants are paid in respect of work which has already started before approval is given.
RANGE OF GRANTS Up to £7,500.
SAMPLE GRANTS Penton Mewsey, Holy Trinity and North Bassett, St Nicholas (£7,500 each); Gosport, Christ Church (£5,000); Easton, St Mary (£3,000) and Warnford, Church of Our Lady (£1,000).
FINANCES *Year* 2012 *Income* £56,371 *Grants* £47,500
TRUSTEES Caroline Edwards; Ven. Adrian Harbidge; John Steel; Lady Joan Appleyard; Canon Paul Townsend.
HOW TO APPLY On a form available to download, together with guidelines and criteria, from the website.
WHO TO APPLY TO Meryl Balchin, Hon. Secretary, c/o Hampshire Record Office, Sussex Street, Winchester, Hampshire SO23 8TH *Tel.* 01962 760230 *email* sec@hihct.org.uk *Website* www.hihct.org.uk

■ Hampshire and Isle of Wight Community Foundation

CC NO 1100417   **ESTABLISHED** 2002
WHERE FUNDING CAN BE GIVEN Hampshire and Isle of Wight.
WHO CAN BENEFIT Individuals and organisations.
WHAT IS FUNDED General charitable purposes, community development.
WHAT IS NOT FUNDED No grants for: individuals; public bodies; organisations for the sole benefit of plants or animals; national charities; party political activity; commercial ventures; proselytising activities such as the active promotion of a specific religion or belief system; bids for major capital projects.
RANGE OF GRANTS Up to £10,000.
SAMPLE GRANTS The Bivol Trust (£27,000); Ocean Youth Trust South (£15,000); The Roberts Centre (£11,000); The Bobby Scheme (£9,500); Age Concern Hampshire (£7,500); Whitchurch Millennium Green Trust (£6,800); Portsmouth Citizens Advice (£6,000); Isle of Wight Rural Community Council (£5,200) and Nepalese Help, Weston Church Youth Project (£5,000).
FINANCES *Year* 2012 *Income* £1,569,657 *Grants* £643,413 *Assets* £5,796,100
TRUSTEES Tom Floyd; Pat James; Lena Samuels; Carole Damper; Michael Woodhall; Miles Brown; Jonathan Moseley; Alistair Stokes; Rebecca Kennelly.
OTHER INFORMATION The foundation administers a variety of funds, many of which will open and close throughout the year whilst new ones are added and others end. Therefore potential applicants should see the foundation's website for details of current open funds, or contact the foundation directly.
HOW TO APPLY There are separate application forms for each fund which can be downloaded from the foundation's website and various deadlines for each fund which can also be viewed on the website.
WHO TO APPLY TO Toni Shaw, Chief Executive Officer, Vertex House, Chineham Court, Lutyens Close, Basingstoke, Hampshire RG24 8AG *Tel.* 01256 776101 *email* grantsadmin@hantscf.org.uk *Website* www.hantscf.org.uk

■ The Hampstead Wells and Campden Trust

CC NO 1094611   **ESTABLISHED** 1971
WHERE FUNDING CAN BE GIVEN The former metropolitan borough of Hampstead.
WHO CAN BENEFIT Organisations, institutions and individuals in Hampstead and Camden, benefiting children, young adults and older people, parents and children, ethnic minority groups, at risk groups, people who are disabled or disadvantaged by poverty, ex-offenders and those at risk of offending, refugees, homeless people, socially isolated people, and victims of abuse and domestic violence.
WHAT IS FUNDED The relief of people in need who are sick, convalescent, have disabilities or are infirm, and the relief generally of people in need or distress.
WHAT IS NOT FUNDED Grants may not be made towards the payment of rates or taxes, or in principle where statutory bodies have the responsibility to help.
TYPE OF GRANT One-off to individuals and organisations, some recurring.
SAMPLE GRANTS Camden Community Law Centre (£20,000); West Hampstead Women's Centre

(£15,500); Camden CAB (£14,000); Caris Camden C4WS Homeless Project (£12,000); Age Concern Camden and Women Like Us (£10,000 each); Hampstead Community Centre (£9,000); CancerKin and KOVE (Kilburn Older Voices Exchange) (£5,000 each); Children's Country Holiday Fund All About Kids (£3,000); Henna Asian Women's Group (£2,000) and Hampstead Theatre (£1,500).

FINANCES *Year* 2011–12 *Income* £637,319 *Grants* £463,008 *Assets* £15,653,584

TRUSTEES Geoff Berridge; Gaynor Bassey; Dr Diana Dick; Francoise Findlay; Dennis Finning; Michael Bieber; Ian Harrison; Gaynor Humphreys; Jocelyne Tobin; Revd Stephen Tucker; Alistair Voaden; Dr Christina Williams; Ted Webster; Charles Perrin; Alistair Jacks; Ilan Jacobs; Michael Katz; Linda Chung.

OTHER INFORMATION In 2011–12 grants totalling £269,000 were awarded to individuals whilst £195,000 was awarded to organisations.

HOW TO APPLY On a form available to download, together with criteria and guidelines, on the website. Applications may be made at any time. The trustees meet eight times a year and in addition requests for smaller grants are considered at more frequent intervals.

WHO TO APPLY TO Sheila Taylor, Director/Clerk to the Trustees, 62 Rosslyn Hill, London NW3 1ND *Tel.* 020 7435 1570 *Fax* 020 7435 1571 *email* grant@hwct.co.uk *Website* www.hwct.org. uk

....

■ Hampton Fuel Allotment Charity

CC NO 211756   **ESTABLISHED** 1811

WHERE FUNDING CAN BE GIVEN Hampton, the former borough of Twickenham, and the borough of Richmond (in that order).

WHO CAN BENEFIT Community groups, voluntary organisations and individuals.

WHAT IS FUNDED Grants towards fuel costs; essential equipment; not for profit organisations which support those in need; hospitals and hospices; organisations supporting people with disabilities; social welfare; housing; education; community.

WHAT IS NOT FUNDED The charity is unlikely to support grants to individuals for private and post-compulsory education; adaptations or building alterations for individuals; holidays, except in cases of severe medical need; decoration, carpeting or central heating; anything which is the responsibility of a statutory body; national general charitable appeals; animal welfare; religious groups, unless offering a non-religious service to the community; commercial and business activities; endowment appeals; political projects; retrospective capital grants; organisations whose free reserves exceed 12 months' running costs; non-charitable social enterprises.

TYPE OF GRANT Various including capital, one-off and loans.

RANGE OF GRANTS £100–£60,000.

SAMPLE GRANTS Richmond Citizens Advice (£55,000); Hampton Hill Cricket Club, Twickenham Brunswick Club for Young People and Age UK Richmond (£50,000 each); Hampton and Hampton Hill Voluntary Care Group and Richmond Youth Partnership (£40,000 each); SPEAR (£39,000); Linden Hall Day Centre (£22,000); Alzheimer's Society (£16,000); Three Wings Trust and Richmond Furniture Scheme (£15,000 each); LBRUT Specialist Children's Services Leaving Care Team and Orange Tree Theatre (£10,000 each);

South West London Stroke Club (£5,000); Learn English at Home (£3,000) and Richmond upon Thames College (£1,500).

FINANCES *Year* 2011–12 *Income* £1,754,241 *Grants* £1,719,066 *Assets* £46,568,246

TRUSTEES David Parish, Chair; Revd Derek Winterburn; Jonathan Cardy; David Cornwell; Stuart Leamy; Jamie Mortimer; Paula Williams; Dr Jane Young; Hilary Hart; Richard Montgomery.

OTHER INFORMATION Of the grant total £885,000 was made in grants to organisations and £834,000 was paid in grants to individuals.

HOW TO APPLY Once applicants are satisfied that they meet the criteria they should contact the clerk to discuss their funding request, or preferably send a brief outline by email (david@hfac.co.uk or 020 8979 5555). If the clerk determines that you meet the criteria and have a reasonable chance of success then he will either invite you to submit an application which will be followed up by a telephone assessment or arrange an assessment visit to your organisation. Detailed application and eligibility guidelines, as well as application forms, are available on the website. Trustees meet to consider applications every two months and feedback can be given to unsuccessful applicants.

WHO TO APPLY TO David White, Clerk to the Trustees, 15 High Street, Hampton, Middlesex TW12 2SA *Tel.* 020 8941 7866 *email* david@hfac.co.uk *Website* www.hfac.co.uk

....

■ The W. A. Handley Charitable Trust

CC NO 230435   **ESTABLISHED** 1963

WHERE FUNDING CAN BE GIVEN Northumberland and Tyneside.

WHO CAN BENEFIT Registered charities only.

WHAT IS FUNDED General charitable purposes with preference for the alleviation of distress, crisis funding, pump-priming finance and operating expenses.

WHAT IS NOT FUNDED No grants to individuals. Grants are only made to registered charities.

TYPE OF GRANT Buildings; capital; core costs; endowments; feasibility studies; one-off; project; research; running costs; recurring costs; salaries; and start-up costs. Funding is available for up to one year.

RANGE OF GRANTS £1,000– £5,000.

SAMPLE GRANTS St Nicholas Cathedral (£20,000); Nunnykirk Centre for Dyslexia (£11,500); RGS Bursary Campaign (£10,500); Holy Island Parochial School Trust, Hexham Abbey Project, Derwenthaugh Boat Station (£10,000 each); Groundworks (£7,500); Christians Against Poverty, Prostate Action, Get Hooked on Fishing, Northumberland Theatre Company (£2,000 each) Holy Island Village Hall, Combat Stress and Depression Alliance (£1,000 each).

FINANCES *Year* 2011–12 *Income* £293,017 *Grants* £303,550 *Assets* £8,412,531

TRUSTEES Anthony Glenton; David Milligan; William Dryden; David Irvin.

OTHER INFORMATION No grants to individuals.

HOW TO APPLY In writing to the correspondent, quoting the applicant's official charity number and providing full back-up information. Grants are made quarterly in March, June, September and December.

WHO TO APPLY TO David Milligan, Trustee, c/o Ryecroft Glenton, 32 Portland Terrace, Newcastle upon Tyne NE2 1QP *Tel.* 01912 811292 *email* davidmilligan@ryecroft-glenton. co.uk

Beatrice Hankey Foundation Limited

CC NO 211093 **ESTABLISHED** 1949
WHERE FUNDING CAN BE GIVEN UK and overseas.
WHO CAN BENEFIT Institutions benefiting Christians.
WHAT IS FUNDED Christian causes.
WHAT IS NOT FUNDED No grants for buildings or equipment.
RANGE OF GRANTS Up to £14,000.
SAMPLE GRANTS Bangladesh Knighthood Fellowship (£4,000); Friends of Burma, Mathieson Music Trust and Hope on the Horizon (£1,000 each); and Christian Response to Eastern Europe and Christian Solidarity Worldwide (£500 each).
FINANCES *Year* 2012 *Income* £49,039 *Grants* £11,750 *Assets* £1,057,351
TRUSTEES Hilary Walker; Angela Stewart; Revd David Faulks; Revd David Savill; Canon David Haokip; Christine Legge; Wendyanne Hill; Selina Ormond; Daphne Sampson; Margaret Faulks; Crispin Wedell; David Walker.
HOW TO APPLY Unsolicited applications cannot be considered.
WHO TO APPLY TO Melanie Churchill, Secretary, 11 Staverton Road, Peterborough PE4 6LY *Tel.* 01733 571794

The Hanley Trust (1987)

CC NO 299209 **ESTABLISHED** 1987
WHERE FUNDING CAN BE GIVEN UK.
WHO CAN BENEFIT General charitable purposes.
WHAT IS FUNDED Charitable organisations.
WHAT IS NOT FUNDED Grants are not made to individuals or to non-registered charities.
RANGE OF GRANTS £2,500 to £50.
SAMPLE GRANTS Butler Trust and Irene Taylor Trust (£2,500 each); Canine Partners and Shelter (£1,000 each); Helen Arkell Dyslexia Centre, Amnesty International and Prader-Willi Syndrome (£500 each); Prison Phoenix Trust, Parentline Plus and Corby Voluntary and Community Services (£250 each); Leicestershire and Rutland Headway, Homestart – Leicester and Youth Brass 2000 (£100 each); and Duke of Cornwall Spinal Appeal – Cornwall (£50).
FINANCES *Year* 2011–12 *Income* £35,019 *Grants* £26,200 *Assets* £1,031,733
TRUSTEES Hon. Sarah Price; William Swan; Hon. Samuel Butler.
HOW TO APPLY In writing to the correspondent.
WHO TO APPLY TO Hon. Sarah Price, Trustee, 21 Buckingham Gate, London SW1E 6LS

The Kathleen Hannay Memorial Charity

CC NO 299600 **ESTABLISHED** 1988
WHERE FUNDING CAN BE GIVEN UK.
WHO CAN BENEFIT Registered charities, universities and schools.
WHAT IS FUNDED Health, welfare, Christian, general
WHAT IS NOT FUNDED No grants to individuals or non-registered charities.
TYPE OF GRANT One-off grants for capital and revenue costs.
RANGE OF GRANTS £5,000–£140,000.

SAMPLE GRANTS Network Training and Counselling and Hullavington Parochial Church Council (£140,000 each); Ripon College – Cuddesdon (£52,000); Save the Children (£50,000); and Children's Burn Trust (£33,000).
FINANCES *Year* 2011–12 *Income* £353,229 *Grants* £666,000 *Assets* £12,315,390
TRUSTEES Simon Weil; Christian Ward; Jonathan Weil; Laura Watkins.
OTHER INFORMATION Accounts for 2011–12 were late at the Charity Commission.
HOW TO APPLY In writing to the correspondent. The trustees' report for 2011/12 states that 'the trustees consider and approve grants annually and although many are made to the same charities each year none are promised or guaranteed.'
WHO TO APPLY TO Martin Betts, R. F. Trustee Co. Ltd, 15 Suffolk Street, London SW1Y 4HG *Tel.* 020 7036 5685

The Doughty Hanson Charitable Foundation

CC NO 1080755 **ESTABLISHED** 2000
WHERE FUNDING CAN BE GIVEN Worldwide.
WHO CAN BENEFIT Registered charities.
WHAT IS FUNDED The relief of poverty distress and suffering, advancing education and appreciation in the arts and science, furthering religious work and other charitable purposes in any part of the world.
SAMPLE GRANTS Private Equity Foundation (£37,500); Voluntariado Jesus con los Ninos (£20,000); Parkinson's Disease Society (£15,000); Women's Aid (£10,000); NSPCC (£5,500); Afghan Action (£1,000); Breast Cancer Campaign (£230)
FINANCES *Year* 2012 *Income* £206,499 *Grants* £200,875 *Assets* £10,953
TRUSTEES Richard Hanson; Stephen Marquardt; Richard Lund; Graeme Stening
HOW TO APPLY In writing to the correspondent – the grants committee meets about four times a year. Only successful applicants receive a response.
WHO TO APPLY TO Julie Foreman, Secretary, PO Box 31064, London SW1Y 5ZP

Lord Hanson Foundation

CC NO 1077014 **ESTABLISHED** 1999
WHERE FUNDING CAN BE GIVEN Worldwide.
WHO CAN BENEFIT Charitable organisations.
WHAT IS FUNDED General charitable purposes.
RANGE OF GRANTS Up to £13,000.
SAMPLE GRANTS Beneficiaries were: Raisa Gorbachev Foundation (£12,000); Hanson Research Trust (£10,000); Royal College of Radiologists, Help for Heroes and Imperial College Health Care Charity Fund (£1,000) and The Children's Charity (£500).
FINANCES *Year* 2011–12 *Income* £38,500 *Grants* £35,000
TRUSTEES Jonathan G. A. Azis; Alan Hagdrup; The Hon Robert Hanson.
HOW TO APPLY In writing to the correspondent.
WHO TO APPLY TO Gillian Ryan, Lord Hanson Foundation, 31 Wilton Row, London SW1X 7NS *Tel.* 020 7245 6996

Think carefully about every application. Is it justified?

601

■ The Haramead Trust

CC NO 1047416   **ESTABLISHED** 1995

WHERE FUNDING CAN BE GIVEN Worldwide, in practice developing countries, UK and Ireland, locally in the East Midlands.

WHO CAN BENEFIT Registered charities and individuals and families in need of direct assistance.

WHAT IS FUNDED Children, social welfare, education, people with disabilities, homeless people, medical assistance, victims and oppressed people and religious activities.

TYPE OF GRANT Core support, building/renovation, equipment, vehicles and project support will all be considered.

RANGE OF GRANTS £1,000–£75,000

SAMPLE GRANTS Scope and Let Children Live (£75,000 each); Leicestershire and Rutland Community Fund (£30,000); NSPCC (£25,000); Leonard Cheshire Disability (£20,000); De Montford University and Project Trust (£15,000 each); and Compassion Africa, Housing Justice, Macmillan Cancer Support and Sense International (£10,000 each).

FINANCES *Year* 2011–12 *Income* £627,753 *Grants* £770,515 *Assets* £107,406

TRUSTEES Simon P. Astill; Winifred M. Linnett; Michael J. Linnett; Robert H. Smith; David L. Tams; Revd Joseph A. Mullen.

HOW TO APPLY In writing to the correspondent. The trustees meet every couple of months and may visit funded projects for monitoring purposes or to assess for future grants.

WHO TO APPLY TO Michael J. Linnett, Trustee, Park House, Park Hill, Gaddesby, Leicestershire LE7 4WH

■ Miss K. M. Harbinson's Charitable Trust

WHERE FUNDING CAN BE GIVEN UK and developing countries.

WHO CAN BENEFIT Development organisations.

WHAT IS FUNDED General charitable purposes and in particular, international development.

RANGE OF GRANTS £1,000–£9,000.

SAMPLE GRANTS Previous beneficiaries have included ActionAid, British Red Cross Worldwide Fund for Nature, Breadline Africa, Care Britain, Ethopiaid Intermediate Technology, Marie Stopes International, Oxfam, Romanian Orphanage Trust, Sight Savers International, UNICEF.

FINANCES *Year* 2011–12 *Income* £151,170 *Grants* £100,000

TRUSTEES A. Maguire; G. L. Harbinson; R. Harbinson.

HOW TO APPLY In writing to the correspondent.

WHO TO APPLY TO The Secretary, 190 St Vincent Street, Glasgow G2 5SP *Tel.* 01412 042833

■ Harbo Charities Limited

CC NO 282262   **ESTABLISHED** 1981

WHERE FUNDING CAN BE GIVEN Worldwide.

WHO CAN BENEFIT Charitable organisations.

WHAT IS FUNDED General charitable purposes and Jewish causes, particularly those which provide financial support and basic necessities to 'the poor', support Jewish education and places of worship for the Jewish community and provide relief of sickness and disability.

SAMPLE GRANTS Previous beneficiaries have included: Beis Chinuch Lebonos Girls School, Beth Rochel d'Satmar, Bobov Trust, Chevras Maoz Ladol, Craven Walk Charitable Trust, Edgware Yeshiva Trust, Keren Yesomim, Kollel Shomrei HaChomoth, Tevini Limited, Tomchei Shabbos, Yad Eliezer, Yesode Ha Torah School and Yeshiva Chachmay Tsorpha.

FINANCES *Year* 2011–12 *Income* £92,954 *Grants* £77,011 *Assets* £743,596

TRUSTEES Harold Gluck; Harry Stern; Barbara Stern.

HOW TO APPLY In writing to the correspondent.

WHO TO APPLY TO Harry Stern, Trustee, 13 Fairholt Road, London N16 5EW

■ The Harborne Parish Lands Charity

CC NO 219031   **ESTABLISHED** 1699

WHERE FUNDING CAN BE GIVEN The ancient parish of Harborne, which includes parts of Harborne, Smethwick, Bearwood and Quinton and Wednesbury.

WHO CAN BENEFIT All grants must benefit people living within the parish.

WHAT IS FUNDED Charities working in the fields of: accommodation and housing; infrastructure and technical support; infrastructure development; healthcare; health facilities and buildings; physical and mental disability organisations; schools; education and training; community centres and village halls; playgrounds and community services; individual need and other charitable purposes.

TYPE OF GRANT Buildings, capital, core costs, interest-free loans, one-off, project, running costs, salaries and start-up costs. Funding for up to one year will be considered.

RANGE OF GRANTS £500–£15,000

SAMPLE GRANTS Cares Sandwell (£15,000); W. Smethwick Enterprise (£12,000); St Albans Community Centre (£6,600); Haven Community Project and St Boniface Church (£6,000 each); Quinton Youth for Christ (£5,000); Bangladeshi Islamic Centre (£4,000); Wednesbury Young Firefighters Association and Smethwick Mini Muslims (£2,000 each); Sandwell Young African Achievers and Beginagen Community Project (£1,000 each); The Rainbow Club (£800) and Cottage Crafts (£500).

FINANCES *Year* 2011–12 *Income* £1,394,737 *Grants* £267,201 *Assets* £14,515,917

TRUSTEES Mike Lloyd; Kerry Bollister; Geoff Hewitt; Buddhi Chetiyawardana; Peter Hollingworth; David Jeffery; Cllr Roger Horton; Rachel Silber; Andrew Lawrence; Cllr Vic Silvester; Nigel Thompson; Frank Wayt.

OTHER INFORMATION In 2011–12 a total of £117,000 was given in grants to organisations.

HOW TO APPLY On a form available from the correspondent. An exact map of the beneficial area can be obtained from the trust (or on its website) and should be consulted before an application is submitted. Further information can be obtained from the trust's website.

WHO TO APPLY TO Julie Boardman, Grant Administrator, 109 Court Oak Road, Harborne, Birmingham B17 9AA *Tel.* 01214 261600 *email* julie.boardman@hplc.org.uk *Website* www. hplc.org.uk

■ The Harbour Charitable Trust

CC NO 234268   **ESTABLISHED** 1962

WHERE FUNDING CAN BE GIVEN UK.

WHO CAN BENEFIT Organisations benefiting children, young adults and students. Support may also be given to teachers and governesses, medical

602

Does the trust you have chosen match your needs? Haphazard applications waste postage and time

professionals, research workers, parents and children and one-parent families.

WHAT IS FUNDED Childcare, education and healthcare, and other charitable organisations.

WHAT IS NOT FUNDED Grants are given to registered charities only.

SAMPLE GRANTS Grants were made in the following categories: Joint Jewish Charitable Trust (£31,000); childcare (£6,000); aged care (£3,000); healthcare (£500); and other donations (£1,000).

FINANCES *Year* 2011–12 *Income* £191,621 *Grants* £41,823 *Assets* £4,240,283

TRUSTEES Barbara Brenda Green; Elaine Knobil; Zena Sandra Blackman; Tamar Eisenstat.

HOW TO APPLY In writing to the correspondent.

WHO TO APPLY TO Mr Aldina, Administrator, Barbican House, 26–34 Old Street, London EC1V 9QQ

■ The Harbour Foundation

CC NO 264927 **ESTABLISHED** 1970

WHERE FUNDING CAN BE GIVEN Worldwide.

WHO CAN BENEFIT Organisations and individuals.

WHAT IS FUNDED Relief of poverty for refugees and homeless people; education; research.

RANGE OF GRANTS £0–£200,000

SAMPLE GRANTS Previous beneficiaries included: Royal College of Music, London; Tel Aviv Foundation, Israel (£15,000 each).

FINANCES *Year* 2011–12 *Income* £1,367,546 *Grants* £801,531 *Assets* £49,035,821

TRUSTEES Rex Harbour; Susan Harbour; Dr Daniel Harbour; Edmond Harbour.

OTHER INFORMATION In 2011–12 the trust made 83 grants totalling £802,000 of which 74 were to charities in the UK.

HOW TO APPLY In writing to the correspondent. Applications need to be received by February, as trustees meet in March.

WHO TO APPLY TO The Trustees, 1 Red Place, London W1K 6PL *Tel.* 020 7456 8180

■ The Harding Trust

CC NO 328182 **ESTABLISHED** 1989

WHERE FUNDING CAN BE GIVEN Mainly, but not exclusively, Staffordshire and surrounding areas.

WHO CAN BENEFIT Charitable organisations.

WHAT IS FUNDED Charities supported are in most cases connected with music and the arts but local welfare charities and hospices are also given support.

TYPE OF GRANT One-off and recurrent.

SAMPLE GRANTS Stoke on Trent Festival (£32,000); Harding Trust Piano Recitals (£18,000); Malvern Theatres Trust (£10,000); European Union Chamber Orchestra and Royal Philharmonic Orchestra (£6,000 each); Clonter Farm Music Trust (£3,500); Help for Heroes and English Haydn Festival (£2,000 each); British Red Cross Society, Midlands Air Ambulance and Codsall Arts Festival (£1,000 each); Tettenhall Operatic Society (£750); and Uttoxeter Choral Society and English Music Festival (£500 each).

FINANCES *Year* 2011–12 *Income* £143,048 *Grants* £115,750 *Assets* £3,656,673

TRUSTEES Geoffrey Snow; Geoffrey Wall; John Fowell; Michael Lloyd.

HOW TO APPLY In writing to the correspondent. The trustees meet annually in spring/early summer. Accounts are available for recurrent applications.

WHO TO APPLY TO Peter O'Rourke, Administrator, Horton House, Exchange Flags, Liverpool L2 3YL *Tel.* 01516 003000 *email* peter. orourke@brabnerscs.com

■ William Harding's Charity

CC NO 310619 **ESTABLISHED** 1978

WHERE FUNDING CAN BE GIVEN Aylesbury.

WHO CAN BENEFIT Individuals and organisations residing and benefiting the population of Aylesbury.

WHAT IS FUNDED To assist young people in education, including at an individual level, by providing scholarships, maintenance allowances, travel awards and grants for equipment. At a wider level, grants are made to the LEA for Aylesbury schools to fund equipment in addition to that which can be provided by the authority. The charity also provides relief in need and for the general benefit of Aylesbury residents.

WHAT IS NOT FUNDED All persons and organisations not based in Aylesbury Town.

TYPE OF GRANT One-off and capital.

RANGE OF GRANTS £250–£15,000 (organisations).

SAMPLE GRANTS Aylesbury Project Community Interest Company (£15,000); QPAC (£12,000); Aylesbury Youth Action (£10,000); Youth Concern Aylesbury (£7,000); IQRA (£5,000); Monday Contact Club and SPACE (£4,000 each); and Buckingham St Youth Club and 14th Vale of Aylesbury Sea Scout (£2,500 each).

FINANCES *Year* 2012 *Income* £834,239 *Grants* £593,855 *Assets* £23,655,766

TRUSTEES Les Sheldon; Anne Brooker; Freda Roberts; Bernard Griffin; Penni Thorne; Roger Evans; William Chapple; Lennard Wakelam; Susan Hewitt.

OTHER INFORMATION Grants to organisations totalled £261,000. Grants were also made to 185 individuals totalling £143,500.

HOW TO APPLY In writing to the correspondent. Trustees meet on a regular basis to consider and determine applications for charitable assistance.

WHO TO APPLY TO John Leggett, Administrator, 14 Bourbon Street, Aylesbury, Buckinghamshire HP20 2RS *Tel.* 01296 318501 *email* doudjag@ pandclip.co.uk

■ The Hare of Steep Charitable Trust

CC NO 297308 **ESTABLISHED** 1987

WHERE FUNDING CAN BE GIVEN UK, with preference for the south of England, especially Petersfield and East Hampshire.

WHO CAN BENEFIT Registered charities only.

WHAT IS FUNDED Charities which benefit the community, in particular the advancement of social, cultural, medical, educational and religious projects.

TYPE OF GRANT Mainly annual contributions but one-off grants are made for special projects.

RANGE OF GRANTS £250–£2,000.

SAMPLE GRANTS In 2000: £1,500 each to Alzheimer's Disease Society, Arthritis and Rheumatism Council – Petersfield, British Heart Foundation, Rainbow House Trust and SSAFA.

FINANCES *Year* 2011–12 *Income* £47,582 *Grants* £50,500 *Assets* £115,024

TRUSTEES S. M. Fowler; Brigadier P. L. F. Baillon; J. R. F. Fowler; S. E. R. Johnson-Hill; Stephanie Grenfell.

HOW TO APPLY 'The trustees already support as many charities as they could wish and would certainly not welcome any appeals from others. Unsolicited requests are not acknowledged.'

WHO TO APPLY TO S. M. Fowler, Hon. Secretary, 56 Heath Road, Petersfield GU31 4EJ *Tel.* 01730 267953

■ The Harebell Centenary Fund

cc no 1003552   **ESTABLISHED** 1991
WHERE FUNDING CAN BE GIVEN UK.
WHO CAN BENEFIT UK and small charitable organisations benefiting children, older people, people who have a disability and animals.
WHAT IS FUNDED Neurological research and animal welfare. This includes charities working in the fields of health, medical studies and research, conservation, heritage, special needs education and holidays and outings.
WHAT IS NOT FUNDED No grants made to individuals.
TYPE OF GRANT One-off, core costs, research, recurring costs, running costs and funding for one year or less will be considered.
RANGE OF GRANTS Up to £10,000.
SAMPLE GRANTS PACE (£10,000); Partially Sighted Society, Meningitis Trust and Penumbra (£7,000 each); St Helena Hospice and Nordoff-Robbins Music School (£5,000 each); and the Blue Cross (£2,000).
FINANCES *Year* 2012 *Income* £182,277 *Grants* £208,000 *Assets* £5,656,658
TRUSTEES Michael Goodbody; Penelope Chapman; Angela Fossick.
OTHER INFORMATION In 2012, grants totalling £208,000 were made to 37 organisations, many of which were hospices.
HOW TO APPLY In writing to the correspondent. The trust meets every six months to consider applications. Unsolicited applications are not requested, as the trustees prefer to make donations to charities whose work they have come across through their own research.
WHO TO APPLY TO Penelope Chapman, Trustee, 50 Broadway, Westminster, London SW1H 0BL *Tel.* 020 7227 7000 *email* pennychapman@bdb-law.co.uk

■ The Hargrave Foundation

cc no 1106524   **ESTABLISHED** 2004
WHERE FUNDING CAN BE GIVEN Worldwide.
WHO CAN BENEFIT Charitable organisations and individuals.
WHAT IS FUNDED General, research, welfare.
FINANCES *Year* 2011–12 *Income* £108,164 *Grants* £34,679 *Assets* £2,775,786
TRUSTEES Stephen Hargrave; Dominic Moseley; Adam Parkin.
HOW TO APPLY In writing to the correspondent.
WHO TO APPLY TO Stephen Hargrave, Trustee, 47 Lambs Conduit Street, London WC1N 3NG

■ The Kenneth Hargreaves Charitable Trust

cc no 223800   **ESTABLISHED** 1957
WHERE FUNDING CAN BE GIVEN UK, with a preference for West Yorkshire.
WHO CAN BENEFIT Registered charities benefiting children, young adults, students, medical professionals, community workers, research workers, teachers and project workers.
WHAT IS FUNDED Health, social welfare, arts, education, the environment and conservation.
WHAT IS NOT FUNDED No grants to individuals. Applications for core funding or salaries are rarely considered.
TYPE OF GRANT Preference is given to capital rather than revenue funding.
RANGE OF GRANTS Usually £100–£2,000.
SAMPLE GRANTS Children with Leukaemia and Opera North (£2,000 each); Northern Ballet and Salvation Army (£1,000 each); Yorkshire Eye

Research (£500); Hope And Homes For Children (£300); Yorkshire Historic Churches and Yorkshire Foundation For Conservation and Craftsmen (£250 each); Hearing Dogs (£200); Born Free Foundation (£150) and Gorilla Organisation (£100).
FINANCES *Year* 2011–12 *Income* £28,991 *Grants* £24,150 *Assets* £735,649
TRUSTEES Dr Ingrid Roscoe; Margaret Hargreaves-Allen; Sheila Holbrook; P. Chadwick; John Roscoe.
OTHER INFORMATION Small one-off grants, especially to groups using volunteers.
HOW TO APPLY In writing to the correspondent including clear details of the intended project, an outline budget and an annual report. The trustees meet quarterly. Only successful applicants will be contacted.
WHO TO APPLY TO Kathryn Hodges, Trust Administrator, 5 Grimston Park Mews, Grimston Park, Grimston, Tadcaster, North Yorkshire LS24 9DB *Tel.* 01937 834730 *email* khargreavestrust@btinternet.com

■ The Harpur Trust

cc no 1066861   **ESTABLISHED** 1566
WHERE FUNDING CAN BE GIVEN The borough of Bedford.
WHO CAN BENEFIT Community groups, schools, individuals (under education object), and organisations. Particularly children and young adults, people with additional support needs, older people, and people disadvantaged by poverty.
WHAT IS FUNDED The promotion of education; the relief of people who are sick or in need, hardship or distress; homelessness; child and adolescent mental health; the provision in the interest of social welfare of facilities for recreation and other leisure-time occupations. The charity's four programmes are: The Education Challenge Fund; Transitions; Resilience or Psychological Fitness; and Isolation.
WHAT IS NOT FUNDED Grants are not made in support of commercial ventures; for any project that relates primarily to the promotion of any religion; in support of projects that do not benefit the residents of the borough of Bedford; to cover costs already incurred; for trips, except in very limited circumstances (contact the grants manager for specific guidance); for services which are the responsibility of the local authority, for example, a school applying for a grant to cover the cost of employing a teacher is unlikely to be successful. However, the trust could consider an application from a school for a creative arts project that involved paying a voluntary organisation to deliver lunch time or after school workshops.
TYPE OF GRANT Capital, revenue, salaries, running costs. The very great majority of grant giving is targeted at organisations. Single and multi-year grants.
RANGE OF GRANTS Usually up to £50,000 a year.
SAMPLE GRANTS Autism Bedfordshire (£74,000); St John's Foundation Special School (£50,000); Family Groups Bedford (£41,000); The Cranfield Trust (£37,000); Alzheimer's Society (£30,000); Full House Theatre Company (£22,000); Road Victims Trust (£15,000); Show Racism the Red Card (£12,000); YMCA Bedfordshire (£10,000); Fun 4 Young People and Anglia Ruskin University (£5,000 each); Pilgrims Oakley Cricket Club (£2,500) and Queens Park Allotment Association (£1,700).

FINANCES *Year* 2011–12 *Income* £50,354,000 *Grants* £578,349 *Assets* £109,978,000

TRUSTEES David Palfreyman; Rae Levene; Michael Womack; Ian David McEwen; Rosemary Wallace; Philip Wallace; Anthony Nutt; Justin Phillimore; Susan Clark; Tina Beddoes; Prof. Stephen Mayson; Hugh Murray Stewart; Peter Budek; Richard O'Quinn; David Meghen; Sally Peck; Dr Deirdre Anderson; David Dixon; Kate Jacques; Dr Jennifer Sauboorah; Dr Anne Egan.

OTHER INFORMATION Grants to organisations: £556,000. Grants to individuals: £94,000. However, £71,000 in grants were withdrawn or not taken up during the year taking the total figure distributed to £578,000.

HOW TO APPLY First, read the guidance notes to make sure your project is eligible. These are available on the charity's website upon completion of a short eligibility questionnaire. The trust is open to informal contact with potential applicants. If you are in doubt about your project or whether you are eligible you are encouraged to call to discuss before applying formally.

The first stage of the formal application process is to submit a preliminary proposal form. Proposals are first considered by trustees before the trust writes to applicants to discuss the outcome, offer feedback and make an invitation to submit a formal, second stage application if applicable. The second stage application may be completed online or by filling out a hard copy form, downloadable from the website, and posting it back to the trust. Be careful to include the required additional information. The trust guidelines detail what information is required depending on the size and type of grant requested.

Applications requesting amounts of up to £5,000 are normally considered within two to three months. Grants of up to £50,000 for a single project in any one year and up to £150,000 for a project over a three year period will be considered by the full grants committee which meets every three months. Decisions for these grants are usually made within three to six months. The trust advise: 'allow more time if you are submitting a request that will be processed during the summer months as there are no committee meeting in July and August. Grants awarded by the committee above £50,000 per year will need to be endorsed by the full trustee body of the Harpur Trust, which meets three times a year. These meetings usually take place in March, July and December. Awards of this size are rare, and the decision making process will almost certainly be longer than for more modest requests.' The trust has produced helpful 'how-to' documents on full cost recovery applications and dealing with outcomes and monitoring which are available on the website. Application deadlines are also published online.

WHO TO APPLY TO Lucy Bardner, Grants Manager, Princeton Court, Pilgrim Centre, Brickhill Drive, Bedford MK41 7PZ *Tel.* 01234 369500 *Fax* 01234 369505 *email* grants@harpur-trust. org.uk *Website* www.bedfordcharity.org.uk

··

■ The Harris Charitable Trust

CC NO 292652   **ESTABLISHED** 1966
WHERE FUNDING CAN BE GIVEN UK, with a preference for Merton.
WHO CAN BENEFIT Registered charities known to the trustees.
WHAT IS FUNDED General charitable purposes.
WHAT IS NOT FUNDED No grants to individuals.
RANGE OF GRANTS £50–£3,000.

SAMPLE GRANTS Merton Crossroads Care Attendants Scheme (£3,000); British Heart Foundation (£2,500); MS Society – Merton (£2,000); Cancer Research (£1,500); Rochester Cathedral Trust (£1,000) and Leukaemia Research Fund (£500).
FINANCES *Year* 2011–12 *Income* £23,000 *Grants* £27,500
TRUSTEES Diana Harris; Colin Harris; Dr Andrew Harris; Thomas Harris.
HOW TO APPLY The trust does not respond to unsolicited applications.
WHO TO APPLY TO Diana Harris, 101 Church Road, Wimbledon, London SW19 5AL

··

■ The Harris Charity

CC NO 526206   **ESTABLISHED** 1883
WHERE FUNDING CAN BE GIVEN Lancashire, with a preference for the City of Preston (formally the borough of Preston.)
WHO CAN BENEFIT Young people.
WHAT IS FUNDED Charities benefiting individuals, children and young people under 25, in the Lancashire area.
TYPE OF GRANT Capital projects and provision of equipment are preferred.
RANGE OF GRANTS £30 to £4,000.
SAMPLE GRANTS Brownedge St Mary's and The Coppice School and Holy Cross High School (£4,000); Leyland (St Mary's) Scout Group (£3,000); St Cuthbert's Playgroup and Youth Group (£1,000) and Friends of Stoneyholme Park (£300).
FINANCES *Year* 2011–12 *Income* £184,521 *Grants* £54,337 *Assets* £3,181,667
TRUSTEES Simon Huck; Edwin Booth; Bridgeen Banks; Dr Anthony Andrews; Timothy Scott; Stanley Smith; William Huck; Rosemary Jolly; Keith Mellalieu; Audrey Scott; Nicola Fielden.
OTHER INFORMATION The grant total includes £3,000 that was given to individuals.
HOW TO APPLY On a form available to download from the website, where criteria and guidelines are also posted, and returned to the correspondent with an sae. The half yearly dates by which the applications must be submitted are 31 March and 30 September. Successful applicants are notified in July and January respectively following the closing date each year. Each request for a grant must be made on an official application form
WHO TO APPLY TO Peter Metcalf, Secretary, c/o Moore and Smalley, Richard House, 9 Winckley Square, Preston, Lancashire PR1 3HP *Tel.* 01772 821021 *Fax* 01772 259441 *email* harrischarity@mooreandsmalley.co.uk *Website* www.theharrischarity.co.uk

··

■ The Harris Family Charitable Trust

CC NO 1064394   **ESTABLISHED** 1997
WHERE FUNDING CAN BE GIVEN UK.
WHO CAN BENEFIT Charitable organisations.
WHAT IS FUNDED Health issues and the alleviation of sickness.
FINANCES *Year* 2011–12 *Income* £408,068 *Grants* £98,855 *Assets* £1,300,967
TRUSTEES Ronnie Harris; Loretta Harris; Charlotte Harris; Sophie Harris; Toby Harris.
HOW TO APPLY According to the trustees' report for 2011/12, 'the charity invites applications for funding of projects through various sources. The applications are reviewed by the trustees that

they are in accordance with the charity's objectives.'

WHO TO APPLY TO Ronnie Harris, Trustee, 64 New Cavendish Street, London W1G 8TB *Tel.* 020 7467 6300

■ The Edith Lilian Harrison 2000 Foundation

CC NO 1085651   **ESTABLISHED** 2000
WHERE FUNDING CAN BE GIVEN UK.
WHO CAN BENEFIT Registered charities.
WHAT IS FUNDED General charitable purposes.
TYPE OF GRANT One-off grants; three years or more.
SAMPLE GRANTS Salisbury Hospice, PDSA and Macmillan Cancer Support (£20,000 each); Transport for All, Centre for Alternative Technology and Cobalt Heart Mind and Body Scanner Appeal (£5,000 each); and Rotary Club of Salisbury (£1,000).
FINANCES *Year* 2011–12 *Income* £78,247 *Grants* £101,000 *Assets* £2,738,208
TRUSTEES Geoffrey Peyer; Clive Andrews; Paul Bradley.
HOW TO APPLY In writing to the correspondent. The trustees meet every six months. At each regular meeting, applications for grants are considered and duly dealt with.
WHO TO APPLY TO Geoffrey Peyer, Trustee, TWM Solicitors LLP, 40 West Street, Reigate RH2 9BT *Tel.* 01737 221212 *email* reigate. reception@twmsolicitors.com

■ The Harrison and Potter Trust

CC NO 224941   **ESTABLISHED** 1970
WHERE FUNDING CAN BE GIVEN Leeds (pre-1974 boundary).
WHO CAN BENEFIT Individuals, or organisations supporting people in need who are resident in Leeds.
WHAT IS FUNDED Individuals can be given grants for heat, lighting, equipment, clothing and holidays. Organisations or projects concerned with homeless, older people, young mothers and unemployed people are supported.
WHAT IS NOT FUNDED The trust cannot commit to repeat grants.
TYPE OF GRANT One-off and project.
RANGE OF GRANTS Up to £5,000
FINANCES *Year* 2012 *Income* £392,028 *Grants* £5,200 *Assets* £4,619,809
TRUSTEES John Campbell; Dr Ian Blomfield; Hilary Vinall; Alison Lowe; Nigel Wainman; Mike Andrews; Martin Payne; The Rector of Leeds; The Lord Mayor of Leeds; Gill Cartwright.
OTHER INFORMATION The grant total for 2012 was much reduced from previous years due to grant-giving being partially suspended. The grant-giving 'facility' has now been restored.
HOW TO APPLY In writing to the correspondent to be considered in February, May, August and November. Individuals must write requesting an application form and these will be considered monthly.
WHO TO APPLY TO Ann Duchart, Clerk, Wrigleys Solicitors, 19 Cookridge Street, Leeds LS2 3AG *Tel.* 01132 046100

■ The John Harrison Charitable Trust

CC NO 277956   **ESTABLISHED** 1979
WHERE FUNDING CAN BE GIVEN UK.
WHO CAN BENEFIT Organisations concerned with multiple sclerosis.
WHAT IS FUNDED Multiple Sclerosis support and research.
SAMPLE GRANTS Previous beneficiaries have included: Andover &RD MS Society (£885); Whizz-Kidz (£5,000).
FINANCES *Year* 2012–13 *Income* £8,837 *Grants* £900,000
TRUSTEES Ian Burch; Iris Sebba; Sian Crookes.
OTHER INFORMATION This was a very substantial increase in spending which in the previous four years had not exceeded £21,000. By way of explanation, the 2011–12 trustees' annual report had stated: 'The trustees intend to make substantial donations in the near future and continue the trust at a much reduced level.'
HOW TO APPLY In writing to the correspondent.
WHO TO APPLY TO David Hull, Administrator, 131 Manor Road, Leyton, London E10 7HW

■ The Peter Harrison Foundation

CC NO 1076579   **ESTABLISHED** 1999
WHERE FUNDING CAN BE GIVEN UK; south east of England.
WHO CAN BENEFIT Registered charities, community amateur sports clubs, friendly or provident societies and organisations in Scotland and Northern Ireland recognised by the HM Revenue and Customs.
WHAT IS FUNDED Charitable activities capable of demonstrating an existing high level of committed voluntary members with strong self-help activities together with well-planned and thought out projects under the following categories: Opportunities Through Sport Programme – support for sporting activities or projects which provide opportunities for children and young people who have disabilities or those who are disadvantaged, to fulfil their potential, and for other personal and life skills to be developed; Special Needs and Care Programme for Children and Young People – only for organisations in south east England; Opportunities Through Education Programme – applications not invited. Grants are also made through the Trustees' Discretionary Programme – again, invitations are not invited.
WHAT IS NOT FUNDED General appeals; retrospective funding; individuals; other grantmaking bodies to make grants on its behalf; projects that replace statutory funding; projects that are the responsibility of the central or local government; holidays in the UK or abroad and expeditions; outdoor activity projects such as camping or outward bound expeditions; overseas projects; projects solely for the promotion of religion.
RANGE OF GRANTS Up to £150,000.
SAMPLE GRANTS Loughborough University (£150,000); British Paralympic Association and the National Maritime Museum (£125,000 each); The Scout Association, Watford Grammar and St Michael's Church (£50,000 each); Dwarf Sports Association (£38,000); The Shakespeare Globe Trust (£36,000) and The Outward Bound Trust (£13,000).
FINANCES *Year* 2011–12 *Income* £2,369,439 *Grants* £1,326,300 *Assets* £52,557,692
TRUSTEES Sir Peter Harrison, Chair; Julia Harrison-Lee; Peter Lee; Nicholas Harrison.

OTHER INFORMATION £139,000 of the grant total was paid as bursaries to individuals to enable them to attend Reigate Grammar School.

HOW TO APPLY The foundation has a two stage application process.

Step 1: Initial enquiry

Potential applicants are asked to first read the information on eligibility and grant programmes available on the foundation's website. If your project meets the criteria for one of the open programmes (i.e. Opportunities through Sport or Special Needs and Care for Children and Young People), then complete the online initial enquiry form. This can be found in the 'application process' section of the foundation's website. Applications are processed as quickly as possible, but be aware that the foundation receives a large number of applications and it may sometimes take up to two months for an initial enquiry form to be considered. Applications are first assessed by the foundation's staff. If it is felt the project will be of interest, they will arrange either to visit the project or to conduct a telephone discussion with the applicant about it. Depending on the outcome of these discussions, you may then be invited to submit a full application. If your initial enquiry is not successful you will be notified by email. The foundation receives many more applications than it is able to support and unfortunately have turn down many good proposals, even though they meet the criteria. No feedback is given on unsuccessful applications.

Step 2: Full application

You will only be asked to complete a full application if your initial enquiry has been successful. The application form will be sent to you by email. Trustees meet regularly to consider applications. If an application is successful the applicant will normally be contacted by telephone followed by a grant offer letter. The letter will explain the conditions which apply to all grant awards and also set out any special conditions which apply to your organisation. It will also confirm details of how and when you will receive the grant and how payment is made. If an application is unsuccessful the applicant will be informed by letter. The main reason for not funding projects is the volume of applications received. Organisations supported by the foundation are required to show how they have used the grant and, depending on the grant amount and the nature of the project, may be asked to undertake a review and evaluation of the project being funded. This will normally be on completion of the project, but for charities receiving their grant in several instalments, interim reports may be requested. Full details of the monitoring information required are given in the foundation's grant offer letter. The foundation aims to ensure that all grant applications that are eligible for consideration within the foundation's grants criteria are given equal consideration, irrespective of gender, sexual orientation, race, colour, ethnic or national origin, or disability.

WHO TO APPLY TO Julia Caines, Administrator, Foundation House, 42–48 London Road, Reigate, Surrey RH2 9QQ *Tel.* 01737 228000 *Fax* 01737 228001 *email* enquiries@peterharrisonfoundation.org *Website* www.peterharrisonfoundation.org

■ The Spencer Hart Charitable Trust

CC NO 800057   ESTABLISHED 1988

WHERE FUNDING CAN BE GIVEN UK and overseas.

WHO CAN BENEFIT Registered charities.

WHAT IS FUNDED General charitable purposes.

RANGE OF GRANTS Most grants made in region of £100 to £10,000.

SAMPLE GRANTS UCLH Charity and National Gallery Trust (£10,000 each); The League of the Helping Hand (£6,000); World Challenge (£1,500); Garsington Opera Limited (£1,250); Food Lifeline and Wigmore Hall Trust (£1,000 each); Human Rights Watch (£700); Meningitis Trust, Deafblind UK and London Cello Society (£500 each) and RETT UK (£250).

FINANCES *Year* 2011–12 *Income* £25,422 *Grants* £40,700

TRUSTEES Julian Korn; Ian Burman.

OTHER INFORMATION In 2011–12 grants were given to 16 organisations.

HOW TO APPLY In writing to the correspondent.

WHO TO APPLY TO The Trustees, c/o Laytons, 2 More London Riverside, London SE1 2AP *Tel.* 020 7842 8000 *Fax* 020 7842 8080 *email* london@laytons.com

■ The Hartley Charitable Trust

CC NO 800968   ESTABLISHED 1989

WHERE FUNDING CAN BE GIVEN Unrestricted.

WHO CAN BENEFIT Organisations.

WHAT IS FUNDED General charitable purposes.

WHAT IS NOT FUNDED No grants to individuals.

TYPE OF GRANT One-off and recurrent grants for core costs, projects, research and salaries, for one year or less.

SAMPLE GRANTS Alzheimer's Society (£30,000); National Association of Clubs for Young People (£15,000); Open Arms Malawi (£7,000); Senior Volunteer Network Trust Network and Celtic Storm – Cornwall Powerchair Football Club (£5,000 each) and Parkinson's Improvement Programme (£500).

FINANCES *Year* 2011–12 *Income* £63,874 *Grants* £62,500 *Assets* £1,708,220

TRUSTEES Richard Hartley; Jane Hartley; Peta Hyland.

HOW TO APPLY In August 2011 the trust told us: 'We are fully committed for four to five years. It would be better if you indicated this in your publications and website, as organisations and individuals are wasting money in putting applications to us.'

WHO TO APPLY TO Rick Hartley, 6 Throstle Nest Drive, Harrogate, Yorkshire HG2 9PB *Tel.* 01423 525100 *email* hartleycharitabletrust@hotmail.com

■ The Alfred And Peggy Harvey Charitable Trust

CC NO 1095855   ESTABLISHED 2003

WHERE FUNDING CAN BE GIVEN UK, with a strong preference for Kent, Surrey and South East London.

WHO CAN BENEFIT Charitable organisations.

WHAT IS FUNDED Care and financial support for the elderly, children and young people with disabilities or living in difficult socio-economic circumstances, blind and deaf people and funding of medical and surgical studies and research.

WHAT IS NOT FUNDED Charitable organisations in Kent, Surrey and south east London only.

RANGE OF GRANTS £1,000–£10,000.

FINANCES *Year* 2011–12 *Income* £70,258 *Grants* £63,350 *Assets* £423,535

TRUSTEES Kevin Custis; Colin Russell; John Duncan.

HOW TO APPLY In writing to the correspondent.

WHO TO APPLY TO Colin Russell, Trustee, c/o Manches LLP, Aldwych House, 81 Aldwych, London WC2B 4RP *Tel.* 020 7404 4433

....

■ William Geoffrey Harvey's Discretionary Settlement

CC NO 800473   **ESTABLISHED** 1968

WHERE FUNDING CAN BE GIVEN Unrestricted with some preference for north west England.

WHO CAN BENEFIT Registered charities.

WHAT IS FUNDED Animal facilities and services to promote the well-being of, and prevent cruelty to, animals and birds.

WHAT IS NOT FUNDED Note, the trustees state that the settlor Mrs Harvey gave them 'a clear indication of the causes she favoured and [they] are guided by that for the moment at least'. New applicants will not be considered.

TYPE OF GRANT Running costs and capital expenditure.

RANGE OF GRANTS £10,000–£40,000

SAMPLE GRANTS Previous beneficiaries include: People's Dispensary for Sick Animals (£40,000); St Tiggywinkles (£26,000); The Donkey Sanctuary (£24,000); Dog's Trust (£20,000) and Home of Rest for Horses (£10,000).

FINANCES *Year* 2011–12 *Income* £141,651 *Grants* £24,000 *Assets* £4,521,525

TRUSTEES G. J. Hull (chair), F. R. Shackleton; S. A. Hull, N. J. Joyce.

OTHER INFORMATION In 2011–12 a single grant of £24,000 was made to the RSPCA.

HOW TO APPLY Previously the trust has stated that the settlor Mrs Harvey gave them 'a clear indication of the causes she favoured and [they] are guided by that for the moment at least', therefore new applicants will not be considered for the time being.

WHO TO APPLY TO Nicola Joyce, c/o Usher Spiby and Co, 76 Manchester Road, Denton, Manchester M34 3PS *Tel.* 01614 328307 *email* sa.hull4harvey@gmail.com

....

■ The Edward Harvist Trust

CC NO 211970   **ESTABLISHED** 1994

WHERE FUNDING CAN BE GIVEN The London boroughs of Barnet, Brent, Camden, Harrow and the City of Westminster.

WHO CAN BENEFIT Registered charities.

WHAT IS FUNDED General charitable purposes.

RANGE OF GRANTS Up to £16,000.

SAMPLE GRANTS PACE (£15,000); Ijad Dance Company (£8,000); Camden Somali Forum (£5,000); Mary Ward Legal Centre (£4,100); St John's Wood Crypt Youth Club (£3,000); Barnet Play Association (£1,500); Iran Institute (£1,100); Friends of Canons Park (£500); and Carramea Community Resource Centre (£260).

FINANCES *Year* 2011–12 *Income* £274,032 *Grants* £235,000

TRUSTEES Howard Bluston; Cllr Gwyneth Hampson; Ilan Jacobs; Graham Old; Shafique Choudhary.

OTHER INFORMATION Income is distributed to the local authorities in proportion to the length of the Edgware Road passing through their area.

Previously (2009/10), this was as follows: London borough of Barnet – (31%) £78,000; London borough of Brent – (27%) £70,000; City of Westminster – (25%) £63,000; London borough of Camden – (11%) £27,000; London borough of Harrow – (6%) £14,000.

HOW TO APPLY In writing to the relevant local authority. Do not write to the correspondent.

WHO TO APPLY TO Jennifer Hydari, London Borough of Harrow, Finance Department, PO Box 21, Civic Centre, Harrow HA1 2UJ *Tel.* 020 8424 1393

....

■ The Haskel Family Foundation

CC NO 1039969   **ESTABLISHED** 1993

WHERE FUNDING CAN BE GIVEN UK.

WHO CAN BENEFIT Jewish people and research workers.

WHAT IS FUNDED The charity is currently funding projects concerned with social policy research and Jewish communal life.

RANGE OF GRANTS Usually up to £12,000.

SAMPLE GRANTS Aldeburgh Music (£15,000); Liberal Judaism and the Rosetree Trust (£5,000 each); Children Leukaemia (£3,500); Jewish Research (£1,100) and The Rainbow Trust (£500).

FINANCES *Year* 2012 *Income* £31,000 *Grants* £11,000 *Assets* £620,000

TRUSTEES A. M. Davis; S. Haskel; M. Nutman; Lord Haskel.

HOW TO APPLY **This trust states that it does not respond to unsolicited applications.**

WHO TO APPLY TO Lord Simon Haskel, 12 Rosemont Road, Richmond upon Thames, Surrey TW10 6QL *Tel.* 020 8948 7711

....

■ Hasluck Charitable Trust

CC NO 1115323   **ESTABLISHED** 2006

WHERE FUNDING CAN BE GIVEN UK.

WHO CAN BENEFIT Children and young people, people with disabilities, older people.

WHAT IS FUNDED Health, welfare, disability, youth, overseas aid.

WHAT IS NOT FUNDED No grants are made to individuals.

RANGE OF GRANTS Up to £4,500.

SAMPLE GRANTS Regular beneficiaries (see the 'Other information' section) received £4,500 each. One-off grants were made to: Alzheimer's Society (£2,500); Riders and World Vision – Somalia Appeal (£1,500 each); Living Hope, Family Care, Just Different, Ipswich Community Playbus and Seafarers UK (£1,000 each); and the Message and Leukaemia and Lymphoma Research (£500 each).

FINANCES *Year* 2011–12 *Income* £96,320 *Grants* £71,700 *Assets* £1,207,268

TRUSTEES Matthew James Wakefield; John Billing.

OTHER INFORMATION Half of the income received by the trust is allocated to eight charities [Barnardo's, Mrs R. H. Hotblack's Michelham Priory Endowment Fund, International Fund for Animal Welfare, Macmillan Cancer Relief, the Riding for the Disabled Association, RNLI, RSPB and Scope], which are of particular interest to the settlor. The remaining monies are distributed to such charitable bodies as the trustees decide.

HOW TO APPLY In writing to the correspondent. Grants are generally distributed in January and July, although consideration is given to appeals received at other times of the year.

WHO TO APPLY TO John Billing, Trustee, Rathbone Trust Company Limited, 4th Floor, 1 Curzon Street, London W1J 5FB *Tel.* 020 7399 0447 *email* john.billing@rathbones.com

■ The Hathaway Trust

CC NO 1064086   ESTABLISHED 1997
WHERE FUNDING CAN BE GIVEN Unrestricted.
WHO CAN BENEFIT Registered charities and individuals.
WHAT IS FUNDED The trust tends to support Jewish organisations and causes.
RANGE OF GRANTS £1,000–£13,000
SAMPLE GRANTS Toimchei Shabbos Manchester (£13,000); JCOM (£8,000); Jewish Teachers Training College (£5,000); Yeshivas Sharei Torah (£4,000); Meleches Machsheves (£2,000); Jewish Rescue and Relief Committee (£1,500) and Manchester Swallow (£1,250). The trust also made 'other grants' totalling £18,500.
FINANCES *Year* 2011–12 *Income* £136,451 *Grants* £86,782 *Assets* £126,633
TRUSTEES Norman Younger; Miriam Younger; Rabbi Stuart Schwalbe; Jonathan Roitenbarg.
OTHER INFORMATION During the year, the trust became involved in a variety of new projects and activities aimed at youths in the area of Greater Manchester 'who have yet to find their place in society'. The aim being to help them realise their potential, develop their skills and capabilities to participate and contribute to society.
HOW TO APPLY The trustees have stated previously that they have adopted a proactive approach to funding and now only fund projects with which they have a personal connection, therefore unsolicited requests will not be considered.
WHO TO APPLY TO The Trustees, 12 Hereford Drive, Prestwich, Manchester M25 0JA

■ The Maurice Hatter Foundation

CC NO 298119   ESTABLISHED 1987
WHERE FUNDING CAN BE GIVEN Unrestricted.
WHO CAN BENEFIT Educational bodies, particularly those with Jewish links, and registered charities.
WHAT IS FUNDED Education, medical research and social welfare
TYPE OF GRANT Grants, often recurring; loans.
SAMPLE GRANTS The largest grant was made to World ORT (£350,000) which has also received substantial support in previous years (£188,000 in 2010/11). Other beneficiaries included: South of England Foundation (Charlton Athletic Community Trust) (£100,000); University College Hospital Charity Fund – towards the Hatter Cardiovascular Institute (£80,000); Ambitious About Autism (£55,000); Jewish Community Secondary School Trust (£25,000); Community Security Trust (£15,000); Norwood Ravenswood (£10,000); Churchill Centre UK, Chief Rabbinate Trust and Social Mobility Foundation (£5,000 each) and Prostate Action (£3,000).
FINANCES *Year* 2011–12 *Income* £485,853 *Grants* £931,283 *Assets* £4,667,782
TRUSTEES Sir Maurice Hatter; Ivor Connick; Jeremy S. Newman; Richard Hatter.
HOW TO APPLY Unsolicited applications will not be considered.

WHO TO APPLY TO Jeremy S. Newman, Trustee, Smith and Williamson, 1 Bishops Wharf, Walnut Tree Close, Guildford, Surrey GU1 4RA *Tel.* 01483 407100

■ The M. A. Hawe Settlement

CC NO 327827   ESTABLISHED 1988
WHERE FUNDING CAN BE GIVEN Lancashire with a preference for the Fylde coastal area.
WHO CAN BENEFIT UK and local organisations and schemes benefiting people of all ages, women, at-risk groups, and children who are ill or disabled, people who are socially isolated, homeless or disadvantaged by poverty.
WHAT IS FUNDED Welfare of older people, women and children, disability, homelessness and other charitable purposes.
TYPE OF GRANT One-off, some recurrent.
RANGE OF GRANTS Up to £1,000.
SAMPLE GRANTS Kensington House Trust Limited (£191,000); Youth Service Events and Young Persons' Visits to Lourdes (£1,000 each); Holy Cross Church and Soup Kitchen (£840) and Fylde Mayor's Charity and Fr Dunstan Cooper (£500 each).
FINANCES *Year* 2011–12 *Income* £64,867 *Grants* £200,000 *Assets* £3,018,623
TRUSTEES M. A. Hawe; G. Hawe; M. G. Hawe.
OTHER INFORMATION The trust states that 'The settlement is committed to the support of the Kensington Foundation to which 96% of the grants (by value) made in this year have gone. [. . .] The Kensington Foundation intends to focus its efforts into developing the Daisy Chain Project at Norcross farm as their main activity.' Grants to individuals totalled £2,500.
HOW TO APPLY In writing to the correspondent.
WHO TO APPLY TO M. A. Hawe, Trustee, 94 Park View Road, Lytham St Annes, Lancashire FY8 4JF *Tel.* 01253 796888

■ The Hawerby Trust

CC NO 1133740   ESTABLISHED 2010
WHERE FUNDING CAN BE GIVEN UK and overseas.
WHO CAN BENEFIT Registered charities.
WHAT IS FUNDED General charitable purposes.
FINANCES *Year* 2012
TRUSTEES Wynne Griffiths; Pamela Griffiths; Kate Griffiths; William Griffiths; Nicholas Griffiths; Max Griffiths; Robert Penrose; Coutts and Co.
HOW TO APPLY In writing to the correspondent.
WHO TO APPLY TO c/o Trustee Dept, Coutts and Co, 440 Strand, London WC2R 0QS *Tel.* 020 7663 6825

■ The Hawkins Foundation

CC NO 1147374   ESTABLISHED 2012
WHERE FUNDING CAN BE GIVEN UK, with a preference for the East Lindsey area of Lincolnshire.
WHO CAN BENEFIT Charities and community groups.
WHAT IS FUNDED General charitable purposes.
TRUSTEES Dianne Hawkins; Gordon Hawkins; Tim Sisson; Deborah Hutchinson; Deana Gibson.
HOW TO APPLY In writing to the correspondent.
WHO TO APPLY TO Dianne Hawkins, 348 Drummond Road, Skegness, Lincolnshire PE25 3AY *Tel.* 01754 761946

■ The Hawthorne Charitable Trust

CC NO 233921   ESTABLISHED 1964

WHERE FUNDING CAN BE GIVEN UK, especially Hereford and Worcester.

WHO CAN BENEFIT Organisations benefiting young people and older people, medical professionals and people disadvantaged by poverty.

WHAT IS FUNDED The trustees make donations, generally on an annual basis, to a large number of charities mainly concerned with the care of young people and older people, the relief of pain, sickness and poverty, the advancement of medical research, particularly into the various forms of cancer, research into animal health, the arts, disability and heritage.

WHAT IS NOT FUNDED Grants are given to registered charities only. No grants to individuals.

TYPE OF GRANT Often recurring.

RANGE OF GRANTS Usually up to £8,000.

SAMPLE GRANTS St Laurence – Winchenford (£5,250); Malvern Festival Theatre Trust Ltd, Canine Partners for Independence, Combat Stress and Elizabeth Finn Trust (£2,500 each); Motor Neurone Disease Association and The Passage (£2,000 each); National Art Collections Fund and Birmingham Hippodrome (£1,000 each) and Asthma Relief (£500).

FINANCES *Year* 2011–12 *Income* £194,582 *Grants* £126,750 *Assets* £7,167,925

TRUSTEES Alexandra Berington; Roger Jackson Clark; Thomas Berington; Richard White.

HOW TO APPLY In writing to the correspondent, including up-to-date accounts. Applications should be received by October for consideration in November.

WHO TO APPLY TO Evaline Sarbout, c/o Baker Tilly, 25 Farringdon Street, London EC4A 4AB *Tel.* 020 3201 8298

■ The Dorothy Hay-Bolton Charitable Trust

CC NO 1010438   ESTABLISHED 1992

WHERE FUNDING CAN BE GIVEN UK, with a preference for the South East of England and overseas.

WHO CAN BENEFIT Charities working with people who are blind or deaf, particularly children, young people and elderly people

WHAT IS FUNDED Welfare needs.

WHAT IS NOT FUNDED The trust states that it does not generally give to individuals.

TYPE OF GRANT One-off and ongoing.

SAMPLE GRANTS Previous beneficiaries have included: Hearing Dogs for the Deaf, Action for Blind People, Sussex Lantern, Telephones for the Blind, Eyeless Trust, British Blind Sport, Esther Benjamin's Trust, East Sussex Association for the Blind, the Seeing Ear and East Kent Cycling Club.

FINANCES *Year* 2011–12 *Income* £22,806 *Grants* £50,000

TRUSTEES Brian Carter; Stephen Gallico.

HOW TO APPLY In writing to the correspondent.

WHO TO APPLY TO The Trustees, Reeves and Co LLP, 24 Chiswell Street, London EC1Y 4YX *Tel.* 020 7382 1820 *email* brian.carter@reeves.co.uk

■ The Charles Hayward Foundation

CC NO 1078969   ESTABLISHED 1961

WHERE FUNDING CAN BE GIVEN Unrestricted, in practice mainly UK with some overseas funding.

WHO CAN BENEFIT Registered charities.

WHAT IS FUNDED Predominantly capital costs for organisations undertaking projects which are preventative or provide early intervention; developmental or innovative; promote or continue good practice and add value to existing services. Priority areas: criminal justice, heritage and conservation, overseas and older people.

WHAT IS NOT FUNDED Grants are not made for: academic chairs; bursaries; church restoration; computers; education; endowment funds; environmental and animal sciences; fundraising activities; general repairs; non-medical academic research; paying off loans; revenue funding or core costs, general funding, continuing funding and replacement funding; replacement of government or lottery funding or activities primarily the responsibility of central or local government or any other responsible body; travel, outings or holidays.

TYPE OF GRANT Capital cost of buildings, extensions, adaptations, equipment and furnishings. Occasionally project funding for start-up or development.

RANGE OF GRANTS Generally £1,000–£25,000.

SAMPLE GRANTS Les Bourgs Hospice (£30,000); St Barnabas House (£20,000); Age UK Norwich and Sutton Women's Aid (£15,000 each); Build Africa (£13,000); International Refugee Trust London (£11,000); Street Child Africa, Heritage Trust for the North West and Wildlife Trust Hampshire and Isle of Wight (£10,000 each); HANDS Volunteer Bureau (£5,000); Lifecycle UK (£4,500); Llanrumney Community Church (£4,000); YMCA North Somerset (£2,000) and St Breward Village Hall (£1,100).

FINANCES *Year* 2012 *Income* £1,484,312 *Grants* £1,179,305 *Assets* £49,442,242

TRUSTEES J. M. Chamberlain; Sir Jack Hayward; S. J. Heath; B. D. Insch; N van Leuven; R. Hayward; A. J. Heath.

OTHER INFORMATION Full guidelines are available on the foundation's website. Priority areas do change quite often so check before applying.

HOW TO APPLY Full guidelines and an application form are available on the foundation's website.

WHO TO APPLY TO Dorothy Napierala, Hayward House, 45 Harrington Gardens, London SW7 4JU *Tel.* 020 7370 7063 *Website* www. charleshaywardfoundation.org.uk

■ The Headley Trust

CC NO 266620   ESTABLISHED 1973

WHERE FUNDING CAN BE GIVEN Unrestricted.

WHO CAN BENEFIT Registered charities working in the areas listed. The trust prefers to support innovative schemes that can be successfully replicated or become self-sustaining.

WHAT IS FUNDED Arts and Heritage UK: arts, heritage and conservation projects in the UK of outstanding importance, including industrial and maritime heritage; grants for regional museums/galleries, particularly for supporting curatorship; national museums and libraries; rural crafts; archaeological projects; support for principally regional museums to purchase unusual or exceptional artefacts; Headley Museums Archaeological Acquisition Fund. Cathedrals and Major Churches: restoration or repair work to the fabric of ancient cathedrals, parish church cathedrals and large churches of exceptional architectural merit. Parish Churches: fabric repairs to listed medieval parish churches in sparsely populated and less prosperous rural areas. Arts and Heritage Overseas: conservation and recording of heritage (including ecclesiastical and vernacular architecture, archaeology and cultural artefacts), primarily in South Eastern Europe (Slovenia, Croatia,

Albania, Macedonia, Bulgaria, Romania, Serbia, Montenegro, Bosnia-Herzegovina, Turkey); raising awareness of heritage issues in these countries, supporting the capacity of new heritage NGOs, and training the next generation of conservation and heritage professionals. Developing Countries: development projects in sub-Saharan Anglophone Africa, and Ethiopia, under the following general headings – water (sanitation, access, better use of water resources), environment (sustainable energy, farming, forestry), education and literacy, healthcare (maternal, disability, trachoma prevention and treatment), and emergency appeals (at the discretion of trustees). Education: bursaries for vocational training in traditional crafts, conservation and heritage skills; bursaries for mainly postgraduate studies in music and dance. Health and Social Welfare: support for elderly people of limited means and dementia sufferers to maintain their independence; housing provision for older people; music therapy for older people; support for older carers of an ill or disabled relative; family and parenting support and access for the disabled; occasional research projects on medical conditions of particular interest to the trustees; small grants providing practical aids for disabled people.

WHAT IS NOT FUNDED Individuals; expeditions.

TYPE OF GRANT One-off, capital and project over three years or less.

SAMPLE GRANTS Lakeland Arts Trust (£210,000); Peabody Trust (£118,000); National Museum of the Royal Navy and Remap (£90,000 each); Art Fund (£75,000); Canterbury Cathedral and the Royal Academy of Music (£60,000 each); Action On Elder Abuse (£58,000); Great Ormond Street Hospital Children's Charity (£50,000); Fight for Sight (£49,000); Council for British Archaeology (£45,000); Ethiopian Heritage Fund (£40,000); Halifax Minster (£30,000); Groundwork Wakefield (£25,000); Central School of Ballet and the Imperial Society of Teachers of Dancing (£20,000 each); Penarth Pier Pavilion (£15,000); Pontefract Museum and the Wessex Children's Hospice Trust (£10,000 each).

FINANCES *Year* 2012–13 *Income* £2,971,000 *Grants* £4,299,000 *Assets* £74,001,000

TRUSTEES Lady Susan Sainsbury; Judith Portrait; Timothy Sainsbury; Sir Timothy Sainsbury; J. Benson; Camilla Sainsbury.

OTHER INFORMATION The figures are higher than usual as the period covered 15 months due to a change in the financial year end of the trust.

HOW TO APPLY See the guidance for applicants in the entry for the Sainsbury Family Charitable Trusts. A single application will be considered for support by all the trusts in the group. However, for this as for many of the trusts, 'the trustees take an active role in their grantmaking, employing a range of specialist staff and advisers to research their areas of interest and bring forward suitable proposals. Many of the trusts work closely with their chosen beneficiaries over a long period to achieve particular objectives. It should therefore be understood that the majority of unsolicited proposals we receive will be unsuccessful', however, the trust states that the 'trustees are prepared to consider unsolicited proposals so long as they closely match one of [its] areas of interest' (see general section).

'Applications should be sent by post with a description (strictly no more than two pages please, as any more is unlikely to be read) of the proposed project, covering: the organisation – explaining its charitable aims and objectives, and

giving its most recent annual income and expenditure, and current financial position. Do not send a full set of accounts; the project requiring funding – why it is needed, who will benefit and in what way; the funding – breakdown of costs, any money raised so far, and how the balance will be raised. All applications will receive our standard acknowledgement letter. If your proposal is a candidate for support from one of the trusts, you will hear from us within eight weeks of the acknowledgement. Applicants who do not hear from us within this time must assume they have been unsuccessful.'

WHO TO APPLY TO Alan Bookbinder, Director, The Peak, 5 Wilton Road, London SW1V 1AP *Tel.* 020 7410 0330 *Fax* 020 7410 0332 *Website* www.sfct.org.uk

---

■ Headley-Pitt Charitable Trust

CC NO 252023   **ESTABLISHED** 1955

WHERE FUNDING CAN BE GIVEN Mainly Ashford, Kent

WHO CAN BENEFIT Older people and those in need.

WHAT IS FUNDED Quaker projects. The trust also administers ten bungalows for the benefit of older people in the community.

WHAT IS NOT FUNDED Sport or animal projects.

TYPE OF GRANT One-off.

RANGE OF GRANTS Up to £2,000.

FINANCES *Year* 2011–12 *Income* £67,377 *Grants* £37,992 *Assets* £2,530,922

TRUSTEES Christopher Pitt; Roger Pitt; Jon Pitt; Stella Pitt.

OTHER INFORMATION During the year 82 organisations received a total of £26,000 and 51 individuals received a total of £12,000.

HOW TO APPLY In writing to the correspondent.

WHO TO APPLY TO Thelma Pitt, Administrator, Old Mill Cottage, Ulley Road, Kennington, Ashford, Kent TN24 9HX *email* thelma.pitt@headley.co.uk

---

■ May Hearnshaw's Charity

CC NO 1008638   **ESTABLISHED** 1992

WHERE FUNDING CAN BE GIVEN UK, particularly South Yorkshire, North Nottinghamshire, Derbyshire, East Lancashire and Cheshire areas.

WHO CAN BENEFIT Registered charities.

WHAT IS FUNDED General with a preference for the promotion of education, advancement of religion and the relief of poverty and sickness.

TYPE OF GRANT One-off, with grants for buildings, core costs, research, recurring costs, running costs and salaries all considered. Funding may be given for up to three years.

RANGE OF GRANTS Usually £500–£5,000.

FINANCES *Year* 2011–12 *Income* £76,818 *Grants* £61,250 *Assets* £1,936,325

TRUSTEES Marjorie West; Michael Ferreday; Richard Law; William Munro.

HOW TO APPLY 'The trustees usually meet three times a year when they decide on and make major grants to charitable organisations but may decide to make grants at any time. They do not include in their consideration appeals received direct from individuals.'

WHO TO APPLY TO Michael Ferreday, Trustee, Barber Harrison and Platt, 2 Rutland Park, Sheffield S10 2PD

■ Heart of England Community Foundation

CC NO 1117345   **ESTABLISHED** 1995

WHERE FUNDING CAN BE GIVEN The city of Coventry and Warwickshire.

WHO CAN BENEFIT Community-based groups and activities benefiting a wide range of social circumstances.

WHAT IS FUNDED General charitable purposes, in particular for the benefit of the local community in Warwickshire and the city of Coventry and people who are disabled, and to promote social and economic development. This includes residential facilities and services, community arts and recreation, respite care and care for carers, support and self-help groups, community services, social issues advice and information and health advocacy.

WHAT IS NOT FUNDED Grants will not usually be considered for the following: general and major fundraising; educational institutions except where the institution or project is aimed at the relief of disadvantage; promotion of religious causes except where the institution or the project is aimed at relief of disadvantage; medical research; organisations with no permanent presence in the beneficial area; animal welfare; political activity; organisations with substantial reserves relative to turnover; salaries and other core costs.

TYPE OF GRANT Buildings, capital, core costs, feasibility studies, one-off, project, research, development costs, salaries, and start-up costs. Funding is available for up to one year.

RANGE OF GRANTS £100–£7,000.

SAMPLE GRANTS Coventry Somali Women's Network (£11,500); Hub @ Blackwell (£10,700); Positive Youth Foundation (£10,000); Friendship Project (£6,000 in two grants); The Open Theatre Company Ltd (£5,000); Support Sport Ltd (£4,500); Write Here Write Now CiC (£3,000); Lower Ford Street Baptist Church (£1,000); and Welford Junior Football Club (£700).

FINANCES *Year* 2012–13 *Income* £2,378,863 *Grants* £284,185 *Assets* £5,025,451

TRUSTEES Brian Clifford Holt; Sally Carrick; David Green; Susan Ong; Peter Shearing; John Taylor; Paul Belfield; Derek Cake; Philip Gordon Ewing; Sandra Garlick; Michelle Vincent.

OTHER INFORMATION The priorities of the trustees are reviewed annually; applicants are encouraged to contact the foundation by telephone to obtain up-to-date information on current priorities. Only one grant will be given to an organisation in any one year from the foundation.

HOW TO APPLY Applications should be completed online. Some schemes have online applications while others have forms which can be downloaded from the site. Applicants are encouraged to telephone the foundation to discuss their project in advance of applying. Grants Officers, who cover specific geographical areas and funds, will be pleased to assist you. Applicants should hear the outcome of their application within 12 weeks.

WHO TO APPLY TO Kat Venton, Grants Officer, PSA Peugeot Citroën, PO BOX 126, Torrington Avenue, Tile Hill, Coventry CV4 0UX *Tel.* 02476 883262 *email* info@heartofenglandcf.co.uk *Website* www.heartofenglandcf.co.uk

■ Heart Research UK

CC NO 1044821   **ESTABLISHED** 1967

WHERE FUNDING CAN BE GIVEN UK.

WHO CAN BENEFIT Community groups, voluntary organisations and people involved in medical research.

WHAT IS FUNDED Medical research and 'Lifestyle interventions' focusing on heart disease in the UK.

WHAT IS NOT FUNDED No grants to government organisations or local authority groups.

TYPE OF GRANT One-off and recurrent.

RANGE OF GRANTS Up to £200,000.

SAMPLE GRANTS University College London and Great Ormond Street Hospital for Children (£186,000); University of Nottingham (£145,000); William Harvey Research Institute, Queen Mary University of London (£112,000); Kings College London (£75,000) and Oxford Spires Four Pillars Hotel (£19,000); The Fresh – Sportsmen Study (£10,000); Heart Smart (£8,000); Northern Star's Healthy Hearts (£5,700); Run for a Healthy Heart (£4,700) and YMCA Fitness Challenge – Love Your Heart (£2,300).

FINANCES *Year* 2012 *Income* £1,820,614 *Grants* £939,152 *Assets* £2,896,887

TRUSTEES K. Loudon; R. Hemsley; Prof. Homer-Vanniasinkam; E. A. Blackmore; Dr D. Dickinson; F. Hamilton MP; J. Jill; A. D. Knight; C. Mortimer; A. G. Oxley; H. Stewart; J. Villiers; K. Watterson; N. White.

HOW TO APPLY Application forms, full guidelines and grant terms and conditions for each programme can be requested by telephone or downloaded from the website. For **Translational Research** grants the deadline is 1 February each year with applications being accepted from the beginning of January. For **Novel and Emerging Technologies** grants outline applications are accepted from 1 March until 1 April each year and the deadline for full applications is 1 July each year. For **Healthy Heart** grants there are two rounds each year, one in May and one in November. **Subway Healthy Heart** grants are available in specific regions at certain times of the year; check the website for these details.

WHO TO APPLY TO M. Clark, Suite 12D, Joseph's Well, Leeds LS3 1AB *Tel.* 01132 347474 *email* mail@heartresearch.org.uk *Website* www.heartresearch.org.uk

■ The Heathcoat Trust

CC NO 203367   **ESTABLISHED** 1945

WHERE FUNDING CAN BE GIVEN Mainly Tiverton, Devon.

WHO CAN BENEFIT Local organisations to Tiverton and individual grants to employees and pensioners of the Heathcoat group of companies.

WHAT IS FUNDED Welfare, educational.

TYPE OF GRANT Recurring and one-off.

RANGE OF GRANTS Usually less than £1,000.

FINANCES *Year* 2011–12 *Income* £305,746 *Grants* £47,151 *Assets* £1,935,640

TRUSTEES Sir Ian Heathcoat Amory; Lady Amory; WF. Heathcoat Amory.

OTHER INFORMATION A further £1,950 was given in grants to individuals.

HOW TO APPLY In writing to the correspondent. There are application forms for certain education grants.

WHO TO APPLY TO Lowman Manufacturing Co Ltd, Secretary, The Island, Lowman Green, Tiverton EX16 4LA *Tel.* 01884 254899 *Website* www.heathcoat.co.uk

■ Heathside Charitable Trust

CC NO 326959 **ESTABLISHED** 1985
WHERE FUNDING CAN BE GIVEN UK.
WHO CAN BENEFIT Charitable organisations, especially Jewish groups.
WHAT IS FUNDED General charitable purposes.
RANGE OF GRANTS £1,000–£141,100.
SAMPLE GRANTS Previously: Joint Jewish Charitable Trust (£141,000); Jewish Education Defence Trust and Community Security Trust (£25,000 each); Jewish Care (£15,000); and British Friends of Jaffa Institute, GRET and Motivation (£10,000 each).
FINANCES *Year* 2012 *Income* £598,382 *Grants* £508,119 *Assets* £2,757,930
TRUSTEES Sir Harry Solomon; Lady Judith Solomon; Geoffrey Jayson; Louise Jacobs; Daniel Solomon; Juliet Solomon.
OTHER INFORMATION In recent years, a list of grants has not been included in the trust's accounts.
HOW TO APPLY In writing to the correspondent, at any time. Trustees meet four times a year.
WHO TO APPLY TO Sir Harry Solomon, 32 Hampstead High Street, London NW3 1QD *Tel.* 020 7431 7739

■ The Charlotte Heber-Percy Charitable Trust

CC NO 284387 **ESTABLISHED** 1981
WHERE FUNDING CAN BE GIVEN Worldwide.
WHO CAN BENEFIT Charitable organisations.
WHAT IS FUNDED General charitable purposes, including: animal welfare; the environment; health; overseas aid; education; and the arts.
WHAT IS NOT FUNDED No grants to individuals.
TYPE OF GRANT One-off grants.
RANGE OF GRANTS £34,000–£1,000.
SAMPLE GRANTS Countryside Foundation (£34,000); ABF The Soldier's Charity (£20,000); Royal Shakespeare Company, Rugby Football Foundation and Ronald McDonald House (£10,000 each); Dumfries and Galloway Action (£8,000); Katherine House Hospice and Lawrence's Roundabout Well Appeal (£5,000 each); Remount (£3,000); St Andrew's Church – Naunton and War Memorial Trust (£2,000 each); and St John Ambulance and the Children's Trust (£1,000 each).
FINANCES *Year* 2011–12 *Income* £253,019 *Grants* £259,000 *Assets* £5,999,580
TRUSTEES Joanna Prest; Charlotte Heber-Percy.
OTHER INFORMATION In 2011–12, grants were made to 51 organisations totalling £259,000.
HOW TO APPLY The correspondent stated that unsolicited applications are not required.
WHO TO APPLY TO The Administrator, Rathbone Trust Company Limited, 1 Curzon Street, London W1J 5FB *Tel.* 020 7399 0820

■ Percy Hedley 1990 Charitable Trust

CC NO 1000033 **ESTABLISHED** 1990
WHERE FUNDING CAN BE GIVEN UK with a preference for Northumberland and Tyne and Wear.
WHO CAN BENEFIT Charitable organisations.
WHAT IS FUNDED General charitable purposes.
RANGE OF GRANTS Up to £5,000, but the majority of grants are for £500.
SAMPLE GRANTS Percy Hedley Foundation (£5,000); Newcastle Royal Grammar School Bursary Fund and Central Newcastle High School GDST Bursary Fund (£3,000 each); St Oswald's

Hospice, Anaphylaxis Campaign and Samaritans – Newcastle (£1,000 each) and Howick Church, Landmark Trust, Stroke Association, Combat Stress, Northumberland Wildlife Trust and The Grassland Trust (£500 each).
FINANCES *Year* 2011–12 *Income* £46,261 *Grants* £42,250 *Assets* £1,364,644
TRUSTEES John Armstrong; Bill Meikle; Fiona Ruffman.
HOW TO APPLY In writing to the correspondent. Trustees meet twice a year. 'We are happy to receive succinct applications. A financial statement can be welcome, but full annual report accounts are too much.'
WHO TO APPLY TO John Armstrong, Trustee, 10 Castleton Close, Newcastle upon Tyne NE2 2HF *Tel.* 01912 815953

■ The Hedley Denton Charitable Trust

CC NO 1060725 **ESTABLISHED** 1996
WHERE FUNDING CAN BE GIVEN Northeast England.
WHO CAN BENEFIT Charitable organisations, including those operating overseas.
WHAT IS FUNDED General charitable purposes.
RANGE OF GRANTS £250–£1,000.
SAMPLE GRANTS North East Promenaders Against Cancer, Brain Research Trust, Stamfordham Parish Church, DEC East Africa Crisis Appeal and Rift Valley Newcastle Justice Project (£1,000 each); Alzheimer's Research Trust, Free Tibet, Henshaw's Society for Blind People, National Youth Orchestra of Great Britain, Northumberland County Scout Council and The Royal National Mission for Deep Sea Fishermen (£500 each) and The Lord's Taverners, Newcastle Gang Show, Wallsend Sea Cadets, Deafblind UK and Consett Churches Detached Youth Project (£250 each).
FINANCES *Year* 2011–12 *Income* £45,445 *Grants* £38,500 *Assets* £1,037,029
TRUSTEES Iain Nicholson; Dorothy Wild; Charles Watts; Charles Nicholson.
HOW TO APPLY In writing to the correspondent. Applications are considered twice during the year and should be received before either the end of April or October.
WHO TO APPLY TO Iain Nicholson, Trustee, c/o Iain Nicholson and Co, 5 West Road, Ponteland, Newcastle upon Tyne NE20 9ST *Tel.* 01661 823863 *email* law@iainnicholson.co.uk

■ The Hedley Foundation

CC NO 262933 **ESTABLISHED** 1971
WHERE FUNDING CAN BE GIVEN UK.
WHO CAN BENEFIT Registered charities benefiting young people including their education, training and health; disabled people and the terminally-ill.
WHAT IS FUNDED Organisations working with young people, local church and community projects, organisations concerned with people who are disabled or seriously ill and medical equipment.
WHAT IS NOT FUNDED Grants are made to UK registered charities only. No support for individuals, churches and cathedrals, core revenue costs, salary or transport funding, or for very large appeals.
TYPE OF GRANT Grants for specific projects only, mostly one-off but a limited number of recurring grants for up to three years are given. No revenue or salary funding.

RANGE OF GRANTS £1,000–£15,000; average grant £3,000.

SAMPLE GRANTS Adventure Unlimited, Aspatria Dreamscheme, Barnet Community Projects, BASIC (Brain and Spinal Injury Centre), Brain Tumour Research Campaign, Community Action North Devon, Derby Kids Camp, Durham Wildlife Trust, Enable NI, Famous Trains Model Railway, Happy Days Children's Charity, Neuromuscular Centre Midlands, Scout Holiday Homes Trust, Warwickshire Association for the Blind, West Edinburgh Time Bank and Young Musicians Symphony Orchestra.

FINANCES *Year* 2011–12 *Income* £1,422,207 *Grants* £955,762 *Assets* £28,325,216

TRUSTEES John F. Meadows Rodwell, Chair; Patrick R. Holcroft; George R. Stratton Broke; Lt Col. Peter G. Chamberlin; Lorna B. Stuttaford; Angus Fanshawe; Lt. Col. Andrew Ford; David Byam-Cook.

HOW TO APPLY Application forms are downloadable from the foundation's website. Once completed in typescript, the form should be printed off and sent by post to the appeals secretary named above, accompanied by a recent copy of your accounts and your e-mail address. Note that the foundation is unable to return any enclosures that are sent in with applications.

The trustees meet six times a year. The closing date for a meeting is three weeks beforehand. All applications will be acknowledged, but, in the case of those short-listed, not until after they have been considered by the trustees. The trustees usually meet in January, March, May, July, September and November. A list of meeting dates for the current year is published on the foundation's website. The foundation receives many more applications than it can fund and urges that applicants should not be surprised, or too disappointed, if they are unsuccessful.

WHO TO APPLY TO Pauline Barker, Appeals Secretary, 1–3 College Hill, London EC4R 2RA *Tel.* 020 7489 8076 *email* pbarker@hedleyfoundation.org.uk *Website* www.hedleyfoundation.org.uk

■ The H. J. Heinz Company Limited Charitable Trust

CC NO 326254   **ESTABLISHED** 1982

WHERE FUNDING CAN BE GIVEN UK.

WHO CAN BENEFIT Organisations benefiting children and young adults, at-risk groups, people disadvantaged by poverty and socially isolated people.

WHAT IS FUNDED The trust typically supports medicine, welfare, education (food technology and nutrition in particular), conservation, community relations and the arts. UK bodies are more likely to be favoured than local groups unless local applicants operate in the immediate vicinity of the company's main operating locations.

WHAT IS NOT FUNDED No grants to individuals. Requests for political or denominational causes or for advertising are not considered.

TYPE OF GRANT One-off.

RANGE OF GRANTS Up to £5,000.

SAMPLE GRANTS Foundation for The Study of Infant Deaths, Children's Sunshine Home, Community Albums, Wigan Stars Nelson's Journey and Hope House Children's Hospice (£5,000 each)

FINANCES *Year* 2012 *Income* £33,673 *Grants* £51,897 *Assets* £46,964

TRUSTEES Drue Heinz; Simon Cowdroy; Nigel Dickie; Chris Humphries; Kelly Barker; P. Jones; S. Digby; C. Winter.

OTHER INFORMATION In 2012 grants were given to 35 organisations.

HOW TO APPLY In writing to the address below, no follow-up telephone calls. Applications are considered once or twice a year. Applicants, whether successful or unsuccessful, are informed of the trustees' decisions.

WHO TO APPLY TO Kelly Barker, Trust Administrator, Hayes Park South Building, Hayes End Road, Hayes, Middlesex UB4 8AL *Tel.* 020 8848 2346 *email* charitable.trust@uk.hjheinz.com *Website* www.heinz.co.uk

■ The Hellenic Foundation

CC NO 326301   **ESTABLISHED** 1982

WHERE FUNDING CAN BE GIVEN UK.

WHO CAN BENEFIT Organisations and individuals, to advance education in the cultural tradition and heritage of Greece, particularly in the subjects of education, philosophy, the arts and science.

WHAT IS FUNDED Projects involving education, research, music and dance, books and library facilities, and university symposia.

WHAT IS NOT FUNDED The foundation is unable to offer scholarships or grants to cover tuition fees and living expenses.

RANGE OF GRANTS Up to £15,000.

SAMPLE GRANTS Previously: Royal Academy Byzantine exhibition (£15,000); Theatro Technis (£1,000); and Aghia Shophia School (£200).

FINANCES *Year* 2012 *Income* £21,811 *Grants* £7,955

TRUSTEES Stamos J. Fafalios; Nicos H. Sideris; Constantinos I. Caroussis; Mary Bromley; George J. D. Lemos; Louisa Williamson; Joanna Caroussis; Nikki Chandris; Pantelis Michelakis.

HOW TO APPLY In writing to the correspondent.

WHO TO APPLY TO The Secretary, 150 Aldersgate Street, London EC1A 4AB *Tel.* 020 7251 5100

■ The Michael Heller Charitable Foundation

CC NO 327832   **ESTABLISHED** 1988

WHERE FUNDING CAN BE GIVEN Worldwide.

WHO CAN BENEFIT Organisations benefiting academics, medical professionals, research workers, scientists, students and teachers.

WHAT IS FUNDED Medical, education and scientific research.

WHAT IS NOT FUNDED No support for individuals.

RANGE OF GRANTS £5,000–£100,000.

FINANCES *Year* 2011–12 *Income* £240,453 *Grants* £202,889 *Assets* £3,756,419

TRUSTEES Morven Heller; Michael Heller; W. S. Trustee Company Ltd.

OTHER INFORMATION A list of beneficiaries was not provided in the trust's accounts.

HOW TO APPLY In writing to the correspondent.

WHO TO APPLY TO Michael Heller, Trustee, 24 Bruton Place, London W1J 6NE *Tel.* 020 7415 5000

■ The Simon Heller Charitable Settlement

CC NO 265405   **ESTABLISHED** 1972

WHERE FUNDING CAN BE GIVEN Worldwide.

WHO CAN BENEFIT Organisations benefiting academics, medical professionals, research workers, scientists, students and teachers as well as people in need.

WHAT IS FUNDED Medical research, scientific and educational research and humanitarian relief.

WHAT IS NOT FUNDED No grants to individuals.
SAMPLE GRANTS Previously: Institute for Jewish Policy Research (£35,000); Jewish Care (£30,000), Aish Hatora (£15,000 in two grants), Spiro Institute (£13,000), Scopus (£12,000 in two grants) and Chief Rabbinate Charitable Trust (£10,000).
FINANCES *Year* 2011–12 *Income* £385,467 *Grants* £338,229 *Assets* £7,161,200
TRUSTEES M. A. Heller; Morven Heller; W. S. Trustee Company Limited.
HOW TO APPLY In writing to the correspondent.
WHO TO APPLY TO The Trustees, 24 Bruton Place, London W1J 6NE *Tel.* 020 7415 5000

■ Help for Health (formerly The Humberside Charitable Health Trust)

CC NO 1091814   **ESTABLISHED** 2002
WHERE FUNDING CAN BE GIVEN Humberside.
WHO CAN BENEFIT Registered charities.
WHAT IS FUNDED Healthcare provision (including facilities and equipment), medical research and medical education.
SAMPLE GRANTS Yorkshire Scan Appeal (£70,000); Dove House Hospice (£50,000); Hull University (£25,000); St John Ambulance (£11,000); and the Motor Neurone Disease Association (£5,000).
FINANCES *Year* 2011–12 *Income* £73,367 *Grants* £194,450 *Assets* £4,151,965
TRUSTEES Keith Gorton; Julie Bielby; Prof. Peter Lee; Stuart Smith; Wendy Thomas; Andrew Mould; Andrew Milner; Richard Field.
HOW TO APPLY On a form available to download from the website. The trustees meet bi-monthly.
WHO TO APPLY TO Andrew Milner, Chair of Trustees, c/o Baker Tilly, 2 Humber Quays, Wellington Street West, Hull HU1 2BN *Tel.* 01964 550725 *email* info@helphealth.org.uk *Website* www.helphealth.org.uk

■ Help the Homeless

CC NO 271988   **ESTABLISHED** 1975
WHERE FUNDING CAN BE GIVEN UK
WHO CAN BENEFIT Small-medium and/or new, registered charities with a turnover of less than £1 million a year. Grants to larger charities are considered if the project is suitably innovative and it is only possible for a large organisation to develop it.
WHAT IS FUNDED Projects which assist individuals in their return to mainstream society, rather than simply offer shelter or other forms of sustenance.
WHAT IS NOT FUNDED Charities with substantial funds are not supported. No grants to individuals.
TYPE OF GRANT Capital costs.
RANGE OF GRANTS Normally up to £3,000. Trustees will also consider applications for larger pump priming grants for major and innovative projects.
SAMPLE GRANTS Bradford City Centre Project, West London Day Centre, Homeless in Action, Say Women and Youth Shelter (£3,000 each); Room at the Inn (£2,800); Furniture Plus, Ross-shire Women's Aid and St George's Hub (£2,000 each); Urban Outreach and South Birmingham Young Homeless Project (£1,500 each) and The Nehemiah Project (£400).
FINANCES *Year* 2011–12 *Income* £74,821 *Grants* £46,084 *Assets* £1,192,725
TRUSTEES F. J. Bergin; T. S. Cookson; T. Rogers; P. Fullerton; J. Rose; S. Holmes.

HOW TO APPLY Application forms can be downloaded from the trust's website. The quarterly deadlines for applications each year are: 31 March, 30 June, 30 September and 31 December.
WHO TO APPLY TO Terry Kenny, Secretary, 6th Floor, 248 Tottenham Court Road, London W1T 7QZ *email* hth@help-the-homeless.org.uk *Website* www.help-the-homeless.org.uk

■ Help the Hospices

CC NO 1014851   **ESTABLISHED** 1984
WHERE FUNDING CAN BE GIVEN UK and overseas.
WHO CAN BENEFIT Hospices, palliative care units and their staff.
WHAT IS FUNDED Grant programmes vary; go to the website for up-to-date details of open and forthcoming programmes.
TYPE OF GRANT One-off and recurrent.
SAMPLE GRANTS St Luke's Hospice (£78,000); St Giles Hospice (£51,000); St Catherine's Hospice (£49,000); Rowcroft – Torbay and S Devon Hospice (£30,000); Farleigh Hospice (£7,000); Children's Hospice Association Scotland (£5,000); Richard House Children's Hospice (£2,000).
FINANCES *Year* 2011–12 *Income* £5,748,000 *Grants* £582,000 *Assets* £6,786,000
TRUSTEES Lee Barker; Peter Holliday; Andrew Ryde; Michael Howard; Bay Green; Paul Dyer; Patrick Beasley; Ros Taylor; Susan Newman; Christine Miles; Rosalind Scott.
OTHER INFORMATION A further £1 million was given in grants to individuals.
HOW TO APPLY The website provides guidelines for each programme and clear information on application procedures and deadlines. Depending on the programme, application forms can be downloaded or completed through the online application system.
WHO TO APPLY TO Grants Team, 34–44 Britannia Street, London WC1X 9JG *Tel.* 020 7520 8200 *Fax* 020 7278 1021 *email* info@helpthehospices.org.uk *Website* www.helpthehospices.org.uk

■ The Helping Foundation

CC NO 1104484   **ESTABLISHED** 2004
WHERE FUNDING CAN BE GIVEN Greater London and Greater Manchester.
WHO CAN BENEFIT Institutions and registered charities.
WHAT IS FUNDED The advancement of education according to the tenets of the Orthodox Jewish Faith; the advancement of the Orthodox Jewish Religion and the relief of poverty amongst the elderly or persons in need, hardship or distress in the Jewish Community.
TYPE OF GRANT Recurrent grants.
RANGE OF GRANTS Mostly up to around £50,000.
SAMPLE GRANTS Previous beneficiaries have included: Asser Bishvil Foundation (£2 million); British Friends of Ezrat Yisrael (£670,000); Notzar Chesed (£236,500); New Rachmistrivka Synagogue Trust (£201,000); TTT (£198,500); Emuno Educational Centre (£163,000); United Talmudical Associates (£160,000); BCG CT (£105,000); Friends for the Centre for Torah Education Centre (£57,000); Toimchei Shabbos Manchester (£30,000); Gateshead Kollel (£20,000); Beis Naduorna (£10,000); and Law of Truth (£5,500).
FINANCES *Year* 2012 *Income* £13,734,804 *Grants* £7,190,102 *Assets* £76,774,112

TRUSTEES Benny Stone; David Neuwirth; Rabbi Aubrey Weis; Rachel Weis.

OTHER INFORMATION A list of beneficiaries was not available.

HOW TO APPLY In writing to the correspondent.

WHO TO APPLY TO Benny Stone, Trustee, 1 Allandale Court, Waterpark Road, Salford M7 4JN *Tel.* 01617 40116

■ The Hemby Trust

CC NO 1073028   **ESTABLISHED** 1998

WHERE FUNDING CAN BE GIVEN Merseyside and Wirral.

WHO CAN BENEFIT Charitable organisations.

WHAT IS FUNDED Social needs, community facilities and services, youth and employment, schools and colleges, help for older people, health, the arts, culture and recreation, the environment and church buildings.

WHAT IS NOT FUNDED Grants will not be given to political organisations, pressure groups or individuals, feasibility studies, organisations outside Merseyside or Wirral, or to replace statutory funding.

TYPE OF GRANT Capital grants.

RANGE OF GRANTS £250–£10,000

SAMPLE GRANTS Fairbridge Merseyside (£10,000); University of Liverpool – Better Births Appeal (£5,000); Zoe's Place Hospice (£4,000); Furniture Resource Centre Ltd. and Tall Ships Youth Trust (£2,000 each); National Youth Orchestra of Great Britain, UK North Blind Sailing Association, The Salvation Army and The Tuesday Club (£1,500 each); Tranmere Residents Association and Wirral Community Narrowboat Trust (£1,000 each); Viking Centre and Youth Club, Liverpool Film Academy Educational Trust and Southport and Formby Beekeepers (£500 each) and Jesus Ministries International North West (£250).

FINANCES *Year* 2011–12 *Income* £95,940 *Grants* £99,458 *Assets* £2,458,454

TRUSTEES Roy Morris; Caroline Tod; Andrew Morris; Nicholas Wainwright; Percival Furlong.

OTHER INFORMATION Grants were distributed to 81 organisations in 2011–12.

HOW TO APPLY Applicants should write to the correspondent for a leaflet which sets out the aims and objectives of the trust and an application form which should be returned with a copy of the applicant's latest accounts. A date will be given for the return of the form if it is to be discussed by the trustees at their next meeting. The trustees meet at the end of March, July and November. Applications are not acknowledged, but the applicant is welcome to telephone the correspondent to check it has been received.

WHO TO APPLY TO Michael Hope, c/o Rathbone Investment Management, Port of Liverpool Building, Pier Head, Liverpool L3 1NW *Tel.* 01704 834887

■ The Christina Mary Hendrie Trust for Scottish and Canadian Charities

SC NO SC014514   **ESTABLISHED** 1975

WHERE FUNDING CAN BE GIVEN Scotland and Canada.

WHO CAN BENEFIT Charities benefiting young people and older people.

WHAT IS FUNDED Charities connected with young people and older people, especially war veterans.

WHAT IS NOT FUNDED Grants are not given to individuals.

TYPE OF GRANT Up to one year.

RANGE OF GRANTS Typical grants £5,000–£50,000+.

SAMPLE GRANTS Camphill Blair Drummond (£20,000); PKAVS, Portage Program and ACCORD Hospice Paisley (£10,000 each); Freeing the Human Spirit and Wester Hailes Youth Society (£9,000 each); Down's Syndrome Scotland and Fernandez Earle Scholarship Foundation (£5,000 each); and Highland Skate Park (£2,000).

FINANCES *Year* 2011–12 *Income* £103,298 *Grants* £224,300 *Assets* £6,046,739

TRUSTEES Charles Cox; John Scott-Moncrieff; Caroline Irwin; Anthony Cox; Mary-Rose Grieve; Susie Hendrie; Andrew Desson; Caron Hughes.

OTHER INFORMATION 33 grants to organisations totalling £224,000 were provided in 2011–12.

HOW TO APPLY Application forms can be accessed via the trust's website. Applications forms must be sent to the trust by post. The trustees meet twice yearly in March and October. To be considered for the meeting in March, applications must be made no later than 15 February and 15 September for the October meeting. Applications are acknowledged via email.

WHO TO APPLY TO Alan Sharp, Secretary, 1 Rutland Court, Edinburgh EH3 8EY *Tel.* 01312 707700 *Website* www.christinamaryhendrietrust.com

■ Henley Educational Trust (formerly Henley Educational Charity)

CC NO 309237   **ESTABLISHED** 1604

WHERE FUNDING CAN BE GIVEN Henley-on-Thames and the parishes of Bix and Rotherfield Greys in Oxfordshire and Remenham in Berkshire only.

WHO CAN BENEFIT Individuals and organisations concerned with the education of children, young adults and people who are disadvantaged. State-maintained schools and colleges in the area defined above.

WHAT IS FUNDED Grants are given to alleviate financial hardship, to support particular educational initiatives and courses and to help meet the cost of educational visits, books and equipment at a local school or college.

WHAT IS NOT FUNDED Applicants for individual grants must be under 25 years of age, and must either be resident in the area of benefit or have attended a state-maintained school in the area for at least two years.

TYPE OF GRANT Mainly one-off grants for core and capital support; also project funding.

RANGE OF GRANTS All applications considered individually.

SAMPLE GRANTS Henley Schools Partnership (£40,000); Gillots (£14,000); Henley College (£6,000); Trinity and Henley Youth Centre (£5,000 each); Henley Youth festival (£4,000); Sacred Heart (£3,000); Valley Road (£2,750) and Crazies Hill (£900).

FINANCES *Year* 2011–12 *Income* £144,765 *Grants* £93,756 *Assets* £3,013,883

TRUSTEES William Hamilton; Marjorie Hall; Guy Norgrove; William Parrish; Maureen Smith; Rosalind Whittaker; Stephan Gawrysiak; Amanda Heath; Colin Homent; Revd Canon Martyn Griffiths.

OTHER INFORMATION The area of benefit is restricted to the parishes of Henley, Bix, Remenham and Rotherfield Greys or the applicants must currently attend or have attended for a minimum of two years the nominated schools within the above areas (see website). Individual applicants must be under 25 years of age.

HOW TO APPLY On a form available to download from the trust's website (www.henleyeducationaltrust.com), where criteria and guidelines are also posted, and returned to the correspondent by post.

WHO TO APPLY TO Claire Brown, Clerk, Syringa Cottage, Horsepond Road, Gallowstree Common, Reading, Berkshire RG4 9BP *Tel.* 01189 724575 *email* henleyeducationalcharity@hotmail.co.uk *Website* www.henleyeducationaltrust.com

■ Philip Henman Trust

CC NO 1054707　　　**ESTABLISHED** 1986
WHERE FUNDING CAN BE GIVEN Worldwide.
WHO CAN BENEFIT UK-registered charities concerned with long term overseas development and UK registered charities working with children in developing countries.
WHAT IS FUNDED Grants are aimed at established major UK registered charity (normally defined as having an income of over £100,000 per annum). The funding from the trust should be important to the project, normally accounting for between 20% and 80% of the total project budget. The project should be partly funded by other sources, voluntary work and central office administration costs can be counted as other source funding.
WHAT IS NOT FUNDED The trust does not fund ongoing concerns.
TYPE OF GRANT Partnership grants for three to five years. Projects must start and finish within five years.
One-off grants are not available.
RANGE OF GRANTS £3,000–£5,000 per year. A maximum of £25,000 over the course of the project.
SAMPLE GRANTS Overseas aid (£40,000); Medical and community work (£5,000); Individuals (£2,000); Other (£850).
FINANCES *Year* 2012–13 *Income* £59,632 *Grants* £47,778 *Assets* £1,852,099
TRUSTEES Joseph Charles Clark; David James Clark; Jason Colin Duffey.
OTHER INFORMATION The grant total includes £2,000 awarded to individuals.
HOW TO APPLY Applications are only considered once a year – the deadline is always 10 September. Applications are no longer accepted by post. Use the online form (available on the 'Applications' page) to submit a request for funding.
WHO TO APPLY TO Joseph Charles Clark, Trustee, 16 Pembury Road, Tonbridge TN9 2HX *Tel.* 01732 362227 *email* info@pht.org.uk *Website* www.pht.org.uk

■ Esther Hennell Charitable Trust

CC NO 261477　　　**ESTABLISHED** 1970
WHERE FUNDING CAN BE GIVEN UK.
WHO CAN BENEFIT Registered charities.
WHAT IS FUNDED General charitable purposes.
WHAT IS NOT FUNDED No grants to individuals.
SAMPLE GRANTS Previous beneficiaries include: Emmanuel Church Wimbledon, Strangers' Rest Mission, Shaftesbury Society, Whitefield Christian Trust, Barnabas Fund, Interserve, Tear Fund, AIM, South Asian Concern and Crosslinks UK.

FINANCES *Year* 2011–12 *Income* £18,568 *Grants* £23,340
TRUSTEES Esther Hennell; Jane Hunt; Nicholas Smith.
HOW TO APPLY In writing to the correspondent.
WHO TO APPLY TO Nicholas Smith, Trustee, Currey and Co, 21 Buckingham Gate, London SW1E 6LS *Tel.* 020 7802 2700

■ The G. D. Herbert Charitable Trust

CC NO 295998　　　**ESTABLISHED** 1986
WHERE FUNDING CAN BE GIVEN UK.
WHO CAN BENEFIT Registered charities.
WHAT IS FUNDED The trust supports medicine, health, welfare and environmental resources. It mainly gives regular grants to a set list of charities, with a few one-off grants given each year.
TYPE OF GRANT Mainly recurrent.
RANGE OF GRANTS Up to £2,500
SAMPLE GRANTS The National Trust, The Abbeyfield Society, Canterbury Oast Trust, Campaign to Protect Rural England, Friends of the Elderly, Marie Curie Cancer Care, NSPCC, Catch 22, Disability Rights UK, St Christopher Hospice and The Woodland Trust (£2,700 each) and Ogbourne St George Parochial Church Council and Wiltshire Wildlife Trust (£600 each).
FINANCES *Year* 2011–12 *Income* £48,454 *Grants* £63,300 *Assets* £1,863,542
TRUSTEES M. E. Beaumont; J. M. Cuxson.
HOW TO APPLY In writing to the correspondent. No applications are invited other than from those charities currently supported by the trust.
WHO TO APPLY TO M. J. Byrne, Trustee, Veale Wasbrough Vizards, Barnards Inn, 86 Fetter Lane, London EC4A 1AD *Tel.* 020 7405 1234

■ The Anne Herd Memorial Trust

SC NO SC014198　　　**ESTABLISHED** 1990
WHERE FUNDING CAN BE GIVEN Scotland, with a preference for the City of Dundee, and the community of Broughty Ferry in particular.
WHO CAN BENEFIT People who are visually impaired.
WHAT IS FUNDED Organisations working in the beneficial area within visually impaired individuals.
FINANCES *Year* 2011–12 *Income* £36,662
HOW TO APPLY In writing to the correspondent. Trustees meet once a year to consider grants, usually in June. Applications should be received by March/April.
WHO TO APPLY TO The Trustees, Bowman Scottish Lawyers, 27 Bank Street, Dundee DD1 1RP

■ The Herefordshire Community Foundation

CC NO 1094935　　　**ESTABLISHED** 2002
WHERE FUNDING CAN BE GIVEN Herefordshire.
WHO CAN BENEFIT Community and voluntary groups and individuals in Herefordshire.
WHAT IS FUNDED General charitable purposes.
RANGE OF GRANTS Up to £27,000.
SAMPLE GRANTS Herefordshire Cider Museum (£27,000); Marches Access Point and SHIRE Herefordshire (£11,000 each); Newton Farm Community Centre (£10,000) and Wye Learn (£7,000).
FINANCES *Year* 2011–12 *Income* £475,349 *Grants* £100,036 *Assets* £1,620,454

Think carefully about every application. Is it justified?

617

TRUSTEES Wilma Gilmour; Will Lindesay; Sally Pettipher; Barbara Parkinson; Nat Hone; Raymond Hunter; David Snow.

OTHER INFORMATION The majority of grants are for less than £1,000.

HOW TO APPLY HCF administers a number of different funds which includes Comic/Sport Relief, ESF Community Grants and PCT Small Schemes. These all have their specific application processes and criteria and the forms are available to download from the website. Applications for under £1,000 can also be made in writing to the foundation and must include the following information: contact details, what is the grant to be used for and when, a budget/costs and why the grant is needed. Initial telephone calls are welcome.

WHO TO APPLY TO David Barclay, Director, The Fred Bulmer Centre, Wall Street, Hereford HR4 9HP *Tel.* 01432 272550 *email* dave.barclay@ herefordshire-cf.co.uk *Website* herefordshirecommunityfoundation.org

....

■ The Herefordshire Historic Churches Trust

CC NO 511181   **ESTABLISHED** 1954

WHERE FUNDING CAN BE GIVEN Old county of Herefordshire.

WHO CAN BENEFIT All Christian places of worship.

WHAT IS FUNDED The restoration, preservation, repair, maintenance and improvement of churches, their contents and their churchyards in Herefordshire.

WHAT IS NOT FUNDED Grants cannot be given for general maintenance of lighting, heating, decoration or furnishings

TYPE OF GRANT Capital, core and start-up costs. Unrestricted funding.

RANGE OF GRANTS Up to £10,000.

SAMPLE GRANTS Beneficiaries included the parishes of: Llangarron, Leintwardine and Hoarwithy (£10,000 each); Woolhope (£5,000); Llanwarne (£4,000); Credenhill (£3,000); Credenhill (£2,000) and Little Dewchurch (£750).

FINANCES *Year* 2012 *Income* £63,687 *Grants* £64,300 *Assets* £751,410

TRUSTEES Earl of Darnley; David Furnival; James Devereux; Lady Susanna McFarlane; Robin Peers; Simon Arbuthnott; Ven Canon Patrick Benson; Ali Jones; Jill Gallimore.

HOW TO APPLY On a form available to download from the website. Deadlines for applications are 15 March and 15 September.

WHO TO APPLY TO Sarah de Rohan, Secretary, Birley Court, Birley, Herefordshire HR4 8ET *Tel.* 01568 720423 *email* derohans@ btinternet.com *Website* www. herefordhistoricchurchestrust.org.uk

....

■ The Heritage of London Trust Ltd

CC NO 280272   **ESTABLISHED** 1980

WHERE FUNDING CAN BE GIVEN All 33 London boroughs.

WHO CAN BENEFIT Listed buildings in London.

WHAT IS FUNDED The restoration of buildings of architectural importance. Grants are mainly given for skilled restoration of notable features of listed buildings, generally (though not exclusively) external work. Examples of buildings assisted are churches, community centres, almshouses, theatres, hospitals, museums and educational establishments.

WHAT IS NOT FUNDED Buildings in private ownership that are not open or available for public use and enjoyment, roof replacements or repairs, restoration schemes where the work has already been completed or general maintenance or repairs.

RANGE OF GRANTS Usually up to £5,000.

SAMPLE GRANTS St Mary and Holy Trinity, Bow, Kings College, Somerset House and St Luke's Church, Charlton (£5,000 each); Blackheath Concert Halls (£4,000); Old Royal Naval College (£3,000); Kew Gardens (£2,600) and Myers tomb at West Norwood Cemetery (£1,000).

FINANCES *Year* 2011–12 *Income* £101,345 *Grants* £52,630 *Assets* £444,639

TRUSTEES James Cayzer-Colvin; Lady Caroline Egremont; Nicholas Bell; Cllr Robert Davies; John Fishburn; Cllr Denise Jones; Alec Forshaw; Michael Hoare; Roger Bright; Geoffrey Hunter; Edward Benyon; Philip Davies; Emily Arnold.

PUBLICATIONS Map: *Historic Buildings in Covent Garden.*

OTHER INFORMATION In 2011–12 grants were given to 16 organisations.

HOW TO APPLY On a form available to download from the website (www.heritageoflondon.com), where criteria, guidelines and application deadlines are also posted.

WHO TO APPLY TO Diana Beattie, Director, Heritage of London Trust, 34 Grosvenor Gardens, London SW1W 0DH *Tel.* 020 7730 9472 *Fax* 020 7117 1125 *email* contact@heritageoflondon. com *Website* www.heritageoflondon.com

....

■ The Hertfordshire Community Foundation

CC NO 299438   **ESTABLISHED** 1988

WHERE FUNDING CAN BE GIVEN Hertfordshire.

WHO CAN BENEFIT Organisations which benefit local people. Many are smaller, less well-known groups or less 'popular' causes that often find it extremely difficult to obtain funds elsewhere.

WHAT IS FUNDED To support the work of local charities and voluntary groups for the benefit of the community, with the following particular concerns: disadvantaged children and families; developing young people; access to education, training and employment; the needs of older people and other community needs. Grants are made for a variety of needs including: running costs; training; staff costs; equipment and new initiatives.

WHAT IS NOT FUNDED No grants are made towards: political groups; animal welfare; projects that are solely environmental; statutory agencies; medical research; religious activities or individuals.

TYPE OF GRANT Project grants up to £5,000 for specific purpose, start-up or development.

RANGE OF GRANTS £100–£10,000 per year for up to three years.

SAMPLE GRANTS Previous beneficiaries include: Citizens Advice – Hertfordshire, Broxbourne and East Hertfordshire Credit Union, Hertfordshire PASS, Satsang Mandal, Hitchin Town Bowls Club, Age Concern Hertfordshire, Hertfordshire Area Rape Crisis and Sexual Abuse Centre, Dacorum Indian Society, Neomari Beadcraft Training Services, Grandparents' Association, and Alzheimer's Disease Society.

FINANCES *Year* 2011–12 *Income* £1,833,429 *Grants* £446,886 *Assets* £6,429,452

TRUSTEES J. Stuart Lewis, Chair; Kate Belinis; Jo Connell; Gerald Corbett; David Fryer; Pat Garrard; Mike Master; Caroline McCaffrey; Brig

John Palmer; John Peters; Penny Williams; Cllr Christopher Hayward.

PUBLICATIONS Leaflets; newsletter; guidelines for applicants.

OTHER INFORMATION For further information on the grant programmes currently available consult the foundation's website.

HOW TO APPLY Ideally, applications should be made online via the foundation's website. However, if it is not possible to apply online, contact the foundation and they will send an application pack by post or email. An initial telephone call or e-mail to check eligibility is also welcomed. Applicants may be contacted by telephone to discuss their work and if it is your first application to the foundation a site visit may be arranged. For amounts of £500 or more the grants committee meets quarterly to review applications.

WHO TO APPLY TO Christine Mills, Grants Manager, Foundation House, 2–4 Forum Place, Fiddlebridge Lane, Hatfield, Hertfordshire AL10 0RN *Tel.* 01707 251351 *email* grants@hertscf.org.uk *Website* www.hertscf.org.uk

....

■ Hesed Trust

CC NO 1000489   **ESTABLISHED** 1990

WHERE FUNDING CAN BE GIVEN UK and overseas.

WHO CAN BENEFIT Christian charities benefiting children, young adults, older people, clergy, students, Christians and evangelists.

WHAT IS FUNDED Christian charitable purposes. The trust will consider funding the advancement of religion and the Free Church umbrella bodies.

WHAT IS NOT FUNDED No support for expeditions and individual requests.

TYPE OF GRANT One-off grants, for one year or less.

RANGE OF GRANTS Up to £45,000

SAMPLE GRANTS Ministries without Borders (£42,000); All Nations Church (£24,000); Blackpool Church and City Church Coventry (£10,000 each); and Covenant Life Church Leicester (£750).

FINANCES *Year* 2010–11 *Income* £179,147 *Grants* £68,206 *Assets* £74,522

TRUSTEES Ronald Eagle; Glyn Rawlings; Charles Smith.

OTHER INFORMATION The accounts for 2011–12 were overdue at the Charity Commission at the time of writing (December 2013), being 319 days late.

HOW TO APPLY In writing to the correspondent.

WHO TO APPLY TO Glyn Rawlings, Trustee, 14 Chiltern Avenue, Cosby, Leicestershire LE9 1UF *Tel.* 01162 862990 *email* glynrawlings@btopenworld.com

....

■ The Hesslewood Children's Trust (Hull Seamen's and General Orphanage)

CC NO 529804   **ESTABLISHED** 1982

WHERE FUNDING CAN BE GIVEN East Yorkshire and North Lincolnshire.

WHO CAN BENEFIT Individuals and organisations in the area defined above, benefiting children and young adults under 25. Support will be given to people in care, or who are fostered or adopted; people who are disabled; people disadvantaged by poverty; ex-offenders and people at risk of offending; homeless people; people living in both rural and urban areas; socially isolated people; and victims of abuse and crime.

WHAT IS FUNDED To provide aid for young individuals in need and to support youth organisations for holidays. Particularly supported are charities working in the fields of education, housing and accommodation, and arts, culture and recreation.

WHAT IS NOT FUNDED No grants to benefit people over the age of 25 will be made.

TYPE OF GRANT One-off. Funding may be given for up to one year. Equipment. Start-up costs.

RANGE OF GRANTS Up to £21,000

SAMPLE GRANTS Hull Compact Ltd. (£21,000); North Ferriby Riding for Disabled (£8,000); Dyslexia Association (£5,000); Endsleigh Holy Child Primary School (£4,500); Barnardo's Sibling Support Service (£2,000); Braveheart Sport Foundation (£1,000).

FINANCES *Year* 2011–12 *Income* £90,742 *Grants* £80,000

TRUSTEES Dudley Moore; Ross Allenby; Dr Christopher Woodyatt; Colin Andrews; David Turner; Revd Timothy Boyns; Gaynel Munn; Deena Lidgett; Dr David Nicholas; Philip Evans. Capt. Philip Watts.

HOW TO APPLY On a form available from the correspondent, with a telephone number if possible. The trustees meet to consider applications at least three times a year. No replies are given to ineligible organisations. This trust informed us that it promotes its work through its own avenues, receiving more applications than it can support.

WHO TO APPLY TO R. E. Booth, Secretary, 1 Canada Drive, Cherry Burton, East Yorkshire HU17 7RQ *Tel.* 01946 550474

....

■ Hexham and Newcastle Diocesan Trust (1947)

CC NO 235686   **ESTABLISHED** 1867

WHERE FUNDING CAN BE GIVEN Diocese of Hexham and Newcastle, overseas.

WHO CAN BENEFIT Roman Catholic organisations.

WHAT IS FUNDED This trust supports the advancement of the Roman Catholic religion in Hexham and Newcastle by both initiating its own projects and giving grants to other organisations.

TYPE OF GRANT One-off and reoccuring.

RANGE OF GRANTS Up to £300,000

SAMPLE GRANTS CAFOD Development and emergency aid (£203,000); Papal Visit (£119,000); National Catholic Fund (£86,000); Catholic Education Service (£46,000); Holy Places (£28,000); Sick and Retired Priests NBF (£25,000); Apostleship of the Sea (£21,000); Day for Life (£13,000); Peter's Pence (£20,000) and Day for Life (£13,000).

FINANCES *Year* 2011–12 *Income* £21,867,000 *Grants* £1,050,000 *Assets* £69,336,000

TRUSTEES Very Revd Seamus Cunningham; Revd Gerard Lavender; Revd James O'Keefe; Revd Martin Stempczyk; Revd Christopher Jackson; Revd John Butters; Msgr Philip Carroll.

HOW TO APPLY Contact the correspondent. The accounts note the following about the grantmaking policy: 'Each year the Bishop, assisted by guidance from the Catholic Bishops' Conference of England and Wales, decides which organisations will benefit from special collections to be taken in the parishes. At a local level, parish priests and their finance committees decide which additional causes they will support to further the work of the Church, by means of special appeals. The amounts raised from such appeals and paid over to charities are sometimes supplemented from general offertory income, where this is approved by the parish priest and the parish finance committee.'

WHO TO APPLY TO Kathleen Smith, St Cuthberts House, West Road, Newcastle upon Tyne NE15 7PY *Tel.* 01912 433300 *Fax* 01912 433309 *email* office@rcdhn.org.uk *Website* rcdhn.org.uk

■ The P. and C. Hickinbotham Charitable Trust

CC NO 216432   **ESTABLISHED** 1947
WHERE FUNDING CAN BE GIVEN UK, with a preference for Leicestershire and Rutland.
WHO CAN BENEFIT Registered charities only. Particular favour is given to Quakers.
WHAT IS FUNDED The trust has a preference for Quaker organisations and general charities based in Leicester, Rutland, North Wales and Northern Ireland.
WHAT IS NOT FUNDED No grants to individuals applying for bursary-type assistance or to large UK charities.
TYPE OF GRANT Usually one-off grants.
RANGE OF GRANTS Up to £15,000, most grants made between £1,000 and £2,000.
SAMPLE GRANTS Beneficiaries included: DeMontfort University – Women in Technology Programme (£9,000); Community Foundation for Northern Ireland and Lyddington Village Hall Trust (£5,000 each); Altnaveigh House (£3,500); Mullaghdun Community Association (£2,000); Belgrave Playhouse (£1,500) LOROS, RNLI, Pen Green Centre and Staffordshire Area Quaker Meeting (£1,000 each).
FINANCES *Year* 2011–12 *Income* £65,283 *Grants* £86,962 *Assets* £3,503,163
TRUSTEES Catherine Hickinbotham; Roger Hickinbotham; Rachel Hickinbotham; Anna Steiger.
HOW TO APPLY In writing to the correspondent, giving a brief outline of the purpose of the grant. Replies will not be sent to unsuccessful applicants. Successful applicants are usually contacted within six weeks.
WHO TO APPLY TO Roger Hickinbotham, Trustee, 9 Windmill Way, Lyddington, Oakham, Leicestershire LE15 9LY *Tel.* 01572 821236 *email* roger@hickinbothamtrust.org.uk *Website* www.hickinbothamtrust.org.uk

■ The Rosalind Hicks Charitable Trust

CC NO 1050135   **ESTABLISHED** 1995
WHERE FUNDING CAN BE GIVEN Preference for Devon.
WHO CAN BENEFIT Charitable organisations.
WHAT IS FUNDED General charitable purposes.
RANGE OF GRANTS £500–£5,000.
SAMPLE GRANTS Exeter Royal Academy for Deaf (£3,500); Handicapped Children's Action (£2,600); Children and Families in Grief (£2,400); Chew Lake Association of Disabled Sailors (£2,000); Dream Holidays (£1,800) Devon Wildlife Trust and Chill'd Out Youth Project (£1,000 each) and PDSA (£500).
FINANCES *Year* 2011–12 *Income* £34,664 *Grants* £29,287 *Assets* £644,612
TRUSTEES Nigel Wollen; Christopher Hart; Alexandra Clementson; James Pritchard; John Mallowan.
OTHER INFORMATION In 2011–12 grants were awarded to 17 organisations.
HOW TO APPLY In writing to the correspondent.

WHO TO APPLY TO The Trustees, c/o Wollen Michelmore Solicitors, Carlton House, 30 The Terrace, Torquay TQ1 1BS *Tel.* 01803 213251 *Fax* 01803 296871

■ The Higgs Charitable Trust

CC NO 267036   **ESTABLISHED** 1982
WHERE FUNDING CAN BE GIVEN UK, with a preference for the former county of Avon.
WHO CAN BENEFIT Mostly medical research trusts or foundations. Organisations benefiting children, young adults, older people and people who are disadvantaged by poverty or homeless.
WHAT IS FUNDED Mainly research into deafness carried out by private charitable foundations. Also considered are charities working in the fields of religious buildings; housing and accommodation; animal facilities and services; conservation and campaigning; and education and training.
TYPE OF GRANT One-off and research. Funding for more than three years will be considered.
RANGE OF GRANTS Up to £18,000.
SAMPLE GRANTS TWJ Foundation (£10,000).
FINANCES *Year* 2012 *Income* £29,483 *Grants* £10,000 *Assets* £801,058
TRUSTEES D. W. M. Campbell; T. W. Higgs; L. Humphris; P. Humphris.
OTHER INFORMATION Governance/support costs for this charity remain very high in relation to the grants total, at almost £5,000. The accounts state: 'During the year the trust entered into transactions with Mogers, Solicitors, of which Mr D W M Campbell is a partner. During the year services to the value of £4,042 were acquired from the firm. These transactions were charged at normal professional rates.' It is not clear from the accounts what these services were.
HOW TO APPLY In writing to the correspondent, not less than two months before the annual general meeting in November.
WHO TO APPLY TO Derwent Campbell, Trustee, 24 Queen Square, Bath BA1 2HY *Tel.* 01225 750000

■ Alan Edward Higgs Charity

CC NO 509367   **ESTABLISHED** 1979
WHERE FUNDING CAN BE GIVEN Within 25 miles of the centre of Coventry only.
WHO CAN BENEFIT Registered charities where their activity will benefit young people either directly, through their family, or through the provision of facilities or services to the community.
WHAT IS FUNDED Activities or projects that contribute to the amelioration of deprivation.
WHAT IS NOT FUNDED No grants for individuals or the funding of services usually provided by statutory services, medical research, travel outside the UK or evangelical or worship activities.
TYPE OF GRANT One-off capital for buildings and equipment; will consider both core and revenue funding of projects.
RANGE OF GRANTS Typically £500–£30,000.
SAMPLE GRANTS Previous grant beneficiaries included: Coventry Institute of Creative Enterprise (£40,000); The Living Environment Trust (£28,000); Belgrade Theatre (£20,000); Family Holiday Association (£10,000); Shakespeare Hospice Appeal (£5,000); Guideposts Trust (£3,000); and the RSPB (£1,000).
FINANCES *Year* 2010–11 *Income* £477,100 *Grants* £236,063 *Assets* £19,122,087

TRUSTEES Peter J. Davis; Marilyn F. Knatchbull-Hugessen; Andrew Young.

OTHER INFORMATION During 2010/11, there were 50 grants awarded. The average grant was for £4,700.

HOW TO APPLY In writing to the clerk to the trustees, along with: a copy of the latest audited accounts; charity number (if registered); a detailed description of the local activities for the benefit of which the grant would be applied; the specific purpose for which the grant is sought; a copy of the organisation's policy that ensures the protection of young or vulnerable people and a clear description of how it is implemented and monitored.

WHO TO APPLY TO Peter Knatchbull-Hugessen, Clerk, Ricoh Arena Ltd, Phoenix Way, Coventry CV6 6GE *Tel.* 02476 221311 *email* clerk@higgscharity.org.uk

---

■ The Graham High Charitable Trust

CC NO 1149046   **ESTABLISHED** 2012

WHERE FUNDING CAN BE GIVEN UK.

WHO CAN BENEFIT Charities and community groups.

WHAT IS FUNDED General charitable purposes, with a specific focus on organisations working with children and young people, older people, people with disabilities and ethnic communities.

TRUSTEES Graham High; Bruce Elkins; Jean High; Michael Chappell.

HOW TO APPLY In writing to the correspondent.

WHO TO APPLY TO Graham High, Trustee, c/o CW Fellowes Accountants) Templars House, Lulworth Close, Chandlers Ford, Hampshire SO53 3TL

■ The High Sheriff's Police Trust for the County of West Midlands (Building Blocks)

CC NO 1075800   **ESTABLISHED** 1999

WHERE FUNDING CAN BE GIVEN West Midlands Police catchment area.

WHO CAN BENEFIT Children and young people in all matters relating to alcohol, drug and solvent abuse.

WHAT IS FUNDED Crime prevention projects in partnership with the police.

WHAT IS NOT FUNDED No grants towards personal applications, circular and capital appeals. No grants outside the benefit area.

SAMPLE GRANTS Barnardo's Dudley Community Routes (£18,000); Cult Racing Cycles (£10,000); Walsall Street Teams – The Nemiah Project (£9,400) and Birmingham Youth Sports Academy and Young Vibes (£5,000 each).

FINANCES *Year* 2011–12 *Income* £8,964 *Grants* £29,000

TRUSTEES Colin Birchall; David Wilkin; Jean McEntire; Ann Worley; David Thompson.

HOW TO APPLY Application forms are available on the trust's website, together with criteria and guidelines. Applicants must have a police partner or a statement of support for the project. The trustees consider applications three times a year.

WHO TO APPLY TO Ann Penfold, Lloyd House, Colmore Circus, Queensway, Birmingham B4 6NQ *Tel* 0845 113 5000 ext. 7800 2294 *email* a.penfold@west-midlands.pnn.police.uk *Website* www.buildingblockscharity.co.uk

---

■ Highcroft Charitable Trust

CC NO 272684   **ESTABLISHED** 1975

WHERE FUNDING CAN BE GIVEN UK and overseas.

WHO CAN BENEFIT Organisations benefiting Jewish people, especially people disadvantaged by poverty.

WHAT IS FUNDED The advancement and study of the Jewish faith and the Torah. The relief of poverty and advancement of education among people of the Jewish faith.

RANGE OF GRANTS Up to £10,000.

SAMPLE GRANTS Previous beneficiaries included: Chevras Maoz Ladal, Kol Yaacov, SOFT and Tevini (£10,000 each); Friends of Beer Miriam, Institute For Higher Rabbinic Studies and Kollel Ohr Yechiel (£5,000 each); Kollel Chibas Yerushalayim (£4,200); Craven Walk Charity Trust (£2,500); London Friends of Kamenitzer (£2,000).

FINANCES *Year* 2011–12 *Income* £17,374 *Grants* £63,000

TRUSTEES Rabbi Richard Fischer; Sarah Fischer.

HOW TO APPLY In writing to the correspondent.

WHO TO APPLY TO Rabbi R. Fischer, Trustee, 15 Highcroft Gardens, London NW11 0LY

■ The Hilden Charitable Fund

CC NO 232591   **ESTABLISHED** 1963

WHERE FUNDING CAN BE GIVEN UK and developing countries.

WHO CAN BENEFIT Charities, voluntary organisations and NGOs. In the UK most grant aid is directed to registered charities. Overseas projects will either work with a UK charity partner or show relevant local legal status. Preference is given to smaller organisations rather than large national charities. Scottish charities are only funded through a block grant to Scottish Community Foundation which they distribute to the sector.

WHAT IS FUNDED Priorities in the UK are homelessness, asylum seekers and refugees, penal affairs and disadvantaged young people. For projects in developing countries, priorities are projects which focus on community development, education, and health. Those which focus on the needs and potential of girls and women are particularly welcome.

WHAT IS NOT FUNDED Grants are not normally made for well-established causes or to individuals, and overseas grants concentrate on development aid in preference to disaster relief.

TYPE OF GRANT Capital, revenue and recurring. Also running costs and project costs.

RANGE OF GRANTS Up to £10,000.

SAMPLE GRANTS Tanzania Development Trust – Tanzania (£30,000 in three grants); Joint Council for the Welfare of Immigrants – London (£15,000); Furniture Recycling Project – Gloucester and St Cuthbert's Centre – London (£7,000 each); Baynards Zambia Trust – Zambia (£6,000); Birmingham Friends of the Earth, 999 Project – Deptford and Irene Taylor Trust – London (£5,000 each); Devon and Cornwall Refugee Support Council (£4,500); Lena Gardens Primary School (£3,500) and Recyke Y'Bike – Newcastle upon Tyne (£3,000).

FINANCES *Year* 2011–12 *Income* £428,752 *Grants* £411,072 *Assets* £11,214,362

TRUSTEES C. Younger; Ms C. Rampton; A. Rampton; Prof. D. Rampton; Prof. C. Rodeck; J. Rampton; Prof. M. Rampton; Maggie Baxter; Ms E. Rodeck; Ms E. Rampton; Ms E. Rodeck; Ms Samia Khatun.

HOW TO APPLY Applications are made via the application form, available on the website. When making an application, grant seekers should note the following guidance from the trust: 'we expect all applicants to complete our application form. Your case for funds should be concise (no more than two sides of A4), but supporting documentation is essential. Ensure your application includes enclosures of: your most recent independently inspected accounts; your most recent annual report and projected income and expenditure for the current financial year'. Be clear in your application form about when the proposed work is to commence, and give the relevant timetable.

Applicants from the UK applying for funds for their project partners must complete both the UK application form and the overseas partner profile form. Application forms, including one for Summer Playschemes, are available from the trust's website or offices. Note that forms must be submitted to the secretary by post as hard copies; forms submitted by email or other electronic means are not accepted. Applicants are advised to ensure that they have read the application guidelines at the top of the form prior to completion. For applicants to the Summer Playschemes fund: applications should be sent by post along with a brief plan or timetable for the scheme and a copy of the applicant's most recent annual report and accounts which should include details of their management committee. Potential applicants in Scotland should contact the Scottish Community Foundation, 22 Calton Road, Edinburgh EH8 8DP; Tel: 0131 524 0300; website: www.scottishcf.org.

WHO TO APPLY TO Rodney Hedley, Secretary, 34 North End Road, London W14 0SH *Tel.* 020 7603 1525 *Fax* 020 7603 1525 *email* hildencharity@hotmail.com *Website* www. hildencharitablefund.org.uk

---

■ The Derek Hill Foundation

CC NO 801590   **ESTABLISHED** 1989
WHERE FUNDING CAN BE GIVEN UK.
WHO CAN BENEFIT Organisations and individuals.
WHAT IS FUNDED The promotion of arts and culture.
TYPE OF GRANT Bursaries and travel costs.
SAMPLE GRANTS The British School at Rome (£12,000); Arvon Foundation (£7,500); The George Orwell Memorial Trust and Thelma Holt (£5,000 each); Llanfyllin Festival Association (£3,000); Welsh National Opera (£2,500); Bulgarian Orphans Fund (£1,500); Yale University Press and Friary Guildford Brass Band (£1,000 each).
FINANCES *Year* 2011–12 *Income* £49,402 *Grants* £68,599 *Assets* £1,415,935
TRUSTEES Rathbone Trust Company Limited; Earl of Gowrie; Lord Armstrong of Ilminster; Josephine Batterham; Ian Paterson.
OTHER INFORMATION Grants to six individuals totalled £2,900
HOW TO APPLY In writing to the correspondent.
WHO TO APPLY TO The Trustees, Rathbone Trust Company Limited, 1 Curzon Street, London W1J 5FB *Tel.* 020 7399 0000

■ The Charles Littlewood Hill Trust

CC NO 286350   **ESTABLISHED** 1978
WHERE FUNDING CAN BE GIVEN UK, with a preference for Nottinghamshire and Norfolk.
WHAT IS FUNDED General charitable purposes.

WHAT IS NOT FUNDED Applications from individuals are not considered. Grants are seldom made for repairs of parish churches outside Nottinghamshire.
TYPE OF GRANT Applications for starter finance are encouraged. Grants are seldom made to endowment or capital funds.
RANGE OF GRANTS £1,000–£15,000, but usually of £5,000 or less.
SAMPLE GRANTS Norfolk Community Foundation (£15,000); Royal Norfolk Agricultural Association (£12,500); The Norfolk Churches Trust (£7,500); St John Waterwing (£6,000); Churches Conservation Trust and Nottinghamshire Wildlife Trust (£5,000 each); Dragon Hall and Family Care (£2,000 each); and Ovarian Cancer Action and Victim Support – Norfolk (£1,000 each).
FINANCES *Year* 2012 *Income* £204,607 *Grants* £161,000 *Assets* £4,157,290
TRUSTEES Charles Barratt; Tim Farr; Nigel Savory; John Pears.
OTHER INFORMATION No grants to individuals.
HOW TO APPLY In writing to the correspondent, including the latest set of audited accounts, at least one month before trustees' meetings in March, July and November. Unsuccessful applications will not be notified.
WHO TO APPLY TO John Thompson, c/o Shakespeares, Park House, Friar Lane, Nottingham NG1 6DN *Tel.* 01476 552429 *Fax* 01159 480234

■ The Hillier Trust

CC NO 1147629   **ESTABLISHED** 2012
WHERE FUNDING CAN BE GIVEN UK.
WHO CAN BENEFIT Charities and community groups.
WHAT IS FUNDED Education, social welfare, the arts and religion, with a preference for those working with children and young people and older people.
TRUSTEES Anthony Hillier; Susan Hillier.
HOW TO APPLY In writing to the correspondent.
WHO TO APPLY TO Anthony Hillier, Trustee, Loose Court Farmhouse, Old Drive, Maidstone, Kent ME15 9SE *Tel.* 01622 691561 *email* tonyhillier@zen.co.uk

---

■ The Hillingdon Community Trust

CC NO 1098235   **ESTABLISHED** 2003
WHERE FUNDING CAN BE GIVEN The London borough of Hillingdon.
WHO CAN BENEFIT Community organisations.
WHAT IS FUNDED Supports community projects, education, the relief of poverty and advocacy in the beneficial area.
WHAT IS NOT FUNDED No grants to individuals, public bodies, religious bodies or organisations that have already received funding in respect of a completed project.
TYPE OF GRANT One-off; recurrent.
RANGE OF GRANTS Small grants: £500–£7,500. Main grants: up to £75,000.
SAMPLE GRANTS HECAB (£60,000); Hillingdon Law Centre (£40,000); 2nd Harlington Scout Group (£37,000); Hillingdon Play Association (£36,000); West London YMCA (£25,000); QPR in the Community (£19,000); West Drayton Youth Football Club and Hayes FM (£15,000 each); Hililngdon Somali Women's Group (£7,500) and Hillingdon Youth Cricket Alliance (£7,000); Hillingdon Cycle Circuit Users' Group (£6,800); Emperors Basketball Club (£5,800); Harlington Hospice and Guru Nanak Sikh

622

Does the trust you have chosen match your needs? Haphazard applications waste postage and time

Academy (£4,000 each); Hillingdon Mathematical Society and Hillingdon Asian Women's Group (£3,000 each) and Garden City Residents' Association (£1,000).

FINANCES *Year* 2011–12 *Income* £1,040,076 *Grants* £897,000 *Assets* £1,380,717

TRUSTEES David Brough, Chair; Mathew Gorman; Gillian Francis-Musanu; Ian Campbell; Steve Coventry; Carole Jones; Hanif Islam; Isabel King; Colin Lowen; Mort Smith; Douglas Mills; Keith Wallis.

OTHER INFORMATION Grants approved for the year were: 32 Small grants totalling £176,000 17 Main grants totalling £721,000

HOW TO APPLY Small grants scheme – Application forms, together with criteria and guidelines, are available to download on the trust's website. Main grants scheme – This is a two-stage process. Initially, applicants complete a two-sided expression of interest form. These are considered by the Main Grants Sub-Committee and the trustees, who shortlist applicants with a reasonable likelihood of being funded. These applicants are then invited to complete and submit a full application for a main grant. Application forms, together with criteria and guidelines and deadlines, are available to download on the trust's website. Initial contact is welcome.

WHO TO APPLY TO Theresa O' Brien, Trust Administrator, Barra Hall, Wood End, Green Road, Hayes, Middlesex UB3 2SA *Tel.* 020 8581 1676 *email* info@ hillingdoncommunitytrust.org.uk *Website* www. hillingdoncommunitytrust.org.uk

■ The Hillingdon Partnership Trust

CC NO 284668   **ESTABLISHED** 1982

WHERE FUNDING CAN BE GIVEN The London borough of Hillingdon.

WHO CAN BENEFIT Organisations benefiting people of all ages, at risk groups, people disadvantaged by poverty and socially isolated people.

WHAT IS FUNDED The trust aims: to build links between the local community and the business sector to secure funding for community initiatives and projects; to relieve people resident in Hillingdon who are sick, disabled, elderly, poor or in other social and economic circumstances; to provide, or assist in providing, equipment and facilities not normally provided by the local authority for the purpose of advancing education or relieving people in need.

SAMPLE GRANTS Harlington Hospice (£52,000) and Hillingdon's Schools Books of the Year literacy and comprehension project (£10,500).

FINANCES *Year* 2011–12 *Income* £325,390 *Grants* £74,719 *Assets* £25,525

TRUSTEES Prof. Ian Campbell; Tony Woodbridge; James Crowe; Air Cmdr Paul Thomas; John Watts; Michael Wisdom; Prof. Heinz Wolff; Albert Kanjee; Nicholas Smith; Miranda Clarke; Peter O'Reilly; David Routledge; Robert Brightwell.

OTHER INFORMATION 'In general the trust does not itself make grants. It does make appeals to its business supporters on behalf of needy organisations and exceptionally, individuals, and the business partners may then provide funds direct to the applicant. Exceptionally, the trust may meet a need by arranging the purchase of necessary items and delivering the essential items to an applicant.'

HOW TO APPLY On a form available from the correspondent.

WHO TO APPLY TO John Matthews, Chief Executive, Room 22–25, Building 219, Epsom Square,

Eastern Business Park, London Heathrow Airport, Hillingdon, Middlesex TW6 2BW *Tel.* 020 8897 3611 *Fax* 020 8897 3613 *email* johnmatthewshpt@lineone.net *Website* www.hillingdonpartnershiptrust.com

■ R. G. Hills Charitable Trust

CC NO 1008914   **ESTABLISHED** 1982

WHERE FUNDING CAN BE GIVEN UK and overseas.

WHO CAN BENEFIT Local and national registered charities.

WHAT IS FUNDED General charitable purposes with some preference for the fields of health, poverty and education.

SAMPLE GRANTS Canterbury Festival Foundation (£10,000); Odyssey Project Limited (£3,500); Swinfen Charitable Trust and Wildwood Trust (£3,000 each); Porchlight and Project Mala (£2,500 each); African Mission, Asthma Relief, Dyslexia Institute, Fynvola Foundation and The Grasslands Trust (£2,000 each); Tall Ships Trust (£1,750); Action Against Hunger and Hope Romania (£1,500 each); and The B 17 Charitable Trust (£1,000).

FINANCES *Year* 2011–12 *Income* £105,203 *Grants* £86,500 *Assets* £3,029,918

TRUSTEES David Pentin; Harvey Barrett.

HOW TO APPLY In writing to the correspondent.

WHO TO APPLY TO Harvey Barrett, Trustee, Furley Page, 39 St Margaret's Street, Canterbury, Kent CT1 2TX *Tel.* 01227 763939

■ The Hilmarnan Charitable Trust

CC NO 500918   **ESTABLISHED** 1971

WHERE FUNDING CAN BE GIVEN Within ten miles of the Moot Hall, Keswick.

WHO CAN BENEFIT People who are older, have disabilities, are poor or sick.

WHAT IS FUNDED Registered charities, local organisations such as hospices.

TYPE OF GRANT One-off

SAMPLE GRANTS Alzheimer's Disease Society – Keswick, the Keswick Heating Fund, Macmillan Nurses, a variety of hospices in the beneficial area and grants towards mobility equipment.

FINANCES *Year* 2012–13 *Income* £28,969 *Grants* £12,251

TRUSTEES Gareth Mendus; Dr Peter White; Catherine Hooper.

HOW TO APPLY In writing to the correspondent. Under the charity's constitution, one of the trustees must be a local GP and applications are normally made to the trustees via the local GP practices when they are aware of a particular need.

WHO TO APPLY TO Gareth Mendus, Trustee, c/o Oglethorpe and Broatch Solicitors, 6 Borrowdale Road, Keswick CA12 5DB *Tel.* 01768 772125 *email* garethmendus@brockbanks.co.uk

■ Hinchley Charitable Trust

CC NO 1108412   **ESTABLISHED** 1973

WHERE FUNDING CAN BE GIVEN UK and overseas.

WHO CAN BENEFIT Mainly evangelical Christian organisations, including Christian youth organisations and Christian organisations in local communities.

WHAT IS FUNDED General charitable purposes, with particular reference to evangelical Christian work, such as the training of Christian leaders, holistic mission and evangelism and Christian influence in the public sphere.

TYPE OF GRANT One-off and recurring, usually for projects, but capital and core costs are considered.

RANGE OF GRANTS Up to £23,000.

SAMPLE GRANTS Langham Partnership (£13,000); Christchurch Canterbury University, ACK Masabit Mission, Faith2Share, Spurgeons College (£10,000 each); Elim Church – Huddersfield (£8,000) and Urban Saints (£7,500).

FINANCES *Year* 2011–12 *Income* £162,742 *Grants* £167,300 *Assets* £2,837,237

TRUSTEES Prof. Brian Stanley; John Levick; Mark Hobbs; Roger Northcott.

HOW TO APPLY The trustees adopt a proactive approach to grantmaking meaning unsolicited applications are rarely supported.

WHO TO APPLY TO Emma Northcott, Secretary, 10 Coplow Terrace, Coplow Street, Birmingham B16 0DQ *Tel.* 01214 556632

■ Lady Hind Trust

CC NO 208877   **ESTABLISHED** 1951

WHERE FUNDING CAN BE GIVEN England with a preference for Nottinghamshire and Norfolk.

WHO CAN BENEFIT Registered and exempt charities, including churches.

WHAT IS FUNDED General charitable purposes with a preference for health, disability, medical and social welfare charities.

WHAT IS NOT FUNDED Grants are not awarded to individuals.

TYPE OF GRANT Core and project support.

RANGE OF GRANTS Up to £20,000, but mostly under £5,000.

SAMPLE GRANTS Royal Norfolk Agricultural Association (£12,500); The Norfolk and Norwich Association for the Blind, The Nottinghamshire Hospice and Notts Mind Network (£10,000); The Benjamin Foundation, Southwell Care Project, Norfolk Wildlife Trust, The Norfolk Churches Trust, Nottingham High School for Boys – Bursary and NSPCC Nottinghamshire (£7,500 each). More typical grants of £5,000 or less included those to: The National Association of Almshouses, Pintsize Theatre Ltd, Friends of Brancaster Church, Rutland House School for Parents, Zibby Garnett Travelling Fellowship, British Trust for Ornithology, ABF The Soldiers Charity, 1st Norwich Sea Scouts Group, Norfolk Historic Buildings Trust, The Anthony Nolan Trust, East Anglia Children's Hospices, Calibre Audio Library, Keeping Abreast, Asthma UK, The Leeds Teaching Hospitals Charitable Foundation, Pregnancy Choices Norfolk, National Search and Rescue Dog Association, Citizens Advice Broxtowe, Blue Sky Development and Regeneration, Friary Drop-In, Sailors Society and Waveney Stardust.

FINANCES *Year* 2012 *Income* £429,548 *Grants* £322,446 *Assets* £12,356,101

TRUSTEES Charles W. L. Barratt; Tim H. Farr; Nigel R. Savory; John D. Pears.

HOW TO APPLY Applications, in writing and with latest accounts, must be submitted at least one month in advance of trustee meetings held in March, July and November. Unsuccessful applicants are not notified. 'The trustees consider all written applications made to them by charitable organisations. Such applications are reviewed by every trustee prior to the trustees' four-monthly meetings and are discussed at such meetings. Grants are awarded at such meeting to those organisations which the trustees collectively consider to be worthy of their support. Grants are awarded principally to institutions based on their level of need and with a geographical bias towards Nottinghamshire and Norfolk.'

WHO TO APPLY TO John Thompson, Administrator, c/o Shakespeares Solicitors, Park House, Friar Lane, Nottingham NG1 6DN *Tel.* 01159 453700 *Fax* 01159 480234 *email* ladyhind@ btinternet.com

---

■ The Hinduja Foundation

CC NO 802756   **ESTABLISHED** 1989

WHERE FUNDING CAN BE GIVEN Worldwide.

WHO CAN BENEFIT Registered charities.

WHAT IS FUNDED Health-care, educational charities, scarcity relief, poverty alleviation, art and culture, sports, social, economic and international development-related research.

RANGE OF GRANTS Up to £10,000

SAMPLE GRANTS International Society for Krishna Consciousness (£17,000 in total); The Sarvam Trust (£10,000); Guru Nanak International Education Trust and Concern for Mental Health (£5,000 each); The Rajasthani Foundation (£2,500); Women's India Association (£2,000); Alzheimer's Research UK (£1,000); Sangam Association of Asian Women (£300); and Shrimad Rajchandra Ashram Dharampur (£100).

FINANCES *Year* 2012 *Income* £76,504 *Grants* £63,751 *Assets* £80,222

TRUSTEES Srichand Hinduja; Gopichand Hinduja; Prakash Hinduja; Shanu Hinduja.

HOW TO APPLY In writing to the correspondent.

WHO TO APPLY TO The Trustees, New Zealand House, 80 Haymarket, London SW1Y 4TE *email* foundation@hindujagroup.com *Website* hindujagroup.com

---

■ Stuart Hine Trust

CC NO 326941   **ESTABLISHED** 1985

WHERE FUNDING CAN BE GIVEN UK and overseas.

WHO CAN BENEFIT Evangelical Christian organisations, churches and missionary societies supported by Stuart Hine during his lifetime or by the trustees since his death.

WHAT IS FUNDED The support of Christian ministry.

SAMPLE GRANTS Wycliff Bible Translators (£159,000).

FINANCES *Year* 2011–12 *Income* £222,832 *Grants* £304,505 *Assets* £370,503

TRUSTEES Raymond Bodkin; Amelia Gardner; Roland Dumford-Slater; Jonathan Birdwood Juby; Leonard Chipping.

PUBLICATIONS A booklet: *How Great Thou Art!* – *The Inspiring Story of Stuart K. Hine and the Making of a Classic Christian Hymn.* This will be published in the near future.

OTHER INFORMATION The trust receives its income mainly from royalties from the hymn 'How Great Thou Art' written by Stuart Hine.

HOW TO APPLY The trust states that 'unsolicited requests for funds will not be considered'. Funds are basically distributed in accordance with the wishes of the settlor.

WHO TO APPLY TO Raymond Bodkin, Trustee, 'Cherith', 23 Derwent Close, Hailsham, East Sussex BN27 3DA *Tel.* 01323 843948

■ The Hinrichsen Foundation

CC NO 272389   **ESTABLISHED** 1976

WHERE FUNDING CAN BE GIVEN UK.

WHO CAN BENEFIT Organisations benefiting musicians; individual musicians.

WHAT IS FUNDED Assisting contemporary composition and its performance, and musicological research.

WHAT IS NOT FUNDED The trust does not support study courses, including those at postgraduate level. Grants are not given for instruments, equipment or recordings.

TYPE OF GRANT Usually one-off for a specific project or part of a project.

RANGE OF GRANTS Variable, generally between £500 and £2,500.

SAMPLE GRANTS ENO (£2,500); Birmingham Contemporary Music Group, Dartington International Summer Festival and Sound Festival (£2,000 each); Wednesdays at the Forge and York Late Music (£1,500 each); and Clod Ensemble and Trio Scordatura (£1,000 each).

FINANCES *Year* 2012 *Income* £522,477 *Grants* £36,172 *Assets* £1,263,661

TRUSTEES Professor Jonathan Cross; Keith Potter; Dr Linda Hirst; Professor Stephen Walsh; Patric Standford; Paul Strang; Sue Lubbock; Tim Berg; Tabby Estell; Eleanor Gussman.

OTHER INFORMATION Grants total includes £6,700 to individuals. Financial information taken from the statement of financial activities.

HOW TO APPLY On a form that can be downloaded from the foundation's website. Visit the website which provides full information on how to apply including a useful FAQ section. Trustees meet quarterly.

WHO TO APPLY TO The Administrator, 2–6 Baches Street, London N1 6DN *email* hinrichsen. foundation@editionpeters.com *Website* www. hinrichsenfoundation.org.uk

■ The Hintze Family Charitable Foundation

CC NO 1101842   **ESTABLISHED** 2003

WHERE FUNDING CAN BE GIVEN England and Wales.

WHO CAN BENEFIT Churches, museums, galleries, libraries, schools and charitable organisations.

WHAT IS FUNDED The trust operates in the following areas: promoting access to museums, libraries and art galleries; supporting Christian churches in England and Wales, particularly the Diocese of Southwark; the relief of sickness and people with terminal illnesses; and the provision of resources and equipment for schools, colleges and universities (in particular to enable the acquisition and retention of antiquarian books to be used as a learning resource).

TYPE OF GRANT Capital and revenue funding, mostly over two to five years.

SAMPLE GRANTS The Prince's Foundation for the Built Environment (£1.3 million) towards unrestricted funding 'for a charity with which [the foundation] has very strong ties' Patrons of the Arts in the Vatican Museum (€1 million) for the restoration of the Scala Sancta; Friends of Harvard University ($1 million over five years) to support the Cultural Entrepreneurship Challenge; Old Vic Theatre (£500,000 over two years) in support of their endowment and building campaigns; Wandsworth Museum (£385,000) to provide funding since the local council decided they could no longer support it; Institute of Economic Affairs (£250,000) in support of their outreach programme; Museum of London (£150,000); St George's Chapel – Windsor (£75,000); Macmillan Cancer Support and The Prince's Teaching Institute (£50,000 each).

FINANCES *Year* 2012 *Income* £5,922,290 *Grants* £4,522,664 *Assets* £3,512,689

TRUSTEES Michael Hintze; David Swain; Brian Hannon.

HOW TO APPLY The trust offers the following application guidance in its latest accounts: 'The foundation invites applications for grants or commitments from charities which serve the objects of the foundation. No specific format is required for applications. Applications, along with potential donations and commitments identified by the Chief Executive and the trustees, are considered in formal trustee meetings.'

WHO TO APPLY TO Dorothy Hintze, Director, CQS, 5th Floor, 33 Grosvenor Place, London SW1X 7HY *Tel.* 020 7201 6862

■ The Hiscox Foundation

CC NO 327635   **ESTABLISHED** 1987

WHERE FUNDING CAN BE GIVEN Worldwide.

WHO CAN BENEFIT Registered charities or individuals.

WHAT IS FUNDED General charitable purposes.

TYPE OF GRANT Usually one-off.

RANGE OF GRANTS £50–£4,000.

SAMPLE GRANTS HART (Humanitarian Aid Relief Trust) (£30,000); Royal Academy (£10,000); The Royal British Legion (£5,500); Richard House Trust (£5,000); Cancer Research Campaign (£3,000); The Rainbow Trust (£2,500), British Consultancy Charitable Trust (£2,000); Alabare Christian Care Centre, Brain Research Trust, Breakthrough Breast Cancer, Fine Cell Work, Little Haven's Children's Hospice, Salisbury Cathedral and SSAFA Forces Help (£1,000 each); Headway East London and Heritage of London Trust (£500 each); Asthma UK and Princess Royal Trust for Carers (£250 each) and Lynsey Ivison Trust (£100).

FINANCES *Year* 2011–12 *Income* £374,679 *Grants* £89,110 *Assets* £3,761,817

TRUSTEES Robert Hiscox; Alexander Foster; Rory Barker; Jade Hallam; Andrew Nix; Amanda Brown.

HOW TO APPLY This foundation does not accept unsolicited applications.

WHO TO APPLY TO Peresha McKenzie, Administrator, c/o Hiscox Underwriting Limited, 1 Great St Helen's, London EC3A 6HX *Tel.* 020 7448 6011

■ The Hitchin Educational Foundation

CC NO 311024   **ESTABLISHED** 1965

WHERE FUNDING CAN BE GIVEN Unrestricted, in practice Hertfordshire.

WHO CAN BENEFIT Individuals and local organisations benefiting children, young adults and students under the age of 25 years.

WHAT IS FUNDED The advancement of education and training.

WHAT IS NOT FUNDED No support for second degrees or the purchase of certain books.

TYPE OF GRANT One-off.

RANGE OF GRANTS Up to £35,000

SAMPLE GRANTS Hitchin Girls' School (£30,000); The Priory School and Hitchin Boys' School (£15,000 each); North Herts Educational Support Care (£500) and Hertfordshire Educational Foundation (£300).Other miscellaneous grants were given to unnamed recipients totalling £25,500.

Think carefully about every application. Is it justified?

625

FINANCES *Year* 2011–12 *Income* £99,480 *Grants* £88,581 *Assets* £1,288,830

TRUSTEES Derrick Ashley; C. Minton; Revd M. Roden; D. Chapallaz; Nigel Brook; Sarah Wren; Susan Cracknell; Bernard Lovewell; Morag Norgan; David Leal-Bennett; Alison Ashley; Anthony Buckland; Roy Shakespeare-Smith; Frank Carr.

OTHER INFORMATION Applicants must have lived in Hitchin or attended a Hitchin school for at least two years.

HOW TO APPLY Apply in writing to the correspondent for an application form.

WHO TO APPLY TO Brian Frederick, Clerk, 33 Birch Close, Broom, Biggleswade SG18 9NR *Tel.* 01767 313892

■ The Henry C. Hoare Charitable Trust

CC NO 1088669　　　ESTABLISHED 2001

WHERE FUNDING CAN BE GIVEN UK.

WHO CAN BENEFIT Charitable organisations.

WHAT IS FUNDED General charitable purposes.

TYPE OF GRANT One-off and annual donations.

SAMPLE GRANTS Beckley Foundation (£10,500); Transform Drug Policy Foundation, Prospect Burma, Future Trees Trust and Autism Research (£10,000 each); Worldwide Volunteers, Tree Aid, The March Foundation, Leaping Frogs Kindergarten, League of Friends of Westminster Hospital, Ataxia UK and Burma Campaign UK (£5,000 each).

FINANCES *Year* 2011–12 *Income* £198,054 *Grants* £147,132 *Assets* £3,787,554

TRUSTEES Henry C. Hoare; Hoare Trustees.

HOW TO APPLY In writing to the correspondent.

WHO TO APPLY TO Trust Administrator, C. Hoare and Co, 37 Fleet Street, London EC4P 4DQ *Tel.* 020 7353 4522

■ The Eleemosynary Charity of William Hobbayne

CC NO 211547　　　ESTABLISHED 1962

WHERE FUNDING CAN BE GIVEN The borough of Ealing with priority given to Hanwell.

WHO CAN BENEFIT Specific beneficiaries as stated in the trust's deed; Organisations and individuals in (a) Hanwell, then (b) borough of Ealing.

WHAT IS FUNDED General charitable purposes, including the relief of need and hardship.

RANGE OF GRANTS Up to about £7,500.

SAMPLE GRANTS St Mary's Church Hanwell (£7,500); Hanwell Neighbourly Care Scheme (£4,800); Educational Charity of William Hobbayne (£4,000); Hanwell Churches Winter Homeless Project (£2,000); EASE Summer Club and St John's Community Kitchen (£1,500 each).

FINANCES *Year* 2011–12 *Income* £140,226 *Grants* £28,105 *Assets* £2,837,339

TRUSTEES Revd Matthew Grayshon, Chair; Mark Cosstick; Roy Price; Allison Rockley; John Sawyer; Bridget Goodman; Angela Wallis; Nicholas Robinson; Robert Coomber; David Muir.

OTHER INFORMATION £4,000 was paid in grants to individuals.

HOW TO APPLY In writing to the correspondent.

WHO TO APPLY TO Caroline Lumb, Clerk, Caroline Lumb, The William Hobbayne Community Centre, St Dunstans Road, London W7 2HB *Tel.* 020 8810 0277 *email* hobbaynecharity@btinternet.com

■ The Hobson Charity Limited

CC NO 326839　　　ESTABLISHED 1985

WHERE FUNDING CAN BE GIVEN UK

WHO CAN BENEFIT Registered charities only, particularly those benefiting people of all ages, students, teachers, at risk groups, people disadvantaged by poverty and socially isolated people.

WHAT IS FUNDED Relief of poverty and distress among people who are elderly and poor; the provision of recreation and leisure facilities; and the advancement of education and other charitable purposes.

WHAT IS NOT FUNDED No grants to individuals, except in exceptional circumstances.

TYPE OF GRANT One-off and recurrent.

RANGE OF GRANTS £1,000–£150,000

SAMPLE GRANTS Historic Royal Palaces (£150,000); Royal Hospital for Neurodisability (£100,000 in three grants); Queenswood School and Great Ormond Street Hospital (£100,000 each); Food Fortnight Ltd (Cook for the Queen) Jubilee (£75,000); Hornsey Trust (£67,000); British School of Osteopathy (£55,000); SSAFA, Classics for All, Almshouse Association and the Police Foundation (£50,000 each); Changing Faces (£40,000); Skills Force Development and the Alnwick Garden Trust (£30,000 each); Army Benevolent Fund (£26,000 in two grants); Muscle Help Foundation (£20,000 in two grants); Eden Trust Project and the Anglican Space Appeal (£15,000 each); Scottish Veterans Garden City Association, Guildhall School of Music, St Peter's Church – Harrogate, British Heart Foundation and Wellbeing of Women (£10,000 each); St Mungo's (£7,000); Concord Prison Trust, Museum of Jurassic Marine Life, St Paul's Church Covent Garden, Oxford Radcliffe Hospitals Charitable Fund and Inner London Scope Nor-West Club (£5,000 each); Canadian Cancer Foundation (£4,000); Open Country (£2,000); and Rotary Club of London Charitable Trust, Hope Centre and WIZO UK (£1,000 each).

FINANCES *Year* 2011–12 *Income* £8,138,535 *Grants* £1,967,534 *Assets* £28,536,705

TRUSTEES Deborah Hobson; Sir Donald Gosling; Sir Ronald F. Hobson; Lady Hobson; J. Richardson.

HOW TO APPLY In writing to the correspondent. The trustees meet quarterly.

WHO TO APPLY TO Deborah Hobson, Trustee and Secretary, Hildane Properties Limited, 7th Floor, 21 Bryanston Street, Marble Arch, London W1H 7PR *Tel.* 020 7495 5599

■ Hockerill Educational Foundation

CC NO 311018　　　ESTABLISHED 1977

WHERE FUNDING CAN BE GIVEN UK, with a preference for the dioceses of Chelmsford and St Albans.

WHO CAN BENEFIT Organisations benefiting young adults, older people, academics, students, teachers and educational support staff, Christians and the Church of England.

WHAT IS FUNDED The foundation makes grants in the field of education in three main areas: individual grants to support the education and training of teachers; grants to organisations to support teachers and research and development in religious education; and grants to develop the church's educational work in the dioceses of Chelmsford and St Albans. The trustees will normally consider applications from corporate bodies or institutions associated with education on Christian principles. Trustees would expect

626

Does the trust you have chosen match your needs? Haphazard applications waste postage and time

any activity, course, project or research supported to be of real benefit to religious education and/or the church's educational work. They will give priority to imaginative new projects which will enhance the Church of England's contribution to higher and further education and/or promote aspects of religious education in schools.

WHAT IS NOT FUNDED Grants are not given for general appeals for funds, 'bricks and mortar' building projects or purposes that are the clear responsibility of another body.

TYPE OF GRANT Renewable for up to three years, or occasionally a maximum of five years, subject to satisfactory progress reports.

FINANCES *Year* 2011–12 *Income* £274,407 *Grants* £233,010 *Assets* £5,340,165

TRUSTEES H. Potter; Jonathan Reynolds; Venerable Elwin Cockett; Lesley Barlow; Colin Graham Bird; Harry Marsh; Revd Paul Bayes; Bishop of Colchester; Janet Scott; Jonathan Longstaff; Revd Dr Alan Smith; Revd Stephen Cottrell.

OTHER INFORMATION The grant total includes £51,000 given to individuals.

HOW TO APPLY On a form available to download from the website. Applications should include some official documentation, such as the most recent annual report and accounts, which clearly show the status, objects and ideals of the organisation and its financial position, and an sae. They should be submitted by 31 March each year. Grants are usually awarded between July and September.

WHO TO APPLY TO Derek J. Humphrey, Secretary, 3 The Swallows, Harlow, Essex CM17 0AR *Tel.* 01279 420855 *email* info@ hockerillfoundation.org.uk *Website* www. hockerillfoundation.org.uk

....

■ Matthew Hodder Charitable Trust

CC NO 1042741   **ESTABLISHED** 1994

WHERE FUNDING CAN BE GIVEN Worldwide.

WHO CAN BENEFIT Organisations and individuals.

WHAT IS FUNDED The trust's charitable concern is with: book publishing; literacy and literature; reading; the book trade (including the provision of books); arts education (including music); provision of financial support for educational purposes; Christian endeavour.

WHAT IS NOT FUNDED Health (unless reading related); social welfare; environment; politics

TYPE OF GRANT Funding for up to three years for capital and core costs.

RANGE OF GRANTS Up to £1,000.

FINANCES *Year* 2012–13 *Income* £37,426 *Grants* £45,800 *Assets* £1,000,821

TRUSTEES Tim Biggs-Davison; David Hicks; Timothy Lambert; Andrew Hodder-Williams; Ben Gutcher.

OTHER INFORMATION The trust has no geographical limits and makes grants to individuals and organisations.

HOW TO APPLY In writing to the correspondent.

WHO TO APPLY TO David Hicks, Administrator, 23 The Retreat, Kings Langley, Hertfordshire WD4 8LT *Tel.* 01923 263128 *email* david@mhct.org.uk

....

■ The Sir Julian Hodge Charitable Trust

CC NO 234848   **ESTABLISHED** 1964

WHERE FUNDING CAN BE GIVEN UK.

WHO CAN BENEFIT Registered charities benefiting people of all ages. Support may also be given to people who are disabled, medical professionals, research workers, scientists, students and teachers and governesses. Support may also be given to people with cancer, paediatric diseases, polio and tuberculosis.

WHAT IS FUNDED General charitable purposes, especially medical research in cancer, polio, tuberculosis and diseases of children. General advancement of medical and surgical science, the advancement of education, religion, and the relief of older people and people who are disabled.

WHAT IS NOT FUNDED No grants to individuals or companies.

RANGE OF GRANTS Usually £500–£2,000.

SAMPLE GRANTS The Conservation Foundation and Strongbones Children's Charitable Trust (£2,000 each); Sense, Douglas Macmillan Hospice and The Firefighters Charity (£1,500 each); National Search and Rescue Dog Association, All Saints Church, Ammanford, Disabled Travel Service, Watford and Three Rivers Furniture Recycling, YHA (England and Wales) Ltd and North Wales Deaf Association (£1,000 each) and Northampton Volunteering Centre (£750).

FINANCES *Year* 2011–12 *Income* £58,774 *Grants* £47,250 *Assets* £1,364,281

TRUSTEES Jonathan Hodge; Joyce Harrison; Derek Jones; Margaret Cason; Eric Hammonds.

HOW TO APPLY In writing to the correspondent. The trust invites applications for grants from charitable institutions. Institutions submit a summary of their proposals to the trustees in a specific format. Applications for grants are considered by the trustees against its objectives.

WHO TO APPLY TO Margaret Cason, Trustee and Secretary, 31 Windsor Place, Cardiff CF10 3UR *Tel.* 02920 787674

....

■ The Jane Hodge Foundation

CC NO 216053   **ESTABLISHED** 1962

WHERE FUNDING CAN BE GIVEN UK and overseas with a preference for Wales.

WHO CAN BENEFIT Charitable organisations.

WHAT IS FUNDED Medical research; education; religion; and general charitable purposes.

WHAT IS NOT FUNDED No grants to individuals.

TYPE OF GRANT One-off and recurring grants and loans.

RANGE OF GRANTS Up to £140,000.

SAMPLE GRANTS Cardiff Business School (£132,000); Royal Welsh College of Music and Drama and George Thomas Memorial Trust (£50,000 each); TENOVUS (£30,000); Ty Hafan (£10,000); Leukaemia and Lymphoma Research and Aberystwyth University (£6,000 each); Race Equality First, the United World College and Welsh National Opera (£5,000 each); Plan International UK (£4,000); PDSA and the Owl Fund (£3,000 each); and the River and Corpus Christie High School (£2,500 each).

FINANCES *Year* 2011–12 *Income* £815,293 *Grants* £855,016 *Assets* £28,292,294

TRUSTEES Joyce Harrison; Derek Jones; I. Davies; Margaret Cason; Eric Hammonds; Jonathan Hodge.

OTHER INFORMATION The foundation described its grantmaking in the 2011–12 accounts: 'from the applications for grants received in the year, applications in respect of £699,000 met the criteria required and amounts were granted to the charities concerned. The level of grants made each year can vary since there is a process of assessment and approval before grants can be made and grants may cover a period of more than one year.'

HOW TO APPLY In writing to the correspondent. Applications for grants are considered by the trustees at regular meetings throughout the year. Applications are acknowledged. The trustees' report for 2011/12 states that 'trustees invite applications for grants from charitable institutions who submit a summary of their proposals in a specific format. Institutions are required to report on completion of the project for which the grant was made.'

WHO TO APPLY TO Jonathan Hodge, Trustee, 31 Windsor Place, Cardiff CF10 3UR *Tel.* 02920 787693 *email* Marion.Pepperell@janehodgefoundation.co.uk

■ The J. G. Hogg Charitable Trust

CC NO 299042   **ESTABLISHED** 1987
WHERE FUNDING CAN BE GIVEN UK.
WHO CAN BENEFIT To benefit people in need and animals in need.
WHAT IS FUNDED Humanitarian causes, overseas charities, wild and domestic animal welfare causes.
WHAT IS NOT FUNDED No grants to individuals. Registered charities only are supported.
SAMPLE GRANTS Previously: Kids Company and Oxfam (£15,000 each); Medicinema and Teddy Bear Air Care (£10,000 each); and Addiction Recovery Foundation (£7,000).
FINANCES *Year* 2011–12 *Income* £14,884 *Grants* £100,061
TRUSTEES Sarah Jane Houldsworth; Joanna Wynfreda Turvey.
HOW TO APPLY In writing to the correspondent. To keep administration costs to a minimum, the trust is unable to reply to unsuccessful applicants.
WHO TO APPLY TO C. M. Jones, Trustees' Accountant, Chantrey Vellacott DFK, Russell Square House, 10 -12 Russell Square, London WC1B 5LF *Tel.* 020 7509 9000 *email* cjones@cvdfk.com

■ The Holden Charitable Trust

CC NO 264185   **ESTABLISHED** 1972
WHERE FUNDING CAN BE GIVEN UK, with a preference for the Manchester area.
WHO CAN BENEFIT Organisations benefiting Jewish people. Children, young adults and students may benefit.
WHAT IS FUNDED Jewish charitable purposes with emphasis on the advancement of education.
SAMPLE GRANTS Previous beneficiaries included: Broom Foundation (£59,000); Ohel Bnei Yaakob (£50,000); Ohr Yerushalayim Synagogue (£33,000); Friends of Beis Eliyahu Trust (£24,000); the FED (£7,500); and King David's School (£5,000).
FINANCES *Year* 2011–12 *Income* £302,123 *Grants* £377,105 *Assets* £687,460
TRUSTEES David Lopian; Marian Lopian; Michael Lopian.
OTHER INFORMATION Grants of less than £5,000 each amounted to £66,996.
HOW TO APPLY In writing to the correspondent.
WHO TO APPLY TO The Clerk, c/o Lopian Gross Barnett and Co., Cardinal House, 20 St Mary Parsonage, Manchester M3 2LG *Tel.* 01618 328721

■ John Holford's Charity

CC NO 223046   **ESTABLISHED** 1984
WHERE FUNDING CAN BE GIVEN The parishes of Clutton and Middlewich, the borough of Congleton and that part of Astbury that lies outside the borough.
WHO CAN BENEFIT Mostly individuals, also organisations including schools.
WHAT IS FUNDED Relief in need and educational visits and trips.
FINANCES *Year* 2012 *Income* £64,724 *Grants* £25,000
TRUSTEES Anita Lockett; Ven Ian Bishop; Revd Jonathan Sharples; Rosamund Mahon; Edward Tudor-Evans; Revd Cannon David Taylor; Jane Shelmerdine; Revd Simon Drew.
OTHER INFORMATION Up to 5% of the income can be used for relief-in-need in the parish of Clutton, with the remainder divided equally between the parish of Middlewich, the borough of Congleton and the part of Astbury outside the borough of Congleton.
HOW TO APPLY On a form available to download on the website.
WHO TO APPLY TO Kerris Owen, The Clerk, Parish Office, St Peter's Church, The Cross, Chester CH1 2LA *Tel.* 07794 654212 *email* jholfordcharity@gmail.com *Website* www.johnholfordcharity.org

■ The Hollands-Warren Fund

CC NO 279747   **ESTABLISHED** 1977
WHERE FUNDING CAN BE GIVEN Maidstone.
WHO CAN BENEFIT Residents of the borough of Maidstone who are in genuine need.
WHAT IS FUNDED Temporary medical and nursing services and/or domestic help for residents.
RANGE OF GRANTS Up to £43,000.
SAMPLE GRANTS Rapid Response (£43,000) and Heart of Kent Hospice (£13,000).
FINANCES *Year* 2011–12 *Income* £65,840 *Grants* £55,000
TRUSTEES Kim Harrington; Daniel Bell; Anthony Palmer; Jane Sankey.
HOW TO APPLY In writing to the correspondent.
WHO TO APPLY TO Kim Harrington, c/o Brachers Solicitors, Somerfield House, 57–59 London Road, Maidstone, Kent ME16 8JH *Tel.* 01622 690691 *email* kimharrington@brachers.co.uk

■ The Hollick Family Charitable Trust

CC NO 1060228   **ESTABLISHED** 1997
WHERE FUNDING CAN BE GIVEN UK and overseas.
WHO CAN BENEFIT Registered charities.
WHAT IS FUNDED General charitable purposes.
TYPE OF GRANT One-off and recurrent.
RANGE OF GRANTS £1,000–£12,000
SAMPLE GRANTS AMREF (£12,000); London Citizens (£7,500); Real Action and King's Head (£5,000 each); Scene and Heard (£2,000); Amref Christmas Concert (£1,500) and Aid to Gaza, Notting Hill Churches Homeless Concern and Macmillan (£1,000 each).
FINANCES *Year* 2011–12 *Income* £776,571 *Grants* £70,000
TRUSTEES Lord Hollick; Lady Hollick; Hon. Caroline Hollick; David Beech; Hon. Georgina Hollick; Hon. Abigail Hollick; Thomas Kemp, Caroline Kemp.
OTHER INFORMATION Previously, grants for less than £1,000 totalled £8,000.
HOW TO APPLY In writing to the correspondent.

who to apply to David Beech, Solicitor, c/o Peter Bryan and Co, Foxglove House, 166 Piccadilly, London W1J 9EF *Tel.* 020 7493 4932 *email* peterbryanco@btinternet.com

....

■ The Holliday Foundation

cc no 1089931　　**established** 2002
where funding can be given UK.
who can benefit Organisations and individuals.
what is funded General charitable purposes.
sample grants National Centre for Young People with Epilepsy and Training for Life (£10,000 each); Charsfield Recreation Ground, Help the hospices (£5,000); Sparkles Home Sri Lanka (£2,500); The Easy Anglian Academy (£1,200) and The Newbury Spring Festival (£1,000).
finances *Year* 2011–12 *Income* £17,544 *Grants* £130,000
trustees David Garrett; Jane Garrett; James Cave; Anthony Wilson; Huw Llewellyn.
other information The trustees review requests for grants and may request further information or visit applicants before deciding whether to make a payment. The trustees will follow up the use of grants where relevant.
how to apply In writing to the correspondent.
who to apply to The Trustees, Salisbury Partners LLP, 25 Hill Street, London W1J 5LW

....

■ The Dorothy Holmes Charitable Trust

cc no 237213　　**established** 1964
where funding can be given UK, with a preference for Dorset.
who can benefit UK registered charities benefiting young adults and older people; people who are sick; clergy; ex-service and service people; legal professionals; unemployed people; volunteers; parents and children; one-parent families; widows and widowers; at risk groups; carers; and people who are disabled.
what is funded Charities working in the fields of advice and information on housing; emergency and short-term housing; residential facilities; respite and sheltered accommodation; information technology and computers; civil society development; support of voluntary and community organisations; health professional bodies; and religion will be considered. Support is also given to healthcare; hospices and hospitals; cancer research; church buildings; heritage; secondary schools and special schools; counselling on social issues; and income support and maintenance.
what is not funded Only applications from registered charities will be considered.
type of grant Buildings; capital; core costs; one-off; project; research; recurring costs; running costs; salaries; and start-up costs. Funding for up to and over three years will be considered.
range of grants Up to £6,000
sample grants Previous beneficiaries included: Wallingford School (£6,000); Children in Touch, Crisis and Christmas and RNLI (£5,000 each); Hyman Cen Foundation (£4,000); Army Benevolent Fund (£3,000); Action on Elder Abuse and Clic Sargent Cancer Fund (£2,000 each); National Autistic Society and Raleigh International (£1,000 each); and Royal Free Hospital Retirement Fellowship (£300).
finances *Year* 2011–12 *Income* £24,914 *Grants* £60,000

trustees Margaret Cody; Dr Susan Roberts; James Roberts.
how to apply In writing to the correspondent, preferably in January to March each year.
who to apply to Michael Kennedy, Smallfield Cody and Co, 5 Harley Place, Harley Street, London W1G 8QD *Tel.* 020 7631 4574

....

■ The Holmes Family Trust (Sheffield)

cc no 1139716　　**established** 2011
where funding can be given UK.
who can benefit Registered charities.
what is funded General charitable purposes, Christian causes and children and young people.
sample grants Not available.
finances *Year* 2011–12 *Income* £0 *Grants* £13,252
trustees Adrian Holmes; Michelle Rigby; Andrew Robertson; Richard Holmes.
other information Accounts had been received at the Charity Commission but were not published online due to the low income. We have no further information regarding the trust.
how to apply In writing to the correspondent.
who to apply to Adrian Holmes, Trustee, Bank Green House, Fox Lane, Millthorpe, Derbyshire S18 7WG *Tel.* 01142 547090

....

■ The Holst Foundation

cc no 283668　　**established** 1981
where funding can be given UK.
who can benefit Mainly musical organisations.
what is funded To promote public appreciation of the musical works of Gustav and Imogen Holst and to encourage the study and practice of music. Funds are almost exclusively for the performance of music by living composers.
what is not funded No support for: the recordings or works of Holst that are already well supported; capital projects; individuals for educational purposes, research, travel, purchase of instruments, equipment or publications; the commissioning of new works, although help is sometimes available for the copying and rehearsal costs of works receiving first performances or festivals (other than Aldeburgh) or orchestras or other large organisations.
range of grants Usually up to £30,000.
sample grants New Music House (£3,800); Holst Birthplace Trust, London Sinfonietta and Birmingham Contemp Music Group (£3,000 each); Aldeburgh Music (£2,500) and Mornington Trust and Tête à Tête Productions (£1,000). A further 22 unlisted grants of less than £1,000 totalled £11,300.
finances *Year* 2011–12 *Income* £75,542 *Grants* £154,056 *Assets* £1,069,327
trustees Rosamund Strode, Chair; Noel Periton; Prof. Arnold Whittall; Peter Carter; Andrew Clements; Julian Anderson.
how to apply In writing to the correspondent. Trustees meet four times a year. There is no application form. Six copies of the application should be sent. Applications should contain full financial details and be as concise as possible. If you are applying to other funders you should also make note of this in your application form. Funding is not given retrospectively.

Think carefully about every application. Is it justified?

629

WHO TO APPLY TO The Grants Administrator, 43 Alderbrook Road, London SW12 8AD *Tel* 020 8673 4215 (answerphone only) *email* holst@dpmail.co.uk *Website* www. holstfoundation.org

---

■ P. H. Holt Foundation

CC NO 1113708 **ESTABLISHED** 1955
WHERE FUNDING CAN BE GIVEN UK, with a preference for Merseyside.
WHO CAN BENEFIT Wherever possible, grants are paid to or through registered charities.
WHAT IS FUNDED General charitable purposes in the UK, especially Merseyside, particularly when original work or work of special excellence is being undertaken.
WHAT IS NOT FUNDED No grants for: individuals; sectarian causes; appeals for help with minibuses, holidays and animal welfare work; organisations based outside of Merseyside (in some circumstances help may be given to organisations in parts of Cheshire West and Chester, Halton and West Lancashire which have strong links with Merseyside).
TYPE OF GRANT One-off and recurrent.
RANGE OF GRANTS Up to £10,000.
SAMPLE GRANTS A full list of grants was not included in the accounts, however, previous beneficiaries included: Speke Baptist Church (£10,000); Lodestar Theatre Company (£6,000); Collective Encounters and Liverpool Arts Interface Ltd (£5,000 each); Plaza Community Cinema (£4,400); Garston and District Community Council (£3,000); Hurricane Film Foundation (£2,500); Creative Ideas in Action and Merseyside Refugee and Asylum Seekers Pre and Post Natal Support Group (£2,000 each); Steps to Freedom (£1,500); Kensington Remembers (£1,000) and China Pearl, Rotunda Community College and Elim Christian Centre (£500 each).
FINANCES *Year* 2011–12 *Income* £754,017 *Grants* £65,000 *Assets* £13,889,974
TRUSTEES Neil Kemsley, Chair; Tilly Boyce; Martin Cooke; Paige Earlam; Nikki Eastwood; Anthony Hannay; Ken Ravenscroft; Elspeth Christie.
HOW TO APPLY From the website: 'there is currently no application form. What we want is a short letter about your project, backed up as appropriate by a budget, your annual report and accounts, and indications of who else is supporting the work or willing to recommend it. Explain how much you hope we will give and why you need that amount. Remember that, with limited resources, we prefer to make fairly small grants but also want them to be significant in their impact; when we make larger grants, it is normally after a series of meetings and discussions.' See the website for detailed criteria and a discussion of the foundation's preferences.
WHO TO APPLY TO Anne Edwards, Trust administrator, LCVS, 151 Dale Street, Liverpool L2 2AH *Tel.* 01512 372663 *email* administrator@ phholtfoundation.org.uk *Website* www. phholtfoundation.org.uk

---

■ The Edward Holt Trust

CC NO 224741 **ESTABLISHED** 1955
WHERE FUNDING CAN BE GIVEN UK with a preference for Greater Manchester.
WHO CAN BENEFIT Registered charities.
WHAT IS FUNDED Primarily the maintenance of a block of ten flats in Didsbury, Manchester, for retired people. Preference to charities which the trustees have special interest in, knowledge of or association with, including cancer, neurological and ageing research.
TYPE OF GRANT Buildings, capital, project and research. Funding is available for up to three years.
SAMPLE GRANTS Didsbury Good Neighbours (£17,500)
FINANCES *Year* 2011–12 *Income* £219,421 *Grants* £108,872 *Assets* £6,814,363
TRUSTEES Richard Kershaw; Mike Fry; David Tully; Edward Tudor-Evans; Angela Roden.
OTHER INFORMATION Holt House expenditure totalled to £91,000 including the cost of refurbishments carried out in the year.
HOW TO APPLY In writing to the correspondent, although the trust informed us that at the time of writing (December 2013) no grants were available. Contact the trust for up-to-date information.
WHO TO APPLY TO Bryan Peak, Secretary, 22 Ashworth Park, Knutsford, Cheshire WA16 9DE *Tel.* 01565 651086 *email* edwardholt@btinternet.com *Website* www. edwardholttrust.btck.co.uk

---

■ The Holywood Trust

SC NO SC009942 **ESTABLISHED** 1981
WHO CAN BENEFIT Young people, the disabled and those suffering from ill health in Dumfries and Galloway. Grants are made both to individuals and to organisations.
WHAT IS FUNDED 'The Holywood Trust assists organisations working with or for young people in Dumfries and Galloway. It does this by means of secondment of staff, management and administrative support, assisting with fundraising activity as well as direct financial support.
TYPE OF GRANT One-off, capital and recurring (usually limited to three years) depending on need.
RANGE OF GRANTS £10–£50,000.
SAMPLE GRANTS Dumfries and Galloway Multi-cultural Association; Mossburn Community Farm – Equine Assisted Learning and Summerhill Community Association.
FINANCES *Year* 2011–12 *Income* £1,799,190
TRUSTEES Valerie McElroy; Charles Jencks; Louisa Jencks; Clara Weatherall; Ben Weatherall.
OTHER INFORMATION In 2011–12 the trust had a total expenditure of £1.5 million
HOW TO APPLY On a form available from the correspondent or available, together with criteria and guidelines, to download from the website. Applications are considered by the trustees at least three times a year.
WHO TO APPLY TO Richard Lye, Trust Administrator, Hestan House, Crichton Business Park, Bankend Road, Dumfries DG1 4TA *Tel.* 01387 269176 *Fax* 01387 269175 *email* funds@ holywood-trust.org.uk *Website* www.holywood-trust.org.uk

---

■ The Homelands Charitable Trust

CC NO 214322 **ESTABLISHED** 1962
WHERE FUNDING CAN BE GIVEN UK.
WHO CAN BENEFIT Registered charities benefiting children, particularly people in at risk groups, or who are victims of abuse or domestic violence. Support may also be given to clergy, medical professionals and research workers.
WHAT IS FUNDED General charitable purposes in accordance with the settlor's wishes. Special

emphasis is given to the General Conference of the New Church, medical research and the care and protection of children. Hospices are also supported.

WHAT IS NOT FUNDED No grants to individuals.

SAMPLE GRANTS Previous beneficiaries included: General Conference of the New Church (£68,000); Broadfield Memorial Fund (£15,000); New Church College (£11,000); Bournemouth Society (£10,000); Jubilee Sailing Trust, Manic Depression Fellowship and National Children's Homes (£2,400 each); and the Attic Charity – Youth Project, Bikeability, Eyeless Trust and Pestalozzi (£1,600 each).

FINANCES *Year* 2011–12 *Income* £260,135 *Grants* £242,000 *Assets* £6,828,083

TRUSTEES Denis Ballard; Nigel Armstrong; Revd Clifford Curry; Robert Curry.

OTHER INFORMATION No list of grantees was available. The trustees state in their 2011–12 annual report that they intend to continue supporting registered charities with a bias towards: General Conference of the New Church; medical research; care and protection of children; and hospices, including those for children.

HOW TO APPLY In writing to the correspondent.

WHO TO APPLY TO Nigel Armstrong, Trustee, c/o Alliotts, 4th Floor, Imperial House, 15 Kingsway, London WC2B 6UN *Tel.* 020 7240 9971

■ The Homestead Charitable Trust

CC NO 293979   **ESTABLISHED** 1986

WHERE FUNDING CAN BE GIVEN UK.

WHO CAN BENEFIT Actors and entertainment professionals, musicians, textile workers and designers, writers and poets, Christians, at risk groups, people disadvantaged by poverty, and socially isolated people.

WHAT IS FUNDED Medical, health and welfare, animal welfare, Christianity and the arts.

TYPE OF GRANT Some recurring.

RANGE OF GRANTS Up to £10,000.

SAMPLE GRANTS Ahkshaya Patra Foundation (£21,000); British Heart Foundation (£15,000); Missionaries of Charity – Calcutta, water.org and Angel Covers (£6,200 each); Nottingham Trent University, National Osteoporosis Society and County History Trust (£5,000 each); Fight Against Blindness (£3,500); Prostate Cancer Charity and Kingswold Trust for Children (£2,000 each); Finsbury Park Community Hub (£1,500); Down's Heart Group and South East Dog Rescue (£1,000 each) and YMCA (£250).

FINANCES *Year* 2011–12 *Income* £88,147 *Grants* £131,142 *Assets* £5,078,028

TRUSTEE Lady N Bracewell-Smith.

OTHER INFORMATION £3,500 was awarded to one individual.

HOW TO APPLY In writing to the correspondent.

WHO TO APPLY TO Lady Nina Bracewell-Smith, Trustee, Flat 7, Clarence Gate Gardens, Glentworth Street, London NW1 6AY

■ The Mary Homfray Charitable Trust

CC NO 273564   **ESTABLISHED** 1977

WHERE FUNDING CAN BE GIVEN UK, with a preference for Wales.

WHO CAN BENEFIT Registered charities.

WHAT IS FUNDED General charitable purposes.

RANGE OF GRANTS Up to £5,000

SAMPLE GRANTS Age Concern, Teenage Cancer Trust and Welsh Sinfonia (£3,000 each); Barnardo's, National Botanic Garden of Wales, Prince's Trust Cymru, St David's Foundation, Wales Millennium Centre and Wildfowl and Wetland Trust (£2,000 each); Y Bont, St Dunstan's, RSPB, Maes-y-Dyfan, Alzheimer's Society and Ashgrove School (£1,000 each).

FINANCES *Year* 2011–12 *Income* £160,316 *Grants* £46,000 *Assets* £1,438,110

TRUSTEES Angela Homfray; Simon Gibson; Josephine Homfray.

HOW TO APPLY In writing to the correspondent. Applications should be made towards the end of the year, for consideration at the trustees' meeting in February or March each year.

WHO TO APPLY TO Angela Homfray, Trustee, 5 Callaghan Square, Cardiff CF10 5BT *Tel.* 02920 264391

■ Sir Harold Hood's Charitable Trust

CC NO 225870   **ESTABLISHED** 1962

WHERE FUNDING CAN BE GIVEN Worldwide.

WHO CAN BENEFIT Roman Catholic charities and churches.

WHAT IS FUNDED Charities dealing with the advancement of the Roman Catholic faith through religious buildings, religious umbrella bodies and other Roman Catholic organisations.

WHAT IS NOT FUNDED No grants to individuals.

TYPE OF GRANT One-off and recurring.

RANGE OF GRANTS Up to £30,000.

SAMPLE GRANTS Downside Fisher Youth Club and the Prison Advice and Care Trust (£30,000 each); Craig Lodge Trust (£25,000); Duchess of Leeds Foundation (£20,000); Diocese of Brentwood (£17,000); San Lorenzo School – Chile and Westminster Cathedral (£14,000 each); Venerable English College – Rome and the Ace of Clubs – Clapham (£10,000); Maryvale Institute (£8,000); HCPT (£7,000); Housing Justice (£5,000); Ten Ten Theatre (£3,000); Young Christian Workers (£2,000); and the Right to Life Charitable Trust (£1,000).

FINANCES *Year* 2011–12 *Income* £555,019 *Grants* £516,700 *Assets* £30,915,348

TRUSTEES Dom James Hood; Lord Nicholas True; Lady True; Margaret Hood; Christian Elwes.

HOW TO APPLY In writing to the correspondent. The trustees meet once a year to consider applications, usually in November.

WHO TO APPLY TO Margaret Hood, Trustee, Haysmacintyre, Fairfax House, 15 Fulwood Place, London WC1V 6AY *Tel.* 020 7722 9088

■ Hope For Youth (NI)

CC NO 264843   **ESTABLISHED** 1972

WHERE FUNDING CAN BE GIVEN Northern Ireland.

WHO CAN BENEFIT Integrated schools; community playgroups; play buses; youth clubs; women's groups; cross-community holiday schemes benefiting children and young adults.

WHAT IS FUNDED Cross-community projects that give disadvantaged 11–18 year olds in Northern Ireland the opportunity to work together on practical projects that foster teamwork, creativity and personal development, especially within the arts or in the great outdoors. Education, arts, media, sport, recreation.

WHAT IS NOT FUNDED No grants for individuals, large capital expenditure or salaries, organisations solely for the welfare of physically or mentally disabled people, or drug or alcohol related projects. No grants for holidays outside the island of Ireland.

TYPE OF GRANT Recurring costs funded for up to one year.

RANGE OF GRANTS £200–£2,000.

SAMPLE GRANTS Music Theatre for Youth, Youth Initiatives, Appletree Childcare, Careers 'N' Kids, Drumaness Cross Community Playgroup, Old Library Trust, Significance Women's Initiative, St Vincent de Paul, The Diamond Centre.

FINANCES *Year* 2012 *Income* £28,845 *Grants* £57,620 *Assets* £81,677

TRUSTEES Johnny Andrews; Julia Corkey; The Viscount Crichton; David Lindsay; Rt Hon William Montgomery; Lady Nicholson; The Viscount Gough; Emma Nicholson; Jonathan Shillington; James Jackson; Noel Lamb.

OTHER INFORMATION Details of 2014 grant round to be made available on website.

HOW TO APPLY On an application form available to download, together with criteria and guidelines, on the website. The trustees meet four or five times a year and receive many more applications than can be accepted.

WHO TO APPLY TO Angela Dickson, c/o Cherton Enterprise Ltd, Unit 8, Belmont Business Park, 240 Belmont Road, Belfast BT4 2AW *Tel.* 02890 769966 *email* angela.dickson@cherton.co.uk *Website* www.hopeforyouthni.com

■ The Hope Trust

SC NO SC000987   **ESTABLISHED** 1912

WHERE FUNDING CAN BE GIVEN Worldwide, with a preference for Scotland.

WHO CAN BENEFIT Individuals and organisations benefiting Christians; Church of England; evangelists; Methodists; Quakers; Unitarians and people with a substance addiction.

WHAT IS FUNDED The provision of education and the distribution of literature to combat the misuse and effects of drink and drugs and to promote the principles of Reformed Churches; charities concerned with the advancement of the Christian religion, Anglican bodies, Free Church, rehabilitation centres and health education.

WHAT IS NOT FUNDED No grants to gap year students, scholarship schemes or to any individuals, with the sole exception of PhD students of theology studying at Scottish universities. No grants for the refurbishment of property.

TYPE OF GRANT Core costs, one-off funding, project, research, recurring costs, running costs, salaries, start-up costs and funding for more than three years will be considered.

RANGE OF GRANTS £100–£6,000.

SAMPLE GRANTS Previous beneficiaries have included Church of Scotland Priority Areas Fund, World Alliance of Reformed Churches, National Bible Society for Scotland, Feed the Minds and Waldensian Mission Aid.

FINANCES *Year* 2012 *Income* £215,413 *Grants* £200,000

HOW TO APPLY In writing to the correspondent. The trustees meet to consider applications in June and December each year. Applications should be submitted by mid-May or mid-November each year.

WHO TO APPLY TO The Secretary, Drummond Miller, 31–32 Moray Place, Edinburgh EH3 6BZ *Tel.* 01312 265151 *email* reception@drummond-miller.co.uk

■ HopMarket Charity

CC NO 244569   **ESTABLISHED** 1964

WHERE FUNDING CAN BE GIVEN The city of Worcester.

WHO CAN BENEFIT 'Needy' people in the city of Worcester. 'Needy' is defined as those 'who, by reason of poverty, sickness or infirmity, whether young or old, are in need of financial assistance, care or attention'. People of all ages, volunteers, and people who are disabled or disadvantaged by poverty.

WHAT IS FUNDED The trust has adopted the following guidelines: 'That as a general principle the funds should be allocated to either capital or revenue projects which fall within the purposes of the charity and which will generate further support for the community. Where revenue funding is made, such support should not imply any ongoing commitment except where the trustees specifically indicate otherwise. Emphasis should be placed on assisting applications which have an affinity to matters which are within the council's sphere of activity.'

WHAT IS NOT FUNDED No grants to, or on behalf of, individuals.

RANGE OF GRANTS £750–£21,500

SAMPLE GRANTS Worcester Housing and Benefits Advice (£21,500); Worcester Play Council (£16,000); Worcestershire Lifestyles (£12,000); Perdiswell Young People's Club (£11,000); Worcester Action For Youth (£4,300); Ethnic Access Link Scheme (£2,750); Gorse Hill Community Primary School (£1,500) and Worcester Leg Club (£1,250).

FINANCES *Year* 2011–12 *Income* £197,195 *Grants* £103,000 *Assets* £1,058,221

TRUSTEE The City Council.

HOW TO APPLY On a form available from the correspondent. Applications should be submitted by the beginning of January or August for consideration in March or September respectively.

WHO TO APPLY TO Finance Services Team Leader, c/o Worcester City Council, Orchard House, Farrier Street, Worchester WR1 3BB *Tel.* 01905 722005

■ The Horizon Foundation

CC NO 1118455   **ESTABLISHED** 2007

WHERE FUNDING CAN BE GIVEN Worldwide.

WHO CAN BENEFIT Registered charities.

WHAT IS FUNDED General, education, women and children

SAMPLE GRANTS Future Hope UK and Rugby School (£65,600 each); UWC Atlantic College and The National Boarding Bursary Foundation (£50,000 each); Eton College (£48,000); The Hotchkiss School (£22,000); University College London (£18,500); School for Oriental and African Studies (£14,000); Medical Aid for Palestinians (£8,000) and Friends of Ubunto Education Fund (£5,000).

FINANCES *Year* 2012–13 *Income* £458,516 *Grants* £454,082 *Assets* £91,820

TRUSTEES Kirkland Caroline Smulders; Patrick Lance Smulders; Coutts and Co.

HOW TO APPLY In writing to the correspondent.

WHO TO APPLY TO Trust Administrator, c/o Coutts and Co, 440 The Strand, London WC2R 0QS *Tel.* 020 7663 6814

■ The Cuthbert Horn Trust

CC NO 291465   **ESTABLISHED** 1985

WHERE FUNDING CAN BE GIVEN Worldwide.

WHO CAN BENEFIT Registered charities.

WHAT IS FUNDED General charitable purposes.

WHAT IS NOT FUNDED No grants are made to individuals.

TYPE OF GRANT One-off and recurrent.

RANGE OF GRANTS £1,000–£10,000.

SAMPLE GRANTS BISYOC and The Island Trust (£3,000 each); and Charleston Trust, Norfolk Wherry Trust, Population Matters, Pesticide Action Network UK and Progressive Farming Trust (£2,000 each).

FINANCES *Year* 2012 *Income* £230,778 *Grants* £26,000 *Assets* £1,387,580

TRUSTEES Alan Flint; Prosper Marr-Johnson; Rory Johnston; Capita Trust Co Ltd.

HOW TO APPLY There are no application forms to complete; applicants should provide in writing as much background about their charity or cause as possible. Applications need to be received by December as the trustees meet as soon as possible after the financial year end. Only successful applications will be notified.

WHO TO APPLY TO Laurie Wilson, Trust Manager, Capita Trust Company Limited, 4th Floor, 40 Dukes Place, London EC3A 7NH *Tel.* 020 3367 8209 *email* lwilson@capitafiduciary.co.uk

■ The Antony Hornby Charitable Trust

CC NO 263285   **ESTABLISHED** 1971

WHERE FUNDING CAN BE GIVEN Unrestricted with a preference for London and the Home Counties.

WHO CAN BENEFIT Registered charities.

WHAT IS FUNDED General charitable purposes, in particular supporting charities involved in medical activities, education and welfare.

WHAT IS NOT FUNDED No grants to individuals. Only registered charities are supported. No grants to localised building projects.

RANGE OF GRANTS £100–£1,500.

SAMPLE GRANTS Pro-Action Hertfordshire and Kings Medical Research Trust (£1,500 each); West London Action for Children, Tring Park School for Performing Arts and Shakespeare Globe Trust (£1,000 each); National Association of Almshouses (£750); Cure Parkinson's Trust, Walking with the Wounded and University of Hertfordshire (£500 each) and Prostate Cancer Charity and Samantha Dickson Brain Tumour Trust (£100 each).

FINANCES *Year* 2011–12 *Income* £39,677 *Grants* £34,045 *Assets* £1,183,184

TRUSTEES Marie Antoinette Hall; Mark Antony Loveday; Michael Wentworth-Stanley; Jane Wentworth-Stanley.

OTHER INFORMATION The grant total includes £23,000 that was distributed via Charities Aid Foundation.

HOW TO APPLY The trust has stated that it is fully committed and does not usually add new names to its list of beneficiaries unless it is a charity known to the trustees, or a very special appeal.

WHO TO APPLY TO Paul Langdon, Saffrey Champness, Lion House, 72–75 Red Lion Street, London WC1R 4GB *Tel.* 020 7841 4000

■ The Horne Foundation

CC NO 283751   **ESTABLISHED** 1981

WHERE FUNDING CAN BE GIVEN UK, mainly Northamptonshire and Oxfordshire.

WHO CAN BENEFIT Preference is given to local organisations benefiting young adults, children and older people, especially people disadvantaged by poverty, with occasional grants also made to UK organisations.

WHAT IS FUNDED Predominantly large grants towards major educational projects that involve new buildings and regular smaller donations to local projects in the Northampton and Oxfordshire area and student bursaries for higher education through Northampton schools.

WHAT IS NOT FUNDED The foundation prefers organisations without religious affiliation.

TYPE OF GRANT Capital and project grants.

RANGE OF GRANTS £1,000–£10,000

SAMPLE GRANTS Marie Curie Cancer Care and Crisis UK Christmas (£10,000 each); Northamptonshire Association of Youth Clubs Octopus Project (£8,000) and Daventry Contract (£1,200).

FINANCES *Year* 2011–12 *Income* £208,109 *Grants* £204,200 *Assets* £6,548,713

TRUSTEES Julie Davenport; Ros Harwood; Tina Horne.

OTHER INFORMATION In 2011–12 grants were given to one national appeal, three organisations and 87 individual students.
Grants given to students were in the form of bursaries for higher education through Northampton schools.

HOW TO APPLY In writing to the correspondent at any time.

WHO TO APPLY TO R. M. Harwood, Secretary, PO Box 6165, Newbury RG14 9FY *email* hornefoundation@googlemail.com

■ The Horne Trust

CC NO 1010625   **ESTABLISHED** 1992

WHERE FUNDING CAN BE GIVEN UK and the developing world.

WHO CAN BENEFIT Charities, hospices and charitable projects.

WHAT IS FUNDED Hospices (particularly children's hospices), medical support and development of self-reliant technology in Africa and the developing world.

RANGE OF GRANTS £1,000–£40,000.

SAMPLE GRANTS World Medical Fund (£20,000); St Andrew's Hospice – Grimsby, Practical Action (IDTG) and Demelza House Children's Hospice (£10,000 each); Ardgowan Hospice – Greenock (£7,500); Acorns Children's Hospice – Worcester, Alzheimer's Society, Donna Louise Children's Hospice – Stoke, Humberstone Hydrotherapy Pool, Julia's House Children's Hospice – Dorset (£5,000 each); Soundabout (£2,500) and Whitby Dog Rescue and Winfield Trust (£1,000 each).

FINANCES *Year* 2011–12 *Income* £788,393 *Grants* £605,900 *Assets* £6,416,621

TRUSTEES Jeff Horne; Jon Horne; Emma Horne.

HOW TO APPLY Normally in writing to the correspondent, although the trust has stated that currently unsolicited applications cannot be supported.

WHO TO APPLY TO J. T. Horne, Trustee, Kingsdown, Warmlake Road, Chart Sutton, Maidstone, Kent ME17 3RP *Tel.* 01622 842638 *email* contact@horne-trust.org.uk

Think carefully about every application. Is it justified?

633

■ The Worshipful Company of Horners' Charitable Trusts

CC NO 292204   **ESTABLISHED** 1985

WHERE FUNDING CAN BE GIVEN Mainly in London.

WHO CAN BENEFIT Registered charities, educational establishments and individuals.

WHAT IS FUNDED General charitable purposes; education in plastics; and scholarships and bursaries in education.

RANGE OF GRANTS £1,000–£25,000

SAMPLE GRANTS Thrive (£25,000); Salters Homers Advanced Physics (£15,000); Polymer Study Tours (£10,000); Lord Mayor's Appeal, Guildhall School Trust and Mudchute Farm (£3,000 each); Blind in Business (£1,400); and Rivertime Trust (£1,000).

FINANCES *Year* 2012 *Income* £727,425 *Grants* £84,502 *Assets* £2,553,832

TRUSTEES Ray Anstis; Jack Bunyer; Dr Brian Ridgewell; Georgina Scott; K. Featherstone; Keith Pinker; Clive Thompson; Newton Grant; Robert Leader.

OTHER INFORMATION Other grants for under £1,000 each amounted to £1,700.

HOW TO APPLY In writing to the correspondent.

WHO TO APPLY TO Hugh Moss, Assistant Clerk, c/o The Horners' Company, 37 Waterloo Road, Bedford MK40 3PQ *email* horners.clerk@ btinternet.com *Website* www.horners.org.uk

■ The Hornsey Parochial Charities

CC NO 229410   **ESTABLISHED** 1890

WHERE FUNDING CAN BE GIVEN Ancient parish of Hornsey in part of the boroughs of Hackney and Haringey.

WHO CAN BENEFIT Individuals and organisations benefiting people disadvantaged by poverty.

WHAT IS FUNDED Supporting those in need and also assisting with education expenses for those young people under the age of 25 years. Financial assistance is granted to individuals and local organisations through bursaries, maintenance allowances, clothing, instruments and books.

WHAT IS NOT FUNDED Residential qualification needed (must have lived in ancient parish of Hornsey for at least a year). No commitment to continuous grants.

FINANCES *Year* 2012 *Income* £53,271 *Grants* £48,000

TRUSTEES Revd Patrick Henderson; Eddie Griffiths; John Hudson; Ann Jones; Peter Kenyon; Vivienne Manheim; Lorraine Marshall; Barbara Simon; Katy Jones; Ann Gillespie; Carol O'Brien; Paula Lanning; Revd Bruce Batstone.

HOW TO APPLY On a form available to download, together with criteria and guidelines, from the website. Initial enquiries by e-mail are welcome.

WHO TO APPLY TO The Clerk to the Trustees, PO Box 22985, London N10 3XB *Tel.* 020 8352 1601 *email* hornseypc@blueyonder.co.uk *Website* www.hornseycharities.com

■ The Hospital of God at Greatham

CC NO 1123540   **ESTABLISHED** 1973

WHERE FUNDING CAN BE GIVEN Darlington, Durham, Gateshead, Hartlepool, Newcastle upon Tyne, Northumberland, North Tyneside, South Tyneside, Stockton on Tees and Sunderland.

WHO CAN BENEFIT Charities, voluntary organisations and individuals. The trust supports children, young adults, older people, at risk groups, carers, people who are disabled, disadvantaged by poverty, homeless or socially isolated, victims of abuse and domestic violence, and people with Alzheimer's disease, epilepsy and hearing loss.

WHAT IS FUNDED Preference is given to projects concerned with local initiatives aimed at disadvantaged people, particularly charities working in the field of social care and with local communities.

WHAT IS NOT FUNDED No grants for: Capital works or appeals; Education/travel/adventure projects; Training/conferences and feasibility studies; Medical equipment and related projects; Organisations that do not have a base in the north east.

TYPE OF GRANT One-off, core funding, running costs and salaries. Funding for one year or more will be considered.

RANGE OF GRANTS £500–£8,000.

SAMPLE GRANTS Newcastle Diocese Discretionary Fund (£7,000); Bishop of Durham Discretionary Fund (£5,000); Credit Union for South East Northumberland (£3,500); After Adoption, Gateshead, Hartlepool and District Hospice, North East Prison After Care Society and Durham Area Disability Leisure Group (£2,000 each); Westgate Baptist Church (£1,500); Willington Community Action Centre Crook, Tees Valley Dance, Hartlepool, Sunderland Community Furniture Society and Retired Fishermen, Wallsend (£1,000 each) and Small Talk, Norton (£500).

FINANCES *Year* 2011–12 *Income* £3,867,519 *Grants* £100,870 *Assets* £39,521,833

TRUSTEES Wendy Mitchell; Ven Ian Jagger; Ven Geoffrey Miller; Barry Winter; John Allen; Stephen Croft; John De Martino; Michael Poole; Peter Shields; Philippa Sinclair; Harvey Madden.

OTHER INFORMATION The charity's main work is the provision of almshouse accommodation and residential care. In 2011–12 grants were given to 73 organisations.

HOW TO APPLY Applications should be made to the correspondent in writing. The grants committee meets three times a year. Grant applications should consist of not more than two sides of A4 and should provide information on: Description of organisation; description of project; how it is to be delivered; evidence of need for the project; amount requested and how it is to be spent s. This should be accompanied by the latest set of audited accounts and/or annual report. The correspondent is happy to answer initial telephone enquiries.

WHO TO APPLY TO David Granath, Administrator, The Estate Office, Greatham, Hartlepool TS25 2HS *Tel.* 01429 870247 *email* david.granath@ hospitalofgod.org.uk *Website* www. hospitalofgod.org.uk

■ The Hospital Saturday Fund

CC NO 1123381   **ESTABLISHED** 1987

WHERE FUNDING CAN BE GIVEN UK, the Republic of Ireland, the Channel Islands and the Isle of Man.

WHO CAN BENEFIT Hospitals, hospices, medically-associated charities and welfare organisations providing similar services worldwide, but mostly in the UK and Republic of Ireland. Individuals can also be directly supported. Must be registered with the Charity Commission or regionally appropriate body (outside of England and Wales).

WHAT IS FUNDED Medical care and research to organisations; specialist equipment, welfare and scholarships to individuals.

WHAT IS NOT FUNDED Organisations should be registered with the Charity Commission, OSCR, Charity Commission for Northern Ireland, Isle of Man General Registry, HM Revenue and Customs, the Revenue Commissioners in Ireland or the appropriate regulatory body in the Channel Islands.

TYPE OF GRANT One-off grants. Organisations are rarely supported in successive years.

RANGE OF GRANTS Mostly £1,000.

FINANCES *Year* 2011–12 *Income* £24,297,006 *Grants* £502,773 *Assets* £20,985,659

TRUSTEES John Greenwood; Jane Laidlaw Dalton; Michael Boyle; John Randel; David Thomas; Christopher Bottomley; Pauline Lee.

OTHER INFORMATION In 2012 £25,000 was granted to individuals.

HOW TO APPLY Applications by letter to the Chief Executive detailing the scope of the request with supporting documentation, the amount requested and a copy of the latest annual report. The letter should clearly state the reason for your application (specific project or running costs); your charity registration number or details of registration with one of the other named bodies and the correct wording for a cheque should your application be successful.

WHO TO APPLY TO Paul Jackson, Chief Executive, 24 Upper Ground, London SE1 9PD *Tel.* 020 7202 1381 *email* charity@hsf.eu.com

■ The Sir Joseph Hotung Charitable Settlement

CC NO 1082710   **ESTABLISHED** 2000

WHERE FUNDING CAN BE GIVEN Worldwide.

WHO CAN BENEFIT Charitable organisations.

WHAT IS FUNDED General charitable purposes.

SAMPLE GRANTS The trust tends to support a small number of organisations known to the settlor, often on a regular basis. St George's Hospital Medical School (£1.8 million); the School of Oriental and African Studies (£175,000); Council for Assisting Refugee Academics (£50,000) and Spinal Research (£1,200).

FINANCES *Year* 2011–12 *Income* £1,384,371 *Grants* £2,023,046 *Assets* £759,818

TRUSTEES Sir Joseph E. Hotung; Sir Robert D. H. Boyd; Victoria F. Dicks.

HOW TO APPLY The trust has previously stated that: 'the trustees have their own areas of interest and do not respond to unsolicited applications'.

WHO TO APPLY TO Sir Joseph Hotung, Trustee, HSBC Private Bank Ltd, 78 St James's Street, London, SW1A 1JB

■ Houblon-Norman/George Fund

CC NO 213168   **ESTABLISHED** 1944

WHERE FUNDING CAN BE GIVEN UK.

WHO CAN BENEFIT Organisations benefiting academics and research workers.

WHAT IS FUNDED Research into the interaction and function of financial and business institutions, the economic conditions affecting them, and the dissemination of knowledge thereof. Fellowships are tenable at the Bank of England. The research work to be undertaken is intended to be full-time work, and teaching or other paid work must not be undertaken during the tenure of the fellowship, without the specific consent of the trustees. In considering applications the trustees will pay particular regard to the relevance of the research to current problems in economics and finance.

TYPE OF GRANT Research fellowship.

SAMPLE GRANTS The Trust made an individual grant totalling £72,000, in the form of one fellowship.

FINANCES *Year* 2011–12 *Income* £164,290 *Grants* £71,680 *Assets* £2,048,743

TRUSTEES Andrew Haldane; Charles Bean; David Prentis

HOW TO APPLY On an application form available from the website.

WHO TO APPLY TO Emma-Jayne Coker, Secretary, Bank of England, Threadneedle Street, London EC2R 8AH *Tel.* 020 7601 3778 *email* ma-hngfund@bankofengland.co.uk *Website* www.bankofengland.co.uk/research/houblonnorman/index.htm

■ The House of Industry Estate

CC NO 257079   **ESTABLISHED** 1968

WHERE FUNDING CAN BE GIVEN The borough of Bedford.

WHO CAN BENEFIT People who are in need and local organisations.

WHAT IS FUNDED Local organisations concerned with unemployed people, youth, counselling and housing.

WHAT IS NOT FUNDED Funds are not given in relief of taxes or other public funds. No recurrent grants are given.

TYPE OF GRANT One-off capital grants or core revenue funding.

RANGE OF GRANTS Up to £25,000

SAMPLE GRANTS Bedford Community Rights; Bedfordshire Garden Carers; Bedford Pilgrims Housing Association; Kempston Summer School; and King's Arms Project.

FINANCES *Year* 2011–12 *Income* £199,305 *Grants* £200,000

TRUSTEES Cllr Colleen Atkins; Cllr Tim Hill; Cllr David Sawyer; Cllr Tom Wootton; Cllr Stephen Moon; Cllr Henry Vann; Cllr James Valentine.

OTHER INFORMATION The Trustees may pay for such items, services or facilities by way of donations or subscriptions to institutions or organisations which provide or which undertake, in return, to provide such items, services or facilities for such persons.

HOW TO APPLY In writing to the correspondent. Criteria and guidelines are available on request.

WHO TO APPLY TO Director of Finance and Corporate Services, Bedford Borough Council, Borough Hall, Cauldwell Street, Bedford MK42 9AP *Tel.* 01234 267422

■ The Reta Lila Howard Foundation

CC NO 1041634   **ESTABLISHED** 1994

WHERE FUNDING CAN BE GIVEN UK and Republic of Ireland.

WHO CAN BENEFIT Children up to the age of 16.

WHAT IS FUNDED Innovative projects that benefit children, and projects concerned with 'the education of young people or to ameliorate their physical and emotional environment'.

WHAT IS NOT FUNDED Grants are not given to individuals, organisations which are not registered charities, or towards operating expenses, budget deficits, (sole) capital projects, annual charitable appeals, general endowment funds, fundraising drives or events, conferences, or student aid.

RANGE OF GRANTS £5,000 –£45,000.

SAMPLE GRANTS Countryside Education Trust (£70,000); Barnardo's (£68,500); Civitas

(£60,000); The Tree Council (£53,000); Farms for City Children (£40,000); Children's Hospice Association Scotland (£35,000); Teach First (£30,000); New Forest Museum and Library (£20,000); The Bridge End Community Centre (£15,000) and Bibles for Children (£10,000).

FINANCES *Year* 2011–12 *Income* £399,484 *Grants* £360,000 *Assets* £14,013,607

TRUSTEES Pilar Bauta; Charles Burnett; Garfield Mitchell; Alannah Weston; Galvin Weston; Melissa Murdoch; Tamara Lila Rebanks.

HOW TO APPLY The trust states that it does not accept unsolicited applications, since the trustees seek out and support projects they are interested in.

WHO TO APPLY TO The Company Secretary, Jamestown Investments, 4 Felstead Gardens, Ferry Street, London E14 3BS *Tel.* 020 7537 1118 *email* jamestown@btinternet.com

■ The Daniel Howard Trust

CC NO 267173   **ESTABLISHED** 1974

WHERE FUNDING CAN BE GIVEN UK and Israel.

WHO CAN BENEFIT Charities benefiting: children; young adults; actors and entertainment professionals; musicians; textile workers and designers; and writers and poets.

WHAT IS FUNDED Culture, education, the environment and welfare. Particularly Jewish causes.

WHAT IS NOT FUNDED Grants are only made to registered charities. No grants to individuals.

TYPE OF GRANT Recurrent and one-off.

RANGE OF GRANTS £500–£52,000

SAMPLE GRANTS Friends of Daniel for Rowing association (£40,000); V&A (£30,000); Tel Aviv Foundation (for Daniel Centre) (£22,000); Council for a Beautiful Israel (£10,000); Ringling Museum of Art (£9,600); Israel Philharmonic (£6,400); The Wharton Fund (£6,100); Israeli Opera Friends Association (£2,500) and Habitat for Humanity (£1,200).

FINANCES *Year* 2011–12 *Income* £39,625 *Grants* £157,121 *Assets* £5,216,205

TRUSTEES Dame Shirley Porter; Linda Streit; Steven Porter; Brian Padgett; Andrew Peggie.

HOW TO APPLY In writing to the correspondent.

WHO TO APPLY TO Sarah Hunt, 22 Arlington Street, London SW1A 1RD

■ The Howe Family Foundation

CC NO 1136256   **ESTABLISHED** 2010

WHERE FUNDING CAN BE GIVEN Throughout England

WHO CAN BENEFIT Organisations and individuals.

WHAT IS FUNDED General charitable purposes.

FINANCES *Year* 2011–12 *Income* £4,100 *Grants* £1,100

TRUSTEES Caroline Howe; Graham Howe.

OTHER INFORMATION A request to the correspondent for further information on the foundation did not produce a response.

HOW TO APPLY In writing to the correspondent.

WHO TO APPLY TO Sylvie Nunn, Administrator, Wrigleys Solicitors LLP, 19–21 Cookridge Street, Leeds LS2 3AG *Tel.* 01132 045726

■ HTA Sheba Foundation UK

CC NO 1135473   **ESTABLISHED** 2010

WHERE FUNDING CAN BE GIVEN Undefined, in practice national.

WHO CAN BENEFIT Charitable organisations.

WHAT IS FUNDED 'Any charitable purpose for the benefit of the community, including the relief of

poverty, advancement of education, in the interest of social welfare, to meet the needs of disabled, children, widows, elderly, people in need, orphans, health and homelessness, as well as the relief of natural disasters.'

SAMPLE GRANTS Not available.

FINANCES *Year* 2011–12 *Income* £3,190 *Grants* £3,420

TRUSTEES Ashik Ahmed; Salma Hashim.

OTHER INFORMATION Accounts had been received at the Charity Commission but due to the low income were not published online.

HOW TO APPLY In writing to the correspondent.

WHO TO APPLY TO Ashik Ahmed, Trustee, 18A Charlemont Road, London E6 6HL *Tel.* 07985 568755

■ The Huddersfield Common Good Trust

CC NO 231096   **ESTABLISHED** 1964

WHERE FUNDING CAN BE GIVEN The old Huddersfield County Borough and its environs (basically all HD Postcodes with the exception of HD6).

WHO CAN BENEFIT Organisations benefiting people of all ages, at-risk groups, carers, people who are disabled, people who are disadvantaged by poverty or who are homeless and victims of domestic violence.

WHAT IS FUNDED Youth and community groups, children, older people and general welfare organisations.

WHAT IS NOT FUNDED No grants to individuals, central/local government departments, religious bodies or national organisations. No grants to help with running costs.

TYPE OF GRANT One-off buildings and capital grants will be considered.

RANGE OF GRANTS £50–£5,000.

SAMPLE GRANTS Honley Scouts (£4,000); Kirkwood Hospice (£2,200); Almondbury Methodist Church (£2,000); Birkby Rose Hill Cricket Club, Oakes Cafe, Lowerhouses Bowling Club and Newsome Football Club (£1,500 each); Huddersfield Woodturners (£625) and U-Turn (£250).

FINANCES *Year* 2012–13 *Income* £30,545 *Grants* £24,805

TRUSTEES Susan Stott; Anthony Russell; Raymond Butterworth; Peter Hoyle; John Lockwood; John Ashworth; Val Javin; Jacqui Goff; Martin Kilburn.

PUBLICATIONS Information leaflet.

HOW TO APPLY Write or email the correspondent, giving details of your organisation. They will need to see a copy of your latest annual accounts, or if you are a new organisation some form of financial plan.

WHO TO APPLY TO Anthony Haigh, Secretary, c/o Methodist Mission, 3–13 Lord Street, Huddersfield HD1 1QA *email* antonyhaigh@btinternet.com *Website* www.hcgtrust.org.uk

■ The Hudson Foundation

CC NO 280332   **ESTABLISHED** 1980

WHERE FUNDING CAN BE GIVEN UK, with a preference for the Wisbech area.

WHO CAN BENEFIT Individuals and organisations benefiting older people and those who are infirm, especially in the Wisbech area.

WHAT IS FUNDED The relief of people who are elderly or infirm.

RANGE OF GRANTS Up to £80,000.

SAMPLE GRANTS Wisbech Grammar School (£42,000); National Trust (£25,000); Wisbech

Swimming Club (£9,100); Fenland Association Community Transport (£7,900); WisARD (£7,500); Wisbech Angles Theatre (£6,000) and Listening Books (£2,000).
FINANCES *Year* 2011–12 *Income* £869,659 *Grants* £124,805 *Assets* £2,008,783
TRUSTEES Hayward A. Godfrey; David W. Ball; Stephen G. Layton.
HOW TO APPLY In writing to the correspondent. Trustees meet quarterly.
WHO TO APPLY TO David W. Ball, Trustee, 1–3 York Row, Wisbech, Cambridgeshire PE13 1EA *Tel.* 01945 461456

■ The Huggard Charitable Trust

CC NO 327501   **ESTABLISHED** 1987
WHERE FUNDING CAN BE GIVEN UK, with a preference for South Wales.
WHO CAN BENEFIT Older people, people who are disabled, people who are disadvantaged by poverty.
WHAT IS FUNDED Advancement of religion, the relief of poverty, disability and the welfare of older people.
RANGE OF GRANTS Up to £12,000.
SAMPLE GRANTS Previously: Amelia Methodist Trust, Vale of Glamorgan, Bro Morgannwg NHS Trust, CURE Fund – Cardiff, Laparoscopy Laser Fund – UHW, SWS Cymru and Whitton Rosser Trust – Vale of Glamorgan.
FINANCES *Year* 2011–12 *Income* £15,823 *Grants* £150,000
TRUSTEES Anne Helme; Stephen Thomas; Anne Chiplen.
HOW TO APPLY The trustees are not inviting applications for funds, they support a list of charities provided by their founder.
WHO TO APPLY TO Stephen Thomas, Trustee, 25 Harvey Crescent, Aberavon, Port Talbot SA12 6DF *Tel.* 01639 681539

■ The Geoffrey C. Hughes Charitable Trust

CC NO 1010079   **ESTABLISHED** 1992
WHERE FUNDING CAN BE GIVEN UK.
WHO CAN BENEFIT Actors and entertainment professionals and musicians.
WHAT IS FUNDED This trust is essentially interested in two areas: nature conservation/environment and performing arts, particularly ballet or opera with a bias towards modern work.
WHAT IS NOT FUNDED No grants to individuals.
FINANCES *Year* 2011–12 *Income* £6,768 *Grants* £115,000
TRUSTEES John Young; Paul Solon; William Bailey.
OTHER INFORMATION In 2009/10 the trust had a total expenditure of £15,000.
HOW TO APPLY In writing to the correspondent.
WHO TO APPLY TO Paul Solon, Trustee, c/o Mills and Reeve, Francis House, 112 Hills Road, Cambridge CB2 1PH *Tel.* 01223 222290

■ The Hull and East Riding Charitable Trust

CC NO 516866   **ESTABLISHED** 1985
WHERE FUNDING CAN BE GIVEN Hull and the East Riding of Yorkshire.
WHO CAN BENEFIT Registered charities only, with a possible preference for organisations working with children/youth, medical/disability and welfare.

WHAT IS FUNDED General charitable purposes.
WHAT IS NOT FUNDED Grants are not normally given to individuals. No grants to organisations or causes of a political nature, or for religious purposes, although requests for maintenance of significant religious buildings may be considered. If a donation has been made the trustees would not expect to receive a further request from the recipient in the immediate future.
TYPE OF GRANT The trust prefers to fund the capital costs of a project, but will consider funding revenue costs over a limited period of time.
RANGE OF GRANTS £100–£15,000.
FINANCES *Year* 2011–12 *Income* £224,707 *Grants* £221,272 *Assets* £5,750,887
TRUSTEES Kate Field; Mary Barker; Adrian Horsley.
HOW TO APPLY In writing to the correspondent, including the aims of the project and benefits hoped for, the costs involved with budgets/ accounts as appropriate, the contribution sought from the trust and details of other funds raised. The trustees meet in May and November and requests for donations will only be considered at those meetings. Applications must be received by 20 April and 20 October. The trust states: 'It is unlikely that the trustees would support the total cost of a project and applicants should be able to demonstrate that funds have been raised or are in the process of being raised from other sources.'
WHO TO APPLY TO J. R. Barnes, Secretary and Administrator, Greenmeades, Kemp Road, Swanland, East Yorkshire HU14 3LY *Tel.* 01482 634664 *email* john@barnes1939.karoo.co.uk

■ Hulme Trust Estates (Educational)

CC NO 532297   **ESTABLISHED** 1964
WHERE FUNDING CAN BE GIVEN Greater Manchester.
WHO CAN BENEFIT Educational establishments.
WHAT IS FUNDED This trust supports educational establishments in the Greater Manchester area.
TYPE OF GRANT Grants awarded to schools and universities in the Greater Manchester area.
SAMPLE GRANTS Brasenose College (£88,000); Manchester University (£44,000); Schools Committee (£29,500); William Hulmes Grammar School (£25,000); Bury Grammar School, Hulme Grammar School Oldham and William Hulmes Grammar School (£5,500 each); Manchester HS for Girls (£4,600) and Manchester Grammar School (£900).
FINANCES *Year* 2012 *Income* £198,326 *Grants* £209,000 *Assets* £9,006,780
TRUSTEES David Claxton; Thomas Hoyle; Ian Thompson; Alan Bowman; Peter Sidwell; Philip Parker; Ian Rankin; Sarah Newman.
HOW TO APPLY In writing to the correspondent.
WHO TO APPLY TO Jonathan Aldersley, Secretary, c/o Butcher and Barlow, 34 Railway Road, Leigh, Lancashire WN7 4AU *Tel.* 01942 674144

■ Human Relief Foundation

CC NO 1126281   **ESTABLISHED** 1995
WHERE FUNDING CAN BE GIVEN Iraq, Jordan, Ethiopia and other regions requiring urgent relief/aid.
WHO CAN BENEFIT Organisations benefiting at risk groups, carers, people who are disabled, people disadvantaged by poverty, refugees, victims of famine, man-made or natural disasters and war. Medical professionals, scientists, unemployed people and volunteers will be supported.

WHAT IS FUNDED General charitable purposes for the relief of poverty, sickness and to protect and preserve good health, and advance education of those in need from impoverished countries, in particular Somalia, Bosnia, Iraq, Bangladesh and Lebanon. Infrastructure, support and development and cultural activity are also funded.

WHAT IS NOT FUNDED No grants to individuals, or for medical expenses, tutors or examination fees.

SAMPLE GRANTS Previous beneficiaries include: Red Crescent UAE; Qatar Charitable Society; Muslim Aid; Islamic Trust; Elrahma Charity Trust; Saudi Arabia (Muslim World League); Darfur Health Clinics; Isakhel Hospital Pakistan; Well Project, Iraq

FINANCES *Year* 2012 *Income* £4,277,435 *Grants* £479,753 *Assets* £2,118,489

TRUSTEES Dr Haytham Al-Khaffaf; Wael Musabbeh; Dr Nooh Al-Kaddo; Dr Haitham Al-Rawi; Mohanned Rahman.

OTHER INFORMATION A list of recent beneficiaries was not included in the accounts.

HOW TO APPLY In writing to the correspondent.

WHO TO APPLY TO Kassim Tokan, Secretary, PO Box 194, Bradford, West Yorkshire BD7 1YW *Tel.* 01274 392727 *Fax* 01274 739992 *Website* www.hrf.org.uk

■ The Humanitarian Trust

CC NO 208575   **ESTABLISHED** 1946

WHERE FUNDING CAN BE GIVEN Worldwide, mainly Israel.

WHO CAN BENEFIT Organisations and individuals.

WHAT IS FUNDED 'The trustees consider grant applications from organisations and individuals in the UK and abroad, especially in the fields of education, health, social welfare, civil society, Jewish communal life and general charitable purposes.'

TYPE OF GRANT One-off grants.

RANGE OF GRANTS up to £10,000

SAMPLE GRANTS Friends of Hebrew University of Jerusalem (£25,000 in two equal awards for scholarships); New Israel Fund (£6,000); Etz Hayyim Synagogue (£5,000); Jerusalem Foundation and Friendship Village (£4,000 each); Share Zedek UK (£3,000); Anne Frank Trust UK (£2,500); Nightingale House and Leo Baeck College (£2,000 each); Glasgow Jewish Educational Forum, Jewish Music Institute and Diabetes UK (£1,000 each) and Tommy's The Baby Charity, Oxford University Jewish Society and University of Warwick (£500 each).

FINANCES *Year* 2011–12 *Income* £136,849 *Grants* £93,480 *Assets* £4,294,209

TRUSTEES Jacques Gunsbourg; Pierre Halban; Anthony Lerman; Emanuelle Gunsbourg-Kasavi.

OTHER INFORMATION Approximate total grant-giving.

HOW TO APPLY In writing to the correspondent, including annual report and accounts, projected budgets and future plans. Applications are considered at trustees' meetings in March and October.

WHO TO APPLY TO J. Myers, Secretary, C/O Prism the Gift Fund, 20 Gloucester Place, London W1U 8HA *Tel.* 020 7486 7760

■ The Michael and Shirley Hunt Charitable Trust

CC NO 1063418   **ESTABLISHED** 1997

WHERE FUNDING CAN BE GIVEN UK and overseas.

WHO CAN BENEFIT Prisoners and/or their families, and people charged with criminal offences and held in custody. Also, animals which are unwanted, sick or ill-treated.

WHAT IS FUNDED Relief of need, hardship or distress of prisoners and/or their families; animal welfare; general charitable purposes.

WHAT IS NOT FUNDED No grants for capital projects, support costs, fines, bail, legal costs, rent deposits and so on.

TYPE OF GRANT One-off.

RANGE OF GRANTS £50–£10,000.

SAMPLE GRANTS St Barnabas Hospice (£6,000); Storybook Dads, DEC East Africa Crisis and Time for Families (£5,000 each); Miracles to Believe in (£2,500); Church Housing Trust (£2,000) and Rocking Horse, Alberts Horse Sanctuary and Dog Action Welfare Group (£1,000 each).

FINANCES *Year* 2011–12 *Income* £206,185 *Grants* £69,328 *Assets* £5,793,378

TRUSTEES Chester Hunt; Deborah Jenkins; Kathy Mayberry; Shirley Hunt; Wanda Baker.

OTHER INFORMATION Grants to 71 individuals (under the prisoners category) totalled £12,000.

HOW TO APPLY In writing to the correspondent. The trustees meet to consider applications 'as and when necessary, and at least annually'.

WHO TO APPLY TO Debra Jenkins, Trustee, Ansty House, Henfield Road, Small Dole, West Sussex BN5 9XH *Tel.* 01903 817116 *Fax* 01903 879995

■ The Albert Hunt Trust

CC NO 277318   **ESTABLISHED** 1979

WHERE FUNDING CAN BE GIVEN UK.

WHO CAN BENEFIT Registered charities.

WHAT IS FUNDED Projects that enhance the physical and mental welfare of individuals, or group of individuals.

WHAT IS NOT FUNDED No grants for research or overseas work.

RANGE OF GRANTS Up to £50,000.

SAMPLE GRANTS Beneficiaries of the largest grants were: Ambitious About Autism (£35,000); Bury Hospice, Sunfield Children's Homes Limited, Cornwall Hospice Care Limited, Home Farm Trust, Hollybank Trust and Chescombe Trust (£25,000 each); Botley Alzheimer's Home, Stroud Court Community Trust and Elizabeth Fitzroy Support (£20,000 each); Cancer Link Aberdeen and North (£15,000); and Douglas Macmillan Hospice (£13,000). Beneficiaries of grants of £10,000 or less included: Ruskin Mill Educational College Ltd, Tagsa Uibhist and St Barnabas Hospice Ltd (£10,000 each); Abbeyfield Society, the Norfolk Hospice and Alexander Devine Children's Hospice Service (£9,000 each); Julian House (£7,000); and the Peace Hospice (£6,000). Beneficiaries of grants of £5,000 or less included: Action on Hearing Loss, Aspire, Bath Institute for Medical Engineering, Birmingham St Mary's Hospice, Combat Stress, Clatterbridge, Community Campus 87, County Air Ambulance Trust, the Eric Lidell Centre, the Fire Fighters Charity, and Hestia Housing and Support. Beneficiaries of grants of £2,000 or less included: Advocacy Matters, Action for Kids, Arcos, Asperger East Anglia, Barnstondale Centre, British Liver Trust, the Bridge Trust, British Wireless for the Blind

Fund, Child Brain Injury Trust, Child Victims of Crime, Down's Heart Group, Dyspraxia Foundation, Friends First Farm, EDP Drug and Alcohol Services, Friends of Priestley Smith School, and Guildford Action.

FINANCES *Year* 2011–12 *Income* £1,627,632 *Grants* £1,658,640 *Assets* £45,419,939

TRUSTEES Breda McGuire; Richard Collis; Coutts and Co.

OTHER INFORMATION Grants were made to 582 institutions totalling £1.8 million.

HOW TO APPLY In writing to the correspondent. All appeals should be by letter containing the following: aims and objectives of the charity; nature of appeal; total target if for a specific project; contributions received against target; registered charity number; any other relevant factors. The correspondent has stated that no unsolicited correspondence will be acknowledged, unless an application receives favourable consideration.

WHO TO APPLY TO The Manager, Coutts and Co., Trustee Department, 440 Strand, London WC2R 0QS *Tel.* 020 7663 6826

■ The Hunter Foundation

SC NO SC027532   **ESTABLISHED** 1998

WHERE FUNDING CAN BE GIVEN UK and overseas.

WHO CAN BENEFIT Charitable organisations, schools and universities.

WHAT IS FUNDED Educational initiatives aimed largely at children; relief of poverty; community development. Focus in the developed world is to invest in national educational programmes that challenge the system wide issues which prevent children from achieving their potential. In the developing world the focus is on investing in holistic developments that embed solutions within communities and countries, again with education being central.

RANGE OF GRANTS £50,000+

SAMPLE GRANTS 'We do not distinguish between funding partners and programme partners – as far as we see it we are all in this together, either as funders or programme deliverers. We have many partners, but as an indication they include: University of Strathclyde; Prince's Scottish Youth Business Trust; Cash for Kids; STV Appeal; Children in Need; Comic Relief; Clinton Foundation; and Ethel Mutharika Maternity Hospital.'

FINANCES *Year* 2012–13 *Grants* £750,000

TRUSTEES Sir Tom Hunter, Chair; Lady Marion Hunter; Jim McMahon; Robert Glennie; Vartan Gregorian.

OTHER INFORMATION As in previous years, our requests for accounts from the foundation were ignored. Grant total is approximate based on previous research.

HOW TO APPLY The foundation has previously stated that it is 'pro-active' and does not seek applications. However, in response to our regular survey the foundation indicated that unsolicited applications are considered, so we repeat previous guidance from the foundation on how to make an approach:
'The Hunter Foundation proactively sources programmes for investment, or works with partners to develop new programmes where a gap or clear need is identified. As such it is very rare indeed for THF to fund unsolicited bids, however if you wish to apply complete a maximum two page summary outlining how your project fits with our aims and objectives and email it to info@thehunterfoundation.co.uk. This summary should include: summary of project; impact of

project; any independent evaluation undertaken of your project/programme; if this is a local programme how it could be scaled to become a national programme; current sources of funding; and funding sought from the Hunter Foundation. Note: we do not have a large staff and thus we will not consider meetings in advance of this information being provided. If your project appears to be of initial interest, we will then contact you to discuss this further.'

WHO TO APPLY TO Sir Tom Hunter, Trustee, Marathon House, Olympic Business Park, Drybridge Road, Dundonald, Ayrshire KA2 9AE *email* info@thehunterfoundation.co.uk *Website* www.thehunterfoundation.co.uk

■ Miss Agnes H. Hunter's Trust

SC NO SC004843   **ESTABLISHED** 1954

WHERE FUNDING CAN BE GIVEN Mainly Scotland, rest of the UK for specified medical research only.

WHO CAN BENEFIT Registered charities assisting people who are blind or visually impaired, help people with health problems or disabilities, including those affected by physical disability or illness and those with mental health problems or learning disabilities, providing training and education for disadvantaged people and assisting in youth projects; organisations undertaking research into cancer, arthritis, tuberculosis.

WHAT IS FUNDED Advancement of health, education and training, research, relief of sickness, provision of help to the disadvantaged, assistance to youth and community projects.

WHAT IS NOT FUNDED As the trust's website specifies, the following are not supported: 'organisations that are not formally recognised as charities; individuals – including students; expeditions; overseas travel or international projects; projects out with Scotland, except for medical research; general appeals or circulars, including contributions to endowment funds; animal welfare; the bricks and mortar aspect of large capital appeals; initiatives focused on sports, arts or the environment except where the subject is being used as a vehicle to engage with one of the trust's core policy groups; statutory requirements of local authorities, hospitals, schools, universities and colleges; projects which are primarily intended to promote political or religious beliefs; organisations under the control of the UK government.'

TYPE OF GRANT Mainly one-off grants to organisations.

RANGE OF GRANTS From £1,000 to £36,000. Average range between £5,000 –£10,000.

SAMPLE GRANTS Arthritis Research UK (£36,000); Breakthrough Breast Cancer (£20,000); Alcohol and Drug Support South West Scotland (£15,500); Macmilllan Cancer Support and Deafblind Scotland (£15,000 each); Deaf Connections (£13,000); Caledonia Youth and Epilepsy Scotland (£12,000 each); South Ayrshire Befriending Project and Cancer Research UK (£8,000); Pass It On (£6,000); Listening Books (£4,500); Chest Heart and Stroke Scotland (£4,000); People First Fraserburgh and Jigsaw (£3,000 each); Capability Scotland (£2,000) and Reidvale Adventure Playground Association (£1,000).

FINANCES *Year* 2011–12 *Income* £709,311 *Grants* £313,567 *Assets* £16,286,174

TRUSTEES Andrew Gray; Walter Thompson; Neil Paterson; Alison Campbell.

HOW TO APPLY In writing to the correspondent. Applicants should provide: a brief description of

the organisation's history, background, aims and objectives; a full description of the project requiring funding; how the need for this work has been identified; difference or changes that the project will make; activities/services to be carried to achieve these changes; projected means of monitoring and evaluating the work; income and expenditure budget for the project; proposed timetable for the project. In addition to that details of a referee who is independent of your organisation but knows your work well and has given permission to be contacted and provide a reference and a copy of your most recent annual report and full audited accounts are required. The Trustees meet twice a year to allocate grants and the closing dates for receipt of applications are 9 February for the June meeting and 1 August for the November meeting.
More details on application criteria and procedure can be found on the trust's website.
WHO TO APPLY TO Jane Paterson, Grants Administrator, Pagan Osborne, 55–56 Queen Street, Edinburgh EH2 3PA *Tel.* 01315 385496 *email* grants@agneshunter.org.uk *Website* www.agneshunter.org.uk

■ The Hunting Horn General Charitable Trust

CC NO 1149358   **ESTABLISHED** 2012
WHERE FUNDING CAN BE GIVEN UK and Africa.
WHO CAN BENEFIT Registered charities.
WHAT IS FUNDED General charitable purposes.
TRUSTEES Martin Oldfield; Sean Dubrovnik Jackson.
HOW TO APPLY In writing to the correspondent.
WHO TO APPLY TO Sean Dubrovnik Jackson, Trustee, 3 Ada Road, Cambridge CB3 9AD *Tel.* 01223 476769

■ The Huntingdon Foundation

CC NO 286504   **ESTABLISHED** 1984
WHERE FUNDING CAN BE GIVEN Mainly Jewish communities in the UK. There is some grant giving in the US.
WHO CAN BENEFIT Organisations benefiting Jewish people.
WHAT IS FUNDED Jewish organisations, particularly schools.
WHAT IS NOT FUNDED No grants to individuals.
RANGE OF GRANTS About £1,000 to £60,000
SAMPLE GRANTS Yavneh College, Beis Yaccov Primary School, Bnos Beis Yaakov Primary School Limited, Menorah High School, Moreshet Hatorah and Simon Marks Jewish Primary School.
FINANCES *Year* 2011–12 *Income* £652,323 *Grants* £277,268 *Assets* £11,036,071
TRUSTEES Benjamin Perl, Chair; Dr Shoshana Perl; R. Jeidel; Jonathan Perl; Naomi Sorotzkin; Joseph Perl.
OTHER INFORMATION The accounts do not list the amounts given to individual recipient organisations.
HOW TO APPLY In writing to the correspondent. The trustees meet several times a year.
WHO TO APPLY TO Benjamin Perl, 8 Goodyers Gardens, London NW4 2HD *Tel.* 020 8202 2282

■ Huntingdon Freemen's Trust

CC NO 1044573   **ESTABLISHED** 1993
WHERE FUNDING CAN BE GIVEN Huntingdon.
WHO CAN BENEFIT Individuals and organisations.
WHAT IS FUNDED Relief in need (including sickness and healthcare provision); provision of pensions; educational needs; and recreational needs.
WHAT IS NOT FUNDED No applications from outside the boundaries of Huntingdon.
RANGE OF GRANTS Up to £25,000.
SAMPLE GRANTS Huntingdon Municipal Pension and Almshouse Charities (£125,000); Huntingdon Gymnastics Club. (£37,500); Natural High (£29,000); Huntingdon Regional College (£17,000); The Boat Club (£15,000); Hinchingbooke Country Park (£12,000); Hunts Forum (£8,000) and Huntingdon Commemoration Hall (£5,000).
FINANCES *Year* 2011–12 *Income* £445,860 *Grants* £480,969 *Assets* £14,729,133
TRUSTEES Edward Bocking; Brian Bradshaw; James Fell; John Hough; Laine Kadic; Dr Adelaide Turnill; Ann Beevor.
OTHER INFORMATION In 2011–12 grants were made in the following categories (to individuals and organisations): Relief in need (£273,000); Education (£138,500) and Recreation (£69,300).
HOW TO APPLY In writing to the correspondent.
WHO TO APPLY TO Karen Clark, Grants Officer, 37 High Street, Huntingdon, Cambridgeshire PE29 3AQ *Tel.* 01480 414909 *email* info@huntingdonfreemen.org.uk *Website* www.huntingdonfreemen.org.uk

■ Hurdale Charity Limited

CC NO 276997   **ESTABLISHED** 1978
WHERE FUNDING CAN BE GIVEN Worldwide.
WHO CAN BENEFIT Organisations benefiting Jewish people.
WHAT IS FUNDED Jewish organisations that promote the Orthodox Jewish way of life.
WHAT IS NOT FUNDED In writing to the trustees.
TYPE OF GRANT One-off and recurring.
RANGE OF GRANTS Up to £250,000
SAMPLE GRANTS Springfield Trust Limited (£750,000); Harofeh Donations Limited (£300,000) and Moundfield Charities Limited (£200,000).
FINANCES *Year* 2011–12 *Income* £1,202,035 *Grants* £1,753,000 *Assets* £15,945,195
TRUSTEES Eva Oestreicher; Pinkas Oestreicher; David Oestreicher; Abraham Oestreicher; Jacob Oestreicher; Benjamin Oestreicher.
HOW TO APPLY In writing to the correspondent.
WHO TO APPLY TO Abraham Oestreicher, Trustee, Cohen Arnold and Co., New Burlington House, 1075 Finchley Road, London NW11 0PU

■ The Hutton Foundation

CC NO 1106521   **ESTABLISHED** 2004
WHERE FUNDING CAN BE GIVEN UK and overseas.
WHO CAN BENEFIT Charitable organisations.
WHAT IS FUNDED Christian causes.
SAMPLE GRANTS International Theological College (£64,000) and Emmanuel College (£7,200) both received grants in previous years. The only other named beneficiary was the Cardinal Hume Centre (£35,000). Other donations totalled £147,000.
FINANCES *Year* 2012 *Income* £96,828 *Grants* £253,023 *Assets* £1,653,253

TRUSTEES Graham Hutton; Amanda Hutton; Richard Hutton; James Hutton; Helen Hutton.

HOW TO APPLY Unsolicited applications are not supported. Those interested in learning more about the foundation are encouraged to contact the secretary.

WHO TO APPLY TO Jackie Hart, Secretary and Treasurer, Hutton Collins Partners LLP, 50 Pall Mall, London SW1Y 5JH *Tel.* 020 7004 7000 *Fax* 020 7004 7001 *email* jackie.hart@ huttoncollins.com *Website* www.huttoncollins. com/about-us/hutton-collins-foundation

■ The Nani Huyu Charitable Trust

CC NO 1082868   **ESTABLISHED** 2000
WHERE FUNDING CAN BE GIVEN UK, particularly but not exclusively within 50 miles of Bristol.
WHO CAN BENEFIT Welfare organisations.
WHAT IS FUNDED 'To assist people who are underprivileged, disadvantaged or ill, young people in matters of health, accommodation and training and those requiring assistance or medical care at the end of their lives.'
SAMPLE GRANTS Womankind and Rainbow (£13,000 each); Southside Family Project (£12,000); Jessie May Trust (£11,000); Young Bristol and FareShare South West (£10,000 each); Fairbridge West and Bristol Drugs Project (£8,000 each); Grounds 4 Change (£7,000); Kingergy (£6,000); Blenheim Scouts (£4,000) and Bristol Children's Help Society (£3,000).
FINANCES *Year* 2011–12 *Income* £161,350 *Grants* £161,000 *Assets* £4,051,260
TRUSTEES Ben Whitmore; Charles Thatcher; Maureen Whitmore; Susan Webb.
HOW TO APPLY In writing to the correspondent.
WHO TO APPLY TO The Trustees, Rusling House, Butcombe, Bristol BS40 7XQ *Tel.* 01275 474433 *email* maureensimonwhitmore@ btinternet.com

■ The P. Y. N. and B. Hyams Trust

CC NO 268129   **ESTABLISHED** 1974
WHERE FUNDING CAN BE GIVEN Worldwide.
WHO CAN BENEFIT Organisations, especially those benefiting Jewish people.
WHAT IS FUNDED Jewish organisations and general charitable purposes.
FINANCES *Year* 2011–12 *Income* £83,576 *Grants* £42,794 *Assets* £1,135,170
TRUSTEES M. Hyams; D. Levy; N. Shah.
HOW TO APPLY In writing to the correspondent, but note, the trust states that funds are fully committed and unsolicited applications are not welcomed.
WHO TO APPLY TO N. Shah, Trustee, Lubbock Fine, Russell Bedford House, City Forum, 250 City Road, London EC1V 2QQ *Tel.* 020 7490 7766

■ The Hyde Charitable Trust – Youth Plus

CC NO 289888   **ESTABLISHED** 1984
WHERE FUNDING CAN BE GIVEN The areas in which the Hyde Group operates (currently London, Kent, Surrey, Sussex and Hampshire).
WHO CAN BENEFIT Schools and registered charities operating in Hyde Group areas.
WHAT IS FUNDED Grants to organisations providing services to residents of Hyde Housing Association and other Hyde Group members.

They trust also provides bursaries directly to residents to improve life opportunities.
WHAT IS NOT FUNDED No funding for: projects outside of the area where Hyde is working – no areas outside the South East of England; sporting, social or fundraising events; medical research, hospices, residential homes for the elderly; any other projects which the trustees deem to fall outside the trust's main criteria.
SAMPLE GRANTS Young Pride Awards (£34,000); Family Support/Parenting (£26,000); Flexible Pot (£16,000); Navi Learning Fund and Activities Communities (£13,000 each); Jobs Plus (£11,000); Older People and Green Living (£9,000); Digital Inclusion (£7,000) and Youth Plus Pilot (£6,000).
FINANCES *Year* 2011–12 *Income* £431,000 *Grants* £130,000 *Assets* £2,433,000
TRUSTEES Geron Walker; Kishwer Falkner; Jonathan Prichard; Julie Hollyman; Jacqueline Puddifoot; Ronald Brookes; Andrew Moncrieff; Sharon Darcy; Christopher Carlisle.
OTHER INFORMATION £300,000 is available for 2013/14.
HOW TO APPLY The trust has informed us that: 'Because the funding available is limited – and targeted at Hyde residents – the Trust does not encourage unsolicited applications.'
WHO TO APPLY TO The Trustees, Hyde Charitable Trust, 30 Park Street, London SE1 9EQ *Tel.* 020 3207 2762 *email* hydeplus@ hyde-housing.co.uk *Website* www.hyde-housing. co.uk/about-us/hyde-plus

■ IBB Charitable Trust

cc no 1146654   established 2012
where funding can be given UK.
who can benefit Registered charities.
what is funded General charitable purposes.
trustees Abigail Winkworth; Mark Lewis; Paul Brampton; Steven Booth.
how to apply In writing to the correspondent.
who to apply Josh Gibbons, Administrator, c/o IBB Solicitors, Capital Court, 30 Windsor Street, Uxbridge, Middlesex UB8 1AB *Tel.* 01895 207287 *email* josh.gibbons@ibblaw.co.uk

■ I. G. O. Foundation Limited

cc no 1148316   established 2012
where funding can be given UK, Israel and the USA.
who can benefit Charities and community groups.
what is funded General charitable purposes, social welfare and the relief of poverty and Jewish causes
trustees Abraham Lipschitz; Bernard Ost; Gita Ost.
how to apply In writing to the correspondent.
who to apply to Bernard Ost, Trustee, 29 Grosvenor Gardens, London NW11 0HE *Tel.* 020 8731 6307

■ The Idlewild Trust

cc no 268124   established 1974
where funding can be given UK.
who can benefit Registered charities only.
what is funded The encouragement of excellence in the performing and fine arts; museums, galleries and other venues concerned with the visual arts and crafts and the preservation for the benefit of the public of buildings and items of historical interest or national importance.
what is not funded Work which has been completed; individuals; new work within churches, e.g. heating systems, annexes, facilities; community-based projects or festivals largely involving and attracting people in the immediate area; education work unless it is within the fine arts (performing or visual arts); education work with pre-school or primary school aged children; endowment or deficit funding; nationwide appeals by large charities; appeals where all or most of the recipients live outside the UK; appeals whose sole or main purpose is to make grants from funds collected; or projects based in the channel islands or Isle of Man.
type of grant Buildings, core costs, endowments, feasibility studies, one-off, projects, research and start-up costs.
range of grants Up to £5,000.
sample grants National Youth Choirs of Great Britain (£4,000); National Theatre (£3,600); Lake District Summer Music (£3,500); Birmingham Royal Ballet, Buxton Festival, Holdgate Church and Oxford University Museum of Natural History (£3,000 each); The National Trust, The Friends of St Bridget's – Skenfrith, The Friends of Portaferry Presbyterian Church and Classical Opera (£2,500); Handel House Museum, Barbican Art Gallery and

Northamptonshire Music and Performing Arts Trust (£2,000 each) and Vale of Glamorgan Festival and Abbot's Hospital (£1,000 each).
finances *Year* 2012 *Income* £177,637 *Grants* £124,000 *Assets* £4,656,192
trustees Jonathan Ouvry; Tony Ford; Dr Tessa Murdoch; Helen McCabe; John Gittens; Tessa Mayhew.
how to apply The trust now uses an online application process. Potential applicants are welcome to telephone the trust to discuss their application and check eligibility; however, opening times are limited so check the website before calling. Trustees meet twice a year usually in May and November – exact dates and deadlines are published on the website. The trust will check your Charity Commission record if your charity's annual returns and accounts are up-to-date. The trust will let you know the outcome of your application within a fortnight of the trustees' meeting. Grants will not be awarded to any one charity more frequently than every two years. Unsuccessful applicants can re-apply immediately.
who to apply to Angela Hurst, Administrator, 1a Taylors Yard, 67 Alderbrook Street, London SW12 8AD *Tel.* 020 8772 3155 *email* info@idlewildtrust.org.uk *Website* www.idlewildtrust.org.uk

■ The Iliffe Family Charitable Trust

cc no 273437   established 1977
where funding can be given UK and Worldwide.
who can benefit The majority of donations are made to charities already known to the trustees. Thereafter, preference is given to charities in which the trust has a special interest.
what is funded Heritage, welfare, education, medical, conservation and religious.
what is not funded No grants to individuals and rarely to non-registered charities.
range of grants Usually up to £40,000.
sample grants Royal Shakespeare Company and Mary Rose Trust (£20,000 each); Berkshire Community Foundation (£16,000); Arthur Rank Centre (£12,000); Coventry University, Godiva Awakes Trust and Prostate Cancer Research (£10,000 each); Game and Wildlife Conservation Trust (£2,500); Army Benevolent Fund and Welsh Guards Afghanistan Appeal (£2,000 each); University of Cambridge Vet School Trust (£1,400); National Rheumatoid Arthritis Society, Marine Society and Sea Cadets and Farm Africa (£1,000); National Trust Newbury (£500) and Hampshire and Isle of Wight Wildlife Trust (£100).
finances *Year* 2011–12 *Income* £96,494 *Grants* £190,030 *Assets* £1,441,223
trustees N. G. E. Petter; G. A. Bremner; Lord Iliffe; Hon. Edward Iliffe.
how to apply In writing to the correspondent. Only successful applications will be acknowledged. Grants are considered at ad hoc meetings of the trustees, held throughout the year.
who to apply to Secretary to the Trustees, Barn Close, Yattendon, Berkshire RG18 0UX *Tel.* 01635 203929

■ Impetus – The Private Equity Foundation (Impetus – PEF)

CC NO 1152262 **ESTABLISHED** 2013

WHERE FUNDING CAN BE GIVEN UK

WHO CAN BENEFIT Registered charities and social enterprises.

WHAT IS FUNDED Funding, management support from the investment team and specialist expertise from pro bono professionals for organisations supporting disadvantaged people particularly children, young people and families.

WHAT IS NOT FUNDED No funding for particular projects or buildings, or for organisations that are not focussed on working with economically disadvantaged young people.

TYPE OF GRANT Development and strategic funding along with management and pro-bono support.

RANGE OF GRANTS £500,000–£1 million

SAMPLE GRANTS Family National Nurse Partnership; Unitas; Greenhouse; Oxford Parent-Infant Project; Business in the Community; Working Chance; HHM and Bundesnetzwerk; I CAN; Ripplez; Resurgo Trust; ThinkForward; Prison Radio Association and Teens and Toddlers.

FINANCES *Year* 2011–12 *Income* £7,600,000

TRUSTEES Johannes Huth; Louis Elson; Marc Boughton; Craig Dearden-Phillips; Stephen Dawson; Charles Green; Andy Hinton; Carl Parker; Karl Peterson; Andrew Sillitoe; Nat Sloane; Ramez Sousou; Nikos Stathopoulos; Chris Underhill.

OTHER INFORMATION The foundation was formed from the merger of the Impetus Trust and Private Equity Foundation. As the foundation is newly registered there are no accounts published yet, however there are some key figures provided on the website: 'in 2011–12 the foundation had an income of £7.6 million. This is a combined total of the incomes of the two previous organisations for the corresponding year. There are currently 48 organisations receiving support from the foundation, each receiving on average £500,000–£1 million, non-financial support. There were 566,000 people helped by the organisations in the combined portfolio in 2011–12.'

HOW TO APPLY Potential applicants can sign up to the foundation's newsletter online and receive a notification when the application process is open. Previously applicants would complete an eligibility checker then a short expression of interest form if they were deemed eligible which would then be assessed by the foundation.

WHO TO APPLY TO Barbara Storch, Portfolio Director, 20 Flaxman Terrace, London WC1H 9PN *Tel.* 020 3747 1001 *email* info@impetus-pef. org.uk *Website* impetus-pef.org.uk

■ The Indigo Trust

CC NO 1075920 **ESTABLISHED** 1999

WHERE FUNDING CAN BE GIVEN Primarily Africa, some UK.

WHO CAN BENEFIT Organisations using technology to improve equality in Africa.

WHAT IS FUNDED Technology-driven projects which focus on innovation, transparency and citizen empowerment. Development can be in any sector, including the health, education, human rights and agricultural spheres.

WHAT IS NOT FUNDED No support for infrastructure, general equipment costs or generic ICT training.

SAMPLE GRANTS Co-Creation Hub Nigeria (£47,000 in four separate project grants); Copenhagen Youth Project (£45,000); iCow and KINU Group (£30,000 each); iLab Liberia (£20,000); Amnesty International (£16,000); SHM Foundation (£15,000); One World UK (£13,000); Map Kibera (£11,000); Wikimedia (£10,000); TEDx Dzorwulu (£4,000) and Institute for Philanthropy (£3,600).

FINANCES *Year* 2011–12 *Income* £166,835 *Grants* £679,125 *Assets* £7,425,029

TRUSTEES Dominic Flynn; Francesca Perrin; William Perrin.

OTHER INFORMATION 10% of grants went to UK based organisations. Trustees do not accept unsolicited applications for this stream.

HOW TO APPLY 'As a flexible funder, we recognise that conditions vary from country to country and organisation to organisation and so the following criteria should be seen more as guidelines than absolute rules. It's also important to stress here that this is very much a work in progress and we welcome feedback and input on the following points. In general, however, when considering proposals we look for some or all of the following elements: the applicant should be operating wholly or partly in at least one African country or else specifically seeking to benefit those who do work and live in Africa; they must be implementing or hoping to implement a technology-driven project or seeking to raise the profile/efficiency of technology as a development tool in Africa; technology must be integrated into a well-devised project, which will have a social impact; the project must be well researched and tackling an unmet need; any technology used must be appropriate, i.e. available and usable by the target population; projects ought to be sustainable, replicable and/or scalable; there should be a robust evaluation mechanism in place that enables the impact of the project to be measured; any organisation must be willing to be transparent and open about their work, unless security concerns mean that such openness would present a credible risk of harm to people involved in the project; we generally only provide approximately £10,000 to projects. The project budget can be higher, although it's very unlikely that we would be able to cover the full cost. We also have a soft spot for the following: local organisations (or strong collaboration with local organisations); open source projects; small organisations (with a budget of less than £500,000); interoperable solutions; two way interactivity and innovation. We also actively encourage collaboration and, in addition to acting as funders, we see one of our key roles as making connections between grantees, other organisations and funders. If you think your project/organisation could be suitable for consideration by us, contact us in the first instance to tell us a little more about it. If you would prefer to submit a concept note or proposal directly, e-mail [us]. We strongly recommend that applicants submit brief proposals and concept notes of **between two and four sides A4** where possible. Remember, if we require further information to be able to come to an assessment or decision, we will be in touch to ask you. By asking applicants to keep proposals brief, we hope to reduce the burden both on them and on us. We do not want applicants to spend lots of time creating proposals or concept notes for us, especially if we are unlikely to fund them. In any event, a typical proposal should contain: brief background information on your organisation, the country/countries it operates in, approximate size etc.; if appropriate, an overview of the project for which you are seeking funding, including details of the technology involved, the numbers/types of people it aims to reach, current status etc.; a statement of need, i.e. what problem does this project address; a rough budget for the project; details of how you will evaluate and monitor the project including milestones or objectives; any other information, which you think we should know or may be helpful, such as details of partners you'll be working with.'

The trust welcomes contact to discuss applications or to answer any questions you may have about applying or eligibility.

WHO TO APPLY TO Fran Perrin, Director, The Peak, 5 Wilton Road, London SW1V 1AP *Tel.* 020 7410 0330 *Fax* 020 7410 0332 *email* info@sfct.org.uk *Website* indigotrust.org.uk

....

■ Infinity Capital Trust

CC NO 1134183   **ESTABLISHED** 2010
WHERE FUNDING CAN BE GIVEN Worldwide
WHO CAN BENEFIT Individuals and organisations.
WHAT IS FUNDED The relief of poverty among persons of the Jewish faith in any part of the world; the advancement of the Jewish religion in any part of the world; the advancement of the education of the public in any part of the world in the knowledge of the Jewish religion and Jewish history and culture; other charitable purposes for the benefit of persons of the Jewish faith in any part of the world as the trustees shall from time to time decide.
SAMPLE GRANTS Not available.
FINANCES *Year* 2011–12 *Income* £0 *Grants* £674
TRUSTEES Rabbi Naftali Chaim Blau; Brian Blau; Judith Wilk.
OTHER INFORMATION Grants are available to individuals and organisations, though the correspondent stated in 2011 that the trustees plan to allow capital to build up and, consequently, will not be making any significant grants for a time.
HOW TO APPLY In writing to the correspondent.
WHO TO APPLY TO Brian Blau, Trustee, Foframe House, 35–37 Brent Street, London NW4 2EF

....

■ The Ingram Trust

CC NO 1040194   **ESTABLISHED** 1994
WHERE FUNDING CAN BE GIVEN UK and overseas, with a local preference for Surrey.
WHO CAN BENEFIT Established registered charities only.
WHAT IS FUNDED General charitable purposes. The trust prefers to support specific projects including special services and equipment. It will support major UK charities together with some local ones in the county of Surrey. Normally the policy is to support a limited number of charities, but with a longer-term commitment to each.
WHAT IS NOT FUNDED No grants to non-registered charities or to individuals. No charities specialising in overseas aid are considered except those dedicated to encouraging self-help or providing more permanent solutions. No animal charities except those concerned with wildlife conservation.
RANGE OF GRANTS Up to £75,000.
SAMPLE GRANTS WWF – UK (£242,000); Shelter (£75,000); NSPCC (£65,000); ActionAid (£52,000); the National Theatre (£50,000); Queen Elizabeth Foundation for Disabled People (£35,000); Almeida Theatre Company Ltd and the Prince's Trust (£30,000 each); Alzheimer's Society (£22,000); Countryside Learning

(£20,000); Rainbow Trust Children's Charity and St Giles Trust (£15,000 each); Pimlico Opera and South East Cancer Help Centre Limited (£12,000 each); The Woodland Trust and The Princess Alice Hospice (£10,000 each); and Age UK – Surrey (£2,000).
FINANCES *Year* 2011–12 *Income* £147,214 *Grants* £909,210 *Assets* £10,586,724
TRUSTEES Christopher Ingram; Clare Maurice; Janet Ingram.
HOW TO APPLY In writing to the correspondent, although the trust states that it receives far more worthy applications than it is able to support.
WHO TO APPLY TO Joan Major, Administrator, Ground Floor, 22 Chancery Lane, London WC2A 1LS *email* theingramtrust@nqpllp.com

....

■ The Inland Waterways Association

CC NO 212342   **ESTABLISHED** 1946
WHERE FUNDING CAN BE GIVEN UK and Ireland.
WHO CAN BENEFIT Organisations promoting the restoration of inland waterways (such as canal and river navigations).
WHAT IS FUNDED Conservation and restoration of inland waterways.
WHAT IS NOT FUNDED No grants to individuals. No retrospective grants for projects where expenditure has already been incurred or committed.
TYPE OF GRANT Capital, feasibility studies, one-off grants, project and research grants. Funding can be given over a number of years.
RANGE OF GRANTS Grants of up to £5,000 are available but grants of up to £3,000 are usually awarded.
SAMPLE GRANTS Pocklington Canal Amenity Society and Shrewsbury and Newport Canals Trust (£5,000 each); Lichfield and Hatherton Canals Restoration Trust (£2,500); and Wilts and Berks Canals Trust (£1,000).
FINANCES *Year* 2012 *Income* £1,336,854 *Grants* £663,044 *Assets* £1,676,788
TRUSTEES Vaughan Welch; Les Etheridge; Alan Platt; Paul Roper; Raymond Carter; Peter Scott; Ivor Caplan; James Shead; Paul Strudwick; Gordon Harrower; Clive Henderson; Gillian Smith; Roger Holmes; Grenville Messham.
OTHER INFORMATION Charitable expenditure during the year totalled approximately £663,000 of which a large amount (£479,000) was designated to 'campaign and restoration costs' which included 'donations and grants' of £37,000.
HOW TO APPLY In writing to the correspondent. Applications should comply with the 'Guidelines for Applicants', also available from the correspondent. Application forms can be downloaded from the IWA website. Applications are considered by the IWA's Restoration Committee. The committee will prioritise work involving practical restoration. Each applicant should provide a full description of the proposal. The guidelines state that proposals should include the following: location plans; proposed programme of activities; information on land ownership and consents; timescales; totals costs of the project; how value for money will be achieved; and maintenance after construction. Applications for up to £2,000 are assessed under a simplified procedure – each application should demonstrate that the grant would be used to initiate or sustain a restoration scheme or significantly benefit a specific small project.

Applications for over £2,000 should demonstrate that the grant would be applied to one of the types of projects (1–6). Applicants should also demonstrate the extent to which the project satisfies one or more of the following conditions: the grant would unlock (lever) a grant several times larger from another body; the grant would not replace grants available from other sources; the project does not qualify for grants from major funding sources; the grant would enable a key project to be undertaken which would have a significant effect on the prospect of advancing the restoration and gaining funds from other sources for further restoration projects; the result of the project would have a major influence over the progress of a number of other restoration projects; and the Inland Waterways Association Restoration Committee would have a major influence in the management of the project, including monitoring of expenditure.

WHO TO APPLY TO Helen Elliott-Adams, Administrator, Island House, Moor Road, Chesham HP5 1WA *Tel.* 01494 783453 *email* iwa@waterways.org. uk *Website* www.waterways.org.uk

■ The Inlight Trust

CC NO 236782   **ESTABLISHED** 1957
WHERE FUNDING CAN BE GIVEN UK.
WHO CAN BENEFIT Registered charities benefiting people from many different religions.
WHAT IS FUNDED Donations are made on a non-denominational basis to charities providing valuable contributions to spiritual development and charities concerned with spiritual healing and spiritual growth through religious retreats.
WHAT IS NOT FUNDED Grants are made to registered charities only. Applications from individuals, including students, are ineligible. No grants are made in response to general appeals from large national organisations. Grants are seldom available for church buildings.
TYPE OF GRANT Usually one-off for a specific project or part of a project. Bursary schemes eligible. Core funding and/or salaries are rarely considered.
RANGE OF GRANTS Up to £20,000.
SAMPLE GRANTS Previous beneficiaries included: Drukpa UK (£10,000); St Albans Cathedral Music Trust (£5,000): Christians in Care (£3,000); and Acorn Christian Healing Foundation (£2,000).
FINANCES *Year* 2012–13 *Income* £298,388 *Grants* £150,000
TRUSTEES Stuart Neil; Wendy Collett; Judy Hayward; Sharon Knight; Sir Thomas Lucas.
OTHER INFORMATION Accounts were received at the Charity Commission but not published online. We have estimated the grants total.
HOW TO APPLY In writing to the correspondent including details of the need the intended project is designed to meet plus an outline budget and the most recent available annual accounts of the charity. Only applications from eligible bodies are acknowledged. Applications must be accompanied by a copy of your trust deed or of your entry in the Charity Commission register. They are considered four times a year. Only successful applicants are informed.
WHO TO APPLY TO Clare Pegden, Administrator, PO Box 2, Liss, Hampshire GU33 6YP *Tel.* 01730 894120

■ The Inman Charity

CC NO 261366   **ESTABLISHED** 1970
WHERE FUNDING CAN BE GIVEN UK.
WHO CAN BENEFIT 'In addition to supporting a wide range of charitable organisations, the charity makes a regular payment (£20,000 per annum) to the Victor Inman Bursary Fund at Uppingham School of which the settlor had been a lifelong supporter.'
WHAT IS FUNDED Medical research; care of the elderly; general welfare; hospices; deaf and blind; care of the physically and mentally disabled and armed forces.
WHAT IS NOT FUNDED No grants to: individuals; young children and infants; maintenance of local buildings (e.g. churches and village halls); animal welfare; wildlife and environmental conservation or religious charities.
RANGE OF GRANTS Most grants are for £5,000 or less.
SAMPLE GRANTS Help the Hospices (£10,000); Wellbeing of Women, Parkinson's UK, Multiple Sclerosis Society, Juvenile Diabetes Research Foundation, Vitalise, Royal British Legion, Changing Faces and St Mark's Hospital Foundation (£5,000 each); Back to Work for the over 40's, The Pavement, Thrift Urban Housing and Farleigh Hospice (£3,500); Hearing Dogs for Deaf People, St Cuthbert's Hospice, Support for Living and Remap (£3,000 each); Cornwall Blind Association, The Royal Star and Garter Homes and Swinfen Telemedicine (£2,000 each) and Communication for Blind and Disabled People (£1,500).
FINANCES *Year* 2012 *Income* £171,771 *Grants* £270,900 *Assets* £4,819,911
TRUSTEES A. L. Walker; B. M. A. Strother; M. R. Matthews; Prof. J. D. Langdon; Neil John Wingerath; Inman Charity Trustees Ltd.
HOW TO APPLY In writing to the correspondent accompanied by the charity's latest report and full accounts. Applications should contain the following: aims and objectives of the charity; nature of the appeal; total target if for a specific project; contributions received against target; registered charity number; any other relevant factors. Directors' meetings are held in April and October; applications should be received by the end of February and August to be considered at the respective meetings. Only successful applicants will be contacted.
WHO TO APPLY TO The Trustees, BM Box 2831, London WC1N 3XX *Website* www.inmancharity. org

■ The Inner London Magistrates Court Poor Box and Feeder Charity

CC NO 1046214   **ESTABLISHED** 1995
WHERE FUNDING CAN BE GIVEN Inner London.
WHO CAN BENEFIT Individuals and organisations.
WHAT IS FUNDED Relief of need, hardship or distress.
WHAT IS NOT FUNDED Not directly for the relief of rates, taxes or other public funds.
RANGE OF GRANTS Usually £250 to £15,000
SAMPLE GRANTS St Mungo's and The Passage (£14,000 each); St Giles Trust and Clean Break (£10,000 each); Youth Courts (£8,500); Centrepoint (£7,000); Freedom Charity (£5,000); West London Day Centre (£3,000) and Youth and Family Court (£2,000).
FINANCES *Year* 2011–12 *Income* £336,604 *Grants* £137,309 *Assets* £3,579,877

TRUSTEES Timothy Workman; Richard Mangnall; Nicholas Evans; Penelope Sinclair; Quentin Purdy; Kevin Griffiths.

OTHER INFORMATION In 2011–12 grants were given to 18 organisations.

HOW TO APPLY In writing to the correspondent.

WHO TO APPLY TO Paula Carter, Administrator, Ealing Magistrates Court, The Court House, Green Man Lane, London W13 0SD

■ The Innocent Foundation

CC NO 1104289   **ESTABLISHED** 2004

WHERE FUNDING CAN BE GIVEN India, Vietnam, Indonesia, Peru, Kenya and Uganda.

WHO CAN BENEFIT Community based projects and non-government organisations in the developing countries where the Innocent Drinks company sources fruit. Organisations must have UK representation or be registered to receive foreign funds.

WHAT IS FUNDED Projects enabling people dependant on subsistence agriculture to build sustainable futures.

WHAT IS NOT FUNDED No grants to individuals. Funding is not currently available in the UK.

TYPE OF GRANT Most funds are allocated in three year partnerships.

SAMPLE GRANTS Send a Cow (£60,000); Practical Action (£57,000); Farm Africa (£50,000); Find Your Feet (£40,000); Jeevika Trust (£25,000); Fauna and Flora International (£24,000); Hope for Children (£12,000); Feedback Madagascar (£10,000); Africa Now (£9,000); Inga Foundation (£3,000) and APD (£1,500).

FINANCES *Year* 2011–12 *Income* £267,092 *Grants* £409,683 *Assets* £618,808

TRUSTEES Adam Balon; Jon Wright; Richard Reed; Christina Archer; Alan Gerbi.

OTHER INFORMATION The Innocent Foundation was set up by Innocent Drinks in 2004. Each year the company gives at least 10% of its profits to charity, the majority to the foundation.

HOW TO APPLY In the first instance, email the correspondent and include the following: Your name; Your organisation's name; Is your organisation a non-profit / registered charity? Do you work with the local community? What level of UK or European representation do you have? Give a summary of your project in no more than 200 words, including how you set up the project, your long term aims and what you would use the money for.

WHO TO APPLY TO Kate Franks, Manager, Fruit Towers, 342 Ladbroke Grove, London W10 5BU *email* manager@innocentfoundation.org *Website* www.innocentfoundation.org

---

■ The International Bankers Charitable Trust (The Worshipful Company of International Bankers)

CC NO 1087630   **ESTABLISHED** 2001

WHERE FUNDING CAN BE GIVEN UK with preference for inner London.

WHO CAN BENEFIT Registered charities only.

WHAT IS FUNDED 'The company will seek to promote recruitment and development of employees in the financial services industry with particular emphasis on those younger people in the immediate area of the city who would not normally be able to aspire to a city job.'

WHAT IS NOT FUNDED The following areas are excluded from company grants: large projects towards which any contribution from the company would have limited impact; general appeals or circulars; replacement of statutory funds; salaries; counselling; course fees for professionals; medical research; fundraising events and sponsorship.

TYPE OF GRANT The company may support: (a) specific projects where a donation from the Company would cover either a significant proportion of the cost or an identified element of it; (b) Long-term funding of scholarships and/ or bursaries.

SAMPLE GRANTS the Brokerage Citylink (£30,000); City Experience (£11,000); Lord George Memorial Scholarship – Dulwich College (£7,500); Brokerage Citylink Essay Competition, Mansion House Scholarship Scheme and the City of London School for Girls (£5,000 each); University Academic Prizes (£3,000); Mudchute Park and Farm (£1,500) and Debt Doctors Foundation, Blind in Business, Into University and ENO Opera Squad Proposal (£1,000 each).

FINANCES *Year* 2011–12 *Income* £142,084 *Grants* £100,232 *Assets* £898,897

TRUSTEE The Worshipful Company of International Bankers.

OTHER INFORMATION 'As a representative of the major commercial activity in the city, banking and financial services, the company combines the traditions of the City Livery Companies with a modern outlook on the financial services sector. With more than 600 members, drawn from over 250 companies and institutions and with almost 50 nationalities represented, the company has a truly international character.'

HOW TO APPLY On a form with can be downloaded from the trust's website. Previous grant recipients must allow two years from the date the original grant was awarded to reapply.

WHO TO APPLY TO Tim Woods, Clerk, 3rd Floor, 12 Austin Friars, London EC2N 2HE *Tel.* 020 7374 0212 *email* clerk@internationalbankers.co.uk *Website* www.internationalbankers.co.uk

---

■ International Spinal Research Trust

CC NO 281325   **ESTABLISHED** 1980

WHERE FUNDING CAN BE GIVEN UK and overseas.

WHO CAN BENEFIT Academic institutions undertaking research into spinal cord injury.

WHAT IS FUNDED A wide range of research activities are funded, with the sole aim of ending the permanence of paralysis caused by spinal cord injury, such as clinical-based programmes and PhD studentships.

WHAT IS NOT FUNDED No commercial organisations or private individuals are funded.

RANGE OF GRANTS £175,000 on average.

FINANCES *Year* 2011–12 *Income* £2,302,470 *Grants* £910,498 *Assets* £717,268

TRUSTEES David Allan; Frances Blois; Martin Curtis; Philippa Herbert; John Hick; Jane Pelly; Dr Ruth McKernan; Robert Shelton; David Thomson.

OTHER INFORMATION Details of all funding opportunities can be found on the website.

HOW TO APPLY The trust advertises in publications such as the British Medical Journal, The Lancet, Nature and Science for people to apply to work on specific research topics. Applications should be made in the form of a letter of intent, of approximately two sides of A4 in length. All applications are reviewed by the Scientific Committee, assisted where appropriate by other scientists in the field. Some applicants will then be invited to make a full application. Unsolicited

....

646   *Does the trust you have chosen match your needs? Haphazard applications waste postage and time*

applications will not be considered. Enquiries by email or telephone are welcome.

WHO TO APPLY TO The Head of Research, Unit 8a Bramley Business Centre, Station Road, Bramley, Guildford, Surrey GU5 0AZ *Tel.* 01483 898786 *email* research@spinal-research.org *Website* www.spinal-research.org

■ The Inverforth Charitable Trust

CC NO 274132   **ESTABLISHED** 1977
WHERE FUNDING CAN BE GIVEN UK.
WHO CAN BENEFIT UK-wide, registered charities only.
WHAT IS FUNDED General charitable purposes.
RANGE OF GRANTS All grants given ranged from £500 to £2,000.
SAMPLE GRANTS Previous beneficiaries have included: Help for Heroes (£5,000); Herriot Hospice Homecare and CHASE Hospice Care for Children (£2,000 each); the ART Fund, British Lung Foundation, Voluntary Services Overseas and National Youth Orchestra of Great Britain (£1,500 each); National Playbus Association, Kidscape, Contact the Elderly and Farms for City Children (£1,000 each); and Book Aid International, Bowel Cancer UK and the Gurkha Welfare Trust (£500 each).
FINANCES *Year* 2012 *Income* £44,832 *Grants* £70,000 *Assets* £3,881,998
TRUSTEES Elizabeth Lady Inverforth; Dr Andrew Weir; Hon. C. Kane.
OTHER INFORMATION No grants were made in 2010.
HOW TO APPLY In writing to the trustees.
WHO TO APPLY TO Clarinda Kane, Secretary and Treasurer, 58A Flood Street, London SW3 5TE

■ Investream Charitable Trust

CC NO 1097052   **ESTABLISHED** 2003
WHERE FUNDING CAN BE GIVEN In practice the UK and Israel.
WHO CAN BENEFIT Registered charities.
WHAT IS FUNDED Jewish, education, relief of poverty, medical and community.
SAMPLE GRANTS Beneficiaries included: Jewish Care, Moreshet Hatorah, Cosmon Belz, Chana, Project Seed, Menorah High School for Girls, Train for Employment and Woodstock Sinclair Trust. Individual grant amounts were not disclosed in the accounts.
FINANCES *Year* 2011–12 *Income* £455,051 *Grants* £518,595 *Assets* £70,262
TRUSTEES Mark Morris; Graham S. Morris.
HOW TO APPLY In writing to the correspondent.
WHO TO APPLY TO The Trustees, Investream Ltd, 38 Wigmore Street, London W1U 2RU *Tel.* 020 7486 2800

■ The Ireland Fund of Great Britain

CC NO 327889   **ESTABLISHED** 1988
WHERE FUNDING CAN BE GIVEN Ireland and Great Britain.
WHO CAN BENEFIT Organisations benefiting people in health, housing, social or psychological need.
WHAT IS FUNDED Marginalised people in society, such as homeless people; survivors of institutional abuse; vulnerable and/or older Irish people; projects that tackle loneliness and isolation; social, cultural or educational activities and projects that help young people.
WHAT IS NOT FUNDED Organisations based outside of England, Scotland or Wales; general appeals – assistance must be sought for clearly specified purposes; individuals; tuition or student fees;

medical costs; purchase of buildings or land; construction or refurbishment projects; events; debt; retrospective costs or salary costs.
RANGE OF GRANTS Up to £45,000.
SAMPLE GRANTS The Irish Women Survivors Support Network (£45,000); St John's Ward – Crumlin (£25,000); Justice for Magdalenes (£14,000); Southwark Irish Pensioners (£10,000); Federation of Irish Societies (£6,100); Irish in Birmingham (£6,000); Irish Heritage Foundation Scotland (£4,200); Coventry Irish Society (£3,500) and St John Bosco Youth Club (£2,000).
FINANCES *Year* 2012–13 *Income* £629,669 *Grants* £354,219 *Assets* £680,181
TRUSTEES Sheila Bailey; Seamus McGarry; Peter Kiernan; John Rowan; Ruth McCarthy; Ivan Fallon; Michael Casey; Ruairi Conneely; Zach Webb; Eileen Kelliher; Rory Godson.
HOW TO APPLY On an application form available to download from the fund's website. Only one application per organisation per year. Staff or donors may visit your organisation.
WHO TO APPLY TO Sheila Bailey, 2nd Floor, Wigglesworth House, 69 Southwark Bridge Road, London SE1 9HH *Tel.* 020 7940 9850 *Fax* 020 7378 8376 *email* shenderson@ irlfunds.org *Website* www.irelandfund.org

■ The Irish Youth Foundation (UK) Ltd (incorporating The Lawlor Foundation)

CC NO 328265   **ESTABLISHED** 1989
WHERE FUNDING CAN BE GIVEN UK.
WHO CAN BENEFIT Community-based organisations working directly with young Irish people.
WHAT IS FUNDED Projects benefiting young Irish people or enhancing their personal and social development, especially if they are disadvantaged or in need. A wide range of projects are supported which include: training/ counselling; drug rehabilitation; advice/ advocacy; youth work; family support; homelessness; educational, cultural and social activities; cross-community initiatives; travellers and disability.
WHAT IS NOT FUNDED The foundation generally does not support: projects for people over 25; general appeals; large/national charities; academic research; alleviating deficits already incurred; individuals; capital bids; overseas travel; or multiple applications from a single organisation.
TYPE OF GRANT Programme development grants; seeding grants; grants to upgrade premises and/or equipment and small grants.
RANGE OF GRANTS Grants for organisations in England, Scotland and Wales fall into the following three categories: Small grants for up to £2,500; Medium grants for over £2,500 and under £12,000; Large grants for one year or more ranging from £12,000– £25,000. The Irish Youth Foundation (UK) and the Irish Youth Foundation (Ireland) have established a joint fund to provide support for community and voluntary groups in Northern Ireland. Grants for organisations in Northern Ireland are up to £5,000.
SAMPLE GRANTS Great Britain beneficiaries included: New Horizon Youth Centre – London, Solace Women's Aid – London and Irish Community Care Merseyside (£9,500 each); Tyneside Irish Cultural Society, Luton Irish Forum, Liverpool Irish Festival Society, Irish Traveller Movement in Britain and Tricycle Theatre Company –

London (£2,000 each); Manchester Irish Education Group (£1,500); Reading Community Radio (£1,000) and Irish Arts Foundation – Leeds (£500). Previous beneficiaries in Northern Ireland included: The National Deaf Children's Society, Northern Ireland (£4,500); Artillery Youth Centre – Belfast (£4,000); Drake Music Project – Newry (£3,500); Down Community Arts – Downpatrick (£3,000); Headliners – Derry (£2,500) and Our Lady Queen of Peace Youth Club – Belfast (£1,000).

FINANCES *Year* 2012 *Income* £343,418 *Grants* £170,000 *Assets* £2,395,833

TRUSTEES John Dwyer, Chair; David Murray; Jim O'Hara; John O'Neill; Mary Clancy; Virginia Lawlor; June Trimble; Richard Corrigan; Ciara Brett.

OTHER INFORMATION Irish Youth Foundation (UK) Ltd merged with the Lawlor Foundation (effective from 30 June 2005). The work of the Lawlor Foundation towards the advancement of education in Northern Ireland continues with support for Irish students and educational organisations.

HOW TO APPLY Applications are assessed on an annual basis and application forms are only available during the annual round either on the website or by request. The application period is short as forms are only available during December with grant awards being made the following May. Unsolicited applications at other times of the year are not accepted. Applications are assessed on the following requirements: need; continuity; track record/evaluation; disadvantaged young people; innovativeness; funding sources; and budgetary control. Faxed or emailed applications are not considered. Unsolicited applications outside the annual round of grant applications will not be considered or acknowledged.

WHO TO APPLY TO Linda Tanner, The Irish Cultural Centre, 26–28 Hammersmith Grove, London W6 7HA *Tel.* 020 8748 9640 *Fax* 020 8748 7386 *email* info@iyf.org.uk *Website* www.iyf.org.uk

··

■ The Ironmongers' Foundation

CC NO 219153–10   **ESTABLISHED** 1964

WHERE FUNDING CAN BE GIVEN UK with some preference for inner London.

WHO CAN BENEFIT 'The Ironmongers' Company aims to help people who are disadvantaged in life to improve their ability to make the most of life. We wish to support projects that develop and nurture the motivation and skills necessary to take advantage of opportunities.'

WHAT IS FUNDED Projects benefiting: children and young people up to the age of 25; educational activities; specific projects with clear aims and objectives to be met within a planned timescale. The company's support should make a recognisable difference; therefore preference will be given to requests which cover a significant element of the cost and to those from smaller organisations.

WHAT IS NOT FUNDED No grants towards: large projects towards which any contribution from the Company would have limited impact; general appeals or circulars; replacement of statutory funds; general running costs (a reasonable proportion of overheads will be accepted as part of project costs); counselling and therapy; course fees for professionals; medical research; fundraising events and sponsorship; retrospective appeals and projects starting

before the date of the relevant Committee meeting; building work; holidays.

TYPE OF GRANT The trustees will consider making grants over more than one year to longer term projects, subject to a satisfactory evaluation of progress at the end of each year.

RANGE OF GRANTS Mostly £1,000–£10,000.

SAMPLE GRANTS Lyric Hammersmith (£17,000); MakeBelieve Arts (£16,000); St Paul's Cathedral School (£12,500); St Vincent's Family Project (£10,000); Museum of London (£8,600); The Comedy Trust (£4,700); University of Sheffield (£4,500); University of Manchester and University of Cambridge (£4,000 each); REAL (£3,400); Liverpool Lighthouse, Froglife Trust and Leaders in Community (£2,500 each); Sheriff's and Recorder Fund (£2,000); City of London and North East Sector Army Cadet Force (£1,000) and City of London Police Widows and Orphans Fund (£200).

FINANCES *Year* 2012–13 *Income* £1,274,493 *Grants* £391,604 *Assets* £23,478,597

TRUSTEE The Ironmongers' Trust Company.

HOW TO APPLY The Company's 'Grant Application Summary Sheet' must be completed and returned including a description of the project, of no more than three A4 pages. Summary sheets can be downloaded from the fund's website. A description of the project on no more than three A4 pages, typed on one side of each sheet, should be provided. Use the following headings: aims and objectives of the organisation; how the need for the work has been identified; why the project is the best way to address this need; the anticipated outcomes and the methods by which the success of the project will be evaluated and a full breakdown of the costs involved, explaining how the figures have been calculated. If your most recent audited accounts are not available on the Charity Commission website enclose a copy. There is no need to send additional material. The Appeals Committee meets twice a year in March and October. The deadlines for receipt of applications are 31 December and 31 July respectively. Note that applications are not accepted by e-mail. Grants must be spent within twelve months from the date of the award. There is a separate application process for iron projects, see the website for more.

WHO TO APPLY TO Helen Sant, Charities Administrator, Ironmongers' Hall, Barbican, London EC2Y 8AA *Tel.* 020 7776 2311 *Fax* 020 7600 3519 *email* helen@ironhall.co.uk *Website* www.ironhall.co.uk

··

■ The Charles Irving Charitable Trust

CC NO 297712   **ESTABLISHED** 1987

WHERE FUNDING CAN BE GIVEN Mainly Gloucestershire.

WHO CAN BENEFIT Charitable organisations.

WHAT IS FUNDED Disability, mental health, older people in the local community, local community projects, homelessness, victim support and the resettlement of offenders.

WHAT IS NOT FUNDED Research, expeditions, computers or equipment are not supported unless benefiting people who are disabled.

TYPE OF GRANT Capital, project and recurring.

RANGE OF GRANTS Mostly in the rage of £50–£1,000. Larger grants are sometimes made.

SAMPLE GRANTS Cheltenham Animal Shelter (£5,000); Dogs for the Disabled (£2,300); Leonard Cheshire Disability and Samaritans, Cheltenham and District (£2,000 each); Listening Books and Macmillan Cancer Support (£1,500 each); Lords Taverners (£1,250) and Whizz-Kidz (£1,200).

FINANCES *Year* 2011–12 *Income* £79,900 *Grants* £78,433 *Assets* £1,918,917

TRUSTEES AP. Hilder; JE. Lane; DJ. Oldham; PW. Shephard.

OTHER INFORMATION The majority of grants are for less than £1,000.

HOW TO APPLY In writing to the correspondent, giving details of the proposed project, its total cost and the amount (if any) already raised or promised from other sources. In 2007–08 the trusted noted 'a decline in the number of grants awarded because of a decline in the number of applications received'.

WHO TO APPLY TO J. E. Lane, Trustee and Secretary, PO Box 868, Cheltenham, Gloucestershire GL53 9WZ *Tel.* 01242 234848

■ Irwin Trust

CC NO 1061646   **ESTABLISHED** 1997

WHERE FUNDING CAN BE GIVEN UK and overseas.

WHO CAN BENEFIT Charities concerned with Christianity, relief of sickness, promotion of health, advancement of education and benefit to the community.

WHAT IS FUNDED General charitable purposes.

RANGE OF GRANTS £150 to £45,000.

SAMPLE GRANTS Goldhill Baptist Church (£45,000); London Institute for Contemporary Christianity (LICC) (£5,000); School of Pharmacy, London and Christian Blind Mission (£2,500 each); Centre for Legal Aid Assistance and Settlement (CLAAS) (£1,000) and Macmillan Cancer Support (£150).

FINANCES *Year* 2011–12 *Income* £46,155 *Grants* £74,950 *Assets* £167,759

TRUSTEES Thomas Irwin; Elizabeth Irwin.

OTHER INFORMATION In 2011–12 the trust gave grants in the following categories: Promotion of the Christian Faith – eight donations totalling £54,000; Relief of Poverty and Sickness – nine donations totalling £12,450 and Education – three donations totalling £8,500.

HOW TO APPLY In writing to the correspondent.

WHO TO APPLY TO Thomas Irwin, Trustee, Beechcroft House, 29 Camp Road, Gerrards Cross, Bucks SL9 7PG

■ The ISA Charity

CC NO 326882   **ESTABLISHED** 1985

WHERE FUNDING CAN BE GIVEN UK.

WHO CAN BENEFIT Registered charities only.

WHAT IS FUNDED Causes related to the arts, health and education in the broadest sense. This can include both UK and overseas initiatives. The charity selects various organisations which help to find the individual beneficiaries.

FINANCES *Year* 2011–12 *Income* £59,327 *Grants* £35,321 *Assets* £1,683,593

TRUSTEES Monique Paice; Adriana Kent; Richard Paice.

HOW TO APPLY The following is taken from the charity's website, from which can be downloaded an application form:

'**How to Apply**'

'When applying for the award bear in mind that we would like either a written report outlining your experience once you return (minimum of 500 words with lots of images) or a blog whilst you are travelling (with at least four entries of 250 words and plenty of pictures). We also encourage winners to share their experience with their school or University when they return and inspire new candidates to apply.'

WHO TO APPLY TO Richard Paice, Trustee, 2 The Mansion, Northwick Park, Blockley, Moreton-in-Marsh GI56 9RJ *Tel.* 01386 700121 *Website* www.isacharity.org

---

■ The Isaacs Charitable Trust

CC NO 264590   **ESTABLISHED** 1972

WHERE FUNDING CAN BE GIVEN UK and Israel.

WHO CAN BENEFIT Registered charities.

WHAT IS FUNDED Jewish charities and general charitable purposes, particularly medical causes. The trustees tend to support favoured projects.

TYPE OF GRANT Recurrent and one-off.

RANGE OF GRANTS £500–£6,000.

SAMPLE GRANTS Previous beneficiaries have included Jewish Care, the Child Resettlement Fund Emunah, the Marie Curie Foundation, Friends of Laniado UK, Norwood Children and Families Trust, Nightingale House, Cancer Research UK, British Heart Foundation, Furniture Trades Benevolent Association, North Western Reform Synagogue, Royal National Lifeboat Institution and Scope.

FINANCES *Year* 2011–12 *Income* £24,000 *Grants* £23,000

TRUSTEES Adam Isaacs; David Isaacs; Stephen Goldberg.

HOW TO APPLY In writing to the correspondent.

WHO TO APPLY TO David Isaacs, Trustee, Flat 26 Leamington House, 23 Stonegrave, Edgware HA8 7TN *Tel.* 020 8958 7854

■ The J. Isaacs Charitable Trust

CC NO 1059865   **ESTABLISHED** 1996

WHERE FUNDING CAN BE GIVEN England and Wales.

WHO CAN BENEFIT Charitable organisations.

WHAT IS FUNDED General charitable purposes.

RANGE OF GRANTS Up to £100,000.

SAMPLE GRANTS Previous beneficiaries included: Jewish Care (£200,000); the Jewish Museum London (£100,000); Community Security Trust (£75,000); Greenhouse Schools Project (£25,000); Policy Exchange Ltd (£15,000); UCLH Fund (£7,500); UK Jewish Film (£5,000); and Royal National Theatre (£1,000).

FINANCES *Year* 2011–12 *Income* £16,176 *Grants* £744,448

TRUSTEES Jeremy Isaacs: Joanne Isaacs; Helen Eastick.

OTHER INFORMATION Due to the low income for 2011–12, accounts were not published on the Commission's website.

HOW TO APPLY This trust's income is fully committed to its current list of donees. New applications are not considered.

WHO TO APPLY TO The Trustees, JRJ Group, 61 Conduit Street, London W1S 2GB *Tel.* 020 7220 2305

■ The Isle of Anglesey Charitable Trust

CC NO 1000818   **ESTABLISHED** 1990
WHERE FUNDING CAN BE GIVEN The Isle of Anglesey only.
WHO CAN BENEFIT Organisations in Anglesey.
WHAT IS FUNDED The provision of amenities and facilities; the preservation of buildings; the conservation and protection of the land; the protection and safeguarding of the environment.
WHAT IS NOT FUNDED Individuals.
TYPE OF GRANT One-off and recurring.
RANGE OF GRANTS 1,000–£270,000
SAMPLE GRANTS Isle of Anglesey County Council – Oriel Ynys Môn (£250,000); Holyhead and Anglesey Wellbeing and Fitness Centre (£180,000); The Castle Players Amateur Dramatic Society (£6,000); Talwn Village Hall (£4,600); Bodedem Cricket Club (£2,900); Treaddur Bay Community Centre (£2,300); Rhosneigr Boys Institute (£2,000); Menai Bridge Community Heritage Trust (£1,600); Almlwch Port Hall (£1,300) and Brynteg Community Hall (£1,100).
FINANCES *Year* 2011–12 *Income* £460,451 *Grants* £557,096 *Assets* £16,275,476
TRUSTEE Isle of Anglesey County Council.
HOW TO APPLY In writing to the correspondent with an application form, following advertisements in the local press in February. The trust considers applications once a year: 'we will take details of any prospective applicants during the year, but application forms are sent out annually in February'.
WHO TO APPLY TO Head of Function (Resources), Isle of Anglesey County Council, County Offices, Llangefni, Anglesey LL77 7TW *Tel.* 01248 752610

■ The ITF Seafarers Trust

CC NO 281936   **ESTABLISHED** 1981
WHERE FUNDING CAN BE GIVEN UK and overseas.
WHO CAN BENEFIT Seafarers of all nations and their dependants.
WHAT IS FUNDED Seafaring organisations; and the social welfare of seafarers of all nations, their families and dependants.
WHAT IS NOT FUNDED Applications for the following are not likely to be supported: Maintenance of buildings and vehicles; Wages and other personnel costs; Retrospective funding for completed projects; Deficits which have already been incurred; Projects which promote particular religious beliefs; Recurring costs.
TYPE OF GRANT Buildings, capital, one-off, project, training and education.
RANGE OF GRANTS Up to £235,000
SAMPLE GRANTS International Committee on Seafarers' Welfare (£235,000); World Maritime University (£162,000); Nautilus Welfare Fund (£150,000); North American Maritime Ministry Association (£124,000); International Christian Maritime Association (£120,000); International Maritime Health Association (£83,000); Ha Tinh Maritime Administration Employees Trade Union (£59,000); Hunter Workers Rehabilitation and Counselling Service (£53,000); Stella Maris Seafarers' Centre (£34,000); Polish Society of Maritime, Tropical and Travel Medicine (£12,000); Forward Seamen's Union of India (£6,000); and Antwerp Mariners Sportsfield (£2,000).
FINANCES *Year* 2012 *Income* £1,602,032 *Grants* £1,888,007 *Assets* £18,446,437

TRUSTEES Theresa Broome; Deidre Fitzpatrick; Paddy Crumlin; Dave Heindel; Stephen Cotton; Lars Lindgren; Brian Orrell; Abdulgani Serang.
HOW TO APPLY On a form available to download, together with criteria and guidelines, on the website. Applications must be supported by an ITF affiliated seafarers' or dockers' trade union and have a proven record of dealing with seafarers' welfare.
WHO TO APPLY TO Theresa Broome, Finance Officer and Trustee, ITF House, 49–60 Borough Road, London SE1 1DR *Tel.* 020 7403 2733 *Fax* 020 7357 7871 *email* trust@itf.org.uk *Website* www.itfglobal.org/seafarers-trust

■ The Ithaca Trust

CC NO 1145502   **ESTABLISHED** 2012
WHERE FUNDING CAN BE GIVEN Greater London.
WHO CAN BENEFIT Registered charities.
WHAT IS FUNDED General charitable purposes, education and social welfare.
TRUSTEES James Midgley; Ralph Fiennes; Julian Wadham.
OTHER INFORMATION Unfortunately at the time of writing (December 2013) the trust's first accounts were overdue with the Charity Commission.
HOW TO APPLY In writing to the correspondent.
WHO TO APPLY TO James Midgley, Trustee, MacIntyre Hudson, New Bridge Street House, 30–34 New Bridge Street, London EC4V 6BJ *Tel.* 020 7429 4100 *email* james.midgley@mhllp.co.uk

■ The J. and J. Benevolent Foundation

cc no 1146602   **established** 2012
where funding can be given UK and overseas.
who can benefit Charitable organisations.
what is funded General charitable purposes, education, relief of poverty and advancement of the Orthodox Jewish religion.
finances *Year* 2012–13 *Income* £305,000 *Grants* £139,195 *Assets* £165,085
trustees Joseph Adler; Judi Adler.
how to apply In writing to the correspondent.
who to apply to Joseph Adler, Trustee, 46 Woodville Road, London NW11 9TN *Tel.* 020 8731 0777

■ The J. and J. Charitable Trust

cc no 1065660   **established** 1997
where funding can be given UK.
who can benefit Registered charities, schools and universities.
what is funded Education, general, Jewish
range of grants Usually up to £10,000.
sample grants Harefield Academy (£145,000); Great Ormond Street Hospital (£7,000); Western Marble Arch Synagogue (£6,200); Myeloma UK and London Business School (£5,000 each); Kisharon (£2,000); British Technion Society (£1,500); The Presidents' Club and the National Society for Epilepsy (£1,000 each); and Jewish Care (£140).
finances *Year* 2011–12 *Income* £62,528 *Grants* £173,998 *Assets* £32,716
trustees Jahnene Green; Jonathan Green.
other information Jonathan Green is a former Goldman Sachs trader and co-founder of London hedge fund GLG.
how to apply In writing to the correspondent.
who to apply to Leon Angel, Administrator, Hazlems Fenton LLP, Palladium House, 1–4 Argyll Street, London W1F 7LD *Tel.* 020 7437 7666 *Fax* 020 7734 0644 *email* leonangel@hazlemsfenton.com

■ J. A. R. Charitable Trust

cc no 248418   **established** 1966
where funding can be given Worldwide.
who can benefit Organisations benefiting older people, students, Roman Catholics, missionaries, and people disadvantaged by poverty.
what is funded The advancement of the Roman Catholic faith; education for people under 30; and the provision of food, clothing and accommodation for people in need over 55.
what is not funded The trust does not normally support a charity unless it is known to the trustees and it does not support individuals.
type of grant One-off and recurring.
range of grants £1,000–£4,000.
sample grants Oxford Oratory and the Passage (£4,000 each); Catholic Children's Society – Brentwood, Liverpool Archdiocesan Youth Pilgrimage, St Joseph's Hospice and the Venerable English College Rome (£3,000 each);

Friends of Tumaini, Little Sisters of the Poor and St Anthony's Church (£2,000 each); and Marriage Care, Tongabezi Trust School and Walsingham Parish (£1,000 each).
finances *Year* 2011–12 *Income* £78,282 *Grants* £59,500 *Assets* £2,441,043
trustees Philip R. Noble; Revd William Young; Revd Paschal Ryan.
how to apply In writing to the correspondent. Note that the trust's funds are fully committed to regular beneficiaries and it states that there is very little, if any, for unsolicited appeals. In order to save administration costs replies are not sent to unsuccessful applicants.
who to apply to Philip R. Noble, Trustee, Hunters, 9 New Square, London WC2A 3QN *Tel.* 020 7412 0050

■ J. D. R. Charitable Trust

cc no 1147073   **established** 2012
where funding can be given UK.
who can benefit Registered charities.
what is funded General charitable purposes.
trustees C. A. Rimer; Mark Rimer; Sarah Rimer.
how to apply In writing to the correspondent.
who to apply to C. A. Rimer, Trustee, The End House, 102 High Street, Marlow, Buckinghamshire SL7 1AQ *Tel.* 01628 486323

■ The J. J. Charitable Trust

cc no 1015792   **established** 1992
where funding can be given Unrestricted.
who can benefit Charities benefiting children with learning difficulties particularly dyslexia, ex-offenders and people at risk of offending.
what is funded Literacy: to improve the effectiveness of literacy teaching in the primary and secondary education sectors for children with general or specific learning difficulties, including dyslexia, and to do the same through agencies working with ex-offenders or people at risk of offending. Environment UK: to support environmental education, particularly supporting projects displaying practical ways of involving children and young adults. Support is rarely given to new educational resources in isolation from the actual process of learning and discovering. More interest is shown in programmes which enable schools to take on the benefits of education for sustainable development across the whole school and beyond, into the local community. Particularly, those projects which help pupils and teachers develop a sense of ownership over time. There is also an interest in sustainable agriculture and bio-diversity; and sustainable transport, energy efficiency and renewable energy in wider society. Environment overseas: to support community-based agriculture projects which aim to help people to help themselves in an environmentally sustainable way. General: especially the education and social welfare of children who are disadvantaged.
what is not funded No grants for: individuals; educational fees; or expeditions. The trust only funds registered charities or activities with clearly defined charitable purposes.
range of grants £3,000–£124,000.
sample grants Ashden Sustainable solutions, better lives (£90,000); British Academy of Film and Television Awards (BAFTA) (£74,000); Shannon Trust (£70,000); Open Book (£60,000); Jolibe Trust (£52,000); Ecofin Research Foundation (£49,000); Lyndhurst

Primary School and Ministry of Stories (£40,000 each); National Energy Foundation (£32,000) and Africa Innovations Institute (£25,000).

FINANCES *Year* 2011–12 *Income* £955,730 *Grants* £736,129 *Assets* £33,268,550

TRUSTEES John Julian Sainsbury; Mark Sainsbury; Judith Portrait; Lucy Guard.

OTHER INFORMATION The trust is one of the Sainsbury Family Charitable Trusts which share a common administration. An application to one is taken as an application to all.

HOW TO APPLY See the guidance for applicants in the entry for the Sainsbury Family Charitable Trusts. A single application will be considered for support by all the trusts in the group. However, for this as for many of the trusts, the following statement from the Sainsbury Family website should be noted: 'the trustees take an active role in their grantmaking, employing a range of specialist staff and advisers to research their areas of interest and bring forward suitable proposals. Many of the trusts work closely with their chosen beneficiaries over a long period to achieve particular objectives. It should therefore be understood that the majority of unsolicited proposals we receive will be unsuccessful'.

WHO TO APPLY TO Alan Bookbinder, Director, The Peak, 5 Wilton Road, London SW1V 1AP *Tel.* 020 7410 0330 *Fax* 020 7410 0332 *email* info@sfct.org.uk *Website* www.sfct.org.uk

■ The J. M. K. Charitable Trust

CC NO 274576 **ESTABLISHED** 1977

WHERE FUNDING CAN BE GIVEN Worldwide.

WHO CAN BENEFIT Registered charities only, benefiting the appreciation of art and music, also assisting religious organisations to help relations with other faiths.

WHAT IS FUNDED There is a preference for charities concerned with Art and Music.

RANGE OF GRANTS £100–£17,000.

SAMPLE GRANTS Royal Academy of Music – Scholarship (£17,000); English Touring Opera (£13,000); Royal Opera House (£5,400); Les Azuriales Opera Trust (£4,000); Friends of the Salzburg Festival (£3,400); Central British Fund for World Jewish Relief (£1,400); London Jewish Cultural Centre and English National Opera (£1,000 each); British Friends of Haifa University (£200) and Opera Holland Park (£100).

FINANCES *Year* 2011–12 *Income* £69,552 *Grants* £60,320 *Assets* £2,033,622

TRUSTEES Jill Karaviotis; Joseph Karaviotis.

HOW TO APPLY Unsolicited applications will not be considered.

WHO TO APPLY TO The Trustees, c/o Saffery Champness, Lion House, 72–75 Red Lion Street, London WC1R 4GB *Tel.* 020 7841 4000

■ The J. R. S. S. T. Charitable Trust

CC NO 247498 **ESTABLISHED** 1955

WHERE FUNDING CAN BE GIVEN UK.

WHO CAN BENEFIT Organisations or individuals undertaking research or action in fields which relate directly to the non-charitable work of the Joseph Rowntree Reform Trust Ltd. Academics and research workers may benefit.

WHAT IS FUNDED The trust works in close association with the Joseph Rowntree Reform Trust Ltd, which is a non-charitable trust of which all the trustees of The JRSST Charitable Trust are

directors, in supporting the development of an increasingly democratic and socially just UK.

WHAT IS NOT FUNDED No student grants are funded.

TYPE OF GRANT Specific finance in particular fields of interest to the trust. Funding is given for up to one year.

RANGE OF GRANTS £2,000– £20,000.

SAMPLE GRANTS Reuters Institute for the Study of Journalism (£20,000); Rowntree Society (£15,000); Democratic Audit (£9,000); Education for Choice (£5,000); Bureau of Investigative Journalism (£4,000); and Institute of Race Relations (£2,000).

FINANCES *Year* 2012 *Income* £105,500 *Grants* £81,710 *Assets* £2,807,644

TRUSTEES Christine Day; Dr Christopher Greenfield; Amanda Cormack; Peadar Cremin; Baroness Sal Brinton; Andrew Neal; Alison Goldsworthy.

OTHER INFORMATION 21 grants were paid to organisations totalling £82,000.

HOW TO APPLY The trustees meet quarterly. They do not invite applications. Initial assessments should be submitted to the Grants and Projects adviser via email. The email should include an outline (up to a side of A4 which includes the amount required) of the proposal. There is no standard application form; however an application should include the following: application registration form (available from the trust's website); proposal (up to four pages long); full project budget; most recent accounts; and CV (if applying as an individual). Applications for small grants of up to £5,000 are considered at any time. The deadline for grants over £5,000 is four to five weeks before the trustees' meeting. All applications should be received before 12 noon on the deadline day.

WHO TO APPLY TO Tina Walker, Administrator, The Garden House, Water End, York YO30 6WQ *Tel.* 01904 625744 *email* info@jrrt.org.uk *Website* www.jrrt.org.uk

■ The Jabbs Foundation

CC NO 1128402 **ESTABLISHED** 2009

WHERE FUNDING CAN BE GIVEN UK

WHO CAN BENEFIT Registered charities; universities and educational/research institutions.

WHAT IS FUNDED Medical research; education; enhancing family relationships.; prevention of crime.

SAMPLE GRANTS 'The Foundation agreed new grants during the year... to fund medical research projects including plasma cell dyscrasias, acute rheumatic fever and heart disease and a small grants programme to early stage research projects. The projects are led by medics of international reputation and standing and grant funding is made available to major university hospitals. The results will be published widely to maximise the benefits to patients with these conditions. In addition, the Foundation committed to making grants to an organisation supporting vulnerable women to provide a case worker and a fund targeted at smaller organisations in Birmingham and the Black Country that aim to provide positive experiences and support to young people vulnerable to entering the criminal justice system.'

FINANCES *Year* 2011–12 *Income* £636,143 *Grants* £642,270 *Assets* £248,186

TRUSTEES Robin Daniels; Dr Alexander Wright.

OTHER INFORMATION No specific beneficiary organisations detailed in the accounts.

HOW TO APPLY In writing to the correspondent.

WHO TO APPLY TO Robin Daniels, Trustee, PO BOX 16067, Harborne, Birmingham, West Midlands B32 9GP *Tel.* 01214 282593

■ **C. Richard Jackson Charitable Trust**

CC NO 1073442　　**ESTABLISHED** 1999
WHERE FUNDING CAN BE GIVEN England and Wales.
WHO CAN BENEFIT Registered charities.
WHAT IS FUNDED General charitable purposes.
RANGE OF GRANTS Typically £5,000 or less.
SAMPLE GRANTS The Prince's Trust (£43,000); Teenage Cancer Trust and St Peter's Church (£5,000 each); The Variety Club Children's Charity and Macmillan Cancer Support (£3,500 each); Kohima Educational Trust (£3,000); Leeds Teaching Hospitals Charitable Foundation and Prince of Wales Hospice (£2,500 each); and Two Ridings Community Fund (£2,000).
FINANCES *Year* 2011–12 *Income* £71,228 *Grants* £77,053 *Assets* £55,213
TRUSTEES Charles Richard Jackson; Jeremy P. Jackson; Lucy Crack.
HOW TO APPLY In writing to the correspondent.
WHO TO APPLY TO Charles Richard Jackson, Trustee, Loftus Hill, Ferrensby, Knaresborough, North Yorkshire HG5 9JT

■ **Elizabeth Jackson Charitable Trust**

CC NO 1083421　　**ESTABLISHED** 1999
WHERE FUNDING CAN BE GIVEN Warwickshire and surrounding areas, particularly Barston (Solihull) and Great Rollright (Oxfordshire).
WHO CAN BENEFIT Organisations and individuals.
WHAT IS FUNDED General charitable purposes.
RANGE OF GRANTS Usually £2,000 to £5,000.
SAMPLE GRANTS Great Rollright School (£15,000); Foundation of Lady Katherine Leveson (£5,000); Animal Health Trust (£3,000) and Motor Neurone Disease Association, ARC – Addington Fund, Myton Hospices, British Forces Foundation, Royal Agricultural Benevolent Institution and Warwickshire and Northamptonshire Air Ambulance (£2,000 each).
FINANCES *Year* 2011–12 *Income* £32,640 *Grants* £35,000 *Assets* £861,524
TRUSTEES Robin Ogg; James Davy; Jeremy Seel.
HOW TO APPLY In writing to the correspondent.
WHO TO APPLY TO Thomas McKenzie, c/o Wright Hassall Solicitors, Olympus House, Olympus Avenue, Tachbrook Park, Warwick CV34 6RJ *Tel.* 01926 886688

■ **Jacobs Charitable Trust**

CC NO 264942　　**ESTABLISHED** 1972
WHERE FUNDING CAN BE GIVEN Unrestricted.
WHO CAN BENEFIT Registered charities and community groups.
WHAT IS FUNDED Jewish causes and the arts.
RANGE OF GRANTS Up to £66,000.
SAMPLE GRANTS St Jude Childcare Centres India (£66,000); Central Synagogue (£19,500); North Shore Health System Foundation (£12,000); Boca Raton Promise (£6,000); Centre for Jewish Life (£2,500); Yesh Din Volunteers for Human Rights (£2,000) and Palm Beach Country Club Foundation (£600).
FINANCES *Year* 2011–12 *Income* £129,572 *Grants* £115,802 *Assets* £51,654

TRUSTEES Lord Jacobs, Chair; Lady Jacobs; Marla Kosec.
HOW TO APPLY In writing to the correspondent.
WHO TO APPLY TO The Rt Hon the Lord Jacobs, Chair, 9 Nottingham Terrace, London NW1 4QB *Tel.* 020 7486 6323

■ **The Ruth and Lionel Jacobson Trust (Second Fund) No 2**

CC NO 326665　　**ESTABLISHED** 1984
WHERE FUNDING CAN BE GIVEN UK, with a preference for North East England
WHO CAN BENEFIT Organisations benefiting people of all ages, medical professionals, parents and children, people with disabilities, people who are sick, people who have had strokes or who are terminally ill, homeless people, refugees and victims of famine.
WHAT IS FUNDED Organisations working in the fields of holiday accommodation and residential facilities, support for voluntary organisations, the Jewish religion, health, animal/bird sanctuaries and nature reserves, special needs education and speech therapy and various community facilities and services.
WHAT IS NOT FUNDED No grants for individuals. Only registered charities will be supported.
TYPE OF GRANT One-off, project and research. Funding is available for one year or less.
RANGE OF GRANTS £50–£10,000; typical grant £100–£500.
SAMPLE GRANTS Newcastle University (£20,000); Calvert Trust (£15,000); United Jewish Israel Appeal (£12,500); WIZO UK (£6,000); Anne Frank Trust (£1,500); and NE Jewish Community Services (£200).
FINANCES *Year* 2011–12 *Income* £168,202 *Grants* £55,100 *Assets* £1,348,224
TRUSTEES Anne Jacobson; Malcolm Jacobson.
HOW TO APPLY In writing to the correspondent. Enclose an sae. Applications are considered every other month.
WHO TO APPLY TO Malcolm Jacobson, Trustee, 14 The Grainger Suite, Dobson House, The Regent Centre, Newcastle upon Tyne NE3 3PF

■ **Jaffe Family Relief Fund**

CC NO 208560　　**ESTABLISHED** 1970
WHERE FUNDING CAN BE GIVEN UK.
WHO CAN BENEFIT Registered charities.
WHAT IS FUNDED People in need.
WHAT IS NOT FUNDED No grants to charities for anything which is not direct relief of poverty in UK.
SAMPLE GRANTS Previously, grants have been made to the following organisations: Bryson House, Catholic Children's Society, Campden Charities, Central Family Service Units, Providence Row, SSAFA Forces Help, West London Action for Children and West London Family Service Unit.
FINANCES *Year* 2011–12 *Income* £48,589 *Grants* £46,177 *Assets* £1,142,917
TRUSTEES James Reinlieb; Dr Robin Jacobson; Gillian Haworth.
HOW TO APPLY In writing to the correspondent, but the trust states 'funds are unlikely to allow us to add to the list of beneficiaries'.
WHO TO APPLY TO Dr Robin Jacobson, Trustee, 24 Manor Way, Beckenham, Kent BR3 3LJ *Tel.* 020 0650 8125

■ John James Bristol Foundation

cc no 288417 **ESTABLISHED** 1983

WHERE FUNDING CAN BE GIVEN Worldwide, in practice Bristol.

WHO CAN BENEFIT Charitable bodies and schools that can clearly show that they are benefiting Bristol residents.

WHAT IS FUNDED Education, health and the elderly are the key focus areas.

WHAT IS NOT FUNDED No grants to individuals.

RANGE OF GRANTS £50–£150,000

SAMPLE GRANTS Barton Hill Settlement (£33,000); The Red Maids' School and Redland High School (£30,000 each); Barnardo's Bristol BASE Project (£25,000); Badminton School (£20,000); University of Bristol – Bowel Cancer Research (£18,000); Crisis Centre Ministries (£10,000); Deafblind UK (£5,000); Bristol Amateur Operatic Society (£4,200); St Dunstan's (£3,000); Huntington FoodCycle (£2,000); Huntington's Disease Association (£2,000) and Relate Avon (£1,000).

FINANCES *Year* 2011–12 *Income* £1,490,734 *Grants* £901,461 *Assets* £53,865,357

TRUSTEES Joan Johnson; David Johnson; Elizabeth Chambers; John Evans; Andrew Jardine; Andrew Webley; John Haworth; Peter Goodwin.

HOW TO APPLY The trustees meet quarterly in February, May, August and November to consider appeals received by 15 January, April, July and October as appropriate. There is no application form and appeals **must be submitted by post**, to the chief executive on no more than two sides of A4. Supporting information, sent by the applicant with their appeal, is available to the trustees at their meeting. All appeal applications are acknowledged, stating the month in which the appeal will be considered by the trustees. If further information is required it will be requested and a visit to the applicant may be made by a representative of the foundation.

WHO TO APPLY TO Julia Norton, Chief Executive, 7 Clyde Road, Redland, Bristol BS6 6RG *Tel.* 01179 239444 *Fax* 01179 239470 *email* info@johnjames.org.uk *Website* www.johnjames.org.uk

■ The Susan and Stephen James Charitable Settlement

cc no 801622 **ESTABLISHED** 1988

WHERE FUNDING CAN BE GIVEN UK.

WHO CAN BENEFIT Registered charities; Jewish organisations.

WHAT IS FUNDED General charitable purposes.

RANGE OF GRANTS £60–£20,000.

SAMPLE GRANTS Norwood Ravenswood (£20,500); Jewish Care (£15,000); Community Security Trust (£11,500); Chai Cancer Care (£10,000); World Jewish Relief (£6,000); United Synagogue (£4,500); British Friends of Haifa University (£2,000); WIZO UK (£1,500); Jewish Women's Aid and Grief Encounter (£1,000 each); Marie Curie Cancer Care and Jewish Childs Day (£500 each); British Friends of Arts Museums of Israel (£250) and North London Hospice (£100).

FINANCES *Year* 2012 *Income* £167,088 *Grants* £96,225 *Assets* £92,273

TRUSTEES Stephen James; Susan James.

OTHER INFORMATION In 2012 grants were given to 29 organisations.

HOW TO APPLY In writing to the correspondent.

WHO TO APPLY TO Stephen James, Trustee, 4 Turner Drive, London NW11 6TX *Tel.* 020 7486 5838

■ The James Trust

cc no 800774 **ESTABLISHED** 1989

WHERE FUNDING CAN BE GIVEN UK and overseas.

WHO CAN BENEFIT Principally Christian organisations benefiting Christians, young adults, older people, people disadvantaged by poverty, disaster victims, and refugees.

WHAT IS FUNDED Churches, Christian organisations and individuals. Support is primarily to Christian causes, the advancement of the Christian religion and Anglican diocesan and Free Church umbrella bodies.

WHAT IS NOT FUNDED No grants to individuals not personally known to the trustees.

TYPE OF GRANT One-off, capital, projects, recurring costs, salaries and start-up costs. Funding is available for up to three years.

RANGE OF GRANTS Usually up to £10,000.

SAMPLE GRANTS Above Bar Church, Church Mission Society, Food for the Hungry, Highfield Church and Wycliffe Translators.

FINANCES *Year* 2011–12 *Income* £46,758 *Grants* £54,535 *Assets* £76,698

TRUSTEES R. J. Todd; G. Blue.

HOW TO APPLY In writing to the correspondent. Unsolicited applications are not acknowledged. Phone calls are welcome before an application is submitted.

WHO TO APPLY TO R. J. Todd, Trustee, 27 Radway Road, Upper Shirley, Southampton, Hampshire SO15 7PL *Tel.* 02380 788249

■ The Marjory Jameson Trust

cc no 1135470 **ESTABLISHED** 2010

WHERE FUNDING CAN BE GIVEN Undefined, in practice national and overseas.

WHO CAN BENEFIT Organisations.

WHAT IS FUNDED The advancement of health and the saving of lives, including establishing nursing/care homes; the advancement of education, including setting up, managing and supporting schools; and the advancement of the Christian faith by establishing, promoting and supporting churches or other Christian organisations.

SAMPLE GRANTS None available.

FINANCES *Year* 2011–12

TRUSTEES Elizabeth Frances Bailey; Colin Dundonald Jameson.

OTHER INFORMATION In 2010/11, the charity had an income of £5,500 and a total expenditure of £817. In 2011–12, the accounts were 320 days late at the Commission. No further information is available.

HOW TO APPLY In writing to the correspondent.

WHO TO APPLY TO Colin Dundonald James, Administrator, 2 Applegarth, Wymondham, Norfolk NR18 0BZ

■ The Jarman Charitable Trust

cc no 239198 **ESTABLISHED** 1964

WHERE FUNDING CAN BE GIVEN Birmingham and district.

WHO CAN BENEFIT Organisations benefiting children, young adults, older people, one-parent families, at-risk groups, homeless people.

WHAT IS FUNDED Welfare work, church building extension schemes and general social services in the Birmingham district. This includes convalescent homes, hospices, hospitals, nursing homes, rehabilitation centres, cancer research, community centres and village halls, day centres, holidays and outings, youth work and playschemes.

WHAT IS NOT FUNDED There is a preference for registered charities. No grants to individuals.

TYPE OF GRANT Annual donations and one-off payments.

SAMPLE GRANTS Coventry Day Centre for the Homeless; Friendship Project for Children; St Anne's Hostel for Men; St Paul's Church; Samaritans – Birmingham; Shakespeare Hospice and Victim Support – East Birmingham.

FINANCES *Year* 2011–12 *Income* £37,910 *Grants* £39,725 *Assets* £841,953

TRUSTEES Dr Geoffrey Jarman; Susan Chilton; Ilfra Jarman.

OTHER INFORMATION In 2011–12 grants were made to 176 organisations.

HOW TO APPLY In writing to the correspondent by the first week in February or the first week in September. Trustees meet in spring and autumn. The trust does not want telephone calls and will not acknowledge applications even if an sae is enclosed. Accounts and/or budgets should be included.

WHO TO APPLY TO Susa Chilton, Trustee, 52 Lee Crescent, Edgbaston, Birmingham, West Midlands B15 2BJ *Tel.* 01212 472622 *email* jarmanct@hotmail.com

---

■ The Barbara Joyce Jarrald Charitable Trust

CC NO 1135228　　**ESTABLISHED** 2010

WHERE FUNDING CAN BE GIVEN Worldwide.

WHO CAN BENEFIT Registered charities.

WHAT IS FUNDED Health, child protection, Christian activities and animal welfare.

SAMPLE GRANTS The Peace Hospice; Nazarene Church; Cancer Research UK; Age UK; Mount Vernon Hospital; YHA (England and Wales) Ltd; Alzheimer's Society; NSPCC; RSPCA; Battersea Dogs and Cats Home; Cats Protection; Brooke Hospital for Animals and The Society for Protection of Animals Abroad.

FINANCES *Year* 2011–12 *Income* £4,875

TRUSTEE NatWest Trust Services.

HOW TO APPLY In writing to the correspondent.

WHO TO APPLY TO NatWest Trust Services, 5th Floor, Trinity Quay 2, Avon Street, Bristol BS2 0PT *Tel.* 05516577371

■ The John Jarrold Trust

CC NO 242029　　**ESTABLISHED** 1965

WHERE FUNDING CAN BE GIVEN Norfolk.

WHO CAN BENEFIT Organisations benefiting academics, research workers and students.

WHAT IS FUNDED General charitable purposes of all kinds and in particular of education and research in all or any of the natural sciences. Social welfare, arts, education, environment/ conservation, medical research, churches. Funds currently very limited.

WHAT IS NOT FUNDED Educational purposes that should be supported by the state will not be helped by the trust. Local groups outside Norfolk are very unlikely to be supported unless there is a personal connection to the trust. Individual educational programmes and gap year projects are not supported.

TYPE OF GRANT One-off.

RANGE OF GRANTS Usually up to £5,000.

SAMPLE GRANTS UEA Jubilee Appeal (£30,000); Hamlet Centre and YMCA Norfolk (£7,500 each); Thorpe St Andrew School (£5,000); Norfolk and Norwich Festival and Theatre Royal Norwich (£3,000 each); Community Action

Norwich, East Anglia Art Fund, Emmaus, Smallpiece Trust and Woodland Trust (£2,000 each); Big C, Childhood First, CLIC Sargent, Criminon UK, Hebron Trust, Leeway Norwich Women's Aid, Mercy Ships, Self Help Africa, Sightsavers, The Hamlet Centre and SNCLS (£1,000 each); Feed the Minds, Friends of the Elderly, Halvergate Parish Council, Leonard Cheshire Disability, Magdalene Group and Theatre Royal Norwich (£500 each); Garveston Parish Council, Geographical Association and Norfolk Titanic Association (£100 each); and Magdalen Gates Primary School (£50).

FINANCES *Year* 2011–12 *Income* £99,283 *Grants* £144,881 *Assets* £2,474,982

TRUSTEES Caroline Jarrold; Juliet Jarrold; Richard Jarrold; Waltraud Jarrold; Joan Jarrold; Peter Jarrold; Antony Jarrold; Charles Jarrold.

HOW TO APPLY Trustees meet in January and June each year and applications should be made in writing by the end of November and April respectively. Grants of up to £250 can be made between meetings.

WHO TO APPLY TO Caroline Jarrold, Trustee, Jarrold and Sons Ltd, St James Works, 12–20 Whitefriars, Norwich NR3 1SH *Tel.* 01603 677360 *email* caroline.jarrold@jarrold.com *Website* www.jarrold.com

---

■ The Jasper Conran Foundation

CC NO 1148876　　**ESTABLISHED** 2012

WHERE FUNDING CAN BE GIVEN UK.

WHO CAN BENEFIT Charities and community groups

WHAT IS FUNDED General charitable purposes, with a particular interest in the welfare of children and young people and people living with HIV.

FINANCES *Year* 2012–13 *Income* £24,000 *Grants* £23,500

TRUSTEES Jasper Conran; Jo Hulf; Bernard Harrington.

OTHER INFORMATION Registered in September 2012, this is the charitable foundation of fashion designer Jasper Conran.

HOW TO APPLY In writing to the correspondent.

WHO TO APPLY TO Rob Litler, Jasper Conran Ltd, 1–7 Rostrevor Mews, London SW6 5AZ *Tel.* 020 7384 0800 *email* info@jasperconran.com *Website* jasperconranfoundation.com

---

■ Jay Education Trust

CC NO 1116458　　**ESTABLISHED** 2006

WHERE FUNDING CAN BE GIVEN Worldwide.

WHO CAN BENEFIT Jewish organisations.

WHAT IS FUNDED 'The objects of the charity are: the relief of poverty in the Jewish Community worldwide; the advancement of religious education according to the beliefs and values of the Jewish Faith worldwide and any charitable purpose at the discretion of the trustees for the benefit of the community.'

SAMPLE GRANTS Chevras Mo'oz Ladol (£276,500); Notzar Chesed (£10,000); Centre for Torah Education Trust (£5,500); Yeshiva Torah Chaim (£5,000); and TTT (£1,500).

FINANCES *Year* 2011–12 *Income* £1,376,010 *Grants* £342,943 *Assets* £925,219

TRUSTEES Rabbi Alfred Schechter; Gabriel Gluck; Shlomo Z. Stauber.

HOW TO APPLY In writing to the correspondent.

WHO TO APPLY TO Rabbi Alfred Schechter, Trustee, 37 Filey Avenue, London N16 6JL

■ JCA Charitable Foundation

CC NO 207031   ESTABLISHED 1891

WHERE FUNDING CAN BE GIVEN Israel.

WHO CAN BENEFIT Projects benefiting Jewish people, particularly children and those living in rural areas.

WHAT IS FUNDED The foundation helps the development of new settlements in Israel, the Kibbutzim and Moshavim, contributes to the resettlement of Jewish people in need, fosters viable agricultural and rural life to support them, and encourages other trusts and foundations to join it in partnership to fulfil its ideals. New projects in education and agricultural research are now the main interests of the JCA.

WHAT IS NOT FUNDED Grants are not awarded for individual students' tuition fees in Israel or elsewhere.

TYPE OF GRANT Loans, grants and feasibility studies. Funding may be given for one year or less.

SAMPLE GRANTS Tel Hai Academic College ($196,000); Dead Sea and Arava Science Center ($171,000); Sha'ar Hanegev High School ($125,000); Ben-Gurion University of the Negev ($92,000); Agricultural Research Organisation ($61,000); Malkishua Drug Rehabilitation Center ($30,000); Kibbutz Ein Gedi ($10,000); Ben Shemen Youth Village ($5,000) and Gilat – The Negev Seminar ($1,000).

FINANCES *Year* 2012 *Income* £5,710,000 *Grants* £1,045,000 *Assets* £25,131,000

TRUSTEES Sir Stephen Waley-Cohen; Baron Alain Philippson; Jacques-Martin Philippson; Dr Ariela Brickner; Jacques Capelluto; Prof. Yona Chen; Marc Vellay; Beatrice Jouan; Isaac Lidor; Mark Sebba; Hana Smouha; Guy Wallier; Peter Lawrence; Dr Mordechai Cohen.

OTHER INFORMATION The amounts given in Sample Grants relate to US dollars.

HOW TO APPLY Full proposals should be sent to the office in Israel. For further information contact the correspondent.

WHO TO APPLY TO Timothy R. Martin, Company Secretary, c/o The Victoria Palace Theatre, Victoria Street, London SW1E 5EA *Tel.* 020 7828 0600 *Fax* 020 7828 6882 *email* thejcafoundation@aol.com *Website* www. ica-is.org.il

■ The Jeffrey Charitable Trust

SC NO SC015990   ESTABLISHED 1972

WHERE FUNDING CAN BE GIVEN Scotland and elsewhere.

WHO CAN BENEFIT Organisations benefiting seafarers and fishermen, volunteers, and people in care, or who are fostered or adopted.

WHAT IS FUNDED Primarily this trust is concerned with medical research, and carer organisations. It also considers holiday and respite accommodation; health; conservation; independent and special schools; tertiary, higher and special needs education; community facilities and transport; and emergency care for refugees and their families.

WHAT IS NOT FUNDED Animal-related charities, medical electives and projects eligible for statutory support are not considered.

TYPE OF GRANT One-off and recurring grants are most commonly made for capital, buildings, core costs, endowment, project, research, running costs, salaries and start-up costs. Funding is available for up to three years.

RANGE OF GRANTS £250–£20,000; typical grant £1,000–£1,500.

SAMPLE GRANTS £20,000 to Glasgow Royal Infirmary for HTR project – diabetes centre; £5,000 to Dunstans Home for the War-blinded for general purposes; £2,500 each to Morrison's Academy Appeal for bursary provision and Donaldson School for the Deaf for a development project; £2,000 each to Erskine Hospital for general purposes, Princess Royal Trust for Carers for general purposes, and Edinburgh Breast Cancer Foundation for general purposes; £1,359 to Salvation Army for general purposes; £1,000 each to Capability Scotland for general purposes and Crieff Parish Church for hall refurbishment.

FINANCES *Year* 2011–12 *Income* £60,852 *Grants* £50,000

TRUSTEES R. B. A. Bolton; R. S. Waddell; M. E. Bolton; Dr A. C. MacCuish.

HOW TO APPLY In writing to the correspondent, although due to continuing support to long-term projects and anticipated repeat grants to other organisations, new requests for assistance are unlikely to be successful.

WHO TO APPLY TO Robert Bolton, 29 Comrie Street, Crieff, Perthshire PH7 4BD *Tel.* 01764 652224 *Fax* 01764 653999

■ Rees Jeffreys Road Fund

CC NO 217771   ESTABLISHED 1950

WHERE FUNDING CAN BE GIVEN UK.

WHO CAN BENEFIT Universities, research bodies, academic staff and students, as well as proposals for roadside projects.

WHAT IS FUNDED The trustees will consider funding lectureships and postgraduate bursaries over an academic year; research projects; physical roadside projects; and transport and alternative transport. Only subjects directly related with road and transportation will be considered.

WHAT IS NOT FUNDED Grants are not given to environmental projects not related to highways, individual works for cycle tracks or works of only local application. Also, operational and administrative staff costs are rarely considered.

TYPE OF GRANT Some one-off capital, some bursaries and others for research and lectureships including salaries and, in some cases, running costs and endowments.

RANGE OF GRANTS Up to £24,000

SAMPLE GRANTS The fund offers the following commentary on its grantmaking in the 2010 accounts: 'The largest proportion of this sum related to bursary awards, which remained a key priority for trustees during 2010, providing vital support and encouragement to nine highly impressive candidates, who, it is anticipated, will make a significant impact upon the UK transport world in future years. Grants for physical projects continued to rely upon the long-standing relationship which the fund has with Wildlife Trusts, and in 2010 the partnership resulted in financial support for four schemes in England and Wales. The fund's chair has continued to express a desire to extend the number of research grant recipients. The trustees see the support that they can give to projects which can influence UK transport policy as a core objective, and they would very much wish to encourage more applicants in this area.' During the year major awards under this heading went to the Road Safety Foundation and to the Sir Colin Buchanan Archive project.

FINANCES *Year* 2012 *Income* £16,883 *Grants* £203,178 *Assets* £6,599,844

TRUSTEES David Bayliss, Chair; Mike Cottell; Tony Depledge; Ann Frye; Prof. Mike McDonald; Prof.

Stephen Glaister; David Hutchinson; Martin Shaw.

HOW TO APPLY Applications should be made in writing to the Fund Secretary and include the following details: the purpose for which funding is sought – outlining the objects, relevance and the proposed methodology of the project including the names of the principal participants; the expected costs by category, along with the project timetable; evidence of the willingness of other parties (where the project requires their contribution or participation) to get involved; and appropriate evidence of the applicant's in-depth knowledge of the subject of the application and their familiarity with previous work in the field.

Applications should not be more than three A4 pages. All necessary supporting material and a digital version of the application should also be submitted.

The trustees meet five times a year, usually in January, April, July, September and November (see the fund's website for specific dates). The deadline for submission of applications or other agenda items is normally a fortnight before the meeting. Informal contact prior to submitting a formal application is welcomed.

WHO TO APPLY TO Brian Smith, Fund Secretary, Merriewood, Horsell Park, Woking, Surrey GU21 4LW *Tel.* 01483 750758 *email* briansmith@reesjeffreys.org *Website* www.reesjeffreys.co.uk

---

■ The Nick Jenkins Foundation

CC NO 1135565   **ESTABLISHED** 2010
WHERE FUNDING CAN BE GIVEN England and Wales; India; Ethiopia.
WHO CAN BENEFIT Organisations.
WHAT IS FUNDED General charitable purposes.
SAMPLE GRANTS The Prince's Trust, Opportunity International UK and Give a Future (£25,000 each); Molecular Oncology and Cell Cycle Chantelle Fund (£20,000); Turning Point Trust and Marie Curie Cancer Care (£2,000 each); Red Squirrel Survival Trust (£1,000) and University of Birmingham (£500).
FINANCES *Year* 2011–12 *Income* £1,596,698 *Grants* £430,000
TRUSTEES Rosemary Connor Rafferty; Alison Clare Jenkins; Nicholas David Jenkins.
HOW TO APPLY In writing to the correspondent.
WHO TO APPLY TO Nicholas Jenkins, Trustee, Bapton Manor, Bapton, Warminster, Wiltshire BA12 0SB

■ The Jenour Foundation

CC NO 256637   **ESTABLISHED** 1968
WHERE FUNDING CAN BE GIVEN UK, with a special interest in Wales.
WHO CAN BENEFIT Registered charities only.
WHAT IS FUNDED General charitable purposes. Both UK charities and local charities in Wales are supported.
WHAT IS NOT FUNDED Registered charities only.
TYPE OF GRANT Capital projects.
RANGE OF GRANTS Usually up to £8,000.
SAMPLE GRANTS Army Benevolent Fund (£9,000); Atlantic College and Cancer Research Wales (£8,000 each); British Heart Foundation and Welsh National Opera (£7,000 each); Macmillan Cancer Care Fund (£6,000); St Arvan's Church – Chepstow, St Woolos Cathedral and British Red Cross (£5,000 each); Wales Millennium Centre, Llandovery College and British Scoliosis Research Foundation (£3,000 each); Parish of

Llanishen (£1,000); and Society for Welfare of Horses and Ponies and Bridge VIS (£500 each).
FINANCES *Year* 2011–12 *Income* £118,534 *Grants* £116,000 *Assets* £3,131,833
TRUSTEES David Jones; Sir Peter Phillips; James Zorab.
OTHER INFORMATION 33 grants were awarded, which totalled £116,000.
HOW TO APPLY Applications should be in writing and reach the correspondent by February for the trustees' meeting in March.
WHO TO APPLY TO Cecilia St Clair, Administrator, Deloitte PCS Ltd, 5 Callaghan Square, Cardiff CF10 5BT *Tel.* 02920 264391

■ The Jephcott Charitable Trust

CC NO 240915   **ESTABLISHED** 1965
WHERE FUNDING CAN BE GIVEN Worldwide.
WHO CAN BENEFIT 'We like to make grants which will make a difference, preference will be given to charities or projects which have difficulty getting started, or raising funds from other sources. This often means that the trust is funding capital projects, e.g. for equipment or materials, rather than running costs. Grants are made to charities in all parts of the world.'
WHAT IS FUNDED Funding priorities: population control – support for schemes, particularly educational ones, which help to control excessive growth in population; the natural environment – projects involved in conserving the natural environment (it does not support projects involving animal welfare or heritage sites or buildings); education – projects will be considered benefiting people of all ages and backgrounds; healthcare projects. Population control The natural environment Education Health
WHAT IS NOT FUNDED The trust does not support: organisations whose administrative expenses form more than 15% of their annual income; individuals; animal welfare; heritage; projects which require long-term funding are not normally considered.
TYPE OF GRANT Pump-priming – helping to get an organisation up and running, or make a significant step forward. Project costs – capital rather than running costs are preferred.
RANGE OF GRANTS Grants are made in the range of £2,000–£10,000, and in exceptional cases only, up to £20,000. The trust prefers to make one–off donations to get many projects started, rather than support fewer projects charities over a long period.
SAMPLE GRANTS Possibilities (£20,000); Catherine Bullen Trust (£15,000) Lessons for Life and Zisize (£10,000 each); Lotus Flower Trust (£8,000); Flora and Fauna International and Kagando (£5,000 each); Potosi (£4,000); and African Village Support (£2,000).
FINANCES *Year* 2011–12 *Income* £211,787 *Grants* £155,778 *Assets* £5,476,948
TRUSTEES James Parker; Lady Jephcott; Judge A. North; Mark Jephcott; Keith Morgan; Diana Ader; Dr David Thomas.
HOW TO APPLY Full and detailed guidelines and application forms can be downloaded from the trust's website. Trustees meet twice a year (in April and October) and must have detailed financial information about each project before they will make a decision. Only applications from eligible bodies are acknowledged, when further information about the project may be requested. Monitoring of grant expenditure is a requirement of all successful grants and donations from the trust.

WHO TO APPLY TO Dr Felicity Gibling, Secretary to the Trustees, The Threshing Barn, Ford, Kingsbridge, Devon TQ7 2LN *Website* www. jephcottcharitabletrust.org.uk

■ The Jerusalem Trust

CC NO 285696   **ESTABLISHED** 1982
WHERE FUNDING CAN BE GIVEN Unrestricted.
WHO CAN BENEFIT Organisations working for the promotion of Christianity in the fields detailed below.
WHAT IS FUNDED *Evangelism and Christian mission in the UK* – particularly Christian projects that develop new ways of working with children and young people; in church planting and evangelistic projects, including those that undertake Christian work with prisoners, ex-prisoners and their families. *Christian education* – including the development of Christian curriculum resource materials for schools in RE and across the curriculum; the recruitment and development of Christian teachers in all subjects; and adult lay Christian training and education. *Christian evangelism and relief work overseas* – specifically the provision of support for indigenous training centres and the provision of Christian literature in Central and Eastern Europe and Anglophone sub-Saharan Africa. *Christian media* – support for media projects that promote Christianity as well as training and networking projects for Christians working professionally in, or considering a career in, the media. *Christian art* – specifically a small number of commissions of works of works of art for places of worship.
WHAT IS NOT FUNDED Trustees do not normally make grants towards building or repair work for churches. Grants are not normally made to individuals.
RANGE OF GRANTS Up to £250,000.
SAMPLE GRANTS National Society for Promoting Religious Education (£150,000); Tear Fund (£110,000); Churches and Media Network (£82,000); Salmon Youth Centre (£60,000); Bible Reading Fellowship (£50,000); Religious Education Movement in Scotland (£40,000); Churches' National Adviser in Further Education (£30,000); African Enterprise (£20,000); and Transform Newham (£15,000).
FINANCES *Year* 2011 *Income* £2,675,000 *Grants* £2,658,000 *Assets* £77,932,000
TRUSTEES Rt Hon. Sir Timothy Sainsbury; Lady Susan Sainsbury; Dr V. E. Hartley Booth; Phillida Goad; Dr Peter Frankopan; Melanie Townsend.
OTHER INFORMATION At the time of writing (November 2013) the trust's accounts for 2012 were not yet available.
HOW TO APPLY See the guidance for applicants in the entry for the Sainsbury Family Charitable Trusts. A single application will be considered for support by all the trusts in the group. However, for this as for many of the trusts, 'proposals are generally invited by the trustees or initiated at their request'.
WHO TO APPLY TO Alan Bookbinder, Director, The Peak, 5 Wilton Road, London SW1V 1AP *Tel.* 020 7410 0330 *Fax* 020 7410 0332 *email* jerusalemtrust@sfct.org.uk *Website* www. sfct.org.uk

■ Jerwood Charitable Foundation

CC NO 1074036   **ESTABLISHED** 1999
WHERE FUNDING CAN BE GIVEN UK.
WHO CAN BENEFIT Organisations benefiting young adults, actors, artists, musicians, research workers, writers, dancers and choreographers, directors, producers and film makers.
WHAT IS FUNDED Project and programme support across the arts throughout the UK. The foundation host an open grants programme as well as proactively funding the Jerwood Visual Arts series of events.
WHAT IS NOT FUNDED The foundation will not consider applications for: building or capital costs (including purchase of equipment); projects in the fields of religion or sport; animal rights or welfare; study fees or course fees; general fundraising appeals which are likely to have wide public appeal; appeals to establish endowment funds for other charities; appeals for matching funding for National Lottery applications; grants for the running and core costs of voluntary bodies; projects which are of mainly local appeal or identified with a locality; medical or mental health projects; social welfare, particularly where it may be considered a government or local authority responsibility; retrospective awards; projects outside Great Britain; schools which are trying to attain Special Schools Status; general touring, production or staging costs; environmental or conservation projects; musical instruments; informal education or community participation projects; education or participation projects for those who have not yet left formal education. The foundation may, where there are very exceptional circumstances, decide to waive an exclusion.
TYPE OF GRANT Principally one-off, usually incorporating challenge funding, but will sometimes be prepared to maintain support if consistency will secure better results.
RANGE OF GRANTS Lower range will be around £5,000–£10,000, and the more substantial grants usually ranging from £10,000–£50,000; but up to £100,000.
SAMPLE GRANTS Royal Court Theatre: Jerwood New Playwrights (£75,000); Jerwood Space re Jerwood Visual Arts (£63,000); Sadler Wells: Summer University (£43,000); Arts Admin: Develop and Create (£25,000); Chris Goode and Company: Monkey Bars (£20,000); National Theatre Wales: Online Artists' Platform (£15,000); OTO Projects: Grassroots Promoters/Emerging Artists Fund (£10,000); Undercurrent Festival: Commissions and Development (£7,500); New School House Gallery: Transformation (£5,000) and Owl Project: Organisational Development (£2,000).
FINANCES *Year* 2012 *Income* £986,802 *Grants* £1,262,411 *Assets* £26,497,065
TRUSTEES Tim Eyles, Chair; Katherine Goodison; Juliane Wharton; Anthony Palmer; Sarah Vine; Thomas Grieve; Rupert Tyler; Phyllida Earle.
OTHER INFORMATION The grants total includes £94,000 given to individuals.
HOW TO APPLY Initial applications should include: a short proposal, not more than two sides of A4, outlining a description of the organisation's aims or a short biography for individuals, and a description of the specific project for which funding is sought and the opportunity it seeks to fulfil; a detailed budget for the project, identifying administrative, management and central costs details of funding already in place for the project, including any other trusts or sources which are being or have been

approached for funds; and, if funding is not in place, details of how the applicant plans to secure the remaining funding. The trustees may decide to contact the applicants for further information including: details of the management and staffing structure, including trustees; and the most recent annual report and audited accounts of the organisation, together with current management accounts if relevant to the project. However, the trust asks that this information is **not** sent unless it is requested. Applications may be made online via the website. Alternatively applicants can send proposals by post. The foundation may wish to enter into discussions and/or correspondence with the applicant which may result in modification and/or development of the project or scheme. Any such discussion or correspondence will not commit the foundation to funding that application. Applications are assessed throughout the year. Successful applicants will be invited to report to the foundation at the completion of their project and to provide photographs of the work or project supported. As the foundation receives a large number of applications, it is not always possible to have preliminary meetings to discuss possible support before a written application is made.

WHO TO APPLY TO Shonagh Manson, Director, 171 Union Street, Bankside, London SE1 0LN *Tel.* 020 7261 0279 *email* info@jerwood.org *Website* www.jerwoodcharitablefoundation.org

....

■ Jesus Hospital Charity

CC NO 1075889 **ESTABLISHED** 1679
WHERE FUNDING CAN BE GIVEN Barnet
WHO CAN BENEFIT Individuals; and local organisations benefiting people of all ages, academics, research workers, scientists, students, unemployed people, volunteers, families, at risk groups, carers, people who are disabled, people with a medical condition or disease, people who are disadvantaged by poverty or who are socially isolated, and victims of abuse, crime and domestic violence.
WHAT IS FUNDED This trust will consider funding: almshouses; support to voluntary and community organisations; support to volunteers; respite care and care for carers; support and self-help groups; ambulances and mobile units; special needs education; training for work; costs of study; academic subjects, sciences and research; and community services.
WHAT IS NOT FUNDED No grants for relief of rates, taxes or other public funds. No provision of almshouse accommodation to anyone male or under the age of 50. No grants outside the Barnet area.
TYPE OF GRANT Capital and one-off. Funding is available for one year or less. Each case is considered on its merits.
SAMPLE GRANTS Mind in Barnet and North London Hospice (£5,000 each); New Barnet Community Centre and Chipping Barnet Day Centre for the Elderly (£2,000 each); High Barnet Good Neighbour Scheme (£1,500) and Church House – Winter Shelter Scheme (£1,000).
FINANCES *Year* 2012 *Income* £602,536 *Grants* £29,027 *Assets* £9,965,933
TRUSTEES Neil Kobish; Brenda Sandford; P. J. Mellows; William Carrington; Ian Lawless; Revd Canon Hall Speers; Catherine Cavanagh; Stephen Payne; Dr Ian Johnston; Malcolm Bye; M. Relfe; Ian Lawless; Janet Hulme.

OTHER INFORMATION The 2012 grant total includes £6,000 that was given to individuals.
HOW TO APPLY Application forms are available to download on the charity's website. Trustees meet every two months to consider applications.
WHO TO APPLY TO Simon Smith, Clerk to the Visitors (Trustees), Ravenscroft Lodge, 37 Union Street, Barnet, Hertfordshire EN5 4HY *Tel.* 020 8440 4374 *Website* www.jesushospitalcharity.org.uk

....

■ Jewish Child's Day

CC NO 209266 **ESTABLISHED** 1947
WHERE FUNDING CAN BE GIVEN Worldwide. In practice, mainly Israel, UK and Eastern Europe.
WHO CAN BENEFIT Organisations caring for Jewish children.
WHAT IS FUNDED Charitable purposes of direct benefit to Jewish children who are disadvantaged, suffering or in need of special care.
WHAT IS NOT FUNDED Individuals are not supported. Grants are not given towards general services, building or maintenance of property or staff salaries.
TYPE OF GRANT 'One-off' and recurring.
RANGE OF GRANTS Up to £70,000.
SAMPLE GRANTS Friends of Givat Ada (£100,000); Beit Uri (£33,000); Friends of Neve-Kineret (£20,000); Manchester Jewish Federation (£15,000); Haifa Centre (£10,000); Schechter Institute of Jewish Studies, Yated – Downs Syndrome Society of Israel and The Jerusalem Therapeutic Riding Center (£3,000); Micha Tel Aviv and Youth Direct (£1,100).
FINANCES *Year* 2011–12 *Income* £1,118,570 *Grants* £687,000 *Assets* £640,853
TRUSTEES Joy Moss, Chair; June Jacobs; Stephen Moss; Virginia Campus; Francine Epstein; Susie Olins; Amanda Ingram; Gaby Lazarus; David Collins.
HOW TO APPLY To apply for a grant contact the correspondent to discuss in the first instance. Applications must be supported by audited accounts in English or with the main heading translated into English. Applications should be submitted by 31 December, 30 April and 31 August for consideration in March, June and October respectively. Organisations with dedicated UK fundraising operations must disclose this in the application.
WHO TO APPLY TO Jackie Persoff, 5th Floor, 707 High Road, North Finchley, London N12 0BT *Tel.* 020 8446 8804 *Fax* 020 8446 7370 *email* info@jcd.uk.com *Website* www.jcd.uk.com

....

■ The Jewish Youth Fund

CC NO 251902 **ESTABLISHED** 1937
WHERE FUNDING CAN BE GIVEN UK.
WHO CAN BENEFIT Jewish youth clubs, centres, movements and groups.
WHAT IS FUNDED Jewish youth work projects, equipment and premises.
WHAT IS NOT FUNDED Grants are not made in response to general appeals. Formal education is not supported.
TYPE OF GRANT Grants are made for a whole variety of Jewish youth work projects. Loans are sometimes offered towards the cost of building.
RANGE OF GRANTS Generally, £1,000–£10,000
SAMPLE GRANTS London Jewish Cultural Centre (£104,000); JLGB (£10,000); Step by Step (£8,000); Camp Simcha (£5,000); Friends of B'nei Akiva (£4,000); FZY, Noam, Habonim Dror

and Kisharon (£3,000 each); and The BBYO Charitable Trust (£1,000).

FINANCES *Year* 2011–12 *Income* £100,196 *Grants* £144,089 *Assets* £3,439,740

TRUSTEES Lady Morris of Kenwood; Adam D. Rose; Philippa Strauss; Lord Jonathan Morris; David Goldberg; David Brown; Elliot Simberg; Stephen Spitz.

HOW TO APPLY On an application form available from the correspondent, enclosing a copy of the latest accounts and an annual report.

WHO TO APPLY TO Julia Samuel, Secretary, Haskell House, 152 West End Lane, London NW6 1SD *Tel.* 020 7443 5169 *email* info@jyf.org.uk

■ The Jigsaw Foundation

CC NO 1149083   **ESTABLISHED** 2012

WHERE FUNDING CAN BE GIVEN UK, with a possible preference for North East England.

WHO CAN BENEFIT Charities, community groups and educational establishments.

WHAT IS FUNDED General charitable purposes, education, social welfare and community and economic development. More specifically, there is a focus on supporting organisations working with children and young people and families facing disadvantage or hardship.

TRUSTEES Sir Peter Vardy; Lady Margaret Vardy; Richard Vardy.

HOW TO APPLY In writing to the correspondent.

WHO TO APPLY TO Victoria Spencer, Venture House, Aykley Meads, Durham DH1 5TS *Tel.* 01913 744710 *email* info@thejigsawfoundation.com *Website* www.thejigsawfoundation.com

■ The Harold Joels Charitable Trust

CC NO 206326   **ESTABLISHED** 1957

WHERE FUNDING CAN BE GIVEN UK and overseas.

WHO CAN BENEFIT Jewish organisations only, with a preference for organisations in the USA.

WHAT IS FUNDED Jewish causes.

RANGE OF GRANTS £50–£20,000

SAMPLE GRANTS United Synagogue (£1,600); and Chai Cancer Care, Nowood, Samaritans, Shaare Zedek UK, St John Ambulance and Tricycle Theatre Company Limited (all grants under £500).

FINANCES *Year* 2011–12 *Income* £27,856 *Grants* £20,960 *Assets* £595,164

TRUSTEES Harold Joels; N. Joels; Valerie Joels; Prof. Norman Joels.

OTHER INFORMATION The grant total includes grants made in the US of £16,347.

HOW TO APPLY In writing to the correspondent.

WHO TO APPLY TO Harold Joels, Trustee, 11a Arkwright Road, London NW3 6AA *email* hjoels7@aol.com

■ The Nicholas Joels Charitable Trust

CC NO 278409   **ESTABLISHED** 1978

WHERE FUNDING CAN BE GIVEN UK and overseas.

WHO CAN BENEFIT Registered charities only, with a preference for Jewish charities.

WHAT IS FUNDED General charitable purposes.

RANGE OF GRANTS Up to £9,000

SAMPLE GRANTS Previous beneficiaries included: World Jewish Relief (£9,000); Norwood (£5,300); Emunah (£4,300); United Jewish Israel Appeal (£3,800); Jewish Care (£2,000);

Zionist Federation (£1,000); United Synagogue (£900); I Rescue (£750); Chinese Disaster Fund (£500); Jewish Women's Aid (£200); and Friends of the Tate Gallery (£100).

FINANCES *Year* 2011–12 *Income* £18,710 *Grants* £25,572

TRUSTEES N. Joels; H. Joels; A. Joels.

OTHER INFORMATION Accounts for the year 2011–12 had been received at the Charity Commission but were not available to view.

HOW TO APPLY In writing to the correspondent.

WHO TO APPLY TO Nicholas Joels, Trustee, 20 Copse Wood Way, Northwood HA6 2UF *Tel.* 01923 841376

■ The Norman Joels Charitable Trust

CC NO 206325   **ESTABLISHED** 1957

WHERE FUNDING CAN BE GIVEN UK, Israel and the Middle East.

WHO CAN BENEFIT Registered charities only.

WHAT IS FUNDED General charitable purposes.

RANGE OF GRANTS £100–£3,500.

SAMPLE GRANTS Previous beneficiaries have included: Friends of Magen David Action in Great Britain, Jewish Aid Committee, Jewish Care, Joint Jewish Charitable Trust, New London Synagogue, Norwood Ravensmead, The Spiro Institute and World Jewish Relief

FINANCES *Year* 2011–12 *Income* £36,164 *Grants* £33,374 *Assets* £1,151,456

TRUSTEES Jessica Joels; Norman Joels; Harold Joels; Myriam Joels.

HOW TO APPLY In writing to the correspondent.

WHO TO APPLY TO The Trustees, Grunberg and Co Ltd, 10 - 14 Accommodation Road, London NW11 8EP *Tel.* 020 8458 0083

■ The Joffe Charitable Trust

CC NO 270299   **ESTABLISHED** 1968

WHERE FUNDING CAN BE GIVEN The Gambia, Kenya, Malawi, Mozambique, South Africa, Tanzania, Uganda, Zambia and Zimbabwe.

WHO CAN BENEFIT Registered charities with good quality leadership, clear objectives and realistic project budgets.

WHAT IS FUNDED The alleviation of poverty and protection/advancement of human rights mainly in the developing world, (poverty for this purpose could include some forms of suffering such as mental or physical disability and lack of education).

WHAT IS NOT FUNDED No grants for: emergency relief, the arts, conflict resolution, formal academic education, micro credit, work directly in the field of HIV/AIDS, individuals, physical infrastructure, large charities with income of over £5 million per annum.

TYPE OF GRANT Grants and loans for up to three years.

RANGE OF GRANTS Around £5,000–£40,000.

SAMPLE GRANTS Ububele Educational and Psychotherapy Trust (£137,000); AFIDEP (£50,000); Acid Survivors International (£44,000); Charities Aid Foundation (£38,000); Transparency International (£25,000); Earth Security Initiative CIC (£18,000); Global Giving (£15,000) and University of California San Francisco Foundation (£12,500). Grants of £10,000 or less totalled £85,000.

FINANCES *Year* 2011–12 *Income* £387,200 *Grants* £706,482 *Assets* £11,022,896

TRUSTEES Lord Joel Joffe, Chair; Lady Vanetta Joffe; Deborah Joffe; Dr Nick Maurice; Mark Poston; Alex Jacobs.

HOW TO APPLY Firstly, applicants must complete an online application form available through the trust's website. The trust aims to respond to applicants within one month if they have been successful. If so, they will be asked to submit a more detailed proposal. As part of the evaluation of your application, the trust may telephone or arrange to meet you with you to discuss it further. The trust aims to let all stage two applicants have a decision within four months of receiving their proposal.

WHO TO APPLY TO Linda Perry, Trust Manager, Liddington Manor, 35 The Street, Liddington, Swindon SN4 0HD *Tel.* 01793 790203 *email* joffetrust@lidmanor.co.uk *Website* www.joffecharitabletrust.org

■ The Elton John Aids Foundation

CC NO 1017336   **ESTABLISHED** 1993

WHERE FUNDING CAN BE GIVEN Unrestricted.

WHO CAN BENEFIT Registered charities.

WHAT IS FUNDED The provision of focused and sustainable funding to frontline programmes that help alleviate the physical, emotional and financial hardship of those living with, affected by or at risk of HIV/AIDS

WHAT IS NOT FUNDED For both UK and international grants the foundation will not fund: academic or medical research; conferences; grants to individuals; repatriation costs; retrospective funding.

TYPE OF GRANT Revenue and specific projects. Core costs; one-off, running costs; and salaries. Funding may be given for one year or up to three years.

RANGE OF GRANTS £200–£1.3 million.

SAMPLE GRANTS Habitat for Humanity; Terrence Higgins Trust; Riders for Health; partners in Health; the Children's Society; Liverpool VCT; Familia Salmada; Simelela Rape Crisis; All Ukrainian Network of People Living with HIV/AIDS; Romanian Angel Appeal; Nwamitwa Community Centre; Paediatric Palliative Care, Zambia; Fair Play – Tackling HIV in Ukraine and Red Badges – Tanzania.

FINANCES *Year* 2012 *Income* £11,987,615 *Grants* £8,899,531 *Assets* £27,944,494

TRUSTEES Sir Elton John, Chair; David Furnish; Lynette Jackson; Frank Presland; Anne Aslett; Marguerite Littman; Johnny Bergius; James Locke; Rafi Manoukian; Scott Campbell.

HOW TO APPLY There are two funds that accept applications: **Pioneer Grants –** Available in: Cameroon, Cote D'Ivoire, Ghana, India, Kenya, Lesotho, Malawi, Myanmar (Burma), Nigeria, Russian Federation, South Africa, Tanzania, Thailand, Uganda, Ukraine, United Kingdom, Zambia and Zimbabwe. **Robert Key Memorial Fund –** Applicants must be applying on behalf of an organisations that is a registered not-for-profit or charitable organisation. Available in the countries listed above under Pioneer Grants, **plus**: Botswana, Democratic Republic of the Congo, Ethiopia, Mozambique, China, Indonesia and Vietnam.

These programmes may change or open and close throughout the year so applicants are advised to check the website before making an application. Applications are made through the online form.

WHO TO APPLY TO Mohamed Osman, Head of Grants, 1 Blythe Road, London W14 0HG *Tel.* 020 7603 9996 *Fax* 020 7348 4848 *email* grants@ejaf.com *Website* www.ejaf.com

■ The Dyfrig and Heather John Charitable Trust

CC NO 1149595   **ESTABLISHED** 2012

WHERE FUNDING CAN BE GIVEN Wales.

WHO CAN BENEFIT Charities and community groups.

WHAT IS FUNDED General charitable purposes, education, social welfare and the arts, with a preference for children and young people.

TRUSTEES Dyfrig John; Heather John; Gareth John; Steffan John.

HOW TO APPLY No grants to unsolicited applications.

WHO TO APPLY TO Dyfrig John, Trustee, 11 Marine Parade, Penarth, South Glamorgan CF64 3BG

■ The Michael John Trust

CC NO 293571   **ESTABLISHED** 1986

WHERE FUNDING CAN BE GIVEN UK.

WHO CAN BENEFIT Scientific research, education, health, disability – UK.

WHAT IS FUNDED Registered charities

TYPE OF GRANT Unrestricted funding.

RANGE OF GRANTS Up to £10,000.

SAMPLE GRANTS Michael Brown Scholarship (£10,000); Westminster Abbey Thanksgiving Service (£5,000); Science and Technology Foundation Trust (£4,000); The Snowdon Award Scheme and Contaminated Blood Inquiry (£1,200).

FINANCES *Year* 2011–12 *Income* £66,075 *Grants* £25,557 *Assets* £1,863,792

TRUSTEES Dr H. P. Jost; M. J. Jost; R. Worby.

OTHER INFORMATION In 2011–12 grants were given to 24 organisations.

HOW TO APPLY In writing to the correspondent. The trustees meet quarterly. As the trust is a small charitable trust, it prefers requests for small, reasonable amounts.

WHO TO APPLY TO Dr Peter Jost, Trustee, Hill House, Mills Grove, Mill Hill, London NW7 1QL *Tel.* 020 3213 1030 *email* michaeljohntrust@btconnect.com

■ The Lillie Johnson Charitable Trust

CC NO 326761   **ESTABLISHED** 1985

WHERE FUNDING CAN BE GIVEN UK, with a preference for the West Midlands.

WHO CAN BENEFIT Charities concerned with children, young people and medical causes.

WHAT IS FUNDED Medical and welfare causes.

WHAT IS NOT FUNDED No support for individuals.

SAMPLE GRANTS LEC – Worcester (£40,000); Family Care Trust and Marie Curie Cancer Care (£10,000 each); British Tinnitus Association and Samaritans Solihull (£5,000 each); Birmingham and Midland Operatic Society – Youth (£4,500); and Blind Veterans UK, Cambridge Performing Arts, Pan Asia Community Housing, Sense, Sunfield Home and Warwickshire Junior Tennis Foundation (£1,000 each).

FINANCES *Year* 2011–12 *Income* £203,899 *Grants* £172,273 *Assets* £5,321,871

TRUSTEES Victor Lyttle; Peter Adams; John Desmond; Verena Adams.

Think carefully about every application. Is it justified?

661

HOW TO APPLY Applications are only considered from charities which are traditionally supported by the trust. The trust stated that it is inundated with applications it cannot support and feels obliged to respond to all of these.

WHO TO APPLY TO John Desmond, Trustee, Heathcote House, 39 Rodbourne Road, Harborne, Birmingham B17 0PN *Tel.* 01214 721279

■ The Johnson Foundation

CC NO 518660   ESTABLISHED 1987

WHERE FUNDING CAN BE GIVEN Merseyside.

WHO CAN BENEFIT Registered charities.

WHAT IS FUNDED Medicine and health, education, relief of poverty and youth projects,

WHAT IS NOT FUNDED Grants are not normally given to individuals.

TYPE OF GRANT One-off, up to two years. Recurrent, core costs, project and research.

RANGE OF GRANTS Usually £1,000–£5,000.

SAMPLE GRANTS Liverpool and Merseyside Theatre Trust (£200,000); Liverpool Heart and Chest Hospital (£50,000); Birkenhead School (£25,000); Age UK Wirral (£19,000); Old Parkonians Youth Development and Sara's Hope Foundation Children's Hospice (£10,000 each); Wirral St John's Hospice (£5,000); Christians Against Poverty and the Princes' Trust (£2,500 each); and the Snowdrop Appeal, Birkenhead Gang Show and Shining Faces in India (£1,000 each).

FINANCES *Year* 2012–13 *Income* £127,283 *Grants* £356,609 *Assets* £3,765,698

TRUSTEES Christopher Johnson; Peter Johnson.

OTHER INFORMATION The trust stated: 'Whilst this trust is prepared to help larger charities, it prefers to support small, local organisations unable to afford professional fundraisers with grants from about £250 to £1,000.'
Grants totalling £375,000 were awarded to 75 organisations.

HOW TO APPLY In writing to the correspondent, including details of what your organisation does and how it is funded, a copy of the latest audited accounts, charity registration number or name of a registered charity through which the grant will be made, why a grant is needed and who will benefit, an annual report and a business plan or statement. Applications are considered in spring and autumn.

WHO TO APPLY TO Peter Johnson, Trustee, c/o Park Group plc, 1 Valley Road, Birkenhead, Wirral CH41 7ED *Tel.* 01516 531700

■ The Reginald Johnson Foundation

CC NO 276003   ESTABLISHED 1978

WHERE FUNDING CAN BE GIVEN Stoke-on-Trent and North Staffordshire.

WHO CAN BENEFIT Registered charities.

WHAT IS FUNDED General charitable purposes.

WHAT IS NOT FUNDED UK charities must apply through a local branch, making it clear in which areas the parent body expects the project to be self-supporting and raise its own funds.

SAMPLE GRANTS Previous beneficiaries include: Volunteer Help Reading (£2,000), Frontline Dance (£1,000) and North Staffs Kidney Patient Association (£350).

FINANCES *Year* 2011–12 *Income* £273 *Grants* £250

TRUSTEES Arthur Burden; Patrick Johnson; Florence McCall.

OTHER INFORMATION In the previous accounting year, this charity's total expenditure was £320,285 and it may be that income and expenditure will increase in the future.

HOW TO APPLY In writing to the correspondent. The trustees meet monthly.

WHO TO APPLY TO Arthur Burden, Trustee, St Georges House, 215–219 Chester Road, Manchester M15 4JE

■ The Johnnie Johnson Trust

CC NO 200351   ESTABLISHED 1961

WHERE FUNDING CAN BE GIVEN UK, with a preference for the West Midlands.

WHO CAN BENEFIT To benefit children and young adults.

WHAT IS FUNDED Heritage and training/adventure breaks for children, youth and welfare organisations.

TYPE OF GRANT Normally one-off.

RANGE OF GRANTS Up to £18,500

SAMPLE GRANTS St Basils (£18,500); Docklands Sailing and Watersports Centre (£17,000); Birmingham Children's Hospital (£16,000); Boys2Men (£15,000); Douglas Bader Foundation (£6,500); Construction Youth Trust (£5,000); Ro-Ro Sailing (£4,000); Get Hooked on Fishing (£3,000); Birmingham Youth Foundation (£2,000); Dodford Children's Holiday Farm (£1,200) and Little Brig Sailing Trust (£350).

FINANCES *Year* 2012 *Income* £120,372 *Grants* £101,698 *Assets* £3,679,283

TRUSTEES Victor Johnson; Peter Johnson; Jane Fordham; G. W. Ballard; Katherine Cross; Christopher Johnson.

OTHER INFORMATION In 2011–12 grants were given to 18 organisations.

HOW TO APPLY In writing to the correspondent.

WHO TO APPLY TO Christopher Jackson, 3 Crumpfields Lane, Webheath, Redditch, Worcestershire B97 5PN *Tel.* 01527 544722

■ The Johnson Wax Ltd Charitable Trust

CC NO 200332   ESTABLISHED 1961

WHERE FUNDING CAN BE GIVEN 20 mile radius of Frimley Green, Surrey.

WHO CAN BENEFIT Local charities.

WHAT IS FUNDED Health, education, local community, environment, arts, sports.

WHAT IS NOT FUNDED No grants to individuals.

RANGE OF GRANTS £4,000 average.

SAMPLE GRANTS Grants were broken down in to the following categories: Health (£122,000); Education (£75,000); Local Community (£50,000); June Community Day (£30,500); Giving Back scheme (£25,000); Arts and sports (£18,500); Environment (£14,000); Employee-led schemes (£10,000) and Samuel C Johnson award (£3,700).

FINANCES *Year* 2011–12 *Income* £250,016 *Grants* £347,969 *Assets* £90,723

TRUSTEES Faye Gilbert; Trevor Jessett; J. Thake.

HOW TO APPLY In writing to the correspondent including the following information: the amount requested and what is it is needed for; – details of how the grant will benefit a broad cross-section of the Frimley Green community and meet a clear social need within it.

WHO TO APPLY TO Faye Gilbert, S. C. Johnson Wax Ltd, Frimley Green, Camberley, Surrey GU16 7AJ *Tel.* 01276 852422 *email* givinguk@scj.com

■ The Joicey Trust

CC NO 244679 **ESTABLISHED** 1965
WHERE FUNDING CAN BE GIVEN Unrestricted but in practice, the county of Northumberland and the old metropolitan county of Tyne and Wear.
WHO CAN BENEFIT Registered charities operating in Northumberland and Tyne and Wear or groups with a specific project within the area defined above. The trust will consider funding organisations benefiting people of all ages, seafarers and fishermen, people who are in care, fostered or adopted and one-parent families.
WHAT IS FUNDED This trust will consider funding activities within the following fields: residential facilities and services; a range of infrastructure, technical support and development; charity or voluntary umbrella bodies; religious buildings; music, dance and theatre; healthcare, facilities and buildings; conservation; education and training; and community facilities and services. UK appeals are not normally supported unless there is specific evidence of activity benefiting the local area.
WHAT IS NOT FUNDED The trust states that it will not support 'bodies not having registered charitable status; personal applications; individuals; groups that do not have an identifiable project within the beneficial area'.
TYPE OF GRANT One-off for capital and revenue projects, with preference for discrete projects over running costs. Also start-up costs, buildings, core costs, projects and salaries.
RANGE OF GRANTS Up to £5,000 with very occasional larger grants.
SAMPLE GRANTS Northumberland Theatre Company (£10,000); Borders Health Board Endowment Funds (£7,500); Leuchie House Short Break Care and Tyne Housing Association (£5,000 each); Corbridge Youth Initiative (£4,000); The Fusiliers Museum of Northumberland (£3,500); Motor Neurone Disease Association and The Northern Police Convalescent and Treatment Centre (£3,000 each); St Paul's Church, Whitley Bay and The Wildlife and Wetlands Trust (£2,000 each); Gilsland Village Hall (£1,500); British Wireless for the Blind (£1,250); Dream Holidays (£650); Motability (£400) and Wansbeck CVS (Holy Sepulchre Over 50's Club) (£50).
FINANCES *Year* 2011–12 *Income* £252,008 *Grants* £223,780 *Assets* £7,054,312
TRUSTEES Rt Hon. Lord Joicey; Rt Hon. Lady Joicey; Hon. A. H. Joicey; R. H. Dickinson; Hon K. J. Crosbie Dawson.
OTHER INFORMATION In 2011–12 grants were given to 172 organisations.
HOW TO APPLY There is no application form and applications should be made in writing to the correspondent. Trustees' meetings are held in January and July and applications should be received not later than the end of November and the end of May respectively. Applications should include a brief description of the project and must include a copy of the previous year's accounts and, where possible, a copy of the current year's projected income and expenditure. In the case of large projects, an indication should be given of how the major sources of funding are likely to be secured, including reference to any Community Fund grant applied for/received. Unsuccessful applicants will not be informed unless an sae is provided.

WHO TO APPLY TO N. A. Furness, Appeals Secretary, c/o Dickinson Dees LLP, St Ann's Wharf, 112 Quayside, Newcastle upon Tyne NE1 3DX *Tel.* 01912 799662 *email* appeals@thejoiceytrust.org.uk

■ The Jones 1986 Charitable Trust

CC NO 327176 **ESTABLISHED** 1986
WHERE FUNDING CAN BE GIVEN UK, mostly Nottinghamshire.
WHO CAN BENEFIT Registered charities.
WHAT IS FUNDED People with disabilities, welfare of older people, welfare of younger people, education and purposes beneficial to the community.
WHAT IS NOT FUNDED No grants to individuals.
RANGE OF GRANTS Up to around £100,000, but mostly between £4,000 and £25,000.
SAMPLE GRANTS Riding for the Disabled – Highland Group (£50,000); Cope Children's Trust (£40,000); Age UK and Kirkby Community Advice Centre (£25,000 each); The Archbishop of York's Southwell Palace Project (£15,000); I CAN and Combat Stress (£10,000 each); Platform 51 (£6,000); Family Care Nottingham, Radford Care Group and Tree Tops Hospice (£5,000 each); Community Concern Erewash (£3,000); Relate (£2,500); Deafblind UK (£1,000) and Happy Days (£500).
FINANCES *Year* 2012 *Income* £487,194 *Grants* £404,819 *Assets* £18,401,939
TRUSTEES Robert Heason; Richard Stringfellow; John David Pears.
HOW TO APPLY In writing to the correspondent. The trust invites applications for grants by advertising in specialist press. Applications are considered for both capital and/or revenue projects as long as each project appears viable.
WHO TO APPLY TO Nigel Lindley, Administrator, Smith Cooper LLP, 2 Lace Market Square, Nottingham NG1 1PB *Tel.* 01159 454300

■ The Dezna Robins Jones Charitable Foundation

CC NO 1104252 **ESTABLISHED** 2004
WHERE FUNDING CAN BE GIVEN Preference for south Wales.
WHO CAN BENEFIT Charitable organisations in south Wales.
WHAT IS FUNDED Medicine; education.
SAMPLE GRANTS University Hospital Wales (£88,000); Neil Boobyer Rugby Solutions Limited (£56,000); Performance Arts Education (£54,000); Tredegar Band and St John's School Porthcawl (£50,000 each); Cory Band (£42,000); St David's Hospice and Save the Children Fund (£5,000 each); Maggie's Cancer Care Centre (£2,000); and Cancer Information and Support Services (£1,000).
FINANCES *Year* 2012–13 *Income* £3,912 *Grants* £371,298 *Assets* £2,268,023
TRUSTEES Bernard Jones; Louise Boobyer; Alexia Cooke.
HOW TO APPLY In writing to the correspondent. Trustees meet at least twice a year.
WHO TO APPLY TO Bernard Jones, Trustee, Greenacres, Laleston, Bridgend CF32 0HN *Tel.* 01656 768584

■ The Marjorie and Geoffrey Jones Charitable Trust

CC NO 1051031   **ESTABLISHED** 1995

WHERE FUNDING CAN BE GIVEN UK, preference south west of England.

WHO CAN BENEFIT Registered charities.

WHAT IS FUNDED General charitable purposes.

RANGE OF GRANTS £1,000–£5,000.

SAMPLE GRANTS Torquay Child Contact Centre (£5,000); Children and Families in Grief (£4,000); British Wireless for the Blind Fund, Devon Wildlife Trust and Parkinson's UK (£3,000 each); Epilepsy Society (£2,500); Changing Faces and The Sailors' Families Society (£2,000 each); and 66 Route Youth Trust, Double Elephant Print Workshop and Home-Start Torbay (£1,000 each).

FINANCES *Year* 2011–12 *Income* £23,353 *Grants* £87,000 *Assets* £1,492,970

TRUSTEES Nigel Wollen; William Coplestone Boughey; Philip Kay; Katrina Vollentine.

HOW TO APPLY In writing to the correspondent. The trustees meet four times a year to consider applications.

WHO TO APPLY TO Sophia Honey, Administrator, Carlton House, 30 The Terrace, Torquay, Devon TQ1 1BN *Tel.* 01803 213251 *email* sophia.honey@wollenmichelmore.co.uk

■ The Muriel Jones Foundation

CC NO 1135107   **ESTABLISHED** 2010

WHERE FUNDING CAN BE GIVEN Undefined.

WHO CAN BENEFIT Registered charities.

WHAT IS FUNDED General charitable purposes.

RANGE OF GRANTS £500–£200,000

SAMPLE GRANTS Medecins San Frontieres (£300,000); Crossflow (£125,000); Anti-Slavery International (£100,000); Animals Asia Foundation (£80,000); Frome Development (£75,000); Kids Company and Compassion in World Farming (CIWF) (£50,000 each); Sport for Life (£40,000); Guide Dogs for the Blind (£28,000); Downside Up (£15,000); Lancashire User Forum (£3,000) and Tonbridge District Mencap (£500).

FINANCES *Year* 2011–12 *Income* £1,192,228 *Grants* £1,187,727 *Assets* £4,603,436

TRUSTEES Richard Brindle; Katie Brindle; Coutts and Co.

OTHER INFORMATION In 2011–12 a total of 23 grants were given to 17 organisations.

HOW TO APPLY In writing to the correspondent.

WHO TO APPLY TO The Administrator, Coutts and Co, 440 Strand, London WC2R 0QS *Tel.* 020 7663 6826

■ The Jordan Charitable Foundation

CC NO 1051507   **ESTABLISHED** 1995

WHERE FUNDING CAN BE GIVEN UK national charities, Herefordshire and Sutherland, Scotland.

WHO CAN BENEFIT UK national charities and local charities and community groups in Herefordshire and Sutherland, Scotland.

WHAT IS FUNDED General charitable purposes, specifically: medical equipment; medical research; grants to elderly people; grants to help people with disabilities including children; grants for animal welfare; grants to assist in the maintenance of Hereford Cathedral.

TYPE OF GRANT One-off, capital and core costs will be considered.

RANGE OF GRANTS Up to £50,000. Mostly up to £10,000.

SAMPLE GRANTS Martha Trust – Hereford (£50,000); County Air Ambulance Trust (£15,000); Brooke Hospital for Animals, Marie Curie Cancer Care and The Special Air Service Regimental Association (£10,000 each); National Trust for Scotland, Royal National Mission for Deep Sea Fishermen and The Royal Start and Garter Home (£5,000 each); Tykes – The Young Karers East Sutherland (£1,000) and Dunrobin Castle Piping Championship (£500).

FINANCES *Year* 2012 *Income* £939,598 *Grants* £396,500 *Assets* £43,658,182

TRUSTEES Sir George Russell; Ralph Stockwell; Christopher Jan Andrew Bliss; Anthony Brierley; Snowport Ltd; Parkdove Ltd.

HOW TO APPLY In writing to the correspondent.

WHO TO APPLY TO Ralph Stockwell, Trustee, Rawlinson and Hunter, 8th Floor, 6 New Street Square, New Fetter Land, London EC4A 3AQ *Tel.* 020 7842 2000 *email* jordan@rawlinson-hunter.com

■ The Joron Charitable Trust

CC NO 1062547   **ESTABLISHED** 1997

WHERE FUNDING CAN BE GIVEN UK.

WHO CAN BENEFIT Registered charities.

WHAT IS FUNDED 'The charity's policy is to make grants to registered charities in the fields of education, medical research and other charities who can demonstrate that the grants will be used effectively.'

SAMPLE GRANTS The Wilderness Foundation (£112,000 for the protection of wilderness areas); Hammersmith Hospital Imperial Healthcare Charity (£63,000 to fund the oncology department for prostate cancer research); St John's Hospice (£10,000); Keeping Kids Company (£5,000); the Wellchild Trust (£2,500); and Breast Cancer Care (£1,000).

FINANCES *Year* 2011–12 *Income* £347,338 *Grants* £193,158 *Assets* £220,000

TRUSTEES Bruce D. G. Jarvis; Sandra C. Jarvis; Joseph R. Jarvis.

HOW TO APPLY 'There is no formal grants application procedure. The trustees retain the services of a charitable grants advisor and take account of the advice when deciding on grants.'

WHO TO APPLY TO Bruce D. G. Jarvis, Chair, 115 Wembley Commercial Centre, East Lane, North Wembley, Middlesex HA9 7UR *Tel.* 020 8908 4655

■ The J. E. Joseph Charitable Fund

CC NO 209058   **ESTABLISHED** 1946

WHERE FUNDING CAN BE GIVEN London, Manchester, Israel, India and Hong Kong.

WHO CAN BENEFIT Jewish people who are poor and in need.

WHAT IS FUNDED Jewish community organisations, especially those catering for people who are socially disadvantaged and young people.

WHAT IS NOT FUNDED No grants to individuals. No support for capital projects.

TYPE OF GRANT Outright cash grants frequently on an annual basis. Very occasionally loans.

RANGE OF GRANTS £500–£10,000.

SAMPLE GRANTS The Future Generation Fund (£11,000); Sir Jacob Sassoon Charity Trust (£8,500); Old Yosef Hai Yeshiva and Edinburgh House Elderly Home (£6,000 each); University Jewish Chaplaincy Board (£5,000); Ezra

U'Marpeh (£4,000); Alyn Paediatric and Adolescence Rehabilitation Centre (£3,500) and British Ort Foundation, ICLEP and Spanish and Portuguese Synagogue Hebrew Classes (£3,000 each).
FINANCES *Year* 2011–12 *Income* £131,251 *Grants* £120,023 *Assets* £4,204,957
TRUSTEES E. Mocatta, Chair; P. Sheldon; J. H. Corre; S. Horesh; A. Simon; R. Shemtob; S. Kendal.
HOW TO APPLY In writing to the correspondent, including a copy of the latest accounts. The trustees respond to all applications which are first vetted by the secretary. The accounts have noted that, 'as in previous years the trust received far more applications that it can support from its limited funds. However, the trust does try, if possible, to respond favourably to one or two new applications per year.'
WHO TO APPLY TO Roger J. Leon, Secretary, 10 Compass Close, Edgware, Middlesex HA8 8HU *Tel.* 020 8958 0126

■ The Lady Eileen Joseph Foundation
CC NO 327549   **ESTABLISHED** 1987
WHERE FUNDING CAN BE GIVEN UK.
WHO CAN BENEFIT Mainly UK organisations benefiting at-risk groups and people who are disadvantaged by poverty or socially isolated.
WHAT IS FUNDED Largely welfare and medical causes. General charitable purposes are also supported.
TYPE OF GRANT One-off.
RANGE OF GRANTS Up to £10,000.
SAMPLE GRANTS Previous beneficiaries include: Second Chance (£7,500); Coldstream Guards Association (£6,500); Alzheimer's Research Trust and Friends of the Home Physiotherapy Service (£5,000 each); Havens Hospices (£4,500); Ellenor Foundation and Queen Alexandra Hospital (£3,000 each); Independent Age and Wellbeing of Women (£2,000 each); and Cystic Fibrosis Trust, Foundation for the Prevention of Blindness and Action for Kids (£1,000 each).
FINANCES *Year* 2012–13 *Income* £9,760 *Grants* £92,000
TRUSTEES Judith M. Sawdy; Thurlstan W. Simpson; Gael Lynn Simpson.
HOW TO APPLY The trust states that unsolicited requests will not be considered.
WHO TO APPLY TO Thurlstan W. Simpson, Trustee, Colbrans Farm, Cow Lane, Laughton, Lewes BN8 6BZ

■ The Josephs Family Charitable Trust
CC NO 1054016   **ESTABLISHED** 1996
WHERE FUNDING CAN BE GIVEN UK.
WHO CAN BENEFIT Registered charities.
WHAT IS FUNDED Jewish, medical research, children, general.
RANGE OF GRANTS Mostly £100 or less.
SAMPLE GRANTS Previous beneficiaries include: United Jewish Israel Appeal (£5,000); Gatehead Academy (£3,000); Kollel Nechovas Israel (£1,000); MS Society (£500); Law of Truth College Talmudical College (£350); Foodlife Line, Norwood Challenges and St Oswald's College (£100 each).
FINANCES *Year* 2012 *Income* £12,893 *Grants* £125,000

TRUSTEES Anthony Josephs; Kate Ison; Howard Gold.
HOW TO APPLY In writing to the correspondent.
WHO TO APPLY TO John Josephs, Treasurer, 55 Moor Court, Newcastle upon Tyne NE3 4DY *Tel.* 01912 851912

■ The Josh Charitable Trust
CC NO 1107060   **ESTABLISHED** 2004
WHERE FUNDING CAN BE GIVEN UK, Israel and Australia.
WHO CAN BENEFIT Registered charities.
WHAT IS FUNDED General charitable purposes.
FINANCES *Year* 2011–12 *Income* £58,315 *Grants* £59,925 *Assets* £8,618
TRUSTEES Joel Cope; Shoshana Raizelle Cope.
OTHER INFORMATION In 2011–12 grants were given to 20 'worthy causes'.
HOW TO APPLY In writing to the correspondent.
WHO TO APPLY TO The Trustees, 1 Lancaster Drive, Prestwich, Manchester M25 0HZ

■ JTH Charitable Trust
SC NO SC000201   **ESTABLISHED** 1989
WHERE FUNDING CAN BE GIVEN Scotland, in particular west Scotland and Glasgow.
WHO CAN BENEFIT Individuals and organisations.
WHAT IS FUNDED Grants are given to a range of organisations, including universities, cultural bodies and those caring for people who are sick. Support may also be given to charities working in the fields of community services, community centres and village halls, special needs education, voluntary and community organisations and volunteers.
WHAT IS NOT FUNDED The following are not usually supported: medical electives, second or further qualifications, payment of school fees or costs incurred at tertiary educational establishments.
TYPE OF GRANT Some grants are made to individuals for educational purposes. Core costs, one-off, project, research, running costs and start-up costs will be considered.
RANGE OF GRANTS £100–£10,000.
SAMPLE GRANTS Previous beneficiaries have included Crossroads (Scotland) Care Attendance Scheme and East Park Home for Inform Children, Royal Blind Asylum and School, University of Glasgow and University of Strathclyde.
FINANCES *Year* 2011–12 *Income* £197,615 *Grants* £200,000
TRUSTEES Gordon M. Wyllie; Christine C. Howat.
HOW TO APPLY In writing to the correspondent. There is no application form for organisations. Applications should contain a summary not longer than one side of A4, backed up as necessary with schedules. A copy of the latest accounts and/or business plan should be included. Costs and financial needs should be broken down where possible. It should be clear what effect the grant will have and details of other grants applied for or awarded should be given. Evidence that the project will enhance the quality of life of the clients and that they are involved in the decision making must be included. 'Applications should include evidence of charitable status, current funding, and the use you are making of that. Projects should be demonstrated to be practical and business-like. It is a condition of any grant given that a report be made as to how the funds have been used. Grants not used for the purposes stated must be returned.' Successful applicants should not reapply in the following year. Unsuccessful

applicants are not acknowledged due to the large number of applications received by the trust. The trustees meet to consider grants in March, June, September and December. Applications should be received in the preceding month.

WHO TO APPLY TO The Trustees, 21 Blythswood Square, Glasgow G2 4BL

■ The Judith Trust

CC NO 1063012   **ESTABLISHED** 1997

WHERE FUNDING CAN BE GIVEN UK.

WHO CAN BENEFIT Organisations concerned with people with a learning disability and mental health needs.

WHAT IS FUNDED Multi-disciplinary preventative and innovative approaches to help those with learning disabilities and mental health problems, especially women, children and Jewish people.

WHAT IS NOT FUNDED No grants to individuals.

TYPE OF GRANT One-off, project and research. Funding may be given for up to three years.

SAMPLE GRANTS No beneficiary sample available.

FINANCES *Year* 2011–12 *Income* £29,944 *Grants* £5,000 *Assets* £442,897

TRUSTEES Dr Annette Lawson; Peter Lawrence; George Lawson; Charlotte Collins; Geraldine Holt; Colin Samson.

PUBLICATIONS Joined Up Care: good practice in services for people with learning disabilities and mental health needs.

HOW TO APPLY In writing to the correspondent; however, note that most grants are made through experts and advisors. The trust does not accept unsolicited applications for funding, but is pleased to hear from organisations who wish the trust to be aware of their work.

WHO TO APPLY TO Dr Annette Lawson, Trustee, 5 Carriage House, 88–90 Randolph Avenue, London W9 1BG *Tel.* 020 7266 1073 *email* judith.trust@lineone.net *Website* www.judithtrust.org.uk

■ The Julian Budd Kids in Sport Trust Limited

CC NO 1141615   **ESTABLISHED** 2011

WHERE FUNDING CAN BE GIVEN South-eastern England with a preference for Buckinghamshire.

WHO CAN BENEFIT Children.

WHAT IS FUNDED Sports and sporting facilities for disadvantaged children.

SAMPLE GRANTS A list of beneficiaries was unavailable. However, the accounts state that grants were used 'for the purchase of sports equipment, including sports wheelchairs for disabled youngsters, training sessions and transportation costs where needed.'

FINANCES *Year* 2011–12 *Income* £58,501 *Grants* £27,539 *Assets* £76,974

TRUSTEES Andy Bristow; Steve Brown; Roger Budd; Will Brown; Andre Calleja; Nick Davidson; Ken Dulieu; Jim Hill; Toby Hefferman; Ann Palmer; Andy Pieroux; Nigel Shirley; Nick Taylor; Simone Whitbread; David Thomas; Ann Whytewood.

HOW TO APPLY In writing to the correspondent.

WHO TO APPLY TO Roger Budd, Trustee, c/o The Clare Foundation, Wycombe Road, Saunderton, Buckinghamshire HP14 4BF *Tel.* 0300 777 7000 *email* info@kidsinsport.org *Website* www.kidsinsport.co.uk

■ The Cyril and Eve Jumbo Charitable Trust

CC NO 1097209   **ESTABLISHED** 2003

WHERE FUNDING CAN BE GIVEN Worldwide.

WHO CAN BENEFIT Charitable organisations.

WHAT IS FUNDED The objectives of the trust are: fresh water projects; projects that deal with grass roots and front line action, and that set up sustainable, ongoing projects so that people can increase their independence and create their own livelihoods; projects that help children (particularly those in countries recovering from war and trauma), older people and people with disabilities.

RANGE OF GRANTS £200–£54,000.

SAMPLE GRANTS Wherever the Need (£54,000); Jewish Care (£12,500); Promise, and World Jewish Relief (£10,000 each); Grief Encounter (£6,000); Forest School Camps (£5,000); Starlight Santa Run (£2,000); Finchley Jewish Primary School (£1,250); Sharpham Trust (£1,000); British Lung Foundation and Property Race Day (£500 each) and Leatherhead Drama Festival (£300).

FINANCES *Year* 2011–12 *Income* £100,702 *Grants* £127,345 *Assets* £1,947,547

TRUSTEES Geoffrey Allan Margolis; Rafiq Ahmed Hayat; Michaela Justice; Fred Kindall.

HOW TO APPLY In writing to the trustees, including full details of the charity who meet on a regular basis to consider applications. Unsuccessful applications are not always acknowledged.

WHO TO APPLY TO Tracy O'Sullivan, Mumbo Jumbo World, 48 Great Marlborough Street, London W1F 7BB *Tel.* 020 7437 0879 *email* tracy@mjw13.com *Website* mjw13.com

■ The Jungels-Winkler Charitable Foundation

CC NO 1073523   **ESTABLISHED** 1999

WHERE FUNDING CAN BE GIVEN UK.

WHO CAN BENEFIT Registered charities.

WHAT IS FUNDED Projects for the benefit of people who are visually impaired., with some preference for arts-related charities.

FINANCES *Year* 2012 *Income* £0 *Grants* £30,000

TRUSTEES Gabrielle Jungels-Winkler; Christopher Jungels-Winkler; Rupert Ticehurst; Alexandra Saunders.

HOW TO APPLY In writing to the correspondent.

WHO TO APPLY TO Jessica Henson, Trustee, Berwin Leighton Paisner LLP, Adelaide House, London Bridge, London EC4R 9HA *Tel.* 020 3400 1000 *email* jessica.henson@blplaw.com

■ The Anton Jurgens Charitable Trust

CC NO 259885   **ESTABLISHED** 1969

WHERE FUNDING CAN BE GIVEN UK with a preference for the south east of England.

WHO CAN BENEFIT UK registered charities.

WHAT IS FUNDED The welfare of children and young people; youth organisations; centres, clubs and institutions; community organisations; day centres and nurseries; and general welfare organisations.

TYPE OF GRANT Generally one-off.

RANGE OF GRANTS £1,000–£15,000.

SAMPLE GRANTS Silcester Parochial Council (£25,000); Highland Hospice (£15,000); Ability Net, Kid's Company and Royal School for Deaf Children – Margate (£10,000 each); child Link

Adoption Society (£8,000); the Fifth Trust (£6,000); Bucks Disability Information Network and Queen Alexandra Hospital Home (£5,000 each); Hope House (£4,000); Haemophilia Society (£3,000); Barnabas Adventure Centres and Vitalise (£2,000 each); and Bury Shopmobility (£1,000).

FINANCES *Year* 2011–12 *Income* £263,000 *Grants* £218,200 *Assets* £6,480,463

TRUSTEES Eric M. C. Deckers; Steven R. D. Jurgens; Frans A. W. Jurgens; F. A. W. Jurgens; Maria E. Edge-Jurgens; Frans C. M. Tilman.

HOW TO APPLY In writing to the correspondent. The trustees meet twice a year in June and October. The trustees do not enter into correspondence concerning grant applications beyond notifying successful applicants.

WHO TO APPLY TO Maria E. Edge-Jurgens, Trustee, Saffrey Champness, Lion House, 72–75 Red Lion Street, London WC1R 4GB *Tel.* 020 7841 4000

··

■ Jusaca Charitable Trust

CC NO 1012966   **ESTABLISHED** 1992

WHERE FUNDING CAN BE GIVEN UK, Israel and worldwide.

WHO CAN BENEFIT Registered charities.

WHAT IS FUNDED Jewish, arts, research, religion, housing.

TYPE OF GRANT Mainly recurrent.

SAMPLE GRANTS No information available.

FINANCES *Year* 2011–12 *Income* £125,179 *Grants* £172,129 *Assets* £1,383,920

TRUSTEES Ralph Neville Emanuel; Sara Jane Emanuel; Carolyn Leonora Emanuel; Maurice Seymour Emanuel; Diana Clare Franklin; Donald Franklin; Rachel Paul.

OTHER INFORMATION The trust aims to distribute at least 50% of donations to Jewish charities in the UK, overseas and Israel, and of the remainder about 40% to be donation to charities operating in the UK and about 60% outside the UK. The majority of grants are given to the same organisations each year in order to provide a long term stream of funding.

HOW TO APPLY Grants are made at the discretion of the trustees. Unsolicited applications are not encouraged.

WHO TO APPLY TO Sara Emanuel, Trustee, 17 Ashburnham Grove, London SE10 8UH

■ The Bernard Kahn Charitable Trust

CC NO 249130   **ESTABLISHED** 1965
WHERE FUNDING CAN BE GIVEN UK and Israel.
WHO CAN BENEFIT Organisations benefiting Jewish people, children and young adults, people disadvantaged by poverty, teachers, governesses and rabbis.
WHAT IS FUNDED Relief of, and assistance to, Jewish people to alleviate poverty; the advancement of religion and education.
WHAT IS NOT FUNDED Jewish causes only.
RANGE OF GRANTS £25–£45,000
SAMPLE GRANTS Marbeh Torah Trust and Achisomoch Aid Company Ltd (£23,000 each); Orthodox Council of Jerusalem Limited and Friends of Be'er Miriam (£20,000 each); Tashbar and Mishkovas Yaacov (£10,000 each); the Menorah Primary School (£5,000); the Rowans Hospice (£3,000); NW London Communal Mikvah Limited and Menorah High School (£1,000 each); Shori Torah (£400); and CRI (£100).
FINANCES *Year* 2011–12 *Income* £52,366 *Grants* £151,503 *Assets* £1,351,230
TRUSTEES Shalom Fuehrer; Yaacov Zvi Kahn.
OTHER INFORMATION Grants were made to 18 organisations totalling £152,000.
HOW TO APPLY In writing to the correspondent.
WHO TO APPLY TO Yaacov Zvi Kahn, Trustee, 24 Elmcroft Avenue, London NW11 0RR

■ The Stanley Kalms Foundation

CC NO 328368   **ESTABLISHED** 1989
WHERE FUNDING CAN BE GIVEN UK and overseas.
WHO CAN BENEFIT Organisations and individuals involved with: Orthodox Jewish education in the UK and Israel; the arts; medicine; and other secular and religious programmes.
WHAT IS FUNDED Encouragement of Orthodox Jewish education in the UK and Israel, particularly by providing scholarships, fellowships and research grants. Other areas supported include the arts, medicine and other programmes, both secular and religious.
TYPE OF GRANT One-off, research, project, bursaries and scholarships.
RANGE OF GRANTS Up to £5,000.
SAMPLE GRANTS Churchillian Centre UK, Dixons City Academy, Lifelites, Oxford Centre for Hebrew and Jewish Studies and Taxpayers Alliance (£5,000 each).
FINANCES *Year* 2011–12 *Income* £99,505 *Grants* £53,051 *Assets* £248,008
TRUSTEES Lord Kalms of Edgware; Lady Pamela Kalms; Stephen Kalms.
HOW TO APPLY In writing to the correspondent, but note that most of the trust's funds are committed to projects supported for a number of years.
WHO TO APPLY TO Jane Hunt-Cooke, 84 Brook Street, London W1K 5EH *Tel.* 020 7499 3494

■ The Kalou Foundation

CC NO 1135173   **ESTABLISHED** 2010
WHERE FUNDING CAN BE GIVEN Worldwide
WHO CAN BENEFIT Individuals and organisations.
WHAT IS FUNDED The provision of facilities in the interests of social welfare for recreation or other leisure time occupation of individuals who have need of such facilities by reason their youth, age, infirmity or disability, financial hardship or social circumstances; the relief of sickness worldwide; other general charitable purposes as determined by the trustees.
FINANCES *Year* 2011–12 *Income* £62,867 *Grants* £0 *Assets* £10
TRUSTEES Salomon Kalou; Jan De Visser; Constance Kalou.
OTHER INFORMATION The 2011–12 accounts state that charitable expenditure was £27,421. However, grant expenditure appears to be zero.
HOW TO APPLY In writing to the correspondent.
WHO TO APPLY TO Stephen Claus, Clerk to the Trustees, Brabners Chaffe Street LLP, Horton House, Exchange Flags, Liverpool L2 3YL *Tel.* 01516 003079 *email* stephen.claus@brabnerscs.com

■ The Karenza Foundation

CC NO 264520   **ESTABLISHED** 1972
WHERE FUNDING CAN BE GIVEN England and Wales.
WHO CAN BENEFIT Charitable organisations.
WHAT IS FUNDED General charitable purposes.
RANGE OF GRANTS Larger grants can be up to £30,000.
SAMPLE GRANTS Charities Aid Foundation (£20,000). Previously: Liver Cancer Surgery Appeal (£2,500); and Aid to Children Everywhere and St Catherine's Hospice (£1,000 each).
FINANCES *Year* 2011–12 *Income* £27,605 *Grants* £20,000 *Assets* £718,798
TRUSTEES E. J. Uren; A. F. Uren.
OTHER INFORMATION The grant total for 2011–12 was considerably down on previous years (2010/11: £50,000). However, income remains steady.
HOW TO APPLY In writing to the correspondent.
WHO TO APPLY TO The Trustees, No. 1 Dorset Street, Southampton, Hampshire SO15 2DP

■ The Boris Karloff Charitable Foundation

CC NO 326898   **ESTABLISHED** 1985
WHERE FUNDING CAN BE GIVEN Worldwide.
WHO CAN BENEFIT UK and local charities benefiting actors, musicians and people disadvantaged by mental or physical illness.
WHAT IS FUNDED Charities supporting the performing arts; cricket.
WHAT IS NOT FUNDED No grants for individuals or charities with large resources.
RANGE OF GRANTS £100–£10,000.
SAMPLE GRANTS Young Vic (£13,000); Surrey County Cricket (£10,000); Soho Theatre (£7,000); LAMDA, RADA, Royal Theatrical Fund and Shakespeare's Globe Trust (£5,000 each); and National Media Museum (£4,000).
FINANCES *Year* 2011–12 *Income* £59,578 *Grants* £53,423 *Assets* £2,125,706
TRUSTEES James Fairclough; Carole Fairclough; Bernard Coleman; Owen Lewis.
HOW TO APPLY In writing to the correspondent.

WHO TO APPLY TO Andrew Studd, Administrator, Russell Cooke Solicitors, 2 Putney Hill, London SW15 6AB *Tel.* 020 8789 9111 *Fax* 020 8780 1194

■ The Ian Karten Charitable Trust

CC NO 281721 ESTABLISHED 1980

WHERE FUNDING CAN BE GIVEN UK and Israel, with some local interest in Surrey and London.

WHO CAN BENEFIT CTEC Centres promoting digital inclusion for people with disabilities, and students who have been awarded Karten Scholarships by universities.

WHAT IS FUNDED The administration of centres for computer-aided training, education and communication (CTEC Centres) for people with severe physical, sensory or cognitive disabilities, or with mental health problems; scholarships for postgraduate study and research in selected subjects at selected universities and for postgraduate training; and the trust makes occasional small donations to some charities in Surrey and London.

WHAT IS NOT FUNDED No grants to individuals.

TYPE OF GRANT Projects: sometimes funded over a period of two years; charities: normally one-off, but in some cases repeated annually; universities: scholarships.

RANGE OF GRANTS £50–£150,000.

SAMPLE GRANTS Scope – Beaumont College (£86,000); Southampton (£37,000); Cedar Foundation – Northern Ireland (£26,000); Bridge College – Manchester and Linkage Colleges (£25,000 each); Percy Hedley (£22,000); Jewish Care – Redbridge (£12,000); White Lodge – Chertsey (£5,800); Jewish Care (£1,500) Commonwealth Jewish Trust and World Jewish Relief (£1,000 each); Spiro Ark (£500) and Community Security Trust (£300).

FINANCES *Year* 2011–12 *Income* £214,329 *Grants* £454,000 *Assets* £6,557,504

TRUSTEES Ian H. Karten, Chair; Mildred Karten; Tim Simon; Angela Hobbs.

OTHER INFORMATION Further funding was given for scholarships to eight institutions, including Haifa University and Southampton University, totalling £62,000; an individual scholarship of £6,800; and the sum of £2,900 was also given in small grants.

HOW TO APPLY The trust currently only considers grants to charities supported in the past. Grants are no longer being made for new CTEC centres. The trustees meet at least twice a year to review grants.

WHO TO APPLY TO Timothy Simon, Trustee, The Mill House, PO Box 386, Lymington SO41 1BD *Tel.* 01590 681345 *Fax* 01483 222420 *email* kartentrust@aol.com *Website* www.karten-network.org.uk

■ The Kasner Charitable Trust

CC NO 267510 ESTABLISHED 1974

WHERE FUNDING CAN BE GIVEN UK and Israel.

WHO CAN BENEFIT Jewish organisations.

WHAT IS FUNDED Jewish charitable purposes.

RANGE OF GRANTS £25–£20,000.

SAMPLE GRANTS British Committee for Israel and U.J.I.A. (£10,000 each); Gevurath Ari Academy Trust (£5,000); Gateshead Talmudical College (£1,600); and British Friends of Nishmas Yisroel, British Friends of Shalom, British Friends of the Hebrew University, Friends of Michas, Friends of Seret Vishnitz, Chashei Dovid, Jewish Genetic Disorder Limited, Neve

Yerushalayim and Union of Orthodox Hebrew (£100 each).

FINANCES *Year* 2011–12 *Income* £146,349 *Grants* £96,260 *Assets* £843,972

TRUSTEES Elfreda Erlich; Baruch Erlich; Josef Kasner; Elfreda Erlich.

HOW TO APPLY In writing to the correspondent. The trust gives grants to most of the organisations that apply. Certain organisations are investigated personally by the trustees and may receive larger grants.

WHO TO APPLY TO Josef Kasner, Trustee, 1a Gresham Gardens, London NW11 8NX *Tel.* 020 8455 7830

■ The Kathleen Trust

CC NO 1064516 ESTABLISHED 1997

WHERE FUNDING CAN BE GIVEN UK, with a preference for London.

WHO CAN BENEFIT Organisations benefiting young musicians.

WHAT IS FUNDED Typically course fees or instrument costs for outstanding young musicians.

SAMPLE GRANTS Oxford Chamber Music Festival (£20,000)

FINANCES *Year* 2011–12 *Income* £27,512 *Grants* £20,000 *Assets* £1,191,355

TRUSTEES E. R. H. Perks; Sir O. C. A. Scott; Lady P. A. Scott; C. N. Withington.

OTHER INFORMATION The trust's main grantmaking priority is individuals.

HOW TO APPLY In writing to the correspondent.

WHO TO APPLY TO E. R. H. Perks, Trustee, Currey and Co, 21 Buckingham Gate, London SW1E 6LS *Tel.* 020 7828 4091

■ The Michael and Ilse Katz Foundation

CC NO 263726 ESTABLISHED 1971

WHERE FUNDING CAN BE GIVEN Worldwide.

WHO CAN BENEFIT International and UK schemes and organisations benefiting Jewish people, at risk groups, and people who are disadvantaged by poverty or socially isolated.

WHAT IS FUNDED Primarily Jewish organisations. Medical/disability and welfare charities are also supported.

TYPE OF GRANT One-off and recurring.

RANGE OF GRANTS Up to £20,000.

SAMPLE GRANTS Jewish Hospice Care (£252,000); Jewish Care (£17,500); Fight for Sight (£15,000); the Worshipful Company of Butchers (£10,000); Bournemouth Orchestral Society (£8,000); Community Security Trust and Norwood Children and Families First (£7,000 each); Hannah Levy House Trust (£2,000); and Council of Christians and Jews, Variety Club of Jersey and Starlight Children's Foundation (£1,000 each).

FINANCES *Year* 2011–12 *Income* £2,060,560 *Grants* £336,000 *Assets* £2,152,165

TRUSTEES Norris Gilbert; Osman Azis.

OTHER INFORMATION Grants to organisations totalled £336,000, of which £9,500 was allocated in grants not exceeding £1,000 each.

HOW TO APPLY In writing to the correspondent

WHO TO APPLY TO Osman Azis, Trustee, Counting House, Trelill, Bodmin PL30 3HZ *Tel.* 01208 851814

■ The Katzauer Charitable Settlement

cc no 275110   **established** 1977
where funding can be given UK, but mainly Israel.
who can benefit Jewish people.
what is funded Jewish organisations, predominantly in Israel.
range of grants Up to £30,000.
sample grants Previous beneficiaries included: Chabad Ra'anana (£26,000); Moriah Community and Meir Hospital (£10,000); Nahalat Yehiel (£6,000); Mercaz Hatorah (£4,000); Rabbi K. Gross (£3,800); Kollel Ra'anana (£3,200); Friends of Lubavitch (£2,900); Beit Hatavshil (£1,000).
finances *Year* 2011–12 *Income* £3,000 *Grants* £5,500
trustees G. C. Smith; E. Moller; M. S. Bailey; W. Lian.
how to apply In writing to the correspondent.
who to apply to Walter Lian, Trustee, c/o Citroen Wells and Partners, Devonshire House, 1 Devonshire Street, London W1W 5DR *Tel.* 020 7304 2000 *email* walter.lian@citroenwells.co.uk

■ The C. S. Kaufman Charitable Trust

cc no 253194   **established** 1967
where funding can be given UK.
who can benefit Organisations benefiting Jewish people.
what is funded Mainly Jewish organisations.
range of grants Up to £30,000.
sample grants Tomchei Yotzei Anglia (£20,000); Ezer Mikoidesh Foundation (£15,000); Kollel Sha'rei Shlomo (£10,000 in two grants); Tomchei Torah Family Relief (£5,000); Jewish Teacher Training College (£3,000 in two grants); SOFT (£1,000 in four grants); Yeshiva Tiferes Yaakov (£750); and ZVT (£150).
finances *Year* 2011–12 *Income* £79,574 *Grants* £87,942 *Assets* £877,193
trustees I. I. Kaufman; L. L. Kaufman; J. J. Kaufman; S. Kaufman.
other information Many of the grants recipients received more than one grant each during the year.
how to apply In writing to the correspondent.
who to apply to The Trustees, 162 Whitehall Road, Gateshead, Tyne and Wear NE8 1TP

■ The Geoffrey John Kaye Charitable Foundation

cc no 262547   **established** 1971
where funding can be given UK and overseas.
who can benefit Jewish people.
what is funded Jewish organisations and other charitable purposes.
type of grant Largely recurrent.
sample grants Animal Shelter A.C. (£6,300).
finances *Year* 2011–12 *Income* £54,396 *Grants* £17,905 *Assets* £1,000,239
trustees G. J. Kaye; S. Rose; J. Pears.
other information Two individuals also received grants totalling £13,000.
how to apply In writing to the correspondent. Note the foundation has previously stated that funds were fully committed.

who to apply to Robert Shaw, Chartered Accountant, Macilvin Moore Reveres, 7 St John's Road, Harrow, Middlesex HA1 2EY *Tel.* 020 8863 1234 *email* charity@mmrca.co.uk

■ The Emmanuel Kaye Foundation

cc no 280281   **established** 1980
where funding can be given UK and overseas.
who can benefit Organisations benefiting medical professionals, research workers, scientists, Jewish people, at-risk groups, people who are disadvantaged by poverty and socially isolated people.
what is funded Medical research, welfare and Jewish organisations.
what is not funded Only registered charities are supported.
range of grants £50–£25,000.
sample grants Previously: St James Conservation Trust (£6,000); Imperial College London and Nightingale (£5,000 each); Royal Academy of Arts and St Michael's Hospice – North Hampshire (£2,500 each); Jewish Care, the Holocaust Education Trust, Shaare Zedek UK, Community Links Trust, Laniado UK and UK Friends of Magen David Adom (£2,000 each); and Caius (£1,500).
finances *Year* 2011–12 *Income* £23,683 *Grants* £25,359
trustees David Kaye; John Forster; Michael Cutler.
other information Accounts were received at the Charity Commission but due to the low income were not published online.
how to apply In writing to the correspondent.
who to apply to The Secretary to the Trustees, Oakleigh House, High Street, Hartley Wintney, Hampshire RG27 8PE *Tel.* 01252 843773

■ The Caron Keating Foundation

cc no 1106160   **established** 2004
where funding can be given UK
who can benefit Small but significant cancer charities and support groups.
what is not funded No grants to individuals.
sample grants Action Cancer Belfast; The Lavender Touch; The Rosemary Foundation; Sarah Lee Trust; Variety Club; and the Rainbow Centre.
finances *Year* 2011–12 *Income* £199,505 *Grants* £0 *Assets* £1,064,378
trustees M. Keating; G. Hunniford.
other information No grants were made during the year due to illness in the trustee's family. Shortly after the year end over £250,000 was paid out in grants, which will appear in the next accounts.
how to apply In writing to the correspondent.
who to apply to Mary Clifford Day, PO Box 122, Sevenoaks, Kent TN13 1UM *email* info@caronkeating.org *Website* www.caronkeating.org

■ The Soli and Leah Kelaty Trust Fund

cc no 1077620   **established** 1999
where funding can be given Not defined.
who can benefit Registered charities.
what is funded General, education, overseas aid, religion
sample grants No list of grant beneficiaries was available.

FINANCES *Year* 2011–12 *Income* £25,000
Grants £25,409
TRUSTEES David Lerer; Frederick Kelaty; Sharon
Mozel Kelaty.
HOW TO APPLY In writing to the correspondent.
WHO TO APPLY Frederick Kelaty, Trustee, Block O,
OCC Building, 105 Eade Road, London N4 1TJ
Tel. 020 8800 2000 *email* freddy.kelaty@
asiatic.co.uk

■ The Kelly Family Charitable Trust

CC NO 1102440   **ESTABLISHED** 2004
WHERE FUNDING CAN BE GIVEN UK.
WHO CAN BENEFIT Registered charities that support
and encourage family welfare and cohesion.
WHAT IS FUNDED 'The trust has decided to prioritise
its funding in favour of charities whose activities
involve all or most family members in initiatives
that support and encourage the family to work
as a cohesive unit in tackling problems that
face one or more of its members. The overall
objective is to reinforce the potential benefit and
support that family members as a unit can give
to each other. Applications are also welcomed
from sports and health-related charities whose
activities comply with the above criteria.'
WHAT IS NOT FUNDED The following will not be
considered: non-registered charities; grants
directly to individuals; national charities (only
regional projects will be considered); general
appeals; organisations with specific religious or
political agendas.
TYPE OF GRANT Capital and revenue grants; core
funding as well as project-based grants.
RANGE OF GRANTS £1,000–£10,000.
SAMPLE GRANTS Homestart Teesside; Quaker Social
Action; Westminster Befriending; Winchester
Young Carers; Relate North East; Parent to
Parent Dundee; Survive; Guy's Gift; Moira
Anderson Foundation; Homestart Perth;
Relationship Scotland (Orkneys); Families
Talking and Meningitis Trust.
FINANCES *Year* 2011–12 *Income* £131,534
Grants £135,324 *Assets* £2,643,691
TRUSTEES Annie Kelly; Brian Mattingley; Jenny Kelly;
Sheldon Cordell; Michael Field; Emma Maier.
OTHER INFORMATION Applications are welcomed from
sports and health-related charities and
particularly from relatively new organisations to
help them become established.
HOW TO APPLY Applications should be made using
the application form, which can be downloaded
from the trust's website. Applications should be
sent by email, and should be supported by
annual accounts where available. Grants are
awarded twice a year to charities and are
usually for amount between £1,000 and
£5,000, but the trustees will consider requests
for higher amounts. Applications must be
submitted by 1 March and 1 September to be
considered at the subsequent meeting. The
trustees will ask for more detail for those
applications that pass the initial screening and
may visit the projects they wish to support.
WHO TO APPLY Stuart Armstrong, Administrator,
8 Mansfield Place, Edinburgh EH3 6NB
Tel. 01313 154879 *email* s.armstrong@kfct.org
Website www.kfct.org.uk

■ Kelsick's Educational Foundation

CC NO 526956   **ESTABLISHED** 1723
WHERE FUNDING CAN BE GIVEN Lakes parish
(Ambleside, Grasmere, Langdale and part of
Troutbeck).
WHO CAN BENEFIT Organisations and individuals
under 25 years of age.
WHAT IS FUNDED Educational needs of individuals;
organisations providing educational benefit to
those under 25. School activities such as
educational visits, field trips, music lessons.
Academic courses and apprenticeships including
equipment.
WHAT IS NOT FUNDED Holidays, course items without
receipts.
TYPE OF GRANT Capital and project support, for
longer than three years.
RANGE OF GRANTS Usually £50–£3,000. With large
grants of up to £50,000 given to schools.
SAMPLE GRANTS Large grants of over £30,000 were
given to Ambleside, Grasmere and Langdale
Primary Schools.
FINANCES *Year* 2011–12 *Income* £366,649
Grants £261,612 *Assets* £6,808,134
TRUSTEES Peter Jackson; Linda Dixon; Leslie
Johnson; Nigel Hutchinson; John Halstead;
Angela Renouf; Helen Fuller; Norman Tyson;
Reginald Curphey; Cannon William Coke;
Nicholas Martin.
OTHER INFORMATION £110,000 to individuals; and
£151,000 to organisations.
HOW TO APPLY Application forms are available from
the correspondent and from the website. The
Kelsick Foundation office is open Monday-Friday:
9.30 to 12.30.
WHO TO APPLY Peter Gordon Frost, Clerk, Kelsick
Centre, St Mary's Lane, Ambleside, Cumbria
LA22 9DG *Tel.* 01539 431289 *Fax* 01539
431292 *email* john@kelsick.plus.com
Website www.kelsick.org.uk

■ The Kemp–Welch Charitable Trust

CC NO 263501   **ESTABLISHED** 1972
WHERE FUNDING CAN BE GIVEN UK.
WHO CAN BENEFIT National and local charities.
WHAT IS FUNDED Medical research, parochial church
councils, care and welfare of both children and
the elderly and educational establishments, arts
and culture, wildlife and the environment.
RANGE OF GRANTS £100 to £5,000.
SAMPLE GRANTS Winchester College (£5,000); Game
and Wildlife Conservation Trust (£2,500);
Cancer Vaccine Institute and National Portrait
Gallery (£1,000 each); The Black Watch
Heritage Appeal, Maytree Respite Centre and
Macmillan Cancer Support (£500 each); Stanley
Hall Opera and The Afghanistan Trust (£250
each) and Save the Children (£100).
FINANCES *Year* 2011–12 *Income* £34,482
Grants £24,200 *Assets* £1,005,496
TRUSTEES Sir John Kemp–Welch; Lady Diana
Elisabeth Kemp–Welch.
OTHER INFORMATION In 2011–12 grants were given
to 41 organisations.
HOW TO APPLY No unsolicited applications.
WHO TO APPLY Sir John Kemp–Welch, Trustee,
74 Melton Court, Onslow Crescent, London
SW7 3JH *Tel.* 020 7581 2164

■ The Kay Kendall Leukaemia Fund

CC NO 290772   **ESTABLISHED** 1984

WHO CAN BENEFIT Organisations conducting research into and treatment of leukaemia.

WHAT IS FUNDED Medical research into and treatment of leukaemia.

WHAT IS NOT FUNDED Circular appeals for general support are not funded.

TYPE OF GRANT Research, capital, equipment, fellowships.

SAMPLE GRANTS Institute of Cancer Research (£489,000); University College London Hospitals Charitable Foundation (£300,000); Paterson Institute for Cancer Research, School of Cancer and enabling Sciences (£233,000); The Teenage Cancer Trust (£150,000); Churchill Hospital (£120,000); Lingen Davies Cancer Research Fund (£100,000); Cardiff University, Department of Haematology (£62,000) and Royal Marsden NHS Trust (£60,000).

FINANCES *Year* 2011–12 *Income* £1,309,000 *Grants* £5,164,000 *Assets* £33,687,000

TRUSTEES Judith Portrait; Timothy J. Sainsbury; Charles Metcalfe.

OTHER INFORMATION The trust is one of the Sainsbury Family Charitable Trusts which share a common administration. An application to one is taken as an application to all.

HOW TO APPLY A preliminary letter or telephone call to the administration offices of the Kay Kendall Leukaemia Fund may be helpful to determine whether or not a proposal is likely to be eligible. Application forms are available by contacting the trust's office. 'Applicants should complete the approved Application Form and include a research proposal (aims, background, plan of investigation, justification for budget). The research proposal should be three to five single-spaced pages for project grants (excluding references, costings and CV) and up to ten single-spaced pages for programme grants. Applications should be submitted by email in addition to the provision of a hard copy with original signature. The trustees will take account of annual inflation and of salary increases related to nationally negotiated pay scales and these should not be built into the application. Salaries should generally be on nationally agreed scales. Tenured or non-time-limited appointments will not be supported. The trustees may, from time to time, set special conditions for the award of a grant. Final decision on the award of a grant is made by the trustees, having taken into account advice from their scientific advisers. The trustees consider proposals twice each year, normally May and October. To allow for the refereeing process, new full proposals for the May meeting should be received by 28 February and for the October/November meeting by 15 July. Late applications may be deferred for six months.

WHO TO APPLY TO Alan Bookbinder, Director, The Peak, 5 Wilton Road, London SW1V 1AP *Tel.* 020 7410 0330 *email* info@kklf.org.uk *Website* www.kklf.org.uk

■ William Kendall's Charity (Wax Chandlers' Company)

CC NO 228361   **ESTABLISHED** 1559

WHERE FUNDING CAN BE GIVEN Greater London and the London borough of Bexley.

WHO CAN BENEFIT Charitable organisations in Greater London working for relief of need; in Bexley, charitable organisations generally.

WHAT IS FUNDED Most donations are for relief of need in London.

WHAT IS NOT FUNDED Grants are not normally made to large charities, charities whose accounts disclose substantial reserves or non-registered charities. Grants are not made to replace cuts in funding made by local authorities or others, schemes or activities which would be regarded as relieving central or local government of their statutory responsibilities or cover deficits already incurred.

TYPE OF GRANT One-off or recurring.

RANGE OF GRANTS £500–£25,000, typical grant £5,000.

SAMPLE GRANTS Copenhagen Youth Project (£27,000); Westside School (£10,000); City of London ACF (£6,000); King Henry's Walk Garden (£4,000); National Autistic Society Bexley, Complementary Cancer Care Trust, Woodlands Farm and 1st Footscray Scouts Group (£2,000 each) and Disabled Christian Fellowship (£500).

FINANCES *Year* 2011–12 *Income* £86,400 *Grants* £82,109 *Assets* £3,057,686

TRUSTEE Wax Chandlers' Company.

HOW TO APPLY The company undertakes its own research and does not respond to unsolicited applications.

WHO TO APPLY TO Georgina Brown, The Clerk to the Wax Chandlers' Company, Wax Chandlers' Hall, 6 Gresham Street, London EC2V 7AD *Tel.* 020 7606 3591 *Fax* 020 7600 5462 *email* info@chandlers.ndonet.com *Website* www.waxchandlers.org.uk/charity

■ The Kennedy Charitable Foundation

CC NO 1052001   **ESTABLISHED** 1995

WHERE FUNDING CAN BE GIVEN Unrestricted, but mainly Ireland with a preference for County Mayo and County Sligo.

WHO CAN BENEFIT Registered charities and individuals.

WHAT IS FUNDED Predominantly organisations connected with the Roman Catholic faith, mainly in Ireland.

RANGE OF GRANTS £200–£50,000; typical grant £1,000–£5,000.

SAMPLE GRANTS Newman Institute (£87,000); Ballintubber Abbey Trust (£23,000); Lower Shankhill Community Association (£18,000); Elizabeth Hardie Ferguson Trust (£10,000); St Ann's Hospice (£6,000); Archdiocese of Cardiff and Diocese of Hexham and Newcastle (£5,000 each); Destination Florida, Lancaster Roman Catholic Diocese Trustees and St Vincent de Paul Society – Wythenshawe (£2,000 each); East Belfast Mission and Society of African Missions (£1,000 each); Leukaemia Research (£500); and NSPCC (£100).

FINANCES *Year* 2011–12 *Income* £98,085 *Grants* £155,988 *Assets* £186,912

TRUSTEES Patrick James Kennedy; Kathleen Kennedy; John Gerard Kennedy; Patrick Joseph Francis Kennedy; Anna Maria Kelly.

HOW TO APPLY The foundation says that 'unsolicited applications are not accepted'.

WHO TO APPLY TO The Trustees, 12th Floor, Bank House, Charlotte Street, Manchester M1 4ET *Tel.* 01612 368191 *Fax* 01612 364814 *email* kcf@pye158.freeserve.co.uk

....

■ The John Thomas Kennedy Charitable Foundation

CC NO 1082421   **ESTABLISHED** 2000
WHERE FUNDING CAN BE GIVEN UK and overseas.
WHO CAN BENEFIT Registered charities.
WHAT IS FUNDED General charitable purposes.
WHAT IS NOT FUNDED No grants to individuals
SAMPLE GRANTS The Cardinal Hume Centre and Co-operation Ireland (£10,000 each); Macmillan Cancer Support (£9,500); SMA Fathers and Signpost Stockport for Carers (£5,000 each); Cheethams School of Music (£2,500); Lupus UK (£2,000); and Broughton House, Friends of Westminster Cathedral and Manchester Outward Bound Association (£1,000 each).
FINANCES *Year* 2012 *Income* £108,000 *Grants* £112,486 *Assets* £1,452,722
TRUSTEES John Kennedy; Veronica Kennedy; Nicholas Shaw.
HOW TO APPLY In writing to the correspondent.
WHO TO APPLY TO John Kennedy, Trustee, Reedham House, 31 King Street West, Manchester M3 2PJ *Tel.* 01618 342574

....

■ The Kennel Club Charitable Trust

CC NO 327802   **ESTABLISHED** 1988
WHERE FUNDING CAN BE GIVEN UK.
WHO CAN BENEFIT Registered charities or research bodies benefiting dogs; research workers and vets; and people who are disabled blind or deaf where dogs are involved (e.g. in support of human beings).
WHAT IS FUNDED The trust describes its objects as 'science, welfare and support'. It supports the furthering of research into canine diseases and hereditary disorders of dogs and also organisations concerned with the welfare of dogs in need and those which aim to improve the quality of life of humans by promoting dogs as practical or therapeutic aids.
WHAT IS NOT FUNDED The trust does not give grants directly to individuals; veterinary nurses can apply to the British Veterinary Nursing Association where bursaries are available. The trustees tend not to favour funding the costs of building work.
TYPE OF GRANT One-off and recurring for set periods.
RANGE OF GRANTS The trust gives both ongoing and one–off grants.
SAMPLE GRANTS Animal Health Trust (£250,000); Hearing Dogs for Deaf People (£30,000); Support Dogs (£24,000); Mayhew Animal Rescue Home and Stokenchurch Dog Rescue (£10,000 each); Pets as Therapy (£7,000); BAARK (£6,000); Bristol Dog Action Welfare Group (£3,000); and Bulldog Rescue and Rehoming Trust and Supporters of Stray and Abandoned Dogs (£2,000 each).
FINANCES *Year* 2012 *Income* £727,995 *Grants* £703,440 *Assets* £2,498,297
TRUSTEES Michael Townsend; Bill King; Steven Dean; Michael Herrtage; John Spurling; Jennifer Fairhall.
OTHER INFORMATION Grants were divided into 'scientific and research project support' which

amounted to £383,000, and 'other grants' totalling £320,000.
HOW TO APPLY Information taken from the trust's website: 'You should state clearly the specific details of the costs for which you are requesting funding, and for what purpose and over what period the funding is required. The trustees meet four times a year and will wish to see your organisation's latest audited and signed report and accounts and (if applicable) the registered number of your charity. Generally, pure building costs or requests from organisations whose concern is not predominantly with the dog (e.g. general animal-sanctuaries) do not receive favourable attention from the trustees. Similarly, grants are rarely made to individuals and not to organisations having a political reason. Grants which are payable over a number of years will be subject to a satisfactory annual review and report of progress. Send information to: Mr Richard Fairlamb (email), The Kennel Club, 1–5 Clarges Street, London W1J 8AB. Tel: 020 7518 6874, fax: 020 7518 1014.'
WHO TO APPLY TO Richard Fairlamb, Administrator, 1–5 Clarges Street, Piccadilly, London W1J 8AB *Tel.* 020 7518 6874 *Fax* 020 7518 1014 *email* dholford@the-kennel-club.org.uk *Website* www.thekennelclub.org.uk/charitabletrust

....

■ Kent Community Foundation

CC NO 1084361   **ESTABLISHED** 2001
WHERE FUNDING CAN BE GIVEN Kent.
WHO CAN BENEFIT Local charities, community groups and voluntary organisations and individuals.
WHAT IS FUNDED Improving the quality of life for people in Kent. The foundation administers a number of funds established by individuals, families and companies. In addition it has its own general fund which enables it to support voluntary groups which fall outside the stated criteria of these funds.
RANGE OF GRANTS £100–£600,000.
FINANCES *Year* 2011–12 *Income* £6,176,332 *Grants* £3,763,381 *Assets* £8,635,462
TRUSTEES Arthur Gulland; Bella Coltrain; Peter Lake; Peter Williams; Ann West; Tim Bull; Vicki Jessel; Georgina Warner; Sarah Hohler.
OTHER INFORMATION Grant schemes change frequently. Consult the foundation's website for details of current programmes and their deadlines.
HOW TO APPLY Further information on applications can be obtained from the Grants Team: admin@kentcf.org.uk
WHO TO APPLY TO Carol Lynch, Chief Executive Officer, 23 Evegate Park Barn, Evegate, Smeeth, Kent TN25 6SX *Tel.* 01303 814500 *email* admin@kentcf.org.uk *Website* www.kentcf.org.uk

....

■ The Nancy Kenyon Charitable Trust

CC NO 265359   **ESTABLISHED** 1972
WHERE FUNDING CAN BE GIVEN UK.
WHO CAN BENEFIT Registered charities only.
WHAT IS FUNDED General charitable purposes. Primarily for people and causes known to the trustees.
RANGE OF GRANTS Up to £11,000.
SAMPLE GRANTS Nancy Oldfield Trust (£10,500); St Nicholas Church, Ashchurch (£3,500); One More Child (£3,000); The Good Shepherd Project and

Think carefully about every application. Is it justified?

....

673

The Starfish Cafe, Cambodia (£2,000 each); Cheltenham Youth for Christ and the Starfish Cafe – Cambodia (£2,000 each); Church Mission Society (£1,500); African Workshop, Epic Arts and Earls Court Community Project (£1,000 each) and Cheltenham Youth for Christ and The Family Haven (£500 each).

FINANCES *Year* 2011–12 *Income* £47,399 *Grants* £40,993 *Assets* £1,476,377

TRUSTEES Lucy Phipps; Maureen Kenyon; Christopher Kenyon; Sally Kenyon; Peter Kenyon; Kieron Kenyon.

OTHER INFORMATION The grant total includes £7,000 that was awarded to individuals.

HOW TO APPLY In writing to the correspondent at any time. Applications for causes not known to the trustees are considered annually in December.

WHO TO APPLY TO Alison Smith, c/o Brook Financial Management Ltd, Meads Barn, Ashwell Business Park, Ilminster, Somerset TA19 9DX *Tel.* 01460 259852

■ Keren Association

CC NO 313119				**ESTABLISHED** 1961
WHERE FUNDING CAN BE GIVEN UK and Israel.
WHO CAN BENEFIT Organisations benefiting children, young adults and Jewish people.
WHAT IS FUNDED The advancement of education; the provision of religious instruction and training in traditional Judaism; general charitable purposes.
SAMPLE GRANTS Previous beneficiaries include: Beis Aharon Trust, Yeshivah Belz Machnovke, U T A, Yetev Lev Jerusalem, Lomdei Tom h Belz Machnovke, Friends of Beis Yaakov, Yeshivat Lomdei Torah, Friends of Arad, Kupat Gmach Vezer Nlsuin, Clwk Yaakov and British Heart Foundation.
FINANCES *Year* 2010–11 *Income* £10,960,910 *Grants* £6,809,790 *Assets* £42,642,028
TRUSTEES E. Englander, Chair; S. Englander; Pinkus Englander; S. Z. Englander; Jacob Englander; H. Z. Weiss; N. Weiss.
OTHER INFORMATION Unfortunately at the time of writing (November 2013) the trust's latest accounts were almost a year overdue with the Charity Commission. A list of grant recipients was not included in the accounts.
HOW TO APPLY In writing to the correspondent.
WHO TO APPLY TO S. Englander, Trustee, 136 Clapton Common, London E5 9AG

■ Kermaville Ltd

CC NO 266075				**ESTABLISHED** 1973
WHERE FUNDING CAN BE GIVEN UK, Israel.
WHO CAN BENEFIT Organisations benefiting Jewish people.
WHAT IS FUNDED Advancement of religion according to the Orthodox Jewish faith and general charitable purposes.
SAMPLE GRANTS Previous beneficiaries include: Yeshivas Imrei Chaim Spinka, Bais Rochel D'Satmar, Keren Tzedoka Vochesed, Kollel Congregation Yetev Lev, Kollel Atzei Chaim, United Talmudical Association, Ponevez Beth Hamedrash and Lolev Charitable Trust.
FINANCES *Year* 2012–13 *Income* £14,960 *Grants* £14,745
TRUSTEE L. Rabinowitz.
HOW TO APPLY In writing to the correspondent.
WHO TO APPLY TO M. Freund, 3 Overlea Road, London E5 9BG *Tel.* 020 8806 5783

■ E. and E. Kernkraut Charities Limited

CC NO 275636				**ESTABLISHED** 1978
WHERE FUNDING CAN BE GIVEN UK.
WHO CAN BENEFIT Charitable organisations.
WHAT IS FUNDED General charitable purposes, Jewish and education.
FINANCES *Year* 2011–12 *Income* £897,381 *Grants* £402,795 *Assets* £6,252,818
TRUSTEES Eli Kernkraut; Esther Kernkraut; Joseph Kernkraut; Jacob Kernkraut.
OTHER INFORMATION Accounts were on file at the Charity Commission, but without a list of grants.
HOW TO APPLY In writing to the correspondent.
WHO TO APPLY TO Eli Kernkraut, Trustee, Eli Kernkraut, The Knoll, Fountayne Road, London N16 7EA *Tel.* 020 8806 7947

■ The Peter Kershaw Trust

CC NO 268934				**ESTABLISHED** 1974
WHERE FUNDING CAN BE GIVEN Manchester and the surrounding district only.
WHO CAN BENEFIT Recipients must be medical or registered charitable organisations or educational establishments normally located in Greater Manchester or north Cheshire.
WHAT IS FUNDED Social welfare; medical research, especially in the field of oncology; educational bursaries.
WHAT IS NOT FUNDED No grants to individuals or for building projects.
TYPE OF GRANT One-off or core costs. Also research, running costs, salaries and start-up costs. Funding may be given for up to three years. For grants of more than one year a report is required before years two and three are confirmed.
RANGE OF GRANTS Up to £25,000.
SAMPLE GRANTS N-Gage (£25,000); South Chadderton Methodist Church (£15,000); Factory Youth Zone (£12,500); Bolton School (£6,000); Broughton House, Manchester Grammar School and Commitment in Communities (£5,000 each); Cornerstone Day Centre, Depaul UK and Disability Snowsport UK (£2,000 each); Ace Centre North (£1,500); and ECHG Sash Project and ECHG Stopover (£500 each).
FINANCES *Year* 2011–12 *Income* £194,623 *Grants* £155,177 *Assets* £6,409,427
TRUSTEES David Tully; Margaret Rushbrooke; Richard Kershaw; Rosemary Adams; Tim Page.
OTHER INFORMATION David Tully and Peter Kershaw are also trustees of Edward Holt Trust (Charity Commission no. 224741) and The Booth Charities (Charity Commission no. 221800); David Tully is also a trustee of CHR Charitable Trust (Charity Commission no. 213579); and Tim Page is also a trustee of Cheadle Royal Industries Charitable Trust (Charity Commission no. 509813).
HOW TO APPLY In writing to the correspondent, however the trust is always oversubscribed. The trustees normally meet twice a year in May and November to consider recommendations for grant aid which will be disbursed in June and December respectively. The trustees' report for 2011/12 states that 'applications for social welfare grants and medical research are received by the secretary in writing. These must give an outline of the organisation and the project for which financial assistance is being sought, together with budgetary forecasts and a copy of the latest financial accounts. Applications for school bursaries are usually

made by the relevant educational establishment on behalf of the pupil. These must give the background to the family circumstances of the pupil together with a financial statement and a justification for why the trust should continue to support the pupil.'

WHO TO APPLY TO Bryan Peak, Administrator, 22 Ashworth Park, Knutsford, Cheshire WA16 9DE *Tel.* 01565 651086 *email* pkershawtrust@btinternet.com *Website* www.peterkershawtrust.org

■ Keswick Hall Trust

CC NO 311246   **ESTABLISHED** 1968
WHERE FUNDING CAN BE GIVEN England, Wales, East Anglia
WHO CAN BENEFIT University of East Anglia, its teachers and students (especially student teachers) and corporate organisations in the dioceses of Ely, Norwich and St Edmundsbury and Ipswich.
WHAT IS FUNDED Grants to support the education and training of religious education (RE) teachers and students, corporate grants to support the teaching of RE, and research and development grants in that subject.
WHAT IS NOT FUNDED The trust does not make grants for buildings, courses in pastoral work or courses which are purely for personal interest. Retrospective applications will not be considered. If an application is received from a student who has already started a course, but has not yet completed it, the application will not be regarded as a retrospective application. The trustees state that they give priority to their own initiatives.
RANGE OF GRANTS Up to £15,000
SAMPLE GRANTS Aldeburgh Parochial Church Council (£15,000); Church Schools East (£11,000); University of East Anglia (£7,500); Reverence for Life (£2,500); and Watson Symposium (£2,000).
FINANCES *Year* 2011–12 *Income* £224,535 *Grants* £71,132 *Assets* £4,052,301
TRUSTEES Andy Mash; David Hicks; Revd Dr Patrick Richmond; David Briggs; Doreen Bartlett; David Broom; Jane Sheat; Jacqueline Watson; Peter Maxwell; Tricia Pritchard.
OTHER INFORMATION The grant total includes £27,000 that was given to 12 individuals
HOW TO APPLY Grant applications should be received by the beginning of the months of January, May or September each year and must be made online at the Keswick Hall Charity website. Preliminary approaches for advice about applications are welcomed by email.
WHO TO APPLY TO Malcolm Green, PO Box 307, Woodbridge IP13 6WL *Tel.* 07760 433409 *email* admin@keswickhalltrust.org.uk *Website* www.keswickhalltrust.org.uk

■ Kettering and District Charitable Medical Trust

CC NO 277063   **ESTABLISHED** 1979
WHERE FUNDING CAN BE GIVEN Kettering and district.
WHO CAN BENEFIT Hospitals and community organisations.
WHAT IS FUNDED Medical equipment.
WHAT IS NOT FUNDED No grants to individuals.
RANGE OF GRANTS Up to £22,000
SAMPLE GRANTS Kettering General – Patient Monitors (£22,000); Kettering General – Refractor (£9,000); Rothwell and Desborough

Surgery – Dermatoscope (£5,000); Summerdale Medical Centre – ECG Machine (£2,000); BRA Group – Tattoo Machine (£1,000) and Headlands Surgery – Induction Loop etc. (£250).
FINANCES *Year* 2012 *Income* £10,394 *Grants* £60,000
TRUSTEES Robert Smith; Gareth Ogden; Martin Hill.
HOW TO APPLY In writing to the correspondent. The trust meets twice a year.
WHO TO APPLY TO Gareth Ogden, Trustee, 73 Windermere Road, Kettering, Northamptonshire NN16 8UF

■ The Ursula Keyes Trust

CC NO 517200   **ESTABLISHED** 1985
WHERE FUNDING CAN BE GIVEN Chester.
WHO CAN BENEFIT Individuals and institutions benefiting at risk groups, and people who are disadvantaged by poverty, socially isolated or sick.
WHAT IS FUNDED The purpose of the trust is to support the financial needs of various organisations and individuals in the Chester area, particularly in the fields of health and social care. A wide range of causes are supported, including cultural and leisure projects, particularly when matched by other fundraising efforts. Funds are mainly directed at the cost of capital projects and equipment rather than as a source of funding for ongoing running costs or salaries. National charities are also considered for support if there is a clear link to a local beneficiary.
WHAT IS NOT FUNDED No support for students or political groups.
TYPE OF GRANT Small and large grants.
RANGE OF GRANTS Most are for under £10,000.
SAMPLE GRANTS Countess of Chester NHS Hospital and King's School (£20,000 each); Marie Curie Cancer Care (£13,000); Claire House (£10,000); Children's Adventure Trust and Chester Childbirth Appeal (£5,000 each); NeuroMuscular Centre (£4,000); Hospice of the Good Shepherd (£3,500); Army Cadet Forces Association and Tarporley War Memorial Hospital (£2,500 each) and Shelter, Deafblind UK and Huntington's Disease Association (£1,000 each).
FINANCES *Year* 2012 *Income* £314,404 *Grants* £168,008 *Assets* £4,958,747
TRUSTEES J. F. Kane; Dr Ian Russell; J. R. Leaman; Euan Elliott; Harold Shaw; John Brimelow; Dr Peter Reid.
OTHER INFORMATION The 2012 grant total includes £36,500 given to individuals.
HOW TO APPLY In writing to the correspondent, together with a form available to download from the website. Applications are considered at the trustees' quarterly meetings in January, April, July and October.
WHO TO APPLY TO Dot Lawless, c/o Baker Tilly, Steam Mill, Chester, Cheshire CH3 5AN *Tel.* 01244 505100 *Fax* 01244 505101 *Website* www.ursula-keyes-trust.org.uk

■ The Mr and Mrs Paul Killik Charitable Trust

CC NO 1145428   **ESTABLISHED** 2012
WHERE FUNDING CAN BE GIVEN UK and overseas.
WHO CAN BENEFIT Registered charities.
WHAT IS FUNDED General charitable purposes, with a specific interest in education, social welfare,

religious activities and the arts. There is a stated preference for overseas aid, although no countries or regions are specified.

TRUSTEES Paul Killik; Karen Killik; Killik and Co Trustees Limited.

OTHER INFORMATION The settlor of the trust, Paul Killik, is a stockbroker and also a trustee of ShareGift (the Orr Mackintosh Foundation).

HOW TO APPLY In writing to the correspondent.

WHO TO APPLY TO Killik and Co Trustees Limited, c/o Killik and Co, Crown House, Crown Street, Ipswich IP1 3HS *Tel.* 020 7337 0500 *email* trusts@killik.com

■ The Robert Kiln Charitable Trust

CC NO 262756   **ESTABLISHED** 1970

WHERE FUNDING CAN BE GIVEN UK, with a special interest in Hertfordshire and Bedfordshire. Occasionally overseas.

WHAT IS FUNDED General charitable purposes with a preference for small organisations.

WHAT IS NOT FUNDED Applications from individuals, large national appeals, churches, schools or artistic projects (such as theatre groups) will not be considered.

TYPE OF GRANT Usually one-off, or instalments for particular projects.

RANGE OF GRANTS £250–£3,500. Mostly £500.

SAMPLE GRANTS Hertford Symphony Orchestra (Children's concert) (£3,500); Ashridge and Flagfen (£2,000 each); North West Wales Dendrochronology Project, Scottish Society for Northern Studies and University of Sheffield (Viking Camp) (£1,500 each); Penmaenmawr Historical Society (£1,200) and Orkney Archaeology Society and Morlaggan Rural Settlement Group (£1,000 each).

FINANCES *Year* 2011–12 *Income* £49,820 *Grants* £40,096 *Assets* £863,123

TRUSTEES Stephen Kiln; Barbara Kiln; Dr Nicholas Akers; Janet Akers.

OTHER INFORMATION The trust stated: 'Most of the income is allocated to regular beneficiaries, where relationship has been built up over many years (55%). The trustees are keen to support new projects, particularly those from small local organisations. The trustees support many charities where they have a particular interest.'

HOW TO APPLY In writing to the correspondent, setting out as much information as seems relevant and, if possible, costings and details of any other support. The trust no longer has twice-yearly distribution meetings and will endeavour to distribute funds within one month of receiving applications, subject to funds being available. The trust does not acknowledge receipt of applications unless an sae is enclosed.

WHO TO APPLY TO Sarah Howell, Secretary to the Trustees, 15a Bull Plain, Hertford SG14 1DX *Tel.* 01992 554962 *email* kilntrust@hemscott.net

■ The Eric and Margaret Kinder Charitable Trust

CC NO 1136528   **ESTABLISHED** 2010

WHERE FUNDING CAN BE GIVEN UK, with a preference for North West England.

WHO CAN BENEFIT Individuals and organisations with a preference for children and young people.

WHAT IS FUNDED Priorities are the advancement of education of young people in music in the North West and assisting in the treatment of Alzheimer's disease.

SAMPLE GRANTS Royal Liverpool Philharmonic (£10,000); Royal Northern College of Music (£3,000).

FINANCES *Year* 2011–12 *Income* £201,205 *Grants* £13,000 *Assets* £956,697

TRUSTEES M. Harris; Ms K. M. Allen; C. W. Kinder.

HOW TO APPLY In writing to the correspondent.

WHO TO APPLY TO The Trustees, Wrigleys LLP, Solicitors, 17–21 Cookridge Street, Leeds LS2 3AG *Tel.* 01132 045724

■ The King Henry VIII Endowed Trust – Warwick

CC NO 232862   **ESTABLISHED** 1964

WHERE FUNDING CAN BE GIVEN The former borough of Warwick only.

WHO CAN BENEFIT Half the income goes to Warwick churches, 30% to Warwick Independent Schools Foundation and 20% for the 'Town Share' – general charitable purposes for the inhabitants of the town of Warwick.

WHAT IS FUNDED General charitable purposes in the former borough of Warwick (in effect now covered by the postcode area CV34). (The grant total in this entry only applies to the grants for general charitable purposes.)

RANGE OF GRANTS Up to £50,000

SAMPLE GRANTS Beneficiaries of the 'Town Share' of the trust's income included: Myton School (£47,000); Warwick Apprenticing Charities (£30,000); Northgate Methodist Church (£17,000); Myton Hospice (£10,000); Warwick Sports Club (£5,000); West End Senior Citizens Club (£3,000) and Heritage Education and Culture WCC (£1,000).

FINANCES *Year* 2012 *Income* £1,456,140 *Grants* £160,032 *Assets* £24,090,033

TRUSTEE Trustees names not disclosed – dispensation given.

OTHER INFORMATION The sum of £1.1 million was distributed in total.

HOW TO APPLY On a form available to download, together with guidelines and criteria, from the trust's website. Trustees meet to make grants six times a year.

WHO TO APPLY TO Jonathan Wassall, Clerk and Receiver, 12 High Street, Warwick CV34 4AP *Tel.* 01926 495533 *Fax* 01926 401464 *email* jwassall@kinghenryviii.org.uk *Website* www.kinghenryviii.org.uk

■ The King/Cullimore Charitable Trust

CC NO 1074928   **ESTABLISHED** 1999

WHERE FUNDING CAN BE GIVEN UK.

WHO CAN BENEFIT Charitable organisations.

WHAT IS FUNDED General charitable purposes.

RANGE OF GRANTS From £500 up to £150,000.

SAMPLE GRANTS Splash (£150,000); Jubilee Sailing Trust and Scannappeal (£25,000 each); Countryside Foundation for Education (£20,000); Sussex Snowdrop Trust (£15,000); Woodland Trust, Alzheimer's Research UK and London Youth (£10,000 each); Leukaemia and Lymphoma Research (£7,500); Music in Hospitals (£5,000); and Chiltern MS Centre and St Agnes Pre-School (£2,000 each).

FINANCES *Year* 2011–12 *Income* £715,783 *Grants* £333,608 *Assets* £6,325,519

TRUSTEES Christopher King; Peter Cullimore; Alastair McKechnie; Christopher Gardner.

HOW TO APPLY In writing to the correspondent.

WHO TO APPLY TO Peter Cullimore, Trustee, 52 Ledborough Lane, Beaconsfield, Buckinghamshire HP9 2DF *Tel.* 01494 678811

....

■ Kingdom Way Trust (Formerly known as Sugarworld Trust)

CC NO 1139646   ESTABLISHED 2011
WHERE FUNDING CAN BE GIVEN UK; Worldwide.
WHO CAN BENEFIT Registered charities; individuals.
WHAT IS FUNDED General charitable purposes, with a preference for the Christian faith.
RANGE OF GRANTS Usually up to £7,500
SAMPLE GRANTS E D and F Man Relief Fund (£75,000); Salvation Army (£7,500).
FINANCES *Year* 2011–12 *Income* £328,941 *Grants* £97,543 *Assets* £327,433
TRUSTEES David Barratt; Revd William Lovatt; Brian Arnott.
OTHER INFORMATION This is the charitable trust of the Sugarworld company.
HOW TO APPLY In writing to the correspondent.
WHO TO APPLY TO David Barratt, Trustee, Chantry House, 22 Upperton House, Eastbourne, East Sussex BN21 1BF *Tel.* 01323 470807 *email* david@sugarworld.eu

....

■ The Kingsbury Charity

CC NO 205797   ESTABLISHED 1986
WHERE FUNDING CAN BE GIVEN Ancient parish of Kingsbury.
WHO CAN BENEFIT Older people in need.
WHAT IS FUNDED Organisations in the ancient parish of Kingsbury.
FINANCES *Year* 2012 *Income* £374,371 *Grants* £38,250 *Assets* £9,526,553
TRUSTEES Valerie Pope; Julia Day; Rose Peacock; Terence Hopkins.
HOW TO APPLY In writing to the correspondent
WHO TO APPLY TO Philomena Hughes, Hon Secretary, 29 Bowater Close, London NW9 0XD *Tel.* 020 8205 9712

....

■ The Mary Kinross Charitable Trust

CC NO 212206   ESTABLISHED 1957
WHERE FUNDING CAN BE GIVEN UK.
WHO CAN BENEFIT Registered charities benefiting research workers, people in prison or leaving prison, young people and people disadvantaged by poverty.
WHAT IS FUNDED General charitable purposes. Donations confined to projects which the trust promotes and manages, particularly in the areas of medical research, to benefit the communities of which trustees have direct knowledge: youth, mental health and penal affairs. Grants made under the heading of youth are often made with crime prevention in mind.
WHAT IS NOT FUNDED No grants to individuals.
TYPE OF GRANT Capital projects, core costs and recurring.
SAMPLE GRANTS Department of Oncology, University of Oxford (£76,000); Scottish Centre for Regenerative Medicine, University of Edinburgh (£50,000); Greenhouse Schools Project (£36,000); Barry and Martin's Trust (£30,000); Centre for Education in the Justice System (£20,000); The Bendrigg Trust (£19,000); Woking YWCA (£10,000); Ballsall Heath Church Centre (£8,000); Gospel Oak Action Link

(£5,000); Warstock Community Centre (£1,500) and Edinburgh Global Partnerships (£500).
FINANCES *Year* 2012–13 *Income* £757,657 *Grants* £374,845 *Assets* £30,835,827
TRUSTEES Elizabeth Shields, Chair; Fiona Adams; Neil Cross; Jonathan Haw; Robert McDougall.
HOW TO APPLY 'Because the trustees have no office staff and work from home, they prefer dealing with written correspondence rather than telephone calls from applicants soliciting funds.' Note: unsolicited applications to this trust are very unlikely to be successful. The majority of new grants are recommended by the chair and the secretary who can authorise small grants of up to £25,000. Other grants are discussed and agreed at trustee meetings.
WHO TO APPLY TO Fiona Adams, Trustee, 36 Grove Avenue, Moseley, Birmingham B13 9RY

....

■ Laura Kinsella Foundation

CC NO 1145325   ESTABLISHED 2012
WHERE FUNDING CAN BE GIVEN Worldwide.
WHO CAN BENEFIT Organisations and individuals.
WHAT IS FUNDED General charitable purposes.
TRUSTEES Stephen Kinsella; Alison Jolly; Michael Dickson.
OTHER INFORMATION The foundation was registered in January 2012 for general charitable purposes. The foundation was set up by Stephen Kinsella OBE, a prominent competition lawyer and partner at Sidley Austin LLP, who is based in Brussels
HOW TO APPLY In writing to the correspondent.
WHO TO APPLY TO Stephen Kinsella, Trustee, c/o Bates Wells and Braithwaite, Scandinavian House, 2–6 Cannon Street, London EC4M 6YH *Tel.* 020 7551 7777 *Fax* 020 7551 7800 *email* mail@bwbllp.com

....

■ Kinsurdy Charitable Trust

CC NO 1076085   ESTABLISHED 1999
WHERE FUNDING CAN BE GIVEN UK.
WHO CAN BENEFIT Registered charities.
WHAT IS FUNDED General charitable purposes.
RANGE OF GRANTS Up to £7,500.
SAMPLE GRANTS All beneficiaries were awarded the same amount: £7,300. Beneficiaries included: the National Trust, the Samaritans, Age UK, Multiple Sclerosis Society, West Berks Community Hospital League of Friends, Macmillan Cancer Support and the Children's Trust.
FINANCES *Year* 2011–12 *Income* £690,368 *Grants* £116,800 *Assets* £3,710,382
TRUSTEES James Mann; Ian Brasington.
HOW TO APPLY The trustees do not respond to unsolicited requests.
WHO TO APPLY TO James Mann, Trustee, c/o Cheviot Asset Management Limited, 90 Long Acre, London WC2E 9RA *Tel.* 020 7438 5600 *email* dominic.goumal@cheviot.co.uk

....

■ Kirkley Poor's Land Estate

CC NO 210177   ESTABLISHED 1976
WHERE FUNDING CAN BE GIVEN The parish of Kirkley and former borough of Lowestoft
WHO CAN BENEFIT Individuals and organisations.
WHAT IS FUNDED Welfare and disability. The trust administers a grocery voucher scheme enabling people of pensionable age in Kirkley to receive a grant each winter to purchase groceries. It cooperates with Kirkley High School to make

Think carefully about every application. Is it justified?

....

677

grants to former pupils whose parents have low incomes to help with their expenses at university or other further education establishments. All funding has to be calculated to reduce identified need, hardship or distress.

WHAT IS NOT FUNDED No grants to well-known charities or only to local branches.

TYPE OF GRANT One-off.

RANGE OF GRANTS Up to £3,575.

SAMPLE GRANTS Past beneficiaries have included: St John's Housing Trust and the Waveney Women's Refuge (£3,575), Waveney Counselling Service (£2,750), Kirkley Church – St Peter and St John, Pakefield Church and Waveney Rape and Abuse (£1,650 each), Waveney Crossroads (£1,550), Salvation Army – Kirkley Branch (£900), Lowestoft Club for the Elderly and Kirkley Pre-school (£500 each).

FINANCES *Year* 2011–12 *Income* £85,609 *Grants* £51,416 *Assets* £1,826,159

TRUSTEES Yvonne Cherry; Jennifer Van Pelt; Michael Leonard Cook; Ralph Alan Castleton; Elaine High; Revd Andrew White; June Ford.

OTHER INFORMATION In total, individuals received £17,000; including 729 vouchers given to older people in Kirkley for the purchase of groceries in the winter.

HOW TO APPLY In writing to the correspondent. Trustees meet two to three times a year.

WHO TO APPLY TO Lucy Walker, Clerk, 4 Station Road, Lowestoft NR32 4QF *Tel.* 01502 514964 *email* kirkleypoors@gmail.com

---

■ The Richard Kirkman Charitable Trust

CC NO 327972   **ESTABLISHED** 1988

WHERE FUNDING CAN BE GIVEN UK, with a preference for Hampshire.

WHO CAN BENEFIT Registered charities and individuals.

WHAT IS FUNDED General charitable purposes, however the trustees are considering financing various plans for alleviating drug addiction.

RANGE OF GRANTS Up to £3,000.

SAMPLE GRANTS British Limbless Ex-Servicemen Association and Rose Road (£4,000 each); Southampton Society for the Blind (£2,500) and Diabetes UK, Mayor of Southampton's Charity Fund, Southampton Churches Rent Deposit Scheme, Southampton Rotary Club Trust Fund, Southampton Young Carers Project and Stroke Association (£2,000 each).

FINANCES *Year* 2011–12 *Income* £52,004 *Grants* £61,400 *Assets* £1,506,726

TRUSTEES M. Howson-Green; F. O. Kirkman; B. M. Baxendale; D. A. Hoare; M. Howson-Green.

OTHER INFORMATION In 2011–12 the total grants figure includes 63 grants of £1,000 or less, given to organisations and individuals totalling £37,000.

HOW TO APPLY The trust carries out its own research for beneficiaries and does not respond to applications by post or telephone.

WHO TO APPLY TO Michael Howson-Green, Trustee, Ashton House, 12 The Central Precinct, Winchester Road, Chandlers Ford, Eastleigh, Hampshire SO53 2GB *Tel.* 02380 274555

■ Kirschel Foundation

CC NO 1067672   **ESTABLISHED** 1998

WHERE FUNDING CAN BE GIVEN UK.

WHO CAN BENEFIT Registered charities.

WHAT IS FUNDED The trust states that its aims and objectives are 'to provide benefits to underprivileged persons, who may be either disabled or lacking resources'. In practice this includes mostly Jewish organisations.

RANGE OF GRANTS Up to £50,000.

SAMPLE GRANTS Hampstead Village Shul (£74,000); Ahavat Shalom Charity Fund (£73,000); Rays of Sunshine (£41,000); Jewish Learning Exchange (£33,000); Gateshead Academy for Torah Studies (£20,000); Jewish Care (£13,000); The Israel Film Festival London (£9,300); Great Ormond Street Hospital and TUT (£5,000); Diabetes UK (£3,000); Immanuel College (£2,500); Keren Hayeled (£2,000) and ETC Youth, Jewish Deaf Association and Beis Yehudis Moscow (£1,000 each).

FINANCES *Year* 2011–12 *Income* £400,454 *Grants* £474,930 *Assets* £304,905

TRUSTEES Laurence Grant Kirschel; Ian Lipman; Stephen Pinshaw.

OTHER INFORMATION Grants of less than £1,000 totalled £13,600.

HOW TO APPLY In writing to the correspondent.

WHO TO APPLY TO Stephen Pinshaw, Trustee, 26 Soho Square, London W1D 4NU *Tel.* 020 7437 4372

■ Robert Kitchin (Saddlers' Company)

CC NO 211169   **ESTABLISHED** 1891

WHERE FUNDING CAN BE GIVEN City of London and contiguous boroughs

WHO CAN BENEFIT Organisations and student welfare.

WHAT IS FUNDED Education and general charitable purposes.

RANGE OF GRANTS £500 to £64,000.

SAMPLE GRANTS In 2011/12 the trust had assets of £3.1 million, which generated an income of £140,000. Total grants paid/allocated to year end 31 March 2012 totalled £130,000. The major beneficiaries were: City University London (£64,000); St Ethelburga's Centre for Reconciliation and Peace (£20,000); City of London Academy Islington (£5,000); Central School of Ballet; English Touring Opera; London Symphony Orchestra (£2,000 each); Meadowgate School (£1,700).

FINANCES *Year* 2011–12 *Income* £135,897 *Grants* £128,629 *Assets* £3,152,722

TRUSTEES P. C. Laurie (Master); P. M. Farmar (Key Warden); P. M. C. Jameson (Quarter Warden); Lt Col G. E. Vere-Laurie DL; D. J. Serrell-Watts; H. J. C. Pulley; E. J. Pearson; D. S. Snowden; M. A. C. Laurie; D. T. L. Hardy; J. T. M. Satchell; H. S. Dyson-Laurie; J. R. Vant; W. J. Dyson-Laurie; I. L. J. Pulley; J. Godrich; D. H. Chandler; P. L. H. Lewis; C. E. Barclay; J. C. Robinson; E. H. Thomas; J. D. G. Welch; N. Mason.

OTHER INFORMATION Each year the charity gives a fixed percentage to two organisations – City University receives 50% of net income, while St Ethelburga's Centre for Reconciliation and Peace receives 15% of net income. The remaining 35% is distributed at the discretion of the trustees.

HOW TO APPLY In writing to the correspondent. However, the discretionary element of the trust's income is fully committed each year and the trustees are unable to respond to applications.

....

■ Ernest Kleinwort Charitable Trust

CC NO 229665   **ESTABLISHED** 1963
WHERE FUNDING CAN BE GIVEN UK.
WHO CAN BENEFIT Registered charities.
WHAT IS FUNDED The main fields of work are wildlife and environmental conservation, care of the elderly, disability, general welfare, hospices, medical research, miscellaneous, family planning and youth care.
WHAT IS NOT FUNDED The trust will not consider funding: large national charities having substantial fundraising potential, income from legacies and or endowment income; organisations not registered as charities or those that have been registered for less than a year; pre-school groups; out of school play schemes including pre-school and holiday schemes; projects which promote a particular religion; charities not funded by any other charity; very small and narrowly specialised activities; local authorities; individuals or charities applying on behalf of individuals; general requests for donations; expeditions or overseas travel; campaigning organisations; charities whose main aim is to raise funds for other charities; charities with substantial cash reserves.
TYPE OF GRANT Grants for start-up, capital costs and ongoing expenses for up to five years.
RANGE OF GRANTS Up to £100,000, but mostly for £10,000 or less.
SAMPLE GRANTS WWF UK (£100,000); River Trust (£70,000); Tusk Trust (£50,000); Chailey Heritage School (£40,000); Crawley Open House and Resource Centre (£30,000); Blond McIndoe Centre for Medical Research (£15,000); Latitude Global Volunteering (£6,600); Adventure Unlimited (£5,000); Bat Conservation Trust (£3,000); Hope in the Valley RDA (£1,000) and Neighbourly Care (£500).
FINANCES *Year* 2011–12 *Income* £50,046 *Grants* £51,700 *Assets* £1,348,968
TRUSTEES Sir Simon Robertson, Chair; Richard Ewing; Alexander Kleinwort; Lady Madeleine Kleinwort; Marina Kleinwort; Sir Richard Kleinwort; Sir Christopher Lever.
HOW TO APPLY The trustees' current policy is to consider written appeals from charities working in the field of the arts, but only successful applications are notified of the trustees' decision. The trustees do not normally respond favourably to appeals from individuals, nor to those unconnected with the arts. The charity requests a copy of the most recent report and financial statements from applicants.
WHO TO APPLY TO Nicholas Kerr-Sheppard, Secretary, c/o Kleinwort Benson Trustees Ltd, 14 St George Street, London W1S 1FE *Tel.* 020 3207 7008 *Website* www.ekct.org.uk

....

■ The Marina Kleinwort Charitable Trust

CC NO 1081825   **ESTABLISHED** 2000
WHERE FUNDING CAN BE GIVEN UK, in particular Sussex; overseas.
WHO CAN BENEFIT Arts organisations.

WHAT IS FUNDED Arts projects.
WHAT IS NOT FUNDED No grants to individuals.
SAMPLE GRANTS Rambert Dance Company (£25,000); LAMDA (£5,000); The Art Room and The Old Vic Theatre Trust (£4,000 each); Notting Hill Churches (£3,500); Endymion Ensemble (£3,000); Almeida Theatre (£2,700); Opera Brava (£2,500) and Polka Theatre (£2,000).
FINANCES *Year* 2011–12 *Income* £1,429,322 *Grants* £1,350,449 *Assets* £51,293,627
TRUSTEES Marina Kleinwort, Chair; David Robinson; Tessa Bremmer.
HOW TO APPLY In writing to the correspondent. Applications should be no longer than two A4 sides, and should incorporate a short (half page) summary. Applications should also include a detailed budget for the project and the applicant's most recent audited accounts. If accounts show a significant surplus or deficit of income, explain how this has arisen. Applicants must also complete and include an Accounts Summary form, which is available on the trust's website.
WHO TO APPLY TO Nicholas Kerr-Sheppard, Secretary, c/o Kleinwort Benson Trustees Ltd, 14 St George Street, London W1S 1FE *Tel.* 020 3207 7337 *email* elizabeth.fettes-neame@ kleinwortbenson.com

....

■ The Sir James Knott Trust

CC NO 1001363   **ESTABLISHED** 1990
WHERE FUNDING CAN BE GIVEN Tyne and Wear, Northumberland, County Durham inclusive of Hartlepool but exclusive of Darlington, Stockton-on-Tees, Middlesbrough, Redcar and Cleveland.
WHO CAN BENEFIT Registered charities only.
WHAT IS FUNDED Support of the welfare of people who are disadvantaged, the young, the elderly, people with disabilities, education and training, medical care, historic buildings, the environment, music and the arts and seafarers' and services' charities.
WHAT IS NOT FUNDED Individuals, replacement of funding withdrawn by local authorities or organisations that do not have an identifiable project within the beneficial area.
SAMPLE GRANTS Beneficiaries included: Sage Gateshead (£30,000 in total); North East Autism Society (£25,000); Northumbria Historic Churches Trust (£20,000); Bowes Museum (£10,000); Disability North and Chillingham Wild Cattle Association (£5,000 each); Embleton Cricket and Football Trust, Red Squirrel Survival Trust and Army Cadet Force – Northumbria (£3,000 each) and Bubble Foundation UK and Independent Age (£2,000 each).
FINANCES *Year* 2011–12 *Income* £1,382,790 *Grants* £1,234,707 *Assets* £38,350,589
TRUSTEES Prof. Oliver James; John Cresswell; Sarah Riddell; Ben Speke.
HOW TO APPLY In writing to the correspondent, giving a brief description of the need, with relevant consideration to the following points: what type of organisation you are and how you benefit the community; how you are organised and managed; how many staff/volunteers you have; if a registered charity, provide your registered number, if not you will need to submit the name and registered number of a charity which is prepared to administer funds on your behalf; what relationship, if any, do you have with similar or umbrella organisations; provide details of your main funding source; provide full details of the project you are currently fundraising for, including the cost, the amount

required and when the funds are needed; give details of who else you have approached and what response have you had; confirm whether you have you applied to the Big Lottery Fund (if not, state why not); and enclose a copy of your latest trustee report and accounts (if you are a new organisation then provide a copy of your latest bank statement). Not all the questions/points may apply to you, but they give an idea of what the trustees may ask when considering applications. Applicants may be contacted for further information. Trustees normally meet in spring, summer and autumn. Applications need to be submitted at least three months before a grant is required. However, if your application is for a grant of less than £1,000, this can usually be processed outside meetings and usually within one month.

WHO TO APPLY TO Vivien Stapeley, Secretary, 16–18 Hood Street, Newcastle upon Tyne NE1 6JQ *Tel.* 01912 304016 *email* info@knott-trust.co.uk *Website* www.knott-trust.co.uk

■ The Kobler Trust

CC NO 275237   **ESTABLISHED** 1963
WHERE FUNDING CAN BE GIVEN UK.
WHO CAN BENEFIT Registered charities. Grants given to individuals only in exceptional circumstances.
WHAT IS FUNDED General charitable purposes with emphasis on the arts and Jewish causes.
WHAT IS NOT FUNDED Grants are only given to individuals in exceptional circumstances.
TYPE OF GRANT No restrictions. These vary from small grants on a one-off basis for a specific project to a continuing relationship.
RANGE OF GRANTS £500–£50,000.
SAMPLE GRANTS Tricycle Theatre (£15,000); Pavilion Opera Educational Trust (£12,000); Arkwright Scholarship (£8,000 in two grants); Jewish Museum London (£5,000); Disability Law Service (£3,000); Place2Be, St Mungo's and Jewish Blind and Disabled (£1,000 each) and Merseyside Thursday Club (£500).
FINANCES *Year* 2011–12 *Income* £89,794 *Grants* £111,460 *Assets* £2,740,740
TRUSTEES A. Xuereb; A. H. Stone; Ms J. L. Evans; J. W. Israelsohn.
HOW TO APPLY Applications should be in writing and incorporate full details of the charity for which funding is requested. Acknowledgements are not generally sent out to unsuccessful applicants.
WHO TO APPLY TO The Trustees, c/o Lewis Silkin LLP, 10 Clifford's Inn Passage, London EC4A 1BL *Tel.* 020 7074 8000 *email* info@lewissilkin.com

■ The Kofia Trust

CC NO 1149116   **ESTABLISHED** 2012
WHERE FUNDING CAN BE GIVEN UK.
WHO CAN BENEFIT Charities and community groups.
WHAT IS FUNDED General charitable purposes.
TRUSTEES Johannes Huth; Christopher Huth; Elisabeth Huth; Helene Huth.
HOW TO APPLY In writing to the correspondent.
WHO TO APPLY TO Ben Brice, c/o Bircham Dyson Bell, 50 Broadway, London SW1H 0BL *Tel.* 020 7783 3523 *email* Kofia.Trust@huth.org.uk

■ The Kohn Foundation

CC NO 1003951   **ESTABLISHED** 1991
WHERE FUNDING CAN BE GIVEN UK and overseas.
WHO CAN BENEFIT Registered charities.
WHAT IS FUNDED General charitable purposes, especially education, Jewish religion, relief of poverty, care of people who are sick or who have a mental illness, medical research, and the arts (particularly music).
RANGE OF GRANTS Up to £160,000
SAMPLE GRANTS Royal Academy of Music (£100,000); Jesus College Oxford (£80,000); University of Manchester (£25,500); Jerusalem Foundation (£15,000); Foundation for Liver Research and Jewish Care (£10,000 each); Rudolf Kempe Society (£7,500); Foundation for Science and Technology (£5,000); Daniel Tumberg Memorial Trust (£2,000); and Sense about Science (£1,000).
FINANCES *Year* 2012 *Income* £385,788 *Grants* £545,515 *Assets* £981,517
TRUSTEES Sir Ralph Kohn, Chair; Lady Zahava Kohn; Anthony A. Forwood.
HOW TO APPLY In writing to the correspondent.
WHO TO APPLY TO Sir Ralph Kohn, Trustee, c/o Wilkins Kennedy and Co, Bridge House, 4 Borough High Street, London SE1 9QR *Tel.* 020 7403 1877 *email* enquiries@wilkinskennedy.com

■ Kollel and Co. Limited

CC NO 1077180   **ESTABLISHED** 1999
WHERE FUNDING CAN BE GIVEN Worldwide.
WHO CAN BENEFIT Jewish organisations.
WHAT IS FUNDED The objects of the charity are the: advancement of education and religion in accordance with the doctrines of the Jewish religion; and the relief of poverty.
RANGE OF GRANTS Up to £128,000.
SAMPLE GRANTS Congregation Beth Hamadrash Vyoel Moshe D'Satmar (£120,000); Ezer V'hatzolah (£85,000); Hadras Kodesh Trust (£34,000); Shaarei Chesed – London (£33,500); Inspirations (£28,500); and Chochmas Shloime Chasidi Talmud Torah Jerusalem (£25,000).
FINANCES *Year* 2012–13 *Income* £856,077 *Grants* £492,985 *Assets* £1,909,190
TRUSTEES S. Low; J. Lipschitz; Z. Rothschild.
OTHER INFORMATION Only the largest grants were listed in the 2012–13 accounts.
HOW TO APPLY Grants are made upon application by the charity concerned. Grants are made in amounts thought appropriate by the directors/trustees.
WHO TO APPLY TO S. Low, Trustee, 7 Overlea Road, London E5 9BG *Tel.* 020 8806 1570

■ Liudmila Korneenko Foundation

CC NO 1149109   **ESTABLISHED** 2012
WHERE FUNDING CAN BE GIVEN UK, Russia, Ukraine and USA.
WHO CAN BENEFIT Charities and community groups.
WHAT IS FUNDED General charitable purposes.
TRUSTEES Leonid Makaron; Liudmila Korneenko; Marina Makaron; Vladimir Makaron.
HOW TO APPLY In writing to the correspondent.
WHO TO APPLY TO Liudmila Korneenko, Trustee, c/o GMDS LLC, 1710 Walton Road, Suite 110, Blue Bell, PA 19422, USA *Tel.* 01610 825 680

■ The KPMG Foundation

CC NO 1086518　　　　**ESTABLISHED** 2001
WHERE FUNDING CAN BE GIVEN UK.
WHO CAN BENEFIT Refugees, young offenders, children and young people who have been in care, children and young people with dyslexia/ literacy difficulties
WHAT IS FUNDED Registered charities
SAMPLE GRANTS Working Chance (£37,000); Oval House, Helena Kennedy Foundation and Luton Churches Educational Trust (£25,000 each); Spartans Community Football (£20,000); Theatre Royal Plymouth and Tower Hamlets Family Intervention Project (£15,000 each); Young Vic (£6,000) and Shine (£500).
FINANCES *Year* 2011–12 *Income* £569,652 *Grants* £250,660 *Assets* £6,069,805
TRUSTEES Marianne Fallon; Gerry Acher; Peter Sherratt; Simon Collins; Surinder Arora; Lisa Harker; Claire Le Masurier; Robin Cartwright.
HOW TO APPLY The KPMG Foundation considers applications for the General Grants programme once a year. 'Throughout the year, we capture all organisations keen to apply for funding on a database. When the trustees agree their funding date at the end of each year for the following year, we write to all organisations on our database providing them with details of the funding date, when applications must be submitted and any specific criteria defined by the trustees. If you would like your details added to our database then email us at: kpmg@kpmg.co.uk
'The trustees meet four times a year. Once a year the trustees will assess all applications and make their funding decisions. If the trustees are keen to progress your application a project/site visit may be undertaken by either one of the trustees or one of the support team. In addition, the trustees may request that a financial due diligence assessment be undertaken, by the Foundation Treasurer, of the charitable organisation seeking funding.'
WHO TO APPLY TO Jo Clunie, Director, KPMG, 15 Canada Square, London E14 5GL *Tel.* 020 7311 4733 *email* kpmgfoundation@kpmg.co.uk *Website* www.kpmg.com

■ The Kreditor Charitable Trust

CC NO 292649　　　　**ESTABLISHED** 1985
WHERE FUNDING CAN BE GIVEN UK, with preferences for London and North East England.
WHO CAN BENEFIT Jewish organisations and UK welfare organisations benefiting Jewish people, at risk groups, and people who are disadvantaged by poverty or socially isolated.
WHAT IS FUNDED Jewish organisations working in education and social and medical welfare.
SAMPLE GRANTS Previous beneficiaries have included: Academy for Rabbinical Research, British Diabetic Association, British Friends of Israel War Disabled, Fordeve Ltd, Jerusalem Ladies' Society, Jewish Care, Jewish Marriage Council Kosher Meals on Wheels, London Academy of Jewish Studies, NW London Talmudical College, Ravenswood, RNID and UNICEF UK.
FINANCES *Year* 2011–12 *Income* £84,334 *Grants* £119,131 *Assets* £1,733
TRUSTEES P. M. Kreditor; M. P. Kreditor; Sharon Kreditor.
HOW TO APPLY In writing to the correspondent.

WHO TO APPLY TO Paul Kreditor, Trustee, Hallswelle House, 1 Hallswelle Road, London NW11 0DH *Tel.* 020 8209 1535 *email* admin@gerald-kreditor.co.uk

■ The Kreitman Foundation

CC NO 269046　　　　**ESTABLISHED** 1975
WHERE FUNDING CAN BE GIVEN UK.
WHO CAN BENEFIT Registered charities and other tax exempt charitable organisations benefiting children, young adults and older people, people who are disabled and people disadvantaged by poverty.
WHAT IS FUNDED Education, health and welfare.
WHAT IS NOT FUNDED No grants to individuals.
TYPE OF GRANT Project costs.
RANGE OF GRANTS £5,000–£56,000.
SAMPLE GRANTS Middlesex University (£56,000); and University of Bristol and Isha Institute of Inner Sciences (£5,000 each).
FINANCES *Year* 2011–12 *Income* £183,437 *Grants* £66,000 *Assets* £4,574,587
TRUSTEES Jill Luck-Hille; Peter Luck-Hille; Gareth Morgan.
OTHER INFORMATION Three grants totalling £66,000 were made.
HOW TO APPLY To the correspondent in writing. The trustees seem to have a list of regular beneficiaries and it may be unlikely that any new applications will be successful.
WHO TO APPLY TO The Trustees, Citroen Wells, Devonshire House, 1 Devonshire Street, London W1W 5DR

■ The Neil Kreitman Foundation

CC NO 267171　　　　**ESTABLISHED** 1974
WHERE FUNDING CAN BE GIVEN Worldwide, in practice UK, USA and Israel.
WHO CAN BENEFIT Registered or exempt charities.
WHAT IS FUNDED Arts and culture; education; health and social welfare; Jewish causes.
WHAT IS NOT FUNDED No grants to individuals.
TYPE OF GRANT Primarily general funds with some small capital grants and core costs.
RANGE OF GRANTS Generally £500–£30,000.
SAMPLE GRANTS Crocker Art Museum (£219,000); The British Museum (£68,000); International Campaign for Tibet and Médecins Sans Frontières (£50,000 each); Sierra Club Foundation (£30,000); Pacific Asia Museum, Pasadena (£25,000); The Ancient India and Iran Trust (£22,000); Release – Legal Emergency and Drugs Service (£16,000); Los Angeles County Museum of Art (£15,000) and School of Oriental and African Studies (£1,600).
FINANCES *Year* 2011–12 *Income* £681,095 *Grants* £417,989 *Assets* £22,990,632
TRUSTEES Neil R. Kreitman; Gordon C. Smith.
OTHER INFORMATION Amounts were converted from dollars at a rate of 0.6436.
HOW TO APPLY In writing to the correspondent.
WHO TO APPLY TO Gordon C. Smith, Trustee, Citroen Wells and Partners, Devonshire House, 1 Devonshire Street, London W1W 5DR *Tel.* 020 7304 2000

■ The Heinz, Anna and Carol Kroch Foundation

CC NO 207622   **ESTABLISHED** 1962

WHERE FUNDING CAN BE GIVEN UK.

WHO CAN BENEFIT Individuals with chronic illnesses; disabled people; people who are disadvantaged by poverty; homeless people; victims of abuse and domestic violence; and victims of war.

WHAT IS FUNDED The foundation exists to support people who have suffered injustice and relieve hardship amongst people with medical conditions.

WHAT IS NOT FUNDED No grants are made to students or for holidays. Overseas applications or projects are not considered.

RANGE OF GRANTS Up to £10,000.

SAMPLE GRANTS Bath Institute of Medical Engineering, Brainwave, Breakthrough Breast Cancer, Eyeless Trust, Northern Friends of ARMS, VISCERAL and University College London.

FINANCES *Year* 2011–12 *Income* £160,927 *Grants* £86,322 *Assets* £4,653,909

TRUSTEES Margaret Cottam; Dr Amatsia Kashti; Daniel Lang; Xavier Lang; Annabel Page; Christopher Rushbrook; John Seagrim.

OTHER INFORMATION In total there were 668 grants made.

HOW TO APPLY Appeals are considered monthly. Applications on behalf of individuals must be submitted through a recognised body, such as social services, GP/consultant, CAB or welfare rights. Applications always receive a reply – include an sae.

WHO TO APPLY TO Beena Astle, Administrator, PO Box 462, Teddington TW11 1BS *Tel.* 020 8977 5534 *Fax* 020 8977 5547 *email* hakf50@ hotmail.com

■ Kupath Gemach Chaim Bechesed Viznitz Trust

CC NO 1110323   **ESTABLISHED** 2005

WHERE FUNDING CAN BE GIVEN UK and Israel.

WHO CAN BENEFIT Registered charities.

WHAT IS FUNDED Jewish causes.

SAMPLE GRANTS Keren Habinyan (£50,000); Kollel Imrei Boruch (£13,000); Talmud Torah Viznitz (£8,000); Mercaz Refuah (£7,000).

FINANCES *Year* 2011–12 *Income* £317,906 *Grants* £123,172 *Assets* £20,641

TRUSTEES Israel Kahan; Saul Weiss; Alexander Pifko.

OTHER INFORMATION During the year, a further £214,843 went to individuals.

HOW TO APPLY In writing to the correspondent.

WHO TO APPLY TO Saul Weiss, Trustee, 171 Kyverdale Road, London N16 6PS *Tel.* 020 8442 9604

■ The Kyte Charitable Trust

CC NO 1035886   **ESTABLISHED** 1994

WHERE FUNDING CAN BE GIVEN UK.

WHO CAN BENEFIT Primarily organisations that benefit the Jewish community.

WHAT IS FUNDED Jewish causes; education; health.

RANGE OF GRANTS Up to £27,000.

SAMPLE GRANTS United Jewish Israel Fund (£27,500); Jewish Care (£26,000); Jewish Community Secondary School (£20,000); Chai Cancer Care and Norwood Ravenswood (£16,000 each); One Family UK and United Kingdom Jewish Film Festival (£5,000 each);

and Rays of Sunshine, WIZO and Union of Jewish Students (£1,000 each).

FINANCES *Year* 2011–12 *Income* £250,013 *Grants* £214,258 *Assets* £69,643

TRUSTEES David Kyte; Tracey Kyte; James Kyte; Ilana Kyte.

OTHER INFORMATION Grants were made to 19 organisations totalling £214,000.

HOW TO APPLY In writing to the correspondent.

WHO TO APPLY TO Carly McKenzie, Administrator, Business Design Centre, 52 Upper Street, London N1 0QH *Tel.* 020 7704 7791

682

Does the trust you have chosen match your needs? Haphazard applications waste postage and time

■ L. P. W. Limited

CC NO 1148784 **ESTABLISHED** 2012
WHERE FUNDING CAN BE GIVEN UK.
WHO CAN BENEFIT Charities and community groups.
WHAT IS FUNDED General, relief of poverty, Jewish causes.
TRUSTEES Irwin Weiler; Paula Weiler; Riki Weiler; Alexander Weiler; Daniela Rosenthal; Monica Rosenthal; Nicholas Rosenthal; Talia Cohen.
HOW TO APPLY In writing to the correspondent.
WHO TO APPLY TO The Trustees, c/o Cohen Arnold, New Burlington House, 1075 Finchley Road, London NW11 0PU *Tel.* 020 8731 0777 *Fax* 020 8731 0778 *email* info@cohenarnold.com

■ The Late Sir Pierce Lacy Charity Trust

CC NO 1013505 **ESTABLISHED** 1992
WHERE FUNDING CAN BE GIVEN UK and overseas.
WHO CAN BENEFIT The trust only supports the Roman Catholic Church or associated institutions which are registered charities and does not fund requests from individuals.
WHAT IS FUNDED Medicine and health, welfare, education, religion and general charitable purposes. Particularly charities working in the field of infrastructure development, residential facilities and services, Christian education, Christian outreach, Catholic bodies, charity or voluntary umbrella bodies, hospices, rehabilitation centres, advocacy, education and training, community services and community issues.
WHAT IS NOT FUNDED The trust only supports the Roman Catholic Church or associated institutions.
TYPE OF GRANT Recurrent small grants of £1,000 or less, buildings, capital, core costs, project, research, start-up costs and funding for more than three years may be considered.
RANGE OF GRANTS Most are less than £500.
SAMPLE GRANTS Previous beneficiaries have included: Crusade of Rescue (£1,400); St Francis' Children's Society (£900); Poor Mission Fund and St Cuthbert's Mayne RC School – special donation (£800 each); Society of St Vincent de Paul (£700); Poor Mission Fund (£600); Catholic Children's Society (£550) and St Francis' Leprosy Guild (£500).
FINANCES *Year* 2011–12 *Income* £26,758 *Grants* £22,820 *Assets* £532,858
TRUSTEE Aviva Insurance Ltd
HOW TO APPLY In writing to the correspondent, at any time.
WHO TO APPLY TO Aviva Insurance Limited, Capita Trust Company, 4th Floor, 40 Dukes Place, London EC3A 7NH *Tel.* 020 3367 8142

■ The K. P. Ladd Charitable Trust

CC NO 1091493 **ESTABLISHED** 2002
WHERE FUNDING CAN BE GIVEN UK and overseas.
WHO CAN BENEFIT Churches and other organisations.
WHAT IS FUNDED 'It is the trustees' present intention that the fund will be applied to support Christian charities and other charitable organisations involved in religious activities. This will be done by supporting churches, missionary work and other organisations both in the UK and overseas.'
RANGE OF GRANTS Up to £20,000. Usually £2,000.
SAMPLE GRANTS London Institute for Contemporary Christianity (£22,500); Eastbury Church Northwood Trust (£20,000); Cross Pollinate Foundation (£7,000); Kepplewray Trust (£6,000); Amnos Ministries and Storehouse Church, Tarporley (£5,000 each); Wycliffe Bible Transistors and London City Mission (£4,000 each); Livability and Salvation Army (£2,000 each) and Church Urban Fund and Romance Academy (£1,000 each).
FINANCES *Year* 2011–12 *Income* £33,681 *Grants* £97,550 *Assets* £1,572,035
TRUSTEES Rosemary Anne-Ladd; Brian Ladd; Kenneth Ladd; Ian Creswick.
OTHER INFORMATION Grants were given to 19 organisations.
HOW TO APPLY 'The trust is fully committed and does not reply to unsolicited requests.'
WHO TO APPLY TO Brian Ladd, Trustee, 34 St Mary's Avenue, Northwood, Middlesex HA6 3AZ

■ John Laing Charitable Trust

CC NO 236852 **ESTABLISHED** 1962
WHERE FUNDING CAN BE GIVEN UK.
WHO CAN BENEFIT Existing and former employees of John Laing plc who are in need; 'charitable organisations, or in exceptional circumstances from not-for-profit companies'.
WHAT IS FUNDED More recently, the trust has concentrated its support on charities which support the following main themes: education; community regeneration; disadvantaged young people; homelessness with a particular emphasis on day centres; and environment.
WHAT IS NOT FUNDED No grants to individuals (other than to Laing employees and/or their dependants).
TYPE OF GRANT Usually one-off, but a small number are supported for an agreed period, often up to three years.
RANGE OF GRANTS £250–£25,000.
SAMPLE GRANTS Bury Lake Young Mariners (£500,000); Young Enterprise London (£30,000); Homeless Link, Hertfordshire Groundwork and TCV (£25,000 each); Fairshare and National Literacy Trust (£20,000 each); Place 2 Be (£15,000); Envision and Outreach (£10,000 each); Darton College, Safe and Sound Derby and Westminster Befriend a Family (£5,000 each); 999 Club and Hounslow Seniors Trust (£2,500 each).
FINANCES *Year* 2012 *Income* £1,935,000 *Grants* £1,236,000 *Assets* £52,771,000
TRUSTEES Christopher Laing; Sir Martin Laing; Lynette Krige; Christopher Waples; Daniel Partridge.
OTHER INFORMATION In in addition to the grant total, £585,000 was distributed to about 515 individuals who were either current or former employees of John Laing plc.
HOW TO APPLY In writing to the correspondent. Telephone enquiries are welcome to avoid abortive work. The trust does not have an application form and applicants are asked to keep the initial request as brief as possible. There is no deadline for receipt of applications. All applications are dealt with on a rolling basis. The trust says that all applications are acknowledged.

WHO TO APPLY TO Jenny Impey, Administrator, 33 Bunns Lane, Mill Hill, London NW7 2DX *Tel.* 020 7901 4216 *email* jenny.impey@laing. com *Website* www.laing.com

....

■ Maurice and Hilda Laing Charitable Trust

CC NO 1058109   **ESTABLISHED** 1996
WHERE FUNDING CAN BE GIVEN UK and overseas.
WHO CAN BENEFIT Registered charities.
WHAT IS FUNDED The advancement of the Christian religion and the relief of poverty both in the UK and overseas. In practice grants awarded fall into three main categories: to organisations seeking to promote Christian faith and values through evangelistic, educational and media activities at home and overseas; to organisations seeking to express Christian faith through practical action to help people in need, for example, those with disabilities, the homeless, the sick, young people, prisoners and ex-offenders; to organisations working to relieve poverty overseas, with a particular emphasis on helping children who are vulnerable or at risk; evangelical activities, theological training and the promotion of Christianity in the UK and overseas. In most cases these grants to overseas projects are made through UK registered charities who are expected to monitor and evaluate the projects on behalf of the trust, providing progress reports at agreed intervals.
WHAT IS NOT FUNDED No grants to groups or individuals for the purpose of education, travel, attendance at conferences or participation in overseas exchange programmes. No grants towards church restoration or repair.
TYPE OF GRANT Usually one-off grants to capital costs or project funding on a one-off or recurring basis. A few grants towards the core costs of national organisations.
RANGE OF GRANTS £0–£650,000
SAMPLE GRANTS Ethiopian Graduate School of Theology (£350,000); The Reculver Trust (£300,000); The Lambeth Fund (£200,000); Mission Aviation Fellowship (£150,000); Mildmay Mission Hospital (£40,000); Caring for Life (£25,000); Prison Fellowship England and Wales (£15,000); Hope UK (£10,000) St Michael and All Angels Church, Amersham and Hope Debt Advice (£5,000 each).
FINANCES *Year* 2012 *Income* £1,568,093 *Grants* £3,068,966 *Assets* £35,710,810
TRUSTEES Andrea Currie; Peter Harper; Simon Martle; Paul van den Bosch; Ewan Harper; Charles Laing; Stephen Ludlow.
OTHER INFORMATION In 2006 the trustees made the decision to work towards winding up the trust by 2020. As such, there will be a controlled increase in the level of future grant expenditure. The trustees are making a number of significant investments to a small number of organisations that they will proactively invite to apply. Charities can still apply for the small grants programme.
HOW TO APPLY In writing to the correspondent. One application only is needed to apply to this or the Kirby Laing Foundation, Martin Laing Foundation or Beatrice Laing Charitable Trust. Multiple applications will still only elicit a single reply, even then applicants are asked to accept non-response as a negative reply on behalf of all these trusts, unless an sae is enclosed. After the initial sifting process, the Maurice and Hilda Laing Trust follows its own administrative procedures. Each application should contain all

the information needed to allow such a decision to be reached, in as short and straightforward a way as possible.

Specifically, each application should say: what the money is for; how much is needed; how much has already been found; and where the rest of the money is to come from. The trustees meet quarterly to consider applications for grants above £10,000. In most cases the trust's administrators will have met with applicants and prepared reports and recommendations for the trustees. Applications for smaller amounts are considered on an ongoing basis throughout the year. The administrators are authorised to make such grants without prior consent up to a maximum of £100,000 in each quarter, the grants to be reported to the trustees and approved retrospectively at the following quarterly meeting.
WHO TO APPLY TO Elizabeth Harley, Trusts Director, 33 Bunns Lane, Mill Hill, London NW7 2DX *Tel.* 020 8238 8890 *Website* www. laingfamilytrusts.org.uk

....

■ The Kirby Laing Foundation

CC NO 264299   **ESTABLISHED** 1972
WHERE FUNDING CAN BE GIVEN Unrestricted, but mainly UK.
WHO CAN BENEFIT Registered charities benefiting disadvantaged sections of the community including people with disabilities or mental illness, people disadvantaged by poverty, and socially isolated people; UK and overseas mission societies.
WHAT IS FUNDED Advancement of the Christian faith, youth development, medical research, care and health organisations, social welfare.
WHAT IS NOT FUNDED No grants for: general appeals or circulars; campaigning or lobbying activities; umbrella, second tier or grantmaking organisations; professional associations or projects for the training of professionals; feasibility studies and social research; individual sponsorship requirements; grants to individuals for educational, medical or travel purposes including gap year projects and overseas exchange programmes; summer activities for children/young people or after-school clubs; state maintained or independent schools other than those for pupils with special educational needs; uniformed groups such as Scouts and Guides; costs of staging one-off events, festivals or conferences; animal welfare; core running costs of hospices, counselling projects and other local organisations; church restoration or repair (including organs and bells).
TYPE OF GRANT Usually capital costs or project funding on a one-off or recurring basis.
RANGE OF GRANTS £100–£120,000
SAMPLE GRANTS University of Oxford (£600,000); Royal Society of Medicine (£125,000); Moorfields Eye Hospital Development and The Education Fellowship (£100,000 each); Restoration of Appearance and Function Trust (£50,000); Queen Elizabeth Hospital Birmingham Charity (£40,000); Wakefield Cathedral (£20,000); Mines Advisory Group and Urban Saints (£10,000 each) and Welsh National Opera (£5,000).
FINANCES *Year* 2012 *Income* £1,850,817 *Grants* £2,504,700 *Assets* £44,833,993
TRUSTEES Lady Isobel Laing; David E. Laing; Simon Webley; Revd Charles Burch.
OTHER INFORMATION See the entry for the Laing Family Foundations for the work of the group as a whole.

Charities can apply for grants of up to £5,000; anything over this amount is by invitation only. The foundation states that it intends to increase the level of grant expenditure with a view to the likely winding down of the foundation in five to ten years.

HOW TO APPLY One application only is needed to apply to this or the Beatrice Laing Trust or Maurice and Hilda Laing Charitable Trust. Multiple applications will still only elicit a single reply. These trusts make strenuous efforts to keep their overhead costs to a minimum. As they also make a very large number of grants each year, in proportion to their income, the staff must rely almost entirely on the written applications submitted in selecting appeals to go forward to the trustees.

Application is by letter including the following information: contact details; confirmation of charitable status; a clear overview of the charity's aims and objectives; precise details of the project for which funding is sought including: project activities; proposed start and end date; a detailed budget breakdown; fundraising strategy: anticipated sources of funding, funds already secured, plans for securing the shortfall; arrangements for monitoring and evaluating the project; a copy of the charity's most recent annual report and audited accounts.

Applicants can include a list of other supporting documents that can be provided upon request such as business plans or architectural drawings for building projects. The trustees meet four times a year to consider the award of grants of over £20,000. Decisions on smaller grants are made on an ongoing basis. For all grants above £5,000 the foundation asks for a report from the charity one year after the grant has been made, describing briefly how the grant has been spent and what has been achieved. For larger and multi-year grants more detailed reports may be required. Where a grant is paid in instalments the usual practice is not to release the second and subsequent instalments until a review of progress has been satisfactorily completed.

WHO TO APPLY TO Elizabeth Harley, 33 Bunns Lane, Mill Hill, London NW7 2DX *Tel.* 020 8238 8890 *Website* www.laingfamilytrusts.org.uk

■ The Christopher Laing Foundation

CC NO 278460   **ESTABLISHED** 1979
WHERE FUNDING CAN BE GIVEN UK,
WHO CAN BENEFIT Applications from headquarter organisations and local organisations will be considered.
WHAT IS FUNDED General charitable purposes, arts and culture, environment, health and sport, with a preference for organisations supporting adults with disabilities.
WHAT IS NOT FUNDED Donations are only made to registered charities.
TYPE OF GRANT Recurrent and one-off. Grants are given for core support, capital funding and project, seed and feasibility funding. Loans may be given.
RANGE OF GRANTS Up to £30,000.
SAMPLE GRANTS Charities Aid Foundation and Fields in Trust (£30,000 each); The Lord's Taverners (£25,000); The Duke of Edinburgh's Award, The John Clements Sports and Community Centre and Hertfordshire Groundwork Trust (£10,000 each); Action of Addiction and Youth Create (£5,000 each); Wooden Spoon (£2,000) and Stroke Association (£1,000).

FINANCES *Year* 2011–12 *Income* £239,412 *Grants* £133,000 *Assets* £6,568,155
TRUSTEES Christopher M. Laing; John Keeble; Peter S. Jackson; Diana C. Laing; Michael R. Warwick Laing.
HOW TO APPLY In writing to the correspondent. The accounts note, 'an enormous and increasing number of requests for donations are received and unfortunately only a small proportion of these requests can be fulfiled.'
WHO TO APPLY TO Vince Cheshire, Administrator, c/o TMF Management UK Ltd, 400 Capability Green, Luton LU1 3AE *Tel.* 01582 439200

■ The David Laing Foundation

CC NO 278462   **ESTABLISHED** 1979
WHERE FUNDING CAN BE GIVEN Worldwide with a preference for the East Midlands and the south of England.
WHO CAN BENEFIT Organisations benefiting children, including those who are in care, fostered or adopted; one-parent families; and people who are disabled.
WHAT IS FUNDED General charitable purposes, with a preference towards young people, disability and the arts.
WHAT IS NOT FUNDED No grants to individuals.
TYPE OF GRANT One-off. Some charities are closely associated with the foundation and would benefit more frequently.
SAMPLE GRANTS Nottinghamshire Community Foundation (£122,000); Hertfordshire Community Foundation and Reach Out Plus (£20,000 each); Wooden Spoon (£16,500); Peterborough Cathedral (£12,000); and Marie Curie Cancer (£11,800).
FINANCES *Year* 2012–13 *Income* £109,543 *Grants* £279,361 *Assets* £4,189,498
TRUSTEES David Laing; Stuart Lewis; Frances Laing; Francis Barlow.
OTHER INFORMATION When supporting larger charities the support will be at headquarters and local levels as, for instance, in support of Save the Children Fund where donations to headquarters will aid the African famine appeal, but support is also given to local branches.
HOW TO APPLY In writing to the correspondent.
WHO TO APPLY TO David Laing, Trustee, The Manor House, Grafton Underwood, Kettering NN14 3AA *email* david@david-laing.co.uk

■ The Martin Laing Foundation

CC NO 278461   **ESTABLISHED** 1979
WHERE FUNDING CAN BE GIVEN UK and worldwide, particularly Malta.
WHO CAN BENEFIT Registered charities.
WHAT IS FUNDED General charitable purposes, including environment and conservation, young people and the elderly, but most grants go to charities and projects which the trustees have a personal connection to.
WHAT IS NOT FUNDED The trust's website states that the following cannot be funded: 'general appeals or circulars; campaigning or lobbying activities; umbrella, second tier or grantmaking organisations; professional associations or projects for the training of professionals; feasibility studies and social research; individual sponsorship requirements; grants to individuals for educational, medical or travel purposes including gap year projects and overseas exchange programmes; summer activities for children/young people or after-school clubs; state maintained or independent schools other

than those for pupils with special educational needs; uniformed groups such as scouts and guides; costs of staging one-off events, festivals or conferences; animal welfare; core running costs of hospices, counselling projects and other local organisations; and church restoration or repair (including organs and bells).'

SAMPLE GRANTS WWF (£35,000); East Anglian Air Ambulance, Student's Education Trust and Macmillan Cancer Support (£10,000 each); John Laing Charitable Trust (£7,500); the Pushkin Trust and Friends of the Castle of Mey (£5,000 each); Norfolk Community Foundation (£4,000); Hands Around The World and Coming Home (£2,000 each); the Nancy Oldfield Trust and Cure Parkinson's Trust (£1,000 each); Spinal Injuries Association (£500); and Choppin's Charity (£250).

FINANCES *Year* 2012–13 *Income* £190,697 *Grants* £242,398 *Assets* £6,418,204

TRUSTEES Edward Laing; Sir Martin Laing; Lady Laing; Nicholas Gregory; Colin Fletcher; Alexandra Gregory; Graham Sillett.

HOW TO APPLY The trustees meet three times a year to consider grants. The trust's website states that 'the Laing Family Trusts are administered and co-ordinated centrally. An application to one is therefore considered as an application to all.' Applications should be made by letter, accompanied by a concise proposal of three to four pages. Information regarding details of the project for which funding is needed, such as project activities and budget breakdown, plus a copy of the charity's most recent annual report and accounts should be included. A list of other supporting documents e.g. annual review, business plan, drawings for capital building projects etc. can also be included. For more information visit the trust's website.

WHO TO APPLY TO Elizabeth Harley, Trusts Director, c/o Laing Family Trusts, 33 Bunns Lane, Mill Hill, London NW7 2DX *Tel.* 020 8238 8890 *Website* www.laingfamilytrusts.org.uk

························

■ The Beatrice Laing Trust

CC NO 211884   **ESTABLISHED** 1952
WHERE FUNDING CAN BE GIVEN UK and overseas.
WHO CAN BENEFIT Mainly registered charities.
WHAT IS FUNDED The welfare of people who are homeless, children, older people, socially excluded and people with physical, mental or learning disabilities. Grants to projects overseas are concentrated upon building the capacity to provide long-term solutions to the problems faced by countries in the developing world, rather than emergency aid. Grants towards the advancement of the evangelical Christian faith are made by the trustees through the JW Laing Trust.
WHAT IS NOT FUNDED No grants to groups or individuals for the purpose of education, travel, attendance at conferences or participation in overseas exchange programmes. No grants towards church restoration or repair.
RANGE OF GRANTS Most grants are between £500 and £10,000, occasionally larger.
SAMPLE GRANTS Together Trust (£50,000); Calvert Trust Exmoor (£50,000); Lurgan YMCA (£50,000); Echoes of Service (£30,000); Emmaus UK (£23,000); Age UK Leeds (£20,000); Crime Diversion Scheme (£10,000); Community Service Volunteers (£5,000); Autism Sussex (£4,000); Doctors of the World (£2,500); Kenyan Orphan Project and Deaf Connections (£2,000 each) and Young People Taking Action (£500).

FINANCES *Year* 2011–12 *Income* £2,241,751 *Grants* £2,019,350 *Assets* £45,938,562
TRUSTEES Sir Martin Laing; David E. Laing; Christopher M. Laing; Charles Laing; Paula Blacker; Alexandra Gregory.
OTHER INFORMATION See the entry for the Laing Family Foundations for the work of the group as a whole.
The trustees have stated that they wish to increase grant expenditure to align it more closely with income, therefore it rose by 26.8% during the year.
HOW TO APPLY In writing to the correspondent. One application only is needed to apply to this or the Kirby Laing Foundation, Martin Laing Foundation or Beatrice Laing Charitable Trust. Multiple applications will still only elicit a single reply, even then applicants are asked to accept non-response as a negative reply on behalf of all these trusts, unless an sae is enclosed. After the initial sifting process, the Maurice and Hilda Laing Trust follows its own administrative procedures. Each application should contain all the information needed to allow such a decision to be reached, in as short and straightforward a way as possible.
Specifically, each application should say: what the money is for; how much is needed; how much has already been found; and where the rest of the money is to come from. The trustees meet quarterly to consider applications for grants above £10,000. In most cases the trust's administrators will have met with applicants and prepared reports and recommendations for the trustees. Applications for smaller amounts are considered on an ongoing basis throughout the year. The administrators are authorised to make such grants without prior consent up to a maximum of £100,000 in each quarter, the grants to be reported to the trustees and approved retrospectively at the following quarterly meeting.
WHO TO APPLY TO Elizabeth Harley, Trusts Director, c/o Laing Family Trusts, 33 Bunns Lane, Mill Hill, London NW7 2DX *Tel.* 020 8238 8890 *Website* www.laingfamilytrusts.org.uk

························

■ The Lambert Charitable Trust

CC NO 257803   **ESTABLISHED** 1969
WHERE FUNDING CAN BE GIVEN UK and Israel.
WHO CAN BENEFIT Organisations supporting older people, children and young people, members of the Jewish faith and people with disabilities.
WHAT IS FUNDED Medicine, social care, education, people with disabilities, homes for the elderly and Jewish causes.
TYPE OF GRANT One-off and recurrent.
RANGE OF GRANTS £250–£15,000.
SAMPLE GRANTS Jewish Care (£15,000); Action on Addiction (£4,000); Medical Engineering Resource Unit and Ro-Ro Sailing Project (£3,000 each); Action Medical Research, Anne Frank Trust, Meningitis Research Foundation, New Horizon Youth Centre and Quaker Social Action (£2,000 each); Jewish Association for the Mentally Ill and Kids' Cookery School (£1,000 each); and Ponevez Yeshivah Israel (£250).
FINANCES *Year* 2011–12 *Income* £90,389 *Grants* £58,250 *Assets* £3,039,424
TRUSTEES Maurice Lambert; Prof. Harold Lambert; Jane Lambert; Oliver Lambert; David Wells.
HOW TO APPLY In writing to the correspondent.
WHO TO APPLY TO George Georghiou, Administrator, Mercer and Hole, 72 London Road, St Albans, Hertfordshire AL1 1NS *Tel.* 01727 869141

■ Community Foundation for Lancashire

cc no 1123229   established 2005

where funding can be given Lancashire.

who can benefit Registered charities and community groups.

what is funded Social welfare and general charitable purposes.

sample grants Blackpool Coastal Housing (£74,000); Blackpool Council Fund (£28,000); Pennine Lancashire Youth Enterprise Fund (£3,000); Jim Hosker Memorial Fund and Surviving Winter Fund (£2,000 each) and Ribble Valley Fund (£200).

finances Year 2011–12 Income £361,200 Grants £119,541 Assets £1,953,750

trustees Peter Robinson; Arthur Roberts; Terry Hephrun; Peter Butterfield; Elizabeth Hall; Pamela Barker; Joanne Turton; Wendy Swift.

how to apply All funds available, together with the criteria, priorities and application process are detailed on the foundation's website.

who to apply to Cathy Elliott, Chief Executive, Suite 22, The Globe Centre, St James Square, Accrington, Lancashire BB5 0RE Tel. 01512 322444 email programmes@lancsfoundation.org.uk Website www.lancsfoundation.org.uk

■ LWS Lancashire Environmental Fund Limited

cc no 1074983   established 1998

where funding can be given Lancashire

who can benefit Environmental organisations.

what is funded Environmental projects which meet the criteria of the ENTRUST scheme.

what is not funded All projects must satisfy at least one objective of the Landfill Tax Credit Scheme. For more information about the scheme contact Entrust, the regulatory body, by visiting their website at www.entrust.org.uk or telephoning 01926 488 300.

type of grant One-off and recurrent.

range of grants £5,000 to £40,000.

sample grants Thornton Methodist Church, Haslingden St Mary's Community Centre and Lytham Hall (£40,000 each); RSPB – Leighton Moss and Clitheroe United Reformed Church (£30,000 each); Leyland Baptist Community Hall (£25,000); Grimsargh Village Hall (£20,000); Lostock Hall (£15,000); Wycoller Riparian Habitat Restoration Project (£11,500); the Meadow Skate Area (£10,000); Oakhill Park (£7,000); and Cliviger Village Hall (£5,000).

finances Year 2012 Income £1,103,153 Grants £1,514,221 Assets £2,135,849

trustees David Tattersall; Cllr Janice Hanson; Gary Mayson.

other information Grants were awarded to 65 organisations and totalled £1.5 million.

how to apply Detailed and helpful guidance notes and application forms for each funding strand are available from the correspondent or may be downloaded from the fund's website. Institutional applications are invited to submit a summary of their proposals in a specified format. The applications are reviewed against specific criteria. The board meets quarterly in January, April, July and October. Staff are willing to have informal discussions before an application is made. Potential applicants are strongly advised to visit the website and view the guidelines before contacting the trust.

who to apply to Andy Rowett, Administrator, The Barn, Berkeley Drive, Bamber Bridge, Preston

PR5 6BY Tel. 01772 317247 Fax 01772 628849 email general@lancsenvfund.org.uk Website www.lancsenvfund.org.uk

■ Duchy of Lancaster Benevolent Fund

cc no 1026752   established 1993

where funding can be given The county palatine of Lancashire (in Lancashire, Greater Manchester and Merseyside), and elsewhere in the country where the Duchy of Lancaster has historical links such as land interests and church livings.

who can benefit Individuals and organisations.

what is funded General charitable causes, but especially youth and education, welfare of people who are disabled or elderly, community help, religion.

type of grant Mainly one-off grants for specific projects. Recurrent grants occasionally given.

range of grants Up to £15,000, but usually £50–£5,000.

sample grants Independence at Home (£15,000); Royal Schools for the Deaf – Seashell Trust (£10,000); Lancaster University Bursary Fund (£9,000); University of Central Lancashire, Abdullah Quilltam Society and Royal Court Trust (£5,000 each); Friends of the Harris Museum and Art Gallery (£3,500); Fields in Trust (£2,500); Country Holidays for Inner City Kids (£1,600) and Carleton Community High School, The Beagle Welfare Scheme and British Dyslexics (£1,000 each).

finances Year 2011–12 Income £385,875 Grants £369,530 Assets £10,596,504

trustees Lord Charles Shuttleworth; Sir Alan Reid; Hon. Justice David Richards; Dame Lorna Muirhead; Robert Hildyard; Chris Adcock; Warren Smith; Geoffrey Driver.

other information During 2011–12 a total of 402 grants were made.

how to apply In writing to the appropriate lieutenancy office (see below), at any time. Applications should be by letter, including as much information as possible. All applications are acknowledged. Lancashire lieutenancy: County Hall, Preston, Lancashire LPRI 8XJ. Greater Manchester lieutenancy: Gaddum House, 6 Great Jackson Street, Manchester M15 4AX. Merseyside lieutenancy: PO Box 144, Royal and Sun Alliance Building, New Hall Place, Old Hall Street, Liverpool L69 3EN.

who to apply to The Secretary, 1 Lancaster Place, Strand, London WC2E 7ED Tel. 020 7269 1700 email info@duchyoflancaster.co.uk Website www.duchyoflancaster.org.uk

■ The Lancaster Foundation

cc no 1066850   established 1997

where funding can be given UK and Africa, with a local interest in Clitheroe.

who can benefit Only charities personally known to the trustees.

what is funded Christian charities only.

sample grants Grand at Clitheroe (£615,000); Message Trust (£212,000); Mary's Meals (£122,000); Saltmine Trust (£96,000); Sparrow Ministries (£60,000); Association Cristiana Manos En Accion (£48,000); Christians against Poverty (£38,000); Revelation life (£25,000); Urban Saints (£10,000); Vision (£5,000); and Bethany Project, United Christian Broadcasters and Stoneyhurst Charity Day (£1,000 each).

FINANCES *Year* 2011–12 *Income* £4,209,357 *Grants* £1,792,515 *Assets* £50,718,183

TRUSTEES Rosemary Lancaster; Dr John Lancaster; Steven Lancaster; Julie Broadhurst.

HOW TO APPLY The trust has previously stated: 'We do not consider applications made to us from organisations or people unconnected with us. All our donations are instigated because of personal associations. Unsolicited mail is, sadly, a waste of the organisation's resources.'

WHO TO APPLY TO Rosemary Lancaster, Trustee, c/o Text House, 152 Bawdlands, Clitheroe, Lancashire BB7 2LA *Tel.* 01200 444404

....

■ LandAid Charitable Trust

CC NO 295157   ESTABLISHED 1986

WHERE FUNDING CAN BE GIVEN Worldwide.

WHO CAN BENEFIT Charitable organisations.

WHAT IS FUNDED Provision of accommodation, assistance with refurbishment projects, running training, life skills and other educational programmes and start-up funding.

WHAT IS NOT FUNDED No grants to individuals.

TYPE OF GRANT One-off. Project funding and capital costs.

RANGE OF GRANTS £5,000–£25,000.

SAMPLE GRANTS Roots and Shoots and St Basils (£150,000 each); FRE Flyers (£85,000); Llamau (£75,000); Fuse Youth Cafe Glasgow and Jericho Foundation (£50,000 each); Goodwin Development Trust and St Edmunds Society (£35,000 each); East Cleveland Youth Housing Trust and Grimsby and Cleethorpes Area Doorstep (£25,000 each); Burley Lodge Centre (£10,000); and Motiv8 South Ltd (£9,500).

FINANCES *Year* 2012–13 *Income* £1,368,532 *Grants* £1,127,515 *Assets* £449,490

TRUSTEES Robin Broadhurst; Robert Bould; Michael Slade; Suzanne Avery; Elizabeth Peace; David Taylor; Lynette Lackey; Timothy Roberts; Robert Noel; Jeremy Newsum; Alistair Elliott; Jenny Buck; David Erwin.

HOW TO APPLY Organisations should apply online through the trust's website. Supporting documentation, including a copy of the latest annual report and financial statements, is required. Written applications for grant support are required to ensure that they fall within the stated criteria; projects are then shortlisted and reviewed by the grants committee. Organisations receiving grant support are required to report on the progress of the project being funded and to provide evidence of the impact of the grant.

WHO TO APPLY TO Joanna Averley, Chief Executive, St Albans House, 5th Floor, 57–59 Haymarket, London SW1Y 4QX *Tel.* 020 3102 7190 *email* enquiries@landaid.org *Website* www.landaid.org

....

■ The Jack Lane Charitable Trust

CC NO 1091675   ESTABLISHED 2002

WHERE FUNDING CAN BE GIVEN Gloucestershire and Wiltshire.

WHO CAN BENEFIT Registered charities.

WHAT IS FUNDED General charitable purposes.

RANGE OF GRANTS Up to £2,500.

SAMPLE GRANTS Previous beneficiaries include: Whizz-Kidz, Mitchemp Trust, Youth Action Wiltshire, Gloucester House Salvation Army, Alzheimer's Support, Doorway Wiltshire Ltd. and Mediation Plus (£2,000 each) and Prospect Hospice and Macmillan Cancer Support (£1,500 each).

FINANCES *Year* 2012–13 *Income* £55,668 *Grants* £45,590 *Assets* £2,149,023

TRUSTEES Jim Toogood; Richard White; Sarah Priday; Christine MacLachlan; David Crampton; Tim Newman; Martin Wright.

HOW TO APPLY In writing to the correspondent or on a form available to download from the trust's website.

WHO TO APPLY TO Emma Walker, Clerk to the Trustees, Agriculture House, 12 High Street, Wotton-Under-Edge, Gloucestershire GL12 7DB *email* admin@jacklane.co.uk *Website* www.jacklane.co.uk

....

■ The Allen Lane Foundation

CC NO 248031   ESTABLISHED 1966

WHERE FUNDING CAN BE GIVEN UK

WHO CAN BENEFIT Organisations whose work is with groups who may be perceived as unpopular such as asylum seekers, lesbian, gay bisexual or transgender people, gypsies and travellers, offenders and ex-offenders, older people, people experiencing mental health problems and people experiencing violence or abuse.

WHAT IS FUNDED Provision of advice or information; advocacy; arts activities where the primary purpose is therapeutic or social; befriending or mentoring; mediation or conflict resolution; practical work, such as gardening or recycling, which benefits both the provider and the recipient; self-help groups; social activities or drop in centres; strengthening the rights of particular groups and enabling their views and experiences to be heard by policy-makers; research and education aimed at changing public attitudes or policy; work aimed at combatting stigma or discrimination; work developing practical alternatives to violence.

WHAT IS NOT FUNDED The foundation does not currently make grants for academic research; addiction, alcohol or drug abuse; animal welfare or animal rights; arts or cultural or language projects or festivals; work with children, young people and families; endowments or contributions to other grantmaking bodies; holidays or holiday play schemes; housing; hospices and medical research; individuals; museums or galleries; overseas travel; particular medical conditions or disorders; physical or learning disabilities; private and/or mainstream education; promotion of sectarian religion; publications; purchase costs of property, refugee community groups working with single nationalities; restoration or conservation of historic buildings or sites; sports and recreation; therapy, counselling; vehicle purchase; work relating to particular medical conditions of illness; work which the trustees believe is rightly the responsibility of the state; work outside the United Kingdom; work which will already have taken place before a grant is agreed; work by local organisations with an income of more than £100,000 per annum or those working over a wider area with an income of more than £250,000. The foundation will not normally make grants to organisations which receive funding (directly or indirectly) from commercial sources where conflicts of interest for the organisation and its work are likely to arise.

TYPE OF GRANT One-off and for up to three years.

RANGE OF GRANTS Usually £500–£15,000.

SAMPLE GRANTS Refugee Survival Trust (£15,000); Rape and Abuse Line (£12,000; Hope Housing (£10,000); Mind Shropshire (£7,500); Cambridge Money Advice Centre and

Lanarkshire Rape Crisis Centre (£5,000 each); Art Beyond Belief and UK Association of Gypsy Women (£3,000 each); Lesbian Immigration Support Group (£1,500); Senior Citizens Lunch Club and Rainbow Families (£1,000 each); Rebound Self Harm Support (£600) and Young at Heart Club (£500).

FINANCES *Year* 2011–12 *Income* £553,123 *Grants* £732,666 *Assets* £16,590,550

TRUSTEES Clare Morpurgo; Zoe Teale; Guy Dehn; Juliet Walker; Fredrica Teale; Margaret Hyde; Philip Walsh.

PUBLICATIONS Every year the foundation hosts a lecture in memory of Sir Allen Lane, the texts of which are published on the foundation's website.

HOW TO APPLY There is no formal application form, but there is a short registration form, available from the website. The registration form should accompany the application. An application should be no more than four sides of A4 but the project budget may be on extra pages. It should be accompanied by your organisation's last annual report and accounts if you produce such documents and the budget for the whole organisation (and the project budget if they are different) for the current year.

'The application should include the following information: the aims of your organisation as a whole; how these aims are achieved; how your proposals make a lasting difference to people's lives rather than simply alleviating the symptoms or current problems; how the proposals reduce isolation, stigma and discrimination or encourage or enable unpopular groups to share in the life of the whole community; why your cause or beneficiary group is an unpopular one; what you want the grant to pay for; what difference a grant would make to your work; the cost of the work; whether you are asking the foundation to meet the whole cost of the work; details of any other sources of funding you are approaching; details of how you know if the work has been successful; details of how the work, and the way it is done, promotes equal opportunities. If you do not think equal opportunities are relevant to your work say why.'

'If further information is needed this will be requested and a visit may be arranged when the application can be discussed in more detail.'

'All applications should be made to the Foundation's office and **not** sent to individual Trustees. If you have any queries about making an application you are encouraged to phone the staff for clarification.'

WHO TO APPLY TO Tim Cutts, Executive Secretary, 90 The Mount, York YO24 1AR *Tel.* 01904 613223 *Fax* 01904 613133 *email* info@ allenlane.org.uk *Website* www.allenlane.org.uk

---

■ Langdale Trust

CC NO 215317   **ESTABLISHED** 1960

WHERE FUNDING CAN BE GIVEN Worldwide, with some preference towards Birmingham.

WHO CAN BENEFIT Registered charities.

WHAT IS FUNDED General charitable purposes, young people, social welfare, health, Christian.

WHAT IS NOT FUNDED No grants to individuals.

RANGE OF GRANTS £1,000–£10,000.

SAMPLE GRANTS Girlguiding (£10,000); Shelter Cymru and Save the Children Fund (£6,000 each); Macmillan Cancer Relief and Make a Wish Foundation (£5,000 each); Buttle UK (£4,000); National Foundation for Conductive Education, Dodford Children's Holiday Farm and Deafblind UK (£3,000 each); and Survival

International, Help the Aged and Off the Rail Contemporary (£1,000 each).

FINANCES *Year* 2011–12 *Income* £134,840 *Grants* £130,000 *Assets* £3,662,857

TRUSTEES Timothy Wilson; Theresa Wilson; Jethro Elvin.

OTHER INFORMATION Grants were made to 42 organisations totalling £130,000.

HOW TO APPLY In writing to the correspondent.

WHO TO APPLY TO Ruth Barron, Administrator, c/o DWF LLP, 1 Scott Place, 2 Hardman Street, Manchester M3 3AA *Tel.* 01618 380487

■ The Langley Charitable Trust

CC NO 280104   **ESTABLISHED** 1980

WHERE FUNDING CAN BE GIVEN UK and worldwide, with a preference for the West Midlands

WHO CAN BENEFIT Individuals and groups benefiting Christians, at risk groups, people who are disadvantaged by poverty, socially isolated or sick.

WHAT IS FUNDED Advancement of the gospel and Christianity; welfare and health.

RANGE OF GRANTS Less than £1,000 to £50,000.

SAMPLE GRANTS Northamptonshire Association of Youth Clubs (£50,000); Coton Green Church and United Christian Broadcasters (£25,000 each); Youth for Christ (£10,000); Sutton Coldfield Vineyard (£2,000); the Gap (£1,000); and Two Rivers School (£400).

FINANCES *Year* 2012 *Income* £100,524 *Grants* £113,360 *Assets* £3,864,895

TRUSTEES John Gilmour; Sylvia Gilmour.

OTHER INFORMATION Grants were made totalling just over £113,000 to seven organisations.

HOW TO APPLY The trustees' report for 2012 states that 'trustees only reply where they require other information. No telephone calls or correspondence will be entered into concerning any proposed or declined applications.'

WHO TO APPLY TO John Gilmour, Trustee, Wheatmoor Farm, 301 Tamworth Road, Sutton Coldfield B75 6JP *Tel.* 01213 080165

■ The Langtree Trust

CC NO 232924   **ESTABLISHED** 1963

WHERE FUNDING CAN BE GIVEN Gloucestershire.

WHO CAN BENEFIT Organisations benefiting the local community; occasionally to individuals if then of direct benefit to the community.

WHAT IS FUNDED General charitable purposes in Gloucestershire only. Priority is given to church projects, youth groups and people who are disabled or disadvantaged. The arts have a lower priority.

WHAT IS NOT FUNDED No grants are given in response to general appeals from large UK organisations. No grants for education.

TYPE OF GRANT Usually one-off for a specific project.

RANGE OF GRANTS £50–£1,000.

FINANCES *Year* 2011–12 *Income* £255,490 *Grants* £42,435 *Assets* £1,349,935

TRUSTEES Paul Haslam; Dr Richard Way; Mike Page; Ann Shepherd; Sally Birch; Katherine Bertram; Will Conway.

OTHER INFORMATION There were 124 grants awarded during the year.

HOW TO APPLY In writing to the correspondent giving a simple, clear statement of the need with the costs of the project, what funding has so far been achieved and/or a recent copy of the annual accounts. Expensive, extensive, glossy appeal brochures are not appreciated. The trustees meet four to six times a year to decide the grant allocation. In exceptional circumstances a grant may be made between meetings. Note that the address is a postal address and Randall and Payne cannot answer any telephone queries.

WHO TO APPLY TO Katherine Bertram, Secretary, c/o Sutton Dipple Accountants Ltd, 8 Wheelwright's Corner, Old Market, Nailsworth, Gloucestershire GL6 0DB *Tel.* 01453 833060 *Fax* 01453 833070 *email* info@suttondipple.co.uk

....

■ The LankellyChase Foundation

CC NO 1107583   **ESTABLISHED** 2005
WHERE FUNDING CAN BE GIVEN UK.
WHO CAN BENEFIT 'We are less interested in the type of organisation than the work taking place – we mainly fund charities but we can fund non-charitable organisations as long as the work itself has charitable purposes and there is no 'private benefit' to non-charitable interests. We are especially keen to hear about work led by people with lived experience of severe and multiple disadvantage. We are open to funding any sort of work – it does not have to be service delivery and can include things like campaigning, journalism, film making or research. In all cases we are looking for people willing to work in an open way and to share ideas with us and the other projects we support.'
WHAT IS FUNDED At the end of 2013 the foundation launched a new funding programme. The following information is taken from the foundation's website:
'**Funds Available – Open Call for Project Ideas:** LankellyChase Foundation's mission is to bring about change to improve the lives of people facing severe and multiple disadvantage. By this we mean people who are experiencing a combination of severe social harms such as homelessness, substance misuse, mental illness, extreme poverty, and violence and abuse. We are not interested in sticking plaster solutions, even if they make people's lives better in the short term, but in changing the fundamentals. We think that: many of the services that are supposed to help people operate in 'silos' (looking at each need on its own) rather than responding to the 'whole person' and that this needs to change; services are too often set up to respond to crisis rather than preventing problems developing in the first place; there is a need to address the lack of power and influence in the hands of people facing severe and multiple disadvantage; people facing severe and multiple disadvantage are often excluded from the market – the services and activities most of us take for granted, including employment, finance and leisure; certain discriminated-against groups face even greater disadvantage and this needs to be brought to light and addressed. We have some ideas about what might make change happen (set out in our 'Theory of Change') but we are clear that we do not have all the answers and we certainly cannot do this alone. These are really thorny issues and success in this area has so far been limited. We are all working in an environment that has changed drastically in recent times. We are convinced that new, radical and even daring ideas are needed and we want to find and support the very best of these as well as working out which current approaches are working well and why. If you think your project (large or small, short or lengthy) can help us towards our mission, we would like to hear from you. We strongly suggest

you read our 'Theory of Change' before applying. We do not make a large number of grants so everyone has to give us something really valuable and different in terms of our overall objectives. If you read these guidelines and our website and think that there is a clear match between your ideas and ours then we want to hear from you.'
WHAT IS NOT FUNDED 'Our focus is always on people who are experiencing a combination of severe social harms, and we are therefore very unlikely to fund work that is about a single issue, such as mental illness alone. Also note that we don't fund work that is focused exclusively on the following: a particular health condition; disability issues; imprisonment and/or prisoner resettlement; issues affecting asylum seekers.'
TYPE OF GRANT Capital, revenue and full project funding for up to three years.
RANGE OF GRANTS Mainly £10,000 to £15,000. Occasionally up to £135,000.
SAMPLE GRANTS Family Action – London (£135,000); Afiya Trust – London (£75,000); Creation Community Development Trust – S. Wales (£60,000); Off the Hook/York Boxing Club and Blackpool Women's Centre (£50,000 each); New Step for African Community, Rochdale (£45,000); Together Women Project – Bradford, Small World Cultural Arts Collective – Keighley and Argyll and Bute Rape Crisis (£36,000 each); Kirckman Concert Society – London (£35,000); Amina – The Muslim Women's Research Centre – Glasgow and National Coalition of Anti-Deportation Campaigns – London (£30,000 each); The Foundation for Families – Yorkshire (£25,000); Female Prisoners Welfare Project – London (£20,000); Artichoke Trust, London (£12,000); Ethex – Oxford (£10,000) and New Harmonie – West Sussex (£5,300).
FINANCES *Year* 2011–12 *Income* £4,858,019 *Grants* £5,727,614 *Assets* £118,777,465
TRUSTEES Suzi Leather, Chair; Hilary Berg; Morag Burnett; Paul Cheng; Martin Clarke; Bobby Duffy; Victoria Hoskins; Marion Janner; Peter Latchford; Clive Martin; Jane Millar; Andrew Robinson; Kanwaljit Singh; Simon Tucker.
HOW TO APPLY The following information is taken from the foundation's website:
'We have a two-stage application process:
Stage 1: Check if we are the right funder for you and send an Expression of Interest
Check if we are the right funder for you; read our 'Theory of Change' [available on the foundation's website] to understand the problems we want to address and the type of change we want to see and support; email us, write to us, phone us or send us a video of yourself talking about your project or idea, whichever works best for you. When telling us about the work you would like to do, tell us the following: what is the change that you are aiming for as a result of your project?; how will you make that change happen?; how will you know that you have succeeded?; in what way will your project shift power to people who face severe and multiple disadvantage?; how will you ensure that your ideas influence and reach beyond your organisation, e.g. locally and/or nationally? Alongside this, you will also need to complete and submit our brief registration form. Your letter/email should be up to a maximum of 1,000 words; and if you are applying by submitting a video, this should be between three and five minutes long. We will send you an email to let you know that we have received your application. We will not share your project ideas with anyone else outside LankellyChase at this stage.'

690

Does the trust you have chosen match your needs? Haphazard applications waste postage and time

'Stage 2: Work with us to build a full proposal
We will contact you within six weeks to let you know whether we think your idea offers something really valuable in the context of our mission. If it does, we will invite you to move forward to stage two. We will then work with you to develop your idea to the point where we can put it to our trustees in the form of a fully developed proposal and ask for funding. This is a process that may take some months and will involve meeting you, probably more than once. Our grants committee, made up of our trustees meets twice a year though we can sometimes make decisions on funding in between meetings.'
'Where do I send my Expression of Interest and registration form? You can email us or send your video to grants@lankellychase.org.uk, or you can use Dropbox by sharing your link or your folder; you can call us on 020 3747 9930. We will ask you the questions listed above and write down what you say; you can write to us. If you are successful, we will call or visit you regularly; we will support you if necessary or get you together with people from other projects we fund. We are keen to bring people together to share ideas and learn what does and doesn't work to improve the lives of people facing severe and multiple disadvantage.'
WHO TO APPLY TO Julian Corner, Chief Executive, First Floor Greenworks, Dog and Duck Yard, Princeton Street, London WC1R 4BH *Tel.* 020 3747 9930 *email* grants@lankellychase.org.uk
Website www.lankellychase.org.uk

■ The R. J. Larg Family Charitable Trust

SC NO SC004946 **ESTABLISHED** 1970
WHERE FUNDING CAN BE GIVEN UK but generally Scotland, particularly Tayside.
WHO CAN BENEFIT Organisations benefiting children, young adults, students and people who are disabled or who have a disease or medical condition.
WHAT IS FUNDED Grants are made for cancer research, amateur music and youth organisations including university students' associations. Funding may also be given to churches, conservation, respite care, hospices, MS and neurological research, care in the community and other community facilities. Other charitable purposes will be considered.
WHAT IS NOT FUNDED Grants are not available for individuals.
TYPE OF GRANT Generally one-off, some recurring. Buildings, core costs, running costs, salaries and start-up costs will be considered. Funding may be given for up to two years.
RANGE OF GRANTS £250–£5,000; typical grant £1,000–£2,000.
SAMPLE GRANTS Previous beneficiaries include High School – Dundee, Whitehall Theatre Trust, Macmillan Cancer Relief – Dundee and Sense Scotland Children's Hospice.
FINANCES *Year* 2013 *Grants* £100,000 *Assets* £141,880
TRUSTEES R. Gibson; D. Brand; S. Stewart.
HOW TO APPLY In writing to the correspondent. Trustees meet to consider grants in February and August.
WHO TO APPLY TO The Trustees, Whitehall House, Yeaman Shore, Dundee DD1 4BJ

■ Largsmount Ltd

CC NO 280509 **ESTABLISHED** 1979
WHERE FUNDING CAN BE GIVEN UK and overseas.
WHO CAN BENEFIT Institutions providing religious education in accordance with the doctrine and principles of traditional Judaism and organisations set up to provide for the Jewish needy.
WHAT IS FUNDED Jewish charitable purposes.
WHAT IS NOT FUNDED Gives mainly to Jewish charitable organisations.
SAMPLE GRANTS A list of beneficiaries was unavailable.
FINANCES *Year* 2012 *Income* £672,791 *Grants* £216,392 *Assets* £4,235,902
TRUSTEES ZM. Kaufman; Simon Kaufman; Naomi Kaufman.
OTHER INFORMATION Accounts for previous years were available without a list of grants.
HOW TO APPLY In writing to the correspondent.
WHO TO APPLY TO Simon Kaufman, Trustee, 50 Keswick Street, Gateshead NE8 1TQ *Tel.* 01914 900140

■ The Lark Trust

CC NO 327982 **ESTABLISHED** 1988
WHERE FUNDING CAN BE GIVEN Mainly Bristol.
WHO CAN BENEFIT Registered charities benefiting people of all ages.
WHAT IS FUNDED Support in the areas of counselling, psychotherapy and the visual arts.
WHAT IS NOT FUNDED No grants to individuals.
TYPE OF GRANT Generally one-off
RANGE OF GRANTS £500 to £3,000
SAMPLE GRANTS Bristol and District Tranquiliser Project and Womankind (£3,000 each); St Peter's Hospice Trust, Windmill Hill City Farm, Positive Action on Cancer, Firebird Theatre and Artists First Spike Island (£2,000 each); Myeloma Foundation and Alive (£1,000) and Wye Valley Music Society (£500).
FINANCES *Year* 2011–12 *Income* £43,899 *Grants* £38,475 *Assets* £1,471,272
TRUSTEES George Tute; Malcolm Tute.
OTHER INFORMATION Grants were given to 22 organisations.
HOW TO APPLY Initially in writing to the correspondent, who will check eligibility and then send a form which must be completed. Trustees do not accept information from charities wishing to build a relationship with them. Applications should be received by the end of January for consideration in March.
WHO TO APPLY TO Alice Meason, c/o Quartet Community Foundation, Royal Oak House, Royal Oak Avenue, Bristol BS1 4AH *Tel.* 01179 897700 *Fax* 01179 897701

■ Laslett's (Hinton) Charity

CC NO 233696 **ESTABLISHED** 1879
WHERE FUNDING CAN BE GIVEN Worcestershire and surrounding area.
WHO CAN BENEFIT Children, older people, clergy and people who are disadvantaged by poverty.
WHAT IS FUNDED Church repairs; general benefit of people who are poor, including homes for older people and educating children; relief of sickness, hospitals and general charitable purposes in Worcestershire and surrounding area.
FINANCES *Year* 2011–12 *Income* £358,399 *Grants* £125,803 *Assets* £15,467,896

TRUSTEES T. J. Bridges; R. J. R. Young; M. Jones; E. A. Pugh-Cook; J. B. Henderson; J. V. Panter; A. P. Baxter; A. E. Lodge; S. P. Inman; P. Wittenberg; G. T. Newman.

OTHER INFORMATION This trust has recently been focussing on the refurbishments of its properties in the hope of generating greater income in the following years, therefore has not been giving many grants that do not further this aim. This position is currently under review.

HOW TO APPLY In writing to the correspondent. Trustees meet quarterly to consider applications.

WHO TO APPLY TO Ian C. Pugh, Kateryn Heywood House, Berkeley Court, The Foregate, Worcester WR1 3QG *Tel.* 01905 726600 *email* admin@lasletts.org.uk

■ **Laufer Charitable Trust**

CC NO 275375   **ESTABLISHED** 1961
WHERE FUNDING CAN BE GIVEN UK.
WHO CAN BENEFIT Charitable organisations.
WHAT IS FUNDED General charitable purposes.
WHAT IS NOT FUNDED No grants to individuals, as grants are only made to registered charities.
TYPE OF GRANT Recurrent core costs for up to one year.
FINANCES *Year* 2012–13 *Income* £65,587 *Grants* £48,800 *Assets* £925,493
TRUSTEES Stanley Laufer; Della Laufer; Simon Goulden; Rowland Aarons; Mark Hoffman.
OTHER INFORMATION As this is a small charity, new beneficiaries are only considered in exceptional circumstances as the income is already allocated for some years to come.
HOW TO APPLY In view of the ongoing support for an existing group of charities, applications are not recommended.
WHO TO APPLY TO Rowland Aarons, Trustee, 342 Regents Park Road, London N3 2LJ *Tel.* 020 8343 1660

■ **The Lauffer Family Charitable Foundation**

CC NO 251115   **ESTABLISHED** 1965
WHERE FUNDING CAN BE GIVEN Commonwealth countries, Israel and USA.
WHO CAN BENEFIT Educational, medical, welfare, cultural and Jewish charities.
WHAT IS FUNDED Education, medical, welfare, cultural and Jewish causes.
WHAT IS NOT FUNDED No support for individuals.
TYPE OF GRANT Starter finance and recurrent for five years.
SAMPLE GRANTS Lyttleton Playing Fields Redevelopment (£35,000); Jewish Learning Exchange (£22,000); British Friends of Sarah Herzog Memorial Hospital (£20,000); Friends of Tifereth Shlomo (£17,000); Chicken Shed Theatre Trust and Teenage Cancer Trust (£8,300 each); British Friends of Ariel (£7,000); Bridge Lane Beth Hamidrash (£5,200); Lincoln College Development Fund (£3,500) and Jewish Women's Aid, The Royal Ballet School and Nightingale (Home for Aged Jews) (£1,000 each).
FINANCES *Year* 2011–12 *Income* £350,414 *Grants* £380,678 *Assets* £5,352,384
TRUSTEES Jonathan Lauffer; Robin Lauffer; Gideon Lauffer.
HOW TO APPLY In writing to the correspondent; applications are considered once a year.

WHO TO APPLY TO Jonathan Simon Lauffer, Trustee, Clayton Stark and Co, 5th Floor, Charles House, 108–110 Finchley Road, London NW3 5JJ *Tel.* 020 7431 4200 *email* jonathanlauffer13@gmail.com

■ **Mrs F. B. Laurence Charitable Trust**

CC NO 296548   **ESTABLISHED** 1976
WHERE FUNDING CAN BE GIVEN UK and overseas.
WHO CAN BENEFIT Organisations benefiting ex-service and service people, retired people, unemployed people and disadvantaged members of society within the UK or overseas to whom the UK owes a duty of care.
WHAT IS FUNDED The aid and support of people who are chronically ill and people who are disabled. The support of justice and human rights organisations and the protection of the environment and wildlife. Charities working in the fields of accommodation and housing legal services, publishing and printing, support to voluntary and community organisations, volunteer bureaux, community arts and recreation, community facilities, special schools and special needs education and literacy will also be considered.
WHAT IS NOT FUNDED No support for individuals. The following applications are unlikely to be considered: appeals for endowment or sponsorship; overseas projects, unless overseen by the charity's own fieldworkers; maintenance of buildings or landscape; provision of work or materials that are the responsibility of the state; where administration expenses, in all their guises, are considered by the trustees to be excessive; or where the fundraising costs in the preceding year have not resulted in an increase in the succeeding years donations in excess of these costs.
TYPE OF GRANT Core costs, one-off, project and start-up costs. Funding is for one year or less.
SAMPLE GRANTS DEC East Africa Crisis Appeal and the Cambridge Foundation (£5,000 each); Halow Project (£4,000); Multiple Sclerosis Trust (£3,500); Shooting Star Chase and Wiltshire Air Ambulance (£2,000 each); Winston's Wish and Brooke Hospital for Animals (£1,500 each); and Fernhurst Recreation (£1,300).
FINANCES *Year* 2011–12 *Income* £80,492 *Grants* £87,500 *Assets* £2,342,866
TRUSTEES Caroline Fry; Camilla Carr; Elizabeth Lyle.
OTHER INFORMATION Smaller grants of £1,000 or less totalled £15,000.
HOW TO APPLY In writing to the correspondent, including the latest set of accounts. Only registered charities will be considered.
WHO TO APPLY TO The Trustees, BM Box 2082, London WC1N 3XX

■ **The Kathleen Laurence Trust**

CC NO 296461   **ESTABLISHED** 1987
WHERE FUNDING CAN BE GIVEN UK.
WHO CAN BENEFIT General charities with specific projects and events.
WHAT IS FUNDED General charitable purposes. The trust particularly favours smaller organisations and those raising funds for specific requirements such as medical research, associations connected with disability and learning difficulties, organisations helping people who are sick, older people and children.

WHAT IS NOT FUNDED No donations are made for running costs, management expenses or to individuals.
TYPE OF GRANT One-off and recurrent grants.
RANGE OF GRANTS £500–£30,000.
SAMPLE GRANTS Arthritis Research UK; Cancer Research UK; British Heart Foundation; Society for Horticultural Therapy; Greenwich Toys and Leisure Library Association; Fair Play for Children; I CAN – Children's Communication Charity; Aylsham Care Trust; QED – UK; Contact the Elderly; Dr Bell's Family Centre; Home Start – Stroud and Dursley; Calvert Trust; Birmingham Settlement; Disability Challengers; and Step by Step – Autistic School.
FINANCES *Year* 2011–12 *Income* £954,468 *Grants* £172,562 *Assets* £787,320
TRUSTEE Coutts and Co.
HOW TO APPLY In writing to the correspondent. Trustees meet in January and June.
WHO TO APPLY TO Trust Manager, Coutts and Co, Trustee Department, 440 Strand, London WC2R 0QS *Tel.* 020 7663 6825

■ The Law Society Charity

CC NO 268736   **ESTABLISHED** 1974
WHERE FUNDING CAN BE GIVEN Worldwide.
WHO CAN BENEFIT Organisations protecting people's legal rights and lawyers' welfare as well as projects from charities without an identifiable legal connection.
WHAT IS FUNDED Charitable activities in the furtherance of law and justice. This includes: charitable educational purposes for lawyers and would-be lawyers; legal research; promotion of an increased understanding of the law; promotion of human rights and charities concerned with the provision of advice, counselling, mediation services connected with the law, welfare directly/indirectly of solicitors, trainee solicitors and other legal and Law Society staff and their families.
WHAT IS NOT FUNDED Projects with a narrow geographical remit are generally not supported. No grants to individuals.
TYPE OF GRANT One-off and recurrent grants.
RANGE OF GRANTS Up to £15,000.
SAMPLE GRANTS Liverpool Mombasa Access to Justice Project and Personal Support Unit (£15,000 each); City of Westminster and Holborn Law Society – Caravana Colombia (£12,500); Just Fair – Economic, Social and Cultural Rights UK (£10,000); Advocates for International Development (£8,000); Fair Trials International (£7,500); UK Lesbian and Gay Immigration Group and Detention Advice Service (£5,000 each) and University of Cape Town (£3,500).
FINANCES *Year* 2011–12 *Income* £275,063 *Grants* £111,850 *Assets* £726,652
TRUSTEE The Law Society Trustees Ltd.
HOW TO APPLY On an application form available to download from the website. Applications are considered at quarterly trustees' meetings, usually held in April, July, September and December.
WHO TO APPLY TO Andrew Dobson, Company Secretary, 110–113 Chancery Lane, London WC2A 1PL *Tel.* 020 7316 5597 *email* lawsocietycharity@lawsociety.org.uk *Website* www.lawsociety.org.uk

■ The Edgar E. Lawley Foundation

CC NO 201589   **ESTABLISHED** 1961
WHERE FUNDING CAN BE GIVEN UK, with a preference for the West Midlands.
WHO CAN BENEFIT Older people, disability, children, community, hospices and medical in the UK
WHAT IS FUNDED Charities involved in the provision of medical care and services to older people, children's charities, and those involved with the advancement of medicine and medical research.
WHAT IS NOT FUNDED No grants to individuals.
TYPE OF GRANT One-off.
RANGE OF GRANTS Average of £1,500.
SAMPLE GRANTS Beneficiaries were listed in the accounts, but without any indication of the size of grant received. They included: Rugby Mountaineering Club, Samaritans, Toynbee Hall, Woking and Sam Beare Hospices, SSAFA Forces Help, Dogs for the Disabled, Inspire Foundation, Newman University College – Birmingham, Cockermouth Mountain Rescue Team and Babies in Prison.
FINANCES *Year* 2011–12 *Income* £187,583 *Grants* £196,500 *Assets* £3,977,371
TRUSTEES J. H. Cooke, Chair; G. Hilton; P. J. Cooke; F. S. Jackson.
HOW TO APPLY Applications should be made in writing to the correspondent by 31 October. Applicants should outline the reasons for the grant request and the amount of grant being sought. Any supporting information that adds to the strength of the application should be included. The trustees make grant decisions in January. The foundation regrets that it is not possible, unless a stamped addressed envelope has been provided, to communicate with unsuccessful applicants and the fact that a grant has not been received by the end of January indicates that it has not been possible to fund it. The trustees advise that around one in seven applications is successful.
WHO TO APPLY TO F. S. Jackson, Trustee, P.O. Box 456, Esher KT10 1DP *Tel.* 01372 805760 *email* frankjackson1945@yahoo.com *Website* www.edgarelawleyfoundation.org.uk

■ The Herd Lawson and Muriel Lawson Charitable Trust

CC NO 1113220   **ESTABLISHED** 1975
WHERE FUNDING CAN BE GIVEN Mainly Cumbria.
WHO CAN BENEFIT Charitable organisations.
WHAT IS FUNDED This trust supports organisations benefiting older people in need, particularly those who are members of evangelical or Christian Brethren churches. A number of other named organisations receive support each year.
SAMPLE GRANTS British Red Cross Society and WWF – UK (£21,000 each); the Christian Workers Relief Fund (£15,000); West Cumbria Hospice (£7,000) the Hospice of St Mary of Furness (£4,500); Ambleside Baptist Church (£4,500); Spring Mount Fellowship (£3,000); Ambleside Welfare Charity (£2,500) the Universal Beneficent Society (£1,500); and Heron Corn Mill Project (£400).
FINANCES *Year* 2011–12 *Income* £217,934 *Grants* £90,000
TRUSTEES John Scott; Peter Matthews; Robert Barker; Brian Herd.
HOW TO APPLY The trust receives more applications than it can deal with and does not seek further unsolicited appeals. 'The trustees have established a number of charities to whom they make grants each year and they very rarely make any donations to other charities.'

WHO TO APPLY TO John Scott, The Estate Office, 14 Church Street, Ambleside, Cumbria LA22 0BT *Tel.* 01539 434758

■ The Lawson Beckman Charitable Trust

CC NO 261378   ESTABLISHED 1970
WHERE FUNDING CAN BE GIVEN UK and overseas.
WHO CAN BENEFIT Mainly headquarters organisations.
WHAT IS FUNDED Jewish organisations, welfare, education, the arts and general purposes.
WHAT IS NOT FUNDED No grants to individuals.
TYPE OF GRANT One-off and recurrent.
RANGE OF GRANTS £1,000–£21,000.
SAMPLE GRANTS Jewish Care (£21,000); Norwood Ravenswood (£11,000); World Jewish Relief (£5,000); United Jewish Israel Appeal (£3,000); Dalaid Limited and the Prince's Teaching Institute (£2,000 each); and the Anne Frank Trust (£1,000).
FINANCES *Year* 2011–12 *Income* £64,518 *Grants* £62,325 *Assets* £2,497,818
TRUSTEES Melvin Lawson; Lynton Stock; Francis Katz.
HOW TO APPLY In writing to the correspondent.
WHO TO APPLY TO Melvin Lawson, Trustee, A. Beckman plc, PO Box 1ED, London W1A 1ED *Tel.* 020 7637 8412

■ The Raymond and Blanche Lawson Charitable Trust

CC NO 281269   ESTABLISHED 1980
WHERE FUNDING CAN BE GIVEN UK, with an interest in West Kent and East Sussex.
WHO CAN BENEFIT Charitable organisations benefiting children, young adults, older people, people with disabilities and people within the armed forces.
WHAT IS FUNDED This trust will consider funding: arts activities and education; building preservation; hospice at home; nursing service; local hospices; hospitals; cancer research; community centres and village halls; guide dogs; care in the community; and armed service charities and benevolent associations.
WHAT IS NOT FUNDED No support for individuals.
TYPE OF GRANT One-off, project and research. Funding is available for up to one year.
RANGE OF GRANTS £250–£5,000. Typically £500–£1,000.
SAMPLE GRANTS The two largest grants during the year were for £5,000 and were awarded to the following charities: Royal British Legion and the Royal London Society for the Blind. Smaller grants included: Crisis, Royal Marsden and Kent Air Ambulance (£2,500 each); Scots Project Trust, Cancer Research UK, Young Lives Foundation and the Heart of Kent Hospice (£2,000 each); Worldwide Volunteering (£1,500); British Lung Foundation, Canine Partners, Fire Fighters Charity and Age Concern (£1,000 each); and the National Autistic Society, the Dame Vera Lynn Trust and Action for Deafness (£500 each).
FINANCES *Year* 2011–12 *Income* £140,183 *Grants* £97,430 *Assets* £1,601,491
TRUSTEES Philip Thomas; Sarah Hill.
OTHER INFORMATION Grants were made to 99 organisations totalling £97,000.
HOW TO APPLY In writing to the correspondent.
WHO TO APPLY TO The Trustees, 28 Barden Road, Tonbridge, Kent TN9 1TX *Tel.* 01732 352183 *email* philip.thomas@worrinlawson.co.uk

■ The Mason Le Page Charitable Trust

CC NO 1054589   ESTABLISHED 1996
WHERE FUNDING CAN BE GIVEN London area.
WHO CAN BENEFIT Organisations benefiting people with cancer and medical research.
WHAT IS FUNDED General charitable purposes, with a preference for supporting charities working in cancer research and care in the London area.
WHAT IS NOT FUNDED No grants to individuals.
SAMPLE GRANTS Previous beneficiaries include: London Chest Hospital and Multiple Sclerosis Society (£5,000 each); Cancer BACUP and Dermatrust (£3,000 each); Harlington Hospice Middlesex and Royal Hospital for Neuro-disability (£2,000 each); The Peaceful Place (£1,500); Sergeant Cancer Care Children (£1,200); and CLIC Sargent (£500).
FINANCES *Year* 2011–12 *Income* £15,925 *Grants* £40,000
TRUSTEES David Morgan; Andrew Stebbings.
HOW TO APPLY In writing to the correspondent.
WHO TO APPLY TO Andrew Stebbings, The Administrator, c/o Pemberton Greenish LLP, 45 Cadogan Gardens, London SW3 2TB *Tel.* 020 7591 3333 *email* charitymanager@pglaw.co.uk

■ The Leach Fourteenth Trust

CC NO 204844   ESTABLISHED 1961
WHERE FUNDING CAN BE GIVEN UK, with some preference for south west England and overseas only via a UK charity.
WHO CAN BENEFIT Grants to registered charities only.
WHAT IS FUNDED General charitable purposes with a preference towards medicine, health, disability and conservation.
WHAT IS NOT FUNDED Only registered charities based in the UK are supported.
TYPE OF GRANT Buildings, capital, core costs, one-off, project, research, running costs, recurring costs, salaries and start-up costs will be considered. Funding may be given for more than three years.
RANGE OF GRANTS £500–£5,000.
SAMPLE GRANTS Previous beneficiaries included: Merlin (£10,000); the Country Trust (£4,500); Hope and Homes for Children (£3,000); Orbis, Deafblind UK and International Otter Survival Fund (£2,000 each); Roy Kinnear Trust and Salvation Army (£1,500 each); and Armed Forced Fund, Dogs for the Disabled and Isles of Scilly Museum (£1,000 each).
FINANCES *Year* 2011–12 *Income* £125,844 *Grants* £90,000
TRUSTEES Roger Murray-Leach; Judith Murray-Nash; Guy Ward; John Henderson; Tamsin Murray-Leach; Grant Nash; Richard Moore.
HOW TO APPLY In writing to the correspondent.
WHO TO APPLY TO Guy Ward, Trustee, Bathurst House, 86 Micklegate, York YO1 6LQ *Tel.* 01904 628551 *email* info@barronyork.co.uk

■ The David Lean Foundation

CC NO 1067074   ESTABLISHED 1997
WHERE FUNDING CAN BE GIVEN UK.
WHO CAN BENEFIT Charitable organisations.
WHAT IS FUNDED Promotion and advancement of education and to cultivate and improve public taste in the visual arts, particularly in the field of film production, including screenplay writing, film direction and editing.

TYPE OF GRANT One-off and recurrent grants.

RANGE OF GRANTS £13,000–£88,000

SAMPLE GRANTS National Film and Television School (£88,000); Royal Academy of Arts (£75,000); British Film Institute (£65,000); British Academy of Film and Television (£31,000); and Film Club UK (£13,000).

FINANCES *Year* 2012 *Income* £949,760 *Grants* £279,878 *Assets* £978,818

TRUSTEES Anthony Reeves; Stefan Breitenstein.

HOW TO APPLY Scholarship grants for students attending the National Film and Television School, Royal Holloway or Leighton Park School, are normally only awarded on the recommendation of the course provider with the trustees. Other applications for grants that would meet the aims of the foundation are invited in writing, enclosing full details of the project and including financial information and two references. Progress reports should be provided when required.

WHO TO APPLY TO The Trustees, The Bradshaws, Oaken, Codsall, Stoke On Trent WV8 2HU *Tel.* 01902 754024 *email* aareeves@davidleanfoundation.com *Website* www.davidleanfoundation.org

---

■ The Leathersellers' Company Charitable Fund

CC NO 278072   **ESTABLISHED** 1979

WHERE FUNDING CAN BE GIVEN UK, particularly London.

WHO CAN BENEFIT Registered charities only.

WHAT IS FUNDED Charities associated with the Leathersellers' Company, the leather and hide trades, education in leather technology and for the welfare of poor and sick former workers in the industry and their dependants. Charities working for the benefit of people in London in the following priority areas: education; disability; children and young people; relief of need. Charities working across the UK can also be supported.

TYPE OF GRANT One-off and recurrent grants.

RANGE OF GRANTS £500–£60,000

SAMPLE GRANTS The Message Trust and National Memorial Arboretum Appeal (£50,000); Colfe's School (£38,000); Research Autism and Leather Conservation Centre (£30,000 each); St Catherine's College (£27,000); Bendrigg Trust and Widehorizons Outdoor Education Trust (£25,000 each); The London Pathway, Edmonton Eagles Amateur Boxing Club and Cancer and Bio Detection Dogs (£20,000 each); Guildhall School Trust (£18,000) and Friendship Works, Me2 Club and New Horizon Youth Centre (£15,000 each).

FINANCES *Year* 2011–12 *Income* £1,472,000 *Grants* £1,552,000 *Assets* £41,194,000

TRUSTEE The Leathersellers Company

OTHER INFORMATION Grants of less than £15,000 totalled £657,000. A further 79 grants individuals for education totalled £167,000.

HOW TO APPLY Applications can be made using the online form on the company's website. Successful applicants to the main grants programme will typically have to pass through a four stage process, which can take up to nine months: Initial assessment – applicants will hear whether they have been successful or unsuccessful within six weeks; consideration by the grants committee; possible visit by committee working group for a detailed assessment; and grants committee final decision. Only one application can be made in a

year. If a charity is in receipt of a multi-year grants or a large single year grant cannot apply for another grants until four years has passed.

WHO TO APPLY TO David Santa-Olalla, Clerk, 21 Garlick Hill, London EC4V 2AU *Tel.* 020 7330 1444 *Fax* 020 7330 1445 *email* enquires@leathersellers.co.uk *Website* www.leathersellers.co.uk

---

■ The Leche Trust

CC NO 225659   **ESTABLISHED** 1963

WHERE FUNDING CAN BE GIVEN UK.

WHO CAN BENEFIT Individuals and organisations benefiting: preservation and conservation of art and architecture; education.

WHAT IS FUNDED (i) 'the promotion of amity and good relations between Britain and third world countries by financing visits to such countries by teachers or other appropriate persons, or providing financial assistance to students from overseas especially those in financial hardship during the last six months of their postgraduate doctorate study in the UK or those engaged in activities consistent with the charitable objects of the trust; (ii) assistance to academic, educational or other organisations concerned with music, drama, dance and the arts; (iii) the preservation of buildings and their contents and the repair and conservation of church furniture (including such items as monuments, but excluding structural repairs to the church fabric); preference is to be given to buildings and objects of the Georgian period; (iv) assistance to conservation in all its aspects, including in particular museums and encouraging good practice in the art of conservation by supporting investigative and diagnostic reports; (v) the support of charitable bodies or organisations associated with the preservation of the nation's countryside, towns, villages and historic landscapes.'

WHAT IS NOT FUNDED No grants are made for: religious bodies; overseas missions; schools and school buildings; social welfare; animals; medicine; expeditions; or British students other than music students.

TYPE OF GRANT Projects and capital costs, not recurring.

RANGE OF GRANTS £400–£20,000.

SAMPLE GRANTS Furniture History Society (£20,000); Warwickshire Museum Service (£8,000); Leeds College of Music (£5,000); London Shobana Jeyasingh Dance Company and NI Opera (£3,000 each); Théâtre Sans Frontières, Sound Festival and Barefaced Theatre Company (£1,000 each); English Folk Dance and Song Society (£600); All Saints Church – Northamptonshire and Sheffield Cemetery Trust – Yorkshire (£500 each); and the Library of Innerpeffary – Scotland (£400).

FINANCES *Year* 2011–12 *Income* £231,206 *Grants* £238,032 *Assets* £5,845,526

TRUSTEES Martin Williams; Dr Ian Bristow; Simon Wethered; Lady Greenstock; Ariane Bankes; Caroline Laing; Thomas Howard.

OTHER INFORMATION Included in the grant total is £23,000 given to individual students.

HOW TO APPLY In writing to the correspondent. Trustees meet three times a year, in February, June and October; applications need to be received the month before. Applications must be submitted via letter along with relevant supporting documents and budgets. Unsuccessful applications will be notified within two weeks. Funding for overseas students is on a rolling programme and students can apply at any time. Applications can only be made by students in the final six months of a PhD course and if they are under 35 years of age. Application forms and guidance notes can be obtained from the secretary.

WHO TO APPLY TO Louisa Lawson, Administrator, 84 Cicada Road, London SW18 2NZ *Tel.* 020 8870 6233 *email* info@lechetrust.org *Website* www.lechetrust.org

■ The Arnold Lee Charitable Trust

CC NO 264437 **ESTABLISHED** 1972
WHERE FUNDING CAN BE GIVEN UK.
WHO CAN BENEFIT Organisations linked to the Jewish community.
WHAT IS FUNDED Established charities of high repute working in the fields of education, health and religious purposes.
WHAT IS NOT FUNDED Grants are rarely made to individuals.
SAMPLE GRANTS Project Seed (£15,000); Aleph Society (£13,000); Policy Exchange Ltd (£7,500); Mesila UK (£6,500); JRoots (£5,000); and the Institute of Jewish Studies (£2,000).
FINANCES *Year* 2012–13 *Income* £465,784 *Grants* £169,076 *Assets* £1,999,884
TRUSTEES Edward Lee; Alan Lee.
OTHER INFORMATION A list of beneficiaries was not available, however two grants were noted in the annual report.
HOW TO APPLY In writing to the correspondent.
WHO TO APPLY TO Hazlems Fenton LLP, Administrator, Hazlems Fenton LLP, Palladium House, 1–4 Argyll Street, London W1F 7LD *Tel.* 020 7437 7666

■ The William Leech Charity

CC NO 265491 **ESTABLISHED** 1972
WHERE FUNDING CAN BE GIVEN Northumberland, Tyne and Wear, Durham and overseas.
WHO CAN BENEFIT Registered charities.
WHAT IS FUNDED Community welfare in particular youth projects, medical care, projects to assist people with disabilities and the maintenance of churches. Projects in the developing world which focus on the needs and welfare of disadvantaged children. Emergency aid to natural disasters is also given. Small registered charities where at least two thirds of the work is done by volunteers
WHAT IS NOT FUNDED No grants for: community centres and similar (exceptionally, those in remote country areas may be supported); running expenses of youth clubs (as opposed to capital projects); running expenses of churches (this includes normal repairs, but churches engaged in social work, or using their buildings largely for 'outside' purposes, may be supported); sport; the arts; individuals or students; organisations which have been supported in the last 12 months (it would be exceptional to support an organisation in two successive years, unless support had been confirmed in advance); holidays, travel, outings; minibuses (unless over 10,000 miles a year is expected); schools; and housing associations.
TYPE OF GRANT One-off and recurring grants, loans, running costs.
RANGE OF GRANTS £100–£100,000; most grants are for £1,000 or less.
SAMPLE GRANTS St Nicholas Cathedral Trust (£50,000); Maggie's (£20,000); CAFOD and The Alnwick Playhouse Trust (£10,000); The Alnwick Garden Trust (£6,000); Central Palz and Team

Kenya (£5,000 each); Northumberland Association of Clubs for Young People (£4,000); South Tyneside Asylum Seeker and Refugee (£2,000); Wallsend Sea Cadets and North Tyneside Disability Forum (£1,000 each); Shine a Light on Aniridia (£500) and Hartlepool Rugby Football Club (£250).
FINANCES *Year* 2011–12 *Income* £476,589 *Grants* £203,551 *Assets* £14,513,902
TRUSTEES Adrian Gifford; Roy Leech; Richard Leech; N. Sherlock; David Stabler; Barry Wallace.
HOW TO APPLY Application letters can be written and submitted on the charity's website, or sent by post. Full guidelines are also available there. Trustees meet every two months to consider applications.
WHO TO APPLY TO Kathleen M. Smith, Secretary, Saville Chambers, 5 North Street, Newcastle upon Tyne NE1 8DF *Tel.* 01912 433300 *email* enquiries@williamleechcharity.org.uk *Website* www.williamleechcharity.org.uk

■ The Lord Mayor of Leeds Appeal Fund

CC NO 512441 **ESTABLISHED** 1982
WHERE FUNDING CAN BE GIVEN Leeds Metropolitan District.
WHO CAN BENEFIT The charities selected by the lord mayor during her/his year of office.
WHAT IS FUNDED Charitable causes.
SAMPLE GRANTS Voluntary Action, Leeds (£34,000)
FINANCES *Year* 2011–12 *Income* £34,554 *Grants* £34,355 *Assets* £62,494
TRUSTEES Peter Gruen; Ann Blackburn; John M. Proctor; Susan Bentley.
HOW TO APPLY The fund does not accept unsolicited applications.
WHO TO APPLY TO Thomas Riordan, Secretary, Leeds City Council, Civic Hall, Leeds LS1 1JF *Tel.* 01132 474283

■ Leeds Building Society Charitable Foundation

CC NO 1074429 **ESTABLISHED** 1999
WHERE FUNDING CAN BE GIVEN Areas where the society's branches are located.
WHO CAN BENEFIT Organisations benefiting the homeless, local community centres, younger people, older people, individuals with disabilities, and deaf and/or blind people.
WHAT IS FUNDED Charities which have benefited include those working in the following areas: provision of shelter, support and resettlement programmes; for the homeless; centres offering facilities for the local community with emphasis on the young and elderly; provision of work experience and skills training for young people with special needs; educational and recreational projects for the deaf and blind; provision of transport for the physically disabled; practical care for the terminally ill; recreational and educational opportunities for children and young people from disadvantaged backgrounds.
WHAT IS NOT FUNDED The Foundation is unlikely to make donations for: The restoration or upgrading of buildings, including churches; Environmental charities (unless there is a benefit to a disadvantaged community); Administration equipment such as IT equipment for a charity's own use; Projects with religious, political or military purposes; Overseas charities or projects; Individuals, including sponsorship of

individuals; Animal welfare projects; Medical research.

TYPE OF GRANT One-off for capital projects.

RANGE OF GRANTS £250–£1,000.

FINANCES *Year* 2012 *Income* £111,089 *Grants* £122,004 *Assets* £11,399

TRUSTEES Paul Taylor; Ann Shelton; Gary Brook; Robert Wade; Martin Richardson; Peter Chadwick; Michael Garnett.

HOW TO APPLY In writing to the correspondent including the following information: The name of your organisation; The name of the project, and brief information about its work; A contact name, address and phone number; Your registered charity number; Details of what the donation would be used for; Who would benefit from the donation; Your nearest Leeds Building Society branch. The trustees meet four times a year in March, June, September and November. The trust is unable to consider applications if support has been provided in the last two years.

WHO TO APPLY TO Janet Lightfoot, Secretary, 105 Albion Street, Leeds, West Yorkshire LS1 5AS *Tel.* 01132 257508 *Website* www.leedsbuildingsociety.co.uk/foundation

■ The Leeds Community Foundation

CC NO 1096892   **ESTABLISHED** 2005

WHERE FUNDING CAN BE GIVEN Leeds.

WHO CAN BENEFIT Community groups and registered charities

WHAT IS FUNDED Social welfare and general charitable purposes.

WHAT IS NOT FUNDED Unless otherwise stated in the grants guidelines for the separate funds, the foundation cannot support: general and major fundraising appeals overseas travel or expeditions for individuals and groups projects that would normally be funded from statutory sources such as City Council, Local Education Authority, Health Authority etc., promotion of purely religious or party political causes, large national charities (except for independent local branches working for local people) work which has already been done before the application has been submitted sponsorship, fundraising events or advertising

RANGE OF GRANTS Usually from below £1,000 to £50,000

FINANCES *Year* 2011–12 *Income* £2,309,608 *Grants* £2,254,000 *Assets* £18,568,127

TRUSTEES Andrew Wriglesworth; Rachel Hannan; Kevin O'Connor; Steve Rogers; Helen Thomson; Nicholas Burr; Jonathan Morgan; Cath Mahoney.

OTHER INFORMATION The foundation runs a number of grant schemes that change frequently. Consult the foundation's website for details of current programmes and their deadlines.

HOW TO APPLY The foundation's website has details of the grant schemes currently being administered and how to apply.

WHO TO APPLY TO The Grants and Community Manager, 51a St Paul's Street, Leeds LS1 2TE *Tel.* 01132 422426 *email* info@leedscf.co.uk *Website* www.leedscf.org.uk

■ Leicestershire and Rutland Community Foundation

CC NO 1135322   **ESTABLISHED** 2002

WHERE FUNDING CAN BE GIVEN Leicestershire, Leicester and Rutland.

WHO CAN BENEFIT Charities and community groups with some preference for smaller groups.

WHAT IS FUNDED General charitable purposes, community development and local projects.

TYPE OF GRANT One-off, running and project costs.

RANGE OF GRANTS Mostly under £1,000 but up to £10,000

SAMPLE GRANTS Age UK Leicestershire and Rutland (£10,000); Network for Change (£8,500); Cottesmore Athletic Football Club and Cruse Bereavement Care (£2,000 each); Pablo's Horse Sanctuary (£1,800); Waltham Primary School (£1,700); 28th Leicester (Wigston) Scout Group, Heart of the Forest Festival and Original Step Performers (£1,000 each); Oasis Family Care (£500); Coalville Amateur Boxing Club (£430); Getting Lutterworth Growing (£390) and Ullesthorpe Environment Group (£190).

FINANCES *Year* 2011–12 *Income* £390,498 *Grants* £196,756 *Assets* £1,113,394

TRUSTEES Mary Arbuckle Chesterton; John Cope Strange; Kally Barot; James Kirkpatrick; Stephen Woolfe; Rick Moore; Ivan Trevor; Joan Valerie Stephens; Sue Tilley; Justine Flack; Stuart Graham Dawkins.

HOW TO APPLY Details of funds are available online. The foundation welcomes enquiries prior to the submission of formal applications either via phone or email. The application process differs depending on the scheme applied for with some schemes using online application forms and others using more traditional paper based forms. Grants panels are held twice yearly and deadlines for applications are around four to six weeks before the panel is due to sit.

WHO TO APPLY TO Hannah Stevens, Funds Coordinator (Lead), Leicestershire and Rutland Community Foundation, 3 Wycliffe Street, Leicester LE1 5LR *Tel.* 01162 624916 *email* grants@llrcommunityfoundation.org.uk *Website* www.llrcommunityfoundation.org.uk

■ Leicestershire Historic Churches Trust

CC NO 233476   **ESTABLISHED** 1964

WHERE FUNDING CAN BE GIVEN County of Leicester.

WHO CAN BENEFIT Churches and chapels.

WHAT IS FUNDED The restoration, preservation, repair, maintenance and improvement of churches and chapels, their churchyards and contents.

WHAT IS NOT FUNDED No grants for electrical work, disability access, reordering of the interior, redecorating, toilets or kitchen facilities, extensions, school or other ancillary buildings.

FINANCES *Year* 2011–12 *Income* £141,499 *Grants* £70,850 *Assets* £212,602

TRUSTEES Richard Bloor; Hon. Lady Brooks; Barrie Byford; Terence Cocks; John Hemes; Revd Derek Hole; James Ireland; David Knowles; Revd Fabian Radcliffe; Revd Timothy Stevens; Richard Wood; Janet Arthur.

HOW TO APPLY On a 'Grant Application Form' obtainable from the correspondent. Criteria and guidelines are available to view on the website. The trustees meet twice a year, usually in April and October. Applications should be submitted by 1 March and 1 September. Churches and chapels have three years in which to claim a grant once a grant has been awarded.

WHO TO APPLY TO Janet Arthur, 20 Gumley Road, Smeeton Westerby, Leicester LE8 0LT *Tel.* 01162 793995 *email* chair@lhct.org.uk *Website* www.lhct.org.uk

■ The Kennedy Leigh Charitable Trust

CC NO 288293   **ESTABLISHED** 1983
WHERE FUNDING CAN BE GIVEN Israel and UK.
WHO CAN BENEFIT Registered charities only.
WHAT IS FUNDED Projects and causes which will improve and enrich the lives of all parts of society, not least those of the young, the needy, the disadvantaged and the underprivileged. The trust's objects require three-quarters of its grantmaking funds to be distributed to charitable institutions within Israel, with the remainder being distributed in the UK and elsewhere.
WHAT IS NOT FUNDED No grants to individuals.
TYPE OF GRANT Capital projects and running costs. Usually up to three years, with the possibility of renewal.
RANGE OF GRANTS £1,000 and over.
SAMPLE GRANTS Sajur Israel Tennis Centre (£50,000) St John Eye Hospital (£27,000); CHAI Lifeline, Dental Volunteers Israel, Oxford Centre for Hebrew Studies and Jewish Association for the Mentally Ill (£25,000 each); Yad Vashem (£19,000); Jerusalem Print Workshop (£11,000); Community Security Trust and Jewish Care (£10,000 each); Krembo Wings (£9,600); Jewish Arab Community Centre (£9,300) and Hand in Hand (£4,800).
FINANCES *Year* 2011–12 *Income* £494,509 *Grants* £305,289 *Assets* £18,118,086
TRUSTEES Lesley Berman; Anthony Foux; Geoffrey Goldkorn; Angela L. Sorkin; Michael Sorkin; Carole Berman.
HOW TO APPLY The trust has informed us that they are not currently giving outside Israel apart from previous commitments.
WHO TO APPLY TO Naomi Shoffman, Administrator, ORT House, 126 Albert Street, London NW1 7NE *Tel.* 020 7267 6500 *email* naomi@klct.org

■ Morris Leigh Foundation

CC NO 280695   **ESTABLISHED** 1980
WHERE FUNDING CAN BE GIVEN England and Wales.
WHO CAN BENEFIT Charitable organisations, with a strong preference for Jewish organisations with interests abroad, especially Israel.
WHAT IS FUNDED General charitable purposes with focus on Jewish faith, including the arts and humanities, education, culture and welfare causes.
TYPE OF GRANT Grants to organisations.
RANGE OF GRANTS £1,000–£15,000.
SAMPLE GRANTS Institute of Jewish Policy Research (£15,000); Jerusalem Foundation (£13,000); JCC Donations Account (£10,000); Nightingale House (£5,000); Norwood School (£3,000) and Jerusalem Museum London (£1,000).
FINANCES *Year* 2011–12 *Income* £35,699 *Grants* £46,500 *Assets* £1,574,046
TRUSTEES Martin Paisner; Howard Leigh.
HOW TO APPLY In writing to the correspondent.
WHO TO APPLY TO Tina Grant-Brook, Administrator, 40 Portland Place, London W1B 1NB *Tel.* 020 7908 6000

■ The Leigh Trust

CC NO 275372   **ESTABLISHED** 1976
WHERE FUNDING CAN BE GIVEN UK and overseas.
WHO CAN BENEFIT Registered charities benefiting children; young adults; older people; unemployed people; volunteers; people who are in care, fostered or adopted; ethnic minority groups; at risk groups; people disadvantaged by poverty; ex-offenders and those at risk of offending; refugees; socially isolated people; people living in urban areas; victims of abuse and crime; and people with substance abuse problems.
WHAT IS FUNDED Grants can be given to legal services, support to voluntary and community organisations, support to volunteers, health counselling, support and self-help groups, drug and alcohol rehabilitation, education and training, social counselling, crime prevention schemes, community issues, international rights of the individual, advice and information (social issues), asylum seekers, racial equality and other charitable causes.
WHAT IS NOT FUNDED The trust does not make grants to individuals.
TYPE OF GRANT Buildings, capital, core costs, one-off, project, recurring costs, running costs, salaries and start-up costs. Funding is available for up to three years.
RANGE OF GRANTS £500–£5,000.
SAMPLE GRANTS The Amber Foundation (£6,000); Action on Addictions, Outside Edge Theatre Company and Shelter (£5,000 each); Music in Detention (£3,000); Bedfordshire Refugee and Asylum Support, Mentoring Plus and One North East London (£2,000 each); and Good News Family Care, Solace and The Trust Women's Project (1,500 each).
FINANCES *Year* 2011–12 *Income* £85,000 *Grants* £106,500 *Assets* £2,900,000
TRUSTEES Hon. David Bernstein; Dr R. M. E. Stone; Caroline Moorehead.
HOW TO APPLY Organisations applying for grants must provide their most recent audited accounts, a registered charity number, a cash flow statement for the next 12 months, and a stamped addressed envelope. Applicants should state clearly on one side of A4 what their charity does and what they are requesting funding for. They should provide a detailed budget and show other sources of funding for the project.
WHO TO APPLY TO The Trustees, Begbies Chettle Agar, Epworth House, 25 City Road, London EC1Y 1AR *Tel.* 020 7628 5801 *Fax* 020 7628 0390

■ Mrs Vera Leigh's Charity

CC NO 274872   **ESTABLISHED** 1976
WHERE FUNDING CAN BE GIVEN UK.
WHO CAN BENEFIT Charitable organisations only.
WHAT IS FUNDED General charitable purposes.
WHAT IS NOT FUNDED According to the 2011/12 accounts grants are only made to charitable organisations.
RANGE OF GRANTS £250–£1,000
SAMPLE GRANTS Royal British Legion (£1,000); WaterAid; Brain Research Trust and British Red Cross (£750 each); Royal National Institute for Blind People; NSPCC; Siloam Christians Ministries and The Samaritans of Guildford (£500 each); Movember and Farnham Amateur Operatic Society (£250 each); and Hampshire and Isle of Wight Air Ambulance (£100).
FINANCES *Year* 2011–12 *Income* £280,234 *Grants* £16,300 *Assets* £12,464

TRUSTEES Terence Cole; John Woollcombe.

HOW TO APPLY In writing to the correspondent. The trustees make grants throughout the year after conferring electronically, or by telephone, or at periodic meetings.

WHO TO APPLY TO Clare Harrison, Administrator, Penningtons Solicitors LLP, Highfield, Brighton Road, Godalming, Surrey GU7 1NS *Tel.* 01483 791800

■ P Leigh-Bramwell Trust 'E'

CC NO 267333   **ESTABLISHED** 1973

WHERE FUNDING CAN BE GIVEN UK, with a preference for Bolton

WHO CAN BENEFIT Registered charities, schools, universities and churches benefiting children, young adults, students and Christians.

WHAT IS FUNDED Specific regular allocations, leaving little opportunity to add further charities. Support is particularly given to Methodist churches and Bolton-based organisations.

WHAT IS NOT FUNDED No grants to individuals.

TYPE OF GRANT Mainly recurrent grants to established beneficiaries.

RANGE OF GRANTS £100–£30,000.

SAMPLE GRANTS Previous beneficiaries include: King's College School (£30,000). Other large beneficiaries included: Leigh-Bramwell Fund (£23,000); The Methodist Church – Bolton (£11,000); Rivington Parish Church (£7,500); The Unicorn School (£7,000); and The Methodist Church – Delph Hill and The Methodist Church – Breightmet (£3,400 each); Barnabus, Bolton Choral Union, Bolton Deaf Society, ChildLine North West, NCH Bypass, West London Mission and YWCA (£500 each).

FINANCES *Year* 2012–13 *Income* £90,083 *Grants* £92,327 *Assets* £2,251,668

TRUSTEES Helen Leigh-Bramwell; Jennifer Leigh Mitchell; Brian Leigh-Bramwell.

HOW TO APPLY In writing to the correspondent; however, note that previous research suggests that there is only a small amount of funds available for unsolicited applications and therefore success is unlikely.

WHO TO APPLY TO L. Cooper, Secretary, Suite 2E, Atria, Spa Road, Bolton BL1 4AG *Tel.* 01204 364656

■ The Lennox and Wyfold Foundation

CC NO 1080198   **ESTABLISHED** 2000

WHERE FUNDING CAN BE GIVEN Worldwide.

WHO CAN BENEFIT Registered charities.

WHAT IS FUNDED General charitable purposes.

SAMPLE GRANTS The Maggie Keswick Jencks Cancer Caring Centres Trust (£27,000) and The Eden Trust (£20,000). Previous beneficiaries included: Breakthrough Breast Cancer; Absolute Return for Kids; RNIB; Deafblind UK; Amber Foundation; Tusk Trust; Elephant Family; St George's Chapel – Windsor; Bucklebury Memorial Hall; Chipping Norton Theatre and Friends Trust; Gloucestershire Air Ambulance; Mary Hare Foundation; and Reform Research Trust.

FINANCES *Year* 2011–12 *Income* £510,415 *Grants* £446,940 *Assets* £35,547,795

TRUSTEES Lennox Hannay; Adam Fleming; Christopher Fleming; Caroline Wilmot-Sitwell.

OTHER INFORMATION Beneficiaries of 92 grants of less than £11,000 were not listed in the accounts.

HOW TO APPLY In writing to the correspondent. Trustees meet once a year to discuss applications.

WHO TO APPLY TO Karen Wall, Secretary, Fleming Family and Partners Ltd, 15 Suffolk Street, London SW1Y 4HG *Tel.* 020 7036 5000 *Fax* 020 7036 5601

■ The Leonard Trust

CC NO 1031723   **ESTABLISHED** 1993

WHERE FUNDING CAN BE GIVEN Overseas and UK, with a preference for Winchester.

WHO CAN BENEFIT Registered charities.

WHAT IS FUNDED Christian, mental health, overseas aid.

WHAT IS NOT FUNDED No grants to individuals. Medical research or building projects are no longer supported.

TYPE OF GRANT Usually one-off.

RANGE OF GRANTS £500–£5,000.

SAMPLE GRANTS Care for the Family, Christian Aid and Christian Missionary Society (£3,000 each); Intercare, Scripture Union and Tower Hamlets Mission (£2,000 each); and VIVA Together for Children (£1,000).

FINANCES *Year* 2012 *Income* £29,120 *Grants* £28,000 *Assets* £191,600

TRUSTEES Dominic Gold; Christopher Smiley.

HOW TO APPLY Unsolicited applications cannot be considered.

WHO TO APPLY TO Tessa E. Feilden, Administrator, 18 Edgar Road, Winchester, Hampshire SO23 9TW *Tel.* 01962 854800

■ The Erica Leonard Trust

CC NO 291627   **ESTABLISHED** 1985

WHERE FUNDING CAN BE GIVEN Mainly Surrey and occasionally overseas.

WHO CAN BENEFIT Registered charities only.

WHAT IS FUNDED General charitable purposes.

WHAT IS NOT FUNDED Only able to support registered charities.

RANGE OF GRANTS Most grants are for £1,000 or less.

SAMPLE GRANTS Previous beneficiaries include: Phoenix Trust (£9,000); Wells for India (£4,000); Leonard Trust (£2,000); The Meath Epilepsy Trust, Kensington Philharmonica Orchestra Trust, International Refugee Trust and Haslemere Educational Museum (£1,000 each); Macmillan Cancer Support, Christian Solidarity World Wide and Rainbow Trust (£750 each); Marie Curie Cancer Care (£500); Coundon Care Centre Charity (£250) and Prisoners Fellowship (£200).

FINANCES *Year* 2011–12 *Income* £22,130 *Grants* £37,725

TRUSTEES Richard Grey; Richard Beeston; Andrew Lodge.

HOW TO APPLY In writing to the correspondent.

WHO TO APPLY TO Richard Grey, Trustee, Old Farmhouse, Farnham Road, Elstead, Surrey GU8 6DB *Tel.* 01252 702230 *email* rcegrey@ aol.com

■ The Mark Leonard Trust

CC NO 1040323   **ESTABLISHED** 1994

WHERE FUNDING CAN BE GIVEN Worldwide, but mainly UK.

WHO CAN BENEFIT Organisations benefiting the environment, children and young adults.

WHAT IS FUNDED Environment: environmental education, particularly supporting projects displaying practical ways of involving children and young adults, as well as sustainable transport, energy efficiency and renewable energy. Youth work: the rehabilitation of young people who have become marginalised and involved in anti-social or criminal activities, as well as extending and adding value to the existing use of school buildings and encouraging greater involvement of parents, school leavers and volunteers in extra-curricular activities. General charitable purposes.

WHAT IS NOT FUNDED Grants are not normally made to individuals.

RANGE OF GRANTS £10,000–£100,000

SAMPLE GRANTS Global Action Plan (£180,000); Sustainable Restaurant Association (£100,000); BioRegional Development Group (£90,000); Ashden: Sustainable solutions, better lives (£60,000); Ecofin Research Foundation (£49,000); National Energy Foundation (£32,000); Only Connect (£25,000); Kaizen Partnership (£23,000); Behaviour Change Ltd (£20,000); Lyndhurst Primary School (£15,000); City University, Rambert School of Ballet and Dance and Centre for Sustainable Energy (£10,000 each).

FINANCES *Year* 2011–12 *Income* £1,014,801 *Grants* £649,740 *Assets* £14,235,209

TRUSTEES Zivi Sainsbury; Judith Portrait; John Julian Sainsbury; Mark Sainsbury.

HOW TO APPLY 'Proposals are generally invited by the trustees or initiated at their request. Unsolicited applications are discouraged and are unlikely to be successful, unless they are closely aligned to the trust's areas of interest.' A single application will be considered for support by all the trusts in the Sainsbury family group.

WHO TO APPLY TO Alan Bookbinder, Director, Sainsbury Family Charitable Trusts, The Peak, 5 Wilton Road, London SW1V 1AP *Tel.* 020 7410 0330 *email* info@sfct.org.uk *Website* www.sfct.org.uk

··

■ **Lesley Lesley and Mutter Trust**

CC NO 1018747   **ESTABLISHED** 1989

WHERE FUNDING CAN BE GIVEN Dorset

WHO CAN BENEFIT Parkinson's Disease Association, Chest Heart and Stroke Association, Multiple Sclerosis Society, Muscular Dystrophy Group of Great Britain, Royal National Institute for the Blind, Rowcroft Hospice for Torbay and Guide Dogs for the Blind (Devon Area Branch).

WHAT IS FUNDED Recipients are named in the trust deed and only those organisations can be funded.

TYPE OF GRANT Recurrent

SAMPLE GRANTS Each year grants are distributed as follows: 35% to Chest Heart and Stroke Association; 35% to Parkinson's Disease Society; 6% to Guide Dogs for the Blind (Devon Area Branch); 6% to Multiple Sclerosis Society; 6% to Muscular Dystrophy Group of Great Britain; 6% to Rowcroft Hospice for Torbay; 6% to Royal National Institute for the Blind.

FINANCES *Year* 2011–12 *Income* £23,576 *Grants* £23,000

TRUSTEE Lloyds TSB Private Banking Ltd.

HOW TO APPLY Applications are not welcome.

WHO TO APPLY TO Yvonne Maidment, c/o Lloyds Bank plc, UK Trust Centre, The Clock House, 22–26 Ock Street, Abingdon, Oxfordshire OX14 5SW *Tel.* 01235 232766

··

■ **Leukaemia and Lymphoma Research Fund**

CC NO 216032   **ESTABLISHED** 1960

WHERE FUNDING CAN BE GIVEN UK.

WHO CAN BENEFIT Hospitals and university medical centres which benefit medical professionals, nurses and doctors; students; and people with leukaemia.

WHAT IS FUNDED Improving treatments, finding the cures and preventing all forms of leukaemia, Hodgkin's disease and other lymphomata, myeloma, the myelodysplasias and aplastic anaemia.

TYPE OF GRANT Capital (equipment), feasibility study, recurring costs, research and salaries.

RANGE OF GRANTS £45,000–£7.7 million.

SAMPLE GRANTS (£7.7 million); University of Birmingham (£3.4 million); University of Oxford (£3.3 million); University of Southampton (£3 million); University College London (£2.5 million); University of Edinburgh (£1 million); University of Cardiff (£645,000) and London Barts (£115,000).

FINANCES *Year* 2012–13 *Income* £20,353,000 *Grants* £33,162,000 *Assets* £15,460,000

TRUSTEES Peter Burrell; Anthony Dart; Maria Clarke; Michelle Cockayne; Angela Knowles; Richard Delderfield; Mike Williams; John Reeve; Lesley Lee; Charles Metcalf; Joanne Bray; Jeremy Bird; John Purser; Mary Grange.

HOW TO APPLY All applications for all forms of funding must be submitted via the fund's online application system. See the website for details.

WHO TO APPLY TO Prof. Chris Bunce, Scientific Director, 39–40 Eagle Street, London WC1R 4TH *Tel.* 020 7405 0101 *Fax* 020 7242 1488 *email* info@beatbloodcancers.org *Website* www.beatbloodcancers.org

··

■ **The Leverhulme Trade Charities Trust**

CC NO 288404   **ESTABLISHED** 1983

WHERE FUNDING CAN BE GIVEN UK.

WHO CAN BENEFIT Charities connected with and benefiting commercial travellers, grocers or chemists, their wives, widows and children, especially those disadvantaged by poverty.

WHAT IS FUNDED Benevolent societies, educational institutions and research costs.

WHAT IS NOT FUNDED No capital grants. No response is given to general appeals.

TYPE OF GRANT One-off and recurrent grants.

SAMPLE GRANTS UCTA Samaritan Fund (£255,000); The Girls' Day School Trust (£216,000); The Royal Pharmaceutical Society – Research Fellowships (£180,000); Royal Pinner School Foundation (£160,000); United Reformed Church Schools (£128,000) and The Royal Pharmaceutical Society – The Pharmacy Practice Research Trust (£68,000).

FINANCES *Year* 2011–12 *Income* £2,031,000 *Grants* £1,754,000 *Assets* £56,837,000

TRUSTEES Sir Iain Anderson; Niall Fitzgerald; Patrick J-P. Cescau; Dr Ashok Ganguly; Paul Polman.

HOW TO APPLY On a form available from the charity's website. Deadlines are 1 November and 1 March.
Undergraduate and postgraduate bursary applications should be directed to the relevant institution.

WHO TO APPLY TO Paul Read, Administrator, 1 Pemberton Row, London EC4A 3BG *Tel.* 020 7042 9883 *email* pdread@leverhulme.ac.uk *Website* www.leverhulme-trade.org.uk

········

■ The Leverhulme Trust

CC NO 288371   **ESTABLISHED** 1925

WHERE FUNDING CAN BE GIVEN Unrestricted.

WHO CAN BENEFIT Universities and other institutions of higher and further education; registered charities; and individuals.

WHAT IS FUNDED Grants are made to institutions for specific research undertakings, for schemes of international academic interchange, fellowships and arts initiatives.

WHAT IS NOT FUNDED When submitting an application to the trust, applicants are advised that the trust does not offer funding for the following costs, and hence none of these items may be included in any budget submitted to the trust: core funding or overheads for institutions; individual items of equipment over £1,000; sites, buildings or other capital expenditure; support for the organisation of conferences or workshops, which are not directly associated with International Networks, Early Career Fellowships; Visiting Fellowships or Philip Leverhulme Prizes; contributions to appeals; endowments; a shortfall resulting from a withdrawal of or deficiency in public finance; UK student fees where these are not associated with a Research Project Grant bid or Arts Scholarships.

TYPE OF GRANT One-off, project, research, recurring, running costs and salaries.

SAMPLE GRANTS University of Cambridge (£5 million); University of Oxford (£4.8 million); University of Manchester (£3.2 million); Durham University (£2.7 million); Newcastle University (£2.2 million); School of Oriental and African Studies (£1.8 million); British Museum (£1.8 million); University of Edinburgh (£1.4 million); University of Liverpool (£1.1 million); Guildhall School of Music and Drama (£892,000); University of Southampton (£762,000); Royal Academy of Music (£717,000) and University of Strathclyde (£512,000).

FINANCES *Year* 2012 *Income* £64,157,000 *Grants* £80,416,000 *Assets* £1,888,350,000

TRUSTEES Sir Michael Perry, Chair; Patrick J. P. Cescau; Niall W. A. Fitzgerald; Dr Ashok S. Ganguly; Paul Polman.

HOW TO APPLY Each programme, scholarship and award has its own individual application deadline and procedure. Full guidelines and application procedures for each award scheme are available from the trust directly or via its website.

WHO TO APPLY TO Reena Mistry, 1 Pemberton Row, London EC4A 3BG *Tel.* 020 7042 9881 *email* enquiries@leverhulme.org.uk *Website* www.leverhulme.org.uk

■ Lord Leverhulme's Charitable Trust

CC NO 212431   **ESTABLISHED** 1957

WHERE FUNDING CAN BE GIVEN UK especially, Cheshire, Merseyside and South Lancashire.

WHO CAN BENEFIT Registered and exempt charities.

WHAT IS FUNDED General charitable purposes. Priority is given to certain charitable organisations and trusts in Cheshire and Merseyside, particularly educational organisations, welfare charities, youth organisations, the arts, churches, and organisations benefiting older people and people with disabilities.

WHAT IS NOT FUNDED No grants to non-charitable organisations.

TYPE OF GRANT Recurrent, one-off and capital.

RANGE OF GRANTS Up to £200,000.

SAMPLE GRANTS Shrewsbury Abbey Renaissance and Royal College of Surgeons (£50,000 each); Lady Lever Art Gallery Annuity and Chester Zoo (£30,000 each); Lady Lever Art Gallery (£27,000) and Community Foundation for Shropshire and Telford (£25,000).

FINANCES *Year* 2011–12 *Income* £544,045 *Grants* £324,362 *Assets* £26,669,305

TRUSTEES A. E. H. Heber-Percy; A. H. S. Hannay.

HOW TO APPLY The trust states: 'Priority is given [. . .] to applications from Cheshire, Merseyside and South Lancashire and the charities supported by the settlor in his lifetime. Others who do not meet those criteria should not apply without prior invitation but should, on a single sheet, state briefly their aims and apply fully only on being asked to do so. A handful of charities have heeded this warning and telephoned our administrator but the continuing volume of applications from charities which plainly do not meet the stated criteria suggests that many applicants do not concern themselves with their target's policies.'

WHO TO APPLY TO S. Edwards, Administrator, Leverhulme Estate Office, Hesketh Grange, Manor Road, Thornton Hough, Wirral CH63 1JD *Tel.* 01513 364828 *Fax* 01513 530265

■ The Joseph Levy Charitable Foundation

CC NO 245592   **ESTABLISHED** 1965

WHERE FUNDING CAN BE GIVEN UK and Israel.

WHO CAN BENEFIT Registered charities benefiting children and young people, older people, health, medical research.

WHAT IS FUNDED Health and community care, religion, social welfare, education, arts, culture and sport.

WHAT IS NOT FUNDED No grants to individuals, under any circumstances.

TYPE OF GRANT Project, research, salaries and start-up costs. Funding may be given for up to and over three years.

RANGE OF GRANTS £250–£1 million.

SAMPLE GRANTS University of St Andrews (£46,000); Dementia UK (£35,000); Jewish Community Secondary School and Target Ovarian Cancer (£25,000 each); Hammerson Home Charitable Trust (£10,000); Shluvim (£7,500); Different Strokes (£3,000); and Sussex Wildlife Trust (£1,000).

FINANCES *Year* 2011–12 *Income* £795,766 *Grants* £944,234 *Assets* £15,787,712

TRUSTEES Jane Jason; Peter L. Levy; Melanie Levy; Claudia Giat; James Jason.

HOW TO APPLY The foundation states on the website that due to current commitments it is no longer able to accept unsolicited applications.

WHO TO APPLY TO Roland Gyallay-Pap, Grants Administrator, 1st Floor, 1 Bell Street, London NW1 5BY *Tel.* 020 7616 1200 *Fax* 020 7616 1206 *email* info@jlf.org.uk *Website* www.jlf.org. uk

■ Lewis Family Charitable Trust

CC NO 259892   **ESTABLISHED** 1962

WHERE FUNDING CAN BE GIVEN UK and Israel.

WHO CAN BENEFIT Charitable bodies and research institutions.

WHAT IS FUNDED Medical research, particularly into possible treatments for cancer, Jewish

Think carefully about every application. Is it justified?

701

community work, general medical support, educational funding, support for the elderly and child care.

WHAT IS NOT FUNDED No grants to individuals.

TYPE OF GRANT Potentially up to three years funding but mostly one-off.

RANGE OF GRANTS Up to £80,000

SAMPLE GRANTS Israel Centre for Social and Economic Progress (£66,000); University of Nottingham (£53,000); United Jewish Israel Appeal (£50,000); Bowel Disease Research Foundation (£40,000); Weizmann Institute (£25,000); Reform Judaism and Norwood (£20,000 each); Centre for Media Research, FRODO and The Common Security Trust (£10,000 each); Council for a Beautiful Israel, Jewish Marriage Council and NSPCC (£5,000 each); and Ajex Museum, Jewish Museum and Lupus UK (£1,000 each).

FINANCES *Year* 2011–12 *Income* £1,667,384 *Grants* £611,788 *Assets* £8,080,052

TRUSTEES Julian Lewis; Deborah Lewis; Benjamin Lewis; Simon Lewis.

OTHER INFORMATION Total grants figure excludes support costs.

HOW TO APPLY In writing to the correspondent.

WHO TO APPLY TO The Secretary, Chelsea House, West Gate, Ealing, London W5 1DR *Tel.* 020 8991 4601

··

■ **The John Spedan Lewis Foundation**

CC NO 240473   **ESTABLISHED** 1964

WHERE FUNDING CAN BE GIVEN UK.

WHO CAN BENEFIT The focus is on applications for small projects connected with the natural sciences, in particular horticulture, environmental education, ornithology and conservation, and from organisations benefiting, in the first instance, children, young adults and research workers.

WHAT IS FUNDED Charitable purposes, in the first instance reflecting the particular interests of John Spedan Lewis, namely horticulture, ornithology, entomology and associated educational and research projects. The trustees will also consider applications from organisations for imaginative and original educational projects aimed at developing serious interest and evident talent, particularly among young people.

WHAT IS NOT FUNDED Local branches of national organisations, or for salaries, medical research, welfare projects, building works or overseas expeditions.

TYPE OF GRANT Mostly one-off donations. Salaries not funded.

RANGE OF GRANTS £60–£12,000.

SAMPLE GRANTS Clyde River Foundation (£6,000); Highland Biological Recording Group, Natural History Museum and Yorkshire Wildlife Trust (£5,000 each); Kent Wildlife Trust and The Manchester Museum (£4,000 each); and Snowdon Trust and Birding for All (£1,000 each).

FINANCES *Year* 2012–13 *Income* £88,194 *Grants* £66,882 *Assets* £2,635,958

TRUSTEES Charlie Mayfield, Chair; David Jones; Dr Vaughan Southgate; Dr John David; Gerrard Keogh-Peters.

HOW TO APPLY In writing to the correspondent with latest report and accounts and a budget for the proposed project.

WHO TO APPLY TO Bridget Chamberlain, Secretary, Partnership House, Carlisle Place, London SW1P

1BX *Tel.* 020 7592 6121 *email* bridget_chamberlain@johnlewis.co.uk

··

■ **The Sir Edward Lewis Foundation**

CC NO 264475   **ESTABLISHED** 1972

WHERE FUNDING CAN BE GIVEN UK and overseas, with a preference for Surrey.

WHO CAN BENEFIT Registered charities.

WHAT IS FUNDED General charitable purposes.

WHAT IS NOT FUNDED Grants are generally only given to charities, projects or people known to the trustees. No grants are given to individuals.

RANGE OF GRANTS £500–£38,000,

SAMPLE GRANTS The Arnold Foundation for Rugby School (£60,000); Arthritis Research UK (£15,000); FareShare (£10,000); The Children's Trust Tadworth, Ex-Services Mental Welfare Society (Combat Stress), Gurkha Welfare Trust and St Bartholomew's Church, Leigh (£5,000 each); Rugby Clubs (£4,000); Opthalmic Aid to Eastern Europe (£3,000); Musicians Benevolent Fund (£2,500); The Airey Neave Trust, St Catherine's Hospice and Wildlife Aid (£2,000); WaterAid (£1,000) and Elizabeth Finn Care (£500).

FINANCES *Year* 2011–12 *Income* £256,266 *Grants* £242,200 *Assets* £7,787,630

TRUSTEES Richard Lewis; Mark Harris; Christine Lewis; Sarah Dorin.

OTHER INFORMATION The trust makes one substantial donation every two or three years, as well as smaller donations each year.

HOW TO APPLY In writing to the correspondent. The trustees meet every six months.

WHO TO APPLY TO Darren Wing, Administrator, Rawlinson and Hunter, The Lower Mill, Kingston Road, Ewell, Surrey KT17 2AE *Tel.* 020 7842 2000

··

■ **John Lewis Partnership General Community Fund**

CC NO 209128   **ESTABLISHED** 1961

WHERE FUNDING CAN BE GIVEN UK.

WHO CAN BENEFIT Registered charities.

WHAT IS FUNDED UK and local registered charities benefiting children and young adults, at risk groups, people who are sick or who have disabilities, people disadvantaged by poverty and those who are socially isolated. Medical professionals and research workers may be considered for funding.

WHAT IS NOT FUNDED Loans are not made and sponsorship is not undertaken. Grants are not made for the promotion of religion, political organisations, advertising or to individuals.

TYPE OF GRANT One-off and recurring grants.

RANGE OF GRANTS £250–£100,000.

SAMPLE GRANTS British Red Cross (£100,000); Retail Trust (£60,000); Fashion and Textile Children's Trust (£25,000); The Voices Foundation (£22,000); Marie Curie Cancer Care (£20,000); Baltic Flour Mills Visual Arts Trust (£16,000); Royal Welsh College of Music and Drama (£7,000); St Finian's Catholic Primary School (£6,000); Stamford Green Primary School (£1,200) and The Norfolk Youth Music Trust (£250).

FINANCES *Year* 2011–12 *Income* £569,460 *Grants* £573,460

TRUSTEES Cathy Houchin; Charlie Mayfield; David Barclay; Ian Hiscock; Derek Bond.

OTHER INFORMATION In 2011–12 grants were awarded to 95 organisations.

HOW TO APPLY The trust provided the following information: 'If you have a cause you think we could support, contact the Waitrose champion for community giving at your local branch (www.waitrose.com) or the John Lewis Community Liaison Coordinator at your local branch (www.johnlewis.com). As we are contacted by so many organisations throughout the year, we cannot always give you a swift reply, but we will reply as soon as possible if we can help.'

WHO TO APPLY TO Partnership House, Carlisle Place, London SW1P 1BX *Website* www.johnlewispartnership.co.uk

The Lewis Ward Trust

CC NO 1100891   **ESTABLISHED** 2003

WHERE FUNDING CAN BE GIVEN UK and overseas

WHO CAN BENEFIT Children, particularly those with special needs or disabilities, are deprived or terminally ill or are lacking adequate nutrition and education.

WHAT IS FUNDED Special projects for children run locally, nationally and internationally. Hospices and special therapy units for children and organisations caring for lepers.

RANGE OF GRANTS Generally £1,000

SAMPLE GRANTS No list of beneficiary organisations was available.

FINANCES *Year* 2012 *Income* £1,787
Grants £33,000

TRUSTEES Margaret Waugh; Revd Gareth Jones (Chair); Kevin Ward; Stephanie Cheetham; Bernard Cheetham.

HOW TO APPLY In writing to the correspondent. 'The trustees meet twice a year, when appeals for grants are considered and depending on monies available, donations are sent to those organisations it is felt are in greatest need.'

WHO TO APPLY TO Margaret Waugh, Trustee, 2 Abraham Court, Lutton Close, Oswestry SY11 2TH *Tel.* 01691 688892

Liberum Foundation

CC NO 1137475   **ESTABLISHED** 2010

WHERE FUNDING CAN BE GIVEN Not defined, in practice UK.

WHO CAN BENEFIT Organisations and individuals.

WHAT IS FUNDED General charitable purposes including education/training; the prevention or relief of poverty; sport/recreation and community development/employment.

WHAT IS NOT FUNDED Adult health; hospitals; animals; older people; the armed services; housing; heritage; environment; and religion.

SAMPLE GRANTS St Giles Trust (£30,000); Tiny Tickers (£29,000); and School Home Support (£24,000).

FINANCES *Year* 2012 *Income* £139,226
Grants £83,610 *Assets* £115,993

TRUSTEES Carolyn Doherty; Simon Stilwell; Antony Scawthorn; Dean Butterfield; Timothy Mayo.

HOW TO APPLY In writing to the Secretary.

WHO TO APPLY TO Justine Rumens, Secretary to the Foundation, Ropemaker Place, Level 12, 25 Ropemaker Street, London EC2Y 9LY *Tel.* 020 3100 2000 *email* info@liberumfoundation.com *Website* www.liberumcapital.com/LiberumFoundation

Lichfield Conduit Lands

CC NO 254298   **ESTABLISHED** 1982

WHERE FUNDING CAN BE GIVEN Lichfield.

WHO CAN BENEFIT Organisations and people under 25 who are in education.

WHAT IS FUNDED General charitable purposes.

RANGE OF GRANTS Up to £20,000.

SAMPLE GRANTS Lichfield Talking News and Community Care (£5,400); The Darwin Walk Trust (£3,000); Erasmus Darwin Foundation and Lichfield Mysteries (£2,500 each); The Lichfield Festival (£2,000); Lichfield and District Arts Association (£1,000); Cruse Bereavement Care: South Staffs (£950); Lichfield and District Live at Home Scheme (£850); The Extra Care Charitable Trust (£800) and AFC Litchfield (£300).

FINANCES *Year* 2012 *Income* £27,629
Grants £19,296 *Assets* £1,052,905

TRUSTEES John Russell; Colin Ablitt; Kathryn Brown; Betty Twivey; Robert White; Muriel Boyle; Christopher Spruce; Nicola Templeton; Thomas Roach; Janet Eagland; Kenneth Humphreys.

OTHER INFORMATION A grants was made to one individual totalling £140.

HOW TO APPLY Application forms are available from the reception at Ansons, along with a map of the beneficial area. They are considered four times a year

WHO TO APPLY TO Simon James, The Warden, c/o Ansons LLP Solicitors, St Mary's Chambers, 5 Breadmarket Street, Lichfield WS13 6LQ *Tel.* 01543 263456 *Fax* 01543 250942 *email* sjames@ansonsllp.com

Lifeline 4 Kids

CC NO 200050   **ESTABLISHED** 1961

WHERE FUNDING CAN BE GIVEN Worldwide.

WHO CAN BENEFIT Organisations supporting children who are disabled (up to 18 years old), such as hospitals, homes, special schools and so on. Individuals and their families are also supported.

WHAT IS FUNDED To assist children who are disabled by providing equipment and services.

WHAT IS NOT FUNDED Building projects, research grants and salaries will not be funded. According to the trust's website, the trust does not fund the following: 'building or garden works; carpets/floor covering; ovens/cookers; refrigerators (unless for medical needs); clothing; shoes (unless specialist); transport costs; tuition/school lessons or fees; driving lessons; and holidays.'

TYPE OF GRANT Equipment purchased by the trust. No cash grants are given.

SAMPLE GRANTS Grants in 2006 included: £5,000 to Central Middlesex Hospital, towards equipment for its outdoor play area; £2,500 to the Living Paintings Trust, funding the production of 20 copies of a new Living Picture Book; £2,400 to the New Jumbulance Travel Trust, providing two portable instant resuscitation packs; £2,000 to Vision Aid, providing a specialised flat screen video magnifier; £1,500 to the Lothian Autistic Society, for equipment for its various play schemes.

FINANCES *Year* 2012 *Income* £25,394
Grants £164,026 *Assets* £393,723

TRUSTEES Roger Adelman, chair; Paul Maurice; Beverley Emden; Roberta Harris; Irving Millman; Jeffrey Bonn.

OTHER INFORMATION This trust does not administer cash grants.

HOW TO APPLY Applications for help indicating specific requirements and brief factual information must initially be made in writing, addressed to the Investigations Officer, or by email (appeals@lifeline4kids.org). Each request will be acknowledged and provided it meets the charity's criteria, an application form will be sent by post. Appeals are discussed and decided upon at monthly meetings. If appropriate, the appeal will be investigated personally by one of the trust's members. If approved, a maximum sum is allocated and the trust takes full responsibility for the purchase and safe delivery of the approved item. Initial telephone calls from applicants are not welcome.

WHO TO APPLY TO Roger Adelman, Trustee, 215 West End Lane, West Hampstead, London NW6 1XJ *Tel.* 0207941661 *Fax* 020 7794 1161 *email* rda@lifeline4kids.org *Website* www. lifeline4kids.org

----

■ The Limbourne Trust

CC NO 1113796   **ESTABLISHED** 2006
WHERE FUNDING CAN BE GIVEN UK and overseas.
WHO CAN BENEFIT Communities throughout the world.
WHAT IS FUNDED Environment, welfare, and arts organisations, particularly where meeting the trust's objectives concerning the advancement of education, the protection of health, and the relief of poverty, distress and sickness.
SAMPLE GRANTS The Reader Organisation (£12,500); Farms for City Children and Jubilee Sailing Trust (£10,000 each); Seachange Arts and CHICKS (£9,000 each); Voluntary Action Maidstone (£7,500); English Pen, Hope and Homes for Children and Vauxhall City Farm (£5,000 each); and Eden Community Outdoors – ECO (£2,000).
FINANCES *Year* 2012–13 *Income* £104,826 *Grants* £107,700 *Assets* £2,681,910
TRUSTEES Elisabeth Thistlethwayte; Katharine Thistlethwayte; Jennifer Lindsay; Jane Chetwynd Atkinson; Jocelyn Magnus.
OTHER INFORMATION Grants totalled nearly £108,000 and were made to 17 organisations.
HOW TO APPLY The trustees' report for 2012/13 states that 'the trustees will seek to identify those projects where the greatest and widest benefit can be attained, and usually will only consider written applications and, where necessary, make further enquiries.'
WHO TO APPLY TO Elisabeth Thistlethwayte, Trustee, Downs Farm, Homersfield, Harleston IP20 0NS

■ Limoges Charitable Trust

CC NO 1016178   **ESTABLISHED** 1991
WHERE FUNDING CAN BE GIVEN UK, with a preference for Birmingham.
WHO CAN BENEFIT Registered charities.
WHAT IS FUNDED Education, health and welfare, heritage and community, animals, youth, environment and nautical projects.
RANGE OF GRANTS £50–£18,000; mostly £200–£1,000.
SAMPLE GRANTS Edward's Trust and Moseley Community Development Trust (£10,000 each); Portsmouth Cathedral (£4,000); Birmingham Civic Society and Birmingham St Mary's Hospice (£2,000 each); University of Birmingham (£1,700) and St Ildierna's Church (£1,600).
FINANCES *Year* 2011–12 *Income* £27,487 *Grants* £64,120 *Assets* £700,597

TRUSTEES Mike Dyer; Albert Kenneth Dyer; Judy Ann Dyke; Andrew Milner.
HOW TO APPLY In writing to the correspondent. Trustees usually meet four times a year to consider applications.
WHO TO APPLY TO Judy Ann Dyke, Trustee, c/o Tyndallwoods Solicitors, 29 Woodbourne Road, Edgbaston, Birmingham B17 8BY *Tel.* 01216 932222 *Fax* 01216 930844

■ The Linbury Trust

CC NO 287077   **ESTABLISHED** 1973
WHERE FUNDING CAN BE GIVEN Unrestricted.
WHO CAN BENEFIT Charities working in the fields listed below.
WHAT IS FUNDED Arts and arts education, especially support for dance and dance education. Medical research into chronic fatigue syndrome, and occasionally other 'unfashionable' areas. Drug abuse, provision of hands-on care to treat and rehabilitate drug users, particularly those which work with young people and the families of drug users. Education, especially support for best practice in the identification and teaching of children and young people with literacy problems, especially dyslexia. Environment and heritage, particularly historical buildings and major art institutions. Social welfare, especially for work helping young people disadvantaged by poverty, educational achievement or difficult family backgrounds, or who are involved in the criminal justice system. Also support for initiatives that improve quality of life of older people and through which they are helped to continue living in their own home. Developing countries, including humanitarian aid, social welfare and educational opportunities.
WHAT IS NOT FUNDED No grants to individuals.
TYPE OF GRANT Running costs, project.
SAMPLE GRANTS British Museum (£2.25 million); Rambert Dance Company (£250,000); Linbury Prize for Stage Design (£158,000); University of Buckingham (£150,000); Salisbury Cathedral (£100,000); Ashden (£75,000); Shakespeare Schools Festival, Medical Aid for Palestinians, Merlin, PSS and Action for Prisoners Families (£50,000 each); University of Bristol (£46,000)
FINANCES *Year* 2011–12 *Income* £6,487,000 *Grants* £6,957,000 *Assets* £145,547,000
TRUSTEES John Sainsbury; Anya Sainsbury; Martin Jacomb; James Spooner.
OTHER INFORMATION The trust is one of the Sainsbury Family Charitable Trusts which share a common administration. An application to one is taken as an application to all.
HOW TO APPLY See the guidance for applicants in the entry for the Sainsbury Family Charitable Trusts. A single application will be considered for support by all the trusts in the group. Note: 'the trustees take a proactive approach towards grantmaking; accordingly, unsolicited applications to the trust are not usually successful'.
WHO TO APPLY TO Alan Bookbinder, Director, The Peak, 5 Wilton Road, London SW1V 1AP *Tel.* 020 7410 0330 *Fax* 020 7410 0332 *Website* www.linburytrust.org.uk

----

■ The Lincolnshire Churches Trust

CC NO 509021   **ESTABLISHED** 1952
WHERE FUNDING CAN BE GIVEN Lincolnshire.
WHO CAN BENEFIT Christian churches generally of any denomination within the Anglican diocese of Lincoln, being at least 100 years old, needing

repairs aimed at excluding wind and weather, achieving safety and security. (Trustees' report from 2012)

WHAT IS FUNDED Preservation, repair and maintenance of churches within the Anglican diocese of Lincoln.

WHAT IS NOT FUNDED No support is available for requirements relating to ritual, heating, lighting or for repairs to gravestones.

TYPE OF GRANT One off grants to churches.

RANGE OF GRANTS £1,000–£6,000.

SAMPLE GRANTS East Barkwith – St Mary (£6,000); Witham on the Hill – St Andrew and Spilsby – St James (£4,000) each; Cranwell – St Andrew, Hameringham – All Saints, Weston – St Mary, Welbourn – St Chad and Wootton – St Andrew (£3,000 each); Asgarby – St Andrew (£2,500); Ingoldmells – SS Peter and Paul (£1,500); Newton by Toft – St Michael; Welton – St Mary; Potterhanworth – St Andrew; Wickenby – SS Peter Lawrence (£1,000 each).

FINANCES *Year* 2012 *Income* £64,945 *Grants* £37,000 *Assets* £454,695

TRUSTEES Nevile Camamile; Baroness Willoughby de Eresby; Catherine Hammant; David Lawrence; Peter Sandberg; Revd Clifford Knowles; Jeffrey Couzens; Graham Cook; Anthony Worth; Henrietta Reeve; Linda Lord; Mona Dickinson; Caroline Mockford; Nicholas Ridley; Peter Milnes; Jane Ford.

HOW TO APPLY In writing to the correspondent.

WHO TO APPLY TO Linda Lord, Trustee, Tower House, Lucy Tower Street, Lincoln LN1 1XW *Tel.* 01522 551200

■ Lincolnshire Community Foundation

CC NO 1092328   **ESTABLISHED** 2002

WHERE FUNDING CAN BE GIVEN Lincolnshire.

WHO CAN BENEFIT Organisations supporting people in Lincolnshire General charitable purposes

WHAT IS FUNDED General charitable purposes

TYPE OF GRANT One-off and up to three years funding.

FINANCES *Year* 2012–13 *Income* £1,120,303 *Grants* £604,855 *Assets* £3,470,473

TRUSTEES Charles Ferens; Stephen Cousins; David Close; Jean Burton; Margaret Serna; Bernadette Jones; Dr Cheryle Berry; Jane Hiles; Paul Scott; Lizzie Milligan-Manby.

HOW TO APPLY Visit the foundation's website for details of current grant schemes. Application forms can be downloaded from the foundation's website or requested by phone.

WHO TO APPLY TO Gordon Hunter, Director, 4 Mill House, Carre Street, Sleaford, Lincolnshire NG34 7TW *Tel.* 01529 307749 *email* lincolnshirecf@btconnect.com *Website* www.lincolnshirecf.co.uk

---

■ The Lind Trust

CC NO 803174   **ESTABLISHED** 1990

WHERE FUNDING CAN BE GIVEN UK.

WHO CAN BENEFIT Churches, charities and individuals involved in social action, youth, community and Christian service.

WHAT IS FUNDED Christian service, youth, community and social action.

SAMPLE GRANTS The Open Youth Trust (£185,000); and other charities not listed. The trustees have made a £5,000 commitment to the Matthew Project.

FINANCES *Year* 2011–12 *Income* £651,562 *Grants* £434,038 *Assets* £20,403,123

TRUSTEES Leslie Brown; Dr Graham Dacre; Gavin Wilcock; Julia Dacre; Russell Dacre; Samuel Dacre

HOW TO APPLY In writing to the correspondent at any time. However, the trust commits most of its funds in advance, giving the remainder to eligible applicants as received.

WHO TO APPLY TO Gavin Croft Wilcox, Trustee, Drayton Hall, Hall Lane, Norwich, Norfolk NR8 6DP *Tel.* 01603 262626 *email* john. savery@dacrepropertyholdings.com

---

■ Lindale Educational Foundation

CC NO 282758   **ESTABLISHED** 1981

WHERE FUNDING CAN BE GIVEN UK and overseas.

WHO CAN BENEFIT Roman Catholic organisations benefiting children, young adults and students.

WHAT IS FUNDED Charities which aim to advance education in accordance with Christian principles and ideals within the Roman Catholic tradition, in particular those organisations that train priests. Most grants are already allocated to specific charities.

WHAT IS NOT FUNDED No grants to individuals.

TYPE OF GRANT Recurrent.

SAMPLE GRANTS Thornycroft Hall (five grants totalling £29,000); Netherhall Educational Association Centre for Retreats and Study (four grants totalling £16,500); and Hazelwood House (two grants totalling £6,500).

FINANCES *Year* 2011–12 *Income* £33,400 *Grants* £51,980 *Assets* £5,344

TRUSTEES Dawliffe Hall Educational Foundation; Greygarth Association; Netherhall Educational Association.

OTHER INFORMATION Grants were made totalling £52,000. A total of eleven grants were made to organisations.

HOW TO APPLY In writing to the correspondent, but note that most funds are already committed.

WHO TO APPLY TO Jack Valero, Administrator, 6 Orme Court, London W2 4RL *Tel.* 020 7243 9417

■ The Linden Charitable Trust

CC NO 326788   **ESTABLISHED** 1985

WHERE FUNDING CAN BE GIVEN UK, with a preference for West Yorkshire

WHO CAN BENEFIT Registered charities and arts organisations.

WHAT IS FUNDED Currently, the trust's policy is to benefit charities specialising in cancer relief and research, those particularly involved with hospices, those involved in arts and also a wider range of charities based in and around Leeds.

The trustees have agreed (2009/10) to make a regular donation to Leeds international Pianoforte Competition of £10,000 per year.

WHAT IS NOT FUNDED No grants to individuals.

RANGE OF GRANTS Up to £20,000.

SAMPLE GRANTS Leeds International and Pianoforte Competition (£10,000); Macmillan Cancer Care (£5,000); Yorkshire Air Ambulance, Henshaws for the Blind and Leeds Lieder (£3,000 each); David Wood Yellow Bird and Caring for Life (£2,000 each); Yorkshire Eye Research, the Sick Children's Trust and West Yorkshire Playhouse (£1,000 each); and Yorkshire Dales Millennium and Phillip Harvey Horse and Do (£500 each).

FINANCES *Year* 2011–12 *Income* £66,032 *Grants* £85,100 *Assets* £2,459,891

TRUSTEES Margaret Heaton Pearson; Gerald Holbrook; John Swales; Robert Swales.
HOW TO APPLY In writing to the correspondent.
WHO TO APPLY TO Baker Tilly Tax and Accounting Ltd, 2 Whitehall Quay, Leeds, West Yorkshire LS1 4HG

■ Lindenleaf Charitable Trust

CC NO 1124672   **ESTABLISHED** 2008
WHERE FUNDING CAN BE GIVEN UK and overseas.
WHO CAN BENEFIT General charitable purposes in particular, poverty; community development.
WHAT IS FUNDED Registered charities.
SAMPLE GRANTS IntoUniversity, BEAT, Shannon Trust and Camfed (£8,000 each); Concern Worldwide (£5,000) and Build It (£3,000).
FINANCES *Year* 2011–12 *Income* £502,975 *Grants* £40,000 *Assets* £2,444,746
TRUSTEES Henry Charles; Paul Greatbatch; Elizabeth Haycox; Thomas Howells; Helen Norton
HOW TO APPLY In writing to the correspondent.
WHO TO APPLY TO Paul Greatbatch, 344 Fulham Road, London SW10 9UH *Tel.* 020 7376 4321 *email* paul_greatbatch@hotmail.com

■ The Enid Linder Foundation

CC NO 267509   **ESTABLISHED** 1974
WHERE FUNDING CAN BE GIVEN UK
WHO CAN BENEFIT Registered charities benefiting children, older people and people who are disabled; universities and teaching hospitals, schools and other educational establishments.
WHAT IS FUNDED Medicine: To fund research, education and capital projects related to all areas of medicine through grants to selected medical universities, institutions and charities. The Arts: To fund projects which aim to develop and encourage individual and group talent in musical, theatre and illustrative art. General: To make donations to projects through other registered UK charities which support and care for the benefit of the public as a whole.
WHAT IS NOT FUNDED No grants to individuals.
TYPE OF GRANT One-off and recurrent.
SAMPLE GRANTS Royal College of Surgeons (£110,000); National Children's Orchestra Bursary (£50,000); Imperial College and Victoria and Albert Museum (£30,000 each); Médecins Sans Frontières (£25,000); Moto Neurone Disease Association (£13,000); Bath Intensive Care Baby Unit and Help for Heroes (£10,000 each); Beatrix Potter Society (£7,000) and Prospect Hospice and WaterAid (£5,000 each).
FINANCES *Year* 2011–12 *Income* £540,170 *Grants* £511,000 *Assets* £13,146,430
TRUSTEES Jack Ladeveze; Audrey Ladeveze; M. Butler; C. Cook; Jonathan Fountain.
OTHER INFORMATION The grants total includes £75,000 in elective and hardship grants to University medical schools.
HOW TO APPLY Apply using the online form on the foundation's website. The deadline is 1 January for the March trustee meeting and 1 September for the December meeting. Grants will be made in April and January. From the foundation's website: 'Unsolicited applications are accepted, but the Trustees do receive a very high number of grant applications which, in line with their grantmaking policy, are mostly unsuccessful. The Trustees prefer to support donations to a charity whose work they have researched and which falls within their guidelines.'
WHO TO APPLY TO Martin Pollock, Secretary, c/o Moore Stephens LLP, 150 Aldersgate Street,

London EC1A 4AB *Tel.* 020 7334 9191 *Fax* 020 7651 1953 *email* info@enidlinderfoundation.com *Website* www.enidlinderfoundation.com

■ The Linmardon Trust

CC NO 275307   **ESTABLISHED** 1977
WHERE FUNDING CAN BE GIVEN UK, with a preference for the Nottingham area.
WHO CAN BENEFIT Registered charities.
WHAT IS FUNDED General charitable purposes.
WHAT IS NOT FUNDED Registered charities only. No grants to individuals.
RANGE OF GRANTS £500–£3,000
SAMPLE GRANTS Animal Health Trust, Bath Cats and Dogs Home, Great North Air Ambulance and Sheltered Work Opportunities Project (£2,000 each); The Nottingham Historic Churches Trust and Age UK Andover and District (£1,250 each) and Demand, Friends of St Francis Special School and Newport Cottage Care Centre (£1,000 each).
FINANCES *Year* 2011–12 *Income* £361,458 *Grants* £36,644 *Assets* £1,225,233
TRUSTEE HSBC Trust Company (UK) Ltd
HOW TO APPLY In writing to the correspondent. The trustees meet quarterly, generally in February, May, August and November. Grants are made throughout the year.
WHO TO APPLY TO Lee Topp, Trust Manager, HSBC Trust Company (UK) Limited, Norwich House, Nelson Gate, Commercial Road, Southampton SO15 1GX *Tel.* 02380 722240

■ The Ruth and Stuart Lipton Charitable Trust

CC NO 266741   **ESTABLISHED** 1973
WHERE FUNDING CAN BE GIVEN UK and overseas
WHO CAN BENEFIT Preference for organisations benefiting Jewish people.
WHAT IS FUNDED Jewish charities and charitable purposes.
WHAT IS NOT FUNDED No grants to individuals.
RANGE OF GRANTS £100–£30,000
SAMPLE GRANTS Community Security Trust (£28,000); United Jewish Israel Appeal (£12,500); The Royal Opera House Foundation (£8,000); Western Marble Arch Synagogue (£4,000); Barbican Centre (£3,000); Chai Cancer Care (£2,500); National Portrait Gallery and Haileybury Youth Trust (£1,000 each); Royal Ballet School (£500); Oxfam (£200) and Motor Neurone Disease Association and Jewish Women's Aid (£100 each).
FINANCES *Year* 2011–12 *Income* £72,190 *Grants* £78,902 *Assets* £592,940
TRUSTEES Sir Stuart Lipton; Lady Lipton; Neil Benson.
OTHER INFORMATION There is no minimum limit for any grant and all grants must be approved unanimously by the trustees.
HOW TO APPLY In writing to the correspondent.
WHO TO APPLY TO Neil Benson, Trustee, c/o Lewis Golden and Co., 40 Queen Ann Street, London W1G 9EL *Tel.* 020 7580 7313

■ The Lister Charitable Trust

CC NO 288730   **ESTABLISHED** 1981
WHERE FUNDING CAN BE GIVEN UK and overseas.
WHO CAN BENEFIT Registered charities which work with young people.

WHAT IS FUNDED General charitable purposes.

WHAT IS NOT FUNDED Applications from individuals, including students, are ineligible. No grants are made in response to general appeals from large UK organisations or to smaller bodies working in areas outside its criteria.

TYPE OF GRANT Usually one-off for specific project or part of a project. Core funding and/or salaries rarely considered. Funding may be given for up to one year.

SAMPLE GRANTS The European Nature Trust (£191,000); the Stroke Association (£40,000); Nyaka School (£19,000); Sponsored Arts for Education and Home Start Ashford (£10,000 each); Oxford Transplant Foundation (£5,000); and Embercombe (£3,000).

FINANCES *Year* 2011–12 *Income* £216,434 *Grants* £304,112 *Assets* £7,659,573

TRUSTEES Noel Lister; David Collingwood; Paul Lister; Penny Horne; Sylvia Lister.

OTHER INFORMATION Grants to ten organisations were made totalling £304,000 in 2011–12.

HOW TO APPLY In writing to the correspondent. Applications should include clear details of the need the intended project is designed to meet, plus an outline budget. Only applications from eligible bodies are acknowledged, when further information may be requested.

WHO TO APPLY TO Nicholas Yellowlees, Administrator, 44 Welbeck Street, London W1G 8DY *Tel.* 020 7486 0800 *email* info@apperleylimited.co.uk

---

■ Frank Litchfield Charitable Trust

CC NO 1038943   **ESTABLISHED** 1994

WHERE FUNDING CAN BE GIVEN Mostly in and around Cambridge.

WHO CAN BENEFIT Charitable organisations.

WHAT IS FUNDED Medical services and relief of poverty amongst those involved in agriculture.

RANGE OF GRANTS Up to £12,000.

SAMPLE GRANTS Therfield Recreation Ground (£12,000); Tomotherapy and Cambridge University (£10,000); Headway Cambridgeshire (£7,500); The Cogwheel Trust (£5,000); and Happy Days and Richmond Fellowship Cambridge (£1,000 each).

FINANCES *Year* 2011–12 *Income* £60,619 *Grants* £50,000

TRUSTEES Michael Womack; David Chater.

HOW TO APPLY In writing to the correspondent. This trust receives more applications each year than it is able to fund.

WHO TO APPLY TO Michael Womack, Trustee, 12 De Freville Avenue, Cambridge CB4 1HR *Tel.* 01223 358012

■ The Andrew and Mary Elizabeth Little Charitable Trust

SC NO SC011185   **ESTABLISHED** 1935

WHERE FUNDING CAN BE GIVEN Mainly Glasgow and the surrounding area.

WHO CAN BENEFIT Organisations based in Scotland such as infirmaries, hospitals, homes for the aged, orphanages and other such institutions, which provide direct or indirect help to disadvantaged people.

WHAT IS FUNDED Welfare needs.

SAMPLE GRANTS Previous beneficiaries have included: Ayrshire Hospice, Glasgow City Mission, Glasgow Marriage Guidance Council, Glasgow Old People's Welfare Committee, St Margaret's of Scotland Adoption Society and Strathclyde Youth Club Association.

FINANCES *Year* 2011–12 *Income* £55,154

HOW TO APPLY In writing to the correspondent. Trustees meet to consider grants once a month. Individuals should provide financial details of income support.

WHO TO APPLY TO The Trustees, Low Beaton Richmond Solicitors, Sterling House, 20 Renfield Street, Glasgow G2 5AP

■ Littlefield Foundation (UK) Limited

CC NO 1148909   **ESTABLISHED** 2012

WHERE FUNDING CAN BE GIVEN UK and the USA.

WHO CAN BENEFIT Charities and community groups.

WHAT IS FUNDED General charitable purposes.

TRUSTEES Horace Joseph Leitch; Cathey Leitch; Jeffrey Brummette.

OTHER INFORMATION Registered in September 2012, the trust's objects are general charitable purposes. The trustees are: H Joseph Leitch who is chief administrative officer and partner at Rubicon Fund Management LLP, which he co-founded in 1999; his wife, Cathey Leitch, who is a historian, author and academic; and Jeffrey Brummette, also co-founder of Rubicon Fund Management and currently at Onewall Advisors, another hedge fund manager. All of the trustees are American-born. Further research suggests that Mr and Mrs Leitch have previously supported the arts, particularly music, and have an interest in sailing.

HOW TO APPLY In writing to the correspondent.

WHO TO APPLY TO Alana Lowe-Petraske, c/o Withers LLP, 16 Old Bailey, London EC4M 7EG *Tel.* 020 7597 6257 *Fax* 020 7597 6543 *email* alana.lowe-petraske@withersworldwide.com

---

■ The Second Joseph Aaron Littman Foundation

CC NO 201892   **ESTABLISHED** 1961

WHERE FUNDING CAN BE GIVEN UK.

WHO CAN BENEFIT Registered charities only.

WHAT IS FUNDED General charitable purposes, with a special preference for Jewish causes, as well as academic and medical research.

WHAT IS NOT FUNDED Applications from individuals are not considered.

TYPE OF GRANT One-off, core costs, replacement of statutory funding.

RANGE OF GRANTS Usually £5,000–£50.

SAMPLE GRANTS Littman Library of Jewish Civilisation (£192,000); Hadassah UK, University Jewish Chaplaincy and Coronary Flow Trust (£5,000 each); Leo Baeck College UK (£2,500); University College London and Great Ormond Street Hospital (£2,000 each); Holocaust Educational Trust (£1,500); and Fight for Sight (£1,000).

FINANCES *Year* 2011–12 *Income* £295,352 *Grants* £245,465 *Assets* £5,557,135

TRUSTEES Robert Littman; Glenn Hurstfield; C. Littman.

OTHER INFORMATION Donations of less than £1,000 totalled £12,000 in 2011–12.

HOW TO APPLY In writing to the correspondent.

WHO TO APPLY TO Robert Littman, Trustee, Manor Farm, Mill Lane, Charlton Mackrell, Somerton, Somerset TA11 7BQ

■ The George John and Sheilah Livanos Charitable Trust

CC NO 1002279 **ESTABLISHED** 1985
WHERE FUNDING CAN BE GIVEN UK.
WHO CAN BENEFIT Registered charities.
WHAT IS FUNDED Medical research and equipment, health, medical charities for children or older people, marine charities and general charitable purposes.
WHAT IS NOT FUNDED No grants to individuals or non-registered charities.
TYPE OF GRANT One-off and recurring grants. Capital grants.
RANGE OF GRANTS £1,000–£125,000.
SAMPLE GRANTS Ovarian Cancer Action (£170,000); Fight for Sight (£126,000); SPARKS (£54,000); Parkinson's Disease Society (£50,000) London Youth and Martlets Hospice (£10,000 each); Brainwave, The Bletchley Park Trust and Listening Books (£5,000 each); Whitechapel Mission (£2,500); Bath Institute of Medical Engineering and Children's Heart Foundation (£2,000 each) and Group B Strep Support (£1,000).
FINANCES *Year* 2012 *Income* £101,627 *Grants* £578,905 *Assets* £1,879,900
TRUSTEES Philip N. Harris; Timothy T. Cripps; Anthony S. Holmes.
HOW TO APPLY 'Unsolicited applications are considered but the trustees inevitably turn down a large number of applications.'
WHO TO APPLY TO Philip N. Harris, Trustee, Jeffrey Green Russell, Waverley House, 7–12 Noel Street, London W1F 8GQ *Tel.* 020 7339 7000

■ Liverpool Charity and Voluntary Services

CC NO 223485 **ESTABLISHED** 1970
WHERE FUNDING CAN BE GIVEN Merseyside only.
WHO CAN BENEFIT Registered charities.
WHAT IS FUNDED General charitable purposes.
FINANCES *Year* 2011–12 *Income* £3,951,266 *Grants* £2,357,173 *Assets* £6,977,547
TRUSTEES Charles Feeny; Sue Newton; Roger Morris; Caroline Clark; Hilary Russell; Andrew Lovelady; Christine Reeves; Heather Akehurst; Adeyinka Olushonde; Perminder Bal.
OTHER INFORMATION The charity acts in a similar manner to a community foundation, administrating the giving of much smaller charitable trusts.
HOW TO APPLY On a form available to download, together with criteria and guidelines, from the website.
WHO TO APPLY TO The Grants Team, 151 Dale Street, Liverpool L2 2AH *Tel.* 01512 275177 *email* info@lcvs.org.uk *Website* www.lcvs.org.uk

■ Liverpool Sailors' Home Trust

CC NO 515183 **ESTABLISHED** 1984
WHERE FUNDING CAN BE GIVEN Merseyside.
WHO CAN BENEFIT Organisations benefiting seafarers, fishermen, ex-service and service people and sea cadets.
WHAT IS FUNDED Charities engaged in maritime activities and based in Merseyside.
WHAT IS NOT FUNDED No grants to individuals.
TYPE OF GRANT One-off and capital grants will be considered.
SAMPLE GRANTS Previous grants have included: £9,000 to The Royal Merchant Navy School Foundation, £4,000 each to Sail Training

Association and Fairbridge Merseyside, £2,000 to Sea Cadet Corps – Ellesmere Port, £1,500 each to RNLI – New Brighton and RNLI – Hoylake and West Kirby, and £1,000 each to BISS and Sea Cadet Corps – Liverpool Mersey Unit.
FINANCES *Year* 2011–12
TRUSTEES Ian Higby; Trevor Hart; Peter Oranmore Copland; John Reginald Hulmes; Lynn Patricia Cook; David Stewart Barbour; Michael Finn.
HOW TO APPLY In writing to the correspondent. Trustees meet to consider grants in March, applications should be sent by 20 January.
WHO TO APPLY TO L. Gidman, Secretary, Room 19, 2nd Floor, Tower Building, 22 Water Street, Liverpool L3 1AB *Tel.* 01512 273417 *Fax* 01512 273417 *email* enquiries@rlsoi-uk. org

■ The Ian and Natalie Livingstone Charitable Trust

CC NO 1149025 **ESTABLISHED** 2012
WHERE FUNDING CAN BE GIVEN UK.
WHO CAN BENEFIT Charities and community groups.
WHAT IS FUNDED General charitable purposes, with a focus on organisations working with children and young people.
TRUSTEES Ian Livingstone; Natalie Livingstone; Mark Levitt.
OTHER INFORMATION As this is a new trust, information is limited. However, research shows that Mr and Mrs Livingstone have supported organisations such as Ovarian Cancer Action and the Serpentine Gallery.
HOW TO APPLY In writing to the correspondent.
WHO TO APPLY TO Mark Levitt, Trustee, c/o Hazlems Fenton LLP, Palladium House, 1–4 Argyll Street, London W1F 7LD *Tel.* 020 7437 7666 *Fax* 020 7734 0644 *email* marklevitt@hazlemsfenton. com

■ Jack Livingstone Charitable Trust

CC NO 263473 **ESTABLISHED** 1971
WHERE FUNDING CAN BE GIVEN UK and worldwide, with a preference for Manchester.
WHO CAN BENEFIT Registered charities benefiting Jewish people, at risk groups, and people who are ill, disadvantaged by poverty or socially isolated.
WHAT IS FUNDED Jewish charities and general charitable purposes.
TYPE OF GRANT One-off and recurrent.
RANGE OF GRANTS Up to £10,000.
SAMPLE GRANTS LCCC Foundation (£105,000); Federation of Jewish Services (£8,000); Community Security Trust and Manchester Jewish Community Care (£5,000 each); Langdon FDN Patrons (£3,000); J Roots Ltd (£2,500); British Friends of Darche Noam (£1,600); South Manchester Synagogue (£1,500); Southport New Synagogue, Project Seed, Stockdales, UK Toremet and Brookvale (£1,000 each).
FINANCES *Year* 2011–12 *Income* £52,417 *Grants* £147,665 *Assets* £1,899,867
TRUSTEES Janice Livingstone; Terence Livingstone; Brian White.
OTHER INFORMATION Grants of less than £1,000 totalled £11,000.
HOW TO APPLY The trust does not respond to unsolicited applications.

WHO TO APPLY TO Janice Livingstone, Trustee, Westholme, The Springs, Bowdon, Altringham, Cheshire WA14 3JH *Tel.* 01619 283232

■ The Elaine and Angus Lloyd Charitable Trust

CC NO 237250   **ESTABLISHED** 1964
WHERE FUNDING CAN BE GIVEN UK, with a preference for Surrey, Kent and the South of England.
WHO CAN BENEFIT Individuals, local, regional and UK organisations benefiting children, young adults, at risk groups, people disadvantaged by poverty and socially isolated people.
WHAT IS FUNDED Health and welfare organisations, churches and education.
TYPE OF GRANT Recurrent and one-off.
RANGE OF GRANTS Up to £7,000. Mostly £1,000–£2,000.
SAMPLE GRANTS Positive Initiative Trust (£7,500); EHAS (£3,800); Diabetes UK; Monday to Wednesday club; Rhema Partnership Anitoch; Rhema New Bible College and Skillaway (£2,000 each); East Kent Hospice Project and Martha Trust (£1,500 each); Croce Rossa Italiana Menaggio; Hever School; National Youth Orchestra of Great Britain; RNLI and The Afghan Connection (£1,000 each). Grants of less than £1,000 totalled £27,000.
FINANCES *Year* 2011–12 *Income* £88,181 *Grants* £78,185 *Assets* £2,479,844
TRUSTEES Angus Lloyd; John Gordon; James Lloyd; Philippa Satchwell-Smith; Virginia Best; Christopher Lloyd; Michael Craig-Cooper; Richard Lloyd.
HOW TO APPLY In writing to the correspondent. The trustees meet regularly to consider grants.
WHO TO APPLY TO Ross Badger, 3rd Floor, North Side, Dukes Court, 32 Duke Street, St James's, London SW1Y 6DF *Tel.* 020 7930 7797

■ The Charles Lloyd Foundation

CC NO 235225   **ESTABLISHED** 1964
WHERE FUNDING CAN BE GIVEN Roman Catholic Dioceses of Menevia and Wrexham.
WHO CAN BENEFIT Roman Catholics.
WHAT IS FUNDED The upkeep of Roman Catholic churches, houses, convents and monasteries, the advancement of religion and the promotion and advancement of music, either religious or secular.
TYPE OF GRANT One-off.
SAMPLE GRANTS Flint Catholic Church (£16,000); and Hawarden Catholic Church and Barmouth Catholic Church (£10,000 each).
FINANCES *Year* 2012–13 *Income* £45,526 *Grants* £36,000 *Assets* £1,421,821
TRUSTEES Richard Thorn; Patrick Walters; Vincent Ryan; Steven Davies.
HOW TO APPLY In writing to the correspondent. Four copies of the income and expenditure pages of the latest financial return; plans and estimates of the project; plus what finances the parish can contribute must be provided once details of the project are known.
WHO TO APPLY TO Vincent Ryan, Trustee, 8–10 Grosvenor Road, Wrexham LL11 1BU *Tel.* 01978 291000 *email* susanelder@allingtonhughes.co.uk

■ Lloyd's Charities Trust

CC NO 207232   **ESTABLISHED** 1953
WHERE FUNDING CAN BE GIVEN UK, with particular interest in East London.
WHO CAN BENEFIT Charitable organisations.
WHAT IS FUNDED General charitable purposes, with a specific interest in education, training, employment and enterprise.
WHAT IS NOT FUNDED The trust's website states that 'Lloyd's Charities Trust will not fund the following: organisations that are not registered charities or non-UK registered charities (except at the occasional discretion of trustees); political parties or lobbying organisations; local charities outside London, unless there is significant involvement from a person currently working in the Lloyd's market, in which case the application must come from that individual; mainstream schools, PTAs and educational establishments unless there is significant involvement from a person currently working in the Lloyd's market, in which case the application must come from that individual; grantmaking bodies to make grants on our behalf; animal welfare causes, zoos, animal rescue; the promotion of religion or other beliefs; individuals, including student grants, bursaries, medical costs or financial assistance; sponsorship of events or individuals including taking tables at gala dinners; advertising including in brochures for charitable events; costs associated with expeditions; and retrospective funding for work that has already taken place. Lloyd's Charities Trust will typically not fund the following: military causes; arts, culture or heritage charities; outward bound courses and adventure experiences; conferences, cultural festivals, exhibitions and events; and churches, cathedrals and other historic buildings.'
SAMPLE GRANTS The Prince's Trust (£75,000); and Bromley By Bow Centre (£50,000).
FINANCES *Year* 2012 *Income* £469,005 *Grants* £403,362 *Assets* £2,483,539
TRUSTEES John Spencer; David Gittings; Lawrence Holder; Iain Wilson; Charles Hamond; Rupert Atkin; Graham Clarke; Chris Harman; Neil Smith; Vicky Mirfin.
HOW TO APPLY Lloyd's Charities Trust makes ad hoc donations, however the majority of funds are committed to supporting the partnership charities the trust works with. The trust has previously stated that as funds are committed over a three-year period 'we are unable to respond positively to the numerous appeals we receive'.
WHO TO APPLY TO Suzanna Nagle, Administrator, 1 Lime Street, London EC3M 7HA *Tel.* 020 7327 6075 *email* communityaffairs@lloyds.com *Website* www.lloyds.com/lct

■ Lloyds Bank Foundation for England and Wales

CC NO 327114   **ESTABLISHED** 1986
WHERE FUNDING CAN BE GIVEN England and Wales.
WHO CAN BENEFIT Registered charities benefiting people who are disabled or disadvantaged.
WHAT IS FUNDED Education and training and social and community needs.
WHAT IS NOT FUNDED The foundation does not fund the following types of organisations and work: *Organisations:* organisations that are **not** registered charities; second or third tier organisations (unless there is evidence of direct benefit to disadvantaged people); charities that

mainly work overseas; charities that mainly give funds to other charities, individuals or other organisations; hospitals, hospices or medical centres; rescue services; schools, colleges and universities.

Types of work: activities which a statutory body is responsible for; capital projects, appeals, refurbishments; environmental work, expeditions and overseas travel; funding to promote religion; holidays or trips; loans or business finance; medical research, funding for medical equipment or medical treatments; sponsorship or funding towards a marketing appeal or fundraising activities; work with animals or to promote animal welfare.

TYPE OF GRANT One-off for a specific project, core funding, two or three year funding. Also capital, recurring costs, running costs and salaries.

RANGE OF GRANTS £500–£250,000

SAMPLE GRANTS Hackney CVS (£250,000); Age Concern in Cornwall and The Isles of Scilly (£188,000); Working With Men (WWM) (£38,000); Norfolk Community Law Service and Sexual Abuse and Rape Advice Centre (£30,000 each); Rainbow Services and Greenwich Mencap (£28,000 each); CVS Tamworth (£27,000); Burnley and Pendle CAB (£22,000); MIND in West Cumbria (£20,000); Hodan Somali Community (£19,000); Broxlow Youth Homelessness (£18,000); Pakistan Association Liverpool (£15,000); Downs Syndrome Association (£12,000); Halton Disability Advice and Appeals Centre (£14,000) and Children and Families in Grief (£8,000).

FINANCES *Year* 2011–12 *Income* £26,693,000 *Grants* £21,492,000 *Assets* £39,236,000

TRUSTEES Prof. Ian Diamond, Chair; Janet Bibby; Rob Devey; Pavita Cooper; Alan Leaman; Philip Grant; Mohammad Naeem; Lord Sandy Leitch; Sir Clive Booth; Dame Denise Platt; Prof. Patricia Broadfoot; Helen Edwards.

OTHER INFORMATION On 15 January 2014 the foundation released the following statement on its website:

'The Lloyds Bank Foundation for England and Wales has today announced its intention to launch a new funding strategy. The new strategy – to be launched in April [2014] – reflects discussions with charities and other funders, and will reinforce the foundation's ongoing commitment to support small and medium sized charities in a challenging economic funding environment.'

'**Creating a flexible and responsive approach to grantmaking:** Following the recent signing of a nine year rolling funding agreement with Lloyds Banking Group and a change of name, the Lloyds Bank Foundation for England and Wales will launch two new funding programmes, along with an optional support programme for successful applicants.'

'These new programmes demonstrate the foundation's ongoing commitment to support charities that have the greatest impact upon improving the lives of disadvantaged people and their communities.'; 'Invest – A flexible, long term core funding programme for organisations delivering clear, targeted outcomes for disadvantaged people'; 'Enable – A smaller and shorter grants programme for organisations that have identified clear development needs';

'Enhance – A programme working alongside the Invest or Enable programme providing an option of tailored in-kind support to strengthen and develop charities' effectiveness. The foundation will continue to process grant requests under the current Community Programme over the coming months. However, to ensure a smooth transition

between the programmes, it will close this programme to new enquiries on 14 February 2014. Further information about the new programmes will be published in April when they will be open for new enquiries.'

'**A trusted partner and respected voice:** As part of the new strategy, the foundation also announced its intention to partner with other funders to identify issues and contribute to policy and practices in the voluntary sector, at a national and local level, to lever positive change.'

HOW TO APPLY Refer to the foundation's website for current information.

WHO TO APPLY TO Tina Claeys, Grant Administration Manager, Pentagon House, 52–54 Southwark Street, London SE1 1UN *Tel.* 0870 411 1223 *Fax* 0870 411 1224 *email* enquiries@lloydstsbfoundations.org.uk *Website* www.lloydstsbfoundations.org.uk

■ Lloyds Bank Foundation for Northern Ireland

IR NO XN72216   **ESTABLISHED** 1986

WHERE FUNDING CAN BE GIVEN Northern Ireland.

WHO CAN BENEFIT Charities registered with HM Revenue and Customs, benefiting children, young adults, older people, volunteers and people who are unemployed, homeless, living in rural communities, disabled or disadvantaged by poverty.

WHAT IS FUNDED Underfunded voluntary organisations which enable people who are disabled and people who are disadvantaged through social and economic circumstances, to make a contribution to the community. The trustees regret that, as the funds available are limited, they cannot support all fields of voluntary and charitable activity. The two main objectives to which funds are allocated are: (a) social and community needs; (b) education and training. For full details of the foundation's funding objectives go to the website.

WHAT IS NOT FUNDED Grants are not usually given for: organisations that are not recognised as a charity by HM Revenue and Customs; individuals, including students; animal welfare; environmental projects including those that deal with geographic and scenic issues – however, the trustees may consider projects that improve the living conditions of disadvantaged individuals and groups; activities that are normally the responsibility of central or local government or some other responsible body; schools, universities and colleges (except for projects specifically to benefit students with special needs); hospitals and medical centres); sponsorship or marketing appeals; fabric appeals for places of worship; promotion of religion; activities that collect funds for subsequent redistribution to others; endowment funds; fundraising events or activities; corporate affiliation or membership of a charity; loans or business finance; expeditions or overseas travel; construction of and extension to buildings; salary or training costs for the pre-school sector. Note: organisations must have a total income of less than £250,000 to be eligible to apply to the Standard Grant Programme.

TYPE OF GRANT Capital, core costs, one-off, project, recurring costs, salaries and start-up costs. Funding is usually one-off, but support for two years or more is considered.

RANGE OF GRANTS Normally a maximum of £5,000, but larger amounts are considered.

SAMPLE GRANTS Northern Ireland Community Addiction Services Ltd (£5,300); Allergy NI and New Belfast Community Arts Initiative (£5,000 each); Foyle Women's Aid (£4,300); Ligoniel Amateur Boxing Club (£3,500); Northern Walking Project (£2,500); Shopmobility Lisburn and Stroke Association (£2,000 each); Windyhall Community Association (£1,650); Donaghmore Open Door Club and Killyleagh Early Years Playgroup (£1,000 each) and Alphabet Playgroup (£450).

FINANCES *Year* 2012 *Income* £1,994,694 *Grants* £1,865,233 *Assets* £2,389,950

TRUSTEES Tony Reynolds; Paddy Bailie; Angela Colhoun; Brian Scott; Hugh Donnelly; Carmel McGukian; Lord Leitch; Janet Leckey; Jim McCooe; Janine Donnelly; Robert Agnew; Sandara Kelso-Robb.

HOW TO APPLY Applications can be made using the online application form. Once registered you will receive a username and password which you can use to access the online grants portal and view and apply for open programmes. Applicants are welcome to contact the foundation or make an appointment to discuss an application. As part of the assessment process the foundation may contact or visit the applicant. If you have not heard from the foundation within four weeks contact them. Guidelines, advice on completing the form, supporting document checklist and monitoring factsheets are all available from the website.

WHO TO APPLY TO Sandara Kelso-Robb, Executive Director, 2nd Floor, 14 Cromac Place, Gasworks, Belfast BT7 2JB *Tel.* 02890 323000 *Fax* 02890 323200 *email* lloydstsbfoundationni.org *Website* www.lloydstsbfoundationni.org

....

■ Lloyds Bank Foundation for the Channel Islands

CC NO 327113   **ESTABLISHED** 1986

WHERE FUNDING CAN BE GIVEN The Channel Islands.

WHO CAN BENEFIT Organisations benefiting children and young people; older people; volunteers; at risk groups; people who are unemployed, carers, disabled, disadvantaged by poverty or homeless; and victims of abuse and domestic violence.

WHAT IS FUNDED The main aims of the foundation are to assist disadvantaged and disabled people and to promote social and community welfare within the Channel Islands. A wide range of activities are supported, and the following examples are meant as a guide only: advice services – addictions (particularly substance misuse rehabilitation), bereavement, counselling, emergency and rescue services, family support, helplines, homelessness, housing, parenting; community relations – crime prevention (particularly activities involving young people), mediation, promotion of volunteering, rehabilitation of offenders, victim support, vulnerable young people; community facilities and services – after school clubs, community centres, family centres, older people's clubs, playschemes, transport, youth organisations; cultural enrichment – improving participation in and access to the arts and national heritage; activities with an educational focus for all ages; improvements to buildings of historic or architectural value which increase their benefit to the community; projects which have a strong focus on benefit to people and the social environment; disabled people – advocacy,

carers, day centres, information and advice, sheltered accommodation, transport; promotion of health – day care, information and advice, mental health, holistic medicine, home nursing, hospices. The trustees will, on an exceptional basis, also fund research projects in health related areas. The foundation also supports education and training, particularly activities which enhance learning opportunities for disabled and disadvantaged people of all ages.

WHAT IS NOT FUNDED No grants for: organisations which are not recognised charities; activities which are primarily the responsibility of the Insular authorities in the Islands or some other responsible body; activities which collect funds to give to other charities, individuals or other organisations; animal welfare; corporate subscription or membership of a charity; endowment funds; environment – conserving and protecting plants and animals, geography and scenery; expeditions or overseas travel; fabric appeals for places of worship; fundraising events or activities; hospitals and medical centres (except for projects which are clearly additional to statutory responsibilities); individuals, including students; loans or business finance; promotion of religion; schools and colleges (except for projects that will benefit disabled students and are clearly additional to statutory responsibilities); sponsorship or marketing appeals; international appeals – trustees may from time to time consider a limited number of applications from UK registered charities working abroad.

TYPE OF GRANT Depends on merit, but usually one-off for a specific project, operational costs, salaries and start-up costs. Funding of up to three years may be considered.

RANGE OF GRANTS £1,000–£110,000.

SAMPLE GRANTS Brighter Futures (£120,000); Guernsey Arts Commission (£90,000); The Bridge Project Guernsey (£75,000); Jersey Youth Trust (£65,000); St Mark's Church (£30,000); Jubilee Sailing Trust (£25,000); Guernsey Voluntary Service (£11,000); Guernsey Bereavement Service (£7,400); Chernobyl Children life line (£5,000) and Helping Wings (£1,700).

FINANCES *Year* 2012 *Income* £1,151,477 *Grants* £1,039,252 *Assets* £1,522,311

TRUSTEES Pauline Torode; John Boothman; Stephen Jones; Dr John Furguson; Patricia Tumelty; Martin Fricker; Sarah Bamford; Simon Howitt; Andrew Dann.

OTHER INFORMATION The grants total includes £41,000 raised by Lloyds TSB staff in the Channel Islands. From 2014 the foundation will be known as the Lloyds Bank Foundation for the Channel Islands.

HOW TO APPLY Applications are only accepted on the foundation's own form which should be submitted with: a copy of your latest report and accounts (or draft accounts if more recent). These should be signed as approved on behalf of your Management Committee or equivalent; a photocopy of your most recent bank statement; if you are applying to fund an employee post: a copy of the job description; income Tax letter of exemption if you are a CI-based organisation and not part of a UK registered charity. The form and guidelines are available from its website or from the foundation's office in Jersey and can be returned at any time. They must be returned by post as the foundation does not accept forms that have been emailed or faxed. All applications are reviewed on a continual basis. The trustees meet three times a year to approve donations in March, July and November and deadlines are usually the middle of the preceding month. Decision-making processes can therefore take up to four months. Applications up to £5,000 are normally assessed within one month and all applicants are informed of the outcome of their application. Applicants are encouraged to discuss their project with one of the foundation's staff before completing an application form. This will help ensure that your project is within its criteria and that you are applying for an appropriate amount. You will also be informed of when you should hear a decision.

WHO TO APPLY TO John Hutchins, Executive Director, PO Box 160, 25 New Street, St Helier, Jersey JE4 8RG *Tel.* 01534 845889 *email* john. hutchins@lloydstsbfoundations.org.uk *Website* www.ltsbfoundationci.org

....

■ Lloyds TSB Foundation for Scotland

SC NO SC009481   **ESTABLISHED** 1986
WHERE FUNDING CAN BE GIVEN Scotland.
WHO CAN BENEFIT Recognised charities which provide support to the Scottish community, enabling people, primarily those in need, to become active members of society and to improve their quality of life.
WHAT IS FUNDED The foundation's current programmes are: Henry Duncan Awards; the Partnership Drugs Initiative; Capacity Building Support and Recovery Initiative Fund.
WHAT IS NOT FUNDED The foundation will not support: charities with an income of more than £500,000 per annum; organisations which are not formally recognised as charities in Scotland; charities which pay their board members or have paid employees who also hold a position as Director on the Board. This principle also applies to charities operating as collectives; individuals – including students; animal welfare; initiatives that are focused on sport, the arts or the environment, except where the subject is being used as a vehicle to engage with at risk or disadvantaged groups to increase life skills; conservation and protection of flora and fauna; mainstream activities and statutory requirements of hospitals and medical centres, schools, universities and colleges; sponsorship or marketing appeals; establishment/ preservation of endowment funds; activities that collect funds for subsequent grantmaking to other organisations and/or individuals; expeditions or overseas travel; major building projects/capital appeals; historic restoration/ historic publications; retrospective funding; promotion of religion/church fabric appeals; hobby groups; one-off events such as gala days.
TYPE OF GRANT Mostly one-off. However the foundation will consider grants over two or three years. Grants are made for buildings, capital, core costs, feasibility studies, project, research, recurring costs, running costs, salaries and start-up costs.
SAMPLE GRANTS Inspiring Scotland (£250,000); Barnardo's Perth and Kincross (£80,000 in two grants); Befriend a Child (£72,000); Tayside Council on Alcohol (£57,000); Pilotlight Scotland (£30,000); Children 1st (£27,000); PLUS (Stirling) Ltd (£8,000); Reality Adventure Works in Scotland Limited (£7,000); Orkney Alcohol Counselling and Advisory Service (£6,000); Loanhead Community Learning Association (£5,000); Getting Better Together (£4,000); Cruse Bereavement Care Scotland (£3,000) and

Scottish Minority Deaf Children's Society (£900).
FINANCES *Year* 2012 *Income* £904,000 *Grants* £2,110,000 *Assets* £6,263,000
TRUSTEES Christine Lenihan, Chair; Prof. Sir John P. Arbuthnott; Prof. Sandy Cameron; James G. D. Ferguson; Jane Mackie; Maria McGill; Ian Small; Iain Webster; Tim Hall.
HOW TO APPLY Application forms for all programmes, complete with comprehensive guidance notes, are available from the foundation. These can be requested by telephone, by email, or through its website. Foundation staff are always willing to provide additional help. Check the foundation's website for details of upcoming application deadlines.
WHO TO APPLY TO Karen Brown, Administrator and Secretary, Riverside House, 502 Gorgie Road, Edinburgh EH11 3AF *Tel.* 01314 444020 *Fax* 01314 444099 *email* enquiries@ ltsbfoundationforscotland.org.uk *Website* www. ltsbfoundationforscotland.org.uk

....

■ The Lo Family Charitable Trust

CC NO 1145845   **ESTABLISHED** 2012
WHERE FUNDING CAN BE GIVEN England, Australia and South East Asia.
WHO CAN BENEFIT Registered charities, churches, hospitals and universities.
WHAT IS FUNDED Christianity, education, health and general charitable purposes.
TRUSTEES Dr Ronald Lo; Judith Lo.
HOW TO APPLY No grants to unsolicited applications.
WHO TO APPLY TO Dr Ronald Lo, Trustee, 174 Leigh Hunt Drive, London N14 6DQ

....

■ Localtrent Ltd

CC NO 326329   **ESTABLISHED** 1982
WHERE FUNDING CAN BE GIVEN UK, with some preference for Manchester.
WHO CAN BENEFIT Charities benefiting Jewish people and the advancement of the Jewish faith.
WHAT IS FUNDED The trustees will consider applications from organisations concerned with Orthodox Jewish faith education and the relief of poverty.
SAMPLE GRANTS Yetev Lev (£41,000); Dushinsky Trust (£20,000) and Kesser Torah School (£7,300).
FINANCES *Year* 2011–12 *Income* £225,856 *Grants* £193,902 *Assets* £748,927
TRUSTEES Hyman Weiss; Mina Weiss; Philip Weiss; Zisel Weiss; Bernardin Weiss; Yocheved Weiss.
HOW TO APPLY In writing to the correspondent.
WHO TO APPLY TO A. Kahan, Administrator, Lopian Gross Barnett and Co, 6th Floor, Cardinal House, 20 St Mary's Parsonage, Manchester M3 2LG *Tel.* 01618 328721

....

■ The Locker Foundation

CC NO 264180   **ESTABLISHED** 1972
WHERE FUNDING CAN BE GIVEN UK and overseas.
WHO CAN BENEFIT Organisations benefiting Jewish people. General charitable purposes with preference for the welfare of the sick and those with disabilities and the teaching of the Jewish religion.
WHAT IS FUNDED Jewish charities, Synagogues, schools and colleges and Jewish education studies.
RANGE OF GRANTS £100–£100,000.

SAMPLE GRANTS Magen David Adom (£65,000); Kahal Chassidim Babov (£64,000); British Friends of Israel War Disabled (£30,000); Chai Cancer Care (£25,000); Jewish Blind and Disabled (£20,000); Youth Aliyah (£17,000); Shaare Zedak Hospital (£15,000); Norwood Children and Families First (£12,000); The Shalom Foundation and World Jewish Relief (£10,000); Jewish Museum (£5,000); Jewish Lads and Girls Brigade (£2,500); North London Hospice (£1,000) and Zionist Foundation (£250).

FINANCES *Year* 2011–12 *Income* £611,584 *Grants* £396,600 *Assets* £4,961,817

TRUSTEES I. Carter; M. Carter; S. Segal.

HOW TO APPLY In writing to the correspondent.

WHO TO APPLY TO Irving Carter, Trustee, 9 Neville Drive, London N2 0QS *Tel.* 020 8455 9280

....

■ The Loftus Charitable Trust

CC NO 297664   **ESTABLISHED** 1987

WHERE FUNDING CAN BE GIVEN UK and overseas.

WHO CAN BENEFIT Jewish organisations benefiting children, young adults and students.

WHAT IS FUNDED Jewish organisations working in the areas of welfare, education and religion.

RANGE OF GRANTS £**FINANCES** *Year* 2011–12 *Income* £243,750 *Grants* £262,612 *Assets* £17,225

TRUSTEES R. I. Loftus; A. L. Loftus; A. D. Loftus.

OTHER INFORMATION Jewish Care (£30,000); Zichron Moshe Educational and Education Trust (£25,000); United Synagogue (£22,000); and Kirsharon and Norwood (£20,000 each); Community Security Trust (£15,000); Tikva Children's Home (£10,000); Nightingale and Lubavitch Foundation (£5,000 each); Magen David Adom UK (£3,000) and Project SEED (£2,500).

HOW TO APPLY The trustees prefer to invite applications rather than considering unsolicited applications.

WHO TO APPLY TO Anthony Loftus, Trustee, Asher House, Blackburn Road, London NW6 1AW *Tel.* 020 7604 5900 *email* post@ rhodesandrhodes.com

....

■ The Lolev Charitable Trust

CC NO 326249   **ESTABLISHED** 1982

WHERE FUNDING CAN BE GIVEN Worldwide.

WHO CAN BENEFIT Individuals and organisations.

WHAT IS FUNDED Orthodox Jewish causes.

FINANCES *Year* 2011 *Income* £3,683,920 *Grants* £3,716,853 *Assets* £5,715

TRUSTEES Abraham Tager; Eve Tager; Michael Tager.

OTHER INFORMATION The latest accounts available at the time of writing (December 2013) were for 2011. £3.3 million of the grant total was given in grants to individuals.

HOW TO APPLY In writing to the correspondent.

WHO TO APPLY TO Abraham Tager, Trustee, 14a Gilda Crescent, London N16 6JP

....

■ The Joyce Lomax Bullock Charitable Trust

CC NO 1109911   **ESTABLISHED** 2005

WHERE FUNDING CAN BE GIVEN UK

WHO CAN BENEFIT Registered charities.

WHAT IS FUNDED General charitable purposes.

SAMPLE GRANTS There were nine beneficiaries, each of which received two grants totalling £5,900.

They were: Age UK; Cancer Research UK; Guide Dogs For The Blind; IWK Health Centre Foundation; The National Trust; Perennial; RAF Benevolent Fund; The Royal British Legion; and Royal Commonwealth Society.

FINANCES *Year* 2011–12 *Income* £846,327 *Grants* £53,100 *Assets* £3,030,402

TRUSTEE HSBC Trust Company (UK) Limited

HOW TO APPLY In writing to the correspondent, although note that 'grants are awarded at the discretion of the trustee but are generally in accordance with a letter of wishes provided by the late Joyce Lomax Bullock'. This seems to dictate that a set list of charities are awarded grants each year.

WHO TO APPLY TO The Trust Manager, Norwich House, Nelson Gate, Commercial Road, Southampton SO15 1GX *Tel.* 02380 723344

....

■ The Trust for London (formerly the City Parochial Foundation)

CC NO 205629   **ESTABLISHED** 2004

WHERE FUNDING CAN BE GIVEN Greater London.

WHO CAN BENEFIT Organisations providing advice, information and individual advocacy, especially those which are user-led or which encourage user involvement, participation and which lead to user empowerment. Organisations developing, promoting and providing education, training and employment schemes. Organisations which are attempting to develop initiatives which tackle violence and hate crimes against the target groups; applications will be considered for work with people who commit crimes and violence as well as work with the victims of it. Organisations who support and help settle asylum seekers, migrants and refugees.

WHAT IS FUNDED Work that aims to bring about policy changes relating to discrimination, isolations and violence and improving people's quality of life; second tier and infrastructure organisations which meet the needs of the targeted groups; projects involving working together with others to meet the needs of their members.

WHAT IS NOT FUNDED The foundation will not support proposals: which do not benefit Londoners; that directly replace or subsidise statutory funding (including contracts); that are the primary responsibility of statutory funders such as local and central government and health authorities; from individuals, or which are for the benefit of one individual; for mainstream educational activity including schools; for medical purposes including hospitals and hospices; for the promotion of religion; for umbrella bodies seeking to distribute grants on the foundation's behalf; for work that has already taken place; for general appeals; for large capital appeals (including buildings and minibuses); or from applicants who have been rejected by the foundation in the last six months. The foundation is unlikely to support proposals: from large national charities which enjoy widespread support; for work that takes place in schools during school hours; where organisations have significant unrestricted reserves (including those that are designated). Generally up to six months expenditure is normally acceptable; or where organisations are in serious financial deficit.

TYPE OF GRANT Core and management costs; work that aims to change policy.

Think carefully about every application. Is it justified?

713

RANGE OF GRANTS £5,000–£120,000 often up to three years.

SAMPLE GRANTS Zacchaeus 2000 Trust (£120,000); Evelyn Oldfield Unit (£110,000); Latin American Women's Rights Service (£90,000); Africans Unite Against Child Abuse (£85,000); Roma Support Group (£60,000); Kensington and Chelsea Social Council (£56,000); London Tenants Federation (£48,000); Harrow CAB (£32,000); Winvisible (£30,000); Community Language Support Service (£20,000); Changing Minds (£15,000); Safety Net People First (£14,000) and Just for Kids Law (£5,000).

FINANCES *Year* 2012 *Income* £9,397,534 *Grants* £11,418,853 *Assets* £234,913,723

TRUSTEE Trust for London Trustee Board.

OTHER INFORMATION The grants total consists of £7.1 million given through the Central Fund and £4.3 million through the City Churches Fund.

HOW TO APPLY The foundation's funding guidelines for 2010–12 are available to download from its website. Alternatively contact the foundation's office for hard copies. It is strongly recommended that potential applicants read the guidelines before making an application. There is a three-stage application process: *Stage one* – An initial proposal to be submitted by post. There are three closing dates for proposals to be submitted by – you may submit your proposal at any time but it will only be assessed once the next closing date has passed. Closing dates are: 7 February for the June Grants Committee; 30 May for the October Grants Committee; 5 October for the February Grants Committee. *Stage two* – All organisations whose initial proposals are shortlisted will be visited by the foundation to assess their suitability for funding. *Stage three* – The grants committee will make the final decision on all funding requests. Applicants will be contacted within ten days of the committee meeting. The whole process can take approximately four and a half months from the closing date for successful applicants.

WHO TO APPLY TO Mubin Haq, Director of Policy and Grants, 6–9 Middle Street, London EC1A 7PH *Tel.* 020 7606 6145 *email* info@trustforlondon. org.uk *Website* www.trustforlondon.org.uk

■ London Catalyst

CC NO 1066739 **ESTABLISHED** 1872

WHERE FUNDING CAN BE GIVEN Greater London, within the boundaries of the M25.

WHO CAN BENEFIT Hospitals, homes and medical charities outside the NHS who are also registered charities; NHS hospitals throughout London; clients of social workers; individuals in need.

WHAT IS FUNDED The charity targets health inequalities and community projects in areas of social deprivation.

WHAT IS NOT FUNDED No grants to: hospitals and homes within the NHS, including specialist clinics and appeals relating to NHS hospitals and special units; charitable organisations not registered with the Charity Commission; hospital league of friends for NHS and independent hospitals; government departments; or individuals.

TYPE OF GRANT Project and one-off.

RANGE OF GRANTS Up to £15,000.

SAMPLE GRANTS Core Arts (£15,000); Green Candle Dance Company (£12,000); Ace of Clubs and Harold Hill Foodbank (£10,000 each); Housing Justice and Age UK Waltham Forest (£7,500 each); Redbridge Concern for Mental Health (£5,000); Streatham Drop In Centre (£4,500);

Frampton Park Baptist Church (£3,500); British Muslim Association of Merton and St Michael, Hodan Somali Community and St George's Women's Fellowship (£1,500 each) and Ascension Community Trust (£600).

FINANCES *Year* 2012 *Income* £353,528 *Grants* £307,180 *Assets* £11,170,931

TRUSTEES Revd Paul Regen; Dr Steve Mowle; Yoke Hopkins; Zoe Camp; Revd Adrian McKenna-Whyte; Peter Moore; Margaret Elliott; Dr Muhammad Bari; Dr Ruth Kosmin; Andrew Davidson.

HOW TO APPLY Forms and guidance can be downloaded from the charity's website or requested by phone or letter. Applications and other grant enquiries are acceptable via email. All applications are reviewed against eligibility criteria and then considered by the grants scrutiny committee before presenting to the trustees for approval.

WHO TO APPLY TO Ian Baker, Grants Administrator, c/o The Peabody Trust, Minster Court, 45 Westminster Bridge Road, London SE1 7JB *Tel.* 020 7021 4204 *email* london.catalyst@ peabody.org.uk *Website* www.londoncatalyst. org.uk

■ The London Community Foundation (formerly Capital Community Foundation)

CC NO 1091263 **ESTABLISHED** 2002

WHERE FUNDING CAN BE GIVEN The London boroughs including the City of London.

WHO CAN BENEFIT Community organisations benefiting unemployed people, volunteers, people disadvantaged by poverty, refugees and people living in urban areas.

WHAT IS FUNDED Community based projects enhancing the quality of life of people in the community and addressing discrimination and disadvantage. Each scheme run by the foundation has its own local grant criteria and awards panel.

WHAT IS NOT FUNDED Generally, no grants for political groups or activities which promote religion.

TYPE OF GRANT Normally one-off for core costs, feasibility studies, project, running costs, salaries and start-up costs. Funding is available for up to two years on some programmes. Most are up to one year.

RANGE OF GRANTS Small grant programmes up to £5,000. Large grants up to £150,000.

SAMPLE GRANTS Participe (£150,000); Oasis Children's Venture (£50,000); Women Like Us (£32,000); Food Cycle (£25,000); Lambeth Mind (£7,500); Camden Plus Credit Union Ltd (£5,000); Voluntary Associations Support (£3,500); Kongolese Centre for Information and Advice (£2,300); Biggin Hill Community Association (£1,500); Southside Young Leaders Academy and Race on the Agenda (£1,000 each) and Hammersmith and Fulham Older Persons Project (£750).

FINANCES *Year* 2011–12 *Income* £6,908,300 *Grants* £3,919,600 *Assets* £13,604,700

TRUSTEES Carole Souter; Gordon Williamson; Clive Cutbill; Stephen Jordan; Donovan Norris; Martin Richards; Davina Judelson; Francis Salway; Rhys Moore; Grant Gordon; Juliet Wedderburn; Tajinder Nijjar; Sanjay Mazumder; Jesse Zigmund.

OTHER INFORMATION The foundation manages and distributes funds on behalf of several donors, including companies, individuals and government programmes and is able to offer a number of grant programmes which cover different areas and types of activity. There were a further 137 grants to individuals made totalling £140,000.

HOW TO APPLY As the foundation offers funds on behalf of different donors, you may apply to each and every programme for which your group is eligible. However, the criteria do vary for each grant programme, so be sure to read the guidance carefully. If you are unsure about your eligibility, call the grants team on Tel: 020 7582 5117 before making an application. What the foundation looks for in an application: demonstration of need; sound governance; sound financial management; sound project planning; good partnership working and strong capacity and ability to deliver. Application forms, guidance notes and deadlines specific to each programme are available from the foundation and/or the website.

WHO TO APPLY TO Kath Sullivan, Unit 7, Piano House, 9 Brighton Terrace, London SW9 8DJ *Tel.* 020 7582 5117 *Fax* 020 7582 4020 *email* enquiries@londoncf.org.uk *Website* www. londoncf.org.uk

....

■ The London Housing Foundation

CC NO 270178   **ESTABLISHED** 1975
WHERE FUNDING CAN BE GIVEN London.
WHO CAN BENEFIT Voluntary organisations tackling single homelessness in London.
WHAT IS FUNDED Project funding as well as organisational support. Particularly around criminal justice, health and employment, training and volunteering initiatives. Small number of research grants are available. Advice and support for mergers.
RANGE OF GRANTS £2,000–£120,000
SAMPLE GRANTS De Paul Trust (£117,000); PACT (£94,000); Revolving Doors (£90,000); London Councils (Andy Ludlow Award) (£50,000); Women in Prison (£47,000); Homeless Link (£35,000); South London YMCA (£28,000); The Passage (£25,000); University of Southampton (£12,000); William Wilberforce Trust (£9,000); One Housing (£5,000) and Boys Clubhouse (£3,500).
FINANCES *Year* 2012–13 *Income* £630,463 *Grants* £659,835 *Assets* £15,997,829
TRUSTEES Simon Down; Ian Brady; Donald Wood; John Stebbing; Jeremy Swain; Derek Joseph; Clare Miller; Eleanor Lesley Stringer; Victoria Rayner.
HOW TO APPLY Applicants are first asked to complete a short application on the Foundation website detailing their project idea. The Foundation will then follow this up with the applicant.
WHO TO APPLY TO Jane Woolley, 57A Great Suffolk Street, London SE1 0BB *Tel.* 020 7934 0177 *email* jane.woolley@lhf.org.uk *Website* www.lhf. org.uk

....

■ The London Law Trust

CC NO 1115266   **ESTABLISHED** 1968
WHERE FUNDING CAN BE GIVEN UK.
WHO CAN BENEFIT Educational and research institutions.
WHAT IS FUNDED Medical research. The London Law Trust's website states at the time of writing (October 2013) the following: 'The London Law Trust has entered into arrangements for funding medical research and leadership development programmes which are being run in conjunction with other institutions. As for the foreseeable

future the trust will be applying all of its available funds on these programmes, it regrets that it is no longer able to accept any new applications for grants.'
WHAT IS NOT FUNDED Applications from individuals, including students, are ineligible.
SAMPLE GRANTS Previous beneficiaries have included: BRIC, British Lung Foundation, Deans and Canons of Windsor, Great Ormond Street and St George's Hospital Medical School (£5,000 each); Envision (£3,000); Activenture and Swan Syndrome (£2,500 each); and Circomedia (£1,000).
FINANCES *Year* 2011–12 *Income* £142,853 *Grants* £111,000 *Assets* £3,902,189
TRUSTEES Prof. Anthony Mellows; Roger Pellant; Sir Michael Hobbs; Sir Ian Gainsford.
OTHER INFORMATION Grants were made to organisations totalling £67,500.
HOW TO APPLY In writing to the correspondent, however funds are currently fully committed.
WHO TO APPLY TO Graham Olgilvie, Administrator, Hunters, 9 New Square, Lincoln's Inn, London WC2A 3QN *Tel.* 020 7412 0050 *email* londonlawtrust@hunters-solicitors.co.uk *Website* www.thelondonlawtrust.org

....

■ London Legal Support Trust

CC NO 1101906   **ESTABLISHED** 2004
WHERE FUNDING CAN BE GIVEN London and the Home Counties.
WHO CAN BENEFIT Voluntary sector legal agencies in London and the Home Counties that employ solicitors or retain the services of solicitors as volunteers to provide free legal advice to poor or disadvantaged members the public; and network organisations that support the above agencies.
WHAT IS FUNDED (i) Legal services and projects that encourage or provide co-operation between voluntary sector agencies and volunteers from private practice. (ii) Crisis intervention to 'keep the doors open' when funding cuts threaten the closure of a voluntary sector legal agency and when the trustees consider that short term funding may lead to sustainable recovery. (iii) One-off capital support to increase the capacity of an agency to deliver its service. (iv) Creation of new social welfare legal and pro bono provision in London and the Home Counties.
WHAT IS NOT FUNDED The trust does not fund: non charitable activity; applications for which the trustees feel that Legal Services Commission funding is suitable and practical within a reasonable time frame, except where the trust's funding is to be used to lever matched funding.
RANGE OF GRANTS £100–£35,000.
SAMPLE GRANTS South West London Law Centre (£77,000); Bar Pro Bono Unit (£35,000); Free Representation Unit (£25,000); Lawworks (£20,000); Hackney Law Centre (£12,000); Release – Legal and Drug Work (£11,000); Personal Support Unit (£7,000); Notre Dame Refugee Centre (£3,600); Queen Mary University (£1,000) and Prisoners Advice Service (£500).
FINANCES *Year* 2011–12 *Income* £634,423 *Grants* £554,334 *Assets* £67,464
TRUSTEES Julian Clark; Richard Dyton; Peter Gardner; Graham Huntley; Steve Hynes; Joy Julien; Marc Sosnow; Jeremy Thomas; John Dunlop; Emma Turnbull; Jeremy Connick; Lorraine Ellam; Amanda Illing; Jessica Clark; George Bacon.
HOW TO APPLY On a form available to download, together with criteria and guidelines, from the website.

WHO TO APPLY TO Robert Nightingale, Chief Executive, 40 Alexander Road, Epsom, Surrey KT17 4BT *Tel.* 020 3088 3656 *email* chair@londonlegalsupporttrust.org.uk *Website* londonlegalsupporttrust.org.uk

■ **The London Marathon Charitable Trust**

CC NO 283813   **ESTABLISHED** 1982
WHERE FUNDING CAN BE GIVEN London and any area where London Marathon stages an event (South Northamptonshire).
WHO CAN BENEFIT Organisations involved with sports, recreation and leisure, including schools.
WHAT IS FUNDED Recreational facilities in London. Grants have been made towards the establishment of play areas and nature trails; improvements to existing leisure facilities; provision of MUGAs (Multi Use Games Areas); and to various rowing organisations to provide new accommodation and boats. Grants are aimed to benefit both the able bodied and people with disabilities and include the sports of athletics, cricket, tennis, gymnastics, sailing, football, boxing, and climbing.
WHAT IS NOT FUNDED Grants cannot be made to 'closed' clubs or schools, unless the facility is available for regular public use. No grants are made for recurring or revenue costs. Individuals are not supported.
RANGE OF GRANTS £750–£732,000
SAMPLE GRANTS LM Playing Field – Greenford (£263,000); London 2012 Legacy – Aquatic Lift (£243,000); LB Waltham Forest – London Playing Fields Foundation (£176,000); LB Enfield – Queen Elizabeth Stadium (£150,000); LB Southwark – Camberwell Baths (£100,000); LB Lambeth – Clapham Common Skate Park (£75,000); LB Richmond – Putney Town Rowing Club (£50,000); RB Kingston – Dickerage Adventure Playground (£45,000); LB Richmond – Royal Deer Park (£30,000) and Chance to Shine – cricket markings in schools (£9,000).
FINANCES *Year* 2011–12 *Income* £20,070,764 *Grants* £4,402,984 *Assets* £15,892,553
TRUSTEES Bernard Atha; Simon Cooper; Eileen Gray; Dame Mary Peters; Joyce Smith; John Graves; James Dudley Henderson Clarke; John Austin; John Disley; Sir Rodney Walker; John Bryant.
OTHER INFORMATION The trust has no connection to the fundraising efforts of the individuals involved in the race, who raise over £40 million each year for their chosen good causes.
The charity spent £1.8 million on staff costs including the payment of eight employees earning £60,000 to £250,000 during the year.
HOW TO APPLY On a form available from the correspondent. Applications are welcomed from London Boroughs and independent organisations, clubs and charities. The trustees meet once a year; the closing date is usually the end of August.
WHO TO APPLY TO David Golton, Secretary, Kestrel House, 111 Heath Road, Twickenham TW1 4AH *Tel.* 020 8892 6646 *email* lmct@ffleach.co.uk

■ **The William and Katherine Longman Trust**

CC NO 800785   **ESTABLISHED** 1988
WHERE FUNDING CAN BE GIVEN UK.
WHO CAN BENEFIT Registered charities.
WHAT IS FUNDED General charitable purposes.

WHAT IS NOT FUNDED Grants are only made to registered charities.
TYPE OF GRANT One-off and recurrent.
RANGE OF GRANTS £1,000–£30,000.
SAMPLE GRANTS Previous beneficiaries include: Vanessa Grant Trust; World Child Cancer Fund; Hope Education Trust; RADA; Action for ME; The Children's Society; Age Concern – Kensington and Chelsea; RSPCA; St Mungo's; and Prisoners Abroad.
FINANCES *Year* 2011–12 *Income* £69,678 *Grants* £259,000 *Assets* £3,198,983
TRUSTEES Paul Harriman; A. C. O. Bell.
HOW TO APPLY The trustees believe in taking a proactive approach in deciding which charities to support and it is their policy not to respond to unsolicited appeals.
WHO TO APPLY TO G. Feeney, Charles Russell LLP, 5 Fleet Place, London EC4M 7RD *Tel.* 020 7203 5196

■ **The Lord's Taverners**

CC NO 306054   **ESTABLISHED** 1950
WHERE FUNDING CAN BE GIVEN Unrestricted, in practice, UK.
WHO CAN BENEFIT Cricket clubs affiliated to a National Governing Body, individual schools or other organisations directly involved in the organisation of youth cricket and which have a genuine need for assistance.
WHAT IS FUNDED Youth cricket, minibuses for organisations supporting young people with disabilities and sports and recreational equipment for young people with disabilities or who are disadvantaged.
WHAT IS NOT FUNDED **Youth cricket:** Only one application in any 12 month period. The following is not normally grant aided: building or renovation of pavilions; sight screens; bowling machines; mowers/rollers; overseas tours; clothing; refreshments; trophies.
Sport for young people with special needs: The following will not normally be considered for a grant: capital costs; general grants; running costs including salaries; individuals (although applications will be considered for equipment to enable an individual to participate in a team/group recreational activity); holidays/overseas tours.
Minibuses: Homes, schools and organisations catering for young people with special needs under the age of 25 years, are entitled to only one minibus per location, although applications are accepted for a replacement.
SAMPLE GRANTS No grants list was available.
FINANCES *Year* 2011–12 *Income* £6,241,418 *Grants* £2,771,722 *Assets* £3,426,662
TRUSTEES John Ayling; John Barnes; Leo Callow; Mike Gatting; Robert Powell; Sally Surridge; Tom Rodwell; Robert Griffiths; Christine Colbeck; Martin Smith; Marilyn Fry.
HOW TO APPLY The trust committee meets regularly to review applications for grant aid. All applications must be presented on the appropriate application forms and should be submitted to the secretary. Application forms with detailed application instructions for the different grant schemes are available from the secretary or on the trust's website.
WHO TO APPLY TO Nicky Pemberton, Head of Foundation, 10 Buckingham Place, London SW1E 6HX *Tel.* 020 7821 2828 *Fax* 020 7821 2829 *email* contact@lordstaverners.org *Website* www.lordstaverners.org

■ The Loseley and Guildway Charitable Trust

CC NO 267178 **ESTABLISHED** 1973
WHERE FUNDING CAN BE GIVEN International and UK, with an interest in Guildford.
WHO CAN BENEFIT Organisations benefiting people with various disabilities and terminal illness, children and victims of natural disasters.
WHAT IS FUNDED Compassionate causes, mainly local or causes with which various members of the More-Molyneux family and trustees are associated.
WHAT IS NOT FUNDED No grants to non-registered charities.
RANGE OF GRANTS £25–£5,000.
SAMPLE GRANTS CHASE and Disability Challengers (£5,000 each); Brooke Hospital, Cherry Trees, Crisis, Gurkha Welfare Trust, National Society for Epilepsy, Phyllis Tuckwell Hospice, RNLI and Wells for India (£1,000 each).
FINANCES *Year* 2011–12 *Income* £61,411
Grants £55,000
TRUSTEES Maj. James More-Molyneux, Chair; Susan More-Molyneux; Michael More-Molyneux; Alexander More-Molyneux; Glye Hodson.
HOW TO APPLY In writing to the correspondent. The trustees meet in February, May and September to consider applications. However, due to commitments, new applications for any causes are unlikely to be successful.
WHO TO APPLY TO Helen O'Dwyer, Secretary, The Estate Offices, Loseley Park, Guildford, Surrey GU3 1HS *Tel.* 01483 405114 *Fax* 01483 302036 *email* charities@loseleypark.co.uk *Website* www.loseley-park.com/charities.asp

■ The Lotus Foundation

CC NO 1070111 **ESTABLISHED** 1998
WHERE FUNDING CAN BE GIVEN UK, especially London and Surrey; occasionally overseas.
WHO CAN BENEFIT Established or newly-formed charities.
WHAT IS FUNDED Social welfare, including: substance abuse, cerebral palsy, brain tumours, cancer, battered women and their children, homelessness and animals in need.
TYPE OF GRANT One-off and Recurrent.
RANGE OF GRANTS £200–£32,000.
SAMPLE GRANTS RAPT (£31,500); British Red Cross and ACLIM and Addiction (£25,000 each); Whizz-Kidz and Macmillan Cancer Relief (£10,000 each); Fine Cell Workers (£7,000); Scope and Variety the Children's Charity (£5,000 each); and Alone in London and Happy Days (£1,000 each).
FINANCES *Year* 2012 *Income* £208,540
Grants £237,432 *Assets* £86,877
TRUSTEES Barbara Starkey; Richard Starkey; Emma Turner.
HOW TO APPLY In writing to the correspondent giving a brief outline of the work, amount required and project/programme to benefit. The trustees prefer applications which are simple and economically prepared rather than glossy 'prestige' and mail sorted brochures. Note: In order to reduce administration costs and concentrate its efforts on the charitable work at hand, unsolicited requests will no longer be acknowledged by the foundation.
WHO TO APPLY TO Barbara Starkey, Trustee, c/o Startling Music Ltd, 90 Jermyn Street, London SW1Y 6JD *Tel.* 020 7930 5133 *Website* www. lotusfoundation.com

■ The Lower Green Foundation

CC NO 1137862 **ESTABLISHED** 2010
WHERE FUNDING CAN BE GIVEN Worldwide.
WHO CAN BENEFIT Organisations and individuals.
WHAT IS FUNDED General charitable purposes.
FINANCES *Year* 2011–12 *Income* £0
Grants £90,000
TRUSTEES Laurence Billett; Marina Sajitz; Sinclair Beecham.
OTHER INFORMATION In 2011–12 the foundation had a total expenditure of £91,160. Previously, almost all expenditure has been accounted for in grants.
HOW TO APPLY In writing to the correspondent.
WHO TO APPLY TO Pam Henness, Administrator, 10–14 Old Church Street, London SW3 5DQ *email* info@lowergreen.com

■ The Lowy Mitchell Foundation

CC NO 1094430 **ESTABLISHED** 2002
WHERE FUNDING CAN BE GIVEN Worldwide.
WHO CAN BENEFIT Charitable organisations chosen at the trustees' discretion.
WHAT IS FUNDED General and Jewish charitable purposes.
RANGE OF GRANTS £100–£20,000.
SAMPLE GRANTS Portobello Media (£20,000); Community Security Trust (£10,000); UK Jewish Film Festival (£5,000); Help for Heroes (£2,000); The Amos Bursary (£1,500); National Theatre (£1,250); Batsheva Dance Company (£1,000) and Pratham UK and Jewish Community Centre (£150 each).
FINANCES *Year* 2011–12 *Income* £5,173
Grants £46,000
TRUSTEES Lord Mitchell; Lady Mitchell; Amanda Weiner; Julia Delew.
OTHER INFORMATION In 2011–12 the foundation had a total expenditure of £56,000. The grants total is an approximation based on previous research.
HOW TO APPLY In writing to the correspondent.
WHO TO APPLY TO Lady Lowy Mitchell, Administrator, 3 Elm Row, London NW3 1AA *Tel.* 020 7431 1534

■ The C. L. Loyd Charitable Trust

CC NO 265076 **ESTABLISHED** 1973
WHERE FUNDING CAN BE GIVEN UK, with a preference for local causes.
WHO CAN BENEFIT Neighbourhood-based community projects and UK organisations benefiting at risk groups, and people who are disabled, disadvantaged by poverty or socially isolated.
WHAT IS FUNDED General charitable purposes. Local charities, UK health and welfare charities and UK animal welfare charities.
WHAT IS NOT FUNDED In writing to the correspondent. Grants are made several times each month.
TYPE OF GRANT One-off and recurrent.
RANGE OF GRANTS Up to £50,000; mostly £1,000 or less.
SAMPLE GRANTS County Buildings Protection Trust (£31,000); Wantage Vale and Downland Museum (£10,000); Coldstream Guards (£5,000); Iran Liberty Association (£3,000); Christian Aid, Mango Tree and Pond Conservation (£1,000 each).
FINANCES *Year* 2011–12 *Income* £85,243
Grants £72,425 *Assets* £2,296,805
TRUSTEES Christopher Loyd; Thomas Loyd; Alexandra Loyd.

OTHER INFORMATION Other grants of less than £1,000 amounted to £50,000.

HOW TO APPLY In writing to the correspondent. Grants are made several times each month.

WHO TO APPLY TO Thomas Loyd, Trustee, The Lockinge Estate Office, Ardington, Wantage OX12 8PP *Tel.* 01235 833200

....

■ LSA Charitable Trust

CC NO 803671   **ESTABLISHED** 1989

WHERE FUNDING CAN BE GIVEN UK.

WHO CAN BENEFIT Individuals and institutions benefiting horticultural researchers, students and people working in horticulture, and former tenants and employees of the former Land Settlement Association Ltd, who are in need.

WHAT IS FUNDED Horticultural research, the promotion of horticultural knowledge, and the relief of poverty.

FINANCES *Year* 2011–12 *Income* £53,601 *Grants* £39,182 *Assets* £1,260,049

TRUSTEES S. R. V. Pomeroy, Chair; B. E. G. Howe; P. Hadley; C. F. Woodhouse; A. M. M. Ross;

HOW TO APPLY For organisations: in writing to the correspondent. Grants to individuals for the relief of poverty are made through the Royal Agricultural Benevolent Institution.

WHO TO APPLY TO Cheryl Boyce, c/o Farrer and Co, 66 Lincoln's Inn Fields, London WC2A 3LH *Tel.* 020 3375 7000

....

■ The Marie Helen Luen Charitable Trust

CC NO 291012   **ESTABLISHED** 1984

WHERE FUNDING CAN BE GIVEN Worldwide and UK, with a preference for Wimbledon.

WHO CAN BENEFIT Charitable organisations and individuals.

WHAT IS FUNDED The trust supports both UK and local charities concerned with cancer relief, homelessness and the relief of hardship, pain and suffering. Grants are also given to relieve developing world poverty.

RANGE OF GRANTS Up to £5,000.

SAMPLE GRANTS Kingston University Student Hardship Fund (£5,000); Macmillan Cancer Relief, Crisis and Mpemba Orphanage in Malawi (£2,000 each); Marie Curie Cancer Care, St Mungo's, Headway, Beating Bowel Cancer and Tenovus (£1,000 each).

FINANCES *Year* 2012 *Income* £42,157 *Grants* £43,500

TRUSTEES Richard Littleton; Nushi Kassam; Jyoti Joshi.

HOW TO APPLY In writing to the correspondent.

WHO TO APPLY TO Richard Littleton, Trustee, Hillcroft, 57 Langley Avenue, Surbiton, Surrey KT6 6QR *Tel.* 020 8946 3979 *email* richard@esppos.com

....

■ Robert Luff Foundation Ltd

CC NO 273810   **ESTABLISHED** 1977

WHERE FUNDING CAN BE GIVEN UK.

WHO CAN BENEFIT Medical research charities.

WHAT IS FUNDED Medical research.

RANGE OF GRANTS Up to £175,000.

SAMPLE GRANTS Cystic Fibrosis Trust (£175,000); Royal Brompton Hospital (£110,000); Bowel Disease Research Foundation (£80,000); International Spinal Research Trust; Blonde McIndoe Research Foundation (£40,000 each);

Alzheimer's Society; Sheffield Teaching Hospital (£50,000 each); Lowe Syndrome Trust (£30,000).

FINANCES *Year* 2011–12 *Income* £409,677 *Grants* £800,000

TRUSTEES Sir Robert Johnson; Lady R. Bodey; R. P. J. Price; Ms G. Favot; J. Tomlinson; Revd Matthew Tomlinson; M. Condon; B. D. Nicholson.

HOW TO APPLY The foundation makes its own decisions about what causes to support. It has stated that 'outside applications are not considered, or replied to'.

WHO TO APPLY TO Michael D. Lock, Secretary, The Garth, Wood Lane, Stanmore, Middlesex HA7 4JZ *Tel.* 020 8954 9006 *email* md.lock@virgin.net

....

■ Henry Lumley Charitable Trust

CC NO 1079480   **ESTABLISHED** 2000

WHERE FUNDING CAN BE GIVEN UK and overseas.

WHO CAN BENEFIT Charitable organisations and individuals.

WHAT IS FUNDED General charitable purposes, with a preference towards medicine, education and the relief of poverty.

TYPE OF GRANT Grants of up to three years.

RANGE OF GRANTS £15,000–£1,000.

SAMPLE GRANTS Royal College of Surgeons (£15,000); Royal Australasian College of Surgeons (£10,000); Stroke Association and Cancer Research UK (£5,000 each); Action on Addiction, Bowel Disease Research Foundation and Meningitis Research Fund (£4,000 each); Juvenile Diabetes Research Foundation, Outward Bound Trust and Royal Star and Garter Home for Disabled Ex-Service Men and Women (£2,500 each); and Royal School of Needlework and Wings for Life Spinal Cord Research (£1,000 each).

FINANCES *Year* 2012 *Income* £86,619 *Grants* £131,500 *Assets* £3,314,030

TRUSTEES Henry Lumley; Peter Lumley; Robert Lumley; James Porter.

HOW TO APPLY In writing to the correspondent.

WHO TO APPLY TO Peter Lumley, Trustee, c/o Lutine Leisure Ltd, Windlesham Golf Club, Bagshot, Surrey GU19 5HY *Tel.* 01276 472273

....

■ Paul Lunn-Rockliffe Charitable Trust

CC NO 264119   **ESTABLISHED** 1972

WHERE FUNDING CAN BE GIVEN UK and developing world.

WHO CAN BENEFIT Mainly smaller and locally based charities and those which may be known to the trustees, or members of their family.

WHAT IS FUNDED The trust makes grants in the following categories: aged; children; disabled; education and students; family; mission; needy, drug addicts, homeless and unemployed people; prisoners; radio/mission; third world; youth; and 'others'. Each year the trustees allocate a proportion of the funds for donation to be applied to charities not previously supported and for special one-off causes.

WHAT IS NOT FUNDED The trustees will not fund individuals; for example, student's expenses and travel grants. Repair and maintenance of historic buildings are also excluded for support.

TYPE OF GRANT Core costs, one-off and start-up costs. Funding for more than three years will be considered.

RANGE OF GRANTS £300–£1,000.

SAMPLE GRANTS Christians Against Poverty (£1,000); Community of Holy Fire (Zimbabwe children) and Parish of St George Hanworth (£600 each); Action for Elder Abuse, Children Country Holiday Fund, Consequences, Forgiveness, Koestler Awards, Parkinson Disease Society, Shepherds Down School, Street Pastors, Under Tree Schools and Way to Life (£500 each); and Gateway Club (£300).

FINANCES *Year* 2011–12 *Income* £204,706 *Grants* £43,102 *Assets* £1,481,537

TRUSTEES Jacqueline Lunn-Rockliffe; James Lunn-Rockliffe; Bryan Boult.

HOW TO APPLY In writing to the correspondent. The trust will generally only reply to written correspondence if an sae has been included.

WHO TO APPLY TO James Lunn-Rockliffe, Trustee, 6A Barnes Close, Winchester, Hampshire SO23 9QX *email* plrcharitabletrust@gmail.com

■ C. F. Lunoe Trust Fund

CC NO 214850   **ESTABLISHED** 1960

WHERE FUNDING CAN BE GIVEN UK.

WHO CAN BENEFIT Universities and ex-employees (and their dependants) of Norwest Holst Group Ltd.

WHAT IS FUNDED Universities associated with the construction industry.

SAMPLE GRANTS I.C.E Quest Fund (£28,000); Leeds University (£11,000) and The Danish Church in London (£10,000).

FINANCES *Year* 2011–12 *Income* £95,698 *Grants* £78,387 *Assets* £1,306,885

TRUSTEES Peter Lunoe,; John Henke; Alexandra Coghill; John Jefkins; John Dodson; Trevor Parks.

OTHER INFORMATION In 2011–12 grants totalling £24,000 was given to 11 individuals.

HOW TO APPLY In writing to the correspondent. However, the majority of the trust's funds go to organisations already known to the trustees and as a result new applications are likely to be unsuccessful.

WHO TO APPLY TO Peter Lunoe, Trustee, 29 Box Lane, Hemel Hempstead, Hertfordshire HP3 0DH *Tel.* 01442 252236

■ The Ruth and Jack Lunzer Charitable Trust

CC NO 276201   **ESTABLISHED** 1978

WHERE FUNDING CAN BE GIVEN UK.

WHO CAN BENEFIT Organisations benefiting children, young adults and students are given priority.

WHAT IS FUNDED Jewish organisations, educational institutions and the arts. Other charitable purposes will be considered.

TYPE OF GRANT Mainly recurrent.

RANGE OF GRANTS £100–10,000.

SAMPLE GRANTS Yesoday Hatorah Schools (£8,500); Kahal Chassidim Bobov and Lubavich Foundation (£6,000); Chai Cancer Care and Trenhill Limited (£3,000 each); British Friends of Ohel Sarah and Weizmann UK (£1,000 each); British Friends of Ezer Mizion and The Committee for the Rescue of Immigrant Children in Israel £500 each); Institute for Higher Rabbinical Studies (£250); and Chesdei Ephraim Limited (£100).

FINANCES *Year* 2011–12 *Income* £56,000 *Grants* £53,142 *Assets* £513,007

TRUSTEES J. V. Lunzer; M. D. Paisner.

HOW TO APPLY In writing to the correspondent. Unsuccessful applicants are not acknowledged.

WHO TO APPLY TO Martin Paisner, Trustee, c/o Berwin Leighton Paisner, Adelaide House, London Bridge, London EC4R 9HA *Tel.* 020 7760 1000

■ Lord and Lady Lurgan Trust

CC NO 297046   **ESTABLISHED** 1987

WHERE FUNDING CAN BE GIVEN England, Northern Ireland and South Africa.

WHO CAN BENEFIT Medical charities, older people, children and the arts.

WHAT IS FUNDED The registered objects of this trust are: the relief and medical care of older people; medical research, in particular cancer research and the publication of the useful results of such research; the advancement of education including education in the arts for the public benefit by the establishment of educational and artistic bursaries; other charitable purposes at the discretion of the trustees.

WHAT IS NOT FUNDED No support for organisations in Scotland. No grants to individuals or for expeditions.

TYPE OF GRANT One-off and recurrent.

RANGE OF GRANTS £1,000–£5,000.

SAMPLE GRANTS Previous beneficiaries have included: Royal College of Music, English National Opera, Queen's University – Belfast, Greater Shankhill Business Forum, Deafblind UK, Help the Aged, Macmillan Cancer Relief, Oesophageal Patients Association, St Joseph's Hospice and WaterAid.

FINANCES *Year* 2012 *Income* £21,871 *Grants* £100,000

TRUSTEES Simon Ladd; Andrew Stebbings; Diana Graves; Brendan Beder.

HOW TO APPLY Complete the downloadable application form which is available on the trust's website. Read the grant policy on the website before completing the form. Trustees meet three or four times a year. There is no deadline for applications. All successful applications will be required to provide a written report within six months of receiving the grant.

WHO TO APPLY TO Andrew Stebbings, Trustee, 45 Cadogan Gardens, London SW3 2AQ *Tel.* 020 7591 3333 *Fax* 020 7591 3300 *email* charitymanager@pglaw.co.uk *Website* www.lurgantrust.org

■ The Lyndhurst Trust

CC NO 235252   **ESTABLISHED** 1964

WHERE FUNDING CAN BE GIVEN UK and overseas, with preferences for North East England and the developing world.

WHO CAN BENEFIT Christian organisations.

WHAT IS FUNDED Charities connected with the propagation of the gospel or the promotion of the Christian religion; the distribution of bibles and other Christian religious works; the support of Christian missions; the provision of clergy; the maintenance of churches and chapels; work with disadvantaged people in society. Funds are given worldwide; there is a preference for the developing world, and in the UK a preference for the north east of England. It tends to support specific charities on a regular basis.

WHAT IS NOT FUNDED No support for individuals or buildings.

RANGE OF GRANTS £500–£20,000.

SAMPLE GRANTS Sowing Seeds (£12,000); Junction 42 (£5,000); Lydia's House, St Luke's Church and Friends International (£3,000 each); Ichthus Christian Fellowship, Newcastle Chaplaincy and St Barnabas Church (£2,000 each); Eden North East and Healing on the Streets (£1,000 each); and Action Foundation, Blue Sky Trust and Trinity Church – Gosforth (£500 each).

FINANCES *Year* 2012 *Income* £42,064
Grants £93,500 *Assets* £1,313,562

TRUSTEES Revd Dr Robert Ward; Jane Hinton; Ben Hinton; Sally Tan.

HOW TO APPLY In writing to the correspondent.

WHO TO APPLY TO The Secretary, PO Box 615, North Shields NE29 1AP

....

■ The Lynn Foundation

CC NO 326944   **ESTABLISHED** 1985
WHERE FUNDING CAN BE GIVEN UK and overseas.
WHO CAN BENEFIT Registered charities, institutions benefiting musicians, textile workers and designers, and artists. Older people and people who are disabled will also benefit.
WHAT IS FUNDED Promotion and encouragement of music, art, Masonic charities, disability, and charities concerned with children and older people.
TYPE OF GRANT One-off grants for core, capital and project support. Loans are also made.
RANGE OF GRANTS Usually £500–£1,000.
FINANCES *Year* 2011–12 *Income* £276,669
Grants £247,802 *Assets* £4,857,769
TRUSTEES Guy Parsons; Ian Fair; John Emmott; Philip Parsons; John Sykes.
HOW TO APPLY In writing to the correspondent.
WHO TO APPLY TO Guy Parsons, Trustee, 17 Lewes Road, Haywards Heath RH17 7SP *Tel.* 01444 454773

....

■ The Lynwood Trust

CC NO 289535   **ESTABLISHED** 1984
WHERE FUNDING CAN BE GIVEN UK and overseas.
WHO CAN BENEFIT Organisations benefiting children, older people and people who are disabled.
WHAT IS FUNDED Advancement of religion and other charitable purposes including churches and missionary organisations.
TYPE OF GRANT One-off and recurrent.
SAMPLE GRANTS Beneficiaries include: Church of Christ (£7,000); Dorothy K Trust and TWFE (£2,000 each); and CARE and North Kent Community Church (£1,000 each).
FINANCES *Year* 2012–13 *Income* £26,265
Grants £19,006 *Assets* £667,757
TRUSTEES Jean Barling; Colin Harmer.
HOW TO APPLY In writing to the correspondent.
WHO TO APPLY TO Colin Harmer, Trustee, Salatin House, 19 Cedar Road, Sutton, Surrey SM2 5DA *Tel.* 020 8652 2700 *email* colinharmer@gmail.com

....

■ John Lyon's Charity

CC NO 237725   **ESTABLISHED** 1578
WHERE FUNDING CAN BE GIVEN The London boroughs of Barnet, Brent, Camden, Ealing, Kensington and Chelsea, Hammersmith and Fulham, Harrow and the Cities of London and Westminster.
WHO CAN BENEFIT Schools and registered charities working with children and young people.
WHAT IS FUNDED Education, training, arts, sport, youth clubs, disability and counselling services, all aimed at improving the lives of children and young people in the charity's beneficial area.

WHAT IS NOT FUNDED Grants are restricted to the London boroughs of Harrow, Barnet, Brent, Ealing, Camden, City of London, City of Westminster, Hammersmith and Fulham and Kensington and Chelsea. Grants are not made: to individuals; for research, unless it is action research designed to lead directly to the advancement of practical activities in the community; for feasibility studies; for medical care and resources; in response to general charitable appeals, unless they can be shown to be of specific benefit to children and young people in one or more of the geographical areas listed; as direct replacements for the withdrawal of funds by statutory authorities for activities which are primarily the responsibility of central or local government; to umbrella organisations to distribute to projects which are already in receipt of funds from the charity; for the promotion of religion or politics; for telephone helplines; as core funding for national charities; for advice and information services; to housing associations.
TYPE OF GRANT Capital costs, revenue costs and recurring costs up to three years. Buildings, core costs, project, salaries and start-up costs.
RANGE OF GRANTS Up to £250,000
SAMPLE GRANTS London Sports Trust and Brent Play Association (£70,000); Harrow Club W10 (£65,000); Skillforce (£53,000); Donmar Warehouse Projects Ltd and HAFPAC (£50,000); St Gregory's Catholic Science College (£48,000); National Numeracy Trust (£46,000); Royal Opera House (£44,000); Carlton primary School (£39,000); HAFAD (£36,000); Tricycle Theatre Company, Mousetrap Theatre Projects and Royal Institution of Great Britain (£35,000 each); Drayton Green Primary School (£34,000); Place2Be, Wigmore Town Hall, Brandon Centre, Tender and Local Employment Access Projects (£30,000 each).
FINANCES *Year* 2011–12 *Income* £6,479,000
Grants £5,323,000 *Assets* £242,889,000
TRUSTEE The Governors of the John Lyon School, Harrow
HOW TO APPLY The charity's main and small grants programmes have a two stage application process: Stage One - Initial Proposal: Write to the Grants Office with the following information: a summary of the main purpose of the project; details of the overall amount requested; the timescale of your project; some indication of how funds from the charity would be allocated. The trust has produced guidelines on how best to write the initial proposal which can be accessed on the website. Trustees meet to decide three times a year in March, June and November. There is no stage two for small grants of less than £2,000. Applications are made by initial proposal letter and the grants team will be in touch if more information is required.
Stage Two – Application Form: If your Initial Proposal is assessed positively, you will be advised whether you will need to complete an application form. Forms are required for all applications to the Main Grants Programme, Access to Opportunity and for requests of over £2,000 to the Small Grants Programme. If you qualify for Stage Two you will be advised by your Grants Officer when your application form must be returned. Applications by fax or email will not be accepted.
The John Lyon's Access to the Arts Fund
The John Lyon Access to the Arts Fund has a **single stage** application process and requests are made by application form. Applications can be

made at any time. Application forms are available via the charity's website.

WHO TO APPLY TO S. Whiddington, Chair of Grants Committee, The Grants Office, 45 Cadogan Gardens, London SW3 2TB *Tel.* 020 7591 3330 *Fax* 020 7591 3412 *email* info@johnlyonscharity.org.uk *Website* www.johnlyonscharity.org.uk

■ The Sir Jack Lyons Charitable Trust

CC NO 212148   **ESTABLISHED** 1960
WHERE FUNDING CAN BE GIVEN UK and Israel.
WHO CAN BENEFIT Charities benefiting children and young people; actors and entertainment professionals; musicians; students; textile workers and designers; writers and poets; at risk groups; those disadvantaged by poverty, and people who are socially isolated.
WHAT IS FUNDED Relief in need, arts, education and humanities. Jewish charities are also supported.
WHAT IS NOT FUNDED No grants to individuals.
TYPE OF GRANT Mainly recurrent.
RANGE OF GRANTS £200–£50,000.
SAMPLE GRANTS Federation CJA (£130,000 in four grants); UJIA (£86,000 in two grants); Jerusalem Foundation (£40,000); Beit Halohem Geneva (£11,000); Yezreel Valley College (£10,000) and Jewish Institute of Music (£7,500).
FINANCES *Year* 2011–12 *Income* £116,650 *Grants* £284,904 *Assets* £2,872,659
TRUSTEES Lady Roslyn Marion Lyons; M. J. Friedman; D. S. Lyons; Miss A. R. J. Maude-Roxby; P. D. Mitchell; Belinda Lyons-Newman.
HOW TO APPLY The trustees have decided that the most effective method of applying the charity's resources is to make distributions to known charitable organisations.
WHO TO APPLY TO Paul Mitchell, Gresham House, 5–7 St Pauls Street, Leeds LS1 2JG *Tel.* 01332 976789

■ The Lyons Charitable Trust

CC NO 1045650   **ESTABLISHED** 1995
WHERE FUNDING CAN BE GIVEN UK.
WHO CAN BENEFIT Registered charities.
WHAT IS FUNDED Health, medical research, children in need and charities concerned with animals.
TYPE OF GRANT Recurrent.
RANGE OF GRANTS £3,000–£20,000.
SAMPLE GRANTS Helen House (£12,000); Streetsmart (£10,000); The Royal Marsden Hospital, Macmillan and St Thomas Hospital (£8,000 each); CLIC (£5,000) and Children with Aids and Cambridge Curwen Print Study Centre (£3,000).
FINANCES *Year* 2011–12 *Income* £213,367 *Grants* £57,000 *Assets* £1,610,815
TRUSTEES M. Scott Gibbon; J. Scott Gibbon; G. Read; Robin Worby.
OTHER INFORMATION Historically, the same charities are supported each year.
HOW TO APPLY In writing to the correspondent. In the past the trust has stated: 'In the light of increased pressure for funds, unsolicited appeals are less welcome and would waste much time and money for applicants who were looking for funds which were not available.'
WHO TO APPLY TO Michael Scott Gibbon, Trustee, 74 Broad Walk, London N21 3BX *Tel.* 020 8882 1336

■ The Lyras Family Charitable Trust

CC NO 328628   **ESTABLISHED** 1990
WHERE FUNDING CAN BE GIVEN UK, Greece, worldwide.
WHO CAN BENEFIT Beneficiaries include: people disadvantaged by poverty and members of the Greek Orthodox religion.
WHAT IS FUNDED (a) Disaster funds worldwide; (b) the relief of poverty; (c) the advancement of religion, in particular within the country of Greece; and (d) other charitable purposes.
RANGE OF GRANTS Up to £5,500.
SAMPLE GRANTS St Sophia's School (£5,000); The Greek Orthodox Charity Organisation (£2,500); Monastery of St John the Baptist and Foundation for Paediatric Osteopathy (£2,000 each); Multiple Sclerosis Society, British Diabetic Association and Alzheimer's Society (£1,000 each); and RNLI and The Smile Train (£500 each).
FINANCES *Year* 2012 *Income* £41,942 *Grants* £45,000
TRUSTEES John C. Lyras; John M. Lyras; Richard Moore.
HOW TO APPLY In writing to the correspondent.
WHO TO APPLY TO Martin Pollock, Secretary, Moore Stephens, 150 Aldersgate Street, London EC1A 4AB *Tel.* 020 7334 9191

■ Sylvanus Lyson's Charity

CC NO 202939   **ESTABLISHED** 1980
WHERE FUNDING CAN BE GIVEN Diocese of Gloucester.
WHO CAN BENEFIT Individuals and organisations benefiting people of all ages, clergy, and Church of England.
WHAT IS FUNDED Religious and charitable work in the areas of youth, community, relief for widows, clergy and people in need.
WHAT IS NOT FUNDED The present policy is to make no grants for the repair or maintenance and improvement of churches or other buildings, other than in very exceptional circumstances.
TYPE OF GRANT Recurrent and one-off.
RANGE OF GRANTS Usually £1,000 to £5,000 with a few larger grants.
SAMPLE GRANTS Diocesan Board of Finance (£32,000); Gloucester Cathedral Stone Masons (£20,000); Gloucester Night Stop (£10,000); Holy Trinity – Tewkesbury (£4,500); Cheltenham Youth for Christ (£4,250); St Paul's Parochial Church Council (£3,750); Pioneer Minister (£3,000).
FINANCES *Year* 2011–12 *Income* £377,958 *Grants* £350,000
TRUSTEES Bernard Day; G. Doswell; Revd Anne Spargo; The Ven. Robert Springett.
HOW TO APPLY In writing to the correspondent.
WHO TO APPLY TO A. Holloway, c/o Rowberry Morris Solicitors, Morroway House, Station Road, Gloucester GL1 1DW *Tel.* 01452 301903

■ The M. and C. Trust

cc no 265391   **ESTABLISHED** 1973
WHERE FUNDING CAN BE GIVEN UK.
WHO CAN BENEFIT Mainly Jewish organisations benefiting Jewish people, at risk groups, people disadvantaged by poverty, and socially isolated people.
WHAT IS FUNDED Primarily Jewish and welfare organisations.
WHAT IS NOT FUNDED No grants to individuals.
TYPE OF GRANT One-off and recurrent grants.
RANGE OF GRANTS £3,000–£10,000
SAMPLE GRANTS World Jewish Relief and Connect – Communication Disability Network (£10,000 each); Helen and Douglas House, Prince's Royal Trust for Carers and Refugee Resources (£7,000 each); Community Security Trust and Deafblind UK (£5,000 each); and Changing Faces and Chicken Shed Theatre Company (£3,000 each).
FINANCES *Year* 2011–12 *Income* £171,648 *Grants* £361,500 *Assets* £4,190,180
TRUSTEES Rachel Lebus; Kate Bernstein; Elizabeth Marks.
HOW TO APPLY In writing to the correspondent.
WHO TO APPLY TO Helen McKie, Administrator, c/o Mercer and Hole Trustees Limited, Gloucester House, 72 London Road, St Albans, Herts AL1 1NS *Tel.* 01727 869141

■ The M. K. Charitable Trust

cc no 260439   **ESTABLISHED** 1966
WHERE FUNDING CAN BE GIVEN Unrestricted, in practice mainly UK.
WHO CAN BENEFIT Orthodox Jewish organisations.
WHAT IS FUNDED Support of Orthodox Jewish organisations.
FINANCES *Year* 2011–12 *Income* £984,690 *Grants* £282,098 *Assets* £7,899,949
TRUSTEES A. Piller; D. Katz; S. Kaufman; Z. Kaufman.
HOW TO APPLY In writing to the correspondent. The trust accepts applications for grants from representatives of Orthodox Jewish charities, which are reviewed by the trustees on a regular basis.
WHO TO APPLY TO Simon Kaufman, Trustee, 50 Keswick Street, Gateshead NE8 1TQ *Tel.* 01914 900140

■ The Madeline Mabey Trust

cc no 326450   **ESTABLISHED** 1983
WHERE FUNDING CAN BE GIVEN UK and overseas particularly Asia.
WHO CAN BENEFIT Registered charities, including UK registered charities and international charities.
WHAT IS FUNDED Principally medical research, children's welfare and education and humanitarian aid.
WHAT IS NOT FUNDED No grants to individuals.
SAMPLE GRANTS Beneficiaries have included: Cancer Research UK, the Education Engineering Trust, Save the Children, UNICEF, Barnardo's, the Disasters Emergency Committee, Help for Heroes, Great Ormond Street Children's Hospital
FINANCES *Year* 2011–12 *Income* £225,012 *Grants* £400,000 *Assets* £166,921
TRUSTEES Alan G. Daliday; Bridget A. Nelson; Joanna L. Singeisen.
OTHER INFORMATION 'Direct charitable expenditure' totalled £414,000. A breakdown of this expenditure and a grants list was not included in the accounts.
HOW TO APPLY In writing to the correspondent. Note, unsuccessful applications are not acknowledged.
WHO TO APPLY TO Joanna Singeisen, Trustee, Madeline Mabey Trust, Woodview, Tolcarne Road, Beacon, Camborne TR14 9AB *Tel.* 01209 710304 *Website* www.mabeygroup.co.uk/about/heritage/the-madeline-mabey-trust

■ The E. M. MacAndrew Trust

cc no 290736   **ESTABLISHED** 1984
WHERE FUNDING CAN BE GIVEN UK.
WHO CAN BENEFIT Charitable organisations.
WHAT IS FUNDED Medical and children's charities.
RANGE OF GRANTS £500–£5,000.
SAMPLE GRANTS MacIntyre (£3,000); Bucks Community Foundation, Calibre Audio Library, The Pepper Foundation, Puzzle Pre-school and Willen Hospice (£2,000 each); and Action Medical Research, Addington Fund, Cancer Research UK, Restore and Scannappeal (£1,000 each).
FINANCES *Year* 2011–12 *Income* £47,114 *Grants* £43,500 *Assets* £987,926
TRUSTEES Amanda Nicholson; John Kempe Nicholson; Sally Grant; Verity Webster.
HOW TO APPLY The trustees state that they do not respond to any unsolicited applications under any circumstances, as they prefer to make their own decisions as to which charities to support.
WHO TO APPLY TO James Thornton, Administrator, J. P. Thornton and Co., The Old Dairy, Adstockfields, Adstock, Buckingham MK18 2JE *Tel.* 01296 714886 *Fax* 01296 714711

■ The R. S. Macdonald Charitable Trust

sc no SC012710   **ESTABLISHED** 1978
WHERE FUNDING CAN BE GIVEN Scotland.
WHO CAN BENEFIT Charities and institutions working in the areas of research and support of neurological conditions, visual impairment, child welfare and animal welfare and community and families.
WHAT IS FUNDED The care and welfare of individuals suffering from neurodevelopmental or neurodegenerative disorders; the care and welfare of individuals who are either blind or suffering from visual impairment; research into neurological and ophthalmic disorders; the care and welfare of children and young persons under the age of eighteen years who have been or are in danger of being abused physically, sexually or mentally; the prevention of cruelty to animals.
WHAT IS NOT FUNDED Grants are not given to non-registered charities, individuals or charitable organisations that cannot demonstrate that they are delivering benefit in Scotland.
TYPE OF GRANT One-off, recurring costs, project and research will be considered. Funding may be given for up to three years and can be revenue or capital funding.

Does the trust you have chosen match your needs? Haphazard applications waste postage and time

RANGE OF GRANTS Average grants are about £20,000.

SAMPLE GRANTS Capability Scotland (£60,000); Muir Maxwell Trust (£40,000); Visability (£36,000); Deafblind Scotland and University of Edinburgh (£25,000 each); Sense Scotland (£15,000); Alcohol Focus Scotland (£13,000); Hidden Gardens Trust and Whizz-Kidz (£10,000 each); Rock Trust (£8,000); National Galleries of Scotland (£4,300);

FINANCES *Year* 2011–12 *Income* £1,752,892 *Grants* £1,539,233 *Assets* £57,192,044

TRUSTEES Richard Sweetman; Richard K. Austin; Donald Bain; Fiona Patrick; John Rafferty.

HOW TO APPLY Applicants are invited to apply by letter; there is no application form. The trustees request that, except in relation to medical or social research, the application letter should not exceed two pages in length. It should explain (as appropriate) what and how the need to be addressed has been identified, the costs involved and the extent to which support has been sought from other sources, the outcome hoped for and how that outcome is to be measured. It should also demonstrate how the subject of the application meets the charitable objects of the trust. Where an application is for help with revenue costs for a particular service there should be an explanation of how this will continue following the expiry of the award.

Along with your letter you may enclose separate papers, providing background information and/or more detailed financial information. If there is a current DVD providing an insight into the work of your organisation you may wish to submit this. Application guidelines, information and award conditions are available from the website.

In addition to the application letter you are required to complete and submit (a) a copy of the applicant's most recently audited accounts and (b) an Organisation Information Sheet. This can be downloaded from the trust's website or obtained from the trust's secretary.

Applications will normally be considered at trustee meeting in May and November. Applications must be received no later than 31 March or 30 September for these meetings.

WHO TO APPLY TO Douglas Hamilton, Director, 21 Rutland Square, Edinburgh EH1 2BB *Tel.* 01312 284681 *email* Dhamilton@rsmacdonald.com *Website* www.rsmacdonald.com

■ The Macdonald-Buchanan Charitable Trust

CC NO 209994   **ESTABLISHED** 1952
WHERE FUNDING CAN BE GIVEN UK, with a slight preference for Northamptonshire.
WHO CAN BENEFIT Registered charities, with a small preference for those benefiting Northamptonshire.
WHAT IS FUNDED General charitable purposes.
WHAT IS NOT FUNDED No grants to individuals.
TYPE OF GRANT Mainly recurrent, up to one year.
RANGE OF GRANTS £50–£15,000.
SAMPLE GRANTS Carrijo and Orrin (£30,000 each); Racing Welfare (£29,000); AMB Charity Trust (£15,000); Royal National Lifeboat Institution (£1,300); the Gurkha Welfare Trust, the Holy Sepulchre Northampton Restoration Trust and Victim Support (£650 each); the Royal Mencap Society, the Scots Guards Association and St John's Hospice (£500 each); the National Association of Almshouses (£400); the Wordsworth Trust and International Fund for

Animal Welfare (£200 each); and the James Mackaness Family Charitable Trust and Warning Zone (£50 each).
FINANCES *Year* 2012 *Income* £145,975 *Grants* £180,300 *Assets* £3,237,759
TRUSTEES Alastair Macdonald-Buchanan; Capt. John Macdonald-Buchanan; Mary Philipson; AJ. Macdonald-Buchanan; Joanna Lascelles; Hugh Macdonald-Buchanan.
OTHER INFORMATION The majority of grants were under £1,000.
HOW TO APPLY In writing to the correspondent, for consideration once a year.
WHO TO APPLY TO Linda Cousins, Administrator, Rathbone Trust Co Ltd, 1 Curzon Street, London W1J 5FB *Tel.* 020 7399 0820 *email* linda.cousins@rathbone.com

■ The Macfarlane Walker Trust

CC NO 227890   **ESTABLISHED** 1963
WHERE FUNDING CAN BE GIVEN UK, with priority for Gloucestershire.
WHO CAN BENEFIT Individuals, registered charities and institutions benefiting: former employees of Walker-Crosweller; musicians; actors and entertainment professionals; artists; students; and scientists.
WHAT IS FUNDED Grants to former employees, and their families, of Walker, Crosweller and Co Ltd; provision of educational facilities particularly for scientific research; encouragement of music, drama and the fine arts. Also support for community facilities and services, and charities in the fields of conservation, alternative transport, and recreation.
WHAT IS NOT FUNDED No grants for tuition fees; gap year trips; large charities; animal charities; foreign charities; or major building projects.
TYPE OF GRANT One-off, research. Funding for up to and over three years will be considered.
RANGE OF GRANTS Up to £2,000.
SAMPLE GRANTS Gloucestershire Society (£2,000); Wellchild and Cotswold Volunteers (£1,500 each); Music Alive, Under The Edge and Root and Branch (£1,000 each); Guideposts (£600); and New Brewery Arts (£500).
FINANCES *Year* 2011–12 *Income* £26,740 *Grants* £22,302 *Assets* £660,783
TRUSTEES David Walker; Nigel Walker; Catherine Walker.
OTHER INFORMATION 19 grants were made to during the year.
HOW TO APPLY In writing to the correspondent.
WHO TO APPLY TO Sophie Walker, Administrator, 4 Shooters Hill Road, London SE3 7BD *Tel.* 020 8858 4701 *email* sophiewalker@mac.com

■ The Mackay and Brewer Charitable Trust

CC NO 1072666   **ESTABLISHED** 1998
WHERE FUNDING CAN BE GIVEN UK.
WHO CAN BENEFIT Charitable organisations.
WHAT IS FUNDED General charitable purposes.
RANGE OF GRANTS £5,750
SAMPLE GRANTS £5,750 each to Hampshire Association for the Care of the Blind, Macmillan Cancer Trust, Marie Curie Cancer Care, National Trust for Scotland, PDSA, Open Doors, Salvation Army, and St John Ambulance.
FINANCES *Year* 2011–12 *Income* £59,511 *Grants* £46,000 *Assets* £35,374
TRUSTEE HSBC Trust Co. (UK) Ltd

HOW TO APPLY In writing to the correspondent.

WHO TO APPLY TO Christopher Stroud, Trust Manager, c/o HSBC Trust Co. (UK) Ltd, 10th Floor, Norwich House, Nelson Gate, Commercial Road, Southampton SO15 1GX *Tel.* 02380 723344

....

■ The Mackintosh Foundation

CC NO 327751   **ESTABLISHED** 1988

WHERE FUNDING CAN BE GIVEN Worldwide. In practice, mainly UK.

WHO CAN BENEFIT Registered charities.

WHAT IS FUNDED Priority is given to the theatre and the performing arts. Also funded are children and education; medicine; homelessness; community projects; the environment; HIV/AIDS; refugees; and other charitable purposes.

WHAT IS NOT FUNDED Religious or political activities are not supported. Apart from the foundation's drama award and some exceptions, applications from individuals are discouraged.

TYPE OF GRANT Capital, project and recurring costs up to three years.

RANGE OF GRANTS Up to £75,000.

SAMPLE GRANTS Mercury Musical Developments (£75,000); Royal Conservatoire of Scotland (£75,000); Charles Dickens Museum (£30,000); Soho Theatre Company (£16,000); Macmillan Cancer Support (£10,000); The Royal Theatrical Fund (£6,000); National Student Drama Festival Ltd (£5,000); Mayor of London's Fund for Young Musicians (£4,000); Leukaemia and Lymphoma Research (£3,000); The Amber Foundation, RSPB – Scotland and Sun and Moon Foundation (£2,500 each) and The Prince's Youth Business International (£2,200).

FINANCES *Year* 2011–12 *Income* £59,236 *Grants* £472,775 *Assets* £9,231,085

TRUSTEES Sir Cameron Mackintosh, Chair; Nicholas Mackintosh; Nicholas Allott; D. Michael Rose; Robert Noble; Bart Peerless; Thomas Schonberg; F. Richard Pappas.

HOW TO APPLY In writing to the correspondent outlining details of the organisation, details of the project for which funding is required and a breakdown of the costs involved. Supporting documents should be kept to a minimum and sae enclosed if materials are to be returned. The trustees meet in May and October in plenary session, but a grants committee meets weekly to consider grants of up to £10,000. The foundation responds to all applications in writing and the process normally takes between four to six weeks.

WHO TO APPLY TO Richard Nibb, Appeals Director, 1 Bedford Square, London WC1B 3RB *Tel.* 020 7637 8866 *email* info@camack.co.uk

....

■ The MacRobert Trust

SC NO SC031346   **ESTABLISHED** 1943

WHERE FUNDING CAN BE GIVEN UK, mainly Scotland.

WHO CAN BENEFIT Recognised charitable organisations benefiting children, young adults and older people, ex-service and service people, seafarers and fishermen, and volunteers. Also artists, musicians, textile workers and designers, and writers and poets. At risk groups, carers, disabled people, people disadvantaged by poverty, and socially isolated people will also be considered.

WHAT IS FUNDED The current grantmaking themes are: services and sea; education and training; children and youth; science, engineering and technology; agriculture and horticulture; Tarland and the local area.

WHAT IS NOT FUNDED Grants are not normally provided for: religious organisations (but attention will be given to youth/community services provided by them, or projects of general benefit to the whole community); organisations based outside the United Kingdom; individuals; general appeals or mailshots; political organisations; student bodies as opposed to universities; fee-paying schools, apart from an Educational Grants Scheme for children who are at, or who need to attend, a Scottish independent secondary school and for which a grant application is made through the Head Teacher; expeditions, except those made under the auspices of recognised bodies such as the British Schools Exploring Society (BSES); community and village halls other than those local to Tarland and Deeside; and departments within a university, unless the appeal gains the support of, and is channelled through, the principal.

TYPE OF GRANT Core/revenue costs, project. Capital including buildings, feasibility studies, one-off, research, recurring and running costs, and salaries and unrestricted funding. Funding may be given for one year or more.

RANGE OF GRANTS Mostly £5,000–£10,000.

SAMPLE GRANTS Northern Police Convalescent and Training Centre (£60,000); University Hospital Birmingham Charities (£50,000); L'Arche Edinburgh (£35,000); Community Service (£20,000); Alzheimer's Research UK and Gamelea Countryside Training Trust (£10,000 each); The National Deaf Children's Trust (£5,000); British Schools Exploring Society (£3,400) Cleveland Housing Advice Centre (£3,000); Girlguiding Scotland (£2,500); Royal Caledonian Horticultural Society (£1,000); St Thomas' Church, Aboyne (£800); Forces Help – Aberdeen (£570) and Fife Opera (£500).

FINANCES *Year* 2011–12 *Income* £2,461,243 *Grants* £535,921 *Assets* £72,679,380

TRUSTEES S. Campbell; C. D. Crole; K. Davis; J. D. Fowlie; C. W. Pagan; J. C. Swan; J. H. Strickland; P. J. Hughesdon; C. Stevenson.

OTHER INFORMATION The education total includes £21,000 given in educational grants to individuals.

HOW TO APPLY The application form and full guidelines can be downloaded from the website, although applications must be posted.
The trustees meet to consider applications twice a year in March and November. To be considered, applications must be received for the March meeting by 31 October previously and for the October meeting by 31 May previously.
Time bars: Unsuccessful applicants must wait for at least one year from the time of being notified before re-applying. Successful applicants must wait for at least two years from the time of receiving a donation before re-applying. When a multi-year donation has been awarded, the time bar applies from the date of the final instalment. Withdrawn applications do not normally face a time bar
The trust stresses the importance of including an informative covering letter; completing *all* sections of the application form and asks that applicants maintain a process of dialogue with the trust: 'We deal with many hundreds of worthy applications each year. If we have to chase you for information, you will understand that our interest might wane.' A further list of additional guidance and feedback on the application procedure is available on the trust website. Applicants are informed of the trustees' decision, and if successful, payments are made immediately after each meeting.

WHO TO APPLY TO Air Comm. R. W. Joseph, Administrator, Cromar, Tarland, Aboyne, Aberdeenshire AB34 4UD *Tel.* 01339 881444 *email* vicky@themacroberttrust.org.uk *Website* www.themacroberttrust.org.uk

■ The Mactaggart Third Fund

SC NO SC014285   ESTABLISHED 1969
WHERE FUNDING CAN BE GIVEN UK and abroad.
WHO CAN BENEFIT Charitable organisations.
WHAT IS FUNDED General charitable purposes.
TYPE OF GRANT One-off.
RANGE OF GRANTS £100–£50,000.
SAMPLE GRANTS Previous beneficiaries included: University of Miami (£50,000); Robin Hood Trust (£13,000); Bahamas National Trust (£11,000); Amazon Conservation Team (£8,000); Mactaggart Community Cybercafé (£7,000); Terrence Higgins Trust (£5,000); Hearing Dogs for Deaf People (£4,000); Harris Manchester College (£2,000); Greatwood (£1,000); and Diabetes UK (£100).
FINANCES *Year* 2011–12 *Income* £11,994,875 *Grants* £397,975
TRUSTEES Sandy Mactaggart; Robert Gore; Fiona Mactaggart; Andrew Mactaggart; Sir John Mactaggart.
OTHER INFORMATION The latest accounts were not available on the charity's website, however, they had been received at the OSCR and the limited published information is replicated here.
HOW TO APPLY 'The trustees are solely responsible for the choice of charitable organisations to be supported. Trustees are proactive in seeking out charities to support and all projects are chosen on the initiative of the trustees. Unsolicited applications are not supported.'
WHO TO APPLY TO The Trustees, 2 Babmaes Street, London SW1Y 6HD *Website* www. mactaggartthirdfund.org

■ Ian Mactaggart Trust

SC NO SC012502   ESTABLISHED 1969
WHERE FUNDING CAN BE GIVEN UK, with a preference for Scotland.
WHO CAN BENEFIT Charitable organisations.
WHAT IS FUNDED The trust supports a wide range of activities including: education and training, culture and the relief of people who are poor, sick, in need or disabled.
WHAT IS NOT FUNDED Unsolicited requests for donations are discouraged.
RANGE OF GRANTS £100–£50,000
SAMPLE GRANTS Previous beneficiaries included: Slough Immigration Aid Unit (£31,000); Robin Hood Foundation (£22,000); Alzheimer's Society (£21,000); Oxfordshire Community Foundation (£20,000); Eagle Hill Foundation (£13,000); Game and Wildlife Conservation Trust (£10,000); Rights of Women (£5,000); Millbrook Early Childhood Education Centre (£3,000); Medical Foundation for the Victims of Torture (£2,500); Breakthrough Breast Cancer (£2,000); Dragon School Trust Ltd (£1,000); and Ashmolean Museum (£750).
FINANCES *Year* 2011–12 *Income* £8,973,482 *Grants* £372,838
TRUSTEES Sir John Mactaggart; Philip Mactaggart; Jane Mactaggart; Fiona Mactaggart; Lady Caroline Mactaggart; Leora Armstrong.
OTHER INFORMATION In 2011–12 the trust had an unusually high income of £8.7 million recorded on the OSCR's website, (it is normally around

£500,000). This was approximately what was declared as assets in the previous accounts.
HOW TO APPLY The trustees are committed to seeking out charitable organisations that they wish to support and therefore they do not respond to unsolicited applications.
WHO TO APPLY TO The Trustees, 2 Babmaes Street, London SW1Y 6HD *Website* www. ianmactaggarttrust.org

■ James Madison Trust

CC NO 1084835   ESTABLISHED 2000
WHERE FUNDING CAN BE GIVEN UK.
WHO CAN BENEFIT Charities and educational institutions.
WHAT IS FUNDED 'The objects of the charity are to support and promote studies of federal government whether within or among states and of related subjects, including the processes that may lead towards the establishment of such government, and to support or promote education and dissemination of knowledge of these subjects. These objects govern all decisions of trustees without the need for further specific annual objectives.'
TYPE OF GRANT Seminars, conferences, studies and publications.
RANGE OF GRANTS £3,500–£155,000
SAMPLE GRANTS Previous beneficiary organisations have included: University of Kent, Federal Trust, University of Edinburgh, Unlock Democracy, University of Middlesex, London Metropolitan University, and University of Cardiff. The trust has also usefully broken down grant totals according to project, as well as by recipient organisations. Previous projects funded by grants have included: Comparative Devolution, Centre for Federal Studies, Federal Trust Projects, Additional Constitutionalism, Autonomy Website, Regions of England, European Foreign and Security Policy, Welsh Papers, Climate Change Research and Book of Federal Studies 06.
FINANCES *Year* 2011–12 *Income* £8,918 *Grants* £170,000
TRUSTEES Robert Emerson; Ernest Wistrich; John Pinder; John Bishop; Richard Corbett.
HOW TO APPLY In writing to the correspondent.
WHO TO APPLY TO David Grace, Administrator, 68 Furnham Road, Chard TA20 1AP *Tel.* 01460 67368

■ The Magdalen and Lasher Charity

CC NO 211415   ESTABLISHED 1951
WHERE FUNDING CAN BE GIVEN Hastings.
WHO CAN BENEFIT Individuals, and organisations benefiting elderly and young people, and people disadvantaged by poverty.
WHAT IS FUNDED Pensions for elderly people in Hastings; playschemes; primary, secondary and special schools; purchase of books, travel and maintenance in schools; literacy; health care, facilities and buildings; community services.
TYPE OF GRANT One-off; one year or less.
SAMPLE GRANTS St Clements and All Saints and Surviving Christmas (£2,000 each); Martha Trust – Mary House and Hastings and Rother Credit Union (£1,000 each); Broomgrove Play Scheme and Halton Baptist Church (£500 each); and Bangladeshi Association Hastings and Rother (£100).

Think carefully about every application. Is it justified?

725

FINANCES *Year* 2012–13 *Income* £1,826,478 *Grants* £114,033 *Assets* £12,750,178

TRUSTEES Ian Steel; Gareth Bendon; John Bilsby; Revd Robert Featherstone; Michael Foster; Donald Burrows; Jill Cooper; Richard Stevens; Clive Morris; Susan Parsons; Joy Waite; Jenny Blackburn; John Hodges; Susan Phillips; Nikki Port; Keith Donaldson.

OTHER INFORMATION The grant total includes £68,000 that was given towards pensions.

HOW TO APPLY On a form available from the correspondent. Guidelines and criteria are available to view on the website.

WHO TO APPLY TO Gill Adamson, Administrator, Old Hastings House, 132 High Street, Hastings, East Sussex TN34 3ET *Tel.* 01424 452646 *email* mlc@oldhastingshouse.co.uk *Website* www.magdalenandlasher.co.uk

■ Magdalen Hospital Trust

CC NO 225878   **ESTABLISHED** 1963

WHERE FUNDING CAN BE GIVEN UK.

WHO CAN BENEFIT Registered charities benefiting: deprived children and young adults up to 25 years; those in care, fostered and adopted; parents and children; one-parent families; people disadvantaged by poverty; and people with HIV/AIDS.

WHAT IS FUNDED Projects for deprived and disabled children and young people, including literacy, special needs education, training for work and personal development, clubs, crime prevention, emergency care, playschemes, and counselling.

WHAT IS NOT FUNDED No grants to non-registered charities, individuals, charities with an income in excess of £150,000 or national charities.

TYPE OF GRANT One-off; project; start-up funding; one year or less.

RANGE OF GRANTS £500–£2,000; typically £1,000.

SAMPLE GRANTS Hope's Place and Blue Horizon's (£2,000 each); Birmingham University Guild of Students, Friends of the Family, Network for Surviving Stalking, Youth for Youth, Young and Free (£1,000 each); and Musical Keys (£500).

FINANCES *Year* 2011–12 *Income* £31,654 *Grants* £19,950 *Assets* £771,110

TRUSTEES B. M. Gregory; B. Lucas; Revd R. Mitchell; Ven. F. R. Hazell; D. Lazenby; Hon. E. Wood; Dr E. Offerman, L. Wood.

HOW TO APPLY An application form and guidelines are available. An sae is required.

WHO TO APPLY TO Norma Hazell, Flat 27, Ramsay Hall, 9–13 Byron Road, Worthing, BN11 3HN *Tel.* 01903 217108 *email* correspondent@ magdalentrust.org.uk *Website* www. magdalentrust.org.uk

■ The SV and PE Magee Family Charitable Trust

CC NO 1135130   **ESTABLISHED** 2010

WHERE FUNDING CAN BE GIVEN Worldwide

WHO CAN BENEFIT Charitable organisations.

WHAT IS FUNDED Religious activities.

SAMPLE GRANTS St Andrews Community Network (£24,000)

FINANCES *Year* 2011–12 *Income* £30,070 *Grants* £24,000

TRUSTEE NatWest Trust Services.

HOW TO APPLY In writing to the correspondent.

WHO TO APPLY TO The Administrator, NatWest Trust Services, 5th Floor, Trinity Quay 2, Avon Street, Bristol BS2 0PT *Tel.* 05516577371

■ The Magen Charitable Trust

CC NO 326535   **ESTABLISHED** 1984

WHERE FUNDING CAN BE GIVEN UK.

WHO CAN BENEFIT Registered charities.

WHAT IS FUNDED Jewish organisations.

SAMPLE GRANTS Previous beneficiaries have included Manchester Yeshiva Kollel, Talmud Educational Trust, Bnos Yisroel School and Mesifta Tiferes Yisroel.

FINANCES *Year* 2011–12 *Income* £135,687 *Grants* £92,180 *Assets* £1,454,387

TRUSTEES Jacob Halpern; Rosa Halpern.

HOW TO APPLY In writing to the correspondent.

WHO TO APPLY TO The Trustees, New Riverside, 439 Lower Broughton, Salford M7 2FX *Tel.* 01617 922626

■ Mageni Trust

CC NO 1070732   **ESTABLISHED** 1998

WHERE FUNDING CAN BE GIVEN UK

WHO CAN BENEFIT Arts organisations; registered charities.

WHAT IS FUNDED Primarily arts projects and other general charitable purposes.

TYPE OF GRANT One-off and recurrent.

RANGE OF GRANTS Up to £10,000.

SAMPLE GRANTS Charities Aid Foundation (£10,000); British Red Cross, Esther Benjamins Trust and LPO Thomas Beecham Group (£5,000 each); National Theatre (£2,500); Foundation for Young Musicians (£2,000); Medicine Sans Frontier and RNLI (£1,000 each); Primavera (£600) and Care International (£500).

FINANCES *Year* 2011–12 *Income* £27,411 *Grants* £52,850 *Assets* £1,107,765

TRUSTEES Garfield Collins; Gillian Collins; Alex Collins.

HOW TO APPLY In writing to the correspondent.

WHO TO APPLY TO Garfield Collins, Trustee, 5 Hyde Vale, Greenwich SE10 8QQ *Tel.* 020 8469 2683 *email* garfcollins@gmail.com

■ The Brian Maguire Charitable Trust

CC NO 1091978   **ESTABLISHED** 2002

WHERE FUNDING CAN BE GIVEN Worldwide.

WHO CAN BENEFIT Organisations.

WHAT IS FUNDED General charitable purposes.

RANGE OF GRANTS £200–£75,000.

SAMPLE GRANTS The Royal Grammar School (£75,000) and St George's, Bristol (£20,000); Wheel Power and Cornwall Mobility Centre (£5,000 each); the Peace Hospice – Starlight Walk (£2,000); The National Trust, Parapet Breast Unit and The Salvation Army (£1,000 each); Barrow Romania Action Group and Galloway's Society for the Blind (£500 each); Disability Recreation Unity Movement (£300); and Watford Philharmonic (£200).

FINANCES *Year* 2011–12 *Income* £77,250 *Grants* £95,000 *Assets* £2,131,367

TRUSTEES Margaret Maguire; Martin Bennett; Burges Salmon Trustees Ltd.

OTHER INFORMATION In 2011–12 grants were given to two organisations.

HOW TO APPLY In writing to the correspondent.

WHO TO APPLY TO The Trustees, Burges Salmon LLP, 1 Glass Wharf, Bristol BS2 0ZX *Tel.* 01179 392000

■ The Mahavir Trust (also known as the K. S. Mehta Charitable Trust)

CC NO 298551   **ESTABLISHED** 1988
WHERE FUNDING CAN BE GIVEN UK
WHO CAN BENEFIT Registered charities, social enterprises and hospitals.
WHAT IS FUNDED General, medical, animal welfare, relief of poverty, overseas aid, religion.
TYPE OF GRANT Unrestricted.
RANGE OF GRANTS £100–£140,000
SAMPLE GRANTS Shantiniketan Ltd (£147,000); Mahavir Foundation Ltd UK (£61,000); Shivanand Mission Virpur India (£3,400); Samast Mahajan Mumbai India (£3,300) and Jain Vishwa Bharti UK (£1,200).
FINANCES *Year* 2011–12 *Income* £273,713 *Grants* £276,047 *Assets* £334,160
TRUSTEES Jay Mehta; Nemish Mehta; Pravinchandra Mehta; Pushpa Mehta; Kumar Mehta; Sheena Mehta Sabharwal; Sangita Mehta.
HOW TO APPLY In writing to the correspondent.
WHO TO APPLY TO Jay Mehta, Trustee, 19 Hillersdon Avenue, Edgware, Middlesex HA8 7SG *Tel.* 020 8958 4883 *email* mahavirtrust@googlemail.com

■ The Makin Charitable Trust

CC NO 1089832   **ESTABLISHED** 2001
WHERE FUNDING CAN BE GIVEN Preference for Merseyside.
WHO CAN BENEFIT Registered charities.
WHAT IS FUNDED 'Learning, religion, the arts and general philanthropy.'
RANGE OF GRANTS Up to £75,000
SAMPLE GRANTS Liverpool Hope University (£75,000); Merseyside Jewish Community Care (£50,000); The Jerusalem Foundation (£41,000) and Liverpool Old Hebrew Congregation (£30,000).
FINANCES *Year* 2011–12 *Income* £1,368 *Grants* £40,000
TRUSTEES Rex Makin; Shirley Makin; Robin Makin
OTHER INFORMATION In 2011–12 the trust had a total expenditure of £40,500.
HOW TO APPLY In writing to the correspondent.
WHO TO APPLY TO Robin Makin, Trustee, c/o E. Rex Makin and Co., Leigh Street, Whitechapel, Liverpool L1 1HQ *Tel.* 01517 094491

■ Malbin Trust

CC NO 1045174   **ESTABLISHED** 1995
WHERE FUNDING CAN BE GIVEN Worldwide.
WHO CAN BENEFIT Charitable organisations and individuals.
WHAT IS FUNDED Jewish causes, general charitable purposes, social welfare.
SAMPLE GRANTS Previously: £10,000 to Chasidei Belz Institutions.
FINANCES *Year* 2010–11 *Income* £64,994 *Grants* £71,947 *Assets* £435,978
TRUSTEES Benjamin Leitner; Benjamin Leitner; Jehuda Waldman; Margaret Leitner.
HOW TO APPLY In writing to the correspondent.
WHO TO APPLY TO Benjamin Leitner, Trustee, 8 Cheltenham Crescent, Salford M7 4FP *Tel.* 01617 927343

■ The Mallinckrodt Foundation

CC NO 1058011   **ESTABLISHED** 1996
WHERE FUNDING CAN BE GIVEN UK and overseas.
WHO CAN BENEFIT Registered charities and charitable organisations.
WHAT IS FUNDED General charitable purposes.
RANGE OF GRANTS £1,000–£13,000.
SAMPLE GRANTS Sisters of Christian Charity, Uruguay The Mallinckrodt Sisters (£13,000); American Academy in Berlin (£10,000); Kennedy School of Government, Harvard (£6,000); Christian Responsibility in Public Affairs (CRPA) (£5,000); St Andrews Youth Club (£2,500); African Medical and Research Foundation (AMREF) (£2,000) and Hemi-Help (£1,000).
FINANCES *Year* 2011–12 *Income* £43,304 *Grants* £55,767 *Assets* £3,326,263
TRUSTEES G. W. Mallinckrodt; C. B. Mallinckrodt; P. S. A. Mallinckrodt; C. L. Fitzalan Howard; E. G. P. Mallinckrodt.
OTHER INFORMATION In 2011–12 grants were given to 12 organisations.
HOW TO APPLY The foundation does not seek or respond to unsolicited applications.
WHO TO APPLY TO Sally Yates, 81 Rivington Street, London EC2A 3AY

■ Man Group plc Charitable Trust

CC NO 275386   **ESTABLISHED** 1978
WHERE FUNDING CAN BE GIVEN UK, with some preference for London.
WHO CAN BENEFIT Registered charities.
WHAT IS FUNDED General charitable purposes in the UK and overseas with some preference for causes near to or linked to the business of Man Group plc.
WHAT IS NOT FUNDED The trust does not normally support: large national charities; charities who use outside fundraising organisations; charities whose administration costs are thought to be excessive; animal charities; applicants who have applied within the previous 12 months; requests that directly replace statutory funding; individuals (unless under a sponsorship scheme); endowment funds; charities where the main purpose is to promote religious beliefs.
SAMPLE GRANTS Foundation and Friends of the Royal Botanic Gardens, Kew (£175,000); Starlight Children's Foundation, Community Links and Refuge (£100,000 each); Skill Force (£94,000); Teach First (£75,000); School-Home Support and The Fostering Network (£50,000); The Boxing Academy (£36,000); Birkbeck, University of London (£25,000); Career Academies UK and University of Oxford (£15,000 each) and Inspire (£10,000).
FINANCES *Year* 2012 *Income* £1,155,378 *Grants* £1,850,628 *Assets* £3,385,299
TRUSTEES Jonathan Aisbitt; Nicholas Taylor; Murray Steel; Jasveer Singh; David Kingsley; Britt Lintner.
HOW TO APPLY The trust has stated that it cannot commit to responding to organisations making unsolicited applications. See the trust's website for criteria.
WHO TO APPLY TO L. Clarke, Secretary to the Trust, Riverbank House, 2 Swan Lane, London EC4R 3AD *Tel.* 020 7144 1000 *email* charitable.trust@man.com *Website* www. man.com/GB/man-charitable-trust

■ The Manackerman Charitable Trust

CC NO 326147   **ESTABLISHED** 1982
WHERE FUNDING CAN BE GIVEN England, with some preference for Manchester.
WHO CAN BENEFIT Jewish causes.
WHAT IS FUNDED Education, religion, relief of poverty.

SAMPLE GRANTS Heathlands (£3,200); TTT Charity (£2,500); Manchester Jewish Federation (£2,000); M.B. Foundation (£1,400); Reshet (£1,250); Child Resettlement Fund (£1,000); and British Friends of New Synagogue Netanya (£1,000).

FINANCES *Year* 2012–13 *Income* £130,325 *Grants* £44,950 *Assets* £616,885

TRUSTEES Jonathan Marks; Vanessa Marks; Michael Hammelburger.

HOW TO APPLY In writing to the correspondent. The trust receives many applications for grants, both by mail and verbally. Each application is considered against the criteria established by the charity. Feedback received is used to monitor the quality of grants.

WHO TO APPLY TO Jonathan Marks, Trustee, 3 Park Lane, Salford M7 4HT *Tel.* 01618 323434

■ Manchester Airport Community Trust Fund

CC NO 1071703   **ESTABLISHED** 1997

WHERE FUNDING CAN BE GIVEN The area which is most affected by Manchester Airport. This includes South Manchester and Tameside, Trafford, Stockport, the borough of Macclesfield and the borough of Congleton up to but not including the towns of Macclesfield and Congleton, Vale Royal, and up to but not including Northwich.

WHO CAN BENEFIT Established groups or charities able to demonstrate clear financial records.

WHAT IS FUNDED Projects which: encourage tree planting, afforestation, landscaping and other environmental improvements or heritage conservation; promote social welfare through recreation, sport and leisure; provide better appreciation of the natural and urban environment.

WHAT IS NOT FUNDED Applications from individuals or organisations working for profit are not considered. Must be based in Manchester/Cheshire area.

RANGE OF GRANTS £200–£3,000, usually £1,000.

SAMPLE GRANTS Denton West Cricket Club (£2,000); Ashlon on Marsey RUFC (£1,000); Friday Club (£700); Body positive (£1,000); Lloyd Hotel Bowling (£1,000); Paramount Boxing Club (£900); Stockport and Brinnington ABC (£2,700) and Hough End Griffins Community Football Club (£200).

FINANCES *Year* 2011–12 *Income* £133,520 *Grants* £85,289 *Assets* £55,809

TRUSTEES Tony Burns; Cllr John Pantall; Myles Hogg; Cllr Don Stockton; Cllr Malcolm Byram; Michael Whetton; Andrew Harrison; Council Michael Smith; Wendy Sinfield.

HOW TO APPLY application form online at www.manchesterairport.co.uk.

WHO TO APPLY TO David Proudfoot, Trust Fund Administrator, The Community Relations Department, Manchester Airport plc, Olympic House, Manchester M90 1QX *Tel.* 01614 898623 *email* trust.fund@manairport.co.uk *Website* www.manchesterairport.co.uk

■ The Manchester Guardian Society Charitable Trust

CC NO 515341   **ESTABLISHED** 1984

WHERE FUNDING CAN BE GIVEN Greater Manchester

WHO CAN BENEFIT Preference is usually shown to smaller charities.

WHAT IS FUNDED General charitable purposes. The emphasis is very much on support in the Greater Manchester area.

WHAT IS NOT FUNDED The trust does not give to individuals.

TYPE OF GRANT Primarily small, single, capital projects.

RANGE OF GRANTS £300–£3,000.

SAMPLE GRANTS The Fusilier Museum, Willow Wood Hospice and Starlight Children's Foundation (£3,000 each); Oldham Sea Cadets (£2,000); Coolshade Community Medical Workshop and CLIC Sargent Cancer Care for Children (£1,500 each); Henshaw Society for blind people and Lower Kersal Young Peoples Project (£1,000 each); Kaleidoscope Craft Club (£770); Manchester Refuge Support Network and Muscular Dystrophy Campaign (£500 each) and St George's Court Action Group (£300).

FINANCES *Year* 2011–12 *Income* £105,030 *Grants* £80,275 *Assets* £3,528,687

TRUSTEES D. Burton; L. Worsley; V. Carter; W. J. Smith; D. G. Wilson; J. P. Wainwright; K. Ahmed; K. Hardinge; J. A. H. Fielden; D. Hawkins; P. Lochery; S. Birtles.

OTHER INFORMATION In 2011–12 grants were given to 85 organisations.

HOW TO APPLY On a form available from the correspondent. Applications are considered on the first Monday in March, June, September and December; they must arrive 14 days before these dates. The trustees do not welcome repeat applications within two years.

WHO TO APPLY TO Joseph Swift, Clerk to the Trustees, c/o Cobbetts LLP, 58 Mosley Street, Manchester M2 3HZ *Tel.* 0845 404 2404 *Fax* 0845 404 2414

■ Lord Mayor of Manchester's Charity Appeal Trust

CC NO 1066972   **ESTABLISHED** 1997

WHERE FUNDING CAN BE GIVEN The City of Manchester.

WHO CAN BENEFIT Registered charities.

WHAT IS FUNDED General charitable purposes.

RANGE OF GRANTS £500– £4,000.

SAMPLE GRANTS 'Food of Love' Campaign (£4,500); Friends of Ghyll Head (£4,000); Army Benevolent Fund, Whitmore Club for Young People and Tours Aid (£1,000 each); and Mines Advisory Group and Broughton House (£500 each).

FINANCES *Year* 2011–12 *Income* £148,829 *Grants* £33,500 *Assets* £796,730

TRUSTEES Arthur Burden; Howard Bernstein; Richard Paver; William Egerton; Lady Mayoress of Manchester; Lord Maj. of Manchester.

HOW TO APPLY Application forms are available from the Mayor's office. Applications are considered quarterly.

WHO TO APPLY TO Amanda Kaye, Head of Lord Mayor's Office, We Love MCR Charity, Lord Mayor's Office, Room 412, Level 4, Town Hall, Manchester M60 2LA *Tel.* 01612 343229 *Fax* 01612 747113 *email* a.scallan@manchester.gov.uk *Website* www.welovemcrcharity@manchester.gov.uk

■ The Mandeville Trust

CC NO 1041880   **ESTABLISHED** 1994

WHERE FUNDING CAN BE GIVEN UK.

WHO CAN BENEFIT Charitable organisations.

WHAT IS FUNDED General charitable purposes, health and young people.

SAMPLE GRANTS Previous beneficiaries have included: University College London and Imperial College for research purposes; and the Berkshire Community Foundation.

FINANCES *Year* 2011–12 *Income* £9,500 *Grants* £6,000

TRUSTEES Robert Mandeville; Pauline Mandeville; Dr Justin Mandeville; Peter Murcott.

HOW TO APPLY In writing to the correspondent.

WHO TO APPLY TO Robert Mandeville, Trustee, The Hockett, Hockett Lane, Cookham, Maidenhead SL6 9UF *Tel.* 01628 484272

■ The Manifold Charitable Trust

CC NO 229501   **ESTABLISHED** 1962

WHERE FUNDING CAN BE GIVEN UK.

WHO CAN BENEFIT Registered charities only.

WHAT IS FUNDED Education, historic buildings, environmental conservation and general. The trust has previously focused much attention on the preservation of churches, however following the death in 2007 of its founder, Sir John Smith, the trust is now allocating most of its grants for educational purposes. The trust still makes grants to the Historic Churches Preservation Trust for onward distribution to churches; however it would seem that the amount has been reduced on previous years.

WHAT IS NOT FUNDED Applications are not considered for improvements to churches as this is covered by a block grant to the Historic Churches Preservation Trust. The trust regrets that it does not give grants to individuals for any purpose.

TYPE OF GRANT One-off; recurring.

SAMPLE GRANTS Eton College; Historic Churches Preservation Trust; Thames Hospice Care; Imperial College; Berkeley Castle Charitable Trust; Maidenhead Heritage Trust; Berkshire Medical Heritage Centre; Gislingham Parochial Church Council; Household Cavalry Museum Trust; Brompton Ralph Parochial Church Council; Morrab Library; Richmond Building Preservation Society; Askham Parochial Church Council and Westray Heritage Trust.

FINANCES *Year* 2012 *Income* £581,456 *Grants* £322,000 *Assets* £8,255,276

TRUSTEE Manifold Trustee Company Limited.

HOW TO APPLY The trust has no full-time staff, therefore general enquiries and applications for grants should be made in writing only, by post or by fax and not by telephone. The trust does not issue application forms. Applications should be made to the correspondent in writing and should: state how much money it is hoped to raise; if the appeal is for a specific project state also (a) how much it will cost (b) how much of this cost will come from the applicant charity's existing funds (c) how much has already been received or promised from other sources and (d) how much is therefore still being sought; list sources of funds to which application has been or is intended to be made (for example local authorities, or quasi-governmental sources, such as the national lottery); if the project involves conservation of a building, send a photograph of it and a note (or pamphlet) about its history; send a copy of the charity's latest income and expenditure account and balance sheet. Applications are considered twice a month, and a reply is sent to most applicants (whether successful or not) who have written a letter rather than sent a circular.

WHO TO APPLY TO Helen Niven, Studio Cottage, Windsor Great Park, Windsor, Berkshire SL4 2HP *email* themanifoldtrust@gmail.com

■ W. M. Mann Foundation

SC NO SC010111   **ESTABLISHED** 1992

WHERE FUNDING CAN BE GIVEN Scotland and other parts of the UK

WHO CAN BENEFIT Organisations based in Scotland or serving the Scottish community.

WHAT IS FUNDED The arts, education, music, health, care and sport.

RANGE OF GRANTS £100 to £10,000.

FINANCES *Year* 2011–12 *Income* £195,652

TRUSTEES W. M. Mann; B. M. Mann; A. W. Mann; S. P. Hutcheon.

OTHER INFORMATION In 2011–12 the foundation had a total expenditure of £71,961.

HOW TO APPLY In writing to the trustees.

WHO TO APPLY TO Bruce M. Mann, Trustee, 201 Bath Street, Glasgow G2 4HZ *Tel.* 01412 484936 *Fax* 01412 212976 *email* mail@wmmanngroup. co.uk

■ R. W. Mann Trust

CC NO 1095699   **ESTABLISHED** 1959

WHERE FUNDING CAN BE GIVEN UK, but grants are practically all confined to organisations in Tyne and Wear, with a preference for North Tyneside.

WHO CAN BENEFIT Local activities or local branches of national charities benefiting children, young adults, older people, academics, seafarers and fishermen, students, teachers and governesses, unemployed people, volunteers, those in care, fostered and adopted, parents and children, one-parent families, widows and widowers, at risk groups, carers, people with disabilities, people disadvantaged by poverty, ex-offenders and those at risk of offending, homeless people, people living in urban areas, and victims of abuse, crime and domestic violence. People with Alzheimer's disease, autism, cancer, cerebral palsy, Crohn's disease, mental illness, motor neurone disease, multiple sclerosis, muscular dystrophy, sight loss and all terminal diseases will be considered.

WHAT IS FUNDED Charities working in the fields of: accommodation and housing; information technology and computers; infrastructure development; professional bodies; charity and umbrella bodies; arts and art facilities; theatre; the visual arts; arts activities and education; cultural activity; health; conservation and environment; education and training; and social care and development. Other charitable purposes will be considered.

WHAT IS NOT FUNDED Large well-established national charities; Individuals; Church buildings except where they are used for community groups; Projects or groups which can attract public funds or which appeal to Community Fund grants or national charitable trusts or other sources except if there is a particular part of the project which other sources would be unlikely to fund; Deficits already incurred or to replace statutory funding.

TYPE OF GRANT Recurrent expenditure, capital or single expenditure. Core costs, feasibility studies, interest-free loans, one-off and project funding, recurring costs, running costs, and salaries up to two years will be considered.

Think carefully about every application. Is it justified?

729

RANGE OF GRANTS £50–£5,000; usually £1,000 or below.

SAMPLE GRANTS Northumberland Clubs for Young People (£6,250); Linskill and N. Tyneside Community Development Trust (£3,050); St Paul's Community Partnership (£2,750); Newcastle CVS (£2,500).

Northumbria Youth Action Ltd; North Shields Sea Cadets Unit 613; Lookwide UK; Learning Disabilities Federation; Friends of the Elderly (£1,000 each); The Catholic Fellowship Newcastle – St Bernadette club; The Outpost Housing Project; Theatre Royal Newcastle (£750 each); Durham Light Infantry (£200).

FINANCES *Year* 2011–12 *Income* £70,527 *Grants* £129,512 *Assets* £2,235,728

TRUSTEES Judy Hamilton, Chair; Guy Javens; Monica Heath.

HOW TO APPLY In writing to the correspondent, with an sae. The Trustees meet monthly. Applicants will usually hear if their application has been successful within two months.

WHO TO APPLY TO John Hamilton, PO Box 119, Gosforth, Newcastle upon Tyne NE3 4WF *Tel.* 01912 842158 *Fax* 01912 858617 *email* john.hamilton@onyx.octacon.co.uk *Website* www.rwmanntrust.org.uk

■ The Leslie and Lilian Manning Trust

CC NO 219846   **ESTABLISHED** 1960

WHERE FUNDING CAN BE GIVEN The north east of England.

WHO CAN BENEFIT Principally charities with local affinities benefiting at risk groups, and people who are disadvantaged by poverty, socially isolated, sick or disabled.

WHAT IS FUNDED Principally health and welfare.

WHAT IS NOT FUNDED No grants to individuals.

RANGE OF GRANTS Usually £500–£1,000.

SAMPLE GRANTS Northumberland Clubs for Young People, Royal National Institute for the Deaf, Leukaemia Research Fund, Great North Air Ambulance and Age UK Northumberland (£1,000 each) and Shandon Way Community Association and 5th Whitley Bay Scouts (£500 each).

FINANCES *Year* 2012–13 *Income* £28,974 *Grants* £22,000 *Assets* £826,739

TRUSTEES David Jones; Ugo Fagandini; Kristian Anderson.

OTHER INFORMATION In 2012–13 grants were given to 23 organisations.

HOW TO APPLY In writing to the correspondent by January for consideration in March.

WHO TO APPLY TO David Jones, Trustee, 44 Midhurst Road, Newcastle upon Tyne NE12 9NU *Tel.* 01912 847661

■ The Manoukian Charitable Foundation

CC NO 1084065   **ESTABLISHED** 2000

WHERE FUNDING CAN BE GIVEN Worldwide.

WHO CAN BENEFIT Registered charities.

WHAT IS FUNDED Social welfare, education, medical, the arts, 'Armenian matters'.

SAMPLE GRANTS Cherie Blair Foundation for Women (£100,000); Elton John Aids Foundation (£55,000); Give a Child a Toy (£30,000); Mission Enfance (£7,600); Our Lady of Lebanon Church and English Heritage (£5,000 each) and NSPCC and The Eve Appeal (£1,000 each).

FINANCES *Year* 2012 *Income* £275,000 *Grants* £229,798 *Assets* £5,951

TRUSTEES Tamar Manoukian; Anthony Bunker; Steven Press; Dr Armen Sarkissian.

OTHER INFORMATION £25,000 was given in individuals grants for 'religious, cultural and educational purposes'.

HOW TO APPLY 'Requests for grants are received from the general public and charitable and other organisations through their knowledge of the activities of the foundation and through personal contacts of the settlor and the trustees.' The trustees meet at least once per year.

WHO TO APPLY TO Anthony Bunker, Trustee, c/o Berwin Leighton Paisner, Adelaide House, London Bridge, London EC4R 9HA *Tel.* 020 7760 1000

■ Maranatha Christian Trust

CC NO 265323   **ESTABLISHED** 1972

WHERE FUNDING CAN BE GIVEN UK and overseas.

WHO CAN BENEFIT Christian organisations and individuals.

WHAT IS FUNDED The promotion of education among young persons and the relief of poverty, particularly among those professing the Christian religion or working to promote such religion.

RANGE OF GRANTS £500–£10,000.

SAMPLE GRANTS CARE (£5,000); Cafe Africa Trust (£3,000); Concordis International (£2,500); and Ashburnham Christian Trust and Stewards Trust (£2,000 each).

FINANCES *Year* 2011–12 *Income* £27,193 *Grants* £105,500 *Assets* £957,124

TRUSTEES Alan Bell; Lyndon Bowring; Viscount Crispin Brentford.

HOW TO APPLY In writing to the correspondent.

WHO TO APPLY TO The Secretary, 208 Cooden Drive, Bexhill-On-Sea TN39 3AH

■ Marbeh Torah Trust

CC NO 292491   **ESTABLISHED** 1985

WHERE FUNDING CAN BE GIVEN UK and Israel.

WHO CAN BENEFIT Jewish charitable organisations.

WHAT IS FUNDED Furtherance of Orthodox Jewish religious education and relief of poverty.

WHAT IS NOT FUNDED Mainly Jewish causes.

RANGE OF GRANTS £3,500–£81,000

SAMPLE GRANTS Yeshiva Marbeh Torah (£124,000); Chazon Avraham Yitzchak (£34,000); Tashbar (£19,000); Yad Gershon (£17,000); Mishkenos Yaakov (£8,000); Torah Bezalel (£6,000); Beis Dovid (£1,000); and British Friends of Igud Hokollim (£300).

FINANCES *Year* 2012 *Income* £227,666 *Grants* £222,600 *Assets* £2,572

TRUSTEES Jacob Elzas; Moishe Elzas; Simone Elzas.

HOW TO APPLY In writing to the correspondent.

WHO TO APPLY TO Moishe Elzas, Trustee, 116 Castlewood Road, London N15 6BE

■ The Marcela Trust

CC NO 1127514   **ESTABLISHED** 2009

WHERE FUNDING CAN BE GIVEN UK

WHO CAN BENEFIT Registered charities and research institutions

WHAT IS FUNDED Medical research, environment and animals.

TYPE OF GRANT Research grants; capital projects.

SAMPLE GRANTS Fauna and Flora International (£170,000); and Consensus Action on Salt and Health (£100,000).

FINANCES *Year* 2011–12 *Income* £5,765,811 *Grants* £270,000 *Assets* £65,677,671

TRUSTEES Brian Groves; Dawn Rose; Dr Martin Lenz; Mark Spragg.

HOW TO APPLY In writing to the correspondent, although potential applicants should be aware that grant recipients may be pre-determined by the directors of OMC Investments Limited.

WHO TO APPLY TO Josephine Paxton, OMC Investments Limited, 2nd Floor, 14 Buckingham Street, London WC2N 6DF *Tel.* 020 7925 8095

■ Marchig Animal Welfare Trust

CC NO 802133   **ESTABLISHED** 1989

WHERE FUNDING CAN BE GIVEN Worldwide.

WHO CAN BENEFIT Organisations and individuals that make positive contributions in protecting animals and promoting and encouraging practical work in preventing animal cruelty and suffering.

WHAT IS FUNDED Projects supported by the trust have included mobile spay/neuter clinics, alternatives to the use of animals in research, poster campaigns, anti-poaching programmes, establishment of veterinary hospitals, clinics and animal sanctuaries. There are no restrictions on the geographical area of work (with the exception of the USA and Canada), types of grants or potential applicants, but all applications must be related to animal welfare and be of direct benefit to animals.

WHAT IS NOT FUNDED The trust will reject any application failing to meet its criteria. Additionally, applications relating to educational studies or other courses, expeditions, payment of salaries, support of conferences and meetings, or activities that are not totally animal welfare related, will also be rejected.

TYPE OF GRANT Based on project.

RANGE OF GRANTS Based on project.

SAMPLE GRANTS UK beneficiaries included: Freshfield Animal Rescue Centre; Prevent Unwanted Pets; Farm Animal and Bird Sanctuary Trust; Rain Rescue; Society for Abandoned Animals; and Save Our Strays. Non-UK beneficiaries included: Gozo SPCA – Malta; Aegean Wildlife Hospital – Greece; Kleinmond Animal Welfare Society – South Africa; Dog and Cat Rescue Samui – Thailand; Free the Bears – Australia; Chats de Quercy – France; Animal House-Jamaica; and McKee Project – Costa Rica.

FINANCES *Year* 2012 *Income* £1,052,879 *Grants* £595,431 *Assets* £18,201,917

TRUSTEES Colin Moor; Les Ward; Dr Jerzy Mlotkiewicz; Alastair Keatinge; Janice McLoughlin.

OTHER INFORMATION As well as giving grants, the trust also makes Marchig Animal Welfare Trust Awards. These awards, which take the form of a financial donation in support of the winner's animal welfare work, are given in either of the following two categories: (a) The development of an alternative method to the use of animals in experimental procedures and the practical implementation of such an alternative resulting in a significant reduction in the number of animals used in experimental procedures; (b) Practical work in the field of animal welfare resulting in significant improvements for animals either nationally or internationally.

HOW TO APPLY On an application form available from the correspondent or via the website. Entries should be submitted by email to:

info@marchigtrust.org or via post. Full support documentation must be submitted with the form. Applications are accepted throughout the year.

WHO TO APPLY TO Alastair Keatinge, Trustee, Caledonian Exchange, 10A Canning Street, Edinburgh EH3 8HE *Tel.* 01316 565746 *email* info@marchigtrust.org *Website* www.marchigtrust.org

■ The Stella and Alexander Margulies Charitable Trust

CC NO 220441   **ESTABLISHED** 1970

WHERE FUNDING CAN BE GIVEN UK.

WHO CAN BENEFIT Charitable organisations benefiting Jewish people.

WHAT IS FUNDED Jewish, general charitable purposes.

WHAT IS NOT FUNDED Mainly Jewish causes.

RANGE OF GRANTS Generally £200–£5,000.

SAMPLE GRANTS Shaare Zedek (£236,000); Jerusalem Foundation – Har Herzl (£187,000); Royal Opera House Foundation and Alma Hebrew College (£25,000 each); Chief Rabbinate Trust and B'nai B'rith Hillel Foundation (£5,000 each); Nightingale House (£2,000); Jewish Literary Trust and Jewish Association of Business Ethics (£1,000 each); Beaconsfield Talking Papers and Cancer Research UK (£500 each); and Lolev Charitable Trust (£200).

FINANCES *Year* 2011–12 *Income* £151,042 *Grants* £469,952 *Assets* £7,458,236

TRUSTEES Martin Paisner; Sir Stuart Lipton; Alexander Sorkin; Marcus Margulies; Leslie Michaels.

HOW TO APPLY In writing to the correspondent.

WHO TO APPLY TO Leslie Michaels, Trustee, 34 Dover Street, London W1S 4NG

■ The Marianne Foundation

CC NO 1136999   **ESTABLISHED** 2010

WHERE FUNDING CAN BE GIVEN Developing countries.

WHO CAN BENEFIT Organisations working with children and young people.

WHAT IS FUNDED Education and training.

SAMPLE GRANTS Navajeevana preschools in the Hambantota district in Southern Sri Lanka; leadership training programmes in Bulawayo in Zimbabwe and the Starehe Girls' School in Kenya.

FINANCES *Year* 2012–13 *Income* £3,392 *Grants* £8,000

TRUSTEES Edward Seymour; Raffaella Taylor-Seymour; Susan Johns; Stephen Gee; Jenefer Greenwood.

HOW TO APPLY In writing to the correspondent.

WHO TO APPLY TO Raffaella Taylor-Seymour, Trustee, 36 Alexandra Road, Flat 5, London N8 0PP *email* info@themariannefoundation.org

■ Mariapolis Limited

CC NO 257912   **ESTABLISHED** 1968

WHERE FUNDING CAN BE GIVEN UK and overseas.

WHO CAN BENEFIT Organisations and individuals.

WHAT IS FUNDED Christian ecumenism, young people and families.

SAMPLE GRANTS Previous beneficiaries have included: Pia Associazione Maschile Opera di Maria; family welfare grants; Anglican Priests Training Fund; Focolare Trust; and 'other'.

FINANCES *Year* 2011–12 *Income* £1,224,555 *Grants* £155,000

TRUSTEES Barry Redmond; Manfred Kochinky.

OTHER INFORMATION This trust promotes the international Focolare Movement in the UK, and grantmaking is only one area of its work. It works towards a united world and its activities focus on peace and cooperation. It has a related interest in ecumenism and also in overseas development. Activities include organising conferences and courses, and publishing books and magazines.

HOW TO APPLY In writing to the correspondent.

WHO TO APPLY TO Rumold Van Geffen, Administrator, 57 Twyford Avenue, London W3 9PZ *Tel.* 020 8992 7666 *email* rumold1949@gmail.com

■ Market Harborough and The Bowdens Charity

CC NO 1041958   **ESTABLISHED** 1994

WHERE FUNDING CAN BE GIVEN The parishes of Market Harborough, Great Bowden and Little Bowden.

WHO CAN BENEFIT Organisations and individuals.

WHAT IS FUNDED The trust supports a wide range of large and small projects, giving towards supporting the community, the improvement of the environment, the arts, healthcare, heritage and relief-in-need.

WHAT IS NOT FUNDED No grants towards sporting projects or to replace statutory funding.

RANGE OF GRANTS Up to £105,000

SAMPLE GRANTS Church of St Peter and St Paul, Great Bowden (£105,000); Harborough Christian Counselling Service (£43,500); Harborough Town F.C. (£37,500); Harborough Youth And Community Trust (£15,000); Market Harborough Family of Schools and Harborough FM (£10,000 each); Shopmobility Market Harborough (£8,000); Little Bowden Primary School and Market Harborough Squash and Racketball Club (£5,000 each); Market Harborough Hockey Club (£1,500) and HomeStart South Leicestershire (£1,000).

FINANCES *Year* 2012 *Income* £628,987 *Grants* £411,415 *Assets* £15,843,558

TRUSTEES Ian Wells; Tim Banks; Dr Julie Jones; David Battersby; John Clare; Janice Hefford; Janet Roberts; George Stamp; Mark Stamp; Adrian Trotter; Alan Walker; Joan Williams; Lennie Rhodes; Paul Beardsmore; Guy Hartopp.

OTHER INFORMATION The grant total includes £93,000 that was given to 80 individuals.

HOW TO APPLY On a form available, together with criteria and guidelines, from the website. Potential applicants are welcome to contact the correspondent directly for further guidance.

WHO TO APPLY TO J. G. Jacobs, Steward, c/o Godfrey Payton and Co, 149 St Mary's Road, Market Harborough, Leicestershire LE16 7DZ *Tel.* 01858 462467 *Fax* 01858 431898 *email* admin@mhbcharity.co.uk *Website* www.mhbcharity.co.uk

■ The Michael Marks Charitable Trust

CC NO 248136   **ESTABLISHED** 1966

WHERE FUNDING CAN BE GIVEN UK and overseas.

WHO CAN BENEFIT Registered charities.

WHAT IS FUNDED Conservation, environment and culture.

WHAT IS NOT FUNDED Grants are given to registered charities only. No grants to individuals or profit organisations.

RANGE OF GRANTS Generally £500–£25,000.

SAMPLE GRANTS British Library (£19,000); The Burlington Magazine (£15,000); The Bach Choir, Suffolk Wildlife Trust and Woodland Trust (£10,000 each); Canterbury Cathedral (£9,000); St Pancras Community Trust (£7,700); London Zoological Society (£6,000); Oxford Philomusica Trust (£5,000); National Library of Scotland (£4,300); Benaki Museum and Harvard Centre of Hellenic Studies (£3,000); Campaign for the Protection of Rural England (£2,000) and Greek Archaeological Committee (UK) (£500).

FINANCES *Year* 2011–12 *Income* £178,110 *Grants* £133,466 *Assets* £5,827,701

TRUSTEES Marina, Lady Marks; Prof. Sir Christopher White; Noel Annesley.

HOW TO APPLY In writing to the correspondent. Applications should include audited accounts, information on other bodies approached and details of funding obtained. The trustees meet twice a year, usually in January and July, to consider applications. Requests will not receive a response unless they have been successful.

WHO TO APPLY TO Lady Marina Marks, 5 Elm Tree Road, London NW8 9JY *Tel.* 020 7286 4633

■ The Marks Family Foundation

CC NO 1137014   **ESTABLISHED** 2010

WHERE FUNDING CAN BE GIVEN UK.

WHO CAN BENEFIT Organisation working with children and young people and older people.

WHAT IS FUNDED General charitable purposes, with a preference for health, arts and culture.

TYPE OF GRANT Usually one-off, unrestricted grants.

RANGE OF GRANTS £250–£20,000

SAMPLE GRANTS West London Synagogue (£20,000); Jewish Care (£12,500); Weizmann Institute (£10,650); Royal National Theatre (£10,000); Orchestra of the Age of Enlightenment (£2,000); Exeter College, Oxford (£1,000); The Lymphoma Association (£500); The Eve Appeal (£300) and Jewish Child's Day and Tel Aviv University Trust (£250 each).

FINANCES *Year* 2011–12 *Income* £116,183 *Grants* £58,350 *Assets* £142,544

TRUSTEES David Marks; Selina Marks; James Marks; Dr Daniel Marks.

OTHER INFORMATION The settlor of the foundation, David Marks, is a partner in Apax Partners LLP private equity investment group and also a trustee of the Apax Foundation and the R and S Cohen Foundation.

HOW TO APPLY The trust has stated that it will not reply to unsolicited applications.

WHO TO APPLY TO David Marks, Trustee, 1 Ambassador Place, Stockport Road, Altrincham, Cheshire WA15 8DB

■ The Ann and David Marks Foundation

CC NO 326303   **ESTABLISHED** 1983

WHERE FUNDING CAN BE GIVEN Worldwide.

WHO CAN BENEFIT Jewish charities.

WHAT IS FUNDED To promote and support health, education and welfare of communities; humanitarian aid.

TYPE OF GRANT One-off and up to three years.

RANGE OF GRANTS Average grant less than £1,000.

SAMPLE GRANTS Finchley Jewish Primary Trust – Morasha (£20,000).

FINANCES *Year* 2012 *Income* £28,853 *Grants* £44,476 *Assets* £574,181

TRUSTEES A. Marks; A. Marks; G. Marks; David Marks; Marcelle Palmer.

HOW TO APPLY Previous research suggested that the trust's funds are mostly committed and unsolicited applications are not welcome.

WHO TO APPLY TO David Marks, Trustee, 1 Ambassador Place, Stockport Road, Altrincham, Cheshire WA15 8DB *Tel.* 01619 413183 *email* davidmarks@mutleyproperties. co.uk

---

■ The Hilda and Samuel Marks Foundation

CC NO 245208   **ESTABLISHED** 1965

WHERE FUNDING CAN BE GIVEN UK and Israel.

WHO CAN BENEFIT Charitable organisations.

WHAT IS FUNDED General charitable purposes; the relief and assistance of poor and needy persons; education; community facilities and services; health.

WHAT IS NOT FUNDED No grants to individuals.

TYPE OF GRANT Buildings and other capital; core costs; project; start-up costs.

FINANCES *Year* 2011–12 *Income* £110,609 *Grants* £178,489 *Assets* £3,134,613

TRUSTEES David Marks; Samuel Marks; Hilda Marks; Rochelle Selby.

HOW TO APPLY The trust primarily supports projects known to the trustees and its funds are fully committed. Therefore unsolicited applications are not being sought.

WHO TO APPLY TO David Marks, Trustee, 1 Ambassador Place, Stockport Road, Altrincham, Cheshire WA15 8DB *Tel.* 01619 413183 *email* davidmarks@mutleyproperties. co.uk

---

■ J. P. Marland Charitable Trust

CC NO 1049350   **ESTABLISHED** 1995

WHERE FUNDING CAN BE GIVEN UK.

WHO CAN BENEFIT Registered charities.

WHAT IS FUNDED General charitable purposes.

RANGE OF GRANTS Up to £16,000.

SAMPLE GRANTS Natural History Museum (£16,000); Guggenheim UK Charitable Trust (£5,500); The Sports Nexus (£5,000); Hospitaller Ltd (£2,000); and Tickets for Troops (£3,000).

FINANCES *Year* 2011–12 *Income* £386,312 *Grants* £75,000

TRUSTEES Lord Jonathan Marland; Lady Penelope Marland; Carol Law; Marcus Marland; Hugo Marland.

HOW TO APPLY In writing to the correspondent.

WHO TO APPLY TO Lord Jonathan Marland, Trustee, Odstock Manor, Odstock, Salisbury SP5 4JA *Tel.* 01722 329781 *email* jmarland@jltgroup. com

---

■ Marmot Charitable Trust

CC NO 1106619   **ESTABLISHED** 2004

WHERE FUNDING CAN BE GIVEN Worldwide.

WHO CAN BENEFIT General charitable purposes, 'green' organisations, conflict resolution.

WHAT IS FUNDED Environment, sustainability, nuclear disarmament and non-proliferation.

RANGE OF GRANTS £1,200–£15,000

SAMPLE GRANTS Unit for Research into Changing Institutions (£15,000); Organic Research Centre (£7,000); Centre for Alternative Technology – Zero Carbon Britain Appeal (£5,000); Earth Resources Research – Nuclear Research for

Parliamentarians and War on Want – Stamp Out Poverty (£4,000 each); Margaret Hayman Charitable Trust and Missionary Society of St Columban (£2,000 each); Christian Peace Education Fund and Quaker Service Memorial Trust (£500 each).

FINANCES *Year* 2011–12 *Income* £102,319 *Grants* £77,300 *Assets* £2,803,679

TRUSTEES Bevis Gillett; Jonathan Gillett; Jeanni Barlow.

HOW TO APPLY The trust has informed us directly that they do not accept unsolicited applications.

WHO TO APPLY TO Bevis Gillett, Trustee, c/o BM Marmot, London WC1N 3XX

■ The Marr-Munning Trust

CC NO 261786   **ESTABLISHED** 1970

WHERE FUNDING CAN BE GIVEN Indian Subcontinent, South-East Asia and Sub-Saharan Africa.

WHO CAN BENEFIT Organisations benefiting refugees, people disadvantaged by poverty, and victims of famine, war and man-made or natural disasters.

WHAT IS FUNDED Overseas aid projects, particularly those likely to improve economic and educational work.

WHAT IS NOT FUNDED No grants to individuals or for work taking place outside the defined beneficial area (Indian Subcontinent, South-East Asia and Sub-Saharan Africa). No retrospective funding.

TYPE OF GRANT Recurrent and one-off.

RANGE OF GRANTS Up to £23,000.

SAMPLE GRANTS Marr-Munning Ashram (£23,000); Gram Niyojan Kendra (£18,000); Friends of Ibba Girls' School (£15,000); Woodford Foundation (£10,000); The Joe Homan Charity (£8,800); Kasilsi Porridge Project (£6,000); Children in Crisis (£4,000); World Wide Cancer (£3,000); Seeds for Africa (£2,000) and Ebenezer Woman Welfare Sangam (£1,900).

FINANCES *Year* 2011–12 *Income* £651,113 *Grants* £316,265 *Assets* £12,376,945

TRUSTEES Glen Barnham; Marianne Elliott; Guy Perfect; Pierre Thomas; Martin Sarbicki; Dr Geetha Oommen.

HOW TO APPLY The trust has an application form available on its website. Completed forms should be emailed to the trust. The trust no longer accepts applications not made on their application form. Applicants must submit the following supporting documentation: a copy of the organisation's most recent audited accounts, a copy of the governing document and if an NGO or charitable organisation based outside the UK, a copy of your registration certificate.

Applicants may also, if they wish, supply further information which they think may help the trustees make their decision, for example, a recent annual report, business plan, project plan, newsletter or newspaper report about your project. If you supply an email address the trust will acknowledge receipt of your application and the outcome. Do not send CDs or memory sticks. Applications are typically reviewed twice yearly and precise dates will be published on the trust's website. No feedback for unsuccessful applicants. More detailed application guidelines, including common reasons why applications are unsuccessful, are available from the website.

WHO TO APPLY TO James Fitzpatrick, Executive Director, 9 Madeley Road, Ealing, London W5 2LA *Tel.* 020 8998 7747 *Fax* 020 8998 9593 *email* info@marrmunningtrust.org.uk *Website* www.marrmunningtrust.org.uk

■ The Michael Marsh Charitable Trust

cc no 220473   established 1958
WHERE FUNDING CAN BE GIVEN Birmingham, Staffordshire, Worcestershire, Warwickshire, Coventry, Wolverhampton and associated towns in the Black Country.
WHO CAN BENEFIT Organisations benefiting children and young people, people who are elderly, at risk groups and people who are disabled, disadvantaged by poverty or socially isolated.
WHAT IS FUNDED Health and welfare charities, community-based organisations, education and training and religious activities.
WHAT IS NOT FUNDED No grants towards animals or entertainment charities. Grants to individuals are only given through charitable institutions on their behalf.
TYPE OF GRANT Generally recurrent
RANGE OF GRANTS Usually £250–£10,000.
SAMPLE GRANTS Marie Curie Cancer Care (£25,000); University of Birmingham (£10,800); St Basils (£7,000); Girlguiding Birmingham and Sunfields Children's Homes (£5,000 each); Enterprise Education Trust (£3,000); Happy Days Children's Charity (£2,000); Parks for Play (£1,500); Home from Hospital Care (£1,000); Midland Actors Theatre (£500) and Troop Aid (£250).
FINANCES Year 2011–12 Income £190,583 Grants £142,424 Assets £3,436,737
TRUSTEES Peter Barber; Susan Bennett; Lee Nuttall
HOW TO APPLY In writing to the correspondent. Trustees meet in June and December, considering all applications received in the preceding six months. However, they will consider on an ad-hoc basis any applications that they consider should not be retained until their next scheduled meeting.
WHO TO APPLY TO Clerk to the Trust, c/o Mills and Reeve, 78–84 Colmore Row, Birmingham B3 2AB Tel. 0870 600 0011 Fax 01214 568483 email marsh.charity@mills-reeve.com

■ The Marsh Christian Trust

cc no 284470   established 1981
WHERE FUNDING CAN BE GIVEN UK.
WHO CAN BENEFIT Registered charities only.
WHAT IS FUNDED General charitable purposes, with a preference towards social welfare; environmental causes; health; education; arts; animal welfare; and overseas appeals.
WHAT IS NOT FUNDED The trust's website states that: 'no grants are made to individuals or towards individual sponsorship proposals; no funding is provided for building work or individual restoration projects; no funding is provided to individual churches, as the Trustees consider it is the responsibility of congregations and the church to maintain these; and no funding is provided for individual hospices or hospitals, as the Trustees consider it is the responsibility of the local and national community to maintain these.'
TYPE OF GRANT Core funding, up to three years.
RANGE OF GRANTS Generally £250–£4,000, with responses to new applications being at the lower end of this scale.
SAMPLE GRANTS English Speaking Union of the Commonwealth (£6,500); Butterfly Conservation (£2,500); Refugee Council (£2,000); Bible Reading Fellowship and Ataxia UK (£1,000 each); Born Free Foundation and Seven Stories (£800 each); Clean Rivers Trust and the Fircroft Trust (£700 each); Barnabas, Barnardo's,

Church Mission Society and Children's Country Holidays Fund (£500 each); Disability Challengers and Mother's Union (£400 each); the Holly Lodge Centre and the Queen Alexandra Hospital Home (£300 each); Amnesty International, Housing Justice and Marie Curie Cancer Care (£250 each); Zoological Society of London (£100); English Heritage (£80); National Army Museum (£50); and NADFAS (£10).
FINANCES Year 2011–12 Income £618,988 Grants £213,182 Assets £6,971,475
TRUSTEES Brian Marsh; Natalie Marsh; L. Ryan; Antonia Marsh; Camilla Kenyon; Charles Micklewright.
HOW TO APPLY In writing to the correspondent. Applications should be one or two sides of A4 plus a copy of the most recent set of accounts. Applications can be made at any point throughout the year.
WHO TO APPLY TO Brian Marsh, Trustee, 36 Broadway, London SW1H 0BH Tel. 020 7233 3112 Website www.marshchristiantrust.org

■ The Charlotte Marshall Charitable Trust

cc no 211941   established 1962
WHERE FUNDING CAN BE GIVEN UK.
WHO CAN BENEFIT Registered charities, institutions benefiting Roman Catholics, children, young adults and students.
WHAT IS FUNDED Educational and religious objects for Roman Catholics.
WHAT IS NOT FUNDED No grants are given to individuals.
RANGE OF GRANTS £300–£8,000.
SAMPLE GRANTS Sacred Heart Primary School (£5,000); Society of St Vincent de Paul (£3,500); Catholic Trust for England and Wales and Kent Association for the Blind (£2,000 each); African Swahili Community Project in the UK and The Clock Tower Sanctuary (£1,500 each); 4Sight, Demelza House Children's Hospice, Pett Level Rescue Boat Association and St John Ambulance Sussex (£1,000 each): and Pestalozzi and St Wilfrid's Hospice (£500 each).
FINANCES Year 2011–12 Income £76,857 Grants £75,306 Assets £520,475
TRUSTEES Elizabeth Cosgrave; Joseph Cosgrave; Kevin Page; John Russell; Rachel Cosgrave.
HOW TO APPLY On a form available from the correspondent. Completed forms must be returned by 31 December for consideration in March.
WHO TO APPLY TO The Trustees, Sidney Little Road, Churchfields Industrial Estate, St Leonards on Sea, East Sussex TN38 9PU Tel. 01424 856655

■ The Jim Marshall Charitable Trust

cc no 328118   established 1989
WHERE FUNDING CAN BE GIVEN Milton Keynes.
WHO CAN BENEFIT Charitable organisations.
WHAT IS FUNDED General charitable purposes, mainly for the benefit of children, young people, families and people who are disabled or sick.
TYPE OF GRANT Up to three years.
RANGE OF GRANTS £1,000–£25,000
SAMPLE GRANTS MK Lions Basketball Club (£10,000); Willen Hospice (£5,000); and Action

4 Youth and MK Victors Boxing Club (£3,000 each).

FINANCES *Year* 2012 *Income* £3,012,525 *Grants* £30,510 *Assets* £3,059,148

TRUSTEES Jonathon Ellery; Kenneth Saunders; Richard Willis; David Cole.

OTHER INFORMATION A total of £4,500 was made in grants of £1,000 or less.

HOW TO APPLY In writing to the correspondent at any time.

Applications will only be considered for those charitable organisations benefiting communities in and around Milton Keynes.

WHO TO APPLY TO The Trustees, Simpson Wreford and Co, Wellesley House, Duke of Wellington Avenue, London SE18 6SS *Tel.* 020 8317 6460

■ The Nora Joan Marshall Charitable Trust

CC NO 220478   **ESTABLISHED** 1964

WHERE FUNDING CAN BE GIVEN Worldwide, with a preference for the UK.

WHO CAN BENEFIT Mainly Christian organisations.

WHAT IS FUNDED The promotion of the Christian faith.

WHAT IS NOT FUNDED Predominantly Christian organisations.

SAMPLE GRANTS Grace Community Church of Worthing (£5,500); Acorn Pregnancy Counselling Centre (£2,400); Caring for Life, Elam and Arab World Ministries (£1,200 each); Biblelands (£1,100); Africa Inland Mission and Through the Roof (£700 each); and Barnabas Fund, Worthing Churches Homeless Project and CMJ (£300 each).

FINANCES *Year* 2012–13 *Income* £27,123 *Grants* £32,770 *Assets* £384,196

TRUSTEES Richard Marshall; Wendy Marshall.

OTHER INFORMATION 24 grants were made during the year totalling £33,000. The same beneficiaries were funded in 2012–13 as in 2011–12.

HOW TO APPLY In writing to the correspondent.

WHO TO APPLY TO Richard Marshall, Trustee, 30 Manor Road, Worthing BN11 4RU

■ The D. G. Marshall of Cambridge Trust

CC NO 286468   **ESTABLISHED** 1982

WHERE FUNDING CAN BE GIVEN UK with a preference for Cambridgeshire.

WHO CAN BENEFIT Community projects, local appeals and local charities benefiting disabled people and people disadvantaged by poverty.

WHAT IS FUNDED Charitable causes in and around Cambridge.

SAMPLE GRANTS Cambridge Community Foundation (£100,000); Royal Aeronautical Society and University of Cambridge (Institute of Marketing) (£50,000 each); Children's Hospices UK (£1,200); Alzheimer's Research UK, Blue Smile, CamRead, Cancer Research UK, Help For Heroes, Newmarket Open Door, Peru's Challenge and Ten For Ten (£500 each); Barnardo's and Heydon District Church Council (£250 each).

FINANCES *Year* 2011–12 *Income* £117,051 *Grants* £219,250 *Assets* £1,790,179

TRUSTEES M. J. Marshall; J. D. Barker; W. C. M. Dastur; R. Marshall.

HOW TO APPLY The charity will consider all applications, providing they are consistent with the objectives of the charity.

WHO TO APPLY TO Sarah Moynihan, Control Building, The Airport, Newmarket Road, Cambridgeshire CB5 8RY *Tel.* 01223 373273

■ Marshall's Charity

CC NO 206780   **ESTABLISHED** 1627

WHERE FUNDING CAN BE GIVEN England and Wales with preference for Kent, Surrey, Lincolnshire and Southwark.

WHAT IS NOT FUNDED No grants to churches outside the counties of Kent, Surrey and Lincolnshire, as defined in 1855. No church funding for the following: cost of church halls and meeting rooms; kitchens; decorations – unless they form part of qualifying repair or improvement work; furniture and fittings; work to bells, brasses or clocks; private chapels or monuments; stained glass – although work to repair ferraments can be supported; grounds, boundary walls and fences; external lighting.

TYPE OF GRANT Building and other capital works; loans.

RANGE OF GRANTS Up to £20,000. Grants to churches usually £3,000 to £5,000. Grants to parsonages usually up to £4,000.

SAMPLE GRANTS Boughton under Blean – SS Peter and Paul; Canterbury Cathedral; Holmwood – St Mary Magdalene; Loose – All Saints; Spalding – St Paul; Sutton – Christ Church; Utterby – St Andrew and Welton – St Mary (£5,000 each); Hernhill – St Michael (£4,000); Mereworth – St Lawrence (£2,000) and Goodnestone – Holy Cross (£1,000).

FINANCES *Year* 2012 *Income* £1,165,820 *Grants* £712,534 *Assets* £16,036,796

TRUSTEES Anthea Nicholson, Chair; Colin Bird; David Lang; Michael Dudding; Colin Stenning; Stephen Clark; Gina Isaac; Bill Eason; Jeremy Hammant; John Heawood; Surbhi Malhotra; Revd Jonathan Rust; Ven. Christine Hardman; Tony Guthrie; Lesley Bosman.

HOW TO APPLY Applicants should write a letter or send an e-mail to the correspondent, giving the name and location of the Church and a brief (30 – 40 words maximum) description of the proposed work. If appropriate the charity will then send out an application form which should be completed and returned within three months. Applicants will also be visited by the surveyor who will submit a report which will be submitted to the committee along with the completed application form. Applications for parsonage grants should be made by the relevant Diocesan Parsonage Board. Trustees usually meet in January, April, July and October.

WHO TO APPLY TO Catherine Dawkins, Clerk to the Trustees, Marshall House, 66 Newcomen Street, London SE1 1YT *Tel.* 020 7407 2979 *Fax* 020 7403 3969 *email* grantoffice@ marshalls.org.uk *Website* www.marshalls.org.uk

---

■ Marshgate Charitable Settlement

CC NO 1081645   **ESTABLISHED** 2000

WHERE FUNDING CAN BE GIVEN England and Wales.

WHO CAN BENEFIT Christian, educational and medical charities.

WHAT IS FUNDED There is an interest in work with children.

RANGE OF GRANTS £500–£38,000, usually £1,000.

SAMPLE GRANTS The Godolphin and Latymer School (£1,000); Tearfund (£2,000); Inter Health (£2,000); CARE (£8,500); Cystic Fibrosis Trust

(£1,000): Chaplaincy Plus (£1,000); The Cans Trust (£2,000); Karis Kids £2,000); Oxfordshire VCH Trust (£200); Stewardship (£2,000); Watson (£200); Wings Like Eagles (£10,000); The Ffald-y-Brenin Trust (£500) and Highmoor Spring Charitable Trust (£38,000).

FINANCES *Year* 2011–12 *Income* £103,039 *Grants* £72,000 *Assets* £63,917

TRUSTEES C. S. H. Hampton; M. J. Hampton; R. Hambler.

HOW TO APPLY In writing to the correspondent.

WHO TO APPLY TO Clifford Hampton, Trustee, Highmoor Hall, Henley-on-Thames, Oxfordshire RG9 5DH *Tel.* 01491 641543

....

■ Sir George Martin Trust

CC NO 223554   **ESTABLISHED** 1956

WHERE FUNDING CAN BE GIVEN West and North Yorkshire.

WHO CAN BENEFIT Registered charities; churches; schools; universities; hospices.

WHAT IS FUNDED Countryside, environment, green issues; children; church appeals; hospices; music and arts; museums; old age; schools, education, universities; social welfare.

WHAT IS NOT FUNDED restoration schemes of church roofs, spires, etc.; applications from overseas; individuals in the area of music and arts; playgroups; any area of education where there is state funding; applications in the old Yorkshire coalfield; university or college appeals, nor appeals from individuals seeking grants for university fees, postgraduate courses, or other courses; overseas seminars or exchange visits by individuals or groups; medical appeals of a capital or revenue nature; medical research projects.

TYPE OF GRANT Grants for capital rather than revenue projects.

RANGE OF GRANTS Usually £100–£3,000 with some larger grants.

SAMPLE GRANTS Forget Me Not Trust; Harrogate International Festival; Marrick Priory and Square Chapel Centre for the Arts. Smaller grants were awarded to: St Jemma's Hospice (£3,000); St Michael's Just 'B' (£2,000); Leeds Women's Aid and Northern Ballet (£1,500 each); and Older Wiser Local Seniors (£500).

FINANCES *Year* 2011–12 *Income* £153,159 *Grants* £179,269 *Assets* £6,348,956

TRUSTEES David Coates, Chair; Martin Bethel; Roger Marshall; Paul Taylor; Marjorie Martin.

OTHER INFORMATION We have no information regarding the larger amounts given.

HOW TO APPLY The following information is taken from the trust's helpful website: 'Email info@sirgeorgemartintrust.org.uk or telephone 01423 810 222 and we will send you our brief application form. This needs to be posted back to us along with a statement of no more than two pages outlining your proposal. Where possible include with your application a copy of your latest Annual Report and Accounts, the specific amount you are looking for from the Sir George Martin Trust and details of any support you have had so far towards your project. The trust prefers to make grants available for capital rather than revenue projects, and is reluctant to give to general running costs, or areas previously supported by state funds. The trust does not normally repeat grants to any charity in any one year, and the maximum number of consecutive grants. The trustees meet in March, July and November of each year, to consider applications. If an application meets the trust's initial criteria, our Secretary will be in touch to arrange a visit to the project prior to the next trustees meeting taking place. Each application will then be reviewed by our five trustees and successful applications will be told following the meeting. Unsuccessful applicants will not be informed because of increased cost of postage. Don't hesitate to contact our Secretary/ Administrator Carla Marshall if you have any questions.'

WHO TO APPLY TO Carla Marshall, Secretary/ Administrator, 6 Firs Avenue, Harrogate, North Yorkshire HG2 9HA *Tel.* 01423 810222 *email* info@sirgeorgemartintrust.org.uk *Website* www.sirgeorgemartintrust.org.uk

....

■ John Martin's Charity

CC NO 527473   **ESTABLISHED** 1714

WHERE FUNDING CAN BE GIVEN Evesham and 'certain surrounding villages' only.

WHO CAN BENEFIT Individuals and charitable or voluntary organisations and schools benefiting the residents of Evesham.

WHAT IS FUNDED Christian activities; social welfare; education; promotion of health.

WHAT IS NOT FUNDED No grants for the payment of rates or taxes, or otherwise to replace statutory benefits.

TYPE OF GRANT One-off capital and project costs.

RANGE OF GRANTS £200–£29,000.

SAMPLE GRANTS St Andrews Parochial Church Council Hampton (£31,000); Heart of England Mencap and St Richard's Hospice (£20,000 each); St Peter's Parochial Church Council Bengeworth and All Saints Parochial Church Council Evesham (£19,000 each); South Worcestershire Citizens Advice (£12,000); Evesham and District Mental Health (£10,000); Evesham Shop Mobility (£6,500); Acquired Aphasia Trust (£5,000); Evesham Methodist Church (£3,000); Life Education Centre (£1,500); and Youth Music Festival (£500).

FINANCES *Year* 2012–13 *Income* £748,942 *Grants* £638,351 *Assets* £20,475,267

TRUSTEES Nigel Lamb; John Smith; Richard Emson; Cyril Scorse; Revd Andrew Spurr; Diana Raphael; Josephine Sandalls; Joyce Turner; Julie Westlake; John Wilson; Revd Mark Binney; Catherine Evans; Gabrielle Falkiner.

OTHER INFORMATION A total of £428,000 was granted to individuals.

HOW TO APPLY Grant applications are considered from organisations in, or supporting, the town of Evesham where the requested support is considered to fit within the governing schemes of the charity. Details of the application procedure for individuals are also contained on the trust's website. There is no limit on the amount of grants that an organisation can apply for but trustees cannot commit to renewals. Requests are considered for both capital items and general expenditure, including project costs. Organisations which show self-help or those which give valid reasons why alternative sources of finance are not available will be given preference. Forms are available from the correspondent or via the 'downloads' page at: www.johnmartins.org.uk/downloads. Applicants are asked to provide the following with their application: the latest set of annual accounts; latest bank statement showing the current balance and name of the organisation; any relevant literature about the organisation e.g. a leaflet or flyer. The annual closing dates for applications are as follows: 1 June, 1 September, 20 November and 1 March.

WHO TO APPLY TO John Daniels, Clerk, 16 Queen's Road, Evesham, Worcestershire WR11 4JN *Tel.* 01386 765440 *email* enquiries@johnmartins.org.uk *Website* www.johnmartins.org.uk

■ The John Mason Family Trust

CC NO 1136856   **ESTABLISHED** 2010
WHERE FUNDING CAN BE GIVEN North West England, with a preference for the diocese of Chester; overseas.
WHO CAN BENEFIT Registered charities.
WHAT IS FUNDED Education, social welfare, religious activities and overseas aid.
WHAT IS NOT FUNDED No grants to individuals.
RANGE OF GRANTS Up to £4,000.
SAMPLE GRANTS Church Urban Fund (£4,000); Alzheimer's Society (£3,000); Power International, The Oesophageal Patients Association and The Hope Centre (£2,500 each); The Christie Hospital Charitable Fund, The Fatima Women's Association and Pancreatic Cancer Action (£2,0–00 each); Next Generation and The Olive Branch (£1,000 each); Frontline Trust (£500) and Hope UK (£385).
FINANCES *Year* 2011–12 *Income* £33,756 *Grants* £30,504 *Assets* £647,906
TRUSTEES Dr John Mason; Joan Mason; Rick Gates.
OTHER INFORMATION In 2011–12 grants were given to 16 organisations.
HOW TO APPLY In writing to the correspondent.
WHO TO APPLY TO The Trustees, Aaron and Partners LLP, 5–7 Grosvenor Court, Foregate Street, Chester CH1 1HG *Tel.* 01244 405555 *email* jmfamilytrust@gmail.com

■ The Mason Porter Charitable Trust

CC NO 255545   **ESTABLISHED** 1968
WHERE FUNDING CAN BE GIVEN UK.
WHO CAN BENEFIT Grants are made only to charities known to the settlor.
WHAT IS FUNDED General charitable purposes, particularly Christian causes.
RANGE OF GRANTS Up to £25,000.
SAMPLE GRANTS St Luke's Methodist Church Hoylake (£23,000); Abernethy Trust Limited (£10,500); Cliff College (£10,000); St John's Hospice in Wirral (£7,000); Proclaim Trust, ECG Trust and Just Care (£5,000 each) and Sisters of Jesus Way; One Rock International; Messengers and Crusade for World Revival (£1,000 each).
FINANCES *Year* 2011–12 *Income* £91,339 *Grants* £84,698 *Assets* £1,706,390
TRUSTEES Sue Newton, Chair; Adeyinka Olushonde; Charles Feeny; Caroline Clark; Deborah Shackelton; Andrew Lovelady; Christine Reeves; Hilary Russell; Heather Akehurst; Perminder Bal.
HOW TO APPLY The trust states that it only makes grants to charities known to the settlor and unsolicited applications are not considered.
WHO TO APPLY TO The Secretary, Liverpool Charity and Voluntary Services, 151 Dale Street, Liverpool L2 2AH *Tel.* 01512 275177

■ The Nancie Massey Charitable Trust

SC NO SC008977   **ESTABLISHED** 1989
WHERE FUNDING CAN BE GIVEN Scotland, particularly Edinburgh and Leith.
WHO CAN BENEFIT Registered charities.

WHAT IS FUNDED Young people; elderly people; education; the arts; and medical research.
WHAT IS NOT FUNDED Grants are not given to individuals.
TYPE OF GRANT Capital, core costs and salaries.
RANGE OF GRANTS £500–£2,000, but can be larger.
SAMPLE GRANTS Scottish National Portrait Gallery (£25,000); Alzheimer's Research Trust and the Queen's Hall (£15,000 each); Edinburgh and Lothian Council on Alcohol, Hearts and Minds, and the Marie Curie Build Appeal (£5,000 each); and Children 1st; SSAFA Forces Help; Greenbank Parish Church; Marie Curie Memorial Foundation; and St Columba's Hospital.
FINANCES *Year* 2011–12 *Income* £249,947 *Grants* £300,000
TRUSTEES Gavin Morton; M. F. Sinclair; E. Wilson.
HOW TO APPLY Write to the correspondent requesting an application form. Trustees meet three times a year in February, June and October. Applications need to be received by January, May or September.
WHO TO APPLY TO Gavin Morton, Trustee, c/o Chiene and Tait, Cairn House, 61 Dublin Street, Edinburgh EH3 6NL *Tel.* 01315 585800 *Fax* 01315 585899

■ The Mathew Trust

SC NO SC016284   **ESTABLISHED** 1935
WHERE FUNDING CAN BE GIVEN City of Dundee, Angus, Perth and Kinross and Fife
WHO CAN BENEFIT Registered charities, schools, universities, social enterprises and individuals.
WHAT IS FUNDED The advancement of education of adults; advancement of vocational and professional training; relief of poverty by providing assistance in the recruitment of people who are unemployed, or who are likely to become unemployed in the near future.
TYPE OF GRANT Capital costs and salaries
FINANCES *Year* 2011–12 *Income* £224,188 *Grants* £250,000
TRUSTEES D. B. Grant, Chair; G. S. Lowden; A. F. McDonald; Prof. P. Howie; The Lord Provost of the City of Dundee.
OTHER INFORMATION In 2011–12 the trust had a total expenditure of £285,000.
HOW TO APPLY In writing to the correspondent.
WHO TO APPLY TO Fiona Bullions, c/o Henderson Loggie, Chartered Accountants, Royal Exchange, Panmure Street, Dundee DD1 1DZ *Tel.* 01382 201234

■ Matliwala Family Charitable Trust

CC NO 1012756   **ESTABLISHED** 1992
WHERE FUNDING CAN BE GIVEN UK and overseas, especially Bharuch – India.
WHO CAN BENEFIT Charitable organisations.
WHAT IS FUNDED The advancement of education for pupils at Matliwala School of Baruch in Gujarat – India, including assisting with the provision of equipment and facilities; advancement of the Islamic religion; relief of sickness and poverty; advancement of education.
FINANCES *Year* 2012–13 *Income* £426,000 *Grants* £215,650 *Assets* £4,370,977
TRUSTEES Ayub Bux; Yousuf Bux; Abdul Patel; Usman Salya; Fatima Ismail.
HOW TO APPLY In writing to the correspondent.
WHO TO APPLY TO Ayub Bux, Trustee, 9 Brookview, Fulwood, Preston PR2 8FG *Tel.* 01772 706501

■ The Matt 6.3 Charitable Trust

cc no 1069985   established 1998
where funding can be given UK.
who can benefit Christian organisations.
what is funded Christian causes.
type of grant One-off. Core costs and start-up costs.
sample grants Christian Centre (Humberside) Limited (£65,000).
finances *Year* 2012–13 *Income* £344,655 *Grants* £67,525 *Assets* £4,328,053
trustees Doris Dibdin; Christine Barnett.
other information Includes £2,400 to individuals.
how to apply The trustees' report states the following: 'due to the fact that the charity's income is largely unpredictable, the trustees have adopted a policy of maximising the reserves in order to provide ongoing funding in future years for the organisations they wish to support.'
who to apply to Ian Harding Davey, Secretary, Progress House, Progress Park, Cupola Way, Off Normanby Road, Scunthorpe DN15 9YJ *Tel.* 01724 863666

■ The Violet Mauray Charitable Trust

cc no 1001716   established 1990
where funding can be given UK.
who can benefit Registered charities.
what is funded General charitable purposes, particularly medical charities and Jewish organisations.
what is not funded No grants to individuals.
type of grant One-off.
range of grants Usually £750–£5,000
sample grants Wikimedia UK (£5,000); Action on Hearing Loss, Aquabox and Straight Talking (£3,000 each); Merlin, Jewish Marriage Council and Jewish Deaf Association (£2,000 each); Bletchley Park Trust and British Institute for Brain-Injured Children (£1,000 each); and British Shalom-Salaam Trust (£750).
finances *Year* 2012–13 *Income* £51,562 *Grants* £48,000 *Assets* £2,016,378
trustees Robert Stephany; John Stephany; Alison Karlin.
other information Grants totalled £48,000 and were made to 28 organisations.
how to apply In writing to the correspondent. Grants are made on an ad hoc basis. Grants are made to assist the funding of projects of other charities.
who to apply to John Stephany, Trustee, 9 Bentinck Street, London W1U 2EL *Tel.* 020 7935 0982

■ The Maxwell Family Foundation

cc no 291124   established 1965
where funding can be given UK.
who can benefit Registered charities in the fields of health, medical research, and the relief of people who are elderly, are sick or who have disabilities.
what is not funded The trust states explicitly that there is no support for unsolicited applications.
range of grants Usually £3,500 or under.
finances *Year* 2011–12 *Income* £25,290 *Assets* £372,252
trustees Eric Maxwell; Paul McLean Maxwell.
how to apply Applications are neither sought nor acknowledged. There appears little purpose in applying to this trust as no application will be supported unless accompanied by a personal request from someone known by the trustees.
who to apply to Eric Maxwell, Trustee, 181 Whiteladies Road, Bristol BS8 2RY *Tel.* 01179 626878

■ Evelyn May Trust

cc no 261038   established 1970
where funding can be given Worldwide.
who can benefit Registered charities.
what is funded Currently the main areas of interest are elderly people, children, medical projects and natural disaster relief, but support is given to a variety of registered charities.
what is not funded No grants to individuals, including students, or to general appeals or animal welfare charities.
type of grant Often one-off for a specific project, but support for general purposes is also given.
sample grants MACS (£3,800); Edward's Trust (£3,000); the Rainbow Centre for Children and Children's Heart Foundation (£2,000 each); and Independent Parental Special Education Advice (£1,000).
finances *Year* 2012 *Income* £30,012 *Grants* £24,030 *Assets* £762,603
trustees Jill McDermid; Kim Gray; Lisa Webb.
other information Grants totalling £24,000 were made to ten organisations.
how to apply In writing to the correspondent.
who to apply to Kim Gray, Trustee, 70 St George's Square, London SW1V 3RD *Tel.* 020 7821 8211

■ Mayfair Charities Ltd

cc no 255281   established 1968
where funding can be given UK and overseas.
who can benefit Registered charities benefiting Orthodox Jews, particularly children and young adults.
what is funded Education, religion and medical welfare charities which support Orthodox Judaism.
type of grant Capital and running costs.
range of grants Typically £500–£2,500, although large donations are also made.
sample grants Previous beneficiaries include: SOFT; Beth Jacob Grammar School For Girls Ltd; Merkaz Lechinuch Torani; Ohr Akiva Institute; Kollel Chibas Yerushalayim; Mesivta Letzeirim; Chevras Maoz Ladal; Congregation Ichud Chasidim; Chaye Olam Institute; United Talmudical Association; Talmud Torah Zichron Gavriel; Friends of Bobov; Regent Charities Ltd; Comet Charities Ltd; Woodstock Sinclair Trust; Yesodei Hatorah School; Beis Aharon Trust; Ezer Mikodesh Foundation; Gateshead Jewish Teachers Training College; Edgware Foundation; Heritage House; Kiryat Sanz Jerusalem; and PAL Charitable Trust.
finances *Year* 2011–12 *Income* £12,641,000 *Grants* £2,792,000 *Assets* £69,821,000
trustees Benzion S. E. Freshwater, Chair; D. Davis; Solomon I. Freshwater.
other information Grants were made to over 300 organisations. A recent list of beneficiaries was unavailable.
how to apply In writing to the correspondent.
who to apply to Jenner, Secretary, Freshwater House, 158–162 Shaftesbury Avenue, London WC2H 8HR *Tel.* 020 7836 1555

■ The Mayfield Valley Arts Trust

CC NO 327665   **ESTABLISHED** 1988

WHERE FUNDING CAN BE GIVEN Unrestricted, but with a special interest in Sheffield and South Yorkshire.

WHO CAN BENEFIT Charities supporting new and emerging artists, as well as music education.

WHAT IS FUNDED Music education; the arts.

WHAT IS NOT FUNDED The trust has stated that 'it will not be involved in the education of individual students nor will it provide grants to individual students; it will not be involved in the provision of musical instruments for individuals, schools or organisations.'

TYPE OF GRANT Up to three years for core costs.

RANGE OF GRANTS £45,000–£5,000

SAMPLE GRANTS Wigmore Hall (£45,000); York Early Music Foundation and Live Music Now (£30,000 each); Music in the Round (£18,000); Prussia Cove (£10,000); and MIR Piano Donation (£5,000).

FINANCES *Year* 2012–13 *Income* £126,149 *Grants* £138,000 *Assets* £2,281,236

TRUSTEES David Brown; David Whelton; John Rider; Anthony Thornton; Priscilla Thornton; James Thornton.

OTHER INFORMATION Grants totalling £138,000 were made to six organisations.

HOW TO APPLY The trust states that no unsolicited applications are considered. The trust has also stated that 'it considers its financial support on a three year cycle. The next review being summer 2016. If a charity/organisation meets our criteria it should submit a summary request at that time.'

WHO TO APPLY TO James Thornton, Trustee, 12 Abbots Way, Abbotswood, Ballasalla, Isle of Man IM9 3EQ *email* jamesthornton@manx.net

■ Mazars Charitable Trust

CC NO 1150459   **ESTABLISHED** 1983

WHERE FUNDING CAN BE GIVEN UK, overseas.

WHO CAN BENEFIT Organisations with charitable purposes.

WHAT IS FUNDED Support is normally only given to projects which are nominated to the management committee by the partners and staff of Mazars (chartered accountants).

WHAT IS NOT FUNDED No grants to individuals, large national charities (rarely), applications from a particular national charity within three years of an earlier grant, or for ongoing funding. Unsolicited appeals are rarely considered.

TYPE OF GRANT Single strategic projects; one-off; research; building; and capital. Funding is for one year or less.

RANGE OF GRANTS £55–£19,000

SAMPLE GRANTS Previously: UK Youth (£25,000); Chickenshed Theatre and Parkinson's Disease Society of the United Kingdom (£15,000 each); The Johari Foundation (£12,000); Hope HIV and The Waterside Charitable Trust (£10,000 each); Emmanuel Global Network (UK) Limited, Hope for Konya and Redbridge Breast Funds (£5,000 each); and Sense and The National Deafblind and Rubella Association (£2,250 each).

FINANCES *Year* 2011–12 *Grants* £250,000

TRUSTEES Phil Verity; Alan Edwards; David Evans; Bob Neate.

OTHER INFORMATION The grants total is an estimation based on previous years.

HOW TO APPLY The trustees operate through the management committee who meet annually to consider nominations for national (major) grants. Some funds are allocated to ten regional

'pots' whose appointed representatives approve smaller grant nominations from within their own region. Nominations for national grants must be known to and be sponsored by team members of Mazars LLP and comply with stated criteria. Applicants known to team members of Mazars LLP can obtain a copy of the stated criteria upon request to the trust administrator. National and regional criteria are regularly reviewed but, in general, the trustees consider that the national grantmaking policy should avoid core funding. Most national grants are therefore made towards one-off projects covering a defined period. Successful national nominations cannot normally be repeated within three years

WHO TO APPLY TO Bryan Rogers, Trust Administrator, 1 Cranleigh Gardens, South Croydon CR2 9LD *Tel.* 020 8657 3053

■ The Robert McAlpine Foundation

CC NO 226646   **ESTABLISHED** 1963

WHERE FUNDING CAN BE GIVEN UK.

WHO CAN BENEFIT Registered charities, schools, hospices and hospitals.

WHAT IS FUNDED Children, disability, older people, medical research, welfare.

WHAT IS NOT FUNDED The trust does not like to fund overheads. No grants to individuals.

TYPE OF GRANT Capital costs and unrestricted funding, one-off and up to one year.

RANGE OF GRANTS Up to £100,000. Average grants between £10,000 and £15,000.

SAMPLE GRANTS Ewing Foundation (£100,000); Royal Marsden NHS Trust (£50,000); Prostate UK (£46,000); National Eye Research Centre (£31,000); the Towers School and 6th Form Centre (£25,000); Community Self Build Agency, Merchants Academy Withywood and Downside Fisher Youth Club (£20,000 each); Age Concern (£15,000); DENS Action Against Homelessness, St John's Youth Centre and James Hopkins Trust (£10,000 each); and Grateful Society, National Benevolent Fund for the Aged and the Golden Oldies (£5,000 each).

FINANCES *Year* 2011–12 *Income* £812,813 *Grants* £640,000 *Assets* £13,747,167

TRUSTEES Adrian McAlpine; Cullum McAlpine; The Hon David McAlpine; Kenneth McAlpine.

OTHER INFORMATION 45 grants were made to organisations totalling £640,000 in 2011–12.

HOW TO APPLY In writing to the correspondent at any time. Considered annually, normally in November.

WHO TO APPLY TO Brian Arter, Administrator, Eaton Court, Maylands Avenue, Hemel Hempstead, Hertfordshire HP2 7TR *Tel.* 01442 233444 *email* b.arter@sir-robert-mcalpine.com

■ The McDougall Trust

CC NO 212151   **ESTABLISHED** 1959

WHERE FUNDING CAN BE GIVEN UK and overseas.

WHO CAN BENEFIT Organisations or individuals carrying out charitable work including research in accord with the trust's objects.

WHAT IS FUNDED The knowledge, study and research of: political or economic science and functions of government and the services provided to the community by public and voluntary organisations; methods of election of and the selection and government of representative organisations whether national, civic, commercial, industrial or social; and representative democracy, its forms, functions and development and also its associated institutions. Special priority is given to electoral research projects.

WHAT IS NOT FUNDED No grants to any political party or commercial organisation, for an individual's education, for social welfare matters, or for general appeals, expeditions or scholarships.

TYPE OF GRANT Usually one-off for a specific project or part of a project or work programme. Applications for small 'pump-priming' grants are welcomed. Feasibility studies and research grants are also considered.

RANGE OF GRANTS Minimum grant £250.

SAMPLE GRANTS Centre for Women and Democracy; Political Studies Association and University of Exeter.

FINANCES *Year* 2011–12 *Income* £29,238 *Grants* £32,444 *Assets* £731,731

TRUSTEES Patrick Noon; Prof. Ron Johnston; Elizabeth Collingridge; Dr Ruth Farmer; David Hill; Nigel Siederer; Michael Steed.

PUBLICATIONS Representation: Journal of Representative Democracy, (quarterly).

OTHER INFORMATION The trustees have established a library called the Lakeman Library for Electoral Studies at the address below. This is available for the use of research workers and the public generally on conditions laid down by the trustees. The trustees also sponsor several prizes in conjunction with the Political Studies Association and the Politics Association.

HOW TO APPLY In writing to the correspondent, including annual accounts. Trustees normally meet six times a year. Brief details of proposal needed. Initial enquiries by telephone accepted. Two deadlines for receipt of applications: 1 May and 1 October. Applications received after a deadline may be held over for consideration at the trustees' discretion.

WHO TO APPLY TO Paul Wilder, Administrator, 6 Chancel Street, London SE1 0UX *Tel.* 020 7620 1080 *Fax* 020 7928 1528 *email* admin@mcdougall.org.uk *Website* www.mcdougall.org.uk

....

■ **The A. M. McGreevy No 5 Charitable Settlement**

CC NO 280666   **ESTABLISHED** 1979

WHERE FUNDING CAN BE GIVEN UK, with a preference for the Bristol and Bath area.

WHO CAN BENEFIT Registered charities.

WHAT IS FUNDED General charitable purposes.

WHAT IS NOT FUNDED No support for individuals.

SAMPLE GRANTS NSPCC, UCL Development Fund and Christchurch Oxford (£25,000 each).

FINANCES *Year* 2011–12 *Income* £36,000 *Grants* £75,000 *Assets* £2,171,900

TRUSTEES Avon Executor and Trustee Co. Ltd; Anthony McGreevy; Elise McGreevy-Harris; Katrina Paterson.

HOW TO APPLY In writing to the correspondent.

WHO TO APPLY TO Karen Ganson, Trust Administrator, KPMG, 100 Temple Street, Bristol BS1 6AG *Tel.* 01179 054000

....

■ **The McKenna Charitable Trust**

CC NO 1050672   **ESTABLISHED** 1995

WHERE FUNDING CAN BE GIVEN England and Wales.

WHO CAN BENEFIT Organisations and individuals.

WHAT IS FUNDED Education, health, disability, relief of poverty, the arts.

SAMPLE GRANTS Clic Sargent and Miracles (£5,000 each); and St Paul's Church (£250).

FINANCES *Year* 2011–12 *Income* £272,456 *Grants* £10,250 *Assets* £310,614

TRUSTEES Howard Jones; John Boyton; Margaret McKenna; Patrick McKenna.

OTHER INFORMATION Three grants totalling £10,250 were made to organisations in 2011–12.

HOW TO APPLY The 2011/12 trustees' report states that 'the trustees will consider applications for grants from individuals and charitable bodies on their merits but will place particular emphasis on the educational needs and the provision of support for disabled people.'

WHO TO APPLY TO John Boyton, Trustee, Ingenious Media plc, 15 Golden Square, London W1F 9JG *Tel.* 020 7319 4000

....

■ **Martin McLaren Memorial Trust**

CC NO 291609   **ESTABLISHED** 1985

WHERE FUNDING CAN BE GIVEN UK

WHO CAN BENEFIT Horticulture students.

WHAT IS FUNDED Horticultural scholarships.

RANGE OF GRANTS £50–£12,000.

SAMPLE GRANTS Ace Trust (£6,000); St John's Smith Square (£2,000); Fairbridge Garden Society and Garden Museum (£500 each); Independence at Home and St Andrews Church (£250 each); Army Benevolent Fund (£100) and Brunswick Club and West Woodhay Church (£50 each).

FINANCES *Year* 2011–12 *Income* £25,154 *Grants* £11,450 *Assets* £585,002

TRUSTEES Sir Kenneth Carlisle; William Francklin; Revd Richard McLaren; Nancy Gordon McLaren; Robert Blower; Diana McLaren.

OTHER INFORMATION The grant total in 2011–12 was considerably lower than that of 2010/11 (£137,000).

HOW TO APPLY In writing to the correspondent.

WHO TO APPLY TO The Trustees, c/o Charles Russell Solicitors, 5 Fleet Place, London EC4M 7RD *Tel.* 020 7203 5000

....

■ **The Helen Isabella McMorran Charitable Foundation**

CC NO 266338   **ESTABLISHED** 1973

WHERE FUNDING CAN BE GIVEN UK and overseas.

WHO CAN BENEFIT Registered charities benefiting children, young adults and older people; those in care, fostered and adopted; Christians, Church of England; people with disabilities; people disadvantaged by poverty; homeless and socially isolated people.

WHAT IS FUNDED Older people's welfare, Christian education, churches, the arts, residential facilities and services, social and moral welfare, special schools, cultural and religious teaching, special needs education, health, medical and religious studies, conservation, animal welfare, bird sanctuaries and heritage.

WHAT IS NOT FUNDED No grants to individuals.

TYPE OF GRANT One-off.

RANGE OF GRANTS £500–£2,000.

SAMPLE GRANTS Cambridge Preservation Society, The Samaritans, National Churches Trust, Save the Children Fund, St John Ambulance, Salvation Army, National Art Collection Fund, DIBS Charitable Trust, Edinburgh Festival Appeal, Royal Commonwealth Society for the Blind and Cambridge House (£1,625 each).

FINANCES *Year* 2011–12 *Income* £27,980 *Grants* £17,875

TRUSTEE NatWest Trust Services

HOW TO APPLY In writing to the correspondent. Brief guidelines are available. The closing date for applications is February each year.

WHO TO APPLY TO NatWest Trust Services, 5th Floor, Trinity Quay 2, Avon Street, Bristol BS2 0PT *Tel.* 05516577371

....

◼ D. D. McPhail Charitable Settlement

CC NO 267588   **ESTABLISHED** 1974
WHERE FUNDING CAN BE GIVEN UK.
WHO CAN BENEFIT Registered charities and hospices, especially those benefiting people who are elderly or disabled.
WHAT IS FUNDED Medical research and welfare.
TYPE OF GRANT Mainly recurrent.
RANGE OF GRANTS Mostly £2,000–£10,000.
SAMPLE GRANTS Pulmonary Hypertension Clinical Trials (£128,000); CHAMPS (£35,000); Dove Cottage Day Hospice and Vocal Eyes (£5,000 each); Diabetes UK, the Cure Parkinson's Trust and BLISS (£2,000 each); and RASCALS (£1,000).
FINANCES Year 2011–12 *Income* £390,052 *Grants* £200,157 *Assets* £8,469,713
TRUSTEES Julia Noble; Patricia Cruddas; Catherine Charles-Jones; Christopher Yates; Tariq Kazi; Michael Craig; Mary Meeks.
OTHER INFORMATION Grants were made to 17 organisations totalling £200,000.
HOW TO APPLY In writing to the correspondent. The charity's accounts for 2011/12 state that: 'to date, the trust has supported small and medium sized charities to make an investment and/or step change in their activities by making a relatively large grant award over a period of two to three years. Trustees identify potential projects for assessment by the executive director. The trust makes no commitment to respond to unsolicited applications. There have also been ongoing smaller grants to causes supported by the founder and trustees.'
WHO TO APPLY TO Sheila Watson, Administrator, PO Box 285, Pinner, Middlesex HA5 3FB

....

◼ The Mears Foundation

CC NO 1134941   **ESTABLISHED** 2010
WHERE FUNDING CAN BE GIVEN UK, India, Indonesia, South Africa, Romania and Sri Lanka.
WHO CAN BENEFIT Charities, voluntary bodies and individuals.
WHAT IS FUNDED Projects in the following areas: economic, community, people development and employment; education and training; overseas aid and famine relief; sport and recreation; environment, conservation and heritage. The foundation follows four 'guiding principles' in its grantmaking: 'to improve the lives of people living within our communities; to help build community cohesion and integration; to provide career and skills development opportunities to those needing them the most; to be a positive contributor to the environment'.
RANGE OF GRANTS Up to £17,000; generally average is under £1,000.
SAMPLE GRANTS The South Africa Project (£17,000); Children's Hospice South West (£5,000); Starlight and The Rainbow Centre (£1,000 each); West Coast Crash and Cerebra (£500 each); Just Different (£250) and Ro-Ro Sailing Project (£200).
FINANCES Year 2011–12 *Income* £40,868 *Grants* £27,572 *Assets* £25,190

TRUSTEES Robert Holt; Margaret Devine; Donna Ellis; Sally Dowler; Dean Webster; Judith Herbert.
OTHER INFORMATION This foundation was established as the next 'logical step' following the successful delivery of two international relief projects in India in 2008 and Sri Lanka in 2009 by Mears Group plc, the social housing and domiciliary care company.
HOW TO APPLY In writing to the correspondent.
WHO TO APPLY TO The Trustees, 1390 Montpellier Court, Gloucester Business Park, Brockworth, Gloucester GL3 4AH *Tel.* 01452 634600 *email* mearsfoundation@mearsgroup.co.uk *Website* www.themearsfoundation.org.uk

....

◼ The James Frederick and Ethel Anne Measures Charity

CC NO 266054   **ESTABLISHED** 1973
WHERE FUNDING CAN BE GIVEN West Midlands.
WHO CAN BENEFIT All categories within the West Midlands area.
WHAT IS FUNDED General charitable purposes. Applicants must usually originate in the West Midlands and show evidence of self-help in their application. Trustees have a preference for disadvantaged people.
WHAT IS NOT FUNDED Trustees will not consider funding students who have a full local authority grant and want finance for a different course of study. Applications by individuals in cases of hardship will not usually be considered unless sponsored by a local authority, health professional or other welfare agency.
TYPE OF GRANT Recurrent grants are occasionally considered. The trustees favour grants towards the cost of equipment.
RANGE OF GRANTS £100–£1,600.
SAMPLE GRANTS Farms for City Children (£7,500); Royal Wolverhampton School (£2,400); Bluecoat School (£1,500); and Sightsavers (£1,000); Birmingham and Midland Limbless Ex-Service Association, BID – Services with deaf people in the West Midlands, Stratford-upon-Avon Athletic Club and Stratford-upon-Avon Shakespeare Hospice (£500 each); All Saints Sea Scouts – Sutton Coldfield, Edwards Trust – Birmingham and Tall Ships Youth Trust – Coventry and Warwicks Branch (£400 each); Birmingham Festival Choral Society and Birmingham Settlement, (£300 each); Small Heath Play Centre, Stratford-upon-Avon Writers Circle and T S Coventry – Sea Cadets (£250 each); Birmingham Focus on Blindness (£200); and Warwick Hospital Cancer Ward (£175).
FINANCES Year 2011–12 *Income* £31,000 *Grants* £17,400 *Assets* £841,000
TRUSTEES J. P. Wagg; M. P. Green; D. A. Seccombe; R. S. Watkins.
HOW TO APPLY In writing to the correspondent. No reply is sent to unsuccessful applicants unless an sae is enclosed. The trustees meet quarterly.
WHO TO APPLY TO Laura Reid, 2nd Floor, 33 Great Charles Street, Queensway, Birmingham B3 3JN

....

◼ The Medlock Charitable Trust

CC NO 326927   **ESTABLISHED** 1985
WHERE FUNDING CAN BE GIVEN Overwhelmingly the areas of Bath and Boston in Lincolnshire.
WHO CAN BENEFIT Small local projects and established organisations benefiting children, adults and young people.

WHAT IS FUNDED General charitable purposes, especially education, medicine, research and social services for the benefit of the local community.

WHAT IS NOT FUNDED No grants to individuals or students.

TYPE OF GRANT One-off capital and revenue grants for up to two years.

RANGE OF GRANTS Mainly less than £10,000.

SAMPLE GRANTS RUH Bath (£1 million); King Edward's School (Junior) (£400,000); The Boston Stump Restoration Trust (£180,000); The Forever Friends Appeal (£50,000); Kind Edward's School, Bath (£106,000); Somerset Masonic Charity (£50,000); Bristol Rugby Community Foundation (£20,000); The Central Amenities Fund, HMS Drake (£10,000); Bath Mencap and Avon Wildlife Trust (£5,000 each); Housing, Training and Support Ltd and Furniture Re-Use Network (£1,000 each) and Daylight Plus Club (£500).

FINANCES *Year* 2011–12 *Income* £832,416 *Grants* £2,629,261 *Assets* £26,529,813

TRUSTEES Leonard Medlock; Jacqueline Medlock; David Medlock; Mark Goodman

HOW TO APPLY In writing to the correspondent. 'The trustees have identified the City of Bath and the borough of Boston as the principal but not exclusive areas in which the charity is and will be proactive. These areas have been specifically chosen as the founder of the charity has strong connections with the City of Bath, the home of the charity, and has family connections of long standing with the borough of Boston. To date the charity has supported and funded a number of projects in these areas by making substantial grants. These grants have been made to fund projects in the areas of education, medicine, research and social services all for the benefit of the local community. During the year, the trustees also receive many applications for assistance from many diverse areas in the United Kingdom. These are all considered sympathetically.'

WHO TO APPLY TO David Medlock, Trustee, c/o Hebron and Medlock Ltd, St Georges Lodge, 33 Oldfield Road, Bath, Avon BA2 3ND *Tel.* 01225 428221

■ The Anthony and Elizabeth Mellows Charitable Settlement

CC NO 281229   **ESTABLISHED** 1980

WHERE FUNDING CAN BE GIVEN UK.

WHO CAN BENEFIT National arts and heritage groups, hospitals, hospices and churches.

WHAT IS FUNDED The acquisition of objects to be used or displayed in houses of the National Trust or churches of the Church of England; the encouragement of hospices and medical research; support of the arts. The trustees can only consider projects recommended to them by those UK institutions with whom they are in close cooperation.

WHAT IS NOT FUNDED Applications from individuals, including students, are ineligible.

TYPE OF GRANT Generally single projects.

RANGE OF GRANTS Up to £3,000

SAMPLE GRANTS Royal Opera House Foundation (£2,700); St John Ambulance Malaysia (£3,000); National Art Collection Fund (£1,100) and St Peter Minsterworth and St Martin-in-the-Fields (£500 each).

FINANCES *Year* 2011–12 *Income* £50,358 *Grants* £14,497 *Assets* £742,103

TRUSTEES Prof. Anthony R. Mellows; Elizabeth Mellows.

HOW TO APPLY Applications are considered when received, but only from UK institutions. No application forms are used. Grants decisions are made three times a year when the trustees meet to consider applications.

WHO TO APPLY TO Prof. Anthony Mellows, Trustee, 22 Devereux Court, Temple Bar, London WC2R 3JR *Tel.* 020 7583 8813

■ Melodor Limited

CC NO 260972   **ESTABLISHED** 1970

WHERE FUNDING CAN BE GIVEN UK and overseas.

WHO CAN BENEFIT Orthodox Jewish institutions.

WHAT IS FUNDED Jewish causes, such as education, relief of poverty and the advancement of religion in accordance with the Orthodox Jewish faith.

TYPE OF GRANT One-off grants and loans.

RANGE OF GRANTS Up to £30,000.

SAMPLE GRANTS Previous beneficiaries include: Centre for Torah Education Trust, Beis Rochel, Chasdei Yoel, Beth Hamedrash Hachodosh, Yeshivas Ohel Shimon, Beis Minchas Yitzhok, Talmud Torah Education Trust, Dushinsky Trust, Kollel Chelkas Yakov, Yetev Lev, Delman Charitable Trust, Ovois Ubonim and Friends of Viznitz.

FINANCES *Year* 2011–12 *Income* £87,499 *Grants* £131,475 *Assets* £570,609

TRUSTEES Hyman Weiss; Philip Weiss; Zisel Weiss; Pinchas Neumann; Yocheved Weiss; Eli Neumann; Esther Henry; Henry Neumann; Janet Bleier; Maurice Neumann; Miriam Friedlander; Rebecca Delange; Rivka Olloch; Rivka Rabinowitz; Pesha Kohn; Yehoshua Weiss.

HOW TO APPLY The trust's accounts for 2011/12 state that 'the governors receive many applications for grants, mainly by mail, but also verbally. Each application is considered against the criteria established by the charity. Although the charity does not advertise, it is well known within its community and there are many requests received for grants. Feedback received is used to monitor the quality of grants.'

WHO TO APPLY TO Bernardin Weiss, Administrator, 10 Cubley Road, Salford M7 4GN *Tel.* 01617 206188

■ The Melow Charitable Trust

CC NO 275454   **ESTABLISHED** 1978

WHERE FUNDING CAN BE GIVEN UK and overseas.

WHO CAN BENEFIT Jewish charities.

WHAT IS FUNDED Jewish charitable purposes.

SAMPLE GRANTS Ezer V'Hatzalah Ltd (£314,000); Lolev Charitable Trust (£179,000); Friends of Kollel Samtar (Antwerp) Ltd (£107,000); and Rehabilitation Trust and Asser Bishvil Foundation (£100,000 each).

FINANCES *Year* 2011 *Income* £1,650,808 *Grants* £1,140,736 *Assets* £12,354,210

TRUSTEES Miriam Spitz; Esther Weiser.

OTHER INFORMATION At the time of writing (December 2013) the trust's 2012 accounts were overdue with the Charity Commission.

HOW TO APPLY In writing to the correspondent.

WHO TO APPLY TO J. Low, 21 Warwick Grove, London E5 9HX *Tel.* 020 8806 1549

■ Meningitis Trust

CC NO 803016 **ESTABLISHED** 1986
WHERE FUNDING CAN BE GIVEN UK.
WHO CAN BENEFIT Organisations researching meningitis.
WHAT IS FUNDED Research into all aspects of the disease.
FINANCES *Year* 2011–12 *Income* £3,196,946 *Grants* £0 *Assets* £1,557,437
TRUSTEES Gill Noble; Richard Greenhalgh; Alastair Irvine; Mitchell Wolfe; Stephen Gazard; Michelle Harvey-Jones; Anna Freeman; Richard Gillett.
OTHER INFORMATION No research grants were made during the year, previously grants have fluctuated from £2,000 to £150,000. There were grants to individuals made totalling £294,000.
HOW TO APPLY On a form available from the website along with guidelines, to be submitted by mid-August. See the website for exact deadlines. Decisions are announced in late December.
WHO TO APPLY TO Financial Grants Officer, Link House, Britton Gardens, Kingswood, Bristol BS15 1TF *Tel.* 01179 476320 *Fax* 01179 600427 *email* catherine@meningitisuk.org *Website* www.meningitisuk.org

■ Menuchar Ltd

CC NO 262782 **ESTABLISHED** 1971
WHERE FUNDING CAN BE GIVEN UK
WHO CAN BENEFIT Jewish organisations.
WHAT IS FUNDED Advancement of religion in accordance with the Orthodox Jewish faith, and relief of people in need.
WHAT IS NOT FUNDED No grants to non-registered charities or to individuals.
TYPE OF GRANT Primarily one-off.
FINANCES *Year* 2011–12 *Income* £738,249 *Grants* £721,515 *Assets* £154,143
TRUSTEES Norman Bude; Gail Bude.
OTHER INFORMATION A list of beneficiaries was not included in the accounts however they did state that grants went to religious organisations.
HOW TO APPLY In writing to the correspondent.
WHO TO APPLY TO The Trustees, c/o Barry Flack and Co, Knight House, 27–31 East Barnet Road, Barnet EN4 8RN *Tel.* 020 8275 5186

■ The Menzies Charity Foundation

CC NO 1136667 **ESTABLISHED** 2010
WHERE FUNDING CAN BE GIVEN Worldwide.
WHO CAN BENEFIT Registered charities working with children and young people and people with disabilities.
WHAT IS FUNDED General charitable purposes. Education; social welfare; community regeneration.
FINANCES *Year* 2012–13 *Income* £7,044
TRUSTEES Julie Adams; Peter Noyce; Tom Govan.
HOW TO APPLY In writing to the correspondent.
WHO TO APPLY TO Peter Noyce, Trustee, Menzies LLP, Menzies, 62 Goldsworth Road, Woking GU21 6LQ *Tel.* 01483 755000 *Fax* 01483 599238 *email* pnoyce@menzies.co.uk

■ Mercaz Torah Vechesed Limited

CC NO 1109212 **ESTABLISHED** 2005
WHERE FUNDING CAN BE GIVEN Worldwide.
WHO CAN BENEFIT Charitable organisations and individuals.

WHAT IS FUNDED The advancement of the Orthodox Jewish faith, Orthodox Jewish religious education, and the relief of poverty and infirmity amongst members of the Orthodox Jewish community.
FINANCES *Year* 2011–12 *Income* £491,115 *Grants* £524,670
TRUSTEES Joseph Ostreicher; Mordche David Rand.
HOW TO APPLY In writing to the correspondent.
WHO TO APPLY TO Joseph Ostreicher, Secretary, 28 Braydon Road, London N16 6QB *Tel.* 020 8880 5366

■ Brian Mercer Charitable Trust

CC NO 1076925 **ESTABLISHED** 1999
WHERE FUNDING CAN BE GIVEN UK and overseas.
WHO CAN BENEFIT Charitable organisations.
WHAT IS FUNDED Advancement of education, promotion of medical and scientific research in particular sight and liver. Visual for young people.
TYPE OF GRANT Mainly recurrent.
RANGE OF GRANTS £1,000 to £50,000.
SAMPLE GRANTS British Liver Trust (£82,000); British Council for the Prevention of Blindness (£59,000); Blackburn Youth Zone (£25,000); Sculpture Residency in Pietrasanta (£21,000); Marie Curie Cancer Care, The Living Paintings Trust and Micro Loan Foundation (£10,000 each); NADFAS North West Area (£9,000); East\(£9,000); Talking Newspapers and Magazines (£3,000); Baines School and Our Lady Catholic College (£2,500 each).
FINANCES *Year* 2011–12 *Income* £511,301 *Grants* £436,844 *Assets* £21,843,868
TRUSTEES Christine Clancy; Kenneth Merrill; Alan Rowntree; Roger Duckworth; Mary Clitheroe.
HOW TO APPLY Via email at least four weeks before trustee meetings. Dates of upcoming trustee meetings can be found on the website, they are generally twice yearly.
WHO TO APPLY TO Alan Rowntree, Trustee, c/o Beever and Struthers, Central Buildings, Richmond Terrace, Blackburn BB1 7AP *Tel.* 01254 686600 *Fax* 01254 682483 *email* info@brianmercercharitabletrust.org *Website* www.brianmercercharitabletrust.org

■ The Mercers' Charitable Foundation

CC NO 326340 **ESTABLISHED** 1982
WHERE FUNDING CAN BE GIVEN UK; strong preference for London and the West Midlands. The foundation is keen to stress that it currently has geographical restrictions on its welfare and educational grantmaking. See individual programme information for details.
WHAT IS FUNDED General welfare, the elderly, conservation, arts, Christian faith activities, educational institutions.
WHAT IS NOT FUNDED These should be read alongside the specific exclusions for the particular category into which an application falls. Excluded appeals: animal welfare charities; endowment appeals; projects that are primarily political; activities that are the responsibility of the local, health or education authority or other similar body; activities that have already taken place; other grantmaking trusts; sponsorship or marketing appeals; loans or business finance; and general or mailshot appeals.
Capital projects: This is restricted to appeals that are within the last 20% of their target. No capital

projects are funded under the Education programme.

TYPE OF GRANT Building and other capital grants with certain restrictions; feasibility studies; one-off grants; project and research grants; recurring and start-up costs. Grants given for up to three years.

RANGE OF GRANTS Usually £5,000–£15,000, but up to over £4 million for special projects.

SAMPLE GRANTS St Paul's School London (£4.2 million); Hammersmith Academy London (£1 million); Guildhall School of Music and Drama (£250,000); London Schools Network (£139,000); Hexham Abbey Northumberland (£100,000); R L Glasspool Charity Trust (£30,000); Quaker Social Action London and Sue Ryder Care (£15,000 each); National Churches Trust and Water City Festival London (£12,000 each); London Sports Trust, Peace Direct, Age UK Camden, Calvert Trust and Contact the Elderly (£10,000 each).

FINANCES *Year* 2011–12 *Grants* £11,761,000

TRUSTEE The Mercers' Company

HOW TO APPLY Applications can be made online via the foundation's website. In addition applicants are required to post: The organisation's most recent statutory report and accounts (produced not later than ten months after the end of the financial year); and a copy of your organisation's bank statement, dated within the last three months.

Grants officers are happy to give advice by telephone or email. Applicants must submit applications four weeks prior to committee meetings. Applications will be acknowledged within ten working days. Committees meet regularly throughout the year. For up to date committee meeting dates consult the trust's website for each grant programme. Approval of successful applications may take up to four weeks from the date of the meeting at which your applications is considered. 'Where possible, applicants awarded, or being considered for, a grant over £10,000 will receive a visit either from staff or from members of the Mercers' Company.' Note: This trust is under the trusteeship of the Mercers' Company and one application to the Company is an application to all its trusts including the Charity of Sir Richard Whittington and the Earl of Northampton's Charity.

WHO TO APPLY TO The Clerk, Mercers' Hall, Ironmonger Lane, London EC2V 8HE *Tel.* 020 7726 4991 *email* info@mercers.co.uk *Website* www.mercers.co.uk

■ Merchant Navy Welfare Board

CC NO 212799   **ESTABLISHED** 1962

WHERE FUNDING CAN BE GIVEN UK

WHO CAN BENEFIT Organisations that help or represent seafarers; merchant navy and sailors.

WHAT IS FUNDED Welfare; medical care. To promote and support the welfare of merchant seafarers and their dependants.

WHAT IS NOT FUNDED No retrospective funding.

TYPE OF GRANT Capital projects, evaluation studies and start-up costs.

RANGE OF GRANTS Up to £50,000.

SAMPLE GRANTS Maritime Charities Funding Group (£50,000); Nautilus Welfare Fund (£41,000); Mission to Seafarers (£33,000); Royal National Mission to Deep Sea Fishermen (£20,000); Royal Alfred Seafarers' Society – Belvedere Care Home, Surrey (£19,000); Sir Gabriel Woods Mariners Horne, Greenock, Scotland (£12,500); Queen Victoria Seamen's Rest, London

(£6,000); Invergordon Seafarers' Centre (£800) and Merchant Navy Medal Fund (£100).

FINANCES *Year* 2012 *Income* £621,702 *Grants* £207,313 *Assets* £12,485,212

TRUSTEES Anthony Dickinson; Barry Bryant; Timothy Springett; Michael Jess; Stephen Todd; Edward McFadyen; Graham Lane; Robert Jones; Ian Ballantyne; Revd Kenneth Peters; Deanne Thomas; Andrew Cassels; Mark Carden; David Colclough.

HOW TO APPLY On a form available to download, together with criteria and guidelines, on the website. The trust is open to enquiries regarding the application process.

WHO TO APPLY TO David Parsons, Chief Executive, 8 Cumberland Place, Southampton SO15 2BH *Tel.* 02380 337799 *email* enquiries@mnwb.org.uk *Website* www.mnwb.org

■ The Merchant Taylors' Company Charities Fund

CC NO 1069124   **ESTABLISHED** 1941

WHERE FUNDING CAN BE GIVEN UK, especially inner London.

WHO CAN BENEFIT Organisations benefiting children, older people, actors and entertainment professionals, medical professionals, musicians, substance abuse, carers, people who are disabled, and homeless people.

WHAT IS FUNDED Areas that may be considered are the arts, social care and community development, disability, older people, poverty, medical studies and research, addiction, homelessness, children, and education, with priority for special needs.

WHAT IS NOT FUNDED No grants for: bricks and mortar, although they will consider contributing to the fitting out or refurbishment of new or existing buildings; medical research, although the Company provides administrative services to a third-party trust with a small reactive capacity in this area, to which such applications may be referred; funds for 'on-granting' to third-party charities or individuals; generalised appeals; very large charities, except occasionally in support of localised work in the Trustees' geographical area of interest; revenue funding.

TYPE OF GRANT One-off grants or three-year tapering grants.

RANGE OF GRANTS Mostly £5,000–£15,000

SAMPLE GRANTS Veterans Aid (£14,000); UNLOCK and Cricket for Change (£10,000 each); Westside School (£9,000); Guildhall School of Music and Drama (£6,000); Addaction (£5,000); St John's Church, Hackney (£3,000); Tailors' Benevolent Institute (£1,500); Master Tailors' Benevolent Association (£1,000); Merchant Taylors' School, Crosby and St Paul's Cathedral Choir School (£500 each) and Brandram Road Community Association (£300).

FINANCES *Year* 2012 *Income* £293,160 *Grants* £95,280 *Assets* £697,966

TRUSTEES Hugh Stubbs; Duncan Macdonald Eggar; Peter Magill; Rupert Bull.

OTHER INFORMATION The Merchant Taylors' Company also administers the Charities for the Infirm (214266) and the Charities for the Poor (214267).

HOW TO APPLY Awards are restricted at present to charities nominated by the Livery Committee. Applications may only be made with the support of a member of the Merchant Taylors' Company or by invitation.

WHO TO APPLY TO Nick Harris, Chief Executive Officer, Merchant Taylor's Hall, 30 Threadneedle Street,

London EC2R 8JB *Tel.* 020 7450 4440 *Fax* 020 7588 2776 *email* charities@merchant-taylors.co.uk *Website* www.merchanttaylors.co.uk

■ The Merchant Venturers' Charity

cc no 264302   **established** 1972
where funding can be given Bristol.
who can benefit Local and regional organisations and local branches of national organisations particularly those supporting the young, aged and disadvantaged; and some individuals.
what is funded Any charitable purpose which enhances the quality of life for all, including learning and the acquisition of skills by supporting education; supporting community activity; and assisting in the preservation of open spaces and heritage.
type of grant Some recurrent.
sample grants South Bristol Consortium for Young People and Clifton Down Charitable Trust (£15,000 each); UWE Primary Transition Programme (£10,000); The Station (£7,000) and Young Bristol, Home Start and Southmead Community Support (£5,000 each).
finances *Year* 2012 *Income* £426,080 *Grants* £143,922 *Assets* £6,267,038
trustee The Standing Committee of the Society of Merchant Venturers of Bristol.
other information Grants were broken down in to the following categories: Community and social (£48,500) and Youth and education (£95,400).
how to apply In writing to the correspondent. A subcommittee of the trustees meets bi-annually while the trustees meet monthly and can, if necessary, consider any urgent business at that meeting.
who to apply to Richard Morris, Treasurer, c/o The Society of Merchant Venturers, Merchants' Hall, The Promenade, Clifton, Bristol BS8 3NH *Tel.* 01179 738058 *Fax* 01179 735884 *email* enquiry@merchantventurers.com

■ The Merchants' House of Glasgow

sc no SC008900   **established** 1605
where funding can be given Glasgow and the west of Scotland.
who can benefit Registered charities benefiting seamen, pensioners and young people (aged 10 to 30) in full-time education.
what is funded Seamen's missions, general charitable purposes, and grants to pensioners and young people in education.
what is not funded The trust will not, unless in exceptional circumstances, make grants to: individuals; churches other than Glasgow Cathedral; organisations that have received support in the two years preceding an application.
type of grant Capital projects.
range of grants Up to £4,000.
sample grants Previous grant recipients have included: Erskine Hospital, the National Youth Orchestra of Scotland, Scottish Motor Neurone Disease, the Castle Howard Trust, Delta, the National Burns Memorial Homes, Quarriers Village and Shelter.
finances *Year* 2012 *Income* £927,735 *Grants* £451,828
trustee The Directors.
how to apply In writing to the correspondent at any time, supported by copy of accounts and

information about the organisation's principal activities.
who to apply to The Directors, 7 West George Street, Glasgow G2 1BA *Tel.* 01412 218272 *Fax* 01412 262275 *email* theoffice@merchantshouse.org.uk *Website* www.merchantshouse.org.uk

■ Mercury Phoenix Trust

cc no 1013768   **established** 1992
where funding can be given Worldwide.
who can benefit Registered charities benefiting people with AIDS and the HIV virus.
what is funded Relief of poverty, sickness and distress of people affected by AIDS and the HIV virus, and to stimulate awareness of the virus throughout the world.
what is not funded No funding for individuals or travel costs.
type of grant One-off, capital, project, running costs.
range of grants Up to £15,000.
sample grants Help Age International – Thailand (£10,500); UNICEF, Azafady – Madagascar and AIDS Care Education and Training UK – Democratic Republic of Congo (£10,000 each); Teaching Aids at Low Cost – Mozambique (£7,500); Joint Efforts for Youth Uganda, Concern Worldwide – Zimbabwe and Build Africa UK – Kenya (£5,000 each); Karunya Social Services Society – India (£3,000); Rural Development Welfare Society – India (£2,000) and Terrence Higgins trust (£1,600).
finances *Year* 2011–12 *Income* £538,569 *Grants* £224,485 *Assets* £1,370,867
trustees Brian May; Henry James Beach; Mary Austin; Roger Taylor.
how to apply Application forms are available on request to 'funding@mercuryphoenixtrust.com'. In addition to a completed application form, the trust requires the following documents: a budget, registration certificate, audited accounts for the last financial year, constitution or memorandum and articles of association, annual report and equal opportunities policy.
who to apply to Peter Chant, Administrator, 22 Cottage Offices, Latimer Park, Latimer, Chesham, Buckinghamshire HP5 1TU *Tel.* 01494 766799 *email* mercuryphoenixtrust@idrec.com *Website* www.mercuryphoenixtrust.com

■ The Mersey Docks and Harbour Company Charitable Fund

cc no 206913   **established** 1811
where funding can be given Merseyside.
who can benefit Seafaring, registered charities on Merseyside.
what is funded The relief of people who are sick, disabled and retired in the dock service or the families of those who were killed in service; and to benefit charities in the town or port of Liverpool.
range of grants £25–£24,000.
sample grants Community Foundation for Merseyside (£24,000); The Mersey Mission to Seafarers (£10,000); Plaza Community Cinema (£3,000); National Museums Liverpool (££2,000); Seafarers UK (£1,000); The Ark (£500) and Marie Curie Cancer Care (£150).
finances *Year* 2012 *Income* £137 *Grants* £39,000

Think carefully about every application. Is it justified?

745

TRUSTEES Gary Hodgson; Mark Whitworth; Ian Charnock.

HOW TO APPLY In writing to the correspondent.

WHO TO APPLY TO Caroline Gill, Secretary, The Mersey Docks and Harbour Company, Maritime Centre, Port of Liverpool, Liverpool L21 1LA *Tel.* 01519 496349

■ Community Foundation for Merseyside

CC NO 1068887   **ESTABLISHED** 1998

WHERE FUNDING CAN BE GIVEN Merseyside, Halton and Lancashire.

WHO CAN BENEFIT Charitable organisations.

WHAT IS FUNDED General charitable purposes, community, regeneration. The foundation manages funds on behalf of parent donors. Funding priorities will vary considerably depending on the requirements of these donors.

WHAT IS NOT FUNDED Each fund administered by the trust has separate guidelines and exclusionary criteria which are available directly from the trust's website.

SAMPLE GRANTS Previously: Halton Voluntary Action; Jo Jo Mind and Body; The Zero Centre; Liverpool Academy of Art; Fire Support Network; and Liverpool Greenbank Wheelchair Basketball Club.

FINANCES *Year* 2011–12 *Income* £3,236,701 *Grants* £1,860,046 *Assets* £6,265,749

TRUSTEES Sue Langfield, Administrator. Michael Eastwood; Abi Pointing; Andrew Wallis; Robert Towers; William Bowley; Sally Yeoman; David McDonnell.

OTHER INFORMATION As the foundation manages a wide range of funds which open and close regularly, they are not detailed here and applicants are advised to visit the website instead to see the most up to date information. During the year there were a further 64 grants totalling £19,000 were awarded to individuals. A list of beneficiaries was not included in the accounts.

HOW TO APPLY Most of the trust's funds can now be applied for online using a standard form. Forms for the other funds are also available online. Once you have submitted the form the foundation will determine which fund the proposal meets. The foundation has a membership scheme available which keeps members up to date on the latest grant schemes. Applications must also include the following documents: constitution; accounts; bank statement; safeguarding policy (where applicable). Unless your organisation has received a grant from the foundation in the last 12 months you *must* submit these documents, otherwise your application will not be considered. Full guidelines and application forms for individual funds are available from the foundation's website.

WHO TO APPLY TO Cathy Elliott, Chief Executive, Third Floor, Stanley Building, 43 Hanover Street, Liverpool L1 3DN *Tel.* 01512 322444 *Fax* 01512 322445 *email* info@cfmerseyside. org.uk *Website* www.cfmerseyside.org.uk

---

■ The Zachary Merton and George Woofindin Convalescent Trust

CC NO 221760   **ESTABLISHED** 1956

WHERE FUNDING CAN BE GIVEN Preference for Sheffield and Lincoln including the following areas: north Nottinghamshire, north Derbyshire and South Yorkshire.

WHO CAN BENEFIT Organisations benefiting carers, disabled people and people disadvantaged by poverty.

WHAT IS FUNDED Convalescent homes, travelling expenses of convalescent poor people, respite care for carers, people in need through illness, and community medicine.

WHAT IS NOT FUNDED No grants to individuals.

TYPE OF GRANT Recurring costs; up to two years.

RANGE OF GRANTS £500–£4,500.

SAMPLE GRANTS Sheffield Churches Council for Community Care (£4,500); Trinity Day Care Trust (£3,000); Macmillan Cancer Support, SHARE Psychotherapy Agency and Sheffield Family Holiday Fund (£2,000 each) and British Red Cross Society, Marie Curie Cancer Care (Lincoln) and Vitalise (£1,000 each).

FINANCES *Year* 2011–12 *Income* £41,204 *Grants* £21,500 *Assets* £977,280

TRUSTEES G. Connell; M. Frampton; N. Hutton; P. Perriam; Dr B. Sharrack; B. Evans; R. Hague; G. Rylands; Dr J. Burton; J. Banks.

HOW TO APPLY In writing to the correspondent, by the middle of March or September.

WHO TO APPLY TO G. J. Smallman, Secretary, c/o Wrigleys Solicitors LLP, Fountain Precinct, Balm Green, Sheffield S1 2JA *Tel.* 01142 675594

■ The Tony Metherell Charitable Trust

CC NO 1046899   **ESTABLISHED** 1992

WHERE FUNDING CAN BE GIVEN UK, especially Hertfordshire and Worcestershire.

WHO CAN BENEFIT Particularly older people and people who have cancer or disabilities.

WHAT IS FUNDED General charitable purposes, including hospices, cancer charities and the care and welfare of people who are elderly or have disabilities.

WHAT IS NOT FUNDED No grants to overseas causes.

RANGE OF GRANTS Up to £5,000.

SAMPLE GRANTS Previous beneficiaries include: H Hospice (£2,800).

FINANCES *Year* 2011–12 *Income* £13,144

TRUSTEES Jemma Eadie; Kate Cooper.

HOW TO APPLY In writing to the correspondent.

WHO TO APPLY TO Jemma Eadie, Trustee, North End Farm, North End, Newbury, Berkshire RG20 0BE

■ The Metropolitan Drinking Fountain and Cattle Trough Association

CC NO 207743   **ESTABLISHED** 1960

WHERE FUNDING CAN BE GIVEN UK, mainly London, and overseas.

WHO CAN BENEFIT Charitable organisations.

WHAT IS FUNDED Projects working to provide clean water supplies in developing countries, the provision of drinking fountains in schools and the restoration of disused drinking fountains. The preservation of the association's archive materials, artefacts, drinking fountains, cattle troughs and other installations.

WHAT IS NOT FUNDED Registered charities only.

SAMPLE GRANTS Restoration of Horse Troughs (£10,000); Busogu Trust, Excellent Development, Appropriate Technology and Village Water (£2,000 each); Teso (£1,400); Friends of Mayow Park (£900); Newport Parish Council (£750); Friends of Hope (£740) and Schools for Kenya (£600).

FINANCES *Year* 2012 *Income* £31,453 *Grants* £31,457 *Assets* £618,661

TRUSTEES J. E. Mills, Chair; R. P. Baber; S. Fuller; Sir J. Smith; M. W. Elliott; M. Nation; A. King; M. Bear; L. Erith; Mark Slater

OTHER INFORMATION Grants paid to schools not exceeding £1,000 each totalled £9,000. During the year 21 fountains were donated to schools throughout the UK.

HOW TO APPLY There are separate application forms depending on whether an application is being made for a schools fountain; a UK project; an overseas project or a restoration work. These forms are all available on the website. In addition the trustees require the following information: a copy of the most recent audited accounts; how has the cost of the project been ascertained, e.g. qualified surveyor; how many people/animals is it estimated would use the fountain/trough in a day; will the charity supervise the project, if not who would; where is it anticipated the remainder of the funds to complete the project will come from.

WHO TO APPLY TO R. P. Baber, Secretary, Oaklands, 5 Queenborough Gardens, Chislehurst, Kent BR7 6NP *Tel.* 020 8467 1261 *email* ralph. baber@tesco.net *Website* www. drinkingfountains.org

■ The Metropolitan Masonic Charity

CC NO 1081205 **ESTABLISHED** 2000
WHERE FUNDING CAN BE GIVEN Throughout London, but not exclusively.
WHO CAN BENEFIT Individuals and organisations within the area of London.
WHAT IS FUNDED General charitable purpose, with particular, albeit not exclusive, focus on the relief of need, poverty or distress, advancement of education.
TYPE OF GRANT One – off grants and sponsorship or undertaking of a research.
RANGE OF GRANTS Normally £100–£6,000.
SAMPLE GRANTS Barts and The London Charity (£1.7 million); Lifelites (£6,000); British School of Osteopathy, Lambeth Summer Projects Trust and London Wing Air Training Corps (£5,000 each); Seventy 4 and Masonic Trout and Salmon Fly Fishing Association (£4,000 each); Barons Court Project, Interact Reading Service, St Bride's Appeal, The Douglas Bader Foundation and The Lee Smith Foundation (£3,000 each); RMBI, Metropolitan Sports and Social, Drop-in Bereavement Centre and DEBRA (£2,000 each) and Children's Country Holiday Fund and Moorfields Eye Hospital (£100 each).
FINANCES *Year* 2011–12 *Income* £1,854,416 *Grants* £1,750,050 *Assets* £775,675
TRUSTEES Michael Birkett; Stuart Henderson; Rex Thorne; Robert Corp-Reader; Brian de Neut.
HOW TO APPLY In writing to the correspondent.
WHO TO APPLY TO Michael Birkett, Trustee, London Masonic Charitable Trust, 33 Great Queen Street, London WC2B 5AA *Tel.* 020 7539 2930 *email* office@metgl.com

■ T. and J. Meyer Family Foundation Limited

CC NO 1087507 **ESTABLISHED** 2001
WHERE FUNDING CAN BE GIVEN UK and overseas.
WHO CAN BENEFIT Charitable organisations.
WHAT IS FUNDED The primary focus of the foundation is on education, healthcare and the environment. The criteria for charities are: organisations which alleviate the suffering of humanity through health, education and environment; organisations with extremely high correlation between what is gifted and what the beneficiary receives; organisations who struggle to raise funds either because either they are new, their size or their access to funds is constrained; organisations who promote long-term effective sustainable solutions.
SAMPLE GRANTS Partners in Health (£200,000); Royal Marsden Cancer Trust (£198,000); Sisters SHJ&Mary (£129,000); Hope and Homes for Children (£63,000); Angkor Children's Hospital (£50,000); Pepo La Tumaini (£35,000); Nyaya Health and Heifer International (£25,000 each); Friends of the Citizens Foundation (£17,000); Healthprom and Rwanda Works (£16,000 each); Qespina (£11,000); Project Muso (£10,000); Riders for Health (£7,900) and Toniic (£4,200).
FINANCES *Year* 2012 *Income* £594,269 *Grants* £935,375 *Assets* £24,781,708
TRUSTEES A. C. Meyer; J. D. Meyer; Q. H. Meyer; I. T. Meyer; M. M. Meyer.
HOW TO APPLY No grants to unsolicited applications. Trustees meet four times a year
WHO TO APPLY TO T. H. Meyer, 3 Kendrick Mews, London SW7 3HG *email* info@tjmff.org

■ Mi Yu Foundation

CC NO 1136451 **ESTABLISHED** 2010
WHERE FUNDING CAN BE GIVEN Worldwide.
WHO CAN BENEFIT Organisations and individuals.
WHAT IS FUNDED The advancement of education of children and young people, in particular those who are orphaned, abandoned or disadvantaged in any part of the world. The relief of poverty, sickness and distress and any other charitable purposes.
FINANCES *Year* 2012 *Income* £1
TRUSTEES Michelle Ambalo; Jeffrey Lermer.
HOW TO APPLY In writing to the correspondent.
WHO TO APPLY TO Jeffrey Lermer, Trustee, 43 Lytton Road, New Barnet, Barnet EN5 5BY *email* jeff. lermer@lermer.co.uk

■ The Mickel Fund

SC NO SC003266 **ESTABLISHED** 1970
WHERE FUNDING CAN BE GIVEN UK, with a preference for Scotland.
WHO CAN BENEFIT Voluntary organisations and charitable groups benefiting people of all ages, especially at risk groups. The trust prefers local charities but does give to UK charities.
WHAT IS FUNDED General charitable purposes including: health and social care professional bodies; hospices; cancer research; immunology, MS and neurological research; health-related volunteer schemes; church and historical buildings; zoos; heritage; art galleries, libraries and museums; sports centres; care in the community; and holidays and outings.
WHAT IS NOT FUNDED No grants to individuals.

TYPE OF GRANT One-off and recurrent, capital including buildings, project and research. Funding is available for more than three years.

RANGE OF GRANTS £100–£10,000.

SAMPLE GRANTS Barnardo's; Macmillan Cancer Support; Guide Dogs for the Blind; Glasgow Association for Mental Health; Royal National Lifeboat Institution; FUSE Youth Cafe; The Royal Zoological Society of Scotland and Erskine Hospital.

FINANCES *Year* 2011–12 *Income* £367,355 *Grants* £100,000

TRUSTEES Mairi Mickel; Bruce Mickel; Findlay Mickel; Alan Hartley; Oliver Bassi.

HOW TO APPLY On an application form available from the charity's website, which should be emailed to the charity upon completion. A check-list of requirements and eligibility criteria is also available on the charity's website.

The following information is provided by the charity:

'The Mickel Fund aims to be a flexible and helpful funder that builds relationships with the organisations we fund. We have a small team who work hard to provide the support required by charities that wish to make applications. We recognise that charities are often dealing with complex issues and we try to provide as much advice and support as we can in addition to donations. We are always happy to answer telephone and e-mail enquiries and to give pre-application support as appropriate. We sometimes meet with potential applicants but only once we have received an application.'

'Our aim is to fund effective people and organisations that can make a difference. We are an independent grant-maker and we are willing to take risks and support new ideas; however, we will also fund ongoing work, which can show it makes a difference. Donations can take the form of core funding including salaries and general running costs, project grants or capital grants for building or equipment.'

WHO TO APPLY TO Lindsay McColl, 1 Atlantic Quay, 1 Robertson Avenue, Glasgow G2 8JB *Tel.* 01412 427528 *email* admin@mickelfund.org.uk *Website* www.mickelfund.org.uk

■ Mickleham Charitable Trust

CC NO 1048337   **ESTABLISHED** 1995

WHERE FUNDING CAN BE GIVEN UK, with a preference for Norfolk.

WHO CAN BENEFIT Registered charities.

WHAT IS FUNDED Relief for the abused and disadvantaged, particularly young people, and the blind.

TYPE OF GRANT Mainly recurrent.

RANGE OF GRANTS £500–£10,000

SAMPLE GRANTS YMCA Norfolk and Norfolk and Norwich Association for the Blind (£20,000 each); Motability for Norfolk (£7,500); Barnardo's and Connects and Co. (£5,000 each) Foundation for Conductive Education and Mercy Ships (£2,000 each) and British Wireless for the Blind, Moorfields Eye Hospital, The Benjamin Foundation, Prisoners of Conscience Appeal Fund, Norwich Door to Door, East Norwich Youth Project and Canine Partners (£1,000 each).

FINANCES *Year* 2011–12 *Income* £123,593 *Grants* £155,500 *Assets* £3,204,713

TRUSTEES Philip Norton; Revd Sheila Nunney; Anne Richardson.

HOW TO APPLY In writing to the correspondent.

WHO TO APPLY TO Philip Norton, Trustee, c/o Hansells, 13–14 The Close, Norwich NR1 4DS *Tel.* 01603 615731 *email* philipnorton@hansells.co.uk

■ Gerald Micklem Charitable Trust

CC NO 802583   **ESTABLISHED** 1988

WHERE FUNDING CAN BE GIVEN UK and East Hampshire

WHO CAN BENEFIT Registered charities benefiting at risk groups and people who are disadvantaged by poverty or socially isolated.

WHAT IS FUNDED Medicine and health, welfare and general charitable purposes.

WHAT IS NOT FUNDED The trust does not make grants to individuals, does not enter into sponsorship arrangements with individuals and does not make grants to organisations that are not UK-registered charities. The areas of charitable activity that fall outside the trust's current funding priorities are: drug/alcohol abuse and counselling; museums, galleries and heritage; performing arts and cultural organisations; churches; and overseas aid.

TYPE OF GRANT One-off and recurrent.

RANGE OF GRANTS £1,000–£6,000.

SAMPLE GRANTS Self Unlimited (£60,000); Cecily's Fund (£6,000); Whizz-Kidz and The Rowans Hospice (£5,000 each); British Schools Exploring Society, CLIC Sargent, Foundation for Paediatric Osteopathy and Target Ovarian Cancer (£4,000 each); I CAN and Kinlochbervie High School (£3,000 each) and Halow Project (£2,000).

FINANCES *Year* 2012 *Income* £220,298 *Grants* £180,000 *Assets* £1,081,778

TRUSTEES Susan J. Shone; Joanna L. Scott-Dalgleish; Helen Ratcliffe.

HOW TO APPLY Applications may be made to the correspondent by letter – not by e-mail. Enquiries prior to any application may be made by email. 'There is no application form. Applications may be made at any time, but preferably not in December, and should be accompanied by the latest report and accounts of the applicant organisation. Applicants should note that, at their main meeting early in the calendar year, the trustees consider applications received up to 31 December each year, but do not carry them forward. Having regard for the time of year when this meeting takes place, it makes sense for applications to be made as late as possible in the calendar year so that the information they contain is most up to date when the trustees meet. **Note:** The trustees receive a very substantial number of appeals each year. It is not their practice to acknowledge appeals, and they prefer not to enter into correspondence with applicants other than those to whom grants are being made or from whom further information is required. Only successful applicants are notified of the outcome of their application.'

WHO TO APPLY TO S. J. Shone, Trustee, Bolinge Hill Farm, Buriton, Petersfield, Hampshire GU31 4NN *Tel.* 01730 264207 *email* mail@geraldmicklemct.org.uk *Website* www.geraldmicklemct.org.uk

■ The Sir John Middlemore Charitable Trust

CC NO 1102736 **ESTABLISHED** 2004
WHERE FUNDING CAN BE GIVEN West Midlands, preference for South Birmingham.
WHO CAN BENEFIT Charities, community groups, social enterprises, CICs.
WHAT IS FUNDED Support for children and young people under the age of 25 with particular focus on disadvantaged and disabled children and young people; children in and leaving care and young carers.
WHAT IS NOT FUNDED No grants to: organisations with an annual income over £150,000 or with reserves of more than six months of operating costs; projects outside the UK; statutory organisations; or political organisations. Grants are not made for: onwards distribution to other organisations; core operating costs; equipment; medical treatment or research.
TYPE OF GRANT One-off.
FINANCES Year 2012–13 Income £66,627 Grants £14,899 Assets £1,433,148
TRUSTEES Dr Douglas Munro Fleming; John Surtees; Doreen Anne Mabbett; John Holmes; James Leo; Reginald Corns.
HOW TO APPLY On an application form available to download from the website or by emailing the correspondent. The trust prefers to receive completed applications via email, however, hard copy applications are also accepted. Unsuccessful applicants cannot re-apply within a 12 month period. Unsuccessful applications are not acknowledged. Trustees meet quarterly to consider applications.
WHO TO APPLY TO Teresa Soden, Company Secretary, 7 Lodge Crescent, West Hagley DY9 0ND *email* office@middlemore.org.uk *Website* www.middlemore.org.uk

■ The Masonic Province of Middlesex Charitable Trust

CC NO 1064406 **ESTABLISHED** 1997
WHERE FUNDING CAN BE GIVEN Middlesex
WHO CAN BENEFIT Masons and others
WHAT IS FUNDED Masonic charities and non-masonic charities
RANGE OF GRANTS £500–£25,000
SAMPLE GRANTS Middlesex Mark Benevolent Fund (£25,000); 1st Harrow Weald Scout Group (£6,000); Royal College of Surgeons (£5,000); Kids Aware and Waldegrave School for Girls (£4,700 each); St George's Youth Club (£3,600); Crest Cancer Information and Support Centre (£3,000); West London Brigades Gym Team (£2,000); Asthma Relief (£1,500) and HDMC – Age Concern (£525).
FINANCES Year 2011–12 Income £66,508 Grants £81,833 Assets £1,850,089
TRUSTEES David Yeaman; Stephen Ramsay; Jonathan Markham Gollow; Adrian Howorth; Peter Gledhill.
OTHER INFORMATION In 2011–12 grants were given to 17 organisations.
HOW TO APPLY On a form is available from the correspondent or the Provincial Office.
WHO TO APPLY TO Peter Gledhill, Secretary of the Trustees, 85 Fakenham Way, Owlsmoor, Sandhurst, Berkshire GU47 0YS *Tel.* 01344 777077 *email* peter.gledhill@btinternet.com

■ Middlesex Sports Foundation

CC NO 1119091 **ESTABLISHED** 2007
WHERE FUNDING CAN BE GIVEN England and Wales
WHO CAN BENEFIT Children and young people, the elderly, disabled and injured sportsmen and sportswomen and the generally disadvantaged.
WHAT IS FUNDED Sport, recreation and social welfare.
RANGE OF GRANTS Up to £12,500 but mostly for £1,500.
SAMPLE GRANTS Great Britain Wheelchair Rugby (£12,500); Fields in Trust (£5,000) and British Polio Fellowship, Sandwell Asian Development Association, Avon Riding Centre for Disabled, Tall Ships Youth Trust, Mencap Sport and Cyclists Fighting Cancer (£1,500 each).
FINANCES Year 2012–13 Income £55,292 Grants £43,250 Assets £1,586,809
TRUSTEES Rhidian Jones; Julian Tregoning; Michael Foxwell; Keith King; Robert Horner; Gareth Rees; Dr Colin Crosby; Charles Hogbin; Howard Walters.
OTHER INFORMATION The grant total includes £1,500 that was donated to individuals.
HOW TO APPLY In writing to the correspondent.
WHO TO APPLY TO Charles Hogbin, Chestnut Cottage, 20a Stubbs Wood, Chesham Bois, Buckinghamshire HP6 6EY *Tel.* 01494 729220 *email* charles.hogbin@btinternet.com

■ Midhurst Pensions Trust

CC NO 245230 **ESTABLISHED** 1965
WHERE FUNDING CAN BE GIVEN Throughout England and Wales.
WHO CAN BENEFIT Old/elderly people connected to the Cowdray Estate, in 'necessitous or straitened circumstances'; other charitable organisations.
WHAT IS FUNDED Support to old/elderly people, advancement of health, relief of poverty and sickness; general charitable purposes.
WHAT IS NOT FUNDED No grants to individuals who do not have a connection to the Cowdray Estate.
TYPE OF GRANT One off grants to individuals and organisations.
SAMPLE GRANTS Birthday House Trust (£110,000). Previous beneficiaries have included: Viscountess Cowdray's Charitable Trust, King Edward VII Hospital – Midhurst, Ladaka School Project and Tibet House Trust.
FINANCES Year 2011–12 Income £84,052 Grants £145,779 Assets £4,033,668
TRUSTEES The Cowdray Trust Limited; Rathbone Trust Company Ltd.
OTHER INFORMATION Only individuals connected to the Cowdray Estate can apply.
HOW TO APPLY In writing to the correspondent.
WHO TO APPLY TO Laura Gosling, Administrator, 4th Floor, Swan House, 17–19 Stratford Place, London W1C 1BQ *Tel.* 020 7907 2100 *email* charity@mfs.co.uk

■ The Migraine Trust

CC NO 1081300 **ESTABLISHED** 1965
WHERE FUNDING CAN BE GIVEN UK and overseas.
WHO CAN BENEFIT Organisations benefiting people suffering from migraines, medical professionals, research workers and scientists.
WHAT IS FUNDED Research grants, fellowships and studentships (studentships are applied for by host institution only) for the study of migraine. Funds provide for research into migraine at

recognised institutions, e.g. hospitals and universities.

SAMPLE GRANTS University of California.

FINANCES *Year* 2012–13 *Income* £567,341 *Grants* £12,000 *Assets* £288,735

TRUSTEES P. J. Goadsby; Jennifer Mills; Mark Wetherall; Brendan Davies; Ian Watmore; Suzanne Marriot; Fayyaz Ahmed; David Cubitt; Denis O'Connor.

PUBLICATIONS Migraine News, Migraine: Understanding and coping with migraine.

OTHER INFORMATION The trust holds the Migraine Trust International Symposia, funds research into migraine, and has a full sufferer service.

HOW TO APPLY Contact the trust to discuss an application.

WHO TO APPLY TO Adam Speller, 2nd Floor, 52–53 Russell Square, London WC1B 4HP *Tel.* 020 7631 6970 *Fax* 020 7436 2886 *email* info@migrainetrust.org *Website* www.migrainetrust.org

■ Miles Trust for the Putney and Roehampton Community

CC NO 246784   **ESTABLISHED** 1967

WHERE FUNDING CAN BE GIVEN The borough of Wandsworth.

WHO CAN BENEFIT Organisations benefiting people of all ages, people disadvantaged by poverty and homeless people.

WHAT IS FUNDED Schools, churches, youth organisations, and social welfare organisations caring for people who are poor, homeless, elderly or sick.

WHAT IS NOT FUNDED No grants to individuals.

TYPE OF GRANT Some recurring, but new grants may be one-off.

RANGE OF GRANTS £100–£5,000 with occasional larger special grants.

SAMPLE GRANTS Wandsworth Bereavement Service and Putney Poor Relief Committee (£3,000 each); and the Work and Play Resource Centre (£1,500).

FINANCES *Year* 2013 *Income* £24,000 *Grants* £24,000

TRUSTEES Andrew Collender; Vanessa Davey; Richard Holman; Kate Caseley; Jessica Walters; Perry Kitchen; Alison Stevens; Mark White; Nicky Scotts; Nick Hudson; Jane Hopper.

HOW TO APPLY In writing to the correspondent. Applications are considered first by a subcommittee of trustees with specialist knowledge of the particular area to which the request for funds relates (church, youth or community); recommendations are then put before full meetings of the Trustees, which are held bi-annually.

WHO TO APPLY TO Angela Holman, Secretary and Administrator, 11 Genoa Avenue, Putney, London SW15 6DY *Tel.* 020 8789 0953 *email* angelaholman@virgin.net

■ Millennium Stadium Charitable Trust

CC NO 1086596   **ESTABLISHED** 2001

WHERE FUNDING CAN BE GIVEN Wales.

WHO CAN BENEFIT The trust supports: not-for-profit organisations; properly constituted voluntary organisations; charitable organisations; voluntary groups working with local authorities (applicant cannot be the local authority); applications from groups of any age (not just youth projects). Priority is given to organisations

serving groups and communities suffering from the greatest disadvantage.

WHAT IS FUNDED Through its grant funding the trust aims to improve the quality of life of people who live and work in Wales. In particular the trust aims to promote education, history, language and culture, particularly for those who face disadvantage or discrimination. The trust makes grants in four programme areas: (1) sport; (2) the arts; (3) the environment; (4) the community. The trust is keen to help young people learn more about their country via exchange programmes and has made provision to support youth exchange programmes which fall in to any of the funding categories of the trust.

WHAT IS NOT FUNDED The trust does not support: projects outside of Wales; day-to-day running costs; projects that seek to redistribute grant funds for the benefit of third party organisations; payments of debts/overdrafts; retrospective requests; requests from individuals; payment to profit making organisations; applications made solely in the name of a local authority. (In addition to the above, successful applicants may not-reapply to the trust until a three year period from the date of grant offer has elapsed. The grant offer letter will advise applicants of the date when they will be eligible to re-apply.)

RANGE OF GRANTS The trust issues funding according to the size of geographical area that an organisation has a remit to cover. National (Wales–wide)–up to £12,500; regional–up to £7,500; local–up to £2,500.

SAMPLE GRANTS Cardiff Foodbank; South Gwent Children's Foundation; The Bridge to Cross Charitable Trust; Rhyl Yacht Club and Take Part Community Group.

FINANCES *Year* 2011–12 *Income* £341,677 *Grants* £367,464 *Assets* £152,086

TRUSTEES Russell Goodway; Ian Davies; Gerald Davies; Paul Glaze; Gerallt Hughes; Peredur Jenkins; Mike John; John Lloyd-Jones; Linda Pepper; Louise Prynne; Huw Thomas; Andrew Walker.

HOW TO APPLY The trust holds three rounds a year one for each type of application – national, regional and local. Deadline dates can be found on the trust's website, along with full guidelines and application forms.

WHO TO APPLY TO Sarah Fox, Suite 1 4, Bessemer Road, Cardiff CF11 8BA *Tel.* 02920 022143 *email* info@millenniumstadiumtrust.org.uk *Website* www.millenniumstadiumtrust.co.uk

■ The Hugh and Mary Miller Bequest Trust

SC NO SC014950   **ESTABLISHED** 1976

WHERE FUNDING CAN BE GIVEN Mainly Scotland.

WHO CAN BENEFIT Registered charities. The trust supports disability causes, with the same 18 organisations receiving the majority of funding each year.

WHAT IS FUNDED Healthcare and disability.

WHAT IS NOT FUNDED Only registered charities are supported. No grants to individuals.

TYPE OF GRANT Capital including buildings, core costs, project, research, recurring costs, running costs and salaries. Funding is available for more than three years.

FINANCES *Year* 2011–12 *Income* £107,738 *Grants* £90,000

TRUSTEES G. R. G. Graham; H. C. Davidson.

OTHER INFORMATION Research indicates that grants are made to regular beneficiaries totalling around £90,000 each year.

HOW TO APPLY The trust states that its funds are fully committed.

WHO TO APPLY TO Andrew S. Biggart, Secretary, c/o Maclay Murray and Spens Solicitors, 1 George Square, Glasgow G2 1AL *Tel.* 01412 485011 *Fax* 01412 715319 *email* andrew.biggart@mms.co.uk

■ The Ronald Miller Foundation

SC NO SC008798   **ESTABLISHED** 1979

WHERE FUNDING CAN BE GIVEN UK, with a preference for Scotland, especially Glasgow.

WHO CAN BENEFIT Charities benefiting children and young adults; students; at risk groups; disabled groups; those disadvantaged by poverty; and socially isolated people.

WHAT IS FUNDED Arts, social welfare, education, environment and health have all been supported

WHAT IS NOT FUNDED No grants to individuals.

RANGE OF GRANTS £1,000–£2,000.

FINANCES *Year* 2011–12 *Income* £181,265 *Grants* £150,000

TRUSTEES C. Fleming-Brown; G. R. G. Graham; J. Simpson; G. F. R. Fleming-Brown.

HOW TO APPLY In writing to the correspondent.

WHO TO APPLY TO The Secretary, Maclay Murray and Spens, 151 St Vincent Street, Glasgow G2 5NJ

■ The Millfield House Foundation

CC NO 271180   **ESTABLISHED** 1976

WHERE FUNDING CAN BE GIVEN North east England particularly Tyne and Wear.

WHO CAN BENEFIT Voluntary agencies and other bodies with charitable objectives working with socially and economically disadvantaged people. Bodies undertaking policy research and advocacy should have close links with or voluntary or community organisations in the region. The foundation will support national as well as local bodies, provided that projects are based in the North East of England (includes regional and sub-regional projects; projects which are locally based may be considered so long as they are of wider benefit).

WHAT IS FUNDED The foundation funds in three ways: 'We invite a limited number of policy-focused organisations to become our strategic partners. We are developing the capacity and policy skills of the North East voluntary sector through placements we are setting up with accomplished policy-focused organisations. Through our open grants programme we support applications from the field.'

WHAT IS NOT FUNDED The foundation 'will not fund straightforward service provision, or mainline university research, or the wide range of other projects that are eligible for support elsewhere'.

TYPE OF GRANT Capacity building; project funding; advocacy and campaigning.

RANGE OF GRANTS Between £5,000 and £360,000 over many years.

SAMPLE GRANTS Regional Refugees Forum North East (£161,000 over three years); Mental Health North East (£70,000); Voluntary Organisations North East (£60,000 over two years); IPPR North and Regional Youth Work Unit North East (£35,000 each); Northumbria University (£31,000); Centrepoint (£22,000); Age UK North Tyneside (£20,000); Cyrenians (£17,000) and Blyth Valley Citizens Advice (£6,100).

FINANCES *Year* 2011–12 *Income* £168,500 *Grants* £277,500 *Assets* £5,268,200

TRUSTEES Grigor McClelland; Stephen McClelland; Sheila Spencer; Robert Williamson; Toby Lowe; Jane Streather; Rhiannon Bearne; Peter Deans; Betty Weallans; John Williamson; Andrew Curry.

PUBLICATIONS Report: 'Funding Policy Change for a Better Society in the North East of England', 1996–2004, available in PDF version.

HOW TO APPLY Applications can only be made using the trusts application form available on their website. The following documents should be attached with the form: a copy of the most recent annual report and accounts or a reference to the Charity Commission website if they are available on there; the governing document; a job description for and requests for funding towards a salaried post. The trustees meet twice a year, in May and November and the deadlines for the trustees' meetings are end March or end September. If the trustees are interested the trust manager may request further information and/or a meeting. For further information potential applicants are strongly advised to visit the trust's website.

WHO TO APPLY TO Fiona Ellis, Trusts Manager, Brunswick House, Whaelton, Morpeth, Northumberland NE61 3UZ *Tel.* 07500 057825 *email* fiona.ellis@mhfdn.org.uk *Website* www.mhfdn.org.uk

■ The Millfield Trust

CC NO 262406   **ESTABLISHED** 1971

WHERE FUNDING CAN BE GIVEN UK and worldwide.

WHO CAN BENEFIT Individuals and organisations benefiting elderly people, Christians, and people in need.

WHAT IS FUNDED Support of religious or other charitable institutions or work. Advancement of the Protestant and Evangelical tenets of the Christian faith and encouragement of missionary activity. Relief of need. Preference to charities of which the trust has special interest, knowledge or association. Funds fully allocated or committed.

TYPE OF GRANT Unrestricted.

RANGE OF GRANTS £100–£14,000

SAMPLE GRANTS Gospel Mission to South America (£14,000); Gideons International (£13,000); Ashbury Evangelical Free Church (£6,000); Mission to Europe (£3,000); Overseas Council for Theological Education and Mission (£2,500); Revival and Armonia (UK) Trust (£2,000 each); Scripture Union (£1,800) and Abacus Trust and Send a Cow (£1,100 each).

FINANCES *Year* 2011–12 *Income* £95,727 *Grants* £75,950 *Assets* £165,633

TRUSTEES Andrew Bunce; David Bunce; Philip Bunce; Stephen Bunce; Rita Winifred Bunce.

OTHER INFORMATION A further £2,000 was given to 'individual evangelists and missionaries' and £80 to pensioners and widows.

HOW TO APPLY No replies to unsolicited applications.

WHO TO APPLY TO D. Bunce, Trustee, Millfield House, Bell Lane, Liddington, Swindon, Wiltshire SN4 0HE *Tel.* 01793 790181

■ The Millhouses Charitable Trust

CC NO 327773   **ESTABLISHED** 1988

WHERE FUNDING CAN BE GIVEN UK and overseas.

WHO CAN BENEFIT Registered charities benefiting Christians, at risk groups, people disadvantaged by poverty, socially isolated people, victims of famine, disasters and war.

WHAT IS FUNDED Overseas aid, social welfare and community services (with a Christian emphasis). A preference is shown for Baptist charities.

WHAT IS NOT FUNDED Grants are made to registered charities only; no grants to individuals.

TYPE OF GRANT Mostly recurrent.

RANGE OF GRANTS £250–£12,000.

SAMPLE GRANTS Previously: NSPCC and Christian Solidarity (£5,000 each); Release International and Barnabas Fund (£2,500 each); Children's Society, Crisis and Oasis (£1,000 each); Rehab UK and Medical foundation (£500 each); and Mercy Ships, Operation Mobilisation and Smile (£250 each).

FINANCES *Year* 2011–12 *Income* £10,258 *Grants* £9,000

TRUSTEES Revd Jeanetta S. Harcus; Dr A. W. Harcus; Dr J. L. S. Alexander; Penelope A. Thornton; Fiona J van Nieuwkerk.

HOW TO APPLY In writing to the correspondent, but note that most of the grants given by this trust are recurrent. If new grants are made, they are usually to organisations known to the trustees.

WHO TO APPLY TO Paul Charles Kurthausen, Administrator, c/o B. W. MacFarlane LLP, Castle Chambers, Castle Street, Liverpool L2 9SH *Tel.* 01512 361494

························

■ The Millichope Foundation

CC NO 282357   **ESTABLISHED** 1981

WHERE FUNDING CAN BE GIVEN UK, especially the West Midlands and Shropshire.

WHO CAN BENEFIT Registered charities, some grants to UK and international organisations; local applications limited to the West Midlands and Shropshire.

WHAT IS FUNDED The foundation makes donations in the UK to arts, culture, conservation and heritage. Grants are made specifically within Shropshire for general charitable purposes. Worldwide conservation projects and disaster funds are also occasionally supported.

WHAT IS NOT FUNDED No grants to individuals or non-registered charities.

TYPE OF GRANT Normally an annual commitment for a period of five years.

RANGE OF GRANTS Usually £500–£5,000.

SAMPLE GRANTS Fauna and Flora International (£20,000); Shropshire Historic Churches Trust (£10,000); Manali School/Hospital (£5,000); Community of the Holy Fire (£2,500); Macmillan Cancer Support and Welsh National Opera (£2,000 each); Age Concern Ludlow, Shropshire Victim Support and Relate Shropshire (£1,000 each); Isle of Jura Music Festival (£500) and Frank Haines Memorial Trust (£200).

FINANCES *Year* 2011–12 *Income* £509,675 *Grants* £239,162 *Assets* £6,081,783

TRUSTEES Bridget Marshall; Sarah Bury; Lindsay Bury; Frank Bury; H. M. Horne.

HOW TO APPLY In writing to the correspondent. Trustees meet several times a year to consider grants.

WHO TO APPLY TO S. A. Bury, Trustee, The Old Rectory, Tugford, Craven Arms, Shropshire SY7 9HS *Tel.* 01584 841234 *email* sarah@millichope.com

························

■ The Mills Charity

CC NO 207259   **ESTABLISHED** 1981

WHERE FUNDING CAN BE GIVEN Framlingham and surrounding district.

WHO CAN BENEFIT Charitable organisations and some individuals.

WHAT IS FUNDED General charitable purposes and social welfare.

SAMPLE GRANTS Sir Hitchams CEVAP School – funding for toilet refurbishment (£26,000); St Michael's Parish Church – funding for kitchen (£10,000); Brandeston Parochial Church Council – funding for repair to church (£5,000) and Disability Advice Service (£1,000).

FINANCES *Year* 2011–12 *Income* £170,633 *Grants* £41,827 *Assets* £7,200,465

TRUSTEES H. Wright; P. Booth; K. Musgrove; M. Kelleway; N. Corke; K. Hunt; Dr C. Wright; Revd M. Vipond.

OTHER INFORMATION Grants totalling £3,644 were given to individuals.

HOW TO APPLY In writing to the correspondent.

WHO TO APPLY TO Chair of the Trustees, PO Box 1703, Framlingham, Woodbridge IP13 9WW *Tel.* 01728 638038 *email* info@themillscharity.co.uk *Website* www.themillscharity.co.uk

························

■ The Millward Charitable Trust

CC NO 328564   **ESTABLISHED** 1989

WHERE FUNDING CAN BE GIVEN UK and overseas

WHO CAN BENEFIT Charitable organisations.

WHAT IS FUNDED Social welfare, performing arts, medical research and animal welfare

TYPE OF GRANT One-off grants.

SAMPLE GRANTS Birds Eye View (£36,000 in three grants); Music in the Round (£6,400); City of Birmingham Symphony Orchestra (£10,000 in two grants); CORD Sudan Appeal and Leamington Music RSPCA (£5,000 each); and Barnardo's, Christian Relief, Howard League for Penal Reform and RSPCA (1,000 each).

FINANCES *Year* 2009–10 *Income* £68,445 *Grants* £84,158 *Assets* £1,996,781

TRUSTEES Maurice Millward; Sheila Millward; John Hulse.

OTHER INFORMATION The trust has had consistently overdue accounts at the Charity Commission. The last financial information available at the time of writing (September 2013) was for 2009/10.

HOW TO APPLY In writing to the correspondent.

WHO TO APPLY TO John Hulse, Trustee, c/o Burgis and Bullock, 2 Chapel Court, Holly Walk, Leamington Spa, Warwickshire CV32 4YS *Tel.* 01926 451000

························

■ The Clare Milne Trust

CC NO 1084733   **ESTABLISHED** 1999

WHERE FUNDING CAN BE GIVEN The south west of England, but Devon and Cornwall in practice.

WHO CAN BENEFIT Voluntary and community groups.

WHAT IS FUNDED Disability projects, especially those for adults in the south west of England, mainly in Devon and Cornwall. Preference is given to small and well-run local and regional charities with strong support from volunteers and with only modest expenditure on fundraising and administration.

WHAT IS NOT FUNDED No grants directly to or for individuals or to national charities.

TYPE OF GRANT Generally a partial contribution towards total cost of a project.

RANGE OF GRANTS Typically £1,000–£25,000.

SAMPLE GRANTS CEDA (£36,000); Bidwell Brook Foundation, Disability Cornwall (£20,000 each); Macular Disease Society (£10,000); Robert Owen Communities (£6,000); Access to Community Education (£5,000); and Cornwall Dyslexia Association (£1,000).

FINANCES *Year* 2012 *Income* £718,862 *Grants* £456,753 *Assets* £22,093,648

TRUSTEES Michael Brown, Chair; Lucie Nottingham; Tim Robinson; Margaret Rogers; Nigel Urwin.

HOW TO APPLY If you think your project meets the trust's criteria, you should write summarising your request on one side of an A4 sheet if possible, with minimal supporting literature; the trust will request a copy of your annual report and accounts later on if necessary. The trustees usually meet four times a year and to save unnecessary administration only applications which fit the trust's criteria will be responded to.

WHO TO APPLY TO Kim Lyons, Secretary, c/o Lee Bolton Monier-Williams Solicitors, 1 The Sanctuary, Westminster, London SW1P 3JT *Tel.* 020 7404 0422 *email* milnetrust@hotmail.co.uk *Website* www.claremilnetrust.com

....

■ Milton Keynes Community Foundation

CC NO 295107　　　**ESTABLISHED** 1987

WHERE FUNDING CAN BE GIVEN Milton Keynes Unitary Authority.

WHO CAN BENEFIT Community groups, community interest companies, social enterprises, sports clubs, parish councils and local registered charities benefiting; people of all ages, at risk groups, carers, disabled people, those disadvantaged by poverty, homeless people, and victims of abuse, crime and domestic violence.

WHAT IS FUNDED The foundation's main priority is to help those in the Milton Keynes Council area who miss out because of poverty, ill health, disability or disadvantage. It also supports important initiatives in the spheres of the arts and leisure.

WHAT IS NOT FUNDED No grants are made to the following types of organisation: statutory organisations – including schools, hospitals and borough councils (applications from parish councils for community projects are accepted); political parties or groups affiliated to a political party; or individuals. Grants are normally not given for: sponsorship and fundraising events; contributions to major appeals; projects outside the beneficial area; political groups; projects connected with promoting a religious message of any kind; work which should be funded by health and local authorities or government grants aid; animal welfare; medical research or treatment; ongoing core costs not related to a particular service or activity; retrospective grants; nor grants to pay off deficits.

TYPE OF GRANT Small grants of up to £1,500; community grants up to £5,000 to cover equipment costs, projects and minor building work, training, publicity and one-off activity costs; arts grants awarded for artistic and cultural activities, particularly of high quality and originality; extraordinary grants for exceptional or urgent causes or for amounts of more than £5,000. The grants team must grant permission before extraordinary grants applications are made.

RANGE OF GRANTS Usually up to £5,000; possibility of more for extraordinary grants.

SAMPLE GRANTS Age UK Milton Keynes (£9,600); Church of Council of All Saints Emberton and Milton Keynes YMCA (£5,000 each); Arabian School of Gymnastics (£4,500); Special Needs Unit Gymnastics (SNUGS) (£4,200); The Children's Society (£3,800); MK Cheerleading Academy (£3,000); Desperate 2 Dance

(£2,400); Conniburrow Community Association (£2,100); Saahil Support Group (£1,400); Tattenhoe Youth Football Club (£1,000); City Discovery Centre (£780) and Age UK MK (£500).

FINANCES *Year* 2011–12 *Income* £2,363,606 *Grants* £466,356 *Assets* £100,002,800

TRUSTEES Judith Hooper; Fola Komolafe; Francesca Skelton; Jane Matthews; Michael Murray; Peter Kara; Peter Selvey; Richard Brown; Roger Kitchen; Ruth Stone; Stephen Norrish; Philip Butler; John Moffoot.

OTHER INFORMATION In 2011–12 there was a further £21,000 given in grants to individuals through the Arts Bursaries programme. **It is important to note that grant schemes can change frequently. For full details of the foundation's current grant programmes and their deadlines consult the website**.

HOW TO APPLY Application forms and guidelines are available on the website or can be requested by telephoning the office. The grants staff can be contacted to assist with any queries or help with applications. Deadlines for small grants programme is the last working Friday of each month and the community grants programme has five deadlines per year. Small grant applications are usually processed within two weeks and community grants, five weeks.

WHO TO APPLY TO Bart Gamber, Grants Director, Acorn House, 381 Midsummer Boulevard, Central Milton Keynes MK9 3HP *Tel.* 01908 690276 *Fax* 01908 233635 *email* info@mkcommunityfoundation.co.uk *Website* www.mkcommunityfoundation.co.uk

....

■ The Edgar Milward Charity

CC NO 281018　　　**ESTABLISHED** 1980

WHERE FUNDING CAN BE GIVEN UK and overseas, with an interest in Reading.

WHO CAN BENEFIT Causes known to the trustees, particularly those supported by the settlor.

WHAT IS FUNDED A limited number of Christian and humanitarian causes. The trustees currently have an established interest in a range of charities. Few new charities will be added to this list.

WHAT IS NOT FUNDED No new applications will be supported.

SAMPLE GRANTS Connect4Life (£5,000); Bransgore Community Church and Global Outreach (£2,000 each); Africa Inland Mission (£1,500); Christian Legal Centre, Greyfriars Missionary Trust, Open Doors and REAP (£1,000 each).

FINANCES *Year* 2012–13 *Income* £51,619 *Grants* £49,460 *Assets* £1,314,867

TRUSTEES J. S. Milward, Chair; M. V. Roberts; G. M. Fogwill; S. M. W. Fogwill; A. S. Fogwill; F. Palethorpe; J. C. Austin.

HOW TO APPLY Unsolicited applications are not normally considered.

WHO TO APPLY TO A. S. Fogwill, Corresponding Secretary, 53 Brook Drive, Corsham, Wiltshire SN13 9AX *Tel.* 01832 270055

....

■ The Keith and Joan Mindelsohn Charitable Trust

CC NO 1075174　　　**ESTABLISHED** 1998

WHERE FUNDING CAN BE GIVEN Birmingham and West Midlands.

WHO CAN BENEFIT Charitable organisations, with a preference for smaller groups who lack the resources of national organisations and where the grant will make a more noticeable difference.

WHAT IS FUNDED General charitable purposes.

TYPE OF GRANT Project grants.

RANGE OF GRANTS Average £1,000–£5,000

SAMPLE GRANTS KIDS – West Midlands; Motor Neurone Disease; Whizz-Kidz, Heartlands Cystic Fibrosis; Birmingham Rathbone; Lady Hoare Trust; Ackers Trust; Autism West Midlands; Elizabeth Dowell Trust; Samaritans Birmingham and World Jewish Relief.

FINANCES *Year* 2011–12 *Income* £15,752 *Grants* £60,000

TRUSTEES Jane Jaffa; Christine Thomas; Gillian Hickman.

HOW TO APPLY In writing to the correspondent, preferably via e-mail. The trustees meet three times a year.

WHO TO APPLY TO Richard Jaffa, Administrator, 32 Malcolmson Close, Edgbaston, Birmingham B15 3LS *Tel.* 01214 546661 *email* rjaffa3266@aol.com

■ The Peter Minet Trust

CC NO 259963   **ESTABLISHED** 1969

WHERE FUNDING CAN BE GIVEN Mainly south east London boroughs, particularly Lambeth and Southwark.

WHO CAN BENEFIT UK registered charities.

WHAT IS FUNDED Registered charities (not individuals), particularly those working in the following areas: community; cultural; health and disability and youth.

WHAT IS NOT FUNDED The trust does not make grants for: individuals; national appeals by large charities; appeals outside the inner boroughs of South East London; appeals whose sole purpose is to make grants from collected funds; research.

TYPE OF GRANT Main grants of £5,000 or small grants of up to £500.

RANGE OF GRANTS £50 –£5,000.

SAMPLE GRANTS Alzheimer's Society, FareShare and Latin American Disabled People's Project (£5,000 each); Slade Gardens Community Play Association and Raw Material (£4,250 each); Cardboard Citizens (£4,000); Somali Mental Health and Advocacy Project (£3,300); Futures Theatre Company, London Philharmonic Orchestra and Springfield Community Flat (£3,000 each); Stockwell Partnership (£2,500); The Guild of Psychotherapists and Bermondsey Artists' Group (£2,000); Dog Kennel Hill Adventure Playground (£1,500); Kings College London (£1,000) and Little Starz Children's Services and Sickle Cell and Young Stroke Survivors (£500 each).

FINANCES *Year* 2011–12 *Income* £202,905 *Grants* £151,438 *Assets* £4,686,066

TRUSTEES J. C. B. South, Chair; Ms P. C. Jones; R. Luff; Simon Hebditch; L. Cleverly.

HOW TO APPLY Using the online application process on the trust's website. Main grants are awarded in February, June and October and applications should be submitted approximately two months beforehand. See the application guidelines for exact dates. Applications for small grants can be made at any time and a decision will be communicated within four weeks. The office is open Monday and Tuesday 9.00–15.00 and Wednesday 10.00–14.00.

WHO TO APPLY TO Rachel Oglethorpe, 1a Taylors Yard, 67 Alderbrook Road, London SW12 8AD *Tel.* 020 8772 3155 *email* info@peterminet. org.uk *Website* www.peterminet.org.uk

■ Minge's Gift and the Pooled Trusts

CC NO 266073   **ESTABLISHED** 1972

WHERE FUNDING CAN BE GIVEN UK, with some preference for the City of London

WHO CAN BENEFIT Registered charities, schools, universities, hospitals, churches and organisations associated with the footwear trade.

WHAT IS FUNDED General charitable purposes as directed by the Master and Wardens of the Cordwainers Company. The income of Minge's Gift is generally allocated for the long-term support of medical and educational establishments and towards disabled and/or disadvantaged young people. The Pooled Trusts mainly support individuals including scholars, the blind, deaf, clergy widows, spinsters of the Church of England, ex-servicemen and their widows and those who served in the merchant services.

WHAT IS NOT FUNDED Grants to individuals are only given through the Pooled Trusts.

TYPE OF GRANT Grants of up to, and in some cases over, three years for core costs, projects, research, and recurring costs; start-up costs are considered.

RANGE OF GRANTS £100–£17,000.

SAMPLE GRANTS University of Northampton (£17,000); Urswick School Hackney, Library Books (£13,000); Royal London Society for the Blind (Dorton House) (£8,000); Capel Manor College (2 Bursaries) (£6,000); University of the Arts, London (£5,300), Footwear Friends (£4,500); University College London (£4,000); Guildhall School of Music and Drama (£2,100); British Footwear Development Trust (£2,000); Lord Mayor's Fund (£1,500); Leather Conservation Centre (£1,000); St Dunstan-in-the-West Church (£700); St Mary Magdalene Enfield (£500); Museum of London (£100.

FINANCES *Year* 2011–12 *Income* £197,397 *Grants* £93,707 *Assets* £2,998,421

TRUSTEE The Master and Wardens of the Worshipful Company of Cordwainers.

OTHER INFORMATION In 2011–12 £11,600 was given to individuals through the pooled trusts.

HOW TO APPLY In writing to the correspondent.

WHO TO APPLY TO John Miller, Company Clerk, The Worshipful Company of Cordwainers, Clothworkers Hall, Dunster Court, Mincing Lane, London EC3R 7AH *Tel.* 020 7929 1121 *Fax* 020 7929 1124 *email* office@cordwainers. org *Website* www.cordwainers.org

■ The Minos Trust

CC NO 265012   **ESTABLISHED** 1972

WHERE FUNDING CAN BE GIVEN UK and overseas with a preference for West Sussex.

WHO CAN BENEFIT Organisations.

WHAT IS FUNDED General charitable purposes, especially Christian causes.

RANGE OF GRANTS £25–£2,000, exceptionally higher.

SAMPLE GRANTS Previous beneficiaries include: Care Trust (£2,500), Tearfund (£2,000) and Ashburnham Christian Trust (£1,500), with £1,000 each to Bible Society, Friends of the Elderly and Youth with a Mission; Worldwide Fund for Nature (£450); Africa Christian Press (£400); Aid to Russian Christians (£300); Gideon's International (£100); Sussex Farming Wildlife Advisory Group and RSPB (£50 each).

FINANCES *Year* 2012–13 *Income* £6,912 *Grants* £16,000

TRUSTEES Revd K. W. Habershon; E. M. Habershon; D. M. Irwin-Clark.

HOW TO APPLY In writing to the correspondent, for consideration on an ongoing basis.

WHO TO APPLY TO The Trustees, Kleinwort Benson Trustees Ltd, 30 Gresham Street, London EC2V 7PG *Tel.* 020 3207 7091

■ Minton Charitable Trust

CC NO 1112106   **ESTABLISHED** 2005

WHERE FUNDING CAN BE GIVEN UK.

WHO CAN BENEFIT Organisations and individuals.

WHAT IS FUNDED 'The advancement and promotion of the education of the public through the provision of, or assisting with, the provision of facilities, support, education, advice and financial assistance.'

RANGE OF GRANTS Up to £200,000.

SAMPLE GRANTS St Giles Trust (£125,000)

FINANCES *Year* 2011–12 *Income* £212,382 *Grants* £126,500 *Assets* £606,949

TRUSTEES Sir Anthony Armitage Greener; Richard Edmunds; Lady Audrey Greener.

HOW TO APPLY In writing to the correspondent.

WHO TO APPLY TO Sir Anthony Armitage Greener, Trustee, Flat 26 Hamilton House, Vicarage Gate, London W8 4HL

■ The Mirfield Educational Charity

CC NO 529334   **ESTABLISHED** 1961

WHERE FUNDING CAN BE GIVEN The urban district of Mirfield.

WHO CAN BENEFIT Individuals and organisations.

WHAT IS FUNDED Education and social and physical training of people under 25

RANGE OF GRANTS £200–£30,000

SAMPLE GRANTS Communities United Project (£8,000); Crossley Fields School (£5,000); Battyeford Sporting Club (£3,000) and Muirfield Ranbows (£225).

FINANCES *Year* 2011–12 *Income* £48,636 *Grants* £29,771 *Assets* £1,385,389

TRUSTEES Dr Howard Grason; Jaqueline Longbottom; Paul Morton; Edward Speight; Martyn Bolt; Christopher Oldfield; Vivien Lees-Hamilton; Christine Sykes; Heather Conolly

HOW TO APPLY In writing to the correspondent.

WHO TO APPLY TO Malcolm Parkinson, c/o Ramsdens Whitfield Hafiam, 7 King Street, Mirfield WF14 8AW *Tel.* 01924 499251 *email* Malcolm. Parkinson@ramsdens.co.uk

■ The Mirianog Trust

CC NO 1091397   **ESTABLISHED** 2002

WHERE FUNDING CAN BE GIVEN UK.

WHO CAN BENEFIT Charitable organisations.

WHAT IS FUNDED General charitable purposes. Currently the trustees give preference to: the relief of poverty; overseas aid and famine relief; accommodation and housing; environment, conservation and heritage.

SAMPLE GRANTS Justice First (£6,100); Medical Aid for Palestine and Freedom of Torture (£3,000); Shelter, Children with Aids, RIDERS and Bwindi Hospice (£2,000); Key (£1,500) and Temwa (£1,000).

FINANCES *Year* 2011–12 *Income* £28,609 *Grants* £34,586 *Assets* £636,957

TRUSTEES Canon William Broad, Chair; Daphne Broad; Elizabeth Jeary.

HOW TO APPLY In writing to the correspondent. The trustees meet twice each year.

WHO TO APPLY TO Canon W. E. L. Broad, Trustee, Moorcote, Thornley, Tow Law, Bishop Auckland DL13 4NU *Tel.* 01388 731350

■ The Laurence Misener Charitable Trust

CC NO 283460   **ESTABLISHED** 1981

WHERE FUNDING CAN BE GIVEN UK.

WHO CAN BENEFIT There is a tendency to benefit those charities in which the settlor was interested.

WHAT IS FUNDED General charitable purposes, particularly Jewish organisations and medical causes.

RANGE OF GRANTS £4,000–£15,000.

SAMPLE GRANTS Jewish Association for the Physically Handicapped, Jewish Care and Nightingale House (£15,000 each); Cancer Research UK (£14,000); Seafarers UK (£10,000); Jews' Temporary Shelter (£8,000); Blond McIndoe Centre, Cassel Hospital Families Centre Appeal, Elimination of Leukaemia Fund, Great Ormond Street Children's Hospital Fund, Sussex Stroke and Circulation Fund, Royal Marsden Hospital and World Jewish Relief (£7,000 each).

FINANCES *Year* 2011–12 *Income* £95,650 *Grants* £174,000 *Assets* £2,442,209

TRUSTEES Jillian Legane; Capt. George Frederick Swaine.

HOW TO APPLY In writing to the correspondent.

WHO TO APPLY TO David Lyons, Administrator, c/o Leonard Jones and Co, 1 Printing Yard House, London E2 7PR *Tel.* 020 7739 8790

■ The Mishcon Family Charitable Trust

CC NO 213165   **ESTABLISHED** 1961

WHERE FUNDING CAN BE GIVEN UK.

WHO CAN BENEFIT Registered charities, particularly Jewish organisations.

WHAT IS FUNDED General charitable purposes. Within the limited funds available each application is considered on its merits with preference given to applications for the relief of poverty from recognised organisations.

TYPE OF GRANT One-off.

RANGE OF GRANTS £20 upwards. Generally £5,000 or less.

SAMPLE GRANTS Jewish Israel Appeal (£37,000); Sick Children's Trust (£6,500); The Board of Deputies Charitable Trust (£6,000); Friends of Progressive Judaism (£5,000); Friends of Alyn (£2,000); The Lubavich Foundation and World Jewish Relief (£1,000 each); One World Action (£450); Jewish Book Council, Jewish Care, NSPCC and Rainbow Trust (£100 each); and The Stroke Association (£50).

FINANCES *Year* 2011–12 *Income* £60,642 *Grants* £92,163 *Assets* £1,812,315

TRUSTEES P. A. Mishcon; R. O. Mishcon; J. Landau.

HOW TO APPLY In writing to the correspondent.

WHO TO APPLY TO The Trustees, Summit House, 12 Red Lion Square, London WC1R 4QD

■ The Misselbrook Trust

CC NO 327928   **ESTABLISHED** 1988

WHERE FUNDING CAN BE GIVEN UK with a preference for the Wessex area.

WHO CAN BENEFIT Registered charities.

WHAT IS FUNDED General charitable purposes.

TYPE OF GRANT One-off and recurrent

RANGE OF GRANTS Up to £10,000, usually under £500.

SAMPLE GRANTS Enham Trust (£2,000); and Aidis Trust, Marwell Preservation Trust and St Dunstan's (£1,000 each).

FINANCES *Year* 2011–12 *Income* £52,640 *Grants* £70,280 *Assets* £1,006,736

TRUSTEES Michael Howson-Green; Brian M. Baxendale; David A. Hoare; M. A. Howson-Green.

OTHER INFORMATION .

HOW TO APPLY In writing to the correspondent

WHO TO APPLY TO Michael Howson-Green, Trustee, Ashton House, 12 The Central Precinct, Winchester Road, Eastleigh, Hampshire SO53 2GB *Tel.* 02380 274555

■ The Brian Mitchell Charitable Settlement

CC NO 1003817   **ESTABLISHED** 1989

WHERE FUNDING CAN BE GIVEN UK.

WHO CAN BENEFIT Registered charities.

WHAT IS FUNDED General charitable purposes including education, the arts and health.

RANGE OF GRANTS Up to £20,000.

SAMPLE GRANTS Glyndebourne Festival Society (£20,000); Shakespeare's Globe Theatre (£15,000); The Skinners School and Macmillan Nurses (£10,000 each); Romanian Orphanage (£8,840); Hospice on the Weald, Archway, ABF, The Bridge Trust, Broomhill Bank School, ACT and St John Ambulance (£5,000 each).

FINANCES *Year* 2011–12 *Income* £770,142 *Grants* £119,660 *Assets* £1,094,947

TRUSTEES Brian Mitchell; Andrew Buss; John Andrews; Michael Conlon; Fraser Moore Reavell.

HOW TO APPLY In writing to the correspondent, although note that the charity has recently identified several regular beneficiaries.

WHO TO APPLY TO The Trustees, Round Oak, Old Station Road, Wadhurst, East Sussex TN5 6TZ *Tel.* 01892 782072 *email* brnmitchell3@googlemail.com

■ The Mitchell Charitable Trust

CC NO 290273   **ESTABLISHED** 1984

WHERE FUNDING CAN BE GIVEN UK, with a preference for London and overseas.

WHO CAN BENEFIT Organisations benefiting: people of all ages; volunteers; Jews; at risk groups; people disadvantaged by poverty; and victims of abuse and domestic violence.

WHAT IS FUNDED Jewish organisations, social welfare, voluntary organisations.

WHAT IS NOT FUNDED No grants to individuals or for non-Jewish religious appeals. Applicants from small charities outside London are unlikely to be considered.

TYPE OF GRANT Some recurring.

RANGE OF GRANTS £50–£38,000.

SAMPLE GRANTS Previous beneficiaries included: Hammersmith Clinical Research (£37,000); Ovarian Cancer Care (£34,500) and Prostate Cancer Research Foundation (£25,000); London School of Economics and Political Science (£6,000); Community Security Trust and Norwood (£5,000 each); National Council for Epilepsy (£500); and Kidney for Kids (£30).

FINANCES *Year* 2011–12 *Income* £39,964 *Grants* £30,372 *Assets* £1,164,296

TRUSTEES Ashley Mitchell; Elizabeth Mitchell; Antonia Mitchell; Keren Mitchell.

HOW TO APPLY In writing to the correspondent. Applications must include financial information. The trust does not reply to any applications unless they choose to support them. Trustees do not meet on a regular basis, thus applicants may not be advised of a grant for a considerable period.

WHO TO APPLY TO Ashley Mitchell, Trustee, 28 Heath Drive, London NW3 7SB *Tel.* 020 7794 5668

■ The Esmé Mitchell Trust

IR NO XN48053   **ESTABLISHED** 1965

WHERE FUNDING CAN BE GIVEN Ireland, but mainly Northern Ireland.

WHO CAN BENEFIT Organisations and individuals who are involved in the arts and cultural activities.

WHAT IS FUNDED General charitable purposes in Ireland as a whole but principally in Northern Ireland with a particular interest in cultural and artistic objects. Part of the trust fund is only available to assist certain heritage bodies as set out in Schedule 3 to the Capital Transfer Act 1984.

WHAT IS NOT FUNDED Grants are not usually given to individuals wishing to undertake voluntary service or further education.

TYPE OF GRANT No time limits have generally been set on grants. The trust has on occasions given grant assistance over a period of two to three years but in general tries not to become involved in commitments of a long-term nature.

RANGE OF GRANTS No restriction

FINANCES *Year* 2013 *Grants* £120,000

TRUSTEES P. J. Rankin; F. Jay-O'Boyle; R. P. Blakiston-Houston.

OTHER INFORMATION The trust makes grants totalling around £120,000 a year. Further information was not available.

HOW TO APPLY Trustees meet about five or six times a year. Guidelines for applicants are available from the trust.

WHO TO APPLY TO Lisa Smyth, Administrator, Cleaver Fulton Rankin Ltd. Solicitors, 50 Bedford Street, Belfast BT2 7FW *Tel.* 02890 243141

■ The MITIE Foundation

CC NO 1148858   **ESTABLISHED** 2012

WHERE FUNDING CAN BE GIVEN UK and the Republic of Ireland.

WHO CAN BENEFIT Charities and community groups.

WHAT IS FUNDED General charitable purposes, education and training and economic and community development. There is a particular interest in supporting organisations working with young people, older people and people with disabilities.

TRUSTEES Ruby McGregor-Smith; Suzanne Baxter; Paul Cooper.

HOW TO APPLY Following a request for further information about the foundation the correspondent stated: 'Whilst we are registered as a grant-maker, amongst other things, this will not be the primary activity of the charity and in fact it is unlikely to be making any grants in the foreseeable future.'

WHO TO APPLY TO Stephen Barthorpe, Caron House, 3 Oak Tree Court, Mulberry Drive, Cardiff Gate, Cardiff CF23 8RS *email* stephen.barthorpe@mitie.com

■ The Mittal Foundation

CC NO 1146604   **ESTABLISHED** 2012
WHERE FUNDING CAN BE GIVEN UK and India.
WHO CAN BENEFIT Registered charities.
WHAT IS FUNDED General charitable purposes, children and young people.
TRUSTEES Sudhir Maheshwari; Bhikham Chand Agarwal; Usha Mittal.
OTHER INFORMATION This foundation is one of the charitable endeavours of steel magnate Lakshmi Mittal, one of the richest people in the world, and his wife Usha, who is a trustee. The remaining trustees, Sudhir Maheshwari and Bhikham Chand Agarwal, hold senior management and directorship positions respectively at ArcelorMittal.
HOW TO APPLY In writing to the correspondent.
WHO TO APPLY TO The Trustees, c/o Mittal Investments Limited, Floor 3, Berkeley Square House, Berkeley Square, London W1J 6BU *Tel.* 020 7659 1033

■ Keren Mitzvah Trust

CC NO 1041948   **ESTABLISHED** 1994
WHERE FUNDING CAN BE GIVEN UK.
WHO CAN BENEFIT Jewish organisations; registered charities
WHAT IS FUNDED General charitable purposes.
TYPE OF GRANT One-off and recurrent.
RANGE OF GRANTS Up to £32,000
SAMPLE GRANTS Friends of Yeshivas Mir (£31,000); CML (£16,000); Cosmon Beiz Limited and Woodstock Sinclair Trust (£11,000 each); Edgware Jewish Primary School and KKL Charity (£10,000 each); Yesamach Levav Foundation (£7,000); NRST (£6,300) and European Beis Din and Centre for Advanced Rabbinics (£5,000).
FINANCES *Year* 2012 *Income* £212,303 *Grants* £199,603 *Assets* £55,101
TRUSTEES Manny Weiss; Alan McCormack; Neil Bradley.
HOW TO APPLY The trust stated that the trustees support their own personal charities.
WHO TO APPLY TO Naomi Crowther, 1 Manchester Square, London W1U 3AB

■ The Mizpah Trust

CC NO 287231   **ESTABLISHED** 1983
WHERE FUNDING CAN BE GIVEN UK and overseas.
WHO CAN BENEFIT Registered charities.
WHAT IS FUNDED Relief of poverty, aid and famine relief and Christianity.
TYPE OF GRANT One-off and recurrent.
RANGE OF GRANTS £50 to £30,000.
SAMPLE GRANTS The Vanessa Grant Trust (£60,000); CARE (£5,000); Micah Trust (£4,000) and The Stewards Trust, The Wilberforce Trust and The Saville Foundation (£1,000 each).
FINANCES *Year* 2011–12 *Income* £73,643 *Grants* £82,500 *Assets* £45,355
TRUSTEES Alan Bell; Julia Bell.
OTHER INFORMATION £500 went in grants to individuals.
HOW TO APPLY No unsolicited applications.
WHO TO APPLY TO A. C. O. Bell, Trustee, Foresters House, Humbly Grove, South Warnborough, Hook, Hampshire RG29 1RY

■ The Mobbs Memorial Trust Ltd

CC NO 202478   **ESTABLISHED** 1963
WHERE FUNDING CAN BE GIVEN Stoke Poges and district within a 35-mile radius of St Giles' Church.
WHO CAN BENEFIT Organisations benefiting: people of all ages; ex-service and service people; volunteers; unemployed; those in care, fostered and adopted; parents and children; at-risk groups; people with disabilities; those disadvantaged by poverty; ex-offenders and those at risk of offending; homeless people; those living in rural areas; socially isolated people; victims of abuse, crime and domestic violence.
WHAT IS FUNDED St Giles' Church and other charitable purposes including: almshouses; sheltered accommodation; community development; support to voluntary and community organisations; combined arts; community arts and recreation; health; conservation and environment; schools and colleges; and community facilities and services.
WHAT IS NOT FUNDED MMT does not normally support applications: from or for individuals or private companies; from national charitable organisations unless a specific need arises with the local area; that should be funded by national or local government; for running costs, apart from exceptional cases within a four miles radius of Stoke Poges.
TYPE OF GRANT Buildings and project. Funding is given for up to three years.
RANGE OF GRANTS Usually between £500 and £10,000.
SAMPLE GRANTS British Red Cross (£5,000); BMX Track – Iver Heath (£4,400); Farnham Royal (£4,000); Action 4 Youth (£3,000); Stoke Poges Old People's Christmas Fund and Stoke Poges Parochial Church Council Account (£2,000 each); and Thames Hospice Care (£1,500).
FINANCES *Year* 2011–12 *Income* £38,847 *Grants* £55,000
TRUSTEES Michael Mobbs; Dr Charles Mobbs; Chris Mobbs; Sandra Greenslade; Alexandra Mobbs.
HOW TO APPLY In writing to the correspondent. Applications can either be posted or emailed.
WHO TO APPLY TO Michael Mobbs, Chair, Cypress Cottage, 89 St John's Road, Newport, Isle of Wight PO30 1LS *email* applications@mobbsmemorialtrust.com *Website* www.mobbsmemorialtrust.com

■ The Modiano Charitable Trust

CC NO 328372   **ESTABLISHED** 1989
WHERE FUNDING CAN BE GIVEN UK and overseas
WHO CAN BENEFIT Charitable organisations, with some preference for Jewish groups.
WHAT IS FUNDED Development work, arts and relief of poverty.
TYPE OF GRANT One-off and recurrent
RANGE OF GRANTS £50–£20,000.
SAMPLE GRANTS Previous beneficiaries have included: Philharmonic Orchestra (£20,000); the Weiznam Institute Foundation (£10,000); DEC Haiti Appeal, St Paul's School and UJIA (£5,000 each); World Jewish Relief (£4,000); Life Action Trust (£3,500); CCJ and The Holocaust Educational Trust (£2,500 each); YMCA and the Reform Research Trust (1,000 each); and British Forces Association, Jewish Assoc. for the Mentally Ill (JAMI) and The St John of Jerusalem Eye Hospital (£100 each).
FINANCES *Year* 2011–12 *Income* £140,001 *Grants* £73,900 *Assets* £167,350

Think carefully about every application. Is it justified?

757

TRUSTEES Barbara Modiano; Laurence Modiano; Michael Modiano.

OTHER INFORMATION No list of grants available in the 2011–12 accounts.

HOW TO APPLY In writing to the correspondent.

WHO TO APPLY TO Michael Modiano, Trustee, Broad Street House, 55 Old Broad Street, London EC2M 1RX *Tel.* 020 7012 0000

■ The Moette Charitable Trust

CC NO 1068886   **ESTABLISHED** 1998

WHERE FUNDING CAN BE GIVEN UK and overseas.

WHO CAN BENEFIT People educationally disadvantaged through poverty.

WHAT IS FUNDED 'The principal activity of the trust is the provision of support of the poor and needy for educational purposes.'

SAMPLE GRANTS Previous beneficiaries have included: Finchley Road Synagogue (£15,000); King David Schools (Manchester) and Manchester Charitable Trust (£2,500); The Purim Fund (£2,000); Yad Voezer and Yeshivas Lev Aryeh (£1,000 each); Hakalo and London School of Jewish Studies (£500); Manchester Jewish Federation (£400); and Manchester Seminary for Girls (£50).

FINANCES *Year* 2011–12 *Income* £101,579 *Grants* £30,283 *Assets* £423,200

TRUSTEES Jonathan Brodie; Simon Lopian; Pearl Lopian.

HOW TO APPLY In writing to the correspondent

WHO TO APPLY TO Simon Lopian, Trustee, 1 Holden Road, Salford M7 4NL *Tel.* 01618 328721

■ The Mole Charitable Trust

CC NO 281452   **ESTABLISHED** 1980

WHERE FUNDING CAN BE GIVEN UK, with a preference for Manchester.

WHO CAN BENEFIT Individuals, registered charities and institutions benefiting children, young adults, Jews and people disadvantaged by poverty.

WHAT IS FUNDED Jewish causes, educational institutions and organisations to relieve poverty.

RANGE OF GRANTS £1,000–£60,000.

SAMPLE GRANTS Previous beneficiaries included: Three Pillars Charity (£60,000); Manchester Jewish Grammar School (£26,000); Chasdei Yoel Charitable Trust and United Talmudical Associates Limited (£20,000 each); Binoh of Manchester (£6,000); Beis Ruchel Girls School (£3,000); Manchester Jewish Federation (£2,500); and Our Kids (£1,000).

FINANCES *Year* 2011–12 *Income* £156,678 *Grants* £160,602 *Assets* £2,371,768

TRUSTEES Leah Pearl Gross; Martin Gross.

HOW TO APPLY The following is taken from the trustees' report 2011/12:

Grant-Making Policy The trustees receive many applications for grants, mainly personal contact, but also verbally. Each application is considered against the criteria established by the Charity. Although the Charity does not advertise, it is well known within its community and there are many requests received for grants. Feedback received is used to monitor the quality of grants.

WHO TO APPLY TO Martin Gross, Trustee, 2 Okeover Road, Salford M7 4JX *Tel.* 01618 328721 *email* martin.gross@lopiangb.co.uk

■ The Mollie Thomas Charitable Trust

CC NO 1149224   **ESTABLISHED** 2012

WHERE FUNDING CAN BE GIVEN UK.

WHO CAN BENEFIT Charities and community groups.

WHAT IS FUNDED General charitable purposes.

FINANCES *Year* 2012–13 *Income* £201,264

TRUSTEES Peggy Thomas; Martin Bell; Pauline Ball.

OTHER INFORMATION No grants were awarded during this first year of operation.

HOW TO APPLY In writing to the correspondent.

WHO TO APPLY TO Peggy Thomas, Trustee, 19 Presely View, Pembroke Dock, Pembrokeshire SA72 6NS

■ The Monatrea Charitable Trust

CC NO 1131897   **ESTABLISHED** 2009

WHERE FUNDING CAN BE GIVEN UK

WHO CAN BENEFIT Registered charities.

WHAT IS FUNDED General charitable purposes.

RANGE OF GRANTS £2,000–£27,000.

SAMPLE GRANTS Children Welfare Home; Samata Samaj; Dr Ambrosoli Memorial Health Care Centre; Prisoners' Advice Service; Family Action; Roses Charitable Trust; Samata Hospital; South Central Youth and Africa Conservation.

FINANCES *Year* 2011–12 *Income* £216,065 *Grants* £235,000 *Assets* £211,946

TRUSTEES Patrick Stephen Vernon; Mary Vernon; Coutts and Co.

HOW TO APPLY In writing to the correspondent.

WHO TO APPLY TO The Trustees, Coutts and Co, 440 Strand, London WC2R 0QS *Tel.* 020 7663 6838

■ The D. C. Moncrieff Charitable Trust

CC NO 203919   **ESTABLISHED** 1965

WHERE FUNDING CAN BE GIVEN UK and worldwide, with a preference for Norfolk and Suffolk.

WHO CAN BENEFIT Registered charities only.

WHAT IS FUNDED General charitable purposes. Trustees already have a list of beneficiaries whose requirements outweigh the trustees' ability to help.

WHAT IS NOT FUNDED No grants for individuals.

RANGE OF GRANTS Usually £400–£2,000. Larger grants for larger one–off projects or certain regularly supported local charities.

SAMPLE GRANTS Previous grants have included those to: All Hallows Hospital, East Anglia's Children's Hospices, the Society for Lincolnshire History and Archaeology, Hemley Church Parochial Church Council, Lowestoft Girl Guides Association and The Scouts Association, BREAK, Strongbones Children's Charitable Trust and East Anglian Air Ambulance Association.

FINANCES *Year* 2011–12 *Income* £43,889 *Grants* £33,000 *Assets* £2,053,079

TRUSTEES M. I. Willis; R. E. James; M. F. Dunne.

HOW TO APPLY In writing to the correspondent. The trust has previously stated that demand for funds exceeded available resources; therefore no further requests are currently invited.

WHO TO APPLY TO R. E. James, Trustee, 8 Quinnell Way, Lowestoft, Suffolk NR32 4WL

■ **Monmouthshire County Council Welsh Church Act Fund**

cc no 507094   established 1996

where funding can be given Blaenau Gwent, Caerphilly, Monmouthshire, Torfaen and Newport

who can benefit Students, at risk groups, and people who are disadvantaged by poverty, socially isolated, disaster victims, or sick.

what is funded Education, relief in sickness and need, people who are blind or elderly, medical and social research, probation, social and recreational, libraries, museums and art galleries and protection of historic buildings relating to Wales, places of worship and burial grounds, emergencies and disasters.

type of grant Mostly for provision, upkeep and repair of religious buildings and community halls.

range of grants Up to £1,000.

sample grants Previous beneficiaries include: Parish Church Llandogo, Parish Church Llangybi, Bridges Community Centre, St David's Foundation Hospice Care and North Wales Society for the Blind.

finances *Year* 2011–12 *Income* £84,349 *Grants* £216,397 *Assets* £4,729,239

trustee Monmouthshire County Council.

how to apply On a form available from the correspondent, this must be signed by a county councillor. They are considered in March, June, September and December.

who to apply to Joy Robson, Head of Finance, Monmouthshire County Council, Innovation House, PO Box 106, Magor, Caldicot NP26 9AN *Tel.* 01633 644657 *Fax* 01633 644260

■ **The Montague Thompson Coon Charitable Trust**

cc no 294096   established 1986

where funding can be given UK.

who can benefit Children with muscular diseases, medical research, environment.

what is funded Relief of sickness in children with muscular dystrophy and/or other muscular diseases, carrying out and provide for research into infant diseases and advancing the education of the public in the study of ecology and wildlife.

what is not funded No grants to individuals.

sample grants Livability (£10,000); The Wildfowl and Wetlands Trust (£7,500); Muscular Dystrophy Campaign (£6,000); Keech Hospice Care (£5,000); Farms for City Children (£4,000); and CP Sport (£1,000).

finances *Year* 2011–12 *Income* £54,723 *Grants* £37,880 *Assets* £1,227,704

trustees Peter Clarke, Chair; John Lister; Philippa Blake-Roberts.

how to apply In writing to the correspondent.

who to apply to Philippa Blake-Roberts, Trustee, Old Rectory, Church Lane, Colton, Norwich NR9 5DE *Tel.* 07766 072592

■ **The Colin Montgomerie Charitable Foundation**

cc no 1072388   established 1998

where funding can be given UK.

who can benefit Charitable organisations.

what is funded The relief of poverty, the advancement of education and religion, and general charitable purposes.

sample grants Previously: British Lung Foundation, Cancer Vaccine Institute, NSPCC – Full Stop Campaign and University of Glasgow MR Scanner Fund.

finances *Year* 2011 *Income* £87,500 *Grants* £40,000

trustees Colin Montgomerie; Guy Kinnings; Jonathan Dudman; Donna Cooksley.

how to apply In writing to the correspondent.

who to apply to Donna Cooksley, Trustee, c/o Catella, Chiswick Gate, 3rd Floor, 598–608 Chiswick High Road, London W4 5RT

■ **The Monument Trust**

cc no 242575   established 1965

where funding can be given Unrestricted, but UK and South Africa in practice.

who can benefit Registered charities working in the fields outlined below.

what is funded Arts and heritage, health and community care particularly HIV/AIDS and Parkinson's, social development particularly rehabilitation of offenders, general.

what is not funded Grants are not normally made to individuals.

range of grants Amounts up to £6 million, mostly under £500,000.

sample grants British Museum (£6 million); Tate Britain (£3 million); Parkinson's Disease Society (£1.2 million); Foyer Federation (£750,000); African Solutions to African Problems (ASAP) (£451,000); Landmark Trust (£400,000); Ashden Sustainable Solutions Better Lives (£390,000); BalletBoyz (£260,000); Children's HIV Association (CHIVA) (£249,000); National Communities Resource Centre (£150,000); Home-Start MAJIK (£60,000); Apples and Snakes (£30,000) and Community Media Trust (£24,000).

finances *Year* 2011–12 *Income* £9,180,000 *Grants* £45,424,000 *Assets* £175,172,000

trustees Stewart Grimshaw; Linda Heathcoat-Amory; Charles Cator.

other information The trust gives the following indication of its current particular area of interest: 'In the arts and heritage category [the trustees] particularly wish to be made aware of significant appeals.'

how to apply See the guidance for applicants in the entry for the Sainsbury Family Charitable Trusts. A single application will be considered for support by all the trusts in the group. The trust 'will consider unsolicited proposals, as long as they demonstrably and closely fit their specific area of interest. However, it should be understood that the majority of unsolicited proposals are unsuccessful.'

who to apply to Alan Bookbinder, Director, The Peak, 5 Wilton Road, London SW1V 1AP *Tel.* 020 7410 0330 *Fax* 020 7410 0332 *Website* www.sfct.org.uk

■ **The Moonpig Foundation**

cc no 1136686   established 2010

where funding can be given Worldwide; Uganda.

who can benefit Organisations and individuals.

what is funded General charitable purposes.

sample grants World Vision – Ntwetwe project (£71,000); XLP Project (£31,000) and World Vision – Child sponsorship (£13,500).

finances *Year* 2011–12 *Income* £141,748 *Grants* £119,941 *Assets* £37,336

trustees Iain Martin; Paul Lantsbury; Nicholas Jenkins; Sophie Dummer; Caroline Clarke.

OTHER INFORMATION The Moonpig Foundation will match any money raised for charity by a Moonpig employee up to a limit of £5,000 in any financial year per employee. Matched funding for 2011–12 amounted to £5,000.

HOW TO APPLY 'The Moonpig Foundation actively seeks projects to fund and does not accept unsolicited applications for grants.'

WHO TO APPLY TO Nicholas Jenkins, Trustee, Bapton Manor, Bapton, Warminster, Wiltshire BA12 0SB

....

■ George A. Moore Foundation

CC NO 262107   **ESTABLISHED** 1970
WHERE FUNDING CAN BE GIVEN Principally Yorkshire and the Isle of Man.
WHO CAN BENEFIT Charitable and voluntary organisations.
WHAT IS FUNDED The trustees select causes and projects from the applications received during the year and also independently research and identify specific objectives where they wish to direct assistance. The type of grants made can vary quite widely from one year to another and care is taken to maintain a rough parity among the various fields covered so that one sphere of activity does not benefit unduly at the expense of another. Areas which are not or cannot be covered by official sources are favoured.
WHAT IS NOT FUNDED No assistance will be given to individuals, courses of study, expeditions, overseas travel, holidays, or for purposes outside the UK. Local appeals for UK charities will only be considered if in the area of interest. Because of present long-term commitments, the foundation is not prepared to consider appeals for religious property or institutions.
TYPE OF GRANT Grants are generally non-recurrent and the foundation is reluctant to contribute to revenue appeals.
RANGE OF GRANTS Mostly under £1,000.
SAMPLE GRANTS National Institute for Cardiovascular Outcomes Research (£50,000); Boston Charitable Foundation (£44,000); Marrick Priory (£25,000); North Yorkshire Waste Action Group (£10,000); 49th Eastfield Scout Group (£5,000); Blood Pressure Association, Disability Action Yorkshire, Living Paintings Trust and Northallerton and District Voluntary Service (£1,000 each); Time Together (£500) and Sulby Horticultural Show (£250).
FINANCES *Year* 2011–12 *Income* £281,331 *Grants* £239,954 *Assets* £5,724,601
TRUSTEES George Moore; Elizabeth Moore; Jonathan Moore; Paul Turner.
HOW TO APPLY In writing to the correspondent. No guidelines or application forms are issued. The trustees meet approximately four times a year, on variable dates, and an appropriate response is sent out after the relevant meeting. For large grants of over £5,000, the trust will normally hold a meeting with the applicant to determine how the money will be spent.
WHO TO APPLY TO Angela James, Chief Administrator, The Stables, Bilton Hall, Bilton-in-Ainsty, York YO26 7NP *Tel.* 01423 359446 *email* info@gamf.org.uk *Website* www.gamf.org.uk

....

■ The Henry Moore Foundation

CC NO 271370   **ESTABLISHED** 1977
WHERE FUNDING CAN BE GIVEN UK and overseas.
WHO CAN BENEFIT Public visual art and educational bodies.
WHAT IS FUNDED Financial support is given to a broad range of institutions promoting the appreciation of the fine arts and in particular the works of Henry Moore through activities such as exhibitions, acquisitions, research and development, artists residencies and fellowships, conferences, lectures and publications.
WHAT IS NOT FUNDED No grants for revenue expenditure. No grant (or any part of grant) may be used to pay any fee or to provide any other benefit to any individual who is a trustee of the foundation.
TYPE OF GRANT One-off and longer term funding.
RANGE OF GRANTS Up to £30,000 depending on grant category.
SAMPLE GRANTS Cubitt Gallery, London: Exhibition and Exhibition Booklet/Publication, *The City is a Burning, Blazing Bonfire*, 29 October-23 December 2011–£6,000; Whitechapel Art Gallery, London: Commission, *Whitechapel Gallery Façade*: Tree of Life by Rachel Whiteread – £12,500; Ashmolean Museum, Oxford: Acquisition, *The Crucifixion with the Virgin Mary and St John*, terracotta, 1785 by Clodion (Claude Michel, 1738–1814) – £15,000; Scottish National Portrait Gallery, Edinburgh: *Sculpture display in the Library*, from November 2011–£10,000; *Glasgow Sculpture Studios Redevelopment Programme*, April 2012-March 2015 £15,000; Art Licks, London: Publication, *Art Licks* magazine, Issues 6–13 (January 2012-December 2013) – £2,500; University of Pennsylvania, Philadelphia in collaboration with Institut National d'Histoire de l'Art, Paris and the Philadelphia Museum of Art: Conference, *Working Group for the Study of Medieval Sculpture (1100–1550): A Transatlantic Collaboration*, January-November 2012–£5,000.
FINANCES *Year* 2011–12 *Income* £1,547,275 *Grants* £886,926 *Assets* £95,943,910
TRUSTEES Marianne Brouwer; Greville Worthington; Dawn Ades; Simon Keswick; Malcolm Baker; Duncan Robinson; Laure Genillard; Henry Channon; David Wilson; Celia Clear.
PUBLICATIONS The Henry Moore Foundation Review.
HOW TO APPLY Applicants should complete an application form which is available on the foundation's website. Applications must be posted to the grants administrator. Applications will be acknowledged by letter. The grants committee meets quarterly; consult the foundation's website for exact dates as the trust advises that applications received late will not be considered until after the meeting. It is advised to leave six months between the grants committee meeting and the project start date as funds cannot be paid for retrospective projects. Applicants should also advise the foundation whether it is envisaged that any trustee will have an interest in the project for which a grant is sought. Organisations may include supporting material with their application and this will be returned if requested.
WHO TO APPLY TO Alice O'Connor, Grants Programme Secretary, Dane Tree House, Perry Green, Much Hadham, Hertfordshire SG10 6EE *Tel.* 01279 843333 *email* admin@henry-moore.org *Website* www.henry-moore.org

....

■ John Moores Foundation

CC NO 253481   **ESTABLISHED** 1963
WHERE FUNDING CAN BE GIVEN Primarily Merseyside (plus Skelmersdale, Ellesmere Port and Halton); Northern Ireland; and overseas.
WHO CAN BENEFIT Voluntary organisations and community groups benefiting people who are

marginalised as a result of social, educational, physical, economic, cultural, geographical or other disadvantage. International relief organisations are also supported, but only organisations proactively selected by the trustees rather than applicants.

WHAT IS FUNDED Grass roots community groups; black and minority ethnic organisations; women including girls; second chance learning; advice and information to alleviate poverty; support and training for voluntary organisations. And, in Merseyside only: people with disabilities; carers; refugees; homeless people; child care; complementary therapies.

WHAT IS NOT FUNDED Generally the foundation does not fund: individuals; projects that are not substantially influenced by their target beneficiaries; national organisations or groups based outside Merseyside even where some of the service users come from the area; statutory bodies or work previously done by them; mainstream education (schools, colleges, universities); faith-based projects exclusively for members of that faith, or for the promotion of religion; capital building costs; festivals, carnivals and fêtes; medicine; holidays, expeditions and outings; gifts, parties etc.; conferences; sport; vehicles; animal charities; arts, crafts, heritage, or local history projects; conservation and environmental projects; employment and enterprise schemes; academic or medical research; uniformed groups (e.g. scouts, cadets, majorettes); sponsorship, advertising or fundraising events. Unsolicited applications which fall outside the policy criteria are not considered. Unsolicited applications for the categories World Crises and One-off exceptional grants are not responded to.

TYPE OF GRANT One-off, revenue, project, equipment and start-up costs. Funding for up to three years. Volunteers' expenses and help towards education and training costs.

RANGE OF GRANTS £100–£50,000, generally around £5,000.

SAMPLE GRANTS Merseyside: Wirral Resource Centre and Toy Library (£11,000); The Debt Advice Network (£10,000); Granby Somali Women's Group (£7,500); Wirral Holistic Care Services (£4,800); Support for Asylum Seekers (3,800); Church Road Neighbourhood Resource Centre (£3,000); Women's Enterprise Breakthrough (£2,500); Kirkby Senior Collaborative (£1,200); Southport Access for Everyone (£1,000) and Stella Marks Social Enterprise (£650). Northern Ireland included: Ardoyne Association and Foyle Sign Language Centre (£5,000 each); Omagh Independent Advice Services and Dialogue for Diversity (£4,500 each); Community Focus Learning (£3,300); Loup Women's Group (£3,200); Roundabout Playgroup (£2,000) and Belfast Butterfly Club (£1,800).

FINANCES *Year* 2011–12 *Income* £1,106,502 *Grants* £618,553 *Assets* £24,040,679

TRUSTEES Barnaby Moores; Kevin Moores; Nicola Eastwood; Alison Navarro; Christina Mee.

OTHER INFORMATION Overseas and exceptional grants are not open to unsolicited applications.

HOW TO APPLY Refer to the foundation's website and make sure your project falls within the criteria. If you are unsure, or if you would like to discuss your application before submitting it, telephone the foundation staff who will be happy to advise you. Application should be made by letter (no more than four sides of A4) accompanied by a completed application form. Application forms and guidance notes can be obtained by letter, phone or email or from the foundation's website. Decisions about which projects to fund

are made by the trustees who meet five to six times a year to consider Merseyside applications and four times a year to consider Northern Ireland applications. As a general rule, Merseyside applicants should allow three to four months for a decision to be made, and applicants from Northern Ireland should allow four to five months. Unsuccessful applicants are advised to wait at least four months before reapplying.

WHO TO APPLY TO Phil Godfrey, Grants Director, 7th Floor, Gostins Building, 32–36 Hanover Street, Liverpool L1 4LN *Tel.* 01517 076077 *email* info@johnmooresfoundation.com *Website* www.jmf.org.uk

■ The Morel Charitable Trust

CC NO 268943   **ESTABLISHED** 1972

WHERE FUNDING CAN BE GIVEN UK and the developing world.

WHO CAN BENEFIT Grants are normally made to projects of which the trustees have personal knowledge. Organisations benefiting people disadvantaged by poverty are prioritised, but those benefiting volunteers, people living in inner city areas and victims of famine will be considered.

WHAT IS FUNDED The arts, particularly drama; organisations working for improved race relations; inner city projects and developing world projects. Charities working in the fields of arts, culture and recreation; health; conservation and environment; education and training; and social care and development.

WHAT IS NOT FUNDED No grants to individuals.

TYPE OF GRANT Project.

RANGE OF GRANTS Usually £500–£5,000

SAMPLE GRANTS Oxfam (£15,000); Christian Aid – Kailahun (£5,000); Motor Neurone Disease (£3,000); Collective Artistes, Computer Aid International, Health Poverty Action, Kaloko Trust, KidzClub Leeds (£2,000 each); African Initiatives and Afrika Eye Bristol (£1,500 each); and Brecon Arts Trust, ACET, Medical Aid Palestine and Renewable World (£1,000 each).

FINANCES *Year* 2011–12 *Income* £55,321 *Grants* £75,450 *Assets* £1,287,941

TRUSTEES James Gibbs; William Gibbs; Benjamin Gibbs; Simon Gibbs; Thomas Gibbs; Dr Emily Parry; Abigail Keane.

OTHER INFORMATION Projects supported are usually connected with places that the trustees have lived and worked, including the cities of Bristol, Leeds, Brecon and London and the countries of Ghana, Zambia, Malawi and the Solomon Islands.

HOW TO APPLY In writing to the correspondent. The trustees normally meet three times a year to consider applications.

WHO TO APPLY TO Simon Gibbs, Trustee, 34 Durand Gardens, London SW9 0PP *Tel.* 020 7582 6901

■ The Morgan Charitable Foundation

CC NO 283128   **ESTABLISHED** 1981

WHERE FUNDING CAN BE GIVEN UK.

WHO CAN BENEFIT Registered charities and institutions benefiting at risk groups and people who are disadvantaged by poverty or socially isolated.

WHAT IS FUNDED The trustees are primarily interested in social welfare causes.

Think carefully about every application. Is it justified?

761

WHAT IS NOT FUNDED No grants to individuals.
RANGE OF GRANTS £1,000–£8,000.
SAMPLE GRANTS Previously: Magen David Adom, World Jewish Relief, Chai Cancer Care, In Kind Direct Charity, Jewish Care, Jewish Blind and Disabled, AfriKids, Aleh Charitable Foundation, Institute for Philanthropy, London Pro Arte Choir, Marie Curie Cancer Care, Ohel Sarah, Pears Foundation, and Royal National Lifeboat Institution.
FINANCES *Year* 2012 *Income* £106,740 *Grants* £60,000
TRUSTEES Albert Morgan; Leslie Morgan; Carmen Gleen; Nelly Morgan; Ronnie Morgan; Molly Morgan.
HOW TO APPLY In writing to the correspondent. Applications will only be considered if accompanied by a copy of the charitable organisation's latest report and accounts. Trustees meet twice a year, usually in April and October. No telephone enquiries please.
WHO TO APPLY TO The Trustees, PO Box 57749, London Nw11 1FD *Tel.* 07968 827709

....

■ The Morgan Foundation

CC NO 1087056   **ESTABLISHED** 2001
WHERE FUNDING CAN BE GIVEN North Wales, Merseyside, West Cheshire and North Shropshire.
WHO CAN BENEFIT Organisations that support children and young people and families.
WHAT IS FUNDED General with a preference for health and social welfare.
WHAT IS NOT FUNDED The foundation will not give grants for the following: animal welfare; arts/heritage; conservation/environment; expeditions and overseas travel; general fundraising appeals; individual and sports sponsorship; large national charities; mainstream education; promotion of specific religions and retrospective funding.
SAMPLE GRANTS OnSide (£500,000); Children Today (£333,000); Wolves Aid (£125,000); Steps to Freedom (£54,000); Christ Church Youth Club (£51,000); Five Children and Families Trust (£45,000); Norris Green Youth Centre (£42,000); Home-Start Flintshire (£36,000); Netherton Park Community Association (£31,000); Cheshire Asperger's Parent Support (£26,000); Clare Mount School (£20,000); Longmynd Adventure Camp (£16,000); Greenbank School Cycle Track (£15,000); St Peter's Collegiate Church (£5,000); North Wales Superkids (£950); Oxfam (£500) and Rett Syndrome Research Trust (£200).
FINANCES *Year* 2012–13 *Income* £1,678,504 *Grants* £1,984,848 *Assets* £13,911,100
TRUSTEES Stephen Morgan, Chair; Vincent Fairclough; Jennie Daly; Rhiannon Walker; Ashley Lewis.
HOW TO APPLY The foundation gives the following guidance about making an application on its website:
'First, ensure that you are eligible under our policy: check that your organisation/project is based within our geographic area; check that your organisation/project is not listed in our exclusions; ring us for an informal chat and request an application form.'
'Before finalising or submitting an application telephone for an informal chat to check that your proposed application falls in line with current policy. We understand that it can be daunting to pick up the phone, but we believe that an initial chat can save you and us lots of wasted time, and we will be happy to give you guidance as to what

specific information we need to process your application. Once you have contacted us by phone and it has been agreed that your application is appropriate, we will ask you to send in a description of your organisation, its history, activities, volunteers, beneficiaries, achievements to date and current funding needs. Enclose copies of most recent reports and accounts. If you have a project in mind, describe its purpose, targets, budget, and timescale. All applications will be acknowledged and we will contact you for any further information we require. All charities and projects will be visited before a grant is approved. Timing of Applications: Trustee Meetings are held regularly throughout the year and there are no specific dates for applications to be received. However, organisations should be aware that applications are considered in chronological order and it can take up to six months for the process to be completed.'
WHO TO APPLY TO Jane Harris, Administrator, PO Box 3517, Chester CH1 9ET *Tel.* 01829 782800 *Fax* 01829 782223 *email* contact@morganfoundation.co.uk *Website* www.morganfoundation.co.uk

....

■ The Mr and Mrs J. T. Morgan Foundation

CC NO 241835   **ESTABLISHED** 1965
WHERE FUNDING CAN BE GIVEN Mainly Wales.
WHO CAN BENEFIT Churches, national and local charities benefiting children, young people, students and Christians.
WHAT IS FUNDED Preference is given to the support of charities in Wales and to the promotion of education and religion in Wales.
WHAT IS NOT FUNDED No grants to individuals.
TYPE OF GRANT One-off.
RANGE OF GRANTS £100–£750
SAMPLE GRANTS Taffs Well United Church (£500); An Open Door into Your Heart (£400); Whizz-Kidz (250); Motor Neurone Disease Association (£250); Special Needs Activity Club (£100); The Arthur Rank Centre (£500).
FINANCES *Year* 2011–12 *Income* £23,231 *Grants* £20,000
TRUSTEES Elaine Phillips; John Aylward; John Morgan.
OTHER INFORMATION Grant totals are usually in the region of £25,000.
HOW TO APPLY In writing to the correspondent.
WHO TO APPLY TO John Morgan, Calvert House, Calvert Terrace, Swansea SA1 6AP *Tel.* 01792 655178 *email* clairephillips@broomfield.co.uk

....

■ Morgan Stanley International Foundation

CC NO 1042671   **ESTABLISHED** 1994
WHERE FUNDING CAN BE GIVEN London boroughs of Tower Hamlets and Newham; Glasgow and overseas.
WHO CAN BENEFIT UK registered charities benefiting unemployed people, at risk groups, carers, and people who are disabled, disadvantaged by poverty or homeless.
WHAT IS FUNDED Grants are focused in the following areas, with a particular emphasis on education, training and employment: (a) services for youth: organisations of which the primary mission is providing educational and leadership activities for young people; (b) job training/remedial education/disabled and homeless support: for adults and young people in order to prepare

these people to become self-supporting; (c) hospitals/health: support for hospitals and innovative healthcare projects in the East End of London. As a rule, the foundation does not support organisations involved in the research of specific diseases.

WHAT IS NOT FUNDED 'The foundation does not make contributions to organisations that fall within the following criteria: organisations which are not registered as a non profit organisation with the appropriate regulatory agencies in their country (unless a state funded school); national or international charities which do not operate in the regions we are located; grants will not be made to either political or religious organisations, 'pressure groups' or individuals outside the firm who are seeking sponsorship either for themselves (e.g. to help pay for education) or for onward transmission to a charitable organisation; programmes that do not include opportunities for employee volunteer engagement.'

TYPE OF GRANT Capital or revenue costs, but not loans.

RANGE OF GRANTS £1,000–£150,000, average grant £5,000.

SAMPLE GRANTS The largest beneficiary during the year was Kids Company, which received £792,500. Local beneficiaries include: East End Community Foundation (£63,000); Career Academies UK (£32,000); School-Home Support (£23,500); Seeds of Peace UK (£18,000); Refuge (£13,000); Old Ford Primary School (£10,000); Clare College, Zoological Society of London and Cystic Fibrosis Trust (£6,000 each); 1st Barking and Dagenham Scout Group and Multiple Sclerosis Society (£4,000 each) and NSPCC and Ayrshire Hospice (£2,000 each). Beneficiaries working overseas include: SOS Children's Villages Italy (£28,000); Movember Europe (£23,000); South Africa Grants (£12,000); Junior Achievement (Italy) (£11,000) and Asociación Manos de Ayuda Social (£5,000).

FINANCES *Year* 2012 *Income* £1,688,186 *Grants* £1,580,087 *Assets* £1,726,789

TRUSTEES Sue Watts; Oliver Stuart; Goran Trapp; Clare Woodman; Hanns Seibold; Rupert Jones; Maryann McMahon; Stephen Souchon; Malcolm Bryant; Stephen Mavin; Fergus O'Sullivan.

HOW TO APPLY The foundation gives the following details on making an initial approach for funding: 'Morgan Stanley International Foundation takes a proactive approach to grantmaking and therefore does not accept unsolicited proposals. If you think your organisation is a match for the criteria set out below, send an email to: communityaffairslondon@morganstanley.com. You will then be sent the guidelines and if your organisation is successful in the first stage of application, you will be invited to complete a full proposal. Grant applications are considered quarterly and the trustees are senior representatives from across the firm's divisions.'

WHO TO APPLY TO Sally Crane, Secretary, 25 Cabot Square, Canary Wharf, London E14 4QA *Tel.* 020 7425 1302 *email* communityaffairslondon@morganstanley. com *Website* www.morganstanley.com

■ Diana and Allan Morgenthau Charitable Trust

CC NO 1062180   **ESTABLISHED** 1997

WHERE FUNDING CAN BE GIVEN Worldwide.

WHO CAN BENEFIT Charitable organisations, with an interest in Jewish groups.

WHAT IS FUNDED Jewish causes, overseas aid, arts, culture, health and education.

RANGE OF GRANTS £200–£35,000.

SAMPLE GRANTS Belsize Square Synagogue (£30,000); The Central British Fund for World Jewish Relief (£18,000); The British Friends of the Jaffa Institute (£10,000); Marie Curie Cancer Care (£5,000); Holocaust Educational Trust (£4,000); Tricycle Theatre Company (£1,700); Lifelites (£1,500); The Royal Marsden Hospital (£250) and The Royal Free Hampstead Charities (£150).

FINANCES *Year* 2011–12 *Income* £131,264 *Grants* £102,196 *Assets* £34,308

TRUSTEES Allan Morgenthau; Diana Morgenthau.

OTHER INFORMATION A further £16,000 was given in grants to individuals.

HOW TO APPLY In writing to the correspondent.

WHO TO APPLY TO Allan Morgenthau, Trustee, Flat 27, Berkeley House, 15 Hay Hill, London W1J 8NS *Tel.* 020 7493 1904

■ The Oliver Morland Charitable Trust

CC NO 1076213   **ESTABLISHED** 1999

WHERE FUNDING CAN BE GIVEN UK.

WHO CAN BENEFIT Registered charities usually chosen through personal knowledge of the trustees.

WHAT IS FUNDED Most of the funds are given to Quaker projects or Quaker-related projects.

WHAT IS NOT FUNDED No grants to individuals.

TYPE OF GRANT Grants are given for core, capital and project support for up to three years.

RANGE OF GRANTS Up to £30,000.

SAMPLE GRANTS Previous beneficiaries have included: Quaker Peace and Service (£32,500); Quaker Home Service – children and young people (£16,000); Refugee Council (£2,000); Leap Confronting Conflict, Living Again, Medical Aid for Palestine and Sightsavers International (£1,000 each); Come to God (£850); and Brooke Animal Hospital (£300).

FINANCES *Year* 2011–12 *Income* £20,344 *Grants* £75,000

TRUSTEES Priscilla Khan; Joseph Rutter; Jennifer Pittard; Kate Lovell; Charlotte Jones; Simon Pittard; Simon Rutter.

HOW TO APPLY 'Most of our grants are for continuing support of existing beneficiaries (approx 90%) so there is little left for responding to new appeals. We receive unsolicited applications at the rate of six or seven each week, 99% are not even considered.'

WHO TO APPLY TO J. M. Rutter, Trustee, Thomas House, Stower Row, Shaftesbury, Dorset SP7 0QW *Tel.* 01747 853524

■ S. C. and M. E. Morland's Charitable Trust

CC NO 201645   **ESTABLISHED** 1957

WHERE FUNDING CAN BE GIVEN UK.

WHO CAN BENEFIT Quaker, local and UK charities which have a strong social bias and some UK-based international charities.

WHAT IS FUNDED Support to Quaker charities and others which the trustees have special interest in, knowledge of or association with, including religious groups, relief of poverty and ill-health, promotion of peace and development overseas.

WHAT IS NOT FUNDED The trust does not usually give to animal welfare, individuals or medical research.

RANGE OF GRANTS Almost all less than £1,000 each.

SAMPLE GRANTS Britain Yearly Meeting (£8,000).

FINANCES *Year* 2011–12 *Income* £40,989 *Grants* £36,470 *Assets* £903,953

TRUSTEES Esther Boyd; Janet Morland; Howard Boyd; David Boyd; Victoria Morland; Rebecca Morland.

OTHER INFORMATION The trust generally makes grants to charities it has supported on a long term basis but each year this list is reviewed and new charities may be added.

HOW TO APPLY In writing to the correspondent. The trustees meet two times a year to make grants, in March and December. Applications should be submitted in the month before each meeting.

WHO TO APPLY TO Victoria Morland, Trustee, 14 Fairmont Terrace, Sherborne DT9 3JS

■ The Morris Charitable Trust

CC NO 802290 **ESTABLISHED** 1989

WHERE FUNDING CAN BE GIVEN UK, with a preference for Islington; and overseas.

WHO CAN BENEFIT Supporting national, international and local community charities.

WHAT IS FUNDED General charitable purposes, placing particular emphasis on alleviating social hardship and deprivation. There is a preference for supporting causes within the borough of Islington.

WHAT IS NOT FUNDED No grants for individuals. No repeat donations are made within 12 months.

TYPE OF GRANT One-off grants for recurring costs for one year or less are priorities. Building and other capital grants, core costs, research grants, running costs, salaries and start-up costs are considered.

RANGE OF GRANTS £1–£7,500; the majority of grants are between £1 and £1,000.

SAMPLE GRANTS Previous beneficiaries include: Age Concern – Islington (an unusually large grant of £25,000); The Bridge School – Islington; (£5,000); and Islington Senior Citizens Fund (£1,000).

FINANCES *Year* 2011–12 *Income* £125,245 *Grants* £123,150 *Assets* £184,865

TRUSTEES Jack A. Morris; Paul B. Morris; Alan R. Stenning; Gerald Morris; Dominic Jones.

PUBLICATIONS Information pamphlet.

HOW TO APPLY By application form available from the trust or downloadable from its website. The completed form should be returned complete with any supporting documentation and a copy of your latest report and accounts.

WHO TO APPLY TO Jack A. Morris, Trustee, c/o Management Office, Business Design Centre, 52 Upper Street, London N1 0QH *Tel.* 020 7359 3535 *Fax* 020 7226 0590 *email* info@morrischaritabletrust.com *Website* www.morrischaritabletrust.com

■ The Bernard Morris Charitable Trust

CC NO 266532 **ESTABLISHED** 1973

WHERE FUNDING CAN BE GIVEN UK.

WHO CAN BENEFIT Charitable organisations and needy individuals.

WHAT IS FUNDED General charitable purposes.

SAMPLE GRANTS Previously: Oxford Synagogue (£16,000); Dragon School Trust (£12,000); One Voice (£2,500), OCJHS – Oxford Centre for Jewish and Hebrew Studies (£2,000), Soundabout (£1,000), the Story Museum (£500) and Centrepoint Homeless (£200).

FINANCES *Year* 2011–12 *Income* £23,076 *Grants* £30,000

TRUSTEES Simon Ryde; Judith Silver; Simon Fineman; Jessica Ryde.

HOW TO APPLY In writing to the correspondent.

WHO TO APPLY TO Simon Ryde, Trustee, 5 Wolvercote Green, Oxford OX2 8BD *Tel.* 01865 516593

■ The Willie and Mabel Morris Charitable Trust

CC NO 280554 **ESTABLISHED** 1980

WHERE FUNDING CAN BE GIVEN UK.

WHO CAN BENEFIT Registered charities benefiting people who are ill, particularly with lupus, cancer, heart trouble, cerebral palsy, arthritis or rheumatism.

WHAT IS FUNDED Welfare and disability.

WHAT IS NOT FUNDED No grants for individuals or non-registered charities.

RANGE OF GRANTS £100–£15,000.

SAMPLE GRANTS St Thomas Lupus Trust (£10,000); UCLH Epilepsy (£7,500); London Centre for Children with Cerebral Palsy (£5,000); St Mary's Church (£4,400); The Prostate Cancer Charity (£2,500); Gainsborough House Society (£550); Historic Royal Palaces (£500); British Heart Foundation (£350); English National Ballet (£200); Dementia UK (£100).

FINANCES *Year* 2011–12 *Income* £129,647 *Grants* £145,231 *Assets* £3,596,815

TRUSTEES Michael Macfadyen; Joyce Tether; Peter Tether; Andrew Tether; Angela Tether; Suzanne Marriott; Verity Tether.

HOW TO APPLY The trustees 'formulate an independent grants policy at regular meetings so that funds are already committed'.

WHO TO APPLY TO Angela Tether, 41 Field Lane, Letchworth Garden City, Hertfordshire SG6 3LD *Tel.* 01462 480583

■ The Peter Morrison Charitable Foundation

CC NO 277202 **ESTABLISHED** 1978

WHERE FUNDING CAN BE GIVEN UK.

WHO CAN BENEFIT Registered charities benefiting at risk groups and people who are disadvantaged by poverty and socially isolated.

WHAT IS FUNDED A wide range of social welfare causes.

RANGE OF GRANTS Up to £10,000

SAMPLE GRANTS Hawk Conservancy Trust Ltd (£10,000); RNLI (£4,300); Grange Park Opera (£3,400); Maccabi GB (£2,000); Alzheimer's Society (£1,000); Cystic Fibrosis Trust (£900); Jewish Care (£500); Langalanga Scholarship Fund (£200) and Friends of the Sick (£50).

FINANCES *Year* 2011–12 *Income* £27,155 *Grants* £55,826 *Assets* £888,295

TRUSTEES M. Morrison; I. R. Morrison; Louise Greenhill; Jane Morrison.

OTHER INFORMATION Ian Morrison is also a trustee of Kemis's Lectureship Charity (Charity Commission no. 1013259); and The Andover Charities (Charity Commission no. 206587).

HOW TO APPLY In writing to the correspondent.

WHO TO APPLY TO J. Payne, Begbies Chettle Agar, Chartered Accountants, Epworth House, 25 City Road, London EC1Y 1AR *Tel.* 020 7628 5801

■ G. M. Morrison Charitable Trust

CC NO 261380   ESTABLISHED 1970

WHERE FUNDING CAN BE GIVEN UK.

WHO CAN BENEFIT Registered charities only.

WHAT IS FUNDED A wide variety of activities in the social welfare, medical and education/training fields. The trustees give priority to those charities already supported. Very few charities are added to the list each year.

WHAT IS NOT FUNDED No support for individuals, charities not registered in the UK, retrospective applications, schemes or activities which are generally regarded as the responsibility of statutory authorities, short-term projects or one-off capital grants (except for emergency appeals).

TYPE OF GRANT Mostly annual.

RANGE OF GRANTS £600 to £3,000, average £803.

SAMPLE GRANTS Save the Children (£3,000); British Red Cross Society – Pakistan Floods Appeal, Royal Society of Arts Endowment Fund (£2,000 each); University of Cambridge (£1,200); Enterprise Education Trust, Psychiatry Research Trust, St Luke's Hospital for the Clergy and YMCA England (£1,050 each); Refugee Council Day Centre (£1,000); Crossroads Care and St Mungo's Association (£850 each); British Lung Foundation and Family Action (£750 each); Missionaries of Africa (£700); Musicians Benevolent Fund (£650); Liverpool School of Tropical Medicine and Salmon Youth Centre (£600 each).

FINANCES *Year* 2011–12 *Income* £344,315 *Grants* £188,000 *Assets* £9,751,424

TRUSTEES N. W. Smith; Elizabeth Morrison; Anthony Cornick; Jane Hunt.

HOW TO APPLY The trust's annual report states: 'Beneficiaries of grants are normally selected on the basis of the personal knowledge and recommendation of a trustee. The trust's grantmaking policy is however to support the recipient of grants on a long term recurring basis. The scope of its giving is determined only by the extent of its resources, and is not otherwise restricted. The trustees have decided that for the present, new applications for grants will only be considered in the most exceptional circumstances, any spare income will be allocated to increasing the grants made to charities currently receiving support. In the future this policy will of course be subject to periodic review. Applicants understanding this policy who nevertheless wish to apply for a grant should write to the [correspondent].' Monitoring is undertaken by assessment of annual reports and accounts which are required from all beneficiaries, and by occasional trustee visits.

WHO TO APPLY TO Anthony Cornick, Trustee, c/o Currey and Co, 21 Buckingham Gate, London SW1E 6LS *Tel.* 020 7802 2700

■ The Stanley Morrison Charitable Trust

SC NO SC006610   ESTABLISHED 1989

WHERE FUNDING CAN BE GIVEN The west coast of Scotland, with a preference for Glasgow and Ayrshire.

WHO CAN BENEFIT Organisations benefiting young adults, and sportsmen and women.

WHAT IS FUNDED Sporting activities in Scotland, with particular emphasis on the encouragement of youth involvement; charities which have as their principal base of operation and benefit the west coast of Scotland, in particular the Glasgow and Ayrshire areas; charities whose funds arise from or whose assistance is provided to people having connection with the licensed trades and in particular the whisky industry; Scottish educational establishments.

TYPE OF GRANT Buildings, project and recurring costs. Grants and funding for up to and over three years will be considered.

RANGE OF GRANTS £100–£10,000.

SAMPLE GRANTS Previous beneficiaries include: Scottish Cricket Union; Princess Royal Trust for Carers; Riding for the Disabled; Mark Scott Foundation; Glasgow University Sports Sponsorship; Grange Cricket Club – Youth Section; Cancer UK Scotland and Scottish Schools' Badminton Union.

FINANCES *Year* 2011–12 *Income* £64,000 *Grants* £30,000

TRUSTEES S. W. Morrison; J. H. McKean; M. E. Morrison; T. F. O'Connell; A. S. Dudgeon.

HOW TO APPLY In writing to the correspondent. Applicants should include details on the purpose of the grant, what funding has already been secured and the actual sum that they are looking for.

WHO TO APPLY TO The Trustees, c/o French Duncan, 375 West George Street, Glasgow G2 4LW *Tel.* 01412 212984 *email* c.wilson@frenchduncan.co.uk

■ Moshal Charitable Trust

CC NO 284448   ESTABLISHED 1981

WHERE FUNDING CAN BE GIVEN UK

WHO CAN BENEFIT Jewish causes.

WHAT IS FUNDED General charitable purposes.

SAMPLE GRANTS The trust's accounts are routinely basic, therefore no sample grants were available for 2010–11.

FINANCES *Year* 2011–12 *Income* £160,076 *Grants* £115,173 *Assets* £370,188

TRUSTEES David Halpern; Lea Halpern.

HOW TO APPLY In writing to the correspondent.

WHO TO APPLY TO The Trustees, c/o Sefton Yodaiken and Co., Fairways House, George Street, Prestwich, Manchester M25 9WS *Tel.* 01617 739411

■ Vyoel Moshe Charitable Trust

CC NO 327054   ESTABLISHED 1986

WHERE FUNDING CAN BE GIVEN UK and overseas.

WHO CAN BENEFIT Registered charities.

WHAT IS FUNDED Education and relief of poverty.

FINANCES *Year* 2010–11 *Income* £622,305 *Grants* £668,415 *Assets* £34,439

TRUSTEES Y. Frankel; B. Berger; S. Seidenfeld.

OTHER INFORMATION Accounts for this trust are consistently filed more than a year overdue at the Charity Commission.

HOW TO APPLY In writing to the correspondent.

Think carefully about every application. Is it justified?

765

WHO TO APPLY TO Berish Berger, Secretary,
2–4 Chardmore Road, London N16 6HX

■ The Moshulu Charitable Trust

CC NO 1071479   ESTABLISHED 1998
WHERE FUNDING CAN BE GIVEN UK.
WHO CAN BENEFIT Charitable organisations.
WHAT IS FUNDED 'Humanitarian' and evangelical
causes.
SAMPLE GRANTS SWYM (£15,900); Christ Church
(£11,700); Tear Fund (£5,400); Partnership UK
(£3,000); Care for the Family (£2,400) and
Seaway Trust (£1,600).
FINANCES *Year* 2011–12 *Income* £0
Grants £47,000
TRUSTEES H. J. Fulls; D. M. Fulls; G. N. Fulls;
S. M. Fulls; G. F. Symons.
HOW TO APPLY In writing to the correspondent.
WHO TO APPLY TO H. J. Fulls, Trustee, Devonshire
Road, Heathpark, Honiton, Devon EX14 1SD
Tel. 01404 540770

■ The Moss Charitable Trust

CC NO 258031   ESTABLISHED 1969
WHERE FUNDING CAN BE GIVEN Worldwide, with an
interest in Dorset, Hampshire and Sussex.
WHO CAN BENEFIT Registered charities, especially
Christian.
WHAT IS FUNDED General charitable purposes,
specifically for the benefit of the community in
the county borough of Bournemouth, and
Hampshire, Dorset and Sussex; advancement of
religion either UK or overseas; advancement of
education; and relief of poverty, disease and
sickness.
TYPE OF GRANT Outright grant or interest-free loan.
RANGE OF GRANTS Up to £8,000, but mostly less
than £5,000.
SAMPLE GRANTS Palawan Partners (£12,000); Christ
Church Westbourne (£6,400); Tamil Church
(£4,400); Chichester Counselling Service
(£3,500); Echo Worldwide (£2,400); Slindon
Parochial Church Council (£2,100); Barnabas
Fund (£1,900); Care Trust (£1,700); Crosslinks
(£1,400); Napam (£1,300); Youth Action for
Holistic development (£1,200); European
Christian Mission (£1,100) and Trinity Methodist
Church (£1,000).
FINANCES *Year* 2011–12 *Income* £119,297
Grants £82,788 *Assets* £146,029
TRUSTEES J. H. Simmons; A. F. Simmons;
D. S. Olby.
OTHER INFORMATION The grants total includes around
£4,600 given by the trust to individuals.
HOW TO APPLY No funds are available by direct
application. Because of the way in which this
trust operates it is not open to external
applications for grants.
WHO TO APPLY TO P. D. Malpas, 7 Church Road,
Parkstone, Poole, Dorset BH14 8UF *Tel.* 01202
730002

■ Brian and Jill Moss Charitable Trust

CC NO 1084664   ESTABLISHED 2000
WHERE FUNDING CAN BE GIVEN Worldwide.
WHO CAN BENEFIT Registered charities only.
WHAT IS FUNDED Jewish causes and healthcare.
WHAT IS NOT FUNDED Donations are made to
registered charities only.

TYPE OF GRANT Capital projects and towards
'ordinary charity expenditure'.
SAMPLE GRANTS Previously: United Jewish Israel
Appeal (£43,000); Magen David Adom UK
(£31,000); Jewish Care (£16,000); World
Jewish Relief (£15,000); Chai Cancer Care
(£12,000); United Synagogue-Tribe (£11,000);
WIZO UK (£6,000); National Jewish Chaplaincy
Board (£5,500); Prostate Cancer Charitable
Trust (£5,000); Myeloma UK (£3,000); Israel
Folk Dance Institute (£500); and Jewish
Museum and Operation Wheelchairs (£250
each).
FINANCES *Year* 2011–12 *Income* £124,040
Grants £172,149 *Assets* £3,250,075
TRUSTEES Brian Peter Moss; Jill Moss; David Paul
Moss; Sarah Levy.
HOW TO APPLY In writing to the correspondent.
Appeals are considered as they are received
and the trustees will make donations throughout
the year.'
WHO TO APPLY TO The Trustees, c/o Deloitte,
5 Callaghan Square, Cardiff CF10 5BT
Tel. 02920 264391

■ The Robert and Margaret Moss Charitable Trust

CC NO 290760   ESTABLISHED 1984
WHERE FUNDING CAN BE GIVEN Oxfordshire, with a
preference for Oxford.
WHO CAN BENEFIT Charitable organisations.
WHAT IS FUNDED Research into human nutrition,
medical research, relief of poverty and
education.
RANGE OF GRANTS Usually £1,000.
SAMPLE GRANTS Vale House Alzheimer's Home
(£10,000); Project Volume and Porch Steppin'
Stone Centre (£1,500 each); Prostate Cancer
Charity, Shelter, Bridewell Organic Gardens,
Donnington Doorstep Family Centre and DEC
East Africa Appeal (£1,000 each) and Deafblind
UK (£700).
FINANCES *Year* 2011–12 *Income* £36,115
Grants £29,960 *Assets* £1,385,928
TRUSTEES John Cole; Dr Tarrant Stein; Maggie
Perrin.
HOW TO APPLY In writing to the correspondent.
WHO TO APPLY TO Helen Fanyinka, c/o Morgan Cole,
Buxton Court, 3 West Way, Oxford OX2 0SZ
Tel. 01865 262600 *email* info@morgan-cole.
com

■ The Moss Family Charitable Trust

CC NO 327529   ESTABLISHED 1987
WHERE FUNDING CAN BE GIVEN England and Wales.
WHO CAN BENEFIT Mainly Jewish organisations.
WHAT IS FUNDED General charitable purposes with
preference to Jewish causes.
WHAT IS NOT FUNDED Neither music nor the arts is
funded.
RANGE OF GRANTS £100–£8,000.
SAMPLE GRANTS Previous beneficiaries include: The
Children's Charity (£10,000); West London
Synagogue (£8,000); Jewish Child's Day
(£5,000); Norwood and the Presidents Club
(£4,000 each) and Hammerson House (£600).
FINANCES *Year* 2011–12 *Income* £100,011
Grants £93,998 *Assets* £15,122
TRUSTEES Stephen Moss; Roger Moss; Virginia
Campus.

HOW TO APPLY In writing to the correspondent. The trust is unlikely to respond to unsolicited applications.

WHO TO APPLY TO K. Sage, Administrator, 28 Bolton Street, Mayfair, London W1J 8BP *Tel.* 020 7491 5108

■ Mosselson Charitable Trust

CC NO 266517 **ESTABLISHED** 1974

WHERE FUNDING CAN BE GIVEN UK.

WHO CAN BENEFIT Charitable organisations working with young people; older people; and those with disabilities.

WHAT IS FUNDED Education; medicine and medical research; women and children's support and welfare; religion; social welfare.

SAMPLE GRANTS Previously a grant of £2,600 was awarded to an individual docker towards visiting Cuba Health Ministry; also £1,000 (in two grants) to Holocaust Education Trust.

FINANCES *Year* 2011–12 *Income* £484,423 *Grants* £77,081 *Assets* £2,266,777

TRUSTEES Dennis Mosselson; Marian Mosselson.

HOW TO APPLY In writing to the correspondent.

WHO TO APPLY TO Dennis Mosselson, Trustee, Denmoss House, 10 Greenland Street, London NW1 0ND *Tel.* 020 7428 1929

■ Mothercare Group Foundation

CC NO 1104386 **ESTABLISHED** 2004

WHERE FUNDING CAN BE GIVEN UK and worldwide.

WHO CAN BENEFIT Children and their mothers.

WHAT IS FUNDED Registered charities and research organisations that promote the general well-being of children and their mothers; offering them the very best chance of good health, education, well-being and a secure start in life. Specifically, the foundation welcomes applications from registered charities and research organisations associated with the following criteria: ensuring the good health and well-being of mums-to-be, new mums and their children; special baby-care needs and premature births; other parenting initiatives relating to family well-being.

WHAT IS NOT FUNDED No response to circular appeals. Support is not given to: animal welfare, appeals from individuals, the arts, elderly people, environment/heritage, religious appeals, political appeals, or sport.

SAMPLE GRANTS The Healing Foundation (£15,000); Wellchild, University of Bristol, Wellbeing of Women and Tommy's (£10,000 each); Meningitis Research Foundation (£7,650); Anthony Nolan Trust (£7,400) and KIDS and PHG Foundation £5,000 each).

FINANCES *Year* 2011–12 *Income* £74,209 *Grants* £109,360 *Assets* £43,964

TRUSTEES Tim Ashby; Lynne Medini.

OTHER INFORMATION Grants of less than £5,000 totalled £24,000.

HOW TO APPLY In writing to the correspondent. Requests for donations will only be considered when made in writing on the application form that can be printed from the company's website. Applications are considered on a quarterly basis. Unsolicited appeals are unlikely to be successful.

WHO TO APPLY TO Lynne Medini, Trustee and Secretary, Cherry Tree Road, Watford, Hertfordshire WD24 6SH *Tel.* 01923 206186 *Website* www.mothercare.com

■ Moto in the Community

CC NO 1111147 **ESTABLISHED** 2005

WHERE FUNDING CAN BE GIVEN UK.

WHO CAN BENEFIT Supports a wide variety of local charities and community projects.

WHAT IS FUNDED Community development and road safety.

WHAT IS NOT FUNDED The trust does not consider applications that are for the promotion of religion or politics or overseas projects.

RANGE OF GRANTS There is no fixed minimum or maximum amount for grants.

SAMPLE GRANTS Breast Cancer Care (£50,000); Padbury Pre-School (£7,000); Darton College (£1,500); The Reader and Wellgate School (£1,000 each); Dosthill Boys Club (£500) and CHAS (£100).

FINANCES *Year* 2012 *Income* £439,306 *Grants* £64,877 *Assets* £345,921

TRUSTEES Suzanne Hollinshead; Brian Lotts; Christopher Rogers; Brian Larkin; Helen Budd; John Thomson; Heather Roberts; Sara Davies; Malcolm Plowes; Jon Shore; Ashleigh Lewis; Ian Kernighan; Gene Macdonald; Nicholas Brokes.

HOW TO APPLY Applications are looked on favourably if the applicant has built a relationship with the local Moto site and discussed opportunities for the Moto site employees to engage with the project/charity. Grants are approved by the trustees every three months. Any questions can be directed to the Moto in the Community Trust Administrator. Application forms, guidelines and criteria are available on the trust's website.

WHO TO APPLY TO Suzanne Hollinshead, Trustee, 37 Beaumont Road, Flitwick, Bedford MK45 1AL *Tel.* 01525 714467 *email* motocharity@talking360.com *Website* www.motointhecommunity.co.uk

■ British Motor Sports Training Trust

CC NO 273828 **ESTABLISHED** 1977

WHERE FUNDING CAN BE GIVEN UK.

WHO CAN BENEFIT Organisations involved with motor sports.

WHAT IS FUNDED Prevention of accidents in motor sports through education and training.

SAMPLE GRANTS Grants towards training projects and equipment totalled £84,000. Beneficiaries include: British Motor Racing Marshals Club Ltd (£19,000); ATLS Lister Hospital (£7,600); Motorsport Marshalling Partnership (£5,000); Castle Combe Racing Club (£2,400); Potteries and Newcastle Motor Club (£1,500) and North Wales Car Club and Scottish Motor Racing Club (£1,000 each). Grants under £1,000 totalled £5,000. Grants towards Rescue Development Projects or Equipment totalled £43,000. Beneficiaries include: Calder Response (£10,000); Emergency Mobile Medical Unit (£5,600) and West Country Rescue (£2,600).

FINANCES *Year* 2012 *Income* £220,103 *Grants* £127,442 *Assets* £3,862,687

TRUSTEES Alan Gow; Nicky Moffitt; Rob Jones; Anthony Andrews; Rt Hon the Lord Rooker; Nick Bunting.

HOW TO APPLY In writing to the correspondent.

WHO TO APPLY TO Allan Dean-Lewis, Secretary, Motor Sport House, Riverside Park, Colnbrook, Berkshire SL3 0HG *Tel.* 01753 765000 *Fax* 01753 682938 *email* safety@msauk.org *Website* www.msauk.org

■ J. P. Moulton Charitable Foundation

CC NO 1109891   **ESTABLISHED** 2005

WHERE FUNDING CAN BE GIVEN UK.

WHO CAN BENEFIT Research institutions, disadvantaged people.

WHAT IS FUNDED Medical research, education, training and counselling

TYPE OF GRANT One-off and recurrent.

RANGE OF GRANTS Up to £500,000.

SAMPLE GRANTS University of Manchester (£491,000); University College London (£396,500); University of Bristol (£300,000); London School of Tropical Medicine (£189,000); Imperial College London (£142,000); University of Cambridge (£65,000); King's College Hospital (£46,000); Brain Tumour Charity (£32,500); Myasthenia Gravis Association (£30,000); King's College London (£13,000); Liverpool Women's NHS Foundation Trust (£11,000); and University of Leicester (£10,000).

FINANCES *Year* 2012 *Income* £72,218 *Grants* £1,726,767 *Assets* £2,041,902

TRUSTEES Jon Moulton; Spencer Moulton; Sara Everett.

OTHER INFORMATION All grants made during the year were for medical research projects.

HOW TO APPLY In writing to the correspondent.

WHO TO APPLY TO Jon Moulton, Trustee, c/o Better Capital LLP, 39–41 Charing Cross Road, London WC2H 0AR *Tel.* 020 7440 0860

■ The Mount Everest Foundation

CC NO 208206   **ESTABLISHED** 1955

WHERE FUNDING CAN BE GIVEN Expeditions from Great Britain and New Zealand.

WHO CAN BENEFIT Organisations, young adults and older people.

WHAT IS FUNDED Support of expeditions for exploration and research in high mountain regions only.

WHAT IS NOT FUNDED Youth, training and commercial expeditions are not eligible.

TYPE OF GRANT Project.

RANGE OF GRANTS £650–£2,700.

FINANCES *Year* 2011–12 *Income* £58,070 *Grants* £43,600 *Assets* £1,127,900

TRUSTEES Sarah Tyacke, Chair; Dr Andy Hodson; David Unwin; Paul Rose; Luke Hughes; Doug Scott; Col. Henry Day; Sqn Ldr Colin Scott.

PUBLICATIONS A map of Central Asia has been produced in collaboration with the Royal Geographical Society.

OTHER INFORMATION In 2011–12 grants were given to 24 expeditions.

HOW TO APPLY Application forms, guidelines and criteria are available to download from the website. Deadlines for receipt of completed application forms are 30 September and 31 January.

WHO TO APPLY TO W. F. Ruthven, Hon Secretary, 1 Sarabeth Drive, Tunley, Bath BA2 0EA. *Tel.* 01761 472998 *email* bill.ruthven@ btinternet.com *Website* www.mef.org.uk

■ The Edwina Mountbatten and Leonora Children's Foundation

CC NO 228166   **ESTABLISHED** 1960

WHERE FUNDING CAN BE GIVEN UK and overseas.

WHO CAN BENEFIT Medical organisations, particularly those benefiting children and nurses and other general charitable purposes.

WHAT IS FUNDED Save the Children Fund (for children who are sick, distressed or in need), the promotion and improvement of the art and practice of nursing, St John Ambulance and charities for the relief of cancer sufferers.

WHAT IS NOT FUNDED No grants for research or to individual nurses working in the UK for further professional training.

TYPE OF GRANT Project grants.

RANGE OF GRANTS £2,000–£32,000.

SAMPLE GRANTS St John Jerusalem Eye Hospital, Brecknock Hospice and Rainbow Trust (£30,000 each); Save the Children (£25,000); Cancer Research UK (£10,000); Home Start Eastleigh (£5,000); Riders for Health and Malaria No More (£3,000 each); Ashram International and Hope 4 the World (£2,000 each) and Queens Nursing Institute (£1,000).

FINANCES *Year* 2011–12 *Income* £153,062 *Grants* £149,000 *Assets* £5,034,241

TRUSTEES Countess Mountbatten of Burma, Chair; Hon. Alexandra Knatchbull; Lord Brabourne; Peter H. T. Mimpriss; Dame Mary Fagan; Lady Brabourne; Myrddin Rees; Sir Evelyn De Rothschild.

HOW TO APPLY Details of how to apply for grants can be obtained from the Trust Secretary. The trustees meet once a year, generally in September/October.

WHO TO APPLY TO John Moss, Secretary, Estate Office, Broadlands, Romsey, Hampshire SO51 9ZE *Tel.* 01794 529750

■ Mountbatten Festival of Music

CC NO 1016088   **ESTABLISHED** 1993

WHERE FUNDING CAN BE GIVEN UK.

WHO CAN BENEFIT Registered charities benefiting (ex) servicemen/women.

WHAT IS FUNDED Charities connected with the Royal Marines and Royal Navy.

WHAT IS NOT FUNDED Charities or organisations unknown to the trustees.

TYPE OF GRANT One-off and recurrent.

SAMPLE GRANTS Royal Marines Charitable Trust Fund (£53,500); CLIC Sargent (15,000); RN Benevolent Trust, Royal Marines Museum and Royal Navy and Royal Marines Children's Fund (£10,000 each); Combat Stress (£4,000); Blind Veterans UK (£3,000); BLESMA (£2,000); and Erskine Hospital and Women's Royal Naval Service Benevolent Trust (£1,000 each).

FINANCES *Year* 2011–12 *Income* £494,667 *Grants* £115,557 *Assets* £54,991

TRUSTEES Commandant General Royal Marines; Director of Royal Marines; Naval Personnel Team (RM) Team Leader

HOW TO APPLY Unsolicited applications are not considered as the trust's income is dependent upon the running and success of various musical events. Any money raised is then disbursed to a set of regular beneficiaries.

WHO TO APPLY TO Lt Col Ian Grant, Corps Secretary, The Corps Secretariat, Building 32, HMS Excellent, Whale Island, Portsmouth PO2 8ER *Tel.* 02392 547201 *email* royalmarines. charities@charity.vfree.com *Website* www. royalmarinesregimental.co.uk

■ The Mountbatten Memorial Trust

CC NO 278691   **ESTABLISHED** 1979

WHERE FUNDING CAN BE GIVEN Mainly UK, but some overseas.

WHO CAN BENEFIT Registered charities.

WHAT IS FUNDED Technological research in aid of disabilities, education and community.

WHAT IS NOT FUNDED No grants are made towards the purchase of technology to assist people with disabilities.

TYPE OF GRANT One off and recurring.

RANGE OF GRANTS £600–£45,000.

SAMPLE GRANTS Atlantic College (£40,000); Canine Partners (£1,600) and British Wireless for the Blind, The Elizabeth Foundation and Sign Health (£1,000 each).

FINANCES *Year* 2011–12 *Income* £37,062 *Grants* £44,600 *Assets* £549,192

TRUSTEES Countess Mountbatten of Burma; Lady Pamela Hicks; Ben Moorhead; Ashley Hicks; Hon. Michael John Knatchbull; Hon. Philip Knatchbull; William Fox and Kelly Knatchbull.

HOW TO APPLY In writing to the correspondent, at any time. Further details of how to apply can be obtained from the Secretary.

WHO TO APPLY TO John Moss, Secretary, The Estate Office, Broadlands, Romsey, Hampshire SO51 9ZE *Tel.* 01794 529750

■ Move on Foundation Limited

CC NO 1147788   **ESTABLISHED** 2012

WHERE FUNDING CAN BE GIVEN UK

WHO CAN BENEFIT Organisations and individuals.

WHAT IS FUNDED Sports; providing facilities, services, advice and information.

TRUSTEES Eunice Barber; Dakar Barry.

OTHER INFORMATION Established in 2012, this trust aims to advance in life and relieve the needs of young people by providing support and activities, in particular sporting activities, which develop their skills, capacities and capabilities to enable them to participate in society as mature and responsible individuals.

HOW TO APPLY In writing to the correspondent.

WHO TO APPLY TO Eunice Barber, Flat 21 Markham House, Kingswood Estate, London SE21 8QQ *Tel.* 020 8670 2871

■ Mrs Waterhouse Charitable Trust (formerly known as the Houghton Dunn Charitable Trust)

CC NO 261685   **ESTABLISHED** 1967

WHERE FUNDING CAN BE GIVEN UK, with an interest in North West England.

WHO CAN BENEFIT Registered charities only, especially those working in North West England.

WHAT IS FUNDED Medical, health, welfare, environment, wildlife, churches and heritage.

WHAT IS NOT FUNDED No grants to individuals.

SAMPLE GRANTS Previous beneficiaries have included: AMEND, Arthritis Research Campaign, Cancer BACUP, Cancer Research UK, Christie Hospital NHS Trust, East Lancashire Hospice Fund, Lancashire Wildlife Trust, Marie Curie Cancer Care, Macmillan Cancer Relief, National Eczema Society, National Trust Lake District Appeal and National Youth Orchestra.

FINANCES *Year* 2012–13 *Income* £301,629 *Grants* £298,000 *Assets* £7,119,413

TRUSTEES Alistair Houghton Dunn; Richard Houghton Dunn.

OTHER INFORMATION Grants were made to 29 organisations during the year; however a list of beneficiaries were not included in the trust's accounts.

HOW TO APPLY In writing to the correspondent.

WHO TO APPLY TO Mark Dunn, Carlton Place, 28–32 Greenwood Street, Altrincham WA14 1RZ

■ The MSE Charity

CC NO 1121320   **ESTABLISHED** 2007

WHERE FUNDING CAN BE GIVEN UK

WHO CAN BENEFIT Individuals and organisations aiming to eradicate financial illiteracy in the UK through education and innovative projects.

WHAT IS FUNDED Financial education; financial planning and advice services.

WHAT IS NOT FUNDED No funding for career development, vocational courses, undergraduate or postgraduate courses. No applications directly from persons under 18 years of age, such applicants will need a parent or guardian to apply on their behalf.

TYPE OF GRANT Project grants.

RANGE OF GRANTS Usually around £5,000.

SAMPLE GRANTS North Liverpool CAB; Whitlawburn Community Resource Centre; Winter Comfort for the Homeless; Building Bridges; Jubilee Family Centre; Financial Inclusion Derbyshire; Durham Christian Partnership; East Ayrshire Carers centre; Solihull Action through Advocacy; Institute of Money Advisers; The Elfrida Society Parents Project and Mancunian Way.

FINANCES *Year* 2011–12 *Income* £230,862 *Grants* £100,855 *Assets* £270,373

TRUSTEES Tony Tesciuba; John Hewison; Katie Birkett; Vanessa Bissessur; Teej Dew.

HOW TO APPLY Applications must be made via the online application form. The trust is open to applications for a month three times a year, usually January, May and September; check the website for upcoming deadlines. It will close to applications either after a month or when 40 completed applications have been received, whichever is the earlier. After a provisional eligibility check the application will be given to the Grant Approval Panel, which meets three times a year. Only one application will be accepted from an organisation within a two year period. If you have a project you consider to be special, and which does not appear to fit into the other criteria, then contact the operations manager directly (stuart@msecharity.org), who will bring it to the attention of the Trustees.

WHO TO APPLY TO Anthony Jeffrey, Administrator, PO Box 240, Gatley, Cheadle SK8 4XT *Tel.* 01618 349221 *email* stuart@msecharity.com *Website* www.msecharity.com

■ The George Müller Charitable Trust

CC NO 1066832   **ESTABLISHED** 1997

WHERE FUNDING CAN BE GIVEN Worldwide.

WHO CAN BENEFIT Individuals and organisations with charitable or Christian principles.

WHAT IS FUNDED Christian organisations; Churches; in practice a preference is shown for children and young people's projects and orphanages.

RANGE OF GRANTS £1,000–£80,000.

SAMPLE GRANTS Rwandan Orphan Project (£80,000); Haven Home Orphanage (£52,000); 25:40 Romania (£31,000); Hebron Hostel Trust (£25,000); Helping Them to Smile Project

Think carefully about every application. Is it justified?

769

(£10,000); Ebenezer Children's Fund (£7,000) and House of Hope (£6,000).

FINANCES *Year* 2012–13 *Income* £2,468,985 *Grants* £399,363 *Assets* £9,330,002

TRUSTEES Quentin Elston; Robert Scott-Cook; Roger Chilvers; Neil Summerton; Tony Davies; Adrian Reed; Kim Conlan; Edward Marsh; Peter Metcalfe; Stewart North.

OTHER INFORMATION Grants are also made to individual Christian workers working in the UK and abroad. £756,000 was paid to 51 individuals in 2012–13. The trust also runs sheltered accommodation for elderly people in Weston-super-Mare and manages a Church partnership scheme which promotes community outreach.

HOW TO APPLY On a form available from the correspondent. Trustees meet in March and November.

WHO TO APPLY TO Tony Davies, Company Secretary, Muller House, 7 Cotham Park, Bristol BS6 6DA *Tel.* 01179 245001 *email* admin@mullers.org *Website* www.mullers.org

■ The Mugdock Children's Trust

SC NO SC006001 **ESTABLISHED** 1920

WHERE FUNDING CAN BE GIVEN Scotland.

WHO CAN BENEFIT Charities benefiting children up to the age of about 14 who are ill or disabled.

WHAT IS FUNDED 'Poor children from Glasgow or other districts of Scotland who are in need of convalescent treatment for sickness or any other disability; organisations of a charitable nature whose objects either consist of or include the provision in Scotland of rehabilitation, recreation or education for children convalescing or still suffering from the effects of illness, injury or disability; organisations of a charitable nature whose objects either consist of or include the provision in Scotland of accommodation or facilities for children who are in need of care or assistance.'

RANGE OF GRANTS £500–£6,000.

SAMPLE GRANTS Abercorn School; Ark Trust; Barnardo's; Camphill Foundation; Cancer and Leukaemia in Childhood; Children First; Children's Heart Federation; Glasgow Children's Holiday Playscheme; Hopscotch Holidays Ltd; Sense; Sighthill Youth Centre; Stepping Stones for Families; Wanderers Youth Club and West Scotland Deaf Children's Society.

FINANCES *Year* 2011–12 *Income* £57,239

TRUSTEES Graham A. Philips; Rosamund Blair; Moira Bruce; Dr Anne Cowan; Joyce Duguid; Avril Meighan; Alastair J. Struthers; Christine Brown; James Morris.

OTHER INFORMATION In 2011–12 the trust had a total expenditure of £58,000.

HOW TO APPLY The trust has stated that it 'will not, as a matter of policy, consider applications which are unsolicited'.

WHO TO APPLY TO J. Simpson, Secretary, Wylie and Bisset Accountants, 168 Bath Street, Glasgow G2 4TP *Tel.* 01415 667000 *Fax* 01415 667001

■ The Mulberry Trust

CC NO 263296 **ESTABLISHED** 1971

WHERE FUNDING CAN BE GIVEN UK, with an interest in Harlow, Essex and surrounding areas, including London.

WHO CAN BENEFIT Charitable organisations.

WHAT IS FUNDED General charitable purposes.

RANGE OF GRANTS £1,000–£50,000.

SAMPLE GRANTS Cambridge Interfaith Project (University of Cambridge (£50,000); Age UK (£49,000); Harlow Parochial Church Council (St Mary's Church) Calm Centre (£20,000); Parents Like Us (£12,000); Harlow Alzheimer's Society (£10,000); Hope UK (£5,000); Youth for Christ (£3,000); Bag Books (£2,000); St George's House, Windsor, Clare College, Harlow Rotary and Sailability (£1,000 each).

FINANCES *Year* 2011–12 *Income* £208,152 *Grants* £256,283 *Assets* £5,862,676

TRUSTEES Ann M. Marks; Charles F. Woodhouse; Timothy J. Marks; Chris Marks; Rupert Marks; William Marks.

HOW TO APPLY The trust states: 'As we are a proactive trust with limited funds and administrative help, we are unable to consider unsolicited applications'.

WHO TO APPLY TO John Marks, Trustee, Farrer and Co, 66 Lincoln's Inn Fields, London WC2A 3LH *Tel.* 020 7242 2002

■ Frederick Mulder Charitable Trust (formerly the Prairie Trust)

CC NO 296019 **ESTABLISHED** 1987

WHERE FUNDING CAN BE GIVEN Worldwide.

WHO CAN BENEFIT Charitable organisations.

WHAT IS FUNDED A small number of organisations working on issues of third world development, climate change and conflict prevention, and particularly to support policy and advocacy work in these areas. The trustees are also interested in supporting innovative and entrepreneurial approaches to traditional problems. Organisations encouraging the development of philanthropy.

WHAT IS NOT FUNDED No grants to individuals or for expeditions.

TYPE OF GRANT One-off and recurrent grants of up to two years.

RANGE OF GRANTS £100–£70,000.

SAMPLE GRANTS The Funding Network (for various projects, TFN London and other TFN groups plus operational costs) (£79,000); 10:10 (carbon emissions) (£35,000); Novim Group (climate change) (£30,000).

FINANCES *Year* 2011–12 *Income* £555,208 *Grants* £172,183 *Assets* £1,558,057

TRUSTEES Dr Frederick Mulder; Hannah Mulder; Robin Bowman; Rhodes Pinto.

OTHER INFORMATION At the end of the year investments stood at £449,000 and the trust transferred a further £631,000 into its CAF Gold account during the year.

HOW TO APPLY In writing to the correspondent.

WHO TO APPLY TO Dr Frederick Mulder, 83 Belsize Park Gardens, London NW3 4NJ *Tel.* 020 7722 2105 *email* info@frederickmulder.com

■ The Edith Murphy Foundation

CC NO 1026062 **ESTABLISHED** 1993

WHERE FUNDING CAN BE GIVEN UK with some preference for Leicestershire.

WHO CAN BENEFIT Organisations benefiting people in need, animals, children and the disabled.

WHAT IS FUNDED Relief for people suffering hardship/distress due to their age, youth, infirmity, disability, poverty or social and economic circumstances. Relief of suffering of animals and provision for the care of unwanted or sick animals. Other general charitable purposes.

TYPE OF GRANT One-off and recurrent.

RANGE OF GRANTS Up to £375,000.

SAMPLE GRANTS De Monfort University (£200,000); Build IT International (£30,000); The Stroke Association and The Harley Staples Cancer Trust (£20,000 each); Marie Curie Cancer Care (£19,000); Vista (£15,000); Leicester Hospitals Charity, Livability, Leeds Mencap and De Montfort University (£10,000 each).

FINANCES *Year* 2011–12 *Income* £777,295 *Grants* £949,605 *Assets* £30,725,007

TRUSTEES David L. Tams; Pamela M. Breakwell; Christopher P. Blakesley; Richard F. Adkinson.

OTHER INFORMATION Grants of less than £10,000 totalled £512,000.

HOW TO APPLY In writing to the correspondent. The foundation states in its annual report: 'The Foundation considers every application received and where there is a need covered by the Foundation's objectives the trustees will consider making a grant.'

WHO TO APPLY TO Richard F. Adkinson, Trustee, c/o Crane and Walton, 113–117 London Road, Leicester LE2 0RG *Tel.* 01162 551901 *email* richard.adkinson@btinternet.com

■ Murphy-Neumann Charity Company Limited

CC NO 229555   **ESTABLISHED** 1963

WHERE FUNDING CAN BE GIVEN UK

WHO CAN BENEFIT Registered charities only.

WHAT IS FUNDED The trust has three main objects: to support projects aimed at helping those in society who suffer economic or social disadvantages or hardship arising from disability and/or social exclusion; to assist those working to alleviate chronic illness and disabling disease; to help fund research into medical conditions (particularly among the very young and the elderly) for which there is not yet a cure.

WHAT IS NOT FUNDED No grants to individuals, or non-registered charities.

TYPE OF GRANT One-off and recurrent grants for general costs (large charities) and specific projects (smaller organisations).

RANGE OF GRANTS £500–£2,500.

SAMPLE GRANTS Evening Argus Christmas Appeal and Contact the Elderly (£2,000 each); Acorn Villages and Autistica (£1,500 each); Hospice in the Weald and Action on Elder Abuse (£1,250 each); Vitalise, Chicks Camping Holidays, Housing the Homeless Central Fund, The Prostate Cancer Charity, Dream Makers, Daisy's Eye Cancer Fund and Tourettes Action (£1,000 each); Lowe Syndrome Trust (£750) and Youth Talk (£500).

FINANCES *Year* 2011–12 *Income* £67,600 *Grants* £59,500 *Assets* £1,499,474

TRUSTEES Mark J. Lockett; Paula Christopher; Marcus Richman.

HOW TO APPLY In writing to the correspondent, in a letter outlining the purpose of the required charitable donation. Telephone calls are not welcome. There are no application forms, guidelines or deadlines. No sae required. Grants are usually given in November and December. Printed grant criteria is available on request.

WHO TO APPLY TO Mark Lockett, Trustee, Hayling Cottage, Upper Street, Stratford St Mary, Colchester, Essex CO7 6JW *Tel.* 01206 323685 *email* mncc@keme.co.uk

■ The John R. Murray Charitable Trust

CC NO 1100199   **ESTABLISHED** 2003

WHERE FUNDING CAN BE GIVEN UK.

WHO CAN BENEFIT Registered charities.

WHAT IS FUNDED 'Arts an literature (although not strictly limited to such areas) and where the award of a grant will have an immediate and tangible benefit to the recipient in question.'

SAMPLE GRANTS National Library of Scotland (£313,000); Wordsworth Trust (£120,000); Bodleian Library (£60,000); Only Connect (£25,000); Lakeland Arts Trust (£20,000); Academy of Ancient Music (£15,000); British School at Athens (£11,000); Fine Cell Work (£10,000); Gilbert White's House (£7,500); Stoke Pages Society (£5,000); John Buchan Heritage Museum (£3,000) and Kings Corner Project (£200).

FINANCES *Year* 2012 *Income* £879,373 *Grants* £912,880 *Assets* £23,720,314

TRUSTEES John R. Murray; Virginia G. Murray; Hallam J. R. G. Murray; John O. G. Murray; Charles J. G. Murray.

HOW TO APPLY The trustees will not consider unsolicited applications for grants.

WHO TO APPLY TO John Murray, Trustee, 50 Albemarle Street, London W1S 4BD *Tel.* 020 7493 4361

■ Peter John Murray Trust

CC NO 1134976   **ESTABLISHED** 2010

WHERE FUNDING CAN BE GIVEN Developing countries, mainly in Africa and the Caribbean.

WHO CAN BENEFIT Charitable organisations.

WHAT IS FUNDED Projects relating needs and wellbeing of pre-school and school aged children where their lives have been seriously affected by violent conflict, poverty, abuse, preventable ill health/incapacity, natural disaster or any other kind of misfortune.

TYPE OF GRANT Mostly recurrent.

FINANCES *Year* 2012 *Income* £1,081

TRUSTEES Recilda Murray; Edith Murray; Peter Murray.

OTHER INFORMATION Note the following statement taken from the trust's website about its funding principles: 'Financial help and various other forms of assistance are provided through our partner organisations that are established voluntary groups and charities providing commendable services within local communities. And it is their local experience and professional practice that we seek to rely on as the leading route to meeting the acute needs and wellbeing of their beneficiaries – seriously affected children with wrecked lives. It is part of our overall objective, when possible and where appropriate, to foster long term relationships with our partners. We seek to be actively engaged in the promotion of our partners' respective causes and indeed enabling seriously affected, desperate children to access basic but essential living needs so they can exist and live a better life.' For more information on becoming a partner organisation, contact the trust directly.

HOW TO APPLY In writing to the correspondent.

WHO TO APPLY TO Peter Murray, Trustee, 78 York Street, London W1H 1DP *Tel.* 020 7692 7007 *email* info@pjm-trust.org *Website* www.pjm-trust.org

■ The Mushroom Fund

CC NO 259954   ESTABLISHED 1969
WHERE FUNDING CAN BE GIVEN UK and overseas, with
a preference for St Helens.
WHO CAN BENEFIT Registered charities. Donations
are made only to charities known to the
trustees.
WHAT IS FUNDED General charitable purposes.
WHAT IS NOT FUNDED No grants to individuals or to
organisations that are not registered charities.
TYPE OF GRANT Unrestricted.
RANGE OF GRANTS Up to £3,000, however generally
under £1,000.
SAMPLE GRANTS Save the Family (£5,000); Liverpool
CVS (£2,000); and Age UK (Mid Mersey), Halton
and St Helens Voluntary Community Action,
SENSE, Samaritans and Walesby Village Hall
(£1,000 each).
FINANCES *Year* 2011–12 *Income* £35,278
Grants £24,900 *Assets* £987,306
TRUSTEES Rosalind Christian; Guy Pilkington; James
Pilkington; Harriet Christian; Liverpool Charity
and Voluntary Services.
HOW TO APPLY The trust does not consider or
respond to unsolicited applications.
WHO TO APPLY TO The Trustees, Liverpool Charity and
Voluntary Services, 151 Dale Street, Liverpool
L2 2AH *Tel.* 01512 275177 *email* enquiries@
charitycheques.org.uk

■ The Music Sales Charitable Trust

CC NO 1014942   ESTABLISHED 1992
WHERE FUNDING CAN BE GIVEN UK, but mostly Bury St
Edmunds and London.
WHO CAN BENEFIT Registered charities benefiting
children and young adults, musicians, disabled
people and people disadvantaged by poverty.
WHAT IS FUNDED The trust supports the education of
children attending schools in the UK, relief of
need, and other charitable purposes. The
trustees are particularly interested in helping to
promote music and musical education for young
people.
WHAT IS NOT FUNDED No grants to individuals.
RANGE OF GRANTS £1,000–£30,000
SAMPLE GRANTS Bury St Edmunds Borough Council
(£6,500); Westminster Synagogue and Bury St
Edmunds Bach Society (£5,000 each); Royal
College of Music (£2,500); St Nicholas Hospice
Care (£2,300); The Salmon Trust – Thurston
Festival and Action Medical Research for
Children for Life (£1,500 each) and Save a Child
– India, Fulfil the Wish, Great Ormond Street
Hospital Children's Charity, Paralympics 2012
and Young People Taking Action (£1,000 each).
FINANCES *Year* 2011 *Income* £75,000
Grants £63,778 *Assets* £29,745
TRUSTEES Robert Wise; T. Wise; Ian Morgan;
Christopher Butler; David Rockberger; Mildred
Wise; A. E. Latham; M. Wise; Miss Jane
Richardson
HOW TO APPLY In writing to the correspondent. The
trustees meet quarterly, generally in March,
June, September and December.
WHO TO APPLY TO Neville Wignall, Clerk, Music Sales
Ltd, Dettingen Way, Bury St Edmunds, Suffolk
IP33 3YB *Tel.* 01284 702600 *email* neville.
wignall@musicsales.co.uk

■ Muslim Hands

CC NO 1105056   ESTABLISHED 1993
WHERE FUNDING CAN BE GIVEN Overseas.
WHO CAN BENEFIT Organisations benefiting people
disadvantaged by poverty and victims of man-
made or natural disasters and war.
WHAT IS FUNDED The relief of poverty and sickness
in the event of natural disasters and areas of
war; help to people in need, particularly
orphans; advancement of the Islamic faith and
distribution of Islamic literature; provision of
schools, training colleges, safe water schemes,
medical centres, and orphan sponsorship
schemes.
SAMPLE GRANTS Grants were given in the following
categories: General (£2.8 million); Orphans
(£2.7 million); Education (£305,500); Health
(£247,000); Emergency Aid (£885,000); Shelter
(£29,500); Safe Water (£717,000); Food
(£1 million) and Masjid (£90,000).
FINANCES *Year* 2012 *Income* £13,230,574
Grants £8,741,682 *Assets* £7,250,836
TRUSTEES Musharaf Hussain; Syed Lakhte
Hassanain; Mohammad Amin-Ul Hasanat Shah;
Saffi Ullah; Sahibzada Ghulam Jeelani.
HOW TO APPLY In writing to the correspondent.
WHO TO APPLY TO Asad Ansari, Administrator,
148–164 Gregory Boulevard, Nottingham
NG7 5JE *Tel.* 01159 117222 *Fax* 01159
117220 *email* contact@muslimhands.org.uk
Website www.muslimhands.org.uk

■ The Mutual Trust Group

CC NO 1039300   ESTABLISHED 1994
WHERE FUNDING CAN BE GIVEN UK.
WHO CAN BENEFIT Organisations benefiting Jewish
people and people disadvantaged by poverty.
WHAT IS FUNDED General charitable purposes. In
particular, for the relief of poverty and the
advancement of Orthodox Jewish religious
education.
SAMPLE GRANTS Yeshivat Kesser Hatalmud
(£217,000); Yeshivat Shar Hashamayim
(£89,000); and 'other' (£1,000).
FINANCES *Year* 2012 *Income* £304,207
Grants £315,644 *Assets* £153,047
TRUSTEES Rabbi Benzion Weitz; Michael Weitz;
Adrian Weisz.
HOW TO APPLY In writing to the correspondent.
WHO TO APPLY TO Rabbi Benzion Weitz, Trustee,
12 Dunstan Road, London NW11 8AA *Tel.* 020
8458 7549

■ MW (CL) Foundation

CC NO 1134917   ESTABLISHED 2010
WHERE FUNDING CAN BE GIVEN Worldwide, with a
preference for the UK.
WHO CAN BENEFIT Charitable organisations,
education providers and Jewish causes.
WHAT IS FUNDED Projects which promote education,
relief of poverty and the advancement of the
Orthodox Jewish faith.
RANGE OF GRANTS £1,000–£70,000
SAMPLE GRANTS Achisomoch (£70,000); Zichron
Mordechai and Devorah Weiz Foundation
(£14,000); Keren Shabbos, N W London
Communal Mikvah Ltd, W S T Charity Ltd
(£10,000 each); Tiferes High School, The Boys
Club House, SEED, Rabbi Zvi Kushalevski
(£5,000 each); Sunderland Talmudical College,
London Academy of Jewish Studies, Beis
Minchat Yitschok Trust (£1,000 each).

FINANCES *Year* 2011–12 *Income* £147,817
Grants £172,765 *Assets* £2,801,192
TRUSTEES Hilary Olsberg; Vivienne Lewin.
OTHER INFORMATION The foundation is closely linked
with the MW (RH) Foundation, MW (GK)
Foundation and MW (HO) Foundation and shares
the same charitable objectives.
HOW TO APPLY In writing to the correspondent.
WHO TO APPLY TO Vivienne Lewin, Trustee,
38 Princes Park Avenue, London NW11 0JT

....

■ MW (GK) Foundation

CC NO 1134916   **ESTABLISHED** 2010
WHERE FUNDING CAN BE GIVEN Worldwide, with a
preference for the UK.
WHO CAN BENEFIT Charitable organisations and
education providers, Jewish causes.
WHAT IS FUNDED Projects which promote education,
relief of poverty and the advancement of the
Orthodox Jewish faith.
RANGE OF GRANTS £1,000–£80,000
SAMPLE GRANTS Mercaz Hatorah Belz Machnovke
(£80,500); Yad Vochessed (£25,500); Beis
Ahron Trust (£16,000); Friends of Dorog
(£6,500); Gateshead Talmudical College
(£2,000); Chasdei Yoel, Kollel Shoimre
Haachomos, Toimche Shaabos (£1,000 each).
FINANCES *Year* 2011–12 *Income* £74,858
Grants £158,760 *Assets* £2,777,201
TRUSTEES Shlomo Klein; Gella Klein.
OTHER INFORMATION The foundation was initially
known as the Weisz Children Foundation and is
closely linked with the MW (CL) Foundation, MW
(RH) Foundation and MW (HO) Foundation.
HOW TO APPLY In writing to the correspondent.
WHO TO APPLY TO Gella Klein, Trustee, 15 Brantwood
Road, Salford M7 4EN

....

■ MW (HO) Foundation

CC NO 1134919   **ESTABLISHED** 2010
WHERE FUNDING CAN BE GIVEN Worldwide, with a
preference for UK.
WHO CAN BENEFIT Charitable organisations,
education providers and Jewish causes.
WHAT IS FUNDED Projects which promote education,
relief of poverty and the advancement of the
Orthodox Jewish faith.
RANGE OF GRANTS £1,000–£55,000
SAMPLE GRANTS Shekel (£55,000); Asser Bishvil
Foundation (£37,500); M H Trust (£17,500);
Chomel Dalim (£8,500); Three Pillars (£6,500);
Beis Chaya Rochel (£3,000); Shemays
(£1,000).
FINANCES *Year* 2011–12 *Income* £169,893
Grants £176,635 *Assets* £3,032,117
TRUSTEES Hilary Olsberg; Rosalind Halpern.
OTHER INFORMATION The foundation was initially
known as the Meir Weisz Foundation and is
closely linked with the MW (CL) Foundation, MW
(GK) Foundation and MW (RH) Foundation.
HOW TO APPLY In writing to the correspondent.
WHO TO APPLY TO David Olsberg, Administrator, 2b
Mather Avenue, Prestwich, Manchester
M25 0LA

....

■ MW (RH) Foundation

CC NO 1134918   **ESTABLISHED** 2010
WHERE FUNDING CAN BE GIVEN Worldwide, with a
preference for the UK.
WHO CAN BENEFIT Charitable organisations and
education providers.

WHAT IS FUNDED Projects which promote education,
relief of poverty and the advancement of the
Orthodox Jewish faith.
SAMPLE GRANTS Asser Bishvil Foundation (£53,500);
Beis Ruchel School (£28,500); Telz Academy
Trust (£18,000); Meir Hatorah (£13,500);
Lowcost Ltd (£10,000); Friends of Boyan, Y A M
F (£5,000 each); Format Charitable Trust,
Merkas Moldos Belz, Toimche Shaabos
Manchester (£1,000 each).
FINANCES *Year* 2011–12 *Income* £252,363
Grants £184,010 *Assets* £2,665,083
TRUSTEES Rosalind Halpern; Jacob Halpern;
H. Olsberg.
OTHER INFORMATION This foundation was initially
known as the Deborah Weisz Foundation and is
closely linked with the MW (CL) Foundation, MW
(GK) Foundation and MW (HO) Foundation.
HOW TO APPLY In writing to the correspondent.
WHO TO APPLY TO Jacob Halpern, Trustee,
29 Waterpark Road, Salford M7 4FT

....

■ MYA Charitable Trust

CC NO 299642   **ESTABLISHED** 1987
WHERE FUNDING CAN BE GIVEN Worldwide
WHO CAN BENEFIT Children, young adults and Jewish
people.
WHAT IS FUNDED Advancement of Orthodox Jewish
religion and education.
SAMPLE GRANTS Previously: ZSV Trust; KZF; Beis
Rochel; Keren Zedoko Vochesed; London
Friends of Kamenitzer Yeshiva; Maos Yesomim
Charitable Trust; Bikkur Cholim De Satmar;
Keren Mitzva Trust and Wlodowa Charity
Rehabilitation Trust.
FINANCES *Year* 2011–12 *Income* £200,545
Grants £182,105 *Assets* £980,213
TRUSTEES Myer Rothfeld; Eve Rothfeld; Hannah
Schraiber; Joseph Pfeffer.
OTHER INFORMATION There was a further £6,500
given in grants to individuals. A list of
beneficiaries was not provided in the accounts.
HOW TO APPLY In writing to the correspondent.
WHO TO APPLY TO Myer Rothfeld, Trustee, Medcar
House, 149a Stamford Hill, London N16 5LL
Tel. 020 8800 3582

....

■ MYR Charitable Trust

CC NO 1104406   **ESTABLISHED** 2004
WHERE FUNDING CAN BE GIVEN In practice, Israel, USA
and England.
WHO CAN BENEFIT Members of the Orthodox Jewish
faith.
WHAT IS FUNDED Advancement of the Orthodox
Jewish religion, relief of sickness and poverty of
recognised members of said faith.
SAMPLE GRANTS Previously: Cong Beth Joseph; HP
Charitable Trust; UTA; Gateshead Jewish
Boarding School; Keren Eretz Yisroel; SCT
Sunderland and GJLC.
FINANCES *Year* 2012 *Income* £93,884
Grants £43,350 *Assets* £1,096,697
TRUSTEES Z. M. Kaufman; S. Kaufman;
A. A. Zonszajn; J. Kaufman.
HOW TO APPLY In writing to the correspondent.
WHO TO APPLY TO Z. M. Kaufman, Trustee,
50 Keswick Street, Gateshead, Tyne and Wear
NE8 1TQ

■ The Kitty and Daniel Nabarro Charitable Trust

CC NO 1002786   **ESTABLISHED** 1991
WHERE FUNDING CAN BE GIVEN UK
WHO CAN BENEFIT Registered charities.
WHAT IS FUNDED Relief of poverty, advancement of medicine and advancement of education. This trust will consider funding: information technology and computers; support and self-help groups; environmental issues; IT training; literacy; training for work; vocational training; and crime prevention schemes.
WHAT IS NOT FUNDED No grants to individuals.
SAMPLE GRANTS Previous beneficiaries include: Cambridge Foundation Discovery Fund (£5,000); and OCD Action (£2,000).
FINANCES *Year* 2011–12 *Income* £20,688 *Grants* £19,440
TRUSTEES Daniel Nabarro; Katherine Nabarro; Allan Watson.
HOW TO APPLY The trustees allocate grants on an annual basis to an existing list of charities. The trustees do not at this time envisage grants to charities which are not already on the list. **This trust states that it does not respond to unsolicited applications.**
WHO TO APPLY TO Daniel Nabarro, Trustee, 24 Totteridge Common, London N20 8NE *email* admin.nabarro.charity@gmail.com

■ The Nadezhda Charitable Trust

CC NO 1007295   **ESTABLISHED** 1992
WHERE FUNDING CAN BE GIVEN UK and worldwide, particularly Zimbabwe.
WHO CAN BENEFIT Christian organisations.
WHAT IS FUNDED Advancement of Christianity in the UK and overseas, particularly Zimbabwe.
WHAT IS NOT FUNDED No grants to individuals.
SAMPLE GRANTS Mind the Gap Africa (£5,700); Family Impact (£2,400); All Saints Kemble (£2,000); Impact Giving (£1,200) and World Horizons (£1,000).
FINANCES *Year* 2011–12 *Income* £28,372 *Grants* £24,701 *Assets* £32,785
TRUSTEES William M. Kingston; Jill M. Kingston; Anthony R. Collins; Ian Conolly.
HOW TO APPLY From the trusts annual report: 'The Trust has continued to operate on the basis of not supporting projects from unsolicited contacts.'
WHO TO APPLY TO Jill Kingston, Trustee, C/o Ballard Dale Syree Watson LLP, Oakmore Court, Kingswood Road, Hampton Lovett, Droitwich Spa WR9 0QH

■ The Naggar Charitable Trust

CC NO 265409   **ESTABLISHED** 1973
WHERE FUNDING CAN BE GIVEN UK and overseas.
WHO CAN BENEFIT Jews.
WHAT IS FUNDED Jewish organisations; medical; the arts.
TYPE OF GRANT Some recurrent.
RANGE OF GRANTS £80–£100,000.
SAMPLE GRANTS Previous beneficiaries include: British Friends of the Art Museums of Israel

(£15,000); Western Marble Arch Synagogue (£11,000); CST (£8,500); The Contemporary Arts Society and The Royal Parks Foundation (£5,000 each) Jewish Care and One Family UK (£2,500 each); Royal Academy of Arts (£1,000); and St John's Wood Society (£15).
FINANCES *Year* 2011–12 *Income* £0 *Grants* £10,000
TRUSTEES Guy Naggar; Hon. Marion Naggar; Marc Zilkha.
HOW TO APPLY In writing to the correspondent.
WHO TO APPLY TO G. Naggar, Trustee, 61 Avenue Road, London NW8 6HR *Tel.* 020 7034 1919

■ The Eleni Nakou Foundation

CC NO 803753   **ESTABLISHED** 1990
WHERE FUNDING CAN BE GIVEN Worldwide, mostly Continental Europe.
WHO CAN BENEFIT Charitable organisations.
WHAT IS FUNDED Advancement of education of the peoples of Europe in each other's culture, history, literature, language, institutions, art, science, religion, music and folklore, and promotion of the exchange of knowledge about the cultures of northern and southern Europe in order to bridge the divide between these cultures and promote international understanding.
TYPE OF GRANT Recurrent and one-off.
RANGE OF GRANTS £1,000–£45,000
SAMPLE GRANTS Previously: £45,000 to Danish Institute at Athens; £17,500 to Hellenic Foundation; £9,000 to Eleni Nakou Scholarship Athens; £1,100 to Scandinavian Society for Modern Greek Studies.
FINANCES *Year* 2011–12 *Income* £591 *Grants* £88,085
TRUSTEE Kleinwort Benson Trustees Ltd.
HOW TO APPLY In writing to the correspondent. Applications are considered periodically. However, the trustees' state: 'It is unusual to respond favourably to unsolicited appeals'.
WHO TO APPLY TO Chris Gilbert, Secretary, Kleinwort Benson Trustees Ltd, 14 St George Street, London W1S 1FE *Tel.* 020 3207 7000 *email* chris.gilbert@kbpb.co.uk

■ The Janet Nash Charitable Settlement

CC NO 326880   **ESTABLISHED** 1985
WHERE FUNDING CAN BE GIVEN UK.
WHO CAN BENEFIT Institutions and individuals.
WHAT IS FUNDED General charitable purposes.
TYPE OF GRANT Recurrent.
SAMPLE GRANTS Get-a-Head Charitable Trust (£15,000); Sense (£5,000); Dyslexia Institute (£4,000); County Air Ambulance Trust (£1,500); and Birmingham Children's Hospital (£1,000).
FINANCES *Year* 2011–12 *Income* £304,122 *Grants* £301,306 *Assets* £84,848
TRUSTEES Ronald Gulliver; Mark Stephen Jacobs; Charlotte Emma Westall.
OTHER INFORMATION In 2011–12 grants were made to individuals totalling £274,806; including £231,724 (Medical) and £43,082 (Hardship).
HOW TO APPLY Absolutely no response to unsolicited applications. In 2007, the trustees stated: 'The charity does not, repeat not, ever, consider any applications for benefit from the public'. Furthermore, that: 'Our existing charitable commitments more than use up our potential funds and were found personally by the trustees

themselves, never as a result of applications from third parties'.

WHO TO APPLY TO Ronald Gulliver, Trustee, The Old Chapel, New Mill Lane, Eversley, Hampshire RG27 0RA *Tel.* 01189 733194

■ The National Art Collections Fund

CC NO 209174   **ESTABLISHED** 1903
WHERE FUNDING CAN BE GIVEN UK.
WHO CAN BENEFIT UK public museums, galleries, historic houses, libraries and archives that are accredited under the Arts Council Scheme. individual UK curators, scholars and researchers.
WHAT IS FUNDED For the purchase of works of art and other objects of aesthetic interest, dating from antiquity to the present day. For travel or other activities to extend and develop their curatorial expertise, collections-based knowledge and art historical interests.
WHAT IS NOT FUNDED Applications where the applicant has already purchased or made a commitment to purchase the object, or made a financial commitment; other costs associated with acquisitions such as the conservation and restoration of works, transport and storage costs, temporary or permanent exhibitions and digitisation projects; applications from individuals, artist's groups, commercial organisations, hospitals, places of worship, schools or higher education institutions; objects that are primarily of social-historical interest; scientific or technological material; letters, manuscripts or archival material with limited artistic or decorative inscription.
TYPE OF GRANT One-off grants.
RANGE OF GRANTS There is no fixed upper or lower limit to the size of grant the committee may offer. There are main grants and small grants schemes.
SAMPLE GRANTS National Gallery (£2 million); Oxford Ashmolean Museum (£855,000); National Maritime Museum (£302,000); London Tate (£270,000); Cambridge Fitzwilliam Museum (£242,000); Towner Contemporary Museum (£135,000); National Museum Cardiff (£115,000); Scottish National Gallery (£78,000); Ben Uri Gallery (£54,000); Wrest Park (£30,000); Touchstones Rochdale (£21,000); The Creative Foundation (£15,000); Hunterian Art Gallery (£10,000); Walker Art Gallery (£8,600); Portsmouth City Museum and Records Office (£5,000) and Essex Collection of Art from Latin America (£2,300).
FINANCES *Year* 2012 *Income* £15,070,000 *Grants* £6,302,269 *Assets* £36,620,000
TRUSTEES David Verey; Paul Zuckerman; Dr Wendy Baron; Prof. Michael Craig-Martin; Christopher Lloyd; Jonathan Marsden; Dr Deborah Swallow; Prof. William Vaughan; Sally Osman; James Lingwood; Richard Calvocoressi; Caroline Butler; Prof. Chris Gosden; Antony Griffiths; Prof. Lisa Tickner; Michael Wilson; Philippa Galnville; Liz Forgan; Alastair Laing.
PUBLICATIONS Review, Art Quarterly, Information notes for grant applicants.
HOW TO APPLY Firstly discuss the application with a member of the programmes office then register on the website to access the online application form. The Art Fund 'actively encourages strong applications from national and designated museums for objects which will enrich their collections and supports their effort s to expand into new collecting areas when appropriate. The

Art Fund considers applications for whatever amount is needed. Applicants are expected also to apply for any public funding for which they might be eligible, and to raise funds from other sources if they can'. There are six deadlines a year for the main grants scheme, telephone the fund for these. Small grants applications can be submitted at any time. Potential applicants for auctions grants should contact the fund at the earliest opportunity. They need a minimum of seven working days notice for an auction in London or ten working days for an auction outside of London. Applications for the small curatorial grants can be submitted at any time. There are three deadlines a year for curatorial grants of more than £1,500; these can be obtained by telephoning the fund. Application forms and deadlines can be downloaded from the website.
WHO TO APPLY TO Sarah Philip, Head of Programmes, Millais House, 7 Cromwell Place, London SW7 2JN *Tel.* 020 7225 4822 *Fax* 020 7225 4848 *email* programmes@artfund.org *Website* www.artfund.org

---

■ The National Churches Trust (formerly the Historic Churches Preservation Trust with the Incorporated Church Building Society)

CC NO 1119845   **ESTABLISHED** 1953
WHERE FUNDING CAN BE GIVEN UK.
WHO CAN BENEFIT Christian churches of architectural or historical importance that are in need of repair. Churches should meet the following criteria: the building must be open for regular public worship – the trust does not currently have grants available for cathedrals, but any other Christian places of worship can apply if they meet the eligibility criteria; it must be sited in England, Northern Ireland, the Isle of Man, Scotland or Wales; the congregation must belong to a denomination that is a member or associated member of Churches Together in Britain and Ireland; and all projects must be overseen by an architect who is either ARB, RIBA or AABC accredited, or by a chartered surveyor who is RICS accredited.
WHAT IS FUNDED To assist, with grants and loans, the efforts of congregations to carry out of essential repairs to the fabric of historic churches and improve their general facilities e.g. accessible toilets, kitchens and meeting rooms. The trust has also been working with WREN (Waste Recycling Environmental Ltd) to administer grants on their behalf to churches sited within a ten mile radius of a landfill site operated by Waste Recycling Group.
WHAT IS NOT FUNDED Be aware that the trust cannot make grants for certain purposes including: non-church buildings (such as church halls and vicarages); bell repairs; organ repairs; repairs to internal furnishings; redecoration, other than after structural repairs; clock repairs; monument repairs. Grantee congregations must be members or associated members of Churches Together in Britain and Ireland.
TYPE OF GRANT Capital costs.
RANGE OF GRANTS From £2,500.
SAMPLE GRANTS St Botoloph, Boston (£50,000) St Vincent, Caythorpe, St Michael and the Holy Angels, West Bromwich and St Wilfred, Halton (£40,000 each); Dunlop Parish Church, Dunlop (£35,000); North Shields Baptist Church

(£20,000); St David, Llanddewi Aberarth (£10,000) and St John the Baptist, Little Maplestead (£5,000).

FINANCES *Year* 2012 *Income* £2,146,529 *Grants* £855,400 *Assets* £4,179,262

TRUSTEES Charlotte Cole; Richard Carr-Archer; John Readman; John Drew; Revd Nicholas Holtam; Jennifer Page; Alastair Hunter; Andrew Day; Nicholas Holtam; Luke March.

PUBLICATIONS 'Keeping Churches Alive – a brief history of the Trust' available directly from the trust or to download from the website.

OTHER INFORMATION In 2008 the Charity Commission appointed the National Churches Trust (NCT) as the sole trustee of the Historic Churches Preservation Trust (HCPT) and also granted a 'uniting direction'. Consequently, the NCT and HCPT are treated as a single charity for administrative, accounting and regulatory purposes. They will however, remain legally distinct so that the HCPT will operate as restricted funds within the NCT. A similar process is envisaged for the Incorporated Church Building Society (ICBS), which has been managed by the HCPT since 1983.

HOW TO APPLY Applicants are advised that each fund has different application procedures. Applications to the Partnership Grants Programme must be made through a local Church trust, a list of which can be found on the trust's website. New guidelines and the online application form are due to be available from February 2014.

WHO TO APPLY TO Alison Pollard, Grants and Local Trusts Manager, 31 Newbury Street, London EC1A 7HU *Tel.* 020 7600 6090 *Fax* 020 7796 2442 *email* info@nationalchurchestrust.org *Website* www.nationalchurchestrust.org

....

■ National Committee of the Women's World Day of Prayer for England and Wales and Northern Ireland (formerly known as Women's World Day of Prayer)

CC NO 233242   **ESTABLISHED** 1932

WHERE FUNDING CAN BE GIVEN UK and worldwide.

WHO CAN BENEFIT Charitable organisations.

WHAT IS FUNDED Promotion of the Christian faith.

WHAT IS NOT FUNDED No grants to individuals.

TYPE OF GRANT Annual, regular or one-off.

RANGE OF GRANTS £200–£21,000.

SAMPLE GRANTS Foundation for Relief and Reconciliation in the Middle East (£30,000); Friends of Ebenezer Child Care (£20,000); Bible Society and Feed the Minds (£15,000 each); United Society for Christian Literature and Wycliffe UK Ltd (£10,000 each); Hope Christian Trust (£8,000); Bible Reading Fellowship, International Bible Reading Association and People International (£3,000 each); Mission India (£2,000); Wales Sunday Schools Council (£1,600); Welsh Council on Alcohol and Drugs (£500); and Christian Aid and Cafod (£300 each).

FINANCES *Year* 2012 *Income* £551,736 *Grants* £277,381 *Assets* £444,281

TRUSTEES Jean Hackett; Mimi Barton; Kathleen Skinner.

PUBLICATIONS Order of service for the Day of Prayer; children's service; Bible study notes on theme for year; annual booklet, Together in Prayer; meditation cards; prayer cards.

HOW TO APPLY In writing to the correspondent.

WHO TO APPLY TO Mary Judd, Administrator, Commercial Road, Tunbridge Wells TN1 2RR *Tel.* 01892 541411 *email* office@wwdp-natcomm.org *Website* www.wwdp-natcomm.org

....

■ The National Express Foundation

CC NO 1148231   **ESTABLISHED** 2012

WHERE FUNDING CAN BE GIVEN West Midlands and South Essex or East London within five miles of the c2c rail line.

WHO CAN BENEFIT Community groups and educational institutions.

WHAT IS FUNDED General, social welfare, education, sport, children and young people.

RANGE OF GRANTS Up to £10,000.

SAMPLE GRANTS Aston Sports and Community Group – funding will help to run activities at youth hubs in Aston for local youngsters after school and during holidays; Handsworth Wood Youth Group – funding will help set up sports activities and provide social and personal skills development for young people in the Handsworth Wood area; One Aim Mix Studio – funding will help to run a gang awareness programme and stage drama workshops with inner-city Birmingham youngsters; Sport4Life – funding will help to launch football courses in Ladywood and volunteer placement for two NEETs; Three Faiths Forum – funding will help to pair schools between the West Midlands and East London to aid better understanding of young people from different communities and backgrounds; and Urban Cycles – funding will help to teach young people road safety as well as provide new bikes for group activities throughout the region. The National Express Foundation is has also awarded funding for bursaries to local educational institutions: South and City College Birmingham – 20 students will benefit from individual bursaries to help fund living costs while they stay in education. The bursaries are worth £20,000 over two years; Stourbridge College – 20 students on resource intensive courses such as construction, arts and sport will benefit from individual bursaries. £20,000 will support bursaries over two years; and the University of Birmingham – eight students from the West Midlands' most deprived areas will benefit from bursaries worth £30,000 over the next three years.

FINANCES *Year* 2012 *Grants* £100,000

TRUSTEES Anthony Vigor; Denise Rossiter; John Fraser; Leslie Dorrington; Madi Pilgrim; Shabana Mahmood.

HOW TO APPLY Applications are required to provide the following information: background to the organisation, membership and funding; evidence of constitution and independent bank account; description of what the funding would be used for; explanation of how the proposed project would benefit the community; timescale and process for delivering the project; proposals for promoting the link with the foundation; plans to evaluate and quantify the benefits. Applicants are asked to indicate what size of grant they are seeking, and explain what they could deliver for the level of grant applied for. The trustees plan to award more small grants (up to a maximum of £5,000) than large grants (up to maximum £10,000). The trustees may choose to support an organisation but offer a smaller amount than has been requested, so it would help if applicants can show what they would deliver for different levels of funding. While the trustees did not set restrictions on how the funding would be applied, they were seeking evidence of innovation in the how projects will be delivered. We will also want to ensure the successful project benefits the maximum number of children and young people in the community it serves.'

WHO TO APPLY TO The Foundation General Manager, National Express House, Digbeth, Birmingham B5 6DD *Tel.* 01214 608423 *email* foundation@nationalexpress.com *Website* nationalexpressgroup.com/foundation

■ The National Hockey Foundation

CC NO 1015550   **ESTABLISHED** 1992
WHERE FUNDING CAN BE GIVEN UK.
WHO CAN BENEFIT Organisations benefiting people under the age of 21.
WHAT IS FUNDED The development of sport at youth level; particularly but not exclusively hockey.
WHAT IS NOT FUNDED Grants will not be awarded for the following: Grants will not be awarded as general donations. The Grant has to be related to a specific project; Grants will not be awarded for day-to-day administrative running costs; Grants are not awarded to individuals; Grants will not be awarded to solely support elite athletes; Grants will not be awarded for fundraising events; Grants will not be awarded to sponsor an award; Grants will not be awarded for projects outside of England; Grants will not be awarded where the project does not provide a lasting benefit or is not sustainable; Grants are generally not awarded to projects where the Trust's input will not make an impact; Grants are not usually awarded for more than 50% of the project cost and Grants are not usually awarded for applications where the primary funding is to support the payment of salaries.
RANGE OF GRANTS Usually between £10,000 and £75,000.
SAMPLE GRANTS Deeside Ramblers Hockey Club (£55,000); Lindum Sports Association, The Hermitage Academy and Bournemouth Hockey Club (£50,000 each); East Grinstead Hockey Club (£40,000); Windrush High School (£20,000); Newport Pagnell Town Football Club and MK Springers (£15,000 each) and MK City Korfball (£5,000).
FINANCES *Year* 2012–13 *Income* £130,717 *Grants* £543,670 *Assets* £2,317,793
TRUSTEES David Laing; David Darling; A. Dransfield; Janet Baker; David Billson; John Cove; John Waters; Michael Fulwood; Benjamin Rea.
HOW TO APPLY On a form available to download, together with criteria and guidelines, from the website. 'If you are unsure as to whether a grant application will meet the requirements you may ask the Trustees by completing the GRANT INDICATION FORM. This will allow the Foundation to provide you with an indication about the suitability of an application without you initially having to complete the full Application Form'.
WHO TO APPLY TO David Billson, 9 Hamlet Green, Northampton, Northants NN5 7AR *Tel.* 01604 589720 *email* nathockfoundation@btinternet. com *Website* www.thenationalhockeyfoundation. com

■ The National Manuscripts Conservation Trust

CC NO 802796   **ESTABLISHED** 1990
WHERE FUNDING CAN BE GIVEN UK.
WHO CAN BENEFIT Grants are made to record offices, libraries, other similar publicly funded institutions including local authority, university and specialist record repositories, and owners of manuscript material which is conditionally exempt from capital taxation or owned by a charitable trust and where reasonable public access is allowed, suitable storage conditions are available, and there is a commitment to continuing good preservation practice.
WHAT IS FUNDED Conservation of manuscripts and archives.
WHAT IS NOT FUNDED The following are not eligible: public records within the meaning of the Public Records Act; official archives of the institution or authority applying except in the case of some older records; loan collections unless exempt from capital taxation or owned by a charitable trust; and photographic, audio-visual or printed materials.
TYPE OF GRANT The grants cover the cost of repair, binding and other preservation measures including reprography, but not cost of equipment. Funding is for up to three years.
RANGE OF GRANTS Up to £16,000.
SAMPLE GRANTS Dr Williams' Library (£22,000); Cambridge Fitzwilliam Museum and Church of England Record Centre (£15,000 each); University of Southampton (£15,500); Bangor University Archive (£12,000); Essex Record Office (£9,500); Glamorgan Archive Aberystwyth University Archive (£4,400); Cornwall Record Office (£3,300); Anglesey Archives (£1,800) and Ceredigion Archives (£1,400).
FINANCES *Year* 2011–12 *Income* £175,130 *Grants* £165,377 *Assets* £2,005,632
TRUSTEES Lord Egremont; B. Naylor; C. Sebag-Montefiore.
HOW TO APPLY On a form available to download from the website, along with guidance notes. Applicants must submit six copies of the application form including six copies of a detailed description of the project. The applicant should also submit one copy of their most recent annual reports and accounts and details of its constitution. The deadlines are usually 1 April and 1 October, check the website for the deadlines and full details of how to apply. 'In deciding whether an application should be awarded a grant, the Trustees take into account the significance of the manuscript or archive, the suitability of the storage conditions, the applicant's commitment to continuing good preservation practice, and the requirement for the public to have reasonable access to it. Written reports on each application are given to the Trustees by specialist staff from The National Archives working on a pro bono basis, but there is no other contribution by volunteers.'
WHO TO APPLY TO Nell Hoare, Secretary, PO Box 4291, Reading, Berkshire RG8 9JA *Tel.* 020 8392 5218 *email* info@nmct.org.uk *Website* www.nmct.co.uk

■ The Nationwide Foundation

CC NO 1065552   **ESTABLISHED** 1997
WHERE FUNDING CAN BE GIVEN UK.
WHO CAN BENEFIT Registered charities
WHAT IS FUNDED 'Organisations bringing empty properties into use for people in need with priority given to schemes including one or more

Think carefully about every application. Is it justified?

777

of the following: projects which are financially sustainable, or which are working towards financial sustainability; projects incorporating training for NEETS and others who are out of work or low skilled; live/work schemes; environmentally friendly practices; asset transfer.'

WHAT IS NOT FUNDED The foundation will not fund: charities with 'unrestricted reserves' which exceed 50% of annual expenditure, as shown in their accounts; charities which are in significant debt as shown in their accounts; promotion of religion or politics; charities which have been declined by the foundation within the last 12 months; applications which do not comply with the foundation's funding criteria/guidelines.

TYPE OF GRANT Project, capital and revenue costs.

RANGE OF GRANTS £15,000 to £140,000.

FINANCES *Year* 2011–12 *Income* £868,165 *Grants* £1,593,661 *Assets* £1,820,006

TRUSTEES Ben Stimson, Chair; Richard Davies; Simon Law; Karen McArthur; Dr Michael McCarthy; Chris Rhodes; Fiona Ellis; Graeme Hughes; Martin Coppack; Juliet Phommahaxay.

HOW TO APPLY On an application form available from the foundation's website.

WHO TO APPLY TO Jennifer Thompson, Grants Officer, Nationwide House, Pipers Way, Swindon SN38 2SN *Tel.* 01793 655113 *Fax* 01793 652409 *email* enquiries@nationwidefoundation. org.uk *Website* www.nationwidefoundation.org. uk

■ Nazareth Trust Fund

CC NO 210503   **ESTABLISHED** 1956

WHERE FUNDING CAN BE GIVEN UK and developing countries.

WHO CAN BENEFIT Young adults, Christian missionaries and victims of famine, war, and man-made or natural disasters – both individually and through registered institutions.

WHAT IS FUNDED Churches, Christian missionaries, Christian youth work, and overseas aid. Grants are only made to people or causes known personally to the trustees.

WHAT IS NOT FUNDED No support for individuals not known to the trustees.

RANGE OF GRANTS £20–£17,000.

SAMPLE GRANTS Harnham Free Church (£8,000); IREF (£5,500 in two grants); Durham Rd Baptist Church (£2,000 in two grants); Crusaders (£1,000); London School of Theology (£300); Christian Viewpoint for Men (£250) and Jubilee Centre and Scripture Union (£100 each).

FINANCES *Year* 2011–12 *Income* £38,174 *Grants* £40,245 *Assets* £37,390

TRUSTEES Revd David R. G. Hunt; Eileen M. Hunt; Dr Robert W. G. Hunt; Elma R. L. Hunt; Philip R. W. Hunt; Nicola M. Hunt.

OTHER INFORMATION A further £1,800 was given in grants to individuals.

HOW TO APPLY 'We only give to people we know personally. Unsolicited applications are unsuccessful.'

WHO TO APPLY TO Dr Robert W. G. Hunt, Trustee, Barrowpoint, 18 Millennium Close, Salisbury, Wiltshire SP2 8TB *Tel.* 01722 349322

■ The NDL Foundation

CC NO 1133508   **ESTABLISHED** 2010

WHERE FUNDING CAN BE GIVEN Worldwide.

WHO CAN BENEFIT Charitable organisations.

WHAT IS FUNDED General; children; sickness; art and culture.

SAMPLE GRANTS Women for Women International (UK) (£42,000); Tumaini Education Trust (£23,000); Kids (£6,000); Swiss Cottage School and Myschoolpulse (£5,000 each); Royal Opera House (£2,500); NSPCC (£2,000); Cancer Research UK (£1,500); Children in Crisis (£1,250) and The Butler Trust (£500).

FINANCES *Year* 2011–12 *Income* £0

TRUSTEES Sylviane Destribats; Laura Destribats; Frank Destribats; Diane Destribats.

OTHER INFORMATION In 2011–12 the trust had zero income and a total expenditure of £251,000, the majority of which was accounted for in grants awarded.

HOW TO APPLY In writing to the correspondent.

WHO TO APPLY TO Sylviane Destribats, Trustee, 8 Bolton Gardens Mews, London SW10 9LW

■ Needham Market and Barking Welfare Charities

CC NO 217499   **ESTABLISHED** 1961

WHERE FUNDING CAN BE GIVEN Needham Market and the parish of Barking.

WHO CAN BENEFIT Projects that benefit the local community especially those in need, hardship or distress.

WHAT IS FUNDED Social welfare in Needham Market and the parish of Barking.

WHAT IS NOT FUNDED Cannot give outside of Needham Market and the parish of Barking. However, grants may be approved to organisations based outside of Needham Market and Barking as long as the application demonstrates visible benefit to the areas.

TYPE OF GRANT One-off and recurring.

RANGE OF GRANTS £100–£1,500.

SAMPLE GRANTS Needham Market Cricket Club (£1,500); Needham Market Community Centre (£1,000); Citizen's Advice Bureau (£500); River Gipping Trust, Bosmere Primary School, and Stowmarket Stroke Support Group (£100 each).

FINANCES *Year* 2011–12 *Income* £38,659 *Grants* £11,296 *Assets* £246,713

TRUSTEES Lt Col Frank Lea; Graham Miller; Jean Annis; Carol Wright; Kay Oakes; Michael Smith; Susan Marsh; Tom Barker; David Bishop; Graham Oxenham; Clive Walker.

OTHER INFORMATION £700 was given in grants to three individuals.

HOW TO APPLY Application forms and guidance can be obtained from the Clerk to the Trustees on 01449 723171. Grants are expected to be taken up as soon as possible.

WHO TO APPLY TO Louise Mills, Clerk, 23 School Street, Needham Market, Ipswich IP6 8BB *Tel.* 01449 723171 *email* nmbwc@btinternet. com *Website* needhammarketbarkingwelfarecharities. onesuffolk.net

■ The Worshipful Company of Needlemakers' Charitable Fund

CC NO 288646   **ESTABLISHED** 1952

WHERE FUNDING CAN BE GIVEN City of London.

WHO CAN BENEFIT Organisations associated with the needlemaking industry, the City of London or education, including the Lord Mayor's and the Master's chosen charities.

WHAT IS FUNDED Education, welfare, religion, general charitable purposes.

RANGE OF GRANTS £100 to £5,000.

SAMPLE GRANTS £5,000 to the Royal School of Needlework and the Royal College of Surgeons of England; £4,000 to St Paul's Cathedral Choir School; £2,000 to Guildhall School of Music and Drama; £1,000 each to City University and City and Guilds of London Institute; and £500 to Royal British Legion City Branch Poppy Appeal.

FINANCES *Year* 2011–12 *Income* £46,590
Grants £45,000

TRUSTEE Worshipful Company of Needlemakers.

HOW TO APPLY In writing to the correspondent, but the trust has stated that it tends to support the same charities each year, so unsolicited applications are unlikely to be successful.

WHO TO APPLY TO Philip Grant, Clerk, PO Box 3682, Windsor SL4 3WR *Tel.* 01753 860690 *email* needlemakers.clerk@yahoo.com *Website* www.needlemakers.org.uk

....

■ The Neighbourly Charitable Trust

CC NO 258488   **ESTABLISHED** 1969

WHERE FUNDING CAN BE GIVEN Bedfordshire and Hertfordshire

WHO CAN BENEFIT Organisations benefiting people with disabilities.

WHAT IS FUNDED General and leisure/adventure trips for people with disabilities.

WHAT IS NOT FUNDED No grants to national charities (except occasionally a local branch) or individuals.

RANGE OF GRANTS Usually £100–£1,500 with some larger grants.

SAMPLE GRANTS Youth Talk Ltd., Rennie Grove Hospice and Earthworks St Albans (£1,500 each); MS Therapy and Sparx Theatre Co (£1,200 each); Stables Christian Centre, Royal Veterinary College and Leonard Cheshire Foundation (£1,000 each); Spotlight Drama Group (£600); Music in Hospitals (£500) and Leighton Buzzard Centre for Healing (£350).

FINANCES *Year* 2011–12 *Income* £78,851
Grants £38,642 *Assets* £2,403,119

TRUSTEES John Sell; Emma Simpson; Jane Wade.

HOW TO APPLY In writing to the correspondent, for consideration at trustees' meetings twice a year.

WHO TO APPLY TO Sharon Long, Secretary, Ashbrittle House, 2a Lower Dagnall Street, St Albans, Hertfordshire AL3 4PA *Tel.* 01727 843603 *email* admin@iplltd.co.uk

....

■ The James Neill Trust Fund

CC NO 503203   **ESTABLISHED** 1974

WHERE FUNDING CAN BE GIVEN Sheffield and its immediate surroundings.

WHO CAN BENEFIT Voluntary organisations.

WHAT IS FUNDED Voluntary work for the benefit of people in the area specified above.

WHAT IS NOT FUNDED Only rarely are grants given to unconnected individuals.

TYPE OF GRANT Ongoing support for established organisations and one-off grants to meet start-up costs or unexpected expenses.

RANGE OF GRANTS Up to £20,000.

SAMPLE GRANTS St Luke's Hospice (£20,000); Dodworth Colliery MW Brass Band, Dyslexia Action, Girlguiding South Yorkshire, MedEquip4Kids, Spinal Injuries Association and Survivors of Depression in Transition (£500 each) and Bluebell Wood Children's Hospice – Cutlers Police Award (£250); Cavendish Cancer Care, South Yorkshire and Hallamshire Clubs for Young People and SVP Furniture Store (£1,000 each); Friends of Whinfell Quarry Garden (£800); British Red Cross (South Yorkshire), The Boys Brigade and The Cathedral Archer Project (£600

each) and Share Psychotherapy and Cruse Bereavement Care Sheffield Branch (£500 each).

FINANCES *Year* 2011–12 *Income* £39,094
Grants £45,896 *Assets* £1,166,819

TRUSTEES Sir Hugh Neill; G. H. N. Peel; Lady Neill; N. R. Peel; A. M. C. Staniforth; J. M. G. Neill.

OTHER INFORMATION During the year pensioners received Christmas hampers amounting to £8,000 in total.

HOW TO APPLY In writing to the correspondent, to arrive in the month of July.

WHO TO APPLY TO Lady Neill, Trustee, Barn Cottage, Lindrick Common, Worksop, Nottinghamshire S81 8BA *Tel.* 01909 562806 *email* neillcharities@me.com

....

■ Nemoral Ltd

CC NO 262270   **ESTABLISHED** 1971

WHERE FUNDING CAN BE GIVEN Worldwide.

WHO CAN BENEFIT Orthodox Jewish communities.

WHAT IS FUNDED General charitable purposes, in practice, religious, educational and other charitable institutions serving Orthodox Jewish communities.

TYPE OF GRANT One-off, recurring, capital and occasionally loans.

FINANCES *Year* 2012 *Income* £133,047
Grants £1,315,000 *Assets* £2,360,571

TRUSTEES Ellis Moore; Rivka Gross; Michael Saberski.

OTHER INFORMATION A list of grant beneficiaries was not included in the trust's accounts.

HOW TO APPLY In writing to the correspondent.

WHO TO APPLY TO Rivka Gross, Secretary, c/o Cohen Arnold and Co., New Burlington House, 1075 Finchley Road, London NW11 0PU *Tel.* 020 8731 0777

....

■ Ner Foundation

CC NO 1104866   **ESTABLISHED** 2004

WHERE FUNDING CAN BE GIVEN UK and Israel.

WHO CAN BENEFIT People of the Jewish faith

WHAT IS FUNDED Advancement of the Orthodox Jewish religion. Community projects, schools, relief of poverty and Yeshivos and seminaries.

FINANCES *Year* 2011–12 *Income* £189,886
Grants £210,400 *Assets* £392,263

TRUSTEES A. Henry; N. Neumann; E. Henry.

HOW TO APPLY In writing to the correspondent.

WHO TO APPLY TO A. Henry, Trustee, 309 Bury New Road, Salford, Manchester M7 2YN

....

■ Nesswall Ltd

CC NO 283600   **ESTABLISHED** 1981

WHERE FUNDING CAN BE GIVEN UK

WHO CAN BENEFIT Orthodox Jewish organisations.

WHAT IS FUNDED Orthodox Jewish causes, including education and relief in need.

SAMPLE GRANTS Previous beneficiaries have included: Friends of Horim Establishments, Torah Vochesed L'Ezra Vesaad and Emunah Education Centre.

FINANCES *Year* 2011–12 *Income* £60,749
Grants £59,725 *Assets* £568,570

TRUSTEES R. Teitelbaum; I. Chersky; H. Wahrhaftig.

HOW TO APPLY In writing to the correspondent, at any time.

WHO TO APPLY TO R. Teitelbaum, Secretary, 28 Overlea Road, London E5 9BG *Tel.* 020 8806 2965

■ Network for Social Change

CC NO 295237   ESTABLISHED 1986

WHERE FUNDING CAN BE GIVEN UK and overseas.

WHO CAN BENEFIT Small projects in the UK and overseas which are likely to affect social change, either through research, public education, innovatory services and other charitable activities.

WHAT IS FUNDED The network is a group of givers who actively seek out projects that they want to fund, rather than responding to applications, in the areas of arts and education for change, economic justice, green planet, health and wholeness, human rights and peace.

RANGE OF GRANTS Up to £130,000

SAMPLE GRANTS The Joseph Rowntree Charitable Trust (£125,000); War on Want (£48,000); STAR (Student Action for Refugees) (£28,000); The Gaia Foundation (£19,000); The Children's Parliament (£16,000); Karma Nirvana Peace and Enlightenment Project for Asian Men and Women, The Holly Hill Charitable Trust, Friends of the Earth Trust Ltd and Manchester Environmental Resource Centre (£15,000 each); New Israel Fund (£13,000); Business and Human Rights Resource Centre (£13,000); Hamlin Fistula UK (£12,000); Civil Liberties Trust (£11,000) and Kanaama Interactive Community Support (£11,000).

FINANCES Year 2011–12 Income £1,199,569 Grants £1,038,603 Assets £204,922

TRUSTEES Sue Gillie; Bevis Gillett; Tom Bragg; Anthony Stoll; P. Boase; C. Freeman; S. Rix; A. Robbins.

HOW TO APPLY The network chooses the projects it wishes to support and does not solicit applications. Unsolicited applications cannot expect to receive a reply. However, the network is conscious that the policy of only accepting applications brought by its members could limit the range of worthwhile projects it could fund. To address this, the network has set up a 'Project Noticeboard' (accessed via the network's website) to allow outside organisations to post a summary of a project for which they are seeking funding. Members of the network can then access the noticeboard and, if interested, contact the organisation for further information with a view to future sponsorship. Projects are deleted from the noticeboard after about six months. Note only 1–2% of project noticeboard entries result in sponsorship and funding.

WHO TO APPLY TO Tish McCrory, Administrator, BM 2063, London WC1N 3XX Tel. 01647 61106 email thenetwork@gn.apc.org Website thenetworkforsocialchange.org.uk

■ The New Appeals Organisation for the City and County of Nottingham

CC NO 502196   ESTABLISHED 1973

WHERE FUNDING CAN BE GIVEN Nottinghamshire.

WHO CAN BENEFIT Individuals and organisations benefiting at-risk groups and people who are disabled, disadvantaged by poverty or socially isolated.

WHAT IS FUNDED Help that is not available from any other source.

WHAT IS NOT FUNDED Appeals to cover debts, arrears, building expenses or educational expenses are not normally considered.

TYPE OF GRANT One-off.

SAMPLE GRANTS Oakfield School (£4,400); Rosehill School (£1,600); Bells Lane and Aspley Tenants and Residents Association (£1,000); Highbury Hospital Ward Redwood 2 (£750); Robert Shaw School (£500); Muslims Women's Organisation (£250) and Nottingham Central Women's Aid (£200).

FINANCES Year 2011–12 Income £59,352 Grants £39,972 Assets £73,021

TRUSTEES Phillip Everett, Joint Chair; Carol Wilson, Joint Chair; L. S. Levin; E. Litman; G. Davis.

OTHER INFORMATION In 2011–12 grants were given to organisations and individuals.

HOW TO APPLY In writing to the correspondent. An initial telephone call from the applicant is welcome.

WHO TO APPLY TO Philip Everett, Grant Secretary, c/o 4 Rise Court, Hamilton Road, Sherwood Rise, Nottingham NG5 1EU Tel. 01159 609644 email enquiries@newappeals.org.uk Website www.newappeals.org

■ Newby Trust Limited

CC NO 227151   ESTABLISHED 1938

WHERE FUNDING CAN BE GIVEN UK.

WHO CAN BENEFIT Welfare, poverty, education, medical, postgraduates and individuals in need.

WHAT IS FUNDED Within the general objects of the trust (medical welfare, relief of poverty, training and education) one category for special support is selected every year.

TYPE OF GRANT Usually one-off for part of a project. Buildings, capital, core costs and salaries may be considered.

RANGE OF GRANTS Normally £150–£10,000.

SAMPLE GRANTS The Bridge Foundation, Snowden Award Scheme, Spinal Injuries Association, Treloar School and College and U Can Do I.T. (£10,000 each); Greenhouse (White City Youth Theatre); Medical Foundation for the Care of Victims of Torture, Birmingham Royal Ballet and Royal School of Needlework (£5,000 each); Action for Children (£2,100); The Textile Conservation Centre Foundation and Canine Partners (£2,000) and Eaves Housing for Women (£1,000).

FINANCES Year 2011–12 Income £382,018 Grants £214,610 Assets £15,098,584

TRUSTEES Anna L. Foxell; Anne S. Reed; Jean M. Gooder; Ben Gooder; Dr Richard D. Gooder; Susan A. Charlton; Evelyn F. Bentley; Nigel Callaghan.

HOW TO APPLY The application procedure differs between each category as follows: Annual special category – unsolicited applications will not be considered; Education, training and research – since 2008 the trust has supported education at the postgraduate or postdoctoral level only by allocating funds to selected universities or institutions in the United Kingdom. These are: City University, London, the London School of Economics and Political Science, the University of Edinburgh and the University of Manchester. Grants are awarded at the discretion of these universities subject to guidelines related to the purposes of the trust; Medical welfare and Relief of poverty – Social Services or similar organisations may apply via the online form on behalf of individuals in need using the pre-application screening form on the trust's website. Responsibility for smaller individual grants is delegated to the Secretary. Main grants are decided at meeting in March and November.

WHO TO APPLY TO Wendy Gillam, Secretary, Hill Farm, Froxfield, Petersfield, Hampshire GU32 1BQ *Tel.* 01730 827557 *email* info@newby-trust.org. uk *Website* www.newby-trust.org.uk

....
■ The Newcomen Collett Foundation

CC NO 312804   **ESTABLISHED** 1988
WHERE FUNDING CAN BE GIVEN London borough of Southwark.
WHO CAN BENEFIT Individuals and small local projects benefiting children, young adults and students under 25.
WHAT IS FUNDED Education of young people under 25 years of age, including community arts and recreation, with priority for dance and ballet, music and theatre.
WHAT IS NOT FUNDED The trust can only help young people living in the London borough of Southwark. People on courses of further education should have lived in Southwark for at least two years before starting their course.
TYPE OF GRANT One-off.
RANGE OF GRANTS Up to £3,000.
SAMPLE GRANTS Gloucester Primary School (£2,650); Oliver Goldsmith Primary School and 1st St James' Guides (£2,500 each); Action Tutoring, The Archway Project and Goodrich Community School (£2,000 each); Graeae Theatre Company, Foundation for Young Musicians and Dulwich Hamlet Football in the Community (£1,500 each); Downside Fisher Youth Club (£1,400); Southwark Education Welfare Office (£1,200) and Lyndhurst Primary School (£1,000).
FINANCES *Year* 2011–12 *Income* £242,047 *Grants* £156,152 *Assets* £2,609,821
TRUSTEES Robin Lovell; Robert Ashdown; Ted Bowman; John Spencer; Dick Edwards; Sylvia Morris; Barbara Lane; Alexander Leiffheidt; Helen Cockerill; Paul Scott; Andrew Covell; Mike Ibbot; Revd Canon Bruce Saunders.
HOW TO APPLY On a form available to download, together with criteria and guidelines, from the website. The governors consider requests four times a year.
WHO TO APPLY TO Catherine Dawkins, Clerk, Marshall House, 66 Newcomen Street, London Bridge, London SE1 1YT *Tel.* 020 7407 2967 *email* grantoffice@newcomencollett.org.uk *Website* www.newcomencollett.org.uk

....
■ The Frances and Augustus Newman Foundation

CC NO 277964   **ESTABLISHED** 1978
WHERE FUNDING CAN BE GIVEN UK.
WHO CAN BENEFIT Mainly professors working in teaching hospitals and academic units.
WHAT IS FUNDED Mainly, but not exclusively, funding for medical research projects and equipment including fellowships of the Royal College of Surgeons.
WHAT IS NOT FUNDED Applications are not normally accepted from overseas. Requests from other charities seeking funds to supplement their own general funds to support medical research in a particular field are seldom supported.
TYPE OF GRANT One-off and recurring. Research and salaries will also be considered. Funding may be given for up to three years.
RANGE OF GRANTS £1,000–£100,000.
SAMPLE GRANTS Peterhouse College – Cambridge (£100,000 towards a new building); University

of Cambridge (£100,000); Royal College of Surgeon (£50,000 towards a one-year fellowship); University College London – Institute of Ophthalmology (£24,000 towards the costs of a gene therapy technical assistant); St Wilfred's Hospice (£23,500); Alzheimer's Research UK (£10,000 for a gene analysis machine); Wellbeing of Women (£10,000); Royal College of Surgeons – Museum (£5,500 for the facial reconstruction of the Irish Giant); and the Dream Team (£1,000).
FINANCES *Year* 2011–12 *Income* £350,088 *Grants* £347,600 *Assets* £11,719,188
TRUSTEES David Sweetnam; Hugh Rathcavan; John Williams; Stephen Cannon.
HOW TO APPLY Applications should include a detailed protocol and costing and be sent to the correspondent. They may then be peer-reviewed. The trustees meet in June and December each year and applications must be received at the latest by the end of April or October respectively. The foundation awards for surgical research fellowships should be addressed to the Royal College of Surgeons of England at 35–43 Lincoln's Inn Fields, London WC2A 3PE, which evaluates each application.
WHO TO APPLY TO Hazel Palfreyman, Administrator, c/o Baker Tilly Chartered Accountants, Hartwell House, 55–61 Victoria Street, Bristol BS1 6AD *Tel.* 01179 452000 *email* hazel.palfreyman@ bakertilly.co.uk

....
■ Newpier Charity Ltd

CC NO 293686   **ESTABLISHED** 1985
WHERE FUNDING CAN BE GIVEN UK.
WHO CAN BENEFIT Jewish organisations.
WHAT IS FUNDED Advancement of the Orthodox Jewish faith and the relief of poverty.
SAMPLE GRANTS Previous beneficiaries include: BML Benityashvut, Friends of Biala, Gateshead Yeshiva, KID, Mesdos Wiznitz and SOFT for redistribution to other charities.
FINANCES *Year* 2011–12 *Income* £1,051,423 *Grants* £539,811 *Assets* £3,082,721
TRUSTEES Charles Margulies; Helen Knopfler; Rachel Margulies.
HOW TO APPLY In writing to the correspondent.
WHO TO APPLY TO Charles Margulies, Trustee, 186 Lordship Road, London N16 5ES *Tel.* 020 8802 4449

....
■ Alderman Newton's Educational Foundation

CC NO 527881   **ESTABLISHED** 1983
WHERE FUNDING CAN BE GIVEN Diocese of Leicester.
WHO CAN BENEFIT Individuals and schools.
WHAT IS FUNDED Church of England education.
TYPE OF GRANT One-off and recurrent. Capital costs; salaries; full project funding.
FINANCES *Year* 2011–12 *Income* £152,000 *Grants* £114,000 *Assets* £3,600,000
TRUSTEES Six nominative trustees; seven co-optative trustees.
HOW TO APPLY On a form available from the correspondent. Applications may be made at any time.
WHO TO APPLY TO Jim Munton, Leicester Charity Link, 20a Millstone Lane, Leicester LE1 5JN *Tel.* 01162 222200 *Website* www.charity-link. org/trust-administration

Think carefully about every application. Is it justified?

....
781

■ The NFU Mutual Charitable Trust

CC NO 1073064   **ESTABLISHED** 1998
WHERE FUNDING CAN BE GIVEN UK.
WHO CAN BENEFIT Organisations.
WHAT IS FUNDED The objects of the trust are the 'promotion and support of charitable purposes in the areas of agriculture, rural development and insurance in the UK – including education, the relief of poverty, social welfare and research – and any other charitable purpose'.
SAMPLE GRANTS The Farming Help Partnership (£75,000); Farming and Countryside Education (£50,000); The National Federation of Young Farmers Clubs/ Wales Young Farmers Clubs (£38,000); Rural Support (£11,700); Shakespeare Hospice at Home Service (£7,500); Bangor University (£2,600); Harper Adams University College (£1,105).
FINANCES *Year* 2012 *Income* £259,339
Grants £450,000
TRUSTEES Lord Curry of Kirkharle; Edmund Bailey; Richard Butler; Sir Ian Grant; Peter Kendall; Nigel Miller; Richard Percy; Lindsay Sinclair; Harry Sinclair.
HOW TO APPLY In writing to the correspondent. Criteria are available to view on the website. The Trustees meet twice a year to consider applications received. These meetings are currently held in June and December.
WHO TO APPLY TO Jim Creechan, Secretary to the Trustees, Tiddington Road, Stratford-upon-Avon, Warwickshire CV37 7BJ *Tel.* 01789 204211 *email* nfu_mutual_charitable_trust@nfumutual. co.uk *Website* www.nfumutual.co.uk

■ The Night Garden Charity

CC NO 1139577   **ESTABLISHED** 2010
WHERE FUNDING CAN BE GIVEN UK.
WHO CAN BENEFIT Registered charities.
WHAT IS FUNDED General charitable purposes.
FINANCES *Year* 2011–12 *Income* £55,000
Grants £55,105 *Assets* £2,611
TRUSTEES Matthew Hansell; Richard Perrin; Derek Shilvock.
OTHER INFORMATION The accounts state that £50,000 was given in grants for the purposes of academic research and £5,000 was given to a variety of local and national charities.
HOW TO APPLY In writing to the correspondent.
WHO TO APPLY TO Matthew Hansell, Trustee, Mills and Reeve LLP, 78–84 Colmore Row, Birmingham B3 2AB *Tel.* 01214 568297 *email* matthew.hansell@mills-reeve.com

■ The Chevras Ezras Nitzrochim Trust

CC NO 275352   **ESTABLISHED** 1978
WHERE FUNDING CAN BE GIVEN UK, with a preference for London.
WHO CAN BENEFIT Organisations benefiting Jewish people who are disadvantaged by poverty.
WHAT IS FUNDED Orthodox Jewish organisations set up to raise money to help the poor in Jewish communities.
RANGE OF GRANTS £10–£4,000.
SAMPLE GRANTS Yesamach Levav Trust (£7,200) and Notzar Chesed (£7,100). Previous beneficiaries included Mesifta, Kupas Tzedoko Vochesed, Beis Chinuch Lenonos, Hachzokas Torah Vochesed Trust, Ezras Hakohol Trust, Woodstock Sinclair Trust, Side by Side, Yeshivas Panim Meiros, Yeahuas Chaim

Synagogue, TYY Trust, Square Yeshiva and Stanislow.
FINANCES *Year* 2011–12 *Income* £262,721
Grants £49,612 *Assets* £13,350
TRUSTEES Kurt Stern; Hertz Kahan; Moshe Rottenberg.
OTHER INFORMATION A further £199,000 was given in grants to individuals.
HOW TO APPLY In writing to the correspondent.
WHO TO APPLY TO Hertz Kahan, Trustee, 53 Heathland Road, London N16 5PQ *Tel.* 020 8800 5187

■ NJD Charitable Trust

CC NO 1109146   **ESTABLISHED** 2005
WHERE FUNDING CAN BE GIVEN UK and Israel.
WHO CAN BENEFIT People of the Jewish faith.
WHAT IS FUNDED The relief of poverty and hardship of members of the Jewish faith; the advancement of Jewish religion through Jewish education.
SAMPLE GRANTS Jewish Care (£15,000); UJIA (£10,000); Jewish Leadership Council (£7,500); Community Security Trust (£6,600); Holocaust Educational Trust (£5,000).
FINANCES *Year* 2011–12 *Income* £100,109
Grants £57,069 *Assets* £185,526
TRUSTEES Nathalie Dwek; Jean Glaskie; Jacob Wolf; Alexander Dwek.
HOW TO APPLY In writing to the correspondent.
WHO TO APPLY TO Alan Dawson, Trust Administrator, Crowe Clark Whitehill, St Bride's House, 10 Salisbury Square, London EC4Y 8EH *Tel.* 020 7842 7306 *email* info@igpinvest.com

■ Alice Noakes Memorial Charitable Trust

CC NO 1039663   **ESTABLISHED** 1994
WHERE FUNDING CAN BE GIVEN Unrestricted.
WHO CAN BENEFIT Organisations and individuals.
WHAT IS FUNDED Animal welfare.
RANGE OF GRANTS £500 to £20,000.
SAMPLE GRANTS University of Cambridge (£20,000); Animal Health Trust (£12,500); RSPCA – Danaher Animal Home for Essex (£10,000); Fauna and Flora International and Red Squirrel Survival Trust (£1,000 each) and Twinkle Trust Animal Aid, The Barn Owl Trust, Scottish Seabird Centre, Safe Haven for Donkeys in the Holy Land and Friends of the Ferals (£500 each)
FINANCES *Year* 2011–12 *Income* £72,594
Grants £68,750 *Assets* £2,107,791
TRUSTEES David Whipps; J. Simpson; Spencer Bayer; Jeremy Hulme.
OTHER INFORMATION The 2011–12 grant total includes £5,000 given to three individuals.
HOW TO APPLY 'Applications for grants fitting the trust's objectives should be sent to the trustees at the charity's registered office.' The trustees meet twice a year.
WHO TO APPLY TO The Trustees, c/o Holmes and Hills, Bocking End, Braintree, Essex CM7 9AJ *Tel.* 01787 475312

■ Nominet Charitable Foundation

CC NO 1125735   **ESTABLISHED** 2008
WHERE FUNDING CAN BE GIVEN UK and overseas.
WHO CAN BENEFIT UK-based initiatives that contribute to a safe, accessible Internet used to improve lives and communities. A small number

of investments in international projects may also be made.

WHAT IS FUNDED Digital technology for social impact, improving young people's economic and social participation and supporting people through life transitions.

WHAT IS NOT FUNDED The trust will not fund the following: hardware infrastructure projects, e.g. a project to equip a school with PCs, or to install Wi-Fi for a community; website improvements where no new functional or service delivery innovations are delivered; website development unless the project and organisation delivers against one of the trust's areas of focus and meets the trust's funding guidelines; organisational running costs per se. Political parties and lobbying parties cannot be funded.

RANGE OF GRANTS Up to £500,000.

SAMPLE GRANTS Online Centres Foundation (£350,000); Sidekick Studios (£300,000); Digitalme (£258,000); We Are What We Do (£209,000); Campaign for Learning (£128,000); UK Youth (£105,000); Alzheimer's Society (£92,000); Cambridge and District CAB (£78,000) and Tyze Personal Networks and Walsall Deaf People's Centre (£50,000 each). Grants of less than £50,000 totalled £654,000.

FINANCES *Year* 2011–12 *Income* £7,147,309 *Grants* £6,507,978 *Assets* £7,048,279

TRUSTEES Nora Nanayakkara; Ian Ritchie; Peter Gradwell; Millie Banerjee; Elaine Quinn; Marcus East; Charles Leadbeater; Louise Ainsworth.

HOW TO APPLY Application processes vary for each programme so potential applicants should check the information on the website. Firstly fill in the self-evaluation checklist on the trusts website. Then applicants must submit the short online application form and if the project is judged to be suitable for the programme they will be invited to submit stage two of the application. Applications processes involve submitting short videos explaining the project. There are various deadlines for the various stages of application; these can be found on the website. Final investment decisions are made in October, December and April. The trust also runs pre-application events across the country and online web chats.

WHO TO APPLY TO Annika Small, Director, Nominet, Minerva House, Edmund Halley Road, Oxford Science Park, Oxford OX4 4DQ *Tel.* 01865 334000 *email* enquiries@nominettrust.org.uk *Website* www.nominettrust.org.uk

····································

■ The Noon Foundation

CC NO 1053654   **ESTABLISHED** 1995

WHERE FUNDING CAN BE GIVEN UK.

WHO CAN BENEFIT Charitable organisations.

WHAT IS FUNDED General charitable purposes including, education, relief of poverty, community relations and alleviation of racial discrimination.

RANGE OF GRANTS £50–£56,000.

SAMPLE GRANTS Previously: Marie Curie Cancer Care; Birkbeck University of London; Breast Cancer Care; Macmillan Cancer Support; Co-existence Trust; Horizon Medical; Garsington Opera; London School of Economics, Oxfam; Muslim Aid and Wellbeing.

FINANCES *Year* 2012 *Income* £9,946 *Grants* £800,000

TRUSTEES Lord Noon; Akbar Shirazi; Zeenat Harnal; A. M. Jepson; A. D. Robinson; Zarmin N. Sekhon.

HOW TO APPLY All applications and queries should be made by e-mail.

WHO TO APPLY TO The Trustees, 25 Queen Anne's Gate, St James's Park, London SW1H 9BU *Tel.* 020 7654 1600 *email* grants@noongroup. co.uk

····································

■ The Norda Trust

CC NO 296418   **ESTABLISHED** 1960

WHO CAN BENEFIT Registered charities only.

WHAT IS FUNDED The trustees allocate funds principally in support of those working for the rehabilitation of prisoners both before and after release and support for the partners and families of prisoners. A special interest is taken in charities and organisations that support immigration detainees and the welfare of young offenders. As funds permit, the trust can also support small local charities whose primary aim should be to improve the quality of life for the most severely disadvantaged communities or individuals. The trustees have a particular interest in helping to support new initiatives where there is a high level of volunteer involvement. When funds allow applications will be considered from charities and organisations that, by the nature of the work they undertake, do not attract popular support.

WHAT IS NOT FUNDED The following areas are not funded by the trust: medical causes; animal causes; individuals; school fees; proselytising.

TYPE OF GRANT Capital, revenue and full project funding. The majority of awards are made on a one off basis, with very few commitments made over two or more years.

RANGE OF GRANTS Up to £15,000.

SAMPLE GRANTS Workhubs Network CIC (£125,000); Samaritans Listening Scheme (£8,000); Detention Action, Dover Detainee Visitors Group and Asylum Welcome (£5,000 each); HOPE, Not Shut Up and TRAIN (£3,000 each) Personal Support Unit (£1,000).

FINANCES *Year* 2012 *Income* £71,868 *Grants* £227,500 *Assets* £2,728,434

TRUSTEES June Macpherson; Peter Gildener.

HOW TO APPLY Via letter or email, outlining the appeal. All applicants should leave at least a year before re-applying. Up to date financial information is required from all applicants. The trust will then make contact to request any further information they need.

WHO TO APPLY TO Martin Ward, Administrator, The Shieling, St Agnes, Cornwall TR5 0SS *Tel.* 01871 553822 *email* enquiries@ thenordatrust.org.uk *Website* www. thenordatrust.org.uk

····································

■ Norfolk Community Foundation

CC NO 1110817   **ESTABLISHED** 2004

WHERE FUNDING CAN BE GIVEN Norfolk.

WHO CAN BENEFIT Organisations which look to benefit the needs of the local community.

WHAT IS FUNDED Charitable purposes that benefit the county of Norfolk with particular interest in the advancement of education, the protection of good health and the relief of poverty and sickness.

WHAT IS NOT FUNDED According to the application guidelines, which were available on the foundation's website, exclusions are as follows: projects benefiting people outside of Norfolk; individuals for their personal needs; retrospective grants; statutory organisations, except parish and town councils; direct replacement of statutory obligation and public funding; organisations controlled by public sector bodies; the purchase of equipment that will become the property of a statutory body; improvements to land or buildings owned by a statutory body (except parish/town councils); improvements to land or buildings where the grant applicant does not have a legal interest in the land/building; projects where the grant awards cannot be spent within 12 months; medical research and equipment; sports projects (unless there is strong evidence of disadvantage or clear evidence of the project widening participation); arts projects (unless there is strong evidence that the project is addressing disadvantage and that people are gaining new and useful life skills); environment projects; promotion of religious or political causes or political lobbying; commercial ventures; general appeals; sponsorship; animal welfare unless the project benefits people; overseas travel or expeditions for individuals and groups; organisations raising funds to redistribute to other causes; and projects that do not directly contribute to community activity. 'The above list is not exhaustive. If in doubt contact the grants team.'

TYPE OF GRANT One-off and one year long projects.

RANGE OF GRANTS Grants are available from £500 and under up to £100,000 for some funds–most are in the range of £2,000–£5,000.

SAMPLE GRANTS Well Community Hospital, The Garage Trust Ltd, Westacre Arts Foundation Ltd, Cringleford Parish Council and Poppy Centre Trust (£100,000 each); The SeaChange Arts Trust (£94,000); Erpingham Parish Council (£88,500); Age UK – Norfolk (£70,000); Feltwell Parish Council (£65,000) and Freethorpe Parish Council (£40,000).

FINANCES *Year* 2012 *Income* £6,695,184 *Grants* £4,108,086 *Assets* £8,232,791

TRUSTEES Richard Packham; Frank Eliel; Bolton Agnew; Carol Bundock; Jackie Higham; Charles Barratt; Charles Mawson; Daniel Chapman; David White.

OTHER INFORMATION The average grant in 2012 was £2,400.
Grants totalling £196,500 were awarded to 83 individuals.

HOW TO APPLY Grants are available all year round and forthcoming deadlines are listed on the website. Online application only, however alternative submissions are possible. For more information contact the grants team on 01603 623958 or email: grants@norfolkfoundation.com. An application pack can be downloaded from the foundation's website, together with guidelines and criteria. Advice and guidance is offered on applications. Applicants can submit a general application if they are unsure of the most suitable grant for their needs. The grants team will then assign the application accordingly. The foundation's website states that 'applicants are advised to submit applications by the middle of the month prior to the targeted grant delivery meeting to allow sufficient time for application assessment and distribution. The foundation also operates a small grants programme, which awards grants of up to £500 throughout the year, for which no grants meeting is required therefore enabling a quicker decision on grants awarded. The foundation seeks to support genuinely good ideas that will make a real difference to the lives of local people. Where applicants do not meet the requirements of this process, the foundation will work with the group or charity to support them to achieve the criteria. Most

Norfolk Community Foundation grants are subject to the following monitoring requirements: four month monitoring, which is usually carried out by phone or email and aims to ensure that there have been no problems in receiving the grant payment and beginning the project. It is also an opportunity to let us know if there are any problems, delays or changes (good or bad) to the original project. End of grant monitoring report: grant recipients will be required to complete and return an end of grant report at the end of the grant term, or when their project completes – whichever is sooner. This should include receipts for items or services purchased where relevant. Selected projects will be telephoned or visited at the end of the grant term to report on final project progress and to collect case studies.' **General criteria:** grants should have a demonstrable impact on a particular need or problem; groups are expected to be clear about their objectives and must be able to demonstrate that the plans are realistic and practical; the project should be accurately costed and evidence provided to support the costs; organisations that are wholly or largely volunteer led will be prioritised; wherever possible, the users of the service should be involved in developing the project; an awareness of equal opportunities issues should be evidenced in the application; and appropriate arrangements must be in place to safeguard vulnerable adults and young people.

WHO TO APPLY TO Olive Thompson, Finance Manager, St James Mill, Whitefriars, Norwich NR3 1SH *Tel.* 01603 623958 *email* info@ norfolkfoundation.com *Website* www. norfolkfoundation.com

....

■ Norie Charitable Trust

CC NO 1073993   **ESTABLISHED** 1999
WHERE FUNDING CAN BE GIVEN UK.
WHO CAN BENEFIT Charitable organisations.
WHAT IS FUNDED General charitable purposes with some preference towards people with disabilities.
RANGE OF GRANTS Up to £6,000.
SAMPLE GRANTS Previous grants have included: Changing Tunes (£5,000), Bath Literary Festival (£3,000); Keynsham Arts and Somerset Crimebeat (£2,000 each); and Bath Film Festival, Pier Art Centre and The Harbour (£1,000 each).
FINANCES *Year* 2011–12 *Income* £21,969
TRUSTEES Christopher Parish; Alexandra Wilson; Kate Bernstein.
HOW TO APPLY In writing to the correspondent.
WHO TO APPLY TO Mary Kitto, Administrator, c/o Hedley Foundation, Victoria House, 1–3 College Hill, London EC4R 2RA *Tel.* 020 7489 8076

....

■ Normalyn Charitable Trust

CC NO 1077985   **ESTABLISHED** 1999
WHERE FUNDING CAN BE GIVEN UK.
WHO CAN BENEFIT Jewish people.
WHAT IS FUNDED General charitable purposes and Jewish causes.
WHAT IS NOT FUNDED Registered charities only.
TYPE OF GRANT One-off.
RANGE OF GRANTS £1,000–£25,000, however the average grant range is £1,001–£5,000.
SAMPLE GRANTS United Synagogue (£21,500); Finchley Jewish Primary School Trust (£8,500); Community Security Trust (£6,000); City of London School Trust (£4,500); Norwood

(£2,500); Chana Charitable Trust, Teach First and UK Jewish Film Festival (£1,000 each).

FINANCES *Year* 2011–12 *Income* £39,153 *Grants* £68,399 *Assets* £34,649

TRUSTEES Daniel Dover; Jeremy Newman; Judith Newman.

HOW TO APPLY The trust does not accept unsolicited applications.

WHO TO APPLY TO Jeremy Newman, Trustee, 26 Allandale Avenue, London N3 3PJ

■ The Norman Family Charitable Trust

CC NO 277616   **ESTABLISHED** 1979

WHERE FUNDING CAN BE GIVEN Primarily Cornwall, Devon and Somerset

WHO CAN BENEFIT Registered charities only, preferably smaller, local charities.

WHAT IS FUNDED Grants are made at the trustees' discretion, mostly in south west England.

WHAT IS NOT FUNDED No grants to individuals. No funding for religious buildings or to assist any organisations using animals for live experimental purposes or generally to fund overseas work.

TYPE OF GRANT One-off, interest-free loans, project, research and start-up costs will be considered. Funding may be given for up to one year.

RANGE OF GRANTS £1,000–£37,000.

SAMPLE GRANTS University of Exeter – Peninsular Foundation (£25,000); Children's Hospice South West and Exmouth Community Transport (£10,000 each); West of England School for Children with Little or No Sight, Topsham Rugby and Football Club, Hospiscare Exeter, Shilhay Community and East Budleigh Community Shop (£5,000 each); Exmouth Community College (£4,900); Knowle Village Hall (£4,000); Fire Fighters Charity (£3,000) and Kingfisher Award Scheme (£2,500).

FINANCES *Year* 2012–13 *Income* £397,186 *Grants* £330,900 *Assets* £8,398,153

TRUSTEES R. J. Dawe, Chair; M. H. Evans; M. B. Saunders; M. J. Webb; C. E. Houghton; S. Gillingham.

HOW TO APPLY Applications can be made using the online form, or by downloading the form, completing it and sending via post. Trustees meet in March, June, September and December to consider grants over £5,000. A subcommittee meets every six to eight weeks to deal with applications for less than £5,000. Meeting dates can be found on the website and applications should be submitted at least two weeks in advance.

WHO TO APPLY TO R. J. Dawe, Chair of the Trustees, 14 Fore Street, Budleigh Salterton, Devon EX9 6NG *Tel.* 01395 446699 *email* info@nfct. org *Website* www.nfct.org

■ The Duncan Norman Trust Fund

CC NO 250434   **ESTABLISHED** 1996

WHERE FUNDING CAN BE GIVEN UK, with a preference for Merseyside.

WHO CAN BENEFIT Registered charities that are known to the trustees.

WHAT IS FUNDED General charitable purposes.

WHAT IS NOT FUNDED No grants to individuals.

RANGE OF GRANTS Generally, less than £1,000

SAMPLE GRANTS Hertford College, Oxford (£2,000); DEC – East Africa Crisis Appeal and LCVS – Thrive at Five Project (£1,000 each).

FINANCES *Year* 2011–12 *Income* £31,866 *Grants* £28,800 *Assets* £826,162

TRUSTEES R. K. Asser; Caroline Chapman; Ms V. S. Hilton; Caroline Elizabeth Lazar; William Stothart; Clare Louise Venner.

OTHER INFORMATION Grants of less than £1,000 each totalled £25,000.

HOW TO APPLY The trust states that it only makes grants to charities known to the settlor and unsolicited applications are not considered.

WHO TO APPLY TO Liverpool Charity and Voluntary Services, 151 Dale Street, Liverpool L2 2AH *Tel.* 01512 275177 *email* enquiries@ charitycheques.org.uk *Website* www. merseytrusts.org.uk

■ The Normanby Charitable Trust

CC NO 252102   **ESTABLISHED** 1966

WHERE FUNDING CAN BE GIVEN UK, with a special interest in North Yorkshire and north east England.

WHO CAN BENEFIT Registered charities.

WHAT IS FUNDED General, particularly Arts, culture, heritage and social welfare.

WHAT IS NOT FUNDED No grants to individuals, or to non-UK charities.

RANGE OF GRANTS £50–£228,000

SAMPLE GRANTS Ley Hall Zealholme (£10,000); Mickleby Village Hall (£7,500); ZANE (£7,000); Yorkshire Air Ambulance, Scarborough and District CAB and the Captain Cook School Room Museum (£5,000 each); Education Centre for Children with Down Syndrome and North Yorkshire Moors Chamber Music Festival (£3,000 each); The Prince's Trust (£2,500); St Hilda's Playgroup (£2,000); Red Squirrel Survival Trust (£1,000) and Braille Chess Association (£500).

FINANCES *Year* 2011–12 *Income* £287,794 *Grants* £94,166 *Assets* £9,728,804

TRUSTEES The Marquis of Normanby; The Dowager Marchioness of Normanby; Lady Lepel Kornicki; Lady Evelyn Buchan; Lady Peronel Phipps de Cruz; Lady Henrietta Burridge.

HOW TO APPLY In writing to the correspondent. Trustees meet two or three times a year to award grants, although there are no regular dates. Note, only successful applications will be acknowledged.

WHO TO APPLY TO The Trustees, 52 Tite Street, London Sw3 4JA

■ The North West Cancer Research Fund

CC NO 223598   **ESTABLISHED** 1948

WHERE FUNDING CAN BE GIVEN North West England and North and Mid Wales.

WHO CAN BENEFIT Those undertaking fundamental cancer research approved by and under the direction of the North West Cancer Research Fund Scientific Committee.

WHAT IS FUNDED Fundamental research into the causes of cancer, including the cost of associated equipment.

WHAT IS NOT FUNDED Funding is not given for research whose primary aim is to develop new forms of treatment or evaluate existing ones, such as drug development, nor for clinical trials.

TYPE OF GRANT Project; research; running and start-up costs; and salaries. Usually for three-year periods subject to review.

RANGE OF GRANTS Average grant size is £35,000 per annum, awarded for three years.

Think carefully about every application. Is it justified?

785

FINANCES *Year* 2011–12 *Income* £1,011,306 *Grants* £750,000

TRUSTEES Michael Barton; Kay Windsor; John Lewys-Lloyd; Wendy Hadwin; Michael Potts; Barbara Smith; Pat Mann; Andrew Renison; Beryl Powell; Olive Cutts; Joan Pettitt; Sheila Gill; Olivia Ley; Kate Cowie; Richard Skelton; Gordon Findlay; Doreen Sands; David Leach; Mary Shepherd.

HOW TO APPLY Application forms can be downloaded, together with criteria and guidelines, from the fund's website, or obtained from the correspondent.

WHO TO APPLY TO Dominique Hare, 22 Oxford Street, Liverpool L7 7BL *Tel.* 01517 092919 *email* research@nwcrf.co.uk *Website* www.nwcrf.co.uk

■ The Northampton Municipal Church Charities

CC NO 259593   **ESTABLISHED** 1969

WHERE FUNDING CAN BE GIVEN The borough of Northampton.

WHO CAN BENEFIT Organisations and individuals in need.

WHAT IS FUNDED Social welfare, disability, religion and education.

TYPE OF GRANT One-off and recurrent.

RANGE OF GRANTS Usually £1,000 for individuals and between £1,000 and £30,000 for organisations.

SAMPLE GRANTS Nene Valley CFR (£18,000); Emmanuel Church (£8,700); Mount Pleasant Baptist Church (£5,000); Northampton Hope Centre (£3,000); Motor Neurone Disease and Broadmead Money Advice Centre (£2,500 each); Crime to Christ (£2,000); Deafblind UK and Listening Books (£1,500 each) and Tools for Self Reliance and Samaritans (£1,000 each).

FINANCES *Year* 2011–12 *Income* £245,585 *Grants* £116,330 *Assets* £3,234,175

TRUSTEES Keith Davidson; James Buckby; Ronald Gate; Ruth Hampson; Clive Fowler; Brian May; Terrence O'Connor; Tony Sanderson; Richard Pestel; Terry Wire.

OTHER INFORMATION From the grants total £6,300 went to individuals, £37,000 went towards pensioners grants, £7,000 went towards Christmas vouchers and £63,000 was given to organisations.

HOW TO APPLY In writing to the correspondent.

WHO TO APPLY TO Clerk to the Trustees, Wilson Browne Solicitors, 4 Grange Park Court, Roman Way, Grange Park, Northampton NN4 5EA *Tel.* 01604 876697 *email* jforsyth@wilsonbrowne.co.uk

■ The Northampton Queen's Institute Relief in Sickness Fund

CC NO 208583   **ESTABLISHED** 1971

WHERE FUNDING CAN BE GIVEN The borough of Northampton.

WHO CAN BENEFIT Organisations benefiting children and young adults, at risk groups, and people who are disadvantaged by poverty or socially isolated.

WHAT IS FUNDED Youth groups, welfare organisations, hospitals and health organisations.

TYPE OF GRANT One-off and recurrent.

RANGE OF GRANTS £1,000–£10,000.

SAMPLE GRANTS Macmillan Cancer Relief (£10,000); Northampton Hope Centre (£4,000); Home Start and Listening Books (£3,000 each); St John Ambulance, Northants Association of Youth Clubs, Northants Association for the Blind, Diabetes UK and Northampton Volunteering Centre (£2,000 each) and Motability (£1,000).

FINANCES *Year* 2011–12 *Income* £28,452 *Grants* £53,000 *Assets* £960,970

TRUSTEES D. M. Orton-Jones, Chair; J. Bradshaw; J. Mackaness; Dr R. Marshall; Dr J. McFarlane; David Hammer; Dr J. Scrivener Birkhead; Dr Charles Fox.

OTHER INFORMATION In 2011–12 grants were made to 21 organisations.

HOW TO APPLY In writing to the correspondent. There are one or two main meetings where applications are considered during the year, although decisions can be made in between.

WHO TO APPLY TO Clerk to the Charity, c/o Shoosmiths, 5 The Lakes, Northampton NN4 7SH *Tel.* 01604 543111

■ The Earl of Northampton's Charity

CC NO 210291   **ESTABLISHED** 2003

WHERE FUNDING CAN BE GIVEN England, with a preference for London and the South East.

WHO CAN BENEFIT Charitable organisations.

WHAT IS FUNDED Welfare causes.

RANGE OF GRANTS £250–£4,000.

SAMPLE GRANTS Trinity Hospital Castle Rising (£10,000); Trinity Hospital Clun (£4,000); Jubilee Trust Almshouses (£2,000) and St Michael's Church Framlingham (£250).

FINANCES *Year* 2011–12 *Income* £1,183,000 *Grants* £16,000 *Assets* £23,044,000

TRUSTEE The Mercers Company.

HOW TO APPLY Note: The trust is currently not accepting any applications. It is under the trusteeship of the Mercers' Company and one application to the Company is an application to all of its trusts including the Mercers' Charitable Foundation and the Charity of Sir Richard Whittington.

WHO TO APPLY TO M. McGregor, Clerk to the Mercers' Company, Mercers' Hall Offices, Mercers' Hall, Ironmonger Lane, London EC2V 8HE *Tel.* 020 7726 4991 *Fax* 020 7600 1158 *email* info@mercers.co.uk *Website* www.mercers.co.uk

■ Northamptonshire Community Foundation

CC NO 1094646   **ESTABLISHED** 2001

WHERE FUNDING CAN BE GIVEN Northamptonshire and surrounding areas.

WHO CAN BENEFIT Registered charities; local organisations.

WHAT IS FUNDED Education; good health; relief of poverty.

WHAT IS NOT FUNDED General exclusions apply as follows: general and major fundraising appeals; statutory work in educational institutions; overseas travel or expeditions for individuals and groups; direct replacement of statutory and public funding; organisations that aim to convert people to any kind of religious or political belief; medical research and equipment; projects operating outside Northamptonshire; animal welfare; large national charities (except for independent local branches working for local people); work that has already finished;

grantmaking bodies applying for funding to redistribute to individuals or groups.

SAMPLE GRANTS Springs Family Centre (£11,000); Serve (£10,000); Deep Roots Tall Trees, Thomas' Fund, Wallaston Cricket Club and Wriggle Dance Theatre (£5,000 each); Blackthorn Good Neighbours and Vineyard Churches – Northampton (£4,000 each); Oundle Cinema Limited (£3,000); Pattishall Parish Hall Association and Rotary Club of Rushden (£2,000 each); and Corby VCS (£1,000).

FINANCES *Year* 2012–13 *Income* £1,310,803 *Grants* £623,807 *Assets* £3,107,865

TRUSTEES David Laing; John Bruce; Wendi Buchanan; Anne Burnett; Linda Davis; Sandra Bell; Robert Tomkinson; Alan Maskell; Sarah Banner; David Knight; Sally Robinson.

HOW TO APPLY The foundation accepts online applications only. Application forms for each funding programme can be downloaded from the foundation's website, where criteria and guidelines are also posted. If you wish to discuss your application then the grants team welcomes calls on 01604 230033.

WHO TO APPLY TO Victoria Miles, Chief Executive, c/o Royal and Derngate, 19 Guildhall Road, Northampton NN1 1DP *Tel.* 01604 230033 *email* enquiries@ncf.uk.com *Website* www.ncf.uk.com

■ The Northcott Devon Foundation

CC NO 201277   **ESTABLISHED** 1960

WHERE FUNDING CAN BE GIVEN Devon.

WHO CAN BENEFIT 'The principal objects of the charity are to provide support for individuals in Devon and to assist registered charities which seek to improve the living conditions of disabled or disadvantaged persons resident in Devon.'

WHAT IS FUNDED (a) Individuals or families living in Devon who are experiencing distress and hardship deriving from disability, illness, injury, bereavement or exceptional disadvantage, in circumstances where such assistance offers long-term benefit. (b) Registered charities operating primarily within Devon, whose objects are broadly in sympathy with those of the foundation, and who seek to improve the living conditions or life experiences of people who are disabled or disadvantaged living in Devon. (c) Young people of limited means undertaking philanthropic activities that are not part of a formal education or training programme, and who live in Devon.

WHAT IS NOT FUNDED The foundation is unable to enter into longer-term financial commitments. Assistance will not be given to statutory agencies, including self-governing National Health Service Trusts, in the performance of their duties. Assistance will not be given to clear any debts owed to statutory agencies or to financial institutions. Other debts will not formally be considered unless agreement has been reached with the creditors for full and final settlement in a substantially reduced sum.

TYPE OF GRANT Usually one-off for a specific purpose or project. Research, capital and buildings will be considered. Core funding is not considered.

RANGE OF GRANTS Usually up to £700.

SAMPLE GRANTS Crosslinks (£700) and The Sir Frances Chichester Trust, Living Options Devon, Helping Hands for Holidays and Magic Carpet (£500 each).

FINANCES *Year* 2011–12 *Income* £188,451 *Grants* £180,855 *Assets* £5,049,007

TRUSTEES Patricia Lane; Maj. Gen. John Grey; Michael Pentreath; George Simey

OTHER INFORMATION Grants to 953 individuals totalled £171,000.

HOW TO APPLY Organisations should initially apply in writing to the correspondent who will supply an application form and statement of policy. Enclose an sae.
Individuals can download a form from the website.
Assistance will not be given unless applicants or their sponsors have checked thoroughly that assistance or benefit is not available from the Department of Social Security or other public funds.

WHO TO APPLY TO Geoffrey Folland, Secretary, 1b Victoria Road, Exmouth, Devon EX8 1DL *Tel.* 01395 269204 *Website* www.northcottdevon.co.uk

■ The Northcott Devon Medical Foundation

CC NO 204660   **ESTABLISHED** 1961

WHERE FUNDING CAN BE GIVEN Devon.

WHO CAN BENEFIT Academics, medical professionals, research workers and postgraduate students.

WHAT IS FUNDED Support of postgraduate, medical research and the improvement of medical practice. Provision of schools, research laboratories, libraries and so on for the promotion of medicine, surgery and other subjects.

WHAT IS NOT FUNDED Tuition fees for medical/nursing undergraduates and living expenses.

RANGE OF GRANTS £400 to £5,000.

SAMPLE GRANTS Peninsula College of Medicine and Dentistry which received funding for 11 projects (£17,500).

FINANCES *Year* 2011–12 *Income* £29,061 *Grants* £17,557 *Assets* £1,204,777

TRUSTEES Dr Christopher Gardner-Thorpe; Prof. Derek Partridge; Dr Andrew Warin; John Thompson.

OTHER INFORMATION 'Whilst grants paid out were less than the previous year (£17,557 compared to £31,960), this is largely a timing issue. Many projects last longer than 12 months.'

HOW TO APPLY On an application form available from the correspondent.

WHO TO APPLY TO R. E. T. Borton, Secretary, Bishop Fleming, Stratus House, Emperor Way, Exeter Business Park, Exeter EX1 3QS *Tel.* 01392 448800 *email* tborton@bishopfleming.co.uk

■ The Community Foundation for Northern Ireland

IR NO XN45242   **ESTABLISHED** 1979

WHERE FUNDING CAN BE GIVEN Northern Ireland and the six border counties of the Republic of Ireland.

WHO CAN BENEFIT Community groups, self-help organisations and voluntary organisations.

WHAT IS FUNDED Priority areas: peace-building; community development; social justice; cross-border development; active citizenship; poverty, social inclusion.

WHAT IS NOT FUNDED No funding for: applicants not based in Northern Ireland, national charities and appeals; activities that duplicate existing services and substitution for statutory funding; retrospective funding; capital build projects and large equipment purchases; vehicles; promotion of religion or party political activity; trips outside NI, holidays, residential costs; dinners, fundraising promotions or other ticketed events;

shopping trips, parties or food (except where food forms a small but essential part of a project); housing associations; individuals (unless a new fund is specifically aimed at helping individuals); projects where the Foundation's contribution is a minor part of a larger funded initiative or organisations that did not comply with reporting requirements of previous grant aid.

TYPE OF GRANT One-off and reoccurring.

RANGE OF GRANTS Generally £1,000–£5,000 but can be up to £150,000.

SAMPLE GRANTS Conflict Resolution Services and Ballymena Inter-Ethnic Forum (£5,000 each); Roe Valley Residents association (£3,000); Foyle Down Syndrome Trust (£2,800); Feeny Community Association and British Red Cross (£2,000 each); Crafts With Love (£1,800); Fall Women's Centre and Newington Day Centre (£1,500 each); Lisburn Sea Cadets (£1,000); Burnfoot Seniors Group (£920); Scotch Youth Group (£450) and Citizens Advice Fermanagh (£280).

FINANCES *Year* 2011–12 *Income* £5,231,232 *Grants* £3,578,617 *Assets* £15,175,937

TRUSTEES Tony McCusker; Les Allamby; Maurna Crozier; Geraldine Donaghy; Brian Dougherty; Conal McFeely; Anne McReynolds; Colin Stutt; John Healy; Kevin Kingston.

PUBLICATIONS Various policy briefs, funder's briefs and models of best practice available on the website.

OTHER INFORMATION Funding programmes are subject to open and close for applications throughout the year. New funds are also established and some end, therefore it is important to contact the foundation or check their comprehensive website for the most recent information.

HOW TO APPLY Applications to any of the funds are made through the same online process. The foundation will match the application with the most suitable fund. There are comprehensive guidelines available on the website for applications. A turnaround time of 12 weeks should be allowed for all applications. There are two parts to the application process: Part A – complete the short online form to answer the questions about the project, beneficiaries and budget and Part B – you will be given a unique link to your own application form in an email along with guidelines on completing it. This part must be printed off and signed by two members of the organisation. Both parts should then be posted to the foundation together with the following documentation: a copy of the governing document; a copy of the most recent accounts or income and expenditure statement; a list of the management committee members and their contact details; a recent original bank statement for the organisation's bank account. The foundation will normally only fund groups located in Northern Ireland however some funds will make grants in the Republic as well. Applicants should check the fund specifications. Applications are assessed by the foundation's staff and recommendations are considered by the trustee's grants subcommittee. Successful applicants will be required to submit both qualitative and quantitative monitoring information for the benefit of both the grant holder and the foundation.

WHO TO APPLY TO Avila Kilmurray, Director, Community House, Citylink Business Park, Albert Street, Belfast BT12 4HQ *Tel.* 02890 245927 *Fax* 02871 371565 *email* info@communityfoundationni.org *Website* www.communityfoundationni.org

■ The Northern Rock Foundation

CC NO 1063906 **ESTABLISHED** 1997

WHERE FUNDING CAN BE GIVEN Cumbria, Northumberland, Tyne and Wear, County Durham and the Tees Valley.

WHO CAN BENEFIT Organisations helping people who are disadvantaged.

WHAT IS FUNDED Current grant programmes are: Managing Money – helps people who are in debt or who have other financial problems and needs; Having a Home – helps vulnerable people who are homeless or at risk of becoming homeless; Enabling Independence and Choice – helps older people, people with mental health problems, people with learning disabilities and carers; Changing Lives – helps young offenders and young people within the criminal justice system, refugees, asylum seekers and migrant communities, and people who misuse alcohol and/or drugs; Safety and Justice for Victims of Abuse – supports people who experience domestic abuse, sexual violence and exploitation and child abuse; Fresh Ideas Fund – provides funding for early stage development of new business ideas to help the charities the foundation supports to grow in size, increase their impact and improve their long term sustainability.

TYPE OF GRANT Capital, core or project funding and for up to three or more years (sometimes renewable after that).

RANGE OF GRANTS Typically £40,000–£250,000.

SAMPLE GRANTS Addaction (£134,000); Middlesbrough First (£114,000); Barrow and District Credit Union Study Group (£99,000); My Sister's Place (£90,000); The Lawnmowers Independent Theatre Company (£80,000); Impact Housing (Eden Rural Foyer) (£75,000); Methodist Asylum Project, Middlesbrough (£66,000); Regional Youth Work Unit (£50,000); North Tyneside Art Studio Ltd (£42,000); Age UK Newcastle upon Tyne (£27,000); Against Violence and Abuse (£25,000) and Teesside Homeless Action Group (£20,000).

FINANCES *Year* 2012 *Income* £493,000 *Grants* £8,683,000 *Assets* £29,000,000

TRUSTEES Alastair Balls; David Chapman; David Faulkner; Jackie Fisher; Julie Shipley; Tony Henfrey; Frank Nicholson; Chris Jobe; Lorna Moran; Mo O'Toole.

OTHER INFORMATION It is not yet clear if the foundation will be able to continue after 2015 when its current programmes end and the reserves are spent. The future of the foundation depends upon the outcome of discussions between the foundation and Virgin Money, who now own Northern Rock plc.

HOW TO APPLY From 2013, the foundation only makes grants on an **invitation to bid basis**. The trustees want to maximise the impact of the funds available and for that reason the foundation is working closely with grant holders it already has a relationship with, with a particular focus on helping organisations to become more resilient.

WHO TO APPLY TO Penny Wilkinson, Chief Executive, The Old Chapel, Woodbine Road, Gosforth, Newcastle upon Tyne NE3 1DD *Tel.* 01912 848412 *Fax* 01912 848413 *email* generaloffice@nr-foundation.org.uk *Website* www.nr-foundation.org.uk

■ The Northmoor Trust

cc no 256818   **established** 1968
where funding can be given UK
who can benefit Local, regional and UK charitable organisations benefiting people who are disadvantaged.
what is funded The direct or indirect relief of poverty, hardship or distress.
what is not funded Grants are only made to organisations which one or more of the trustees have direct personal knowledge. No grants to individuals, or organisations concerned with religion, medicine or the arts. Occasionally grants are made to educational charities where the guiding criteria are met. The trust does not respond to general appeals.
type of grant One-off and recurrent.
range of grants £5,000–£20,000.
sample grants Good Vibrations (£15,000); Family Friends and Tower Hamlets Friends and Neighbours (£10,000 each); and WISH (£6,000).
finances *Year* 2011–12 *Income* £51,482 *Grants* £41,000 *Assets* £1,207,282
trustees Viscount Runciman; Dame Ruth Runciman; Frances Bennett; Cathy Eastburn.
how to apply In writing to the correspondent, including the latest accounts and annual report, a list of the main sources of funding and a budget for the current year including details of other grant applications made. For first time applicants, a general description of aims and achievements to date and an outline of plans for future development. Applications should arrive by mid-February for preliminary consideration in March, decisions are made in May. Applicants may be visited or asked to provide additional information for the May meeting. The trustees may also visit applicants between the two meetings.
who to apply to Hilary Edwards, Secretary, 44 Clifton Hill, London NW8 0QG *Tel.* 020 7372 0698

■ The Northumberland Village Homes Trust

cc no 225429   **established** 1880
where funding can be given Tyne and Wear, Durham, Cleveland and Northumberland.
who can benefit Individuals and youth organisations benefiting those under 21years of age who are disadvantaged by poverty.
what is funded The relief of poverty distress and sickness among children and young persons under the age of 21 years, with a preference for those who are resident in Tyne and Wear, Durham, Cleveland and Northumberland.
what is not funded No personal applications will be considered unless supported by a letter from a registered charity or local authority, or unless the applicant is personally known to one of the trustees. No applications will be considered for 'gap year' projects or for work relating to medical research or such matters.
range of grants £1,000–£5,000.
sample grants The Evening Chronicle Sunshine Fund (£3,000); Nightstop Teesside and Macmillan Cancer Support (£2,500 each); Barnardo's and Westgate Baptist Church (The Hub Kidz Club) (£2,000 each); Trinity Youth and Children (£1,500); Families Talking Tees Valley Mediation and The National Autistic Society (£1,000 each); East Durham Play and Community (£500) and The Sick Children's Trust (£300).

finances *Year* 2011–12 *Income* £54,100 *Grants* £36,000 *Assets* £1,281,745
trustees Claire Macalpine; Lord Gisborough; Eileen Savage; Diana Barkes; Richard Savage.
other information In 2011–12 grants were given to 29 organisations.
how to apply Applications should be made by 30 September for consideration in November. Applications should be in writing and state: whether the applicant is an individual, private charity or registered charity; the objects (if a charity); the amount required and what it is for; and any other sources of funding.
who to apply to Eileen Savage, Trustee, c/o Savage Solicitors, Robson House, 4 Middle Street, Corbridge NE45 5AT *Tel.* 01434 632505

■ The Northumbria Historic Churches Trust

cc no 511314   **established** 1980
where funding can be given The dioceses of Durham and Newcastle.
who can benefit Churches that are at least 100 years old.
what is funded The restoration, preservation, repair, maintenance, reconstruction, improvement and beautification of churches, their contents and their churchyards.
what is not funded 'The trust is unable to help with work on bells, organs, church halls, decoration (unless consequential), notice boards, publications, heating, re-orderings, new facilities or routine maintenance.'
type of grant One-off, feasibility studies and buildings. Funding is for one year or less.
range of grants £500–£5,000.
sample grants St Peter – Wolviston, St Johns Chapel – Bishop Auckland and St Cuthbert – Norham (£5,000 each); St Mary the Virgin – Stamfordham (£4,000); Holy Trinity – Washington (£2,500); St Peter – Monkseaton (£2,000) and Heddon Methodist Church (£1,000).
finances *Year* 2011–12 *Income* £50,859 *Grants* £49,800 *Assets* £191,822
trustees Lt Gen Robin Brimms; Elizabeth Conran; Christopher Downs; Philip Scrope; Jeremy Kendall; Gillian Walker; Alyson Smith; Roger Norris; Revd Terence Hurst, Peter Ryder; Revd Canon Robert McTeer; Revd Canon John Ruscoe; Sir Josslyn Gore-Booth.
other information No grants to individuals.
how to apply On a form available to download, together with guidelines and criteria, from the website. Initial telephone calls to discuss applications are welcomed.
who to apply to Peter De Lange, Secretary, 27 Devonshire Road, Sheffield S17 3NT *Tel.* 01142 367594 *email* Secretary@NorthumbriaHCT.org.uk *Website* www.northumbriahct.org.uk

■ The Northwood Charitable Trust

sc no SC014487   **established** 1972
where funding can be given Scotland, especially Dundee and Tayside.
who can benefit Registered charities.
what is funded General charitable purposes. In the past, grants have been given to a university and to medical and educational projects.
type of grant One-off and recurring grants.

SAMPLE GRANTS Previous beneficiaries include: Tenovus Medical Projects; Tayside Orthopaedic and Rehabilitation Technology Centre; Macmillan Cancer Relief Scotland; Brittle Bone Society; Dundee Repertory Theatre; Dundee Samaritans; Dundee Age Concern; Couple Counselling Tayside; and Tayside Association for the Deaf.

FINANCES *Year* 2011–12 *Income* £2,176,939 *Grants* £2,000,000

TRUSTEES Brian Harold Thomson; Andrew Francis Thomson; Lewis Murray Thomson.

OTHER INFORMATION The grants total is an estimate based upon previous years.

HOW TO APPLY The trust has previously stated that funds are fully committed and that no applications will be considered or acknowledged.

WHO TO APPLY TO Brian McKernie, Secretary, c/o William Thomson and Sons, 22 Meadowside, Dundee DD1 1LN *Tel.* 01382 201534

■ The Norton Foundation

CC NO 702638   **ESTABLISHED** 1990

WHERE FUNDING CAN BE GIVEN UK, with a preference for Birmingham, Coventry and the County of Warwick.

WHO CAN BENEFIT Children and young people under 25 years of age who are in need of care or rehabilitation or aid of any kind, particularly as a result of deprivation, maltreatment or neglect or who are at risk of becoming involved with anti-social behaviour or offending.

WHAT IS FUNDED Grants to support vocational development, entry to employment, establishing a home, provision of equipment and personal development.

WHAT IS NOT FUNDED No grants for the payment of debts that have already been incurred.

TYPE OF GRANT One-off capital grants and smaller recurring grants. Unrestricted funding.

RANGE OF GRANTS Up to £5,000 for organisations. A one–off capital grants of £100,000 every five years.

SAMPLE GRANTS Alcester Town Council and free@last (£100,000 each); Construction Youth Trust (£5,000); Coventry City Mission (£3,250); Volunteer Reading Help Birmingham Branch; The Jericho Foundation; Life Space Trust and Pan-Asia Community Housing (£2,000 each); Envision and Brathay Trust (£5,000 each); Tall Ships Youth Trust (£1,200); The Salvation Army; Cruse Bereavement Care and Bedworth Heath Youth Project (£1,000 each).

FINANCES *Year* 2011–12 *Income* £127,800 *Grants* £267,054 *Assets* £4,131,844

TRUSTEES R. H. Graham, Suggett Chair; Alan Bailey; Michael R. Bailey; Parminder Singh Birdi; Jane Gaynor; Sarah V. Henderson; Richard G. D. Hurley; Brian W. Lewis; Robert K. Meacham; Richard C. Perkins; Louise Sewell.

OTHER INFORMATION £34,000 was given in grants to individuals.

HOW TO APPLY On a form, available with guidance notes from the trusts website. Applications from organisations are normally processed by the trustees at their quarterly meetings. The trust expects that it will make the next capital donation of £100,000 in summer 2015. Applications for this are being accepted from Monday 3 November 2014, when the application form and process for this award will become available on the trust's website.

WHO TO APPLY TO Richard C. Perkins, Administrator, PO Box 10282, Redditch, Worcestershire B97 9ZA *Tel.* 01527 544446 *email* correspondent@nortonfoundation.org *Website* www.nortonfoundation.org

---

■ The Norton Rose Charitable Foundation

CC NO 1102142   **ESTABLISHED** 2004

WHERE FUNDING CAN BE GIVEN Worldwide.

WHO CAN BENEFIT Registered charities and organisations conducting charitable activities worldwide.

WHAT IS FUNDED Education, social welfare, medical.

RANGE OF GRANTS Up to £200,000.

SAMPLE GRANTS Barretstown (£100,000) and The Capital Community Foundation (£47,000).

FINANCES *Year* 2011–12 *Income* £489,751 *Grants* £400,253 *Assets* £89,221

TRUSTEES Simon Cox; Patrick Farrell; Glenn Hall; Campbell Steedman.

OTHER INFORMATION In 2011–12 grants were given to 40 organisations.

HOW TO APPLY 'In many cases, the charities we support are those we have supported in the past, but new charities are considered at all the regular trustee meetings. The trustees also meet on an ad hoc basis to consider specific urgent requests such as the support of major disaster relief appeals.'

WHO TO APPLY TO Patrick Farrell, Secretary, 3 More London Riverside, London SE1 2AQ *Tel.* 020 7283 6000 *Website* www.nortonrose.com

---

■ The Norwich Church of England Young Men's Society

CC NO 206425   **ESTABLISHED** 1892

WHERE FUNDING CAN BE GIVEN Norfolk.

WHO CAN BENEFIT Churches and charitable organisations.

WHAT IS FUNDED Religious and youth related activities mainly local but also overseas.

RANGE OF GRANTS £100–£7,500.

SAMPLE GRANTS Previous beneficiaries have included: Swardeston Cricket Club – Youth Section (£7,500); Norwich Cathedral (£2,500); Ashcroft Project and East Norfolk Youth for Christ (£1,000 each); Nancy Oldfield Trust (£750); Norfolk Deaf Association, Hamlet Centre Trust and Nelsons Trust (£500 each); Sewell Community Group (£250); and Norfolk and Norwich Diabetes Trust (£100).

FINANCES *Year* 2012 *Income* £195,446 *Grants* £13,334 *Assets* £1,441,812

TRUSTEES John Pidgen; John Copeman; Revd Canon David Sharp; Mike Preston; Chris Futter.

OTHER INFORMATION The grant total for 2012 is significantly down on previous years'. However, income and expenditure remain about the same.

HOW TO APPLY In writing to the correspondent. Applications are considered quarterly and only successful ones are acknowledged. The society also informed us that 'because of serious financial constraints, successful applications for grants are being severely restricted'.

WHO TO APPLY TO C. J. Free, Secretary, 3 Brigg Street, Norwich, Norfolk NR2 1QN *Tel.* 01603 628572

■ The Norwich Town Close Estate Charity

CC NO 235678 **ESTABLISHED** 1892

WHERE FUNDING CAN BE GIVEN Within a 20-mile radius of the Guildhall of the city of Norwich.

WHO CAN BENEFIT Only charities based in the area specified will be supported.

WHAT IS NOT FUNDED No grants to: individuals who are not Freemen (or dependants of Freemen) of the city of Norwich; charities more than 20 miles from Norwich; or charities which are not educational. Revenue funding for educational charities is not generally given.

TYPE OF GRANT Buildings, capital, one-off and project. Funding for up to one year will be considered.

RANGE OF GRANTS £500–£35,000.

SAMPLE GRANTS Norfolk Record Office (£34,000); Cultural Communities Consortium (£30,000); Whittingham Boathouses Foundation (£25,000); Morley Church of England VA Primary School and Hamlet Centre Trust (£20,000 each); CAST (Centre for the Advancement of Science and Technology), Community Action Norwich and Stalham Brass Band (£10,000 each); Hethersett High School and Science College (£6,700); Norwich City (FC) Community Sports Foundation (£6,000); Asperger East Anglia, The Wherry Yacht Charter Charitable Trust and Mancroft Advice project (£5,000 each); Norfolk SEN Network (£3,000); Hub Community Project (£2,500) and The Chermond Trust (£760).

FINANCES *Year* 2011–12 *Income* £722,000 *Grants* £276,000 *Assets* £19,627,000

TRUSTEES David Fullman; John Rushmer; Michael Quinton; Brenda Ferris; Geoffrey Loades; Philip Blanchflower; Anthony Hansell; Nigel Back; Richard Gurney; Jeanette Southgate; Robert Self; Pamela Scutter; Brenda Arthur; Heather Tyrrell; Michael Quinton; John Symonds.

OTHER INFORMATION In 2011–12 the charity also gave £165,000 in grants to individuals. There are close links with Norwich Consolidated Charities and Anguish's Educational Foundation. They share their administration processes and collaborate on grantmaking.

HOW TO APPLY After a preliminary enquiry, in writing to the clerk. When submitting an application the following points should be borne in mind: brevity is a virtue – if too much written material is submitted there is a risk that it may not all be assimilated; the trustees like to have details of any other financial support secured; an indication should be given of the amount that is being sought and also how that figure is arrived at; the trustees will not reimburse expenditure already incurred; nor, generally speaking will the trustees pay running costs, e.g. salaries.

WHO TO APPLY TO David Walker, Clerk, David Walker, 1 Woolgate Court, St Benedict's Street, Norwich NR2 4AP *Tel.* 01603 621023 *email* david. walker@norwichcharitabletrusts.org.uk

■ The Norwood and Newton Settlement

CC NO 234964 **ESTABLISHED** 1952

WHERE FUNDING CAN BE GIVEN England and Wales.

WHO CAN BENEFIT Methodist and other mainstream non-conformist churches. Church of England only in exceptional circumstances.

WHAT IS FUNDED New building work in Methodist and other Free Churches. Smaller national charities in which the Settlor expressed a particular interest and other charitable causes that commend themselves to the trustees.

WHAT IS NOT FUNDED Projects will not be considered where an application for National Lottery funding has been made or is contemplated. No grants to individuals, rarely to large UK charities and not for staff/running costs, equipment, repairs or general maintenance.

TYPE OF GRANT One-off capital grants.

RANGE OF GRANTS £1,000–£20,000.

SAMPLE GRANTS New Malden Baptist Church (£320,000); Lichfield Methodist Church, Staffordshire (£15,000); Shirrell Heath Methodist Church, Hampshire (£10,000); The Crown Centre, Plymouth; Sea Mills Community Initiative, Bristol; Christ Church Methodist Church, Addiscombe, Croydon; Trinity Methodist Church, Skipton and Tissington Methodist Chapel, Derby (£5,000 each); Horton Heath Methodist Church, Wimborne (£3,000) and YMCA England Memorial at the National Arboretum (£1,000).

FINANCES *Year* 2011–12 *Income* £333,457 *Grants* £228,000 *Assets* £7,269,693

TRUSTEES P. Clarke; D. M. Holland; Stella Holland; R. Lynch; Susan Newsom.

HOW TO APPLY In writing to the correspondent. In normal circumstances, within seven days an applicant will be sent either a refusal or an application form. Applications are then considered at the quarterly trustee meetings. The trust states:

'At all times applicants are kept informed of the Trustees' time scale.'

WHO TO APPLY TO David M. Holland, Trustee, 126 Beauly Way, Romford, Essex RM1 4XL *Tel.* 01708 723670

■ The Noswad Charity

CC NO 282080 **ESTABLISHED** 1981

WHERE FUNDING CAN BE GIVEN UK.

WHO CAN BENEFIT Emphasis is on charities that benefit the arts and people who are disabled, particularly ex-service people.

WHAT IS FUNDED The trustees continue to support those charitable bodies that they have hitherto supported.

WHAT IS NOT FUNDED No grants to individuals.

RANGE OF GRANTS £600–£2,600.

SAMPLE GRANTS Typically grants are made to Douglas Bader Foundation, Royal Air Force Benevolent Fund, BLESMA, RADAR, Macmillan Cancer Relief and National Arts Collections Fund. It also supports scholarships for postgraduate piano students at London music colleges.

FINANCES *Year* 2011–12 *Income* £22,564

TRUSTEES James Mills; Charles Bardswell; Henry Bromley Davenport.

OTHER INFORMATION In 2011–12 the charity had a total expenditure of £33,700.

HOW TO APPLY In writing to the correspondent.

WHO TO APPLY TO Charles Bardswell, Trustee, c/o Belmont and Lowe Solicitors, Priory House, 18–25 St John's Lane, London EC1M 4HD *Tel.* 020 7608 4600 *Fax* 020 7608 4601

■ The Notgrove Trust

CC NO 278692 **ESTABLISHED** 1979

WHERE FUNDING CAN BE GIVEN Generally in the Gloucestershire area.

WHO CAN BENEFIT Local or special interests of the trustees.

WHAT IS FUNDED Any local charities can be considered.

WHAT IS NOT FUNDED No grants available to support individuals or medical research.

TYPE OF GRANT Except in special circumstances, single donations only will be considered.

RANGE OF GRANTS £1,000 to £23,000.

SAMPLE GRANTS Fair Shares (£23,000); Cheltenham Festivals (£7,000); Woodchester Play Group, Tom Roberts Adventure Centre and Disabled Sailors Association (£5,000 each); Sherborne Church of England Primary School, Furniture Recycling Project and Family Haven (£3,000 each); Hunt Servants Fund (£2,500); Cotswold Riding for the Disabled and Kate's Home Nursing (£2,000 each); and Fields in Trust and Cirencester Cyber Cafe (£1,000 each).

FINANCES *Year* 2011–12 *Income* £169,662 *Grants* £144,250 *Assets* £5,927,242

TRUSTEES David Acland; Elizabeth Acland; Harry Acland.

OTHER INFORMATION In 2011–12 there were 53 grants awarded.

HOW TO APPLY Applications are considered from Gloucestershire charities or from an organisation having an established connection with the trustees. Applicants should include a copy of their latest accounts. Speculative appeals from outside of Gloucestershire are strongly discouraged and unlikely to get a positive response. Past donations to charities outside Gloucestershire should not be taken as an indication of likely future support. The trust has stated telephone calls are unwelcome and due to a lack of clerical support, unsuccessful appeals will not be acknowledged.

WHO TO APPLY TO David Acland, Trustee, Elmbank Farmhouse, Cold Aston, Cheltenham, Gloucestershire GL54 3BJ *Tel.* 01451 810652

■ **The Nottingham General Dispensary**

CC NO 228149   **ESTABLISHED** 1963

WHERE FUNDING CAN BE GIVEN Nottingham and Nottinghamshire.

WHO CAN BENEFIT Individuals or other organisations.

WHAT IS FUNDED The alleviation of need or aid in recovery through the provision of items and services not readily available from ordinary channels. Charities working in the fields of: respite; professional bodies; councils for voluntary service; and health will be considered.

TYPE OF GRANT One-off preferred. Capital, project, recurring costs. Funding for up to three years will be considered.

RANGE OF GRANTS £25–£4,000; mostly under £1,000.

SAMPLE GRANTS Vitalise Skylarks (£1,500); Transplant Sport UK, Spinal Injuries Association, Sign Help and Life Education Centres (£1,000 each); Listening Books (£900); Painful Bladder Group and Bilborough Carers Support Group (£800 each); CAKE Carers (£750); Rushcliffe Stroke Survivors Group (£710); Asian Fathers Special Needs Support Group (£645); Deafblind UK and Peter Le Marchant Trust (£500 each); Bereavement Keyworth (£350); and Heartline Association (£260).

FINANCES *Year* 2011–12 *Income* £41,180 *Grants* £45,000

TRUSTEES Andy Roylance; David Levell; Dr Ian McLachlan; Pauline Johnston; William Bendall; Dr Stanley Harris; Alan Hopwood; Dr Angela Truman.

OTHER INFORMATION In 2011–12 the charity had a total expenditure of £60,000. Research suggests that grants totalled around £45,000.

HOW TO APPLY In writing to the correspondent, supported by medical evidence.

WHO TO APPLY TO Nigel Cullen, Freeth Cartwright LLP, Cumberland Court, 80 Mount Street, Nottingham NG1 6HH *Tel.* 01159 015558

■ **The Nottingham Gordon Memorial Trust for Boys and Girls**

CC NO 212536   **ESTABLISHED** 1976

WHERE FUNDING CAN BE GIVEN Nottingham and its immediate surrounding area.

WHO CAN BENEFIT Children and young people up to the age of 25.

WHAT IS FUNDED Relief in need, education and educational trips.

TYPE OF GRANT One off preferred.

RANGE OF GRANTS Up to £2,500.

SAMPLE GRANTS Previously: £2,500 to the Nottinghamshire Probation Service; £1,500 to the Nottingham Outward Bound Association.

FINANCES *Year* 2012 *Income* £45,696 *Grants* £44,100 *Assets* £1,167,046

TRUSTEES Nigel Cullen; John Tordoff; Jean Ramsden; Linda Clifford; Peter Hill; Revd Paul Watts; John Foxon; Anthony King; Bill Hammond; Revd Ian Wiseman.

HOW TO APPLY On a form available from the correspondent. Trustees meet twice yearly.

WHO TO APPLY TO Anna Chandler, Clerk to the Trustees, Freeth Cartwright LLP, Cumberland Court, 80 Mount Street, Nottingham NG1 6HH *Tel.* 01159 015562 *email* anna.chandler@ freethcartwright.co.uk

---

■ **Nottinghamshire Community Foundation**

CC NO 1069538   **ESTABLISHED** 1998

WHERE FUNDING CAN BE GIVEN Nottinghamshire.

WHO CAN BENEFIT Individuals, community groups and charities.

WHAT IS FUNDED The charity aims to promote good health and social conditions amongst all communities within the County of Nottinghamshire.

WHAT IS NOT FUNDED Refer to the foundation's website for exclusions specific to each fund.

RANGE OF GRANTS Up to £140,000.

SAMPLE GRANTS Grassroots Nottinghamshire (£134,000); Fair Share Trust (£77,000); One Nottingham (£59,000); Active at 60 (£33,000); Winter Surviving Appeal (£8,000); and Keepmoat (£2,500).

FINANCES *Year* 2011–12 *Income* £768,323 *Grants* £561,037 *Assets* £2,332,699

TRUSTEES Christopher Hughes; Frances Walker; Philip Marsh; Paul McDuell; Alistair MacDiarmid; Simon Tipping; Hugh Strickland; Paul Bacon; Amanda Farr; Diana Meale.

OTHER INFORMATION The following funds were available at the time of writing (August 2013): RTC Fund; Comic Relief (Sports Relief Standard Local Communities Programme); The Jones Trust Community Fund; Freemasons Fund; Dragon's Den – Nottingham City Homes; Joan Oliver Fund; The Bramley Fund; Dave Hartley Fund; Kynan Eldridge Fund; and Jessie Spencer Fund.

HOW TO APPLY Refer to the foundation's website for full details of how to apply to the various programmes currently being administered. Trustees meet four times a year to consider applications; this includes the Annual General Meeting.

WHO TO APPLY TO Nina Dauban, Chief Executive, Pine House B, Southwell Road West, Rainworth, Mansfield, Nottinghamshire NG21 0HJ *Tel.* 01623 620202 *email* enquiries@nottscf. org.uk *Website* www.nottscf.org.uk

■ The Nottinghamshire Historic Churches Trust

CC NO 518335   **ESTABLISHED** 1985
WHERE FUNDING CAN BE GIVEN Nottinghamshire.
WHO CAN BENEFIT Churches and chapels.
WHAT IS FUNDED The trust gives grants for the preservation and repair of historic churches and chapels in Nottinghamshire and for the monuments, fittings and furniture and so on, of such churches.
WHAT IS NOT FUNDED Works of routine maintenance (such as repainting a door, non-specialist cleaning, etc.), new buildings, extensions, meeting rooms Coffee areas, sinks, new furniture, routine decoration (unless needing to use some specialist materials), routine electrical work (new switches, lights, cables for new installations), repair of modern furniture, fixtures, fittings, overhead projector screens, sound systems, new bells and bellframes, any work that has already started or been completed before application made.
RANGE OF GRANTS Up to £5,000.
SAMPLE GRANTS All Saints – Collingham and St Michael and All Angels – Bramcote (£5,000 each); St Mary's – Greasley (£3,500); St Peter's – Clayworth (£2,500); St Martin of Tours – Bilborough (£2,000); St Mary's – Radcliffe-on-Trent (£700) and St Andrew's – Eakring (£250).
FINANCES *Year* 2011–12 *Income* £70,092 *Grants* £44,300 *Assets* £265,474
TRUSTEES Richard Craven-Smith-Milnes; Malcolm Stacey; Dr Christopher Brooke; Dr Jenny Alexander; David Atkins; Prof. John Beckett; Graham Beaumont; Graeme Renton; Peter Hoare; Anthony Marriott; Revd Canon Keith Turner; Prof. Michael Jones.
HOW TO APPLY Grant application forms along with guidance notes are available to download from the trust's website.
Alternatively, these can be obtained by ringing or writing to the correspondent.
WHO TO APPLY TO Linda Francis, Grants Administrator, 15 Tattershall Drive, Beeston, Nottingham NG9 2GP *Tel.* 07757 800919 *email* linda.francis15@ntlworld.com *Website* www.nottshistoricchurchtrust.org.uk

■ The Nottinghamshire Miners' Welfare Trust Fund

CC NO 1001272   **ESTABLISHED** 1990
WHERE FUNDING CAN BE GIVEN Nottinghamshire.
WHO CAN BENEFIT Miners or ex-miners who are retired, redundant or unemployed.
WHAT IS FUNDED The trust supports miners or ex-miners in need living in Nottinghamshire, who are retired or redundant and still unemployed, and their dependants.
RANGE OF GRANTS £150–£9,000
SAMPLE GRANTS Previous beneficiaries: CISWO – social worker funding (£8,800); CISWO – National Schemes of Benefit 2006 (£8,000); Edwinstowe Physiotherapy Clinic (£3,0000;

North East Midlands Brass Band Association (£500); and Newstead Youth and Community Centre (£400).
FINANCES *Year* 2012 *Income* £116,848 *Grants* £85,155 *Assets* £3,332,837
TRUSTEES J. Longden; Michael Ball; Jeffrey Wood; Michael Stevens.
OTHER INFORMATION In 2012 grants to individuals totalled £76,000.
HOW TO APPLY In writing to the correspondent at any time.
WHO TO APPLY TO D. A. Brookes, Secretary, Coal Industry Social Welfare Organisation, Welfare Offices, Berry Hill Lane, Mansfield NG18 4JR *Tel.* 01623 625767 *Fax* 01623 626789

■ Novi Most International

CC NO 1043501   **ESTABLISHED** 1995
WHERE FUNDING CAN BE GIVEN Bosnia-Herzegovina.
WHO CAN BENEFIT Bosnians disadvantaged and displaced by war, especially children and young people.
WHAT IS FUNDED Christian youth-based ministry to meet physical, spiritual, emotional and social needs, with particular emphasis on long-term support of children and young people traumatised by war. Reconciliation and community development initiatives are also supported.
WHAT IS NOT FUNDED Grants seldom given to projects not connected with evangelical churches or where the trust's own staff or partners are not involved.
TYPE OF GRANT One-off and recurring.
FINANCES *Year* 2011–12 *Income* £315,243 *Grants* £89,483 *Assets* £115,834
TRUSTEES Simon Evans; Revd David Stillman; Peter Flory; Christine Harris; Andrew Silley.
PUBLICATIONS New Bridge and Bosnia Prayer Briefing.
HOW TO APPLY Funds fully committed for the foreseeable future. Unsolicited applications are not encouraged or acknowledged. Projects that fall outside of the trust's stated objectives will not be considered.
WHO TO APPLY TO Kathleen Flory, Company Secretary, Bushell House, 118–120 Broad Street, Chesham, Buckinghamshire HP5 3ED *Tel.* 01694 793242 *email* chesham@novimost. org *Website* www.novimost.org

■ The Nuffield Foundation

CC NO 206601   **ESTABLISHED** 1943
WHERE FUNDING CAN BE GIVEN UK and Commonwealth.
WHO CAN BENEFIT Charitable and voluntary organisations, and universities benefiting children, young adults and older people; research workers; students; legal professionals; those in care, fostered and adopted; parents and children; one-parent families; at risk groups; carers; disabled people; those disadvantaged by poverty; refugees; travellers; and people suffering from arthritis and rheumatism. Grants are not made to individuals except under the bursary and studentship schemes.
WHAT IS FUNDED Research, experiment or practical development under the following programmes: Law and Society; Children and Families; Education and Open Door.
WHAT IS NOT FUNDED The foundation normally makes grants only to UK organisations, and support work that will be mainly based in the UK, although the trustees welcome proposals for

collaborative projects involving partners in European or Commonwealth countries. There are different exclusions for different programmes so consult the full guidelines for each area before applying. There are a number of things the foundation does not fund under any of its funding programmes, these include: general appeals; buildings or capital costs; applications solely for equipment – grants for equipment are allowed when they are part of a project that is otherwise acceptable; support or attend conferences or seminars; projects that could be considered by a government department, a Research Council or a more appropriate charity; the establishment of Chairs, or other permanent academic posts; grants for the production of films or videos, or for exhibitions; funding for school fees, a university course, or a gap year project; or requests for funding for financial help from or on behalf of individuals in distress.

TYPE OF GRANT One-off grants for projects.

RANGE OF GRANTS £5,000–£250,000.

SAMPLE GRANTS University of Cambridge (£339,000); Institute for Fiscal Studies (£296,000); London School of Economics (£219,000); CHIVA Africa (£150,000); King's College London (£117,000); University of Oxford (£101,000); Institute for Public Policy Research (£68,000); University of Stirling (£39,000); ASA Advice Now (£25,000) and Lexicon Limited (£20,000).

FINANCES *Year* 2012 *Income* £4,933,000 *Grants* £5,000,000 *Assets* £237,841,000

TRUSTEES Prof. Genevra Richardson; Lord Krebs; Prof. Sir David Watson; Prof. David Rhind; Dr Colette Bowe; Prof. James Banks; Prof. Terrie Moffitt.

OTHER INFORMATION Many of the funding programmes have individual funding criteria and guidelines which are not listed here. Consult the trust's excellent website before applying.

HOW TO APPLY The application process is the same for all of the research and innovation grant programmes, that is: Law in Society; Children and Families; Education and Open Door. The foundation publishes the extensive 'Grants for Research and Innovation – Guide for Applications' available to download from the website, which should be read by any potential applicant.

The first stage is to submit an outline application which will be considered and then the proposal may be shortlisted for consideration by trustees. In this case applicants will be asked to submit a full application. Trustees meet three times a year to consider applications, in March, July and November. Deadlines for these meetings are four months before for outline applications then two months before for full applications; exact deadlines are available on the website.

'We welcome cross-disciplinary collaborations or applications that straddle our own areas of interest. If your application meets the criteria of more than one programme, then submit the outline to the most suitable category and note if you think there is an overlap. You do not need to submit it to more than one programme.'

The contacts for the four funding programmes are: **Children and Families** and **Law in Society**: Alison Rees – arees@nuffieldfoundation.org; **Education**: Kim Woodruff – kwoodruff@nuffieldfoundation.org; **Open Door**: Rocio Lale-Montes – rlale-montes@nuffieldfoundation.org.

Applicants for the Nuffield Research Placements should contact their local contact, a list of which can be found on the website.

WHO TO APPLY TO Clerk to the Trustees, 28 Bedford Square, London WC1B 3JS *Tel.* 020 7631 0566 *Fax* 020 7232 4877 *email* info@nuffieldfoundation.org *Website* www.nuffieldfoundation.org

....

■ Nutrisport Trust

CC NO 1147530   **ESTABLISHED** 2012

WHERE FUNDING CAN BE GIVEN UK.

WHO CAN BENEFIT Organisations and institutions.

WHAT IS FUNDED Education and training.

TRUSTEES Kenneth Adams; Conor Davis.

HOW TO APPLY Following contact with the trust in October 2012, the trustees stated that grants are only made directly to individuals, presumably those sought out by the trust.

WHO TO APPLY TO Kenneth Adams, Trustee, Midford Castle, Midford, Bath, Somerset BA2 7BU

O

■ The Father O'Mahoney Memorial Trust

CC NO 1039288   **ESTABLISHED** 1993

WHERE FUNDING CAN BE GIVEN Overseas

WHO CAN BENEFIT Organisations and individuals benefiting 'impotent people and those disadvantaged by poverty'.

WHAT IS FUNDED The relief of 'impotent and poor' people in all parts of the world except the UK.

WHAT IS NOT FUNDED UK organisations.

RANGE OF GRANTS Depends on finances; maximum usually £5,000.

SAMPLE GRANTS Friends of the Holy Land and African Mission (£3,500 each); SPICMA (£3,000); CAFOD (£2,500); ACAT, Street Child Africa, Medical Foundation and Uganda Development (£2,000 each); Romania Challenge (£1,500) and St John of Jerusalem Eye Hospital (£500).

FINANCES *Year* 2011–12 *Income* £44,373 *Grants* £51,746 *Assets* £76,484

TRUSTEES Christopher Carney-Smith; Creina Hearn; Don Maclean; Michael Moran; Revd Gerard Murray; Anthony Sanford; Maureen Jennings; Brenda Carney; Hugh Smith.

HOW TO APPLY In writing to the correspondent. The trustees meet every two months to consider applications.

WHO TO APPLY TO Revd Gerry Murray, Our Lady of the Wayside Church, 566 Stratford Road, Shirley, Solihull, West Midlands B90 4AY *Tel.* 01217 441967 *email* trust@olwayside.fsnet.co.uk

■ The Sir Peter O'Sullevan Charitable Trust

CC NO 1078889   **ESTABLISHED** 2000

WHERE FUNDING CAN BE GIVEN Worldwide.

WHO CAN BENEFIT Charitable organisations.

WHAT IS FUNDED Animal welfare.

TYPE OF GRANT Recurrent.

SAMPLE GRANTS Blue Cross, Brooke Hospital for Animals, Compassion in World Farming, World Horse (formerly International League for the Protection of Horses), the Racing Welfare Charities and the Thoroughbred Rehabilitation Centre.

FINANCES *Year* 2011–12 *Income* £432,855 *Grants* £300,000 *Assets* £106,330

TRUSTEES Christopher Spence; Sir Peter O'Sullevan; Nigel Payne; Geoffrey Hughes; Michael Dillon; John McManus; Michael Keer-Dineen.

HOW TO APPLY In writing to the correspondent although applications are very unlikely to be successful as the trust supports the same six charities every year.

WHO TO APPLY TO Nigel Payne, Trustee, The Old School, Bolventor, Launceston, Cornwall PL15 7TS *Tel.* 07768 025265 *email* nigel@earthsummit.demon.co.uk *Website* www.thevoiceofracing.com

■ The Oak Trust

CC NO 231456   **ESTABLISHED** 1963

WHERE FUNDING CAN BE GIVEN UK with a preference for East Anglia.

WHO CAN BENEFIT Registered charities. Preference to charities that the trust has special interest in, knowledge of or association with, and with a turnover of below £1 million.

WHAT IS FUNDED General charitable purposes. Consideration is specifically given for disadvantage, personal development through adventure, the environment, medicine and life changing benefits.

WHAT IS NOT FUNDED No support to individuals.

TYPE OF GRANT One-off and recurrent.

RANGE OF GRANTS £250–£4,000.

SAMPLE GRANTS The Cirdan Sailing Trust (£3,000); Christian Aid (£2,000); Save the Children Fund; Voice and School Home Support (£1,000 each); Dhaka Ahsania Mission and Tower Hamlets Mission (£750 each) and Essex Youthbuild; Practical Action; MS Society; Tools for Self-Reliance and FareShare (£500 each).

FINANCES *Year* 2011–12 *Income* £27,719 *Grants* £22,750 *Assets* £666,595

TRUSTEES Revd A. C. C. Courtauld; J. Courtauld; Dr Elizabeth Courtauld; Miss C. M. Hart.

HOW TO APPLY Applications must be submitted via the online form on the trust's website. Details of the next submission date are included on the application form. Applicants will receive an acknowledgement of their application and notification of the outcome within ten days of the review meeting by email.

WHO TO APPLY TO Bruce Ballard, Clerk to the Trustees, Birkett Long, Number One, Legg Street, Chelmsford, Essex CM1 1JS *Tel.* 01206 217300 *email* julienc@summershall.com *Website* www.oaktrust.org.uk

■ The Oakdale Trust

CC NO 218827   **ESTABLISHED** 1950

WHERE FUNDING CAN BE GIVEN UK, especially Wales, and overseas.

WHO CAN BENEFIT Organisations doing social and medical work benefiting at risk groups, carers, disabled people, those disadvantaged by poverty, ex-offenders and those at risk of offending, homeless people, refugees, and victims of crime, famine and war.

WHAT IS FUNDED The trust gives preference to Welsh charities engaged in social work, medical support groups and medical research. Some support is given to UK charities working overseas and to conservation projects at home and abroad. Some arts and community arts activities, infrastructure support and development, community facilities and services, mediation, peace and disarmament will also be considered. The trust also supports Quaker activities.

WHAT IS NOT FUNDED No grants to individuals, holiday schemes, sport activities or expeditions.

TYPE OF GRANT Single outright grants. Buildings, capital, core costs, feasibility studies, one-off, project, research, recurring costs, salaries and start-up costs will be considered. Funding may be given for up to one year.

RANGE OF GRANTS Average grant £900.

SAMPLE GRANTS The Brandon Centre (£7,000); F.P.W.P Hibiscus (£5,000); Quaker Service Memorial Trust (£4,000); Cambridge Female Education Trust (£2,000); Play Montgomeryshire, Action for Prisoners Families and International Refugee Trust (£1,000 each);

The Brecon Cathedral Choir Appeal, Roy Castle Lung Cancer Foundation and the Benefits Advice Shop (£750 each); Rethink, Disabled Workers Co-operative and Valleys Healing and Life (£500 each) and Hearing Dogs for Deaf People, The National Lobster Hatchery and Freeplay Network (£250 each).

FINANCES *Year* 2011–12 *Income* £303,550 *Grants* £164,050 *Assets* £8,778,681

TRUSTEES Flavia Cadbury; Rupert Cadbury; Bruce Cadbury; Olivia Tatton-Brown; Dr Rebecca Cadbury.

HOW TO APPLY An online application form is available on the trust's website. The trust gives the following guidelines:

'Applications can be submitted online or sent in by post if preferred. An official application form is available for download although applicants are free to submit requests in any format so long as applications are clear and concise, covering – aims and achievements, plans and needs supported by a budget for the project in question. Applicants applying for a grant in excess of £1,000 are asked to submit a recent set of audited accounts **only** if not already available on the Charity Commission web site. Give a web address where supporting information is available on-line. In order to minimise the waste of time and material, large organisations in particular are asked to submit one application only per trustees' meeting and to avoid sending in duplicate applications. The trustees meet twice a year in April and October to consider applications and to award grants. No grants are awarded between meetings. The deadline for applications for the April meeting is the 1 March and for the October meeting the 1 September. The trust is administered by the trustees at no cost and in view of the numerous requests received unsuccessful applicants are not normally notified and similarly applications are not acknowledged even when accompanied by a stamped addressed envelope.'

WHO TO APPLY TO Rupert Cadbury, Administrator and Trustee, Tansor House, Tansor, Oundle, Peterborough PE8 5HS *Tel.* 01832 226386 *email* oakdale@tanh.co.uk *Website* www.oakdaletrust.org.uk

---

■ The Oakley Charitable Trust

CC NO 233041   **ESTABLISHED** 1963
WHERE FUNDING CAN BE GIVEN UK, but predominantly the Midlands and Channel Isles.
WHO CAN BENEFIT Registered charities.
WHAT IS FUNDED Welfare, health, education, arts, conservation and animal welfare.
WHAT IS NOT FUNDED No grants to individuals can be considered. Grants are only made to registered charities.
TYPE OF GRANT One-off, core costs, project, research, recurring costs and buildings. Funding is available for one year or less.
RANGE OF GRANTS £50–£2,000.
SAMPLE GRANTS Cats Protection League and the Dyspraxia Foundation (£2,000 each); Acorns Children's Hospice and Jersey Animal Shelter (£1,500 each); Birmingham Hippodrome Stage Appeal and Durrell Wildlife Conservation Trust (£1,000 each); and Acquired Aphasia Trust, Brain Tumour UK, Listening Books, North Wales Coast Light Railway, Raynaud's and Scleroderma Association and Warwickshire and Northamptonshire Air Ambulance (£500 each).
FINANCES *Year* 2011–12 *Income* £103,344 *Grants* £49,350 *Assets* £1,910,972

TRUSTEES Christine M. Airey; Geoffrey M. W. Oakley; Simon M. Sharp.
HOW TO APPLY In writing to the correspondent. Trustees usually meet in March, July and November.

'We receive a large number of applications from many charities operating in the same or very similar areas, e.g. specific cancer research/youth work etc. Our policy is to only support one such charity in a particular field. Due to a very high number of unsolicited applications we only respond to successful applicants.'

WHO TO APPLY TO Geoffrey M. W. Oakley, Trustee, 10 St Mary's Road, Harborne, Birmingham B17 0HA *Tel.* 01214 277150

■ The Oakmoor Charitable Trust

CC NO 258516   **ESTABLISHED** 1969
WHERE FUNDING CAN BE GIVEN UK.
WHO CAN BENEFIT Registered charities.
WHAT IS FUNDED General charitable purposes.
WHAT IS NOT FUNDED No grants to individuals.
RANGE OF GRANTS Up to £10,000.
SAMPLE GRANTS Marine Society and Sea Cadets (£15,000); Byways (£5,000); National Gallery Trust (£2,500); Newnham College Cambridge; Smile Support and Care and The Soldiers Charity (£1,000 each); Winchester Festival; RNLI; Hertford House Trust and Friends of St Cross Winchester (£500 each); Grange Park Opera (£300); Irish Guards Appeal (£200).
FINANCES *Year* 2011–12 *Income* £31,205 *Grants* £40,900 *Assets* £1,535,919
TRUSTEES Rathbone Trust Company Ltd; Peter M. H. Andreae; Rosemary J. Andreae.
HOW TO APPLY The trust states that it does not respond to unsolicited applications.
WHO TO APPLY TO The Administrator, Rathbone Trust Company Limited, 4th Floor, 1 Curzon Street, London W1J 5FB *Tel.* 020 7399 0807

■ The Odin Charitable Trust

CC NO 1027521   **ESTABLISHED** 1993
WHERE FUNDING CAN BE GIVEN UK.
WHO CAN BENEFIT Registered charities.
WHAT IS FUNDED General charitable purposes with preference for: the arts; care for people who are disabled and disadvantaged people; hospices, homeless people, prisoners' families, refugees, gypsies and 'tribal groups' research into false memories and dyslexia.
WHAT IS NOT FUNDED Applications from individuals are not considered.
RANGE OF GRANTS £1,000–£5,000.
SAMPLE GRANTS BFMS (£47,000); Helen Arkell Dyslexia Centre and Julian House (£5,000 each); Bath Recital Arts Centre (£3,500); St Peter's Hospice; Music Alive and Asylum Aid (£3,000); Roma Support Group; Castle Gate Family Trust and Music in Prisons (£2,500 each); UCanDoIt; City Gate Community Project and Young and Free (£2,000 each).
FINANCES *Year* 2011–12 *Income* £402,388 *Grants* £413,000 *Assets* £5,033,536
TRUSTEES S. G. P. Scotford; A. H. Palmer; Donna Kelly; Pia C. Cherry.
HOW TO APPLY All appeals should be by letter containing the following:
aims and objectives of the charity nature of appeal total target if for a specific project contributions received against target registered Charity Number any other relevant factors. Letters should be accompanied by a set of the charitable organisation's latest report and full

accounts and should be addressed to the correspondent. Trustees meet twice a year to approve grants.

WHO TO APPLY TO S. G. P. Scotford, Trustee, PO Box 1898, Bradford-on-Avon, Wiltshire BA15 1YS *email* kelly.donna@virgin.net

---

■ The Ofenheim Charitable Trust

CC NO 286525   **ESTABLISHED** 1983
WHERE FUNDING CAN BE GIVEN Worldwide, in practice UK with some preference for East Sussex.
WHO CAN BENEFIT Registered charities.
WHAT IS FUNDED General charitable purposes, in particular health, welfare, arts and the environment.
WHAT IS NOT FUNDED No grants to individuals.
TYPE OF GRANT Mainly recurring grants, but one-off donations are also made.
RANGE OF GRANTS Up to £20,000; mainly £5,000 or less.
SAMPLE GRANTS Trinity Hospice and Barnardo's (£12,000 each); Stroke Association and Friends of the Elderly (£10,000 each); National Youth Orchestra of Great Britain (£9,000); Toynbee Hall (£5,500); Wallace Collection (£4,000); Centrepoint (£3,300); Greenwich, Deptford and Rotherhithe Sea Cadet Unit (£3,000); and the Koestler Trust (£2,000).
FINANCES *Year* 2011–12 *Income* £318,101 *Grants* £352,180 *Assets* £11,855,471
TRUSTEES Roger Jackson Clark; Rory McLeod; Alexander Clark; Fiona Byrd.
HOW TO APPLY In writing to the correspondent. 'The trustees' policy has been to provide regular support for a number of charities and to respond to one-off appeals to bodies where they have some knowledge [. . .] They will consider all applications for grants and make awards as they see fit.'
WHO TO APPLY TO The Trustees, Baker Tilly, The Pinnacle, 170 Midsummer Boulevard, Milton Keynes MK9 1BP *Tel.* 01908 687800 *email* geoff.wright@bakertilly.co.uk

---

■ Ogilvie Charities Deed No.2 (including the Charity of Mary Catherine Ford Smith)

CC NO 211778   **ESTABLISHED** 1890
WHERE FUNDING CAN BE GIVEN England and Wales, mainly London, Essex and Suffolk.
WHO CAN BENEFIT England and Wales, mainly London, Essex and Suffolk.
WHAT IS FUNDED Social welfare.
WHAT IS NOT FUNDED No payment of running costs.
TYPE OF GRANT One-off usually. Grants for individuals must be made through medical and other social workers. Funding may be given for up to one year.
RANGE OF GRANTS Less than £1,000.
SAMPLE GRANTS Children's Country Holidays (£1,000); and Bedford Institute Association (£100).
FINANCES *Year* 2011 *Income* £59,023 *Grants* £40,000 *Assets* £1,587,668
TRUSTEES Patrick Grieve; Belinda Grant; Felicity Lowe; Margaret Smith; Allan Howell; Jean Goyder; Jolyon Sunderland Hall; Simon Gibbs; Edward Wright.
OTHER INFORMATION Ogilvie Charities Deed No. 2 is primarily to benefit the Ogilvie Charities Deed No. 1. Any remaining income is applied to making grants to any charity for the benefit of people in Essex, Suffolk or London which are for

specific fundraising projects. Charity of Mary Catherine Ford – Grants are given from this fund to other charities to help them with a specific project. The grant total was shared between individuals and organisations.
HOW TO APPLY In writing to the correspondent. Preliminary telephone enquiries are acceptable. Applicant organisations must send details of their project and copies of annual accounts. Grants are awarded for specific fundraising projects, not running costs and are allocated in October or November. Grants for individuals must be made through medical and other social workers.
WHO TO APPLY TO Gillian Galvan, General Manager, The Gate House, 9 Burkitt Road, Woodbridge, Suffolk IP12 4JJ *Tel.* 01394 388746 *email* ogilviecharities@btconnect.com *Website* www.theogilvietrust.org.uk

---

■ The Ogle Christian Trust

CC NO 1061458   **ESTABLISHED** 1938
WHERE FUNDING CAN BE GIVEN Worldwide.
WHO CAN BENEFIT Registered charities benefiting Bible students, pastors, Christians, evangelists and victims of famine.
WHAT IS FUNDED The trust's main concern is the promotion of Biblical Christianity. Currently it includes: new initiatives in evangelism; support for the publishing and distribution of scriptures and Christian literature; training of Bible students and pastors; and Christian social enterprise and famine relief.
WHAT IS NOT FUNDED Applications from individuals are discouraged; those granted require accreditation by a sponsoring organisation. Grants are rarely made for building projects. Funding will not be offered in response to general appeals from large national organisations.
TYPE OF GRANT Normally short-term commitments. Salaries will not be funded. About half the grants go to regularly supported organisations.
RANGE OF GRANTS Average grant £1,000–£5,000.
SAMPLE GRANTS Operation Mobilisation (£22,000); CCSM (£8,000); OMF International UK (£6,000); RedCliffe College (£4,000); ELAM Ministries and South Asian Concern (£3,000 each); Dehra Dun and France Mission Trust (£2,000 each); INNOVISTA (£1,500) and Release International (£1,000).
FINANCES *Year* 2011 *Income* £128,965 *Grants* £114,650 *Assets* £2,321,932
TRUSTEES F. J. Putley; R. J. Goodenough; S. Proctor; L. M. Quanrud; Dr D. Harley.
OTHER INFORMATION The grants total includes £2,000 given to individuals.
HOW TO APPLY In writing to the correspondent, accompanied by documentary support and an sae. Trustees meet in May and November, but applications can be made at any time.
WHO TO APPLY TO F. J. Putley, Trustee, 43 Woolstone Road, Forest Hill, London SE23 2TR *Tel.* 020 8699 1036

■ Oglesby Charitable Trust

CC NO 1026669   **ESTABLISHED** 1992
WHERE FUNDING CAN BE GIVEN The North West of England.
WHO CAN BENEFIT Charitable organisations.
WHAT IS FUNDED Educational grants and building projects; environmental improvement projects; improving the life and welfare of the underprivileged, where possible, by the

encouragement of self-help; and medical aid and research

WHAT IS NOT FUNDED The trust will not support: non registered charities; those whose activities are for the purpose of collecting funds for redistribution to other charities; animal charities; charities whose principal operation area is outside the UK; church and all building fabric appeals; conferences; continuing running costs of an organisation; costs of employing fundraisers; expeditions; general sports, unless strongly associated with a disadvantaged group; holidays; individuals; loans or business finance; religion; routine staff training; sectarian religions; sponsorship and marketing appeals.

RANGE OF GRANTS Usually between £5,000–£20,000. Small grants of less than £1,000 are available.

SAMPLE GRANTS Previous beneficiaries include: Action for Kids, Alcohol Drug Abstinence Service, Centre for Alternative Technology, Cheadle Hulme School, Cheetham's School, Fairbridge – Family Contact Line, Halle Youth Orchestra, Manchester City Art Gallery, Manchester University Arts and Drama, Motor Neurone Disease, National Asthma Campaign, National Library For The Blind, Stroke Research and Whitworth Art Gallery.

FINANCES *Year* 2011–12 *Income* £1,023,959 *Grants* £769,911 *Assets* £1,286,566

TRUSTEES Jean Oglesby; Michael Oglesby; Robert Kitson; Kate Vokes; Jane Oglesby; Chris Oglesby; Peter Renshaw.

OTHER INFORMATION The trust also has a small grants programme, the Acorn Fund, which is administered by Forever Manchester: www.forevermanchester.com, 0161 214 0940.

HOW TO APPLY The trust's website currently states: '**Due to an unprecedented number of applications for funding over recent months, caused by the economic downturn, the trustees have decided to close the fund to new applications for the next few months until the current backlog has been attended to.**' To apply when the trust is open to applications, complete the Stage 1 Application Form. The trustees undertake to respond to this in six weeks. If this response is positive, then applicants will be required to complete a more detailed form under Stage 2. By Stage 2, wherever possible, the trustees will require a proper Financial Plan prepared by the applicant. This should contain clear and measurable goals, which will be reviewed at regular intervals by the parties. In cases where the applicant does not possess either the skills or the resources to prepare such a Plan, the Trust may be prepared to assist. Finally, the trustees will want to interview the applicant(s) at their place of operation or project site, both prior to the granting of funds and during the lifetime of the project, to monitor its progress. In addition the trustees will expect regular communication from the applicant, either verbal or by letter, to keep them informed of how the project is moving forward.

WHO TO APPLY TO PO Box 336, Altrincham, Cheshire WA14 3XD *email* oglesbycharitabletrust@ bruntwood.co.uk *Website* www. oglesbycharitabletrust.co.uk

■ The Oikonomia Trust

CC NO 273481   **ESTABLISHED** 1977
WHERE FUNDING CAN BE GIVEN UK and overseas.
WHO CAN BENEFIT Organisations benefiting evangelists.

WHAT IS FUNDED Evangelical work, famine and other relief through Christian agencies, particularly when accompanied with the offer of the Gospel. The trust states it is not looking for new outlets as those it has knowledge of are sufficient to absorb its available funds.

WHAT IS NOT FUNDED No grants made in response to general appeals from large national organisations.

RANGE OF GRANTS £500–£5,000.

SAMPLE GRANTS Barnabas Trust (£5,500); Slavic Gospel Association (£5,000); Bethel Church (£4,000); Asia Link, Association of Evangelists and Caring for Life (£3,000 each); Japan Mission (£2,500); Starbeck Mission (£2,000); People International (£1,000); and Carey Outreach Ministries (£500).

FINANCES *Year* 2011–12 *Income* £0 *Grants* £60,000

TRUSTEES Douglas Metcalfe; Richard Metcalfe; Stephen Metcalfe; Colin Mountain; Revd Robert Owens.

HOW TO APPLY In writing to the correspondent, although the trust has stated that most grants are made to the same organisations each year and as such new applications are unlikely to be successful. If an applicant desires an answer, an sae should be enclosed. Applications should arrive in January.

WHO TO APPLY TO Colin Mountain, Trustee, 98 White Lee Road, Batley, West Yorkshire WF17 8AF *Tel.* 01924 502616 *email* colin.mountain@ gmail.com

■ Oizer Charitable Trust

CC NO 1014399   **ESTABLISHED** 1992
WHERE FUNDING CAN BE GIVEN UK with a preference for Greater Manchester.
WHO CAN BENEFIT Registered charities, schools, individuals.
WHAT IS FUNDED Education and welfare with preference to Orthodox Jewish causes.
SAMPLE GRANTS B'nos Yisroel (£2,250) and Chasdei Yoel (£1,000).
FINANCES *Year* 2011–12 *Income* £373,286 *Grants* £236,082 *Assets* £1,767,458
TRUSTEES Joshua Halpern; Cindy Halpern.
HOW TO APPLY In writing to the correspondent. The trustees' report for 2011/12 states that 'the trustees have identified a number of Orthodox Jewish charities which profess and teach the principles of traditional Judaism or which carry out activities which advance religion in accordance with the Orthodox Jewish faith. Grants are given on application to the trustees by these or similar charities.'
WHO TO APPLY TO Joshua Halpern, Trustee, Lopian Gross Barnett and Co, 6th Floor, Cardinal House, 20 St Mary's Parsonage, Manchester M3 2LG *Tel.* 01618 328721

■ The Old Broad Street Charity Trust

CC NO 231382   **ESTABLISHED** 1964
WHERE FUNDING CAN BE GIVEN UK and overseas.
WHO CAN BENEFIT Registered charities benefiting children, young adults, students, people working in a bank or financial institution, actors and entertainment professionals, musicians, textile workers and designers, and writers and poets.
WHAT IS FUNDED General charitable purposes with an emphasis on arts and education. Funding scholarships for people serving in a bank or

financial institution in the UK to spend time in any seat of learning (principally INSEAD) to attain the highest level of executive management.

WHAT IS NOT FUNDED The trustees only support organisations of which they personally have some knowledge.

TYPE OF GRANT One-off and project grants for one year or less.

RANGE OF GRANTS £5,000 –£10,000.

SAMPLE GRANTS Foundation Henri Cartier-Bresson (£43,000); Hospital of St Cross and Almshouse of Noble Property (£10,000); Whitechapel Gallery (£1,000) and Serpentine Gallery (£500).

FINANCES *Year* 2011–12 *Income* £29,413 *Grants* £54,352 *Assets* £1,508,571

TRUSTEES Simon Jennings; Eric Frank; Christopher J. Sheridan; Clare Gough.

OTHER INFORMATION In addition to the grant total, £48,000 was given in scholarships.

HOW TO APPLY In writing to the correspondent. The annual report states that 'general appeal for funding are sent in to the registered office by post or email. They are collated and distributed to the trustees for consideration on an annual basis.'

WHO TO APPLY TO Simon Jennings, Secretary to the Trustees, Rawlinson and Hunter, Eighth Floor, 6 New Street Square, London EC4A 3AQ *Tel.* 020 7842 2000 *email* obsct@rawlinson-hunter.com

....
■ Old Possum's Practical Trust

CC NO 328558   **ESTABLISHED** 1990

WHERE FUNDING CAN BE GIVEN UK.

WHO CAN BENEFIT Registered charities and individuals of all ages.

WHAT IS FUNDED The increase of knowledge and appreciation of any matters of historic, artistic, architectural, aesthetic, literary, musical, theatrical or scientific interest; human and animal welfare.

WHAT IS NOT FUNDED The trust does not support the following: activities or projects already completed; capital building projects; personal training and education e.g. tuition or living costs for college or university; projects outside the UK; medical care or resources; feasibility studies; national charities having substantial amounts of potential funding likely from other sources.

RANGE OF GRANTS Mainly £500–£5,000.

SAMPLE GRANTS High Tide (£80,000); First Story (£45,000); Story Vault (£25,000); Chickenshed Theatre Company (£10,000); Arete (£5,000); English Stage Co (£3,800); Gersington Opera (£1,000); Big Heart Bike Ride and Southampton Amateur Boxing Club (£500 each) and Fitzroy (£300).

FINANCES *Year* 2011–12 *Income* £213,714 *Grants* £205,160 *Assets* £6,155,275

TRUSTEES Judith Hooper; Deidre Simpson; Clare Reihill.

OTHER INFORMATION This trust was established by Valerie Eliot in 1990, 25 years after her husband T S Eliot's death.

HOW TO APPLY Applications can only be made online through the trust's website. The trustees meet regularly to consider applications but state in the latest accounts that: 'the emphasis will be on continued support of those institutions and individuals who have received support in the past. Unfortunately we have to disappoint the great majority of applicants who nevertheless continue to send appeal letters The Trustees do not welcome telephone calls or emails from applicants soliciting funds'. To keep administration costs to a minimum the trust does not give reasons for unsuccessful applications or allow applicants to appeal a decision.

WHO TO APPLY TO The Trustees, PO Box 5701, Milton Keynes MK9 2WZ *email* generalenquiry@old-possums-practical-trust.org.uk *Website* www.old-possums-practical-trust.org.uk

....
■ The John Oldacre Foundation

CC NO 284960   **ESTABLISHED** 1981

WHERE FUNDING CAN BE GIVEN UK.

WHO CAN BENEFIT Universities, agricultural colleges and innovative projects benefiting students and research workers.

WHAT IS FUNDED Research and education in agricultural sciences.

WHAT IS NOT FUNDED No grants towards tuition fees.

TYPE OF GRANT One-off, recurrent, feasibility, project, research and funding of up to three years will be considered.

RANGE OF GRANTS Up to £57,000.

SAMPLE GRANTS Royal Agricultural College (2 grants totalling £40,000); Nuffield Farming Trust and University of Exeter (£20,000 each); Reading University and Wolverhampton University (£19,000 each); NIAB (£15,000) and Game and Wildlife Conservation Trust (£12,000).

FINANCES *Year* 2011–12 *Income* £194,657 *Grants* £237,313 *Assets* £7,845,444

TRUSTEES Henry Shouler; Stephen Charnock; Ian Bonnett.

HOW TO APPLY In writing to the correspondent stating how the funds would be used and what would be achieved.

WHO TO APPLY TO Stephen J. Charnock, Trustee, Bohicket, 35 Broadwater Close, Burwood park, Walton on Thames, Surrey KT12 5DD

....
■ The Oldham Foundation

CC NO 269263   **ESTABLISHED** 1974

WHERE FUNDING CAN BE GIVEN UK and overseas.

WHO CAN BENEFIT Organisations benefiting young people, older people, people disadvantaged by poverty in the UK and overseas, Church of England and former employees of Oldham International Limited.

WHAT IS FUNDED Arts, culture and recreation; conservation and environment; and churches; relief of former employees of Oldham International Limited.

WHAT IS NOT FUNDED No grants for UK appeals or individuals.

TYPE OF GRANT Annual grant to former employees. Grants usually one-off.

RANGE OF GRANTS £50–£20,000; typical grant £250–£1,000.

SAMPLE GRANTS Cheltenham Music Festival (£11,000); Cheltenham Literature Festival (£10,400); Classic FM (£4,000); CABE (£3,000 each); St Peter's Church – Winchcombe (£2,000); Cheltenham Bach Choir, Merlin, the Kambia Appeal and International Red Cross (£1,000 each); Churches Conservation Trust (£500); SENSE and Barnardo's (£250 each); Green Island Holiday Trust (£100); and Grandmothers United (£50).

FINANCES *Year* 2010–11 *Income* £59,408 *Grants* £56,381 *Assets* £1,214,348

TRUSTEE John Wetherherd Sharpe.

OTHER INFORMATION 28 grants were made totalling £56,000.

HOW TO APPLY In writing to the correspondent. Applications should include clear details of projects, budgets and/or accounts where appropriate. Telephone calls are not welcomed. The trustees meet annually but applications can be considered between meetings. Inappropriate appeals are not acknowledged.

WHO TO APPLY TO John Wetherherd Sharpe, Trustee, c/o Broad Quay House, Broad Quay, Bristol BS1 4DJ *Tel.* 01179 069313

■ The Olga Charitable Trust

CC NO 277925   **ESTABLISHED** 1979
WHERE FUNDING CAN BE GIVEN UK and overseas.
WHO CAN BENEFIT National organisations benefiting children, young adults, at risk groups, people disadvantaged by poverty, socially isolated people, and carers.
WHAT IS FUNDED Health and welfare, youth organisations, children's welfare, carers' organisations. All must be known to the trustees.
RANGE OF GRANTS £500–£12,000.
SAMPLE GRANTS Holy Trinity Church, St Andrews (£10,000); Sightsavers (£6,000); Imperial College Healthcare Charity (£5,000); Crisis and The Cystic Fibrosis Trust (£2,000 each); Brain Tumour Campaign, British Red Cross, Cancer Research UK, RNLI, Save the Children, The Ruth Winston Centre and ZAWT (£1,000 each); and The Great North Air Ambulance Pride of Cumbria (£500).
FINANCES *Year* 2011–12 *Income* £48,964 *Grants* £58,400 *Assets* £933,905
TRUSTEES HRH. Princess Alexandra; James Robert Bruce Ogilvy.
HOW TO APPLY In writing to the correspondent, although the trust states that its funds are fully committed and applications made cannot be acknowledged.
WHO TO APPLY TO Adam Broke, Accountant, International Press Centre, 76 Shoe Lane, London EC4A 3JB *Tel.* 020 7353 1597

■ Open Gate

CC NO 1081701   **ESTABLISHED** 2000
WHERE FUNDING CAN BE GIVEN UK with a preference towards Derbyshire and the surrounding areas. Africa, Asia, South and Central America.
WHO CAN BENEFIT Charitable organisations.
WHAT IS FUNDED Small-scale environmental, technological and educational projects in Derbyshire and the surrounding conurbations as well as in developing countries.
WHAT IS NOT FUNDED No grants to individuals or overseas based charities.
TYPE OF GRANT Project grants for up to three years. Capital grants, core costs, full project funding. Unrestricted.
RANGE OF GRANTS £400–£10,000.
SAMPLE GRANTS Highfields Happy Hens (£10,000); Whirlow Hall Farm Trust (£5,500); Derbyshire Wildlife Trust, Excellent Development and Self Help Africa (£5,000 each); Y Care International and CAFOD (£3,500 each); International Children's Trust, Children of the Andes and Book Aid International (£3,000 each); Computer Aid International, Africa Educational Trust and Rural Solar Lighting (£2,500 each); Farms for City Children, Diocese of Bath and Wells and Sheffield Wildlife Trust (£2,000 each); the Albrighton Trust and Good News Family Care (£1,500 each); Faraja Support and Dedicated Active Dads (£1,000 each); International Alert

and Groundwork Derby and Derbyshire (£500 each); and Cutthorpe Primary School (£400).
FINANCES *Year* 2011–12 *Income* £57,914 *Grants* £228,515 *Assets* £1,318,273
TRUSTEES Mary Wiltshire; Ned Wiltshire; John Wiltshire; Jane Methuen; Tom Wiltshire; Alice Taylor; Lesley Williamson.
OTHER INFORMATION Grants totalled £229,000 and were awarded to 96 organisations.
HOW TO APPLY The website states that 'there is no specific format for applications. However an application should include details of project costs as well as outcomes.' Applications cannot be made via email, post only. Quarterly meetings are held in the middle of January, April, July and October. Applications need to be received six weeks in advance of the meetings.
WHO TO APPLY TO Mary Wiltshire, Trustee, Brownhouse Farm, Ashleyhay, Wirksworth, Matlock, Derbyshire DE4 4AH *Tel.* 01629 822018 *Website* www.opengatetrust.org.uk

■ The Raymond Oppenheimer Foundation

CC NO 326551   **ESTABLISHED** 1984
WHERE FUNDING CAN BE GIVEN UK and worldwide.
WHO CAN BENEFIT National organisations and localised institutions' appeals.
WHAT IS FUNDED General charitable purposes.
WHAT IS NOT FUNDED No grants to individuals.
TYPE OF GRANT One-off.
FINANCES *Year* 2012–13 *Income* £443
TRUSTEES One Charterhouse Street Limited; Thirty Five Ely Place Limited.
HOW TO APPLY In writing to the correspondent.
WHO TO APPLY TO Richard Dewes, Administrator, 1 Charterhouse Street, London EC1N 6SA *Tel.* 020 7421 9800

■ Ormonde Foundation

CC NO 259057   **ESTABLISHED** 1969
WHERE FUNDING CAN BE GIVEN Preference for Oxfordshire.
WHO CAN BENEFIT Mainly local rather than national charities with emphasis on specific projects, rather than donations to general funds. Organisations benefiting Church of England charities in Oxfordshire, people with autism and people suffering from sight loss and blindness.
WHAT IS FUNDED Grants are limited to those fields where the trustees have a personal knowledge of the project or charity concerned, with particular emphasis on Church of England churches in Oxfordshire and charities assisting blind people and people with autism.
TYPE OF GRANT One-off.
RANGE OF GRANTS Approximately 40 grants are made annually with a maximum grant of £1,000.
SAMPLE GRANTS £1,200 to St Luke's Hospital for the Clergy; £1,000 each to Nuffield Orthopaedic Centre, Oxfordshire Historic Churches Trust, Reeds School and Relate; £750 to Fight for Sight; £700 each to King Edward VII's Hospital for Officers, Listening Books and St Mary's Church – Wooton; £550 to Holy Trinity Church; £500 each to All Hallow's Development Trusts, Priscilla Bacon Hospice – Norwich and Williams Trust.
FINANCES *Year* 2011–12 *Income* £20,660 *Grants* £25,000
TRUSTEES Rupert Ponsonby; Luke Ponsonby.
HOW TO APPLY In writing to the correspondent.

WHO TO APPLY TO Luke Ponsonby, Trustee, Ledwell House, Ledwell, Chipping Norton, Oxfordshire OX7 7AN *Tel.* 01608 683752

....

■ The Ormsby Charitable Trust

CC NO 1000599   **ESTABLISHED** 1990
WHERE FUNDING CAN BE GIVEN UK, London and the South East.
WHO CAN BENEFIT Registered charities.
WHAT IS FUNDED Mainly organisations concerned with people who are sick, older people and young people.
WHAT IS NOT FUNDED No grants to individuals, animals or religious causes.
RANGE OF GRANTS £500–£5,000.
SAMPLE GRANTS Beneficiaries included: Newbury Community Resource Centre (£3,500); Honeypot House (£3,000); In Kind and Crisis (£2,000 each); St Michael's Hospice (North Hampshire) (£1,900); Marie Curie and Action 4 Blind (£1,500 each); REACT, Move Europe and NSPCC (£1,00 each) and Wheelyboat Trust, Teenage Cancer and The Living Paintings Trust (£500 each).
FINANCES *Year* 2011–12 *Income* £43,689 *Grants* £32,500 *Assets* £1,709,139
TRUSTEES Rosemary Ormsby David; Angela Ormsby Chiswell; Katrina Ormsby McCrossan.
HOW TO APPLY In writing to the correspondent. Grants are made to organisations known to the trustees.
WHO TO APPLY TO K. McCrossan, Trustee, The Red House, The Street, Aldermaston, Reading RG7 4LN *Tel.* 01189 710343

....

■ The Orrin Charitable Trust

CC NO 274599   **ESTABLISHED** 1977
WHERE FUNDING CAN BE GIVEN Scotland, the rest of the United Kingdom, occasionally overseas.
WHO CAN BENEFIT Registered charities.
WHAT IS FUNDED General charitable purposes.
WHAT IS NOT FUNDED Grants are not given to individuals.
TYPE OF GRANT One-off.
RANGE OF GRANTS Up to £10,000, however, the average grant range is less than £1,000.
SAMPLE GRANTS The Harrow Development Trust (£7,500); National Galleries of Scotland (£5,000); Atlantic Salmon Conservation Trust, Wheelyboat Trust, and ABF The Soldiers' Charity (£3,000 each); and St Mary's and All Souls, Coldstream (£500).
FINANCES *Year* 2011–12 *Income* £156,408 *Grants* £27,000 *Assets* £610,645
TRUSTEES Alexander Macdonald Buchanan; Elizabeth Macdonald Buchanan; Hugh Macdonald Buchanan.
HOW TO APPLY The trust will not accept any unsolicited appeals.
WHO TO APPLY TO Mary Kitto, Administrator, c/o Hedley Foundation, Victoria House, 1–3 College Hill, London EC4R 2RA *Tel.* 020 7489 8076

....

■ The O'Sullivan Family Charitable Trust

CC NO 1123757   **ESTABLISHED** 2008
WHERE FUNDING CAN BE GIVEN Unrestricted, UK in practice.
WHO CAN BENEFIT Children and young people, care homes, genetic research

WHAT IS FUNDED Organisations supporting the advancement of health or relief for those in need because of ill health, disability, financial hardship or other disadvantage
TYPE OF GRANT Grants to individuals and organisations.
RANGE OF GRANTS Usually up to £30,000, exceptionally more.
SAMPLE GRANTS Galway University Foundation (£32,000); University of Southampton (£30,000); The Rose Road Foundation (£20,000); The Duke of Edinburgh International Award (£15,000); The Cheshire Residential Homes Trust (£10,000); The Honey Pot Children's Charity (£7,000); Canine Partners (£5,000); Bal Ashram (£3,000); On Course Foundation (£2,500); DEBRA (£2,000) and Romsey Good Neighbours (£1,000).
FINANCES *Year* 2011–12 *Income* £168,333 *Grants* £498,284 *Assets* £5,182,667
TRUSTEES D. O'Sullivan; F. O'Sullivan; E. O'Sullivan; S. O'Sullivan and T. O'Sullivan.
HOW TO APPLY In writing to the correspondent.
WHO TO APPLY TO Diana O'Sullivan, Trustee, 36 Edge Street, London W8 7PN

....

■ The Ouseley Trust

CC NO 527519   **ESTABLISHED** 1989
WHERE FUNDING CAN BE GIVEN England, Wales and Ireland.
WHO CAN BENEFIT Cathedrals, choirs, parish churches, and choir schools. Children who are members of choirs of recognised choral foundations. Funding is only given to individuals through organisations.
WHAT IS FUNDED Projects that promote and maintain to a high standard the choral services of the Church of England, the Church in Wales or the Church of Ireland. Support may include: courses of instruction; endowment grants; choir school fees; and the purchase of music.
WHAT IS NOT FUNDED Under normal circumstances, grants will not be awarded for building projects, the making of recordings, the purchase of furniture or liturgical objects, the repair of organs, the purchase of pianos or other instruments, the design or acquisition of robes, or tours and visits.
RANGE OF GRANTS Up to £50,000.
SAMPLE GRANTS Blackburn Cathedral, Chester Cathedral and Sheffield Cathedral (£10,000 each); Dean Close School (£8,000); Salisbury Cathedral (£7,000); St Mary the Virgin – Bury (£4,000); King's College School – Cambridge (£3,000); and Hereford Sixth Form College and St James the Great – Derby (£1,000 each).
FINANCES *Year* 2012 *Income* £152,912 *Grants* £129,600 *Assets* £3,840,839
TRUSTEES Dr Christopher Robinson, Chair; Revd Canon Mark Boyling; Dr Stephen Darlington; Gillian Perkins; Canon Martin Pickering; Adam Ridley; Dr John Rutter; Canon Richard White; Timothy Byram-Wigfield; Paul Mason; Adrian Barlow.
HOW TO APPLY Applicants are strongly advised to obtain a copy of the trust's guidelines (either from the correspondent or their website, currently under construction at the time of writing) before drafting an application. Applications must be submitted by an institution on a form available from the correspondent. Closing dates for applications are 31 January for the March meeting and 30 June for the October meeting.

WHO TO APPLY TO Martin Williams, Clerk, PO Box 281, Stamford, Lincolnshire PE9 9BU *Tel.* 01780 752266 *email* ouseleytrust@ btinternet.com *Website* www.ouseleytrust.org.uk

....

■ The Owen Family Trust

CC NO 251975   **ESTABLISHED** 1967
WHERE FUNDING CAN BE GIVEN UK, with a preference for West Midlands.
WHO CAN BENEFIT Schools (independent and church), Christian youth centres, churches, community associations, national organisations benefiting people of all ages, and people with Alzheimer's disease, cancer and strokes.
WHAT IS FUNDED Mainly support for projects known personally by the trustees. Christian outreach projects are supported, with consideration also given to the arts, conservation, cancer research, Christian education, church and related community buildings.
WHAT IS NOT FUNDED The trust states 'No grants to individuals unless part of a charitable organisation'.
TYPE OF GRANT Buildings, capital, and recurring costs will be considered. Funding may be given for more than three years.
RANGE OF GRANTS £100–£15,000.
SAMPLE GRANTS Black Country Living Museum and Lichfield Cathedral (£5,000 each); Birmingham Federation of Clubs for Young People and NAYC Action Centre UK (£3,000 each); Sutton Coldfield YMCA (£2,500); Birmingham Royal Ballet (£2,000); Little Aston Village Hall (£1,500) and Chaplaincy Plus, St Giles Hospice, Elmhurst School for Dance and Shakespeare Birthplace Trust (£1,000 each).
FINANCES *Year* 2012–13 *Income* £45,000 *Grants* £84,935 *Assets* £1,087,595
TRUSTEES Grace Jenkins; David Owen.
HOW TO APPLY In writing to the correspondent including annual report, budget for project and general information regarding the application. Organisations need to be a registered charity; however an 'umbrella' body which would hold funds would be acceptable. Only a small number of grants can be given each year and unsuccessful applications are not acknowledged unless an sae is enclosed. The trustees meet quarterly.
WHO TO APPLY TO David Owen, Trustee, C/o Rubery Owen Holdings Limited, PO Box 10, Wednesbury WS10 8JD *Tel.* 01215 263131

....

■ Oxfam (GB)

CC NO 202918   **ESTABLISHED** 1958
WHERE FUNDING CAN BE GIVEN Africa, Asia, Caribbean, Central America, Eastern Europe, countries of the former Soviet Union, Great Britain, Middle East, South America.
WHO CAN BENEFIT Organisations which benefit people of all ages who are disadvantaged by poverty, disabled or victims of famine, disasters or war.
WHAT IS FUNDED Organisations worldwide working for the relief of hunger, disease, exploitation and poverty. Organisations working in public education in the UK and Ireland.
WHAT IS NOT FUNDED Applications for individuals are not considered.
SAMPLE GRANTS Research and Development Foundation (£4.6 million); Concern Worldwide (£3.6 million); Sindh Agricultural and Forestry Workers Coordinating Organisation (£3.3 million); Humanitarian Initiative Just Relief Aid (£2.6 million); Arid Lands Development

Focus (£930,000); Save the Children UK (£570,000); and Volunteers To Support International Efforts In Developing Africa (£276,000).
FINANCES *Year* 2011–12 *Income* £385,500,000 *Grants* £90,600,000 *Assets* £73,900,000
TRUSTEES Vanessa Godfrey; Karen Brown; James Darcy; Maja Darawula; Rajiv Joshi; Matthew Martin; David Pitt – Watson; Majorie Scardino; Nkoyo Toyo; Tricia Zipfel; Gavin Stewart; Steve Walton.
OTHER INFORMATION In 2011–12 there were 1296 grants made to 873 organisations.
HOW TO APPLY Applications should be made to the Regional Management Centre in the region concerned.
WHO TO APPLY TO Joss Saunders, 2700 John Smith Drive, Oxford Business Park South, Oxford OX4 2JY *Tel.* 0870 333 2444 *email* enquiries@ oxfam.org.uk *Website* www.oxfam.org.uk

....

■ City of Oxford Charity

CC NO 239151   **ESTABLISHED** 2004
WHERE FUNDING CAN BE GIVEN The city of Oxford only.
WHO CAN BENEFIT Charitable organisations, schools and individuals.
WHAT IS FUNDED Educational needs, such as help with school uniforms, attending school trips and books and materials.
FINANCES *Year* 2012 *Income* £322,695 *Grants* £100,000
TRUSTEES Robin Birch; Judith Iredale; Dorothy Tonge; Tony Woodward; Verena Brink; John Gould; Dr Jason Tomes; Jean Fooks; Michael Lancashire; Dr Richard Wittington; Roger Smith; Ben Lloyd-Shogbesan; Alan Armitage; Dr Alan Bogg; Ivan Coulter; Gillian Sanders; Steve Curran; Catherine Hilliard.
OTHER INFORMATION The charity also runs almshouses situated in St Clements – Oxford and provides grants for their upkeep.
HOW TO APPLY Application forms can be downloaded form the charity's website. Trustees meet to consider applications every six weeks.
WHO TO APPLY TO David Wright, Clerk, 11 Davenant Road, Oxford OX2 8BT *Tel.* 01865 247161 *email* enquiries@oxfordcitycharities.fsnet.co.uk *Website* www.oxfordcitycharities.org

....

■ The Oxfordshire Community Foundation

CC NO 1046432   **ESTABLISHED** 1995
WHERE FUNDING CAN BE GIVEN Oxfordshire.
WHO CAN BENEFIT Community-based non-profit organisations constituted in Oxfordshire. Beneficiaries of all ages, social circumstances, family situations and medical conditions will be considered, although the following are prioritised: parents and children; at risk groups; carers; disabled people; people disadvantaged by poverty; homeless people; immigrants; those living in rural areas; socially isolated people; victims of domestic violence; those with hearing loss, mental illness, and sight loss; and substance misusers.
WHAT IS FUNDED Specific projects up to one year with outputs related to poverty, unemployment, education and health promotion, including charities working in the fields of infrastructure and technical support, infrastructure development, charity or voluntary umbrella bodies, residential facilities and services, self-help groups, campaigning for health issues,

health related volunteer schemes, equal opportunities and various community facilities and services.

WHAT IS NOT FUNDED Refer to the foundation's website for exclusions specific to each fund.

TYPE OF GRANT One-off; capital. Core costs; salaries; start-up costs. One-year start-up for projects, training and equipment. Unrestricted.

RANGE OF GRANTS Generally between £500 and £5,000.

SAMPLE GRANTS Abingdon Bridge, Chabad, Goring on Thames Sailing Club, Steeple Aston Youth Club, Sunflower Toddler Group, and UK Dads and the Potential Project (£7,000 each); Azad Hill FC (£6,900); Parasol Project (£6,800); Oxford Concert Party (£6,600); and Fusion £6,200).

FINANCES *Year* 2011–12 *Income* £385,622 *Grants* £211,611 *Assets* £2,099,536

TRUSTEES Anna Moon; Lady North; Colin Alexander; Glyn Benson; Nigel Williams; Ian Lenagan; John Hemingway; Jane Wates; Prof. Ann Buchanan; David Astor.

PUBLICATIONS *The Other Oxfordshire.*

HOW TO APPLY Refer to the foundation's website for full details of how to apply to the various programmes currently being administered.

WHO TO APPLY TO Grants Manager, Oxfordshire Community Foundation, 3 Woodin's Way, Oxford OX1 1HD *Tel.* 01865 798666 *email* ocf@ oxfordshire.org *Website* www.oxfordshire.org

■ The P. F. Charitable Trust

CC NO 220124   **ESTABLISHED** 1951
WHERE FUNDING CAN BE GIVEN Unrestricted, with local interests in Oxfordshire and Scotland.
WHO CAN BENEFIT Voluntary organisations and charitable groups.
WHAT IS FUNDED General charitable purposes.
WHAT IS NOT FUNDED No grants to individuals or non-registered charities.
TYPE OF GRANT One-off and recurring, buildings, core costs, project, research and running costs. Funding may be given for up to three years.
RANGE OF GRANTS Mainly up to £50,000.
SAMPLE GRANTS Eton College Appeal and Soldiers of Oxfordshire Trust (£100,000 each); Charities Aid Foundation (£96,000); Scottish Community Foundation (£58,000) and Blind Veterans UK, Prior's Court Foundation, Oxford Radcliffe Hospitals Charitable Funds, Oxfordshire Community Foundation and Queen Elizabeth Fields Challenge (£50,000 each).
FINANCES *Year* 2011–12 *Income* £2,593,760 *Grants* £2,158,500 *Assets* £93,692,544
TRUSTEES Robert Fleming; Philip Fleming; Rory D. Fleming.
OTHER INFORMATION Grants of less than £50,000 each totalled £1.6 million.
HOW TO APPLY Applications to the correspondent in writing. Trustees usually meet monthly to consider applications and approve grants.
WHO TO APPLY TO The Secretary to the Trustees, c/o Fleming Family and Partners, 15 Suffolk Street, London SW1Y 4HG *Tel.* 020 7036 5685

■ The Doris Pacey Charitable Foundation

CC NO 1101724   **ESTABLISHED** 2004
WHERE FUNDING CAN BE GIVEN UK and Israel.
WHO CAN BENEFIT Charitable organisations.
WHAT IS FUNDED Jewish, medical, educational and social.
TYPE OF GRANT One-off and recurrent.
RANGE OF GRANTS £500–£138,000
SAMPLE GRANTS OR Movement and Jewish Chaplaincy (£50,000 each); UJIA – Jewish Curriculum (£40,000); UJIA – Hemed Project (£25,000); ALEF (£11,000); Heart Cells Foundation (£10,000); Surrey Opera (£9,300) and Courtauld Institute of Art and Nightingale (£5,000 each).
FINANCES *Year* 2010–11 *Income* £104,005 *Grants* £205,560 *Assets* £5,883,333
TRUSTEES J. D. Cohen; R. Locke; L. Powell.
HOW TO APPLY Unsolicited applications are not considered.
WHO TO APPLY TO J. D. Cohen, Trustee, 30 Old Burlington Street, London W1S 3NL *Tel.* 020 7468 2600

■ Padwa Charitable Foundation

CC NO 1019274   **ESTABLISHED** 1992
WHERE FUNDING CAN BE GIVEN UK.
WHO CAN BENEFIT Organisations and individuals.
WHAT IS FUNDED Relief of poverty and disability; advancement of education, as well as general charitable purposes.
RANGE OF GRANTS Up to £5,000.
SAMPLE GRANTS Field Lane (£10,500); CancerKin (£2,500); and Abbeyfield (£1,500).
FINANCES *Year* 2011–12 *Income* £1,955,261 *Grants* £19,539 *Assets* £12,355,733
TRUSTEES Roy Evenden; Jeremy Randall; Alan Goreham; Neil Fulton.
OTHER INFORMATION Grants to individuals totalled £2,200.
HOW TO APPLY In writing to the correspondent.
WHO TO APPLY TO Jeremy Randall, Trustee, 1 Doughty Street, London WC1N 2PH *Tel.* 0845 230 0706 *email* jr@walpolegroup.com

■ The Paget Charitable Trust

CC NO 327402   **ESTABLISHED** 1986
WHERE FUNDING CAN BE GIVEN Worldwide, with an interest in Loughborough.
WHO CAN BENEFIT Normally only British registered charities.
WHAT IS FUNDED Sheer need is paramount, and, in practice, nothing else can be considered. There is a preference for the unglamorous, for maximum achievement with minimal resources. Priorities include the developing world, deprived children, old age, 'green' projects, and animal welfare. The trust does sometimes give ongoing support, thus leaving fewer funds for new applicants.
WHAT IS NOT FUNDED The trust states that 'sheer need is paramount, in practice, nothing else is considered'. Grants are only given to registered UK charities. Overseas projects can only be funded via UK charities; no money can be sent directly overseas. The trust does not support individuals (including students), projects for people with mental disabilities, medical research or AIDS/HIV projects.
RANGE OF GRANTS £50–£5,000
SAMPLE GRANTS Oxfam (£4,000); Farms for City Children (£3,000); ActionAid, Childhood First, Freedom from torture and Children's Family Trust (£2,000 each); Vitalise (£1,500); Wells for India, Tree Aid, Toynbee Hall, St Nicholas Hospice, Splash, Refugee Council, Quaker Social Action, Deafblind UK and Concern Worldwide (£1,000 each) and Dhaka Ahsania Mission, Feed the Children, Cambodia's Dump Children, Asthma UK, Afghan Action and Jubilee Action (£500 each).
FINANCES *Year* 2011–12 *Income* £197,338 *Grants* £150,975 *Assets* £8,074,970
TRUSTEES Joanna Herbert-Stepney; Meg Williams.
OTHER INFORMATION No grants to individuals. The full registered name of the trust is The Joanna Herbert-Stepney Charitable Settlement.
HOW TO APPLY In writing to the correspondent; there is no application form. The trustees meet in spring and autumn. The trust regrets that it cannot respond to all applications.
WHO TO APPLY TO Joanna Herbert-Stepney, Trustee, Old Village Stores, Dippenhall Street, Crondall, Farnham, Surrey GU10 5NZ *Tel.* 01252 850253

■ The Paladin Vince-Odozi Charitable Trust

cc no 1148792 **established** 2012
where funding can be given UK and Africa.
who can benefit Charities and community groups.
what is funded Education and training, relief of poverty and economic development, with a particular emphasis on organisations working with children and young people.
trustees Dr Kathryn Vince-Odozi; Nilam Statham; Sylvester Vince-Odozi.
how to apply In writing to the correspondent.
who to apply to Dr Kathryn Vince-Odozi, Trustee, c/o Paladin Capital Ltd, Afon House, Worthing Road, West Sussex RH12 1TL *Tel.* 01403 211380 *email* kvo@paladincapital.co.uk

■ The Palmer Foundation

cc no 278666 **established** 1979
where funding can be given Tower Hamlets.
who can benefit Selected registered charities chosen by the trustees. Children and young adults at Coopers' Company and Coborn School and Strode's College will be considered.
what is funded Grants and donations to charitable organisations and payments for educational scholarships, bursaries and prizes at Coopers' Company and Coborn School and Strode's College.
type of grant Recurrent grants for up to three years will be considered.
sample grants Welfare (£1,500); Educational (£8,000); City of London (£5,500); Young people (£3,600); and 'Other' (£5,000).
finances *Year* 2011–12 *Income* £31,555 *Grants* £23,694 *Assets* £777,715
trustee The Coopers' Company.
how to apply The trust conducts its own research and does not respond to unsolicited applications.
who to apply to Adrian Carroll, Clerk to the Trustees, Coopers' Hall, 13 Devonshire Square, London EC2M 4TH *Tel.* 020 7247 9577 *email* clerk@coopers-hall.co.uk *Website* www. coopers-hall.co.uk

■ Eleanor Palmer Trust

cc no 220857 **established** 1558
where funding can be given Former urban districts of Chipping Barnet and East Barnet.
who can benefit Charities benefiting people disadvantaged by poverty, hardship or distress.
what is funded Relief in need.
what is not funded Anything other than relief-in-need is not considered. Capital costs are not funded.
type of grant One-off, funding up to three years will be considered.
range of grants £100–£5,000.
finances *Year* 2011–12 *Income* £1,403,428 *Grants* £48,258 *Assets* £4,042,212
trustees Anthony Grimwade; Anthony Alderman; Helena Davis; Stephen Lane; Margaret King; Wendy Prentice; Revd Samuel Hall Speers; David Tait; Christopher Dallison; Deborah Layde.
other information Grants are broken down as follows: amenities for and grants for residents: £9,000; grants for relief in need: £37,000; lunch club for residents £2,600.
how to apply On a form available to download, together with guidelines and criteria, from the website. The trust states that 'successful applicants are required to provide feedback on the outcomes of the project and how they matched their expectations.'
who to apply to Fred Park, Clerk to the Trustees, 106b Wood Street, Barnet, Hertfordshire EN5 4BY *Tel.* 020 8441 3222 *email* info@eleanorpalmertrust.org.uk *Website* www.eleanorpalmertrust.org.uk

■ The Panacea Society

cc no 227530 **established** 1926
where funding can be given UK, with a strong preference for Bedford and its immediate region.
who can benefit Christian organisations, universities and registered charities.
what is funded Research, scholarships and conferences in the field of historical theology, in particular: Prophecy; the Book of Revelation; The Second Coming of Christ; Jewish Apocalyptic literature and Christian Theology and Millennialism and Christian millenarian movements. Poverty, sickness and social related grants are made through the Bedfordshire and Luton Community Foundation and Community and Voluntary Services Bedfordshire.
what is not funded The society will not make grants: to political parties or political lobbying; to pressure groups which support commercial ventures; or which could be paid out of central or local government funds.
sample grants Bedford Project – Charity's properties, chapel and gardens, archives and library (£302,000); Bedford Hospitals Charity, Cambridge University and Goldsmiths College (£75,000 each); Kings College London (£54,000); Bedfordshire and Luton Community Foundation (£50,000); Gray Research Scholarship (£21,000) and Buntan Meeting Broomhall (£2,400).
finances *Year* 2012 *Income* £773,211 *Grants* £501,000 *Assets* £24,763,431
trustees G. Allan; L. Aston; Revd Dr Jane Shaw; Prof. C. Rowland; Dr J. Meggitt.
other information The grants total includes £300,000 used to support the charity's own properties, chapel and gardens, archives and library.
how to apply The trust has previously stated that it receives many applications that they are unable or unwilling to support. Read the grant criteria carefully before submitting an application. Unsolicited applications are not responded to. Any organisation considering applying for funding support should make a formal application in writing to the correspondent. The application should set out the purpose for which the funding is required, and explain how it falls within the funding criteria and complies with their requirements. Full information on the work of the applicant body together with details of how the proposed funding will be applied should be given. The correspondent will acknowledge receipt of an application, and indicate if the application falls within their parameters. At this point the society may call for additional information, or indicate that it is unable to consider the application further. Most applications fail because they fall outside the criteria, however the society does not provide additional reasons why it is unable to support a particular application. When all relevant information has been received the application will be discussed at the next meeting of the society's trustees together with other valid applications. The trustees may at that meeting

refuse or defer any application or request further information without giving reasons. Applicants will be advised in writing of the trustees' decision.

'At the end of 2010 and after much consideration, the Society decided that it would approach its Poverty and Sickness grantmaking in a different manner. Rather than invite organisations and groups to apply directly to the Society, for 2011 onwards funding would be provided to specialist funders working within the not for profit sector with the remit to then deal with all applications directly on behalf of the Society.'

'The Bedfordshire and Luton Community Foundation working in partnership with Community and Voluntary Service Mid and North Beds manage the Society's non-educational grantmaking activities within the local community.'

'Educational grants are still awarded and assessed directly by the Society.'

WHO TO APPLY TO David McLynn, Executive Officer, 14 Albany Road, Bedford MK40 3PH *Tel.* 01234 359737 *email* admin@panacea-society.org *Website* www.panacea-society.org

----

■ Panahpur

CC NO 1130367   **ESTABLISHED** 1911
WHERE FUNDING CAN BE GIVEN UK, overseas in particular India.
WHO CAN BENEFIT Christian charities and individuals, especially Christian missionary organisations.
WHAT IS FUNDED Social and impact investment.
RANGE OF GRANTS £500–£38,000.
SAMPLE GRANTS Mission Now Cambodia (£51,000); Youth for Christ International (£35,000); Republica (£12,000); Interhealth (£9,400); Transworld Radio (£8,600); Romance Academy (£6,000); Molly's Network (£5,000); Cinnamon Network (£4,000); Ambassadors in Sport (£2,100); Serving in Mission (£1,500) and Door of Hope (£1,300).
FINANCES *Year* 2011–12 *Income* £144,308 *Grants* £146,794 *Assets* £4,973,610
TRUSTEES Paul East; Andrew Perry; Larissa Rwakasiisi; Laurence East; Andrew Matheson.
OTHER INFORMATION The grants total includes £36,000 given in grants to individuals.
HOW TO APPLY The trustees do their own research and do not respond to unsolicited applications.
WHO TO APPLY TO James Perry, Trustee, 84 High Street, Tonbridge, Kent TN9 1AP

■ The Panton Trust

CC NO 292910   **ESTABLISHED** 1983
WHERE FUNDING CAN BE GIVEN UK and overseas.
WHO CAN BENEFIT Worldwide organisations concerned with animal wildlife; UK: the environment.
WHAT IS FUNDED The trust states that it is 'concerned with any animal or animals or with wildlife in any part of the world, or with the environment of the UK or any part thereof. The trustees consider applications from a wide variety of sources and favour smaller charities which do not have the same capacity for large-scale fundraising as major charities in this field'.
TYPE OF GRANT Grants are made for strategic planning and project funding and can be for up to three years.
RANGE OF GRANTS Up to £5,000.

SAMPLE GRANTS St Tiggywinkles Wildlife Hospital (£4,000); PDSA (£3,000); Sunshine Club, Flora and Fauna International and William Ellis School (£2,000 each); and Dogs Trust, Gorilla Organisation, Wroxton Parish Council, Moor Bear Rescue and Barn Owl Trust (£1,000 each).
FINANCES *Year* 2011–12 *Income* £60,969 *Grants* £38,800 *Assets* £185,759
TRUSTEES L. M. Slavin; R. Craig.
HOW TO APPLY In writing to the correspondent.
WHO TO APPLY TO Laurence Slavin, Trustee, Ramsay House, 18 Vera Avenue, Grange Park, London N12 1RA *Tel.* 020 8370 7700

■ The James Pantyfedwen Foundation

CC NO 1069598   **ESTABLISHED** 1998
WHERE FUNDING CAN BE GIVEN Wales.
WHO CAN BENEFIT Welsh people; and organisations in Wales benefiting children, young adults, clergy, musicians, students, Christians, at risk groups, people disadvantaged by poverty and homeless people.
WHAT IS FUNDED Church buildings; religious purposes; students (mainly for postgraduate study); registered charities; local Eisteddfodau; and Sunday Schools. Charities working in the field of Christian education; religious umbrella bodies; infrastructure, support and development; cultural activity; academic research; and various community services and facilities will be considered.
WHAT IS NOT FUNDED No grants are made for revenue funding of any kind.
TYPE OF GRANT One-off
RANGE OF GRANTS Up to a maximum of £20,000 in special cases. Generally £1,000–£5,000.
SAMPLE GRANTS Grants were broken down as follows: Educational purposes (students) – £113,000; Religious buildings – £107,000; Eisteddfodau – £64,500; Registered charities – £13,000; Religious purposes – £14,000; Urdd Gobaith Cymru – £10,000; Special Projects – £41,000; Books – £2,000.
FINANCES *Year* 2011–12 *Income* £499,160 *Grants* £364,323 *Assets* £13,217,230
TRUSTEES Dr Carwyn Tywyn; Revd Dr Geraint Tudur; Revd Dr Barry Morgan; Revd Peter Thomas; Garry Nicholas; Revd W. Bryn Williams; Revd Dr R. Alun Evans; Dr Rhidian Griffiths; Ifan Hughes; Emrys Jones; Geraint Jones; Gwerfyl Jones; David Lewis; Prof. Derec Morgan; Revd Enid Morgan; William Phillips; Ken Richards; Roy Sharp; Dr Eryn White.
OTHER INFORMATION Organisations and individuals
HOW TO APPLY On forms available to download, together with guidelines and criteria, on the website. Applications from churches and registered charities can be submitted at any time (trustees meet about five times a year in March, May, July, September and December); student applications should be submitted before 31 July in the academic year for which the application is being made. Applications to the special projects funds are considered twice a year and should be received by 15 June or 15 November for consideration in July or December respectively. All unsuccessful applicants receive a reply.
WHO TO APPLY TO Richard H. Morgan, Executive Secretary, Pantyfedwen, 9 Market Street, Aberystwyth SY23 1DL *Tel.* 01970 612806 *Fax* 01970 612806 *email* pantyfedwen@btinternet.com *Website* www.jamespantyfedwenfoundation.org.uk

■ The Paphitis Charitable Trust

CC NO 1112721 **ESTABLISHED** 2005
WHERE FUNDING CAN BE GIVEN UK and overseas.
WHO CAN BENEFIT Charitable organisations.
WHAT IS FUNDED General charitable purposes, particularly children's charities.
RANGE OF GRANTS £50 to £14,000.
SAMPLE GRANTS Cancer for Care (£14,000); Friends of Orleans Infant School (£6,000); England Footballers Association and The Kiklos Trust (£5,000 each); Skidz and Peter Jones Foundation (£2,500 each); G B Smith Boxing (£2,000); Sam Bearce Hospice and Street Children's Charity Ball (£1,000 each); Mawsley FC and Institute of Cancer Research (£500 each); Stoke Town Ladies FC (£300); Millwall Community Scheme (£200) and Willow Foundation (£100).
FINANCES *Year* 2011–12 *Income* £49,430 *Grants* £59,483
TRUSTEES Malcolm Cooke; Richard Towner; Kypros Kyprianou; Ann Mantz; Ian Childs.
OTHER INFORMATION This trust was set up by entrepreneur Theo Paphitis.
HOW TO APPLY In writing to the correspondent.
WHO TO APPLY TO Ann Mantz, Trustee, 2nd Floor, 22–24 Worple Road, London SW19 4DD *Tel.* 020 8971 9890

■ The Paragon Trust

CC NO 278348 **ESTABLISHED** 1979
WHERE FUNDING CAN BE GIVEN UK and overseas.
WHO CAN BENEFIT Charities and occasionally certain individuals but only those known to the trustees.
WHAT IS FUNDED A wide range of charitable bodies.
TYPE OF GRANT The majority of donations are standing orders.
RANGE OF GRANTS £500–£5,000.
SAMPLE GRANTS Compassion in World Farming 'YouTube Video Project' (£8,000); British Red Cross (£3,000); Zane Zimbabwe (£2,500); Canterbury Cathedral and Médecins Sans Frontières (£2,000 each); Dallington Parochial Church Council Spire Restoration Fund (£1,500); Send a Cow, Army Benevolent Fund, Prison Reform Trust and The Art Fund (£1,000 each) and Women's Holiday Fund, Hospice in the Weald and Changing Faces (£500 each).
FINANCES *Year* 2011–12 *Income* £84,579 *Grants* £100,000
TRUSTEES The Lord Wrenbury; Revd Canon R. Coppin; Ms L. J. Whistler; P. Cunningham; Dr Fiona Cornish; Patricia Russell.
HOW TO APPLY The trust states that it does not respond to unsolicited applications; all beneficiaries 'are known personally to the trustees and no attention is paid to appeal literature, which is discarded on receipt. Fundraisers are therefore urged to save resources by not sending literature.'
WHO TO APPLY TO Stuart Goodbody, c/o Thomson Snell and Passmore Solicitors, 3 Lonsdale Gardens, Tunbridge Wells, Kent TN1 1NX *Tel.* 01892 510000

■ Paraton Trust

CC NO 1146495 **ESTABLISHED** 2012
WHERE FUNDING CAN BE GIVEN UK and overseas, with a preference for the North of England and Scotland.

WHO CAN BENEFIT Organisations working with children and young people, older people and people with disabilities.
WHAT IS FUNDED Relief of poverty, advancement of the Christian faith, economic and community development and social welfare.
FINANCES *Year* 2012 *Income* £147,500 *Grants* £59,689 *Assets* £87,811
TRUSTEES Peter Fullarton; Anne Fullarton.
HOW TO APPLY In writing to the correspondent.
WHO TO APPLY TO Peter Fullarton, Trustee, 23 Rayleigh Road, Harrogate, North Yorkshire HG2 8QR

■ The Park Charitable Trust

CC NO 1095541 **ESTABLISHED** 2003
WHERE FUNDING CAN BE GIVEN UK.
WHO CAN BENEFIT Charitable organisations.
WHAT IS FUNDED 'The objects of the charity are the advancement of the Jewish Faith; the advancement of Jewish education; the relief of poverty amongst the Jewish community; the relief of patients suffering from cancer and heart conditions; giving financial support to hospitals and furthering such other charitable purposes as the trustees may from time to time determine in support of their charitable activities.'
FINANCES *Year* 2011–12 *Income* £846,555 *Grants* £366,606 *Assets* £1,625,149
TRUSTEES D. Hammelburger; M. Hammelburger; E. Pine.
HOW TO APPLY In writing to the correspondent.
WHO TO APPLY TO E. Pine, Trustee, 69 Singleton Road, Salford M7 4LX

■ The Park House Charitable Trust

CC NO 1077677 **ESTABLISHED** 1999
WHERE FUNDING CAN BE GIVEN UK and overseas, with a preference for the Midlands, particularly Coventry and Warwickshire.
WHO CAN BENEFIT Charitable organisations.
WHAT IS FUNDED General charitable purposes, with preference towards social welfare and Christian causes.
WHAT IS NOT FUNDED No grants to individuals.
TYPE OF GRANT Normally one-off for general funds.
RANGE OF GRANTS £2,000–£100,000.
SAMPLE GRANTS Scottish International Relief and St Joseph and the Helpers Charity (£100,000 each); Aid to the Church in Need, Columban Fathers, CAFOD and St John of Jerusalem Eye Hospital (£10,000 each); Smile Train, Y Care International and The Passage (£5,000 each); Community of Holy Fire (£4,000) and Bibles for Children (£3,000).
FINANCES *Year* 2012 *Income* £300,658 *Grants* £368,000 *Assets* £1,416,189
TRUSTEES N. P. Bailey; M. Bailey; P. Bailey.
HOW TO APPLY In writing to the correspondent. The trust has stated that it does not expect to have surplus funds available to meet the majority of applications.
WHO TO APPLY TO Paul Varney, Dafferns LLP, One Eastwood, Harry Weston Road, Binley Business Park, Coventry CV3 2UB *Tel.* 02476 221046

■ The Frank Parkinson Agricultural Trust

CC NO 209407   **ESTABLISHED** 1943

WHERE FUNDING CAN BE GIVEN UK.

WHO CAN BENEFIT Mainly corporate entities benefiting the improvement of agriculture and horticulture.

WHAT IS FUNDED The improvement and welfare of British agriculture, primarily to agricultural colleges and affiliated institutions.

WHAT IS NOT FUNDED Grants are given to corporate bodies and the trust is not able to assist with financial help to any individuals undertaking postgraduate studies or degree courses.

TYPE OF GRANT Short-term: two to four years preferred. One-off will also be considered.

RANGE OF GRANTS One–off at Chair's discretion: smallest £200; largest over three years £100,000.

SAMPLE GRANTS St George's House and Yorkshire and Harrogate Beekeepers' Association (£5,000 each); John Innes Centre (£2,400) and AgriFood Charities Partnership (£250).

FINANCES *Year* 2012 *Income* £59,847 *Grants* £12,650 *Assets* £1,247,747

TRUSTEES C. Bourchier; J. S. Sclanders; Prof. Paul Webster; D. Gardner.

PUBLICATIONS A history of the trust since its inception in 1943, including an outline of projects previously funded, is available in a book entitled Tale of Two Trusts, which is available from the correspondent.

HOW TO APPLY In writing to the correspondent. The trustees meet annually in April and applicants are expected to make an oral presentation. Further details of the whole application process can be found in the useful 'Guidelines for Grant Applications' which is available from the trust. Note, however: 'The chair has the authority to approve small grants between annual meetings, but these are only for minor sums and minor projects.'

WHO TO APPLY TO Janet Smith, Secretary to the Trustees, 11 Alder Drive, Pudsey LS28 8RD *Tel.* 01132 578613 *email* janetpudsey@live.co.uk

■ The Samuel and Freda Parkinson Charitable Trust

CC NO 327749   **ESTABLISHED** 1987

WHERE FUNDING CAN BE GIVEN UK.

WHO CAN BENEFIT Registered charities specified by the founder of the trust.

WHAT IS FUNDED General charitable purposes.

RANGE OF GRANTS £5,000–£25,000.

SAMPLE GRANTS Salvation Army (£26,000); The Leonard Cheshire Foundation (£25,000); Church Army and RNLI (£15,000) and RSPCA, Animal Concern, Animal Rescue Cumbria and Animal Welfare (£5,000 each).

FINANCES *Year* 2011–12 *Income* £105,255 *Grants* £101,000 *Assets* £3,008,469

TRUSTEES John Crompton; Judith Todd; Michael Fletcher.

OTHER INFORMATION The trust supports the same eight beneficiaries each year, although for varying amounts.

HOW TO APPLY The founder of this charity restricted the list of potential beneficiaries to named charities of his choice and accordingly the trustees do not have discretion to include further beneficiaries, although they do have complete discretion within the stated beneficiary list.

WHO TO APPLY TO Trust Administrator, Regent House, 25 Crescent Road, Windermere, Cumbria LA23 1BJ *Tel.* 01539 446585

■ The Parthenon Trust

CC NO 1051467   **ESTABLISHED** 1995

WHERE FUNDING CAN BE GIVEN Unrestricted.

WHO CAN BENEFIT Charitable organisations.

WHAT IS FUNDED International aid, medical research, assistance to the disadvantaged including people with disabilities, culture and heritage, medical treatment and care, education, promotion of civil society and research on current affairs.

WHAT IS NOT FUNDED No grants for individuals, scientific/geographical expeditions or projects which promote religious beliefs.

TYPE OF GRANT Normally one-off grants for general purposes.

RANGE OF GRANTS £2,500–£400,000

SAMPLE GRANTS Cancer Research UK; Friends of Diva Opera; Mont Blanc Foundation; Ungureni Trust; International Committee of the Red Cross; UNICEF UK; Ashoka Africa; Downside Up; Cecily's Fund; Andover Young Carers; Basingstoke-Hoima Partnership for Health; Esther Benjamins Trust; Leprosy Mission; North Hampshire Medical Fund; Trinity Winchester; United Aid for Azerbaijan; Feet First World Wide; Kariandusi School Trust and Langalanga Scholarship Fund.

FINANCES *Year* 2012 *Income* £14,965 *Grants* £0

TRUSTEES Dr J. M. Darmady; J. E. E. Whittaker; Y. G. Whittaker.

OTHER INFORMATION The trust states that 'No grant giving or other charitable activities were undertaken in 2012, but it is expected that activities will resume in the coming months.'

HOW TO APPLY In writing to the correspondent. Anyone proposing to submit an application should telephone the secretary beforehand. Unsolicited written applications are not normally acknowledged. Most grants are awarded at a trustees' meeting held early in the new year, although grants can be awarded at any time.

WHO TO APPLY TO J. E. E. Whittaker, The Secretary, Les Mouriaux House, St Anne, Alderney, Channel Islands GY9 3UD *Tel.* 01481 823821

■ Arthur James Paterson Charitable Trust

CC NO 278569   **ESTABLISHED** 1979

WHERE FUNDING CAN BE GIVEN UK

WHO CAN BENEFIT Organisations benefiting children, older people, retired people, at risk groups, socially isolated people and those disadvantaged by poverty.

WHAT IS FUNDED Medical research, welfare of older people and children.

TYPE OF GRANT One-off.

RANGE OF GRANTS Under £5,000.

SAMPLE GRANTS Glenalmond College and Worcester College (£6,200 each); Shine and Eureka (£4,000 each); Woodlands Hospice and Home Start Bristol (£3,900 each) and British Eye Research and British Forces (£1,100 each).

FINANCES *Year* 2012–13 *Income* £45,411 *Grants* £30,340 *Assets* £1,692,736

TRUSTEE Royal Bank of Canada Trust Corporation Ltd.

HOW TO APPLY There are no application forms. Send your application with a covering letter and include the latest set of report and accounts. Deadlines are February and August.

WHO TO APPLY TO Anita Carter, Trust Administrator, Royal Bank of Canada Trust Corporation Limited, Riverbank House, 2 Swan Lane, London EC4R 3BF *Tel.* 020 7653 4756 *email* anita. carter@rbc.com

---

■ The Constance Paterson Charitable Trust

CC NO 249556   **ESTABLISHED** 1966
WHERE FUNDING CAN BE GIVEN UK.
WHO CAN BENEFIT Organisations benefiting children, older people, retired people, ex-service and service people, at risk groups, socially isolated people and those disadvantaged by poverty. Carers, disabled people, homeless people, victims of abuse, crime or domestic violence and people with dyslexia are also considered.
WHAT IS FUNDED Medical research, health care, welfare of older people and children (including accommodation and housing) and service people's welfare.
WHAT IS NOT FUNDED No grants to individuals.
TYPE OF GRANT One-off grants, which can be for capital costs (including buildings), core or running costs, project or research funding, or salaries.
RANGE OF GRANTS Up to £2,000.
SAMPLE GRANTS Ambitious About Autism, Golden Oldies, Joe Glover Trust, Thames Hospice Care and The Speech Language and Hearing Centre (£2,000 each) and It's your Choice, Forest Bus Ltd, The Eyeless Trust and Extend Exercise Trading Ltd (£1,500 each).
FINANCES *Year* 2012–13 *Income* £31,209 *Grants* £16,190 *Assets* £1,195,159
TRUSTEE Royal Bank of Canada Trust Corporation Ltd.
HOW TO APPLY In writing to the correspondent, including covering letter and latest set of annual report and accounts. The trust does not have an application form. Deadlines for applications are June and December.
WHO TO APPLY TO Anita Carter, Trust Administrator, Royal Bank of Canada Trust Corporation Limited, Riverbank House, 2 Swan Lane, London EC4R 3BF *Tel.* 020 7653 4756 *email* anita. carter@rbc.com

---

■ Miss M. E. Swinton Paterson's Charitable Trust

SC NO SC004835   **ESTABLISHED** 1989
WHERE FUNDING CAN BE GIVEN Scotland.
WHO CAN BENEFIT Organisations benefiting Christians and young people.
WHAT IS FUNDED Support to the Church of Scotland and other Christian groups in the maintenance of church buildings and in their work with young people.
WHAT IS NOT FUNDED No grants to individuals or students.
RANGE OF GRANTS £500–£1,000.
SAMPLE GRANTS Previous beneficiaries include: L'Arche Edinburgh Community, Livingstone Baptist Church, Lloyd Morris Congregational Church, Haddington West Parish Church, Acorn Christian Centre, Stranraer YMCA, Care for the Family, Boys' and Girls' Clubs of Scotland, Fresh Start, Friends of the Elms, Iona Community, Edinburgh Young Carers' Project, Epilepsy Scotland, Stoneykirk Parish Church, Scotland Yard Adventure Centre, Atholl Centre, Scottish

Crusaders, Disablement Income Group Scotland and Artlink.
FINANCES *Year* 2012–13 *Income* £50,143 *Grants* £40,000
TRUSTEES Michael A. Noble; J. A. W. Somerville; C. S. Kennedy; R. J. Steel.
HOW TO APPLY In writing to the correspondent. Trustees meet once a year in July to consider grants.
WHO TO APPLY TO The Trustees, Lindsays' Solicitors, Calendonian Exchange, 19a Canning Street, Edinburgh EH3 8HE

■ The Patrick Charitable Trust

CC NO 213849   **ESTABLISHED** 1962
WHERE FUNDING CAN BE GIVEN UK, with a special interest in Cornwall and West Midlands.
WHO CAN BENEFIT Registered charities.
WHAT IS FUNDED General charitable purposes.
WHAT IS NOT FUNDED No grants to individuals.
TYPE OF GRANT One-off or recurrent.
RANGE OF GRANTS £100 to £25,000. Usually below £10,000.
SAMPLE GRANTS Oundle School Foundation (£25,000); Brain Tumour UK (£10,000); Birmingham Royal Ballet (£6,000); Elmhurst School for Dance and Birmingham Hippodrome (£5,000 each); The Peck Wood Centre and Lord Lieutenant's Fund for Youth (£3,000 each); Muscular Dystrophy Campaign (£2,000); The Scouts Association and Motor Neurone Disease Association (£1,000 each); Project for the regeneration of Druids Heath, Birmingham and Canoldir Male Choir (£300 each) and Barts and the London Charity (£100).
FINANCES *Year* 2011–12 *Income* £109,392 *Grants* £100,832 *Assets* £6,491,494
TRUSTEES J. Alexander Patrick; Mary Patrick; Heather Cole; William Bond-Williams; Nigel Duckitt; Graham Wem.
OTHER INFORMATION In 2011–12 grants were given to 31 organisations.
HOW TO APPLY In writing to the correspondent at any time. The trust endeavours to reply to all applications with a decision.
WHO TO APPLY TO J. A. Patrick, Trustee, The Lakeside Centre, 180 Lifford Lane, Birmingham B30 3NU *Tel.* 01214 863399

■ The Jack Patston Charitable Trust

CC NO 701658   **ESTABLISHED** 1989
WHERE FUNDING CAN BE GIVEN Preferably Leicestershire and Cambridgeshire.
WHO CAN BENEFIT Charitable organisations, including rural churches.
WHAT IS FUNDED Preservation of wildlife and the environment, advancement of religion and preservation of rural church fabric.
WHAT IS NOT FUNDED No grants to individuals.
TYPE OF GRANT Single payments.
RANGE OF GRANTS Up to £3,000.
SAMPLE GRANTS Train A Priest Fund, St Andrew's Church, Whittlesey and The Peterborough Cathedral Trust (£3,000 each); The Countryside Restoration Trust, East Anglia Children's Hospices and Friends of St Catherine's Church, Houghton on the Hill (£2,500 each); British Trust for Ornithology (£2,000); Cambridge Past Present and Future and RNIB (Talking Books Service) (£1,500 each); The Barn Owl Trust (£1,000) and Leicester Hedgehog Rescue and

Think carefully about every application. Is it justified?

809

Shepreth Wildlife Conservation Charity (£500 each).

FINANCES *Year* 2011–12 *Income* £97,030 *Grants* £85,500 *Assets* £3,616,437

TRUSTEES Allan Veasey; Charles Applegate.

OTHER INFORMATION In 2011–12 grants were given to 48 organisations.

HOW TO APPLY In writing to the correspondent.

WHO TO APPLY TO Charles Applegate, Trustee, Buckles Solicitors LLP, Grant House, 101 Bourges Boulevard, Peterborough PE1 1NG *Tel.* 01733 888888 *Fax* 01733 888800 *email* www.buckles-law.co.uk

■ Ambika Paul Foundation

CC NO 276127   **ESTABLISHED** 1978

WHERE FUNDING CAN BE GIVEN Mainly UK and India.

WHO CAN BENEFIT Large organisations, registered charities, colleges and universities benefiting children, young adults and students.

WHAT IS FUNDED Main areas of interest are young people and education.

WHAT IS NOT FUNDED Applications from individuals, including students, are mainly ineligible. Funding for scholarships is made directly to colleges/ universities, not to individuals. No expeditions.

RANGE OF GRANTS Usually £100–£5,000.

SAMPLE GRANTS Loreto College, India (£76,000); Zoological Society of London (£15,000); Shri Venkateswara (£11,000); Indian Orthopaedic Society (£10,000); Lamu Dispensary (£5,000); Anglican Communion Ministries (£2,600); Bharatiya Vidya Bhawan (£1,500) and Sindi Nari Sabha and CST (protecting Jewish community) (£500 each).

FINANCES *Year* 2011–12 *Income* £576,345 *Grants* £121,556 *Assets* £7,530,393

TRUSTEES Lord Paul of Marylebone; Lady Aruna Paul; Hon. Angad Paul; Hon. Anjli Paul; Hon. Ambar Paul; Hon. Akash Paul.

HOW TO APPLY In writing to the trustees at the correspondence address. Acknowledgements are sent if an sae is enclosed. However, the trust has no paid employees and the enormous number of requests it receives creates administrative difficulties.

WHO TO APPLY TO Lord Paul of Marylebone, Trustee, Caparo House, 103 Baker Street, London W1U 6LN *Tel.* 020 7486 1417 *email* georgina.mason@caparo.com

■ Paycare Charity Trust

CC NO 240378   **ESTABLISHED** 1964

WHERE FUNDING CAN BE GIVEN Generally in the East and West Midlands, Staffordshire and Shropshire and other areas where the association operates.

WHO CAN BENEFIT Mainly NHS hospitals and registered, medically related charities benefiting: children; young adults; older people; ex-service and service people; medical professionals, nurses and doctors; research workers; volunteers; people in care; at risk groups; carers; disabled people; those disadvantaged by poverty; homeless people; victims of abuse and domestic violence.

WHAT IS FUNDED Provision of equipment and patient amenities to NHS hospitals, hospices, convalescent homes and other medically related charities in the area where the parent association operates. These include: support to volunteers; health professional bodies; councils for voluntary service; advancement of respite; sheltered accommodation; health; special schools; speech therapy; special needs education; scholarships; medical research; specialist research; and community services.

WHAT IS NOT FUNDED Appeals must be from officials of the appealing body and submitted on official stationery. Appeals are not accepted from, or on behalf of, individuals or for provision of vehicles or general running costs.

TYPE OF GRANT Mainly medical equipment. Grants are not made towards running costs or administration.

RANGE OF GRANTS £100–£1,300.

SAMPLE GRANTS Blind Veteran's UK (£1,300); Multiple Sclerosis Therapy Centre (£1,000); University of Warwick and The Fire Fighters Charity (£950 each); Brain Tumour Research (£800); St Mark's Parish Church (£750); Tiny Tim's Children Centre (£700); Queen Alexandra Hospital Home (£500); Beating Bowel Cancer (£250) and The Respite Association (£140).

FINANCES *Year* 2012 *Income* £31,073 *Grants* £23,194 *Assets* £44,959

TRUSTEES Eric Booth; Gerald Lewis; Helen Lisle; David Clegg; Patricia Stokes; Nicholas Webb.

OTHER INFORMATION In 2011–12 grants were made to 34 organisations.

HOW TO APPLY Application forms are available from the correspondent. Any hospital or registered charity may apply for a grant and all such applications are considered by the trustees who meet four times a year. '[The] reason for the rejection of appeals is due usually to an excessive amount involved.' Each application is considered on merit.

WHO TO APPLY TO Janet Wrighton, Secretary, Paycare House, George Street, Wolverhampton WV2 4DX *Tel.* 01902 371007 *email* enquiries@paycare.org

■ The Payne Charitable Trust

CC NO 241816   **ESTABLISHED** 1965

WHERE FUNDING CAN BE GIVEN Christian in Wales, West Midlands, Cumbria and India.

WHO CAN BENEFIT Missionaries, churches, and people engaged in the propagation of the Christian gospel.

WHAT IS FUNDED To support religious and charitable objects. The main area of interest is the support of evangelical Christians in the promotion and proclamation of the Christian gospel.

WHAT IS NOT FUNDED No grants for repairs to church buildings or towards education.

TYPE OF GRANT One-off grants and loans; capital support.

RANGE OF GRANTS Up to £30,000.

SAMPLE GRANTS Dayspring Trust for India (£30,000); Andrew League Trust (£28,500); Crusaders (£6,000); SASRA (£2,250); Nate and Ali Ussery – missionaries (£1,500); Armed Forces Christian Union and Heart Cry for Wales (£1,000 each); OAC West Midlands (£500); and Keith and Dorothy Ward – missionaries (£100).

FINANCES *Year* 2011–12 *Income* £48,606 *Grants* £41,000

TRUSTEES John Payne; Eric Payne.

OTHER INFORMATION Due to the large number of applications, some considerable time can elapse before communication can be sent.

HOW TO APPLY In writing to the correspondent. Applications should be submitted between 1 January and 21 March only, for grants made from the following 1 May. The trustees regret that they cannot support many of the deserving organisations that apply for a grant. Due to the large number of applications, some considerable time can elapse before communication can be sent.

WHO TO APPLY TO John Payne, Trustee, Fourwinds, Copthorn Road, Colwyn Bay LL28 5YP *Tel.* 01492 532393 *email* john@copthornehouse.com

■ The Harry Payne Trust

CC NO 231063   **ESTABLISHED** 1939

WHERE FUNDING CAN BE GIVEN Birmingham and the immediately surrounding areas of the West Midlands.

WHO CAN BENEFIT Voluntary organisations and charitable groups only. Support will be considered for a wide variety of medical conditions, but particularly where there is evidence of social disadvantage. The trust operates a non-discriminatory policy as regards religion.

WHAT IS FUNDED Priority is given to charitable work in Birmingham, where the trust was founded. Funding may be given to churches and religious ancillary buildings; family planning and Well Women clinics; hospices and hospitals; pre-school and special needs education; advice centres and community services and other charitable organisations.

WHAT IS NOT FUNDED No grants to individuals or organisations outside the beneficial area.

TYPE OF GRANT Capital (including buildings), one-off, research, running costs (including salaries), recurring costs and start-up costs will be considered. Funding may be given for up to three years.

RANGE OF GRANTS £100–£4,000, typical grant £250.

SAMPLE GRANTS Balsall Heath Church Centre (£4,000); Karis Neighbour Centre and Birmingham Settlement (£2,000 each); Garma and Deusa Schools Project and British Red Cross: East Africa Appeal (£1,000 each); Personal Support Unit, Women and Theatre and La Pepiniere Ministries Birmingham (£500 each); National Benevolent Fund for the Aged, Friends Community Centre, Joseph Leckie Community Association, Rollercoasters Playscheme, Shaan: The Asian Men's Project and Yemeni Educational Project (£250 each); and Community Transport Helpline (£180).

FINANCES *Year* 2011–12 *Income* £58,063 *Grants* £51,520 *Assets* £1,297,430

TRUSTEES Duncan Cadbury; Robert King; Fiona Adams; Valerie Dub; Stuart King; Donald Payne; Joseph Devlin; Kate Hazlewood.

HOW TO APPLY On a form available to download from the trust's website, where criteria and guidelines are also posted. Applications should include the organisation's most recent set of audited accounts and must be submitted by the end of May for the summer meeting and the end of November for the winter meeting. Applications are only considered from organisations with a turnover of less than £1 million. Successful applications will be acknowledged as soon as possible after the meeting at which they are considered. If it is not possible to complete and submit the application form electronically, the trust's preferred method, contact the secretary in the first instance.

WHO TO APPLY TO Robert King, Secretary, 1 Matthews Close, Rushton, Kettering, Northamptonshire NN14 1QJ *Tel.* 01536 418905 *email* robcking@harrypaynetrust.org.uk *Website* www.harrypaynetrust.org.uk

■ The Peacock Charitable Trust

CC NO 257655   **ESTABLISHED** 1968

WHERE FUNDING CAN BE GIVEN UK with a possible preference for London and the south of England.

WHO CAN BENEFIT Registered charities benefiting children and young adults, ex-service and service people, disabled people, ex-offenders, at risk groups and carers. Also people with Alzheimer's disease, arthritis and rheumatism, cancer, hearing loss, heart disease, mental illness, multiple sclerosis, and substance abuse.

WHAT IS FUNDED Charities which the trustees have special knowledge of, interest in, or association with, in the fields of medical research, disability, and some youth work.

WHAT IS NOT FUNDED No donations are made to individuals and only in rare cases are additions made to the list of charities already being supported.

TYPE OF GRANT Capital, project and some recurring.

RANGE OF GRANTS £1,500–£105,000.

SAMPLE GRANTS The Prince's Youth Business Trust (£103,000); Cancer Research UK (£95,000); Marie Curie Cancer Care (£75,000); The Jubilee Sailing Trust (£50,000); British Heart Foundation (£36,000); SENSE (£20,000); Cruse Bereavement Care (£9,000); The National Trust (£6,000); Centrepoint 8:59 (£5,000) and Royal Academy of Arts (£4,000).

FINANCES *Year* 2011–12 *Income* £402,466 *Grants* £1,486,200 *Assets* £39,169,544

TRUSTEES Charles Peacock; Bettine Bond; Dr Clare Sellors.

OTHER INFORMATION Of the grant total, only £29,000 was given to new applicants.

HOW TO APPLY In writing to the correspondent. The trustees meet three times a year with representatives from the Charities Aid Foundation (CAF) to decide on the grants to be made. The trust makes a lot of recurring grants therefore new applications are unlikely to be successful.

WHO TO APPLY TO The Administrator, c/o Charities Aid Foundation, Kings Hill, West Malling, Kent ME19 4TA *Tel.* 01732 520081

■ The Susanna Peake Charitable Trust

CC NO 283462   **ESTABLISHED** 1981

WHERE FUNDING CAN BE GIVEN UK, with a preference for the South West of England, particularly Gloucestershire.

WHO CAN BENEFIT Registered charities.

WHAT IS FUNDED General charitable purposes.

WHAT IS NOT FUNDED No grants to individuals.

TYPE OF GRANT Usually one-off grants.

RANGE OF GRANTS Usually £500–£5,000.

SAMPLE GRANTS Longborough School (£10,000); Speech, Language and Hearing Centre (£6,000); Gloucester County Council for the Blind and Rutland Houses School Parents (£5,000 each); Charity Search and Cotswold Care Hospice (£4,000 each); Friends of St Lawrence Church and Training for Life (£3,000 each); PDSA and WaterAid (£2,000 each); Victim Support (£1,000); and Kidscape (£100).

FINANCES *Year* 2011–12 *Income* £154,155 *Grants* £156,500 *Assets* £5,512,200

TRUSTEES Susanna Peake; David Peake.

HOW TO APPLY In writing to the correspondent. 'The trustees meet on an ad hoc basis to review applications for funding, and a full review is undertaken annually when the financial statements are available. Only successful applications are notified of the trustees' decision.'

WHO TO APPLY TO The Administrator, Rathbone Trust Company Limited, 1 Curzon Street, London W1J 5FB *Tel.* 020 7399 0811

■ The David Pearlman Charitable Foundation

CC NO 287009   **ESTABLISHED** 1983
WHERE FUNDING CAN BE GIVEN UK.
WHO CAN BENEFIT Jewish people.
WHAT IS FUNDED General charitable purposes.
SAMPLE GRANTS Previously:
British Friends of Igud Hakolelim B'Yerushalayim (£60,000); Lolev Charitable Trust (£30,000); Jewish Care (£16,000); Chevras Mo'oz Ladol (£15,000); Norwood (£12,000); the Duke of Edinburgh Trust (£7,000); Community Security Trust (£6,000); Life's 4 Living Trust Ltd (£6,400); Children Number One Foundation (£3,750); the Variety Club Children's Charity (£2,750); London Academy of Jewish Studies (£1,500); Jewish Music Institute and United Jewish Israel Appeal (£1,000).
FINANCES *Year* 2011–12 *Income* £177,661 *Grants* £86,184 *Assets* £2,530,459
TRUSTEES D. A. Pearlman; M. R. Goldberger; S. Appleman; J. Hager.
HOW TO APPLY In writing to the correspondent.
WHO TO APPLY TO D. Goldberger, Trustee, New Burlington House, 1075 Finchley Road, London NW11 0PU *Tel.* 020 8731 0777

■ The Pears Family Charitable Foundation

CC NO 1009195   **ESTABLISHED** 1991
WHERE FUNDING CAN BE GIVEN Worldwide.
WHO CAN BENEFIT Charitable organisations.
WHAT IS FUNDED The foundation invests in five main areas:
Identity, community and citizenship in the UK: the foundation promotes citizenship and a positive contribution to British society. The foundation invests in programmes that build respect and understanding between people of different backgrounds as well as address issues of special needs and social exclusion.
Jewish contribution to society: the foundation supports organisations and entrepreneurs who place social action and responsibility at the heart of Jewish identity. The foundation also supports NGO's working to enhance civil and human rights and has a particular focus on issues of equality between Arabs and Jews in Israel.
Education on genocide: the foundation invests in Holocaust education in the UK and international campaigns against genocide and crimes against humanity.
Israel as a global citizen: the foundation supports Israel by being a critical friend and encourages the country to keep faith with its founders' vision to be a force for good in the world. The foundation invests in Israel's academic expertise, particularly in public health and agriculture, its contribution to international development, and scientific co-operation between British and Israeli universities.
Exploring philanthropy: the foundation invests in special initiatives focusing on understanding and promoting philanthropy. This includes a collaboration with City University's Centre for Giving and Philanthropy to publish the annual Family Foundations Giving Trends series which

tracks the spending of the UK's largest family foundations. The foundation also maintains a dialogue with peers within and beyond the philanthropy sector.
TYPE OF GRANT Core, project and capital.
RANGE OF GRANTS Up to £1 million
SAMPLE GRANTS Marie Curie Cancer Care (£1 million); The Three Faiths Forum (£600,000); The Duke of Edinburgh's Award (£250,000); Institute for Philanthropy (£200,000); University of Leeds (£150,000); New Israel Fund UK (£138,000) and Haven House Children's Hospice (£100,000).
FINANCES *Year* 2011–12 *Income* £6,456,967 *Grants* £8,642,238 *Assets* £16,981,710
TRUSTEES Trevor Pears; Mark Pears; David Pears.
HOW TO APPLY 'Note that we do not accept unsolicited applications. The foundation has a full time staff, and specialist consultants, who proactively research areas of interest, creating strategic plans and partnerships with organisations seeking to effect sustainable change. The trustees meet quarterly to review the strategic direction of the foundation and to consider major proposals.'
WHO TO APPLY TO The Trustees, Clive House, 2 Old Brewery Mews, London NW3 1PZ *Tel.* 020 7433 3333 *email* contact@pearsfoundation.org. uk *Website* www.pearsfoundation.org.uk

---

■ The Pedmore Sporting Club Trust Fund

CC NO 263907   **ESTABLISHED** 1973
WHERE FUNDING CAN BE GIVEN West Midlands.
WHO CAN BENEFIT Registered charities and individuals.
WHAT IS FUNDED General charitable purposes.
WHAT IS NOT FUNDED No grants towards running costs or salaries.
TYPE OF GRANT Recurrent
RANGE OF GRANTS £150–£10,000
SAMPLE GRANTS Ladies Fighting Breast Cancer (£10,000); Mary Stevens Hospice (£5,000); Stambermlll Scouts (£4,000); Creating Chances Trust (£3,000); Stourbridge CAB (£3,400); Riding for the Disabled (£2,500); Glasshouse College, Stourbridge (£2,000); Midland Air Ambulance (£1,000); Birmingham Children's Hospital (£500) and Dodford Children's Farm (£150).
FINANCES *Year* 2012 *Income* £41,748 *Grants* £56,547 *Assets* £283,972
TRUSTEES R. Herman-Smith; R. Williams; T. Hickman; J. Price.
HOW TO APPLY In writing to the correspondent or by email. The trustees meet to consider grants in January, May, September and November and typically will consider 30–40 applications.
WHO TO APPLY TO Alan Nicklin, Secretary, Pedmore Sporting Club Trust, Nicklin and Co, Church Court, Stourbridge Road, Halesowen B63 3TT *email* psclub@pedmorehouse.co.uk *Website* www.pedmoresportingclub.co.uk

---

■ The Dowager Countess Eleanor Peel Trust

CC NO 214684   **ESTABLISHED** 1951
WHERE FUNDING CAN BE GIVEN Worldwide, in practice UK, with a preference for Lancashire (especially Lancaster and District), Cumbria, Greater Manchester, Cheshire and Merseyside.
WHO CAN BENEFIT Registered charities and universities.

WHAT IS FUNDED General charitable purposes, particularly medical charities, charities for the elderly and socially disadvantaged people.

WHAT IS NOT FUNDED Grants are not made to charities substantially under the control of central or local government or charities primarily devoted to children. Applications from individuals are not considered, except for medical research grants and annual travelling fellowship awards.

TYPE OF GRANT The trust prefers to support projects rather than running costs.

RANGE OF GRANTS Mostly between £1,000 and £5,000.

SAMPLE GRANTS Peel Studentship Trust – University of Lancaster (£35,000); University of Manchester (£28,000); Mood Swing Network and the British Red Cross (£10,000 each); Genesis Breast Cancer Prevention Appeal (£9,500); Marfan Trust (£8,000); Tax Help for Older People (£4,000); Coalition for the Removal of Pimping, FareShare and Relate Lancashire and Cumbria (£5,000 each); and the Olive Branch (£1,500).

FINANCES *Year* 2011–12 *Income* £574,647 *Grants* £306,450 *Assets* £15,116,702

TRUSTEES Sir Robert Boyd; John W. Parkinson; Michael Parkinson; Prof. Richard Ramsden; Prof. Margaret Pearson; Julius Manduell.

HOW TO APPLY The trustees apply the following criteria in making grants: 1. There is no geographical limitation on applications; however applications from charities in the 'preferred Locations' of Lancashire (especially Lancaster and District), Cumbria, Greater Manchester, Cheshire and Merseyside will receive preference over applications from other geographical areas; 2. The trustees focus on small to medium sized charities where grants will make a difference. Applications from large well-funded charities (with income in excess of £2.5 million per annum) will normally be rejected, unless the project is a capital project; 3. The trustees aim to support fewer charities with larger average grants (£5,000 or more); 4. The trustees' preference is to support capital projects or project driven applications and not running costs, although the trustees are flexible to take account of the needs of smaller charities (with an income of up to £2.5 million) which operate in the trust's preferred locations. For charities in this category the trust will consider supporting revenue projects and running costs in addition to capital projects. The trustees scrutinise the financial position of all applicants. Those with income accounts showing substantial surpluses are unlikely to be supported; 5. The trustees do make grants to disaster appeals which are considered on a case by case basis. The trustees feel it is important to know the charities to which grants are or may be awarded. They will therefore from time to time arrange to visit the charity and/or arrange for the charity to make a presentation to a trustees meeting. Applications for grants along with the required supporting information, should be forwarded by post or email. The following information is required: a general outline of the reasons for the application; the amount of grant applied for; the latest annual report and audited accounts; if the application is for a major capital project, details of the cost of the project together with information regarding funds already in hand or pledged. A grant application form can be downloaded from the trust's website or completed online. *Applications for Medical Research Grants*: applications for medical research grants will be categorised as appropriate for a 'minor grant' (£10,000 or less) or a 'major grant' (greater than £10,000 per annum for a defined research project for one to three years). Applications to be considered for a major grant will be assessed en-block annually at the trustee's March meeting. Applications will be competitive and will be met from funds set aside for this purpose. The following additional information is required: aims, objectives and direction of the research project; the institution where the research will be carried out and by whom (principal researchers); an outline of costs and of funding required for the project and details of any funds already in hand. A brief (but not too technical) annual report on the progress of projects receiving major grants will be requested from the research team. *Minor medical grants:* these are for sums up to a maximum of £10,000 and ordinarily are for areas such as 'pilot study costs' or equipment. Applications for Minor Grants are considered at each of the trustees meeting which are ordinarily held in March, July and November each year.

WHO TO APPLY TO Allan J. Twitchett, Secretary, Trowers and Hamlins LLP, 3 Bunhill Row, London EC1Y 8YZ *Tel.* 020 7423 8000 *email* secretary@peeltrust.com *Website* www.peeltrust.com

....

■ Pegasus (Stanley) Trust

CC NO 1108684   **ESTABLISHED** 2005

WHERE FUNDING CAN BE GIVEN Mainly Shropshire.

WHO CAN BENEFIT Organisations and individuals.

WHAT IS FUNDED The main object of the trust is relief in need for people who have had cancer and/or strokes, grants are also given to other charities.

RANGE OF GRANTS £500–£25,000.

FINANCES *Year* 2011–12 *Income* £49,400 *Grants* £42,161 *Assets* £24,834

TRUSTEES Henry Carpenter; Harry Rollo Gabb; Caspar Gabb; Frank Bury.

OTHER INFORMATION The trust organises an annual event in May at Stanley Hall, in Shropshire, to raise funds.

HOW TO APPLY In writing to the correspondent.

WHO TO APPLY TO Harry Rollo Gabb, Trustee, 84 Faroe Road, London W14 0EP *email* ACSULW@aol.com *Website* www.pegasustrust.org

....

■ The Pell Charitable Trust

CC NO 1135398   **ESTABLISHED** 2010

WHERE FUNDING CAN BE GIVEN UK

WHO CAN BENEFIT Registered charities.

WHAT IS FUNDED General charitable purposes, with a preference for the arts, particularly music.

WHAT IS NOT FUNDED No grants to individuals.

RANGE OF GRANTS £100 to £16,000.

SAMPLE GRANTS Royal National Theatre; British Red Cross; Duke of Edinburgh's Awards; Welsh National Opera; Royal Opera House Foundation; Caudwell Children; Donmar Warehouse Projects; Wylye Valley Disabled Children Riding; Almeida Theatre; English National Opera; London Fund for Young Musicians.

FINANCES *Year* 2011–12 *Income* £56,573 *Grants* £52,786 *Assets* £186,352

TRUSTEES Marian Pell; Gordon Pell; Nicholas Pell; Coutts and Co.

HOW TO APPLY In writing to the correspondent.

WHO TO APPLY TO Trustee Dept, Coutts and Co, 440 Strand, London WC2R 0QS *Tel.* 020 7663 6825

■ The Peltz Trust

CC NO 1002302   **ESTABLISHED** 1991
WHERE FUNDING CAN BE GIVEN UK and Israel.
WHO CAN BENEFIT Charitable organisations.
RANGE OF GRANTS £1,000–£20,000.
SAMPLE GRANTS Birkbeck College (£50,000); British Technion Society (£21,000); Central Synagogue General Charities Fund (£13,000); Norwood Ravencourt (£10,000); City of London School, UK Friends of Magen David Adom, One Family and United Jewish Israel Appeal (£5,000 each); Nightingale House (£2,500); AISH Hatorah UK Ltd (£1,500); Willow Foundation (£1,000); and Mousetrap Theatre Projects (£500).
FINANCES *Year* 2011–12 *Income* £1,005,623 *Grants* £159,775 *Assets* £639,941
TRUSTEES Martin Paisner; Daniel Peltz; Hon. Elizabeth Wolfson Peltz.
HOW TO APPLY In writing to the correspondent. The trustees meet at irregular intervals during the year to consider appeals from appropriate organisations.
WHO TO APPLY TO Martin Paisner, Trustee, Berwin Leighton Paisner, Adelaide House, London Bridge, London EC4R 9HA *Tel.* 020 3400 2356

■ The Pen Shell Project

CC NO 1147958   **ESTABLISHED** 2012
WHERE FUNDING CAN BE GIVEN UK.
WHO CAN BENEFIT Charities and community groups.
WHAT IS FUNDED Healthcare and related research.
TRUSTEES Charles Wansbrough; Amelia Heighington; Digby Leighton Squires; Elaine Heighington.
OTHER INFORMATION The website states the following: 'The Charity exists to make grants in certain specialised fields of healthcare and related research as directed by the Trustees.'
HOW TO APPLY The charity states that it 'does not encourage unsolicited applications'.
WHO TO APPLY TO Dominic Flynn, Administrator, c/o Portrait Solicitors, 21 Whitefriars Street, London EC4Y 8JJ *email* info@penshellproject.org *Website* penshellproject.org/index.html

■ The Pennycress Trust

CC NO 261536   **ESTABLISHED** 1970
WHERE FUNDING CAN BE GIVEN UK and worldwide, with a preference for Cheshire and Norfolk.
WHO CAN BENEFIT Voluntary organisations and charitable groups only.
WHAT IS FUNDED General charitable purposes. Support is given to a restricted list of registered charities only, principally in Cheshire and Norfolk, in the fields of: arts and cultural heritage; education; infrastructure, support and development; science and technology; community facilities; campaigning on health and social issues; health care and advocacy; medical studies and research; and animal welfare.
WHAT IS NOT FUNDED No support for individuals.
TYPE OF GRANT Recurrent and one-off.
RANGE OF GRANTS Usually £100–£500.
SAMPLE GRANTS Previous beneficiaries have included All Saints' Church – Beeston Regis, Brain Research Trust, Brighton and Hove Parents' and Children's Group, British Red Cross, Crusaid, Depaul Trust, Elimination of Leukaemia Fund, Eyeless Trust, Genesis Appeal, Help the Aged, Matthew Project, RUKBA, St Peter's – Eaton Square Appeal, Salvation Army, Tibet Relief Fund, West Suffolk Headway, Women's Link and Youth Federation.

FINANCES *Year* 2011–12 *Income* £78,578 *Grants* £63,383 *Assets* £2,099,860
TRUSTEES Lady Aline Cholmondeley; Anthony J. M. Baker; C. G. Cholmondeley; Sybil Sassoon.
HOW TO APPLY In writing to the correspondent. 'No telephone applications please.' Trustees meet regularly. They do not have an application form as a simple letter will be sufficient.
WHO TO APPLY TO Doreen Howells, Secretary to the Trustees, Flat D, 15 Millman Street, London WC1N 3EP *Tel.* 020 7404 0145

■ People's Postcode Trust

SC NO SC040387   **ESTABLISHED** 2009
WHERE FUNDING CAN BE GIVEN Scotland, Wales and England.
WHO CAN BENEFIT Registered charities and community organisations.
WHAT IS FUNDED Welfare, health, sports, community, rights, environment. The trust currently runs two grant programmes: 1.) Small Grants Programme – £500 to £10,000 for projects of up to six months in length in Scotland and England, and up to £5,000 in Wales and 2.) Dream Fund – Up to £250,000 for charities to run projects of up to 24 months in length they have always dreamed of but never had the opportunity to bring to life. See the website for up-to-date details of all programmes.
WHAT IS NOT FUNDED No grants for running costs.
RANGE OF GRANTS £500 to £250,000
SAMPLE GRANTS Enable Scotland and Impact Arts (£99,000); Manchester International Festival and The Biospheric Project (£91,000); Wild Things! and the Dolphin Conservation Society (£74,000); 1st/2nd Derbyshire Scout Group and Autism Ventures Scotland (£10,000 each); Birkenhead YMCA (£6,000); Friends of Cambuslang Park (£3,500) and Kemistry (£700).
FINANCES *Year* 2012 *Income* £9,401,012 *Grants* £9,500,000
TRUSTEES Lawson Muncaster; Stephen Naysmith; Mike Pratt; Judy Hills.
OTHER INFORMATION Note: 'People's Postcode Trust funds areas where players of People's Postcode Lottery are at the highest intensity. This means that we currently only accept applications in England from the following areas: The NORTH (includes North East, North West, and Yorkshire and Humber); The SOUTH excl. Greater London (includes South East and South West); The MIDLANDS (includes East Midlands and West Midlands) and GREATER LONDON.'
HOW TO APPLY On forms available to download from the website along with guidelines and criteria. Funding deadlines differ depending on the region and the programme; check the website for the next deadlines. Applicants will be informed of a decision six to eight weeks after the deadline.
WHO TO APPLY TO Joe Ray, Grants Officer, 76 George Street, Edinburgh EH2 3BU *Tel.* 01315 557287 *email* info@postcodetrust.org.uk *Website* www.postcodetrust.org.uk

■ The Performing Right Society Foundation

CC NO 1080837   **ESTABLISHED** 2000
WHERE FUNDING CAN BE GIVEN UK.
WHO CAN BENEFIT Music creators, performers and promoters who are involved in creatively adventurous or pioneering musical activity.

WHAT IS FUNDED A huge range of new music activity, for example, unsigned band showcases, festivals, residencies for composers, ground breaking commissions, live electronica, training of music producers, cross art form commissioning and special projects.

WHAT IS NOT FUNDED The foundation will not offer funding for: companies limited by shares; recording costs (recording costs can only be supported through Momentum Music Fund); projects that contain no element of live performance; technological development if it does not contain a significant aspect of new music creation; the purchase of vans and cars; bursaries, tuition/education costs, or scholarships; capital projects (e.g. building work); any project raising funds for another charity; buying equipment/building a studio; organisations or projects that have been running for less than 18 months and musicians that have not been; active for 18 months; retrospective activity; activity that falls before the trust's decision date; organisations based outside the UK; artists and music creators based outside of the UK; British artists no longer permanently resident in the UK; international tours/recording internationally; radio stations/broadcasting costs; start-up companies or labels; a roster of artists on a record label; and editing, mastering or distribution of work.

TYPE OF GRANT Usually one year funding for revenue costs.

SAMPLE GRANTS Arts and Refugees Network Yorks and Humber; Brass Band Heritage Trust; Contemporary Music East (CME); 2 for the Road; Focus Wales; Get it Loud in Libraries; Hackney Music Development Trust; London Contemporary Orchestra; Metta Theatre; Oh Yeah Music Centre; Orange Hill Productions; and Workers Union Ensemble.

FINANCES *Year* 2012 *Income* £2,089,999 *Grants* £1,182,214 *Assets* £621,812

TRUSTEES Prof. Edward Gregson; Simon Platz; Baroness Estelle Morris; Sally Millest; Paulette Long; Mick Leeson; Stephen McNeff; Simon Darlow; Ameet Shah; Vanessa Swann; John Reid.

OTHER INFORMATION A list of grant recipients was not included in the accounts. However, details of previously funded projects are available on the foundation's website, though without information on the individual grant awards.

HOW TO APPLY Apply via the trust's website. The application forms for each programme also include full guidelines for applicants. Deadlines for applications vary from programme to programme. Contact the foundation or go to the website for further information. The foundation stresses that it funds NEW music.

WHO TO APPLY TO Fiona Harvey, Operations Director, 29–33 Berners Street, London W1T 3AB *Tel.* 020 7306 4233 *Fax* 020 7306 4814 *email* info@prsformusicfoundation.com *Website* www.prsformusicfoundation.com

....
■ B. E. Perl Charitable Trust

CC NO 282847　　　　**ESTABLISHED** 1981
WHERE FUNDING CAN BE GIVEN UK.
WHO CAN BENEFIT Orthodox Jewish organisations, particularly schools.
WHAT IS FUNDED The advancement of education in, and the religion of, the Orthodox Jewish faith and other general charitable purposes.

SAMPLE GRANTS Hasmonean High School, JNF, Society of Friends of the Torah and Yavenh College.

FINANCES *Year* 2011–12 *Income* £1,854,556 *Grants* £74,865 *Assets* £15,553,335

TRUSTEES Benjamin Perl, Chair; Dr Shoshanna Perl; Jonathan Perl; Joseph Perl; Naomi Sorotzkin; Rachel Jeidal.

OTHER INFORMATION Note the following statement taken from the trust's 2011–12 annual report and accounts: 'The trustees have considered and approved plans for the establishment of a major educational project in the UK. It is anticipated that the cost of this project will be in the order of £5 million and it is the intentions of the trustees to accumulate this amount over the next ten years. During the period an amount of £500,000 (2011–£500,000) was transferred to the Educational Reserve in order to fund this project. The Educational Reserve for this purpose stands at £3 million as at the balance sheet date.'

HOW TO APPLY In writing to the correspondent.

WHO TO APPLY TO Benjamin Perl, Trustee, Foframe House, 35–37 Brent Street, Hendon, London NW4 2EF

....
■ The Persson Charitable Trust (formerly Highmoore Hall Charitable Trust)

CC NO 289027　　　　**ESTABLISHED** 1984
WHERE FUNDING CAN BE GIVEN UK and overseas.
WHO CAN BENEFIT Registered charities benefiting: Christians; at risk groups; and victims of famine, man-made and natural disasters and war.
WHAT IS FUNDED Christian mission societies and relief agencies.
WHAT IS NOT FUNDED No grants to non-registered charities.
TYPE OF GRANT Mainly recurrent
SAMPLE GRANTS Bible Reading Fellowship (£111,000); Tearfund – Christian Relief (£55,000); All Nations Christian College (£12,000); and Christian Solidarity Worldwide (£10,000).
FINANCES *Year* 2011–12 *Income* £254,149 *Grants* £221,100 *Assets* £614,812
TRUSTEES Paul Persson; Andrew Persson; John Persson; Ann Persson.
HOW TO APPLY The trust states that it does not respond to unsolicited applications. Telephone calls are not welcome.
WHO TO APPLY TO Paul Persson, Trustee, Long Meadow, Dark Lane, Chearsley, Aylesbury, Buckinghamshire HP18 0DA *Tel.* 01844 201955 *email* paulpersson@xalt.co.uk

....
■ The Persula Foundation

CC NO 1044174　　　　**ESTABLISHED** 1994
WHERE FUNDING CAN BE GIVEN Predominantly UK; overseas grants are given, but this is rare.
WHO CAN BENEFIT Mainly small registered charities benefiting at risk groups, people who are socially isolated, disadvantaged by poverty or homeless, people with cancer or disabilities, including visual impairment, deafness, spinal injuries and multiple sclerosis, and animals.
WHAT IS FUNDED Original and unique projects of national benefit in the areas of homelessness, disability, and human and animal welfare.

WHAT IS NOT FUNDED No grants to individuals, including sponsorship, for core costs, buildings/building work or to statutory bodies.

TYPE OF GRANT Up to two years.

RANGE OF GRANTS Up to £50,000.

SAMPLE GRANTS Impact Youth Project Work (£45,000); WSPA Humane Slaughter (£35,000); Amnesty International UK (£25,000); Parent Circle Families Forum (£20,000)

FINANCES *Year* 2011–12 *Income* £807,000 *Grants* £709,000 *Assets* £40,018

TRUSTEES J. Richer; D. Robinson; R. Richer; H. Oppenheim; Robert Rosenthal; Jonathan Levy.

HOW TO APPLY In writing to the correspondent. Trustees meet every two months. The foundation states: 'We consider applications which fit our broad criteria, but they must also fulfill the following: They must come from a registered charity or other appropriate organisation; The project should be an original idea, and not duplicating an existing service or suchlike; The project should be or have the potential to be of national application, rather than local to one area; We will not consider applications from charities that have substantial financial reserves (three to six months running costs), and ask to see an annual report from any charity making an application; Any charity with whom we work must be prepared to co-operate in a professional manner, for example, meet deadlines, return calls, perform mutually agreed work, in short, to behave 'commercially' The project, in most cases, must fall within the remit of one or more GRPs. They must provide value for money. This list is by no means exhaustive, nor is it final. We will attempt to consider every application but, in general, the above should apply.'

WHO TO APPLY TO Fiona Brown, Chief Executive, Gallery Court, Hankey Place, London SE1 4BB *Tel.* 020 7551 5343 *Fax* 020 7357 8685 *email* fiona@persula.org

··

■ The Jack Petchey Foundation

CC NO 1076886   **ESTABLISHED** 1999

WHERE FUNDING CAN BE GIVEN London, Essex and the Algarve, Portugal.

WHO CAN BENEFIT Registered charities and organisations supporting young people aged between 11 and 25.

WHAT IS FUNDED Support for young people through different programmes including: Achievement Award Scheme, Small Grants Scheme and the Individual Grants for Volunteering scheme. The foundation also runs the Petchey Academy, Jack Petchey's Speak Out Challenge!; Step Into Dance; Panathlon Challenge and TS Jack Petchey. For details of all these programmes visit the foundation's website.

WHAT IS NOT FUNDED The foundation will not accept applications: from private schools; from profit making companies; that directly replace statutory funding; from individuals or for the benefit of one individual (unless under the Individual Grants for Volunteering); for work that has already taken place; which do not directly benefit people in the UK; for medical research; for animal welfare; for endowment funds; that are part of general appeals or circulars; building or major refurbishment projects; conferences and seminars; projects where the main purpose is to promote religious beliefs.

SAMPLE GRANTS SpeakersBank Limited (£546,000); Royal Academy of Dance RAD (£440,000); School Planners (£80,000); ETTA (£70,500);

Army Cadet Force (£67,000); Panathlon Challenge (£42,500); Boys' Brigade and Community Links (£19,000 each); YMCA and STEMNET (£10,000 each).

FINANCES *Year* 2012 *Income* £5,647,217 *Grants* £4,932,875 *Assets* £67,696

TRUSTEE Jack Petchey Foundation Company

HOW TO APPLY Application forms for each of the grant schemes can be downloaded from the foundation's website. A typical application process takes six to eight weeks and applicants may be visited by a grants officer. Organisations must have in place: constitution/memorandum and articles of association; bank or building society accounts; public liability insurance; child protection policy; income and expenditure records (applicants may direct assessors to their Charity Commission record).

WHO TO APPLY TO Gemma Dunbar, Head of Grants, Exchange House, 13–14 Clements Court, Clements Lane, Ilford, Essex IG1 2QY *Tel.* 020 8252 8000 *Fax* 020 8477 1088 *email* mail@jackpetcheyfoundation.org.uk *Website* www.jackpetcheyfoundation.org.uk

··

■ The Petplan Charitable Trust

CC NO 1032907   **ESTABLISHED** 1994

WHERE FUNDING CAN BE GIVEN UK.

WHO CAN BENEFIT Animal charities and organisations benefiting students, research workers and veterinarians.

WHAT IS FUNDED Veterinary research, animal therapy, veterinary studies, animal welfare, education in animal welfare, and other charitable purposes. Help is limited to dogs, cats, rabbits and horses only, those being the animals insured by Pet Plan.

WHAT IS NOT FUNDED No grants to individuals or non-registered charities. The trust does not support or condone invasive procedures, vivisection or experimentation of any kind.

RANGE OF GRANTS Scientific grants: £4,000–£99,000. Welfare and education grants: up to £7,000.

SAMPLE GRANTS Royal Veterinary College (£133,000); University of Cambridge (£86,000); Ashbourne and District Animal Welfare Society (£20,000); Rain Rescue (£12,000); University of Edinburgh, Gable farm Dogs and Cats Home (£10,000 each); Animal Health Trust (£9,400); Wood Green Animal Shelter (£7,500); Oldies Club (£5,000); Labrador Rescue England (£2,000); Camp Nibble (£1,500); Joseph Clark School (£500) and English Springer Spaniel Welfare (£100).

FINANCES *Year* 2012 *Income* £682,722 *Grants* £681,053 *Assets* £378,792

TRUSTEES David Simpson, Chair; Clarissa Baldwin; Patsy Bloom; John Bower; Ted Chandler; Neil Brettell.

HOW TO APPLY Closing dates for scientific and welfare applications vary so check the trust's website first. Grant guidelines and application forms can also be downloaded from the trust's website.

WHO TO APPLY TO Catherine Bourg, Administrator, Great West House GW2, Great West Road, Brentford, Middlesex TW8 9EG *Tel.* 020 8580 8013 *Fax* 020 8580 8186 *email* catherine.bourg@allianz.co.uk *Website* www.petplantrust.org

■ The Pharsalia Charitable Trust

cc no 1120402　　**established** 2007
where funding can be given Unrestricted, with a particular interest in Oxford
what is funded General charitable purposes.
range of grants £100–£60,000.
sample grants The Vale House Appeal (£15,000); The Haig Housing Trust and Oxford Radcliffe Hospital Charitable Funds (£5,000 each); Bromsgrove Day Centre (£1,700); DEC East Africa Appeal, Helen and Douglas House, Motability, Sobell House Hospice and the Salvation Army (£1,000 each); Glacier Trust and Royal British Legion (£500 each) and Alzheimer's Research UK (£250).
finances *Year* 2011–12　*Income* £73,308　*Grants* £47,877　*Assets* £2,242,157
trustees Nigel Stirling Blackwell; Christina Blackwell; Trudy Sainsbury.
how to apply In writing to the correspondent.
who to apply to Trudy Sainsbury, Trustee, The Ham, Ickleton Road, Wantage, Oxfordshire OX12 9JA　*Tel.* 01235 426524

■ The Phillips and Rubens Charitable Trust

cc no 260378　　**established** 1970
where funding can be given UK.
who can benefit Registered charities, especially Jewish causes.
what is funded Jewish organisations, especially those in the fields of education, children's charities, the arts, and medical groups.
what is not funded No grants are made to individuals.
type of grant Recurrent and one-off.
sample grants The Phillips Family Charitable Trust (£80,000); United Jewish Israel Appeal (£42,000); Charities Aid Foundation (£25,000); Jewish Community Secondary School (£20,000); Simon Wiesenthal Centre (£16,000); Holocaust Educational Trust and Jewish Care (£7,500 each); The Churchill Centre United Kingdom, The Community Security Trust and British ORT (£5,000 each) and Nightingale House and UK Friends of the Association for the Wellbeing of Israel's Soldiers (£2,500 each).
finances *Year* 2011–12　*Income* £304,828　*Grants* £270,857　*Assets* £8,743,310
trustees Michael L. Philips; Ruth Philips; Martin D. Paisner; Paul Philips; Gary Philips; Carolyn Mishon.
other information Grants of less than £2,500 each totalled £17,000.
how to apply In writing to the correspondent at any time, although the trust has stated that the majority of grants are to beneficiaries they already support.
who to apply to M. L. Phillips, Trustee, 67–69 George Street, London W1U 8LT

■ The Phillips Charitable Trust

cc no 1057019　　**established** 1995
where funding can be given UK, with a preference for the Midlands, particularly Northamptonshire.
who can benefit Seafarer organisations, animal welfare organisations, the National Trust and English Heritage, and smaller one-off grants for national or local projects.
what is funded Seafaring and animal welfare and local community work.
type of grant Recurrent
range of grants £500–£15,000

sample grants Peterborough 900 (£15,000); Sportsaid Eastern (£10,000); Morning Star Trust and Prince's Trust (£4,000 each); Pitsford Sportsfield Charity and National Association for the Blind (£3,000 each); ABF The Soldiers' Charity (£2,500); Ro-Ro Sailing Project and Northampton Counselling Service (£2,000 each); Wildlife Trust (£1,500); Sailors Families Society and Brook Farm Animal Sanctuary (£1,000 each).
finances *Year* 2011–12　*Income* £72,554　*Grants* £63,863　*Assets* £2,546,669
trustees M. J. Ford; M. J. Percival; A. M. Marrum; P. R. Saunderson; S. G. Schanschieff.
other information In 2011–12 a total of 21 organisations received grants.
how to apply In writing to the correspondent.
who to apply to Angela Moon, Clerk, c/o Hewitsons, 7 Spencer Parade, Northampton NN1 5AB　*Tel.* 01604 230400　*email* GILL_EVANS@BTOPENWORLD.COM

■ The Phillips Family Charitable Trust

cc no 279120　　**established** 1979
where funding can be given UK.
who can benefit Registered charities only.
what is funded General charitable purposes, mainly Jewish organisations, and those concerned with older people, children, refugees and education.
what is not funded No grants to individuals.
type of grant Grants are given for core, capital and project support.
range of grants Up to £15,000, but mostly £5,000 or less.
sample grants London School of Jewish Studies (£6,000); Community Security Trust and United Synagogue (£5,000 each); Jewish Leadership Council (£4,500); Jewish Learning Exchange (£4,000); Norwood Ravenswood (£3,200); London Jewish Cultural Centre (£3,000); Tree of Life, Council of Christians and Jews, Interface Parent Carer Forum and Beth Shalom Limited (£1,000 each) and Chabad Lubavitch UK.
finances *Year* 2012–13　*Income* £80,000　*Grants* £70,028　*Assets* £25,059
trustees Michael L. Phillips; Ruth Phillips; Martin D. Paisner; Paul S. Phillips; Gary M. Phillips.
how to apply In writing to the correspondent. Note, the trust informed us that there is not much scope for new beneficiaries.
who to apply to Paul S. Phillips, Trustee, 67–69 George Street, London W1U 8LT　*Tel.* 020 7487 5757

■ Philological Foundation

cc no 312692　　**established** 1982
where funding can be given The City of Westminster and the London borough of Camden.
who can benefit Schools in the City of Westminster and the London borough of Camden, and their pupils and ex-pupils under 25 years of age.
what is funded Individuals may receive grants for educational expenses and tuition fees; schools in the area may benefit over a wide range of purposes.
what is not funded No support for schools not in Westminster or Camden and individuals who did not attend school in the City of Westminster or London borough of Camden. The foundation does not give bursaries, scholarships or loans.
range of grants £200–£2,000.

FINANCES *Year* 2011–12 *Income* £80,286 *Grants* £50,141 *Assets* £891,377

TRUSTEES Peter Sayers; Serena Standing; Gwyneth Hampson; Margery Hall; John Adams; David Jones; Gerald Margolis; Rita Brightmore; Carolyn Keen.

HOW TO APPLY There is an application form available for schools which may be obtained from the foundation. Individuals should apply in writing to the clerk. Trustees meet typically in January, March, June, September and December. Applications should be submitted several weeks before the relevant meeting. Successful applicants may reapply after one year.

WHO TO APPLY TO Audrey Millar, Clerk, Flat 15, Fitzwarren House, Hornsey Lane, London N6 5LX *Tel.* 020 7281 7439 *email* audreymillar@btinternet.com

■ The David Pickford Charitable Foundation

CC NO 243437   **ESTABLISHED** 1965

WHERE FUNDING CAN BE GIVEN UK (with a preference for Kent and London) and overseas.

WHO CAN BENEFIT Mainly, but not solely, young people particularly young people with special needs, and Christian evangelism.

WHAT IS FUNDED Support of a residential Christian youth centre in Kent for those in the 15 to 25 age group and other similar activities, mainly Christian youth work.

WHAT IS NOT FUNDED No grants to individuals. No building projects.

TYPE OF GRANT One-off and recurrent.

RANGE OF GRANTS £250–5,000.

SAMPLE GRANTS CARE; Chaucer Trust; Oasis Trust; Brighter Future and Pastor Training international; Toybox; Alpha International, Flow Romania and Mersham Parish Church; Compassion; Samaritans and Lionhart.

FINANCES *Year* 2011–12 *Income* £39,045 *Grants* £72,800 *Assets* £1,077,962

TRUSTEES C. J. Pickford; E. J. Pettersen;

HOW TO APPLY In writing to the correspondent. The deadline for applications is November. Applications will not be acknowledged. The correspondent states: 'It is our general policy only to give to charities to whom we are personally known.' Unsolicited applications are rarely funded. Those falling outside the criteria mentioned above will be ignored.

WHO TO APPLY TO E. J. Pettersen, Trustee, Benover House, Rectory Lane, Saltwood, Hythe, Kent CT21 4QA *Tel.* 01303 268322

■ The Pickwell Foundation

CC NO 1149424   **ESTABLISHED** 2012

WHERE FUNDING CAN BE GIVEN UK, with a possible preference for Devon.

WHO CAN BENEFIT Registered charities and community groups.

WHAT IS FUNDED General, education, social welfare, the environment; children and young people.

TRUSTEES Richard Elliott; Tracey Elliott; Susannah Baker; Stephen Baker.

HOW TO APPLY In writing to the correspondent.

WHO TO APPLY TO Richard Elliott, Trustee, Pickwell Manor, Georgeham, Braunton, Devon EX33 1LA *Tel.* 01271 890110 *email* richard@pickwellmanor.co.uk

■ The Bernard Piggott Charitable Trust

CC NO 260347   **ESTABLISHED** 1970

WHERE FUNDING CAN BE GIVEN North Wales and Birmingham.

WHO CAN BENEFIT Organisations benefiting children, young adults, medical, actors and entertainment professionals, and Church of England and Wales.

WHAT IS FUNDED Church of England; Church of Wales; education; medical charities, both care and research; drama and the theatre; youth and children.

WHAT IS NOT FUNDED No grants to individuals.

TYPE OF GRANT Usually one-off capital. No further grants within two years.

RANGE OF GRANTS £250–£2,000. Average about £1,000.

SAMPLE GRANTS The Joseph Foote Trust and Wales Air Ambulance (£2,000 each); InterAct Reading Service and Llandysilio Church Parochial Church Council (£1,500 each); Christian Mountain Centre Pensarn Harbour, Inclusion 4U, Birmingham Clubs for Young People, Combat Stress, Relate, Elmhurst, Motor Neurone Disease Association and Birmingham Children's Hospital (£1,000 each); Northfield Festival of Music and Speech (£750) and BUDS (Better Understanding of Dementia in Sandwell) (£500).

FINANCES *Year* 2011–12 *Income* £105,110 *Grants* £68,900 *Assets* £1,385,038

TRUSTEES Mark Painter; Derek Lea; Nigel Lea; Richard Easton; Venerable Paul Davies.

HOW TO APPLY The trustees meet in May/June and November. Applications should be in writing to the secretary including annual accounts and details of the specific project including running costs and so on. General policy is not to consider any further grant to the same institution within the next two years.

WHO TO APPLY TO Jenny Whitworth, Administrator, 4 Streetsbrook Road, Shirley, Solihull, West Midlands B90 3PL *Tel.* 01217 441695

■ The Pilgrim Trust

CC NO 206602   **ESTABLISHED** 1930

WHERE FUNDING CAN BE GIVEN UK, but not the Channel Islands and the Isle of Man.

WHO CAN BENEFIT Local and UK charities and recognised public bodies.

WHAT IS FUNDED Preservation and conservation (covering ecclesiastical buildings, secular buildings), learning and social welfare.

WHAT IS NOT FUNDED Grants are not made to: individuals; non-UK registered charities or charities registered in the Channel Islands or the Isle of Man; projects based outside the United Kingdom; projects where the work has already been completed or where contracts have already been awarded; organisations that have had a grant awarded by the trust within the past two years. Note: this does not refer to payments made within that timeframe; projects with a capital cost of over £1 million pounds where partnership funding is required; projects where the activities are considered to be primarily the responsibility of central or local government; general appeals or circulars; projects for the commissioning of new works of art; organisations seeking publishing production costs; projects seeking to develop new facilities within a church or the re-ordering of churches or places of worship for wider community use; any social welfare project that falls outside the trustees' current priorities; arts and drama projects – unless they can demonstrate that they are linked to clear educational goals for prisoners or those with drug or alcohol problems; drop in centres – unless the specific work within the centre falls within one of the trustees' current priority areas; youth or sports clubs, travel or adventure projects, community centres or children's play groups; organisations seeking funding for trips abroad; organisations seeking educational funding, e.g. assistance to individuals for degree or post-degree work or school, university or college development programmes; one-off events such as exhibitions, festivals, seminars, conferences or theatrical and musical productions.

TYPE OF GRANT Infrastructure costs for specific projects (salary and running costs up to a maximum of three years), capital grants. Also buildings, one-off, research and start-up costs.

RANGE OF GRANTS Small grants of less than £5,000 and main grants of over £5,000.

SAMPLE GRANTS National Cataloguing Scheme (£500,000); Association of Independent Museums (£323,000); Prison Reform Trust (£300,000); Church Building Council (£150,000); SPODA (£105,000); City and Guilds of London Art School (£50,000); The University of Oxford Development Trust (£43,000); Action on Addiction (£30,000); The Mavisbank Trust (£24,000); Up-2-Us (£17,000); Dunfermline Heritage Trust (£9,000); and Female Prisoners Welfare Project – Hibiscus (£5,000).

FINANCES *Year* 2012 *Income* £1,625,647 *Grants* £3,500,000 *Assets* £54,150,147

TRUSTEES Sylvia Jay; Tim Knox; Paul Richards; Mark Jones; Alan Moses; John Podmore; James Fergusson; David Verey; Prof. Colin Blakemore; Lady Riddell; Sarah Staniforth; Michael Baughan.

HOW TO APPLY Applications for both the small grants fund and the main grants can be made using the trust's online form. Applicants should read the application guidelines available on the website in full before applying. There are no deadlines; applications are considered at quarterly trustee meetings. The trust welcomes informal contact prior to an application via phone or email.

WHO TO APPLY TO Georgina Nayler, Director, 55a Catherine Place, London SW1E 6DY *Tel.* 020 7834 6510 *email* info@thepilgrimtrust.org.uk *Website* www.thepilgrimtrust.org.uk

---

■ The Cecil Pilkington Charitable Trust

CC NO 249997   **ESTABLISHED** 1966

WHERE FUNDING CAN BE GIVEN UK, particularly Sunningwell in Oxfordshire and St Helens.

WHO CAN BENEFIT Registered charities only.

WHAT IS FUNDED This trust supports conservation and medical research causes across the UK. It also has general charitable purposes.

WHAT IS NOT FUNDED No grants to individuals or non-registered charities.

RANGE OF GRANTS £500–£60,000.

SAMPLE GRANTS Psychiatry Research Trust (£50,000); Prostate Cancer Research Centre (£33,000); Peninsular Medical School Foundation (£24,000); Allergy UK, Epilepsy Research, Oxford Preservation Trust and Beating Bowel Cancer (£2,000 each) and British Horse Loggers Charitable Trust and Gordon Russell Trust (£1,000 each).

FINANCES *Year* 2010–11 *Income* £241,919 *Grants* £122,878 *Assets* £7,822,778

TRUSTEES A. P. Pilkington; R. F. Carter Jonas; M. R. Feeny.

OTHER INFORMATION The latest accounts available at the time of writing (October 2013) were for 2010/11.

HOW TO APPLY The trust does not respond to unsolicited appeals.

WHO TO APPLY TO Anthony Bayliss, Duncan Sheard Glass, Castle Chambers, 43 Castle Street, Liverpool L2 9TL

■ The Elise Pilkington Charitable Trust

CC NO 278332   **ESTABLISHED** 1979

WHERE FUNDING CAN BE GIVEN UK.

WHO CAN BENEFIT Organisations benefiting equines and older people in need.

WHAT IS FUNDED Welfare and relief work as well as prevention of cruelty.

TYPE OF GRANT Project costs, not running costs.

FINANCES *Year* 2011–12 *Income* £89,564 *Grants* £160,843 *Assets* £2,766,396

TRUSTEES Caroline Doulton, Chair; Tara Economakis; Revd Rob Merchant; Helen Timpany.

OTHER INFORMATION £95,000 in ten grants was given to prevent cruelty to equine animals and £66,000 in 12 grants to provide help for the aged, infirm or poor.

HOW TO APPLY In writing to the correspondent including: 'Five copies of your full application letter along with five copies of your latest consolidated statement of financial activity and balance sheet (we don't need five full sets of the accounts).'

'Detail in your application what percentage of your income is actually used for charitable purposes. In the case of equine application, outline the number of equines your charity currently has in the centre, the number taken in during the last twelve months and the number rehomed during the same period. The deadlines are 28 March for consideration in May and 30 September for consideration in October. Successful applicants must wait three years before reapplying.'

WHO TO APPLY TO Kenton Lawton, Trust Administrator, Ridgecot, Lewes Road, Horsted Keynes, Haywards Heath, West Sussex RH17 7DY *Tel.* 01825 790304 *Website* elisepilkingtontrust.org.uk

---

■ The Pilkington Charities Fund

CC NO 225911   **ESTABLISHED** 1964

WHERE FUNDING CAN BE GIVEN Worldwide, in practice mainly UK with a preference for Merseyside.

WHO CAN BENEFIT Registered charities.

WHAT IS FUNDED Health, social welfare, people with disabilities, older people and victims of natural disaster or war.

WHAT IS NOT FUNDED Applications from unregistered organisations and individuals are not considered.

TYPE OF GRANT Capital (including buildings), core costs, one-off, project, research, recurring costs. Funding for more than three years will be considered.

RANGE OF GRANTS Up to £10,000, although exceptional large grants are made.

SAMPLE GRANTS Action for Addiction and UK Neurology Research Campaign (£10,000 each); Church Housing Trust and Medical Aid for

Palestinians (£5,000 each); Wirral Autistic Society (£4,000); Fairbridge and Toxteth Town Hall Community Resource Centre (£3,000 each); St John's Hospice and The Florence Institute Trust (£2,000 each) and Blood Pressure Association (£1,000).

FINANCES *Year* 2011–12 *Income* £668,240 *Grants* £419,500 *Assets* £19,025,051

TRUSTEES Neil Pilkington Jones; Jennifer Jones; Arnold Philip Pilkington.

HOW TO APPLY In writing to the correspondent. Applications should include charity registration number, a copy of the latest accounts and details of the project for which support is sought. Grants are awarded twice a year, in November and April.

WHO TO APPLY TO Jennifer Jones, Trustee, Rathbones, Port of Liverpool Building, Pier Head, Liverpool L3 1NW *Tel.* 01512 366666 *email* sarah.nicklin@rathbones.com

■ The Sir Harry Pilkington Trust

CC NO 206740   **ESTABLISHED** 1962
WHERE FUNDING CAN BE GIVEN UK, in practice Merseyside.

WHO CAN BENEFIT Charitable organisations.

WHAT IS FUNDED General charitable purposes with a preference for arts and culture, youth work and health and general social welfare.

RANGE OF GRANTS £1,000–£3,000.

SAMPLE GRANTS Liverpool Charity and Voluntary Services (£160,000); Fazakerley Community Federation (£2,600); Croxteth and Gilmoss Community Council and Belle Vale Adventure Playground (£2,000 each); Woodchurch Amateur Boxing Club, West Derby Tuition and Choices Lifelong Learning (£1,500 each) and East 14 Film and Theatre Productions, Liverpool Homeless Football Club, Somali Welfare Development Trust and Woodlands Christian Revival Centre (£1,000 each).

FINANCES *Year* 2011–12 *Income* £189,560 *Grants* £208,150 *Assets* £5,042,947

TRUSTEE Liverpool Charity and Voluntary Services.

HOW TO APPLY In writing to the correspondent. The trust welcomes an initial phone call to discuss the proposal.

WHO TO APPLY TO The Trustees, Liverpool Charity And Voluntary Services, 151 Dale Street, Liverpool L2 2AH *Tel.* 01512 275177

■ The Austin and Hope Pilkington Trust

CC NO 255274   **ESTABLISHED** 1967
WHERE FUNDING CAN BE GIVEN Unrestricted, but see exclusions field.

WHO CAN BENEFIT Registered charities only. National projects are preferred to those with a local remit.

WHAT IS FUNDED The trust has a three-year cycle of funding. (2012 – community, medical; 2013 – children, youth; 2014 – music and the arts, elderly.) These categories are then repeated in a three-year rotation.

WHAT IS NOT FUNDED Grants only to registered charities. No grants to individuals, including individuals embarking on a trip overseas with an umbrella organisation. Overseas projects are no longer supported. National organisations are more likely to be supported than purely local organisations. Charities working in the following areas are not supported: religion (including repair of Church fabric); animals (welfare and

conservation); scouts, guides, cubs, brownies; village halls; individual hospices (national organisations can apply); capital appeals; schools; and minibuses.

TYPE OF GRANT Grants are usually awarded for one year only.

RANGE OF GRANTS Grants are usually between £1,000 and £3,000, with the majority being £1,000. Exceptionally, grants of up to £10,000 are made, but these are usually for medical research projects.

SAMPLE GRANTS Cancer Research UK (£10,000); Genesis Breast Cancer Prevention (£5,000); CLIC Sargent, Shelter, Tommy's and Westminster Befriend a Family (£3,000 each); and Emmaus, Kirby Trust, April Centre, Big Issue, Cardiff bond Board, Housing for Woman, Lesbian and Gay Foundation, Sign Health and Spadework (£1,000 each).

FINANCES *Year* 2012 *Income* £328,329 *Grants* £308,686 *Assets* £9,526,929

TRUSTEES Jennifer Jones; Deborah Nelson; Penny Shankar.

OTHER INFORMATION 2011 was the last year grants will be made to overseas projects. This will be reviewed in 2014. To mark the end of financial support for overseas charities, the trustees awarded a grant of £10,000 to Oxfam's East Africa Famine Appeal in 2011.

HOW TO APPLY Applicants are strongly advised to visit the trust's website as projects supported and eligibility criteria change from year to year. Grants are made twice a year, with deadlines for applications being 1 June and 1 November. Applications should be made in writing to the correspondent – do not use signed for or courier. To apply for a grant, submit *only* the following: A letter summarising the application, including acknowledgement of any previous grants awarded from the trust; a maximum of two sides of A4 (including photographs) summarising the project; a detailed budget for the project; a maximum of two sides of A4 (including photographs) summarising the charity's general activities; the most recent accounts and annual report.
'Do not send CDs, DVDs, or any other additional information. If we require further details, we will contact the charity directly. Charities are therefore advised to send in applications with sufficient time before the June or November deadlines to allow for such enquiries.' With the increased level of applications, the trust has stated that all successful applicants will in future be listed on their website on the 'recent awards' after each trustee meeting. All applicants will still be contacted by letter in due course. Early applications are strongly encouraged.

WHO TO APPLY TO Karen Frank, Administrator, PO Box 124, Stroud, Gloucestershire GL6 7YB *email* admin@austin-hope-pilkington.org.uk *Website* www.austin-hope-pilkington.org.uk

■ The Col W. W. Pilkington Will Trusts – The General Charity Fund

CC NO 234710   **ESTABLISHED** 1964
WHERE FUNDING CAN BE GIVEN Mainly UK, with a preference for Merseyside.

WHO CAN BENEFIT Registered charities only.

WHAT IS FUNDED Medical, arts, social welfare, drugs misuse, international and environmental charities.

WHAT IS NOT FUNDED No support for non-registered charities, building projects or individuals.

TYPE OF GRANT Generally annual.

SAMPLE GRANTS Everyman Theatre Liverpool, Anti-Slavery and Prisoner's Education Trust (£1,500 each); Hope UK, Lupus UK, Tourettes Action, Bug Life, Tree Aid and Minority Rights Group International (£1,000 each) and North End Writers and Hope Centre St Helens (£700).

FINANCES *Year* 2011–12 *Income* £62,865 *Grants* £37,000 *Assets* £1,771,648

TRUSTEES Arnold Pilkington; Jennifer Jones; Neil Pilkington Jones.

HOW TO APPLY In writing to the correspondent, outlining clear statement of need and including recent accounts.

WHO TO APPLY TO Sarah Nicklin, Administrator, Rathbones, Port of Liverpool Building, Pier Head, Liverpool L3 1NW *Tel.* 01512 366666

■ Miss A. M. Pilkington's Charitable Trust

SC NO SC000282   **ESTABLISHED** 1972

WHERE FUNDING CAN BE GIVEN UK, with a preference for Scotland.

WHO CAN BENEFIT Registered charities.

WHAT IS FUNDED General charitable purposes, including conservation/environment, health and social welfare.

WHAT IS NOT FUNDED Grants are not given to overseas projects or political appeals.

FINANCES *Year* 2012–13 *Income* £129,979 *Grants* £130,000

OTHER INFORMATION The grants total is an approximate amount based on previous years.

HOW TO APPLY The trustees state that, regrettably, they are unable to make grants to new applicants since they already have 'more than enough causes to support'.

WHO TO APPLY TO The Clerk, Carters Chartered Accountants, Pentland House, Saltire Centre, Glenrothes, Fife KY6 2AH

■ The DLA Piper Charitable Trust

CC NO 327280   **ESTABLISHED** 1986

WHERE FUNDING CAN BE GIVEN UK.

WHO CAN BENEFIT Charitable organisations.

WHAT IS FUNDED General charitable purposes.

WHAT IS NOT FUNDED No grants to individuals.

TYPE OF GRANT Mainly single donations.

RANGE OF GRANTS £1,000–£30,000. Average grant under £1,000.

SAMPLE GRANTS British Red Cross – Japan Tsunami Appeal (£30,000); Room to Read (£21,000); British Red Cross – Queensland Floods and Marie Curie Big Build (£15,000 each); The Prince's Trust (£5,000); Cancer Research (£3,300 in five grants) and Weston Park Hospital Cancer Charity (£1,300).

FINANCES *Year* 2011–12 *Income* £75,245 *Grants* £120,219 *Assets* £55,077

TRUSTEES N. G. Knowles; P. Rooney; S. Mahon.

HOW TO APPLY In writing to the correspondent, for consideration every three months. Applications from members, partners and employees of DLA Piper for grants in support of charities are encouraged.

WHO TO APPLY TO G. J. Smallman, Secretary, Wrigleys Solicitors LLP, Fountain Precinct, Balm Green, Sheffield S1 1RZ *email* godfrey. smallman@wrigleys.co.uk

■ The Worshipful Company of Plaisterers' Charitable Trust

CC NO 281035   **ESTABLISHED** 1980

WHERE FUNDING CAN BE GIVEN England and City of London.

WHO CAN BENEFIT Former freemen and liverymen of the company; students and competitions in colleges related to the plastering trade; and selected City of London charities, in particular the Lord Mayor's Appeal. Individuals and organisations.

General charitable grants with a focus primarily on charities and worthy good causes with a plastering emphasis; London/ City charities with a 'people' focus towards the disabled and disadvantaged; charities connected with HM Forces.

WHAT IS FUNDED Grants for relief in need, general charitable purposes and training promotion.

SAMPLE GRANTS The Lord Mayor's Appeal and St Paul's Cathedral (£5,000 each); The League of Remembrance (£2,000); SSAFFA and St Mary le Bow Homeless Charity (£1,000 each); Otley College and Children's Country Holiday Fund (£750 each); St Botolph's Church and Guildhall School of Music and Drama (£500 each) and British Red Cross and City of London Freemen's School (£300 each).

FINANCES *Year* 2011–12 *Income* £169,165 *Grants* £37,214 *Assets* £928,175

TRUSTEES Sir Robert Ross; Robert Dalrymple; Robin Doran; Prof. Hubert Lacey; Nigel Bamping; Richard Walker; Michael Lepper.

OTHER INFORMATION £500 to individuals.

HOW TO APPLY In writing to the correspondent.

WHO TO APPLY TO The Trustees, Plaisterers Hall, 1 London Wall, London EC2Y 5JU *Tel.* 020 7796 4333

■ The Platinum Trust

CC NO 328570   **ESTABLISHED** 1990

WHERE FUNDING CAN BE GIVEN UK.

WHO CAN BENEFIT Charities benefiting people with disabilities.

WHAT IS FUNDED The relief of children with special needs and adults with mental or physical disabilities 'requiring special attention'.

WHAT IS NOT FUNDED No grants for services run by statutory or public bodies, or from mental-health organisations. No grants for: medical research/ treatment or equipment; mobility aids/ wheelchairs; community transport/disabled transport schemes; holidays/exchanges/holiday playschemes; special-needs playgroups; toy and leisure libraries; special Olympic and Paralympics groups; sports and recreation clubs for people with disabilities; residential care/ sheltered housing/respite care; carers; conservation schemes/city farms/horticultural therapy; sheltered or supported employment/ community business/social firms; purchase/ construction/repair of buildings; and conductive education/other special educational programmes.

RANGE OF GRANTS Usually £5,000–£45,000.

SAMPLE GRANTS United Kingdom Disabled People's Council (£32,500); Centre for Studies on Inclusive Education and Disability, Pregnancy and Parenthood International (£30,000 each); Parents for Inclusion (£27,000); Alliance for Inclusive Education and Independent Panel for Special Education Advice (£20,000 each); Crescent Support Group and Vassal Centre Trust (£15,000 each); Disabled Parents Network (£10,000); Worldwide Volunteering (£5,000);

and Earthworks and The Cambridge Foundation (£2,500).

FINANCES *Year* 2011–12 *Income* £330,032 *Grants* £235,475 *Assets* £271,514

TRUSTEES Georgios K. Panayiotou; Stephen Marks; Christopher Organ.

HOW TO APPLY The trust does not accept unsolicited applications; all future grants will be allocated by the trustees to groups they have already made links with.

WHO TO APPLY TO The Secretary, Sedley Richard Laurence Voulters, 89 New Bond Street, London W1S 1DA *Tel.* 020 7079 8814

■ G. S. Plaut Charitable Trust Limited

CC NO 261469 **ESTABLISHED** 1970
WHERE FUNDING CAN BE GIVEN Predominantly UK.
WHO CAN BENEFIT Voluntary organisations and charitable groups only.
WHAT IS FUNDED General charitable purposes including sickness, disability, Jewish, Christian, elderly, young people.
WHAT IS NOT FUNDED No grants to individuals or for repeat applications.
TYPE OF GRANT One-off and recurrent grants to organisations.
RANGE OF GRANTS Average grant £1,000–£5,000.
SAMPLE GRANTS Veterans Aid and Anglo Jewish Association and British Eye Research Foundation (£4,500 each); Victoria County History of Essex Appeal (£4,000); British Retinitis Pigmentosa Society (£3,500); Chilterns Multiple Sclerosis Centre and Médecins Sans Frontières (£2,500 each); Southend Toy Library, Magen David Adorn UK, Home Farm Trust and Cancer Research UK (£2,000 each); Action For Kids, Ben-Gurion University Foundation, Council of Christians and Jews, Tall Ships Youth Trust and Sight Savers International (£1,000 each) and Home-Start Dundee (£250).
FINANCES *Year* 2012–13 *Income* £61,032 *Grants* £47,250 *Assets* £1,533,116
TRUSTEES A. D. Wrapson; T. A. Warburg; W. E. Murfett; B. A. Sprinz; R. E. Liebeschuetz; Dr J. D. Hall.
HOW TO APPLY In writing to the correspondent. Applications are reviewed twice a year. Only successful applications are acknowledged.
WHO TO APPLY TO Dr Richard Speirs, Secretary, 39 Bay Road, Wormit, Newport-on-Tay, Fife DD6 8LW

■ Polden-Puckham Charitable Foundation

CC NO 1003024 **ESTABLISHED** 1970
WHERE FUNDING CAN BE GIVEN UK and overseas.
WHO CAN BENEFIT Registered charities only.
WHAT IS FUNDED 'In the limited areas described [here] we support projects that seek to influence values and attitudes, promote equity and social justice, and develop radical alternatives to current economic and social structures.
Peace and Sustainable Security: We support the development of ways of resolving violent conflicts peacefully, and of addressing their underlying causes.
Environmental Sustainability: We support work that addresses the pressures and conditions leading towards global environmental breakdown; particularly national initiatives in UK which promote sustainable living.'

WHAT IS NOT FUNDED The foundation does not fund: organisations that are large; organisations that are outside UK (unless they are linked with a UK registered charity and doing work of international focus); work outside the UK (unless it is of international focus); grants to individuals; travel bursaries (including overseas placements and expeditions); study; academic research; capital projects (e.g. building projects or purchase of nature reserves); community or local practical projects (except innovative projects for widespread application); environmental/ ecological conservation; international agencies and overseas appeals; general appeals; human rights work (except where it relates to peace and environmental sustainability).

TYPE OF GRANT Core costs and project funding for up to three years.
RANGE OF GRANTS Normally £5,000 to £10,000.
SAMPLE GRANTS European Leadership network (£40,000); Quaker United Nations Office (£22,000); British American Security Information Council (£20,000); Carbon Tracker Initiative (£15,000); Protect the Local Globally (£11,000); Localise West Midlands and SpinWatch (£10,000); Campaign Against Arms Trade (£9,000); Mines and Communities (£6,000); Oil Depletion Analysis Centre (£5,000); UK Without Incineration Network (£4,000) and Environmental Funders Network (£2,000).
FINANCES *Year* 2011–12 *Income* £495,131 *Grants* £327,100 *Assets* £13,445,950
TRUSTEES Harriet Gillett; Bevis Gillett; Val Ferguson; Angela Seay; Jonathan Gillett.
HOW TO APPLY The trustees meet twice a year in spring and autumn. Application forms and guidance notes can be downloaded from the foundation's website and must be submitted via email. Applicants are also asked to submit their latest set of audited accounts and an annual report, preferably via email. Note: the foundation is happy to provide brief feedback on applications one week after the trustees have made a decision.
WHO TO APPLY TO Bryn Higgs, Secretary, BM PPCF, London WC1N 3XX *Tel.* 020 7193 7364 *email* ppcf@polden-puckham.org.uk *Website* www.polden-puckham.org.uk

---

■ The Polestar Digital Foundation

CC NO 1147337 **ESTABLISHED** 2012
WHERE FUNDING CAN BE GIVEN UK.
WHO CAN BENEFIT Charities and community groups.
WHAT IS FUNDED General charitable purposes.
TRUSTEES Elaine Skinner; Clive Busby.
HOW TO APPLY In writing to the correspondent.
WHO TO APPLY TO Clive Busby, Trustee, 23 Birchwood Grove, Hampton, Middlesex TW12 3DU *Tel.* 0845 052 3607

■ The George and Esme Pollitzer Charitable Settlement

CC NO 212631 **ESTABLISHED** 1960
WHERE FUNDING CAN BE GIVEN UK.
WHO CAN BENEFIT Registered charities, particularly Jewish organisations.
WHAT IS FUNDED General charitable purposes and Jewish causes.
RANGE OF GRANTS Usually around £2,000 each.
SAMPLE GRANTS Jewish Museum (£10,000); Royal Hospital for Neuro-disability (£5,000); and Big

Issue, Coram, I Can, Macmillan Cancer Support, Marie Curie Cancer Care, Médecins Sans Frontières, The National Brain Appeal, Samaritans, SBS Association and Target Ovarian Cancer (£2,000 each).

FINANCES *Year* 2011–12 *Income* £122,267 *Grants* £95,000 *Assets* £2,920,118

TRUSTEES J. Barnes; Catherine Alexander Charles; R. F. C. Pollitzer.

OTHER INFORMATION All grants bar two were for £2,000 each.

HOW TO APPLY In writing to the correspondent.

WHO TO APPLY TO L. E. Parrock, Saffery Champness, Beaufort House, 2 Beaufort Road, Clifton, Bristol BS8 2AE *Tel.* 01179 151617

■ The J. S. F. Pollitzer Charitable Settlement

CC NO 210680   **ESTABLISHED** 1960

WHERE FUNDING CAN BE GIVEN UK and overseas.

WHO CAN BENEFIT Registered charities only.

WHAT IS FUNDED General charitable purposes.

WHAT IS NOT FUNDED No grants to individuals or students, i.e. those without charitable status.

TYPE OF GRANT One-off.

RANGE OF GRANTS Typically £1,000 each.

SAMPLE GRANTS Happy House; Home Start Richmond; Renewable World; Clean Rivers Trust; Merlin Theatre; Jackdaws Music Education Trust; Manchester Camerata; Orchard Vale Trust; Tourettes Action; Autism Plus; The Hope Centre; Noah's Ark Appeal; Dorset and Somerset Air Ambulance; National Osteoporosis Society; Brain Research UK; Relatives and Residents Association (£1,000 each)

FINANCES *Year* 2011–12 *Income* £52,058 *Grants* £19,000 *Assets* £733,017

TRUSTEES R. F. C. Pollitzer, Chair; E. Pettit; S. C. O'Farrell.

HOW TO APPLY In writing to the correspondent. Grants are distributed twice a year, usually around April/May and November/December.

WHO TO APPLY TO J. R. Webb, Mary Street House, Mary Street, Taunton, Somerset TA1 3NW *Tel.* 01823 286096

■ The Pollywally Charitable Trust

CC NO 1107513   **ESTABLISHED** 2005

WHERE FUNDING CAN BE GIVEN UK.

WHO CAN BENEFIT Jewish institutions of primary, secondary and further education and those caring for the poor and sick.

WHAT IS FUNDED Jewish causes, education, and welfare.

RANGE OF GRANTS Up to £15,000.

SAMPLE GRANTS Kehillas Machzikei Hadass Edgware Trust (£20,000); Joshua Trust and Edgware Foundation (£18,000 each); and Camp Simcha and Ezer Bekovoid Limited (£1,000 each).

FINANCES *Year* 2012–13 *Income* £76,569 *Grants* £60,329 *Assets* £19,502

TRUSTEES Jeremy Waller; Jeremy Pollins; Sarah Waller; Stephany Pollins.

OTHER INFORMATION 25 grants were awarded to organisations and totalled £60,000.

HOW TO APPLY In writing to the correspondent.

WHO TO APPLY TO Jeremy Waller, Trustee, Premier House, 8th Floor, c/o Waller Pollins Ltd, 112 Station Road, Edgware HA8 7BJ *Tel.* 020 8238 5858

■ The Polonsky Foundation

CC NO 291143   **ESTABLISHED** 1985

WHERE FUNDING CAN BE GIVEN UK, Israel and the USA

WHO CAN BENEFIT Registered charities, universities and educational and arts institutions.

WHAT IS FUNDED 'To support higher education internationally, principally in the arts and social sciences, and programmes favouring the study and resolution of human conflict. Much of this work is part of ongoing programmes being undertaken in conjunction with various Departments of the Hebrew University of Jerusalem and the Bezalel Academy of Art and Design, as well as other organisations within the United States and the United Kingdom.'

RANGE OF GRANTS Up to £250,000.

SAMPLE GRANTS British Friends of the Hebrew University (£251,500); New York Public Library (£162,500); University of Cambridge (£74,000); University of Oxford (£48,000); Royal Academy of Music (£20,000); Open Book Publishers (£15,000); Guildhall School Trust (£6,000); Guy's and St Thomas' Charity (£2,000); and The Jewish Museum (£1,000).

FINANCES *Year* 2011–12 *Income* £1,094,367 *Grants* £1,205,499 *Assets* £49,917,390

TRUSTEES Dr Georgette Bennett; Dr Leonard Polonsky; Valarie Smith; Marc Polonsky.

HOW TO APPLY In writing to the correspondent.

WHO TO APPLY TO The Trustees, 8 Park Crescent, London W1B 1PG

■ The Ponton House Trust

SC NO SC021716   **ESTABLISHED** 1993

WHERE FUNDING CAN BE GIVEN The Lothians.

WHO CAN BENEFIT Organisations benefiting disadvantaged groups, principally young and elderly people.

WHAT IS FUNDED Grants are given mainly to support small charities working with young people, elderly people and disadvantaged groups.

WHAT IS NOT FUNDED No grants to individuals or non-charitable organisations.

TYPE OF GRANT One-off.

RANGE OF GRANTS Up to £6,300.

SAMPLE GRANTS Edinburgh Voluntary Organisations Trust (£9,000), for onward distribution to individuals; Bethany Christian Trust and Lothian Autistic Society (£1,500 each); Garvald Training Centre, Venture Scotland, Circle, Children 1st and Partners for Advocacy (£1,000); Rock Trust (£900); and Maggie's Cancer Caring Centres (£750).

FINANCES *Year* 2011–12 *Income* £49,185 *Grants* £40,000

TRUSTEES Revd John Munro, Chair; Shulah Allan; Patrick Edwardson; Ian Boardman; James Verth; David Jack; Jane Sturgeon.

HOW TO APPLY On an application form available from the trust's website, where full guidelines are also available.

WHO TO APPLY TO David S. Reith, Secretary, c/o Lindsays WS, Caledonian Exchange, 19A Canning Street, Edinburgh EH3 8HE *Tel.* 01312 291212 *Fax* 01312 295611 *email* info@ pontonhouse.org.uk *Website* www.pontonhouse. org.uk

■ The Popocatepetl Trust

CC NO 1133690   **ESTABLISHED** 2010

WHERE FUNDING CAN BE GIVEN Worldwide, with a preference for the UK.

WHO CAN BENEFIT Registered charities.

WHAT IS FUNDED Grants are given to UK charities that in turn support projects involving the advancement of education of children and adults worldwide with an emphasis on seriously disadvantaged communities in the developing world.

SAMPLE GRANTS Izara Khom Loi Trust (£35,000); The Thai Children's Trust (£27,000); The Students Education Trust (£10,000); Karen Hill Tribes Trust (£8,000) and The International Children's Trust, Prospect Burma and Children on the Edge (£6,400 each).

FINANCES *Year* 2011–12 *Income* £8,724 *Grants* £95,000

TRUSTEES Eleanor Broad; Grania Bryceson; Elizabeth Deliere; Monique Surridge; David Williams.

HOW TO APPLY In Writing to the Correspondent

WHO TO APPLY TO Elizabeth Deliere, Longview, 7 Clumps Road, Lower Bourne, Farnham, Surrey GU10 3HF *Tel.* 01252 794238

■ Edith and Ferdinand Porjes Charitable Trust

CC NO 274012   **ESTABLISHED** 1973

WHERE FUNDING CAN BE GIVEN UK and overseas.

WHO CAN BENEFIT Jewish organisations; registered charities.

WHAT IS FUNDED General charitable purposes, particularly Jewish causes.

SAMPLE GRANTS The London School of Jewish Studies (£30,000); Jewish Book Council (£17,000); Yesodey Hatorah Grammar School (£10,000); International Institute for Jewish Genealogy (£7,900); Shaare Zedek (£5,000) and British Friends of OHEL Sarah (£2,500).

FINANCES *Year* 2011–12 *Income* £55,982 *Grants* £72,353 *Assets* £1,466,128

TRUSTEES M. D. Paisner; A. S. Rosenfelder; H. Stanton.

HOW TO APPLY In writing to the correspondent.

WHO TO APPLY TO M. D. Paisner, Trustee, Adelaide House, London Bridge, London EC4R 9HA *Tel.* 020 7760 1000

■ The John Porter Charitable Trust

CC NO 267170   **ESTABLISHED** 1974

WHERE FUNDING CAN BE GIVEN Worldwide, but mainly UK and Israel.

WHO CAN BENEFIT Registered and exempt charities.

WHAT IS FUNDED Education, culture, environment, health and welfare.

WHAT IS NOT FUNDED No grants to individuals.

RANGE OF GRANTS Up to £58,000.

SAMPLE GRANTS Foundation de l'Ecole Internationale de Verbier (£58,000); Core of Culture Dance Preservation and (£15,000 each); British Friends of Arts Museum Israel (£7,000); Israel Philharmonic Orchestra Foundation, University of Oxford and Maccabi GB (£5,000 each); Friends of the Menton Festival of Music (£4,000) and English National Ballet, Friends of the Mariinsky Theatre and World Land Trust (£1,000 each).

FINANCES *Year* 2011–12 *Income* £257,584 *Grants* £148,286 *Assets* £9,948,770

OTHER INFORMATION In 2011–12 grants were given to 16 organisations.

HOW TO APPLY In writing to the correspondent.

WHO TO APPLY TO The Trustees, c/o Blink Rothenberg, 12 York Gate, London NW1 4QS *Tel.* 020 7544 8863

■ The Porter Foundation

CC NO 261194   **ESTABLISHED** 1970

WHERE FUNDING CAN BE GIVEN Israel and the UK.

WHO CAN BENEFIT Registered charities and community organisations.

WHAT IS FUNDED Jewish, arts, schools, welfare, health.

WHAT IS NOT FUNDED The foundation makes grants only to registered charitable organisations or to organisations with charitable objects that are exempt from the requirement for charitable registration. Grants will not be made to: individuals; general appeals such as direct mail circulars; charities which redistribute funds to other charities; third-party organisations raising money on behalf of other charities; or cover general running costs.

TYPE OF GRANT Usually project-based and capital.

SAMPLE GRANTS Porter Foundation Switzerland (£40,000); New Israel Fund and The Israel Opera Trust (£25,000); English National Opera (£15,000); British Friends of the Council for a Beautiful Israel (£13,000); The Royal Parks Foundation (£10,000); British Friends of the Verbier Festival and Academy (£7,000); The royal National Theatre (£2,500) and Mencap, Sadler Wells Trust Ltd, Kisharon and Whitechapel Gallery (£1,000 each).

FINANCES *Year* 2011–12 *Income* £922,961 *Grants* £1,503,453 *Assets* £39,118,305

TRUSTEES Albert Castle; Dame Shirley Porter; Steven Porter; Sir Walter Bodmer; John Porter; Linda Streit.

OTHER INFORMATION During recent years the foundation has cut back on the number of beneficiaries supported and is making fewer, larger grants, mainly to the connected Porter School of Environmental Studies at Tel Aviv University, or the university itself, and to other causes in Israel. This has led to a temporary reduction in UK-based activity. A limited number of community awards continue to be given, though usually to organisations already known to the foundation.

HOW TO APPLY An initial letter summarising your application, together with basic costings and background details on your organisation, such as the annual report and accounts, should be sent to the director. Speculative approaches containing expensive publicity material are not encouraged. If your proposal falls within the foundation's current funding criteria you may be contacted for further information, including perhaps a visit from the foundation staff. There is no need to fill out an application form. Applications fulfilling the criteria will be considered by the trustees, who meet three times a year, usually in March, July and November. You will hear shortly after the meeting whether your application has been successful. Unfortunately, it is not possible to acknowledge all unsolicited applications (unless a stamped, addressed envelope is enclosed). If you do not hear from the foundation, you can assume that your application has been unsuccessful. Due to limits on funds available, some excellent projects may have to be refused a grant. In such a case the trustees may invite the applicant to re-apply in a future financial year, without giving a commitment to fund.

WHO TO APPLY TO Paul Williams, Executive Director, Silex Administration S.A., 22 Arlington Street, London SW1A 1RD *Tel.* 0204991957 *email* theporterfoundation@btinternet.com

■ Porticus UK

cc no 1069245　　**ESTABLISHED** 1998
WHERE FUNDING CAN BE GIVEN UK.
WHO CAN BENEFIT Registered charities.
WHAT IS FUNDED The charity's four areas of interest are: strengthening family relationships; enriching education; transformation through faith; and ethics in practice.
WHAT IS NOT FUNDED No grants to non-registered charities. Applications for the following will not be considered: high profile appeals; major capital projects or restoration of buildings; grants to individuals; endowment appeals; overseas projects (including travel).
RANGE OF GRANTS £10,000 to £25,000.
FINANCES *Year* 2012 *Income* £550,215 *Grants* £4,000,000.
TRUSTEES Louise A. Adams; Mark C. L. Brenninkmeyer; Stephen R. M. Brenninkmeyer; Bert Brenninkmeyer.
OTHER INFORMATION Porticus UK is not in itself a grantmaker – it advises and assesses grants on behalf of several foundations in the Netherlands, including Stichting Porticus. In 2012 the charity assessed 443 applications resulting in 209 new grants. Total funds available amount to around £4 million each year.
HOW TO APPLY On an application form available from the charity's website. Applications can be submitted at any time. The charity also says that: 'if you are unsure whether your project/ organisation fits in with our guidelines, you are welcome to submit an initial brief outline of your organisation and funding requirements'.
WHO TO APPLY TO Jane Leek, 4th Floor, Eagle House, 108–110 Jermyn Street, London SW1Y 6EE *Tel.* 020 7024 3503 *Fax* 020 7024 3501 *email* porticusuk@porticus.com *Website* www. porticusuk.com

■ The Portishead Nautical Trust

cc no 228876　　**ESTABLISHED** 1964
WHERE FUNDING CAN BE GIVEN Bristol and North Somerset.
WHO CAN BENEFIT People under 25 years of age who are disadvantaged or at risk; voluntary and charitable groups working with such people, with young offenders and with people with addictions.
WHAT IS FUNDED Projects with young people who are disadvantaged; educational support for such people; counselling services; and youth groups.
WHAT IS NOT FUNDED No grants for further education costs of non-disadvantaged people.
TYPE OF GRANT One-off, project, recurring costs and running costs will be considered. Funding may be given for up to three years.
RANGE OF GRANTS Usually £100–£5,000.
SAMPLE GRANTS Portishead Youth Centre (£75,000); Dyslexia Action (£22,500); Trinity Sailing, Handicapped Children's Action Group and North Somerset Housing (£1,500); Tall Ships Youth Trust and Over the Wall (£1,000 each); Places for People (£750); and Farms for City Children (£230).
FINANCES *Year* 2011–12 *Income* £82,229 *Grants* £121,170 *Assets* £1,785,301
TRUSTEES Sheila Belk; Dr Gerwyn Owen; M. Hoskins; Iris Perry; Tean Kirby; Peter Dingley-Brown; Stephen Gillingham; M. Cruse; Colin Crossman; Wendy Bryant.
OTHER INFORMATION In 2011–12 grants totalling £3,800 were given to individuals.
HOW TO APPLY In writing to the correspondent.

WHO TO APPLY TO Elizabeth Knight, Secretary, 108 High Street, Portishead, Bristol BS20 6AJ *Tel.* 01275 847463

■ The Portrack Charitable Trust

cc no 266120　　**ESTABLISHED** 1973
WHERE FUNDING CAN BE GIVEN Some preference for Scotland.
WHO CAN BENEFIT Charitable organisations.
WHAT IS FUNDED General charitable organisations.
WHAT IS NOT FUNDED Grants are not given to individuals.
RANGE OF GRANTS Usually £1,000 to £2,000, occasionally more.
SAMPLE GRANTS Maggie's Cancer Centres (£45,000 in three grants); Payment to Medical Aid for Palestinians (£6,000 in two grants); Dumfries and Galloway Endowment Fund (£5,000); Victoria and Albert Museum (£3,000); Human Rights Watch Charitable Trust, Who Care Trust, Dumfries and Galloway Mental Health and Musicians Benevolent Fund (£2,000 each) and Lifelites, British Eye Research Foundation, Princess Royal Trust for Carers, Just for Kids Law and St John's Hospice (£1,000 each).
FINANCES *Year* 2011–12 *Income* £103,963 *Grants* £124,000 *Assets* £4,672,817
TRUSTEES Charles Jencks; Keith Galloway; John Jencks.
OTHER INFORMATION Charles Alexander Jencks is also a trustee of the Keswick Foundation Limited (Charity Commission no. 278449); and Keith Galloway is also a trustee of Rockliffe Charitable Trust (Charity Commission no. 274117).
HOW TO APPLY In writing to the correspondent.
WHO TO APPLY TO George Holmes, Butterfield Bank, 99 Gresham Street, London EC2V 7NG *Tel.* 020 7776 6700

■ The J. E. Posnansky Charitable Trust

cc no 210416　　**ESTABLISHED** 1962
WHERE FUNDING CAN BE GIVEN UK and overseas.
WHO CAN BENEFIT Charitable organisations.
WHAT IS FUNDED Jewish charities, health, social welfare, humanitarian.
WHAT IS NOT FUNDED No grants to individuals.
TYPE OF GRANT One-off.
RANGE OF GRANTS Typically £250–£30,000.
SAMPLE GRANTS UJIA and Magen David Adom UK (£20,000 each); WIZO UK (£15,000); Friends of Alyn (£13,000); Jewish Care (£7,500); British Technion Society and World Jewish Relief (£5,000 each); Sight Savers International and WaterAid (£2,500 each); British Limbless Ex-Servicemen, Hazon Yeshaya and Terrance Higgins Trust (£1,000 each); Amnesty International, Jewish Childs Day and The Council for Christians and Jews (£500) and The Sue Ryder Foundation (£250).
FINANCES *Year* 2011–12 *Income* £109,121 *Grants* £121,750 *Assets* £3,629,087
TRUSTEES G. Raffles; A. Posnansky; P. A. Mishcon; E. J. Feather; N. S. Posnansky.
HOW TO APPLY Unsolicited applications will not be considered.
WHO TO APPLY TO N. S. Posnansky, Trustee, Sobell Rhodes, Monument House, 215 Marsh Road, Pinner, Middlesex, London HA5 5NE *Tel.* 020 8429 8800 *Fax* 020 7435 1516

■ The Mary Potter Convent Hospital Trust

cc no 1078525   **ESTABLISHED** 1999
WHERE FUNDING CAN BE GIVEN Nottinghamshire.
WHO CAN BENEFIT Organisations and individuals.
WHAT IS FUNDED Relief of medical and health problems.
WHAT IS NOT FUNDED No grants to non-registered charities, or for capital/building costs.
TYPE OF GRANT Mainly one-off grants, but payments over two or three years may be considered.
SAMPLE GRANTS Friary Drop-in (£6,000); Radford Visiting Scheme and RELATE (£5,000 each) and Clic Sargent, Motor Neurone Disease Association and Notts Mind Network (£4,000 each).
FINANCES *Year* 2011–12 *Income* £75,817 *Grants* £63,014 *Assets* £2,713,476
TRUSTEES Edward Szpryt; Christopher Bain; Sister Ann Hough; Dr John Curran; Martin Witherspoon; Frederick Pell; Sister Jeanette Connell; Mervyn Jones; Joanne Stevenson.
OTHER INFORMATION In 2011/2 there were 35 grants awarded. The grant total includes £5,400 that was given to individuals.
HOW TO APPLY In writing to the correspondent. Unsuccessful applicants will not be notified.
WHO TO APPLY TO Martin Witherspoon, Secretary to the Trustees, c/o Massers Solicitors, 15 Victoria Street, Nottingham NG1 2JZ *Tel.* 01158 511603 *email* martinw@massers. co.uk

■ The David and Elaine Potter Foundation

cc no 1078217   **ESTABLISHED** 1999
WHERE FUNDING CAN BE GIVEN UK and overseas with particular emphasis on the developing world.
WHO CAN BENEFIT Charitable organisations working in the areas of education, science, human rights, and the general strengthening of civil society.
WHAT IS FUNDED Advancement of education and scientific research. Most grants are made for scholarships and other related activities that will improve understanding, governance and the promotion of a civil society; research through the creation of institutions and other means; human rights activism; initiatives that support democratic governance; and agencies and charities carrying out development, research and educational projects. Limited grants are also made for the arts.
WHAT IS NOT FUNDED No grants to individuals, animal welfare charities or humanitarian aid. Requests for endowment, capital campaigns, construction, equipment purchases and debt reduction will not be considered.
TYPE OF GRANT Capital, revenue, project funding over multiple years.
RANGE OF GRANTS £500–£150,000.
SAMPLE GRANTS UCT Trust (£151,000); Reprieve (£60,000); Business Bridge Project and Birmingham Centre for the Rule of Law (£50,000 each); Philharmonia Orchestra Trust Ltd (£39,000); Room to Read (£30,000); London Youth Support Trust (£25,000); Kasslesbai Project (£21,000) and The Almeida Theatre (£5,000).
FINANCES *Year* 2012 *Income* £656,614 *Grants* £817,171 *Assets* £19,871,246
TRUSTEES Michael S. Polonsky; Michael Langley; Dr David Potter; Elaine Potter; Samuel Potter.
HOW TO APPLY The trust has informed us that they have temporarily stopped accepting unsolicited applications. Potential applicants should check the website to find out when this changes.
WHO TO APPLY TO Kathryn Oatey, Director, 6 Hamilton Close, London NW8 8QY *Tel.* 020 7289 3911 *Fax* 020 7286 3699 *email* info@ potterfoundation.com *Website* www. potterfoundation.com

■ The Powell Foundation

cc no 1012786   **ESTABLISHED** 1992
WHERE FUNDING CAN BE GIVEN Within the Milton Keynes Unitary Council area.
WHO CAN BENEFIT Individuals and local organisations benefiting older people and people of any age with disabilities.
WHAT IS FUNDED Grants for the benefit of older people and mentally and physically disabled people. Localised charities working in the fields of community development including supporting voluntary organisations, community arts and recreation, community facilities and services for people with disabilities, healthcare and special needs education.
SAMPLE GRANTS Milton Keynes Community Foundation (£154,000); the Pace Centre (£17,000).
FINANCES *Year* 2011–12 *Income* £145,079 *Grants* £172,975 *Assets* £3,921,928
TRUSTEES Roger Norman; Robert Hill; Paul Smith.
OTHER INFORMATION Each year a large grant is awarded to Milton Keynes Community Foundation to be distributed in grants to voluntary groups that meet the foundation's criteria.
HOW TO APPLY Visit the trust's website for full guidelines and details of how to apply. Application forms are available on request from the grants team who can either post or e-mail the forms.
WHO TO APPLY TO Julia Upton, Chief Executive, c/o Milton Keynes Community Foundation, Acorn House, 381 Midsummer Boulevard, Central Milton Keynes MK9 3HP *Tel.* 01908 690276 *Fax* 01908 233635 *email* information@ mkcommunityfoundation.co.uk *Website* www. mkcommunityfoundation.co.uk

■ The Praebendo Charitable Foundation

cc no 1137426   **ESTABLISHED** 2010
WHERE FUNDING CAN BE GIVEN England, Scotland and Wales.
WHO CAN BENEFIT Organisations supporting children and young people; elderly people; people with disabilities, other charities and the general public/mankind and individuals.
WHAT IS FUNDED Education/training; advancement of health or saving of lives; people with disabilities; the prevention or relief of poverty; and religious activities.
FINANCES *Year* 2011–12 *Income* £49,205 *Grants* £39,500 *Assets* £162,184
TRUSTEES Susan Christmas; Helen Leech.
OTHER INFORMATION A list of grant beneficiaries was unavailable.
HOW TO APPLY In writing to the correspondent.
WHO TO APPLY TO Helen Leech, Administrator and Trustee, Drift House, First Drift, Wothorpe, Stamford, Lincolnshire PE9 3JL *Tel.* 01780 489082

■ The W. L. Pratt Charitable Trust

CC NO 256907   **ESTABLISHED** 1968

WHERE FUNDING CAN BE GIVEN UK, particularly York, and overseas.

WHO CAN BENEFIT Charitable organisations.

WHAT IS FUNDED In the UK: to support religious and social objectives with priority for York and district, including health and community services. Overseas: to help the developing world by assisting in food production and relief of famine and disease.

WHAT IS NOT FUNDED No grants to individuals. No grants for buildings or for upkeep and preservation of places of worship.

SAMPLE GRANTS York Minister Development Campaign (£5,000); York Diocesan Board of Finance (£3,750); Christian Aid, York Cancer Relief and York Samaritans (£1,000 each); British Humanitarian Aid Limited, British Red Cross, Guide Dogs for the Blind, Oxfam, RNLI, and St John Ambulance (£500 each); and Action Research, Age UK, Marie Curie Memorial Foundation and Wellbeing/Birthright (£250 each).

FINANCES *Year* 2011–12 *Income* £49,010 *Grants* £39,653 *Assets* £1,665,867

TRUSTEES John Pratt; Christopher Tetley; Christopher Goodway.

HOW TO APPLY In writing to the correspondent. Applications will not be acknowledged unless an sae is supplied. Telephone applications are not accepted.

WHO TO APPLY TO Christopher Goodway, Trustee, Grays, Duncombe Place, York YO1 7DY *Tel.* 01904 634771 *email* christophergoodway@grayssolicitors.co.uk

■ The Premier League Charitable Fund

CC NO 1137208   **ESTABLISHED** 2010

WHERE FUNDING CAN BE GIVEN England and Wales.

WHO CAN BENEFIT Charitable organisations, particularly those who are directly involved in provision of sports activities.

WHAT IS FUNDED General charitable purposes, with particular focus on activities in connection with football; education and training; advancement of health; disability; sport and recreation; economic and community development.

TYPE OF GRANT Grants to organisations.

RANGE OF GRANTS £1,000 to £89,000.

FINANCES *Year* 2011–12 *Income* £12,411,269 *Grants* £8,121,060 *Assets* £8,333,466

TRUSTEES William Bush; David Barnes; Thomas Finn; Dr Therese Coffey.

HOW TO APPLY In writing to the correspondent.

WHO TO APPLY TO Monica Golding, Head of Premier League Charitable Fund, The F. A. Premier League, 30 Gloucester Place, London W1U 8PL *Tel.* 020 7864 9000 *email* creatingchances@premierleague.com *Website* www.premierleague.com/en-gb

■ Premierquote Ltd

CC NO 801957   **ESTABLISHED** 1985

WHERE FUNDING CAN BE GIVEN Worldwide.

WHO CAN BENEFIT People of the Jewish faith.

WHAT IS FUNDED Jewish charitable purposes, relief of poverty, general charitable purposes.

SAMPLE GRANTS Previously: Achisomoch, Belz Yeshiva Trust, Beth Jacob Grammar School for Girls Ltd, British Friends of Shuvu, Friends of Ohel Moshe, Friends of Senet Wiznitz, Friends of

the United Institutions of Arad, Kehal Chasidei Bobov, Meadowgold Limited, Menorah Primary School, North West London Communal Mikvah and Torah Vedaas Primary School.

FINANCES *Year* 2011–12 *Income* £845,891 *Grants* £412,139 *Assets* £6,037,060

TRUSTEES D. Last; L. Last; H. Last; M. Weisenfeld.

OTHER INFORMATION Grants for over £1,000 each totalled £345,000 and those for under £1,000 each, £67,000.

HOW TO APPLY In writing to the correspondent.

WHO TO APPLY TO D. Last, Trustee, 18 Green Walk, London NW4 2AJ *Tel.* 020 7247 8376

■ Premishlaner Charitable Trust

CC NO 1046945   **ESTABLISHED** 1995

WHERE FUNDING CAN BE GIVEN UK and worldwide.

WHO CAN BENEFIT Jewish people and people disadvantaged by poverty.

WHAT IS FUNDED To advance Orthodox Jewish education; to advance the religion of the Jewish faith in accordance with the orthodox practice; to relieve poverty; other general charitable purposes.

SAMPLE GRANTS Chochmas Shlomo Chasidi (£23,000); Chen Vochessed Vrachamim and Beis Rochel (£13,000 each); Emunoh Educational Centre (£10,000); U.T.A. (£9,500); Yeshiva Gedola Sevenoaks (£7,500); J and R Charitable Trust (£6,500) and Vaad Horabonim, Binyan Torah Charity and Tevini (£5,000 each).

FINANCES *Year* 2011–12 *Income* £181,225 *Grants* £150,544 *Assets* £388,060

TRUSTEES C. Freudenberger; C. M. Margulies.

OTHER INFORMATION Other donations under £5,000 each totalled £35,000.

HOW TO APPLY In writing to the correspondent.

WHO TO APPLY TO C. M. Margulies, Trustee, 186 Lordship Road, London N16 5ES *Tel.* 020 8802 4449

■ The Tom Press Charitable Foundation

CC NO 1136548   **ESTABLISHED** 2010

WHERE FUNDING CAN BE GIVEN Undefined.

WHO CAN BENEFIT Individuals and organisations benefitting children and young people.

WHAT IS FUNDED Advancement of health, providing relief to children who are suffering from life-threatening illness; promotion of medical research into childhood illness and advancing the education of children with learning difficulties and those undergoing treatment in hospital. The foundation also aims to improve learning facilities in schools including the provision of libraries, language or IT facilities and equipment.

TYPE OF GRANT One-off. Capital costs, core costs and full project funding.

FINANCES *Year* 2012 *Income* £308

TRUSTEES Sue Press; Matthew Press; Mark Vines; Andy Press.

HOW TO APPLY Applications forms can be obtained by emailing the correspondent. Applications are reviewed on a quarterly basis and the foundation regrets to inform applicants that because of limited funds, not every appeal can be funded.

WHO TO APPLY TO Andy Press, Trustee, Maybrook, 19 Valley Way, Gerrards Cross SL9 7PL *Tel.* 01753 887921 *email* info@tompressfoundation.com *Website* www.tompressfoundation.com

■ The Douglas Prestwich Charitable Trust

CC NO 1017597   ESTABLISHED 1993

WHERE FUNDING CAN BE GIVEN UK, with a possible preference for the south of England.

WHO CAN BENEFIT Hospices and other organisations benefiting older people and people with disabilities.

WHAT IS FUNDED Help to older people, especially through hospices, and help for people with disabilities, especially through mechanical and other aids.

RANGE OF GRANTS .

SAMPLE GRANTS Previous beneficiaries include: Douglas Prestwich Award, Compaid, Disabled Living Foundation, Motability and the Mobility Trust.

FINANCES *Year* 2011–12 *Income* £2,924 *Grants* £4,342

TRUSTEES Margaret Prestwich; Olivia Meekin; David Monro.

HOW TO APPLY In writing to the correspondent; however, note the trust stated that its 'present policy [] is only to consider grants to institutions which it has already assisted and where the need continues to be shown'.

WHO TO APPLY TO David Monro, 8 Great James Street, London WC1N 3DF

■ The William Price Charitable Trust

CC NO 307319   ESTABLISHED 1989

WHERE FUNDING CAN BE GIVEN Fareham's town parishes of St Peter and St Paul, Holy Trinity with St Columba and St John the Evangelist. Note this area is that of the Fareham town parishes and not the borough of Fareham.

WHO CAN BENEFIT Schools and individuals under the age of 25 in the parishes.

WHAT IS FUNDED Schools for educational benefits not normally provided by the local education authority, and individuals for help with fees, travel, outfits, clothing, books and so on. Also promoting education in the doctrines of the Church of England.

WHAT IS NOT FUNDED Grants cannot be given to persons who live outside the area of the Fareham town parishes or to any organisation or establishment other than those outlined in this entry.

TYPE OF GRANT One-off.

RANGE OF GRANTS £1,000–£5,000

SAMPLE GRANTS Schools and colleges (£106,000); churches (£8,500); individual hardship grants (£12,000); other individual grants (£2,800) and Fareham Welfare Trust (£7,000).

FINANCES *Year* 2011–12 *Income* £158,420 *Grants* £136,283 *Assets* £6,112,400

TRUSTEE William Price Trust Company.

OTHER INFORMATION In 2011–12 grants were made to 25 organisations and 103 individuals.

HOW TO APPLY On a form available to download from the website, together with guidelines and criteria. 'Whenever possible applications should be made through the establishment concerned, although individual requests are also accepted. Larger grants are considered by trustees on a six-monthly basis with closing dates for applications of 1 March and 1 September. Smaller grants for individuals are considered quickly and normally in less than one month.'

WHO TO APPLY TO Dr C. D. Thomas, Clerk, 24 Cuckoo Lane, Stubbington, Fareham, Hampshire PO14 3PF *Tel.* 01329 663685 *email* mazchris@tiscali.co.uk *Website* www.pricestrust.org.uk

■ The Lucy Price Relief-in-Need Charity

CC NO 516967   ESTABLISHED 1982

WHERE FUNDING CAN BE GIVEN The parish of Baginton in Warwickshire only.

WHO CAN BENEFIT Individuals up to the age of 25 and organisations benefiting such people.

WHAT IS FUNDED Education, sports and youth work.

SAMPLE GRANTS No grants list available.

FINANCES *Year* 2012 *Income* £3,963 *Grants* £32,000

TRUSTEES Jean Fawcett; Roger Horsfall; Alan Brown; Nigel Thomas; Susan Williams; Louise Given.

OTHER INFORMATION Grants are given to individuals and organisations.

HOW TO APPLY On a form available from the correspondent, or any of the trustees.

WHO TO APPLY TO Della Thomas, 19 Holly Walk, Baginton, Coventry CV8 3AE *Tel.* 07884 182904

■ Sir John Priestman Charity Trust

CC NO 209397   ESTABLISHED 1931

WHERE FUNDING CAN BE GIVEN Counties of Sunderland, Durham and York (in relation to churches).

WHO CAN BENEFIT Organisations, charities or other voluntary bodies, benefiting children and older people, clergy, people of the Church of England, people disadvantaged by poverty – within the county borough of Sunderland, counties of Durham and York (in relation to the churches).

WHAT IS FUNDED General charitable purposes, in particular, relief of poverty, benefit to the old, infirmary and children; establishment and maintenance of hospitals and convalescent homes; advancement of education; benefit of the Church of England; building, restoration, altering, enlarging, maintaining and furnishing of the churches.

WHAT IS NOT FUNDED Organisations operating outside of charity's beneficial area.

TYPE OF GRANT The trustees support a number of charities by way of regular annual grants, but otherwise the trustees' aim where possible to award grants for specific projects as opposed to general running costs. 'The trustees generally award modest grants to a relatively large number of bodies rather than a few large grants.'

RANGE OF GRANTS £400–£14,000.

SAMPLE GRANTS **Establishment and maintenance of hospitals for the poor of Durham County:** Marie Curie Memorial Foundation (£2,500). **Charitable organisations:** Outward Bound Trust (£14,000); Grace House North East (£10,000); Rookhope Village Hall (£7,500); Hartlepool Hospice, Sunderland Hillview Crusaders, P.D.S.A. Sunderland and Governors of Durham School (£4,000 each); Sunderland Victim Support Scheme (£2,500); Handicapped Children's 'Action Group', Auckland Youth and Community Centre, Durham Choristers School and Sunderland Scout Council (£2,000 each) and Farrington Detached Football Club, Happy Days Sunderland and Dystonia Society (£1,000 each). **Maintenance of churches and church**

buildings: St Anne's Church, Bishop Auckland, St Wilfred's Church, Monk Fryston, Selby Abbey Organ Appeal and St Mary's Church, Horden (£8,000 each); St John's Church Hall and St James' Church, Burnopfield (£6,000 each); Greenside Ryton Parish of Coatham and Dormanstown (£5,000); Parish of Blaydon and Swalwell (£4,000); Christ Church, Felling and Friends of Durham Cathedral (£3,000 each) and Archbishop of York Discretionary Account, All Saints Church, Northallerton and Holy Trinity Church, Seaton Carew (£2,000 each).**Relief and maintenance of Clergy/Church officials and their families:** Durham Diocesan Board of Finance (£7,000); Church of England Pensions Board (£3,000); Bishop of Durham's Discretionary Fund (Clergy Holidays) (£2,000) and Ordination book tokens (£800).

FINANCES *Year* 2012 *Income* £385,832 *Grants* £353,418 *Assets* £10,267,737

TRUSTEES Peter Taylor; Richard Farr; Timothy Norton; Anthony Coates; Thomas Greenwell.

OTHER INFORMATION Only in special circumstances grants are awarded outside of the specified geographical area or to individuals. A number of charities are supported by way of annual grants, however, as the trustees' report from 2012 states,' the trustees aim where possible to award grants for specific projects as opposed to general running costs. The trustees' policy is generally to award modest grants to a relatively large number of bodies rather than a few large grants. The charities supported cover a wide range of activities. In this way the trustees aim to provide for a wide variety of needs of persons resident in the geographical area of the trust.'

HOW TO APPLY In writing to the correspondent. As the previous system entry notes, 'the trustees meet in January, April, July and October. Applications should include clear details of the need the project is designed to meet plus estimates, where appropriate, and details of amounts subscribed to date.'

WHO TO APPLY TO The Trustees, McKenzie Bell, 19 John Street, Sunderland, Tyne and Wear SR1 1JG *Tel.* 01915 674857

■ The Primrose Trust

CC NO 800049   **ESTABLISHED** 1986

WHERE FUNDING CAN BE GIVEN UK.

WHO CAN BENEFIT Registered charities.

WHAT IS FUNDED General charitable purposes.

WHAT IS NOT FUNDED Grants are given to registered charities only.

SAMPLE GRANTS Animal Health Trust (£85,000); St Mary's School Calne (£30,000); British Hen Welfare Trust (£21,000); Langford Trust and World Veterinary Service (£20,000 each) and Swan Advocacy Network (£5,000).

FINANCES *Year* 2011–12 *Income* £137,411 *Grants* £181,000 *Assets* £3,549,318

TRUSTEES M. G. Clark; Susan Boyes-Korkis.

HOW TO APPLY In writing to the correspondent, including a copy of the most recent accounts. The trust does not wish to receive telephone calls.

WHO TO APPLY TO Steven Allan, 5 Callaghan Square, Cardiff CF10 5BT *Tel.* 02920 264394

■ The Prince of Wales's Charitable Foundation

CC NO 1127255   **ESTABLISHED** 1979

WHERE FUNDING CAN BE GIVEN Unrestricted.

WHO CAN BENEFIT Registered charities mainly in which the Prince of Wales has a particular interest.

WHAT IS FUNDED Culture, the environment, business and enterprise, medical welfare, education, children and youth and overseas aid.

WHAT IS NOT FUNDED No grants to individuals.

TYPE OF GRANT One-off grants for capital or core expenditure.

RANGE OF GRANTS Typically up to £5,000; large grants are also made.

SAMPLE GRANTS The Great Steward of Scotland's Dumfries House Trust (£1.1 million); The Soil Association (£200,000); The Prince's Foundation for Building Community (£144,000); The Prince of Wales Foundation and The Prince's Trust (£100,000); The Prince's Regeneration Trust (£90,000); Scottish Business in the Community (£47,000) Children and the Arts (£45,000); The Prince's Countryside Fund (£25,000); United World Colleges (£23,000); The British Horse Loggers (£11,000) and The Environmental Law Foundation (£10,000).

FINANCES *Year* 2011–12 *Income* £14,117,000 *Grants* £2,468,000 *Assets* £18,079,000

TRUSTEES John Varley; Michael Rake; William James; Amelia Fawcett.

HOW TO APPLY Fill out the online eligibility form in the first instance which will give you access to the full online application form, should you be eligible. The main grants programme is not open to unsolicited applications. Organisations can apply for up to £5,000 from the small grants programme.

WHO TO APPLY TO David Hutson, The Prince of Wales's Office, Clarence House, St James's, London SW1A 1BA *Tel* 020 7930 4832 ext. 4788 *Website* www.princeofwalescharitable foundation.org.uk

---

■ Princess Anne's Charities

CC NO 277814   **ESTABLISHED** 1979

WHERE FUNDING CAN BE GIVEN UK.

WHO CAN BENEFIT Registered charities, especially charities in which Princess Anne has a particular interest.

WHAT IS FUNDED Social welfare; medical research; children and youth; environment and wildlife; armed forces; and general charitable purposes.

WHAT IS NOT FUNDED No grants to individuals.

TYPE OF GRANT Project, capital and revenue funding. Loans and contracts may also be issued.

SAMPLE GRANTS Previous beneficiaries have included: Butler Trust, the Canal Museum Trust Cranfield Trust, Dogs Trust, Dorothy House Foundation, Durrell Wildlife Conservation Trust, the Evelina Children's Hospital Appeal, Farms for City Children, Farrer and Co Charitable Trust, Fire Services National Benevolent Fund, the Home Farm Trust, Intensive Care Society and International League for the Protection of Horses.

FINANCES *Year* 2011–12 *Income* £149,582 *Grants* £124,025 *Assets* £5,006,491

TRUSTEES Hon. M. T. Bridges; Sir T. J. H. Laurence; B. Hammond.

HOW TO APPLY The Trustees receive numerous grant application letters throughout the year which are considered by the Trustees at their meeting. They discuss the merits of the applications against the criteria for support referred to above, having taken account of the funds available to them.

WHO TO APPLY TO Capt. N. Wright, Farrer and Co LLP, 66 Lincoln's Inn Fields, London WC2A 3LH

■ Prison Service Charity Fund

CC NO 801678   **ESTABLISHED** 1989
WHERE FUNDING CAN BE GIVEN UK.
WHO CAN BENEFIT Charitable organisations.
WHAT IS FUNDED The trust does not accept outside applications – the applicant must be a member of staff.
RANGE OF GRANTS Up to £2,000, most grants are for less than £1,000.
SAMPLE GRANTS Leeds Prison Charity Fund (£2,000); The Twins Appeal and the David Cross Appeal (£1,600 each); Five Charity Appeal, The Alfie Gough Trust and Steps to America Appeal (£1,000 each); Help for Heroes (£750); Chadsgrove Special School (£670); Claire House Children's Hospice and Prostate Cancer Charity (£600 each); Neurofibromatosis Association; Woodlands Hospice (£500); MS Society (£300) and Lymphoma and Leukaemia Association (£220).
FINANCES *Year* 2012 *Income* £165,755 *Grants* £130,130 *Assets* £699,450
TRUSTEES A. N. Joseph, Chair; P. Ashes; J. Goldsworthy; P. McFall; C. F. Smith; K. Wingfield; J. White; Bob Howard.
HOW TO APPLY The trust does not accept outside applications – the person making the application must be a member of staff.
WHO TO APPLY TO Neville Joseph, The Lodge, 8 Derby Road, Garstang, Preston PR3 1EU *Tel.* 01995 604997 *email* bob@pscf.co.uk *Website* www.prisonservicecharityfund.co.uk

---

■ The Privy Purse Charitable Trust

CC NO 296079   **ESTABLISHED** 1987
WHERE FUNDING CAN BE GIVEN UK.
WHO CAN BENEFIT Registered charities.
WHAT IS FUNDED General charitable purposes. 'The main aims of the trustees are to make grants to charities of which The Queen is patron and to support ecclesiastical establishments associated with The Queen.'
RANGE OF GRANTS Most grants are usually up to £1,000.
SAMPLE GRANTS Chapel Royal – Hampton Court Palace (£87,000); Chapel Royal – St James's Palace (£53,000); Chapel Royal – Windsor Great Park (£25,000) and Game and Wildlife Conservation Trust (£10,000).
FINANCES *Year* 2011–12 *Income* £518,298 *Grants* £406,393 *Assets* £2,562,360
TRUSTEES Michael Stevens; Sir Alan Reid; Christopher Geidt.
HOW TO APPLY The trust makes donations to a wide variety of charities, but does not respond to unsolicited applications.
WHO TO APPLY TO Michael Stevens, Trustee, Buckingham Palace, London SW1A 1AA *Tel.* 020 7930 4832

■ The Proven Family Trust

CC NO 1050877   **ESTABLISHED** 1995
WHERE FUNDING CAN BE GIVEN Cumbria, Halton, Knowsley, Liverpool, St Helens, Sefton, Warrington and Wirral.

WHO CAN BENEFIT Organisations benefiting children and older people; those in care, fostered and adopted; and animals. Support may be given to at risk groups and people who are disabled, disadvantaged by poverty, homeless, victims of abuse or domestic violence or who have Alzheimer's disease, arthritis and rheumatism, asthma, cancer, motor neurone disease, multiple sclerosis, Parkinson's disease or sight loss.
WHAT IS FUNDED Charities working in the fields of holiday and respite accommodation; volunteer bureaux; religious and historic buildings; health; community facilities and services; and animal welfare. Other charitable purposes will be considered.
WHAT IS NOT FUNDED No grants to individuals.
TYPE OF GRANT One-off grants for up to three years. Research grants will be considered.
RANGE OF GRANTS Up to £1,000.
SAMPLE GRANTS Action for Kids, Cockermouth Youth Action Limited, Cumbria Cerebral Palsy, Cumbria County Scout Council, Harvest Trust, Kids First, Kingsway Christian Fellowship, Liverpool Blind and Deaf, Pain Research Institute, Parents Against Drugs, Penrith Methodist Church, Roundabout Centre, Shakespeare Centre Kendal, Student Partnership Worldwide and West Derby Community Association.
FINANCES *Year* 2011–12 *Income* £36,912 *Grants* £32,550 *Assets* £629,548
TRUSTEES Graham Quigley; Michael Taxman; Colin Worthington; Simon Griffiths; David Kerr.
HOW TO APPLY In writing to the correspondent for consideration twice a year.
WHO TO APPLY TO Colin Worthington, Trustee, 35 The Mount, Papcastle, Cockermouth, Cumbria CA13 0JY *Tel.* 01900 823324

■ The Provincial Grand Charity of the Province of Derbyshire

CC NO 701963   **ESTABLISHED** 1989
WHERE FUNDING CAN BE GIVEN Derbyshire.
WHO CAN BENEFIT Masons and dependants; other charitable organisations.
WHAT IS FUNDED Masonic charities and general charitable purposes.
SAMPLE GRANTS Previous beneficiaries include: Blythe House Hospice (£1,000); WORK, Derby Kids' Camp and Ryder-Cheshire Volunteers (£500 each); Brin's Cottage, Lennox Children's Cancer Fund and Ian Appeal (£300 each); and Guide Association Chesterfield HQ and 3rd Wingerworth Scout Group, Muscular Dystrophy Campaign and Nicholson Court Social Club (£250 each).
FINANCES *Year* 2011–12 *Income* £90,320 *Grants* £30,745 *Assets* £1,377,966
TRUSTEES Graham Rudd; Graham Sisson; Peter Hodcroft.
OTHER INFORMATION The grants total includes non-Masonic donations of £24,000.
HOW TO APPLY In writing to the correspondent.
WHO TO APPLY TO Graham Sisson, Secretary, 21 Netherfield Road, Chapel-en-le-Frith, High Peak SK23 0PN *Tel.* 01298 812801 *email* secretary@derbyshiremason.org *Website* www.derbyshiremason.org

---

■ The Puebla Charitable Trust

CC NO 290055 **ESTABLISHED** 1984
WHERE FUNDING CAN BE GIVEN Worldwide.
WHO CAN BENEFIT Organisations benefiting people disadvantaged by poverty living in both urban and rural areas.
WHAT IS FUNDED 'At present, the council limits its support to charities which assist the poorest sections of the population and community development work – either of these may be in urban or rural areas, both in the UK and overseas.'
WHAT IS NOT FUNDED No grants for capital projects, religious institutions, research or institutions for people who are disabled. Individuals are not supported and no scholarships are given.
TYPE OF GRANT Up to three years.
SAMPLE GRANTS Shelter, South West London Law Centres, Child Poverty Action Group and Family Action (£20,000 each) and Action on Disability and Development and Mines Advisory Group (£15,000 each).
FINANCES *Year* 2011–12 *Income* £97,748 *Grants* £110,000 *Assets* £2,378,080
TRUSTEES J. Phipps; M. A. Strutt.
HOW TO APPLY In writing to the correspondent. The trustees meet in July. The trust is unable to acknowledge applications.
WHO TO APPLY TO The Clerk, Ensors, Cardinal House, 46 St Nicholas Street, Ipswich IP1 1TT *Tel.* 01473 220022

■ The Richard and Christine Purchas Charitable Trust

CC NO 1083126 **ESTABLISHED** 2000
WHERE FUNDING CAN BE GIVEN UK.
WHO CAN BENEFIT Medical organisations.
WHAT IS FUNDED Medical research, medical education and patient care
FINANCES *Year* 2011–12 *Income* £22,333 *Grants* £20,000
TRUSTEES Daniel Auerbach; Pauline Auerbach; Dr Douglas Rossdale; Robert Auerbach.
OTHER INFORMATION Previously the trust has part-funded the post of Consultant Speech Therapist at the Charing Cross Hospital in association with Macmillan Cancer Relief.
In 2011–12 the trust had a total expenditure of £23,830. More detailed financial information was not available.
HOW TO APPLY In writing to the correspondent.
WHO TO APPLY TO Daniel Auerbach, Trustee, 46 Hyde Park Gardens Mews, London W2 2NX *Tel.* 020 7580 2448

■ The Puri Foundation

CC NO 327854 **ESTABLISHED** 1988
WHERE FUNDING CAN BE GIVEN Nottinghamshire, India (particularly the towns of Mullan Pur near Chandigarh and Ambala).
WHO CAN BENEFIT Organisations benefiting: children; young adults; students; older people; Hindus; the disabled; at risk groups; those disadvantaged by poverty; and socially isolated people.
WHAT IS FUNDED Welfare and community centres. The trust aims to: relieve those in conditions of need, hardship or distress; advance education; provide facilities for recreation; and relieve and rehabilitate young unemployed people in the Nottinghamshire area.
WHAT IS NOT FUNDED No grants are given for holidays.

RANGE OF GRANTS Minimum of £50.
SAMPLE GRANTS London Southbank University (£1,000,000); The Puri Foundation for Education in India (£191,500); Global Human Rights (£44,000); Graham Budd Actions (£18,600); Ava Campaign Project (£15,000); Nottingham High School (£3,000) and Indian Gymkhana Club (£2,000).
FINANCES *Year* 2011–12 *Income* £852,999 *Grants* £1,267,939 *Assets* £2,710,194
TRUSTEES Nathu Puri; Anil Puri; Mary McGowan.
OTHER INFORMATION In 2011–12 grant expenditure was broken down in to the following categories: Education (£1.2 million); Human Rights (£44,000); General support (£20,000) and Recreation (Special Projects) (£15,000).
HOW TO APPLY In writing to the correspondent.
WHO TO APPLY TO Nathu Puri, Trustee, Environment House, 6 Union Road, Nottingham NG3 1FH *Tel.* 01159 013000 *Fax* 01159 013100

■ Mr and Mrs J. A. Pye's Charitable Settlement

CC NO 242677 **ESTABLISHED** 1965
WHERE FUNDING CAN BE GIVEN UK, with a special interest in the Oxfordshire region and, to a lesser extent, in Reading, Cheltenham and Bristol.
WHO CAN BENEFIT Organisations benefiting children and young adults are given priority, although those benefiting older people will also be funded.
WHAT IS FUNDED General charitable purposes at the trustees' discretion. Of particular interest are: environmental – this subject particularly deals with organic farming matters, conservation generally and health related matters such as pollution research and some wildlife protection; adult health and care – especially causes supporting: post-natal depression, schizophrenia, mental health generally and research into the main causes of early death; children's health and care – for physical, mental and learning disabilities, respite breaks and so on; youth organisations – particularly projects encouraging self-reliance or dealing with social deprivation; education – nursery, primary, secondary or higher/institutions (not individuals); regional causes around Oxford, Reading, Cheltenham and Bristol – under this category the trustees will consider academic and arts projects.
WHAT IS NOT FUNDED No grants for: organisations that are not recognised charities; activities which are primarily the responsibility of government or some other responsible body; activities which collect funds for subsequent re-distribution to other charities; corporate affiliation or membership of charities; endowment funds; expeditions or overseas charities; fabric appeals for places of worship, other than in geographical locations indicated above; fundraising events or activities; hospitals or medical centres (except for projects that are clearly additional to statutory responsibilities); individual, including students; overseas appeals; promotion of religion.
TYPE OF GRANT One-off, core costs, projects, research, recurring, running and start-up costs, and salaries. Capital costs may be considered. Funding may be given for up to or more than three years. Also interest-free loans.
RANGE OF GRANTS £250–£135,000.
SAMPLE GRANTS Organic Research Centre (£75,000); University College Oxford (£50,000);

Association for Post Natal Illness (£20,000);
Children with AIDS Charity (£12,000); Falcon
Rowing and Canoeing Club (£5,000); St John's
Family Resource Unit (£4,000); English Music
Festival (£2,500); Crisis, Guide Association, The
Willow Trust and Wolvercote Young People's
Club in Oxford (£1,000 each).

FINANCES *Year* 2012 *Income* £654,261
Grants £471,250 *Assets* £11,245,321

TRUSTEES Simon Stubbings; David S. Tallon; Patrick
Mulcare.

OTHER INFORMATION There was a further £163,000
given in loans. About half the grants given were
for £1,000 or less including £34,000 given in
grants of less than £500 each.

HOW TO APPLY All applications should be sent to the
administrative office (and not to individual
trustees). These are reviewed on a continual
basis and the trustees meet quarterly to make
their decisions. Any decision can therefore take
up to four months before it is finally taken.
However, all applicants are informed of the
outcome of their applications and all
applications are acknowledged. Telephone
contact will usually be counter-productive. There
are no application forms but the following
information is essential: the registered charity
number or evidence of an organisation's tax
exempt status; brief description of the activities
of the charity; the names of the trustees and
chief officers [more important than patrons];
details of the purpose of the application and
where funds will be put to use; details of the
funds already raised and the proposals for how
remaining funds are to be raised; the latest
trustees report and full audited or independently
examined accounts (which **must** comply with
Charity Commission guidelines and
requirements); details of full name of the bank
account, sort code, and number into which any
grant should be paid; the charity's email
address.

WHO TO APPLY TO David S. Tallon, Trustee, c/o
Mercer and Hole Chartered Accountants,
Gloucester House, 72 London Road, St Albans,
Hertfordshire AL1 1NS *Tel.* 01727 869141
email pyecharitablesettlement@mercerhole.co.
uk *Website* www.pyecharitablesettlement.org

■ The Pyne Charitable Trust

CC NO 1105357   **ESTABLISHED** 2004

WHERE FUNDING CAN BE GIVEN UK and overseas,
particularly Malawi, Moldova, Slovakia and
Ukraine.

WHO CAN BENEFIT Organisations and individuals.

WHAT IS FUNDED Christian and health causes.

SAMPLE GRANTS Good Shepherd Mission
(£110,000); Teen Challenge London £200) and
Release International (£15).

FINANCES *Year* 2011–12 *Income* £107,262
Grants £110,215 *Assets* £24,443

TRUSTEES Michael Brennan; Pauline Brennan; Mike
Mitchell.

OTHER INFORMATION A further £6,500 was given in
grants to individuals.

HOW TO APPLY Ongoing support appears to be given
to projects selected by the trustees.

WHO TO APPLY TO Pauline Brennan, Secretary,
26 Tredegar Square, London E3 5AG *Tel.* 020
8980 4853

■ The Quarry Family Charitable Trust

CC NO 1147766   **ESTABLISHED** 2012
WHERE FUNDING CAN BE GIVEN UK and overseas.
WHO CAN BENEFIT Charities supporting children and young people, older people and people with disabilities.
WHAT IS FUNDED General charitable purposes with a particular interest in education and sport.
TRUSTEES Jill Whitehouse; Gareth Quarry; Oliver Quarry.
HOW TO APPLY In writing to the correspondent.
WHO TO APPLY TO Jill Whitehouse, Trustee, Montrose House, Petersham Road, Richmond, Surrey TW10 7AD *Tel.* 020 8940 2362 *email* trustees@tqft.co.uk *Website* www.tqft.co.uk

■ Quartet Community Foundation (formerly the Greater Bristol Foundation)

CC NO 1080418   **ESTABLISHED** 1987
WHERE FUNDING CAN BE GIVEN West England – Bristol, North Somerset, South Gloucestershire, Bath and North East Somerset.
WHO CAN BENEFIT Any charity aimed at increasing opportunities and enhancing the quality of life in the area; particularly smaller, low-profile community groups and people at a particular disadvantage through discrimination.
WHAT IS FUNDED There are a number of specific schemes which support the four geographical beneficial areas, aiming to help local communities. Grants are made for a wide range of charitable purposes including: education, the protection of good health, relief of poverty and sickness, social welfare and the environment. For further information on types of grants and guidance towards the most appropriate fund(s) for your organisation contact the foundation or visit their website.
WHAT IS NOT FUNDED The foundation does not give grants to: individuals; general appeals; statutory organisations or the direct replacement of statutory funding; political groups or activities promoting political beliefs; religious groups promoting religious beliefs; arts projects with no community or charitable element; sports projects with no community or charitable element; medical research, equipment or treatment; animal welfare; or projects that take place before an application can be processed.
SAMPLE GRANTS Voluntary Action North Somerset (£120,000); Moonstone Therapy Centre Appeal (£100,000); Arnosvale (£95,000); Somerset Wood Recycling (£50,000); Easton Community Children's Centre (£40,000); Second Step Housing Association (£20,000); Oxford Food Bank (£10,000); St John's Hospice (£7,800); Swindon Bats Sport and Social Club (£6,000) and Room 13 Hareclive and Chiltern CAB (£5,000 each).
FINANCES *Year* 2011–12 *Income* £4,053,171 *Grants* £2,865,535 *Assets* £18,095,003
TRUSTEES John Kane; Alexander Hore-Ruthven; Tim Ross; William Lee; Richard Hall; Lin Whitfield; John Cullum; Jane Moss; Hilary Neal; Vernon Samuels; David Harvey; Christopher Sharp; Lesley Freed.
PUBLICATIONS Various research papers available online.
OTHER INFORMATION Full information on all grants programmes and how to apply can be found on the fund's website.
HOW TO APPLY Before you apply to the community foundation check that your group or project meets the following requirements: you must be a small charity, community group or local voluntary organisation operating in the West of England i.e. Bath and North East Somerset, Bristol, North Somerset or South Gloucestershire; you do not need to be a registered charity but you must be able to provide a copy of your group's constitution or set of rules; your group must be managed by a board of trustees or management committee; you must be able to provide the foundation with up-to-date financial information for your group. Applicants should refer to the fund's website for details on how to apply to each grants programme. The funding team can be contacted for any help or advice concerning grants applications.
WHO TO APPLY TO Alice Meason, Royal Oak House, Royal Oak Avenue, Bristol BS1 4GB *Tel.* 01179 897700 *Fax* 01179 897701 *email* info@quartetcf.org.uk *Website* www.quartetcf.org.uk

■ The Queen Anne's Gate Foundation

CC NO 1108903   **ESTABLISHED** 2005
WHERE FUNDING CAN BE GIVEN UK and Asia.
WHO CAN BENEFIT Charitable organisations.
WHAT IS FUNDED 'The foundation seeks to support projects and charities within the following broad criteria. It seeks to make a contribution that is meaningful in the context of the project/charity with which it is working. It tries to focus in particular on projects which might be said to make potentially unproductive lives productive. This tends to mean a bias towards educational, medical and rehabilitative charities and those that work with underprivileged areas of society. There is an attempt to focus a significant proportion of donations on Asia, Malawi and the UK.'
SAMPLE GRANTS Hong King Polytechnic University (£63,000); Friends of the Citizens Foundation (£50,000); Christian Friends of Korea (£31,000); Merlin and Families for Children (£30,000 each); CINI UK and The Marylebone Project (£25,000 each); English National Opera (£21,000); Indochina Starfish Foundation (£20,000); Support Street Children (£19,000); H. H. Maharaja Hanwant Singhji Charitable Foundation (£16,000); Hackney Music Development Trust and City of Exeter YMCA Community Projects (£10,000 each) and Mid-Wales Music Fund.
FINANCES *Year* 2011–12 *Income* £70,025 *Grants* £589,883 *Assets* £2,609,469
TRUSTEES N. T. Allan; J. M. E. Boyer; Roger Wortley.
HOW TO APPLY In writing to the correspondent. Trustees meet twice a year.
WHO TO APPLY TO The Trustees, WillcoxLewis LLP, The Old Coach House, Bergh Apton, Norwich, Norfolk NR15 1DD *Tel.* 01508 480100

■ Queen Mary's Roehampton Trust

CC NO 211715 **ESTABLISHED** 1928
WHERE FUNDING CAN BE GIVEN UK.
WHO CAN BENEFIT Ex-servicemen or women who were disabled in service and their dependants.
WHAT IS FUNDED Grants are made to charities supporting ex-service personnel who suffered disability while in service that provide welfare services, residential or nursing homes and their widows/widowers and dependants.
WHAT IS NOT FUNDED Grants are not made directly to individuals.
TYPE OF GRANT Annual recurring, one-off. Also capital and project. Funding may be given for up to two years.
RANGE OF GRANTS Usually £1,000–£50,000.
SAMPLE GRANTS Royal Naval Benevolent Trust (£35,000); Erskine Hospital (£30,000); Haig Homes (£25,000); Combat Stress (£20,000); British Ex-Services Wheelchair Sports Association (£17,000); Scottish Veterans' Garden City Association (£15,000); Veterans Aid (£10,000); Royal Navy and Royal Marine Children's Fund (£7,500); William Simpson's Home, Stirling (£5,000); Spinal Injuries Association (£3,000) and Women's Naval Service Benevolent Trust (£2,000).
FINANCES *Year* 2011–12 *Income* £507,655 *Grants* £437,500 *Assets* £11,709,021
TRUSTEES Simon Brewis; Cathy Walker; James Macnamara; Gordon Paterson; Colin Green; Paul Cummings; Stephen Farringdon; Beverley Davies; Debbie Bowles; Stephen Coltman; Barry Thornton.
HOW TO APPLY On a standard application form available from the correspondent. Representatives of the trust may visit beneficiary organisations.
WHO TO APPLY TO Col Stephen Rowland-Jones, Clerk to the Trustees, 2 Sovereign Close, Quidhampton, Salisbury, Wiltshire SP2 9ES *Tel.* 01722 501413 *email* qmrt@hotmail.co.uk

■ The Queen's Silver Jubilee Trust

CC NO 272373 **ESTABLISHED** 1976
WHERE FUNDING CAN BE GIVEN UK, Channel Islands, Isle of Man, Commonwealth, Canada.
WHO CAN BENEFIT Registered charities.
WHAT IS FUNDED Organisations working with young people, aged 14–30, across the UK, Commonwealth, Channel Islands and the Isle of Man, particularly those that support disadvantaged young people or those that enable young people to volunteer in their local community, broadly defined.
WHAT IS NOT FUNDED Grants are only made to registered charities. No grants to individuals.
TYPE OF GRANT One-off and recurring.
RANGE OF GRANTS Up to £10,000.
SAMPLE GRANTS The Prince's Trust (£1.2 million); Sentebale (£142,000); Canadian Youth Foundation/Memorial University (£100,000); Rock YK (£80,000); Create (Arts) Ltd (£62,000); Youth United (£60,000); Dance United Northern Ireland (£53,000); Southbank Sinfonia and The Lyric Theatre Belfast (£50,000 each) and Educate Girls and The Schola Foundation (£35,000 each).
FINANCES *Year* 2011–12 *Income* £226,000 *Grants* £1,867,000 *Assets* £35,670,000
TRUSTEES Rt Hon Christopher Geidt; Sir Fred Goodwin; Stephen Hall; Sir Alan Reid; Peter Mimpriss; Michael Marks.

OTHER INFORMATION The trust is currently spending out, so it is unlikely that grants to new applicants will be made.
HOW TO APPLY In choosing beneficiaries, the Trust will not normally accept unsolicited applications but will identify and build trusted, strategic relationships with its charity partners, usually through multi-year grants.
WHO TO APPLY TO Anne Threlkeld, Administrator, Buckingham Palace, London SW1A 1AA *Tel.* 020 7930 4832 *email* anne.threlkeld@ royal.gsx.gov.uk *Website* www. queenssilverjubileetrust.org.uk

■ Quercus Trust

CC NO 1039205 **ESTABLISHED** 1993
WHERE FUNDING CAN BE GIVEN UK.
WHO CAN BENEFIT Established organisations and registered charities.
WHAT IS FUNDED Mainly the arts, and other purposes which seek to further public knowledge, understanding and appreciation of any matters of artistic, aesthetic, scientific or historical interest.
WHAT IS NOT FUNDED No grants to individuals.
RANGE OF GRANTS £500–£70,000.
SAMPLE GRANTS Wayne McGregor Foundation (£1 million); Royal National Theatre (£100,000); Sadler's Wells Trust (£66,000); Royal Opera House Covent Garden Ltd (£50,000); Harley Street Osteopaths Ltd (£32,000); Dance UK (£26,000); Hofesh Shechter Company (£10,000); Rambert Trust Ltd (£7,500); Hunger Project Trust (£5,000); Starlight Children's Foundation (£2,000) and Tate Foundation (£850).
FINANCES *Year* 2011–12 *Income* £144,546 *Grants* £1,358,364 *Assets* £3,937,583
TRUSTEES Lady Angela Bernstein; Kate E. Bernstein.
HOW TO APPLY The trust states in its grantmaking policy that: 'Proposals for distributions are generated internally.' No external applications for funding will be considered. The trust has informed us that 'they do not now consider, or even acknowledge unsolicited applications. Their available funds are fully absorbed by projects known to them.'
WHO TO APPLY TO Helen Price, Trust Administrator, Gloucester House, 72 London Road, St Albans, Hertfordshire AL1 1NS *Tel.* 01727 869141

■ Quothquan Trust

CC NO 1110647 **ESTABLISHED** 2004
WHERE FUNDING CAN BE GIVEN Birmingham and surrounding area, West Midlands.
WHO CAN BENEFIT Christian organisations and individuals.
WHAT IS FUNDED Promotion of Christian faith through specific projects and initiatives aimed at relieving the poverty and sickness, assisting the elderly, the ill, the socially and economically disadvantaged, advancement of religious education.
WHAT IS NOT FUNDED No grants are given towards: anything that does not have the promotion of Christianity as part of its ethos; activities that are the primary responsibility of central or local government; animal welfare; church buildings for restorations, improvements, renovations or new building; environmental projects such as conservation and protection of wildlife and landscape; expeditions and overseas trips; hospitals and health centres; individuals are not normally supported; large national charities are

not normally supported, even for local projects; loans and business finance; medical research projects; overseas appeals, unless there is a recommendation from someone known personally to the trustees; promotion of any non-Christian religion; and schools, universities and colleges.

TYPE OF GRANT Grants are generally made on a one – off basis with an exception to the regular monthly grants.

RANGE OF GRANTS .

SAMPLE GRANTS A list of specific beneficiaries was not included in the annual accounts.

FINANCES *Year* 2012 *Income* £1,518,963 *Grants* £284,500 *Assets* £2,898,919

TRUSTEES Archie Gilmour; Janet Gilmour.

OTHER INFORMATION Grants totalling £73,500 were made to 37 individuals.

HOW TO APPLY In writing to the correspondent. See the website for guidelines and criteria. The applications for grants are aimed to be considered quarterly.

WHO TO APPLY TO Archie Gilmour, Trustee, Dale Farm, Worcester Lane, Four Oaks, Sutton Coldfield B75 5PR *Tel.* 01213 233236 *Website* www.quothquantrust.org.uk

■ R. J. M. Charitable Trust

CC NO 288336   **ESTABLISHED** 1983
WHERE FUNDING CAN BE GIVEN UK and worldwide.
WHO CAN BENEFIT Jewish organisations.
WHAT IS FUNDED Jewish charitable purposes.
RANGE OF GRANTS £50–£100,000.
SAMPLE GRANTS One to One (£10,000); Yeshun (£8,000); North Salford Synagogue (£7,400); South Manchester Synagogue (£5,000); Manchester Jewish Philanthropic (£3,000); Manchester Kellel (£2,000); Navas Chesed, OHR Elcharan and Sunderland Talmud (£1,000); British Friends Masat Moshe (£560); British Friends Israel War (£250) and Crisis (£20).
FINANCES *Year* 2011–12 *Income* £121,000 *Grants* £176,450 *Assets* £117,430
TRUSTEES Joshua Rowe; Michelle Rowe.
HOW TO APPLY In writing to the correspondent.
WHO TO APPLY TO Joshua Rowe, Trustee, 84 Upper Park Road, Salford M7 4JA *Tel.* 01617 208787 *email* joshua@broomwell.com

■ R. S. Charitable Trust

CC NO 1053660   **ESTABLISHED** 1996
WHERE FUNDING CAN BE GIVEN UK.
WHO CAN BENEFIT Registered charities.
WHAT IS FUNDED Jewish causes and the relief of poverty.
SAMPLE GRANTS Previous beneficiaries have included British Friends of Tshernobil, Forty Ltd, NRST, Society of Friends of the Torah, Talmud Hochschule, Viznitz, Yeshiva Horomo and Yeshivas Luzern.
FINANCES *Year* 2011–12 *Income* £580,744 *Grants* £267,327 *Assets* £2,073,755
TRUSTEES Harvey Freudenberger; Michelle Freudenberger; Stuart Freudenberger; Max Freudenberger.
HOW TO APPLY In writing to the correspondent.
WHO TO APPLY TO Max Freudenberger, Trustee, 138 Stamford Hill, London N16 6QT

■ The R. V. W. Trust

CC NO 1066977   **ESTABLISHED** 1958
WHERE FUNDING CAN BE GIVEN UK.
WHO CAN BENEFIT Organisations and individuals, particularly composers, musicians and music students.
WHAT IS FUNDED The trust's current grantmaking policies are as follows: (1) To give assistance to British composers who have not yet achieved a national reputation. (2) To give assistance towards the performance and recording of music by neglected or currently unfashionable 20th century British composers, including performances by societies and at festivals which include works by such composers in their programmes. (3) To assist UK organisations that promote public knowledge and appreciation of 20th and 21st century British music. (4) To assist education projects in the field of music. (5) To support postgraduate students of composition taking first masters degrees at British universities and conservatoires.

WHAT IS NOT FUNDED No grants for Concerts, concert series or concert tours which do not include music by 20th and 21st century British composers; Concerts for which income from box office receipts, together with support from other organisations, is forecast to amount to less than half of the estimated expenditure; Commissions purely for youth or children's ensembles; Grants for musicals, rock or pop music, ethnic music, jazz or dance music or multi-media and theatrical events in which music is not the primary art-form; 'Workshops' with no planned public performance; Grants to organisations directly administered by local or other public authorities; Grants to managing agents and commercial promoters; Vocal or instrumental tuition; The making, purchase or repair of musical instruments, computer or multi-media equipment; The construction or restoration of buildings. Grants cannot be made for the furtherance or performance of the founder's own work (Ralph Vaughan Williams).
RANGE OF GRANTS £2,000–£25,000
SAMPLE GRANTS Vaughan Williams Memorial Library/ English Folk Dance and Song Society (£25,000); Huddersfield Contemporary Music Festival (£12,000); Cheltenham Music Festival (£6,000); Northern Ireland Opera and National Youth Orchestra Composers' Course (£5,000); Royal Philharmonic Society Composition Prize (£4,500); British Youth Opera (£3,000); Little Missenden Festival (£2,500) and Stone Records and Onyx Brass (£2,000 each).
FINANCES *Year* 2012 *Income* £362,874 *Grants* £264,625 *Assets* £1,596,069
TRUSTEES Hugh Cobbe; Michael Kennedy; Lord Armstrong; Andrew Hunter Johnston; Sir John Manduell; Jeremy Dale Roberts; Anthony Burton; Prof. Nicola Lefanu; Musicians Benevolent Fund.
OTHER INFORMATION The grant total includes £20,000 to students studying masters in composition.
HOW TO APPLY In writing to the correspondent including the information detailed in the application guidelines which are available on the trust's website. For applicants for postgraduate funding there is a form available on the website. The trust will only fund up to 50% of the cost of any event. Trustees meet three times a year, in February, June and October to consider applications which should be received by 2 January, 1 May or 1 September respectively. Applications can be made either by email or post but a signed copy of the covering letter must be posted.
WHO TO APPLY TO Helen Faulkner, Administrator, 7–11 Britannia Street, London WC1X 9JS *Tel.* 020 7239 9139 *email* helen@rvwtrust.org.uk *Website* www.rvwtrust.org.uk

■ The Monica Rabagliati Charitable Trust

CC NO 1086368   **ESTABLISHED** 2001
WHERE FUNDING CAN BE GIVEN UK.
WHO CAN BENEFIT Charitable organisations. 'The trustees have decided to prioritise small/ medium sized organisations where possible.'
WHAT IS FUNDED Mostly support for 'organisations that focus on the alleviation of child suffering and deprivation'. The trust also supports humanitarian and medical causes.
RANGE OF GRANTS £5,000 or less.
SAMPLE GRANTS Nilyana Projects, The Special Yoga Centre and Travelling Light Theatre Company (£5,000 each); SignHealth (£4,700); Children's

Safety Education Foundation (£3,800); Outward Bound Trust (£3,000); Getaway Girls (£2,500); Keynsham and District Mencap Society (£2,000) and Foundation UK and Youth at Risk (£1,000 each).

FINANCES *Year* 2011–12 *Income* £37,332 *Grants* £59,950 *Assets* £1,815,999

TRUSTEES S. G. Hambros Trust Company Limited; R. L. McLean

HOW TO APPLY On a form available to download from the website. Grants are given twice yearly.

WHO TO APPLY TO Rachel Iles, S. G. Hambros Bank Limited, Norfolk House, 31 St James's Square, London SW1Y 4JR *Tel.* 020 7597 3065 *Website* www.rabagliati.org.uk

....

■ Rachel Charitable Trust

CC NO 276441   **ESTABLISHED** 1978

WHERE FUNDING CAN BE GIVEN Unrestricted.

WHO CAN BENEFIT Charitable organisations, mostly Jewish groups.

WHAT IS FUNDED General charitable purposes, in practice, mainly Jewish organisations.

SAMPLE GRANTS Previous beneficiaries include: British Friends of Shuut Ami, Children's Hospital Trust Fund, Cometville Limited, Encounter – Jewish Outreach Network, Chosen Mishpat Centre, Gertner Charitable Trust, Hertsmere Jewish Primary School, Jewish Learning Exchange, London Millennium Bikeathon, Manchester Jewish Grammar School, Project Seed, Shaarei Zedek Hospital, Shomrei Hachomot Jerusalem, Yeshiva Ohel Shimon Trust, Yeshiva Shaarei Torah Manchester.

FINANCES *Year* 2011–12 *Income* £3,745,240 *Grants* £2,728,570 *Assets* £4,973,915

TRUSTEES Leopold Noe; Susan Noe; Simon Kanter.

OTHER INFORMATION A separate list of donations made during the year was available from the trustees for £25.

HOW TO APPLY In writing to the correspondent.

WHO TO APPLY TO Robert Chalk, Secretary, F. & C. Reit Asset Management, 5 Wigmore Street, London W1U 1PB *Tel.* 020 7016 3549

....

■ The Racing Foundation

CC NO 1145297   **ESTABLISHED** 2012

WHERE FUNDING CAN BE GIVEN UK

WHO CAN BENEFIT Charities, universities and other research institutes.

WHAT IS FUNDED Horseracing industry; welfare and education; equine research.

WHAT IS NOT FUNDED Only one application, whether successful or not, may be submitted in any one year. No grants can be given for the following: work which does not deliver benefits associated with the UK horseracing and thoroughbreeding industry; the promotion of religion; work that addresses gambling addiction (unless specifically focussed on participants within the horseracing and thoroughbred breeding industry; retrospective funding; any work which is not legally charitable. The foundation will also not be able to provide match funding for projects funded by the British horseracing grants scheme. No general appeals or mailshots will be considered. The trustees will also not recognise any personal approaches in support of an application.

TYPE OF GRANT Capital costs, core costs, salaries.

SAMPLE GRANTS HEROS (Homing Ex-Racehorses Organisation Scheme); Moorcroft Racehorse Welfare Centre, National Horseracing Museum and New Astley Club – Newmarket.

FINANCES *Year* 2013 *Grants* £357,000

TRUSTEES Michael Harris; Roger Weatherby; Kirsten Rausing; Sir Ian Good.

OTHER INFORMATION The foundation was established in 2012 with funding derived from the UK government's sale of the Horserace Totalisator Board ('Tote'). It is expected to receive the proceeds from this sale over the seven year period from 2012–19, with the money being invested to provide a sustainable future income stream. The foundation has already received a £19 million endowment, to which it hopes to add a further £16 million by 2015, with the possibility of a further £50 million by 2021. Founding members include the British Horseracing Authority, The Horsemen's Group and the Racecourse Association. The foundation aims to use these funds to achieve a lasting legacy for the sport of horseracing. The foundation officially launched in October 2012. The trust has forecast that it plans to distribute the following: 2014–£700,000; 2015–£1 million. The first round of grants made in 2013 amounted to £228,000 with £129,000 scheduled for payment later in the year and £99,000 committed for future payment.

HOW TO APPLY The following information is provided by the foundation:

'**Equine Science grants:** Grants are managed and assessed in association with the Horserace Betting Levy Board. To make an application you must apply through the HBLB website by registering with their equine grants system. To ensure your grant is considered by the Racing Foundation you must mark the relevant box on the application summary. Applications will be scrutinised by a number of external peer reviewers and HBLB's Veterinary Advisory Committee. The Racing Foundation trustees make the final decision. The scheme tends to open in Spring and close in Summer with awards made in the Winter. Exact closing dates are posted on the website.'

'**All other grants:** *First stage:* In the first instance, charities must submit an online application. This will require charities to provide basic details about their organisation, upload a copy of the charity's most recent annual accounts and upload a short proposal. The short proposal should be prepared as a Word document or PDF, and should address the following in no more than 600 words: what you would like the Racing Foundation to fund; how you know that there is a need for this work; what difference the work will make and who will benefit from it. If you are successful in your first stage application, you will be invited to submit a second stage application form.'

'*Second stage:* At the second stage, charities will be asked to complete a more detailed application form. Small charities submitting grant applications for less than £5,000 will be asked to complete a simple version of the second stage application form and will be offered assistance to do so. During the application process, the Racing Foundation may ask to speak to you on the phone, or visit your charity, to obtain more information about your grant application. We will contact you if this is the case. Applications are considered twice a year with a spring and autumn funding round. In the past the rounds have closed for first stage applications in December and June in, however, applicants are encourage to check the website for exact dates.'

WHO TO APPLY TO Chris Mills, Executive Officer, 75 High Holborn, London WC1V 6LS *Tel.* 0300 321 1873 *email* chris.mills@racingfoundation.co.uk *Website* www.racingfoundation.co.uk

■ Racing Welfare

CC NO 1084042   **ESTABLISHED** 2000

WHERE FUNDING CAN BE GIVEN UK

WHO CAN BENEFIT Organisations that offer services to people who work in, or are retired from, the horse racing industry.

WHAT IS FUNDED Welfare in the horse racing industry.

RANGE OF GRANTS Up to £50,000

SAMPLE GRANTS Sports Chaplaincy Offering Resources and Encouragement (SCORE) (£50,000); New Astley Club (£30,000) and British Racing School (£26,000).

FINANCES *Year* 2012 *Income* £1,958,000 *Grants* £334,000 *Assets* £21,679,000

TRUSTEES Gary Middlebrook; Samuel Morshead; Baroness Ann Mallalieu; John Maxse; Jacqueline Fanshawe; Gen. Sir Sam Cowan; Raymond Henley; Antonia Deuters; Simon Clarke; Joey Newton; Gavin Macechern.

OTHER INFORMATION The grant total includes £228,000 that was given to individuals.

HOW TO APPLY In writing to the correspondent.

WHO TO APPLY TO Lesley Graham, Robin McAlpine House, 20B Park Lane, Newmarket, Suffolk CB8 8QD *Tel.* 01638 560763 *email* info@racingwelfare.co.uk *Website* www.racingwelfare.co.uk

■ The Mr and Mrs Philip Rackham Charitable Trust

CC NO 1013844   **ESTABLISHED** 1992

WHERE FUNDING CAN BE GIVEN Norfolk.

WHO CAN BENEFIT Registered charities

WHAT IS FUNDED General charitable purposes, although there is some preference for asthma charities and Samaritans.

WHAT IS NOT FUNDED No grants to individuals.

RANGE OF GRANTS Up to £6,000

SAMPLE GRANTS Samaritans – Norwich (£6,000); Papworth Hospital Charity and The Norfolk Hospice Tapping House (£5,000 each); Royal Agricultural Benevolent Institution (£2,500); Victim Support and Wellspring Family Centre (£1,000 each) and The Prince's Trust (£500).

FINANCES *Year* 2011–12 *Income* £49,596 *Grants* £35,750 *Assets* £1,175,890

TRUSTEES Neil Sparrow; Charles Barratt; Ann Rush.

OTHER INFORMATION In 2011–12 grants were given to 17 organisations.

HOW TO APPLY In writing to the correspondent.

WHO TO APPLY TO Neil Sparrow, Trustee, c/ Birketts LLP, Kingfisher House, 1 Gilders Way, Norwich NR3 1UB *Tel.* 01603 232300 *Fax* 01603 230533

■ Richard Radcliffe Charitable Trust

CC NO 1068930   **ESTABLISHED** 1998

WHERE FUNDING CAN BE GIVEN UK.

WHO CAN BENEFIT Charitable organisations.

WHAT IS FUNDED The trust stated its policy as being to support, through making grants to other organisations, the following charitable activities: to assist physically disabled people; to provide technical training to give young people a start in life; to support hospice care for people who are terminally ill; to provide help for people who are severely deaf and/or blind.

TYPE OF GRANT Mainly recurrent.

RANGE OF GRANTS Between £1,000– £10,000.

FINANCES *Year* 2011–12 *Income* £48,675 *Grants* £103,000 *Assets* £1,343,633

TRUSTEES Dr P. A. Radcliffe; Miss M. Radcliffe; Miss P. Radcliffe; A. M. Bell.

HOW TO APPLY In writing to the correspondent.

WHO TO APPLY TO Dr Paul A. Radcliffe, Boycott House, Welsh Lane, Stowe, Buckingham MK18 5DJ *Tel.* 01280 813352

■ The Radcliffe Trust

CC NO 209212   **ESTABLISHED** 1714

WHERE FUNDING CAN BE GIVEN UK.

WHO CAN BENEFIT Registered or exempt charities. Organisations and schemes benefiting musicians and those involved in the crafts.

WHAT IS FUNDED (1) Music: 'The Radcliffe Trust supports classical music performance and training especially chamber music, composition and music education. Particular interests within music education are music for children and adults with special needs, youth orchestras and projects at secondary and higher levels, including academic research. (2) Craft: The Radcliffe Trust supports the development of the skills, knowledge and experience that underpin the UK's traditional cultural heritage and crafts sectors. This includes support for craft and conservation training, for practical projects and for strategic projects which demonstrate clear benefits to individuals and to the sector. However, the Trust remains committed to flexible, open and inclusive grant-giving and will consider other projects, should they fall broadly within its remit. The Radcliffe Trust wishes to promote standards of excellence through all its support.

WHAT IS NOT FUNDED No grants to individual applicants. No retrospective grants are made, nor for deficit funding, core costs, general appeals or endowment funds. No new building appeals.

RANGE OF GRANTS Mostly £1,000–£5,000.

SAMPLE GRANTS Church Buildings Council (£20,000); The Allegri String Quartet (£16,000); University of Buckingham Fund (£15,000); Guideposts Trust and Nordoff Robbins (£5,000 each); Abingdon Museum and Buxton Arts Festival (£4,000 each); Clod Ensemble and Quilters Guild (£2,000 each); Endellion Quartet (£1,000); and Orpheus Foundation (£600).

FINANCES *Year* 2011–12 *Income* £407,972 *Grants* £316,940 *Assets* £15,093,160

TRUSTEES Felix Warnock, Chair; Sir Henry Aubrey-Fletcher; Lord Balfour of Burleigh; Christopher Butcher; Mary Ann Sieghart; Timothy Wilson.

OTHER INFORMATION Breakdown of grants: Music (£160,000); heritage and crafts (£140,000); tercentenary (£15,000); miscellaneous (£2,000).

HOW TO APPLY 'The trustees meet twice yearly to oversee the charity's activities and to make decisions on grants. The trust works with specialist advisers in each of its main sectors of activity: Mrs Sally Carter, Music Adviser and Ms Carole Milner, Heritage and Crafts Adviser. There is also a Music Panel and a Heritage and Crafts Committee which each meet twice a year to consider applications. The day-to-day running of the trust's financial and administrative affairs and processing of grant applications is undertaken by The Trust Partnership. Note that it is advisable to submit an application well in advance of the deadline. Music Deadline: 31 January for the June trustee meeting; 31 August for the December trustee meeting. Heritage and Crafts Deadline: 31 January for the June trustee

meeting; 31 July for the December trustee meeting. All applications must include: a cover letter, which should include official address, telephone number, email address and charity registration number. The letter should be headed with the project title and the applicant should make clear his/her position in the charity. Note that this letter should NOT include information on the project itself as this should be within the grant request; no more than three pages outlining the proposal and the specific request to the trust. This should be structured as follows: 'the project title; a summary of the request in no more than 40 words; the timing of the project; the project background and description; a budget including a financial breakdown and total cost of the project as well as other income secured or requested and from what sources; the amount requested either as a one-off or recurrent grant; an indication of past grants from the Radcliffe Trust (year, amount and purpose); other relevant supporting information, although applicants should be aware that this may not be circulated to trustees. The cover letter and grant request should be emailed to the administrator as Word or Excel documents and a hard copy also sent by post.'
For full details of the trust's guidelines visit its website.
WHO TO APPLY TO Belinda Hunt, Administrator, 6 Trull Farm Buildings, Tetbury, Gloucestershire GL8 8SQ *Tel.* 01285 841900 *email* radcliffe@thetrustpartnership.com *Website* www.theradcliffetrust.org

---

■ The Bishop Radford Trust

CC NO 1113562   **ESTABLISHED** 2006
WHERE FUNDING CAN BE GIVEN UK.
WHO CAN BENEFIT Christian organisations, including churches.
WHAT IS FUNDED The promotion of 'the work of the Christian church in a manner consistent with the doctrines and principles of the Church of England'. This includes the renovation, construction and maintenance of churches, the education of church workers and church ministry.
SAMPLE GRANTS Anglican Investment Agency Trust (£125,000); Bible Society (£50,000); International Needs (£42,000); Bible Reading Fellowship (£41,000); Exeter College, Oxford (£27,000); Bristol Diocese (£25,000); Viva Network (£22,000); Wakefield Diocese (£20,000); Cuddesdon Ripon College (£15,000); Arthur Rank Centre (£13,000); Lambeth Partnership (£10,000); London Diocesan Board for Schools (£6,300); St Peter's Hereford (£1,000) and Queen Alexandra Hospital Home (£500).
FINANCES *Year* 2011–12 *Income* £1,974,777 *Grants* £495,050 *Assets* £6,937,035
TRUSTEES Stephen Green; Janian Green; Suzannah O'Brien; Ruth Dare.
HOW TO APPLY In writing to the correspondent.
WHO TO APPLY TO D. Marks, Administrator, Devonshire House, 1 Devonshire Street, London W1W 5DR *Tel.* 020 7304 2000 *email* thebishopradfordtrust@ntlworld.com

■ The Ragdoll Foundation

CC NO 1078998   **ESTABLISHED** 2000
WHERE FUNDING CAN BE GIVEN UK and worldwide.
WHO CAN BENEFIT Projects that involve children during their early years, although appropriate projects for older children will be considered.
WHAT IS FUNDED Arts projects with children which: promote the development of children through children's imaginative thinking; encourage innovation and innovative thinking and influence good practice elsewhere; offer creative solutions that deal with the causes of problems in childhood; ensures effective evaluation of projects to promote sharing and learning; or above all demonstrate how the voices of children can be heard.
WHAT IS NOT FUNDED Grants are not given for: replacement of statutory funding; work that has already started or will have been completed whilst the application is being considered; promotion of religion; animal welfare charities; vehicles, emergency relief work; general fundraising or marketing appeals; open ended funding arrangements; loans or business advice; charities which are in serious deficit; holidays; any large capital; endowment or widely distributed appeal; specialist schools; school fees for people over 17 years of age; and gap year funds.
RANGE OF GRANTS Typically £500–£20,000, although large-scale grants will be considered.
SAMPLE GRANTS What Makes Me Happy – Film production costs, amortisation and marketing Series I and 2 (£137,600) and Heel and Toe – A grant for a sensory floor was awarded to the North East based charity, helping children with cerebral palsy and dyspraxia (£960).
FINANCES *Year* 2011–12 *Income* £138,281 *Grants* £138,575 *Assets* £17,010
TRUSTEES Katherine Wood; Peter Hollingsworth; Peter Thornton; Anne Wood; Carole Thomson.
OTHER INFORMATION 'The Ragdoll Foundation is dedicated to developing the power of imaginative responses in children through the arts. It owns 15% of its parent company and springs from the same philosophical roots. This can be summed up by the quotation from Sylvia Ashton-Warner in her book *Teacher*, which has greatly influenced Anne's work: *I see the mind of a five year old as a volcano with two vents; destructiveness and creativeness. And I can see that to the extent that we widen the creative channel, we atrophy the destructive one.*'
HOW TO APPLY To register interest in future funding schemes email the foundation. The email should contain the following details – your name, organisation, title of the proposed project and indicative project timescale.
WHO TO APPLY TO Karen Newell, Development Co-ordinator, 9 Timothy's Bridge Road, Stratford Enterprise Park, Stratford-upon-Avon, Warwickshire CV37 9NQ *Tel.* 01789 404100 *email* info@ragdollfoundation.org.uk *Website* www.ragdollfoundation.org.uk

---

■ The Rainford Trust

CC NO 266157   **ESTABLISHED** 1973
WHERE FUNDING CAN BE GIVEN Worldwide, with a preference for areas in which Pilkington plc have works and offices, especially St Helens and Merseyside.
WHO CAN BENEFIT Individuals and charitable and voluntary organisations.
WHAT IS FUNDED The trust's accounts stated that its objectives are to: 'apply money for charitable

purposes and to charitable institutions within the St Helens MBC area, and other places in the UK or overseas where Pilkington has employees. This does not prejudice the trustees' discretion to help charities that operate outside those areas.' Further to this the trust's charitable purposes are to support: 'the relief of poverty, the aged, the sick, helpless and disabled, and the unemployed' and 'the advancement of education including the arts, and other purposes with wide benefit for the community such as environmental and conservation projects'.

WHAT IS NOT FUNDED Funding for the arts is restricted to St Helens only. Applications from individuals for grants for educational purposes will be considered only from applicants who are normally resident in St Helens.

SAMPLE GRANTS Clonter Opera (£13,000); The Citadel Arts Centre (£10,000); The Foundation for the Prevention of Blindness and Practical Action (£2,000 each); West Coast Crash Wheelchair Rugby (£1,500); Sue Ryder, Birchley Hall, National Benevolent Fund for the Aged, Health Poverty Action, Tibet Relief Fund and Rainford Carers Support Group (£1,000 each); Park Farm ACYP Centre (£850); Riders for Health (£800) and Galapagos Conservation Trust (£500).

FINANCES *Year* 2011–12 *Income* £192,896 *Grants* £99,678 *Assets* £7,231,402

TRUSTEES Dr F. Graham; A. J. Moseley; H. Pilkington; Lady Pilkington; D. C. Pilkington; S. D. Pilkington; L. F. Walker; Dr Clarissa Pilkington; John Pilkington.

HOW TO APPLY On a form available from the correspondent. Applications should be accompanied by a copy of the latest accounts and cost data on projects for which funding is sought. Applicants may apply at any time. Trustees normally meet in November, March and July. A sub-appeals committee meets about ten times a year and they can either refuse, grant or pass on an application to the Trustees.

WHO TO APPLY TO William Simm, Executive Officer, c/o Pilkington plc, Prescot Road, St Helens, Merseyside WA10 3TT *Tel.* 01744 20574 *email* rainfordtrust@btconnect.com

■ The Peggy Ramsay Foundation

CC NO 1015427   ESTABLISHED 1992
WHERE FUNDING CAN BE GIVEN British Isles.
WHO CAN BENEFIT Writers who have some writing experience who need time to write and cannot otherwise afford to do so; companies which might not otherwise be able to find, develop or use new work; and projects which may facilitate new writing for the stage.

WHAT IS FUNDED The advancement of education by the encouragement of the art of writing and the relief of poverty amongst stage writers and their families.

WHAT IS NOT FUNDED No grants are made for productions or writing not for the theatre. Adaptations and plays intended primarily for younger audiences are accepted only in special circumstances which imply wider originality. Commissioning costs are often considered as part of production costs. Course fees are not considered. Aspiring writers without some production record are not usually considered.

TYPE OF GRANT Grants awarded for projects, recurring costs and salaries, for up to three years.

SAMPLE GRANTS Pearson Management Services (£14,000); Alfred Fagon Prize Award (£6,500) and Society of Authors (£1,500).

FINANCES *Year* 2012 *Income* £255,288 *Grants* £123,067 *Assets* £5,224,323

TRUSTEES G. Laurence Harbottle; Simon P. H. Callow; Michael Codron; Sir David Hare; John Tydeman; Harriet Walter; Tamara C. Harvey; Neil Adleman; Rupert J. Rhymes; Holly Kendrick.

OTHER INFORMATION There was a further £101,000 given in 53 grants to individuals.

HOW TO APPLY Applications should be made in writing, including: a short letter explaining the need, the amount hoped for and the way in which any grant would be spent; a full CV not limited to writing; separate sheet answers to these questions: 1. when and where was the first professional production of a play of yours, 2. who produced the play which qualifies you for a grant, 3. when and where was your qualifying play produced, what was its run and approximate playing time and has it been revived, 4. for that production were the director and actors all professionals engaged with Equity contracts, 5. did the audience pay to attend. Trustees meet quarterly, but applications are considered between meetings. Allow six to eight weeks for a definitive answer. Urgent appeals can be considered at other times. All appeals are usually acknowledged. Grants are considered at four or five meetings during the year, although urgent appeals can be considered at other times. All appeals are usually acknowledged.

WHO TO APPLY TO Laurence Harbottle, Trustee, Harbottle and Lewis Solicitors, Hanover House, 14 Hanover Square, London W1S 1HP *Tel.* 020 7667 5000 *Fax* 020 7667 5100 *email* laurence.harbottle@harbottle.com *Website* www.peggyramsayfoundation.org

■ The Joseph and Lena Randall Charitable Trust

CC NO 255035   ESTABLISHED 1967
WHERE FUNDING CAN BE GIVEN Worldwide.
WHO CAN BENEFIT Registered charities (mainly headquarters organisations) benefiting at risk groups and people who are disadvantaged by poverty or socially isolated.

WHAT IS FUNDED Regular support to a selection of charities, providing medical, educational and cultural facilities.

WHAT IS NOT FUNDED No grants to individuals.

SAMPLE GRANTS Cancer Research UK, Community Security Trust, Diabetes UK, Downe House 21st Century Appeal, Holocaust Educational Trust, Jewish Care, Jewish Deaf Association, LPO, LSE Foundation, Motor Neurone Disease Association, ROH Foundation and Transplant Trust.

FINANCES *Year* 2012–13 *Income* £121,719 *Grants* £79,085 *Assets* £2,182,422

TRUSTEE Rofrano Trustee Services Ltd.

HOW TO APPLY The trust stated in its 2012/13 annual report: 'The Trustee received many appeals during the year, and a number of new charities have received the benefit of our philanthropy for the first time. All appeals are vetted but we desist from replying in the case of circular letters, or to letters inadequately franked, nor to appeals from individuals or from organisations lacking accreditation. We have always favoured appeals from established charities with proven track records that are successful and efficient in delivering services without being top heavy in terms of management and salaries.'

WHO TO APPLY TO David Anthony Randall, Administrator, Europa Residence, Place des Moulins, Monte-Carlo MC98 000 *Tel* 00377 9350 0382 *email* rofrano.jlrct@hotmail.fr

....

■ The Rank Foundation Limited

CC NO 276976   **ESTABLISHED** 1953

WHERE FUNDING CAN BE GIVEN UK.

WHO CAN BENEFIT Charities or churches working in the areas of promoting Christianity, promoting education and general charitable purposes.

WHAT IS FUNDED The promotion of Christian principles through film and other media; encouraging and developing leadership amongst young people; supporting disadvantaged young people and those frail or lonely through old age or disability.

WHAT IS NOT FUNDED Grants to registered charities only. Appeals from individuals or appeals from registered charities on behalf of named individuals will not be considered; neither will appeals from overseas or from UK-based organisations where the object of the appeal is overseas. In an endeavour to contain the calls made upon the foundation to a realistic level, the directors have continued with their policy of not, in general, making grants to projects involved with: agriculture and farming; cathedrals and churches (except where community facilities form an integral part); culture; university/school building and bursary funds; medical research.

TYPE OF GRANT Small grants are largely one-off. Major grants can be re-occurring.

RANGE OF GRANTS Mostly small grants up to £7,500.

SAMPLE GRANTS Gap Scheme (£358,000); Time to Shine (£235,000); Arthur Rank Centre (£60,000); Essex Boys and Girls Clubs (£38,000); Mersey Youth Support Trust (£30,000); Lower Wensleydale Youth Project (£28,000); Scripture Union Mission Trust (£27,000); Music in Hospitals, Special Olympics Great Britain and Blackburn Cathedral (£20,000 each); Macular Disease Society and Caring for Ex-Offenders (£15,000 each); Changing Faces (£12,000) and Counselling Prayer Trust (£10,000).

FINANCES *Year* 2012 *Income* £1,350,000 *Grants* £6,998,000 *Assets* £206,507,000

TRUSTEES Lord St Aldwyn; James Cave; Andrew Cowan; Mark Davies; Lindsay Fox; Joey Newton; Lucinda Onslow; Lord Shuttleworth; Hon. Caroline Twiston-Davies; Johanna Ropner; Rose Fitzpatrick; Daniel Simon; Nicholas Buxton; Jason Chaffer.

PUBLICATIONS *Journeying Together; History of The Rank Foundation.*

HOW TO APPLY If you are interested in a major grant (over £7,500) you should contact the respective executive director. If you would like to submit an application for a major grant, in either the Special Project or Community Care category, then you should email a one page outline to the respective executive, details of which can be found on the 'contact us' section of the website. This should contain the following information: organisation objectives, location and structure (staff numbers); outline of what you do and where; what you are seeking support for – details of the specific programme including costs; any evidence of partnership working or summary of existing evaluation. For small grants (under £7,500) complete the short eligibility

quiz online to confirm your application is eligible. This takes you to a short online form to which you can attach supporting documentation. The following information is required: charity name and registration number; brief details about the project and the sum to be raised – ensure you include a clear aim or list of objectives; details of the amount raised so far towards the target and if relevant, briefly mention how you intend to raise the rest; a copy of the last audited accounts and annual report. There are two committees: appeals and community care and education and youth which both meet quarterly. Note: due to the overwhelming number of appeals, the foundation can only fund about 25% of current applications. If you are unsure whether your appeal is likely to succeed then contact the grants administrator for further advice. Due to overwhelming demand, unsolicited appeals are extremely unlikely to attract a grant in connection with salaries, general running costs or major capital projects.

WHO TO APPLY TO Rosamond McNulty, Administrator, 12 Warwick Square, London SW1V 2AA *Tel.* 020 7834 7731 *email* rosamond.mcnulty@rankfoundation.co.uk *Website* www.rankfoundation.com

....

■ The Joseph Rank Trust

CC NO 1093844   **ESTABLISHED** 1929

WHERE FUNDING CAN BE GIVEN Unrestricted. In practice, UK and Ireland.

WHO CAN BENEFIT Registered charities benefiting Methodists, children, young adults, older people, and people with disabilities.

WHAT IS FUNDED The adaptation of Methodist Church properties with a view to providing improved facilities for use both by the church itself and in its work in the community in which it is based. Projects that demonstrate a Christian approach to the practical, educational and spiritual needs of people

WHAT IS NOT FUNDED The Trust does not consider applications for delayed church maintenance (for example roof repairs), overseas projects, organ appeals, for completed capital projects, to repay loans, from individuals, for educational bursaries, for medical research, gap years, intern placements, from individual hospices, from social enterprises that have no charitable status, community interest companies, organisations registered under the Industrial and Provident Societies Act 1965, or from registered charities for the benefit of named individuals.

TYPE OF GRANT One-off and recurring.

RANGE OF GRANTS £10,000–£325,000

SAMPLE GRANTS The Exodus Project, Barnsley (£60,000); Battle Methodist Church (£60,000); Bradford Court Chaplaincy Service and The Retreat Association (£45,000 each); Churches Together in Herald Green Youth Initiative (£42,000); SMART Community Project, St Martin's Church (£30,000); Hull Civic Society (£25,000); Youth Link Northern Ireland (£24,000); Heaton Methodist Church (£20,000); Department of Youth and Children's Work – Methodist Church in Ireland (£7,600) and West Orchard United Reformed Church (£5,000).

FINANCES *Year* 2011–12 *Income* £2,599,000 *Grants* £2,326,000 *Assets* £75,892,000

TRUSTEES Tony Reddall; Colin Rank; David Cruise; Gay Moon; James Rank; Mike Shortt; Sue Warner; John Irvine; Darren Holland; Carole Holmes.

Think carefully about every application. Is it justified?

....

841

HOW TO APPLY Ongoing commitments, combined with the fact that the trustees are taking an increasingly active role in identifying projects to support, means that uncommitted funds are limited and it is seldom possible to make grants in response to unsolicited appeals.

If applicants consider that their work might fall within the areas of interest of the trust the following basic information is required: charity name and charity registration number; an outline of the project for which funding is sought; details of the total amount required to fund the project in its entirety; details of the amount already raised, or irrevocably committed, towards the target; a copy of the most recent annual report and audited accounts. Applicants should endeavour to set out the essential details of a project on no more than two sides of A4 paper, with more detailed information being presented in the form of appendices. Applications should be in hard copy. In normal circumstances, papers received before the middle of February, May, August and November may be considered in March, June, September and December respectively. Visits to appeals may be made by the secretary and trustees. All appeals are acknowledged and the applicants advised that if they do not receive a reply by a specified date it has not been possible for the trustees to make a grant.

WHO TO APPLY TO Dr John Higgs, Secretary, Worth Corner, Turners Hill Road, Crawley RH10 7SL *Tel.* 01293 873947 *email* secretary@ranktrust.org *Website* www.ranktrust.org

■ Ranworth Trust

CC NO 292633 **ESTABLISHED** 1985
WHERE FUNDING CAN BE GIVEN UK and developing countries, with a preference for East Norfolk.
WHO CAN BENEFIT Local registered charities in East Norfolk and international charities.
WHAT IS FUNDED General charitable purposes with a focus on care and education in the community in East Norfolk and providing technological initiative and support in developing countries.
WHAT IS NOT FUNDED No grants to non-registered charities.
RANGE OF GRANTS £1,000 to £350,000.
SAMPLE GRANTS Practical Action and WaterAid (£20,000 each); Cancer Research UK and Médecins Sans Frontières (£15,000 each); Alzheimer's Research Trust and Sightsavers (£10,000 each); Hope and Homes for Children and Marie Curie Cancer Care (£5,000 each); Fairhaven Church of England VA Primary School – South Walsham (£3,500); Coeliac Society (£2,000); and Canine Partners for Independence (£1,000).
FINANCES *Year* 2011–12 *Income* £167,980 *Grants* £189,800 *Assets* £4,109,442
TRUSTEES Jacquetta Cator; Charles Cator; Mark Cator.
OTHER INFORMATION In 2010 a grant of £350,000 was given to Norfolk Community Foundation to establish 'The Ranworth Grassroots Fund'. The aim of the fund is to support a wide range of charitable, voluntary and community activities across Norfolk.
WHO TO APPLY TO Jacquetta Cator, Trustee, The Old House, Ranworth, Norwich NR13 6HS *Website* www.ranworthtrust.org.uk

■ The Fanny Rapaport Charitable Settlement

CC NO 229406 **ESTABLISHED** 1963
WHERE FUNDING CAN BE GIVEN North west England.
WHO CAN BENEFIT Registered charities only.
WHAT IS FUNDED The trust supports mainly, but not exclusively, Jewish charities and health and welfare organisations.
WHAT IS NOT FUNDED No grants to individuals.
SAMPLE GRANTS Previous beneficiaries included Brookvale, Christie Hospital NHS Trust, Community Security Trust, Delamere Forest School, the Heathlands Village, King David Schools, Manchester Jewish Federation, South Manchester Synagogue, United Jewish Israel Appeal and World Jewish Relief.
FINANCES *Year* 2011–12 *Income* £21,031 *Grants* £35,387
TRUSTEES Jan Fidler; Nathan Marks.
HOW TO APPLY Trustees hold meetings twice a year in March/April and September/October with cheques for donations issued shortly thereafter. If the applicant does not receive a cheque by the end of April or October, the application will have been unsuccessful. No applications are acknowledged.
WHO TO APPLY TO J. S. Fidler, Trustee, Kuit Steinart Levy Solicitors, 3 St Mary's Parsonage, Manchester M3 2RD *Tel.* 01618 323434

■ The Rashbass Family Trust

CC NO 1135961 **ESTABLISHED** 2010
WHERE FUNDING CAN BE GIVEN Undefined. In practice the Barnet district of London
WHO CAN BENEFIT Individuals and organisations supporting children and young people; older people; people with disabilities; those of a particular ethnic or racial origin; other charities and the general public.
WHAT IS FUNDED General charitable purposes; education/training; advancement of health or saving of lives; disability; prevention or relief of poverty; religious activities.
FINANCES *Year* 2012–13 *Income* £177,515 *Grants* £121,321 *Assets* £69,260
TRUSTEES Jacqueline Rashbass; Andrew Rashbass.
OTHER INFORMATION Grants were all made to institutions with objectives as follows: The advancement of religion – £96,000; The advancement of education – £15,000; The prevention of relief of poverty – £3,700; The relief of those in need, by reason of youth, age, ill-health, disability, financial hardship or other disadvantage – £3,200; The advancement of health or the saving of lives – £2,350; Other charitable purposes – £1,100
HOW TO APPLY In writing to the correspondent.
WHO TO APPLY TO Jacqueline Rashbass, Administrator and Trustee, 17 Wykeham Road, London NW4 2TB *Tel.* 07974 151494

■ The Ratcliff Foundation

CC NO 222441 **ESTABLISHED** 1959
WHERE FUNDING CAN BE GIVEN UK, with a preference for local charities in the Midlands, North Wales and Gloucestershire.
WHO CAN BENEFIT Any organisation that has charitable status for tax purposes.
WHAT IS FUNDED General charitable purposes.
WHAT IS NOT FUNDED No grants to individuals.
RANGE OF GRANTS £2,000–£12,000; most are for £5,000 or less.

SAMPLE GRANTS Previously: Avoncroft Museum of Historic Buildings; Multiple Births Foundation; Harbury Village Hall; Cottage and Rural Enterprises Ltd; White Ladies Aston Parochial Church Council; Focus Birmingham; Full House Furniture; Recycling Service Ltd; Gloucestershire Wildlife Trust; and Colwyn Choral Society.

FINANCES *Year* 2011–12 *Income* £214,379 *Grants* £200,000

TRUSTEES David M. Ratcliff, Chair; Edward H. Ratcliff; Carolyn M. Ratcliff; Gillian Mary Thorpe; Michael Fea; Christopher J. Gupwell.

HOW TO APPLY In writing to the correspondent.

WHO TO APPLY TO Christopher J. Gupwell, Secretary and Trustee, Woodlands, Earls Common road, Stock Green, Redditch B96 6TB *Tel.* 01386 792116 *email* chris.gupwell@btinternet.com

■ The Ratcliff Pension Charity

CC NO 234613   **ESTABLISHED** 1967

WHERE FUNDING CAN BE GIVEN The borough of Tower Hamlets, with a preference for the Stepney area.

WHO CAN BENEFIT Individuals and organisations benefiting older people, young people, at-risk groups, and people who are disadvantaged by poverty, socially isolated or in need.

WHAT IS FUNDED The welfare of older people, general welfare and community organisations.

SAMPLE GRANTS Individuals in need (£10,400); Community centres and churches (£5,000); young people charities (£4,000); elderly, disabled and welfare charities (£12,500); Urgent need payments in Tower Hamlets (£5,000) and shelters for the homeless (£3,750).

FINANCES *Year* 2011–12 *Income* £38,879 *Grants* £40,784 *Assets* £477,092

TRUSTEE The Coopers' Company.

HOW TO APPLY In writing to the correspondent.

WHO TO APPLY TO Adrian Carroll, Clerk, Coopers' Hall, 13 Devonshire Square, London EC2M 4TH *Tel.* 020 7247 9577 *email* clerk@coopers-hall. co.uk *Website* coopers-hall.co.uk

■ The Ratcliffe Charitable Trust

CC NO 802320   **ESTABLISHED** 1989

WHERE FUNDING CAN BE GIVEN UK with a preference for the midlands and Wales.

WHO CAN BENEFIT Registered charities.

WHAT IS FUNDED General charitable purposes.

SAMPLE GRANTS Barnardo's, Family Holiday Association, New Martin Community Youth Trust, Motor Neurone Disease Association, Orchdale Vale Trust Limited, VSO, Cancer Care Dorset, GUTS, British Council for the Prevention of Blindness, British Laser Appeal, Save the Children, Brainwave, Compaid Trust, Chicks (camping for inner city kids) and South West Thames Kidney Fund.

FINANCES *Year* 2011–12 *Income* £43,294 *Grants* £31,500 *Assets* £1,009,466

TRUSTEES George Vellam; Tim Adams; David Robbins.

HOW TO APPLY In writing to the correspondent.

WHO TO APPLY TO The Trustees, c/o Barlow Robbins LLP, 55 Quarry Street, Guildford, Surrey GU1 3UE *Tel.* 01483 543200 *email* nicolaedmondson@barlowrobbins.com

■ The E. L. Rathbone Charitable Trust

CC NO 233240   **ESTABLISHED** 1921

WHERE FUNDING CAN BE GIVEN UK, with a strong preference for Merseyside.

WHO CAN BENEFIT Registered charities.

WHAT IS FUNDED General charitable purposes, especially social work charities. Preference to charities that the trust has special interest in, knowledge of, or association with.

WHAT IS NOT FUNDED No grants to individuals seeking support for second degrees.

RANGE OF GRANTS £250–£5,000.

SAMPLE GRANTS Liverpool Community and Voluntary Services (£5,000); Brathay Trust and Personal Service Society (£3,000 each); Prenton High School for Girls and Clatterbridge Centre for Oncology (£2,500 each); Catholic Children's Society, Honey Rose Foundation, Lifelites, Merseyside Youth Association, Options for Supported Living and Wood Street Mission (£2,000 each); Local Solutions (£1,500); Wirral Community Narrow Boat Trust (£1,400); Tomorrow's People, NSPCC, Fairbridge in Merseyside and Autistics (£1,000 each) and Clothing Solutions (£500).

FINANCES *Year* 2011–12 *Income* £74,000 *Grants* £67,260 *Assets* £1,930,942

TRUSTEES J. B. Rathbone; S. K. Rathbone; Caroline Rathbone; R. S. Rathbone.

HOW TO APPLY In writing to the correspondent.

WHO TO APPLY TO Liese Van Alwon, Rathbone Investment Management Ltd, Port of Liverpool Building, Pier Head, Liverpool L3 1NW *Tel.* 01512 366666

■ The Eleanor Rathbone Charitable Trust

CC NO 233241   **ESTABLISHED** 1947

WHERE FUNDING CAN BE GIVEN UK, with the major allocation for Merseyside; also international projects (Africa, the Indian Sub-Continent, plus exceptionally Iraq and Palestine).

WHO CAN BENEFIT Organisations benefiting general charitable projects in Merseyside; women; and unpopular and neglected causes.

WHAT IS FUNDED (1) Merseyside: charities and projects which are based in or delivered in Merseyside (particularly the more deprived areas) and meet the funding priorities. (2) Holiday Fund: Small grants for holidays and outings provided by charities helping disadvantaged children and adults from Merseyside. (3) National: Charities and projects which meet the priorities and have a nationwide reach. (4) International: Projects in Sub-Saharan Africa, the Indian Sub-Continent and exceptionally Iran, Palestine and Haiti. projects must be sponsored and monitored by a UK registered charity and do one or more of the following: benefit women or orphaned children; demonstrate local involvement in scoping and delivery; aim to repair the damage in countries recently ravaged by international or civil war; deliver clean water and sanitation.

WHAT IS NOT FUNDED Grants are not made in support of: any activity which relieves a statutory authority of its obligations; individuals, unless (and only exceptionally) it is made through a charity and it also fulfils at least one of the other positive objects mentioned above; medical research; gap-year projects; lobbying or campaigning organisations or organisations whose primary purpose is the promotion of a religion, church or sect.

TYPE OF GRANT Most donations are on a one-off basis, although requests for commitments over two or more years are considered.

RANGE OF GRANTS £100–£3,000 and exceptionally higher.

SAMPLE GRANTS Asylum Link; Buttle UK; DADA; Merseyside Congolese Association; Tomorrow's Women; The Basement; Art 4 Dementia; Counsel and Care; Islington Law Centre; Tonybee Hall; Working Families; Wirral Swallows and Amazons; Build it International; Burma Assist; Jeevika Trust; Women and Children First and ZOA-UK

FINANCES *Year* 2011–12 *Income* £279,353 *Grants* £318,182 *Assets* £7,730,853

TRUSTEES William Rathbone; Jenny Rathbone; Andrew Rathbone; Angela Morgan; Mark Rathbone.

HOW TO APPLY Using the online form including supporting documents which you can also print out and send by post. Receipt of applications and those that are unsuccessful are not acknowledged. Applications are accepted at any time and are considered at the Trustee meetings which occur three times a year.

WHO TO APPLY TO Liese van Alwon, Administrator, 546 Warrington Road, Rainhill, Merseyside L35 4LZ *Tel.* 01514 307914 *email* eleanorrathbonetrust@gmail.com *Website* www.eleanorrathbonetrust.org.uk

■ The Sigrid Rausing Trust

CC NO 1046769   **ESTABLISHED** 1995

WHERE FUNDING CAN BE GIVEN Unrestricted.

WHO CAN BENEFIT Charitable or voluntary organisations.

WHAT IS FUNDED Advocacy, research and litigation; detention, torture and death penalty; human rights defenders; free expression; transitional justice; women's rights; LGBTI rights; xenophobia and intolerance; transparency and accountability.

WHAT IS NOT FUNDED Individuals and faith based groups.

TYPE OF GRANT One year grants; multiyear grants.

RANGE OF GRANTS Up to £750,000.

SAMPLE GRANTS Peace Brigades International (£450,000); Zero Mercury Campaign (£480,000 over three years); Reporters Without Borders (£390,000 over three years); Central American Women's Fund (£285,000); Women's Legal Centre (£210,000 over three years); Hotline for Migrant Workers (£195,000 over three years); Adalah (£180,000 over three years); African Refugee Development Center (£120,000 over three years); Council for Assisting Refugee Academics (£100,000 over one year) and London Mining Network (£60,000 over three years).

FINANCES *Year* 2012 *Income* £13,242,053 *Grants* £16,975,400 *Assets* £3,743,316

TRUSTEES Dr Sigrid Rausing; Joshua Mailman; Susan Hitch; Andrew Puddephatt; Geoff Budlender; Jonathan Cooper.

HOW TO APPLY The trust does not accept unsolicited applications for funding. The trust's website does, however, offer the following advice: From time to time, they may request proposals from organisations working in particular fields. Details of requests will be made available on the trust's website. If you have not been invited to apply, but wish to let the trust know about your work, you can send an email describing your organisation to: research@srtrust.org.

Programme officers review emails regularly, but are unlikely to be able to meet with you in person.

WHO TO APPLY TO Sheetal Patel, Administrator, 12 Penzance Place, London W11 4PA *Tel.* 020 7313 7727 *email* info@srtrust.org *Website* www.sigrid-rausing-trust.org

■ The Ravensdale Trust

CC NO 265165   **ESTABLISHED** 1973

WHERE FUNDING CAN BE GIVEN Merseyside, particularly St Helens.

WHO CAN BENEFIT Registered charities.

WHAT IS FUNDED General, health, welfare, children, young people, conservation, heritage and Christian causes.

WHAT IS NOT FUNDED No grants to individuals.

TYPE OF GRANT One-off and recurrent.

RANGE OF GRANTS £100–£5,000.

SAMPLE GRANTS Rainhill Guide House (£19,600); Prescot Guide House and YWCA St Helens (£5,000 each); URC St Helens (£3,000); Liverpool Hope University – Music Department and The Hope Centre (£2,500 each); Arena and Willowbrook Hospice (£2,000 each); Victim Support (£1,500); Alderhey Imagine Appeal and Derbyshire Hill Family and Community Association (£1,000 each); and Home Start Liverpool (£500).

FINANCES *Year* 2011–12 *Income* £41,228 *Grants* £125,000

TRUSTEES Jane Fagan; Mark Feeny; Christine Cudmore.

OTHER INFORMATION In 2011–12 the trust had a total expenditure of £133,671. Grants totalled about £125,000.

HOW TO APPLY In writing to the correspondent. No application form. No acknowledgement of applications are made. Grants are paid in May and October.

WHO TO APPLY TO Jane Fagan, Trustee, c/o Brabners Chaffe Street, Horton House, Exchange Flags, Liverpool L2 3YL *Tel.* 01516 003000 *Fax* 01516 003300

■ The Rawdon-Smith Trust

CC NO 500355   **ESTABLISHED** 1964

WHERE FUNDING CAN BE GIVEN Coniston and those parishes bordering Coniston Water.

WHO CAN BENEFIT Local organisations.

WHAT IS FUNDED The preservation of the area called the 'Bed of Coniston Water' for the benefit of the public; other charitable purposes including education, welfare, animal welfare and preservation of churches.

WHAT IS NOT FUNDED No grants to individuals.

SAMPLE GRANTS Blawith and Nibthwaite Village Hall, Coniston Care and Coniston Primary School (£3,000 each), St Andrew's Parochial Church Council (£1,500); and Old People's Welfare (£1,000).

FINANCES *Year* 2012 *Income* £97,095 *Grants* £30,335 *Assets* £5,517

TRUSTEES Anthony Robinson; Richard Blackburn; Vera Grant; Ian Stancliffe

OTHER INFORMATION In 2012 grants were given to 22 organisations and ranged between £180 and £4,000.

HOW TO APPLY In writing to the correspondent. The trustees meet in February, May, August and November.

WHO TO APPLY TO Pamela Hull, Secretary, Brantwood Lodge, Coniston, Cumbria LA21 8AD
Tel. 01539 441997 *email* hull.pamela@btconnect.com

....

■ The Rayden Charitable Trust

CC NO 294446   **ESTABLISHED** 1985
WHERE FUNDING CAN BE GIVEN UK.
WHO CAN BENEFIT Jewish organisations.
WHAT IS FUNDED General charitable purposes.
SAMPLE GRANTS Previously: NWJDS (£7,000); Or Chadash (£6,500); Yesodey Hatorah (£3,000); Holocaust Education and Jewish Care (£2,500); and Central London Mikveh and CTN Jewish Life (£1,000 each).
FINANCES *Year* 2011–12 *Income* £40,185 *Grants* £44,790 *Assets* £3,452
TRUSTEES Shirley Rayden; Clive Rayden; Paul Rayden.
HOW TO APPLY In writing to the correspondent.
WHO TO APPLY TO The Trustees, c/o Beavis Morgan LLP, 82 St John Street, London EC1M 4JN *Tel.* 020 7417 0417

....

■ The Roger Raymond Charitable Trust

CC NO 262217   **ESTABLISHED** 1971
WHERE FUNDING CAN BE GIVEN UK (and very occasionally large, well-known overseas organisations).
WHO CAN BENEFIT Mainly headquarters organisations. Overseas grants are only made to large, well-known organisations (such as Sight Savers International and UNICEF).
WHAT IS FUNDED Older people, education and medical causes.
WHAT IS NOT FUNDED Grants are rarely given to individuals.
TYPE OF GRANT One-off and recurrent.
SAMPLE GRANTS Bloxham School (£125,000) and Macmillan Cancer Support (£2,000).
FINANCES *Year* 2011–12 *Income* £482,765 *Grants* £146,811 *Assets* £11,685,308
TRUSTEES R. W. Pullen; M. G. Raymond; Alisdair Kruger Thomson.
OTHER INFORMATION Most support goes to Bloxham School each year.
HOW TO APPLY The trust stated that applications are considered throughout the year, although funds are not always available.
WHO TO APPLY TO Russell Pullen, Suttondene, 17 South Border, Purley, Surrey CR8 3LL *Tel.* 020 8660 9133 *email* russell@pullen.cix.co.uk

....

■ The Rayne Foundation

CC NO 216291   **ESTABLISHED** 1962
WHERE FUNDING CAN BE GIVEN UK.
WHO CAN BENEFIT Registered charities.
WHAT IS FUNDED Medicine, education, social welfare and the arts. Under these four headings the foundation encourages applications which apply to its evolving list of areas of special interest: art in deprived communities; developing numeracy skills; improved quality of life for older people; improved palliative care in the community. Excellent applications outside these areas are also welcomed.
WHAT IS NOT FUNDED Grants are not made: to individuals; to organisations working outside the UK; for work that has already taken place; for repayment of debts; for endowments; to those who have applied in the last twelve months. Do not send 'round robin' or general appeals.
TYPE OF GRANT Salaries and all types of project costs plus a reasonable contribution to overheads (there is no fixed percentage); general running or core costs (normally for a maximum of three years); capital costs of buildings and equipment (unless specifically stated in certain sectors).
RANGE OF GRANTS Up to £50,000.
SAMPLE GRANTS Kenilworth Children's Centre and Nursery School (£60,000); Emmaus UK (£50,000); Leap Confronting Conflict (£40,000); Turner Contemporary (£30,000); Youth Dementia UK (£21,000); Pro Contact Expert Services (£15,000); ArtsEkta (£12,000); Stonewall Equality Limited (£10,000); London International Festival of Theatre (£5,000); North Derbyshire Stroke Support Group (£4,000) and Dance Umbrella (£3,000).
FINANCES *Year* 2011–12 *Income* £1,199,058 *Grants* £1,614,208 *Assets* £74,450,148
TRUSTEES The Hon Robert Rayne, Chair; Lord Claus Moser; Lady Jane Rayne; Lady Hilary Browne-Wilkinson; Prof. Dame Margaret Turner-Warwick; Prof. Anthony Newman Taylor; The Hon Natasha Rayne; The Hon Nicholas Rayne; Sir Emyr Jones Parry.
HOW TO APPLY Applying for a grant is a two-stage process. First you must fill in the Stage One Application Form available from the foundation's website, which you can complete and email to applications@raynefoundation.org.uk or print out and post. If it is not possible for you to access the first stage application online you should call the trust on 020 7487 9650. 'If you can demonstrate that the Foundation's aims will be met, we will contact you to make a more detailed application. We aim to respond to all Stage One proposals within one month of receipt. Continuation funding – if you have previously received a grant from the foundation, you must complete a satisfactory monitoring report before reapplying. Organisations can only hold one grant at a time. Use the two-stage process for all applications, even if you are asking the foundation to continue funding the same project.'
WHO TO APPLY TO Morin Carew, Grants Administrator, 100 George Street, London W1U 8NU *Tel.* 020 7487 9656 *email* info@raynefoundation.org.uk *Website* www.raynefoundation.org.uk

....

■ The Rayne Trust

CC NO 207392   **ESTABLISHED** 1958
WHERE FUNDING CAN BE GIVEN Israel and UK.
WHO CAN BENEFIT Registered charities.
WHAT IS FUNDED The trust's mandate, as determined by the trustees, is to understand and engage with the needs of UK and Israeli society. The trust is involved in social bridge building. Jewish organisations and charities supporting the arts and social welfare and benefiting children, older and young people, at risk groups and people disadvantaged by poverty or socially isolated are supported.
WHAT IS NOT FUNDED No grants to: organisations with free reserves that are higher than 75% of annual expenditure; individuals; retrospective applications; repayment of debts; organisations which have had a grant in the last year; general appeals or endowments.
TYPE OF GRANT Capital expenditure and recurrent expenses.

SAMPLE GRANTS The Chicken Shed Theatre Trust (£25,000); Michael Sobell Sinai School (£15,000) and The Place2Be (£3,000). Grants of less than £10,000 totalled £41,000.

FINANCES *Year* 2011–12 *Income* £284,214 *Grants* £118,430 *Assets* £18,793,984

TRUSTEES Lady Jane Rayne; the Hon. Robert A. Rayne; Damian Rayne.

OTHER INFORMATION Grants were broken down into broken down into £87,000 in the UK and £32,000 in Israel.

HOW TO APPLY Firstly fill out the Stage One application form, available to download from the website, and submit it to the correspondent. Applicants will be contacted within a month about whether or not they are invited to make a more detailed Stage Two application.

WHO TO APPLY TO Nurit Gordon, 100 George Street, London W1U 8NU *Tel.* 020 7487 9650 *email* ngordon@raynetrust.org *Website* www.raynefoundation.org.uk/RayneTrust

....

■ The John Rayner Charitable Trust

CC NO 802363   **ESTABLISHED** 1989

WHERE FUNDING CAN BE GIVEN England, with a preference for Merseyside and Wiltshire.

WHO CAN BENEFIT Registered charities. There is a preference for small charities in the UK to receive the largest donations.

WHAT IS FUNDED General charitable purposes including medical and disability, children and older people, community projects, carers, youth work, medical research and development and for the arts.

WHAT IS NOT FUNDED No grants to individuals or non-registered charities.

TYPE OF GRANT One-off and recurrent grants. Funding may be given for up to three years.

RANGE OF GRANTS Up to £5,000.

SAMPLE GRANTS Room to Read (£5,000); Alzheimer's Society, Live Music Now North West, Marie Curie Cancer Care, Prospect Hospice, Royal Marsden and Theodora Children's Trust (£3,000 each); Combat Stress; Home Start Wiltshire, Swindon Sea Cadet Unite, Wiltshire Bobby Van Trust and YKids (£2,000 each) and The Royal Blind Society and Wirral Society for Blind and Partially Sighted (£1,000 each).

FINANCES *Year* 2011–12 *Income* £25,087 *Grants* £35,000 *Assets* £767,528

TRUSTEES J. Wilkinson; Dr J. M. H. Rayner; Louise McNeilage.

HOW TO APPLY In writing to the correspondent by 31 January each year. Trustees meet to allocate donations in February/March. Only successful applicants will be contacted. There are no application forms or guidelines.

WHO TO APPLY TO J. Wilkinson, Trustee, Manor Farmhouse, Church Street, Great Bedwyn, Marlborough, Wiltshire SN8 3PE *Tel.* 01672 870362

....

■ The Sir James Reckitt Charity

CC NO 225356   **ESTABLISHED** 1921

WHERE FUNDING CAN BE GIVEN Hull and the East Riding of Yorkshire, UK and occasional support of Red Cross or Quaker work overseas.

WHO CAN BENEFIT Registered charities covering a wide range of causes, including Quaker causes and occasional relief for victims of overseas disasters.

WHAT IS FUNDED Community based groups and projects in the city of Hull and the county of East Yorkshire; Quaker causes and organisations throughout the UK; national or regional charities focussed on social welfare, medicine, education or the environment, particularly in Hull and East Yorkshire; individuals or groups from Hull or East Yorkshire.

WHAT IS NOT FUNDED Grants are normally made only to registered charities. Local organisations outside the Hull area are not supported, unless their work has regional implications. Grants are not normally made to individuals other than Quakers and residents of Hull and the East Riding of Yorkshire. Support is not given to causes of a warlike or political nature. No replacement of statutory funding or activities which collect funds to be passed on to other organisations, charities or individuals.

TYPE OF GRANT Start-up and core costs; purchase of equipment and materials; building improvements; training costs; project development costs.

RANGE OF GRANTS Up to £100,000

SAMPLE GRANTS Friends School Lisburn (£100,000); Britain Yearly Meeting (£90,000); Mount School York Foundation (£19,000); Pickering Quaker Meeting (£9,000); Home Start Hull and Woodlands Home (£4,000 each); Multiple Sclerosis Society (£3,000); Field Studies Council (£2,500); Yorkshire Quaker Arts Projects and Yorkshire Friends Holiday School (£2,000 each).

FINANCES *Year* 2012 *Income* £1,285,011 *Grants* £1,320,411 *Assets* £29,986,305

TRUSTEES William Upton; James Harrison Holt; Caroline Jennings; Philip James Harrison Holt; Robin James Upton; Sarah Helen Craven; Charles Maxsted; Simon J. Upton; Simon E. Upton; James Marshall; Edward Upton; Rebecca Holt; Dr Karina Mary Upton; Andrew Palfeman; James Atherton.

PUBLICATIONS A History of the Sir James Reckitt Charity 1921–1979 by B N Reckitt; A History of the Sir James Reckitt Charity 1921–1999 by G M Atherton.

OTHER INFORMATION The grant total includes 226 grants to individuals totalling £58,000 for social work.

HOW TO APPLY In writing to the correspondent. The application should include the following key points: the name and address of your organisation; telephone number and email address; the nature of your organisation; its structure, aims and who it serves; and its links with other agencies and networks; the project or funding need. What is the grant to be used for and who will benefit from it; when is the funding required; the date of the project or event; the bank account payee name of your organisation; any links to the Hull and East Yorkshire region, or the Quakers (which together are the charity's funding priorities); a copy of your latest Annual Report and Accounts or equivalent. Applications are measured against the charity's guidelines and decisions are taken at a twice-yearly meeting of trustees in May and October. Applications should be submitted by 31 March and 30 September respectively.

WHO TO APPLY TO James McGlashan, Administrator, 7 Derrymore Road, Willerby, East Yorkshire HU10 6ES *Tel.* 01482 655861 *email* charity@thesirjamesreckittcharity.org.uk *Website* www.thesirjamesreckittcharity.org.uk

■ Eva Reckitt Trust Fund

CC NO 210563 **ESTABLISHED** 1940
WHERE FUNDING CAN BE GIVEN UK and overseas.
WHO CAN BENEFIT Charitable organisations.
WHAT IS FUNDED Welfare and relief-in-need; organisations supporting the extension and development of education and victims of war.
WHAT IS NOT FUNDED Grants are generally not given to individuals, although individual cases may be supported through other charities which are able to monitor the use of the funds.
RANGE OF GRANTS £500–£3,000.
SAMPLE GRANTS Navjyoti (£3,000); Rise and Shine School (£2,300); Workaid, Wythenshawe Law Centre, Islamic Relief, Peace Brigades International and Canon Collins Trust (£1,000 each) and Land Mines Museum Cambodia, Tourism Concern, Project Harar – Ethiopia, St Martin-in-the-Fields Christmas Appeal and The Pirate Castle (£500 each).
FINANCES *Year* 2012 *Income* £23,490 *Grants* £37,050 *Assets* £637,019
TRUSTEES Anna Bunney; Meg Whittaker; David Birch; Diana Holliday.
HOW TO APPLY In writing to the correspondent.
WHO TO APPLY TO David Birch, Trustee, 1 Somerford Road, Cirencester, Gloucestershire GL7 1TP *email* eva.reckitt.trust@gmail.com

■ The Red Arrows Trust

CC NO 283461 **ESTABLISHED** 1981
WHERE FUNDING CAN BE GIVEN UK.
WHO CAN BENEFIT Royal Air Force and general charities.
WHAT IS FUNDED General charitable purposes.
SAMPLE GRANTS No information on beneficiaries was available.
FINANCES *Year* 2012–13 *Income* £22,763 *Grants* £20,000
TRUSTEES Roger Bowder; Keith Harkness; Mark Dunkley
HOW TO APPLY The trustees meet to consider grants in March and September and applications need to be received by February and August.
WHO TO APPLY TO Keith Harkness, Trustee, Orchard House, 67 Ankle Road, Melton Mowbray LE13 0QJ *Tel.* 01664 566844

■ Red Hill Charitable Trust

CC NO 307891 **ESTABLISHED** 1997
WHERE FUNDING CAN BE GIVEN South East England is defined as East Anglia, London and Home Counties west to Hampshire.
WHO CAN BENEFIT Charitable organisations.
WHAT IS FUNDED The promotion of education, including social and physical training, of individuals under the age of 25 who have emotional and/or behavioural difficulties and disorders.
WHAT IS NOT FUNDED No grants to individuals. Research projects are not normally considered.
TYPE OF GRANT The trustees prefer to make grants for a year at a time, and are reluctant to take on any open-ended commitments.
RANGE OF GRANTS Generally £1,000–£5,000.
SAMPLE GRANTS Dandelion (£10,000); Dolphin House (£5,500); Woodside (£5,000); Enterprise Educational Trust (£4,500); Challenger Centre and Bay House School (£1,000 each); and Roseacre Junior School (£800).
FINANCES *Year* 2011–12 *Income* £55,574 *Grants* £87,997 *Assets* £2,552,872

TRUSTEES Dr D. E. Wilson, Chair; A. Bunting; K. Hall; W. Mather; R. Barton; B. Head; P. Stockell; B. Law; J. Moore; M. Startup.
HOW TO APPLY On a form available from the trust's website, which should be completed and emailed to the trust. The trustees hold meetings twice yearly, in early March and early October. Applications should reach the correspondent at the beginning of the previous month to be sure of being considered.
WHO TO APPLY TO The Clerk, 6 Clarendon Close, Bearsted, Maidstone ME14 4JD *Tel.* 01622 739287 *Website* www.redhilltrust.org

■ The Red Rose Charitable Trust

CC NO 1038358 **ESTABLISHED** 1994
WHERE FUNDING CAN BE GIVEN UK with a preference for Lancashire and Merseyside.
WHO CAN BENEFIT Charities working with older people who or people who have physical or mental disabilities.
WHAT IS FUNDED Welfare causes and educational expenses for students.
SAMPLE GRANTS Help the Aged, Mencap and Make-a-Wish Foundation (£2,000 each); Rethink, Mango Tree, Sense, The Leprosy Mission, Motor Neurone Disease Association and Hope House Children's Hospices (£1,000 each) and Local Solutions and The National Autistic Society (£500 each).
FINANCES *Year* 2011–12 *Income* £35,815 *Grants* £32,500 *Assets* £915,065
TRUSTEES James N. L. Packer; Jane L. Fagan; Julian B. Rathbone.
HOW TO APPLY In writing to the correspondent.
WHO TO APPLY TO J. N. L. Packer, Trustee, c/o Rathbone Trust Company, Port of Liverpool Building, Pier Head, Liverpool L3 1NW *Tel.* 01512 366666

■ The C. A. Redfern Charitable Foundation

CC NO 299918 **ESTABLISHED** 1989
WHERE FUNDING CAN BE GIVEN UK.
WHO CAN BENEFIT Registered UK charities.
WHAT IS FUNDED General charitable purposes, with some preference for those concerned with health and welfare.
WHAT IS NOT FUNDED No grants for building works or individuals.
TYPE OF GRANT Core costs, one-off, project and research. Funding is available for one year or less.
RANGE OF GRANTS £250–£50,000. The majority were between £250–£5,000.
SAMPLE GRANTS Saints and Sinners and South Bucks Riding for the Disabled People (£30,000); White Ensign (£10,000); The Special Yoga Centre, Live Music Now and Help for Heroes, Canine Partners for Independence; Chicks Country Hospital for Inner City Kids and St Luke's Primary School (£5,000 each); Fund for Epilepsy (£3,000); Heads Up, The Para Dressage Training Trust and St Christopher's Hospice (£2,000 each); Vitalise, Institute of Hepatology, Fight for Sight and Hertfordshire Red Cross (£1,000); Bromley Churches Housing Action (£800) and The Royal Star and Garter Home (£500).
FINANCES *Year* 2011–12 *Income* £186,722 *Grants* £184,000 *Assets* £4,416,136
TRUSTEES William Maclaren; David Redfern; Simon Ward; Julian Heslop.

HOW TO APPLY The trustees meet regularly to discuss the making of grants but do not invite unsolicited grant applications.

WHO TO APPLY TO The Administrator, PricewaterhouseCoopers, 9 Greyfriars Road, Reading, Berkshire RG1 1JG *Tel.* 01189 597111

■ **The Reed Foundation**

CC NO 264728　　　**ESTABLISHED** 1972
WHERE FUNDING CAN BE GIVEN UK and developing countries.
WHO CAN BENEFIT Charitable organisations.
WHAT IS FUNDED General charitable purposes, with an interest in the arts, education, women's causes and children and young people.
SAMPLE GRANTS The Prince's Trust (£45,000); Classical Opera (£20,000); Bluebell Railway Trust (£15,000); Pop Up Tai Chi (£10,000); Birmingham Royal Ballet (£7,100); Zambia Orphans of Aid UK (£5,000); London Youth Support Trust (£3,800); Supporting Dalit Children (£3,200); Autism Plus (£1,700); Workaid (£1,300) and Intercountry Adoption Centre (£1,000).
FINANCES *Year* 2011 *Income* £1,047,667 *Grants* £1,596,565 *Assets* £14,429,552
TRUSTEES Alec Reed; James A. Reed; Richard A. Reed; Alex M. Chapman.
OTHER INFORMATION At the time of writing (November 2013) the trust's 2012 accounts were overdue with the Charity Commission.
HOW TO APPLY In writing to the correspondent. The trust states that it does not respond to unsolicited applications.
WHO TO APPLY TO Sir Alec Reed, Trustee, 6 Sloane Street, London SW1X 9LE *Tel.* 020 7201 9980 *email* reed.foundation@reed.co.uk

■ **The John and Sally Reeve Charitable Trust**

CC NO 1150448　　　**ESTABLISHED** 2013
WHERE FUNDING CAN BE GIVEN UK and overseas.
WHO CAN BENEFIT Registered charities.
WHAT IS FUNDED General charitable purposes, including education, social welfare, the arts, conservation, children and young people and older people in the UK, and also overseas aid in developing countries.
TRUSTEES John Reeve; Sally Reeve; Emily Sullivan; Royal Bank of Canada Trust Corporation Limited.
HOW TO APPLY In writing to the correspondent.
WHO TO APPLY TO Ian Wyatt, Administrator, Royal Bank of Canada Trust Corporation Limited, Riverbank House, 2 Swan Lane, London EC4R 3BF *Tel.* 020 7653 4146

■ **Richard Reeve's Foundation**

CC NO 1136337　　　**ESTABLISHED** 1928
WHERE FUNDING CAN BE GIVEN Camden, City of London and Islington.
WHO CAN BENEFIT Individuals up to the age of 25 (in certain circumstances up to the age of 40)
WHAT IS FUNDED Educational costs: uniforms, books, travel expenses, living costs, equipment; and organisation projects that benefit a significant number of children at a time.
WHAT IS NOT FUNDED No grants for building costs, independent school fees, furniture/household

goods, school meals, holidays, school outings or to replace statutory funding.
TYPE OF GRANT Up to three years. Capital costs, full project funding and core costs.
RANGE OF GRANTS £350–£50,000
SAMPLE GRANTS The organisations to benefit were: School/Home Projects (£94,000); Christ's Hospital (£20,000); Hugh Myddleton School (£7,000); Gospel Oak Primary School; Islington Mind; City YMCA; Minority Matters; All Change Arts (Combination of £24,500 divided between the projects).
FINANCES *Year* 2011–12 *Income* £584,634 *Grants* £355,543 *Assets* £17,026,828
TRUSTEES Billy Dove; Sylvan Dewing; John Tickle; Charlynne Pullen; Mavis Hughesdon; Mark Jessett; Michael Bennett; Sarah Betteley; Shannon Farrington; Nigel Thomson.
OTHER INFORMATION Grants were made to organisations totalling £131,000 and 478 individuals totalling £224,000.
HOW TO APPLY Initially in writing to the correspondent outlining the request. Criteria and guidelines are available from the foundation's website. Completed proposals should be returned by the middle of February, May, August or November for consideration by the end of the next calendar month.
WHO TO APPLY TO Cath Moffat, Grants Officer, 2 Cloth Court, London EC1A 7LS *Tel.* 020 7726 4230 *email* clerk@richardreevesfoundation.org.uk *Website* www.richardreevesfoundation.org.uk

■ **The Rehoboth Trust**

CC NO 1114454　　　**ESTABLISHED** 2006
WHERE FUNDING CAN BE GIVEN UK and Israel.
WHO CAN BENEFIT Christians
WHAT IS FUNDED Christian churches and ministers
SAMPLE GRANTS Elm Church Kensington Temple (£17,000); 'Others' (£1,150).
FINANCES *Year* 2012 *Income* £28,458 *Grants* £28,000
TRUSTEES Shakti Sisodia, Chair; Andrea Sisodia; Lyndon Bowring; Jonathan Gwilt.
OTHER INFORMATION Grants are given to both organisations and individuals.
HOW TO APPLY In writing to the correspondent.
WHO TO APPLY TO Shakti Sisodia, Chair, 71 Rydal Gardens, Hounslow TW3 2JJ *Tel.* 020 8893 3700

■ **The Max Reinhardt Charitable Trust**

CC NO 264741　　　**ESTABLISHED** 1973
WHERE FUNDING CAN BE GIVEN UK.
WHO CAN BENEFIT Charitable organisations.
WHAT IS FUNDED The trust supports organisations benefiting people who are deaf and fine arts promotion.
WHAT IS NOT FUNDED No grants to individuals.
SAMPLE GRANTS Previously: Paintings in Hospitals, The Art Room, Auditory Verbal UK and Modern Art Museum, Oxford, Deafblind UK, and Dogs Trust, Friends of the Earth, National Trust, Thrive, West London Homeless, Young and Free and Zane.
FINANCES *Year* 2011–12 *Income* £24,627 *Grants* £29,852
TRUSTEES Joan Reinhardt; Veronica Reinhardt; Magdalen Wade.
HOW TO APPLY In writing to the correspondent.
WHO TO APPLY TO The Secretary to the Trustees, Flat 2, 43 Onslow Square, London SW7 3LR

■ Relief Fund for Romania Limited

CC NO 1046737 **ESTABLISHED** 1989
WHERE FUNDING CAN BE GIVEN Romania.
WHO CAN BENEFIT Romanian charities.
WHAT IS FUNDED Street children; work with people who are elderly, infirm or have disabilities; children in hospital; medical programmes in isolated rural areas; 'begging children' and the Roma community; children and adults with special needs in institutions; families at risk; people with tuberculosis; medical disability and the mental health arena; and children and adolescents with physical disabilities.
WHAT IS NOT FUNDED Excepting specific specialist skills training.
SAMPLE GRANTS Grant beneficiaries included: Services for elderly people – Day Care Speranta-Bacau; Day Care Motoseni; Home Care Bacau and Home Care Villages. Services for children-Mozaic centre; 6 Glue clubs; Impart (children with handicap). Services for youth; families and professionals.
FINANCES *Year* 2011–12 *Income* £63,885 *Grants* £59,419
TRUSTEES A. Adams; N. Ratiu; S. Cucos.
HOW TO APPLY A brief, two-page proposal should be sent by post or e-mail to the correspondent. Applicants who interest the trustees will then be asked to complete a second, more detailed proposal.
WHO TO APPLY TO E. Parry, Secretary, 18 Fitzharding Street, London W1H 6EQ *Tel.* 020 8761 2277 *Fax* 020 8761 0020 *email* mail@ relieffundforromania.co.uk *Website* www. relieffundforromania.co.uk

■ REMEDI

CC NO 1063359 **ESTABLISHED** 1973
WHERE FUNDING CAN BE GIVEN UK.
WHO CAN BENEFIT Charitable organisations, hospitals and universities.
WHAT IS FUNDED With a broad remit, REMEDI supports research projects in any medical condition which causes impairment, activity limitation, restriction in participation and reduced quality of life for which rehabilitation is an appropriate response. 'We particularly support pilot or incubator projects which have the potential to lead to bigger projects. Also, each year we will fund a major research project in a specific condition which has been chosen by our Trustees. Generally grants are awarded for one/two years only. Where the Trustees exceptionally approve the support of a three or four year project, funding of the latter part will be conditional upon satisfaction with progress. Consequently a mid-term review will be held to ascertain progress and recommend continued funding.'
TYPE OF GRANT Projects lasting one to two years. Projects lasting longer may also be considered in exceptional circumstances.
SAMPLE GRANTS Dr Isabel White – King's College, London; Dr Lindsay Pennington – Newcastle University; and Dr Richard Wilkie et al – Leeds University.
FINANCES *Year* 2010–11 *Income* £100,849 *Grants* £83,851 *Assets* £141,548
TRUSTEES Dr Anthony Clarke; Dr Adrian Heagerty; Michael Hines; Prof. Tony Ward; Prof. Nick Bosanquet; David Feld.
HOW TO APPLY Firstly, applicants should email a short summary (two pages of A4) of their project, including a breakdown of costs, proposed start date and length of the research

programme. If the project is considered of interest to the trustees you will then be asked to complete a full application form. Full applications are peer reviewed and, if successful, passed on to the trustees for a final decision at their biannual meetings (usually in June and December). On the completion of the research project a final report must be submitted before the final 10% of the award can be released. For full guidelines visit the trust's website.
WHO TO APPLY TO Rosie Wait, Director, Elysium House, 126–128 New Kings Road, London SW6 4LZ *Tel.* 020 7384 2929 *email* info@ remedi.org.uk *Website* www.remedi.org.uk

■ The Rest Harrow Trust

CC NO 238042 **ESTABLISHED** 1964
WHERE FUNDING CAN BE GIVEN UK.
WHO CAN BENEFIT Registered charities benefiting people who are in poor health, disabled, disadvantaged by poverty or homeless.
WHAT IS FUNDED Main areas of interest are older people, education, disability, housing, poverty, and youth. Particularly Jewish organisations.
WHAT IS NOT FUNDED No grants to non-registered charities or to individuals.
TYPE OF GRANT Occasionally one-off for part or all of a particular project.
RANGE OF GRANTS £100–£5,500. The majority were under £500 each.
SAMPLE GRANTS Pinhas Rutenberg Educational Trust (£15,000); Nightingale (£3,000); Weizmann UK (£2,000); Cheltenham Ladies' College (£1,000); World Jewish Relief (£1,000); Friends of Israel Educational Foundation and Age UK (£500 each); Action Medical Research, African Revival, Campaign to Protect Rural England, Combat Stress, Down's Syndrome Association and Project Harar Ethiopia (£200 each).
FINANCES *Year* 2012–13 *Income* £76,573 *Grants* £51,900 *Assets* £936,481
TRUSTEES J. B. Bloch; Judith S. Portrait; H. O. N and V. Trustee Limited; Dominic B. Flynn.
OTHER INFORMATION Grants are usually made to national bodies rather than local branches, or local groups.
HOW TO APPLY In writing to the correspondent. Applications are considered quarterly. Only submissions from eligible bodies are acknowledged.
WHO TO APPLY TO Judith S. Portrait, c/o Portrait Solicitors, 21 Whitefriars Street, London EC4Y 8JJ

■ Reuben Foundation

CC NO 1094130 **ESTABLISHED** 2002
WHERE FUNDING CAN BE GIVEN UK and overseas.
WHO CAN BENEFIT Charitable organisations, with a possible preference for those operating in the UK, Israel, India and Iraq.
WHAT IS FUNDED Healthcare, education and general charitable purposes.
RANGE OF GRANTS Up to £800,000 for major projects.
SAMPLE GRANTS Lyric Theatre (£850,000); University College London (£400,000); Oxford University (£300,000); Nancy Reuben Primary School (£300,000); ARK (£160,000); British Film Institute (£150,000); Impact Scholarships (£31,000); Community Security Trust (£25,000); Leaders Magazine (£15,000); and Jewish Care, Mayo Clinic and Princess Royal Trust for Carers (£10,000 each).

FINANCES *Year* 2012 *Income* £3,978,746
Grants £2,088,577 *Assets* £66,511,670

TRUSTEES Richard Stone; Simon Reuben; Malcolm Turner; Annie Benjamin; Patrick O'Driscoll; James Reuben; Dana Reuben.

OTHER INFORMATION A further £73,000 was given in 20 grants to individuals.

HOW TO APPLY The foundation's website states that applications for grants are made by invitation only. The latest accounts however state that 'The Trustees welcome applications from any institution or individual which meets the criteria [of the objectives] without geographical restriction.' Potential applicants are therefore advised to contact the foundation to discuss an application.

WHO TO APPLY TO Patrick O'Driscoll, Trustee, 4th Floor, Millbank Tower, 21–24 Millbank, London SW1P 4PQ *Tel.* 020 7802 5000 *Fax* 020 7802 5002 *email* contact@reubenfoundation.com *Website* www.reubenfoundation.com

····················

■ The Nathaniel Reyner Trust Fund

CC NO 223619 **ESTABLISHED** 1965

WHERE FUNDING CAN BE GIVEN Merseyside area.

WHO CAN BENEFIT Registered charities and Christian organisations helping children, young adults, older people, clergy, Baptists, Church of England, Christians, evangelists and Methodists.

WHAT IS FUNDED The promotion of evangelical Christianity and also general charitable purposes, particularly the advancement of Christian religion and Christian religious buildings.

WHAT IS NOT FUNDED No grants to individuals, medical research, the arts or denominations other than URC or Baptist unless there is a clear and overriding ecumenical or community objective.

RANGE OF GRANTS Up to £5,000.

SAMPLE GRANTS Baptist Missionary Society Merseyside Auxiliary and North West Baptist Association (£3,500 each); Heswall United Reformed Church, Parkgate and Neston United Reformed Church and The United Reformed Church Caradoc Mission (£2,500 each); Council for World Mission and Laird Street Baptist Church Family Support Centre (£1,000 each); Adelaide House, After Adoption, the Aspire Trust Ltd, BIRD, Contact the Elderly, Listening Ear, Shaftesbury Youth Club and Weston Spirit (£500 each).

FINANCES *Year* 2011–12 *Income* £31,899

TRUSTEES Stuart Keenan; Roger Watson; Muriel Proven; Neville Ward; Derek Craig; Jenny Hope.

OTHER INFORMATION In 2011–12 the trust had a total expenditure of £26,223.

HOW TO APPLY In writing to the correspondent. Trustees meet in April and November.

WHO TO APPLY TO Lawrence Downey, Secretary, 56 Freshfield Road, Formby, Liverpool L37 3HW *Tel.* 01704 879330 *email* lawrencedowney@btconnect.com

····················

■ The Rhododendron Trust

CC NO 267192 **ESTABLISHED** 1974

WHERE FUNDING CAN BE GIVEN UK and overseas.

WHO CAN BENEFIT Registered charities.

WHAT IS FUNDED Overseas charities, UK social welfare charities and UK cultural charities.

WHAT IS NOT FUNDED The trust does not support medical research, individual projects, or local community projects in the UK.

TYPE OF GRANT Preferably project-based.

RANGE OF GRANTS £500 or £1,000 each.

SAMPLE GRANTS Action for Blind People, Brandon Centre, De Paul UK, Street Child Africa and Find Your Feet (£1,000 each) and Womankind Worldwide, Tree Aid, Solace, Rethink, Phoenix Dance Theatre, Medical Aid for Palestinians, Ice and Fire Theatre Company, Anti-Slavery International, Contact the Elderly and Edinburgh Young Carers (£500 each).

FINANCES *Year* 2011–12 *Income* £62,401
Grants £48,500 *Assets* £1,526,929

TRUSTEES Peter Edward Healey; Dr Ralph Walker; Sarah Ray; Sarah Oliver.

HOW TO APPLY In writing to the correspondent at any time. The majority of donations are made in March. Applications are not acknowledged.

WHO TO APPLY TO The Administrator, 6 Bridge Street, Richmond, North Yorkshire DL10 4RW

····················

■ The Rhondda Cynon Taff Welsh Church Acts Fund

CC NO 506658 **ESTABLISHED** 1977

WHERE FUNDING CAN BE GIVEN Rhondda-Cynon-Taff, Bridgend and Merthyr Tydfil County Borough Councils, i.e. the former county of Mid Glamorgan, with the exception of Rhymney Valley which is now outside the area of benefit.

WHO CAN BENEFIT Churches, youth organisations and musical groups benefiting children, young adults, Christians, at risk groups, and people who are disadvantaged by poverty or socially isolated.

WHAT IS FUNDED Churches; youth activities; and welfare.

WHAT IS NOT FUNDED No grants to students, individuals, or projects of other local authorities. Grants are not given for running costs.

SAMPLE GRANTS Bridgend United Church, Trecynon Free Library and Institute and Welsh Religious Buildings Trust, Trecynon (£10,000 each); Darranlas Community Building, Mountain Ash (£7,500); Brackla Tabernacle Church, Bridgend and Aberaman Motorcycle Club (£5,000 each); Treherbert and District Pensioners and Widows Association (£4,400) and Wesley Methodist Church, Merthyr Tydfil (£3,200).

FINANCES *Year* 2011–12 *Income* £362,263
Grants £178,249 *Assets* £10,680,000

TRUSTEE Rhondda Cynon Taff County Borough Council.

OTHER INFORMATION In 2011–12 grants were given to 37 organisations, with 21 organisations receiving grants of more than £2,000 (Total: £155,416) and 16 organisations receiving grants of less than £2,000 (£22,833).

HOW TO APPLY The charity invites applications for funding of projects through advertising in the local press.

WHO TO APPLY TO George Sheldrick, Rhondda Cyon Taff Council, Accounts Section, Bronwydd House, Porth CF39 9DL *Tel.* 01443 680373 *Fax* 01443 680592

····················

■ Daisie Rich Trust

CC NO 236706 **ESTABLISHED** 1964

WHERE FUNDING CAN BE GIVEN UK, with a preference for the Isle of Wight.

WHO CAN BENEFIT Organisations and individuals.

WHAT IS FUNDED General charitable purposes.

TYPE OF GRANT Mostly recurrent.

RANGE OF GRANTS £250–£10,000.

SAMPLE GRANTS Earl Mountbatten Hospice (£6,000); Hampshire and Isle of Wight Air Ambulance and Isle of Wight Scout Council (£5,000 each); SSAFA Forces Help – Isle of Wight branch (£4,000); CLIC Sargent, West Wight Sports Centre and Storeroom 2010 (£3,000 each); Shanklin Voluntary Youth and Community Centre, Quay Arts, Penny Brohn Cancer Care and Isle of Wight Citizens Advice (£2,000 each); Brading Roman Villa and Isle of Wight Foodbank (£1,000 each); Freshwater Independent Lifeboat (£650) and Greater Ryde Benevolent Trust, People's Dispensary for Sick Animals and St John's Church – Ryde (£500 each).

FINANCES *Year* 2012–13 *Income* £162,346 *Grants* £127,069 *Assets* £3,387,631

TRUSTEES Adrian H. Medley, Chair; Ann C. Medley; Maurice J. Flux; David J. Longford; James R. Woodward Attrill.

OTHER INFORMATION In 2011–12 grants to ex-employees of Upward and Rich Ltd, their dependants and other individuals totalled £28,845.

HOW TO APPLY Contact the correspondent for an application form. The trustees hold regular meetings to decide on grant applications and are assisted by information gathered by the administrator.

WHO TO APPLY TO L. Mitchell, Administrator, The Hawthorns, Main Road, Arreton, Newport, Isle of Wight PO30 3AD *Tel.* 07866 449855 *email* daisierich@yahoo.co.uk

··

■ The Sir Cliff Richard Charitable Trust

CC NO 1096412   **ESTABLISHED** 1969

WHERE FUNDING CAN BE GIVEN UK and overseas.

WHO CAN BENEFIT Registered charities only, benefiting a broad spectrum, including: children, adults and young people; Baptists, Methodists, Anglicans and Evangelists; people who are disabled or have a medical condition.

WHAT IS FUNDED Smaller, grass-roots projects are often preferred, for general charitable purposes that reflect the support, Christian commitment and interest of Sir Cliff Richard, including: special schools, special needs education and vocational training; community centres, village halls, playgrounds and play schemes; care in the community and community transport; respite care and care for carers; cancer, MS and neurological research; Christian education and outreach; missionaries and evangelicals; and animal homes and welfare.

WHAT IS NOT FUNDED Capital building projects, church repairs and renovations are all excluded. No support for individuals.

TYPE OF GRANT Usually small one-off sums for operational needs.

RANGE OF GRANTS Up to £5,000.

SAMPLE GRANTS Genesis Trust (£3,500) and Arts Centre Trust (£2,500).

FINANCES *Year* 2011–12 *Income* £75,754 *Grants* £91,112 *Assets* £306,841

TRUSTEES William Latham; Malcolm Smith; Sir Cliff Richard.

OTHER INFORMATION Smaller grants of less than £2,000 were made totalling £85,000.

HOW TO APPLY Applications should be from registered charities only, in writing, and for one-off needs. All applications are acknowledged. Grants are made quarterly in January, April, July and October.

WHO TO APPLY TO William Latham, Trustee, Harley House, 94 Hare Lane, Claygate, Esher, Surrey

KT10 0RB *Tel.* 01372 467752 *email* general@ cliffrichard.org

··

■ The Clive Richards Charity

CC NO 327155   **ESTABLISHED** 1986

WHERE FUNDING CAN BE GIVEN UK, with a preference for Herefordshire.

WHO CAN BENEFIT Individuals and registered charities benefiting children and older people, musicians, Roman Catholics, people who are disabled or disadvantaged by poverty and victims of crime.

WHAT IS FUNDED The assistance of education, people with disabilities, the arts, conservation and religion, mostly in the county of Herefordshire, especially in church schools.

TYPE OF GRANT One-off, project and buildings. Interest-free loans are considered. Grants may be for up to two years.

RANGE OF GRANTS From £1,000.

SAMPLE GRANTS Chance to Shine (£175,000); Archbishop McGrath School (£150,000); Balliol College (£100,000); The Hereford Castle Society (£85,000); Canine Partners (£70,000); Whitecross High School (£30,000); Mary Rose (£20,000); Belmont Abbey (£12,000); The St Kentigem Hospice (£10,000); Welsh National Opera (£5,0000); Seafarers UK (£2,500); Leominster Shopmobility (£2,000) and Bargoed Male Voice Choir (£1,000).

FINANCES *Year* 2011–12 *Income* £1,263,458 *Grants* £942,401 *Assets* £714,026

TRUSTEES Peter Henry; Clive Richards; Sylvia Richards.

HOW TO APPLY In writing to the correspondent. The trustees meet monthly to consider applications. Note, the trust has previously stated that due to its resources being almost fully committed it is extremely selective in accepting any requests for funding.

WHO TO APPLY TO Peter Henry, Trustee, Lower Hope, Ullingswick, Herefordshire HR1 3JF *Tel.* 01432 820557

··

■ The Violet M. Richards Charity

CC NO 273928   **ESTABLISHED** 1977

WHERE FUNDING CAN BE GIVEN UK, with a preference for East Sussex, particularly Crowborough.

WHO CAN BENEFIT Organisations benefiting: older people; medical professionals; researchers; medical students; and people with a medical condition.

WHAT IS FUNDED The trust's objects are the relief of age and ill health, through the advancement of medical research (particularly into geriatric problems), medical education, homes and other facilities for older people and those who are sick. The trust is currently focussing on supporting a small number of long term projects over a few years.

WHAT IS NOT FUNDED No support for individuals.

RANGE OF GRANTS £5,000–£55,000.

SAMPLE GRANTS Sole beneficiary for 2011/12: Stroke Association (£39,000).

FINANCES *Year* 2011–12 *Income* £60,436 *Grants* £38,965 *Assets* £1,854,662

TRUSTEES E. H. Hill; G. R. Andersen; C. A. Hicks; M. Burt; Dr J. Clements.

HOW TO APPLY In writing to the correspondent, however the trust states in its accounts that the trustees 'prefer to be proactive with charities of their own choice, rather than reactive to external applications.' The trustees generally meet to consider grants twice a year in the spring and the autumn. There is no set format for applying and only successful applications are acknowledged. Due to the change of grant policy to focus on a smaller number of projects, external applications are unlikely to be successful and are therefore discouraged.

WHO TO APPLY TO Charles Hicks, Secretary, c/o Wedlake Bell, 52 Bedford Row, London WC1R 4LR *Tel.* 020 7395 3155 *email* chicks@wedlakebell.com

....

■ The Richmond Parish Lands Charity

CC NO 200069 **ESTABLISHED** 1786
WHERE FUNDING CAN BE GIVEN Richmond, Kew, North Sheen, East Sheen, Ham, Petersham and Mortlake.
WHO CAN BENEFIT Charitable organisations and individuals.
WHAT IS FUNDED The charity's objects are: the relief of poverty in the London Borough of Richmond upon Thames; the relief of sickness and distress in the borough; the provision and support of leisure and recreational facilities in the charity's beneficial area; the provision educational facilities and support for people in Richmond wishing to undertake courses; any other charitable purpose for the benefit of the inhabitants of Richmond. Strategic priorities are reviewed periodically – the current priority is addressing social isolation.
WHAT IS NOT FUNDED Projects and organisations located outside the benefit area, unless it can be demonstrated that a substantial number of residents from the benefit area will gain from their work. UK charities (even if based in the benefit area), except for that part of their work which caters specifically for the area.
TYPE OF GRANT One-off and recurring; core costs.
RANGE OF GRANTS Up to around £50,000; small grants of £500 or less are considered separately.
SAMPLE GRANTS Citizens Advice (£56,000); Integrated Neurological Services (£46,000); Cambrian Community Centre (£30,000); Addiction Support and Care Agency (£24,000); Three Wings Trust (£19,000); Richmond Good Neighbours (£11,000); Trans-generational Change and Ethnic Minority Advisory Group (£7,000 each); Kingston and Richmond Advocacy (£4,400); Marshgate After School Club (£2,300); Young Science Events Richmond (£1,000); and Community Mental Health Team (£500).
FINANCES *Year* 2011–12 *Income* £1,903,703 *Grants* £1,094,000 *Assets* £65,302,430
TRUSTEES Ashley Casson; Niall Cairns; Rita Biddulph; Vivienne Press; Susan Goddard; Sue Jones; Ian Durant; Paul Cole; Ros Sweeting; Rosie Dalzell; Tim Sketchley; Kate Ellis; Lisa Blakemore; Gill Moffett; Roger Clark.
OTHER INFORMATION The grant total includes £228,000 to 1,021 individuals and £867,000 to 98 organisations. A further £833,000 was spent on rent subsidies relating to the charity's social housing.
HOW TO APPLY There are separate application forms and guidelines available on the website for the various types of grants. Be sure that you fill in each section and provide the required documents. Regularly funded organisations must apply by specific deadlines which are available on the website. One-off unsolicited applications for funding for more than £500 will be considered in December and March. Application forms should arrive at the RPLC

office by 15 November and 15 February. Potential applicants should check the charity's website to be sure of the deadlines. Eligible applications must be received at least ten working days before the meeting at which they will be considered – check the charity's website for upcoming deadlines. You will be advised by letter within fourteen days of the meeting whether or not your application has been successful. Following agreement for a grant you will be sent a conditions of grant form setting out the terms and conditions of the grant. Payment will be arranged on receipt of a signed agreement. A monitoring and evaluation form will also be required on completion of your next application form.

WHO TO APPLY TO Jonathan Monckton, Director, The Vestry House, 21 Paradise Road, Richmond, Surrey TW9 1SA *Tel.* 020 8948 5701 *Fax* 020 8332 6792 *email* grants@rplc.org.uk *Website* www.rplc.org.uk

....

■ Ridgesave Limited

CC NO 288020 **ESTABLISHED** 1983
WHERE FUNDING CAN BE GIVEN UK and overseas.
WHO CAN BENEFIT Individuals and organisations benefiting Jewish people and those disadvantaged by poverty.
WHAT IS FUNDED The advancement of religion in accordance with the Orthodox Jewish faith; the relief of poverty; education and other charitable purposes.
RANGE OF GRANTS Previously £40–£170,000.
SAMPLE GRANTS Previous beneficiaries include: Keren Associates Ltd, BAT, UTA, CM L, TYY, Square Foundation Ltd, Ateres Yeshua Charitable Trust, Side by Side, My Dream Time, British Friends of Rinat Aharon, Chanoch Lenaar, and All in Together Girls.
FINANCES *Year* 2011–12 *Income* £1,293,944 *Grants* £2,217,244 *Assets* £2,442,118
TRUSTEES Joseph Weiss; Zelda Weiss; E. Englander.
OTHER INFORMATION No grants list was available.
HOW TO APPLY In writing to the correspondent. 'The trustees consider all requests they receive and make donation based on the level of funds available.'
WHO TO APPLY TO Zelda Weiss, Trustee, 141b Upper Clapton Road, London E5 9DB

....

■ The Ripple Effect Foundation

CC NO 802327 **ESTABLISHED** 1989
WHERE FUNDING CAN BE GIVEN UK, with a preference for the South West of England, some overseas.
WHO CAN BENEFIT Registered charities.
WHAT IS FUNDED General charitable purposes, particularly the broad fields of environmental work, empowering young people in the UK and third world development.
WHAT IS NOT FUNDED No grants made to individuals.
TYPE OF GRANT Multiple year funding available.
SAMPLE GRANTS COUL UK (£16,000); CHICKS (£6,000); Network for Social Change (£3,500); Devon Community Foundation (£1,800) and New Economic Foundation (£1,800).
FINANCES *Year* 2011–12 *Income* £30,478 *Grants* £29,075 *Assets* £1,343,728
TRUSTEES Caroline D. Marks; I. R. Marks; I. S. Wesley.
HOW TO APPLY The trust states that it does not respond to unsolicited applications.
WHO TO APPLY TO Nicola Gannon, Trustee, Marlborough Investment Consultants Ltd,

Wessex House, Oxford Road, Newbury,
Berkshire RG14 1PA *Tel.* 01635 814470

■ The Sir John Ritblat Family Foundation

cc no 262463   **established** 1971
WHERE FUNDING CAN BE GIVEN UK.
WHO CAN BENEFIT Charitable organisations, with
some preference for Jewish and arts groups.
WHAT IS FUNDED General charitable purposes.
WHAT IS NOT FUNDED No grants to individuals.
SAMPLE GRANTS Henry Jackson Society (£25,000);
Jewish Care (£11,000); Hertford House Trust
and The Outward Bound Trust (£10,000 each);
The Wallace Collection (£5,500); Weizmann UK
(£4,300); Mayor of London's Fund for Young
Musicians (£4,000); Central Synagogue
(£2,600); Weizmann Institute and Museum of
London (£2,000); The Art Fund (£1,500); The
Board of Deputies of British Jews and Open
Europe (£1,000 each); Tate Foundation (£850)
and Zoë's Place – Baby Hospice (£125).
FINANCES *Year* 2011–12 *Income* £34,254
Grants £103,424 *Assets* £526,498
TRUSTEES Sir John Ritblat; N. S. J. Ritblat;
C. B. Wagman; J. W. J. Ritblat.
HOW TO APPLY The trust has previously stated that
its funds are fully committed.
WHO TO APPLY TO The Clerk, c/o Baker Tilly, The
Pinnacle, 170 Midsummer Boulevard, Milton
Keynes, Buckinghamshire MK9 1BP *Tel.* 01908
687800

■ The River Farm Foundation

cc no 1113109   **established** 2006
WHERE FUNDING CAN BE GIVEN UK.
WHO CAN BENEFIT Charities providing support to
children, the homeless and other disadvantaged
groups.
WHAT IS FUNDED General charitable purposes.
SAMPLE GRANTS The River Farm America Foundation
(£2 million); The Busoga Trust (£30,000); The
University of Oxford (£20,000); Centrepoint
(£15,000); Microloan Foundation, WaterAid and
Richard House Trust (£9,000 each); NSPCC
(£6,000); Cats Protection and Oxford Infant
Parent Project (£3,000 each); Royal British
Legion and Prisoners Abroad (£2,000 each) and
Skidmore College (£900).
FINANCES *Year* 2011–12 *Income* £588,372
Grants £2,250,648 *Assets* £30,292,614
TRUSTEES Mark Haworth; Nigel Jeremy Langstaff;
Michael David Willcox.
OTHER INFORMATION The trustees have stated that
they are aiming to increase the number and
level of grants.
HOW TO APPLY Trustees meet at least twice a year
to review applications made and consider
grantmaking. 'This strategy will continue to be
implemented for as long as the number of
applications remains small. As the activities of
the foundation expand in the future, it is
envisaged that a more refined administrative
process of assessment will be put in place.'
WHO TO APPLY TO M. D. Willcox, Trustee, The Old
Coach House, Sunnyside, Bergh Apton, Norwich
NR15 1DD *Tel.* 01508 480100 *email* info@
willcoxlewis.co.uk

■ River Legacy

cc no 1146997   **established** 2012
WHERE FUNDING CAN BE GIVEN UK
WHO CAN BENEFIT Community organisations.
WHAT IS FUNDED Paddle sports. This charity aims to
promote better river access by providing
funding, facilities and support for paddle sports
in England and Wales. Projects that are eligible
include purchases of land, building access
steps and other 'physical' projects that benefit
the wider community.
SAMPLE GRANTS Symonds Yat Rapid Preservation
Group – The rapids at Symonds Yat were
purchased by canoeists for canoeists in order to
maintain the rapids which were at risk of being
lost for good – (£2,000)
TRUSTEES John Hillier; Christopher Hughes; Andrew
Turton; Lynden Wales; Richard Hales; Steven
Wales; Bryony Bromley.
HOW TO APPLY On a form available from the website.
WHO TO APPLY TO Orlando Hampton, Secretary, Kings
Acre, Kingswood Lane, Saughall, Chester
CH1 6DE *Tel.* 07966 999635 *email* team@
river-legacy.org.uk *Website* www.river-legacy.org.
uk

■ The River Trust

cc no 275843   **established** 1977
WHERE FUNDING CAN BE GIVEN UK, with a preference
for Sussex.
WHO CAN BENEFIT Organisations benefiting
Christians.
WHAT IS FUNDED Evangelical Christian charities.
WHAT IS NOT FUNDED No grants to individuals. The
trust does not support 'repairs of the fabric of
the church' nor does it give grants for capital
expenditure.
TYPE OF GRANT Certain charities are supported for
more than one year.
RANGE OF GRANTS £500–£13,000.
SAMPLE GRANTS Youth With A Mission (£16,000);
Youth With A Mission Scotland (£8,000); Care
Trust (£6,800); St Stephen's Society (£4,000);
Care for the Family (£3,700); Marriage
Foundation, Release International and
Stewardship Trust (£2,000 each); Society of
Mary and Martha, Bible Society and Beauty from
Ashes (£1,000 each).
FINANCES *Year* 2011–12 *Income* £89,560
Grants £103,150 *Assets* £633,260
TRUSTEE Kleinwort Benson Trustees Ltd.
HOW TO APPLY In writing to the correspondent. It is
unusual for unsolicited appeals to be
successful. Only successful applicants are
notified of the trustees' decision. Some
charities are supported for more than one year,
although no commitment is usually given to the
recipients.
WHO TO APPLY TO The Trustees, Kleinwort Benson
Trustees Ltd, 14 St George Street, London
W1S 1FE *Tel.* 020 3207 7008 *email* elizabeth.
fettes-neame@kleinworth.com

■ Rivers Foundation (formerly The Rivers Charitable Trust)

cc no 1078545   **established** 1999
WHERE FUNDING CAN BE GIVEN UK and overseas
WHO CAN BENEFIT Charitable organisations.
WHAT IS FUNDED The trust supports educational
projects in the UK and abroad whether it is in
terms of actual buildings, educational materials
or paying for children's education. The trust

seeks welfare projects to support via small charities with well-targeted schemes.

TYPE OF GRANT One-off grants. Recurring costs and running costs.

RANGE OF GRANTS £200–£20,000.

SAMPLE GRANTS Operation Smile (£15,000); Switchback (£5,000); Mathari Children's Foundation (£9,300); Switchback (£5,000); C.H.A.N.C.E for Nepal (£4,000) and CNCF Sponsor a Child (£240).

FINANCES *Year* 2011–12 *Income* £59,832 *Grants* £35,040 *Assets* £680,080

TRUSTEES Alan Rivers; Keith Constable; Christine Bolton; Cass Chapman; Susan Rivers.

HOW TO APPLY In writing to the correspondent.

WHO TO APPLY TO Trustees, 190A Campden Hill Road, Kensington, London W8 7TH

....

■ Rix-Thompson-Rothenberg Foundation

CC NO 285368   **ESTABLISHED** 1982

WHERE FUNDING CAN BE GIVEN UK.

WHO CAN BENEFIT People with a learning disability.

WHAT IS FUNDED Projects connected with the care, education, training, development and leisure activities of people with a learning disability, particularly those that will enhance opportunity and lifestyle.

WHAT IS NOT FUNDED Applications for specific learning details are not supported.

RANGE OF GRANTS £1,000–£6,000 (2010).

SAMPLE GRANTS Half Moon (£6,400); Self Unlimited (£5,800); Southend University Hospital Foundation Trust and No Handbags (£5,000); Create (£4,700); Soundabout (£4,400); Leeds Mencap and London Symphony Orchestra (£4,000); Tell me a Tale (£3,600); United Response (£2,700) and East Bristol Information and Advice Centres (£2,300).

FINANCES *Year* 2012 *Income* £118,319 *Grants* £129,083 *Assets* £1,344,188

TRUSTEES Lord Rix; David Rothenberg; Loretto Lambe; Fred Heddell; Barrie Davis; Jonathan Rix; Brian Baldock; Suzanne J. Marriott.

OTHER INFORMATION There was a further £15,000 given to individuals through the 'care fund'. 'The foundation maintains a close relationship with the Baily Thomas Charitable Fund which gives it substantial donations towards the annual grantmaking activity.'

HOW TO APPLY In the first instance potential applicants should discuss the proposed work with the administrator by phone, email or letter at least four months before a board meeting, which are held in June and December. They may then be invited to complete an application form and submit it with a copy of their latest audited accounts. Applications received without going through this process will not be acknowledged or considered.

WHO TO APPLY TO The Administrator, RTR Administrative Office, White Top Research Unit, Springfield House, 15/16 Springfield, Dundee DD1 4JE *Tel.* 01382 385157 *email* P-RTR@dundee.ac.uk

....

■ Thomas Roberts Trust

CC NO 1067235   **ESTABLISHED** 1997

WHERE FUNDING CAN BE GIVEN UK.

WHO CAN BENEFIT Organisations benefiting people with a disability or illness.

WHAT IS FUNDED The trust mainly makes grants to medical (particularly cancer support and research), disability and welfare organisations. It also considers applications from employees and former employees of the Thomas Roberts Group Companies.

RANGE OF GRANTS From £100 to £6,000.

SAMPLE GRANTS Cancer Research UK; Macmillan Cancer Relief; Marie Curie Cancer Care; Age Concern; Winchester Churches Nightshelter; Diabetes UK; Riding for the Disabled; Parkinson's Disease Society and Breast Cancer Campaign

FINANCES *Year* 2011–12 *Income* £22,375 *Grants* £42,000

TRUSTEES R. E. Gammage; J. Roberts; G. Hemmings.

HOW TO APPLY In writing to the correspondent. Applicants are required to provide a summary of their proposals to the trustees, explaining how the funds would be used and what would be achieved.

WHO TO APPLY TO James Roberts, Trustee, Sheridan House, 40–43 Jewry Street, Winchester, Hampshire SO23 8RY *Tel.* 01962 843211 *Fax* 01962 843223 *email* trtust@thomasroberts.co.uk

....

■ The Robertson Trust

SC NO SC002970   **ESTABLISHED** 1961

WHERE FUNDING CAN BE GIVEN Scotland.

WHO CAN BENEFIT Registered charities only.

WHAT IS FUNDED Priority areas: health, care, education and training and community arts and sport. Other areas supported: animal conservation and welfare; community facilities and services; heritage; culture and science; environment; saving lives.

WHAT IS NOT FUNDED The trust does not support: individuals or organisations which are not recognised as charities by the Office of the Scottish Charity Regulator (OSCR); general appeals or circulars, including contributions to endowment funds; local charities whose work takes place outside Scotland; generic employment or training projects; community projects where the applicant is a housing association; core revenue costs for playgroups, nurseries, after school groups, etc.; projects which are exclusively or primarily intended to promote political beliefs; students or organisations for personal study, travel or for expeditions whether in the United Kingdom or abroad; medical research; organisations and projects whose primary object is to provide a counselling, advocacy, advice and/or information service. The trust is unlikely to support: charities which collect funds for onward distribution to others; umbrella groups which do not provide a direct service to individuals e.g. CVS; feasibility studies and other research; charities already in receipt of a current donation from the trust.

TYPE OF GRANT One-off, annual, pledges (to give grants if a target figure is raised), and recurring.

RANGE OF GRANTS £500–£250,000

SAMPLE GRANTS Border Health Board Endowment Funds (£250,000); Scottish Opera (£200,000); Crossroads Caring Scotland (£150,000); Glasgow School of Art (£100,000); Citizens Advice (£80,000); Factory Skatepark (£45,000); REACH Community Health Project (£30,000); St Andrew's Hospice (£20,000); Wigtownshire Animal Welfare Association (£14,000); Kyle Public Hall (£10,000); Depression and Anxiety Support and Help Group (£4,000); Clann an Latha an De (£2,000) and Friends of Elmbank (£500).

FINANCES *Year* 2011–12 *Income* £14,410,000 *Grants* £14,650,000 *Assets* £418,184,000

TRUSTEES Sir Ian Good; Richard Hunter; Dame Barbara Kelly; Shonaig Macpherson; David Stevenson; Ian Curle; Mark Laing; Sandy Cumming; Andrew Walls; Heather Lamont; Judy Cromarty; Kintail Trustees Limited.

OTHER INFORMATION Applicants should refer to the trust's excellent website.

HOW TO APPLY Applicants are advised to read the guidelines available to download on the trust's website. There are two ways to apply: by application form which is available on the trusts website, to be returned with the supporting documents, or by letter which should include the following details: a brief description of the organisation, including past developments and successes; a description of the project – what you want to do, who will be involved, where will it take place and how it will be managed; how you have identified the need for this work; what you hope will be the outputs and outcomes of this work and the key targets you have set; how you intend to monitor and evaluate the work so that you know whether or not you have been successful; the income and expenditure budget for this piece of work; how you propose to fund the work, including details of funds already raised or applied for; the proposed timetable. In addition the trust will also require three supporting documents. These are: a completed copy of the Organisation Information Sheet, which is available from the trust's website or the trust office; a copy of your most recent annual report and accounts. These should have been independently examined or audited; a job description, if you are applying for salary costs for a specified worker. The trust requests that applicants do not send a constitution or memorandum and articles. If there is any other bulky information which you feel may be relevant, such as a feasibility study, business plan or evaluation, then you should refer to it in your application, so that the assessment team can request it if required. The trust welcomes enquires from potential applicants and wishes to provide the support required by charities in order to make applications.

WHO TO APPLY TO Lesley Macdonald, Assessment Manager, 152 Bath Street, Glasgow G2 4TB *Tel.* 01413 537300 *email* enquires@ therobertsontrust.org.uk *Website* www. therobertsontrust.org.uk

■ Edwin George Robinson Charitable Trust

CC NO 1068763   **ESTABLISHED** 1998
WHERE FUNDING CAN BE GIVEN UK.
WHO CAN BENEFIT Medical research organisations.
WHAT IS FUNDED The trustees favour applications from smaller organisations for specific research projects.
WHAT IS NOT FUNDED No grants to individuals or for general running costs for small local organisations.
RANGE OF GRANTS Mostly £500–£6,500.
SAMPLE GRANTS Previous beneficiaries include: Marie Curie Cancer Care, Diabetes UK, Bath Institute of Medical Engineering, Deafness Research, Brainwave, Action for Medical Research, Ness Foundation, Cure Parkinson's, Holly Lodge Centre and Salvation Army.
FINANCES *Year* 2011–12 *Income* £12,419 *Grants* £40,000
TRUSTEES E. C. Robinson; S. C. Robinson.

OTHER INFORMATION Accounts were received by the Charity Commission but were not available to view.
HOW TO APPLY In writing to the correspondent.
WHO TO APPLY TO Edwin Robinson, Trustee, 71 Manor Road South, Esher, Surrey KT10 0QB *Tel.* 020 8398 6845

■ Robyn Charitable Trust

CC NO 327745   **ESTABLISHED** 1988
WHERE FUNDING CAN BE GIVEN UK and overseas.
WHO CAN BENEFIT Organisations benefiting children and young people, older people and those with disabilities.
WHAT IS FUNDED Education and social welfare in any part of the world.
WHAT IS NOT FUNDED No grants to individuals.
SAMPLE GRANTS Previous beneficiaries have included: One to One Children's Fund, The Purcell School, Variety Club, The Honeypot Charity, Malawi Against Aids and Teenage Cancer Trust.
FINANCES *Year* 2011–12 *Income* £6,636 *Grants* £69,733
TRUSTEES Malcolm Webber; Mark Knopfler; Ronnie Harris.
OTHER INFORMATION Accounts were received at the Charity Commission but were unavailable to view. Grants totalled around £70,000.
HOW TO APPLY In writing to the correspondent.
WHO TO APPLY TO Malcolm Webber, Trustee, c/o Harris and Trotter, 64 New Cavendish Street, London W1G 8TB *Tel.* 020 7467 6300

■ The Rochester Bridge Trust

CC NO 207100   **ESTABLISHED** 1399
WHERE FUNDING CAN BE GIVEN Kent.
WHO CAN BENEFIT Charitable bodies.
WHAT IS FUNDED The maintenance and reconstruction of the Rochester bridges, Medway tunnel and any other crossings of the River Medway. After this has been achieved, grants can be made for other general charitable purposes. Around £100,000 is available for charities each year.
WHAT IS NOT FUNDED No grants to individuals. No funding for revenue. No grants for pet-care charities or general animal charities. Grants will not be made for the purchase of vehicles or trailers (apart from heritage vehicles) nor for office equipment, including IT equipment and furniture, that supports the running of an organisation rather than being available directly for the beneficiaries of a charity or contributing directly to a charity's objectives. Grants will not be made towards construction, improvement, refurbishment or other projects associated with community centres, village halls, parish halls, club or association buildings, sports pitches or mainstream schools or colleges. Grants are not made to individual mainstream schools and colleges, whether funded by the private, state, faith or charitable sectors, except for projects aimed at promoting interest and learning in the fields of civil engineering, history of Rochester, history of the River Medway, or agriculture. These projects are actively encouraged. Grants will not be made to nursing or care homes and childcare nurseries, except those providing support to severely disabled people and/or seriously disadvantaged children. The Trust will not fund routine maintenance work to any type of building. The Trust will not make general grants to major projects where its contribution

would be a very small proportion of the total required (e.g. less than 10%).

TYPE OF GRANT Capital including equipment, buildings and one-off.

RANGE OF GRANTS Up to £5,000.

SAMPLE GRANTS Maidstone Museum (£7,000); Friends of Bower Grove School (£6,000); Royal Aeronautical Society, Medway Branch (£4,000); Arkwright Trust (£3,900); Thanet Kidz Club, Ramsgate (£2,000); 457th Bomb Group Association – Connington (£1,500); Holy Trinity Church – East Peckham (£1,000); Gravesend and Rochester Agricultural Association (£350).

FINANCES *Year* 2011–12 *Income* £2,431,964 *Grants* £42,771 *Assets* £75,539,412

TRUSTEES Frank Gibson; Rodney Chambers; Paul Harriot; Dr Anne Logan; Paul Oldham; Russell Race; Russell Cooper; John Spence; Richard Thornby; Anthony Goulden; Alan Jarrett; Michael Snelling; Philip Filmer; Peter Homewood.

OTHER INFORMATION In 2011–12 grants were made to 15 organisations.

HOW TO APPLY New applicants are directed to the trust's website, where the trust's criteria, guidelines and application process are posted. According to the trust, there will be no grant funding available in 2014.

WHO TO APPLY TO Sue Threader, Bridge Clerk, The Bridge Chamber, 5 Esplanade, Rochester, Kent ME1 1QE *Tel.* 01634 846706 *email* bridgeclerk@rbt.org.uk *Website* www.rbt.org.uk

■ The Rock Foundation

CC NO 294775   ESTABLISHED 1986

WHERE FUNDING CAN BE GIVEN Worldwide.

WHO CAN BENEFIT Charitable organisations, especially those which are built upon a clear biblical basis and which, in most instances, receive little or no publicity.

WHAT IS FUNDED Christian ministries and other charitable work.

SAMPLE GRANTS Proclamation Trust (£23,000); Crosslinks and Lennox (£16,000 each); Carter (£14,000); Cranleigh Baptist Church (£13,000); Jackman (£12,000); Relite Africa Trust (£8,000), Baltic Reformed Theological Seminary (£6,500) and Lahore Evangelical Ministries (£6,000).

FINANCES *Year* 2011–12 *Income* £176,307 *Grants* £221,321 *Assets* £209,079

TRUSTEES Richard Borgonon; Andrew Green; Kevin Locock; Jane Borgonon; Colin Spreckley; Peter Butler.

OTHER INFORMATION The grant total includes £142,000 given to 32 individuals.

HOW TO APPLY The trust has stated: 'the trust identifies its beneficiaries through its own networks, choosing to support organisations it has a working relationship with. This allows the trust to verify that the organisation is doing excellent work in a sensible manner in a way which cannot be conveyed from a written application. As such, all appeals from charities the foundation do not find through their own research are simply thrown in the bin. If an sae is included in an application, it will merely end up in the foundation's waste-paper bin rather than a post box.' They do not respond to unsolicited applications.

WHO TO APPLY TO Richard Borgonon, Park Green Cottage, Barhatch Road, Cranleigh, Surrey GU6 7DJ *Tel.* 01483 274556

■ The Rock Solid Trust

CC NO 1077669   ESTABLISHED 1999

WHERE FUNDING CAN BE GIVEN Worldwide.

WHO CAN BENEFIT Christian charities and Christian projects

WHAT IS FUNDED The advancement of the Christian religion; the maintenance, restoration and repair of the fabric of Christian church; the education and training of individuals; relief of need.

RANGE OF GRANTS £100–£20,000

SAMPLE GRANTS Previously: Clifton College Development Trust (£25,000); Crisis Centre Ministries (£20,000); Debate Mate (£5,000); Dolphin Society and Holy Trinity Cuckfield (£1,000 each); GL Enterprises (£500); Paralympics GB and Naomi House/Jacksplace (£200 each).

FINANCES *Year* 2011–12 *Income* £13,357 *Grants* £20,000

TRUSTEES J. D. W. Pocock; T. P. Wicks; T. G. Bretell.

OTHER INFORMATION In 2011–12 the trust had an expenditure of £29,000.

HOW TO APPLY In writing to the correspondent. Support is given 'generally where the trustees can get personally involved. The trustees do not make donations to unknown persons or groups.'

WHO TO APPLY TO J. D. W. Pocock, Trustee, Beedings House, Nutbourne Lane, Nutbourne, Pulborough, West Sussex RH20 2HS

■ The Roddick Foundation

CC NO 1061372   ESTABLISHED 1997

WHERE FUNDING CAN BE GIVEN Worldwide.

WHO CAN BENEFIT Charitable organisations.

WHAT IS FUNDED Arts, education, environmental, human rights, humanitarian, medical, poverty, social justice

WHAT IS NOT FUNDED The trust states that it is 'particularly not interested in the following: funding anything related to sport; funding fundraising events or conferences; and sponsorship of any kind'.

RANGE OF GRANTS Up to £300,000.

SAMPLE GRANTS Arundel Festival; The Basement; Chestnut Tree Hospice; ClientEarth; Community Action Fund for Women in Africa; Get Paper Industries; The Marine Foundation; Red Rag Productions; Shine Trust; Slow Food UK; SumOfUs; and Transition Chichester.

FINANCES *Year* 2012–13 *Grants* £1,298,963

TRUSTEES Justine Roddick; Samantha Roddick; Gordon Roddick; Christina Schlieske.

OTHER INFORMATION Information is taken from the foundation's website, which does not give the amount given to individual grant recipients.

HOW TO APPLY The foundation does not accept or respond to unsolicited applications. 'Grants made by the foundation are at the discretion of the board of trustees. The board considers making a grant and, if approved, notifies the intended recipient.'

WHO TO APPLY TO Karen Smith, PO Box 112, Slindon Common, Arundel, West Sussex BN18 8AS *Tel.* 01243 814788 *email* karen@theroddickfoundation.org *Website* www.theroddickfoundation.org

■ The Rofeh Trust

CC NO 1077682   ESTABLISHED 1999

WHERE FUNDING CAN BE GIVEN UK.

WHO CAN BENEFIT Charitable organisations.

WHAT IS FUNDED General charitable purposes, with a possible preference for Jewish causes.

FINANCES *Year* 2011–12 *Income* £53,011 *Grants* £56,285 *Assets* £928,712

TRUSTEES Martin Dunitz; Ruth Dunitz; Vivian Wineman; Henry Eder.

HOW TO APPLY In writing to the correspondent.

WHO TO APPLY TO Martin Dunitz, 44 Southway, London NW11 6SA

■ Rokach Family Charitable Trust

CC NO 284007   **ESTABLISHED** 1981

WHERE FUNDING CAN BE GIVEN UK.

WHO CAN BENEFIT Jewish organisations; registered charities.

WHAT IS FUNDED Advancement of the Jewish religion; general charitable purposes.

SAMPLE GRANTS Belz Heritage Foundation and Machzikei Hadass Ltd (£83,000 each); Cosmon Belz Ltd (£60,000); Before Trust and R.S.T. (£5,000); Beis Yaakov Primary School (£4,700); Belz Mercaz Torah Vechesed and Kehal Chasidei Wiznitz (£3,000 each) and Torah 5759 Ltd and WST Charity Ltd (£2,500 each).

FINANCES *Year* 2011–12 *Income* £572,534 *Grants* £274,958 *Assets* £2,447,529

TRUSTEES N. Rokach; H. Rokach; E. Hoffman; M. Feingold; A. Gefilhaus; N. Brenig.

OTHER INFORMATION Accounts are consistently late when submitted to the Charity Commission. Investment management costs and governance totalled £129,000.

HOW TO APPLY In writing to the correspondent.

WHO TO APPLY TO Norman Rokach, Trustee, 20 Middleton Road, London NW11 7NS *Tel.* 020 8455 6359

■ The Helen Roll Charitable Trust

CC NO 299108   **ESTABLISHED** 1988

WHERE FUNDING CAN BE GIVEN UK.

WHO CAN BENEFIT Registered charities only, including universities, schools, colleges, research institutions, groups helping disadvantaged people, theatres, animal welfare charities, and environmental and wildlife organisations.

WHAT IS FUNDED General charitable purposes, particularly: education, especially higher education; libraries and museums; the arts; health and animal welfare.

WHAT IS NOT FUNDED No support for individuals or non-registered charities.

TYPE OF GRANT Generally one-off for specific projects, but within a framework of charities whose work is known to the trustees.

RANGE OF GRANTS £600–£13,000.

SAMPLE GRANTS Home Farm Trust (£12,000); Pembroke College Oxford and West Oxfordshire Citizen's Advice Bureau (£10,000 each); Museum of Modern History and Wildlife Trust (£5,000 each); Oxford University Botanic Garden (£3,500); Sick Children's Trust (£3,000); Community of the Holy Fire (£2,500); Snowden Award Scheme (£2,000); Compassionate Friends (£1,500) and People's Dispensary for Sick Animals (£1,000).

FINANCES *Year* 2011–12 *Income* £47,242 *Grants* £118,300 *Assets* £1,616,323

TRUSTEES Christine Chapman; Christine Reid; Patrick J. R. Stopford; Paul Strang; Frank R. Williamson; Jennifer C. Williamson; Peter R. Williamson; Stephen G. Williamson.

HOW TO APPLY In writing to the correspondent during the first fortnight in February. Applications should be kept short, ideally on one sheet of A4. Further material will then be requested from those who are short-listed. The trustees

normally make their distributions in March. Applications by email are welcomed.

WHO TO APPLY TO The Trustees, c/o Wenn Townsend Accountants, 30 St Giles, Oxford OX1 3LE *Tel.* 01865 559900 *email* helen.roll@aol.co.uk

---

■ The Sir James Roll Charitable Trust

CC NO 1064963   **ESTABLISHED** 1997

WHERE FUNDING CAN BE GIVEN UK.

WHO CAN BENEFIT Registered charities.

WHAT IS FUNDED Mainly the promotion of mutual tolerance, commonality and cordiality in major world religions; promotion of improved access to computer technology in community-based projects other than political parties or local government; funding of projects aimed at early identification of specific learning disorders; and any other charitable projects as the trustees see fit.

RANGE OF GRANTS £1,000–£10,000, although mostly £1,000.

SAMPLE GRANTS St Clement's Parochial Church Council (£6,000); DEC East Africa Crisis Appeal (£5,000); REACT (£2,600); British Blind Sport, Challenging Behaviour Foundation, Independence at Home Ltd and Jubilee Sailing Trust Ltd (£1,300 each); Fair Trials International, Dystonia Society and OCD Action (£1,000 each) and International Refugee Trust (£500).

FINANCES *Year* 2011–12 *Income* £197,956 *Grants* £154,980 *Assets* £4,076,454

TRUSTEES N. T. Wharton; B. W. Elvy; J. M. Liddiard.

HOW TO APPLY In writing to the correspondent.

WHO TO APPLY TO Nicholas Wharton, Trustee, 5 New Road Avenue, Chatham, Kent ME4 6AR *Tel.* 01634 830111

■ The Roman Research Trust

CC NO 800983   **ESTABLISHED** 1990

WHERE FUNDING CAN BE GIVEN UK, but preference given to Wiltshire and neighbouring counties to the west.

WHO CAN BENEFIT Individuals and organisations benefiting postgraduate students, professional archaeologists and non-professionals of equivalent standing.

WHAT IS FUNDED Excavation, recording, analysis and publication of Romano-British archaeological research not otherwise funded or for which existing funds are insufficient. Romano-British archaeological exhibitions in museums and other places accessible to the public; educational programmes related to Roman Britain.

WHAT IS NOT FUNDED Undergraduate or postgraduate courses.

TYPE OF GRANT Project and research. Funding is for one year or less.

RANGE OF GRANTS £200–£10,000. Typical grant £2,000.

SAMPLE GRANTS Previously: £5,000 each to University of Oxford for excavation of the amphitheatre at Frilford, and Wiltshire Archaeology and Natural History Society for work on the Littlecoat excavation archive; £2,000 to University of Sheffield for excavation and geophysical survey at Chedworth Villa; £1,500 to Primary Latin Project for illustrations for 'Minimus 2' £1,000 to Liverpool Museum for analysis of Roman artefacts from the Wirral;

Think carefully about every application. Is it justified?

857

£500 to Yorkshire Archaeological Society for publication of excavations at Newton Kyme.

FINANCES *Year* 2011–12 *Income* £54,328 *Grants* £31,653 *Assets* £1,301,503

TRUSTEES Prof. Michael Fulford; Dr John Pearce; Robin Birch; Prof. Amanda Claridge; Paul Booth; Jenny Hall; Dr David Bird; Neil Holbrook.

OTHER INFORMATION No organisations were granted awards during 2011–12. The grant total was dispersed between 11 individual applicants as follows: £29,000 for general archaeological purposes and £3,000 for bursary awards.

HOW TO APPLY By 15 November and 15 April annually. Application forms and guidelines are available from the correspondent or the Roman Research website.

WHO TO APPLY TO Dr Ellen Swift, Honorary Secretary, SECL, Cornwallis Building, University of Kent, Canterbury, Kent CT2 7NF *Tel* 01227 827 159 ext. 7898 *email* E.V.Swift@kent.ac.uk *Website* rrt.classics.ox.ac.uk

---

■ The Gerald Ronson Foundation

CC NO 1111728   **ESTABLISHED** 2005

WHERE FUNDING CAN BE GIVEN UK and overseas.

WHO CAN BENEFIT Registered charities.

WHAT IS FUNDED General charitable activities with a preference for Jewish causes.

RANGE OF GRANTS Up to £200,000.

SAMPLE GRANTS Jewish Community Secondary School (£200,000); Jewish Care (£100,000); Great Ormond Street Hospital (£75,000); King David Schools (£55,000); Royal Opera House Foundation (£43,500); Action for Stammering Children (£30,000); and Young Epilepsy (£20,000).

FINANCES *Year* 2012 *Income* £951,126 *Grants* £1,021,152 *Assets* £11,104,600

TRUSTEES Gerald Ronson, Chair; Dame Gail Ronson; Alan Goldman; Jonathan Goldstein; Lisa Ronson; Nicole Ronson Allalouf; Hayley Ronson.

OTHER INFORMATION A number of grants are made to organisations with which the trustees have a connection.

HOW TO APPLY In writing to the correspondent. 'The trust generally makes donations on a quarterly basis in June, September, December and March. In the interim periods, the Chair's Action Committee deals with urgent requests for donations which are approved by the trustees at the quarterly meetings.'

WHO TO APPLY TO Jeremy Trent, Secretary, H. W. Fisher and Company, Acre House, 11–15 William Road, London NW1 3ER *Tel.* 020 7388 7000 *email* jtrent@hwfisher.co.uk

---

■ The C. A. Rookes Charitable Trust

CC NO 512437   **ESTABLISHED** 1980

WHERE FUNDING CAN BE GIVEN South Warwickshire, especially Stratford-upon-Avon.

WHO CAN BENEFIT Small local projects, innovative projects and UK organisations benefiting older people in particular.

WHAT IS FUNDED Older people, general charitable purposes.

WHAT IS NOT FUNDED No grants to individuals for educational purposes.

TYPE OF GRANT One-off and recurrent.

RANGE OF GRANTS Up to £3,000.

SAMPLE GRANTS Good Companions Club (£2,000); The Salvation Army, Macmillan Cancer Support,

Parochial Church Committee of Saint Helen's, Nuneaton and North Warwickshire Riding for the Disabled (£1,000 each); Stratford on Avon Music Festival, Stratford on Avon Samaritans, Cancer Research UK, Marie Curie Cancer Care, The Jennifer Trust, The Myton Hospices, Guide Dogs, Acorns, Ingleby Foundation, Armonico Consort Limited, Orchestra of the Swan and Warwickshire Clubs for Young People (£500 each).

FINANCES *Year* 2011–12 *Income* £7,076 *Grants* £14,250 *Assets* £273,019

TRUSTEE Christopher Ironmonger.

HOW TO APPLY In writing to the correspondent at any time including an sae.

WHO TO APPLY TO Christopher Ironmonger, The Old School, Tiddington, Stratford-upon-Avon, Warwickshire CV37 7AW *Tel.* 01789 269415

■ Mrs L. D. Rope Third Charitable Settlement

CC NO 290533   **ESTABLISHED** 1984

WHERE FUNDING CAN BE GIVEN UK and overseas, with a particular interest in Suffolk.

WHO CAN BENEFIT For unsolicited applications, charities who work at grassroots level within their community, generally small in size, that are little catered for from other sources, or those that are based in particularly deprived areas. Charities with a large and committed volunteer base and those that have relatively low administration costs, in terms of staff salaries.

WHAT IS FUNDED Relief of poverty, advancement of education, advancement of religion and other charitable purposes.

WHAT IS NOT FUNDED The following categories of unsolicited applications will not be successful: overseas projects; national charities; requests for core funding; buildings; medical research/ health care (outside of the beneficial area); students (a very limited amount is available for foreign students); schools (outside of the beneficial area); environmental charities and animal welfare; the arts; matched funding; repayment of debts for individuals.

TYPE OF GRANT For unsolicited requests, grants are usually one-off and small scale. Funding is given for one year or less.

RANGE OF GRANTS Generally £100–£2,000.

SAMPLE GRANTS Mrs L D Rope Second Charitable Settlement (£100,000); CAFOD (£75,000); Disability Information and Advice, Lowestoft (£30,000); Ipswich CAB (£22,000); Kesgrave High School (£14,000); Juvenile Diabetes Research Foundation (£10,000); Buckingham Emergency Food Appeal (£8,000); and African Mission (£6,000).

FINANCES *Year* 2011–12 *Income* £1,321,193 *Grants* £1,109,327 *Assets* £51,912,715

TRUSTEES Crispin Rope; Jeremy Heal; Ellen Jolly; Catherine Scott; Paul Jolly.

OTHER INFORMATION Grants to organisations totalled £716,000 and to individuals totalled £384,000. Of total grants made £336,000 was granted in response to unsolicited applications.

HOW TO APPLY Send a concise letter (preferably one side of A4) explaining the main details of your request. Always send your most recent accounts and a budgeted breakdown of the sum you are looking to raise. The trust will also need to know whether you have applied to other funding sources and whether you have been successful elsewhere. Your application should say who your trustees are and include a daytime telephone number.

Does the trust you have chosen match your needs? Haphazard applications waste postage and time

WHO TO APPLY TO Crispin Rope, Trustee, Crag Farm, Boyton, Near Woodbridge, Suffolk IP12 3LH *Tel.* 01473 333288

■ Rosa – the UK fund for women and girls

CC NO 1124856   **ESTABLISHED** 2008
WHERE FUNDING CAN BE GIVEN UK.
WHO CAN BENEFIT Charitable organisations.
WHAT IS FUNDED Women's organisations and projects supporting women. Women's safety, economic justice, health and wellbeing, and representation in society
WHAT IS NOT FUNDED Religious causes or political parties.
RANGE OF GRANTS £2,000–£50,000.
SAMPLE GRANTS AnyBody; Platform 51; End Violence Against Women; Fawcett Society; Women's Budget Group; UK Feminista; Southall Black Sisters and collaborative work against Female Genital Mutilation.
FINANCES *Year* 2011–12 *Income* £135,799 *Grants* £3,800 *Assets* £109,567
TRUSTEES Marilyn List; Maggie Baxter; Gillian Egan; Lindsay Driscoll; Prof. Ruth Pearson.
HOW TO APPLY The fund encourages organisations running projects or initiatives which match the current strategic priorities of the fund to contact them to discuss how the fund may be able to help. Potential applicants may contact the trust via email, phone or by visiting the office. The fund changes its priorities regularly so applicants are encouraged to visit the website regularly.
WHO TO APPLY TO Jo Shaw, Executive Director, c/o Women's Resource Centre, United House, 4Th Floor, North Road, London N7 9DP *Tel.* 020 7697 3466 *email* info@rosauk.org *Website* www.rosauk.org

---

■ The Rosca Trust

CC NO 259907   **ESTABLISHED** 1966
WHERE FUNDING CAN BE GIVEN The boroughs of Southend-on-Sea, Castle Point and Rochford District Council only.
WHO CAN BENEFIT Registered charities.
WHAT IS FUNDED The trust supports registered health and welfare charities particularly those working with young and older people in its beneficial area.
WHAT IS NOT FUNDED Grants are not given outside the beneficial area or to individuals.
RANGE OF GRANTS Usually £250–£5,000.
SAMPLE GRANTS St Mark's Church, Southend and Southend United Community and Education Trust (£3,000 each); Dial Southend and SOS Domestic Abuse Project (£2,500 each); Livability, Barons Court Community Library and Info Centre and 5th Canvey Air Scout Group (£2,000 each); Rochford and Rayleigh Citizens Advice and South East Essex Advocacy For Older People (£1,500 each); Brentwood Catholic Children's Society, Southend Race Equalities Network and Application for a World Change in Borneo (£1,000 each) and St Christopher's Fostering Service and Asylum Seekers Conference (£500 each).
FINANCES *Year* 2011–12 *Income* £126,604 *Grants* £73,455 *Assets* £655,288
TRUSTEES Ken Crowe; Cheryl Higgins; Christopher Bailey; Daphne Powell; Maureen Sarling.
HOW TO APPLY In writing to the correspondent. Applications are reviewed in January, April and

September. An sae is appreciated. Preliminary telephone calls are considered unnecessary.
WHO TO APPLY TO Ken Crowe, Trustee, 19 Avenue Terrace, Westcliff-on-Sea, Essex SS0 7PL *email* kenbarcrowe@blueyonder.co.uk

---

■ The Rose Foundation

CC NO 274875   **ESTABLISHED** 1977
WHERE FUNDING CAN BE GIVEN In and around London.
WHO CAN BENEFIT Registered charities.
WHAT IS FUNDED The main emphasis is on financing building projects for other charities, where the cost is less than £200,000. A policy of seeking small self-contained projects usually in London or the Home Counties has been adopted. The trustees' policy is to offer assistance where needed with the design and construction process, ensuring wherever possible that costs are minimised and the participation of other contributing bodies can be utilised to maximum benefit.
WHAT IS NOT FUNDED The foundation can support any type of building project (decoration, construction, repairs, extensions, adaptations) but not the provision of equipment (such as computers, transportation and so on). Items connected with the finishes, such as carpets, curtains, wallpaper and so on, should ideally comprise a part of the project not financed by the foundation. Funding will not be given for the purchase of a building or a site or for the seed money needed to draw up plans.
TYPE OF GRANT Part-funding building projects.
RANGE OF GRANTS Typically £5,000–£10,000.
SAMPLE GRANTS St John Ambulance (£550,000); New Amsterdam Charitable Foundation (£87,000); Fred Hollows Foundation (£48,000); University College School (£12,000); Jewish Care (£9,500); All Souls Church of England Primary School and Cancer Research UK (£7,000 each); Soho Theatre Company (£6,000); Cardinal Hume Centre, Flash Musicals and Zoological Society of London (£5,000 each); Regent's Park Open Air Theatre (£4,000); and Body and Soul (£3,000).
FINANCES *Year* 2011–12 *Income* £943,046 *Grants* £911,433 *Assets* £22,012,893
TRUSTEES Martin Rose; Alan Rose; John Rose; Paul Rose.
HOW TO APPLY In writing to the correspondent including details of the organisation and the registered charity number, together with the nature and probable approximate cost of the scheme and its anticipated start and completion dates. Applications can be submitted anytime between 1 July and 31 March (the following year). The foundation hopes to inform applicants of its decision by the second week in July.
WHO TO APPLY TO Martin Rose, Trustee, 28 Crawford Street, London W1H 1LN *Tel.* 020 7262 1155 *Website* www.rosefoundation.co.uk

---

■ The Cecil Rosen Foundation

CC NO 247425   **ESTABLISHED** 1966
WHERE FUNDING CAN BE GIVEN UK.
WHO CAN BENEFIT Organisations benefiting people who are disabled or have diabetes, hearing and sight loss, heart disease or mental illness. Medical professionals and research workers are also considered.
WHAT IS FUNDED General charitable purposes especially to assist people who are blind, deaf, physically or mentally disabled; also for

research into causes of heart disease, diabetes and mental illness.

WHAT IS NOT FUNDED No grants to individuals.

TYPE OF GRANT Research is considered.

SAMPLE GRANTS The Jewish Blind and Physically Handicapped Society (£135,000).

FINANCES *Year* 2011–12 *Income* £445,880 *Grants* £282,700 *Assets* £5,675,562

TRUSTEES Malcolm Ozin; John Hart; Peter Silverman.

OTHER INFORMATION Only one grant beneficiary was listed in the accounts.

HOW TO APPLY The correspondent has previously stated that 'no new applications can be considered'. Unsuccessful applications are not acknowledged.

WHO TO APPLY TO Malcolm Ozin, Trustee, 22 Lisson Grove, London NW1 6TT *Tel.* 020 7258 2070

■ Rosetrees Trust

CC NO 298582   **ESTABLISHED** 1987

WHERE FUNDING CAN BE GIVEN UK.

WHO CAN BENEFIT Independent vetted medical research projects, especially if departmentally backed and peer reviewed. The vast majority of grants are made through university and medical schools.

WHAT IS FUNDED Medical research only.

WHAT IS NOT FUNDED No support for individuals, or for non-medical research.

TYPE OF GRANT Project and research funding for up to three years will be considered. Seed corn funding for a preliminary or pilot report is also available.

RANGE OF GRANTS About £200–£300,000.

SAMPLE GRANTS UCL and Royal Free (£400,000); King's College (£179,000); Hebrew University (£130,000); Royal College of Surgeons (£123,000); Imperial College (£101,000); Institute of Cancer Research (£51,000); University of Oxford (£41,000); University of Cambridge (£31,000); Barts and Queen Mary (£30,000); St George's Hospital (£30,000); University of Manchester (£16,000).

FINANCES *Year* 2011–12 *Income* £1,727,486 *Grants* £1,517,096 *Assets* £37,420,743

TRUSTEES Richard Ross; Clive Winkler; James Bloom; Lee Mesnick.

PUBLICATIONS A brochure, which outlines the trust's approach to the 100 projects it helps fund and its future plans, is available.

OTHER INFORMATION The trust is very keen to share the expertise it has developed over the years, which is available to co-donors at no cost. Organisations interested in sharing this knowledge should contact the trust directly. Six-monthly progress reports in layman's terms are a condition of any grant made. These should give the trustees a clear and concise picture of whether anticipated targets have been achieved. Peer review and endorsement are required.

HOW TO APPLY In writing to the correspondent. Applicants must complete a simple pro forma which sets out briefly in clear layman's terms the reason for the project, the nature of the research, its cost, its anticipated benefit and how and when people will be able to benefit. Proper reports in this form will be required at least six-monthly and continuing funding will be conditional on these being satisfactory. The trust has previously stated: 'The trustees are not medical experts and require short clear statements in plain English setting out the particular subject to be researched, the objects and likely benefits, the cost and the time-scale. Unless a charity will undertake to provide two concise progress reports each year, they should

not apply as this is a vital requirement. It is essential that the trustees are able to follow the progress and effectiveness of the research they support.'

WHO TO APPLY TO Sam Howard, Chief Executive, Russell House, 140 High Street, Edgware, Middlesex HA8 7LW *Tel.* 020 8952 1414 *email* richard@rosetreestrust.co.uk *Website* www.rosetreestrust.co.uk

---

■ The Rothera Charitable Settlement

CC NO 283950   **ESTABLISHED** 1982

WHERE FUNDING CAN BE GIVEN UK and overseas.

WHO CAN BENEFIT Registered charities.

WHAT IS FUNDED Welfare, animals, overseas aid, medical

RANGE OF GRANTS Usually between £300–£500.

SAMPLE GRANTS Alzheimer's Society (£1,000); N.S.P.C.C (£650); Médecins Sans Frontières and Children's Brain Tumour Research (£550 each); Christian Aid; Malt Cross Trust; Special Care Baby Unit Fundraising Society and WaterAid (£500); RNLI and National Eye Research Centre (£450 each); NORSACA and The Abbeyfield Society (£300 each).

FINANCES *Year* 2012 *Income* £37,858 *Grants* £31,950

TRUSTEES Catherine Rothera; Susan Rothera.

HOW TO APPLY Charities are selected at the discretion of the trustees.

WHO TO APPLY TO Catherine Rothera, Trustee, The Dumbles, Lowdham Road, Epperstone, Nottingham NG14 6BB *Tel.* 01159 663005 *email* crothera3@btinternet.com

---

■ The Rothermere Foundation

CC NO 314125   **ESTABLISHED** 1964

WHERE FUNDING CAN BE GIVEN UK.

WHO CAN BENEFIT Registered charities and individual graduates of the Memorial University of Newfoundland.

WHAT IS FUNDED Establishment and maintenance of 'Rothermere Scholarships' to be awarded to graduates of the Memorial University of Newfoundland to enable them to undertake further periods of study in the UK; and general charitable causes.

TYPE OF GRANT Fellowship grants, scholarships, other educational grants.

SAMPLE GRANTS St Peter's College, Oxford (£130,000); Wycombe Abbey School (£80,000); Harmsworth Professorship (£77,000); London Library (£50,000); Shakespeare North (£25,000); National Osteoporosis Society (£10,000); St Christopher's Hospice, St Bride's Church, Salisbury International Arts and Coram's Field (£5,000 each) and Arts Logistics (£950).

FINANCES *Year* 2011–12 *Income* £850,574 *Grants* £569,000 *Assets* £25,422,826

TRUSTEES Rt Hon. Viscount Rothermere; Viscountess Rothermere; V. P. W. Harmsworth; J. G. Hemingway.

OTHER INFORMATION Three fellowship grants were awarded totalling £57,000.

HOW TO APPLY In writing to the correspondent. Trustees meet twice a year to consider grant applications.

WHO TO APPLY TO Vyvyan Harmsworth, Secretary, Beech Court, Canterbury Road, Challock, Ashford, Kent TN25 4DJ *Tel.* 01233 740641

■ The Rotherwick Foundation

CC NO 1058900   **ESTABLISHED** 1996

WHERE FUNDING CAN BE GIVEN Within a 20-mile radius of either Ashdown Park Hotel, Wych Cross, East Sussex; Grand Hotel, Eastbourne, East Sussex; or Tylney Hall Hotel, Rotherwick, Hampshire.

WHO CAN BENEFIT Individuals and charitable organisations.

WHAT IS FUNDED Education; health; social welfare.

TYPE OF GRANT Funding is available for over to two years.

SAMPLE GRANTS Previous beneficiaries include: Brighton and Sussex Medical School, Lord Wandsworth College and Plumpton College (£20,000 each); St Peter and St James Hospice – Lewes and University of Sussex (£16,000 each); Beacon Community College – Crowborough and Marie Curie Cancer Care (£15,000); Hospice in the Weald, and Eastbourne Multiple Sclerosis Society (£10,000 each).

FINANCES *Year* 2011–12 *Income* £10,000

TRUSTEES Andrew Dixon; Graeme Bateman; Thomas Mugleston.

HOW TO APPLY In writing to the correspondent.

WHO TO APPLY TO Graeme Bateman, Trustee, Ashdown Park, Wych Cross, Forest Row, East Sussex RH18 5JR *Tel.* 01342 820227 *email* rotherwickfoundation@ashdownpark.com

■ The Rothley Trust

CC NO 219849   **ESTABLISHED** 1959

WHERE FUNDING CAN BE GIVEN Northumberland, North and South Tyneside, Newcastle upon Tyne, Gateshead and the former counties of Cleveland and Durham (including Darlington) and Cleveland.

WHO CAN BENEFIT Registered charities only.

WHAT IS FUNDED Children, community, education, disability, medical, third world and youth. Apart from a few charities with which the trust has been associated for many years, its activities are now directed exclusively towards north east England (Northumberland to Cleveland inclusive). Developing world appeals, arising from this area only, will be considered.

WHAT IS NOT FUNDED No grants for further education, the repair of buildings used solely for worship, the advancement of religion, advancement in the arts, heritage or science, advancement of amateur sport (unless it has the means of alleviating the problems within the trust's approved categories above), advancement of human rights, conflict resolution or reconciliation (except family mediation), advancement of environmental protection or improvement, advancement of animal welfare and organisations focused on the elderly.

TYPE OF GRANT Mainly one-off donations towards specific projects and not running costs. Start-up costs, buildings, equipment, resources and capital grants will be considered.

RANGE OF GRANTS Typical grant £300.

SAMPLE GRANTS St John Ambulance – Northumbria, Durham Association of Clubs for Young People and Consett Churches Detached Youth Project (£3,000 each); Citizens Advice Newcastle upon Tyne and Greggs Foundation (Hardship Fund) – Newcastle upon Tyne (£2,200 each); Combat Stress and Brathay Hall Trust – Cumbria (£2,000 each) and The MAD Foundation (£1,500).

FINANCES *Year* 2011–12 *Income* £243,339 *Grants* £163,230 *Assets* £6,406,377

TRUSTEES Dr Angus Armstrong; Alice Brunton; Julia Brown; Charles Bucknall; Anne Galbraith; Mark Bridgeman; Gerard Salvin; Hume Hargreave; David Holborn.

OTHER INFORMATION Grants of less than £1,500 each to organisations totalled £131,000 and grants to individuals totalled £10,500.

HOW TO APPLY Write to the correspondent including a copy of latest accounts/annual reports. An sae is appreciated. Full details can be found at the trust's website (www.rothleytrust.org.uk) where criteria, guidelines and application process are posted.

WHO TO APPLY TO Diane Lennon, Secretary, Mea House, Ellison Place, Newcastle upon Tyne NE1 8XS *Tel.* 01912 327783 *email* mail@rothleytrust.co.uk *Website* www.rothleytrust.org.uk

■ The Roughley Charitable Trust

CC NO 264037   **ESTABLISHED** 1972

WHERE FUNDING CAN BE GIVEN Birmingham area (excluding Wolverhampton, Coventry, Worcester and the Black Country towns).

WHO CAN BENEFIT Registered charities; some UK and international projects supported but only where the trustees have a special interest.

WHAT IS FUNDED General charitable purposes. Funds are mostly committed to projects known to the trustees.

WHAT IS NOT FUNDED No support for animal charities, for individuals, for unsolicited projects outside of the Birmingham area or for Birmingham branches of national charities.

RANGE OF GRANTS Mostly £500 to £3,000. Larger grants to projects where trustees have special knowledge.

SAMPLE GRANTS Hope Projects West Midlands (£25,000); Mac (£13,000); Emmaus UK, Appropriate Technology Asia and Tree Aid (£10,000 each); Medical Foundation for the Care of Victims of Torture (£9,000); Birmingham Centre for Arts Therapies and Martineau Gardens (£5,000 each); Royal Birmingham Society of Artists and The Ernest Mason Youth Foundation (£3,000 each); West Midlands Quaker Peace Education Project and The Dorothy Parkes Centre Smethwick (£2,500 each); Women and Theatre and Birmingham Royal Ballet – Freefall Dance Company (£2,000 each); Birmingham Clubs for Young People (£1,500); Northern Star Community Arts Project (£1,000) and Walsall Scouts (20th) and South Sudanese East Bank Community Association (£500 each).

FINANCES *Year* 2011–12 *Income* £170,487 *Grants* £156,500 *Assets* £3,331,255

TRUSTEES Dee Newton; J. R. L. Smith; Martin Smith; Victor Thomas.

HOW TO APPLY Applications should be made online via the trust's website, where the trust's criteria and guidelines are also available.

WHO TO APPLY TO J. R. L. Smith, Trustee, 90 Somerset Road, Edgbaston, Birmingham B15 2PP *Tel.* 01214 546833 *email* correspondent@roughleytrust.org.uk *Website* www.roughleytrust.org.uk

■ Mrs Gladys Row Fogo Charitable Trust

SC NO SC009685 **ESTABLISHED** 1970

WHERE FUNDING CAN BE GIVEN Edinburgh, Lothians and Dunblane.

WHO CAN BENEFIT Research workers and people with neurological diseases, but other medical research and charitable purposes are considered.

WHAT IS FUNDED Medical research, particularly in the field of neuroscience; also to local charity projects and to small charities mostly in Central Scotland.

WHAT IS NOT FUNDED No grants to individuals.

TYPE OF GRANT One-off

RANGE OF GRANTS Usually £1,000 to £8,000.

SAMPLE GRANTS SHEFC Brain Imaging Research Centre (£187,000); Macmillan Cancer Relief (£8,000); RNLI (£6,000); Alzheimer Scotland Action on Dementia, Age Concern and Salvation Army (£5,000 each); Multiple Sclerosis Society, Muscular Dystrophy Campaign and The Wishbone Trust (£4,500 each); Drum Riding for the Disabled, Invalids at Home and Stobhill Kidney Patient's Association (£4,000 each); The Sandpiper Trust £3,500) and Erskine Hospital and Cancer Support Scotland – Tak Tent (£3,000).

FINANCES *Year* 2012–13 *Income* £141,764 *Grants* £70,000

TRUSTEES E. J. Cuthbertson; A. W. Waddell; Dr C. Brough.

HOW TO APPLY In writing to the trustees. Trustees meet once a year to consider applications, usually in September.

WHO TO APPLY TO The Trustees, c/o Brodies LLP Solicitors, 15 Atholl Crescent, Edinburgh EH3 8HA *Tel.* 01312 283777 *Fax* 01312 283878 *email* Mailbox@brodies.co.uk

■ Rowanville Ltd

CC NO 267278 **ESTABLISHED** 1973

WHERE FUNDING CAN BE GIVEN UK and Israel.

WHO CAN BENEFIT Jewish organisations.

WHAT IS FUNDED Established organisations for the advancement of religion in accordance with the Orthodox Jewish faith.

RANGE OF GRANTS Up to £50,000.

SAMPLE GRANTS Friends of Beis Yisrael Trust (£45,500); Yesamach Levav Trust (£30,000); North West Sephardish Synagogue (£22,000); Achisomoch Aid Co. Limited (£16,500); Sunderland Talmudical College (£15,000); Beth Jacob Grammar School for Girls (£9,000); Gateshead Talmudical College (£3,000); and Jewish Rescue and Relief Committee (£1,000).

FINANCES *Year* 2011–12 *Income* £732,265 *Grants* £669,927 *Assets* £4,580,741

TRUSTEES Joseph Pearlman; Ruth Pearlman; Michael Neuberger; Montague Frankel.

HOW TO APPLY The trust has previously stated that applications are unlikely to be successful unless one of the trustees has prior personal knowledge of the cause, as this charity's funds are already very heavily committed.

WHO TO APPLY TO Ruth Pearlman, Secretary, 8 Highfield Gardens, London NW11 9HB *Tel.* 020 8458 9266

■ The Christopher Rowbotham Charitable Trust

CC NO 261991 **ESTABLISHED** 1970

WHERE FUNDING CAN BE GIVEN Bolton, Cheshire, Gateshead, Lancashire, Newcastle upon Tyne, North Tyneside and Northumberland, Kensington, City of London.

WHO CAN BENEFIT Registered charities.

WHAT IS FUNDED The trustees prefer to give regular grants and are especially interested in: people with physical or mental disability – improving their quality of life through equipment, activities and holidays; young people – with particular emphasis on improving prospects of employment by education and meaningful activities; health – improving the quality of life of the ill, their carers and the old either at home or in hospital.

WHAT IS NOT FUNDED Grants are only given to registered charities. No grants to individuals or overseas charities and no grants for capital building costs. The trust prefers to give regular grants but does not fund salaries.

RANGE OF GRANTS Up to £3,500.

SAMPLE GRANTS Children's Magical Taxi Tour and Bath Institute of Medical Engineering (£1,250 each); and the Arnold Foundation, Lionheart and Jubilee Sailing Trust (£1,000 each).

FINANCES *Year* 2011–12 *Income* £26,801 *Grants* £19,500 *Assets* £1,002,158

TRUSTEES C. A. Jackson, Chair; R. M. Jackson; Miss V. J. Lindsay.

OTHER INFORMATION Grants were given to 23 organisations.

HOW TO APPLY In writing to the correspondent. There are no application forms, guidelines or deadlines. Telephone calls are not welcome. No SAE is required; applications are not acknowledged. Trustees meet annually in the autumn. Applications can be sent at any time.

WHO TO APPLY TO C. A. Jackson, Chair, 18 Northumberland Square, North Shields, Tyne and Wear NE30 1PX

■ The Rowing Foundation

CC NO 281688 **ESTABLISHED** 1981

WHERE FUNDING CAN BE GIVEN UK.

WHO CAN BENEFIT Organisations and clubs whose requirements may be too small or who may be otherwise ineligible for an approach to the National Lottery or other similar sources of funds.

WHAT IS FUNDED The aid and support of young people (those under 18 or 23 if still in full-time education) and people who are disabled of all ages, through their participation in water sports, particularly rowing. Grants have also been made towards the purchase of buoyancy aids, splash suits, canoes and the promotion of taster rowing courses for youth clubs, sailing and other water sports clubs.

WHAT IS NOT FUNDED The foundation does not give grants to individuals, only to clubs and organisations, and for a specific purpose, not as a contribution to general funds.

TYPE OF GRANT One-off project grants.

RANGE OF GRANTS £500–£2,000.

SAMPLE GRANTS Eastbourne RC; Eton Excelsior RC; Flushing and Mylor Pilot Gig Club; Portland Gig Club; City of Cambridge Rowing Club; The Great River Race Co; Hollowell Scullers and University of Northampton RC.

FINANCES *Year* 2012 *Income* £13,000 *Grants* £26,000

Does the trust you have chosen match your needs? Haphazard applications waste postage and time

TRUSTEES John Buchan; Simon Goodey; Philip J. Phillips; Iain Reid; Roger S. Smith; John Chick; Frances Dale.

HOW TO APPLY Applications should be made on a form, available to download from the foundation's website. Applications deadlines are usually mid-May, August and November. Trustees have some preference for new applicants.

WHO TO APPLY TO Pauline Churcher, Secretary, 2 Roehampton Close, London SW15 5LU *Tel.* 020 8878 3723 *Fax* 020 8878 6298 *email* applications@therowingfoundation.org.uk *Website* www.therowingfoundation.org.uk

■ The Rowland Family Foundation

CC NO 1111177   **ESTABLISHED** 2005
WHERE FUNDING CAN BE GIVEN UK and overseas.
WHO CAN BENEFIT Charitable organisations.
WHAT IS FUNDED Principal objectives include the relief of poverty, the advancement of education and religion and other purposes beneficial for the community.
RANGE OF GRANTS From £2,000.
SAMPLE GRANTS Chailey Heritage School (£190,000); Child Welfare Scheme (£120,000) and Bevan Trust (£5,000).
FINANCES *Year* 2011–12 *Income* £105,747 *Grants* £315,000 *Assets* £4,770,348
TRUSTEES A. M. Rowland; N. G. Rowland.
HOW TO APPLY In writing to the correspondent.
WHO TO APPLY TO Lucy Gibson, Harcus Sinclair, 3 Lincoln's Inn Fields, London WC2A 3AA *Tel.* 020 7242 9700 *email* lucy.gibson@harcus-sinclair.co.uk

■ The Rowlands Trust

CC NO 1062148   **ESTABLISHED** 1997
WHERE FUNDING CAN BE GIVEN West and South Midlands including Hereford and Worcester, Gloucester, Shropshire and Birmingham.
WHO CAN BENEFIT Organisations benefiting people of all ages, research workers, disabled people and those disadvantaged by poverty.
WHAT IS FUNDED Medical and scientific research; the welfare of elderly, infirm, poor and disabled people; support for music and the arts; the environment; the encouragement of education and training for individuals to better themselves.
WHAT IS NOT FUNDED No support for individuals or to animal charities. No support is given for revenue funding.
TYPE OF GRANT One-off, capital including buildings, project and research.
RANGE OF GRANTS £500–£25,000
SAMPLE GRANTS Ruskin Mill Trust (£30,000); Shenley Academy and Baverstock Foundation School (£15,000 each); Hereford Cathedral (£12,000); Carpet Museum Trust (£10,000); Cure Leukaemia, Avoncroft Museum of Historic Buildings and West Midlands Central Accident Resuscitation and Emergency Team (£5,000 each); Focus, Birmingham (£3,000); Sight Concern Worcestershire, Castle Froma – Leamington Spa and Roses Theatre Trust Tewkesbury (£2,000 each); Cowley Parochial Church Council Gloucestershire and Royal Birmingham Society of Artists (£1,000 each) and Ledbury Poetry Festival (£800).
FINANCES *Year* 2012 *Income* £216,895 *Grants* £433,168 *Assets* £4,937,608
TRUSTEES A. C. S. Hordern, Chair; F. J. Burman; A. M. I. Harris; G. Barber; T. Jessop.

HOW TO APPLY Applications forms are available from the correspondent and are the preferred means by which to apply. Completed forms should be returned with a copy of the most recent accounts. The trustees meet to consider grants four times a year.

WHO TO APPLY TO Gemma Wilkinson, Clerk to the Trustees, c/o Mills and Reeve, 78–84 Colmore Row, Birmingham B3 2AB *email* gemma.wilkinson@mills-reeve.com

■ The Joseph Rowntree Charitable Trust

CC NO 210037   **ESTABLISHED** 1904
WHERE FUNDING CAN BE GIVEN Unrestricted, in practice mainly UK.
WHO CAN BENEFIT Registered charities, voluntary organisations and charitable groups.
WHAT IS FUNDED The trust funds work under the following four themes: equalities, rights and justice; power and accountability; peace and security; and sustainable future.
WHAT IS NOT FUNDED Generally, the trust does not make grants for: the personal support of individuals in need; educational bursaries; travel or adventure projects; medical research; building, buying or repairing buildings; business development or job creation; general appeals; providing care for elderly people, children, people with learning difficulties, people with physical disabilities, or people using mental health services; work which has already been done; work in larger, older national charities which have an established constituency of supporters; work in mainstream education; academic research, except as an integral part of policy and campaigning work that is central to the trust's areas of interest; work on housing and homelessness; the arts, except where a project is specifically concerned with issues of interest to the trust; work which the trust believes should be funded from statutory sources, or which has been in the recent past; work which tries to make a problem easier to live with, rather than getting to the root of it; local work in Britain (except racial justice work in West Yorkshire); work outside the UK, Ireland and South Africa (except for groups working elsewhere within Europe at a European level). Further specific exclusions are included for individual programmes and information on these can be found on the trust's website. Within its areas of interest, the trust makes grants to a range of organisations and to individuals. It is not necessary to be a registered charity to apply to the trust. However, it can only support work which is legally charitable.
TYPE OF GRANT Single and multi-year funding for core and project costs.
FINANCES *Year* 2012 *Income* £5,465,000 *Grants* £6,293,000 *Assets* £157,919,000
TRUSTEES Margaret Bryan, Chair; Peter Coltman; Christine Davis; Jenny Amery; Linda Batten; Helen Carmichael; Michael Eccles; Stan Lee; Emily Miles; Susan Seymour; Hannah Torkington; Imran Tyabji; Catriona Worrall.
OTHER INFORMATION The Joseph Rowntree Charitable Trust is a Quaker trust and the value base of the trustees, as of the founder Joseph Rowntree (1836–1925), reflects the religious convictions of the Society of Friends.
HOW TO APPLY In October 2013 the trust released the following statement on its future activities: 'Over the past 18 months, JRCT has undertaken a strategic review. Many people fed into this

process and we are grateful for these contributions. We reaffirm that our mission is to be a Quaker trust which seeks to transform the world by supporting people who address the root causes of conflict and injustice. For the next five to ten years we will continue to be a responsive grantmaking body, and will group our work into four themes: equalities, rights and justice; power and accountability; peace and security; and sustainable future. Under these four themes, we expect to continue to fund work in a number of areas where we have had a long term commitment, including for example promoting human rights, racial justice, democratic and corporate accountability and challenging militarism, as well as strengthening work in the area of sustainability. We will also continue our funding programme focused on the transformation of the Northern Ireland conflict. Sadly, we will be ending our funding in the Republic of Ireland, where we have supported some excellent work over the last two decades. We will also be closing our Quaker Concerns programme, although we will continue to consider applications from Quaker organisations under the above themes where they fit our published policies.'

'We are currently developing detailed guidance on our priorities within these new themes. This guidance will be published in May 2014, and the first deadline for applications under these new themes will be 1 September 2014. In the meantime, all our existing programmes are closed to applicants who are not current grantees, with the exception of our Northern Ireland programme which continues unchanged. If you are a current grantee and are considering applying to the trust before September 2014, contact the office first for further guidance. We appreciate that it is always disruptive for organisations in the field when funders alter their priorities. We will aim to be as supportive and transparent as possible in relation to these changes.'

WHO TO APPLY TO Nick Perks, Trust Secretary, The Garden House, Water End, York YO30 6WQ *Tel.* 01904 627810 *Fax* 01904 651990 *email* jrct@jrct.org.uk *Website* www.jrct.org.uk

···

■ The Joseph Rowntree Foundation

CC NO 210169 **ESTABLISHED** 1904
WHERE FUNDING CAN BE GIVEN UK, with some preference for York and Bradford.
WHO CAN BENEFIT Organisations carrying out social science research.
WHAT IS FUNDED This is not a conventional grantmaking foundation. It supports research, of a rigorous kind, usually carried out in universities or research institutes, but also has a wide range of other activities not necessarily involving grants of any kind. The foundation initiates, manages and pays for an extensive social research programme. It does not normally respond to unsolicited applications and many of its programmes issue formal and detailed requests for proposals. However modest proposals for minor gap-filling pieces of work in the foundation's fields of interest may sometimes be handled less formally and more rapidly. For 2012–14 the foundation's strategic objectives are research into 'Poverty in the UK', 'Place' and 'Ageing Society'. The foundation does run a grants program for the City of York called the York Committee.

WHAT IS NOT FUNDED With the exception of funds for particular projects in York and the surrounding area, the foundation does not generally support: projects outside the topics within its current priorities; development projects which are not innovative; development projects from which no general lessons can be drawn; general appeals, for example from national charities; conferences and other events, websites or publications, unless they are linked with work which the foundation is already supporting; grants to replace withdrawn or expired statutory funding, or to make up deficits already incurred; educational bursaries or sponsorship for individuals for research or further education and training courses; grants or sponsorship for individuals in need. Grants from the York Committee are not given to: animal welfare groups; archaeological work; individuals; routine maintenance or construction of buildings; medical research; overseas visits or overseas holidays.
TYPE OF GRANT Project and research. Funding can be given for up to two years.
RANGE OF GRANTS Up to £100,000.
FINANCES *Year* 2012 *Income* £8,189,000 *Grants* £5,339,000 *Assets* £261,339,000
TRUSTEES Don Brand; Dr Ashok Jashapara; Bharat Mehta; Tony Stoller; Dame Mavis McDonald; Steven Burkeman; Graham Millar; Prof. Dianne Willcocks; Tony Stoller; Gillian Ashmore; Jas Baines.
PUBLICATIONS Findings – short briefing papers summarising the main findings of projects in the Research and Development Programme; Special Reports designed to present research results with clarity and impact.
OTHER INFORMATION The foundation's excellent website gives full details of its work.
HOW TO APPLY The foundation does not respond to unsolicited applications. Instead, it issues 'calls for proposals' and invites submissions to them. Detailed information, including guidance and a proposal registration form, is available from the foundation's website. The York Committee has its own application guidelines and form, available on the foundation's website. Meetings to decide grants are held four times a year, usually February, May, August and November.
WHO TO APPLY TO Julia Unwin, Chief Executive, The Homestead, 40 Water End, York YO30 6WP *Tel.* 01904 629241 *Fax* 01904 620072 *Minicom* 01904 615910 *email* info@jrf.org.uk *Website* www.jrf.org.uk

···

■ Joseph Rowntree Reform Trust Limited

ESTABLISHED 1904
WHERE FUNDING CAN BE GIVEN UK.
WHO CAN BENEFIT Campaigning organisations and individuals who have reform as their objective and are ineligible for charitable support.
WHAT IS FUNDED The promotion of political and democratic reform and the defence of civil liberties. The trust's main aims are to: correct imbalances of power; strengthen the hand of individuals, groups and organisations who are striving for reform; foster democratic reform, civil liberties and social justice.
WHAT IS NOT FUNDED The trust is not a registered charity and provides grants for non-charitable political and campaigning activities. Examples of work for which the trust does not make grants are: the personal support of individuals in need; educational bursaries; travel and adventure

projects; building, buying or repairing properties; business development or job creation; general appeals; academic research; work which the trust believes should be funded from statutory sources, or which has been in the recent past; administrative or other core costs of party organisations.

TYPE OF GRANT Salaries; full project funding.

SAMPLE GRANTS Paladin National Stalking Advocacy (£70,000); Open Rights Group (£43,000); Privacy International (£40,000); MedConfidential (£38,000); Democratic Audit (£4,500); and Option A Team (£4,000).

FINANCES *Year* 2013 *Grants* £1,000,000 *Assets* £30,000,000

TRUSTEES Dr Christopher Greenfield, Chair; Tina Day; Mandy Cormack; Dr Peadar Cremin; Alison Goldsworthy; Andrew Neal.

PUBLICATIONS The trust produces a range of reports, all of which are available on its website.

OTHER INFORMATION The trust is not a charity and therefore pays tax on its income. Very little financial information was available; the trust budgets £1 million each year for grants.

HOW TO APPLY Applicants should email a one page outline to the correspondent before making a formal application. If accepted, a full application can then be made. The trust does not have a standard form, but any application should include: an Application Registration Form (available to download from the website); up to four pages setting out the proposal; a full budget for the project; the most recent audited accounts; a CV, if applying as an individual. Trust staff make an initial assessment of applications and are authorised to reject those that are clearly inappropriate. All staff rejections are reported to the directors at their next meeting, when they consider all remaining applications. The meetings take place at quarterly intervals in March, July, October and December and the deadline for applications is approximately four or five weeks prior to the trust meeting. Applications for small grants of up to £5,000 can, however, be considered at any time and applicants should hear of the decision within two weeks.

WHO TO APPLY TO Tina Walker, Trust Secretary, The Garden House, Water End, York YO30 6WQ *Tel.* 01904 625744 *Fax* 01904 651502 *email* info@jrrt.org.uk *Website* www.jrrt.org.uk

······································

■ Royal Artillery Charitable Fund

CC NO 210202   **ESTABLISHED** 1964

WHERE FUNDING CAN BE GIVEN UK and overseas.

WHO CAN BENEFIT Service charities.

WHAT IS FUNDED Welfare of service and ex-service personnel.

RANGE OF GRANTS £1,000–£55,000.

SAMPLE GRANTS Royal Artillery Sports (£65,000); Regiments and Batteries (£64,000); Army Benevolent Fund (£55,000); Gunner Magazine (£18,000); RA Memorials (£8,100); King Edward VII Hospital (£2,800); Veterans Aid (£2,000) and Scottish Veterans Garden City Association (£500).

FINANCES *Year* 2012 *Income* £1,105,696 *Grants* £216,953 *Assets* £14,238,980

TRUSTEES Maj. Gen. J. Milne; Col. A. Jolley; Col. C. Fletcher-Wood; Maj. ATG. Richards; Maj. AJ. Dines; Brig. D. E. Radcliffe; Col. M. J. Thornhill; Brig. S. Humphrey; Maj. J. Leighton; Col. W. Prior; Col. R. Lee; Brig. K. Ford.

OTHER INFORMATION A further £799,000 was given in grants directly to individuals.

HOW TO APPLY In writing to the correspondent.

WHO TO APPLY TO Lt Col I. A. Vere Nicoll, Trustee, Artillery House, Royal Artillery House, Larkhill, Wiltshire SP4 8QT *Tel.* 01980 845698 *email* AC-RHQRA-RACF-WelfareClk2@mod.uk *Website* www.theraa.co.uk

······································

■ Royal British Legion

CC NO 219279   **ESTABLISHED** 1921

WHERE FUNDING CAN BE GIVEN UK. Grants in Scotland are made by Poppyscotland.

WHO CAN BENEFIT People who have served in the Armed Forces, their widow(er) s and dependants, and those organisations which help them. Beneficiaries include those who have served in a hostile area with bodies such as the Mercantile Marines, the Allied Civil Police forces, the Home Guard, the Voluntary Aid Society and the Polish Resettlement Corps.

WHAT IS FUNDED The welfare of men and women who have served in the armed forces.

WHAT IS NOT FUNDED Memorials, commercial ventures, or any potential commercial ventures, for example clubs. Grants are not normally given for core costs, for example, administration or running costs of an organisation that is supporting ex-Service personnel. However, there may be exceptions to this, and the Royal British Legion aims to respond flexibly to applications, and is prepared to negotiate if there are special circumstances, for example, if the withholding of grant would harm the interests of ex-Service personnel.

TYPE OF GRANT One-off and recurring costs.

SAMPLE GRANTS The Officers' Association (£1.9 million); Imperial College of Science, Technology and Medicine (£1.7 million); Royal Commonwealth Ex-Service League (£654,000); Goodwin Trust (£500,000); Skill Force (£450,000); MediCinema (£410,000); Thrive (£205,000); Age Concern Liverpool and Sefton and Alabaré Christian Care Centres (£180,000 each); Stoll (£149,000); and Community Housing and Therapy (£105,000). Grants from Poppyscotland included: Citizens Advice Scotland (£183,000); and Scottish Veterans Garden City (£150,000).

FINANCES *Year* 2011–12 *Income* £132,816,000 *Grants* £7,742,000 *Assets* £277,116,000

TRUSTEES John Crisford; Terry Whittles; Denise Edgar; Bill Parkin; Keith Prichard; Neil Salisbury; Martyn Tighe; Lt Col David Whimpenny; Adrian Burn; Dr Diana Henderson; Maj. Gen. David Jolliffe; Anthony Macauley; Catherine Quinn; David Spruce; Wendy Bromwich.

PUBLICATIONS *The Legion* magazine.

OTHER INFORMATION A further £18.2 million was given to individuals. For further information, see *The Guide to Grants for Individuals in Need* also published by the Directory of Social Change.

HOW TO APPLY In the first instance you should contact Scarlet Harris, External Grants Officer (Tel. 020 3207 2138 or Email: externalgrants@britishlegion.org.uk) in order to explore whether you may be eligible for a grant, and at what level, so that you can be advised further on the detailed requirements. Following this, you will be sent an application form which will explain on it the information you need to send in depending on the size of grant you are asking for. Successful applicants, depending on the level of grant applied for, can expect to receive an award in between two and six months of sending in a correctly completed application form, available from the legion's website.

WHO TO APPLY TO External Grants Officer, Haig House, 199 Borough High Street, London SE1 1AA *Tel.* 0845 772 5725 *Fax* 020 3207 2218 *email* info@britishlegion.org.uk *Website* www.britishlegion.org.uk

■ Royal Docks Trust (London)

CC NO 1045057   **ESTABLISHED** 1995
WHERE FUNDING CAN BE GIVEN Part of the London Borough of Newham.

WHO CAN BENEFIT The trust supports the community in that part of the London borough of Newham that lies to the south of the London – Tilbury Trunk Road (A13) known as Newham Way.

WHAT IS FUNDED General charitable purposes. Areas of specific interest are: educational and vocational training; recreational and leisure-time pursuits; advancement of public education in the arts; general improvement of the physical and social environment; relief of poverty and sickness; housing for people with disabilities or are otherwise in need; and preservation of buildings of historical or architectural significance.

WHAT IS NOT FUNDED No grants to individuals. It does not give revenue, top-up or retrospective funding.

RANGE OF GRANTS Up to £30,000

SAMPLE GRANTS Grant recipients were: Royal Docks Learning and Activity Centre and Ascension Eagles Cheerleaders (£30,000 each); West Silverton Community Foundation (Britannia Youth) (£29,900); St Mark's Community Centre, Beckton (£20,000); Ascension Community Trust – Garden Cafe Regeneration (£16,200); Theatre Venture (£9,000); Ascension Community Trust – Positive Ageing Project (£14,000); Thames 21 (Angling Action Beckton Lake) (£10,800); Kingsford Community Theatre Project (£6,000) and Women United (Girls into Sport) (£2,700).

FINANCES *Year* 2011–12 *Income* £181,043 *Grants* £211,992 *Assets* £6,588,395

TRUSTEES Robert Michael Heaton; Alan Taylor; William Thomas; Sid Keys; Stephen William Nicholas; Eric Sorensen (Chair); Charulata Patel; Ken Wilson; Cllr Stephen Ernest Brayshaw; Cllr Conor McAuley; Cllr Paul William; Leslie Schafer; Dennis Eric James; Richard Ernest Gooding; Kayar Raghavan; Amanda Williams.

OTHER INFORMATION Minor Community Grants amounted to £15,000.

HOW TO APPLY The trust operates an annual joint grants programme with the London Borough of Newham and applications are invited in the autumn for grants from the following year's programme. For an application form or for more information contact Stephen Collins at: Community Support Unit, Culture and Community Department, London Borough of Newham, 292 Barking Road, East Ham, London, E6 3BA; Tel: 020 8430 2433; e-mail: Stephen.Collins@newham.gov.uk. Further information and application forms for minor grants can also be obtained from the trust's website.

WHO TO APPLY TO Stephen Collins, Administrator, Community Support Unit, London Borough of Newham, Building 1000, Dockside Road, London E16 2QU *Tel.* 020 8430 2433 *email* stephen.collins@newham.gov.uk *Website* www.royaldockstrust.org.uk

■ Royal Masonic Trust for Girls and Boys

CC NO 285836   **ESTABLISHED** 1982
WHERE FUNDING CAN BE GIVEN UK.

WHO CAN BENEFIT Charities and individual children of Freemasons.

WHAT IS FUNDED This trust predominantly makes grants to individual children of Freemasons who are in need. However grants are also made to UK organisations working with children and young people; it also supports bursaries at cathedrals and collegiate chapels. Non-masonic charities can currently apply to the Stepping Stones scheme which gives grants to charities and programmes working to alleviate poverty and improve educational outcomes among those children and young people who face financial hardship and are educationally disadvantaged.

SAMPLE GRANTS Aspire; British Exploring Society; Child Victims of Crime; Family Support Work; Home-Start Sutton; National Autistic Society; SkillForce; White Lodge Centre; Young Lives Foundation and Youth at Risk.

FINANCES *Year* 2012 *Income* £6,872,000 *Grants* £617,000 *Assets* £123,816,000

TRUSTEE Council members appointed by a resolution of a General Court.

OTHER INFORMATION There was a further £6 million paid to individuals connected with Freemasonry and £382,000 through the TalentAid scheme.

HOW TO APPLY To apply to the Stepping Stones scheme: send a one page initial enquiry, comprising the charity's registration number, main area of work, the amount of funding requested and a description of the programme or project, including its location. If the enquiry fits the aims and requirements of the scheme, a full application form will be sent out.

WHO TO APPLY TO Leslie Hutchinson, Chief Executive, Freemasons' Hall, 60 Great Queen Street, London WC2B 5AZ *Tel.* 020 7405 2644 *Fax* 020 7831 4094 *email* info@rmtgb.org *Website* www.rmtgb.org

■ The RRAF Charitable Trust

CC NO 1103662   **ESTABLISHED** 2004
WHERE FUNDING CAN BE GIVEN UK and the developing world.

WHO CAN BENEFIT Charitable organisations.

WHAT IS FUNDED General, medical research, children who are disadvantaged, religious organisations, aid for the developing world and support for the elderly.

RANGE OF GRANTS £500–£50,000.

SAMPLE GRANTS Previously: Refugee Support Network (£14,000); Dove Association and Kids Company (£7,000 each); Reaching Orphans for Care (£5,800); Hamlin Fistula (£5,000); Blues in Schools (£3,000); and Living Links (£1,500).

FINANCES *Year* 2011–12 *Income* £24,986 *Grants* £26,360

TRUSTEES Rathbone Trust Company Limited; Claire Tufnell; Emilie Rathbone; Joanne McArthy; Rosemary McArthy; Elizabeth Astley-Arlington.

HOW TO APPLY In writing to the correspondent. Only successful applicants are notified of the trustees' decision.

WHO TO APPLY TO The Administrator, Rathbone Trust Company Limited, 1 Curzon Street, London W1J 5FB *Tel.* 020 7399 0807

■ The Alfred and Frances Rubens Charitable Trust

CC NO 264430   **ESTABLISHED** 1972
WHERE FUNDING CAN BE GIVEN UK.
WHO CAN BENEFIT Registered charities only.
WHAT IS FUNDED General charitable purposes and Jewish causes.
WHAT IS NOT FUNDED No grants for national appeals.
TYPE OF GRANT Recurrent. Annually.
RANGE OF GRANTS £25–£10,500.
SAMPLE GRANTS Wiener Library Endowment Trust (£10,500); Friends of the Jewish Museum, Jewish Care and Norwood Ravenswood (£2,000 each); British ORT, Chai Lifeline, Council of Christians and Jews, Friends of Philharmonia, Jewish Association for the Mentally Ill, Jewish Blind and Disabled, Marine Conservation Society, Simon Wiesenthal Centre, The Manchester Jewish Museum and World Jewish Relief (£500 each).
FINANCES *Year* 2011–12 *Income* £26,957 *Grants* £24,492 *Assets* £660,060
TRUSTEES J. F. Millan; A. E. Gutwin; W. C. Lambros.
HOW TO APPLY The trust states that it does not respond to unsolicited applications.
WHO TO APPLY TO J. F. Millan, Trustee, 4 Court Close, St John's Wood Park, London NW8 6NN

■ The Rubin Foundation

CC NO 327062   **ESTABLISHED** 1986
WHERE FUNDING CAN BE GIVEN UK and overseas.
WHO CAN BENEFIT Organisations benefiting Jewish people, students and people who are sick.
WHAT IS FUNDED Primarily, but not exclusively, Jewish charities. Also, medical charities, arts organisations and universities.
RANGE OF GRANTS Up to £50,000.
SAMPLE GRANTS Chai Lifeline Cancer Care (£50,500); The Prince's Trust (£50,000); West London Synagogue and the International Business Leaders' Forum (£25,000 each); Parliamentary Committee against Anti-Semitism Foundation (£15,000); Children and The Arts and the Roundhouse Trust (£10,000 each); Chickenshed Theatre Company (£6,000); Cherie Blair Foundation for Women (£3,000); Footwear Benevolent Society (£2,000); and the Politics and Economic Research Trust (£1,000).
FINANCES *Year* 2011–12 *Income* £309,330 *Grants* £374,743 *Assets* £480,004
TRUSTEES Alison Mosheim; Angela Rubin; Robert Rubin; Andrew Rubin; Carolyn Rubin.
HOW TO APPLY The foundation has previously stated that 'grants are only given to people related to our business', such as charities known to members of the Rubin family and those associated with Pentland Group Ltd. Unsolicited applications are very unlikely to succeed.
WHO TO APPLY TO Robert Rubin, Trustee, The Pentland Centre, Lakeside House, Squires Lane, Finchley, London N3 2QL *Tel.* 020 8346 2600

■ William Arthur Rudd Memorial Trust

CC NO 326495   **ESTABLISHED** 1983
WHERE FUNDING CAN BE GIVEN In practice UK and Spain.
WHO CAN BENEFIT UK and certain Spanish charities.
WHAT IS FUNDED General charitable purposes.
RANGE OF GRANTS £1,000–£5,000.
FINANCES *Year* 2012 *Income* £48,557 *Grants* £34,800 *Assets* £800,463

TRUSTEES Miss A. A. Sarkis; D. H. Smyth; R. G. Maples.
OTHER INFORMATION The trust's accounts state that donations were made to registered charities in the UK and to certain Spanish charities; however, no grants list was provided.
HOW TO APPLY 'As the objects of the Charity are not linked to any specific areas of charitable activity, the Trustees receive a large number of applications for donations. They review the applications received and any wishes expressed by the Settlor at their annual meeting and make their awards'
WHO TO APPLY TO Alexandra Sarkis, Trustee, 12 South Square, Gray's Inn, London WC1R 5HH *Tel.* 020 7405 8932 *email* mail@mmandm.co.uk

■ The Rufford Foundation (formerly The Rufford Small Grants Foundation)

CC NO 1117270   **ESTABLISHED** 2006
WHERE FUNDING CAN BE GIVEN Worldwide, with a focus on 'non-advanced' economies.
WHO CAN BENEFIT Individuals and small groups outside of the developed world.
WHAT IS FUNDED Conservation of threatened animals, habitats and organisms.
WHAT IS NOT FUNDED The following is generally not eligible for funding: projects in first world countries; pure research; expeditions; a conference or seminar.
RANGE OF GRANTS Up to £25,000.
SAMPLE GRANTS Fauna and Flora International (£50,000); Romulus Abila – Kenya, Rovshan Abbasov – Azerbaijan, Sandra M Duran – Brazil and Maksim Tarantavich – Belarus (£6,000 each).
FINANCES *Year* 2011–12 *Income* £6,536,623 *Grants* £1,897,067 *Assets* £31,621,214
TRUSTEES John Laing; Elizabeth Brunwin; Hugo Edwards; Sarah Barbour; Robert Reilly.
OTHER INFORMATION A detailed breakdown, including project summaries, of recent grant recipients is available on the trust's website.
HOW TO APPLY Applications should be completed online at the foundation's website, where criteria and guidelines are also posted. Applications are considered on a rolling basis, there is no deadline.
WHO TO APPLY TO Josh Cole, Grants Director, 6th Floor, 248 Tottenham Court Road, London W1T 7QZ *Tel.* 020 7436 8604 *email* josh@rufford.org *Website* www.ruffordsmallgrants.org/rsg

■ Rugby Football Foundation

CC NO 1100277   **ESTABLISHED** 2003
WHERE FUNDING CAN BE GIVEN England
WHO CAN BENEFIT Community sports clubs, with a particular interest in rugby.
WHAT IS FUNDED The foundation promotes 'community participation in healthy recreation by providing facilities for playing rugby union football and other sports (facilities means land, buildings, equipment and organising sporting activities)'.
RANGE OF GRANTS Up to £5,000.
FINANCES *Year* 2011–12 *Income* £17,900,324 *Grants* £504,673 *Assets* £3,261,015
TRUSTEES R. Appleby; Leroy Angel; Peter Baines; Peter Grace; Stephen Brown; Malcolm Wharton.

OTHER INFORMATION As well as grants, the foundation offers up to £100,000 in interest free loans. In 2011–12 interest free loans were made totalling £829,000.

HOW TO APPLY Application forms, guidance notes and criteria for all schemes are available to download on the website. Application forms for the grant schemes should be completed online at the foundation's website, printed and signed and then posted with the necessary supporting documents. Applicants can click on the email button to send an electronic copy to the foundation ahead of the printed and signed copy which will speed up the application.

WHO TO APPLY TO Fran Thornber, Administrator, Rugby House, Twickenham Stadium, 200 Whitton Road, Twickenham TW2 7BA *Tel.* 020 8831 6703 *email* foundation@therfu.com *Website* www.rugbyfootballfoundation.org

....

■ The Rugby Group Benevolent Fund Limited

CC NO 265669   **ESTABLISHED** 1973

WHERE FUNDING CAN BE GIVEN Preference for the Midlands.

WHO CAN BENEFIT Employees and ex-employees of the Rugby Group Limited; young people; older people; charitable organisations

WHAT IS FUNDED Relief-in-need; general charitable purposes.

SAMPLE GRANTS Thomley Hall Activity Centre and Winterton/Newport Drive Playing Fields Association (£50,000 each); Futures Unlocked (£30,000); The Bradby Club (£20,000); Chinnor Community Swimming Pool (£11,000); Friends for the Renovation of Long Itchington Church (£10,000); Oakfield Cricket Club (£9,000); Rutland Railway Museum (£5,500); Barrington Village Hall (£3,500); St Andrew's School, Chinnor (Children in Touch) (£2,000) and Haslington Parish Council (Wildlife Area) (£1,000).

FINANCES *Year* 2012 *Income* £53,862 *Grants* £304,327 *Assets* £2,489,623

TRUSTEES Graham Fuller; Ian Southcott; Christopher Coates; Norman Jones; Nigel Appleyard; Jim Wootten; Geoff Thomas.

OTHER INFORMATION Grants of less than £1,000 totalled £7,000 and were given to 16 organisations. Around £37,000 was donated to individuals in the form of cash, fuel and Christmas hampers.

HOW TO APPLY On a form available to download on the fund's website, where guidelines and criteria are also posted. Applications are considered on a rolling basis.

WHO TO APPLY TO Daphne Murray, Secretary, Cemex House, Coldharbour Lane, Thorpe, Egham, Surrey TW20 8TD *Tel.* 01932 583181 *Website* www.rugbygroupbenevolentfund.org.uk

....

■ The Russell Trust

SC NO SC004424   **ESTABLISHED** 1985

WHERE FUNDING CAN BE GIVEN UK, especially Scotland.

WHO CAN BENEFIT Registered charities.

WHAT IS FUNDED General charitable purposes.

WHAT IS NOT FUNDED Only registered charities or organisations with charitable status are supported.

TYPE OF GRANT One-off, unrestricted grants, particularly to pump-prime new projects.

RANGE OF GRANTS Usually in the range of £250–£2,000. Three or four larger grants of £20,000 may be awarded annually.

SAMPLE GRANTS No grants list was available, but donations were broken down as follows: youth work; health and welfare; education; local; music and the arts; church; preservation/conservation; archaeology; University of St Andrews.

FINANCES *Year* 2011–12 *Income* £268,113 *Grants* £200,845

TRUSTEES Fred Bowden; Cecilia Croal; Graeme Crombie; David Erdal; Don Munro; Iona Russell; Alan Scott; C. A. G. Parr.

HOW TO APPLY On a form available from the correspondent. A statement of accounts must be supplied. Trustees meet quarterly, although decisions on the allocation of grants are made more regularly.

WHO TO APPLY TO Iona Russell, Administrator and Trustee, Markinch, Glenrothes, Fife KY7 6PB *Tel.* 01592 753311 *email* russelltrust@trg.co.uk

....

■ Ryklow Charitable Trust 1992

CC NO 1010122   **ESTABLISHED** 1992

WHERE FUNDING CAN BE GIVEN UK and overseas, with a preference for the East Midlands.

WHO CAN BENEFIT Organisations, generally to small or start-up charities, and individuals.

WHAT IS FUNDED Projects in the developing world, especially those which are intended to be self-sustaining or concerned with education; help for vulnerable families, minorities and the prevention of abuse or exploitation of children and young persons; and conservation of natural species, landscape and resources.

WHAT IS NOT FUNDED Only organisations which are UK registered, have a UK sponsor, or are affiliated to a UK registered charity will be considered.

RANGE OF GRANTS £500 to £3,000

SAMPLE GRANTS Safe and Sound and Field Row Unitarian Chapel Belper.

FINANCES *Year* 2011–12 *Income* £23,535 *Grants* £222,532

TRUSTEES Andrew Williamson; Ernest J. S. Cannings; Philip W. Hanson; Sheila Taylor.

HOW TO APPLY The trust is no longer accepting unsolicited applications. The trustees actively seek out charities which they invite to apply.

WHO TO APPLY TO Stephen Marshall, c/o Robinsons Solicitors, 10–11 St James Court, Friar Gate, Derby DE1 1BT *Tel.* 01332 291431 *email* stephen.marshall@robinsons-solicitors.co.uk

....

■ The J. S. and E. C. Rymer Charitable Trust

CC NO 267493   **ESTABLISHED** 1974

WHERE FUNDING CAN BE GIVEN East Yorkshire.

WHO CAN BENEFIT People who have retired from rural industry or agriculture.

WHAT IS FUNDED Housing for retired people who have spent the major part of their working lives in rural industry or agriculture; general charitable purposes in the specified area.

WHAT IS NOT FUNDED No grants to charities outside East Yorkshire.

RANGE OF GRANTS £10–£1,000.

SAMPLE GRANTS Recipients include local churches, community healthcare and NSPCC (regional branch).

FINANCES *Year* 2011–12 *Income* £39,141
Grants £44,999
TRUSTEES Carol Rymer; Timothy Rymer; Giles Brand.
HOW TO APPLY In writing to the correspondent.
WHO TO APPLY TO D. Milburn, Southburn Offices,
Southburn, Driffield, East Yorkshire YO25 9ED
Tel. 01377 227764 *Fax* 01377 227802
email charitable.trust@jsr.co.uk

Think carefully about every application. Is it justified?

869

■ S. F. Foundation

CC NO 1105843   **ESTABLISHED** 2004
WHERE FUNDING CAN BE GIVEN Worldwide.
WHO CAN BENEFIT Jewish organisations.
WHAT IS FUNDED The trust gives grants towards the 'advancement and furtherance of the Jewish religion and Jewish religious education and the alleviation of poverty amongst the Jewish community throughout the world.'
FINANCES *Year* 2011–12 *Income* £5,414,036 *Grants* £1,700,000 *Assets* £16,852,035
TRUSTEES Hannah Jacob; Rivka Niederman; Miriam Schrieber.
HOW TO APPLY 'The charity accepts applications for grants from representatives of various charities, which are reviewed by the trustees on a regular basis.'
WHO TO APPLY TO Rivka Niederman, Secretary, 143 Upper Clapton Road, London E5 9DB *Tel.* 020 8802 5492

■ S. O. Charitable Trust

CC NO 326314   **ESTABLISHED** 1982
WHERE FUNDING CAN BE GIVEN Gateshead.
WHO CAN BENEFIT Jewish people.
WHAT IS FUNDED Jewish causes.
SAMPLE GRANTS The largest grants were to: Donations to synagogues, Od Yosefah Chai (£500 each); TYA (£5,000); Sasson Vesimola (£7,000); Yeshaya memorial fund (£3,050).
FINANCES *Year* 2011–12 *Income* £68,480 *Grants* £16,050 *Assets* £734,231
TRUSTEES Rabbi Simon Ohayon; N. Ohayon; S. Ohayon.
OTHER INFORMATION The accounts for 2011–12 were overdue at the charity commission.
HOW TO APPLY In writing to the correspondent.
WHO TO APPLY TO Rabbi Simon Ohayon, Trustee, 19 Oxford Terrace, Gateshead, Tyne and Wear NE8 1RQ *Tel.* 01914 770408

■ The Michael Sacher Charitable Trust (formerly known as the Jeremy and John Sacher Charitable Trust)

CC NO 206321   **ESTABLISHED** 1957
WHERE FUNDING CAN BE GIVEN UK and Israel.
WHO CAN BENEFIT Charitable organisations, with a preference for Jewish organisations.
WHAT IS FUNDED General, including arts, culture and heritage; medical and disability; community and welfare; education, science and technology; children and youth; and religion.
RANGE OF GRANTS £100–£30,000.
SAMPLE GRANTS Community Security Trust; Kings College London; The National Gallery; Royal Opera House Foundation; New Israel Fund; Beaminster Festival; Army Benevolent Fund and Dorset Children's Hospice.
FINANCES *Year* 2012–13 *Income* £160,854 *Grants* £71,964 *Assets* £5,316,582
TRUSTEES Simon Sacher; Jeremy Sacher; Hon. Rosalind Sacher; Elisabeth Sacher.

HOW TO APPLY In writing to the correspondent at any time.
WHO TO APPLY TO The Trustees, c/o H. W. Fisher and Co, Acre House, 11–15 William Road, London NW1 3ER *Tel.* 020 7388 7000

■ The Michael Harry Sacher Trust

CC NO 288973   **ESTABLISHED** 1984
WHERE FUNDING CAN BE GIVEN UK and overseas
WHO CAN BENEFIT Registered charities.
WHAT IS FUNDED General charitable purposes with a preference for arts, education, animal welfare, Jewish organisations and health. Requests are generally only considered if they are from organisations that are personally known to the trustees.
WHAT IS NOT FUNDED No grants to individuals or organisations which are not registered charities.
RANGE OF GRANTS £250–£30,000.
SAMPLE GRANTS Previous beneficiaries have included: British Friends of the Art Museums of Israel; National Gallery Trust; Jewish Care; Nightingale House; Jeremy and John Sacher Charitable Trust; Whale and Dolphin Conservation Society; The Mariinsky Theatre Trust and Venice in Peril.
FINANCES *Year* 2011–12 *Income* £73,015 *Grants* £71,676 *Assets* £2,302,691
TRUSTEES Nicola Shelley Sacher; Michael Harry Sacher.
HOW TO APPLY In writing to the correspondent.
WHO TO APPLY TO The Trustees, c/o H. W. Fisher and Co, Acre House, 11–15 William Road, London NW1 3ER *Tel.* 020 7388 7000

■ Raymond and Beverly Sackler 1988 Foundation

CC NO 327864   **ESTABLISHED** 1988
WHERE FUNDING CAN BE GIVEN UK and overseas
WHO CAN BENEFIT The trust has a list of regular beneficiaries.
WHAT IS FUNDED Grants are given to the arts, sciences and medical research.
TYPE OF GRANT Annual grants.
SAMPLE GRANTS Yale University (£1.2 million); Weill Cornell Medical College (£820,000); and University College London – Cancer Centre (£75,000).
FINANCES *Year* 2012 *Income* £0 *Grants* £640,000
TRUSTEES C. Mitchell; Dr R. R. Sackler; Sackler; R. Smith; Dr R. S. Sackler; A. Wikstrom; A. Mattessich.
OTHER INFORMATION Formerly known as The Raymond and Beverley Sackler Foundation
HOW TO APPLY No grants to unsolicited applications.
WHO TO APPLY TO Christopher Mitchell, Trustee, 9th Floor, New Zealand House, 80 Haymarket, London SW1Y 4TQ *Tel.* 020 7930 4944

■ The Sackler Trust

CC NO 1132097   **ESTABLISHED** 1988
WHERE FUNDING CAN BE GIVEN UK.
WHO CAN BENEFIT Large institutions benefiting, arts and culture or medical research or actors and entertainment professionals, musicians, textile workers and designers, and writers and poets.
WHAT IS FUNDED Arts and culture, science and medical research generally
TYPE OF GRANT Some recurring; others one-off.
RANGE OF GRANTS Up to £500,000

SAMPLE GRANTS Garden Museum (£100,000); The Prince's Foundation for Children and the Arts (£75,000); Watts Gallery (£60,000); Amnesty International (£50,000); The Charleston Trust Centenary Project (£35,000); and Houghton Hall and Commonwealth Youth Orchestra (£25,000 each).

FINANCES *Year* 2012 *Income* £7,457,372 *Grants* £443,550 *Assets* £51,654,071

TRUSTEES Dame Theresa Sackler; Peter Stormonth Darling; C. B. Mitchell; R. M. Smith; Marissa Sackler; Sophia Dalrymple; Michael Sackler; Marianne Mitchell.

HOW TO APPLY In writing to the correspondent.

WHO TO APPLY TO Christopher Mitchell, Trustee, 9th Floor, New Zealand House, 80 Haymarket, London SW1Y 4TQ *Tel.* 020 7930 4944

■ The Ruzin Sadagora Trust

CC NO 285475   **ESTABLISHED** 1982

WHERE FUNDING CAN BE GIVEN UK and Israel.

WHO CAN BENEFIT Jewish people.

WHAT IS FUNDED Upkeep and activities of the Ruzin Sadagora Synagogue in London; other associated institutions; and Jewish charities.

SAMPLE GRANTS Previous grant beneficiaries include: Beth Israel Ruzin Sadagora (£196,000); Friends of Ruzin Sadagora (£180,000); Beth Kaknesset Ohr Yisroel (£91,600); Mosdos Sadigur (£40,000); Yeshivas Torah Temimah (£9,000); Chevras Moaz Lodol (£6,500); Pardes House (£2,000).

FINANCES *Year* 2011–12 *Income* £515,881 *Grants* £453,839 *Assets* £412,359

TRUSTEES Rabbi I. M. Friedman; Sara Friedman.

HOW TO APPLY In writing to the correspondent.

WHO TO APPLY TO Rabbi I. M. Friedman, Trustee, 269 Golders Green Road, London NW11 9JJ *Tel.* 020 8806 9514

■ The Saddlers' Company Charitable Fund

CC NO 261962   **ESTABLISHED** 1970

WHERE FUNDING CAN BE GIVEN UK.

WHO CAN BENEFIT Registered charities and institutions.

WHAT IS FUNDED Grants are made by the company in the following categories: City of London; saddlery trade; equestrian; education; disability charities, service charities and general charitable purposes.

TYPE OF GRANT Usually one-off for one year.

RANGE OF GRANTS Up to around £30,000.

SAMPLE GRANTS Saddlers' Scholarships and Bursaries at Alleyn's School (£130,000); British Horse Society (£32,000); Riding for the Disabled Association (£27,500); City and Guilds of London Institute (£7,000); Birmingham Cathedral (£5,000); Royal Veterinary College and Leather Conservation Centre (£4,000 each); ABF – The Soldiers Charity and the Footsteps Foundation (£2,000 each); Centrepoint and Transport for All (£1,000 each).

FINANCES *Year* 2011–12 *Income* £410,928 *Grants* £360,689 *Assets* £9,096,032

TRUSTEES Campbell Pulley; D. J. Serrell-Wattes; David Hardy; David Snowden; Edward Pearson; Hugh Dyson-Laurie; Iain Pulley; John Vant; Jonathan Godrich; Michael Bullen; Michael Laurie; Peter Laurie; Peter Lewis; Tim Satchell; William Dyson-Laurie; Mark Farmar; David Chandler; Paul Farmar; Petronella Jameson;

Charles Barclay; John Robinson; Hugh Thomas; James Welch; Lt Col. G. E. Vere-Laurie.

HOW TO APPLY In writing to the correspondent. Applications must be submitted by 31 May and 1 November. Grants are made in January and July, following trustees' meetings. Charities are asked to submit reports at the end of the following year on their continuing activities and the use of any grant received. Between 30% – 40% of grants are made to new applicants.

WHO TO APPLY TO Nigel Lithgow, Clerk to the Company, Saddlers' Hall, 40 Gutter Lane, London EC2V 6BR *Tel* 020 7726 8661/6 *Fax* 020 7600 0386 *email* clerk@saddlersco.co.uk *Website* www.saddlersco.co.uk

■ Erach and Roshan Sadri Foundation

CC NO 1110736   **ESTABLISHED** 2005

WHERE FUNDING CAN BE GIVEN Worldwide.

WHO CAN BENEFIT Registered charities, community groups and religious institutions.

WHAT IS FUNDED The main objects of the foundation are: providing financial assistance for education and welfare purposes; relieving poverty by alleviating homelessness; and assisting members of the Zoroastrian religious faith.

WHAT IS NOT FUNDED Applications are unlikely to be successful if they: involve animal welfare or heritage; are a general appeal from large UK organisations.

TYPE OF GRANT One-off grants for project costs.

RANGE OF GRANTS Up to around £25,000.

SAMPLE GRANTS The British Forces Foundation (£25,000); On Course (£22,000); Honeypot (£18,000); World Federation (£12,500); Bobby Van Trust (£10,000); Manthan (£9,000); The Passage (£5,000); Calcutta Rescue (£3,500); and Charlie's Charity (£1,500).

FINANCES *Year* 2011–12 *Income* £84,367 *Grants* £426,960 *Assets* £3,635,736

TRUSTEES Margaret Lynch; Shabbir Merali; Darius Sarosh; Jehangir Sarosh; Sammy Bhiwandiwalla.

HOW TO APPLY On a form which can be downloaded from the foundation's website, along with full and detailed guidelines. Forms can be returned by post or email. Meetings are held four times a year. Note: 'Unsolicited material sent in addition to the clear and concise requirements of the application form is very likely to prove detrimental to your application. The trustees insist that additional items such as annual reports, glossy brochures, Christmas cards and accounts are not sent unless specifically requested.'

WHO TO APPLY TO Mark Cann, Administrator, 10a High Street, Pewsey, Wiltshire SN9 5AQ *Tel.* 01672 569131 *email* markcann@ersf.org.uk *Website* www.ersf.org.uk

■ Saga Charitable Trust

CC NO 291991   **ESTABLISHED** 1985

WHERE FUNDING CAN BE GIVEN Developing countries.

WHO CAN BENEFIT Charitable organisations and projects.

WHAT IS FUNDED The prime objective is to benefit under-privileged communities at destinations in developing countries that host Saga Holidaymakers. It aims not just to donate money, but to invest in projects that will 'empower and support' local communities, provide practical help to those in need, and offer increased opportunities for disadvantaged groups to benefit from tourism.

WHAT IS NOT FUNDED No grants to individuals.

SAMPLE GRANTS Centre for Early Childhood Development (CECD), South Africa (£23,500); The Umdoni and Vulamehlo HIV/Aids Association, South Africa (£20,000); Hailer Foundation, Kenya (£15,500); Mome Doudon School, St Lucia (£13,500); Vatsalya School, India (£5,500); Women's Empowerment through Education and Skills Development Programme (OCCED), Nepal (£4,000) and This Life, Cambodia (£130).

FINANCES *Year* 2011–12 *Income* £495,573 *Grants* £237,793 *Assets* £308,598

TRUSTEES Susan Hooper; Timothy Pethick; Makala Thomas; Helen Adamson; Andrew Stringer; Aynsley Jardin; James Duguid.

HOW TO APPLY In writing to the correspondent at any time. 'Project funding is agreed by our Board of Trustees, who take care to ensure there is a reliable local sponsor to account for all expenditure.'

WHO TO APPLY TO Helen Wathen, The Saga Building, Enbrook Park, Folkestone, Kent CT20 3SE *Tel.* 0800 096 6770 *email* contact@sagacharitabletrust.org *Website* www.sagacharitabletrust.org

....

■ The Jean Sainsbury Animal Welfare Trust

CC NO 326358   **ESTABLISHED** 1982

WHERE FUNDING CAN BE GIVEN UK registered charities.

WHO CAN BENEFIT UK registered national and international animal welfare charities.

WHAT IS FUNDED Projects concerned with animal welfare and wildlife.

WHAT IS NOT FUNDED No grants are given to charities which: are mainly engaged with the preservation of specific species of wild animals; have available reserves equal to more than one year's running costs (unless it can be demonstrated that reserves are being held for a designated project); are offering sanctuary to animals, with no effort to re-home, foster or rehabilitate; do not have a realistic policy for animals that cannot be given a reasonable quality of life; are involved with assistance animals e.g. Hearing Dogs for the Deaf, Riding for the Disabled; spend more than a reasonable proportion of their income on administration or cannot justify their costs per animal helped; are registered outside the UK. No support is given to veterinary schools (unless the money can be seen to be directly benefiting the type of animals the Trust would want to support). No individuals are supported.

TYPE OF GRANT Capital, buildings, campaigning, core costs, project, running costs and recurring costs. Funding for up to one year is available.

RANGE OF GRANTS £100–£12,000.

SAMPLE GRANTS All Creatures Great and Small (£30,000); North Clwyd Animal Rescue (£20,000); RVC Beaumont Sainsbury Animal Hospital (£15,000); Doris Banham Dog Rescue (£10,000); Southern Wildlife Animal Rescue (£7,000); Mayhew Animal Home, Caring for Cats – Yorkshire and Humber and Scratching Post (£5,000); South Yorkshire English Springer Spaniel Rescue (£4,000); Gambia Horse and Donkey Trust and Wildlife Vets International (£3,000 each); RSPCA Cardiff and District (£2,000) and Friends of the Tsunami Animal People Alliance (£500).

FINANCES *Year* 2012 *Income* £391,084 *Grants* £311,462 *Assets* £12,564,563

TRUSTEES Colin Russell; Gillian Tarlington; James Keliher; Mark Spurdens; Adele Sparrow; Valerie Pike; Michelle Francine Allen.

OTHER INFORMATION The grant total comprised of £281,000 given to charities working in the UK and £31,000 to UK charities working overseas

HOW TO APPLY On a form available from the correspondent or to download from the trust's website. Applicants should complete and return nine copies of the form, their latest set of audited accounts and any other information which may be relevant to the application. Note: the trust requests that you do not send originals as these cannot be returned. There are three trustees' meetings every year, usually in March, July and November and applications should be submitted by 15 January, 15 May and 15 September respectively. Further application information and policy guidelines are available by visiting the website.

WHO TO APPLY TO Madeleine Orchard, Administrator, PO Box 469, London W14 8PJ *Tel.* 020 7602 7948 *email* orchardjswelfare@gmail.com *Website* jeansainsburyanimalwelfare.org.uk

....

■ The Alan and Babette Sainsbury Charitable Fund

CC NO 292930   **ESTABLISHED** 1953

WHERE FUNDING CAN BE GIVEN UK and overseas.

WHO CAN BENEFIT Registered charities and research institutes.

WHAT IS FUNDED Projects in the following fields: civil liberties, scientific and medical research, youth work, overseas projects and general charitable purposes.

WHAT IS NOT FUNDED Grants are not normally made to individuals.

TYPE OF GRANT One-off and ongoing, core costs, capital, project and running costs.

RANGE OF GRANTS £5,000–£150,000.

SAMPLE GRANTS Dose Adjustment for Normal Eating (£150,000 towards reducing waiting lists for the DAFNE course in West Essex); University of Oxford (£100,000, towards research into the beneficial effects of licensed drugs on multiple sclerosis); Salmon Youth Centre (£30,000 over two years towards core costs); Tsofen-High Technology Centre (£20,000, towards its new teacher training programme); Survivor's Fund (£12,000, towards the costs of establishing and running sewing co-operative for survivors of the Rwandan Genocide in Eastern Rwanda; Female Prisoners Welfare Project Hibiscus (£10,000, towards the completion of 'A Dangerous Journey', an educational anti-trafficking film aimed at women considered to be at risk from traffickers in West Africa); The Ashden Awards (£6,500, towards the organisation's core costs in 2012/13) and Toppesfield Village Hall Committee (£5,000, towards renovation costs of the community village and shop).

FINANCES *Year* 2011–12 *Income* £407,878 *Grants* £414,232 *Assets* £13,346,059

TRUSTEES The Hon. Sir Timothy Sainsbury; Judith Portrait; John Julian Sainsbury; Lindsey Anderson.

HOW TO APPLY The trust states that: 'proposals are likely to be invited by the trustees or initiated at their request. Unsolicited applications will only be successful if they fall precisely within an area in which the trustees are interested'. A single application will be considered for support by all the trusts in the Sainsbury family group.

WHO TO APPLY TO Alan Bookbinder, Director, The Peak, 5 Wilton Road, London SW1V 1AP
Tel. 020 7410 0330 *Fax* 020 7410 0332
Website www.sfct.org.uk

■ The Sainsbury Family Charitable Trusts

WHERE FUNDING CAN BE GIVEN See individual trusts.
WHO CAN BENEFIT Registered charities and institutions.
WHAT IS FUNDED See the entries for the individuals trusts.
WHAT IS NOT FUNDED No grants are normally given to individuals by many of the trusts (though a number of them fund bursary schemes and the like operated by other organisations). Grants are not made for educational fees or expeditions.
FINANCES *Grants* £114,500,000
OTHER INFORMATION The trusts are: Gatsby Charitable Foundation; Linbury Trust; Monument Trust; True Colours Trust; Jerusalem Trust; Headley Trust; Kay Kendal Leukaemia Fund; Ashden Trust; Staples Trust; J J Charitable Trust; Alan and Babette Sainsbury Trust; Three Guineas Trust; Glass-House Trust; Woodward Charitable Trust; Mark Leonard Trust; Tedworth Trust; and the Indigo Trust.
HOW TO APPLY 'Do not send more than one application. It will be considered by all relevant trusts. The trusts only fund registered charities or activities with clearly defined charitable purposes. The trustees take an active role in their grantmaking, employing a range of specialist staff and advisers to research their areas of interest and bring forward suitable proposals. Many of the trusts work closely with their chosen beneficiaries over a long period to achieve particular objectives. It should therefore be understood that the majority of unsolicited proposals we receive will be unsuccessful. As a rule the Gatsby, Glass-House, Linbury, Staples and Tedworth trusts do not consider unsolicited proposals. The other trusts will consider exceptional proposals which fit closely their specific areas of interest. There are no application forms, except in a small number of clearly defined areas: the Woodward Charitable Trust; the Kay Kendall Leukaemia Fund; the Headley Museums Archaeological Acquisition Fund.'
'Applications to all other trusts should be sent by post, with a description (strictly no more than two pages please, as any more is unlikely to be read) of the proposed project, covering: the organisation – explaining its charitable aims and objectives, and giving its most recent annual income and expenditure, and current financial position – do not send a full set of accounts; the project requiring funding – why it is needed, who will benefit and in what way; the funding – breakdown of costs, any money raised so far, and how the balance will be raised. At this stage do not send supporting books, brochures, DVDs, annual reports or accounts. All applications will receive our standard acknowledgement letter. If your proposal is a candidate for support from one of the trusts, you will hear from us within eight weeks of the acknowledgement. Applicants who do not hear from us within this time must assume they have been unsuccessful.'
WHO TO APPLY TO Alan Bookbinder, Director, The Peak, 5 Wilton Road, London SW1V 1AP
Tel. 020 7410 0330 *Fax* 020 7410 0332
Website www.sfct.org.uk

■ Saint Luke's College Foundation

CC NO 306606 **ESTABLISHED** 1977
WHERE FUNDING CAN BE GIVEN UK and overseas, with some preference for Exeter and Truro.
WHO CAN BENEFIT Individuals and universities, colleges and other agencies operating at university level.
WHAT IS FUNDED *Corporate awards* are made to departments of theology and RE in universities, colleges and other agencies operating at university level, to enhance their capacity to provide theological and religious education. The awards are usually small and short-term and, consequently, priority is given to pump-priming initiatives, and other such situations where, if the initiative proves itself, it may enable the grant-holder to demonstrate success to bodies which engage in longer-term funding. *Personal awards* are made to support individuals who are studying Theology or RE; or who are undertaking research leading to a Masters' degree or PhD in these fields.
WHAT IS NOT FUNDED Funding is not available for building work or to provide bursaries for institutions to administer. Schools are not supported directly (although support is given to teachers who are taking eligible studies). Grants are not normally made for periods in excess of three years.
TYPE OF GRANT Normally for a specific project or part of a project, or for a specific course or piece of research. Grants can be made for periods of up to three years.
RANGE OF GRANTS £1,000–£5,000.
SAMPLE GRANTS University of Exeter Dept of Theology (£28,000); Exeter Diocesan Board of Education (£15,000); University College Plymouth St Mark and St John (£13,000); National Association of Teachers of Religious Education (£2,800) and South West Youth Ministries (£720).
FINANCES *Year* 2011–12 *Income* £184,004
Grants £150,145 *Assets* £3,844,387
TRUSTEES Prof. Mark Overton; The Bishop Of Exeter; Prof. Grace Davie; Dr Barbara Wintersgill; Dr Michael Wykes; David Cain; Alice Hutchings; Dick Powell; The Revd Dr David Rake; Very Revd Dr Jonathan Draper; Dr Karen Stockham; Phillip Mantell.
OTHER INFORMATION The grants total includes £21,000 to individuals.
HOW TO APPLY From 1 January each year, applicants can request an application pack from the correspondent. Applications are considered once a year and should be received by 1 May for grants starting in September.
WHO TO APPLY TO Dr David Benzie, Director, 15 St Maryhaye, Tavistock, Devon PL19 8LR
Tel. 01822 613143 *email* director@st-lukes-foundation.org.uk *Website* www.st-lukes-foundation.org.uk

■ Saint Sarkis Charity Trust

CC NO 215352 **ESTABLISHED** 1954
WHERE FUNDING CAN BE GIVEN UK and overseas.
WHO CAN BENEFIT Smaller registered charities benefiting Armenians and offenders.
WHAT IS FUNDED Primarily charitable objectives with an Armenian connection including Armenian religious buildings; and other small charities developing innovative projects to support prisoners in the UK.
WHAT IS NOT FUNDED The trust does not give grants to: individual applicants; organisations that are not registered charities; and registered charities

Think carefully about every application. Is it justified?

873

outside the UK, unless the project benefits the Armenian community in the UK and/or overseas. The trust does not fund: general appeals; core costs or salaries (as opposed to project costs); projects concerning substance abuse; or medical research.

TYPE OF GRANT Mainly confined to one-off project grants.

RANGE OF GRANTS £1,600–£71,000

SAMPLE GRANTS Armenian Church of St Sarkis (£35,000); Oxfam (£25,000); Lankelly Chase Foundation (£20,000); Centre for Armenian Information and Advice and Armenian Patriarchate (re Jerusalem Library) (£16,000 each); Tufenkian Foundation (£13,000); PRIME (£10,000); London Armenian Poor Relief (£8,500); Read Together (£5,200); and University of London (£300).

FINANCES *Year* 2011–12 *Income* £245,341 *Grants* £147,793 *Assets* £7,912,440

TRUSTEES Martin Sarkis Essayan; Boghos Parsegh (Paul) Gulbenkian; Rita Vartoukian; Robert Brian Todd.

HOW TO APPLY In writing to the correspondent. There is no standard application form so applicants should write a covering letter including: an explanation of the exact purpose of the grant; how much is needed, with details of how the budget has been arrived at; details of any other sources of income (firm commitments and those still being explored); the charity registration number; the latest annual report and audited accounts; and any plans for monitoring and evaluating the work. **Note: The trust is no longer accepting unsolicited applications for prisoner support projects.**

WHO TO APPLY TO Louisa Hooper, Secretary to the Trustees, 50 Hoxton Square, London N1 6PB *Tel.* 020 7012 1408 *email* info@saintsarkis. org.uk *Website* www.saintsarkis.org.uk

---

■ The Saintbury Trust

CC NO 326790 **ESTABLISHED** 1985

WHERE FUNDING CAN BE GIVEN West Midlands and Warwickshire (which the trust considers to be postcode areas B, CV, DY, WS and WV), Worcestershire, Herefordshire and Gloucestershire (postcode areas WR, HR and GL).

WHO CAN BENEFIT Registered charities.

WHAT IS FUNDED General charitable purposes with a preference for: addiction; arts and leisure; care of the dying; childhood and youth; community work; disability; education; environment; health; heritage; homelessness; old age; other special needs; and prisons.

WHAT IS NOT FUNDED No grants to animal charities, individuals (including individuals seeking sponsorship for challenges in support of charities), 'cold-calling' national charities or local branches of national charities. The trust only gives grants to charities outside of its beneficial area if the charity is personally known to one or more of the trustees.

RANGE OF GRANTS £500–£90,000

SAMPLE GRANTS Enham (£25,000); Rehabilitation for Addicted Prisoners Trust and Alzheimer's Research Trust (£10,000 each); Birmingham Bach Choir (£6,000); Birmingham Boys' and Girls' Union and Emmaus (£5,000 each); Birmingham Settlement and Wildfowl and Wetlands Trust (£4,000 each); University Hospital Birmingham (£3,000); The Refugee and Migrant Centre and Hearing Dogs for Deaf People (£2,000 each) and The ASHA Centre,

Sport 4 Life and Warley Woods Community Trust (£1,000 each).

FINANCES *Year* 2012 *Income* £222,079 *Grants* £172,000 *Assets* £6,272,000

TRUSTEES Victoria K. Houghton; Anne R. Thomas; Jane P. Lewis; Amanda E. Atkinson-Willes; Harry O. Forrester; C. E. Brogan.

HOW TO APPLY In writing to the correspondent. Applications are considered in twice a year, usually in April and November.

WHO TO APPLY TO J. P. Lewis, Trustee, P. O. Box 464, Abinger Hammer, Dorking, Surrey RH4 9AF *Tel.* 01306 730119 *email* saintburytrust@ btinternet.com

---

■ The Saints and Sinners Trust

CC NO 200536 **ESTABLISHED** 1961

WHERE FUNDING CAN BE GIVEN Mostly UK.

WHO CAN BENEFIT Registered charities.

WHAT IS FUNDED General charitable purposes, mainly welfare and medical. Priority is given to requests for grants sponsored by members of Saints and Sinners.

WHAT IS NOT FUNDED No grants to individuals or non-registered charities.

RANGE OF GRANTS £500–£10,000 but generally in the range of £1,000–£3,000.

SAMPLE GRANTS The Crimestoppers Trust (£128,000); The Gosling Foundation (£41,000); Marine Conservation Society and South Bucks Riding for the Disabled (£5,000 each); National Talking Newspapers and Magazines (£3,000); Police Rehabilitation Trust, Cowes Sea Cadets and The Stroke Association (£2,000 each) and International Childcare Trust, UCanDoIT and Sandy Gail's Afghanistan Appeal (£1,000 each).

FINANCES *Year* 2012 *Income* £97,257 *Grants* £251,279 *Assets* £79,877

TRUSTEES N. W. Benson; Sir Donald Gosling; David Edwards; I. A. N. Irvine.

HOW TO APPLY Applications are not considered unless nominated by members of the club.

WHO TO APPLY TO N. W. Benson, Trustee, Lewis Golden and Co., 40 Queen Anne Street, London W1G 9EL *Tel.* 020 7580 7313

■ The Salamander Charitable Trust

CC NO 273657 **ESTABLISHED** 1977

WHERE FUNDING CAN BE GIVEN Worldwide.

WHO CAN BENEFIT Registered charities benefiting children, young adults, people disadvantaged by poverty and people who have disabilities.

WHAT IS FUNDED The trust has a list of charities, in the fields of advancement of education and religion, and relief of poverty or physical disability, to which it gives on an annual basis. No other charities are funded.

WHAT IS NOT FUNDED No grants to individuals. Only registered charities are supported.

RANGE OF GRANTS £250–£2,500, generally £1,000 or less.

SAMPLE GRANTS SAT-7 Trust, All Nations Christian College, All Saints in Branksome Park, Birmingham Christian College, Christian Aid, Churches Commission on overseas students, FEBA Radio, International Christian College, London Bible College, Middle East Media, Moorland College, St James Parochial Church Council in Poole, SAMS, Trinity College and Wycliffe Bible Translators.

FINANCES *Year* 2011–12 *Income* £77,000 *Grants* £73,000 *Assets* £1,569,195

TRUSTEES Sheila M. Douglas; Alison Hardwick; Phillip Douglas.

OTHER INFORMATION Grants were made to 100 organisations.

HOW TO APPLY The trust's income is fully allocated each year, mainly to regular beneficiaries. The trustees do not wish to receive any further new requests.

WHO TO APPLY TO Kate Douglas, The Old Rectory, 5 Stamford Road, South Luffenham, Oakham, Leicestershire LE15 8NT

■ The Salt Foundation

CC NO 511978   **ESTABLISHED** 1981

WHERE FUNDING CAN BE GIVEN Saltaire and Shipley.

WHO CAN BENEFIT Individuals and schools benefiting children, young adults, older people and students. During the year the foundation concentrated on its commitment to maintain one of its properties, Victoria Hall, but hopes to resume normal grantmaking in the near future.

WHAT IS FUNDED Education.

WHAT IS NOT FUNDED No grants to replace statutory funding.

TYPE OF GRANT One-off grants (although applicants may reapply), capital, project and recurring costs for funding of one year or less.

SAMPLE GRANTS Saltaire Community Festival Ltd (£6,000).

FINANCES *Year* 2011–12 *Income* £314,383 *Grants* £6,000 *Assets* £326,412

TRUSTEES Alex McClelland; Geraldine Whelan; James Flood; Robert Sowman; Ted Watson; Norman Roper; John Briggs; John Carroll; Paula Truman.

OTHER INFORMATION The foundation stated in 2009 that it has not made grant awards for the past three years because of the need to repair property for which it has responsibility.

HOW TO APPLY Usually in writing to the correspondent, however, we received notification from the correspondent in December 2013 that 'all grants have been suspended for the foreseeable future until economic climate improves'.

WHO TO APPLY TO Marjorie Davies, Clerk, 17 Springfield Road, Baildon, Shipley, Yorkshire BD17 5NA *Tel.* 01274 591508 *email* marjoriedavies@tiscali.co.uk

■ The Salt Trust

CC NO 1062133   **ESTABLISHED** 1977

WHERE FUNDING CAN BE GIVEN UK.

WHO CAN BENEFIT Charitable organisations.

WHAT IS FUNDED General charitable purposes.

SAMPLE GRANTS The trust stated that it 'supported an aid organisation, a food bank, a crisis debt counselling centre, church workers, hardship grants, and other works in keeping with the purposes of the charity.'

FINANCES *Year* 2011–12 *Income* £47,674 *Grants* £41,465 *Assets* £14,878

TRUSTEES Norman Adams; Dianne Parsons; Robert Parsons; Stephen Williams.

HOW TO APPLY The trust does not accept unsolicited applications.

WHO TO APPLY TO Jill Jameson, 10 Tarragon Way, Pontprennau, Cardiff CF23 8SN *Tel.* 02920 733422

■ Salters' Charitable Foundation

CC NO 328258   **ESTABLISHED** 1989

WHERE FUNDING CAN BE GIVEN Greater London and the UK

WHO CAN BENEFIT Priority is given to funding small nationwide charities and organisations connected with the City of London, where the trusts contribution would make a 'real difference'. As a matter of general policy, the company supports those charities where Salters are involved.

WHAT IS FUNDED The trust makes donations for a wide range of charitable purposes including, children and young people, health, homelessness, the developing world, the environment and members of the armed forces.

WHAT IS NOT FUNDED See the foundation's guidelines for information on restrictions.

TYPE OF GRANT Project grants – three year grants of up to £20,000; General grants – a limited amount of small donations up to £3,000.

RANGE OF GRANTS £150– £9,000 but mostly under £2,000.

SAMPLE GRANTS Mental Health Foundation (£18,000); Excellent Development Ltd (£17,000); Target Tuberculosis (£15,000); Drapers' Charitable Fund (£10,000); The Guildhall School Trust (£7,500); Arkwright Scholarships Trust (£4,000); The Passage (£2,000); The Royal Navy Benevolent Trust and Rehabilitation for Addicted Prisoners Trust (£1,500 each) and WWF UK (£500).

FINANCES *Year* 2011–12 *Income* £512,739 *Grants* £192,244 *Assets* £661,404

TRUSTEE The Salters' Company.

OTHER INFORMATION In June 2010 the foundation was amalgamated with the Salters' Company Charity for Relief of Need (charity number: 244092).

HOW TO APPLY Applicants must follow the relevant Guidelines ('Project Grant' or 'General Support') depending on the type of grant they are requesting: Project Grant applicants need to fill in an application form, available from the foundation's website when the programme is open; General Support applicants need to submit a covering letter, supporting document and annual report and accounts. Applications can be made via email or post. All supported organisations are regularly reviewed and visited by the Charities Development Manager, members of the Charity Committee and other interested parties within the Company.

WHO TO APPLY TO Vicky Chant, Charities Development Manager, The Salters' Company, Salters' Hall, 4 Fore Street, London EC2Y 5DE *Tel.* 020 7588 5216 *email* charities@salters. co.uk *Website* www.salters.co.uk

■ The Andrew Salvesen Charitable Trust

SC NO SC008000   **ESTABLISHED** 1989

WHERE FUNDING CAN BE GIVEN UK, with a preference for Scotland.

WHO CAN BENEFIT Organisations benefiting children who are ill and people who are disabled or homeless.

WHAT IS FUNDED Grants are made to a variety of charitable organisations who work for sick children, people who are disabled, homeless people and a range of other causes.

WHAT IS NOT FUNDED No grants to individuals.

SAMPLE GRANTS Previous beneficiaries have included Bield Housing Trust, William Higgins Marathon Account, Multiple Sclerosis Society in Scotland,

Royal Zoological Society of Scotland, Sail Training Association, Scottish Down's Syndrome Association and Sick Kids Appeal.
FINANCES *Year* 2011–12 *Income* £641,598 *Grants* £1,264,864
TRUSTEES A. C. Salvesen; Ms K. Turner; V. Lall.
HOW TO APPLY The trustees only support organisations known to them through their personal contacts. The trust has previously stated that all applications sent to them are 'thrown in the bin'.
WHO TO APPLY The Trustees, c/o Meston Reid and Co., 12 Carden Place, Aberdeen AB10 1UR *Tel.* 01224 625554 *email* info@mestonreid.com

■ Basil Samuel Charitable Trust

CC NO 206579   **ESTABLISHED** 1959
WHERE FUNDING CAN BE GIVEN Worldwide, in practice, mainly UK.
WHO CAN BENEFIT Registered charities.
WHAT IS FUNDED General charitable purposes but mainly, medical, socially supportive, educational and cultural charities.
WHAT IS NOT FUNDED Only applications from registered charities are considered.
TYPE OF GRANT 'One-off' and recurring.
RANGE OF GRANTS £1,000–£100,000
SAMPLE GRANTS Macmillan Cancer Support (£48,000); Historic Royal Palaces, National Hospital for Neurology and Neurosurgery and Westminster Abbey Foundation (£25,000 each); Jewish care (£10,000); Chair Lifeline Cancer Care, London's Air Ambulance and The Samaritans (£5,000 each); M.E.R.L.I.N (£2,000 each) and Friends of the Elderly and The National Autistic Society (£1,000 each).
FINANCES *Year* 2011–12 *Income* £388,275 *Grants* £397,500 *Assets* £9,760,678
TRUSTEES Coral Samuel; Richard M. Peskin.
HOW TO APPLY In writing to the correspondent. The trustees meet on a formal basis annually and regularly on an informal basis to discuss proposals for individual donations.
WHO TO APPLY TO Coral Samuel, Trustee, c/o Smith and Williamson, 25 Moorgate, London EC2R 6AY *Tel.* 020 7131 4376

■ Coral Samuel Charitable Trust

CC NO 239677   **ESTABLISHED** 1962
WHERE FUNDING CAN BE GIVEN UK.
WHO CAN BENEFIT Registered charities only.
WHAT IS FUNDED General charitable purposes, including educational, cultural and socially supportive charities.
WHAT IS NOT FUNDED Grants are only made to registered charities.
RANGE OF GRANTS £350–£10,000.
SAMPLE GRANTS Historic Royal Palaces (£25,000); The Foundation of the College of St George (£12,000); Glyndebourne Arts Trust (£10,000); Academy of St Martin-in-the-Fields, Jewish Music Institute and The Royal Horticultural Society (£5,000 each); Save Britain's Heritage (£2,000); Chicken Shed Theatre Co. and The Hertford House Trust (£1,000 each) and Museum of London (£500).
FINANCES *Year* 2011–12 *Income* £210,819 *Grants* £142,500 *Assets* £5,179,067
TRUSTEES Coral Samuel; Peter Fineman.
HOW TO APPLY In writing to the correspondent.
WHO TO APPLY TO Coral Samuel, Trustee, c/o Smith and Williamson, 25 Moorgate, London EC2R 6AY *Tel.* 020 7131 4376

■ The M. J. Samuel Charitable Trust

CC NO 327013   **ESTABLISHED** 1985
WHERE FUNDING CAN BE GIVEN UK and overseas.
WHO CAN BENEFIT Charitable organisations.
WHAT IS FUNDED The trust supports a wide range of causes, many of them Jewish, environmental or to do with mental health.
WHAT IS NOT FUNDED No grants to individuals.
TYPE OF GRANT Core costs, project and research. Funding of up to two years will be considered.
SAMPLE GRANTS The Game and Wildlife Conservation Trust (£30,000); Oxfam (£25,000); Fact Check (£15,000); Spey Foundation (£10,000); Dress for Success London (£3,000); Osteoporosis Society (£2,000); Kindwood College Appeal (£1,500) and Mells Church of England School and The Anna Freud Centre (£1,000 each).
FINANCES *Year* 2011–12 *Income* £101,103 *Grants* £101,950 *Assets* £3,524,897
TRUSTEES Hon. Michael Samuel; Hon. Julia A. Samuel; Viscount Bearsted.
OTHER INFORMATION In addition 13 other donations were made to institutions of less than £1,000 each, totalling £4,000.
HOW TO APPLY In writing to the correspondent. The trustees have regular contact during the year to consider recommendations for, and make final decisions on, the awarding of grants.
WHO TO APPLY TO Lindsay Sutton, Secretary, Mells Park, Mells, Frome, Somerset BA11 3QB *Tel.* 020 7402 0602

■ The Peter Samuel Charitable Trust

CC NO 269065   **ESTABLISHED** 1975
WHERE FUNDING CAN BE GIVEN UK, with some preference for local organisations in South Berkshire, Highlands of Scotland and East Somerset.
WHO CAN BENEFIT Registered charities benefiting medical professionals, scientists, at-risk groups and people disadvantaged by poverty.
WHAT IS FUNDED Medical sciences, the quality of life in local areas, heritage and land/forestry restoration.
WHAT IS NOT FUNDED No grants to purely local charities outside Berkshire or to individuals.
TYPE OF GRANT Single and annual donations.
RANGE OF GRANTS £200–£20,000.
SAMPLE GRANTS The Game and Wildlife Conservation Trust and Marie Curie Cancer Care (£10,000 each); Anna Freud Centre (£7,000); Child Bereavement Trust (£6,000); Oxfam (£5,000); Community Security Trust and World Jewish Relief (£2,000 each); The Countryside Foundation for Education and Highland Hospice (£1,000 each) and Connexions Thames Valley and Anthony Nolan (£500 each).
FINANCES *Year* 2011–12 *Income* £113,430 *Grants* £91,700 *Assets* £3,875,212
TRUSTEES Hon. Viscount Bearsted; Hon. Michael Samuel.
OTHER INFORMATION The Hon Michael Samuel is also a trustee of: Col. Wilfred Horatio Micholls Deceased Charitable Trust Fund (Charity Commission no. 267472); The Hon. A G Samuel Charitable Trust (Charity Commission no. 1090481); The M J Samuel Charitable Trust (Charity Commission no. 327013); and The Peter Samuel Royal Free Fund (Charity Commission no. 200049).
HOW TO APPLY In writing to the correspondent. Trustees meet twice-yearly.

WHO TO APPLY TO Jenny Dance, Administrator, The Estate Office, Farley Hall, Castle Road, Farley Hill, Berkshire RG7 1UL *Tel.* 01189 730047 *email* pa@farleyfarms.co.uk

■ The Samworth Foundation

CC NO 265647   ESTABLISHED 1973
WHERE FUNDING CAN BE GIVEN Derby, Leicestershire, Nottinghamshire and Africa.
WHO CAN BENEFIT Registered charities only.
WHAT IS FUNDED General charitable purposes.
WHAT IS NOT FUNDED No grants to individuals.
RANGE OF GRANTS Between £10 and £100,000.
SAMPLE GRANTS Tearfund (FACT) (£57,000); Camfed, New Londoner's Project and Barnardo's (£50,000 each); New Horizon Youth Centre and Restless Development Zimbabwe (£49,000 each); The Women's Trust Project (£30,000); Médecins Sans Frontières (£25,000); University of Leicester (£20,000); Belvoir Castle Cricket Trust (£12,000); Compassion UK and Leicestershire and Rutland Crimebeat (£5,000 each); and Sue Ryder Care and Thorpe Satchville Village Hall (£1,000 each).
FINANCES *Year* 2011–12 *Income* £2,646,633 *Grants* £759,156 *Assets* £13,267,542
TRUSTEES Bob Dowson; Alison Price; Viccy Stott.
OTHER INFORMATION Grants were made to 35 organisations.
HOW TO APPLY The foundation's grantmaking policy is to support a limited number of causes known to the trustees. Unsolicited applications are not normally considered.
WHO TO APPLY TO W. A. Bateman, c/o Samworth Brothers (Holdings) Ltd, Chetwode House, 1 Samworth Way, Melton Mowbray, Leicestershire LE13 1GA *Tel.* 01664 414500 *Fax* 01664 414501

■ The Sandhu Charitable Foundation

CC NO 1114236   ESTABLISHED 2006
WHERE FUNDING CAN BE GIVEN Worldwide.
WHO CAN BENEFIT Charities and charitable causes
WHAT IS FUNDED General charitable purposes
SAMPLE GRANTS Variety, The Children's Charity (£32,500); Anne Frank Trust (£20,500); Magic Bus UK (£20,000); Latymer Foundation (£10,000); Choices Ealing, Coram, Enterprise Education Trust, Friendship Works Listening Books, Smile Train UK, Tree of Hope Children's Charity and The Ear Foundation (£5,000 each); Cystic Fibrosis and RNLI (£4,000 each); and EveryChild and Sightsavers (£3,000 each).
FINANCES *Year* 2011–12 *Income* £650,253 *Grants* £212,000 *Assets* £4,570,991
TRUSTEES Bim Sandhu, Chair; Sean Carey.
HOW TO APPLY The charity supports individual charities or charitable causes, mainly on a single donation basis, which the trustees identify.
WHO TO APPLY TO The Trustees, First Floor, Santon House, 53–55 Uxbridge Road, Ealing, London W5 5SA *Tel.* 020 3478 3900 *email* nsteele@thesantongroup.com

■ The Sandra Charitable Trust

CC NO 327492   ESTABLISHED 1987
WHERE FUNDING CAN BE GIVEN UK with slight preference for south east England.
WHO CAN BENEFIT Organisations benefiting children and young people, hospices, education, people with disabilities, people disadvantaged by poverty, the arts, and individual grants for nurses.
WHAT IS FUNDED Animal welfare and research, environmental protection, social welfare, health and youth development.
WHAT IS NOT FUNDED No grants to individuals other than nurses.
TYPE OF GRANT One-off and recurring.
RANGE OF GRANTS Typically £5,000 or less.
SAMPLE GRANTS Kids (£50,000); The Florence Nightingale Foundation and Goring Health Charities (£30,000 each); Second Chance (£28,000); Arundel Castle Cricket Foundation (£25,000); Sparks (£17,000); Project Rainbow and Vale House (£10,000 each); Barnardo's and the National Portrait Gallery (£5,000 each); Children with Cancer UK (£4,000); Changing Faces and the North Berwick Pipe Band (£3,000 each); Thames Valley Air Ambulance and the Pegasus School Trust (£2,000 each); and Alzheimer's Research UK, Families Against Neuroblastoma, Rotary Doctor Bank and Woodland Heritage (£1,000 each).
FINANCES *Year* 2011–12 *Income* £686,007 *Grants* £605,923 *Assets* £17,598,895
TRUSTEES Richard Moore; Michael Macfadyen.
OTHER INFORMATION £517,500 was donated to 117 organisations and £88,500 to 149 individuals.
HOW TO APPLY The trust states that 'unsolicited applications are not requested, as the trustees prefer to support charities whose work they have researched ... the trustees receives a very high number of grant applications which are mostly unsuccessful'.
WHO TO APPLY TO Keith Lawrence, Secretary, c/o Moore Stephens, 150 Aldersgate Street, London EC1A 4AB *Tel.* 020 7334 9191 *Fax* 020 7651 1953 *email* keith.lawrence@moorestephens.com

■ The Sands Family Trust

CC NO 1136909   ESTABLISHED 2010
WHERE FUNDING CAN BE GIVEN Undefined, in practice the UK and overseas.
WHO CAN BENEFIT Organisations and individuals.
WHAT IS FUNDED General charitable purposes. Support is currently focused on the 'advancement of education, the relief of poverty and support and encouragement of the performing arts.'
FINANCES *Year* 2011–12 *Income* £8,202
TRUSTEES Cripps Trust Corporation Ltd; Betsy Tobin; Peter Sands.
OTHER INFORMATION In 2011–12 the trust had a total expenditure of £151,597.
HOW TO APPLY In writing to the correspondent.
WHO TO APPLY TO Heartwood Wealth Management, Administrator, c/o Heartwood Wealth Management, 77 Mount Ephraim, Tunbridge Wells, Kent TN4 8BS *Tel.* 01892 701801 *email* info@heartwoodwealth.com

■ Santander UK Foundation Limited

CC NO 803655 **ESTABLISHED** 1990

WHERE FUNDING CAN BE GIVEN UK, with a particular interest in the London Borough of Camden; Milton Keynes covering Buckinghamshire, Northamptonshire and Bedfordshire; Leicestershire and Rutland; Sheffield covering South Yorkshire; Bradford covering West Yorkshire; Teesside covering the area from Redcar to Darlington and Sunderland; Merseyside; Greater Glasgow; and Northern Ireland.

WHO CAN BENEFIT Registered, excepted or exempt charities. Industrial and Provident societies can only be supported if they are founded under charitable, not membership, rules.

WHAT IS FUNDED The Santander Foundation has two grants programmes to help disadvantaged people in the UK: *Community Plus* provides grants of up to £5,000. The scheme is open to small local UK charities or local projects of national charities with funding available to cover salaries, equipment or materials and *Central Fund* offers grants of up to £10,000. The scheme is open to charities and Credit Unions anywhere in the UK for projects related to education, training or financial capability.

WHAT IS NOT FUNDED Donations are not made for: statutory duties; part of a major capital appeal; a specific individual (this includes Gap Year funding, overseas travel, medical treatment or holidays); lobbying or political parties; the benefit of a single religious or single ethnic group; causes outside the UK; gaining specialist school status; commercial sponsorship or for fundraising events, conferences or advertising.

TYPE OF GRANT All funding is for one off donations. Grants are available to buy tangible items such as equipment or training materials. Grants are also available to fund project costs such as sessional worker fees, salaries, room hire or other costs incurred in the delivery of the charitable priorities.

RANGE OF GRANTS Usually up to £10,000.

SAMPLE GRANTS RDA Centre in Cleveland and Voluntary Action South Leicestershire (£30,000 each); Marie Curie Cancer Care (£28,000) and Wigton Youth Station, Synthonia Scout Group, Lonsdale District Carers, Red Balloon Learner Centre Merseyside, Eden Credit Union Study Group, Howgill Family Centre and Big Issue Foundation (£10,000 each).

FINANCES *Year* 2012 *Income* £5,347,327 *Grants* £4,127,489 *Assets* £12,366,094

TRUSTEES Lord Burns; Simon Lloyd; Jennifer Scardino; Steven Williams; Angela Wakelin.

OTHER INFORMATION In 2012 grants were made to 2,037 organisations.

HOW TO APPLY The following guidance on making an application is given on the foundation's website. 'We have made applying to us as straightforward as possible and do not use an application form. We operate a rolling programme, with no deadlines for applications. Download and print off the grant application cover sheet which you can use as a checklist as you put together your application [available from the foundation's website]. You need to write us a letter on the headed notepaper of your charity which should include your registered charity number or whatever is appropriate for your charitable status. The letter should include the following: how much you are asking for?; what will this pay for? Include a simple budget detailing the main costs; how will disadvantaged people directly benefit? Include an estimate of the long term difference this grant will make; how does this meet one or both of our charitable priorities?; if the funding is for an existing project, tell us how our funding fits your funding strategy and what the project has achieved so far; if the funding is for a new project, tell us how you identified the need for this piece of work; If you are asking for revenue funding for salaries or running costs tell us what your funding strategy is to replace this funding at the end of our grant; if applicable, which other funders are you applying to? Make sure the letter is signed by two people, one of whom must be a trustee of the charity. If it helps explain what your project will do, you may want to include a flyer, newsletter or other sample training material that is produced for the beneficiaries. Do **not** include: annual reports and accounts; DVDs or CDs; business plan or constitution; any other bulky items, plastic binders or covers. If you want confirmation that we have received your application, enclose a self-addressed postcard or envelope with your application letter. We will post this to you when we open your application. If you do not receive any other correspondence from us within six weeks then you should assume that your application has been unsuccessful. We regret that due to the very high volume of requests received, we do not notify unsuccessful applicants or offer feedback on why your application has not been successful. We regret that we cannot accept online or emailed applications.'

WHO TO APPLY TO Alan Eagle, Foundation Manager, Santander House, 201 Grafton Gate East, Milton Keynes MK9 1AN *Tel.* 01908 343224 *email* grants@santander.co.uk *Website* www.santanderfoundation.org.uk

■ The Sants Charitable Trust

CC NO 1078555 **ESTABLISHED** 1999

WHERE FUNDING CAN BE GIVEN UK.

WHO CAN BENEFIT Organisations.

WHAT IS FUNDED General charitable purposes.

RANGE OF GRANTS £300–£60,000

SAMPLE GRANTS Holy Trinity Brompton (£26,000); William Wilberforce Trust (£10,000); Children in Crisis, Family Links and Footsteps Foundation (£5,000 each); Wings (£3,000); Harry Mahon Cancer Research Trust and Tube Station (£1,000 each); trinity College (£300) and The Boxing Academy (£100).

FINANCES *Year* 2011–12 *Income* £99,387 *Grants* £57,486 *Assets* £1,091,495

TRUSTEES Alexander Sants; Caroline Sants; Hector W. H. Sants; John H. Ovens.

HOW TO APPLY In writing to the correspondent.

WHO TO APPLY TO The Trustees, 17 Bradmore Road, Oxford OX2 6QP *Tel.* 01865 310813

■ The Peter Saunders Trust

CC NO 1108153 **ESTABLISHED** 2005

WHERE FUNDING CAN BE GIVEN South Meirionnydd, Wales.

WHO CAN BENEFIT Charities, community groups and individuals.

WHAT IS FUNDED General charitable purposes.

WHAT IS NOT FUNDED No grants to students for university education.

TYPE OF GRANT One-off, recurrent.

RANGE OF GRANTS Up to £20,000

SAMPLE GRANTS Recent grants to organisations have included: Neuadd Egryn – restoration of the village hall (£20,000) and Ensemble Cymru – to develop classical music workshops in schools.

878

Does the trust you have chosen match your needs? Haphazard applications waste postage and time

FINANCES *Year* 2012–13 *Income* £2,871 *Grants* £70,000.

TRUSTEES Lynda Bennett; Peter Saunders; Ifor Williams; Theresa Hartland; Keith Bartlett; Ieuan Saunders.

OTHER INFORMATION Grants are also made to individuals to promote educational opportunities.

HOW TO APPLY The website notes: 'We deliberately do not have an application form because each application will be different. Simply write to us and explain the merits of your project. There is some information that we need to help the trustees make a decision.' Detailed guidelines on what to include are available from the trust's website.

'Applications from an organisation should be accompanied by a copy of your last set of accounts and a copy of your constitution, if available.'

WHO TO APPLY TO Peter Saunders, Founding Trustee, c/o The Sure Chill Company, Pendre, Tywyn, Gwynedd LL36 9LW *Tel.* 01654 713939 *email* enquiries@petersaunderstrust.co.uk *Website* www.petersaunderstrust.co.uk

....

■ The Scarfe Charitable Trust

CC NO 275535　　　　**ESTABLISHED** 1978
WHERE FUNDING CAN BE GIVEN UK, with an emphasis on Suffolk.

WHO CAN BENEFIT Individuals and organisations working in the fields of arts, music, medical research and the environment.

WHAT IS FUNDED This trust will consider funding: conservation; environmental interests; medical research; hospices; arts and arts facilities; churches; religious ancillary buildings; art galleries and cultural centres; libraries and museums; and theatres and opera houses.

TYPE OF GRANT Capital, core costs, one-off, project, research, recurring costs and running costs. Funding is normally for one year or less.

RANGE OF GRANTS £50–£10,000.

SAMPLE GRANTS Aldeburgh Music (£8,000); Gainsborough's House and Woodbridge Tide Mill (£2,500); Aldeburgh Young Musicians (£1,800); East Anglia's Children's Hospices, John Peel Centre for Creative Arts and Suffolk Wildlife Trust (£1,000 each); Rosemary Hinton and Happy Days (£750 each); Canine Partners and Royal Northern College of Music (£500 each); Action on Hearing Loss, SCOPE and The Salvation Army (£375 each); St Peters Parochial Church Council (£200) and Friends of the Royal Academy (£90).

FINANCES *Year* 2011–12 *Income* £56,800 *Grants* £110,304 *Assets* £1,208,664

TRUSTEES Sean McTernan; Eric Maule; John McCarthy.

HOW TO APPLY In writing to the correspondent by post or email. The trustees meet quarterly to consider applications.

WHO TO APPLY TO Eric Maule, Trustee, Salix House, Falkenham, Ipswich, Suffolk IP10 0QY *Tel.* 01394 448339 *Fax* 01394 448339 *email* ericmaule@hotmail.com

....

■ The Schapira Charitable Trust

CC NO 328435　　　　**ESTABLISHED** 1989
WHERE FUNDING CAN BE GIVEN UK.

WHO CAN BENEFIT Organisations benefiting Jewish people.

WHAT IS FUNDED Jewish charitable purposes, health and education generally.

RANGE OF GRANTS £500–£136,000.

SAMPLE GRANTS British Friends of the Rabbi Meir Baal Hanes Charity (Kollel Shromrel Hachomos) (£136,000); The New Rachmistrivke Synagogue Trust (£91,000); Emuno Educational Centre Limited (£84,000); Kahal Chassidim Bobov (£33,000); Friends of Mir (£22,000); Keren Association Limited (£17,000); United Jewish Israel Appeal (£10,000); Rowanville Limited (£8,400); Entindale Ltd (£5,500); Yeshivas Lev Simcha Limited (£2,000) and Friends of Sanz Institutions (£1,000).

FINANCES *Year* 2011 *Income* £215,355 *Grants* £608,850 *Assets* £5,958,543

TRUSTEES Isaac Y. Schapira; Michael Neuberger; Suzanne L. Schapira.

HOW TO APPLY In writing to the correspondent.

WHO TO APPLY TO Isaac Yehuda Schapira, Trustee, 2 Dancastle Court, 14 Arcadia Avenue, Finchley, London N3 2JU *Tel.* 020 8371 0381 *email* londonoffice@istrad.com

....

■ The Annie Schiff Charitable Trust

CC NO 265401　　　　**ESTABLISHED** 1973
WHERE FUNDING CAN BE GIVEN UK, overseas.

WHO CAN BENEFIT Orthodox Jewish institutions supporting religious, educational and relief of poverty aims.

WHAT IS FUNDED The relief of poverty generally and payment to needy individuals of the Jewish faith, for the advancement of education and religion.

WHAT IS NOT FUNDED No support for individuals and non-recognised institutions.

RANGE OF GRANTS £400–£22,000.

SAMPLE GRANTS Friends of Beis Yisrael Trust and Menorah Grammar School Trust (£15,000 each); Elanore Limited (£10,000); WST Charity Limited (£8,000); Friends of Ohel Moshe (£6,000); Tifres High School, EMET and Yesamech Levav Trust (£5,000 each); North West Separdish Synagogue (£3,000); British Friends of Nadvorne (£1,500); Golders Charitable Trust (£1,100); Beth Jacob Grammar School for Girls Limited (£1,000) and Ezra U'Marpeh (£500).

FINANCES *Year* 2011–12 *Income* £62,538 *Grants* £115,235 *Assets* £86,193

TRUSTEES Joseph Pearlman; Ruth Pearlman.

HOW TO APPLY In writing to the correspondent. Grants are generally made only to registered charities.

WHO TO APPLY TO Joseph Pearlman, Trustee, 8 Highfield Gardens, London NW11 9HB *Tel.* 020 8458 9266

....

■ The Schmidt-Bodner Charitable Trust

CC NO 283014　　　　**ESTABLISHED** 1981
WHERE FUNDING CAN BE GIVEN UK and overseas.

WHO CAN BENEFIT Jewish organisations and other registered charities.

WHAT IS FUNDED Health, education and welfare.

RANGE OF GRANTS £3,000–£50,000.

SAMPLE GRANTS Nightingale House (£60,000); Menorah High School for Girls and Oak Family UK (£50,000 each); World Jewish Relief (£15,500); Prostate Action (£10,000); and Chabad Lubavich UK, the Prince's Trust and United Jewish Israel Appeal (£5,000 each).

FINANCES *Year* 2011–12 *Income* £42,061 *Grants* £241,100 *Assets* £2,179,991

TRUSTEES Harvey Rosenblatt; Daniel Dover; Martin Paisner.

HOW TO APPLY In writing to the correspondent. 'All applications received are considered by the trustees on their own merit for suitability of funding.'

WHO TO APPLY TO Harvey Rosenblatt, Trustee, 5 Fitzhardinge Street, London W1H 6ED *Tel.* 020 7486 3111

....

■ The R. H. Scholes Charitable Trust

CC NO 267023   ESTABLISHED 1974
WHERE FUNDING CAN BE GIVEN England.
WHO CAN BENEFIT Registered charities, particularly those benefiting children and young adults, the Church of England, and people who are disabled or disadvantaged by poverty.
WHAT IS FUNDED Preference is given to charities that the trustees have a special interest in, knowledge of, or association with. If any new charities are to be supported it will be in the fields helping children and young people who are disadvantaged or disabled. Particularly charities working in the fields of: residential facilities; respite and sheltered accommodation; Anglican bodies; music and opera; special schools and special needs education; training for community development; care in the community; day centres; holidays and outings; play schemes; and research into medicine.
WHAT IS NOT FUNDED Grants only to registered charities. No grants to individuals, animal charities, expeditions or scholarships. The trust tries not to make grants to more than one charity operating in a particular field, and does not make grants to charities outside England.
TYPE OF GRANT Both recurrent and one-off grants are made depending upon the needs of the beneficiary. Core costs, project and research. Funding for more than three years will be considered.
RANGE OF GRANTS £100–£1,200.
SAMPLE GRANTS Church of England Pensions Board, the Friends of Lancing Chapel and National Churches Trust.
FINANCES *Year* 2011–12 *Income* £22,269 *Grants* £20,000
TRUSTEES Roger Pattison; Henrietta Sleeman.
HOW TO APPLY The trust has informed us that all of its funds are fully committed and they cannot accept unsolicited applications.
WHO TO APPLY TO Roger Pattison, Trustee, Danehurst Corner, Danehurst Crescent, Horsham, West Sussex RH13 5HS *Tel.* 01403 263482 *email* roger@rogpat.plus.com

....

■ The Schreib Trust

CC NO 275240   ESTABLISHED 1977
WHERE FUNDING CAN BE GIVEN UK.
WHO CAN BENEFIT Jewish people, especially those disadvantaged by poverty.
WHAT IS FUNDED Relief of poverty and advancement of religion and religious education.
RANGE OF GRANTS Around £500–£80,000.
SAMPLE GRANTS Previous beneficiaries have included: Lolev, Yad Eliezer, Ponovitz, Craven Walk Charity Trust, Shaar Hatalmud, Beis Rochel, Beth Jacob Building Fund, Toiras Chesed and Oneg Shabbos.
FINANCES *Year* 2011–12 *Income* £479,876 *Grants* £444,804 *Assets* £430,338

TRUSTEES A. Green; R. Niederman; D. Schreiber; I. Schreiber.
OTHER INFORMATION No grants list was available.
HOW TO APPLY In writing to the correspondent.
WHO TO APPLY TO Rivka Niederman, Trustee, 147 Stamford Hill, London N16 5LG *Tel.* 020 8802 5492

....

■ The Schreiber Charitable Trust

CC NO 264735   ESTABLISHED 1972
WHERE FUNDING CAN BE GIVEN UK.
WHO CAN BENEFIT Registered charities benefiting Jewish people.
WHAT IS FUNDED Jewish with a preference for education, social welfare and medical causes.
RANGE OF GRANTS £100–£50,000.
SAMPLE GRANTS Friends of Rabbinical College Kol Tora, Jerusalem Foundation, SOFT, Gateshead Talmudical College, Dalaid Limited and Aish Hatorah UK Limited.
FINANCES *Year* 2011–12 *Income* £310,746 *Grants* £250,000
TRUSTEES Graham S. Morris; David A. Schreiber; Sara Schreiber.
HOW TO APPLY The trust states that the trustees 'regularly appraise new opportunities for direct charitable expenditure and actively seek suitable causes to reduce the unrestricted fund to the appropriate level'.
WHO TO APPLY TO Graham S. Morris, Trustee, PO Box 35547, The Exchange, 4 Brent Cross Gardens, London NW4 3WH *Tel.* 020 8457 6500 *email* graham@schreibers.com

....

■ Schroder Charity Trust

CC NO 214050   ESTABLISHED 1944
WHERE FUNDING CAN BE GIVEN Worldwide, in practice mainly UK.
WHO CAN BENEFIT Preference for UK-registered charities with a proven track record and those in which the trust has a special interest.
WHAT IS FUNDED General charitable purposes, particularly: health and welfare, community, education, international relief and development, young people, arts, culture and heritage, the environment and rural issues.
WHAT IS NOT FUNDED No grants to individuals.
TYPE OF GRANT One-off and recurring.
RANGE OF GRANTS Up to £5,000.
SAMPLE GRANTS Army Benevolent Fund; Alzheimer's Research UK; Asperger's Syndrome Foundation; Civil Liberties Trust; Country Holidays for Inner City Kids; Foundation for Social Improvement; Game Conservancy Trust; Listening Books; National Youth Theatre; Raleigh International Trust; Samaritans; Toynbee Hall UK; and the Young Women's Christian Association (YWCA). All grants were for £5,000 or less.
FINANCES *Year* 2011–12 *Income* £201,212 *Grants* £159,382 *Assets* £7,454,607
TRUSTEES Claire Fitzalan Howard; Charmaine Mallinckrodt; Bruno Schroder; T. B. Schroder; Leonie Fane; Frederick Schroder.
HOW TO APPLY In writing to the correspondent. Applicants should briefly state their case and enclose a copy of their latest accounts or annual review. Requests will be acknowledged in writing. The trust does not have the capacity to correspond with organisations on the progress of their application. Therefore, if you have not heard from the trust after six months, you can assume that the application has not been successful.

WHO TO APPLY TO Sally Yates, Secretary,
81 Rivington Street, London EC2A 3AY

■ The Schroder Foundation

CC NO 1107479   **ESTABLISHED** 2005
WHERE FUNDING CAN BE GIVEN Worldwide, in practice mainly UK.
WHO CAN BENEFIT Charitable causes with a previous track record and organisations in which the foundation has a special interest.
WHAT IS FUNDED General mainly within the areas of the environment, education, arts, culture and heritage, social welfare, the community and international relief and development.
SAMPLE GRANTS Schroder Fund at the University of Cambridge (£1.7 million) – the donation is part of a long-standing relationship with the university and pays for the Schroder Professorship of German and the study of German there; Freya van Moltke Stiftung (£88,000); Carbon Disclosure Project, Priors Court Foundation and Voluntary Services Overseas (£50,000 each); School Home Support (£35,000); London Youth Support Trust (£30,000); Fauna and Flora International (£25,000); West London Action for Children (£20,000); Cumberland Lodge – Windsor, One Voice Europe and the Royal National Institute for the Deaf (£10,000 each).
FINANCES *Year* 2011–12 *Income* £1,558,088 *Grants* £2,665,396 *Assets* £10,580,312
TRUSTEES Bruno Schroder, Chair; Edward Mallinckrodt; Nicholas Ferguson; Charmaine Mallinckrodt; Leonie Fane; Claire Howard; Richard Robinson; Philip Mallinckrodt.
HOW TO APPLY This trust **does not** respond to unsolicited applications. 'The trustees identify projects and organisations they wish to support and the foundation does not make grants to people or organisations who apply speculatively.'
WHO TO APPLY TO Sally Yates, Secretary,
81 Rivington Street, London EC2A 3AY

■ The Schuster Charitable Trust

CC NO 234580   **ESTABLISHED** 1964
WHERE FUNDING CAN BE GIVEN UK, with a particular interest in Oxfordshire.
WHO CAN BENEFIT Charitable and voluntary organisations.
WHAT IS FUNDED General charitable purposes.
WHAT IS NOT FUNDED No grants to individuals.
SAMPLE GRANTS Worton Parochial Church Council (£5,000); Stephen Spender Trust, Oxfordshire Association for Young People, Cancer Research and Hope and Homes for Children (£2,000 each); Action on Addiction (£1,500); Banbury Young Homelessness Project, Bridwell Historical Gardens, Oxford Family Mediation and Princess Royal Trust for Carers (£1,000 each) and Listening Books and PDSA (£500 each).
FINANCES *Year* 2011–12 *Income* £39,614 *Grants* £38,269 *Assets* £111,651
TRUSTEES Joanna Clarke; Richard Schuster; Peter Schuster.
HOW TO APPLY In writing to the correspondent, for consideration at meetings twice a year in June and December. No reply is made without an sae.
WHO TO APPLY TO Joanna Clarke, Trustee, New House Farm, Nether Worton, Chipping Norton, Oxon OX7 7AX

■ Foundation Scotland

SC NO SC022910   **ESTABLISHED** 1995
WHERE FUNDING CAN BE GIVEN Scotland.
WHO CAN BENEFIT Small organisations helping to build and sustain local communities.
WHAT IS FUNDED There are two broad programmes, under which there are a range of different funds.
Scotland-wide programmes – includes express grants (up to £2,000); grants for women's projects; and comic relief local communities grants.
Local grants programmes – there are a variety of programmes which benefit people in specific areas of Scotland. Each has different grant levels, deadline dates and decision making practices. A list of local programmes is available on the foundation's website.
WHAT IS NOT FUNDED The foundation does not usually fund: individuals or groups which do not have a constitution; groups other than not-for-profit groups; groups whose grant request is for the advancement of religion or a political party (this means the foundation won't fund grant requests to support the core activities of religious or political groups); the purchase of second hand vehicles; trips abroad; the repayment of loans, payment of debts, or other retrospective funding; payments towards areas generally understood to be the responsibility of statutory authorities; groups who will then distribute the funds as grants or bursaries; applications that are for the sole benefit to flora and fauna. Applicants are invited to demonstrate the direct benefit to the local community and/or service users in cases where the grant application is concerned with flora and fauna; projects which do not benefit people in Scotland. Note different grant programmes may have additional restrictions.
TYPE OF GRANT Capital, revenue and full project funding.
RANGE OF GRANTS Usually between £250 and £5,000–occasionally larger grants are made.
FINANCES *Year* 2011–12 *Income* £11,131,000 *Grants* £6,930,000 *Assets* £16,401,000
TRUSTEES Bob Benson; Gillian Donald; Beth Edberg; Colin Liddell; Ian McAteer; Jimmy McCulloch; John Naylor; Ella Simpson; Lady Emily Stair; Tom Ward.
OTHER INFORMATION Note that grant schemes change frequently and potential applicants should consult the foundation's website for details of current programmes and their deadlines.
HOW TO APPLY The foundation has a comprehensive website with details of the grant schemes currently being administered. Organisations are welcome to contact the grants team to discuss their funding needs before making any application. Trustees meet at least four times a year.
WHO TO APPLY TO Alice Dansey-Wright, Programmes Administrator, Empire House, 131 West Nile Street, Glasgow G1 2RX *Tel.* 01413 414960 *Fax* 01413 414972 *email* nick@scottishcf.org *Website* www.foundationscotland.org.uk

■ Scott (Eredine) Charitable Trust

CC NO 1002267   **ESTABLISHED** 1990
WHERE FUNDING CAN BE GIVEN UK.
WHO CAN BENEFIT Charitable organisations.
WHAT IS FUNDED Service and ex-service charities; and medical and welfare causes.
SAMPLE GRANTS Scots Guards Charitable Trust (£52,000); Hampshire Youth Options

(£10,000); Combat Stress and King Edward VII's Hospital for Officers (£5,500 each); Combined Services Disabled Ski Team (£5,000); Taste For Adventure Centre (£4,000); Tusk Trust (£3,000); RNLI (£2,000); and Malawi Trust Boat (£1,000).

FINANCES *Year* 2012 *Income* £259,152 *Grants* £250,000 *Assets* £231,974

TRUSTEES Lt Col. Michael Scott; Keith Bruce-Smith; Amanda Scott.

HOW TO APPLY In writing to the correspondent.

WHO TO APPLY TO Keith Bruce-Smith, Trustee, Harcus Sinclair, 3 Lincoln's Inn Fields, London WC2A 3AA *Tel.* 020 7242 9700

··

■ The Frieda Scott Charitable Trust

CC NO 221593   **ESTABLISHED** 1962

WHERE FUNDING CAN BE GIVEN Old county of Westmorland and the area covered by South Lakeland District Council.

WHO CAN BENEFIT Small local charities, parish halls, youth groups and occasionally locally based work of larger charities.

WHAT IS FUNDED A very wide range of registered charities concerned with social welfare, community projects, the upkeep of village halls and voluntary sector infrastructure support and development.

WHAT IS NOT FUNDED Applications are not considered if they are from outside the beneficial area. No grants to individuals. No grants for retrospective funding, parish councils, health establishments, schools or educational establishments, places of worship or promoting religion, environmental causes, multi-year grants (except for start-ups), animal charities, wildlife or heritage causes, gardens or allotments (unless addressing disadvantage), property buying (other than in exceptional circumstances), sporting activity, museums and art galleries, national charities (with exceptions made for branches operating in the beneficial area).

TYPE OF GRANT Capital including building costs, core costs, one-off, project, research, recurring costs, running costs, salaries and start-up costs. The Trustees are unwilling to commit to funding more than one year at any one time.

RANGE OF GRANTS £300–£15,000

SAMPLE GRANTS Workbase (£15,000); Westmoreland Music Council (£12,500); Eden Community Outdoors – Young Cumbria (£10,000); Citizens Advice – Eden (£8,000); Kirkby Stephen Mountain Rescue Team (£6,000); CRUSE Bereavement Care Cumbria, Blackwell Sailing and Shopmobility – Kendal and South Lakes (£5,000 each); South Lakeland Credit Union Study Group (£4,000); Temple Sowerby Victory Hall and South Westmorland Association for Social and Moral Welfare Moral Welfare – Springfield Hostel (£3,500 each); Manchester Camerata and Beck Community Play Area (£2,500 each); Kendal Family Drop in Centre (£2,000); Lindale Village Hall Committee (£800) and Staveley Choral Society (£300).

FINANCES *Year* 2011–12 *Income* £297,633 *Grants* £149,239 *Assets* £6,546,477

TRUSTEES Sally Barker; Richard Brownson; Stuart Fairclough; Claire Hensman; Philip Hoyle; Margaret Wilson.

OTHER INFORMATION Note: the trust asks that charities do not apply to both the Frieda Scott and Francis C Scott Charitable Trusts at the same time. If unsure, contact the trust for further guidance.

44 organisations were given grants in 2011–12, with the average grant being £3,800.

HOW TO APPLY An application form is available from the correspondent, or from the trust's website, which should be returned by email or post with the latest set of audited accounts. Potential applicants are welcome to ring for an informal discussion before submitting an application. Applications are considered at meetings in March, June, September and December and should be sent to the Grants Coordinator at least a month beforehand. Grants of less than £3,500 are considered by the small grants committee in between main trustee meetings.

WHO TO APPLY TO Naomi Brown, Secretary, Stricklandgate House, 92 Stricklandgate, Kendal, Cumbria LA9 4PU *Tel.* 01539 742608 *email* info@fcsct.org.uk *Website* www.friedascott.org.uk

··

■ The Francis C. Scott Charitable Trust

CC NO 232131   **ESTABLISHED** 1963

WHERE FUNDING CAN BE GIVEN Cumbria and north Lancashire (comprising the towns of Lancaster, Morecambe, Heysham and Carnforth).

WHO CAN BENEFIT Mostly registered charities addressing the needs of 0–21 year olds in the most deprived communities of Cumbria and north Lancashire. Organisations who are pursuing charitable objectives and have not-for-profit aims/constitution may be considered. Applications from national organisations will only be considered if the beneficiaries and project workers are based within the beneficial area.

WHAT IS FUNDED There is an emphasis on community services, support and development for youth organisations, family support services and community development projects.

WHAT IS NOT FUNDED The trust does not consider appeals: from individuals; from statutory organisations; from national charities without a local base/project; from charities with substantial unrestricted reserves; from medical/ health establishments; from schools/ educational establishments; from infrastructure organisations/second-tier bodies; for projects principally benefiting people outside Cumbria/ north Lancashire; for retrospective funding; for expeditions or overseas travel; for the promotion of religion; for animal welfare.

TYPE OF GRANT Most grants are multi-year revenue grants (i.e. salaries and running costs); capital projects that make a tangible difference to a local community are also supported.

RANGE OF GRANTS Up to £275,000.

SAMPLE GRANTS Whitehaven Community Trust (£60,000); Whitehaven Foyer (£50,000); Safety Net Advice 8 Support Centre – Carlisle (£20,000); Walney Community Trust (£18,000); Aspatria Dreamscheme, Cumbria Starting Point and Self-Injury Support in North Cumbria (£15,000 each); Distington Club for Young People (£10,000); Leonard Cheshire North West (£7,500); University of Cumbria (£5,000); New Rainbow Pre School (£4,000); Child and Family Connect (£2,000); and the Egremont Amenity Committee (£1,000).

FINANCES *Year* 2012 *Income* £773,789 *Grants* £872,017 *Assets* £27,692,365

TRUSTEES Susan Bagot, Chair; Joanna Plumptre; Alexander Scott; Madeleine Scott; Don Shore; Clare Spedding; Peter Redhead; Melanie Wotherspoon.

OTHER INFORMATION Applicants should refer to the trusts website which is very comprehensive and covers all aspects of the grantmaking process.

HOW TO APPLY The trust is always pleased to hear from charities that need help. If an organisation thinks that it may come within the trust's criteria it is encouraged to contact the director for an informal discussion before making an application. Application forms are available to download from the trust's website or can be requested by phone, email or post. Applications should be completed and returned with the latest set of accounts (via email or post). Applications for over £4,000 should be submitted at least four weeks before the trustee's meetings in late February, June, October and November. Check the website for the latest deadlines. Applications for grants of less than £4,000 will be considered at small grants meetings every three to four weeks.

WHO TO APPLY TO Chris Batten, Director, Stricklandgate House, 92 Stricklandgate, Kendal, Cumbria LA9 4PU *Tel.* 01539 742608 *Fax* 01539 741611 *email* info@fcsct.org.uk *Website* www.fcsct.org.uk

■ Sir Samuel Scott of Yews Trust

CC NO 220878   **ESTABLISHED** 1951

WHERE FUNDING CAN BE GIVEN UK.

WHO CAN BENEFIT Medical research bodies benefiting medical professionals and research workers.

WHAT IS FUNDED Medical research.

WHAT IS NOT FUNDED No grants for: core funding; purely clinical work; individuals (although research by an individual may be funded if sponsored by a registered charity through which the application is made); research leading to higher degrees (unless the departmental head concerned certifies that the work is of real scientific importance); medical students' elective periods; or expeditions (unless involving an element of genuine medical research).

TYPE OF GRANT One-off, project.

RANGE OF GRANTS Usually £1,000–£10,000.

SAMPLE GRANTS Gray Institute at the University of Oxford (£106,500); Cure Parkinson's Trust and Diabetes UK (£10,000 each); Alzheimer's Research UK and the Motor Neurone Disease Association (£5,000 each); British Lung Foundation (£4,000); Leukaemia and Lymphoma Research (£3,000); Blond McIndoe Research Foundation and the National Eye Research Centre (£2,000 each); and the British Council for Prevention of Blindness and the Inspire Foundation (£1,000 each).

FINANCES *Year* 2011–12 *Income* £106,730 *Grants* £205,046 *Assets* £5,781,739

TRUSTEES Lady Phoebe Scott; Hermione Stanford; Edward Perks.

HOW TO APPLY In writing to the correspondent. Trustees hold their half-yearly meetings in April and October and applications have to be submitted two months before. There are no special forms, but applicants should give the following information: the nature and purpose of the research project or programme; the names, qualifications and present posts of the scientists involved; reference to any published results of their previous research; details of present funding; and if possible, the budget for the next 12 months or other convenient period. All applications are acknowledged and both successful and unsuccessful applicants are notified after each meeting of the trustees. No telephone calls.

WHO TO APPLY TO The Secretary, c/o Currey and Co, 21 Buckingham Gate, London SW1E 6LS *Tel.* 020 7802 2700

■ The Sir James and Lady Scott Trust

CC NO 231324   **ESTABLISHED** 1907

WHERE FUNDING CAN BE GIVEN The borough and district of Bolton.

WHO CAN BENEFIT Only registered charities, or not-for-profit organisations that are in the process of becoming a charity, will be considered.

WHAT IS FUNDED The trustees give priority to projects which help disadvantaged people or communities in Bolton. These have included projects which help elderly people, people with disabilities, young people, children and ethnic minority groups.

WHAT IS NOT FUNDED The trust does not consider applications for church restoration, medical causes, expeditions and scholarships.

TYPE OF GRANT Recurring costs; one-off; capital costs including buildings; core costs; endowment; feasibility studies; project research; running costs; salaries; and start-up costs. Funding is available for one year or less.

RANGE OF GRANTS Up to £3,000.

SAMPLE GRANTS Street Soccer Academy, Befriending Refugees and Asylum Seekers and Bibby's Farm Camp and Activities Centre (£3,000 each); St Philip's Community Hall (£2,400); North Bolton Support Group and CATS Youth Theatre (£2,000 each); Bolton Lads and Girls Club and Diversity in Barrier-Breaking Communications (£1,500 each); Volunteer Reading Help (£1,000) and Deafblind UK (£240).

FINANCES *Year* 2011–12 *Income* £47,248 *Grants* £41,584 *Assets* £2,498,436

TRUSTEES Christopher Scott; Madeleine Scott; William Swan.

OTHER INFORMATION Grants of £17,044 were made to former employees of members of the family of the settlor.

HOW TO APPLY In writing to the correspondent. All proposals should include: brief outline of what your organisation does, its constitution, articles, etc. (if appropriate) and a list of the key individuals involved; specifics of the project and who will benefit; how the money would be spent; timescales. Kindly note that any offers of funding should be taken up within three months of notification.

WHO TO APPLY TO Chris Batten, Secretary, Stricklandgate House, 92 Stricklandgate, Kendal, Cumbria LA9 4PU *Tel.* 01539 742608 *Fax* 01539 741611 *email* chris@fcsct.org.uk *Website* www.sjlst.org.uk

■ The Scott Trust Foundation

CC NO 1027893   **ESTABLISHED** 1993

WHERE FUNDING CAN BE GIVEN UK and overseas.

WHO CAN BENEFIT To benefit children, young adults, students and journalists.

WHAT IS FUNDED 'The Scott Trust Charitable Fund was established in March 2005 by the Scott Trust Foundation. Its purpose is to foster, promote and support one of the key objectives of the Scott Trust, namely 'promoting the causes of freedom of the press and liberal journalism both in Britain and elsewhere'. Proposals which answer the following criteria will be considered for support: independent journalism; media literacy; journalistic training; journalistic ethics.

WHAT IS NOT FUNDED As a rule the charitable trust will not fund: building projects; fellowships, internships, bursaries other than its own unless there are exceptional circumstances; new lecture series other than those planned at Kings Place. Small community projects with limited impact will *not* be considered. However, projects such as these might well be considered by individual Guardian Media Group companies, a list of which can be made available on request.

TYPE OF GRANT One-off.

FINANCES *Year* 2011–12 *Income* £260,000 *Assets* £51,681

TRUSTEES Alan Rusbridger; Geraldine Proudler; Jonathan Scott; Liz Forgan; Will Hutton; Andrew Graham; Anthony Salz; Maleiha Malik; Andrew Miller; Heather Stewart.

HOW TO APPLY On a form available from the correspondent, or from the trust's website, together with a latest set of audited accounts. An initial telephone call is welcomed.

WHO TO APPLY TO Philip Boardman, Trust Secretary, PO Box 68164, Kings Place, 90 York Way, London N1P 2AP. *email* scott.trust@guardian.co.uk

■ The Storrow Scott Will Trust

CC NO 328391   **ESTABLISHED** 1989
WHERE FUNDING CAN BE GIVEN Northern England
WHO CAN BENEFIT Charitable organisations.
WHAT IS FUNDED General charitable purposes.
WHAT IS NOT FUNDED Grants for individuals and for the purchase of depreciating assets such as mini-buses will not be considered.
RANGE OF GRANTS Up to £10,000.
SAMPLE GRANTS The Anaphylaxis Campaign, Camphill Village Trust, Great North Air Ambulance Service and Northumberland Clubs for Young People (£4,000 each); Songs Bird Survival (£2,000); Alnwick District Playhouse, Tynedale Hospice at Home and National Rheumatoid Arthritis Society (£1,000 each) and Brinkburn Music Festival, Newcastle Society for Blind People and Haltwhistle Swimming and Leisure Centre (£500 each).
FINANCES *Year* 2011–12 *Income* £46,830 *Grants* £36,000 *Assets* £772,961
TRUSTEES Geoffrey Meikle; John North Lewis; Alison North Lewis.
OTHER INFORMATION In 2011–12 grants were given to 16 organisations.
HOW TO APPLY In writing to the correspondent. There are no formal application forms.
WHO TO APPLY TO The Trustees, c/o Dickinson Dees, One Trinity Gardens, Broad Chare, Newcastle upon Tyne NE1 2HF *Tel.* 01912 799000 *Fax* 01912 799100

■ Scottish Coal Industry Special Welfare Fund

SC NO SC001200   **ESTABLISHED** 1932
WHERE FUNDING CAN BE GIVEN Scotland.
WHO CAN BENEFIT Miners.
WHAT IS FUNDED The fund was set up to improve the conditions of people employed in the mining industry and their families. It supports individuals in need and also the provision of recreational facilities, youth clubs and courses.
FINANCES *Year* 2011–12 *Income* £54,757 *Grants* £90,000

TRUSTEES Keith Jones, Chair; William Menzies; Robert McGill.
OTHER INFORMATION In November 2005 we reported that the fund's website contained only basic information, and that potential applicants should check it for further details on recent beneficiaries and other information as it develops. Over five years later there have been no developments.
Total expenditure for 2011–12 was £118,351. In the absence of further information we have estimated £90,000 as being the grants given.
HOW TO APPLY 'If you feel you, your group or organisation would qualify for some financial assistance from the fund, write to us to request a grant. Include as much information as possible in your letter to avoid any delay caused by questions raised by the trustees prior to grant issue. It is also extremely important to highlight your link to the coal mining industry in your grant request. The trustees meet quarterly to consider grant requests.' In November 2005 the trust stated that it intended to have an application form available to download from its website – as at December 2009 this had still not happened.
WHO TO APPLY TO Ian McAlpine, Secretary, c/o CISWO, Second Floor, 50 Hopetoun Street, Bathgate, West Lothian EH48 4EU *Tel.* 01506 635550 *Fax* 01506 631555 *email* ian.mcalpine@ciswo.org.uk *Website* www.sciswf.org.uk

■ The Scottish International Education Trust

SC NO SC009207   **ESTABLISHED** 1970
WHERE FUNDING CAN BE GIVEN Scotland.
WHO CAN BENEFIT Scots (by birth or upbringing) taking advanced studies for which support from public funds is not available.
WHAT IS FUNDED Grants are given to organisations and individuals whose concerns lie in education, the arts or the areas of economic or social welfare.
WHAT IS NOT FUNDED No grants to commercial organisations, for capital work, general maintenance, or for courses (e.g. undergraduate study) for which there is support from statutory bodies/public funds.
TYPE OF GRANT Normally one-off.
RANGE OF GRANTS Usually £1,000 to £3,000.
SAMPLE GRANTS Previous beneficiaries include Royal Scottish Academy of Music and Drama, Scottish International Piano Competition, Scottish Schools Debating Council and Scotland Yard Adventure Centre.
FINANCES *Year* 2011–12 *Income* £36,142 *Grants* £60,000
TRUSTEES Sir Sean Connery; Sir Jackie Stewart; Gerda Stevenson; Alex Salmond; David Michie; George Donald; Ginnie Atkinson; William Sweeney; Lord Sutherland of Houndwood; Edward Davidson.
OTHER INFORMATION In 2011–12 the trust had a total expenditure of £70,000.
HOW TO APPLY In writing to the correspondent. Guidelines for applicants are available to view on the trust's website.
WHO TO APPLY TO Gavin McEwan, Turcan Connell, Princes Exchange, 1 Earl Grey Street, Edinburgh EH3 9EE *Tel.* 01312 251113 *email* SIET@turcanconnell.com *Website* www.scotinted.org.uk

■ The Scouloudi Foundation

CC NO 205685   **ESTABLISHED** 1962

WHERE FUNDING CAN BE GIVEN UK charities working domestically or overseas.

WHO CAN BENEFIT (a) The Institute of Historical Research, University of London, for publications, research and fellowships ('Historical Awards'), (b) registered charities in the fields of elderly people; children and youth; environment; famine relief and overseas aid; disability; the humanities (archaeology, art, history, libraries, museums, records); medicine, health and hospices; social welfare; and welfare of armed forces and sailors.

WHAT IS FUNDED Candidates fulfilling the Institute of Historical Research's criteria may apply to the Institute for their research and publication costs to be funded. 'Special Donations' are made for extraordinary appeals and capital projects, and not day-to-day expenditure or staff costs. No applications for 'Regular Donations' are invited as these are normally specially selected.

WHAT IS NOT FUNDED Donations are not made to individuals, and are not normally made for welfare activities of a purely local nature. The trustees do not make loans or enter into deeds of covenant.

TYPE OF GRANT There are three categories of grant: an annual donation for historical research and fellowships to the Institute of Historical Research at the University of London; recurring grants to a regular list of charities; and 'special donations' which are one-off grants, usually in connection with capital projects.

RANGE OF GRANTS Typically £1,000–£2,000.

SAMPLE GRANTS University of London – Institute of Historical Research (£72,000); and Friends of the Elderly; British Institute for Brain Injured Children; Straight Talking Peer Education; Campaign to Protect Rural England; Campaign to Protect Rural England; Crossroads Caring for Carers; British Records Association; and Help the Hospices (£1,250 each).

FINANCES *Year* 2012–13 *Income* £223,146 *Grants* £188,288 *Assets* £6,146,018

TRUSTEES Sarah Baxter; David Marnham; James Sewell.

PUBLICATIONS Notes for the guidance of applicants for 'Special Donations' and 'Historical Awards'.

HOW TO APPLY Only Historical grants are open to application. Copies of the regulations and application forms for 'Historical Awards' can be obtained from: The Secretary, The Scouloudi Foundation Historical Awards Committee, c/o Institute of Historical Research, University of London, Senate House, Malet Street, London WC1E 7HU.

WHO TO APPLY TO The Trustees, c/o Haysmacintyre, 26 Red Lion Square, London WC1R 4AG *Tel.* 020 7969 5500 *Fax* 020 7969 5600

■ The Screwfix Foundation

CC NO 1151375   **ESTABLISHED** 2013

WHERE FUNDING CAN BE GIVEN UK

WHO CAN BENEFIT Registered charities, particularly those local to Screwfix Stores.

WHAT IS FUNDED The repair, maintenance, improvement or construction of homes, community facilities or other buildings for those in need.

TYPE OF GRANT Capital costs.

RANGE OF GRANTS £250–£5,000.

TRUSTEES Matthew Smith; John Maggs; Jonathan Mewett.

OTHER INFORMATION The foundation was established in 2013 by Screwfix Ltd, supplier of trade tools, plumbing, electrical, bathrooms and kitchens.

HOW TO APPLY On a form available to download from the website. Applicants complete the eligibility checklist at the start of the form first.

WHO TO APPLY TO Matthew Smith, Trustee, Trade House, Mead Avenue, Yeovil, Somerset BA22 8HT *Tel.* 01935 414100 *email* foundation@screwfix.com *Website* www.screwfix.com

■ Seafarers UK (King George's Fund for Sailors)

CC NO 226446   **ESTABLISHED** 1917

WHERE FUNDING CAN BE GIVEN UK and Commonwealth.

WHO CAN BENEFIT Organisations caring for seafarers whether these are officers or ratings, men or women, past or present of the Royal Navy, the Merchant Navy, the Fishing Fleets and their dependants.

WHAT IS FUNDED Registered nautical charities and other registered charities which assist seafarers and their dependants in distress, provide training for young people to become sailors, provide training for sailors and support for other institutions which promote safety at sea.

WHAT IS NOT FUNDED The fund does not make any grants directly to individuals except in exceptional cases but rather helps other organisations which do this. However, the fund may be able to advise in particular cases about a suitable organisation to approach. Full details of such organisations are to be found in The Guide to Grants for Individuals in Need, *published by DSC.*

TYPE OF GRANT Annual grants for general purposes; capital grants for specific projects such as new buildings, modernisations, conversions, etc.; and interim grants may be considered at any time. Core costs, feasibility studies, recurring and running costs will also be considered.

RANGE OF GRANTS up to £200,000

SAMPLE GRANTS Marine Society and Sea Cadets (£300,000 in total); Nautilus Welfare Funds (£178,000); Mission to Seafarers (£141,000); Seamen's Hospital Society (£121,000); Royal Navy and Royal Marines Children's Fund (£100,000); UK Sailing Academy (£82,500); Sailors' Children's Society (£75,000); Royal Liverpool Seamen's Orphan Institution (£60,000); International Seafarers Assistance Network (£50,000); Combat Stress (£40,000); Community Network (£29,000); Queen Victoria Seamen's Rest (£22,000); Alabare Christian Care Centres (£15,000); Not Forgotten Association (£10,000); and the Falkland Islands Memorial Chapel Trust and Gardening Leave (£5,000 each).

FINANCES *Year* 2012 *Income* £3,360,000 *Grants* £2,508,667 *Assets* £39,318,000

TRUSTEES Peter Mamelok; Vice Admiral Peter Wilkinson; Michael Acland; Christian Marr; Simon Rivett-Carnac; Maj. Patrick Dunn; Capt. R. Barker; P. J. Buxton; T. Cadman; M. Carden; M. Dickinson; Jeffery Evans; J. Monroe; J. Saunders Watson; Ms D. Sterling.

PUBLICATIONS 'Flagship' and the 'Nautical Welfare Guide'.

OTHER INFORMATION The trust has a very informative and useful website that should be referred to.

HOW TO APPLY Applicants to the main grants scheme should download the form available on the trust's website and use the guidance notes also available. There is a deadline for this scheme each year which is published on the website. Those to the Marine Society and Sea Cadets scheme should use the specific form and guidelines available on the website. Applications to the small grants scheme should download the small grants form and guidelines available on the website. There are no closing dates for the schemes which awards grants of up to £5,000. Only one application from an organisation can be considered in any 12 month period.

WHO TO APPLY TO Dennis Treleaven, Head of Grants, 8 Hatherley Street, London SW1P 2YY *Tel.* 020 7932 5984 *Fax* 020 7932 0095 *email* dennis. treleaven@seafarers-uk.org *Website* www. seafarers-uk.org

■ Seamen's Hospital Society

CC NO 231724   **ESTABLISHED** 1999
WHERE FUNDING CAN BE GIVEN UK.
WHO CAN BENEFIT Medical, care and welfare organisations working with seafarers and to individual seafarers and their dependants.
WHAT IS FUNDED Welfare causes.
SAMPLE GRANTS Seafarers' Advice and Information Line (£230,000); Nautilus Welfare Fund (£32,500); MCFG Development Programme (£30,000); Merchant Seamen's War Memorial Society (£17,500); Royal National Mission to Deep Sea Fishermen (£10,000); Scottish Nautical Welfare Society (£3,000); Apostleship of the Sea and Queen Victoria Seamen's Rest (£2,500 each); and Annual National Service for Seafarers (£150). The society mostly supports the same organisations each year, although this may reflect the application received from relevant organisations rather than a specific policy.
FINANCES *Year* 2012 *Income* £461,895
  Grants £328,328 *Assets* £7,812,058
TRUSTEES Jeffery C. Jenkinson; Peter McEwan; Rupert Chichester; Alexander R. Nairne; Capt. Colin Stewart; Dr Charlotte Mendes da Costa; Capt. Duncan Glass; Mark Carden; Comm. Frank Leonard; Max Gladwyn; Graham Lane.
OTHER INFORMATION Individuals were awarded £146,000 in grants.
HOW TO APPLY On a form available from the correspondent. Applicants are encouraged to contact the correspondent before making application.
WHO TO APPLY TO Peter Coulson, General Secretary, 29 King William Walk, Greenwich, London SE10 9HX *Tel.* 020 8858 3696 *Fax* 020 8293 9630 *email* admin@seahospital.org.uk *Website* www.seahospital.org.uk

■ The Searchlight Electric Charitable Trust

CC NO 801644   **ESTABLISHED** 1988
WHERE FUNDING CAN BE GIVEN UK, with a preference for Manchester.
WHO CAN BENEFIT Registered charities. In the past the trustees have stated that it is their policy to only support charities already on their existing list of beneficiaries, or those already known to them.
WHAT IS FUNDED General charitable purposes.
WHAT IS NOT FUNDED No grants for individuals.
SAMPLE GRANTS Previously: UJIA; CST; Bnei Akiva Sefer Torah; Guide Dogs for the Blind; Young Israel Synagogue; the Federation; Langdon College; Heathlands; Lubavitch Manchester; Manchester Eruv Committee; Reshet and the Purim Fund; Sense; Nightingales and Chabad Vilna.
FINANCES *Year* 2011–12 *Income* £19,273
  Grants £65,000
TRUSTEES D. M. Hamburger, Chair; H. E. Hamburger; M. E. Hamburger.
OTHER INFORMATION Expenditure totalled £70,000. No more financial information was available but based upon previous years grants probably totalled around £65,000.
HOW TO APPLY In writing to the correspondent, but note that in the past the trustees have stated that it is their policy to only support charities already on their existing list of beneficiaries or those already known to them.
WHO TO APPLY TO H. E. Hamburger, Trustee, Searchlight Electric Ltd, 900 Oldham Road, Manchester M40 2BS *Tel.* 01612 033300 *email* heh@slightdemon.co.uk

■ The Searle Charitable Trust

CC NO 288541   **ESTABLISHED** 1982
WHERE FUNDING CAN BE GIVEN UK.
WHO CAN BENEFIT Established youth organisations benefiting those disadvantaged by poverty.
WHAT IS FUNDED Projects/organisations connected with sailing for youth development.
WHAT IS NOT FUNDED No grants for individuals or for appeals not related to sailing.
TYPE OF GRANT One-off, recurring costs, project and core costs. Funding is available for up to three years.
SAMPLE GRANTS Rona Sailing Project (£54,000).
FINANCES *Year* 2011–12 *Income* £87,962
  Grants £54,076 *Assets* £3,802,948
TRUSTEES Andrew D. Searle; Victoria C. Searle.
OTHER INFORMATION The Rona Sailing Project is the main regular beneficiary, although small grants are occasionally made to other charities.
HOW TO APPLY In writing to the correspondent.
WHO TO APPLY TO Sarah Sharkey, 30 Watling Street, St Albans, Hertfordshire AL1 2QB

■ The Samuel Sebba Charitable Trust

CC NO 253351   **ESTABLISHED** 1967
WHERE FUNDING CAN BE GIVEN UK and Israel.
WHO CAN BENEFIT Charitable bodies with a preference for Jewish organisations.
WHAT IS FUNDED Social welfare; palliative care; refugees; youth at risk; education; environment; human rights and social justice.
WHAT IS NOT FUNDED No grants to individuals.
RANGE OF GRANTS Up to £100,000.
SAMPLE GRANTS Green Environment Fund (£93,000); King Solomon High School (£75,000); New Israel Fund (£55,000); Music of Remembrance (£33,000); Cystic Fibrosis Trust (£30,000); Deafblind UK (£25,000); Board of Deputies of British Jews and Brighton Voices in Exile (£20,000 each); Israeli Centre for Third Sector Research (£16,500); and Jewish Women's Aid (£15,000).
FINANCES *Year* 2011–12 *Income* £6,314,617
  Grants £2,293,444 *Assets* £58,464,212
TRUSTEES Leigh Sebba; Victor Klein; Lady Winston; Sallie Tangir; Yoav Tangir; Roger Adelman; Odelia Sebba.
HOW TO APPLY Organisations applying must provide proof of need, they must forward the most recent audited accounts, a registered charity

number, and most importantly a cash flow statement for the next 12 months. All applications should have a stamped addressed envelope enclosed. It is also important that the actual request for funds must be concise and preferably summarised on one side of A4. The trustees meet quarterly. However, because of ongoing support to so many organisations already known to the trust, it is likely that unsolicited applications will, for the foreseeable future, be unsuccessful.

WHO TO APPLY TO David Lerner, Chief Executive, 25–26 Enford Street, London W1H 1DW *Tel.* 020 7723 6028 *Fax* 020 7724 7412

....

■ The Seedfield Trust

CC NO 283463   **ESTABLISHED** 1981
WHERE FUNDING CAN BE GIVEN Worldwide.
WHO CAN BENEFIT Registered charities benefiting: Christians; evangelists; victims of famine, man-made and natural disasters, and war; people disadvantaged by poverty; retired clergy; and missionaries.
WHAT IS FUNDED To support the preaching and teaching of the Christian faith throughout the world, including publication and distribution of Scripture, Christian literature and audio-visual aids. To assist in the relief of hardship and poverty, including retired ministers and missionaries.
WHAT IS NOT FUNDED No grants to individuals.
TYPE OF GRANT The trust rarely makes grants towards core funding or for activities that may require funding over a number of years, preferring to make one-off project grants.
RANGE OF GRANTS Up to £10,000.
SAMPLE GRANTS Overseas Missionary Fellowship (£8,000); George Muller Charitable Trust (£5,000); Gideons International (£3,000); International Nepal Fellowship and Scripture Union (£2,000 each); Bible Study and Evangelism Fellowship, Church Urban Fund, Light for the Blind and Toy Box (£1,000 each).
FINANCES *Year* 2012 *Income* £110,894 *Grants* £89,750 *Assets* £2,478,456
TRUSTEES Paul Vipond; Keith Buckler; David Ryan; Janet Buckler; Valerie James; Eric Proudfoot.
HOW TO APPLY In writing to the correspondent, for consideration by the trustees who meet twice each year. Enclose an sae for acknowledgement.
WHO TO APPLY TO Janet Buckler, Trustee, 3 Woodland Vale, Lakeside, Ulverston, Cumbria LA12 8DR *Tel.* 01539 530359

....

■ Leslie Sell Charitable Trust

CC NO 258699   **ESTABLISHED** 1969
WHERE FUNDING CAN BE GIVEN UK, with some preference for the Bedfordshire, Hertfordshire and Buckinghamshire area.
WHO CAN BENEFIT Scout and Guide associations and individuals.
WHAT IS FUNDED Assistance for Scout and Guide associations.
TYPE OF GRANT Usually one-off payments for a small project, such as building repair works, transport, trips or equipment.
RANGE OF GRANTS Up to £5,000.
FINANCES *Year* 2011–12 *Income* £140,891 *Grants* £87,506 *Assets* £3,081,567
TRUSTEES Mary Wiltshire; Adrian Sell; Nicola Coggins.
HOW TO APPLY On an application form available from the trust's website. Applications should include

clear details of the project or purpose for which funds are required, together with an estimate of total costs and details of any funds raised by the group or individual for the project. The trust states that: 'Applications are usually treated sympathetically provided they are connected to the Scouting or Guide movement'. Applications to the Peter Sell Annual Award usually have to be submitted by the end of September. See the trust's website for full guidelines and future deadlines.

WHO TO APPLY TO Sharon Long, Secretary, Ashbrittle House, 2a Lower Dagnall Street, St Albans, Hertfordshire AL3 4PA *Tel.* 01727 843603 *Fax* 01727 843663 *email* admin@iplltd.co.uk *Website* www.lesliesellct.org.uk

....

■ Sellata Ltd

CC NO 285429   **ESTABLISHED** 1980
WHERE FUNDING CAN BE GIVEN UK.
WHO CAN BENEFIT Charitable organisations.
WHAT IS FUNDED The advancement of religion and the relief of poverty.
FINANCES *Year* 2011–12 *Income* £245,874 *Grants* £115,273 *Assets* £339,990
TRUSTEES Eliezer Benedikt; Nechy Benedikt; Pinchas Benedikt; Joseph Stern.
OTHER INFORMATION A list of beneficiaries was not available.
HOW TO APPLY In writing to the correspondent.
WHO TO APPLY TO Eliezer Benedikt, Trustee, 29 Fountayne Road, London N16 7EA

....

■ SEM Charitable Trust

CC NO 265831   **ESTABLISHED** 1973
WHERE FUNDING CAN BE GIVEN Mainly South Africa, Israel and UK.
WHO CAN BENEFIT Mainly educational institutions benefiting disabled people, children and young adults.
WHAT IS FUNDED Mainly recommendations of the settlor, particularly charities working in the fields of the education of disadvantaged and disabled people; and the empowerment of grassroots people in developing countries.
WHAT IS NOT FUNDED No grants to individuals.
TYPE OF GRANT Recurring and one-off.
RANGE OF GRANTS Mostly under £2,000.
SAMPLE GRANTS Natal Society for Arts (£65,000); Africa Ignite (£7,400); Avon Riding Centre (£5,000); Disabled on Line Limited and Magen David Adom UK (£3,000 each); Downs Syndrome Association, Dressability, Keren Laham, Manchester Jewish Community Care and Rutland House (£2,000 each); Friends of the Elderly, Garden Science and Lotem Limady Teva Meshulavium (£1,000 each) and The fifth Trust; Talking with Hands and Haifa LGBT Forum (£500 each).
FINANCES *Year* 2011–12 *Income* £45,895 *Grants* £130,500 *Assets* £959,929
TRUSTEES Sarah Radomir; Michael Radomir; David Wolmark.
HOW TO APPLY In writing to the correspondent.
WHO TO APPLY TO David Ashman, The Trustees, Reeves and Co LLP, 37 St Margaret's Street, Canterbury, Kent CT1 2TU *Tel.* 01227 768231 *email* david.ashman@reeves.co

■ The Seneca Trust

CC NO 1137147 **ESTABLISHED** 2010
WHERE FUNDING CAN BE GIVEN UK
WHO CAN BENEFIT Charities or other voluntary bodies
WHAT IS FUNDED Social welfare, education, children and young people
SAMPLE GRANTS Grants were made to ten organisations and two individuals. A list of beneficiaries was not included in the accounts.
FINANCES *Year* 2012 *Income* £105,775 *Grants* £79,010 *Assets* £32,905
TRUSTEES Tatjana May; Adam Sweidan; Natalie Wade.
OTHER INFORMATION The settlors of the trust are Kevin Gundle, co-founder of Aurum Funds Limited and also a trustee of Absolute Return for Kids (ARK), and his wife Deborah, who amongst other things has been involved in publishing and film production – her most recent venture is NetBuddy, an online resource offering tips, help and advice for parents and carers of children with learning disabilities.
HOW TO APPLY In writing to the correspondent.
WHO TO APPLY TO Natalie Wade, Trustee, c/o Aurum Fund Management, Ixworth House, 37 Ixworth Place, London SW3 3QH *Tel.* 020 7589 1130 *Fax* 020 7581 1780 *email* ir@aurumfunds.com

■ The Ayrton Senna Foundation

CC NO 1041759 **ESTABLISHED** 1994
WHERE FUNDING CAN BE GIVEN Worldwide, with a preference for Brazil.
WHO CAN BENEFIT Children's health and education charities.
WHAT IS FUNDED The relief of poverty and the advancement of education, religion and health, particularly the provision of education, healthcare and medical support for children.
WHAT IS NOT FUNDED No grants to individuals.
FINANCES *Year* 2012 *Income* £108,537 *Grants* £0 *Assets* £572,254
TRUSTEES Viviane Lalli; Milton Guerado Theodoro da Silva; Neyde Joanna Senna da Silva; Leonardo Senna da Silva; Christopher Bliss; Stephen Howard Ravenscroft.
OTHER INFORMATION Again, in this accounting year, the foundation did not make any charitable donations (£2.8 million in 2009). There is no indication in either the trustees' report or the accounts as to why no donations were made during the course of 2012.
HOW TO APPLY In writing to the correspondent.
WHO TO APPLY TO Christopher Bliss, Trustee, 8th Floor, 6 New Street Square, London EC4A 3AQ *Tel.* 020 7842 2000

■ The Seven Fifty Trust

CC NO 298886 **ESTABLISHED** 1988
WHERE FUNDING CAN BE GIVEN UK and worldwide.
WHO CAN BENEFIT Registered charities benefiting Christians.
WHAT IS FUNDED Trustees mainly give to causes they have supported for many years.
WHAT IS NOT FUNDED No support for unsolicited requests.
RANGE OF GRANTS Up to £20,000.
SAMPLE GRANTS All Saints Church (£21,000); St Matthew's Church (£6,000); Universities and Colleges Christian Fellowship (£4,500); Overseas Missionary Fellowship (£3,500); and Care for the Family (£2,500).
FINANCES *Year* 2011–12 *Income* £81,995 *Grants* £65,290 *Assets* £1,942,335

TRUSTEES Revd Andrew Cornes; Katherine Cornes; Cannon Jonathan Clark; Mary Clark.
OTHER INFORMATION Grants are also made to individuals.
HOW TO APPLY Unsolicited applications will not be considered.
WHO TO APPLY TO Revd Andrew Cornes, Trustee, All Saints Vicarage, Church Road, Crowborough, East Sussex TN6 1ED *Tel.* 01892 667384

■ SF Group Charitable Fund for Disabled People

CC NO 1104927 **ESTABLISHED** 2004
WHERE FUNDING CAN BE GIVEN East and west Midlands and parts of the north west of England.
WHO CAN BENEFIT Individuals, organisations and national and local charities.
WHAT IS FUNDED Disabled individuals and organisations that provide care for those with physical or mental disabilities.
TYPE OF GRANT Small, one-off grants.
RANGE OF GRANTS Up to a maximum of £5,000.
SAMPLE GRANTS Previous beneficiaries have included: Acorns Children's Hospice (£5,000 part-funding for a specialist nurse); Green Acres Day Centre (£4,100 for a walking frame); and Willow Wood Day Centre (£2,900 for a combined hoist).
FINANCES *Year* 2012 *Income* £91,675 *Grants* £98,452 *Assets* £206,768
TRUSTEES Warwick; R. Yong.
HOW TO APPLY Initial applications can be made by filling in a short application form. This can be done online at the SF Group website, or by completing the form attached to its information leaflet which can be request by phone or email. The fund manager will contact potential recipients within two weeks of receiving applications to discuss requests in more detail.
WHO TO APPLY TO Brenda Yong, Fund Manager, FREEPOST NAT13205, Nottingham NG8 6ZZ *Tel.* 01159 425646 *email* brenda.yong@sfcharity.co.uk *Website* www.sfcharity.co.uk

■ The Cyril Shack Trust

CC NO 264270 **ESTABLISHED** 1972
WHERE FUNDING CAN BE GIVEN UK.
WHO CAN BENEFIT Voluntary organisations and charitable groups only.
WHAT IS FUNDED General charitable purposes, with a preference for Jewish organisations.
WHAT IS NOT FUNDED No grants for expeditions, travel bursaries, scholarships or to individuals.
TYPE OF GRANT Capital; recurring.
SAMPLE GRANTS No grants list was available. Previous beneficiaries have included Finchley Road Synagogue, Nightingale House and St John's Wood Synagogue.
FINANCES *Year* 2011–12 *Income* £117,978 *Grants* £123,953 *Assets* £699,346
TRUSTEES Jonathan Shack; Cyril Shack.
HOW TO APPLY In writing to the correspondent.
WHO TO APPLY TO The Clerk, c/o Lubbock Fine, Chartered Accountants, Russell Bedford House, City Forum, 250 City Road, London EC1V 2QQ *Tel.* 020 7490 7766

■ The Jean Shanks Foundation

CC NO 293108 **ESTABLISHED** 1985
WHERE FUNDING CAN BE GIVEN UK.
WHO CAN BENEFIT People involved in medical research, i.e. medical schools, medical Royal Colleges and similar bodies.
WHAT IS FUNDED Medical research and education, with a preference for the area of pathology.
WHAT IS NOT FUNDED No grants for capital items. No grants for research which is already supported by another grant giving body or for projects of the type normally dealt with by bodies such as the MRC or Wellcome Trust.
TYPE OF GRANT Scholarships, research – up to three years.
RANGE OF GRANTS £5,000–£70,000.
SAMPLE GRANTS Royal College of Pathologists (£70,000); University of Oxford (£24,000); University of Cambridge (£21,000); University of Nottingham (£20,000); University of Birmingham, University of Manchester, University of Cardiff, University of Liverpool and Brighton and Sussex Medical School (£9,000 each); and University of Dundee (£5,500).
FINANCES *Year* 2012–13 *Income* £286,177 *Grants* £315,040 *Assets* £17,767,370
TRUSTEES Eric Rothbarth; Prof. Andrew Carr; Alistair Jones; Dr Julian Axe; Prof. Adrienne Flanagan; Prof. Sir James Underwood.
HOW TO APPLY In writing to the correspondent. Full grant guidelines are available on the foundation's website.
WHO TO APPLY TO Paula Price-Davies, Administrator, Peppard Cottage, Peppard Common, Henley on Thames, Oxon RG9 5LB *email* administrator@ jeanshanksfoundation.org *Website* www. jeanshanksfoundation.org

■ The Shanley Charitable Trust

CC NO 1103323 **ESTABLISHED** 2003
WHERE FUNDING CAN BE GIVEN Worldwide.
WHO CAN BENEFIT Recognised international charities.
WHAT IS FUNDED The relief of poverty.
SAMPLE GRANTS WaterAid (£100,000); Save the Children (£40,000); and Self Help Africa (£15,000).
FINANCES *Year* 2011–12 *Income* £581,715 *Grants* £155,000 *Assets* £3,028,875
TRUSTEES C. A. Shanley; Roger Lander; Steve Atkins.
OTHER INFORMATION The trust's income includes an exceptional donation of £500,000.
HOW TO APPLY In writing to the correspondent.
WHO TO APPLY TO Steve Atkins, Trustee, Knowles Benning Solicitors, 32 High Street, Shefford, Bedfordshire SG17 5DG *Tel.* 01462 814824

■ The Shanti Charitable Trust

CC NO 1064813 **ESTABLISHED** 1997
WHERE FUNDING CAN BE GIVEN UK, with preference for West Yorkshire, and developing countries (especially Nepal).
WHO CAN BENEFIT Charitable organisations.
WHAT IS FUNDED General, Christian, international development.
WHAT IS NOT FUNDED No grants to gap year students, or political or animal welfare causes.
SAMPLE GRANTS International Nepal Fellowship (£10,500); St John's Church (£9,000); Protac/ Theotac, Nepal (£8,000); Development Associates International (£6,500); St John's Under 5's (£1,750); Marie Curie (£1,000); and Emmaus UK (£500).

FINANCES *Year* 2011–12 *Income* £33,877 *Grants* £37,250 *Assets* £128,554
TRUSTEES Barbara Gill; Andrew Gill; Ross Hyett.
HOW TO APPLY In writing to the correspondent. Note most beneficiaries are those the trustees already have contact with.
WHO TO APPLY TO Barbara Gill, Trustee, Parkside, Littlemoor, Queensbury, Bradford, West Yorkshire BD13 1DB

■ ShareGift (The Orr Mackintosh Foundation)

CC NO 1052686 **ESTABLISHED** 1995
WHERE FUNDING CAN BE GIVEN UK.
WHO CAN BENEFIT UK registered charities.
WHAT IS FUNDED General charitable purposes, guided by the wishes of the donors of shares, from where its income derives.
WHAT IS NOT FUNDED No grants to non-UK registered charities.
RANGE OF GRANTS up to £50,000.
SAMPLE GRANTS Royal Society for the Protection of Birds (£50,000); the Prince's Trust (£30,000); Thomas Coram Foundation for Children (£26,000); Walking with the Wounded and CAFOD (£25,000 each); the James Trust (£20,000); Cable and Wireless Worldwide Foundation and the Daily Telegraph Christmas Appeal (£15,000 each); ICSA Education and Research Foundation (£10,000); Multiple Sclerosis Society and the British Red Cross (£7,500 each); Back-Up Trust, the Federation of Groundwork Trusts and Survival International Charitable Trust (£5,000 each); and Action for Prisoners' Families, Battersea Dogs' and Cats' Home, David Shepherd Wildlife Foundation and North West Air Ambulance (£1,000 each).
FINANCES *Year* 2011–12 *Income* £1,271,224 *Grants* £886,755 *Assets* £284,543
TRUSTEES Stephen Scott; Baroness Mary Goudie; Paul Killik.
HOW TO APPLY Applications for funding are not accepted and no response will be made to charities that send inappropriate applications. ShareGift's trustees choose to support UK registered charities which reflect the broad range of charities which are of interest to the people and organisations that help to create the charity's income by donating their unwanted shares, or by supporting the charity's operation in other practical ways However, charities wishing to receive a donation from ShareGift's trustees can increase their chances of doing so by encouraging their supporters to donate unwanted shares to ShareGift and to make a note of their charitable interests when so doing, using the regular donation form provided by ShareGift. In addition, ShareGift is willing to use its extensive experience of share giving philanthropically to help charities which wish to start receiving gifts of shares themselves. Charities are, therefore, welcome to contact ShareGift to discuss this further. ShareGift advises that, as basic training on share giving is now available elsewhere, charities wishing to benefit from their advice should ensure that they have first researched share giving generally and put some thought into how their charity intends to initiate and run a share giving appeal or strategy. Further information on this and other issues is available on the charity's website.

WHO TO APPLY TO Lady Mackintosh, 2nd Floor, 17 Carlton House Terrace, London SW1Y 5AH *Tel.* 020 7930 3737 *Fax* 020 7839 2214 *email* help@sharegift.org.uk *Website* www. sharegift.org

....

■ The Linley Shaw Foundation

CC NO 1034051   **ESTABLISHED** 1993
WHERE FUNDING CAN BE GIVEN UK.
WHO CAN BENEFIT Registered charities in rural locations.
WHAT IS FUNDED The conservation, preservation and restoration of the natural beauty of the countryside of the UK for the public benefit. In particular, charities that organise voluntary workers to achieve these objectives.
WHAT IS NOT FUNDED No grants to non-charitable organisations, or to organisations whose aims or objects do not include conservation, preservation or restoration of the natural beauty of the UK countryside, even if the purpose of the grant would be eligible. No grants to individuals.
RANGE OF GRANTS £500–£16,000.
SAMPLE GRANTS Beneficiaries were: Protect Rural England; The National Trust; Cornwall Wildlife Trust; Nottinghamshire Wildlife Trust; Pond Conservation: The Water Habitats Trust; Moor Trees; John Muir Trust; The Conservation Volunteers; Leicestershire and Rutland Wildlife Trust; Bardon Mill and Henshaw CVH Project Group; Campaign to Protect Rural England; Derbyshire Wildlife Trust.
FINANCES *Year* 2011–12 *Income* £247,491 *Grants* £60,317
TRUSTEE National Westminster Bank plc.
HOW TO APPLY In writing to the correspondent. All material will be photocopied by the trust so avoid sending 'bound' copies of reports and so on. Evidence of aims and objectives are needed, usually in the forms of accounts, annual reports or leaflets, which cannot be returned. Applications are considered in February/early March and should be received by December/early January.
'Regular meeting are held by the Trustees where they discuss any applications received and consider which grants they wish to award.'
WHO TO APPLY TO The Trust Section, NatWest Trust Services, 5th Floor, Trinity Quay 2, Avon Street, Bristol BS2 0PT *Tel.* 05516577371

....

■ The Shears Foundation

CC NO 1049907   **ESTABLISHED** 1994
WHERE FUNDING CAN BE GIVEN Northumberland, Tyne and Wear, Durham and West Yorkshire.
WHO CAN BENEFIT Registered charities only.
WHAT IS FUNDED The foundation was established in 1994, and 'aims to fund selected organisations and projects in the fields of community development, environmental issues, sustainable development, health and welfare and cultural development, all with an emphasis on education and raising awareness. There is also a proportion devoted to overseas projects in the same fields'.
WHAT IS NOT FUNDED No grants for domestic animal welfare or religious organisations.
RANGE OF GRANTS Up to £100,000.
SAMPLE GRANTS Community Foundation for Tyne and Wear and Northumberland (£100,000 for the Linden Fund and £50,000 for the Local Environmental Action Fund); Alnwick Garden (£60,000); Whitley Fund for Nature (£50,000);

and Samling Foundation and Bradford Grammar School (£30,000 each).
FINANCES *Year* 2011–12 *Income* £493,819 *Grants* £610,500 *Assets* £11,242,248
TRUSTEES Trevor Halliday Shears; Peter John Randal Shears; Peter John Randal Shears; Patricia Shears; G. Lyall.
HOW TO APPLY In writing to the correspondent.
WHO TO APPLY TO Trevor Halliday Shears, Trustee, 35 Elmfeld Road, Gosforth, Newcastle upon Tyne NE3 4BA

....

■ The Sheepdrove Trust

CC NO 328369   **ESTABLISHED** 1989
WHERE FUNDING CAN BE GIVEN UK, but especially north Lambeth, London, where applicable.
WHO CAN BENEFIT Registered charities only.
WHAT IS FUNDED General charitable purposes, particularly sustainability, biodiversity, organic farming, educational research and spiritual care.
TYPE OF GRANT One-off and recurrent.
SAMPLE GRANTS Wildlife Conservation Partnership (£74,000); GM Education Programme (£46,500); Slow Food UK Trust (£31,000); Friends of Kennington Park (£24,000); Watermill Theatre (£15,000); Mother Meera School – India and Vauxhall City Farm (£10,000 each); and the Pasture Fed Livestock Association and the Comedy School Charitable Trust (£5,000 each).
FINANCES *Year* 2012 *Income* £443,901 *Grants* £411,155 *Assets* £18,633,134
TRUSTEES Juliet E. Kindersley; Peter D. Kindersley; Harriet R. Treuille; Barnabas G. Kindersley.
HOW TO APPLY In writing to the correspondent.
WHO TO APPLY TO Juliet E. Kindersley, Trustee, Sheepdrove Organic Farm, Lambourn, Berkshire RG17 7UN *Tel.* 01488 674726

....

■ The Sheffield and District Hospital Services Charitable Fund

CC NO 246057   **ESTABLISHED** 1965
WHERE FUNDING CAN BE GIVEN Mostly South Yorkshire, also UK.
WHO CAN BENEFIT NHS hospitals and trusts; registered charities.
WHAT IS FUNDED Medical equipment and general charitable purposes.
RANGE OF GRANTS Up to £100,000.
SAMPLE GRANTS St Catherine's Hospice (£102,000); Age UK Sheffield (£47,500); Weston Park Hospital Development Fund (£30,000); British Heart Foundation (£25,000); Leonard Cheshire Disability Services and Sheffield Royal Society for the Blind (£20,000 each); University of Sheffield (£10,000); Speakup Self Advocacy Ltd (£5,000); Shopmobility (£3,000) and Derby Hospitals Charity (£1,700).
FINANCES *Year* 2011–12 *Income* £852,613 *Grants* £834,075 *Assets* £959,953
TRUSTEES Graham Moore; David Whitney; Dr John Hammond; Dr Catherine Ryan.
OTHER INFORMATION In 2011–12 there were 176 grants awarded. All but 3 (£3,000) of them were to organisations.
HOW TO APPLY In writing to the correspondent.
WHO TO APPLY TO J. Gill, Secretary, Westfield House, 87 Division Street, Sheffield S1 1HT *Tel.* 01142 502339 *email* charity@westfieldhealth.com *Website* www.westfieldhealth.com

■ The Sheldon Trust

CC NO 242328   **ESTABLISHED** 1965

WHERE FUNDING CAN BE GIVEN West Midlands.

WHO CAN BENEFIT Registered charities.

WHAT IS FUNDED The relief of poverty and distress in society, concentrating on community projects. Aftercare, hospice at home, respite care, self-help and support groups, and rehabilitation centres are also considered. Facilities for people who are disadvantaged or disabled, particularly for young people aged 16–25 who are not in training, education or employment. Encouragement of local voluntary groups, recreational facilities, youth, community, rehabilitation for drugs, alcohol, and solvent abuse, religion, older people, mental health and learning difficulties.

WHAT IS NOT FUNDED No grants to charities with an income over £1 million and/or free unrestricted reserves to the value of more than six months of their annual expenditure.

SAMPLE GRANTS Action in the Community Trust (£31,000); Worth Unlimited and Rona Sailing School (£10,000 each); Cruise Bereavement Care – Coventry and Warwickshire (£9,000); The Spring Playgroup (£7,500); Yeldall Christian Centre (£5,000); Inclusion4U (£3,000) and Bag Books (£2,000).

FINANCES *Year* 2011–12 *Income* £196,083 *Grants* £223,423 *Assets* £3,878,170

TRUSTEES A. Bidnell; Revd R. S. Bidnell; J. K. R. England; R. Beatton; R. Gibbins; Paul K. England.

HOW TO APPLY Applications should be submitted online, via the website. Trustees meet twice a year to consider applications, in March and September. Applications should usually be submitted two months prior to the meeting, although trustees may stop considering applications once sufficient numbers are received so sending applications early is advised. Precise deadlines are posted on the website. Holiday applications differ from the other schemes. Application forms are made available online from the beginning of March and are usually accepted until late April/early May. Exact deadlines are posted on the website.

A copy of the organisation's most recent signed accounts; a budget for the project for the current financial year; and, if the application envisages a salary, a job description. These documents can be uploaded at the end of the online application form. Applications will not be considered until all the relevant documentation has been received. The trust does not accept draft accounts. Do not send any other information as it will be discarded. All applicants will be informed of the funding decision within seven days of the Trustees meeting. Successful applicant will receive confirmation of the grant offer and any related conditions. Do not contact the office before this time. Unsuccessful applicants can re-apply after two years. Successful applicants will not be considered for a period of two years following receipt of a grant (or final payment of repeat funding).

WHO TO APPLY TO The Trust Administrator, Pothecary Witham Weld Solicitors, 70 St George's Square, London SW1V 3RD *Tel.* 020 7821 8211 *email* charities@pwwsolicitors.co.uk *Website* www.pwwsolicitors.co.uk/charitable-applications/charity-details/the-sheldon-trust

■ The Patricia and Donald Shepherd Charitable Trust

CC NO 272948   **ESTABLISHED** 1973

WHERE FUNDING CAN BE GIVEN Worldwide, particularly the north of England and Scotland.

WHO CAN BENEFIT Mainly local organisations – particularly those in the north of England.

WHAT IS FUNDED General charitable purposes. Local charities or charities with which the trustees have personal knowledge of, interest in or association with particularly those supporting young people.

TYPE OF GRANT Mainly one-off.

SAMPLE GRANTS York Museum Trust (£12,500); Police Treatment Centres, Henshaws Society for the Blind, York Cemetery Trust and York Air Museum (£10,000 each); Special Boat Service Association (£5,000); Marrick Priory (£3,000); North Yorkshire Business and Education Partnership, ABF the Soldier's Charity and Involve Learning Centre (£2,000 each); and York Minster Fund (£1,000).

FINANCES *Year* 2011–12 *Income* £140,446 *Grants* £123,720 *Assets* £511,852

TRUSTEES Patricia Shepherd; Iain Robertson; Jane Robertson; Michael Shepherd; Christine Shepherd; Patrick Shepherd; Joseph Shepherd; Rory Robertson; Annabel Robertson.

HOW TO APPLY In writing to the correspondent. The trustees meet frequently. Applications should include details of the need to be met, achievements and a copy of the latest accounts.

WHO TO APPLY TO The Trustees, 5 Cherry Lane, Dringhouses, York YO24 1QH

■ The Sylvia and Colin Shepherd Charitable Trust

CC NO 272788   **ESTABLISHED** 1973

WHERE FUNDING CAN BE GIVEN North east England, but mostly within a 25-mile radius of York.

WHO CAN BENEFIT Registered charities only, benefiting children and older people, retired people and people who are disabled.

WHAT IS FUNDED In the medium-term the policy is to build up the trust's capital base. Currently the main areas of interest are community initiatives, care of older people, childcare, people who are mentally or physically disabled, conservation, and medical support and equipment.

WHAT IS NOT FUNDED Applications from individuals will not be considered and support does not extend to organisations working outside the areas defined above and excludes overseas activities.

TYPE OF GRANT Usually for specific projects on an enabling basis. Core funding or ongoing support will not normally be provided.

RANGE OF GRANTS £100–£5,000, typically £100–£500.

SAMPLE GRANTS York Minster Fund and Church of Our Lady (£5,000 each); Ataxia UK and St Peter's School Foundation (£3,000 each); Handicapped Children's Action Group (£2,000); York Guildhall Orchestra (£1,500); St Leonard's Hospice and Yorkshire Air Ambulance (£1,000 each); Age Concern (£750); Tall Ships Youth Trust, The British Stammering Association, The Captain Cook Schoolroom Museum and Leonard Cheshire Disability (£500 each); British Blind Sport and University of York Dept. of Music (£300 each); Northern Ballet (£200) and Alzheimer's Society (£100).

FINANCES *Year* 2011–12 *Income* £145,018 *Grants* £138,604 *Assets* £2,894,425
TRUSTEES Sara Dickson; David Dickson; Sylvia Shepherd; Lucy Dickson; Sophie Dickson.
HOW TO APPLY In writing to the correspondent.
WHO TO APPLY TO Sara Dickson, Trustee, 15 St Edward's Close, York YO24 1QB *Tel.* 01904 702762

■ The Archie Sherman Cardiff Foundation

CC NO 272225 **ESTABLISHED** 1976
WHERE FUNDING CAN BE GIVEN UK, Canada, Australia, New Zealand, Pakistan, Sri Lanka, South Africa, India, Israel, USA and other parts of the British Commonwealth.
WHO CAN BENEFIT Charitable organisations.
WHAT IS FUNDED Health, education, training, overseas aid, community and Jewish causes.
WHAT IS NOT FUNDED No grants to individuals.
SAMPLE GRANTS The Israel Children's Centres (£50,000); Jewish Child's Day (£35,000); JNF Charitable Trust (£30,000); The British Friends of the Bar-Ilan University (£19,000) and British Friends of the Hebrew University of Jerusalem (£5,000).
FINANCES *Year* 2011–12 *Income* £101,870 *Grants* £139,100 *Assets* £2,244,850
TRUSTEE Rothschild Trust Corporation Ltd.
HOW TO APPLY In writing to the correspondent.
WHO TO APPLY TO The Trustees, Rothschild Trust Corp Ltd, New Court, St Swithin's Lane, London EC4P 4DU *Tel.* 020 7280 5000

■ The Archie Sherman Charitable Trust

CC NO 256893 **ESTABLISHED** 1967
WHERE FUNDING CAN BE GIVEN UK and Israel.
WHO CAN BENEFIT Charitable organisations.
WHAT IS FUNDED Most grants are to Jewish organisations. Other causes supported are the arts, education, health, welfare and overseas aid.
TYPE OF GRANT Capital, buildings and project. Funding may be given for more than three years.
SAMPLE GRANTS The Jacqueline and Michael Gee Charitable Trust (£156,000); WIZO UK (£141,000); the Diana and Allan Morgenthau Charitable Trust (£131,000); and the Rosalyn and Nicholas Springer Charitable Trust (£125,000); Jewish Child's Day (£60,000); Rabin Medical Centre (£47,000); Royal Academy of Arts (£41,000); Ben-Gurion University Foundation (£28,500); Norwood Ravenswood (£25,000); Community Security Trust (£15,000); Islington Community Theatre (£10,000); British Friends of the Jaffa Institute (£3,500); and Glyndebourne Arts Trust (£1,500).
FINANCES *Year* 2011–12 *Income* £1,504,548 *Grants* £956,241 *Assets* £20,243,835
TRUSTEES Michael J. Gee; Allan H. S. Morgenthau; Eric A. Charles.
HOW TO APPLY In writing to the correspondent. Trustees meet every month except August and December.
WHO TO APPLY TO Michael Gee, Trustee, 27 Berkeley House, 15 Hay Hill, London W1J 8NS *Tel.* 020 7493 1904 *email* trust@sherman.co.uk

■ The R. C. Sherriff Trust

CC NO 272527 **ESTABLISHED** 1976
WHERE FUNDING CAN BE GIVEN The borough of Elmbridge.
WHO CAN BENEFIT Local individuals for art training bursaries (short courses only) and local amateur and professional organisations planning arts activities of a developmental nature.
WHAT IS FUNDED The trust is primarily concerned with arts development projects and funds charities, schools and constituted organisations working with one or more art form for the benefit of members of the local community, especially where a professional artist is involved. The trust has funded projects concerned with music, dance, drama, visual arts, crafts, literature, film and new media.
WHAT IS NOT FUNDED Any project taking place outside the borough cannot be supported unless the principal beneficiaries are Elmbridge residents. The trust does not give retrospective grants; it does not fund higher education courses or long-term vocational training; and it rarely agrees to be the sole funder of a project, applicants are expected to raise funds from a variety of sources.
TYPE OF GRANT Capital, one-off, event underwriting, project and school funds. Funding of up to three years will be considered.
RANGE OF GRANTS £180–£12,000; typical grant £1,000.
SAMPLE GRANTS Riverhouse (£12,000); Elmbridge Community Link (£2,500); Oatlands School and Ember Sports Club (£2,000 each); Music in Hospitals and Molesey Youth Centre (£1,800 each); Churches Together and The Medicine Garden (£1,500 each) and Dynamo Dance Project and Elmbridge Youth Theatre (£1,000 each).
FINANCES *Year* 2012 *Income* £288,988 *Grants* £45,465 *Assets* £3,633,660
TRUSTEES Cllr Nigel Cooper; Cllr Shweta Barch; Ruth Lyon; Cllr Tannia Shipley; Cllr James Vickers; Alison Clarke; Barry Cheyne; Frank Renton; Wendy Smithers; Brian Nathan.
PUBLICATIONS Arts Focus
OTHER INFORMATION Grants to individuals and schools are unlikely to exceed £500 and grants to organisations and venues are unlikely to exceed £2,500.
HOW TO APPLY On a form which can be downloaded from the website or obtained from the trust office. Application deadlines, grant decision dates and full grant guidelines are also available. Trustees meet four times a year to consider applications. Applicants are advised to discuss their proposals and check their eligibility, with the Director, in advance. The website will also give information on past and current projects and successful applications.
WHO TO APPLY TO Loretta Howells, Director, Case House, 85–89 High Street, Walton on Thames, Surrey KT12 1DZ *Tel.* 01932 229996 *email* arts@rcsherrifftrust.org.uk *Website* www.rcsherrifftrust.org.uk

■ The Shetland Charitable Trust

SC NO SC027025 **ESTABLISHED** 1976
WHERE FUNDING CAN BE GIVEN Shetland only.
WHO CAN BENEFIT Self-help and voluntary organisations benefiting the inhabitants of Shetland.
WHAT IS FUNDED Social welfare; art and recreation; environment and amenity.

WHAT IS NOT FUNDED Funds can only be used to benefit the inhabitants of Shetland.

TYPE OF GRANT Project, one-off, capital, running and recurring costs, agricultural ten-year loan scheme.

RANGE OF GRANTS Up to £2.5 million.

SAMPLE GRANTS Shetland Recreational Trust (£2.6 million); Support to Rural Care Model (£2.5 million); Shetland Amenity Trust (£1 million); Shetland Arts Development Agency (£732,000); Shetland Youth Information Service (£189,000); COPE Limited (£155,000); Voluntary Action Shetland (£144,500); Shetland Churches Council Trust (£54,000); Swan Trust (£44,000); and Festival Grants (£30,000).

FINANCES *Year* 2011–12 *Income* £9,532,000 *Grants* £10,626,000 *Assets* £216,878,000

TRUSTEES Bobby Hunter, Chair; Jonathan Wills; Malcolm Bell; Allison Duncan; Betty Fullerton; Robert Henderson; Catherine Hughson; Ian Kinniburgh; Andrea Manson; Keith Massey; Stephen Morgan; Ian Napier; Drew Ratter; James Smith; Amanda Westlake.

HOW TO APPLY Applications are only accepted from Shetland-based charities. The trustees meet every two months. The trust has different contact points for different categories of grant: arts grants, development grants, senior citizens club grants and support grants – contact Michael Duncan on 01595 743828; and social assistance grants – contact the duty social worker at duty@shetland.gov.uk

WHO TO APPLY TO Michael Duncan, 22–24 North Road, Lerwick, Shetland ZE1 0NQ *Tel.* 01595 744994 *Fax* 01595 744999 *email* mail@shetlandcharitabletrust.co.uk *Website* www.shetlandcharitabletrust.co.uk

■ SHINE (Support and Help in Education)

CC NO 1082777 **ESTABLISHED** 1999

WHERE FUNDING CAN BE GIVEN Greater London and Manchester.

WHO CAN BENEFIT Organisations working with underachieving 7 to 18 year olds living in disadvantaged areas.

WHAT IS FUNDED Educational programmes which give young people the extra support and attention they need to learn the basic but essential tools for life. SHINE also supports projects that help talented children from poor neighbourhoods to recognise and then realise their full potential. Projects include intensive one-to-one literacy and numeracy support, Saturday learning programmes, homework clubs and computer-assisted study projects.

WHAT IS NOT FUNDED Shine will not fund: individuals; bursaries or any kind of student fees; projects outside of the UK; direct replacement of statutory funding; programmes where the primary aim is the personal development of young people rather than raising academic achievement levels; short term or one off projects; programmes narrowly targeted at specific beneficiary groups, with some exceptions; parenting programmes, where the primary focus is the parent rather than the child; activities promoting particular political or religious beliefs; projects taking place outside Greater London or Manchester (except for the Serious Fun strand and projects that are replicating on a national scale).

TYPE OF GRANT Start-ups, pilots, core costs and development or replication of projects.

RANGE OF GRANTS Up to around £150,000.

SAMPLE GRANTS SHINE @Chingford Hall (£180,000); SHINE @St Mary's Primary School (£165,000); Lift for Learning – DigiSmart (£150,000); London Bubble Theatre Company (£131,500); The Lyric – Hammersmith (£93,500); SHINE @ Clapham Park (£77,000); SHINE @ Axis (£60,000); Tutor Trust (£45,000); Serious Fun Kings School – Ely (£35,000); The Latin Programme (£25,000); Serious Fun Derrick Wood School (£20,000); Serious Fun Perse School (£12,000); Serious Fun Sheffield High School (£3,000).

FINANCES *Year* 2011–12 *Income* £2,283,065 *Grants* £2,194,807 *Assets* £5,419,825

TRUSTEES Jim O'Neill, Chair; David Blood; Mark Heffernan; Henry Bedford; Gavin Boyle; Mark Ferguson; Cameron Ogden; Dr Krutika Pau; Natasha Pope; Richard Rothwell; Stephen Shields; Bridget Walsh; Dr Caroline Whalley.

HOW TO APPLY Potential applicants must check the charity's website for current guidelines and application criteria.

WHO TO APPLY TO Paul Carbury, Chief Executive, 1 Cheam Road, Ewell Village, Surrey KT17 1SP *Tel.* 020 8393 1880 *email* info@shinetrust.org.uk *Website* www.shinetrust.org.uk

■ The Barnett and Sylvia Shine No 2 Charitable Trust

CC NO 281821 **ESTABLISHED** 1980

WHERE FUNDING CAN BE GIVEN Worldwide.

WHO CAN BENEFIT Registered charities.

WHAT IS FUNDED General charitable purposes.

WHAT IS NOT FUNDED No grants to individuals.

TYPE OF GRANT Usually one-off.

SAMPLE GRANTS The Samaritans, African Medical and Research Foundation, CAMFED International and Oxfam (£5,000 each); Médecins Sans Frontières and Macmillan Cancer Support (£3,000 each) and British Shalom-Salaam Trust, Children's Country Holidays Fund, NSPCC and UNICEF (£2,000 each).

FINANCES *Year* 2011–12 *Income* £42,045 *Grants* £55,000 *Assets* £1,320,863

TRUSTEES Martin Paisner; Barbara J. Grahame; Rodney Grahame.

HOW TO APPLY In writing to the correspondent. The trustees consider applications at formal and informal meetings.

WHO TO APPLY TO Martin Paisner, Trustee, Berwin Leiton Paisner, Adelaide House, London Bridge, London EC4R 9HA *Tel.* 020 7760 1000

■ The Bassil Shippam and Alsford Trust

CC NO 256996 **ESTABLISHED** 1967

WHERE FUNDING CAN BE GIVEN UK, with a preference for West Sussex.

WHO CAN BENEFIT Organisations benefiting young and older people, people with learning disabilities, Christians and health and educational purposes.

WHAT IS FUNDED General charitable purposes. Support is concentrated on local charities located in West Sussex rather than on UK appeals, with emphasis on Christian objects and youth.

TYPE OF GRANT Capital grants for up to three years.

RANGE OF GRANTS Mostly under £1,000.

SAMPLE GRANTS Chichester Boys' Club (£8,000); St Wilfrid's Hospice (£5,000); West Wittering Village Hall (£2,500); and the Tall Ships Trust (£1,000).

FINANCES *Year* 2011–12 *Income* £145,131 *Grants* £75,342 *Assets* £3,771,080

TRUSTEES John Shippam; Christopher Doman; Molly Hanwell; Simon MacFarlane; John Shippam; Richard Tayler; Susan Trayler; Stanley Young; Janet Bailey.

OTHER INFORMATION Grants were also made to individuals totalling £4,700.

HOW TO APPLY In writing to the correspondent, including a copy of the latest set of reports, accounts and forecasts. The trustees meet three times a year to consider applications.

WHO TO APPLY TO Iain MacLeod, Administrator, Thomas Eggar LLP, The Corn Exchange, Baffins Lane, Chichester, West Sussex PO19 1GE *Tel.* 01243 786111 *Fax* 01243 775640

....

■ The Shipwrights' Company Charitable Fund

CC NO 262043 **ESTABLISHED** 1971

WHERE FUNDING CAN BE GIVEN UK, with a preference for the City of London.

WHO CAN BENEFIT Individuals and organisations with a maritime connection. Emphasis is given to those benefiting young people, church work and the City.

WHAT IS FUNDED Maritime training, sailors' welfare and maritime heritage. Churches and Anglican bodies are also supported.

WHAT IS NOT FUNDED Any application without a clear maritime connection.

TYPE OF GRANT Annual donations, general donations and outdoor activity bursaries. Buildings, capital, core costs, one-off, project and start-up costs. Funding for one year or less will be considered.

RANGE OF GRANTS Mainly £500–£5,000. Larger grants can be made from unspent surpluses from previous years.

SAMPLE GRANTS Tall Ships Youth Trust (£20,000 for bursaries); George Green's School (£14,500 in three grants); Marine Society and Sea Cadets (£13,000); Jubilee Sailing Trust (£5,000 for bursaries); British Maritime Federation (£2,000); and Thames Shipwright and the Ahoy Centre (£1,000 each).

FINANCES *Year* 2011–12 *Income* £151,164 *Grants* £85,786 *Assets* £2,588,233

TRUSTEES The Worshipful Company of Shipwrights; William Everard; Simon Sherrard; Sir Jock Slater; Simon Robinson; Graham Clarke; Archibald Smith.

HOW TO APPLY In writing to the correspondent. Application forms and further guidelines are available from the trust's website. Applications are considered in February, June and November.

WHO TO APPLY TO The Clerk, Ironmongers' Hall, Shaftesbury Place, Barbican, London EC2Y 8AA *Tel.* 020 7606 2376 *Fax* 020 7600 8117 *email* clerk@shipwrights.co.uk *Website* www.shipwrights.co.uk

....

■ The Shirley Foundation

CC NO 1097135 **ESTABLISHED** 1996

WHERE FUNDING CAN BE GIVEN UK

WHO CAN BENEFIT Registered charities and research institutions.

WHAT IS FUNDED The main areas of interest are information technology and autism (not excluding Aspergers Syndrome) which occasionally extend to learning disabilities in general. The foundation's mission is 'the facilitation and support of pioneering projects with strategic impact in the field of autism spectrum disorders, with particular emphasis on medical research'.

WHAT IS NOT FUNDED No grants to individuals, or for non-autism-specific work. The foundation does not make political donations.

TYPE OF GRANT Capital and revenue grants and full project funding.

SAMPLE GRANTS Edinburgh Development Trust – Autism Research Laboratories (£1 million); Autistica (£500,000); and Paintings in Hospitals – Autism and Disability Loan Scheme (£250,000).

FINANCES *Year* 2011–12 *Income* £69,394 *Grants* £1,750,000 *Assets* £1,803,577

TRUSTEES Dame Stephanie Shirley, Chair; Prof. Eve Johnstone; Michael Robert Macfadyen; Anne McCartney Menzies.

OTHER INFORMATION The foundation appears to have developed a pattern of making a few substantial grants every other year.

HOW TO APPLY 'Trustees meet twice yearly but applications for support are received throughout the year. Only those within the foundation's Mission are considered; applicants are reminded that projects should be innovative in nature with the potential to have a strategic impact in the field of Autism Spectrum Disorders. Research proposals should be aimed ultimately at determining causes of autism. Researchers should refer to the 'Guidance: Application for a medical research grant' downloadable [from the foundation's website]. In the first instance a simple letter with outline proposal should be sent to Dame Stephanie Shirley at the registered address or emailed.'

WHO TO APPLY TO Anne McCartney Menzies, Trustee, c/o James Cowper LLP, North Lea House, 66 Northfield End, Henley-on-Thames, Oxfordshire RG9 2BE *Tel.* 01491 579004 *Fax* 01491 574995 *email* steve@steveshirley.com *Website* www.steveshirley.com/tsf

....

■ Shlomo Memorial Fund Limited

CC NO 278973 **ESTABLISHED** 1980

WHERE FUNDING CAN BE GIVEN Unrestricted.

WHO CAN BENEFIT Organisations benefiting Jewish people.

WHAT IS FUNDED Jewish causes.

SAMPLE GRANTS Previous beneficiaries include: Amud Haolam, Nachlat Haleviim, Torah Umesorah, Beit Hillel, ZSV Charities, Layesharim Tehilla, British Friends of Tashbar Chazon Ish, Chazon Ish, Mei Menuchos, Mor Uketsio, Shoshanat Hoamakim, Millennium Trust, and Talmud Torah Zichron Meir.

FINANCES *Year* 2011–12 *Income* £10,985,980 *Grants* £1,430,477 *Assets* £44,052,869

TRUSTEES Amichai Toporowitz, Chair; Hezkel Toporowitz; Eliyah Kleineman; Channe Lopian; Chaim Y. Kaufman.

OTHER INFORMATION A list of grant beneficiaries was not included in the trust's accounts.

HOW TO APPLY In writing to the correspondent.

WHO TO APPLY TO Channe Lopian, Secretary, Cohen Arnold and Co., New Burlington House, 1075 Finchley Road, London NW11 0PU *Tel.* 020 8731 0777 *Fax* 020 8731 0778

■ The Shoe Zone Trust

CC NO 1112972 **ESTABLISHED** 2005
WHERE FUNDING CAN BE GIVEN Preference for
Leicestershire and Rutland and for certain
charities operating in the Philippines and other
countries.
WHO CAN BENEFIT Children and young people.
WHAT IS FUNDED The objects of the charity are to
make grants and donations to other charities to
relieve the financial hardship and poverty and/or
advancement of education, mainly for children
and young persons under the age of 18
particularly in Leicestershire and Rutland and for
certain charities operating in the Philippines.
SAMPLE GRANTS Shepherd of the Hills – Philippines
(£61,000); Ministries without Borders
(£18,000); CRLC (£12,000) and 500 Miles
(£5,000).
FINANCES *Year* 2012 *Income* £40,457
Grants £98,964 *Assets* £22,606
TRUSTEES Michael Smith; John Smith; Anthony
Smith.
HOW TO APPLY In writing to the correspondent.
WHO TO APPLY TO The Trustees, Haramead Business
Centre, Humberstone Road, Leicester LE1 2LH
Tel. 01162 223007 *Website* www.shoezone.
net/sztrust.html

■ The J. A. Shone Memorial Trust

CC NO 270104 **ESTABLISHED** 1974
WHERE FUNDING CAN BE GIVEN Merseyside and
overseas.
WHO CAN BENEFIT Registered charities known to the
trustees.
WHAT IS FUNDED Christian and local causes in
Merseyside and mission work overseas.
RANGE OF GRANTS Usually up to £10,000.
SAMPLE GRANTS Toxteth Tabernacle and Mission
Aviation Fellowship (£5,000 each); ABF The
Soldiers' Charity (£3,000); Penshurst Retreat
Centre (£2,500); Royal Liverpool Philharmonic
Society, College of St Barnabas, Wirral
Churches' Ark Project and Titus Trust (£2,000
each); TearFund and Local Solutions (£1,000
each).
FINANCES *Year* 2011–12 *Income* £33,252
Grants £46,000
TRUSTEES Anthony Shone; James Stileman;
Liverpool Charity and Voluntary Services; Emma
Crowe.
HOW TO APPLY The trust does not respond to
unsolicited applications.
WHO TO APPLY TO The Trustees, Liverpool Charity and
Voluntary Services, 151 Dale Street, Liverpool
L2 2AH *Tel.* 01512 275177

■ Community Foundation for Shropshire and Telford

CC NO 1012215
WHERE FUNDING CAN BE GIVEN Shropshire, Telford and
Wrekin.
WHO CAN BENEFIT Community projects, local charities
and community groups.
WHAT IS FUNDED General charitable purposes which
address community need.
WHAT IS NOT FUNDED Individuals, animal charities,
statutory organisations, e.g. schools /hospitals,
those applying for equipment that would
become the property of a statutory authority,
purely social activities, capital building costs
(although applications for access adaptations
may be considered depending on the
circumstances), promotion of political or

religious beliefs or campaigning, salaries or
contributions to a general appeal with no set
timescales (e.g. an appeal for a minibus). No
retrospective grants. Note that further
restrictions may apply to different grant
schemes.
TYPE OF GRANT One-off, start-up, project grants.
RANGE OF GRANTS Up to £2,000.
SAMPLE GRANTS Previous beneficiaries include:
Afasic Wrekin; Brookside Family Playhouse;
IMPACT Alcohol Advisory Service; Marks Pit
Stop; Parent Partnership; the Salvation Army Kip
Project; Telford Christian Council – New Start
Project; and Wellington and district YMCA.
FINANCES *Year* 2011–12 *Income* £330,636
Grants £229,876 *Assets* £264,852
TRUSTEES David Dixon; Richard Pennells; Nicole
Howarth; Mike Lowe; John Cuffley; William
Parkinson; Robert Hicklin; Joseph Evans; Pat
McLaughlin; Alan Bowyer
HOW TO APPLY Applicants are directed, where
possible, to the foundation's website where the
foundation's criteria, guidelines and application
process are posted. The foundation welcomes
contact prior to the formal submission of an
application in order to help applicants prepare
the best possible application.
WHO TO APPLY TO Lynne Carney, Grants Officer, The
Academy, 1 Brassey Road, Old Potts Way,
Shrewsbury SY3 7FA *Tel.* 01743 343879
email contact@cfshropshireandtelford.org.uk
Website www.cfshropshireandtelford.org.uk

■ The Barbara A. Shuttleworth Memorial Trust

CC NO 1016117 **ESTABLISHED** 1992
WHERE FUNDING CAN BE GIVEN UK, with a preference
for West Yorkshire.
WHO CAN BENEFIT Organisations benefiting people
with disabilities, particularly children.
WHAT IS FUNDED Charities working with children who
are disabled and associated causes. Grants are
given especially for equipment and premises,
but holidays and outings, training courses, and
other needs are also considered.
TYPE OF GRANT Capital grants.
SAMPLE GRANTS The Being Bel Trust (£2,500);
Whizz-Kidz (£1,900); Hollybank Special School
(£1,400); Sunny Day's Children's Fund
(£1,000); Making a Difference (£800); Disability
Awareness UK, Seeing Ear, Alstrom Syndrome
UK and Naomi House Children's Hospice (£500
each) and West Yorkshire ADHD Support Group
and Autism Plus (£200 each).
FINANCES *Year* 2011–12 *Income* £27,457
Grants £33,500 *Assets* £510,467
TRUSTEES John Alistair Baty, Chair; Barbara Anne
Shuttleworth; John Christopher Joseph Eaton;
William Fenton.
HOW TO APPLY In writing to the correspondent.
WHO TO APPLY TO John Baty, Chair, Baty Casson
Long, 23 Moorhead Terrace, Shipley BD18 4LB
Tel. 01274 584946 *email* baty@btinternet.com

■ The Mary Elizabeth Siebel Charity

CC NO 1001255 **ESTABLISHED** 1990
WHERE FUNDING CAN BE GIVEN Within a 12-mile radius
of Newark Town Hall.
WHO CAN BENEFIT Individuals and organisations
benefiting older people who are ill, have
disabilities or who are disadvantaged by poverty,
and their carers.

WHAT IS FUNDED Hospice at home, respite care for carers and care in the community. Preference is given to assisting people who wish to live independently in their own homes.

TYPE OF GRANT Flexible, but one-off grants preferred for buildings, capital and core costs.

SAMPLE GRANTS £16,000 to Crossroads Care.

FINANCES *Year* 2011–12 *Income* £114,041 *Grants* £91,716

TRUSTEES P. Blatherwick; D. McKenny; R. White; A. Austin; S. Watson; Miss J. Moore.

OTHER INFORMATION The grant total includes £85,000 given to individuals.

HOW TO APPLY In writing to the correspondent, requesting an application form. The trustees meet every couple of months to discuss applications.

WHO TO APPLY TO Frances Kelly, Administrator, c/o Tallents Solicitors, 3 Middlegate, Newark, Nottinghamshire NG24 1AQ *Tel.* 01636 671881 *email* fck@tallents.co.uk

David and Jennifer Sieff Charitable Trust

CC NO 206329   **ESTABLISHED** 1970
WHERE FUNDING CAN BE GIVEN UK.
WHO CAN BENEFIT Registered charities.
WHAT IS FUNDED General charitable purposes.
WHAT IS NOT FUNDED No grants to individuals.
RANGE OF GRANTS £80 to £13,000.
SAMPLE GRANTS Community Security Trust (£12,500); British Refugee Council (£7,000); The Southbank Centre, Save the Children and Home of Horseracing Trust (£5,000 each); Holocaust Centre (£3,500); International Centre for the Study of Radicalisation (£2,500); East Anglian Air Ambulance and Anglo-Israel Association (£1,000 each); British Friends of Heifa University (£500); Age UK London (£250); Starlight Children's Foundation (£200) and Life Action Trust (£80).
FINANCES *Year* 2011–12 *Income* £35,301 *Grants* £80,320 *Assets* £534,620
TRUSTEES Hon. Sir David Sieff; Lady Jennifer Sieff; Lord Wolfson of Sunningdale.
OTHER INFORMATION In 2011–12 grants were given to 66 organisations.
HOW TO APPLY In writing to the correspondent.
WHO TO APPLY TO The Trustees, H. W. Fisher and Company, Acre House, 11–15 William Road, London NW1 3ER *Tel.* 020 7388 7000

The Julius Silman Charitable Trust

CC NO 263830   **ESTABLISHED** 1971
WHERE FUNDING CAN BE GIVEN UK.
WHO CAN BENEFIT Charitable organisations.
WHAT IS FUNDED Support of at risk groups and humanitarian causes, focusing on Jewish organisations.
WHAT IS NOT FUNDED No grants to individuals.
TYPE OF GRANT One-off and recurrent.
RANGE OF GRANTS Up to £3,000.
SAMPLE GRANTS Kids for Kids (£2,600); Neve Michael and New Israel Fund (£1,000 each); Anti-Slavery, Norwood, Motability and Heads Up (£500 each); World Jewish Relief, Friendship Way and Jewish Childs Day (£250 each); and Samaritans of Bath, Wiltshire Splash and Cancer Research (£100 each).
FINANCES *Year* 2012–13 *Income* £20,112 *Grants* £25,000

TRUSTEES Stephen Silman; Christine Smith; Rachel Dickson.
HOW TO APPLY The trust has stated that they are no longer taking any unsolicited applications.
WHO TO APPLY TO Christine Smith, Trustee, Roselands, 2 High Street, Steeple Ashton, Wiltshire BA14 6EL *Tel.* 01380 870421

The Leslie Silver Charitable Trust

CC NO 1007599   **ESTABLISHED** 1991
WHERE FUNDING CAN BE GIVEN UK, but mostly West Yorkshire.
WHO CAN BENEFIT Small local projects, new organisations and established organisations primarily benefiting children, young adults and Jewish causes.
WHAT IS FUNDED Medicine and health; welfare; sciences and humanities; the advancement of the Jewish religion, synagogues, Jewish religious umbrella bodies; arts, culture and recreation; community facilities; and other charitable purposes.
WHAT IS NOT FUNDED No grants to individuals or students.
TYPE OF GRANT One-off grants.
RANGE OF GRANTS £500–£10,000.
SAMPLE GRANTS Leeds Jewish Welfare (£10,000); The Zone and UJIA (£5,000 each); Coexistence Trust, Holocaust Centre, Variety Club Leeds and World Jewish Relief (£2,000 each); Donisthorpe Hall (£1,500); Ezer Mizion (£1,000) and Holocaust Education (£500).
FINANCES *Year* 2011–12 *Income* £32,762 *Grants* £30,900 *Assets* £90,317
TRUSTEES Leslie H. Silver; Mark S. Silver; Ian J. Fraser.
HOW TO APPLY Organisation should submit a summary of their proposals 'in a specific format, together with outline appeals'.
WHO TO APPLY TO Ian J. Fraser, Trustee, R. S. M. Tenon Ltd, 2 Wellington Place, Leeds LS1 4AP *Tel.* 01132 445451

The Simmons and Simmons Charitable Foundation

CC NO 1129643   **ESTABLISHED** 2009
WHERE FUNDING CAN BE GIVEN London, with a preference for the City of London and Tower Hamlets.
WHO CAN BENEFIT Registered charities.
WHAT IS FUNDED Social welfare, education.
RANGE OF GRANTS Up to £10,000.
SAMPLE GRANTS The Mayor's Fund for London and Five Talents UK Ltd (£10,000 each); Bingham Appeal, Red Balloon, Opportunity International UK, Pennies Foundation, Big Issue Foundation and Twist (£5,000 each); Visionpath (£4,000); Stillbirth and Neonatal Death Charity (£2,500); Sunshine Action – Hong Kong (£2,200); Law Society riot helpline (£2,000); and YMCA (£1,000).
FINANCES *Year* 2011–12 *Income* £197,964 *Grants* £61,703 *Assets* £180,038
TRUSTEES Richard Dyton; Michele Anahory; Fiona Loughrey; Colin Passmore.
HOW TO APPLY On an application form available to download from the firm's website.
WHO TO APPLY TO The Trustees, Simmons and Simmons LLP, Citypoint, 1 Ropemaker Street,

London EC2Y 9SS *Tel.* 020 7628 2020
Fax 020 7628 2070 *email* diversity@simmons-simmons.com *Website* www.simmons-simmons.com

■ The Simpson Education and Conservation Trust

CC NO 1069695　　**ESTABLISHED** 1998
WHERE FUNDING CAN BE GIVEN UK and overseas, with a preference for the neotropics (South America).
WHO CAN BENEFIT Charitable organisations.
WHAT IS FUNDED Advancement of education, including medical and scientific research; the conservation and protection of the natural environment and endangered species of plants and animals with special emphasis on the protection of forests and endangered avifauna in the neotropics (South America).
WHAT IS NOT FUNDED No grants to individuals.
TYPE OF GRANT One-off or up to three years, for development or project funding.
RANGE OF GRANTS Up to £25,000.
SAMPLE GRANTS Jocotoco Foundation in Ecuador (£25,000); RBG Kew for Peru (£3,000); Linnean Society for Tanzania, Dodwell Trust for Madagascar and Second Sight Trust for India (£1,000 each); and Lord Treloar School Trust (£500).
FINANCES *Year* 2011–12 *Income* £30,038 *Grants* £31,656 *Assets* £20,953
TRUSTEES Dr Nigel Simpson, Chair; Prof. Donald Broom; Dr Michael Lock; Prof. Stanley Chang; Dr Katherine Simpson.
HOW TO APPLY In writing to the correspondent. The day-to-day activities of this trust are carried out by e-mail, telephone and circulation of documents, since the trustees do not all live in the UK.
WHO TO APPLY TO Nigel Simpson, Trustee, Honeysuckle Cottage, Tidenham Chase, Chepstow, Gwent NP16 7JW *Tel.* 01291 689423 *Fax* 01291 689803

■ The Simpson Foundation

CC NO 231030　　**ESTABLISHED** 1961
WHERE FUNDING CAN BE GIVEN UK.
WHO CAN BENEFIT Registered charities only, particularly those benefiting Roman Catholics.
WHAT IS FUNDED The support of charities favoured by the founder in his lifetime and others with similar objects; mainly Catholic charities.
WHAT IS NOT FUNDED No grants to non-registered charities or individuals.
SAMPLE GRANTS Sisters of Providence and of the Immaculate Conception (£2,000); Apostleship of the Sea, The Passage and Friends of the Holy Trinity Monastery (£1,000 each); and Cardinal Hume Centre, Stonor Chapel and St Mungo's (£500 each).
FINANCES *Year* 2011–12 *Income* £37,453 *Grants* £23,000 *Assets* £313,863
TRUSTEES Charles Bellord; Peter Hawthorne; Patrick Herschan.
HOW TO APPLY In writing to the correspondent, at any time. No telephone applications will be considered.
WHO TO APPLY TO Patrick Herschan, Trustee, Pothecary Witham Weld, 70 St George's Square, London SW1V 3RD *Tel.* 020 7821 8211 *Fax* 020 7630 6484

■ The Huntly and Margery Sinclair Charitable Trust

CC NO 235939　　**ESTABLISHED** 1964
WHERE FUNDING CAN BE GIVEN UK.
WHO CAN BENEFIT Generally to registered charities.
WHAT IS FUNDED Well-established charities in particular.
RANGE OF GRANTS Up to £10,000.
SAMPLE GRANTS Injured Jockeys Fund (£5,000); Changing Faces (£4,000); Zetland Foundation (£3,000); Gloucester Cathedral and R.N.L.I Special Appeal (£2,000); Army Benevolent Fund, Eton College, Action Water and Macmillan Cancer Support (£1,000 each) and National Parrot Sanctuary, Elkstone Church and Maggie's Cheltenham (£500 each).
FINANCES *Year* 2011–12 *Income* £46,522 *Grants* £42,000 *Assets* £1,349,298
TRUSTEES A. M. H. Gibbs; M. A. H. Windsor; J. Floyd.
HOW TO APPLY Unsolicited applications are rarely successful and due to the high number such requests the trust is not able to respond to them or return any printed materials supplied.
WHO TO APPLY TO Wilfrid Vernor-Miles, Administrator, Hunters Solicitors, 9 New Square, Lincoln's Inn, London WC2A 3QN

■ Sino-British Fellowship Trust

CC NO 313669　　**ESTABLISHED** 1948
WHERE FUNDING CAN BE GIVEN UK and China.
WHO CAN BENEFIT Institutions benefiting individual postgraduate students.
WHAT IS FUNDED Scholarships to Chinese citizens to enable them to pursue their studies in Britain. Grants to British citizens in China to educate/train Chinese citizens in any art, science or profession.
TYPE OF GRANT Fees; fares; and allowances.
RANGE OF GRANTS Up to around £50,000.
SAMPLE GRANTS Royal Society (£51,500); British Library (£22,000); China Scholarship Council (£21,500); Great Britain China Educational Trust (£20,000); Hong Kong University (£15,000); Universities China Committee London (£13,000); Needham Research Institute (£8,000); and Universities China Committee London (£4,000).
FINANCES *Year* 2012 *Income* £469,722 *Grants* £329,148 *Assets* £13,270,006
TRUSTEES Prof. Sir Brian Heap; Ling Thompson; Prof. Hugh Baker; Anne Ely; Peter Ely; Dr Jeremy Langton; Lady Pamela Youde.
OTHER INFORMATION Of total grants made £255,500 went to organisations in the UK and China. The remainder was spent on individual scholarships for students.
HOW TO APPLY On a form available by writing to the correspondence address.
WHO TO APPLY TO Anne Ely, Trustee, Flat 23 Bede House, Manor Fields, London SW15 3LT *Tel.* 020 8788 6252

■ SITA Cornwall Trust Limited

CC NO 1127288　　**ESTABLISHED** 2008
WHERE FUNDING CAN BE GIVEN Cornwall
WHO CAN BENEFIT Community organisations.
WHAT IS FUNDED Natural environment and the community. In particular, projects that will provide essential social and environmental benefit to communities in Cornwall.
RANGE OF GRANTS Up to £100,000.

Think carefully about every application. Is it justified?

897

SAMPLE GRANTS Wendron Football Club (£50,000); Hayle and District Bowling Club (£35,000); Forder Community Hall (£25,000); Callington Bowling Club (£18,000); Mary Newman's Cottage (£11,500) and Breage Toddlers Kingdom (£5,000).

FINANCES *Year* 2011–12 *Income* £590,792 *Grants* £440,922 *Assets* £1,026,430

TRUSTEES George Hocking; Richard Thomas; Paul Brinsley; Andrew Saunders; Charlie David; SITA. UK; Lee Rouse; Betty Hale.

OTHER INFORMATION In 2011–12 grants were awarded to 28 projects.

HOW TO APPLY On a form available to download on the website, where criteria and guidelines are also posted. The trust states that 'if you require further information, clarification or have any questions contact the office, and we will be able to answer all your queries.'

WHO TO APPLY TO Wendy Reading, Unit 1 Ashleigh Meadow, Tregondale, Menheniot, Liskeard, Cornwall PL14 3RG *Tel.* 01579 346816 *email* wendyreading@btconnect.com *Website* www.sitacornwalltrust.co.uk

■ Six Point Foundation

CC NO 1143324   **ESTABLISHED** 2012
WHERE FUNDING CAN BE GIVEN UK
WHO CAN BENEFIT Organisations benefiting Holocaust survivors and Jewish refugees.
WHAT IS FUNDED Projects that will improve health and wellbeing.
WHAT IS NOT FUNDED No grants for Holocaust education projects.
TYPE OF GRANT Usually project costs but capital costs may be considered.
RANGE OF GRANTS Up to £30,000
SAMPLE GRANTS London Jewish Cultural Centre (£107,000 in two grants); London Association of Jewish Refugees (£98,000); The Holocaust Centre (£90,000); Birmingham Jewish Community Centre (£37,000); Holocaust Survivors Centre/Shalvata (Jewish Care) (£23,000); Golden Years (£22,000); Senior N'Shei (£21,000) and North London Bikur Cholim and Bikur Cholim Limited (£15,000 each).
FINANCES *Year* 2012–13 *Income* £830,082 *Grants* £910,555 *Assets* £4,024,054
TRUSTEES Frank Harding; Susan Grant; Vivienne Woolf; Julian Challis; Nigel Raine; Lionel Curry; Joanna Lassman.
OTHER INFORMATION This foundation aims to spend out by 2016. There were an additional 123 grants given to individuals for welfare purposes totalling £88,000.
HOW TO APPLY Applicants should firstly contact the foundation to discuss an application and agree a deadline for submission of an initial proposal. Guidance notes for this proposal are available to download from the website. If this initial proposal is successful, applicants will then be asked for more specific and detailed information. Applications will be acknowledged upon receipt and applicants should allow up to six months in total to complete the application process. Trustees meet five times a year to consider proposals and a site visit may be required.
WHO TO APPLY TO Susan Cohen, Executive Director, 25–26 Enford Street, London W1H 1DW *Tel.* 020 3372 8881 *email* info@ sixpointfoundation.org.uk *Website* www. sixpointfoundation.org.uk

■ The Skelton Bounty

CC NO 219370   **ESTABLISHED** 1934
WHERE FUNDING CAN BE GIVEN Lancashire (as it existed in 1934).
WHO CAN BENEFIT Registered charities benefiting young, older and infirm people.
WHAT IS FUNDED Restricted to Lancashire charities (not national ones unless operating in Lancashire from a permanent establishment within the county predominantly for the benefit of residents from that county) assisting young, elderly and infirm people.
WHAT IS NOT FUNDED No grants to individuals, religious charities or medical or scientific research.
TYPE OF GRANT Capital expenditure preferred.
RANGE OF GRANTS Up to £8,500.
SAMPLE GRANTS Lancashire Partnership Against Crime – Preston (£4,400); Garston Adventure Playground – Liverpool, 62' Southport St Cuthbert's Scout Group and Jubilee Sailing Trust – Lydiate (£3,000 each); Netherton Park Community Association (£2,500); Royal Liverpool Philharmonic Society and Methodist Homes for the Aged – Derby (£2,000 each); Plaza Community Cinema – Liverpool (£1,500); Live Music Now North West – Lymm (£1,000); The Dystonia Society – London (£750) and Harvest Trust – Llandysul (£500).
FINANCES *Year* 2011–12 *Income* £97,637 *Grants* £90,112 *Assets* £2,047,083
TRUSTEES William Fulton; Patricia Wilson; Margo Pitt; Dennis Mendoros; Jacqueline Lundy; Dame Lorna Muirhead DBE; Roger Morris; Caroline Reynolds.
OTHER INFORMATION In 2011–12 grants were given to 51 organisations.
HOW TO APPLY On a form available from the correspondent. Requests for application forms should be made as soon as possible after 1 January each year. The completed form should be returned before 31 March immediately following. Applications received after this date will not be considered. The trustees meet annually in July, with successful applicants receiving their grant cheques in late July/early August. Applications should include the charitable registration number of the organisation, or, where appropriate, a letter confirming charitable status.
WHO TO APPLY TO The Trustees, c/o Liverpool Charity and Voluntary Services, 151 Dale street, Liverpool L2 2AH

■ The Charles Skey Charitable Trust

CC NO 277697   **ESTABLISHED** 1979
WHERE FUNDING CAN BE GIVEN UK.
WHO CAN BENEFIT Organisations which the trustees have come across from their own research.
WHAT IS FUNDED General charitable purposes.
TYPE OF GRANT Grants are given on a one-off and recurring basis for core and capital support.
RANGE OF GRANTS £500–£10,000.
SAMPLE GRANTS Lloyds Patriotic Fund (£10,000); Trinity Hospice (£8,500); Roses Charitable Trust (£7,500); Battle of Britain Monument Fund (£5,000); Camphill Village Trust (£4,000); Dagenham Gospel Trust (£3,000); WaterAid (£2,500); Institute of Cancer Research (£1,500); and Rugbeian Society and King Edward VII Hospital for Officers (£1,000 each).
FINANCES *Year* 2011–12 *Income* £285,211 *Grants* £88,000 *Assets* £3,949,318

TRUSTEES Christopher Berkeley; John Leggett; Revd James Leggett; David Berkeley; Edward Berkeley; James Carleton.

HOW TO APPLY The trust has previously stated that no written or telephoned requests for support will be entertained.

WHO TO APPLY TO John Leggett, Trustee, Flint House, Park Homer Road, Colehill, Wimborne, Dorset BH21 2SP

....

■ Skipton Building Society Charitable Foundation

CC NO 1079538   **ESTABLISHED** 2000

WHERE FUNDING CAN BE GIVEN England and Wales.

WHO CAN BENEFIT Registered charitable organisations.

WHAT IS FUNDED General charitable purposes with particular priority to the charities that benefit children, through education and/or welfare, or the elderly and their care.

WHAT IS NOT FUNDED Donations supporting political activities; to non-registered charities or individuals, including students; to activities which are primarily the responsibility of central or local government or other responsible bodies; towards running costs including rent or staff wages, training of employed and volunteer staff; towards restoration or upkeep of buildings or monuments; towards expeditions or overseas travel; towards fundraising events and activities, sponsorship or marketing appeals, or any other activities which collect funds for subsequent redistribution to other charities or individuals; towards the cost or maintenance of vehicles; to healthcare, including medical research and health education; to large national charities; to capital projects; to animal welfare organisations; towards loans or business finance; to overseas activities or charities; towards promotion of religion or the restoration or upkeep of places of worship; from charities which have applied to the foundation within the previous 12 months.

TYPE OF GRANT Direct donations

RANGE OF GRANTS £500–£10,000, normally not exceeding £5,000.

SAMPLE GRANTS Goldhill Play Association (£5,000); U Can Do It (£2,600); Peter Pan Nursery (£2,000); Bradford and District Autistic Support Group (£1,700); Oakhaven Hospice Trust (£1,500); Delamere Toy Library (£1,000); Trinity Care Service (£500).

FINANCES *Year* 2011–12 *Income* £120,849 *Grants* £110,769 *Assets* £64,360

TRUSTEES Richard Twigg; Lord Hope of Thornes; Ethne Bannister; Richard Robinson; Rachel Ramsden; Kitty North.

HOW TO APPLY Written application found on foundation's website together with enclosed organisation's latest two years' annual accounts, a specific breakdown of how the donation will be used and an explanation of the benefit to its recipients.

WHO TO APPLY TO John Gibson, Secretary, The Bailey, Skipton, North Yorkshire BD23 1DN *Fax* 01756 705743 *Website* www. skiptoncharitablefoundation.co.uk

....

■ The John Slater Foundation

CC NO 231145   **ESTABLISHED** 1963

WHERE FUNDING CAN BE GIVEN UK, with a strong preference for the north west of England especially West Lancashire.

WHO CAN BENEFIT Registered charities.

WHAT IS FUNDED Welfare, including animal welfare, and general charitable purposes.

WHAT IS NOT FUNDED No grants to individuals.

RANGE OF GRANTS £500–£10,000.

SAMPLE GRANTS The Dogs Trust (£10,000); Trinity Hospital Bispham (£9,000); Adlington Community Centre (£8,000); Casterton School (£7,500); Verona Association Thornton Cleveleys and the North West Air Ambulance Trust (£6,000 each); Macmillan Cancer Relief (£5,000); Veterans Aid (£4,000); Cottingley Cornerstone Centre (£3,000); Wildlife Hospital Trust (£2,000); and Blackpool and Flyde Society for the Blind and the Marine Conservation Society (£1,000 each).

FINANCES *Year* 2011–12 *Income* £292,535 *Grants* £140,150 *Assets* £4,030,432

TRUSTEES D. J. Coke; B. A. Cook; H. Docherty; J. A. W. Doyle; N. G. Hinshelwood; D. J. Nibloe; V. Wales; D. L. Wells. (HSBC Trust Co. (UK) Ltd.)

HOW TO APPLY The foundation's website states: 'The foundation is presently fully committed to its programme of giving and unfortunately is not able to receive any further new requests of any nature at this time. Should this situation change an appropriate announcement will be made on [the foundation's] website.'

WHO TO APPLY TO Richard Thompson, Trust Manager, HSBC Trust Services, 10th Floor, Norwich House, Nelson Gate, Commercial Road, Southampton SO15 1GX *Tel.* 02380 722231 *Fax* 02380 722250 *Website* johnslaterfoundation.org.uk

....

■ Sloane Robinson Foundation

CC NO 1068286   **ESTABLISHED** 1998

WHERE FUNDING CAN BE GIVEN England and Wales.

WHO CAN BENEFIT Overseas students studying in the UK and British students studying abroad.

WHAT IS FUNDED Advancement of the education of the public through development of long term relationships with academic institutions as well as financial support to private individuals

WHAT IS NOT FUNDED On the undergraduate level and in funding fellowships and professorships at universities and places of higher education for both teaching and research grants should not be focused on religion, social sciences and languages, but no such restrictions apply on the postgraduate level. Funding of overseas programmes should be focused on the studies in which the country concerned offers better courses (e.g. Chinese history in China). Only in exceptional circumstances funding will be provided for the provision of sporting facilities

TYPE OF GRANT Grants to institutions on an ongoing relationship basis and grants to private individuals.

RANGE OF GRANTS £5,000– £156,000.

SAMPLE GRANTS Rugby School (£156,000); Keble College – Oxford and Lincoln College-Oxford (£53,000 each) Oxford University and School of Oriental and African Studies (£5,000 each).

FINANCES *Year* 2011–12 *Income* £21,574 *Grants* £357,065 *Assets* £16,536,242

TRUSTEES George Robinson; Hugh Sloane; Michael Willcox.

HOW TO APPLY Direct written communication with the correspondent. The foundation is very selective in grantmaking process, therefore only successful candidates will be notified.

WHO TO APPLY TO Michael Willcox, Trustee, The Old Coach House, Sunnyside, Bergh Apton, Norwich NR15 1DD *Tel.* 01508 480100 *email* info@ willcoxlewis.co.uk

■ Rita and David Slowe Charitable Trust

CC NO 1048209　　**ESTABLISHED** 1995
WHERE FUNDING CAN BE GIVEN UK and overseas.
WHO CAN BENEFIT Registered charities.
WHAT IS FUNDED General charitable purposes.
WHAT IS NOT FUNDED No grants are made to individuals (including gap year students) or religious bodies.
RANGE OF GRANTS £5,000–£13,000.
SAMPLE GRANTS Computer Aid International (£12,500) and Shelter, Books Abroad, Wells for India, Excellent Development, HERA, Big Issue Foundation and Crisis (£10,000 each). Most beneficiaries are supported on a recurrent basis.
FINANCES *Year* 2011–12 *Income* £263,532 *Grants* £82,500 *Assets* £853,820
TRUSTEES Elizabeth Slowe; Graham Weinberg; Jonathan Slowe; Lilian Slowe; Robert Slowe.
HOW TO APPLY In writing to the correspondent.
WHO TO APPLY TO The Trustees, 32 Hampstead High Street, London NW3 1JQ *Tel.* 020 7435 7800

■ Ruth Smart Foundation

CC NO 1080021　　**ESTABLISHED** 2000
WHERE FUNDING CAN BE GIVEN Worldwide, but mainly UK and USA.
WHO CAN BENEFIT Registered charities and charitable organisations.
WHAT IS FUNDED Relief of animal suffering
TYPE OF GRANT One-off.
RANGE OF GRANTS £250–£12,000.
SAMPLE GRANTS Fauna and Flora International Africa Programmes (£12,000); Mauritian Wildlife Foundation (£6,000); Durrell Wildlife Conservation, Friends of Mauritian Wildlife (£4,000 each); San Francisco Zoological Society (£3,000) and The Trees for Life (£250).
FINANCES *Year* 2012 *Income* £143,494 *Grants* £85,473 *Assets* £4,304,843
TRUSTEES Wilfrid Vernor-Miles; John Vernor-Miles; Paul Williams.
HOW TO APPLY 'The trustees support a number of charities on a regular basis and in practice finds that their income is fully committed and there is little, if any, surplus income available for distribution in response to unsolicited appeals.'
WHO TO APPLY TO The Trustees, c/o Hunters Solicitors, 9 New Square, Lincoln's Inn, London WC2A 3QN *Tel.* 020 7412 5105

■ The SMB Charitable Trust

CC NO 263814　　**ESTABLISHED** 1962
WHERE FUNDING CAN BE GIVEN UK and overseas.
WHO CAN BENEFIT Organisations for the advancement of the Christian religion and the relief of need, hardship or distress.
WHAT IS FUNDED Christian and welfare organisations. Accommodation and housing, various community services, healthcare, health facilities and buildings, famine/emergency aid, medical studies and research, and environmental and wildlife projects and campaigning will also be considered.
WHAT IS NOT FUNDED Grants to individuals are not normally considered, unless the application is made through a registered charity which can receive the cheque.
TYPE OF GRANT One-off grants, project grants and grants for recurring costs are prioritised. Also considered are building and other capital grants,

funding for core and running costs, funding for salaries and start-up costs.
RANGE OF GRANTS Up to £4,000.
SAMPLE GRANTS London City Mission (£4,000); British Red Cross (£3,000); Baptist Missionary Society and Hospice of Hope (£2,500 each); Fegans Child and Family Care, In Golden Company and Leprosy Mission (£2,000 each); University and Colleges Christian Fellowship (£1,500); Torch Trust, World Wildlife Fund, Toybox in Nicaragua and Royal National College for the Blind (£1,000 each).
FINANCES *Year* 2011–12 *Income* £349,285 *Grants* £238,450 *Assets* £8,605,136
TRUSTEES Eric Anstead; Philip Stanford; Barbara O'Driscoll; Jeremy Anstead; Claire Swarbrick.
HOW TO APPLY In writing to the correspondent, including the aims and principal activities of the applicant, the current financial position and details of any special projects for which funding is sought. Application forms are not used. Trustees normally meet in March, June, September and December and applications should be received before the beginning of the month in which meetings are held. Because of the volume of appeals received, unsuccessful applicants will only receive a reply if they enclose an sae. However, unsuccessful applicants are welcome to reapply.
WHO TO APPLY TO Barbara O'Driscoll, Trustee, 15 Wilman Road, Tunbridge Wells, Kent TN4 9AJ *Tel.* 01892 537301 *Fax* 01892 618202 *email* smbcharitabletrust@googlemail.com

■ The Smith and Pinching Charitable Trust

CC NO 1100486　　**ESTABLISHED** 2003
WHERE FUNDING CAN BE GIVEN Norfolk, Suffolk, Cambridgeshire, Essex and Hertfordshire.
WHO CAN BENEFIT Charitable organisations that benefit the areas of Norfolk, Suffolk, Cambridgeshire, Essex and Hertfordshire. Individuals.
WHAT IS FUNDED General charitable purposes; social welfare; health; sports and recreation.
WHAT IS NOT FUNDED Causes which fall within the beneficial areas only.
RANGE OF GRANTS £50–£6,000.
SAMPLE GRANTS Polar Endeavour (£6,000); the J's Hospice, Royal Norwich Agricultural Association and Mancroft Advice Project (£500 each); Waveney Counselling Service and SERV Norfolk Blood Bikes (£300 each); Happy Days Children's Trust (£200); Jubilee Family Centre, Catton Park Trust and Just Different (£100 each); and City of Norwich Athletics Club (£50).
FINANCES *Year* 2011–12 *Income* £48,286 *Grants* £11,924 *Assets* £20,872
TRUSTEES Scott Pinching; David Hughff; Michael Chapman.
OTHER INFORMATION 29 grants were given totalling £12,000.
HOW TO APPLY On a form available to download from the website and returned to the correspondent by post. Trustees meet on a quarterly basis. Unsolicited requests are not supported. Unsuccessful applicants should not apply for at least two years.
WHO TO APPLY TO Scott Pinching, Trustee, 295 Aylsham Road, Norwich NR3 2RY *Tel.* 01603 789966 *email* info@smith-pinching.co.uk *Website* www.spcharitabletrust.co.uk

■ The Mrs Smith and Mount Trust

CC NO 1009718   **ESTABLISHED** 1992

WHERE FUNDING CAN BE GIVEN London and south east England, i.e. Norfolk, Suffolk, Cambridgeshire, Hertfordshire, Essex, Kent and Surrey.

WHO CAN BENEFIT Organisations benefiting people with mental illness or learning disability, homelessness and family support. Counselling is also supported with these categories.

WHAT IS FUNDED The trust has three main areas of interest mental illness/learning difficulties, family support within other two areas and homelessness.

WHAT IS NOT FUNDED The trustees do not consider building costs, only refurbishment or alterations necessary to bring them up to health and safety/fire regulations. No grants to individuals.

TYPE OF GRANT One-off and continuing revenue grants are considered.
Up to three years funding.

RANGE OF GRANTS £1,000 to £7,000.

SAMPLE GRANTS YESU (£7,000); Autistic Way (£6,000); Dens Action Against Homeless and Kingston churches Action on Homelessness (£5,000 each); The Cara Trust, Hackney Migrant Centre and Richmond Borough Mind £4,000 each); Tonbridge and District Mencap Society (£3,000); Suffolk Artlink (£2,500) and Musical Keys (£1,000).

FINANCES *Year* 2011–12 *Income* £209,584 *Grants* £176,939 *Assets* £5,906,725

TRUSTEES Gillian Barnes; Richard Fowler; Douglas Mobsby; Lisa Weaks.

OTHER INFORMATION In 2011–12 grants were made to 46 organisations.

HOW TO APPLY All applications must be submitted using the online application form which can be downloaded from the website, where full guidelines and criteria are also available to view. The trustees meet three times per year in March, July and November and application forms and supporting documentation must reach the trust's offices by the end of January, May and September respectively.

WHO TO APPLY TO Jayne Day, Administrator, c/o Pothecary Witham Weld Solicitors, 70 St George's Square, London SW1V 3RD *Tel.* 020 7821 8211 *email* charities@pwwsolicitors.co.uk *Website* www.pwwsolicitors.co.uk

■ The N. Smith Charitable Settlement

CC NO 276660   **ESTABLISHED** 1978

WHERE FUNDING CAN BE GIVEN Worldwide.

WHO CAN BENEFIT Registered charities.

WHAT IS FUNDED General charitable purposes but mainly social work, medical research, education, environment/animals, arts and overseas aid.

WHAT IS NOT FUNDED Grants are only made to registered charities and not to individuals.

TYPE OF GRANT Appeals for capital equipment are preferred over salary costs.

RANGE OF GRANTS £500–£2,000.

SAMPLE GRANTS Disasters Emergency Committee (£5,000); Oxfam GB, Kidney Research UK and Genesis Appeal (£2,000 each); Epilepsy Research UK and Live Music Now (£1,500 each); and Anthony Nolan Bone Marrow Trust, Just Drop In, Fair Trials International and Pimlico Opera (£1,000 each). Numerous beneficiaries received grants for less than £1,000.

FINANCES *Year* 2011–12 *Income* £264,775 *Grants* £143,450 *Assets* £4,096,066

TRUSTEES Anne Merricks; John Williams-Rigby; Graham Wardle; Janet Adam.

HOW TO APPLY In writing to the correspondent. The trustees meet twice a year.

WHO TO APPLY TO Anne Merricks, Linder Myers, Phoenix House, 45 Cross Street, Manchester M2 4JF *Tel.* 01618 326972 *Fax* 01618 340718

■ The Smith Charitable Trust

CC NO 288570   **ESTABLISHED** 1983

WHERE FUNDING CAN BE GIVEN UK and overseas.

WHO CAN BENEFIT Registered charities, usually large, well-known UK organisations, which are on a list of regular beneficiaries.

WHAT IS FUNDED General charitable purposes particularly health.

WHAT IS NOT FUNDED No grants to animal charities or to individuals.

RANGE OF GRANTS £3,000–£12,000.

SAMPLE GRANTS Sue Ryder Care (£11,000); British Red Cross, RNIB and Research Institute for the Care of the Elderly (£7,400 each); Action for Children and St Nicholas' Hospice (£5,600 each) and The Marine Society and Sea Cadets, The Salvation Army, Providence Row Charity, The Royal British Legion, SCOPE and MIND (£3,700 each).

FINANCES *Year* 2011–12 *Income* £125,631 *Grants* £121,106 *Assets* £6,804,026

TRUSTEES A. G. F. Fuller; P. A. Sheils; R. I. Turner; R. J. Weetch.

HOW TO APPLY Unsolicited applications are not considered.

WHO TO APPLY TO Paul Shiels, Trustee, c/o Moon Beever Solicitors, 24–25 Bloomsbury Square, London WC1A 2PL *Tel.* 020 7637 0661

■ The E. H. Smith Charitable Trust

CC NO 328313   **ESTABLISHED** 1989

WHERE FUNDING CAN BE GIVEN UK, some preference for the Midlands.

WHO CAN BENEFIT Local and national organisations.

WHAT IS FUNDED General charitable purposes.

WHAT IS NOT FUNDED No grants to political parties. Grants are not normally given to individuals.

RANGE OF GRANTS Up to around £5,000 each; usually less than £500.

SAMPLE GRANTS Bible Learning Centre (£8,000); Hearing Dogs Charity Training Centre (£650); Perrywoods F C (£600) and Rubery F C (£500).

FINANCES *Year* 2011–12 *Income* £34,436 *Grants* £19,980 *Assets* £192,735

TRUSTEES Kenneth Avery Smith; David Ensell.

HOW TO APPLY In writing to the correspondent at any time.

WHO TO APPLY TO K. H. A. Smith, Trustee, Westhaven House, Arleston Way, Solihull, West Midlands B90 4LH *Tel.* 01217 137100

■ The Henry Smith Charity

CC NO 230102   **ESTABLISHED** 1628

WHERE FUNDING CAN BE GIVEN UK. Specific local programmes in east and west Sussex, Hampshire, Kent, Gloucestershire, Leicestershire, Suffolk and Surrey.

WHO CAN BENEFIT Charitable organisations.

WHAT IS FUNDED The trustees use the following programme areas to classify their grants: Black, Asian and Minority Ethnic (BAME); Carers; Community Service; Disability; Domestic and Sexual Violence; Drugs, Alcohol and Substance Misuse; Ex-Service Men and Women; Family Services; Healthcare; Homelessness; Lesbian,

Think carefully about every application. Is it justified?

901

Gay, Bisexual and Transgender; Mental Health; Older People; Prisoners and Ex-offenders; Prostitution and Trafficking; Refugees and Asylum Seekers; and Young People.

WHAT IS NOT FUNDED Grants are not made towards the following: local authorities and areas of work usually considered a statutory responsibility; state maintained schools, colleges, universities and friend/parent teacher associations, or independent schools not exclusively for students with special educational needs; organisations not providing direct services to clients such as umbrella, second tier or grantmaking organisations; youth clubs, except those in areas of high deprivation; uniformed groups such as Scouts and Guides, except those in areas of high deprivation; community centres, except those in areas of high deprivation; community transport organisations or services; professional associations or projects for the training of professionals; start-up costs or organisations unable to demonstrate a track record; individuals, or organisations and charities applying on their behalf; projects that promote a particular religion, or capital appeals for places of worship; arts projects, except those which can clearly demonstrate a therapeutic or rehabilitative benefit to disabled people, prisoners or young people who experience educational, social and economic disadvantage, including young people in, or leaving, care; education projects except those which can clearly demonstrate a rehabilitative benefit to disabled people, prisoners or young people who experience educational, social and economic disadvantage, including young people in, or leaving, care; leisure, recreation or play activities, except those exclusively for disabled people or those which can clearly demonstrate a significant rehabilitative benefit to people with mental health problems or that significantly improve opportunities and maximise the potential of young people who experience educational, social and economic disadvantage; overseas trips; projects taking place or benefiting people outside the UK; residential holidays for young people (except those that qualify under the Holiday Grants scheme); counselling projects, except those in areas of high deprivation and with a clearly defined client group; environmental projects where the primary purpose is conservation of the environment; Citizens Advice or projects solely providing legal advice; core running costs of hospices; feasibility studies; social research; campaigning or lobbying projects; projects where website development or maintenance is the focus of the bid; IT equipment (unless as direct support costs for a funded staff member); capital projects to meet the requirements of the Disability Discrimination Act; applicants declined within the previous six months; Organisations that do not have charitable aims (e.g. companies limited by shares and commercial organisations are not eligible to apply); mailshots or general appeals.

TYPE OF GRANT Capital and revenue; one-off grants and recurrent grants for up to three years.

RANGE OF GRANTS Small grants: £500–£10,000; Large grants: over £10,000.

SAMPLE GRANTS Centre for Mental Health (£240,000); Care and Repair Neath Port Talbot (£117,500); Action Medical Research (£90,000); Age UK Hammersmith and Fulham (£71,000); Calderdale SmartMove (£56,500); Copenhagen Youth Project (£49,000); Rhubarb Farm CIC (£40,500); Zone Youth Enquiry

Service Plymouth (£22,500); Centre Project (£10,000); and the Deal Festival of Music and the Arts (£5,000).

FINANCES *Year* 2012 *Income* £10,547,000 *Grants* £26,629,000 *Assets* £715,715,000

TRUSTEES Carola Godman Law; James Hambro; Anna McNair Scott; Merlyn Lowther; Noel Manns; Anne Allen; Rt Hon Claire Countes; Diana Barran; Marilyn Gallyer; Mark Newton; Peter Smallridge; Tristan Millington Drake; Nicholas Acland; Miko Geidroyc; Vivian Hunt; Bridget Biddell; Patrick Maxwell; Sir Richard Thompson.

OTHER INFORMATION £25.5 million of the grant total went to organisations and a further £1.5 million was made in grants to individuals.

HOW TO APPLY 'Each of our grant programmes has a slightly different application and assessment process. You will find information about how to make your application in the guidelines for each type of grant. Some of our grants require you to fill in an application form. For others there is no application form; instead we provide guidance about to structure your application and what supporting documents you need to send us. Ensure you send us all the supporting documents we ask you to include with your application. Incomplete applications will be returned unread. We strongly recommend that you download and read the guidelines of the relevant grant programme carefully before you start your application. It is important that you follow our guidance on how to apply. Guidelines for each programme can be downloaded from the Grant Programmes section of the charity's website.'

WHO TO APPLY TO Richard Hopgood, Director, Applications, 6th Floor, 65 Leadenhall Street, London EC3A 2AD *Tel.* 020 7264 4970 *Fax* 020 7488 9097 *Website* www. henrysmithcharity.org.uk

···

■ The Leslie Smith Foundation

CC NO 250030 **ESTABLISHED** 1964

WHERE FUNDING CAN BE GIVEN UK with a preference for London, Berkshire, Devon, Cornwall, Middlesex, Norfolk, Somerset and Wiltshire

WHO CAN BENEFIT Registered charities, with a preference for those benefiting children with illnesses, both terminal and non-terminal, in the UK (excluding respite care and research); orphans; and schools, specifically special needs schools based in the UK.

WHAT IS FUNDED Preference is given to charities which the trust has special interest in, knowledge of, or association with, but with an emphasis on: counselling services; children's and young persons' welfare; health and allied services; ex-servicemen's welfare; and other causes the trustees deem appropriate.

WHAT IS NOT FUNDED Grants are given to registered charities only. No grants for individuals.

TYPE OF GRANT Buildings, capital, one-off, research and recurring costs. Funding is available for up to one year.

RANGE OF GRANTS £500–£15,000.

SAMPLE GRANTS Comic Relief and the Paul Strickland Scanner Centre Appeal (£15,000 each); Gaddum Centre and Whizz-Kidz (£10,000 each); Cystic Fibrosis Holiday Fund for Children, Prisoners Abroad and Water for All (£5,000 each); and Norfolk Accident Rescue Service (£2,000).

FINANCES *Year* 2011–12 *Income* £59,063 *Grants* £152,500 *Assets* £2,589,644

TRUSTEES Michael Willcox; Huw Young Jones.

HOW TO APPLY In writing to the correspondent, including a summary of the project and a copy of the latest accounts. Only successful applications are acknowledged.

WHO TO APPLY TO The Trustees, c/o Willcox and Lewis, The Old Coach House, Sunnyside, Bergh Apton, Norwich NR15 1DD *Tel.* 01508 480100 *Fax* 01508 480001 *email* info@willcoxlewis.co.uk

■ The Martin Smith Foundation

CC NO 1072607   ESTABLISHED 1998
WHERE FUNDING CAN BE GIVEN UK.
WHO CAN BENEFIT Organisations and individuals.
WHAT IS FUNDED Projects supporting art, music, sports and education.
TYPE OF GRANT One-off and recurrent.
RANGE OF GRANTS £50–£750,000
SAMPLE GRANTS Orchestra of St John's (£19,000); Bath Mozartfest, International Musicians Seminar Prussia Cove and Vocal Futures (£5,000 each); The Becket Collection (£4,000); Orchestra of the Age of Enlightenment and St Anne's College (£3,000 each); Tetbury Music Festival (£2,500); Wigmore Hall (£2,200); Insideworld Imagine (£2,000); Garsington (£1,500) and Kambia Appeal, Oxford Lieder and Tetbury Parish Council/Long Newton Church (£1,000 each).
FINANCES *Year* 2011–12 *Income* £107,668 *Grants* £56,920 *Assets* £69,463
TRUSTEES Martin Smith, Chair; Elise Smith; Jeremy Smith; Katherine Wake; Elizabeth Buchanan; Bartholomew Peerless.
HOW TO APPLY This trust does not consider unsolicited applications. 'The charity continues to look for new recipients and also, from time to time, review past and ongoing projects for possible financial assistance they may require.'
WHO TO APPLY TO Martin Smith, Trustee, PO Box 838, Oxford OX1 9LF

■ The Stanley Smith UK Horticultural Trust

CC NO 261925   ESTABLISHED 1970
WHERE FUNDING CAN BE GIVEN UK and overseas.
WHO CAN BENEFIT Grants are made to individuals or to institutions benefiting botany and horticulture.
WHAT IS FUNDED Grants are made to individual projects which involve the advancement of amenity horticulture and horticultural education. In the past, assistance has been given to: the creation, preservation and development of gardens to which the public is admitted; the cultivation and wider distribution of plants derived by breeding or by collection from the wild, to research; and to the publication of books with a direct bearing on horticulture.
WHAT IS NOT FUNDED Grants are not made for projects in commercial horticulture (crop production) or agriculture, nor are they made to support students taking academic or diploma courses of any kind, although educational institutions are supported.
TYPE OF GRANT Capital (including buildings), core costs, feasibility studies, interest-free loans, one-off, research and start-up costs. Grants are normally made as a contribution to cover the costs of identified projects. In exceptional cases grants are made over a three-year period.
RANGE OF GRANTS Up to £30,000.
SAMPLE GRANTS Hackfalls Arboretum – New Zealand (£5,000); Alpine Garden Society Publications,

Fauna and Flora International and PlantNetwork (£2,500 each); University of East London and Suffolk Punch Trust (£2,000); University of Lincoln (£1,500); Wentworth Castle Heritage Trust (£1,000) and Prenton High School (£500).
FINANCES *Year* 2011–12 *Income* £136,466 *Grants* £84,388 *Assets* £3,325,069
TRUSTEES C. D. Brickell; Lady Renfrew; J. B. E. Simmons; A. De Brye; P. R. Sykes; Dr D. A. H. Rae; E. Reed.
OTHER INFORMATION A scholarship worth £30,000 was also awarded to the Royal Botanic Garden, Edinburgh.
HOW TO APPLY In writing to the correspondent. *Guidelines for Applicants* are available from the trust. The director is willing to give advice on how applications should be presented. Grants are awarded twice a year, in spring and autumn. To be considered in the spring allocation, applications should reach the director before 15 February of each year; for the autumn allocation the equivalent date is 15 August. Potential recipients are advised to get their applications in early.
WHO TO APPLY TO Dr James Cullen, Director, Cory Lodge, PO Box 365, Cambridge CB2 1HR *Tel.* 01223 336299 *Fax* 01223 336278

■ Philip Smith's Charitable Trust

CC NO 1003751   ESTABLISHED 1991
WHERE FUNDING CAN BE GIVEN UK with a preference for Gloucestershire.
WHO CAN BENEFIT Local and national registered charities.
WHAT IS FUNDED The trust makes grants mainly in the fields of welfare, the environment, older people, children and the armed forces.
RANGE OF GRANTS £100–£10,000.
SAMPLE GRANTS Save the Children (£10,000); League of Friends of Moreton-in-Marsh Hospital and the Gamekeepers Welfare Charitable Trust (£5,000 each); St James Parochial Church Council Chipping Campden (£4,000); The Savation Army (£2,500); and the Army Benevolent Fund and Church Urban Fund (£1,000 each).
FINANCES *Year* 2011–12 *Income* £31,572 *Grants* £84,850 *Assets* £1,002,977
TRUSTEES Hon. Philip R. Smith; Mary Smith.
HOW TO APPLY In writing to the correspondent. The trustees meet regularly to consider grants. A lack of response can be taken to indicate that the trust does not wish to contribute to an appeal.
WHO TO APPLY TO Helen D'Monte, Bircham Dyson Bell, 50 Broadway, London SW1H 0BL *Tel.* 020 7783 3685 *Fax* 020 7222 3480 *email* helendmonte@bdb-law.co.uk

■ Smithcorp Charitable Trust

CC NO 1147006   ESTABLISHED 2012
WHERE FUNDING CAN BE GIVEN UK and overseas.
WHO CAN BENEFIT Registered charities.
WHAT IS FUNDED General, social welfare.
SAMPLE GRANTS The Wave Project; Children's Hospice South West; and RNLI.
FINANCES *Year* 2012 *Income* £81,571 *Grants* £25,032 *Assets* £41,166
TRUSTEES Daniel Smith; Adam Smith; Dominic Smith.
OTHER INFORMATION 'Some our recent overseas projects have included building school classrooms in Tanzania and renovating a primary school in Vietnam.'

HOW TO APPLY In writing to the correspondent.
WHO TO APPLY TO Daniel Smith, Trustee, First Floor, Clifton Heights, Triangle West, Bristol BS8 1EJ
email contact@smithcorpcharity.org
Website www.smithcorpcharity.org

■ The R. C. Snelling Charitable Trust

CC NO 1074776   **ESTABLISHED** 1999
WHERE FUNDING CAN BE GIVEN Within a 30 mile radius of the village of Blofield in Norfolk.
WHO CAN BENEFIT UK registered charities, children, young and older people.
WHAT IS FUNDED Medical, educational, religious, welfare or environmental resources
WHAT IS NOT FUNDED The trust gave the following list of ineligible expenditures: salaries; sponsorship for less than one year; general appeals where the need could be met several times over by grantors; national appeals; continued assistance with running costs.
TYPE OF GRANT One-off.
RANGE OF GRANTS Usually £250–£5,000.
SAMPLE GRANTS Norfolk Community Foundation (£35,000); Blofield Primary School (£10,000); The Light Dragoons Colonel's Appeal (£5,000); East Anglia's Children's Hospice (£3,000); St Barnabas Counselling (£2,500); Norwich Foodbank and Daylight Christian Prison Trust (£2,000 each); Community Action Norwich (£1,000); Norfolk Eating Disorders Association (£500); Twirlesque Majorettes (£300) and St Peter's Lingwood (£250).
FINANCES *Year* 2011–12 *Income* £77,030 *Grants* £72,300 *Assets* £1,242,862
TRUSTEES Roy Snelling; Philip Buttinger; Roland Cogman; Toby Wise; Nigel Savoury; Stephan Phillips; Colin Jacobs.
HOW TO APPLY An online application form can be completed from the company's website. The trust is happy to receive queries via email.
WHO TO APPLY TO The Trustees, R. C. Snelling Ltd, Laundry Lane, Blofield Heath, Norwich NR13 4SQ *Tel.* 01603 711737 *email* trust@snellings.co.uk *Website* www.snellings.co.uk/charitable-trust.aspx

■ The Snowball Trust

CC NO 702860   **ESTABLISHED** 1989
WHERE FUNDING CAN BE GIVEN Coventry and Warwickshire.
WHO CAN BENEFIT Individuals or institutions for the benefit of children up to 21 years of age who are disabled.
WHAT IS FUNDED The provision of moveable equipment for sick and disabled children.
WHAT IS NOT FUNDED Applications for administration and maintenance costs, salaries, fees, short-term respite care and holidays are rejected.
TYPE OF GRANT Capital and one-off.
RANGE OF GRANTS Generally £500–£5,000, although there are no upper or lower limits.
FINANCES *Year* 2011–12 *Income* £96,251 *Grants* £62,928 *Assets* £90,812
TRUSTEES Ian Smedley; Elaine Hancox; David Fisher; Dr Alan Rhodes; Dominic Parker.
OTHER INFORMATION Grants totalled £63,000 of which £20,000 went to institutions and £43,000 to individuals.
HOW TO APPLY On a form available from the correspondent.

WHO TO APPLY TO The Trustees, c/o Dafferns LLP, One Eastwood, Harry Weston Road, Binley Business Park, Coventry CV3 2UB

■ The Sobell Foundation

CC NO 274369   **ESTABLISHED** 1977
WHERE FUNDING CAN BE GIVEN Unrestricted, in practice, England and Wales, Israel and the Commonwealth of Independent States (CIS).
WHO CAN BENEFIT Small national or local registered charities or organisations registered with the Inland Revenue.
WHAT IS FUNDED Jewish charities; medical care and treatment; care and education for children and adults with physical and/or mental disabilities; homelessness; care and support for the elderly; care and support for children from disadvantaged backgrounds.
WHAT IS NOT FUNDED No grants to individuals.
TYPE OF GRANT One-off, capital, project, running costs, buildings, core costs and recurring costs. Funding may be given for up to and over three years.
RANGE OF GRANTS £450–£300,000
SAMPLE GRANTS Previous beneficiaries included: Jewish Care (£300,000), towards the building a new day care centre at their Golders Green campus; and Leonard Cheshire Disability (£85,000), to expand Sobell Lodge care home in Kent. Approximately 53% of grants are made to UK non-Jewish charities, 31% to Israeli charities and charities in the CIS, 15% to UK Jewish charities and 1% to other overseas charities.
FINANCES *Year* 2011–12 *Income* £1,954,000 *Grants* £3,500,000
TRUSTEES Susan Lacroix; Roger Lewis; Andrea Scouller.
OTHER INFORMATION Unfortunately at the time of writing only the foundation's Summary Information Return was available, which contains limited information.
HOW TO APPLY Applications should be made in writing to the administrator using the application form obtainable from the foundation or printable from its website. The application form should be accompanied by: current year's summary income and expenditure budget; most recent annual report; most recent full accounts; and Inland Revenue certificate of exemption (if required). It will generally be two to three months before applicants are notified of the trustees' decision. The trustees receive a large number of applications for funding from registered charities during the year and support as many as possible of those which fall within the foundation's objectives. They aim to deal with requests within three months of receipt and to respond to each application received, whether or not a grant is made. Trustees meet every three to four months and major grants are considered at these meetings. Requests for smaller amounts may be dealt with on a more frequent basis. Most applications are dealt with on an ongoing basis, and there are no deadlines for the receipt of applications. Organisations should wait 12 months before reapplying.
WHO TO APPLY TO Penny Newton, Administrator, PO Box 2137, Shepton Mallet, Somerset BA4 6YA *Tel.* 01749 813135 *Fax* 01749 813136 *email* enquiries@sobellfoundation.org.uk *Website* www.sobellfoundation.org.uk

■ Social Business Trust (Scale-Up)

cc no 1136151   **established** 2010
where funding can be given United Kingdom
who can benefit Organisations.
what is funded General charitable purposes.
what is not funded Any organisation not meeting the trust's selection criteria.
type of grant Cash grants and in-kind services. Support usually provided instalments each being conditional upon achievement of certain milestones.
sample grants London Early Years Foundation (£815,000); Inspiring Futures Foundation (£574,000); Moneyline (£293,000); The Challenge Network (£214,000); Timewise (£176,000).
finances Year 2011–12 Income £2,264,207 Grants £558,930 Assets £152,901
trustees Damon Buffini; Paul Armstrong; Simon Milton; Jonathan Myers; Tim Curry; Alan Hirzel.
other information Be aware that it may take up to seven months to complete the full process to investment
how to apply The trust's website provides its selection criteria, however, if unsure, applicants are welcome to contact the correspondent directly. To be eligible the organisation: should be registered as a charity or demonstrate a clear charitable purpose, such as a community interest company (CIC); must have annual revenue in excess of £1.5 million, including a significant proportion of earned income (income that is not grants or donations); needs to have at least one year's audited trading accounts; a minimum of 1,000 people per year must benefit, directly or indirectly, from the organisation's goods or services; needs to be based predominately in the UK; must not have strong political or religious links.
Written communication to the trust must include a one-page covering letter; a summary of *no more than four pages* outlining who you are and what you do; your growth strategy and where you think Social Business Trust can help you most; latest audited accounts. As an appendix a business plan or three to five year strategic plan may be included.
Within your four page summary, you may also wish to include: growth objectives; financial projections for the next three years, separating earned income from grants and donations; measurement of your current social impact and how this will grow; the key members of your management team.
The trust aims to respond within ten working days to confirm the receipt of application and review it within six weeks. Successful applicants are contacted to obtain further details and unsuccessful applicants are informed in writing. Successful applications have to go through an initial review stage with the investment manager, alongside other applications and the approved applicants are invited to work with the core team to present their application to the investment committee to receive the final approval.
who to apply to Adele Blakebrough, Chief Executive, First Floor, 13 St Swithin's Lane, London EC4N 8AL *Tel.* 020 3011 0770 *email* adele@socialbusinesstrust.org *Website* www.socialbusinesstrust.org

■ Solev Co Ltd

cc no 254623   **established** 1967
where funding can be given UK.
who can benefit Individuals and organisations benefiting Jewish people.
what is funded Principally Jewish causes.
type of grant Longer than three years.
range of grants £1,000–£5,000.
sample grants Previous beneficiaries include: Dina Perelman Trust Ltd (£100,000); Songdale Ltd (£40,000); Society of Friends of the Torah (£3,900); Finchley Road Synagogue (£2,300); NW London Talmudical College (£1,500); Yesodey Hatorah School (£700); and Gateshead Talmudical College (£400).
finances Year 2011–12 Income £675,315 Grants £301,940 Assets £5,306,574
trustees Romie Tager; Simon Tager; Joseph Tager; Chaim Frommer.
other information No information on grant beneficiaries has been included in the charity's accounts in recent years.
how to apply In writing to the correspondent.
who to apply to Romie Tager, Trustee, 1 Spaniards Park, Columbas Drive, London NW3 7JD *Tel.* 020 7420 9500

■ The Solo Charitable Settlement

cc no 326444   **established** 1983
where funding can be given UK and Israel.
who can benefit Organisations benefiting Jewish people, people with disabilities, research workers and medical professionals.
what is funded Jewish organisations, medical research, arts and disability.
range of grants Between £100–£15,000.
sample grants Norwood (£14,000); Jewish Leadership Council (£7,500); Mothers and Daughters Support Group (£2,200); and Israel Tennis Centres (£1,000).
finances Year 2011–12 Income £258,676 Grants £48,713 Assets £5,587,687
trustees Peter D. Goldstein; Edna A. Goldstein; Paul Goldstein; Dean Goldstein; Jamie Goldstein; Tammy Ward.
how to apply In writing to the correspondent.
who to apply to The Trustees, c/o Gallaghers Accountants, Titchfield House, 2nd Floor, 69–85 Tabernacle Street, London EC2A 4RR *Tel.* 020 7490 7774 *Fax* 020 7490 5354 *email* partners@gallaghers.co.uk

■ Dr Richard Solomon's Charitable Trust

cc no 277309   **established** 1978
where funding can be given Overseas.
who can benefit Voluntary groups and charitable organisations only.
what is funded General, international development. The trust has previously stated that it prefers to support 'ecologically sound democratic projects'.
what is not funded Individuals are not supported.
range of grants Up to £21,000.
sample grants INDEPO, Institute for Rural Development, Bolivia (£10,000); Rift Valley Tree, Appropriate Technology, Wells for India and Village Water (£3,000 each) and Sunseed Tanzania (£1,000).
finances Year 2011–12 Income £28,783 Grants £22,873 Assets £308,721
trustees Richard Solomon; Zoe Solomon; Diana Huntingford; Zachary Solomons.

HOW TO APPLY In writing to the correspondent.

WHO TO APPLY TO Dr Richard Solomons, Trustee, Fell Edge Farm, Moorside Lane, Addingham, Ilkley, West Yorkshire LS29 9JX *Tel.* 01943 830841

....

■ David Solomons Charitable Trust

CC NO 297275   ESTABLISHED 1986
WHERE FUNDING CAN BE GIVEN UK.
WHO CAN BENEFIT UK and local charitable organisations benefiting people who have learning difficulties and their carers.
WHAT IS FUNDED Research into, or the treatment and care of, people with mental disabilities.
WHAT IS NOT FUNDED No grants to individuals.
TYPE OF GRANT One-off, project and salaries. Administrative expenses and large building projects are not usually funded, although grants can be made towards furnishing or equipping rooms.
RANGE OF GRANTS Up to £2,000.
SAMPLE GRANTS Down's Syndrome Association (£8,000); Columcille Centre (£3,000 in total); Acre Housing and Wessex Autistic Society (£2,000 each); Advocacy Trust Gloucester, Autism Sussex Ltd, Forest Forge Theatre Company, Papworth Trust and the Children's Adventure Farm Trust (£1,000 each); and Bedford Local Mencap, Ferring Country Centre and Outreach 3 Way (£500).
FINANCES *Year* 2011–12 *Income* £103,786 *Grants* £85,100 *Assets* £2,261,474
TRUSTEES Michael Chamberlayne; John Drewitt; Jeremy Rutter; Dr Richard Solomons; Dr Leila Cooke; Diana Huntingford.
HOW TO APPLY The trustees conduct their own research into potential applicants.
WHO TO APPLY TO Graeme Crosby, Administrator, Jasmine Cottage, 11 Lower Road, Breachwood Green, Hitchin, Hertfordshire SG4 8NS *Tel.* 01438 833254 *email* g.crosby@waitrose.com

....

■ Friends of Somerset Churches and Chapels

CC NO 1055840   ESTABLISHED 1996
WHERE FUNDING CAN BE GIVEN The historic county of Somerset.
WHO CAN BENEFIT Churches and chapels.
WHAT IS FUNDED The repair of churches and chapels, which are open for worship in Somerset.
WHAT IS NOT FUNDED No grants to individuals. No support for new work, reordering or repairs to moveable items.
RANGE OF GRANTS Up to £5,000.
SAMPLE GRANTS St Michael, Brent Knoll and All Saint's, East Pennard (£5,000 each); St George, Hinton St George (£3,000); Virgin Mary, Cheddon Fitzpaine (£2,000); Holy Chapel, High Ham (£1,500) and St Mary's, Barrington (£500).
FINANCES *Year* 2011–12 *Income* £34,854 *Grants* £48,500 *Assets* £121,804
TRUSTEES Hugh Playfair; John Wood; David Sisson; Dr Robert Dunning; Jennifer Beazley; Jane Venner-Pack; Peter Wallis; Paul Heal; Angela Dudley; Chris Hawkings; John Reed.
PUBLICATIONS 'Jewels of Somerset' – Stained Glass in parish churches from 1830 was published in 2012.
HOW TO APPLY Application forms and guidelines are available from the correspondent or to download from the website. Trustees meet four times a year.

WHO TO APPLY TO Angela Dudley, Grants Secretary, Whynot Cottage, Wellow, Bath BA2 8QA. *Tel.* 01225 859999 *email* chedburn@chedburn.com *Website* www.fscandc.org.uk

....

■ Songdale Ltd

CC NO 286075   ESTABLISHED 1961
WHERE FUNDING CAN BE GIVEN UK and Israel.
WHO CAN BENEFIT People of the Orthodox Jewish faith.
WHAT IS FUNDED Jewish general charitable purposes.
SAMPLE GRANTS A list of grant beneficiaries was not included in the accounts but previously grants have been given to: Cosmon Belz Ltd, Kollel Belz, BFOT, Ezras Yisroel, Forty Limited, Darkei Ovois, Germach Veholachto, Keren Nedunnia Lchasanim, Belz Nursery and Bais Chinuch.
FINANCES *Year* 2011–12 *Income* £233,336 *Grants* £213,842 *Assets* £2,542,309
TRUSTEES M. Grosskopf; M. Grosskopf; Y. Grosskopf.
HOW TO APPLY In writing to the correspondent.
WHO TO APPLY TO Yechiel Grosskopf, Trustee, 6 Spring Hill, London E5 9BE *Tel.* 020 8806 5010

....

■ The E. C. Sosnow Charitable Trust

CC NO 273578   ESTABLISHED 1977
WHERE FUNDING CAN BE GIVEN UK and overseas.
WHO CAN BENEFIT Cultural institutions; UK and international organisations benefiting children, young people, students, older people and people who are disadvantaged.
WHAT IS FUNDED Education; medical organisations; emergency overseas aid; disability; the arts; and disadvantage.
WHAT IS NOT FUNDED No grants are made to individuals.
TYPE OF GRANT One-off.
RANGE OF GRANTS £200–£5,500.
SAMPLE GRANTS Friends of Ascent and Weizman UK (£10,000 each); LSE (£5,000); Royal National Theatre and Youth Aliyah (£3,000 each); Holocaust Educational Trust (£2,500); British Technion Society and Society for Children with Diabetes (£1,000 each) and Parkinson's UK (£500).
FINANCES *Year* 2011–12 *Income* £63,352 *Grants* £52,600 *Assets* £1,849,528
TRUSTEES E. R. Fattal; F. J. M. Fattal; Miss A. E. Fattal; R. Fattal.
HOW TO APPLY In writing to the correspondent.
WHO TO APPLY TO The Trustees, PO Box 13398, London SW3 6ZL

....

■ The Souter Charitable Trust

SC NO SC029998   ESTABLISHED 1991
WHERE FUNDING CAN BE GIVEN UK, but with a preference for Scotland; overseas.
WHO CAN BENEFIT Grants are given to a variety of organisations supporting people of all ages; people who are in care, fostered or adopted; Christians; evangelists; carers; people disadvantaged by poverty; refugees; or victims of famine, man-made or natural disasters or war.
WHAT IS FUNDED Relief of human suffering, particularly projects with a Christian emphasis.

WHAT IS NOT FUNDED Building projects, individuals, personal education grants and expeditions are not supported.

TYPE OF GRANT One-off and recurring grants.

RANGE OF GRANTS Mostly £1,000 or less.

SAMPLE GRANTS Previous beneficiaries include: The Message Trust; Christians Against Poverty; Youth for Christ; Against Malaria Foundation; Mary's Meals; Chest Heart and Stroke Scotland; and Tearfund.

FINANCES *Year* 2011–12 *Income* £3,260,891 *Grants* £6,000,000

TRUSTEES Brian Souter; Betty Souter.

OTHER INFORMATION Total grants figure is approximate.

HOW TO APPLY In writing to the correspondent. Keep applications brief and no more than two sides of A4 paper: if appropriate, send audited accounts, but do not send brochures, business plans, dvds and so on. The trust states that it will request more information if necessary. The trustees meet every two months or so, and all applications will be acknowledged in due course, whether successful or not. A stamped addressed envelope would be appreciated. Subsequent applications should not be made within a year of the initial submission.

WHO TO APPLY TO Dion Judd, Administrator, PO Box 7412, Perth PH1 5YX *Tel.* 01738 450408 *email* enquiries@soutercharitabletrust.org.uk *Website* www.soutercharitabletrust.org.uk

....

■ The South Square Trust

CC NO 278960   **ESTABLISHED** 1979

WHERE FUNDING CAN BE GIVEN UK, with a preference for London and the Home Counties.

WHO CAN BENEFIT The trust assists in two areas with general donations to registered charities, and support of individual students undertaking full-time undergraduate or postgraduate courses connected with the fine and applied arts within the UK. Individuals are considered especially for courses related to goldsmithing, silversmithing, and metalwork but also for music, drama and dance. Preference is given to students commencing undergraduate studies – students must be at least 18 years old. The trust has established scholarships and bursaries with schools connected with the fine and applied arts and a full list of these schools can be obtained from the clerk to the trustees. Where a school is in receipt of a bursary, no further assistance will be given to individuals as the school will select candidates themselves.

WHAT IS FUNDED Annual income is allocated in awards to individuals for educational purposes, specifically help with tuition fees but living expenses will be considered for courses as specified above. Donations are also considered to registered charities working in fields of the elderly, medical research and equipment, support groups, community groups, horticulture, green issues and other projects connected with the fine and applied arts.

WHAT IS NOT FUNDED No support for building projects, salaries or individuals wishing to start up a business. No grants given to individuals under 18 or those seeking funding for expeditions, travel, courses outside UK, short courses or courses not connected with fine and applied arts.

TYPE OF GRANT Registered charities: single donations to assist with specific projects, one-off expenses, core costs and research. Individual students: funding may be given for the duration of a course, for up to three years,

payable in three term instalments to help with tuition fees or living expenses.

RANGE OF GRANTS Individuals: £500–£1,500; charities: £300–£2,000.

SAMPLE GRANTS Fields in Trust and Woodlands Trust (£3,500 each); and World Child Cancer (£2,000).

FINANCES *Year* 2011–12 *Income* £191,754 *Grants* £182,475 *Assets* £3,648,041

TRUSTEES Christopher Grimwade; Paul Harriman; Brand Inglis; Andrew Blessley; Stephen Baldock.

OTHER INFORMATION £164,000 went to 41 organisations and £18,500 to individuals.

HOW TO APPLY In writing to the correspondent with details about your charity and the reason for requesting funding. Note, however, that the trust is not accepting applications until after July 2014 – check the trust's website for up-to-date information.

WHO TO APPLY TO Nicola Chrimes, Clerk to the Trustees, PO Box 169, Lewes, East Sussex BN7 9FB *Tel.* 01825 872264 *Website* www.southsquaretrust.org.uk

....

■ The Stephen R. and Philippa H. Southall Charitable Trust

CC NO 223190   **ESTABLISHED** 1947

WHERE FUNDING CAN BE GIVEN UK, but mostly Herefordshire.

WHO CAN BENEFIT Registered charities.

WHAT IS FUNDED General charitable purposes, with a preference for promoting education and conservation of the natural environment and cultural heritage.

RANGE OF GRANTS Up to about £20,000.

SAMPLE GRANTS Hereford Waterworks Museum Trust (£5,000); Bristol Museums Development Trust and Home-Start Herefordshire (£2,000 each); and Midlands Air Ambulance, Herefordshire Carers' Support and Britain Yearly Meeting Fund (£1,000 each).

FINANCES *Year* 2011–12 *Income* £76,671 *Grants* £28,600 *Assets* £3,231,341

TRUSTEES Philippa Southall; Anna Southall; Candia Compton.

OTHER INFORMATION The trust has previously stated that it uses its surplus income for world emergencies and the development of Hereford Waterworks Museum.

HOW TO APPLY The trust makes several repeat donations and has previously stated that: 'no applications can be considered or replied to'.

WHO TO APPLY TO Philippa Southall, Trustee, Porking Barn, Clifford, Hereford HR3 5HE

....

■ The W. F. Southall Trust

CC NO 218371   **ESTABLISHED** 1937

WHERE FUNDING CAN BE GIVEN UK and overseas.

WHO CAN BENEFIT Registered charities, especially imaginative new grassroots initiatives and smaller charities where funding will make a significant difference.

WHAT IS FUNDED Work of the Society of Friends; peace-making and conflict resolution; alcohol, drug abuse and penal affairs; environmental action; homelessness; community action; and overseas development.

WHAT IS NOT FUNDED No grants to individuals or large national charities.

TYPE OF GRANT Normally one-off payments.

RANGE OF GRANTS Up to £55,000; usually £100–£5,000.

SAMPLE GRANTS Yearly Meeting – Society of Friends (£55,000); Woodbrooke Quaker Study Centre (£10,000); International Voluntary Services and Quaker Social Action (£5,000 each); Salt of the Earth (£4,000); and Campaign Against Arms Trade and World Orthopaedic Concern (£3,000 each).

FINANCES *Year* 2011–12 *Income* £273,356 *Grants* £248,062 *Assets* £7,824,371

TRUSTEES Donald Southall, Chair; Joanna Engelkamp; Claire Greaves; Mark Holtom; Daphne Maw; Annette Wallis.

HOW TO APPLY On a form available from the trust's website. Further guidance on making an application is given as follows: 'When making an application, grant seekers should bear in mind the points below. We expect all applicants to complete the funding application form. Ensure your application includes details regarding the following: your most recent annual report; projected income and expenditure for the coming year; your reserves; particular features of your costs, e.g. high transport costs in rural areas; details of other funding expected; any significant achievements and/or problems or difficulties; any 'matching funding' arrangements e.g. European Social Fund support; timetable for when the proposed work is to start and finish; applications should be accompanied by a stamped addressed envelope.'

WHO TO APPLY TO Margaret Rowntree, Secretary, c/o Rutters Solicitors, 2 Bimport, Shaftesbury, Dorset SP7 8AY *Tel.* 01747 852377 *Fax* 01747 851989 *email* M.Rowntree@Rutterslaw.co.uk *Website* wfsouthalltrust.org.uk

---

■ The Southdown Trust

CC NO 235583   **ESTABLISHED** 1963
WHERE FUNDING CAN BE GIVEN UK.
WHO CAN BENEFIT Young people aged 17 to 26 years.
WHAT IS FUNDED Grants towards the education of the specified age group.
WHAT IS NOT FUNDED No grants towards courses in the following subjects: law, journalism, women's studies, counselling, veterinary studies, computer/IT studies and media studies.
RANGE OF GRANTS Up to £13,000
SAMPLE GRANTS Winchester College (£13,000); Christ church Oxford (£7,500); Silcock Trust (£3,000); Joint Educational Trust and Reed's school (£2,000 each) and Coventry University and EBET (£300 each).
FINANCES *Year* 2011–12 *Income* £86,528 *Grants* £45,540 *Assets* £979,706
TRUSTEES John Wyatt; Hugh Wyatt; Meriel Buxton; John McBeath.
OTHER INFORMATION In 2011–12 grants to individuals totalled £17,440.
HOW TO APPLY In writing to the correspondent.
WHO TO APPLY TO John Wyatt, Secretary and Trustee, Holmbush, 64 High Street, Findon, Worthing, West Sussex BN14 0SY

■ R. H. Southern Trust

CC NO 1077509   **ESTABLISHED** 1999
WHERE FUNDING CAN BE GIVEN England, Wales, Scotland, Republic of Ireland, Australia, Belgium, India.
WHO CAN BENEFIT Charitable organisations.
WHAT IS FUNDED Advancement of education (including medical and scientific research); relief of poverty; disability; and preservation, conservation and protection of the environment

(especially climate change). The trust favours projects where the work is innovative, connected to other disciplines/bodies and has diverse application.

TYPE OF GRANT Mainly long term core funding and special projects.
RANGE OF GRANTS £1,000–£30,000
SAMPLE GRANTS New Economics Foundation (£23,000); Equal Adventure (£20,000); Accord – Just Change, Salt of the Earth, World Development Movement and Oxford Research Group (£10,000 each); Action Village India (£7,500); Corporate Europe Observatory and Friends of the Earth (£5,000 each); El Rural Links – Tamwed (£4,000); and CSIRO (£1,000).
FINANCES *Year* 2011–12 *Income* £100,505 *Grants* £174,115 *Assets* £2,864,167
TRUSTEES Marion Wells; James Bruges.
OTHER INFORMATION The trust made additional payments to individuals and businesses totalling £34,886.
HOW TO APPLY The trust's website states: 'The trust funds are fully committed for the foreseeable future. Do not apply for funding and waste your time and resources and ours. Thank you.'
WHO TO APPLY TO Marion Wells, Trustee, 23 Sydenham Road, Cotham, Bristol BS6 5SJ *Tel.* 01179 425834 *Website* www.rhsoutherntrust.org.uk

---

■ The Southover Manor General Education Trust

CC NO 299593   **ESTABLISHED** 1988
WHERE FUNDING CAN BE GIVEN Sussex.
WHO CAN BENEFIT Schools, colleges and individuals under the age of 25.
WHAT IS FUNDED The trustees support the 'education of boys and girls under 25 by providing books and equipment, supporting provision of recreational and educational facilities, scholarships and awards'.
WHAT IS NOT FUNDED No grants for people over 25 years of age. Organisations and individuals outside Sussex are not supported.
TYPE OF GRANT Capital and projects.
RANGE OF GRANTS Up to £20,000.
SAMPLE GRANTS A New Beginning Rwanda and Little Horsted C of E School (£10,000 each).
FINANCES *Year* 2011–12 *Income* £114,292 *Grants* £97,100 *Assets* £2,428,231
TRUSTEES B. Hanbury; Charles Davies-Gilbert; Chloe Teacher; Jennifer Gordon-Lennox; Clare Duffield; John Wakely; John Farmer; Wenda Bradley; Jennie Peel.
OTHER INFORMATION Grants were made to 27 organisations and one individual and included money for the following projects: Library facilities, including books and furniture; Building works; IT and other equipment and Playground and playing field equipment.
HOW TO APPLY In writing to the correspondent.
WHO TO APPLY TO J. Foot, The Secretary to the Trustees, Old Vicarage Cottage, Newhaven Road, Iford, Lewes, East Sussex BN7 3PL *email* southovermanor@btinternet.com

---

■ The Southwold Trust

CC NO 206480   **ESTABLISHED** 1962
WHERE FUNDING CAN BE GIVEN Southwold and Reydon.
WHO CAN BENEFIT Registered charities.
WHAT IS FUNDED General charitable purposes.
RANGE OF GRANTS £960– £8,000 (2011/12)

SAMPLE GRANTS Southwold and Reydon Recreation Development Council (£8,000); Sole Bay Care Fund and Southwold Surgery Care Fund (£5,000 each); Southwold Parochial Charity (£2,000) Voluntary Health Centre and East Suffolk Blind Association (£1,500 each) and Andrew Matthews Trust (£960).

FINANCES Year 2011–12 Income £62,304 Grants £25,460 Assets £161,773

TRUSTEES Bernard Segrave-Daly; Edna Utting; Robert Temple; John Denny; Robert Lee; John French; Hugh Fuller; Sir Richard Dales; Michael Mayhew; David Gaffney; Carol Scilly.

HOW TO APPLY In writing to the correspondent.

WHO TO APPLY TO David Gaffney, Treasurer, c/o Margary and Miller, 73 High Street, Southwold, Suffolk IP18 6DS Tel. 01502 723308

....

■ The Sovereign Health Care Charitable Trust

CC NO 1079024   **ESTABLISHED** 1955

WHERE FUNDING CAN BE GIVEN UK, with a preference for Bradford.

WHO CAN BENEFIT Generally local organisations benefiting older people, at risk groups, and people with disabilities, disadvantaged by poverty or socially isolated.

WHAT IS FUNDED Sovereign Health Care Charitable Trust funds work to do with health and well-being that is wholly charitable and usually undertaken either by registered charities or by organisations that have been established for charitable purposes, are properly constituted and have a bank account. In general the trust favours initiatives that touch people's lives and clearly make a difference. Grants are usually quite modest – a few thousand pounds at most. Large medical research initiatives where the trust's contribution would not be significant are unlikely to be a high priority.

'In terms of specific diseases and conditions, the charitable trust gives priority to those that are particularly prevalent in Bradford, especially: heart disease; chest/lung disease; lung cancer; stroke; diabetes; breast cancer; bowel cancer; prostate cancer; and oral cancer. Other priorities are: hospitals and hospices, disease prevention, healthy lifestyle and health promotion; deprivation, poverty or homelessness; disability; and mental health. The trust will also consider applications concerned with carers and with education and training where it relates to one of the other priority areas, though these do not have as high a priority.'

WHAT IS NOT FUNDED No grants to individuals.

TYPE OF GRANT Buildings, core costs, one-off grants, project, research, running costs.

RANGE OF GRANTS Up to £30,000.

SAMPLE GRANTS Bradford Teaching Hospitals Foundation Trust (£221,000); Yorkshire Air Ambulance (£28,500); Marie Curie Cancer Care (£25,000); the Bradford Soup Run (£15,000); Leeds Rugby Foundation (£10,000); Calderdale and Huddersfield NHS Foundation Trust (£8,000); Deafblind UK (£7,500); Christians Against Poverty and Skipton Extended Learning For All (£5,000 each); Bradford Toy Library (£4,000); Barnardo's (£2,000); Clothing Solutions for Disabled People (£1,500); and Behind Closed Doors, Hope For Justice and SSAFA Forces Help (£1,000 each).

FINANCES Year 2012 Income £900,000 Grants £739,015 Assets £281,536

TRUSTEES Mark Hudson, chair; Michael Austin; Dennis Child; Michael Bower; Russ Piper; Kate Robb-Webb; Robert Dugdale; Stewart Cummings.

HOW TO APPLY The following information is given in the trust's guidelines:

'The charitable trust is keen not to burden the organisations it supports with too much paper work and 'jumping through hoops'. On the other hand, just sending a newsletter in the hope that this will trigger a cheque in return will not succeed.'

'The trustees needs to know what you do, what you want money for, how much it's going to cost and, when appropriate, how you'll know that the money has made a difference. There is no application form; just write to the trust with the appropriate information. The kind of detail the trust expects from a local self-help group wanting a couple of hundred pounds will be different from the information it expects from a large charity wanting several thousand pounds for a new initiative.'

'Trustees meet six times a year. From the trust receiving an application to the applicant receiving a cheque (or not) usually takes about two or three months. In the case of disasters and emergencies the trust may be able to act much more quickly. The trust notifies all applicants about the outcome of their request.'

'The trust is likely to look at the copy of your latest report and accounts if it is available on the Charity Commission's website. If it's not available (you're a small charity or not a registered charity at all), then it would be helpful to have some figures about the organisation's finances, as well as figures about the work or activity you want the funding for. If you're in a difficult financial situation, explain what's going on and the steps you are taking to improve things. Conversely, if your accounts show huge 'free' reserves, you might want to explain why you still need a grant.' The deadlines for consideration at the following trustees' meeting are: 15 February; 15 April; 15 June; 15 August; 15 October; 15 December.

WHO TO APPLY TO The Secretary, Royal Standard House, 26 Manningham Lane, Bradford, West Yorkshire BD1 3DN Tel. 01274 729472 Fax 01274 722252 email charities@ sovereignhealthcare.co.uk Website www. sovereignhealthcare.co.uk

....

■ Spar Charitable Fund

CC NO 236252   **ESTABLISHED** 1964

WHERE FUNDING CAN BE GIVEN UK.

WHO CAN BENEFIT Registered charities, mostly well-known national organisations.

WHAT IS FUNDED General charitable purposes, with some preference for projects benefiting young people.

SAMPLE GRANTS NSPCC (£71,000); Spar Charitable Fund (£20,000); and Grocery Aid (£5,000).

FINANCES Year 2012–13 Income £81,597 Grants £114,079 Assets £879,640

TRUSTEES Kevin Hunt; Martin Agnew; Peter Dodding; Philip Marchant; Claire Bolton; Mark Gillett; Patrick Doody; Dominic Hall; Bryan Walters.

OTHER INFORMATION This trust tends to choose one main beneficiary, which receives most of its funds, with smaller grants being made to similar beneficiaries each year.

HOW TO APPLY In writing to the correspondent.

WHO TO APPLY TO Philip Marchant, Trustee, Mezzanine Floor, Hygeia Building, 66 - 68 College Road, Harrow, Middlesex HA1 1BE Tel. 020 8426 3700 email philip.marchant@ spar.co.uk

Think carefully about every application. Is it justified?

909

■ Sparks Charity (Sport Aiding Medical Research For Kids)

CC NO 1003825 **ESTABLISHED** 1991

WHERE FUNDING CAN BE GIVEN UK.

WHO CAN BENEFIT Research units at UK hospitals and universities.

WHAT IS FUNDED Medical research to enable children to be born healthy and to stay healthy.

WHAT IS NOT FUNDED The charity is unable to consider: applications which are concurrently submitted to other funding bodies; grants for further education, for example, MSc/PhD course fees; grants towards service provision or audit studies; grants for work undertaken outside the UK; grants towards 'top up' funding for work supported by other funding bodies; or grants to other charities.

TYPE OF GRANT Project grants up to the value of £150,000, Research Training Fellowships and Programme grants.

RANGE OF GRANTS £50,000–£150,000. Applications outside this range will be considered.

SAMPLE GRANTS St Michael's Hospital, Bristol/Oslo University (£318,500); University of Manchester (£148,500); Cambridge University Hospitals (£115,500); University of Liverpool (£89,500); Chailey Heritage Clinical Services (£72,500); and Oxford University Hospitals (£66,500).

FINANCES *Year* 2012–13 *Income* £4,608,166 *Grants* £2,400,705 *Assets* £434,908

TRUSTEES Sir Trevor Brooking; Hugh Emeades; Roger Uttley; Julian Wilkinson; Floella Benjamin; Jonathon Britton; Victoria Glaysher; Guy Gregory; David Orr; Frank van den Bosch; Robert Booker; Martin Jepson; Dr Simon Newell.

HOW TO APPLY Sparks funds project grants up to the value of £150,000, Research Training Fellowships and Programme grants. Application forms and full guidelines are available on the charity's website.

WHO TO APPLY TO John Shanley, Chief Executive, 6th Floor, Westminster Tower, 3 Albert Embankment, London SE1 7SP *Tel.* 020 7091 7750 *email* info@sparks.org.uk *Website* www.sparks.org.uk

■ Sparquote Limited

CC NO 286232 **ESTABLISHED** 1982

WHERE FUNDING CAN BE GIVEN England and Wales.

WHO CAN BENEFIT Charitable organisations of Jewish community.

WHAT IS FUNDED General charitable purposes, advancement of religion, relief of sickness and poverty, education and training – focus on Jewish community.

TYPE OF GRANT Grants to organisations.

RANGE OF GRANTS Up to £40,000.

SAMPLE GRANTS Previous grant beneficiaries include: The Wlodowa Charity and Rehabilitation Trust (£41,000); the Telz Academy Trust (£30,000); British Friends of Mosdos Tchernobyl (£20,000); the Society of Friends of the Torah (£19,000); the Gevurath Ari Torah Trust (£15,000); Beis Nadvorna Charitable Trust (£10,000); the Edgware Foundation and Penshurst Corporation Limited (£5,000 each); Gateshead Institute for Rabbinical Studies (£3,500); Dina Perelman Trust Limited (£1,800); and American Friends (£1,000)

FINANCES *Year* 2011–12 *Income* £499,439 *Grants* £120,199 *Assets* £4,285,634

TRUSTEES David Reichmann; Dov Reichmann; Anne-Mette Reichmann.

HOW TO APPLY In writing to the correspondent.

WHO TO APPLY TO Anne-Mette Reichman, Trustee, Cohen Arnold, New Burlington House, 1075 Finchley Road, London NW11 0PU *Tel.* 020 8731 0777

■ The Spear Charitable Trust

CC NO 1041568 **ESTABLISHED** 1962

WHERE FUNDING CAN BE GIVEN UK.

WHO CAN BENEFIT Individuals and organisations, particularly employees and former employees of J W Spear and Sons plc, their families and dependants.

WHAT IS FUNDED Welfare of employees and former employees of J W Spear and Sons plc, their families and dependants; also general charitable purposes, with some preference for animal welfare, the environment and health.

WHAT IS NOT FUNDED Appeals from individuals are not considered.

SAMPLE GRANTS RSPCA – Enfield (£8,000); Camphill Village Trust and Tel Aviv University (£5,000 each); Centre for Alternative Technology and the Elm Farm Research Centre (£3,000 each); Bowel Disease Research Foundation and Lake Malawi Projects (UK) (£2,000 each); and ABF – The Soldiers' Charity, Canine Partners, Furniture Recycling Project and Wood Street Mission (£1,000 each).

FINANCES *Year* 2012 *Income* £168,833 *Grants* £144,985 *Assets* £4,893,049

TRUSTEES Philip Harris; Francis Spear; Hazel Spear; Nigel Gooch.

OTHER INFORMATION During the year former employees of J W Spear and Sons plc, their families and dependants received £4,500.

HOW TO APPLY In writing to the correspondent.

WHO TO APPLY TO Hazel Spear, Secretary, Roughground House, Beggarmans Lane, Old Hall Green, Ware, Hertfordshire SG11 1HB *Tel.* 01920 823071 *Fax* 01920 823071

■ Spears-Stutz Charitable Trust

CC NO 225491 **ESTABLISHED** 1964

WHERE FUNDING CAN BE GIVEN Worldwide.

WHO CAN BENEFIT Registered charities.

WHAT IS FUNDED General charitable purposes, relief of poverty, Jewish causes, museums and arts organisations.

RANGE OF GRANTS £250 to £30,000

SAMPLE GRANTS Previous beneficiaries include: Cancer Macmillan Fund, Royal Academy Trust, Royal Academy of Arts, Wellbeing, King Edward Hospital, Help the Aged and Westminster Synagogue.

FINANCES *Year* 2011–12 *Income* £156,150 *Grants* £116,940 *Assets* £4,323,343

TRUSTEES Glenn Hurstfield; Jonathan Spears.

OTHER INFORMATION This trust was previously known as the Roama Spears Charitable Settlement. A list of grants was not provided in the accounts.

HOW TO APPLY In writing to the correspondent.

WHO TO APPLY TO The Trustees, c/o Berkeley Law, 4th Floor, 19 Berkeley Street, London W1J 8ED *Tel.* 020 7399 0930

■ The Worshipful Company of Spectacle Makers' Charity

CC NO 1072172 **ESTABLISHED** 1998

WHERE FUNDING CAN BE GIVEN Worldwide, with a preference for the City of London.

WHO CAN BENEFIT Registered charities.

WHAT IS FUNDED Work concerned with visual impairments, with a preference for national rather than local causes.

WHAT IS NOT FUNDED No grants are made to individuals.

TYPE OF GRANT Specific projects, not general funds.

SAMPLE GRANTS Fight for Sight; Treloar Trust; British Council for the Prevention of Blindness; British Wireless for the Blind Fund; Skillforce; and Vision Aid Overseas.

FINANCES *Year* 2011–12 *Income* £71,638 *Grants* £100,760 *Assets* £659,691

TRUSTEES Christine Tomkins; Venerable John Morrison; Liz Shilling; Edward Middleton; James Osborne; Nigel Andrew; Michael Rudd.

OTHER INFORMATION The charity's accounts list a number of grant beneficiaries, without the grant amounts.

HOW TO APPLY In writing to the correspondent including details of how the grant will be used and a copy of the latest audited accounts. Note: the trustees meet in early spring to decide on grants, meaning that applications received between June and March are unlikely to be addressed quickly.

WHO TO APPLY TO John Salmon, Clerk, Apothecaries Hall, Blackfriars Lane, London EC4V 6EL *Tel.* 020 7236 2932 *email* clerk@spectaclemakers.com *Website* www.spectaclemakers.com

■ The Jessie Spencer Trust

CC NO 219289   **ESTABLISHED** 1962

WHERE FUNDING CAN BE GIVEN UK, with some preference for Nottinghamshire.

WHO CAN BENEFIT Registered charities, with a preference for those in Nottinghamshire.

WHAT IS FUNDED General charitable purposes.

WHAT IS NOT FUNDED Grants are rarely made for the repair of parish churches outside Nottinghamshire.

TYPE OF GRANT Grants are made towards both capital and revenue expenditure. They can be recurrent for up to ten years.

RANGE OF GRANTS £100–£10,000.

SAMPLE GRANTS Nottinghamshire Historic Churches Trust (£10,000); Framework Housing Association and Bromley Home Library (£5,000 each); Motability (£2,000); Independent Parental Special Education Advice, Alzheimer's Research UK and Dove Cottage Day Hospice (£1,000 each); and Clifton Methodist Church, Army Cadet Force Association, Listening Books and Happy Days Children's Charity (£500 each).

FINANCES *Year* 2012–13 *Income* £141,653 *Grants* £91,150 *Assets* £4,080,218

TRUSTEES Victor Semmens; B. Mitchell; David Wild; Andrew Tiplady.

HOW TO APPLY In writing to the correspondent, including the latest set of audited accounts, at least three weeks before the trustees' meetings in March, June, September and December. Unsuccessful applications will not be notified.

WHO TO APPLY TO John Thompson, Administrator, c/o 4 Walsingham Drive, Corby Glen, Grantham, Lincolnshire NG33 4TA *Tel.* 01476 552429 *email* jessiespencer@btinternet.com

■ The Spero Foundation

CC NO 1136810   **ESTABLISHED** 2010

WHERE FUNDING CAN BE GIVEN UK and overseas.

WHO CAN BENEFIT Organisations and individuals.

WHAT IS FUNDED General; education and training; health; community development; sports and recreation; arts; and heritage.

FINANCES *Year* 2011–12 *Income* £0 *Grants* £105,000

TRUSTEES Andrew Peggie; Brian Padgett; Joanna Landau; Eden Landau; Jonathan Emmutt.

OTHER INFORMATION Due to the trust's low income in 2011–12, only basic financial information was available from the Charity Commission. The grant total is an estimation based on this information.

HOW TO APPLY In writing to the correspondent.

WHO TO APPLY TO Sarah Hunt, 22 Arlington Street, London SW1A 1RD *Tel.* 020 7499 1957

■ The Ralph and Irma Sperring Charity

CC NO 1048101   **ESTABLISHED** 1995

WHERE FUNDING CAN BE GIVEN The parishes situated within a five-mile radius of the church of St John the Baptist, Midsomer Norton.

WHO CAN BENEFIT Organisations and individuals in the beneficial area.

WHAT IS FUNDED Grants are given to: provide or assist with the provision of residential accommodation; for the relief of people who are elderly, disabled or in need; assist with the establishment of village halls, recreation grounds, charitable sports grounds and playing fields; further the religious or other charitable work of the Anglican churches in the parishes; support hospitals and their leagues of friends; and further education of children and young people at educational institutions.

FINANCES *Year* 2011–12 *Income* £218,475 *Grants* £98,251 *Assets* £5,813,540

TRUSTEES Revd Christopher Chiplin; Ted Hallam; Sally Blanning; Kenneth Saunders; Noreen Busby; Dr John Haxell.

HOW TO APPLY In writing to the correspondent.

WHO TO APPLY TO Ted Hallam, Trustee, Thatcher and Hallam Solicitors, Island House, Midsomer Norton, Radstock BA3 2HJ *Tel.* 01761 414646 *email* sperringcharity@gmail.com

■ The Spielman Charitable Trust

CC NO 278306   **ESTABLISHED** 1979

WHERE FUNDING CAN BE GIVEN Bristol and the surrounding area.

WHO CAN BENEFIT Charities and voluntary organisations.

WHAT IS FUNDED The trust concentrates its resources on caring for and educating children and young people and the elderly in Bristol and the South West of England, but also uses donations for general charitable purposes.

RANGE OF GRANTS Up to £25,000.

SAMPLE GRANTS Teenage Cancer Trust (£25,000); The Wheels Project (£15,000); NSPCC, Bristol Children's Help Society, Royal Welsh College and WE Care and Repair (£10,000 each) and Girlguiding, Children's Hospice, Colston Society, Farmlink and The Prince's Trust (£5,000 each). Donations of less than £5,000 were made to 44 charities.

FINANCES *Year* 2012–13 *Income* £239,161 *Grants* £239,733 *Assets* £5,729,585

TRUSTEES C. J. L. Moorsom; P. A. Cooper; K. Hann.

OTHER INFORMATION The following are the statistics in respect of certain key activities undertaken in 2012–13: Grants made to organisations helping disadvantaged children and their parents in Bristol, including boys clubs and scout groups (£129,000); Grants made to Art and Theatre organisations (£23,000); Grants given to organisations helping young Individuals with cancer or a terminal illness or who are deaf, blind or suffering other disabilities (£69,500); Grants made to a number of Bristol Charities helping elderly people and the disabled or to elderly individuals (£16,000) and Grants made to Schools (£2,000).

HOW TO APPLY In writing to the correspondent.

WHO TO APPLY TO June Moody, 17 St Augustine's Parade, Bristol BS1 4UL *Tel.* 01179 291929 *email* g-s.moody@btconnect.com

....

■ Split Infinitive Trust

CC NO 1110380   **ESTABLISHED** 2005

WHERE FUNDING CAN BE GIVEN UK, however Yorkshire and regional area is preferred.

WHO CAN BENEFIT Individuals, projects by companies and organisations with charitable status.

WHAT IS FUNDED Arts, education and the alleviation of sickness, poverty, hardship and distress.

WHAT IS NOT FUNDED Grants for general running costs, for projects outside the UK, and charities seeking funds for their own grant disbursement.

TYPE OF GRANT One-off grants to individuals and organisations.

RANGE OF GRANTS Generally between £500 and £2,000.

SAMPLE GRANTS Echoes Foundation (£1,200) The Voices Foundation, I CAN, Polka Theatre, Hidden Gem Productions and Northern Bullitts (£1,000 each).

FINANCES *Year* 2011–12 *Income* £62,536 *Grants* £40,990 *Assets* £123,906

TRUSTEES Sir Alan Ayckbourn; Heather Stoney; Paul Allen; Neil Adleman; Elizabeth Bell.

OTHER INFORMATION Nine individuals were awarded grants ranging from £2,000 to £1,000.

HOW TO APPLY **Individual applicants** are required to fill in an application form and provide a covering letter and an acceptance from the course of study (for students) or evidence of the project/ commission and/or a CV (for non-students). **Organisations** are asked to complete an application form and provide a project plan and a detailed budget breakdown. Both application forms can be found on the trust's website.

WHO TO APPLY TO Heather Stoney, Trustee, PO BOX 409, Scarborough YO11 9AJ *email* splitinfin@pendon.eclipse.co.uk *Website* www.splitinfinitivetrust.co.uk

....

■ The Spoore, Merry and Rixman Foundation

CC NO 309040   **ESTABLISHED** 1958

WHERE FUNDING CAN BE GIVEN The (pre-1974) borough of Maidenhead and the ancient parish of Bray, not the whole of Royal Borough of Windsor and Maidenhead.

WHO CAN BENEFIT People under the age of 25 living in the beneficial area.

WHAT IS FUNDED The trust was set up to benefit people 'who need financial assistance in way of scholarships, bursaries, maintenance allowances or other benefits' to further their education.

WHAT IS NOT FUNDED Deals only with the (pre-1974) borough of Maidenhead and the ancient parish of Bray.

SAMPLE GRANTS Norden Farm Centre for the Arts (£40,000). Previous beneficiaries include: The Bridge Trust (£10,000); Larchfield Primary and Nursery School (£7,820); Ellington Primary and Nursery School (£5,385).

FINANCES *Year* 2012 *Income* £338,764 *Grants* £285,504 *Assets* £9,255,542

TRUSTEES Dorothy Kemp; Ann Redgrave; Ian Thomas; Leo Walters; Grahame Fisher; Tony Hill; Asghar Majeed; Barbara Wielchowski; David Coppinger; The Mayor of the Royal Borough of Windsor and Maidenhead.

OTHER INFORMATION Grants to 46 organisations totalled £106,000 with a further £180,000 given in grants to 129 individuals.

HOW TO APPLY On a form available to download, together with guidelines and criteria, on the foundation's website. Applications are considered in January, April, July and October.

WHO TO APPLY TO Clerk to the Trust, PO Box 4229, Slough SL1 0QZ *email* clerk@smrfmaidenhead.org *Website* www.smrfmaidenhead.org.uk

....

■ Sported Foundation

CC NO 1123313   **ESTABLISHED** 2008

WHERE FUNDING CAN BE GIVEN UK

WHO CAN BENEFIT Community organisations that work with young people, aged between 11 and 25, in disadvantaged areas.

WHAT IS FUNDED Sport and social welfare.

WHAT IS NOT FUNDED No grants for capital costs such as building facilities. No grants to school based projects.

RANGE OF GRANTS Usually up to £10,000, but can be higher.

SAMPLE GRANTS The Dracaena Centre Ltd (£25,000); Community Action Through Sport (£16,000); Trelya and Grapevine (£15,000 each); Coventry Boys Club (£14,000); Salle Ursa Fencing Club (£7,000); Longford Short Football Project (£4,000) and The Grangers Club (£1,500).

FINANCES *Year* 2012 *Income* £230,727 *Grants* £1,475,672 *Assets* £5,864,342

TRUSTEES Sir Keith Mills; Lady Maureen Mills; Alexander Mills; Richard Powles; Dermot Heffernan; Alan Pascoe; Baroness Susan Campbell; Nigel Keen.

HOW TO APPLY Application forms and full criteria and guidelines for each region are available online at the foundation's website.

WHO TO APPLY TO Emma Blackwell, Member Services Co-ordinator, 8th Floor, 20 St James's Street, London SW1A 1ES *Tel.* 020 7389 1907 *email* info@sported.org.uk *Website* www.sported.org.uk

....

■ Rosalyn and Nicholas Springer Charitable Trust

CC NO 1062239   **ESTABLISHED** 1997

WHERE FUNDING CAN BE GIVEN UK and Israel.

WHO CAN BENEFIT Organisations, particularly those supporting Jewish people, and individuals.

WHAT IS FUNDED The promotion of welfare, education and personal development, particularly amongst the Jewish community. Grants are made in the following categories: medical, health and sickness; education and training; arts and culture; religious activities; relief of poverty; and general charitable purposes.

RANGE OF GRANTS Up to £25,000, but mostly £1,000 or less.

SAMPLE GRANTS United Jewish Israel Appeal (£26,500); Magen David Adom UK (£13,000); British Council Of Shears Zedek (£11,000); Community Security Trust (£6,000); The Ear Foundation (£5,000); Chicken Shed Theatre Trust (£4,000); Proms at St Jude's (£2,500); Lifelites (£2,000); Regent's Park Open Air Theatre (£1,000); and CancerKin, Train for Employment, Royal Ballet School and British Emunah (£500 each).

FINANCES *Year* 2011–12 *Income* £125,019 *Grants* £142,122 *Assets* £30,868

TRUSTEES Rosalyn Springer; Nicholas Springer.

HOW TO APPLY The trust has previously stated that it only supports organisations it is already in contact with. 99% of unsolicited applications are unsuccessful and because of the volume it receives, the trust is unable to reply to such letters. It would therefore not seem appropriate to apply to this trust.

WHO TO APPLY TO Nicholas Springer, Trustee, 15 Park Village West, London NW1 4AE *Tel.* 020 7253 7272

■ The Springfields Employees' Medical Research and Charity Trust Fund

CC NO 518005   **ESTABLISHED** 1985

WHERE FUNDING CAN BE GIVEN Preston and South Ribble, Blackpool, Wyre and Fylde areas

WHO CAN BENEFIT Organisations benefiting disabled people.

WHAT IS FUNDED Grants to hospitals and local medical and welfare charities for medical equipment.

WHAT IS NOT FUNDED Support is only provided for specific pieces of equipment therefore funding is not available for items such as projects and salaries. Grants will not be provided to applicants outside the area of benefit unless it can be demonstrated that the research will benefit residents from within the area.

TYPE OF GRANT One-off grants.

RANGE OF GRANTS Up to £4,000.

SAMPLE GRANTS Breast Cancer Campaign (£4,000); Little Sisters of the Poor (£1,900); Fight for Sight (£1,400); The Genesis Appeal (£1,250); Dolly Mops (£500); Medequip4Kids (£3,100); Galloway's Society for the Blind (£2,300); Lee Smith Foundation (£1,200); FSID Program (£800); Listening Books (£3,000); Fylde Citizens Advice (£37).

FINANCES *Year* 2012 *Income* £45,454 *Grants* £45,000

TRUSTEES Steven Hart; Ian Driver; Jackie Humphreys.

HOW TO APPLY In writing to the correspondent.

WHO TO APPLY TO Ian Driver, Welfare Officer and Trustee., Westing House, Springfields Fuels Limited, Springfields, Salwick, Preston PR4 0XJ *Tel.* 01772 764578 *Fax* 01772 762929 *email* driverir@westinghouse.com

---

■ Springrule Limited

CC NO 802561   **ESTABLISHED** 1992

WHERE FUNDING CAN BE GIVEN England and Wales.

WHO CAN BENEFIT Jewish organisations.

WHAT IS FUNDED Advancement of the Orthodox Jewish faith and the relief of poverty.

TYPE OF GRANT One-off grants to organisations.

SAMPLE GRANTS Previously: Beis Yaakov Institutions, Friends of Horim and Torah Vechesed (£25,000 each); and Yad Eliezer (£5,000).

FINANCES *Year* 2011–12 *Income* £110,890 *Grants* £1,056,147 *Assets* £2,480,086

TRUSTEES Malka Jacober; Robert Nevies; Jacque Monderer; Hessie Monderer; Rivka Nevies.

HOW TO APPLY In writing to the correspondent.

WHO TO APPLY TO R. Nevies, Trustee, 45 Cheyne Walk, London NW4 3QH

■ The Spurrell Charitable Trust

CC NO 267287   **ESTABLISHED** 1960

WHERE FUNDING CAN BE GIVEN UK, with some preference for Norfolk.

WHO CAN BENEFIT Registered charities.

WHAT IS FUNDED General charitable purposes.

WHAT IS NOT FUNDED No grants to individuals.

RANGE OF GRANTS Up to £7,500, on average around £1,000.

SAMPLE GRANTS Merlin (£10,000; East Anglian Air Ambulance (£7,000); Break (£5,000); Aylesbury High School (£3,000); Alzheimer's Research Trust, Brain and Spine Foundation, Camphill Village Trust and North Norfolk Multiple Sclerosis Society (£1,200 each); Norfolk Deaf Association, Norwich and Central Norfolk MIND, Wireless for the Bedridden and Woodlands Trust (£600 each) and Felbrigg Crusaders, Sheringham and Cromer Choral Society and Sustead Village Hall Fund (£300 each).

FINANCES *Year* 2011–12 *Income* £64,395 *Grants* £71,900 *Assets* £2,308,431

TRUSTEES Ingeburg Spurrell; Martyn Spurrell.

HOW TO APPLY 'Income has fallen steadily over the last few years and is now insufficient to meet essential commitments. Therefore, new appeals are very unlikely to be considered.'

WHO TO APPLY TO Martyn Spurrell, Trustee, 78 Wendover Road, Aylesbury HP21 9NJ *Tel.* 01892 541565

■ The Geoff and Fiona Squire Foundation

CC NO 1085553   **ESTABLISHED** 2001

WHERE FUNDING CAN BE GIVEN UK.

WHO CAN BENEFIT Charitable organisations.

WHAT IS FUNDED General charitable purposes.

RANGE OF GRANTS £1,000–£250,000.

SAMPLE GRANTS Salisbury Cathedral (£400,000); UCLH Charitable Foundation – Cancer Centre Appeal (£250,000); Teenage Cancer Trust (£207,000); SENSE Holiday Fund and Orpheus Centre (£100,000 each); Lord's Tavemers (£64,000); Special Olympics Great Britain (£35,000); Starlight Children's Foundation (£30,000); Friends of Shepherds Down School (£20,000); Exeter House School (£10,000); Music for Youth (£7,500); Southern Spinal Injuries Trust (£5,000); NHMET Ark Annual Lecture (£3,500); and Deaf Blind UK and Brendoncare Club (£1,000 each).

FINANCES *Year* 2011–12 *Income* £689,517 *Grants* £1,290,573 *Assets* £10,930,100

TRUSTEES Geoff W. Squire; Fiona Squire; B. P. Peerless.

HOW TO APPLY The trust has previously stated: 'the trustees have in place a well-established donations policy and we do not therefore encourage unsolicited grant applications, not least because they take time and expense to deal with properly.'

Think carefully about every application. Is it justified?

913

WHO TO APPLY TO Fiona Squire, Trustee, The Walton Canonry, 69 The Close, Salisbury, Wiltshire SP1 2EN

■ St Andrew's Conservation Trust

CC NO 282157   **ESTABLISHED** 1980

WHERE FUNDING CAN BE GIVEN Preference for the south west of England.

WHO CAN BENEFIT Charitable organisations.

WHAT IS FUNDED The conservation, restoration and preservation of monuments, sculptures and artefacts of historic or public interest which are upon or attached to property owned by any charitable organisation. The trust also makes grants for the training of conservators and facilities.

Aid is granted to 'conservation projects involving decorative or artistic features in parish churches, abbeys and cathedrals in the South West of England and in South Wales'.

WHAT IS NOT FUNDED No support is given for conservation or restoration of churchyard table tombs except in very restricted circumstances.

RANGE OF GRANTS £100–£10,000.

SAMPLE GRANTS Hinton St Geroge, Somerset: C16 monuments (Poulett Memorial Chapel) (£5,000); Mells, Somerset: Wall memorials, Cornworthy, Devon: Wall Monument (£2,000 each); Townstal, Devon: C14 Effigy (£500).

FINANCES *Year* 2012 *Income* £23,240 *Grants* £30,000

TRUSTEES Gerard Leighton; Hugh Playfair; Simon Pomeroy; Alan Thomas; Elsa van der Zee; John Reed; Simon Quilter; John Bucknall.

PUBLICATIONS Accounts from 2009 available from the Charity Commission website. Accounts for 2010 were overdue.

HOW TO APPLY On a form available to download from the website. Grant applications should arrive with the Trust either before end-March, or before end-September in each year.

WHO TO APPLY TO Simon Pomeroy, Trustee, c/o Duddle Farm, Nr Bockhampton, Dorchester, Dorset DT2 8QL *Tel.* 01305 264516 *Website* www.standrewsconservationtrust.org.uk

■ St Christopher's Educational Trust (incorporating the Hughes and Stevens Bequest)

CC NO 313864   **ESTABLISHED** 1971

WHERE FUNDING CAN BE GIVEN UK.

WHO CAN BENEFIT Organisations and individuals connected to the Church of England.

WHAT IS FUNDED Education and the support of children and youth organisations.

TYPE OF GRANT Small grants, usually one-off but can be for up to three years. Some part-funded projects.

RANGE OF GRANTS Up to £15,000.

SAMPLE GRANTS National Society (£15,000 and £2,500); St Mary and St Giles Centre (£10,000); York St John University Messy Church (£7,000); BRAVE School Ecumenical Project Royston and Buntingford (£2,000); Bradford and Ripon and Leeds (£1,500) and St John's College Nottingham (£1,000).

FINANCES *Year* 2012 *Income* £207,790 *Grants* £46,500 *Assets* £134,819

TRUSTEES Dr David Sellick; Revd Prof. Leslie Francis; Revd Canon David Isaac; J. Swallow; Ven. Paul Wheatley; Revd Mary Hawes; Revd Canon John Bull; Revd Janina Ainsworth; Karen Counsell.

OTHER INFORMATION The merger of St Christopher's Trust and the Hughes and Stevens Bequest was finalised during 2012. The merged charity is now known as The St Christopher's Educational Trust (incorporating the Hughes and Stevens Bequest). In 2012 grants were awarded to seven individuals totalling £7,500.

HOW TO APPLY In writing to the correspondent.

WHO TO APPLY TO Lindsey Anderson-Gear, Clerk to the Trustees, Church House, Great Smith Street, Westminster, London SW1P 3NZ *email* stchristopherstrust@hotmail.co.uk

■ The St Hilda's Trust

CC NO 500962   **ESTABLISHED** 1904

WHERE FUNDING CAN BE GIVEN The diocese of Newcastle (Newcastle upon Tyne, North Tyneside and Northumberland).

WHO CAN BENEFIT Deprived communities of the diocese of Newcastle (Newcastle upon Tyne, North Tyneside and Northumberland), with extra focus on children and young people.

WHAT IS FUNDED General charitable purposes, especially smaller scale projects benefiting children and young people in deprived communities.

WHAT IS NOT FUNDED Beneficiaries outside of the trust's operational area.

RANGE OF GRANTS £1,000–£5,000.

FINANCES *Year* 2012 *Income* £69,638 *Grants* £78,135 *Assets* £1,582,092

TRUSTEES Revd Canon Alan Craig; Rosemary Nicholson; Rt Revd Martin Wharton; Dr Martin Wilkinson; Neil Brockbank; David Welsh.

OTHER INFORMATION No published list of beneficiaries.

HOW TO APPLY In writing to the correspondent.

WHO TO APPLY TO Josie Pinnegar, Secretary, Newcastle Diocesan Board of Finance, Church House, St John's Terrace, North Shields, Tyne and Wear NE29 6HS *Tel.* 01912 704100 *email* j.pinnegar@newcastle.anglican.org

■ St James's Trust Settlement

CC NO 280455   **ESTABLISHED** 1980

WHERE FUNDING CAN BE GIVEN UK and USA.

WHO CAN BENEFIT Registered charities.

WHAT IS FUNDED Projects in the areas of health, education and social justice.

WHAT IS NOT FUNDED No grants to individuals.

TYPE OF GRANT Core costs, one-off, project, research, recurring costs, salaries and start-up costs. Funding is for up to three years.

SAMPLE GRANTS Homeopathy Action Trust (£15,000); CARIS (£12,000); and Highbury Vale Blackstock Trust (£10,000).

FINANCES *Year* 2011–12 *Income* £158,122 *Grants* £317,326 *Assets* £3,312,074

TRUSTEES Jane Wells; Cathy Ingram; Simon Taffler.

OTHER INFORMATION The grants total includes £37,000 to three organisations in the UK and £280,500 to 39 organisations in the USA.

HOW TO APPLY The trust states that it 'does not seek unsolicited applications for grants and, without paid staff, are unable to respond to such applications'.

WHO TO APPLY TO The Trustees, c/o Begbies Accountants, Epworth House, 25 City Road, London EC1Y 1AR *Tel.* 020 7628 5801 *Fax* 020 7628 0390 *email* admin@ begbiesaccountants.co.uk

914

Does the trust you have chosen match your needs? Haphazard applications waste postage and time

....
■ St James's Place Foundation

CC NO 1144606   **ESTABLISHED** 1994

WHERE FUNDING CAN BE GIVEN UK.

WHO CAN BENEFIT Registered charities supporting children and young people (up to the age of 25) with mental or physical conditions, life threatening or degenerative illnesses. Hospices are also supported, regardless of the ages of their clients.

WHAT IS FUNDED The foundation's main themes are: cherishing the children; combatting cancer; supporting hospices.

WHAT IS NOT FUNDED The foundation has a policy of not considering an application from any charity within two years of receiving a previous application. The foundation does not provide support for: charities with reserves of over 50% of income; administrative costs; activities primarily the responsibility of statutory agencies; replacement of lost statutory funding; research; events; advertising; holidays; sponsorship; contributions to large capital appeals; single faith charities; social and economic deprivation; charities that are raising funds on behalf of another charity.

TYPE OF GRANT One-off.

RANGE OF GRANTS Up to £10,000.

FINANCES Year 2013 Grants £3,600,000

TRUSTEES Malcolm Cooper-Smith, Chair; David Bellamy; Mike Wilson; Andrew Croft; Hugh Gladman; David Lamb.

OTHER INFORMATION Following a strategic review, the foundation was wound up in 2012 and re-registered with the Charity Commission with a new registered charity number. As a result, no accounts were available for the new iteration of the foundation, although the foundation estimates grantmaking will be in the region of £3.6 million.

HOW TO APPLY The following information is given on the foundation's website.

'The foundation is only able to consider applications from UK registered charities as well as Special Needs Schools in the UK. We accept applications from national, regional and local charities operating in England, Scotland, Wales and Northern Ireland. Important note: we do not accept unsolicited applications from charities operating overseas. The Small Grants Programme is available to smaller UK registered charities working nationally, regionally or locally in the UK with an annual income of up to £750,000. The amount applied for should be up to a maximum of £10,000 in any two-year rolling period. If an applicant is unsuccessful then a period of twelve months must elapse before re-applying. If you believe that your application falls within the funding policy of the foundation, you are welcome to apply. There are no deadlines or closing dates. Small Grants are considered on receipt and in rotation. The whole procedure can take between four to six months (sometimes longer if many applications are received) so it is advisable to apply in good time if funds are required for a certain date. Each application is considered on its merits based on the information provided in the online application form and the due diligence carried out by the foundation team. We will acknowledge receipt of your application by email. Applications for a Small Grant will normally receive a visit from a representative of the foundation, who will subsequently report to the trustees. Following the trustees' decision, successful applicants will be notified. Applications can be made online via the foundation's website.'

'**Supporting Hospices:** the foundation is proud to support hospices in the United Kingdom. However, we do not currently invite applications from individual hospices. Instead we will be working with Help the Hospices, the umbrella organisation supporting independent hospices in the UK, who will distributes funds to hospices on our behalf. For more information, visit the Help the Hospices website: www.helpthehospices.org.uk.'

'**Major Grants Programme:** the foundation's Major Grants Programme remains closed to unsolicited applications. Check the foundation's website for up-to-date information.'

WHO TO APPLY TO Mark Longbottom, c/o St James's Place Wealth Management plc, St James's Place House, 1 Tetbury Road, Cirencester, Gloucestershire GL7 1FP Tel. 01285 878562 email mark.longbottom@sjp.co.uk Website www.sjpfoundation.co.uk

....
■ Sir Walter St John's Educational Charity

CC NO 312690   **ESTABLISHED** 1992

WHERE FUNDING CAN BE GIVEN The boroughs of Wandsworth or Lambeth, with a preference for Battersea.

WHO CAN BENEFIT Children and young persons under the age of 25 years residing in the London Boroughs of Wandsworth or Lambeth and in need of financial assistance. Particular preference is given to those residing in the former Metropolitan Borough of Battersea. Grants are awarded both to individuals and local schools, colleges, youth clubs, and voluntary and community organisations. Priority is given to activities benefiting disadvantaged children.

WHAT IS FUNDED Promotion of education and training of children and young persons under the age of 25 years who are resident in the London Boroughs of Wandsworth or Lambeth and who are in need of financial assistance. The charity gives priority to those activities that benefit the following groups of local children and young people: living in areas of particular social disadvantage; young refugees and asylum seekers; young carers; children and young people with disabilities; children in and leaving state care.

The charity also plays a proactive role in supporting the development of new educational initiatives and projects, curriculum enrichment programmes, play schemes and workshops. Individual grants are primarily made to students undertaking Further Education courses.

WHAT IS NOT FUNDED School pupils under 16 and full-time students on university degree courses are not normally supported. Student funding is not usually given towards the cost of a computer or laptop. Maintenance grants are not available.

TYPE OF GRANT One-off and up to three year strategic grants to organisations, individual grants.

RANGE OF GRANTS Generally £1,000–£5,000.

SAMPLE GRANTS South Thames Crossroads' Young Carers' Project (£90, 000); South Thames College (£5,000); Providence House Community Centre (£2,500); and Futures Theatre Company (£1,000).

FINANCES Year 2011–12 Income £133,743 Grants £98,373 Assets £3,481,303

TRUSTEES Daphne Daytes; Peter Dyson; John O'Malley; Sarah Rackham; Colonel Julian Radcliffe; Jenny Scribbins; Cllr Sheldon Wilkie; Barry Fairbank; Godfrey Allen; Colonel Martin

Stratton; Michael Bates; Canon Simon Butler; Cllr Ademamola Aminu; Wendy Speck; Rosemary Summerfield.

OTHER INFORMATION South Thames Crossroads' Young Carers' Project (£90, 000); South Thames College (£5,000); Providence House Community Centre (£2,500); Futures Theatre Company (£1,000).

HOW TO APPLY Further details for both organisations and individuals can be obtained and applications discussed with the charity's manager Susan Perry by email (manager@swsjcharity.org.uk) or phone (020 7498 8878).

Organisations: small education grants and strategic grants available, application proposals should be discussed with Susan Perry.

Individuals: Application form must be completed after the initial approach In order to proceed the application eligible candidates must satisfy the following conditions: applicants for student grants must be under 25 and must have been permanently resident in Wandsworth or Lambeth for at least six months; grants are not normally made to school pupils under 16 or to full-time students on university degree courses; grants will be awarded only to students who are following a validated, approved or recognised course; applicants must provide evidence that they have a good prospect of successfully completing the course on which they are being supported; the award of a grant should have a critical effect on the grant-holder's opportunity to study. Eligible candidates include: further education students aged 16 to 24; further education students aged 16 to 24 – lone parents; students on foundation or access courses in art, dance and drama (in exceptional circumstances); students with disabilities; students affected by unforeseen circumstances.

WHO TO APPLY TO Susan Perry, Manager, Office 1A, Culvert House, Culvert Road, London SW11 5DH *Tel.* 020 7498 8878 *email* manager@swsjcharity.org.uk *Website* www.swsjcharity.org.uk

....
■ The St Laurence Relief In Need Trust

CC NO 205043   **ESTABLISHED** 1962
WHERE FUNDING CAN BE GIVEN The ancient parish of St Laurence, then the borough of Reading.
WHO CAN BENEFIT Persons resident generally, or individually, in the area of the ancient parish of St Laurence in Reading and, thereafter, persons resident generally, or individually, in the county borough of Reading.
WHAT IS FUNDED Persons, generally or individually, who are in conditions of need, hardship or distress.
WHAT IS NOT FUNDED No grants to individuals outside the ancient parish of St Laurence, Reading or the county borough of Reading, even when supported by social services or similar agencies.
TYPE OF GRANT One-off.
RANGE OF GRANTS £1,000 annual to £10,000 one–off.
FINANCES *Year* 2012 *Income* £57,426 *Grants* £58,794 *Assets* £124,303
TRUSTEES Patricia Thomas; Cllr Rosemary Williams; Revd Christopher Russell; Nicholas Burrows; Stewart Hotston; Lorraine Joslin.
OTHER INFORMATION In 2012 a total of 38 organisations shared £56,000 and two individuals received grants totalling £3,000.

HOW TO APPLY In writing to the correspondent, supplying latest accounts or details of bank balances and so on, together with reason for application. The trustees meet twice a year in April and November. Informal contact via email is welcomed before an application is submitted.
WHO TO APPLY TO Jason Pyke, Treasurer, c/o Vale and West, Victoria House, 26 Queen Victoria Street, Reading RG1 1TG *Tel.* 01189 573238

....
■ St Michael's and All Saints' Charities Relief Branch (The Church Houses Relief in Need Charity)

CC NO 202750   **ESTABLISHED** 1980
WHERE FUNDING CAN BE GIVEN City of Oxford.
WHO CAN BENEFIT Charitable organisations, with an interest in Christian groups.
WHAT IS FUNDED Health and welfare.
WHAT IS NOT FUNDED Individuals are very rarely supported.
SAMPLE GRANTS Leys Youth Programme (£11,000); Donnington Doorstep Family Centre (£10,000); Archway Foundation (£8,000); Oxford Sexual Abuse and Rape Crisis Centre (£6,000); Innovista International (£5,000); Abbeyfield Oxenford Society (£3,000); ACT (£2,000); and Blackbird Leys Neighbourhood Support Scheme (£1,000).
FINANCES *Year* 2012 *Income* £86,538 *Grants* £106,939 *Assets* £1,416,913
TRUSTEES Patrick Beavis; Michael Lear; Lord Krebs; Ruth Loseby; Prudence Dailey; Robert Earl; Samia Shibli; The Very Revd Robert Wilkes; Simon Stubbings; Prof. Henry Woudhuysen; The Ven Martin Gorick.
HOW TO APPLY In writing to the correspondent.
WHO TO APPLY TO Rupert Sheppard, Administrator, 2 Churchill Place, Yarnton, Kidlington, Oxfordshire OX5 1GQ *Tel.* 01865 240940 *email* rupert.sheppard@smng.org.uk

....
■ St Monica Trust (formerly known as St Monica Trust Community Fund)

CC NO 202151   **ESTABLISHED** 1962
WHERE FUNDING CAN BE GIVEN Preference for the south west of England, particularly Bristol and the surrounding area.
WHO CAN BENEFIT Older people; disability.
WHAT IS FUNDED Accommodation and support; respite care.
WHAT IS NOT FUNDED No grants to fund buildings, adaptations to buildings or minibus purchases.
TYPE OF GRANT Capital items, running costs.
RANGE OF GRANTS Grants of up to £15,000 each are available to organisations.
SAMPLE GRANTS Previously: Citizen's Advice Bureau (£9,800); St Peter's Hospice, Headway Bristol and Motor Neurone Disease Association (£7,500 each); IT Help@Home (£5,000); the New Place (£3,900); Bristol and Avon Chinese Women's Group (£2,000); Bath Institute of Medical Engineering (£1,500); and Western Active Stroke Group (£1,000).
FINANCES *Year* 2012 *Income* £23,747,000 *Grants* £584,000 *Assets* £217,719,000
TRUSTEES John Kane; Trevor Smallwood; Stuart Burnett; Richard Wynn-Jones; Jane Cork; John Laycock; Andrew Yates; Peter Rilett; Helen Moss; Dr Rebecca Slinn; Lady Paula Wills;

Michael Lea; Charles Griffiths; Revd Canon Neil Heavisides.

OTHER INFORMATION Grants are also made to individuals.

HOW TO APPLY On a form available from the correspondent, or to download from the fund's website. All applicants must submit a form together with additional information that is requested, for example, an annual report. Applications are considered once a year; see the fund's website for deadline dates.

WHO TO APPLY TO Robert Whetton, Administrator, Cote Lane, Bristol BS9 3UN *Tel.* 01179 494006 *email* info@stmonicatrust.org.uk *Website* www.stmonicatrust.org.uk

■ The Late St Patrick White Charitable Trust

CC NO 1056520   **ESTABLISHED** 1995

WHERE FUNDING CAN BE GIVEN UK.

WHO CAN BENEFIT Registered charities.

WHAT IS FUNDED Large UK charities catering for people who are elderly or who have disabilities, and local groups in Hampshire. The trust has a list of regular beneficiaries, although grants are available to other organisations.

RANGE OF GRANTS Between £1,000 and £5,000.

SAMPLE GRANTS Age Concern, Age UK, Arthritis Care, Cancer Research UK, Barnardo's, Guide Dogs for the Blind, The Salvation Army and Visability (£4,500 each).

FINANCES *Year* 2012–13 *Income* £47,072 *Grants* £31,500 *Assets* £2,185,576

TRUSTEE HSBC Trusts Co. (UK) Ltd.

HOW TO APPLY In writing to the correspondent. Applications are considered in February, May, August and November.

WHO TO APPLY TO R. Thompson, Trust Manager, HSBC Trust Co UK Ltd, Norwich House, Nelson Gate, Commercial Road, Southampton SO15 1GX *Tel.* 02380 722240

■ St Peter's Saltley Trust

CC NO 528915   **ESTABLISHED** 1980

WHERE FUNDING CAN BE GIVEN The dioceses of Worcester, Hereford, Lichfield, Birmingham and Coventry.

WHO CAN BENEFIT Organisations benefiting people of all ages, teachers, governors, unemployed people and volunteers.

WHAT IS FUNDED The advancement of education and religion via projects in the dioceses named above.

WHAT IS NOT FUNDED The trust is unable to fund the following: Individuals; Subsidies for the existing, ongoing work of an organisation and capital costs (e.g., building renovations, ongoing staff salaries).

TYPE OF GRANT Project funding for up to three years will be considered.

RANGE OF GRANTS Up to £8,500.

SAMPLE GRANTS Queen's Foundation – Unlock Birmingham (£8,000); Mission Apprentice Scheme (£7,000); WMCFEC Development (£6,500); Green Blade Theatre (£5,000); North Warwickshire and Hinckley College (£4,700) and Through Life Discipleship (£2,400).

FINANCES *Year* 2012–13 *Income* £130,483 *Grants* £60,747 *Assets* £3,018,699

TRUSTEES Revd Anthony Priddis; David Urquart; Ven Hayward Osborne; Gordon Thornhill; Revd Jonathan Gledhill; Dr Peter Kent; Canon Robert Jones; Colin Hopkins; Revd Dr John Inge; Canon

Paul Wilson; Philip Sell; Dr Paula Gooder; Kathleen Kimber; Revd Christopher Cocksworth; Jill Stolberg.

OTHER INFORMATION The grant total includes £2,000 that was given to individuals.

HOW TO APPLY The trust states that: 'If you are interested to explore how we might work with you, contact us for a further conversation.' Full criteria and guidelines are available on the trust's website.

WHO TO APPLY TO Lin Brown, Bursar and Clerk to the Trustees, Grays Court, 3 Nursery Road, Edgbaston, Birmingham B15 3JX *Tel.* 01214 276800 *email* bursar@saltleytrust.org.uk *Website* www.saltleytrust.org.uk

■ St Teilo's Trust

CC NO 1032405   **ESTABLISHED** 1993

WHERE FUNDING CAN BE GIVEN Wales.

WHO CAN BENEFIT Christian organisations.

WHAT IS FUNDED Evangelistic initiatives in parishes, for example, Alpha courses, evangelistic events and literature distribution.

WHAT IS NOT FUNDED No grants towards equipment or buildings.

SAMPLE GRANTS Previous beneficiaries include: Llandeilo PC, Gobaith Gymru, St Michael's Aberystwyth, Cilcoed Christian Centre, Parish of Bargoed, Postal Bible School and St David's Diocesan Council.

FINANCES *Year* 2011–12 *Income* £3,337 *Grants* £40,000

TRUSTEES Revd Canon Stuart Bell; Revd Peter Bement; Claire Mansel Lewis; Patrick Mansel Lewis; Revd Dr William Strange; Revd Bob Capper; John Settatree.

OTHER INFORMATION No grants list was available.

HOW TO APPLY In writing to the correspondent. Trustees meet in February, May and September. Applications should be sent by January, April and August. Guidelines are available from the trust.

WHO TO APPLY TO Patrick Mansel Lewis, Stradey Estate Office, 53 New Road, Llanelli SA15 3DP *Tel.* 01554 773059 *email* info@saintteilostrust.org.uk *Website* www.saintteilostrust.org.uk

■ The Stafford Trust

SC NO SC018079   **ESTABLISHED** 1991

WHERE FUNDING CAN BE GIVEN UK, with a preference for Scotland.

WHO CAN BENEFIT Charities registered in the UK.

WHAT IS FUNDED Animal welfare, medical research, local community projects, relief in need, HM Services personnel, overseas appeals, environment and sea rescue.

WHAT IS NOT FUNDED The trust does not support: religious organisations; political organisations; retrospective grants; student travel or expeditions; general appeals or mail shots.

RANGE OF GRANTS Mostly £500–£10,000. Occasionally recurring grants of up to three years.

FINANCES *Year* 2012–13 *Income* £380,694 *Grants* £250,540 *Assets* £14,710,291

TRUSTEES A. Peter M. Walls; Hamish N. Buchan; Gordon M. Wyllie; Angus Morgan.

OTHER INFORMATION 'The Stafford Trust was set up in 1991 by the late Mrs Gay Stafford of Sauchie Estate near Stirling. During her lifetime, Mrs Stafford made substantial gifts to the Trust and on her death in 2005, the residue of her estate was bequeathed to the trust.'

Think carefully about every application. Is it justified?

917

HOW TO APPLY The trust has a short application form which can be downloaded from its website. Applicants are invited to complete the form using their own words without the restrictions of completing set questions. Also supply the following, where appropriate: a brief description of your charity; a copy of your most recent annual report and accounts; a description of the project/funding requirement – what do you want to achieve and how will it be managed (the trustees look for clear, realistic and attainable aims); what is the expenditure budget for the project and the anticipated timescale; what funds have already been raised and what other sources are being approached; the need for funding must be clearly demonstrated; what will be the benefits of the project and how do you propose to monitor and evaluate whether the project has been successful; if applicable, what plans do you have to fund the future running costs of the project?

WHO TO APPLY TO Margaret Kane, Administrator, c/o Dickson Middleton CA, PO Box 14, 20 Barnton Street, Stirling FK8 1NE *Tel.* 01786 474718 *Fax* 01786 451392 *email* staffordtrust@dicksonmiddleton.co.uk *Website* www.staffordtrust.org.uk

------

■ The Stanley Foundation Ltd

CC NO 206866   **ESTABLISHED** 1962
WHERE FUNDING CAN BE GIVEN UK.
WHO CAN BENEFIT Charitable organisations.
WHAT IS FUNDED Medical care and research, education and social welfare, culture.
WHAT IS NOT FUNDED No grants to individuals.
RANGE OF GRANTS £1,000–£30,000.
SAMPLE GRANTS Place 2 Be (£32,000); London Library (£22,000); Royal Opera House (£21,000); Holburne Museum (£15,000); National Theatre (£12,000); Tusk (£11,000); Cancer Research (£10,000); Camden Psychotherapy Unit (£7,000); Friends of Roy Kinnear House (£5,000); Multiple Sclerosis Society (£2,000); and Riding for the Disabled (£750).
FINANCES *Year* 2011–12 *Income* £99,541 *Grants* £203,050 *Assets* £3,140,099
TRUSTEES P. Hall; G. Stanley; N. Stanley; S. R. Stanley; E. Stanley; S. H. Hall; J. N. Raymond.
HOW TO APPLY In writing to the correspondent.
WHO TO APPLY TO N. Stanley, Secretary, N. C. Morris and Co, 1 Montpelier Street, London SW7 1EX *email* nick@meristan.com

------

■ The Stanton Ballard Charitable Trust

CC NO 294688   **ESTABLISHED** 1986
WHERE FUNDING CAN BE GIVEN City of Oxford and the immediate neighbourhood.
WHO CAN BENEFIT Individuals, charities, institutions and organisations.
WHAT IS FUNDED Residents of the City of Oxford who are in conditions of need, hardship or stress; voluntary organisations providing services and facilities for such people; provision of leisure services; and the promotion of education.
WHAT IS NOT FUNDED No grants towards buildings or salaries.
RANGE OF GRANTS £100– £6,000
SAMPLE GRANTS Rose Hill and Donnington Advice Centre (£6,000); Oxfordshire County Council (£5,600); Connection (£5,000); Oxford Citizens

Housing Association (£3,000); St Bartholomew's Health Centre (£2,000); Barton Information Centre (£1,000); Listening Books (£500); Oxford Family Mediation (£450); Universal Benefit Society (£250); and First Wednesday Lunch Club (£100).
FINANCES *Year* 2011–12 *Income* £109,072 *Grants* £28,943 *Assets* £2,644,343
TRUSTEES Rosamund Nicholson; Christopher Impey; Mary Tate; John Martin; Keith Pawson; Tony Woodward; Martin Slade; Howard Minns; Dianna Marsh.
HOW TO APPLY On an application form available from the correspondent on receipt of an sae.
WHO TO APPLY TO Janet Minns, Secretary, PO Box 81, Oxfordshire OX4 4ZA *Tel.* 0870 760 5032

■ The Staples Trust

CC NO 1010656   **ESTABLISHED** 1992
WHERE FUNDING CAN BE GIVEN UK and overseas.
WHO CAN BENEFIT Charities working in the fields of international development, environment and women's issues organisations benefiting victims of abuse and domestic violence.
WHAT IS FUNDED Overseas development: projects which contribute to the empowerment of women, the rights of indigenous people, improved shelter and housing, income-generation in disadvantaged communities and sustainable agriculture and forestry. There is a particular interest in development projects which take account of environmental sustainability and, in many cases, the environmental and developments benefits of the project are of equal importance. Environment: support for projects in developing countries, Central and Eastern Europe and the UK. Grants for renewable energy technology, training and skills upgrading and, occasionally, research. In Central and Eastern Europe, particular interest is given to providing training opportunities for community/business leaders and policy makers, and in contributing to the process of skill-sharing and information exchange. In the UK, there is an interest in helping communities protect, maintain and improve areas of land and to support work aimed at informing rural conservation policy. Women's issues: the interest is in domestic violence issues. The priority is for innovative or strategic programmes of support with a national focus (particularly work to tackle domestic violence from the male perpetrator perspective), also smaller grants to assist local refuge services and women's self-help groups. General. Frankopan Scholarship Fund, established to assist exceptionally talented students from Croatia to further or complete their studies (in any discipline).
WHAT IS NOT FUNDED Normally, no grants to individuals.
TYPE OF GRANT One off and recurring for up to three years.
SAMPLE GRANTS St Paul's Girls' School (£50,000); University of Cambridge – World Oral Literature Project (£20,000); Survival International Charitable Trust and Daughters of Eve (£15,000 each); First Story (£10,000); KickStart International (£7,500); Anthony Nolan Bone Marrow Trust and the Royal Society of Literature (£5,000 each); and Eagle House School (£2,000).
FINANCES *Year* 2011–12 *Income* £500,681 *Grants* £504,940 *Assets* £11,864,264
TRUSTEES Jessica Frankopan; Peter Frankopan; James Sainsbury; Judith Portrait.

OTHER INFORMATION The trust is one of the Sainsbury Family Charitable Trusts which share a common administration. New grants approved during the year totalled £220,000.

HOW TO APPLY See the guidance for applicants section in the entry for the Sainsbury Family Charitable Trusts. A single application will be considered for support by all the trusts in the group. However, for this, as for many of the family trusts, 'proposals are generally invited by the trustees or initiated at their request. Unsolicited applications are discouraged and are unlikely to be successful, even if they fall within an area in which the trustees are interested'.

WHO TO APPLY TO Alan Bookbinder, Director, The Peak, 5 Wilton Road, London SW1V 1AP *Tel.* 020 7410 0330 *Fax* 020 7410 0332 *Website* www.sfct.org.uk

■ The Star Charitable Trust

CC NO 266695   **ESTABLISHED** 1974
WHERE FUNDING CAN BE GIVEN UK.
WHO CAN BENEFIT Charitable organisations.
WHAT IS FUNDED General charitable purposes.
SAMPLE GRANTS A list of grants was not available.
FINANCES *Year* 2011–12 *Income* £9,199 *Grants* £37,569
TRUSTEES D. A. Rosen; David Taglight.
HOW TO APPLY In writing to the correspondent.
WHO TO APPLY TO The Trustees, PO Box 63302, London N2 2BU

■ The Peter Stebbings Memorial Charity

CC NO 274862   **ESTABLISHED** 1977
WHERE FUNDING CAN BE GIVEN UK, with a preference for London, and developing countries.
WHO CAN BENEFIT Registered charities.
WHAT IS FUNDED In the UK the grants are focused towards: medical research and care; and social welfare. The main areas of interest are: homelessness; hospices; mental health/counselling; drug and alcohol therapeutic support; offender support; community regeneration; vulnerable families, women and children; and the promotion of human rights. The charity supports charities that operate in the developing world, including projects that support the community through: education; basic skills and tools; health; sustainability; micro finance; and the promotion of human rights.
WHAT IS NOT FUNDED The charity will not assist: individuals; large national or international charities; animal welfare; publications and journals (unless as part of a supported project); general appeals; any charity whose beneficiaries are restricted to particular faiths; educational institutions, unless a particular project the trustees wish to support; arts organisations, unless there is a strong social welfare focus to the work (e.g. community arts projects).
TYPE OF GRANT Project costs, although core costs will be considered for charities known to the trustees.
RANGE OF GRANTS Up to £100,000.
SAMPLE GRANTS Royal Marsden Hospital Project (£100,000); Liver Group (£59,500); The Maya Centre (£30,000); The Irene Taylor Trust (£20,000); St Christopher Hospice (£15,000); The AHOY Centre and Power International (£10,000 each); African Revival, Childreach International, Marylebone Project and the Sick Children's Trust (£5,000 each); The Rainbow Trust Children's Charity (£3,000); and Bart's City Life Saver (£2,000).
FINANCES *Year* 2011–12 *Income* £238,387 *Grants* £463,901 *Assets* £7,336,150
TRUSTEES Andrew Stebbings; Nicholas Cosin; Jennifer Clifford.
HOW TO APPLY An application form is available from the charity's website.
WHO TO APPLY TO Andrew Stebbings, Trustee, Pemberton Greenish LLP, 45 Cadogan Gardens, London SW3 2AQ *Tel.* 020 7591 3349 *Fax* 020 7591 3412 *email* charitymanager@pglaw.co.uk *Website* peterstebbingsmemorialcharity.org

■ The Steel Charitable Trust

CC NO 272384   **ESTABLISHED** 1976
WHERE FUNDING CAN BE GIVEN Mainly UK with 30% of all grants made to organisations in the Luton and Bedfordshire areas.
WHO CAN BENEFIT Registered charities.
WHAT IS FUNDED General, including social welfare; culture; recreation; health; medical research; environment; and overseas aid.
WHAT IS NOT FUNDED Individuals, students and expeditions are not supported.
TYPE OF GRANT 'One-off' and recurring.
RANGE OF GRANT £1,000–£50,000
SAMPLE GRANTS North Devon Hospice (£50,000); Keech Hospice Care (£40,000); University of Bedfordshire – bursaries and Cancer Research UK (£25,000 each); National Deaf Children's Society (£20,000); SSAFA Forces Help (£15,000); London Youth Rowing Ltd and the People's Dispensary for Sick Animals (£10,000 each); Ilkeston School Specialist Arts College (£6,000); Caryl Jenner Productions Limited and the British Federation of Brass Bands (£5,000 each); Familylives (£3,000); Royal Liverpool Philharmonic Society and Victim Support (£2,000 each); and South Northants Volunteer Bureau and the Bedford and District Society for People with Learning Disabilities (£1,000 each).
FINANCES *Year* 2011–12 *Income* £1,044,308 *Grants* £1,003,425 *Assets* £21,588,564
TRUSTEES Nicholas E. W. Wright; John A. Childs, Chair; John A. Maddox; Anthony W. Hawkins; Wendy Bailey; Dr Mary Briggs; Philip Lawford.
HOW TO APPLY All applicants must complete the online application form. Applications submitted by post will not be considered. There is no deadline for applications and all will be acknowledged. Trustees meet regularly during the year, usually in February, May, August and November. All successful applicants will be notified by email and will be required to provide written confirmation of the details of the project or work for which they are seeking a grant. Payment is then made in the following month. To comply with the Data Protection Act 1998, applicants are required to consent to the use of personal data supplied by them in the processing and review of their application. This includes transfer to and use by such individuals and organisations as the trust deems appropriate. The trust requires the assurance of the applicant that personal data about any other individual is supplied to the trust with his/her consent. At the point of submitting an online application, applicants are asked to confirm this consent and assurance.

WHO TO APPLY TO Carol Langston, Administrator, Holme Farm, Fore Street, Bradford, Holsworthy, Devon EX22 7AJ *Tel.* 01409 281403 *email* administrator@steelcharitabletrust.org.uk *Website* www.steelcharitabletrust.org.uk

■ The Steinberg Family Charitable Trust

cc no 1045231   ESTABLISHED 1995
WHERE FUNDING CAN BE GIVEN UK, with a preference for Greater Manchester.
WHO CAN BENEFIT Charitable organisations, with a preference for Jewish groups.
WHAT IS FUNDED General charitable purposes.
WHAT IS NOT FUNDED Registered charities only.
RANGE OF GRANTS Generally £150–£20,000
SAMPLE GRANTS Aish (£75,000); Fed, Hathaway Trust, UJIA and World Jewish Relief (£50,000) and Integrated Education Fund (£25,000).; SEED (£22,000); and Hale Adult Hebrew Education Trust (£20,000); Centre for Social Justice and Policy Exchange (£15,000); Ascent, Ezer Layeled, Imperial War Museum; MDA Israel, Menachim Begin Heritage Foundation and Yeshiva Bais Yisroel (£10,000 each); Chai Cancer Care and Holocaust Centre (£7,500 each); Hamayon and Hazon Yeshaya (£5,000 each); Henshaw's Society, Jewish Education in Manchester, NATA and Rainbow Trust (£2,500 each); and Prostate Cancer Charity (£1,000).
FINANCES *Year* 2011–12 *Income* £1,052,303 *Grants* £1,490,405 *Assets* £22,060,785
TRUSTEES Beryl Steinberg; Jonathan Steinberg; Lynne Attias.
HOW TO APPLY In writing to the correspondent on letter-headed paper, including evidence of charitable status, the purpose to which the funds are to be put, evidence of other action taken to fund the project concerned, and the outcome of that action.
WHO TO APPLY TO The Trustees, Lime Tree Cottage, 16 Bollingway, Hale, Altrincham WA15 0NZ *Tel.* 01619 038854 *email* admin@steinberg-trust.co.uk

■ The Hugh Stenhouse Foundation

sc no SC015074   ESTABLISHED 1968
WHERE FUNDING CAN BE GIVEN Mainly Scotland, with an emphasis on the west coast.
WHO CAN BENEFIT Charities benefiting children; young adults; those in care, fostered and adopted; and people disadvantaged by poverty. The foundation had stated that it tends to support smaller charities.
WHAT IS FUNDED General charitable purposes, including welfare, young people, and nature reserves, woodlands and bird sanctuaries.
WHAT IS NOT FUNDED Grants are not given for political appeals or to individuals.
TYPE OF GRANT Recurring, one-off and core costs. Funding is available for more than three years.
SAMPLE GRANTS Maxwelton Chapel Trust (£24,000); Glasgow City Mission and Hopscotch (£2,000 each); Salvation Army (£1,700); REACT and the Safety Zone (£1,600 each); Lilias Graham Trust (£1,000); Visibility (£800); and Erskine Hospital (£650).
FINANCES *Year* 2011–12 *Income* £60,729
TRUSTEES A. D. Irvine Robertson; M. R. L. Stenhouse; R. G. T. Stenhouse; R. C. L. Stewart.
OTHER INFORMATION In 2011–12 the foundation had a total expenditure of £67,000.

HOW TO APPLY In writing to the correspondent. Trustees meet in March and September. Applications should be received by February and August respectively.
WHO TO APPLY TO David Robertson, c/o Bell Ingram Ltd, Durn, Isla Road, Perth PH2 7HF *Tel.* 01738 621121

■ The Stephen Barry Charitable Trust

cc no 265056   ESTABLISHED 1973
WHERE FUNDING CAN BE GIVEN England and Wales, Chile, Israel, Philippines, Rwanda, United States of America.
WHO CAN BENEFIT Charitable organisations.
WHAT IS FUNDED General charitable purposes.
TYPE OF GRANT One-off grants to organisations.
RANGE OF GRANTS Up to £50,000
SAMPLE GRANTS National Portrait Gallery (£50,000); National Gallery and Youth Aliyah (£15,000 each); Alzheimer's Research Trust (£5,000); Hampstead Synagogue (£4,000); Dartmouth Caring (£3,000); British Museum and Comunidad Israelita de Santiago (£2,000 each); Tate Foundation, New Israel Fund, Jewish Care and Weizmann Institute Foundation (£1,000 each); Royal Court: English Stage Company, Prostate Action and Drug Farm 112316 (£500 each); Global Warming Foundation, Institute of Economic Affairs and Iain Rennie Hospice at Home (£250 each); Age Concern (£150) and Kensington Society and All Saints Church (£25 each).
FINANCES *Year* 2012–13 *Income* £85,721 *Grants* £104,845 *Assets* £1,427,847
TRUSTEES Nicolas Barry; Oliver Barry; Stephen Barry; Linda Barry, Lucinda Barry.
OTHER INFORMATION 31 grants were made in total.
HOW TO APPLY In writing to the correspondent.
WHO TO APPLY TO Stephen Barry, Trustee, 19 Newman Street, London W1T 1PF *Tel.* 020 7580 6696 *email* sjb@limecourt.com

■ C. E. K. Stern Charitable Trust

cc no 1049157   ESTABLISHED 1992
WHERE FUNDING CAN BE GIVEN UK and overseas.
WHO CAN BENEFIT Orthodox Jewish charities.
WHAT IS FUNDED Orthodox Jewish causes.
FINANCES *Year* 2011–12 *Income* £103,883 *Grants* £35,380 *Assets* £875,628
TRUSTEES Simon Kaufman; Chaya Stern; Z. M. Kaufman; Zvi Stern.
HOW TO APPLY In writing to the correspondent.
WHO TO APPLY TO Z. M. Kaufman, Trustee, 50 Keswick Street, Gateshead NE8 1TQ

■ The Sigmund Sternberg Charitable Foundation

cc no 257950   ESTABLISHED 1968
WHERE FUNDING CAN BE GIVEN Worldwide.
WHO CAN BENEFIT Registered charities.
WHAT IS FUNDED Interfaith activities to promote racial and religious harmony, in particular between Christian, Jewish and Muslim faiths, and the education in, and understanding of, their fundamental tenets and beliefs.
WHAT IS NOT FUNDED No grants to individuals.
TYPE OF GRANT One-off or recurring.
RANGE OF GRANTS Up to £80,000, although most grants are of £1,000 or less.

SAMPLE GRANTS Three Faiths Forum (£143,000); The Movement for Reform Judaism (£70,000); The Board of Deputies Charitable Foundation (£17,000); Leo Baeck College Centre for Jewish Education (£5,800); The Times/Sternbeck Active Life Award and UCL Development Fund (£5,000 each); World Congress of Faiths (£3,300); Oxford Centre for Hebrew and Jewish Studies (£2,000 each); Friends of the Hebrew University of Jerusalem (£1,600) and Age Exchange Theatre Trust (£1,000).
There were a further 87 grants of less than £1,000 totalling £11,000.
FINANCES *Year* 2011–12 *Income* £441,794 *Grants* £266,523 *Assets* £4,321,294
TRUSTEES Sir S. Sternberg; V. M. Sternberg; Lady Sternberg; Revd M. C. Rossi Braybrooke; M. A. M. Slowe; R. Tamir; M. D. Paisner.
HOW TO APPLY In writing to the correspondent.
WHO TO APPLY TO Jan Kariya, Star House, 104/108 Grafton Road, London NW5 4BA *Tel.* 020 7431 4200

■ Stervon Ltd

CC NO 280958   **ESTABLISHED** 1980
WHERE FUNDING CAN BE GIVEN UK.
WHO CAN BENEFIT Jewish people.
WHAT IS FUNDED Jewish causes and general charitable purposes.
SAMPLE GRANTS Previous beneficiaries include: Eitz Chaim; Rehabilitation Trust; Chasdei Yoel; Beis Yoel; Friends of Horeinu; Beis Hamedrash Hachadash; Tashbar; Tov V' Chessed; Beth Sorah Schneirer; Asser Bishvil.
FINANCES *Year* 2011 *Income* £202,916 *Grants* £199,715 *Assets* £184,407
TRUSTEES A. Reich; Gabriel Rothbart.
OTHER INFORMATION Unfortunately more recent information was not available as the charity consistently files its accounts late with the Charity Commission. Details on recent beneficiaries are also absent from the accounts.
HOW TO APPLY In writing to the correspondent.
WHO TO APPLY TO A. Reich, Secretary, 109 St Ann's Road, Prestwich, Manchester M25 9GE *Tel.* 01617 375000

■ The Stevenage Community Trust

CC NO 1000762   **ESTABLISHED** 1990
WHERE FUNDING CAN BE GIVEN The borough of Stevenage and the surrounding villages of Aston, Benington, Cromer, Datchworth, Graveley, Knebworth, Little Wymondley, Old Knebworth, Walkern, Watton-at-Stone, Weston, and Woolmer Green.
WHO CAN BENEFIT Organisations and individuals in need who are recommended by a third party agency.
WHAT IS FUNDED General charitable purposes including community projects, disability, older people, children and youth.
WHAT IS NOT FUNDED Religious, education and political appeals are not supported.
TYPE OF GRANT Maximum £2,000 through the grant committee, larger grant requests go the full Board of Trustees.
RANGE OF GRANTS £50–£2,000.
SAMPLE GRANTS Barclay School Karting Club (£2,000); Crossroads Day Care (£1,700); Turn the Tide Boating Building Project (£1,500); Phoenix Group for Deaf Children (£1,000); Stevenage Women's Refuge (£700); Stevenage Hindu Gujarati Association (£550) and Stevenage Storm Netball Club (£440).

FINANCES *Year* 2011–12 *Income* £93,109 *Grants* £51,006 *Assets* £476,509
TRUSTEES Ken Follett; Cllr Richard Henry; Martin Addinson; Darren Isted; Signe Sutherland; Bavna Joshi; Cllr Sherma Batson; Alex Lang; Graham Clark; Ian Morton; Janis Daniel; Mike Phoenix; Robert Stewart; Jeannette Thomas; Paul Beasley; Rob Case.
HOW TO APPLY On a form available from the trust by post, e-mail, telephone or from the website. Grants applications are considered quarterly, however, the trust states that it 'can and does react to individuals in need speedily. It does this with referrals from Third Party Agencies and is unique in that it can offer this service to those most in need.'
WHO TO APPLY TO Martin Addinson, Unit B, Mindenhall Court, High Street, Stevenage SG1 3UN *Tel.* 01438 525390 *email* enquiries@stevenagecommunitytrust.org *Website* www.stevenagecommunitytrust.org

----

■ The June Stevens Foundation

CC NO 327829   **ESTABLISHED** 1988
WHERE FUNDING CAN BE GIVEN UK, but mostly Gloucestershire.
WHO CAN BENEFIT Charitable organisations mainly for older and young people and animals.
WHAT IS FUNDED General charitable purposes
WHAT IS NOT FUNDED No grants to individuals.
RANGE OF GRANTS £200–£2,000.
SAMPLE GRANTS Greek Animal Welfare Fund (£2,000); Brooke Hospital for Animals and the Royal British Legion (£1,500 each); Gloucestershire Historic Churches Trust (£1,000); Cirencester House for Young People and Gloucestershire Playing Fields Association (£750 each); and Cotswold Care Hospice and Women's Holiday Fund (£500 each).
FINANCES *Year* 2011–12 *Income* £16,824 *Grants* £35,000
TRUSTEES June Stevens; Alan Quinton; Anthony Tahourdin.
OTHER INFORMATION The grant total is based on previous research.
HOW TO APPLY In writing to the correspondent.
WHO TO APPLY TO Anthony Tahourdin, Trustee, c/o Herrington and Carmichael, Unit 8 Waters Edge, Riverside Way, Camberley GU15 3YL *Tel.* 01252 686222

■ Stevenson Family's Charitable Trust

CC NO 327148   **ESTABLISHED** 1986
WHERE FUNDING CAN BE GIVEN Worldwide, in practice mainly UK.
WHO CAN BENEFIT Registered charities.
WHAT IS FUNDED Culture and arts, conservation and heritage, education, health, overseas aid and general charitable purposes.
WHAT IS NOT FUNDED No grants to individuals.
TYPE OF GRANT One-off and recurring.
RANGE OF GRANTS £150–£50,000
SAMPLE GRANTS Royal National Theatre and the Foundation and Friends of the Royal Botanic Gardens, Kew (£100,000 each); St Michael and All Angels, Sunninghill (£60,000); Berkshire Community Foundation (£40,000); the Abbotsford Trust and the Strawberry Hill Trust (£25,000 each); Royal Marines Charitable Trust Fund and the Watts Gallery Trust (£10,000 each); Berkshire County Blind Society and Prior's Court Foundation (£5,000 each); and

Whitechapel Art Gallery and Charleston Trust (£1,000 each).
FINANCES *Year* 2012–13 *Income* £227,894 *Grants* £501,220 *Assets* £2,062,987
TRUSTEES Sir Hugh Stevenson; Lady Catherine Stevenson.
HOW TO APPLY 'No unsolicited applications can be considered as the charity's funds are required to support purposes chosen by the trustees.'
WHO TO APPLY TO Sir Hugh Stevenson, Trustee, Old Waterfield, Winkfield Road, Ascot SL5 7LJ

■ **The Steventon Allotments and Relief-in-Need Charity**

CC NO 203331 **ESTABLISHED** 1987
WHERE FUNDING CAN BE GIVEN Parish of Steventon only.
WHO CAN BENEFIT Residents and groups in the parish of Steventon.
WHAT IS FUNDED Projects benefiting the local community, impoverished individuals, churches, schools, older people and the maintenance of the allotments.
WHAT IS NOT FUNDED Parish of Steventon only.
RANGE OF GRANTS Up to £20,000
SAMPLE GRANTS St Michael's School (£22,000 in two grants); Steventon Friendly Association (£2,500); DAMASCUS (£1,000); Steventon Open Gardens (£300); St Michael's Church Hall (£275) and North Star (£250).
FINANCES *Year* 2012 *Income* £112,339 *Grants* £47,540 *Assets* £2,547,396
TRUSTEES Carole Denton; Wendy Lucas; Robin Wilkinson; Steven Ward; Kevin Curley; Bill Temple; Philip Brew.
OTHER INFORMATION The grant total includes £17,000 that was given to individuals.
HOW TO APPLY In writing to the correspondent. The trustees meet monthly.
WHO TO APPLY TO Patrina Effer, Clerk, 19 Lime Grove, Southmoor, Abingdon, Oxfordshire OX13 5DN *Tel.* 01865 821055 *email* sarinc@patrina.co.uk

■ **The Stewards' Charitable Trust**

CC NO 299597 **ESTABLISHED** 1988
WHERE FUNDING CAN BE GIVEN Principally the UK.
WHO CAN BENEFIT Organisations and clubs benefiting young sportsmen and women.
WHAT IS FUNDED Support of rowing at all levels, from grassroots upwards.
WHAT IS NOT FUNDED No grants to individuals or for building or capital costs.
TYPE OF GRANT Preferably one-off and especially where there are matched funds raised elsewhere.
RANGE OF GRANTS £3,000–£150,000.
SAMPLE GRANTS British Rowing Scholarships; London Youth Rowing; Rowing Foundation; Project Oarsome; Henley Rowing Club; Ball Cup Regatta; and Regatta for the Disabled.
FINANCES *Year* 2011–12 *Income* £337,285 *Grants* £250,000 *Assets* £5,552,553
TRUSTEES Michael Sweeney; Christopher Davidge; C. L. Baillieu; R. C. Lester; Sir Steve Redgrave.
HOW TO APPLY In writing to the correspondent. Applications are usually first vetted by Amateur Rowing Association.
WHO TO APPLY TO Daniel Grist, Secretary, Regatta Headquarters, Henley Bridge, Henley-on-Thames, Oxfordshire RG9 2LY *Tel.* 01491 572153 *Fax* 01491 575509 *Website* www.hrr.co.uk

■ **The Stewards' Company Limited (incorporating the J. W. Laing Trust and the J. W. Laing Biblical Scholarship Trust)**

CC NO 234558 **ESTABLISHED** 1947
WHERE FUNDING CAN BE GIVEN Unrestricted.
WHO CAN BENEFIT Organisations involved with training people in religious education. About half the trust's funds are given for work overseas.
WHAT IS FUNDED Christian evangelism, especially but not exclusively that of Christian Brethren assemblies. Grants given overseas are made under the following categories: church buildings; scriptures and literature; education and orphanages; education of missionaries' children; national evangelists and missionaries' vehicles. Grants given in the UK are categorised under: church buildings; evangelistic associations; scriptures and literature; teachers and evangelists; and youth and children. Substantial funds are also transferred to the Beatrice Laing Trust (see separate entry).
TYPE OF GRANT Usually one-off.
RANGE OF GRANTS About £15,000–£1 million.
SAMPLE GRANTS Echoes of Service (£619,000); Beatrice Laing Trust (£466,000); UCCF – The Christian Unions (£393,000); Retired Missionary Aid Fund (£225,000); Interlink (£140,000); London School of Theology (£47,500); Langham Partnership (£35,000); Scripture Union (£20,000); and the Stapleford Centre (£17,000).
FINANCES *Year* 2011–12 *Income* £2,137,580 *Grants* £4,900,844 *Assets* £125,182,904
TRUSTEES Brian Chapman; Alexander McIlhinney; Paul Young; Dr John Burness; William Adams; Andrew Griffiths; Prof. Arthur Williamson; Philip Page; Denis Cooper; Alan Paterson; Glyn Davies; Ian Childs; John Gamble; Philip Symons; William Wood; Andrew Street; Keith Bintley; John Aitken.
OTHER INFORMATION Grants totalling £47,500 were awarded to individuals.
HOW TO APPLY In writing to the correspondent.
WHO TO APPLY TO Brian Chapman, Secretary, 124 Wells Road, Bath BA2 3AH *Tel.* 01225 427236 *Fax* 01225 427278 *email* stewardsco@stewards.co.uk

■ **The Andy Stewart Charitable Foundation**

CC NO 1114802 **ESTABLISHED** 2006
WHERE FUNDING CAN BE GIVEN Worldwide.
WHO CAN BENEFIT Charitable organisations.
WHAT IS FUNDED Spinal injuries care and research, other healthcare, animal welfare and assisting young people
SAMPLE GRANTS Typical beneficiaries include: Spinal Research; Sir Peter O'Sullivan Charitable Trust; Spinal Injuries; Moorcroft Trust; Brompton Foundation; and Racing Welfare.
FINANCES *Year* 2012 *Income* £18,909 *Grants* £80,000
TRUSTEES Andy Stewart; Mark Stewart; Paul Stewart.
HOW TO APPLY In writing to the correspondent.
WHO TO APPLY TO The Trustees, Bridger, 14 Glategny Esplanade, St Peter Port, Guernsey GY1 1WP

■ Sir Halley Stewart Trust

CC NO 208491 **ESTABLISHED** 1924

WHERE FUNDING CAN BE GIVEN UK and some work in Africa.

WHO CAN BENEFIT Charitable organisations and researchers.

WHAT IS FUNDED Research, innovative projects, feasibility and pilot studies and development projects in medical, social, educational and religious fields.

WHAT IS NOT FUNDED According to the trust's website, the trust will be unable to help with funding for any of the following: general appeals of any kind; the purchase, erection or conversion of buildings; capital costs; university overhead charges; the completion of a project initiated by other bodies. The trust does not usually fund but may consider the following: projects put forward indirectly through other 'umbrella' or large charities; educational or 'gap' year travel projects; running costs of established organisations or conferences; climate change issues; personal education fees or fees for taught courses-unless connected with research which falls within current priority areas. (Applications for such research work are normally made by a senior researcher seeking support for a student, or if coming directly from the student it should have project supervisor's written support; the trust does not favour grantmaking to enable the completion of a project or PhD.) Grants are only ever paid to UK registered charities and never to individuals.

TYPE OF GRANT One-off and project grants. Feasibility studies, research and salaries will also be considered. Funding may be given for up to three years.

RANGE OF GRANTS £10,000–£28,000.

SAMPLE GRANTS Newcastle University, Institute of Health and Society (£27,500); Bail for Immigration Detainees (BID) and Bradford Court Chaplaincy Service (£25,000 each); RECOOP – Resettlement and Care for Older Ex-Offenders and Prisoners (£23,500); World Horizons Limited (£20,000); Cardiff University, School of Biosciences, (£19,500); CO'DEC Research centre, St John's College, Durham (£10,000).

FINANCES *Year* 2011–12 *Income* £919,000 *Grants* £810,000 *Assets* £23,855,000

TRUSTEES Joanna Womack; Prof. Phyllida Parsloe; Dr Caroline Berry; Barbara Clapham; Dr Duncan Stewart; George Russell; Lord Stewartby; Prof. John Wyatt; Prof. John Lennard-Jones; Michael Collins; Prof. Philip Whitfield; W. Kirkman; Brian Allpress; Prof. Gordon Wilcock; Caroline Thomas; Theresa Bartlett; Louisa Elder; Amy Holcroft; Prof. Jane Gilliard.

PUBLICATIONS The trust has a helpful website with clear guidelines for applicants.

OTHER INFORMATION The grant total was £17,000 less than stated in the accounts for 2011–12 as according to the administrator, 'Each Trustee has £1,000 to make small grants through individual CAF accounts. These are accounted for as 'personal grants' and we do not record those.'

HOW TO APPLY The following applicant guidelines are taken from the trust's website: applications should be submitted from those directly involved in the project as opposed to fundraisers or development officers; applicants should make sure that their project fits the trust's objects and falls within its current priority areas; initial telephone enquiries to the trust's office are welcomed to discuss the suitability of an application. The trust does not have an application form. Applicants should write to the administrator always including a one-page lay 'executive' summary of the proposed work. The proposal should state clearly: what the aims of the project are and why it is believed to be innovative; how the project fits the trust's objects and current priority areas; what the overall budgeted cost of the project is and how much is being requested from the trust; what the grant will be used for and how long the project will take to have practical benefits; how the project/research results will be disseminated. Applications for young researchers should be accompanied by a letter of support from a senior colleague or research supervisor. Development projects should indicate where they would hope to obtain future funding from. A CV of key individuals who will be responsible for the project and where appropriate; job description, set of audited accounts and annual report should also be provided. There are no set application deadlines and applications are accepted anytime during the year. When the trust has received your application they will make contact (normally within two weeks) either to ask for further information; to tell you the application will be going forward to the next stage of assessment and what the timetable for a final decision will be; or to tell you that they are unable to help. The 2011–12 accounts also note: 'it is a deliberate policy of the trust to maintain as much personal and informal contact with applicants as possible, to keep paper work to the minimum consistent with efficient administration, and to make decisions on applications within four months.' Unsuccessful applicants are sent a personalised letter, or email, which explains the reason for rejection.

WHO TO APPLY TO Susan West, Administrator, 22 Earith Rd, Willingham, Cambridge CB24 5LS *Tel.* 01954 260707 *email* email@sirhalleystewart.org.uk *Website* www.sirhalleystewart.org.uk

■ The Stewarts Law Foundation

CC NO 1136714 **ESTABLISHED** 2010

WHERE FUNDING CAN BE GIVEN Undefined, in practice national and developing world.

WHO CAN BENEFIT Charitable organisations and activities.

WHAT IS FUNDED General charitable purposes; prevention or relief of poverty and homelessness; disability organisations; furtherance of the arts; advancement of education; overseas humanitarian agencies and environmental protection.

RANGE OF GRANTS £2,000 –£25,000

SAMPLE GRANTS Backup Trust and Headway (£25,000 each); SOS Children's Villages, St George's Crypt and The World Land Trust (£20,000 each); ACE Africa, Second Sight and Street Kids International (£15,000 each) and Royal College of Art (£13,000).

FINANCES *Year* 2011–12 *Income* £294,356 *Grants* £312,333 *Assets* £38,906

TRUSTEES John Cahill; Stuart Dench; Paul Paxton; James Healy-Pratt; Stephen Foster; Julian Chamberlayne; Daniel James Herman; Andrew Dinsmore; Kevin Grealis; Clive Zietman; Jane M. Colston; Sean N. Upson; Muiris L. P. Lyons; Emma L. Hatley; Debbie J. Chism.

HOW TO APPLY 'Trustees are invited to select from a number of organisations in each of the Foundation's selected Charitable categories. The Trustees vote as to whether the grant is approved, and agree the amount of the grant. A majority vote is needed for the grant to be given. It is not the policy of the Trustees to accept direct applications for funds.'

WHO TO APPLY TO John Cahill, Trustee, 5 New Street Square, London EC4A 3BF *Tel.* 020 7822 8000 *email* info@stewartslaw.com *Website* www.stewartslaw.com/the-stewarts-law-foundation

■ The David and Deborah Stileman Charitable Trust

CC NO 1148313 **ESTABLISHED** 2012
WHERE FUNDING CAN BE GIVEN UK.
WHO CAN BENEFIT Charities and community groups.
WHAT IS FUNDED General charitable purposes.
TRUSTEES David Stileman; Deborah Stileman; Cripps Trust Corporation Limited (Mary-Anne Gribbon; Jonathan Christopher Langridge; Simon Leney; Anne Lewis; Fiona McIntosh; Peter Scott; Michael Stevens; Gavin Tyler; Christopher Wilkinson).
HOW TO APPLY In writing to the correspondent.
WHO TO APPLY TO Mary-Anne Gribbon, Administrator, c/o Cripps Harries Hall LLP, Wallside House, 12 Mount Ephraim Road, Tunbridge Wells, Kent TN1 1EG *Tel.* 01892 506012 *email* mary-anne.gribbon@crippslaw.com

■ The Leonard Laity Stoate Charitable Trust

CC NO 221325 **ESTABLISHED** 1950
WHERE FUNDING CAN BE GIVEN England and Wales with a preference for the southwest of England, Bristol, Cornwall, Devon, Dorset and Somerset (especially west Somerset).
WHO CAN BENEFIT Methodist organisations benefiting children and young adults, people who are disabled and people disadvantaged by poverty. Community organisation projects and small local innovatory projects with a strong emphasis on self-help are preferred.
WHAT IS FUNDED The broad categories the trust supported are: medical and disability; churches; youth and children; community projects; disadvantage; and environment.
WHAT IS NOT FUNDED No grants to: individuals unless supported by a registered charity; large projects (over £500,000 and/or with more than £250,000 still to raise); general appeals by national charities; the running expenses of a charity.
TYPE OF GRANT Usually one-off for a specific project or part of a project.
RANGE OF GRANTS Typically £100–£1,000.
SAMPLE GRANTS Peasedown St John Methodist Church, Bath (£2,000); Positive Action Cancer, Frome (£1,500); Watchet Market House Museum (£1,200); Crisis Centre Ministries, Bristol, Methodist Homes for the Aged, Derby, Plymouth Foodbank, Exeter Community Transport Association and Youth Drop-in Centre, Tiverton (£1,000 each); Stratton Community Garden Project, Radstock, Curzon Community Cinema, Clevedon and Sound Waves Music and Therapy Trust, Bude (£500 each); Salvation Army, London (£250); and Help for Heroes, Salisbury and Bath Child Contact Centre (£100 each).
FINANCES *Year* 2011–12 *Income* £76,037 *Grants* £77,700 *Assets* £1,787,118
TRUSTEES Sarah Boughton; Stephen Duckworth; Susan Harnden; Dr Christopher Stoate; Philip Stoate; Revd Anthony Jones; Dr Pam Stoate.

OTHER INFORMATION Although the trust does not want to rule out anywhere in England and Wales, it is a comparatively small trust and is forced to be very selective. Therefore, the further an applicant is from the trusts core area the less likely they are to be successful.
HOW TO APPLY There is no special application form, but applications should be in writing; neither telephone nor email applications will be entertained. Supply clear details of: the need the intended project is designed to meet; the amount raised so far, with a breakdown of how much has been raised from within the local community and how much from other grantmaking bodies or other sources. Also supply where possible: your registered charity number or, for unregistered organisations, a copy of your constitution; accounts or budgets; an e-mail address for follow-up correspondence or application acknowledgement. Whilst applications can be considered at any time, the bulk are decided at the trust's half-yearly meetings in mid-March and September of each year. Thus December to February and June to August are probably the best times to submit applications.
WHO TO APPLY TO Philip J. Stoate, Secretary, 41 Tower Hill, Williton, Taunton TA4 4JR *Tel.* 08712847780 *email* charity@erminea.org.uk *Website* www.stoate-charity.org.uk

■ The Stobart Newlands Charitable Trust

CC NO 328464 **ESTABLISHED** 1989
WHERE FUNDING CAN BE GIVEN UK.
WHO CAN BENEFIT Registered charities.
WHAT IS FUNDED General charitable purposes at the discretion of the trustees; mainly Christian organisations and missionary societies.
WHAT IS NOT FUNDED No grants for individuals.
TYPE OF GRANT Mainly recurrent.
RANGE OF GRANTS Up to £250,000
SAMPLE GRANTS Caring for Life (£1 million); World Vision (£360,000); Mission Aviation Fellowship (£250,000); Operation Mobilisation (£175,000); Every Home Crusade (£35,000); London City Mission (£28,000); Living Well Trust (£22,000); and Release International, Trans World Radio and Christian Aid (£10,000).
FINANCES *Year* 2012 *Income* £2,276,858 *Grants* £2,277,250 *Assets* £211,324
TRUSTEES Richard Stobart; Ronnie Stobart; Peter Stobart; Linda Rigg.
HOW TO APPLY Unsolicited applications are most unlikely to be successful.
WHO TO APPLY TO Ronnie Stobart, Trustee, Mill Croft, Newlands, Hesket Newmarket, Wigton, Cumbria CA7 8HP *Tel.* 01697 478531

■ The Edward Stocks-Massey Bequest Fund

CC NO 526516 **ESTABLISHED** 1910
WHERE FUNDING CAN BE GIVEN Burnley.
WHO CAN BENEFIT Charitable organisations.
RANGE OF GRANTS £280–£5,000 (2011/12)
SAMPLE GRANTS Burnley Mechanics Institute Trust (£5,000); Burnley Municipal Choir, Burnley Municipal Symphony Orchestra, Burnley Youth Theatre and Rosanne Duckworth (Individual, to purchase a Piccoli trumpet) (£1,000 each); Arncliffe Press (History of Mechanics Institute 1855–1987), Beauty in the Universe, Burnley

and Pendle Music Society and Burnley Junior Alliance Band (£500 each).

FINANCES *Year* 2011–12 *Income* £32,442 *Grants* £50,500 *Assets* £922,536

TRUSTEES A. David Knagg; Neil Beecham.

OTHER INFORMATION Burnley Borough Council received £16,000 and Lancashire County Council received £15,000 in grants. £8,000 went to organisation/individual grants and £7,000 in scholarship awards.

HOW TO APPLY On a form available from the correspondent.

WHO TO APPLY TO Saima Afzaal, Burnley Borough Council, Town Hall, Manchester Road, Burnley BB11 1JA *Tel.* 01282 425011

■ The Stokenchurch Educational Charity

CC NO 297846   **ESTABLISHED** 1987

WHERE FUNDING CAN BE GIVEN The parish of Stokenchurch.

WHO CAN BENEFIT Local nursery, primary and middle schools; children, young adults and students under the age of 25 residing in the Parish of Stokenchurch. Community groups.

WHAT IS FUNDED Grants are given for educational purposes and to a lesser extent, to the community.

WHAT IS NOT FUNDED No grants to applicants from outside the Parish of Stokenchurch.

RANGE OF GRANTS £100–£9,000

SAMPLE GRANTS Previous beneficiaries: Stokenchurch Primary School (£9,000); The Mary Towerton School (£450); Radnage C of E Infant School (£440); Ibstone C of E Infant School (£405); Stokenchurch Medical Centre (£300); Living Springs (£150); Studley Green Youth Club (£130); and Stokenchurch Village Fete (£100).

FINANCES *Year* 2011–12 *Income* £83,276 *Grants* £41,155 *Assets* £1,870,409

TRUSTEES M. Shurrock, Chair; A. Palmer; A. Saunders; F. Downes; Revd A. France; Cllr C. Baker.

HOW TO APPLY On a form available from the correspondent. The trustees place an annual advertisement in the local press and two public places in Stokenchurch inviting applications. Educational applications must be received by 30 November of each academic year, community grants by 30 September each year.

WHO TO APPLY TO Martin Sheehy, Fish Partnership LLP, The Mill House, Boundary Road, Loudwater, High Wycombe HP10 9QN *Tel.* 01628 527956 *email* martins@fishpartnership.co.uk

■ The Stoller Charitable Trust

CC NO 285415   **ESTABLISHED** 1982

WHERE FUNDING CAN BE GIVEN UK, with a preference for the Greater Manchester area.

WHO CAN BENEFIT Established UK charities and local causes benefiting children and young adults.

WHAT IS FUNDED Preference for medically related causes, though other charitable purposes will be considered.

WHAT IS NOT FUNDED No grants to individuals.

TYPE OF GRANT Buildings, capital, one-off, project, research, recurring costs and start-up costs will be considered. Funding may be given for up to three years.

SAMPLE GRANTS Previous beneficiaries include: Bauern Helfen Baeurn; Onside North West; Broughton House; Central Manchester

Children's Hospitals; Live Music Now; Christie Hospital, Greater Manchester Appeal; Imperial War Museum North; National Memorial Arboretum; Cancer Research UK; Oldham Liaison of Ex-Services Associations; Church Housing Trust; Commandery of John of Gaunt; Mines Advisory Group; Salvation Army; and Windermere Air Show.

FINANCES *Year* 2011–12 *Income* £202,721 *Grants* £405,500 *Assets* £5,358,065

TRUSTEES Norman K. Stoller; Roger Gould; Sheila M. Stoller; Andrew Dixon.

HOW TO APPLY In writing to the correspondent. Applications need to be received by February, May, August or November. The trustees usually meet in March, June, September and December.

WHO TO APPLY TO Alison M. Ford, Secretary, Wrigley Partington Chartered Accountants, Sterling House, 501 Middleton Road, Chadderton, Oldham OL9 9LY *Tel.* 01616 220222 *Fax* 01616 275446 *email* enquiries@ stollercharitabletrust.co.uk

■ The M. J. C. Stone Charitable Trust

CC NO 283920   **ESTABLISHED** 1981

WHERE FUNDING CAN BE GIVEN UK.

WHO CAN BENEFIT UK charities and smaller scale local organisations.

WHAT IS FUNDED General with a preference for education, medicine and health, conservation and religion.

RANGE OF GRANTS Usually up to £50,000.

SAMPLE GRANTS Tennis for Free and the Diamond Jubilee Trust (£100,000 each); Bradfield Foundation (£50,000); Centre for Social Justice (£27,000); Game and Wildlife Trust (£18,000); Countryside Learning (£10,000); University of the Highlands and Islands, Evelina Children's Hospital, National Autistic Society, Wheelpower and the Outward Bound Trust (£5,000 each); Pestalozzi World Trust and Making the Change (£1,000 each).

FINANCES *Year* 2012 *Income* £310,223 *Grants* £389,769 *Assets* £756,279

TRUSTEES Michael Stone; Louisa Stone; Charles Stone; Andrew Stone; Nicola Farquhar.

HOW TO APPLY In writing to the correspondent. 'The charitable trust makes grants to core charities on an annual basis. Grants to other charities are made on receipt of applications and after discussions between the trustees.'

WHO TO APPLY TO Michael Stone, Trustee, Estate Office, Ozleworth Park, Wotton-under-Edge, Gloucestershire GL12 7QA *Tel.* 01453 845591

■ The Stone Family Foundation

CC NO 1108207   **ESTABLISHED** 2005

WHERE FUNDING CAN BE GIVEN Worldwide.

WHO CAN BENEFIT Charities and international aid organisations.

WHAT IS FUNDED Relief of need or hardship. 'Since September 2010, the foundation's main focus has been on water, sanitation and hygiene (WASH). Our goal is to find and support lasting and effective ways to promote good sanitation, safe water and good hygiene across the world.'

WHAT IS NOT FUNDED No grants to individuals.

RANGE OF GRANTS Up to £1 million.

SAMPLE GRANTS Opportunity International (£733,500); WaterAid (£591,000); Water and Sanitation for the Urban Poor (£508,000); IDE Cambodia (£469,000); Acumen Fund

(£415,000); Rethink (£137,000); Room to Read (£100,000); Samaritans (£60,000); Hillside Clubhouse (£45,000); Paragon Charitable Trust (£28,000); University of Oxford Development Trust (£17,000); and Rainforest Saver Foundation (£6,500).

FINANCES *Year* 2012 *Income* £4,212,736 *Grants* £4,368,650 *Assets* £43,646,026

TRUSTEES Coutts and Co; John Kyle Stone; Charles H. Edwards.

OTHER INFORMATION Loans are also available.

HOW TO APPLY The foundation is advised on potential grant recipients by New Philanthropy Capital, and states that it is not looking for new organisations to support at present. Check the foundation's website for up-to-date information.

WHO TO APPLY TO The Clerk, Coutts and Co, 440 Strand, London WC2R 0QS *Tel.* 020 7663 6825 *email* sff@thinknpc.org *Website* www. thesff.com

■ The Samuel Storey Family Charitable Trust

CC NO 267684   **ESTABLISHED** 1974

WHERE FUNDING CAN BE GIVEN UK, with a preference for Yorkshire.

WHO CAN BENEFIT Registered charities.

WHAT IS FUNDED General charitable purposes.

WHAT IS NOT FUNDED No grants to individuals.

RANGE OF GRANTS Typically less than £1,000.

SAMPLE GRANTS Hope and Homes for Children (£25,000); York University (£20,000); St John the Evangelist, Edinburgh (£6,000); Peter Buckley Learning Centre (£2,500); Archbishop of York Youth Trust (£2,000); and Justice First Ltd, Music at Paxton, Pebbles Project, Rainbow Trust and Smile Support and Care (£1,000 each).

FINANCES *Year* 2011–12 *Income* £164,205 *Grants* £99,538 *Assets* £4,731,675

TRUSTEES Hon. Sir Richard Storey; Wren Hoskyns Abrahall; Kenelm Storey.

HOW TO APPLY In writing to the correspondent. The trust informed us that, 'in order to give appropriately, we only really do so to personalised applications'.

WHO TO APPLY TO Hon. Sir Richard Storey, Trustee, 21 Buckingham Gate, London SW1E 6LS *Tel.* 020 7802 2700

■ Peter Stormonth Darling Charitable Trust

CC NO 1049946   **ESTABLISHED** 1995

WHERE FUNDING CAN BE GIVEN UK.

WHO CAN BENEFIT Organisations benefiting children, young adults, and sportsmen and women.

WHAT IS FUNDED Preference for heritage, education, healthcare and sports facilities.

WHAT IS NOT FUNDED No grants to individuals.

RANGE OF GRANTS Up to £12,000.

SAMPLE GRANTS Winchester College Wykeham Campaign (£50,000); Friends of East Sussex Hospices and Westminster Abbey (£12,500 each); National Trust Scotland (£5,000); Chailey Heritage and Fields in Trust (£2,500 each); Royal Commonwealth Ex-Services League (£1,500); and Arthritis Research UK (£1,000).

FINANCES *Year* 2012 *Income* £192,368 *Grants* £131,000 *Assets* £3,634,056

TRUSTEES John Rodwell; Peter Stormonth Darling; Elizabeth Cobb; Arabella Johannes; Christa Taylor.

HOW TO APPLY This trust states that it does not respond to unsolicited applications.

WHO TO APPLY TO Peter Stormonth Darling, Trustee, Soditic Ltd, 12 Charles II Street, London SW1Y 4QU

■ Peter Storrs Trust

CC NO 313804   **ESTABLISHED** 1970

WHERE FUNDING CAN BE GIVEN UK.

WHO CAN BENEFIT Registered charities.

WHAT IS FUNDED The advancement of education.

TYPE OF GRANT One-off and recurring

RANGE OF GRANTS £1,500–£5,400.

SAMPLE GRANTS Peter House (£5,400); Daylight Christian Prison Trust (£4,000); British Schools Exploring Society (£3,000); African Medical, British Bible Society, Hope and Homes for Children, Marie Curie Memorial, Radley College, SENSE, Voluntary Services Overseas, Excellent Development Ltd, The Archway Project and Wiltshire Guild of Spinners, Weavers and Dyers (£2,000 each) and Signalong Group (£1,500).

FINANCES *Year* 2011–12 *Income* £118,007 *Grants* £104,850 *Assets* £2,494,328

TRUSTEES Geoffrey Adams; Arthur Curtis; Julie Easton.

OTHER INFORMATION Grants were split between recurring (£60,850) and one-off (£40,000).

HOW TO APPLY In writing to the correspondent. Applications are considered every three to six months. Note the trust receives far more applications than it is able to support, many of which do not meet the criteria outlined above. This results in a heavy waste of time and expense for both applicants and the trust itself.

WHO TO APPLY TO The Trustees, c/o Smithfield Accountants, 117 Charterhouse Street, London EC1M 6AA *Tel.* 020 7253 3757

■ The Strangward Trust

CC NO 1036494   **ESTABLISHED** 1993

WHERE FUNDING CAN BE GIVEN Mainly Bedfordshire, Cambridgeshire and Northamptonshire.

WHO CAN BENEFIT Organisations concerned with people with mental and physical disabilities.

WHAT IS FUNDED Funding for care and treatment of people with physical or mental disabilities, including direct help and assistance in the purchase of services and equipment.

TYPE OF GRANT One-off, capital, core costs. Funding is for one year or less.

RANGE OF GRANTS Rarely over £2,500.

SAMPLE GRANTS Grant beneficiaries include: Grafham Water Sailability (£15,000); Masonic Trout and Salmon Flyfishing Club (£10,000); East Anglia's Children's Hospices (£5,000); Stepping Stones (£2,500); Narcolepsy UK and Over the Wall (£1,500 each) and National Portage Association (£250).

FINANCES *Year* 2011–12 *Income* £137,969 *Grants* £61,595 *Assets* £3,171,645

TRUSTEES Ross Jones, Chair; Anne Allured; Paul Goakes; Clare O'Callaghan.

OTHER INFORMATION Full details and guidelines are available from the correspondent.

HOW TO APPLY Applications forms are available from the correspondent. Attach a copy of your latest accounts (if relevant) and any other supporting documentation (e.g. copy estimates, medical reports etc., when applying).The trustees meet twice a year (March and September) to decide upon donations. Applications should be submitted by the end of February and August. The trustees will consider every application submitted to them that meets the criteria of the trust. It is important that applications on behalf of national charities identify a specific need for funding in the geographic area referred to above to be considered. The trustees will consider projects where there is an annual ongoing requirement for funds for period of up to five years. Successful applicants will be expected to keep the trust informed on their projects. Only successful applicants will be notified of the outcome of their application.

WHO TO APPLY TO Ross Jones, Chair, Glebe House, Catworth, Huntingdon PE28 0PA *Tel.* 01832 710171 *email* strangwardtrust@aol.com

---

■ The Strasser Foundation

CC NO 511703   **ESTABLISHED** 1978
WHERE FUNDING CAN BE GIVEN Staffordshire.
WHO CAN BENEFIT Organisations and individuals.
WHAT IS FUNDED General charitable purposes.
RANGE OF GRANTS Up to £1,000.
SAMPLE GRANTS Donna Louise Trust, Children's Hospice, Douglas Macmillan Hospice – Stoke-on-Trent and Royal British Legion (£1,000 each); Vitalise – for work with the disabled in Staffordshire, Spinal Injuries Association and Newcastle-under-Lyme Music Festival for Music, Speech and Drama – contribution for new piano (£500 each); Sense – for work with Deafblind in Staffordshire (£350); Moorlands South Community Mental Health Team (£250); Educational grant to student (£150).
FINANCES *Year* 2011–12 *Income* £21,267 *Grants* £22,000
TRUSTEES Alan Booth; Tony Bell.
OTHER INFORMATION Grants of up to £1,000 are made to organisations and individuals in need.
HOW TO APPLY In writing to the correspondent. The trustees meet quarterly. Applications are only acknowledged if an sae is sent.
WHO TO APPLY TO The Trustees, c/o Knight and Sons, The Brampton, Newcastle-under-Lyme, Staffordshire ST5 0QW *Tel.* 01782 619225

■ Stratford-upon-Avon Town Trust

CC NO 1088521   **ESTABLISHED** 2001
WHERE FUNDING CAN BE GIVEN Stratford-upon-Avon.
WHO CAN BENEFIT Organisations benefiting people living in the Stratford-upon-Avon council area.
WHAT IS FUNDED Relief of need, hardship and distress; relief of sickness, disability, old age and infirmity; support of facilities for education, including the advancement of learning and knowledge; support for recreations and other leisure-time facilities; advancement of the Christian religion.
WHAT IS NOT FUNDED No grants to organisations outside Stratford-upon-Avon.
TYPE OF GRANT Capital and revenue grants for up to three years.
RANGE OF GRANTS Up to £50,000.
SAMPLE GRANTS King Edward IV Grammar School (£625,500); Stratford-upon-Avon Christmas Lights (£60,000); Shakespeare Hospice (£50,000); Citizens Advice (£45,000); Warks Police Authority (£43,500); Stratford upon Avon College (£30,500); Stratford High School (£28,500); and Stratford Methodist Church (£25,000); and Holy Trinity Church (£7,000).
FINANCES *Year* 2012 *Income* £3,293,844 *Grants* £1,854,918 *Assets* £52,343,963
TRUSTEES John Lancaster, Chair; Cllr Jenny Fradgley; Jean Holder; Rosemary Hyde; Cllr Juliet Short; Carole Taylor; Tim Wightman;

Clarissa Roberts; Rob Townsend; Charles Bates; Cllr Ian Fradgley.
HOW TO APPLY Application forms can be completed via the trust's website. Awards are made on a quarterly basis. The latest application deadlines are listed on the trust's website.
WHO TO APPLY TO Helen Munro, Chief Executive, 14 Rother Street, Stratford-upon-Avon, Warwickshire CV32 6LU *Tel.* 01789 207111 *Fax* 01789 207119 *email* admin@stratfordtowntrust.co.uk *Website* www.stratfordtowntrust.co.uk

---

■ The Strawberry Charitable Trust

CC NO 1090173   **ESTABLISHED** 2000
WHERE FUNDING CAN BE GIVEN Not defined but with a preference for Manchester.
WHO CAN BENEFIT Registered charities.
WHAT IS FUNDED The relief of poverty and hardship mainly amongst Jewish people and the advancement of the Jewish religion.
RANGE OF GRANTS Up to £32,000.
SAMPLE GRANTS Previous beneficiaries included: United Jewish Israel Appeal; Community Security Trust; The Fed; Lubavitch South Manchester; King David School; World Jewish Relief; Belz and St John's Wood Synagogue; Action on Addiction; Mew Children's Hospital; and Tickets for Troops.
FINANCES *Year* 2010–11 *Income* £3,522 *Grants* £90,000
TRUSTEES Emma Myers; Laura Avigdori; Anthony Leon.
OTHER INFORMATION Unfortunately the trust's accounts for 2011–12 had not been filed with the Charity Commission at the time of writing.
HOW TO APPLY In writing to the correspondent.
WHO TO APPLY TO Anthony Leon, Trustee, 4 Westfields, Hale, Altrincham WA15 0LL *Tel.* 01619 808484 *email* anthonysula@hotmail.com

---

■ The W. O. Street Charitable Foundation

CC NO 267127   **ESTABLISHED** 1973
WHERE FUNDING CAN BE GIVEN UK, with a preference for the North West of England, primarily Lancashire and Jersey.
WHO CAN BENEFIT Registered charities.
WHAT IS FUNDED Support is given for education, relief of poverty, helping people in financial difficulties (particularly people who are elderly, blind or who have disabilities), the relief of sickness and social welfare generally.
WHAT IS NOT FUNDED No grants towards: schools, colleges or universities; running or core costs; religion or church buildings; medical research; animal welfare; hospices; overseas projects or charities; NHS trusts. Applications directly from individuals are not considered.
TYPE OF GRANT One-off and recurring grants.
RANGE OF GRANTS Generally £1,000 to £15,000
SAMPLE GRANTS W O Street Jersey Charitable Trust (£40,000); Emmott Foundation (£30,000); The Fusilier Museum (£20,000); Ribblesdale High School and THOMAS Organisation (£5,000 each); Sahir House (£4,000); New Brighton Community Association (£3,000); Rochdale Connections Trust (£2,500); Norfolk Deaf Association (£2,000); and Fylde Community Link (£600).
FINANCES *Year* 2012 *Income* £300,502 *Grants* £407,531 *Assets* £15,033,761
TRUSTEES Barclays Bank Trust Co. Ltd; Clive Cutbill.

HOW TO APPLY In writing to the correspondent. Applications are considered on a quarterly basis, at the end of January, April, July and October.

WHO TO APPLY TO The Trust Officer, Barclays Bank Trust Co. Ltd, Osborne Court, Gadbrook Park, Rudheath, Cheshire CW9 7UE *Tel.* 01606 313179

■ The A. B. Strom and R. Strom Charitable Trust

CC NO 268916   **ESTABLISHED** 1971
WHERE FUNDING CAN BE GIVEN UK.
WHO CAN BENEFIT Registered charities.
WHAT IS FUNDED A set list of charities working with older people, schools/colleges, hospitals and Christian causes.
SAMPLE GRANTS Previously, grants in excess of £1,000 each were made to Yeshivas Hanegev (£10,000), JRRC (£10,000 in two grants) and Redcroft and Russian Immigrants (£5,000 each).
FINANCES *Year* 2011–12 *Income* £5,380 *Grants* £32,914
TRUSTEES Regina Strom; Debbie Weissbraun.
OTHER INFORMATION Accounts were received at the Commission but due to the low income were not available to view online.
HOW TO APPLY In writing to the correspondent. Note that the same organisations are supported each year.
WHO TO APPLY TO Regina Strom, Trustee, c/o 11 Gloucester Gardens, London NW11 9AB *Tel.* 020 8455 5949 *email* m@michaelpasha. worldonline.co.uk

■ The Sudborough Foundation

CC NO 272323   **ESTABLISHED** 1976
WHERE FUNDING CAN BE GIVEN UK, with a preference for Northamptonshire.
WHO CAN BENEFIT Educational establishments and other charities.
WHAT IS FUNDED Students in need or for scholarships; general charitable purposes.
WHAT IS NOT FUNDED Individuals; Non-registered charities; Political or pressure groups; Religious Groups and National Charities (although local branches may apply for local-based projects).
RANGE OF GRANTS Up to £5,000.
SAMPLE GRANTS Home Farm Trust and Northampton General Hospital (£5,000 each); The Gordon Robinson Memorial Trust (£3,000); Parkinson Disease Society (£2,500); Northampton Scouts Gang Show, Wildlife Trust and Pancreatic Cancer Research Fund (£2,000 each); Northampton Counselling Service, Royal College Of Music and University Of Northants Max Engel Memorial Award (£1,500 each); Guilsborough Playing Fields Association (£1,000); Greenfields School and Sports College (£500) and Guide Association Midlands (£100).
FINANCES *Year* 2011–12 *Income* £77,616 *Grants* £60,700 *Assets* £1,376,884
TRUSTEES Richard Engel; Lady Lowther; Elizabeth Engel; William Reason; Susan Leathem; Simon Powis; Julian Woolfson; Rachel Engel.
HOW TO APPLY On a form available to download on the website.
WHO TO APPLY TO Richard Engel, Chair, 8 Hazelwood Road, Northampton NN1 1LP *email* chair@ sudboroughfoundation.org.uk *Website* www. sudboroughfoundation.org.uk

■ Sueberry Ltd

CC NO 256566   **ESTABLISHED** 1968
WHERE FUNDING CAN BE GIVEN UK and overseas.
WHO CAN BENEFIT Jewish organisations; UK welfare and medical organisations benefiting children and young adults; at risk groups; people who are disadvantaged by poverty, or socially isolated people.
WHAT IS FUNDED General, medical, educational and religious activities.
TYPE OF GRANT Mostly recurrent.
FINANCES *Year* 2011–12 *Income* £172,504 *Grants* £147,526 *Assets* £99,860
TRUSTEES D. S. Davis, Chair; C. Davis; H. Davis; J. Davis; M. Davis; A. D. Davis; S. M. Davis; Y. Davis.
HOW TO APPLY In writing to the correspondent.
WHO TO APPLY TO D. S. Davis, Trustee, 18 Clifton Gardens, London N15 6AP

■ Suffolk Community Foundation (formerly The Suffolk Foundation)

CC NO 1109453   **ESTABLISHED** 2005
WHERE FUNDING CAN BE GIVEN Suffolk.
WHO CAN BENEFIT Registered charities and community groups.
WHAT IS FUNDED The foundation has a range of different funds designed for small community and voluntary groups working to help local people across Suffolk. Each scheme tends to have a different application procedure and size of award. Note: grant schemes can change frequently. Potential applicants are advised to consult the foundation's website for details of current programmes and their deadlines.
WHAT IS NOT FUNDED No funding for: projects not benefiting people living in Suffolk; individuals for their personal needs; direct replacement of statutory obligation and public funding; general large appeals; medical research and equipment; statutory work in educational institutions; promotion of religious or political causes; sponsored events; fundraising events; retrospective grants; animal welfare; overseas travel or expeditions for individuals and groups. Note: different programmes may have further exclusions. Organisations are advised to read the guidelines carefully before making an application.
TYPE OF GRANT One-off grants for capital and revenue costs and full project funding.
RANGE OF GRANTS Small grants averaging around £2,000.
SAMPLE GRANTS Suffolk County Council (£476,000); The Henry Smith Foundation (£377,500); Healthy Ambitions (£300,000); Community First (£275,000) and Comic Relief (£28,000)
FINANCES *Year* 2011–12 *Income* £2,689,122 *Grants* £1,624,734 *Assets* £3,549,100
TRUSTEES David Barclay; James Dinwiddy; The Countess of Euston; Stephen Fletcher; Revd Canon Graham Hedger; Claire Horsley; Lady Howes; Graeme Kalbraier; Sir David Rowland; Nigel Smith; Gulshan Kayembe; James Buckle; Very Revd Dr Frances Ward; Iain Jamie; Terence Ward; Peter Newnham; Judge Caroline Ludlow.
OTHER INFORMATION In 2011–12 grants were given to 514 organisations.
HOW TO APPLY The foundation's website has details of the grant schemes currently being administered and how to apply.
WHO TO APPLY TO Julie Rose, Grants Officer, The Old Barns, Peninsula Business Centre, Wherstead,

Ipswich, Suffolk IP9 2BB *Tel.* 01473 602602
email info@suffolkfoundation.org.uk
Website www.suffolkfoundation.org.uk

■ The Suffolk Historic Churches Trust

CC NO 267047　　　　**ESTABLISHED** 1973
WHERE FUNDING CAN BE GIVEN Suffolk.
WHO CAN BENEFIT Churches and chapels over 100 years old of all denominations.
WHAT IS FUNDED The preservation, repair, maintenance, restoration and improvement of churches in Suffolk.
WHAT IS NOT FUNDED The trust does normally make grants for: electrical work; furnishings and fittings; churchyard walls; brasses and bells; monuments; redecoration, unless needed as part of an eligible project; new buildings or extensions to existing buildings.
TYPE OF GRANT One off for specific project.
RANGE OF GRANTS £300–£10,000. Higher than the maximum is only given in exceptional circumstances.
SAMPLE GRANTS Haverhill and Woodbridge; (£10,000 each); Monk Soham (£8,000); Hesset (£7,000); Ashfield cum Thorpe, Bawdsley and Bacton (£5,000 each); Ashfield; Falkenham; Freston; Greater Whelnetham; Ipswich – Bramford Road Methodist; Leavenheath; Raydon and Withersfield (£1,000 each).
FINANCES *Year* 2011–12 *Income* £218,872 *Grants* £155,750 *Assets* £674,882
TRUSTEES Robert Rous, Chair; Sir Christopher Howes; The Venerable David Jenkins; Jonathan Penn; Martin Favell; Diana Hunt; Christopher Spicer; Robert Williams; Simon Tennent; Celia Stephens; Clive Paine; Patrick Grieve; The Hon Charles Boscawen; Edward Bland; Geoffrey Probert.
HOW TO APPLY Application forms can be downloaded from the trust's website. The Grants Committee normally meets in the second week of January, April, July and October. Applications received by the end of the month prior to the meeting are considered at the meeting.
WHO TO APPLY TO Julie Lonergan, Brinkleys, Hall Street, Long Melford, Suffolk CO10 9JR *Tel.* 01787 883884 *Website* www.shct.org.uk

■ The Alan Sugar Foundation

CC NO 294880　　　　**ESTABLISHED** 1986
WHERE FUNDING CAN BE GIVEN UK
WHO CAN BENEFIT Registered charities.
WHAT IS FUNDED General charitable purposes. Grants are made to causes of current and ongoing interest to the trustees.
WHAT IS NOT FUNDED No grants for individuals or to non-registered charities.
TYPE OF GRANT One-off and recurring, capital and project.
RANGE OF GRANTS £500–£200,000.
SAMPLE GRANTS Jewish Care; Sport Relief; Macmillan Cancer; BBC Children in Need; Prostate Cancer Charitable Fund; Cancer Research UK; and St Michael's Hospice.
FINANCES *Year* 2011–12 *Income* £2,997 *Grants* £220,000
TRUSTEES Lord Alan Sugar; Colin Sandy; Simon Sugar; Daniel Sugar; Louise Baron.
OTHER INFORMATION Unfortunately the accounts were not available to view due to the low income, but it is estimated that grants were made totalling around £220,000.

HOW TO APPLY **This trust states that it does not respond to unsolicited applications.** All projects are initiated by the trustees.
WHO TO APPLY TO Colin Sandy, Trustee, Amshold House, Goldings Hill, Loughton, Essex IG10 3RW *Tel.* 020 3225 5560 *email* colin@amsprop.com

■ The Summerfield Charitable Trust

CC NO 802493　　　　**ESTABLISHED** 1989
WHERE FUNDING CAN BE GIVEN Gloucestershire.
WHO CAN BENEFIT Registered charities local to Gloucestershire.
WHAT IS FUNDED 'The trustees are particularly interested in helping the arts, museums and the built heritage; the environment and natural heritage; community work; education, sport and recreation; and vulnerable or disadvantaged sectors of society.'
The trustees are interested in hearing from those involved in helping older people, people in need and the arts. Viewed especially favourably are: the needs of people living in rural areas; ventures which make a point of using volunteers (and which train volunteers); applicants who show clear indications that they have assessed the impact of their project upon the environment; and joint appeals from groups working in similar areas, who wish to develop a partnership. The trustees particularly welcome innovative ideas from: small, voluntary groups; schemes that indicate planning for long-term self-sufficiency; and projects that demonstrate active involvement with the beneficiaries.
WHAT IS NOT FUNDED No grants for: medical research; private education; animal welfare appeals; fund trips abroad; projects that have already taken place; individuals; churches; and no repeat grants.
TYPE OF GRANT Usually one-off. The trustees prefer to award one-off grants to help fund specific projects rather than to make payments for revenue items. The trustees will occasionally consider start-up costs and grants for up to three years.
RANGE OF GRANTS £500–£29,000.
SAMPLE GRANTS Previous beneficiaries include: Cheltenham Arts Festivals Ltd (£29,000); Art Shape Limited and Brewery Arts (£20,000 each); Forest of Dean Music Makers (£15,000); Abbey Schools (£12,000); and Cotswold Players, Global Dimension Trust, Gloucester Emergency Accommodation Resource, Thomas Morley Trust and Uplands Care Service (£10,000 each).
FINANCES *Year* 2012 *Income* £297,729 *Grants* £413,142 *Assets* £9,300,000
TRUSTEES Edward Gillespie; Katrina Beach; Vanessa Arbuthnott; Anthony McClaran; James Millar.
OTHER INFORMATION In 2012 grants were broken down in to the following categories: Disadvantaged and vulnerable sectors (£151,000 in 26 grants); Arts, museums and built heritage (£115,600 in 20 grants); Community work (£42,700 in 13 grants); Education, sport and recreation (£64,800 in 21 grants); Environment and natural heritage (£39,200 in six grants).
HOW TO APPLY The trust has an online application process. All forms, criteria and guidelines are available to download on its website. The trustees meet quarterly; usually in January, April, July and October (see the trust's website for deadline dates). The Trustees prefer to

support projects that will take place, or start, within six months of receiving the grant. It is therefore important when applying to be clear about timescales and be confident they will fit in with the timing of the quarterly meetings.

WHO TO APPLY TO Lavinia Sidgwick, Administrator, PO Box 287, Cirencester, Gloucestershire GL7 9FB *Tel.* 01285 721211 *Fax* 01285 720843 *email* admin@summerfield.org.uk *Website* www.summerfield.org.uk

···
■ The Bernard Sunley Charitable Foundation

CC NO 1109099   **ESTABLISHED** 1960
WHERE FUNDING CAN BE GIVEN Unrestricted, but a preference for southern England.
WHO CAN BENEFIT Registered charities and Community Amateur Sports Clubs (CASC).
WHAT IS FUNDED General charitable purposes; with grants categorised under: education; arts; religion; community; children and youth; elderly; health; social welfare; environment; animal welfare; amateur sport; emergency and armed services; and overseas.
WHAT IS NOT FUNDED 'We would reiterate that we do not make grants to individuals; we still receive several such applications each week. This bar on individuals applies equally to those people taking part in a project sponsored by a charity such as VSO, Duke of Edinburgh Award Scheme, Trekforce, Scouts and Girl Guides, and so on., or in the case of the latter two to specific units of these youth movements.'
TYPE OF GRANT Capital grants for up to a maximum of three years.
RANGE OF GRANTS £100–£250,000; typical grant £5,000–£10,000.
SAMPLE GRANTS National Gallery – Sunley Room exhibitions (£240,000); Howard League for Penal Reform and Canterbury Cathedral Development Limited (£100,000 each); Canterbury Christ Church University St Gregory's Development Project (£50,000); Country Trust (£36,000); Royal Academy of Arts (£25,000); Children's Hospice South West (£20,000); Off The Fence Trust (£15,000); and Factory Youth Zone (Manchester) Ltd, Sheltered Work Opportunities Project, Friends of Westfield School, Guildhall School Development Fund, Addaction, Parkinson's UK, St Andrew's House – Coventry, Combat Stress and Taverham Recreation Facility (£10,000 each).
FINANCES *Year* 2011–12 *Income* £3,217,000 *Grants* £2,548,619 *Assets* £84,757,000
TRUSTEES Joan Tice; Bella Sunley; Sir Donald Gosling; Dr Brian Martin; Anabel Knight; William Tice; Inigo Paternina.
HOW TO APPLY 'There is no application form, but applicants should send a letter of application to the Director (see below) by post, enclosing the latest approved set of annual report and accounts (but only if these are not on the Charity Commission's website). Give an email address, where possible, for subsequent correspondence. The letter should include the following: the purpose of the charity and its objectives; the need and purpose of the project including who will benefit and how; the cost of the project, including a breakdown of costs where appropriate; the amount of money raised and from whom, and how it is planned to raise the shortfall; if applicable, how the running costs of the project will be met once the project is established; any other documentation that the applicant feels will help to support or explain the appeal.'
'Processing of grants is continuous so applications can be sent at any time. All applications will be acknowledged by email on receipt, and a decision made within three months, with an answer one way or the other. Following an application, do not reapply for at least twelve months (from the date of your original application) as it will be declined automatically.'
WHO TO APPLY TO John Rimmington, Director, 20 Berkeley Square, London W1J 6LH *Tel.* 020 7408 2198 *Fax* 020 7499 5859 *email* office@bernardsunley.org *Website* www.bernardsunley.org

···
■ The Sunny Skies Foundation

CC NO 1147435   **ESTABLISHED** 2012
WHERE FUNDING CAN BE GIVEN UK and overseas.
WHO CAN BENEFIT Charities and community groups.
WHAT IS FUNDED General, social welfare, overseas aid.
TRUSTEES R. Hardy; L. Hardy; Abacus Trustees (UK) Ltd (Andrew Robins; Louise Somerset; Kevin Stokes; Roland Wyatt; Oluremi Adejumo).
HOW TO APPLY In writing to the correspondent.
WHO TO APPLY TO Abacus Trustees (UK) Ltd, c/o R. B. C. International Wealth Planning, The Quadrangle, Imperial Square, Cheltenham, Gloucestershire GL50 1PZ *Tel.* 01242 548400 *Fax* 01242 548401 *email* sunnyskies@rbc.com

···
■ Community Foundation for Surrey

CC NO 1111600   **ESTABLISHED** 2005
WHERE FUNDING CAN BE GIVEN Surrey.
WHO CAN BENEFIT Organisations and individuals.
WHAT IS FUNDED Strengthening communities in Surrey.
TYPE OF GRANT Surrey Community Foundation has an ongoing grant programme consisting of a number of funds established by individuals, families, trusts and companies. The foundation also administers *Grassroots Grants*, a national programme (2008–11) to support small, voluntary led community groups to build stronger more active communities. Grants for running costs or capital items of between £250 and £5,000 are available for small groups with an average annual income of less than £20,000.
FINANCES *Year* 2011–12 *Income* £840,164 *Grants* £764,435 *Assets* £5,404,303
TRUSTEES Prof. Patrick Dowling, Chair; Bridget Biddell; Stephen Blunt, Secretary; Matthew Bowcock; David Frank; Peter Hampson; Gordon Lee-Steere; Jim McAllister; Tracey Reddings; Andrew Wates; Richard Whittington; Graham Williams.
HOW TO APPLY An expression of interest form is available at the funder's website, which all individuals and groups are advised to check for more details, as all funds have their own criteria and closing dates.
WHO TO APPLY TO Prof. Patrick Dowling, Chair, Surrey Community Foundation, 1 Bishops Wharf, Walnut Tree Close, Guilldford, Surrey GU1 4RA *Tel.* 01483 409230 *email* info@cfsurrey.org.uk *Website* www.cfsurrey.org.uk

■ The Surrey Historic Buildings Trust Ltd

CC NO 279240   **ESTABLISHED** 1979

WHERE FUNDING CAN BE GIVEN Surrey.

WHO CAN BENEFIT Individuals or groups.

WHAT IS FUNDED Preservation of the historical, architectural and constructional heritage existing in Surrey.

WHAT IS NOT FUNDED No support for local authority-owned buildings or the general upkeep of places of worship (although specific artefacts or architectural features may attract a grant).

RANGE OF GRANTS Up to £6,000; usually £1,000 to £3,000.

SAMPLE GRANTS St Martin's Church, Blackheath; Betchworth Castle, Betchworth Park, Dorking, (£3,000 each); The Medicine Garden, Cobham; (£2,000 each); and Potters Farm Barn (£1,000).

FINANCES *Year* 2011–12 *Income* £33,402 *Grants* £25,400 *Assets* £470,642

TRUSTEES David Davis; Angela Fraser; N. Westbury; Roger Hargreaves

HOW TO APPLY On an application form available from the correspondent or the website. Applicants should, where possible, produce two detailed estimates. In the case of highly specialized work, a single estimate may be acceptable. The application cannot be considered unless photographs of the building accompany it and, where available, plans should also be submitted.

WHO TO APPLY TO Jacqui Hird, Assistant Honorary Secretary, Surrey Historical Buildings Trust, Room 122, County Hall, Penrhyn Road, Kingston upon Thames, Surrey KT1 2DN *Tel.* 020 8541 9122 *email* jacqui.hird@surreycc.gov.uk *Website* surreycc.gov.uk

■ The Sussex Community Foundation

CC NO 1113226   **ESTABLISHED** 2006

WHERE FUNDING CAN BE GIVEN East Sussex, West Sussex or Brighton and Hove.

WHO CAN BENEFIT Charities and community groups whose work benefits people in East Sussex, West Sussex or Brighton and Hove.

WHAT IS FUNDED The foundation is particularly interested in supporting groups that work towards the advancement of education, the protection of good health both mental and physical and the relief of poverty and sickness

WHAT IS NOT FUNDED According to the foundation's guidance notes (obtained from the foundation's website August 2013), 'Sussex Community Foundation will not support requests from or for: organisations that are part of central, local or regional government; organisations that discriminate on the basis of race, religion, creed, national origin, disability, age, sexual orientation, marital status; individuals – including scholarships, sponsorships and other forms of financial assistance – apart from those applying to the Paul Rooney Foundation and to the Westdene Trust; fundraising activities such as benefits, charitable dinners, or sponsored events; goodwill advertising, dinner programmes, books, magazines or articles in professional journals; political activities; major capital appeals; small contributions to major campaigns; grants which will be used to make awards to a third party; sports sponsorships; projects which only benefit animals; projects seeking funds to improve the buildings or assets of the local authority e.g.; Friends or

Parents of school groups looking for funds for playgrounds, school equipment etc.; projects whose wider community appeal or benefit is limited; groups who have not returned monitoring from previous SCF awards.'

TYPE OF GRANT Grants of up to one year.

RANGE OF GRANTS Mostly £1,000–£5,000.

SAMPLE GRANTS Fletcher in Rye CIC (£25,500); Keep Out Crime Diversion Scheme (£20,000); Moulsecoomb Forest Garden and Wildlife Project and City Gate Community Projects (FareShare Project) (£15,000 each); AMAZE and Kent Community Foundation (£10,000 each); Kaleidoscope, Fun in Action for Children and Central Sussex Citizens Advice – Horsham (£6,000).

FINANCES *Year* 2011–12 *Income* £2,200,439 *Grants* £828,765 *Assets* £4,713,515

TRUSTEES Neil Hart; Trevor James; Richard Pearson; Elizabeth Bennett; John Peel; Kathleen Gore; Steve Manwaring; Sharon Phillips; Mike Simpkin; Humphrey Price; Michael Martin; David Allam; Charles Drayson; Consuelo Brooke.

HOW TO APPLY This information was obtained from the foundation's website, as well as its application guidance notes: Applicants must have a hard copy of the signed application and supporting documents. Applicants have to be able to show that they are not-for-profit, but do not always have to be a charity. All applicants must be working for the benefit of the people of Sussex. Only one fund can be applied for at a time. There are four grants rounds a year, occasionally more. The deadline is approximately eight weeks prior to the panel meeting. The 'SCF General Application form' is used for most funds; however there are certain funds which have separate forms of their own. For more information consult the foundation's website. Each of the funds listed under 'Download Available Funds' link, which is available on the 'Apply for Funding' page, are open to applications. Application forms and guidance notes can be downloaded from the foundation's website. Alternatively applicants can request forms by post or email by ringing 01273 409 440. On receipt of the application, the foundation will contact applicants to advise them on when they are likely to hear back on the decision.

WHO TO APPLY TO Kevin Richmond, Administrator, Suite B, Falcon Wharf, Railway Lane, Lewes BN7 2AQ *Tel.* 01273 409440 *email* info@sussexgiving.org.uk *Website* www.sussexgiving.org.uk

■ The Sussex Historic Churches Trust

CC NO 282159   **ESTABLISHED** 1981

WHERE FUNDING CAN BE GIVEN Sussex.

WHO CAN BENEFIT Churches of any denomination over 100 years old and of some architectural or historical significance.

WHAT IS FUNDED Preservation, repair, maintenance and restoration of churches in Sussex.

WHAT IS NOT FUNDED No grants for bells.

TYPE OF GRANT Interest-free loans and buildings will be considered.

RANGE OF GRANTS £1,000–£10,000, typical grants £5,000.

SAMPLE GRANTS Previous beneficiaries included: Saint John the Baptist – Kirdford (£15,000); Saint Peter – Westhampnett (£10,000); Saint Mary – Salehurst (£6,000); Saint Mary – Bepton and Southwick, C.C.C. (£5,000 each); Saint

Mary – Broadwater, Saint John the Baptist – Crawley, Saint Peter ad Vincula – Folkington and Saint Dunstan – Mayfield (£3,000 each).

FINANCES *Year* 2011–12 *Income* £117,052 *Grants* £85,500 *Assets* £1,108,268

TRUSTEES Philip Jones; Lady Pamela Wedgwood; John Barkshire; The Venerable Roger Combes; The Venerable Douglas H. McKittrick; Sara Stonor; Christopher Whittick; Graham Pound.

HOW TO APPLY In writing to the correspondent giving an outline of the work to be done and some indication of the financial state of the parish or congregation. An application form will then be sent to you, if what you propose qualifies for help. Applications must be made before work is started.

WHO TO APPLY TO John Barkshire, Daneshouse, High street, Burwash, Etchingham TN19 7EH *Tel.* 01435 882646 *email* jbarkshire19@gmail. com *Website* www.sussexhistoricchurches.org. uk

■ The Adrienne and Leslie Sussman Charitable Trust

CC NO 274955   **ESTABLISHED** 1977

WHERE FUNDING CAN BE GIVEN UK, in practice Greater London, particularly Barnet.

WHO CAN BENEFIT Registered charities.

WHAT IS FUNDED General, Jewish.

WHAT IS NOT FUNDED No grants to branches of UK charities outside Barnet, non-registered charities and individuals.

SAMPLE GRANTS Previous beneficiaries have included: BF Shvut Ami, Chai – Lifeline and B'nai B'rith Hillel Fund, Child Resettlement, Children and Youth Aliyah, Finchley Synagogue, Jewish Care, Nightingale House, Norwood Ravenswood and Sidney Sussex CLL.

FINANCES *Year* 2011–12 *Income* £68,760 *Grants* £46,230 *Assets* £2,006,361

TRUSTEES Adrienne Sussman; Debra Sussman; Martin Paisner; Adam Sussman; Neal Sussman.

OTHER INFORMATION A recent list of beneficiaries was not available.

HOW TO APPLY In writing to the correspondent.

WHO TO APPLY TO Adrienne Sussman, Trustee, 25 Tillingbourne Gardens, London N3 3JJ *Tel.* 020 8346 6775

■ The Sutasoma Trust

CC NO 803301   **ESTABLISHED** 1990

WHERE FUNDING CAN BE GIVEN UK and overseas.

WHO CAN BENEFIT Individuals and organisations.

WHAT IS FUNDED Bursaries and support to institutions in the field of social sciences, humanities and humanitarian activities. General grants may also be made.

TYPE OF GRANT Mainly recurrent.

SAMPLE GRANTS Lucy Cavendish College Fellowship (£19,500); University of Bergen (£12,000); Manipal Centre for Philosophy and Humanities (£9,000 in total); Livingstone Anglican Children's Project – Zambia (£7,000); HAU Journal of Ethnographic Theory (£4,000); Link Numeracy Project (£2,000); and the Medical Foundation Allotment Project and the Welfare Association (£1,000 each).

FINANCES *Year* 2011–12 *Income* £103,653 *Grants* £98,600 *Assets* £2,618,201

TRUSTEES Dr Angela Hobart; Marcel Burgauer; Jane Lichtenstein; Prof. Bruce Kapferer; Dr Sally Wolfe; Dr Piers Vitebsky.

HOW TO APPLY In writing to the correspondent.

WHO TO APPLY TO Jane Lichtenstein, Trustee, PO Box 157, Haverhill, Suffolk CB9 1AH *Tel.* 07768 245384 *email* sutasoma.trust@btinternet.com

■ Sutton Coldfield Charitable Trust

CC NO 218627   **ESTABLISHED** 1898

WHERE FUNDING CAN BE GIVEN The former borough of Sutton Coldfield, comprising three electoral wards: New Hall, Vesey and Four Oaks.

WHO CAN BENEFIT Individuals in need and organisations, without restriction, in Sutton Coldfield.

WHAT IS FUNDED General charitable purposes, with grants categorised under the following: relief of poverty; religion; education; health and saving lives; citizenship and community development; arts, culture, heritage and science; repair of historic buildings; and amateur sport.

WHAT IS NOT FUNDED No awards are given to individuals or organisations outside the area of benefit, unless the organisations are providing essential services in the area.

TYPE OF GRANT The trustees will consider making grants for buildings, projects, research, start-up costs, and capital and running costs for up to three years or as one-off payments. No cash payments are made; payments are made via invoices or vouchers.

RANGE OF GRANTS Up to £75,000.

SAMPLE GRANTS Previous beneficiaries include: St Giles Hospice; John Willmott School; Boldmere Swimming Club; New Hall Ward Advisory Board; New Hall Primary School; Holy Trinity (CE) Parish Church; Boldmere Methodist Church; Victim Support; Walmley Women's Institute; and Sutton Coldfield Asian Society.

FINANCES *Year* 2011–12 *Income* £1,567,565 *Grants* £905,855 *Assets* £45,080,147

TRUSTEES Dr Freddie Gick, Chair; Dr Stephen Martin; Neil Andrews; Susan Bailey; Malcolm Cornish; John Gray; Carole Hancox; Rodney Kettel; David Owen; Jane Rothwell; David Roy; Cllr Margaret Waddington; Michael Waltho; Rt Revd Andrew Watson; Linda Whitfield; Jim Whorwood.

OTHER INFORMATION As well as providing grants to organisations, the charities maintain 46 almshouses and provides grants for fees, maintenance, clothing and equipment to individuals. In 2011–12 grants to individuals totalled £45,000.

HOW TO APPLY To make a grant application: contact the trust, either by letter, or by telephoning 0121 351 2262; outline your needs and request a copy of the trust's guidelines for applicants; if appropriate, seek a meeting with a member of staff in making your application; ensure that all relevant documents, including estimates and accounts, reach the charity by the requested dates. Receipt of applications is not normally acknowledged unless a stamped addressed envelope is sent with the application. Applications may be submitted at any time. The grants committee meets at least eight times a year. The board of trustees must approve requests for grants over £30,000. At all stages, staff at the trust will give assistance to those making applications. For example, projects and applications can be discussed, either at the trust's office or on site. Advice about deadlines for submitting applications can also be given. (There are application forms for individuals, who must obtain them from the trust.)

WHO TO APPLY TO Ernest Murray, Clerk to the Trustees, Lingard House, Fox Hollies Road, Sutton Coldfield, West Midlands B76 2RJ *Tel.* 01213 512262 *Fax* 01213 130651 *Website* www.suttoncoldfieldcharitabletrust.com

....

■ The Sutton Trust

CC NO 1067197   ESTABLISHED 1998

WHERE FUNDING CAN BE GIVEN UK only.

WHO CAN BENEFIT Educational institutions, and other groups that organise formal education projects or undertake educational research.

WHAT IS FUNDED The trust's programmes fall under the headings of: early years; schools; university; professions.

TYPE OF GRANT Core costs, feasibility studies, interest-free loans, one-off, project, research, recurring costs, running costs, salaries and start-up costs. Capital and equipment grants are not considered. Grants are usually provided for one to two years only, but can be extended up to a maximum of three years, and further in exceptional circumstances.

SAMPLE GRANTS Cambridge University (various projects); Durham University; Feltham School; Snapethorpe Primary School; and Policy Exchange.

FINANCES *Year* 2012 *Income* £1,597,354 *Grants* £1,065,703 *Assets* £383,086

TRUSTEES Sir Peter Lampl; David Backinsell; Glyn Morris.

OTHER INFORMATION Individual grant amounts were not listed in the accounts.

HOW TO APPLY 'The trust takes a proactive approach to the work it wishes to support and tends to develop programmes itself, contacting the organisations it wants to partner with. The vast majority of unsolicited proposals we receive are unsuccessful. We are however willing to consider exceptional proposals which fit closely with our specific areas of interest.'

'If you feel your organisation has a programme which might interest us, first complete a funding enquiry on the Contact Us page [on the trust's website], including a couple of paragraphs describing your idea. If the idea is in line with our current priorities you may be asked to submit a brief proposal.'

WHO TO APPLY TO The Trust Administrator, 9th Floor, Millbank Tower, 21–24 Millbank, London SW1P 4QP *Tel.* 020 7802 1660 *Fax* 020 7802 1661 *email* info@suttontrust.com *Website* www.suttontrust.com

....

■ The Suva Foundation Limited

CC NO 1077057   ESTABLISHED 1999

WHERE FUNDING CAN BE GIVEN Unrestricted with a preference for Henley-on-Thames.

WHO CAN BENEFIT Charitable organisations.

WHAT IS FUNDED General charitable purposes, with a preference for education, health, medicine and culture.

SAMPLE GRANTS Cancer Research UK (£101,000); Langley Academy (£77,500 in support costs and a grant); Alfred Dunhill Links Foundation (£25,000); Rowing For Our Wounded (£20,000); Crazies Hill Educational Trust (£5,000); Henley Festival Trust (£2,500); and Lambrook School Trust Limited (£1,000).

FINANCES *Year* 2011–12 *Income* £286,258 *Grants* £245,175 *Assets* £9,911,267

TRUSTEES Annabel Nicoll; Paddy Nicoll.

OTHER INFORMATION The foundation is a regular supporter of the Langley Academy.

HOW TO APPLY This trust does not accept unsolicited applications.

WHO TO APPLY TO Cristina Wade, Administrator, 61 Grosvenor Street, London W1K 3JE *Tel.* 020 3011 1100

....

■ Swan Mountain Trust

CC NO 275594   ESTABLISHED 1977

WHERE FUNDING CAN BE GIVEN UK.

WHO CAN BENEFIT Organisations benefiting mental health patients and prisoners, ex-offenders and potential offenders.

WHAT IS FUNDED Mental health (not disability), penal affairs and prisoners' education.

WHAT IS NOT FUNDED No grants for annual holidays, debt repayment, large appeals or for causes outside the trust's two main areas of work.

TYPE OF GRANT One-off.

RANGE OF GRANTS Up to £5,000, however on average under £1,000.

SAMPLE GRANTS Prisoner's Education Trust (£5,000); Scottish Association for Mental Health (£3,000); Asha Women's Centre, Synergy Theatre and The Zahid Mubarek Trust (£2,000 each); Birmingham Centre for Arts Therapies (£1,500); Hope Housing, Training and Support Trust and Young Minds (£1,000 each); and Fair Shares (£500).

FINANCES *Year* 2012–13 *Income* £47,397 *Grants* £42,270 *Assets* £1,074,639

TRUSTEES Dodie Carter; Janet Hargreaves; Peter Kilgarriff; Calton Younger.

HOW TO APPLY In writing to the correspondent, enclosing an up-to-date report on fundraising, and a copy of the most recent annual report and accounts (or any financial information available). The trustees meet in early February, June and October each year, but can occasionally reach decisions quickly in an emergency. Applications should be made at least four weeks before the trustees' next meeting. The trust tries to be as responsive as it can be to appropriate applicants. Individual applications are no longer accepted.

WHO TO APPLY TO Janet Hargreaves, Trustee, 7 Mount Vernon, London NW3 6QS *Tel.* 020 7794 2486 *email* info@swanmountaintrust.org.uk *Website* swanmountaintrust.org.uk

....

■ Swansea and Brecon Diocesan Board of Finance Limited

CC NO 249810   ESTABLISHED 1967

WHERE FUNDING CAN BE GIVEN Diocese of Swansea and Brecon (Neath Port Talbot, Powys and Swansea).

WHO CAN BENEFIT Clergy and organisations in the diocese of Swansea and Brecon.

WHAT IS FUNDED The majority portion of the board's expenditure is on clergy stipends, emoluments and housing, with the balance being spent on Diocesan activities, grants and administration.

WHAT IS NOT FUNDED Applications from outside of the diocese.

TYPE OF GRANT One – off grants to organisations.

FINANCES *Year* 2012 *Income* £3,516,834 *Grants* £3,519,583 *Assets* £3,990,807

TRUSTEES Archdeacon Randolph Thomas; Gwyn Lewis; Gillian Knigh; Rt Revd John Davies; The Venerable Robert Williams; Clive Rees; Revd Canon Peter Williams; Nicolas Paravicini; Revd Alan Jevons; Peter Davies; Professor Peter Townsend; The Revd Canon Janet Russell.

....

HOW TO APPLY The charity does not respond to unsolicited applications.

WHO TO APPLY TO Heather Price, Administrator, Diocesan Centre, Cathedral Close, Brecon, Powys LD3 9DP *Tel.* 01874 623716 *Website* www.churchinwales.org.uk/swanbrec

....

■ Swimathon Foundation

CC NO 1123870   **ESTABLISHED** 2008
WHERE FUNDING CAN BE GIVEN UK
WHO CAN BENEFIT Community groups including swimming clubs, older people' s organisations, youth groups, disability groups and other charities.
WHAT IS FUNDED Swimming. In particular, the promotion of swimming in local communities.
WHAT IS NOT FUNDED Organisations which exist to promote religion itself, and groups where the community must participate in religious services in order to benefit, are not eligible to apply. Hydrotherapy pools are not eligible to apply for a Swimathon Foundation grant if they are not a Swimathon pool and organisations which promote a political party or activity are not eligible to apply.
RANGE OF GRANTS Between £300 and £2,500.
FINANCES *Year* 2011–12 *Income* £2,886,831 *Grants* £93,266 *Assets* £320,097
TRUSTEES Anthony Kendall; Ralph Riley; Philip Stinson; Graham Batterham.
HOW TO APPLY All applications should be submitted using the online application form which is available, together with criteria and guidelines, from the Foundation's website.
WHO TO APPLY TO c/o Cox Costello and Horne Limited, Langwood House, 63–81 High Street, Rickmansworth, Hertfordshire WD3 1EQ *Tel.* 01923 771977 *email* info@ swimathonfoundation.org *Website* www. swimathonfoundation.org

....

■ The John Swire (1989) Charitable Trust

CC NO 802142   **ESTABLISHED** 1989
WHERE FUNDING CAN BE GIVEN UK.
WHO CAN BENEFIT Charitable organisations; universities; schools.
WHAT IS FUNDED General charitable purposes, especially arts, welfare, education, medicine and research.
RANGE OF GRANTS Generally £1,000–£100,000.
SAMPLE GRANTS University College Oxford (£1 million); Eton College (£213,000); Catching Lives, Kew Gardens and Selling Village Hall (£20,000 each); Kent Wildlife Trust and National Trust (£11,000 each); Mary Rose Museum and The Stroke Association (£10,000 each); Canterbury Festival and Royal British Legion (£6,000 each); Smile Support and Care and Stour Music (£5,000 each); Pilgrims Hospices in Kent, RAFT and Wildlife and Wetlands Trust (£2,000 each); Atlantic Salmon Trust and Deal Festival (£1,500 each); and 999 Club, British Heart Foundation, Canterbury Choral Society, Chatham Historic Dockyard Trust, Dover Boat Trust, Essex Yeomanry, Family Links Gurkha Welfare Trust, I CAN, Maggie's Centres, NSPCC, National Back pain Association, Prostate Research Campaign UK and Reeds School (£1,000 each).
FINANCES *Year* 2012 *Income* £2,286,860 *Grants* £1,798,037 *Assets* £27,417,546

TRUSTEES Sir John Swire; J. S. Swire; B. N. Swire; Michael Robinson; Lady M. C. Swire.
HOW TO APPLY In writing to the correspondent explaining how the funds would be used and what would be achieved.
WHO TO APPLY TO Michael Todhunter, Charities Administrator, Swire House, 59 Buckingham Gate, London SW1E 6AJ *Tel.* 020 7834 7717

....

■ The Swire Charitable Trust

CC NO 270726   **ESTABLISHED** 1976
WHERE FUNDING CAN BE GIVEN Worldwide.
WHO CAN BENEFIT Regional and UK organisations.
WHAT IS FUNDED Children, the arts and heritage, medical research, welfare, the environment and general charitable purposes.
RANGE OF GRANTS £1,000–£25,000
SAMPLE GRANTS Alzheimer's Research UK (£75,000); Marine Society and Sea Cadets (£50,000); Royal Ballet School (£30,000); Air League Trust (£26,000); Royal Academy of Arts and Textile Conservation Centre Foundation (£25,000 each); Walking with the Wounded (£15,000); British Red Cross, Combat Stress, Eden Project, Monte San Martino Trust St Mungo's and Voluntary Services Overseas (£10,000 each); Action for ME (£7,500); Ambitious about Autism, Children in Crisis and The Florence Institute (£5,000 each); Canine Partners, Dementia UK and Grey Coat Hospital (£2,500 each); and Survival International (£1,000).
FINANCES *Year* 2012 *Income* £750,280 *Grants* £742,486 *Assets* -£31,057
TRUSTEES Sir J. Swire; Sir Adrian Swire; B. N. Swire; J. S. Swire; M. Swire; J. W. J. Hughes-Hallett.
HOW TO APPLY In writing to the correspondent. Applications are considered throughout the year.
WHO TO APPLY TO Swire House, 59 Buckingham Gate, London SW1E 6AJ *Tel.* 020 7834 7717

....

■ The Adrian Swire Charitable Trust (formerly The Sammermar Trust)

CC NO 800493   **ESTABLISHED** 1988
WHERE FUNDING CAN BE GIVEN UK and overseas.
WHO CAN BENEFIT Charitable organisations.
WHAT IS FUNDED General charitable purposes.
RANGE OF GRANTS £1,000–£125,000.
SAMPLE GRANTS Eton College (£213,000); Collegiate Church of St Mary (£100,000); BSES (£75,000); The Inkerman Housing Association (£45,000); Brain Tumour Charity and Crisis Skylight Oxford (£20,000 each); British Lung Foundation (£11,000); Game and Wildlife Conservation Trust (£6,000); Independent Advice Centre (£5,000); Sparsholt Church (£3,000); 999 Club (£2,000) and Spitfire Society (£1,000).
FINANCES *Year* 2012 *Income* £969,842 *Grants* £996,600 *Assets* £18,026,825
TRUSTEES Lady Judith Swire; Timothy Cox; Richard Leonard; M. B. Swire; M.V.Allfrey.
HOW TO APPLY In writing to the correspondent. The trust states that: 'although the trustees make some grants with no formal applications, they normally require organisations to submit a request saying how the funds could be used and what would be achieved'. The trustees usually meet monthly.
WHO TO APPLY TO The Trustees, Swire House, 59 Buckingham Gate, London SW1E 6AJ *Tel.* 020 7834 7717

■ The Hugh and Ruby Sykes Charitable Trust

CC NO 327648 **ESTABLISHED** 1987

WHERE FUNDING CAN BE GIVEN Principally South Yorkshire, also Derbyshire.

WHO CAN BENEFIT Registered charities.

WHAT IS FUNDED Principally local charities but some major UK charities are supported. The trust has major commitments with several medical charities. It is the policy of the trust to distribute income and preserve capital.

WHAT IS NOT FUNDED No grants are made to individuals. Most grants are made to organisations which have a connection to one of the trustees.

FINANCES *Year* 2012–13 *Income* £173,510 *Grants* £76,765 *Assets* £1,891,594

TRUSTEES Sir Hugh Sykes; Lady Ruby Sykes.

OTHER INFORMATION A list of beneficiaries was not included in the accounts.

HOW TO APPLY Applications can only be accepted from registered charities and should be in writing to the correspondent. In order to save administration costs, replies are not sent to unsuccessful applicants. If the trustees are able to consider a request for support, they aim to express interest within one month.

WHO TO APPLY TO Brian Evans, Administrator, The Coach House, Brookfield Manor, Hathersage, Hope Valley, Derbyshire S32 1BR *Tel.* 01433 651190 *email* info@brookfieldmanor.com

■ The Charles and Elsie Sykes Trust

CC NO 206926 **ESTABLISHED** 1954

WHERE FUNDING CAN BE GIVEN UK, with a preference for Yorkshire.

WHO CAN BENEFIT Registered charities only.

WHAT IS FUNDED People who are blind or partially sighted; children and youth; cultural and environmental heritage; people who are deaf, hard of hearing or speech impaired; people with disabilities; education; hospices and hospitals; medical research; medical welfare; mental health and mental disability; welfare of older people; overseas aid; services and ex-services; social and moral welfare; trades and professions; and sundry.

WHAT IS NOT FUNDED Unregistered and overseas charities are not considered. Individuals, local organisations not in the north of England, and recently-established charities are unlikely to be successful.

TYPE OF GRANT One off and recurring.

RANGE OF GRANTS £2,000–£25,000.

SAMPLE GRANTS Harrogate Citizens Advice (£51,500); Alzheimer's Research UK (£25,000); Association of the Friends of Connaught Court (£10,000); Caring for Life (£7,500); Bierley Community Association Ltd, British Heart Foundation, Doncaster Housing for Young People, Sheffield Mencap and Gateway and Swaledale Festival (£5,000 each); and Carers' Resource, Harrogate (£2,000).

FINANCES *Year* 2012 *Income* £455,777 *Grants* £488,900 *Assets* £12,847,004

TRUSTEES John Ward, Chair; Anne Brownlie; Martin Coultas; Michael Garnett; Barry Kay; Dr Michael McEvoy; Peter Rous; Dr Rosemary Livingstone; Sara Buchan.

HOW TO APPLY Only applications from registered charities are considered, with a preference for those in, or benefiting people in, Yorkshire. Application forms can be requested from the trust or downloaded from the trust's website. The form should then be sent to the trust along with a copy of the organisation's latest accounts, annual report and any other relevant information. It is more favourable for the application if the accounts are current. If a grant is required for a particular project, full details and costings should be provided. Applications from schools, playgroups, cadet forces, scouts, guides, and churches must be for outreach programmes, and not for maintenance projects. Successful applications will receive a donation which may or may not be subject to conditions.

WHO TO APPLY TO Judith Long, Secretary, Barber Titleys Solicitors, 6 North Park Road, Harrogate, Yorkshire HG1 5PA *Tel.* 01423 817238 *Fax* 01423 851112 *Website* www. charlesandelsiesykestrust.co.uk

■ The Sylvanus Charitable Trust

CC NO 259520 **ESTABLISHED** 1968

WHERE FUNDING CAN BE GIVEN Europe and North America.

WHO CAN BENEFIT Organisations benefiting Roman Catholics and animals.

WHAT IS FUNDED The traditional Catholic Church and animal welfare, including wildlife sanctuaries.

WHAT IS NOT FUNDED No grants for expeditions, scholarships or individuals.

TYPE OF GRANT One-off and recurring.

RANGE OF GRANTS £1,000–£5,000.

SAMPLE GRANTS Society of St Pius X (£5,000); Fauna and Flora International (£3,000); Durrell Wildlife Conservation Trust (£2,000); and Animal Health Trust and Help in Suffering (£1,000 each).

FINANCES *Year* 2012 *Income* £83,870 *Grants* £30,924 *Assets* £2,281,886

TRUSTEES John C. Vernor Miles; Alexander D. Gemmill; Wilfred E. Vernor Miles; Gloria Taviner.

OTHER INFORMATION This trust has a sterling section for European grants and a dollar section for USA grants. The financial information in this entry relates to the Sterling section.

HOW TO APPLY The trustees usually make grants to charities known personally to them but occasionally make grants in response to unsolicited appeals. When considering applications for funding the trustees take into account how many years' reserves are held by an applicant and the proportionate costs of administration and fundraising. They also consider the degree to which the trustees have been informed of progress made since previous grants. The Trustees do not give grants to individuals. In writing to the correspondent. The trustees meet once a year.

WHO TO APPLY TO Gloria Taviner, Trustee, Hunters Solicitors, 9 New Square, London WC2A 3QN *Tel.* 020 7412 0050 *Fax* 020 7412 0049 *email* gt@hunters-solicitors.co.uk

■ The Hugh Symons Charitable Trust

CC NO 1137778 **ESTABLISHED** 2010

WHERE FUNDING CAN BE GIVEN Not defined, but a possible preference for Poole, Bradford and Sidmouth where the companies offices are based.

WHO CAN BENEFIT Registered charities.

WHAT IS FUNDED General charitable purposes.

FINANCES *Year* 2011–12 *Income* £10,000
Grants £3,000

TRUSTEES Barry E. Glazier; Geoffrey H. Roper;
Katherine A. Roper; Pauline H. Roper.

OTHER INFORMATION 'Hugh Symons Information
Management is one of the UK's leading
scanning and microfilming bureaux, processing
millions of images per month. The company was
established in 1974 and provides a full range of
scanning and microfilming bureau services from
our Records Management Centres in Poole
(head office), Bradford (northern head office)
and Sidmouth.'

HOW TO APPLY In writing to the correspondent.

WHO TO APPLY TO Geoffrey H. Roper, Trustee,
Stubhampton House, Stubhampton, Blandford
Forum, Dorset DT11 8JU *Tel.* 01258 830135

■ The Stella Symons Charitable Trust

CC NO 259638   ESTABLISHED 1968

WHERE FUNDING CAN BE GIVEN UK and overseas.

WHO CAN BENEFIT Registered charities.

WHAT IS FUNDED Residential facilities and services;
infrastructure, support and development; the
advancement of religion; arts, culture and
recreation; health; conservation and
environment; education and training; and social
care and development will be considered.

WHAT IS NOT FUNDED The trustees do not normally
favour projects which provide a substitute for
the statutory obligations of the state or projects
which in their opinion should be commercially
viable operations. No grants to individuals or to
politically biased organisations.

TYPE OF GRANT Outright gifts and larger sums on
loan on beneficial terms. Buildings, capital, core
costs, one-off, project, research, recurring and
running costs, salaries, and start-up costs.
Funding for up to and over three years will be
considered.

RANGE OF GRANTS The majority of grants are for
£250.

SAMPLE GRANTS National Trust (£1,300); Chestnut
Tree Hospice (£1,000); and 2nd Warwick Sea
Scout Group, Animal Care Trust, Avon Riding
Centre for the Disabled, Bala Orphanage Kenya,
Brain Research UK, Brighton and Hove
Unemployed Workers Association, Médecins
Sans Frontières (UK), Miscarriage Association
and Troop Aid (£250 each).

FINANCES *Year* 2011–12 *Income* £63,464
Grants £48,260 *Assets* £1,619,118

TRUSTEES Jonathan Bosley; Mervyne Mitchell;
Katherine Willis.

HOW TO APPLY In writing to the correspondent.

WHO TO APPLY TO Jonathan Bosley, 20 Mill Street,
Shipston-on-Stour, Warwickshire CV36 4AW

■ T. and S. Trust Fund

CC NO 1095939   **ESTABLISHED** 2002
WHERE FUNDING CAN BE GIVEN Greater London, Gateshead, Manchester City.
WHO CAN BENEFIT Jewish organisations and the Jewish community.
WHAT IS FUNDED 'The advancement of education according to the tenets of the Orthodox Jewish Faith, the advancement of the Orthodox Jewish Religion and the relief of poverty amongst the elderly or persons in need, hardship and distress in the Jewish Community.'
TYPE OF GRANT One-off and recurrent.
RANGE OF GRANTS £1,000–£59,000.
SAMPLE GRANTS Orphan Children Fund; Centre for Advanced Rabbinics; New Hall Charitable Trust; Rozac Charitable Trust; Etz Chaim School; Yeshaya Adler Memorial Fund; and Tashbar.
FINANCES *Year* 2011–12 *Income* £68,326 *Grants* £74,912 *Assets* £142,548
TRUSTEES Shoshana Sandler; Ezriel Salomon.
HOW TO APPLY In writing to the correspondent.
WHO TO APPLY TO Aaron Sandler, Administrator, 96 Whitehall Road, Gateshead, Tyne And Wear NE8 4ET *Tel.* 01914 825050

■ The Tabeel Trust

CC NO 266645   **ESTABLISHED** 1974
WHERE FUNDING CAN BE GIVEN Worldwide with a preference for Clacton (Essex).
WHO CAN BENEFIT Evangelical Christian organisations.
WHAT IS FUNDED Christian charitable purposes, where the trustees have an existing interest.
RANGE OF GRANTS Up to £10,000.
SAMPLE GRANTS Scargill House Building Project (£10,000); Spacious Places (£8,000); Sorted Magazine (£5,000); Barnabas Fund (£3,000); Galeed House and Retrak – Street Children Programme in Ethiopia and Uganda (£2,000 each); and Arise and Shine Children's Home – Kenya and Evangelical Alliance (£1,000 each).
FINANCES *Year* 2011–12 *Income* £28,721 *Grants* £67,000 *Assets* £1,068,872
TRUSTEES Douglas Brown; Barbara Carter; Dr Mary Clark; Jean Richardson; James Davey; Sarah Taylor; Nigel Davey.
HOW TO APPLY Only charities with which a trustee already has contact should apply. Grants are considered at trustees' meetings in May and November.
WHO TO APPLY TO Barbara Carter, Trustee, 3 Oak Park, West Byfleet, Surrey KT14 6AG *Tel.* 01932 343808

■ The Tajtelbaum Charitable Trust

CC NO 273184   **ESTABLISHED** 1974
WHERE FUNDING CAN BE GIVEN Generally UK and Israel.
WHO CAN BENEFIT Jewish organisations benefiting children, young adults and students will be considered. Support may be given to older and sick people.
WHAT IS FUNDED Orthodox synagogues, education establishments, hospitals and homes for older people.
RANGE OF GRANTS £500–£150,000.
SAMPLE GRANTS Previous beneficiaries include: United Institutions Arad, Emuno Educational Centre, Ruzin Sadiger Trust, Gur Foundation, Before Trust, Beth Hassidei Gur, Comet Charities Limited, Delharville, Kupat Gemach Trust, Centre for Torah and Chesed, Friends of Nachlat David and Friends of Sanz Institute.
FINANCES *Year* 2011–12 *Income* £725,156 *Grants* £456,100 *Assets* £4,500,459
TRUSTEES Ilsa Tajtelbaum; Jacob Tajtelbaum; Emanuel Tajtelbaum; Eli Jaswon.
HOW TO APPLY In writing to the correspondent.
WHO TO APPLY TO Ilsa Tajtelbaum, Trustee, PO Box 33911, London NW9 7ZX

■ The Gay and Keith Talbot Trust

CC NO 1102192   **ESTABLISHED** 2004
WHERE FUNDING CAN BE GIVEN Worldwide.
WHO CAN BENEFIT Charities working in developing countries.
WHAT IS FUNDED General charitable purposes including research and development of Cystic Fibrosis, Fistula work and overseas aid.
TYPE OF GRANT One off and recurring. Capital costs, revenue costs and full project funding.
SAMPLE GRANTS CAFOD (£50,000, for water projects in Sudan); International Nepal Fellowship (£19,000, for a fistula repair camp); International Refugee Trust (£16,000, for aid in Sudan); Jesuit Missions (£10,000, to supprt torture victims in Zimbabwe); Medical Missionaries of Mary (£10,000 in total); Impact Foundation (£10,000 in total); Our Lady of Windermere and St Herbert (£500); and Amnesty International (£100).
FINANCES *Year* 2012–13 *Income* £120,211 *Grants* £115,787 *Assets* £109,590
TRUSTEES Gay Talbot; Keith Talbot.
HOW TO APPLY In writing to the correspondent.
WHO TO APPLY TO Keith Talbot, Chair, Fold Howe, Kentmere, Kendal, Cumbria LA8 9JW *Tel.* 01539 821504 *email* rktalbot@yahoo.co.uk

■ The Talbot Trusts

CC NO 221356   **ESTABLISHED** 1928
WHERE FUNDING CAN BE GIVEN Sheffield and immediate surrounding areas.
WHO CAN BENEFIT Organisations directly benefiting people who are sick, convalescent, disabled or infirm.
WHAT IS FUNDED Items, services or facilities which are calculated to relieve suffering or assist recovery.
WHAT IS NOT FUNDED No grants are given towards the direct relief of rates, taxes or other public funds and no commitment can be made to repeat or renew grants. Grants are not normally given to: non-registered charities or other organisations; individuals; appeal requests; research or educational costs; or to finance fundraising initiatives.
TYPE OF GRANT One-off, capital, core costs, running costs, salaries and start-up costs. Funding may be given for up to one year.
RANGE OF GRANTS Usually £500–£5,000
SAMPLE GRANTS Sheffield Family Service Unit (Family Action) and Happy Days (£4,000 each); Diabetes UK Sheffield Adult Branch and Listening Books (£3,000 each); Steelers Wheelchair Basketball Team and Brainwave

Think carefully about every application. Is it justified?

937

(£2,000 each); Sheffield Family Holiday Fund (£1,300); Sheffield MENCAP and Gateway and Association For Spina Bifida and Hydrocephalus (£1,000 each) and Children's Heart Foundation (£600).
FINANCES *Year* 2011–12 *Income* £85,514 *Grants* £66,631 *Assets* £2,046,994
TRUSTEES Dr Brenda Jackson; Godfrey Smallman; Dr Jeremy Wight; Ronald Jones; Jo Frisby; Tim Plant.
HOW TO APPLY On a form available from the correspondent, for consideration in July and December.
WHO TO APPLY TO Neil Charlesworth, Clerk, 11 Russett Court, Maltby, Rotherham S66 8SP *Tel.* 01709 769022

■ The Talbot Village Trust
CC NO 249349   **ESTABLISHED** 1867
WHERE FUNDING CAN BE GIVEN The boroughs of Bournemouth, Christchurch and Poole; the districts of east Dorset and Purbeck.
WHO CAN BENEFIT Community organisations (such as schools, churches, youth clubs, playgroups and so on).
WHAT IS FUNDED Youth, older people and church-related charities.
WHAT IS NOT FUNDED No grants for individuals.
TYPE OF GRANT Grants and loans. Mainly for capital costs.
RANGE OF GRANTS Up to £50,000.
SAMPLE GRANTS Strouden Park Community Association (£20,000); Richmond Hill St Andrew's United Reform Church (£15,000); Motability (£10,000); Dorset Blind Association (£7,000); Motor Neurone Disease Association East Dorset and New Forest (£4,500); and the Bus Stop Club (£1,000).
FINANCES *Year* 2012 *Income* £2,177,329 *Grants* £576,949 *Assets* £37,775,849
TRUSTEES Christopher Lees, Chair; James Fleming; Sir George Meyrick; Sir Thomas Salt; Russell Rowe; Earl of Shaftesbury.
HOW TO APPLY In writing to the correspondent.
WHO TO APPLY TO Gary S. Cox, Clerk, Dickinson Manser LLP, 5 Parkstone Road, Poole, Dorset BH15 2NL *Tel.* 01202 673071 *email* garycox@dickinsonmanser.co.uk

■ Tallow Chandlers Benevolent Fund
CC NO 246255   **ESTABLISHED** 1966
WHERE FUNDING CAN BE GIVEN London, mostly City of London.
WHO CAN BENEFIT Charitable organisations, schools and universities.
WHAT IS FUNDED Medical research, care of people with disabilities and the encouragement of excellence at schools and universities. It also helps City of London-based charities and charities where a liveryman or freeman is actively involved. Youth clubs are particularly supported.
RANGE OF GRANTS Up to £20,000.
SAMPLE GRANTS London Youth (£20,000); Bart's (£15,000); The Bridge School and St Christopher's Hospice (£10,000 each); and the Poppy Factory, St Paul's Choir School, City of London Boys, City of London Girls, Reeds School, Guildhall School Trust, Imperial College, SOAS, King Edwards (Wifley), Guildhall – Milton Court project (£5,000 each).

FINANCES *Year* 2011–12 *Income* £599,019 *Grants* £177,500 *Assets* £5,323,063
TRUSTEES C. P. Tootal; R. A. B. Nicolle; D. R. Newnham.
HOW TO APPLY In writing to the correspondent. 'Every request for assistance will be considered first by the clerk and the chair and then shortlisted for consideration by the education and charity committee.'
WHO TO APPLY TO Brig. R. M. Wilde, Clerk to the Trustees, Tallow Chandlers Hall, 4 Dowgate Hill, London EC4R 2SH *Tel.* 020 7248 4726 *email* clerk@tallowchandlers.org *Website* www.tallowchandlers.org

■ Talteg Ltd
CC NO 283253   **ESTABLISHED** 1981
WHERE FUNDING CAN BE GIVEN UK, with a preference for Scotland.
WHO CAN BENEFIT Registered charities benefiting Jewish people, children, young adults and people disadvantaged by poverty.
WHAT IS FUNDED To support the advancement of religion, especially Jewish, and the relief of poverty. Educational and other charitable purposes are also supported.
SAMPLE GRANTS Previous beneficiaries include: British Friends of Laniado Hospital, Centre for Jewish Studies, Society of Friends of the Torah, Glasgow Jewish Community Trust, National Trust for Scotland, Ayrshire Hospice, Earl Haig Fund – Scotland and RSSPCC.
FINANCES *Year* 2012 *Income* £304,447 *Grants* £203,124 *Assets* £4,081,022
TRUSTEES Fred Berkley; Adam Berkley; Delia Lynn Berkley; Maxwell Berkley.
OTHER INFORMATION A list of grants was not included in the accounts.
HOW TO APPLY In writing to the correspondent.
WHO TO APPLY TO Fred Berkley, Trustee, Gordon Chambers, 90 Mitchell Street, Glasgow G1 3NQ *Tel.* 01412 213353

■ The Tangent Charitable Trust
CC NO 289729   **ESTABLISHED** 1984
WHERE FUNDING CAN BE GIVEN UK.
WHO CAN BENEFIT Registered charities and voluntary organisations.
WHAT IS FUNDED General charitable purposes.
RANGE OF GRANTS £1,000–£15,000.
SAMPLE GRANTS JAMI (£15,000); UCS Centennial Trust (£10,000); Great Ormond Street Hospital Children's Charity; Parochial Church Council of Easton Grey for 2008; and for 2009; Marwar Foundation – Indian Head Injury Foundation (£2,000); The President's Club Charity Trust (£1,300); United Synagogue (£1,100); Wellbeing of Women; Jewish Community Centre for London (£1,000 each).
FINANCES *Year* 2011–12 *Income* £50,020 *Grants* £33,000
TRUSTEES Michael Green; Tessa Green; Rebecca Marks; Catherine Robinson.
HOW TO APPLY In writing to the correspondent.
WHO TO APPLY TO Beverley Matthews, 21 South Street, London W1K 2XB *Tel.* 020 7663 6402

■ The Lady Tangye Charitable Trust

CC NO 1044220   ESTABLISHED 1995

WHERE FUNDING CAN BE GIVEN UK and worldwide, with some preference for the Midlands.

WHO CAN BENEFIT Charitable organisations, with a preference for work in the Midlands or developing world.

WHAT IS FUNDED General charitable purposes, with Christian and environmental causes are well-represented in the grants list.

SAMPLE GRANTS Previous beneficiaries have included: West Midland Urban Wildlife Trust (£3,000); Spana, ChildLine – Midlands and Aid to the Church in Need (£2,000 each); Amnesty International, Priest Training Fund and Crew Trust (£1,500 each); St Saviour's Church, Walsall and District Samaritans, Life and European Children's Trust (£1,000 each); and Charity Ignite – Big Ideal (£500).

FINANCES Year 2011–12 *Income* £29,815 *Grants* £33,500 *Assets* £946,547

TRUSTEES Gitta Clarisse Gilzean Tangye; Colin Ferguson Smith.

OTHER INFORMATION The schedule to the accounts, detailing grant beneficiaries, was not published on the Commission's website.

HOW TO APPLY In writing to the correspondent.

WHO TO APPLY TO Colin Ferguson Smith, Trustee, 55 Warwick Crest, Arthur Road, Birmingham B15 2LH *Tel.* 01214 544698

■ The David Tannen Charitable Trust

CC NO 280392   ESTABLISHED 1974

WHERE FUNDING CAN BE GIVEN UK and Israel.

WHO CAN BENEFIT Jewish organisations.

WHAT IS FUNDED Relief of poverty, education and the advancement of the Jewish religion.

RANGE OF GRANTS About £1,000–£100,000.

SAMPLE GRANTS Previous beneficiaries included: Cosmon Beiz Academy, Gevurath Ari Trust, Telz Academy Trust, Friends of Ohr Elchonon, Beis Ahron Trust, Wlodowa Charity, Chai Cancer Care, Kollel Skver Trust, Centre for Torah Trust, Gateshead Talmudical College, Jewish Women's Aid Trust, Torah 5759 Ltd and YTAF.

FINANCES Year 2011–12 *Income* £1,179,616 *Grants* £221,830 *Assets* £22,460,413

TRUSTEES Jonathan Miller; Alan Rose; David Tannen.

OTHER INFORMATION A list of beneficiaries was not included in the trust's accounts.

HOW TO APPLY In writing to the correspondent.

WHO TO APPLY TO Jonathan Miller, c/o Sutherland House, 70–78 West Hendon Broadway, London NW9 7BT *Tel.* 020 8202 1066

■ The Tanner Trust

CC NO 1021175   ESTABLISHED 1993

WHERE FUNDING CAN BE GIVEN UK, with a slight preference for the South of England, and overseas.

WHO CAN BENEFIT Foundations, schools, societies, charities and projects.

WHAT IS FUNDED General charitable purposes.

WHAT IS NOT FUNDED No grants to individuals.

RANGE OF GRANTS Up to £15,000.

SAMPLE GRANTS Homeopathic Action Trust (£12,000); Addington Fund (£10,000); National Trust (£7,000); Woodland Trust (£6,000); UNICEF and Phoenix Stroke Appeal (£5,000

each); Seeds for Africa and Sense (£4,000 each); Sheffield Industrial Museum Trust (£2,000) and Royal Hospital for Neuro Disability (£1,500).

FINANCES Year 2011–12 *Income* £461,736 *Grants* £396,766 *Assets* £5,409,147

TRUSTEES Alice P. Williams; Lucie Nottingham.

HOW TO APPLY The trust states that unsolicited applications are, without exception, not considered. Support is only given to charities personally known to the trustees.

WHO TO APPLY TO Celine Lecomte, Trust Administrator, Blake Lapthorn, Harbour Court, Compass Road, Portsmouth PO6 4ST *Tel* 023 9222 1122 ext. 552

■ The Lili Tapper Charitable Foundation

CC NO 268523   ESTABLISHED 1974

WHERE FUNDING CAN BE GIVEN UK.

WHO CAN BENEFIT Organisations benefiting Jewish people.

WHAT IS FUNDED Preference to charitable purposes or institutions which are for the benefit of Jewish people.

WHAT IS NOT FUNDED No grants to individuals.

SAMPLE GRANTS Previous beneficiaries include: UJIA, CST, Manchester Jewish Foundation, Teenage Cancer Trust, Keshet Eilon, Israel Educational Foundation, Chicken Shed Theatre Company and Jewish Representation Council.

FINANCES Year 2011–12 *Income* £38,998 *Grants* £79,145 *Assets* £3,128,352

TRUSTEES Michael Webber; Dr Jonathan Webber.

OTHER INFORMATION No details of grant beneficiaries were available for 2011–12.

HOW TO APPLY The trust states that it does not respond to any unsolicited applications.

WHO TO APPLY TO Michael Webber, Trustee, Yew Tree Cottage, Artists Lane, Nether Alderley, Macclesfield SK10 4UA *Tel.* 01625 582320

■ The Mrs A. Lacy Tate Trust

CC NO 803596   ESTABLISHED 1990

WHERE FUNDING CAN BE GIVEN East Sussex.

WHO CAN BENEFIT Individuals and organisations benefiting at risk groups and people who are disabled, disadvantaged by poverty or socially isolated.

WHAT IS FUNDED Welfare, disability and medical charities.

TYPE OF GRANT Often recurrent.

RANGE OF GRANTS £250–£2,000.

SAMPLE GRANTS Fellowship of St Nicholas, Salvation Army Hastings Project and Pett Level Rescue Boat Association (£2,000 each); Public Playing Fields and Recreational Grounds, Sedlescombe (£1,500); Seaview Project (£1,000); Seaford Young Musicians/Seaford Rock and Jazz Orchestra (£700); Jump Trampoline Club (£600); Brighton Unemployed Centre Families Project, Expedition Training Courses for Volunteers and Autism Sussex Ltd (£500 each) and Brighton and Hove Parents and Children's Group and Age Concern Brighton Hove Portslade (£250 each).

FINANCES Year 2011–12 *Income* £53,260 *Grants* £46,115 *Assets* £154,799

TRUSTEES Linda Burgess; Lesley Macey; Ian Stewart; June Roberts.

OTHER INFORMATION Grants to organisations totalled £28,000. Grants to 73 individuals totalled £18,000.

HOW TO APPLY In writing to the correspondent.
WHO TO APPLY TO Ian Stewart, c/o Heringtons
Solicitors, 39 Gildredge Road, Eastbourne, East
Sussex BN21 4RY *Tel.* 01323 411020

■ The Taurus Foundation

CC NO 1128441   **ESTABLISHED** 2009
WHERE FUNDING CAN BE GIVEN UK
WHO CAN BENEFIT Registered charities.
WHAT IS FUNDED General charitable purposes.
RANGE OF GRANTS Up to £10,000.
SAMPLE GRANTS The Purcell School (£28,000);
Concordia Foundation, Jewish Care, Just for
Kids Law and Norwood Ravenswood (£10,000
each); Core Arts, Hillside Clubhouse and Magic
Me (£5,000 each); and Royal Opera House
(£2,500).
FINANCES *Year* 2011–12 *Income* £144,084
Grants £106,010 *Assets* £909,410
TRUSTEES Denis Felsenstein; Michael Jacobs; Alan
Fenton; Anthony Forwood; Priscilla Fenton;
Wendy Pollecoff; Carole Cook.
HOW TO APPLY No grants to unsolicited applications.
WHO TO APPLY TO Carole Cook, Trustee, Forsters
LLP, 31 Hill Street, London W1J 5LS *Tel.* 020
7863 8333 *email* carole.cook@forsters.co.uk

■ The Tay Charitable Trust

SC NO SC001004   **ESTABLISHED** 1951
WHERE FUNDING CAN BE GIVEN UK, with a preference
for Scotland, particularly Dundee.
WHO CAN BENEFIT Registered charities.
WHAT IS FUNDED General charitable purposes.
WHAT IS NOT FUNDED Grants are only given to
registered charities. No grants to individuals.
TYPE OF GRANT One-off and recurring.
RANGE OF GRANTS Up to £5,000.
SAMPLE GRANTS Beneficiaries of grants of £1,000 or
more included: V&A at Dundee (£10,000);
University of Dundee and Ninewells Cancer
Campaign (£5,000 each); Cerebral Palsy Africa
(£3,000); Factory Skatepark, John Muir Trust
and National Trust for Scotland (£2,000 each);
St Giles' Cathedral, Trees for Life, Victim
Support Dundee, Changing Faces and Dundee
Science Centre (£1,000 each). 131
organisations received a grant of less than
£1,000.
FINANCES *Year* 2011–12 *Income* £209,029
Grants £224,950 *Assets* £5,541,267
HOW TO APPLY No standard form; applications in
writing to the correspondent, including a
financial statement. 'The trustees regret to say
they now do not notify applicants who have not
succeeded due to the cost of postage.'
WHO TO APPLY TO E. A. Mussen, Trustee, 6 Douglas
Terrace, Broughty Ferry, Dundee DD5 1EA

■ C. B. and H. H. Taylor 1984 Trust

CC NO 291363   **ESTABLISHED** 1946
WHERE FUNDING CAN BE GIVEN West Midlands, Ireland
and overseas.
WHO CAN BENEFIT Approximately 60% of funds
available are currently given to the work and
concerns of the Religious Society of Friends.
The remaining funds are allocated to those
charities in which the trustees have a special
interest, particularly in the West Midlands.
Applications are encouraged from minority
groups and woman-led initiatives.
WHAT IS FUNDED The general areas of benefit are:
(i) The Religious Society of Friends (Quakers)

and other religious denominations.
(ii) Healthcare projects. (iii) Social welfare:
community groups; children and young people;
older people; disadvantaged people; people with
disabilities; homeless people; housing
initiatives; counselling and mediation agencies.
(iv) Education: adult literacy schemes;
employment training; youth work. (v) Penal
affairs: work with offenders and ex-offenders;
police projects. (vi) The environment and
conservation work. (vii) The arts: museums and
art galleries; music and drama. (viii) Ireland:
cross-community health and social welfare
projects. (ix) UK charities working overseas on
long-term development projects.
WHAT IS NOT FUNDED The trust does not fund:
individuals (whether for research, expeditions,
educational purposes and so on); local projects
or groups outside the West Midlands; or
projects concerned with travel or adventure.
Applications form UK registered charities only.
TYPE OF GRANT One-off and sometimes three year
long reccurent.
RANGE OF GRANTS Mainly £500–£2,000.
SAMPLE GRANTS Britain Yearly Meeting (£37,500);
Oxfam East Africa (£8,000); Quaker Social
Action (£7,500); Cape Town Quaker Peace
Centre (£6,000); Ulster Quaker Service
Committee (£7,000); Samaritans Birmingham
(£4,000); Birmingham Association of Youth
Clubs (£3,000); Freedom from Torture and
Medical Aid for Palestinians (£2,000 each); and
Construction Youth Trust, Birmingham Royal
Ballet, Cerebral Palsy Birmingham and the
International Childcare Trust (£1,000 each).
FINANCES *Year* 2011–12 *Income* £341,150
Grants £282,250 *Assets* £9,935,395
TRUSTEES Constance Penny; Elizabeth Birmingham;
Clare Norton; John Taylor; Thomas Penny;
Robert Birmingham; Simon Taylor.
HOW TO APPLY There is no formal application form.
Applicants should write to the correspondent
giving the charity's registration number, a brief
description of the charity's activities, and details
of the specific project for which the grant is
being sought. Applicants should also include a
budget of the proposed work, together with a
copy of the charity's most recent accounts.
Trustees will also wish to know what funds have
already been raised for the project and how the
shortfall will be met. The trust states that it
receives more applications than it can support.
Therefore, even if work falls within its policy it
may not be able to help, particularly if the
project is outside the West Midlands.
Applications should be submitted at least six
weeks in advance of the trustees' meeting.
Trustees meet twice each year, in May and
November. Applications will be acknowledged if
an sae is provided.
WHO TO APPLY TO Clare Norton, Trustee,
266 Malvern Road, Worcester WR2 4PA
Tel. 01905 412434 *email* claregn@talktalk.net

■ The Cyril Taylor Charitable Trust

CC NO 1040179   **ESTABLISHED** 1994
WHERE FUNDING CAN BE GIVEN Generally in Greater
London.
WHO CAN BENEFIT Organisations benefiting students.
WHAT IS FUNDED General charitable purposes; to
advance the education of the students of
Richmond College and the American
International University in London.
FINANCES *Year* 2011–12 *Income* £188,160
Grants £199,740 *Assets* £199,740

TRUSTEES Sir Cyril Taylor, Chair; Clifford D. Joseph; Robert W. Maas; Peter A. Tchereprine; Stephen Rasch; Christopher Lintott; Lady June Taylor; Michael Berry; William Gertz; Jack Burg; Thomas Kiechle.

HOW TO APPLY In writing to the correspondent.

WHO TO APPLY TO Christopher Lintott, Trustee, Penningtons, Abacus House, 33 Gutter Lane, London EC2V 8AR *Tel.* 020 7457 3000 *Fax* 020 7457 3240 *email* chris.lintott@ penningtons.co.uk

....
■ Humphrey Richardson Taylor Charitable Trust

CC NO 1062836 ESTABLISHED 1997

WHERE FUNDING CAN BE GIVEN Surrey and South London Boroughs.

WHO CAN BENEFIT State schools, choirs, amateur orchestras and individuals.

'The advancement of public education in and appreciation of the art and science of music and allied performing arts. The Trust's aims are to encourage and support music education at state primary, secondary and tertiary levels and to seek the continuing performance of live music in society, particularly by amateur performers.'

WHAT IS FUNDED Tuition fees, purchasing of instruments, music building-projects and grants to musical societies.

WHAT IS NOT FUNDED Projects or causes that are not associated with music.

RANGE OF GRANTS £250–£45,000

SAMPLE GRANTS Guildford Country School (£45,000); Winston Churchill School (£28,000); Sutton Music Service (£20,000); Royal College of Music (£19,000); University of Surrey (£18,000); Marden Lodge Primary (£10,000); Southbank Sinfonia (£7,000); Croydon Music and Arts (£6,000); Arthur Davison Family Concerts (£5,500); Croydon Symphony Orchestra (£5,000); London Mozart Players (£3,000); Riverside Opera (£2,000) and Amy Johnson Primary (£400).

FINANCES *Year* 2012 *Income* £459,959 *Grants* £390,227 *Assets* £11,193,976

TRUSTEES William Malings; Rowena Cox; Colin Edgerton; Ian Catling; Michael Wood; Stephen Oliver.

OTHER INFORMATION Grants were made in the following categories: Capital Projects (£43,000); Concerts (£65,000); Tuition Fees and Bursaries (£120,000) and Instrument and Equipment Purchases (£161,000). Grants were made to individuals totalling £1,000.

HOW TO APPLY In writing to the correspondent. Criteria and guidelines for schools, musical societies and individuals are available to view on the website.

WHO TO APPLY TO B. M. Bennett, Administrator, c/o Palmers, 28 Chipstead Station Parade, Chipstead, Coulsdon, Surrey CR5 3TF *Tel.* 01737 557546 *Fax* 01737 554093 *email* hrtaylortrust@btconnect.com *Website* www.hrtaylortrust.org.uk

....
■ The Connie and Albert Taylor Charitable Trust

CC NO 1074785 ESTABLISHED 1998

WHERE FUNDING CAN BE GIVEN West Midlands.

WHO CAN BENEFIT Organisations concerned with medical research, hospices, education and recreation, and preservation.

WHAT IS FUNDED Research into the cure and causes of cancer, blindness and heart disease; provision and maintenance of nursing homes for people who are elderly or unable to look after themselves; provision of maintenance of hospices for people with terminal illnesses; facilities for the education and recreation of children and young people; the preservation, protection and improvements of any amenity or land of beauty, scientific or of horticultural interest and any building of historical, architectural or artistic or scientific interest.

RANGE OF GRANTS Up to £100,000.

SAMPLE GRANTS St Vincent's and St George's (£75,000); Donna Louise Children's Hospice (£40,000); Williams Syndrome Foundation (£30,000); Cure Leukaemia (£20,000); Norman Laud Association and the Black Country Museum (£15,000 each); Birmingham Royal Ballet (£10,000); and the Royal Wolverhampton Hospital (£2,000).

FINANCES *Year* 2012 *Income* £140,828 *Grants* £448,400 *Assets* £4,682,470

TRUSTEES Alan Foster; Harry Grundy; Richard D. Long.

HOW TO APPLY In writing to the correspondent, the trustees prefer to receive applications via email. The trust may visit applicants/beneficiaries. The trust's annual report has the following information:

'The trustees normally meet quarterly to consider what grants they will make and to review any feedback they have received. Where possible they attempt to arrange these meetings to coincide with visits to organisations for which substantial donations are being considered. Nominations for grants are actively sought through the charity's website and from other sources. In all cases the trustees ask organisations to submit a formal application for specific projects. Decisions as to whether to make donations are made by all three trustees. Follow-up visits and feedback received are used to monitor the quality of grants made. No applications from individuals are considered. The trustees have been long-term supporters of certain projects. However, no ongoing pledge is for longer than three years, although a pledge may occasionally be extended.'

WHO TO APPLY TO Harry Grundy, Trustee, The Farmhouse, Darwin Park, Abnalls Lane, Lichfield, Staffordshire WS13 8BJ *email* applications@ taylortrust.co.uk *Website* www.taylortrust.co.uk

....
■ The Taylor Family Foundation

CC NO 1118032 ESTABLISHED 2007

WHERE FUNDING CAN BE GIVEN UK and overseas, with a preference for London and the south east.

WHO CAN BENEFIT Children and young people. 'The objectives of the Taylor Family Foundation are to help and support children and young people, particularly those from disadvantaged backgrounds, in the areas of education, health, recreation and the performing arts.'

WHAT IS FUNDED Registered charities and statutory bodies.

WHAT IS NOT FUNDED No grants to individuals.

TYPE OF GRANT One off grants and recurring grants. No grants to individuals.

RANGE OF GRANTS £500–£60,000

SAMPLE GRANTS A generous grant of (£450,000) to Royal Opera House Foundation and International Inspiration Foundation UNICEF received (£333,000). Other beneficiaries include Merton College Oxford (£50,000); Straight Talking (£24,000); Build Africa (£23,000); Rainbow House Trust (£20,000); Beat Bullying

Think carefully about every application. Is it justified?

....
941

(£15,000); Home Start Merlon (£15,500); Special Boat Services (£5,000) and Daisy Garland (£800).

FINANCES *Year* 2011–12 *Income* £1,250,309 *Grants* £1,476,569 *Assets* £399,372

TRUSTEES Ian R. Taylor; Cristina A. Taylor; Neville P. Shepherd.

OTHER INFORMATION Grants were given to 34 organisations totalling £1,500,000.

HOW TO APPLY In writing to the correspondent. The trust welcomes written applications and invites charities and relevant organisations to contact them with their report of activities and a copy of their accounts.

WHO TO APPLY TO Neville Shepherd, Trustee, Hill Place House, 55a High Street, Wimbledon, London SW19 5BA *Tel.* 020 8605 2622 *email* info@thetaylorfamilyfoundation.co.uk *Website* www.thetaylorfamilyfoundation.co.uk

■ A. P. Taylor Trust

CC NO 260741   **ESTABLISHED** 1969

WHERE FUNDING CAN BE GIVEN The parishes of Hayes and Harlington (as they existed on 9 January 1953).

WHO CAN BENEFIT Charitable organisations.

WHAT IS FUNDED The provision of recreational and leisure activities.

RANGE OF GRANTS The majority of grants are for £500 or less.

SAMPLE GRANTS Previous beneficiaries have included: Harlington Locomotive Society, Hillingdon Table Tennis Club, Station Road Allotment Society, Broughton Pensioners, Immaculate Heart of Mary Senior Citizens' Club, Westcombe Lodge Club, Hayes Town Women's Institute and Royal British Legion Women's Section.

FINANCES *Year* 2011–12 *Income* £82,018 *Grants* £50,000 *Assets* £1,224,999

TRUSTEES Timothy McCarthy; Sean Fitzpatrick; Peter Chidwick; Alan Woodhouse.

OTHER INFORMATION Grants were made to 81 organisations totalling £50,000.

HOW TO APPLY In writing to the correspondent.

WHO TO APPLY TO Sean Fitzpatrick, Homeleigh, 68 Vine Lane, Hillingdon, Middlesex UB10 0BD *Tel.* 01895 812811 *email* enquiries@ aptaylortrust.org.uk *Website* www.aptaylortrust. org.uk

■ Rosanna Taylor's 1987 Charity Trust

CC NO 297210   **ESTABLISHED** 1987

WHERE FUNDING CAN BE GIVEN UK and overseas, with a preference for Oxfordshire and West Sussex.

WHO CAN BENEFIT Registered charities only.

WHAT IS FUNDED General charitable purposes, including support for medical, cancer, children's development and environmental charities.

WHAT IS NOT FUNDED No grants to individuals or non-registered charities.

RANGE OF GRANTS £500–£24,000.

SAMPLE GRANTS Previous beneficiaries include: Charities Aid Foundation (£24,000); Pearson Taylor Trust (£10,000); Disaster Emergencies Committee – Haiti Appeal (£5,000); and Resonance FM (£500).

FINANCES *Year* 2011–12 *Income* £11,349 *Grants* £56,404

TRUSTEE The Cowdray Trust Limited.

OTHER INFORMATION 2011–12 accounts had been received at the Charity Commission but were unavailable to view.

HOW TO APPLY In writing to the correspondent. Acknowledgements are not sent to unsuccessful applicants.

WHO TO APPLY TO Laura Gosling, Trust Administrator, 4th Floor, Swan House, 17–19 Stratford Place, London W1C 1BQ *Tel.* 020 7907 2100 *email* charity@mfs.co.uk

■ Tearfund

CC NO 265464   **ESTABLISHED** 1968

WHERE FUNDING CAN BE GIVEN Worldwide, but mainly in developing countries.

WHO CAN BENEFIT Evangelical Christian organisations which benefit at risk groups; people who are disabled, disadvantaged by poverty or socially isolated; and victims of famine, man-made or natural disasters, and war.

WHAT IS FUNDED Evangelical Christian ministry to meet all needs – physical, mental, social and spiritual. Funding is given to partner organisations only.

TYPE OF GRANT Project/partner.

RANGE OF GRANTS Smallest £1,000; typical £15,000.

FINANCES *Year* 2012–13 *Income* £60,046,000 *Grants* £21,912,000 *Assets* £27,563,000

TRUSTEES Deepak Mahtani; David Andrew Thompson Todd; Simon Laver; Robert Camp; H. C. Mather; Craig Rowland; Jillian Garner; Julia Caroline Ogilvy; Revd Mark Melluish; David Campanale; Jenny Baker; Stephanie Heald.

PUBLICATIONS Tear Times.

HOW TO APPLY The trust works only with selected partner organisations and therefore they do not accept unsolicited requests or approaches.

WHO TO APPLY TO Andrew Slatter, Secretary, 100 Church Road, Teddington, Middlesex TW11 8QE *Tel.* 020 8943 7795 *email* enquiry@tearfund.org *Website* www. tearfund.org

■ The Tedworth Charitable Trust

CC NO 328524   **ESTABLISHED** 1990

WHERE FUNDING CAN BE GIVEN Unrestricted, but UK in practice.

WHO CAN BENEFIT Registered charities.

WHAT IS FUNDED Parenting, family welfare and child development; environment and the arts; general.

WHAT IS NOT FUNDED Grants are not normally made to individuals.

TYPE OF GRANT One-off and core costs.

RANGE OF GRANTS Up to £60,000.

SAMPLE GRANTS Resurgence (£60,000); Home-Start (£40,000); Open Trust (£37,000); Foundation for Democracy and Sustainable Development (£35,000); Best Beginnings (£25,000); Family Links (£20,000); Women's Environmental Network (£12,500); and Vocal Futures (£9,000).

FINANCES *Year* 2011–12 *Income* £416,428 *Grants* £416,092 *Assets* £10,534,365

TRUSTEES Margaret Sainsbury; Jessica M. Sainsbury; Timothy J. Sainsbury; Judith S. Portrait.

OTHER INFORMATION The trust is one of the Sainsbury Family Charitable Trusts which share a common administration. An application to one is taken as an application to all.

HOW TO APPLY 'Proposals are likely to be invited by the trustees or initiated at their request. Unsolicited applications are unlikely to be successful, even if they fall within an area in which the trustees are interested.' A single application will be considered for support by all the trusts in the Sainsbury family group.

WHO TO APPLY TO Alan Bookbinder, Director, The Peak, 5 Wilton Road, London SW1V 1AP *Tel.* 020 7410 0330 *Fax* 020 7410 0332 *Website* www.sfct.org.uk

■ Tees Valley Community Foundation

CC NO 1111222   **ESTABLISHED** 1988
WHERE FUNDING CAN BE GIVEN The former county of Cleveland, being the local authority areas of Hartlepool, Middlesbrough, Redcar and Cleveland and Stockton-On-Tees.
WHO CAN BENEFIT Registered charities and constituted community groups.
WHAT IS FUNDED General charitable purposes. The foundation makes grants from various different funds, each with its own criteria.
WHAT IS NOT FUNDED No grants for: major fundraising appeals; sponsored events; promotion of religion; retrospective funding; holidays or social outings; existing operating costs, e.g. salaries, rent, overheads; groups with excessive unrestricted or free reserves; groups in serious deficit; replacement of statutory funding; meeting any need which is the responsibility of central or local government; religious or political causes; fabric appeals; or animal welfare. Each fund has separate exclusions which are available on the foundation's website.
TYPE OF GRANT Capital or revenue.
RANGE OF GRANTS Mostly under £12,000.
FINANCES *Year* 2011–12 *Income* £906,843 *Grants* £806,640 *Assets* £11,043,842
TRUSTEES Chris Hope, Chair; Brian Beaumont; Rosemary Young; Marjory Houseman; Neil Kenley; Alan Kitching; Keith Robinson; Peter Rowley; Wendy Shepherd; Jeff Taylor; Keith Smith; Eileen Martin.
PUBLICATIONS Periodic newsletter.
OTHER INFORMATION As with all community foundations grant schemes change frequently. Contact the foundation or check their website for details of current programmes and their deadlines.
HOW TO APPLY Application forms are available on the foundation's website. Applicants can received a maximum of £5,000 in any 12 month period from one or a combination of funds.
WHO TO APPLY TO Hugh McGouran, Wallace House, Fallon Court, Preston Farm Industrial Estate, Stockton-on-Tees TS18 3TX *Tel.* 01642 260860 *Fax* 01642 313700 *email* info@ teesvalleyfoundation.org *Website* www. teesvalleyfoundation.org

■ Tegham Limited

CC NO 283066   **ESTABLISHED** 1981
WHERE FUNDING CAN BE GIVEN Barnet and Israel.
WHO CAN BENEFIT Registered charities.
WHAT IS FUNDED Jewish Orthodox faith and the relief of poverty.
FINANCES *Year* 2011–12 *Income* £350,199 *Grants* £37,265 *Assets* £1,923,055
TRUSTEES Nizza Fluss; Daniel Fluss.
OTHER INFORMATION No details of beneficiaries were included in the accounts.
HOW TO APPLY The trust has stated that it has enough causes to support and does not welcome other applications.

WHO TO APPLY TO Nizza Fluss, Trustee, c/o Gerald Kreditor and Co, Hallswelle House, 1 Hallswelle Road, London NW11 0DH *email* admin@ geraldkreditor.co.uk

■ The Templeton Goodwill Trust

SC NO SC004177   **ESTABLISHED** 1938
WHERE FUNDING CAN BE GIVEN Glasgow and the West of Scotland (the Glasgow postal area).
WHO CAN BENEFIT Scottish registered charities.
WHAT IS FUNDED General charitable purposes. It is interested in supporting organisations which help others. Types of beneficiaries include: youth organisations, medical research charities, churches, ex-services' organisations and other organisations concerned with social work and providing caring services for all age groups.
WHAT IS NOT FUNDED Support is given to Scottish registered charities only. Individuals are not supported and grants are generally not given to arts or cultural organisations.
TYPE OF GRANT Discretionary, both continuing annual sums and 'one-off' support grants.
RANGE OF GRANTS £450–£4,600.
SAMPLE GRANTS Previous beneficiaries include: Girl Guides Association (£6,500); SSAFA (£4,200); Salvation Army, Scout Association (£4,000 each); Scottish Furniture Trades Benevolent Association (£3,300); Cancer Research UK and Marie Curie Memorial Foundation (£2,800 each); Tenovus Scotland (£2,500); Scottish Bible Society (£1,900); Dyslexia Scotwest (£1,000); The Fishermen's Mission (£700); and Diabetes UK Scotland (£500).
FINANCES *Year* 2012–13 *Income* £208,319 *Grants* £100,000
TRUSTEES J. H. Millar, Chair; B. Bannerman; W. T. P. Barnstaple; C. Barrowman.
HOW TO APPLY In writing to the correspondent, preferably including a copy of accounts. Applications should be received by April as the trustees meet once a year, at the end of April or in May. Initial telephone calls are welcome. An sae is required from applicants to receive a reply.
WHO TO APPLY TO W. T. P. Barnstaple, Trustee and Administrator, 12 Doon Street, Motherwell ML1 2BN *Tel.* 01698 262202

■ The Ten Ten Charitable Trust

CC NO 1149206   **ESTABLISHED** 2012
WHERE FUNDING CAN BE GIVEN UK.
WHO CAN BENEFIT Charities, community group, schools and prisons.
WHAT IS FUNDED General charitable purposes, education and performing arts, with a preference for organisations working with children and young people, including young offenders, and older people.
TRUSTEES Martin O'Brien; Anna O'Brien; Clare O'Brien.
HOW TO APPLY In writing to the correspondent.
WHO TO APPLY TO Martin O'Brien, Trustee, 109 Nether Street, London N12 8AB

■ The Tennis Foundation

CC NO 298175   **ESTABLISHED** 1987
WHERE FUNDING CAN BE GIVEN UK.
WHO CAN BENEFIT County and local authority organisations, clubs and schools and individuals, with a particular interest in young

people, older people and people with a disability.

WHAT IS FUNDED The foundation promotes participation in tennis. It categorises its activities as: Junior development (including development and support) and places to play (including community and local authority sites); Tennis development (including supporting the field team, national associations, county associations and clubs); Coaching; Education (including schools, colleges, universities and further education colleges); Competitions and Tennis for disabled people which incorporates a performance and development programme for disabled people.

TYPE OF GRANT Capital and revenue grants.

SAMPLE GRANTS Beneficiaries include: Tennis Scotland (£325,000) and Win Tennis (£300,000). Previous beneficiaries include: Advanced Apprenticeship in Sporting Excellence (£443,000); Win Tennis – High performance centre funding (£300,000); Tennis Scotland (£343,000); Give it Your Max (£36,000) and Clissold Park Development Fund (£10,000).

FINANCES *Year* 2011–12 *Income* £17,309,000 *Grants* £5,630,000 *Assets* £8,016,000

TRUSTEES Jonathan Lane; Sir Geoffrey Cass; Catherine Sabin; Victor Farrow; Charles Trippe; Anthony Lemons; Funke Awoderu; Mathew Stocks; Ian Hewitt; Paul Zanon; Jeffrey Hunter; Nick Basing; Dame Tessa Jowell; Baroness Margaret Ford; Baroness Tanni Grey-Thompson.

HOW TO APPLY Initial enquiries should be made by telephone.

WHO TO APPLY TO Joanna Farquharson, Secretary, National Tennis Centre, 100 Priory Lane, London SW15 5JQ *Tel.* 0845 872 0522 *email* info@tennisfoundation.org.uk *Website* www.tennisfoundation.org.uk

....

■ Tesco Charity Trust

CC NO 297126   **ESTABLISHED** 1987
WHERE FUNDING CAN BE GIVEN Worldwide.

WHO CAN BENEFIT National and local charity appeals benefiting children's welfare and education, older people and people with disabilities.

WHAT IS FUNDED Main areas of interest are: local charities promoting welfare and education of children, people who are elderly and people who are disabled.

WHAT IS NOT FUNDED No grants to political organisations, individuals or towards new buildings. The trust will not make donations to other trusts or charities for onward transmission to other charitable organisations.

TYPE OF GRANT Generally one-off, or for one year or less.

RANGE OF GRANTS Up to £2.2 million

SAMPLE GRANTS Alzheimer's Society (£2.2 million); CLIC Sargent (£984,000); Disabilities and Health (£386,000); Children/ Youth (£292,000); British Red Cross (£100,000); British ORT (£47,000); Caravan (£45,000); Restless Development (£31,000); Action Medical Research (£30,000); Barking Badgers (£2,000); Muscular Dystrophy Campaign (£2,000).

FINANCES *Year* 2011–12 *Income* £6,939,000 *Grants* £5,300,000 *Assets* £2,900,000

TRUSTEES Lucy Neville-Rolfe; Paul Smythe; Paul Dickens; Juliet Crisp; Christophe Roussel; R. Sheely; D. North.

HOW TO APPLY Community Awards Scheme: Applications should be made via the charity's website. There are two categories of Community Awards: '1. Grants to support children's welfare

and/or children's educations (including special needs schools); 2. Grants to support elderly people and/or adults and children with disabilities. There are two rounds of funding every year for each category, see the timescales below. Applications made outside the timescales for your category cannot be accepted. Decisions will not be finalised for approximately three months after the closing date of each round. Consider this when completing your application. Grants for children's education and children's welfare: applications should be made between 1 December and 31 January or 1 May and 30 June. Grants for older people and adults and children with disabilities: applications should be made between: 1 February and 31 March or 1 August and 30 September. Note that charities can only make one application per year. **Larger Grants (Trust Meeting Grant):** A certain amount of budget is available at each Tesco Charity Trust meeting. However the number of donation requests we receive always exceeds the funds available. Therefore some good applications, while meeting our criteria, may have to be refused. To apply for a trust meeting grant and for information on deadlines for applying, email: michelina.filocco@uk.tesco.com with details of your project. If your project fits within our criteria we will send you an application form.'

WHO TO APPLY TO Dame Lucy Neville-Rolfe, Chair, Tesco House, Delamare Road, Cheshunt, Hertfordshire EN8 9SL *Tel.* 01992 806973 *email* charity.enquiries@uk.tesco.com *Website* www.tescoplc.com/tescocharitytrust

....

■ The C. Paul Thackray General Charitable Trust

CC NO 328650   **ESTABLISHED** 1990
WHERE FUNDING CAN BE GIVEN Worcestershire, South Shropshire, Herefordshire. Developing countries.

WHO CAN BENEFIT Organisations benefiting people with special needs, people from developing countries, and sick people.

WHAT IS FUNDED The trustees' areas of interest in Worcestershire, South Shropshire and Herefordshire are the care, rehabilitation and education of those with special needs, complementary medicine and the protection of the local environment. International interests lie in training and technology for developing countries, simple medical assistance of mass benefit, the protection of human rights, ecology and conservation.

WHAT IS NOT FUNDED Grants are not made for disaster appeals, appeals for medical or educational equipment, charities for domestic pets, politics, religion, the arts and heritage, unregistered charities and individuals.

RANGE OF GRANTS £400–£19,000.

SAMPLE GRANTS The Paul Thackray Heritage Foundation (£12,000); Victory Outreach (£3,300); Marie Curie Cancer Care and Checkpoint Christian Youth Trust (£1,600 each); Friends of the Earth Trust, Help for Heroes and Hearing Dogs for Deaf People (£1,100); Kids Company (£800); Shelter and Medical Foundation (£650 each); Maggs Day Centre and The Howard League for Penal Reform (£550 each) and British Blind Sport, Family Education Trust and Durrell Wildlife Conservation Trust (£300 each).

FINANCES *Year* 2010–11 *Income* £32,962 *Grants* £46,600 *Assets* £1,038,719

TRUSTEES Matthew Wrigley; Paul Thackray; Louise Thackray; Celia Adams; Polly Roberts.

OTHER INFORMATION Grants were made to 50 organisations totalling £47,000.

HOW TO APPLY In writing to the correspondent. The trustees meet on an annual basis to consider applications for grants.

WHO TO APPLY TO Matthew Wrigley, Trustee, 19 Cookridge Street, Leeds LS2 3AG *Tel.* 01132 446100

■ Thackray Medical Research Trust

CC NO 702896   **ESTABLISHED** 1990

WHERE FUNDING CAN BE GIVEN Worldwide.

WHO CAN BENEFIT Charitable organisations, university departments and individual researchers.

WHAT IS FUNDED Provision of medical supplies to the developing world and research into the history of medical procedures and products.

TYPE OF GRANT 'Pump-priming', start-up or organisational expenses where alternative funding is not available for medical supply organisations.

SAMPLE GRANTS Thackray Museum (£156,500); Worldshare (£5,000).

FINANCES *Year* 2012–13 *Income* £237,873 *Grants* £161,500 *Assets* £6,518,489

TRUSTEES William Kendall Mathie; Matthew Wrigley; Martin Schweiger; Christin Thackray; John Campbell; Steven Burt; Ian Mallinson.

OTHER INFORMATION The trust initiated and supported the establishment of the award-winning Thackray Museum in Leeds, one of the largest medical museums in the world, and continues to support the research resource there.

HOW TO APPLY Application forms and guidance notes are available from the trust's website. Applications are usually considered in October and April but may be considered at other times. The closing date for applications is the last day of July and January respectively.

WHO TO APPLY TO The Chair of the Trustees, c/o Thackray Museum, Beckett Street, Leeds LS9 7LN *email* johncampbell99@talktalk.net *Website* www.tmrt.co.uk

■ The Thames Wharf Charity

CC NO 1000796   **ESTABLISHED** 1990

WHERE FUNDING CAN BE GIVEN UK.

WHO CAN BENEFIT Charitable organisations.

WHAT IS FUNDED General charitable purposes.

WHAT IS NOT FUNDED No grants for the purchase of property, motor vehicles or holidays

SAMPLE GRANTS World Wildlife Fund UK (£8,500); Milestone Academy (£5,000); Camden City, Islington and Westminster Bereavement Service (£4,200); Cycle to Cannes (£4,000); DEC – East Africa Crisis Appeal, Great Ormond Street Hospital and UNICEF UK (£1,500 each); Macmillan Cancer Support (£1,000); MIND (£500); and Antenatal Results and Choices (£550).

FINANCES *Year* 2011–12 *Income* £442,875 *Grants* £20,545 *Assets* £1,339,953

TRUSTEES Avtar Lotay; Patrick Burgess; Graham Stirk; Audrey Gale.

HOW TO APPLY In writing to the correspondent.

WHO TO APPLY TO Kenneth Hawkins, Administrator, HW Lee Associates, New Derwent House, 69/73 Theobalds Road, London WC1X 8TA *Tel.* 020 7025 4600 *Fax* 020 7025 4666

■ The John P. Gommes Foundation (formerly known as The Britto Foundation)

CC NO 1010897   **ESTABLISHED** 1992

WHERE FUNDING CAN BE GIVEN UK, Israel and USA.

WHO CAN BENEFIT Children and organisations benefiting the people of Israel.

WHAT IS FUNDED The largest grants were to Israeli organisations (The trustees emphasised that these causes were 'Israeli' rather than 'Jewish') with arts, sporting and children's organisations also supported.

SAMPLE GRANTS Weizmann UK (£25,000); Spanish and Portuguese Jews' Congregation (£11,000); Pinner Synagogue and British Friends of the Ad Museums of Israel (£10,000 each); Kids Kidney research, International Bible Students and Coldstream Guards (£5,000); Natan Foundation (£3,000); Columbia College (£2,000); and Laniado UK (£1,000).

FINANCES *Year* 2011–12 *Income* £226 *Grants* £115,000 *Assets* £0

TRUSTEES J. C. Y. P. Gommes; H. K. Lewis; A. I. Leventis.

OTHER INFORMATION Based on the limited information available, it appears that the trust has donated its entire assets.

HOW TO APPLY The trustees stated: 'Applications are not sought at this time – trustees choose causes.'

WHO TO APPLY TO The Trustees, 659 Uxbridge Road, Pinner HA5 3LW *Tel.* 020 7429 4100

■ The Thistle Trust

CC NO 1091327   **ESTABLISHED** 2002

WHERE FUNDING CAN BE GIVEN UK.

WHO CAN BENEFIT Charitable institutions or projects in the UK.

WHAT IS FUNDED The promotion of study and research in the arts; and furthering public knowledge and education of art.

WHAT IS NOT FUNDED No grants to individuals.

RANGE OF GRANTS Up to £8,000.

SAMPLE GRANTS Juventus Lyrica Associacion De Ope (£8,000); Awards for Young Musicians and the Bach Choir (£2,500 each); Bush Theatre and RADA (£2,000); and the Academy of St Martin-in-the-Fields, Handel House Museum, National Youth Orchestra of Scotland and Theatre Peckham (£1,000 each).

FINANCES *Year* 2011–12 *Income* £37,027 *Grants* £42,955 *Assets* £1,134,775

TRUSTEES Lady Madeleine Kleinwort; Catherine Trevelyan; Neil Morris; Donald McGilvray; Nicholas Kerr-Sheppard; Selina Kleinwort Dabbas.

HOW TO APPLY In writing to the correspondent including most recent report and financial accounts. The trustees meet at least once a year with only successful applicants notified of the trustees' decision.

WHO TO APPLY TO Elizabeth Fettes-Neame, Trust Officer, Kleinwort Benson Trustees Ltd, 14 St George Street, London W1S 1FE *Tel.* 020 3207 7337 *email* elizabeth.fettes-neame@ kleinwortbenson.com

Think carefully about every application. Is it justified?

945

■ The Loke Wan Tho Memorial Foundation

CC NO 264273   **ESTABLISHED** 1972
WHERE FUNDING CAN BE GIVEN Worldwide.
WHO CAN BENEFIT Registered charities only.
WHAT IS FUNDED Medical studies and research; conservation and environment; and overseas aid.
TYPE OF GRANT One-off project and research grants.
SAMPLE GRANTS North Hampshire Hospice Charity (£50,000); and Stichting Orchidee (£20,000).
FINANCES *Year* 2011–12 *Income* £130,922 *Grants* £69,772 *Assets* £5,623,000
TRUSTEES Tanis Tonkyn; Alan Tonkyn.
HOW TO APPLY In writing to the correspondent.
WHO TO APPLY TO The Secretary to the Trustees, RBC Trust Company (International) Ltd, La Motte Chambers, St Helier, Jersey, Channel Islands JE1 1BJ *Tel.* 01534 602000

■ The David Thomas Charitable Trust

CC NO 1083257   **ESTABLISHED** 2000
WHERE FUNDING CAN BE GIVEN UK, in particular Gloucester and surrounding districts.
WHO CAN BENEFIT Institutions and registered charities.
WHAT IS FUNDED Social welfare and general charitable purposes.
RANGE OF GRANTS Up to £5,000.
SAMPLE GRANTS Gloucester Outbound (£5,000); Sue Ryder Care (£4,000); Oxfam and Minchinhampton Centre for the Elderly (£3,000 each); The Nelson Trust, The National Autistic Society and Tetbury Hospital (£2,000 each) and James Hopkins Trust, Tetbury Music Festival and Cotswold Care Hospice (£1,000 each).
FINANCES *Year* 2011–12 *Income* £51,190 *Grants* £30,000 *Assets* £1,875,483
TRUSTEES Charles Clark; James Davidson.
OTHER INFORMATION In 2011–12 grants were given to 13 organisations.
HOW TO APPLY In writing to the correspondent.
WHO TO APPLY TO The Trustees, c/o R. F. Trustee Co. Limited, 15 Suffolk Street, London SW1Y 4HG *Tel.* 020 7036 5685

■ The Thomas Lilley Memorial Trust

CC NO 1039529   **ESTABLISHED** 1960
WHERE FUNDING CAN BE GIVEN UK, with some preference for the Newbury area and Isle of Man.
WHO CAN BENEFIT Individuals and organisations.
WHAT IS FUNDED General charitable purposes.
WHAT IS NOT FUNDED No grants are made to individuals for educational or gap year activities.
RANGE OF GRANTS Usually up to £2,000.
SAMPLE GRANTS All Saints Church, Cuddesdon, Samaritans, Isle of Man, Action Medical Research, Army Benevolent Fund, Greater London Fund for the Blind, National Deaf Children's Society, Shelter and Voluntary Services Overseas.
FINANCES *Year* 2011–12 *Income* £33,237 *Grants* £24,500 *Assets* £796,380
TRUSTEES John F. Luke; Peter T. A. Lilley.
OTHER INFORMATION The amount available each year in individual grants in determined by the trust's income for that year.
HOW TO APPLY In writing to the correspondent.

WHO TO APPLY TO Trust Administrator, C/O Moors Andrew Thomas, Clarence Moors House, 94 Wilderspool Causeway, Warrington, Cheshire WA4 6PU *Tel.* 01925 652999

■ The Arthur and Margaret Thompson Charitable Trust

SC NO SC012103   **ESTABLISHED** 1973
WHERE FUNDING CAN BE GIVEN The towns or burghs of Kinross and Perth.
WHO CAN BENEFIT Registered charities in the beneficial area.
WHAT IS FUNDED General charitable purposes.
FINANCES *Year* 2011–12 *Income* £163,684 *Grants* £70,000
TRUSTEES Dr D. P. Anderson; Revd Dr J. P. L. Munro; J. Greig; D. L. Sands; A. G. Dorward; I. D. Donaldson.
OTHER INFORMATION The trust gives grants to individuals and organisations.
HOW TO APPLY The trustees meet to consider applications about every four months.
WHO TO APPLY TO The Trustees, Miller Hendry, 10 Blackfriars Street, Perth PH1 5NS

■ The Maurice and Vivien Thompson Charitable Trust

CC NO 1085041   **ESTABLISHED** 2000
WHERE FUNDING CAN BE GIVEN UK.
WHO CAN BENEFIT UK registered charities.
WHAT IS FUNDED General charitable purposes.
SAMPLE GRANTS Leicestershire First (£29,000).
FINANCES *Year* 2011–12 *Income* £30,832 *Grants* £36,810 *Assets* £1,081,089
TRUSTEES Maurice Thompson; Vivien Thomson; Paul Rhodes.
OTHER INFORMATION Leicestershire First has also been the main beneficiary in previous years, and of which the three trustees of this trust are also on the board.
HOW TO APPLY In writing to the correspondent.
WHO TO APPLY TO Maurice Thompson, Trustee, 2 The Orchard, London W4 1JX *Tel.* 020 8995 1547

■ The Thompson Family Charitable Trust

CC NO 326801   **ESTABLISHED** 1985
WHERE FUNDING CAN BE GIVEN UK.
WHO CAN BENEFIT Registered charities only.
WHAT IS FUNDED General charitable purposes, although the trustees are mostly interested in educational, medical and veterinary organisations, particularly those concerned with horses and horseracing.
WHAT IS NOT FUNDED No grants to individuals.
TYPE OF GRANT The trust makes one-off grants, recurring grants and pledges.
RANGE OF GRANTS Generally £200–£5,000, occasionally larger.
SAMPLE GRANTS Oracle Cancer Trust (£1 million); Macmillan Cancer Support (£500,000 in total); Great Ormond Street Children's Hospital Charity (£300,000 in total); Haberdashers' Aske's Boys' School Foundation (£200,000); Starlight Children's Foundation, Stroke Association, Prostate Cancer Charity, British Heart Foundation and Dementia UK (£100,000 each); Parkinson's UK (£70,000); Changing Faces (£50,000); Cambridge Women's Aid (£40,000 in total); East Anglia's Children's Hospices (£10,000); Racing Welfare Charities (£9,500 in

total); Leukaemia and Lymphoma Research (£5,000); and Gentleman's Night Out Child Sponsorship (£3,000).

FINANCES *Year* 2011–12 *Income* £5,530,174 *Grants* £2,878,800 *Assets* £82,537,462

TRUSTEES David B. Thompson; Patricia Thompson; Katherine P. Woodward.

OTHER INFORMATION The trust regularly builds up its reserves to enable it to make large donations in the future, for example towards the construction of new medical or educational facilities. 'It is the policy of the charity to hold reserves which will enable [it] to make major donations for capital projects in the near future (for example, to fund the construction and endowment of new medical or educational facilities) and appropriate projects are currently being investigated. [. . .] In addition to such capital projects it is envisaged that grants to other charities will in future be made at a higher annual level than in recent years.'

HOW TO APPLY In writing to the correspondent.

WHO TO APPLY TO Katherine P. Woodward, Hillsdown Court, 15 Totteridge Common, London N20 8LR

■ The Thompson Family Foundation

CC NO 1145556   **ESTABLISHED** 2012

WHERE FUNDING CAN BE GIVEN UK

WHO CAN BENEFIT Registered charities.

WHAT IS FUNDED General charitable purposes.

TRUSTEES Bruce Thompson; Catherine Thompson; Nicolas Acomb.

HOW TO APPLY In writing to the correspondent.

WHO TO APPLY TO Bruce Thompson, Trustee, c/o H. W. Fisher and Company, Acre House, 11–15 William Road, London NW1 3ER *Tel.* 020 7388 7000 *Fax* 020 7380 4900 *email* info@hwfisher.co.uk

■ The Thompson6 Charitable Trust

CC NO 1137853   **ESTABLISHED** 2010

WHERE FUNDING CAN BE GIVEN UK

WHO CAN BENEFIT Registered charities.

WHAT IS FUNDED General charitable purposes

RANGE OF GRANTS £1,000 to £10,000

SAMPLE GRANTS St Elizabeth's Centre; The Kusasa Project; Hospice in the Weald; Demelza Hospice Centre for Children and The University of Bristol.

FINANCES *Year* 2012–13 *Income* £72,741 *Grants* £33,000 *Assets* £201,842

TRUSTEE Coutts and Co.

HOW TO APPLY In writing to the correspondent.

WHO TO APPLY TO Coutts and Co, Trustee Dept, 440 Strand, London WC2R 0QS *Tel.* 020 7663 6825

■ The Len Thomson Charitable Trust

SC NO SC000981   **ESTABLISHED** 1989

WHERE FUNDING CAN BE GIVEN Scotland, with a preference for Midlothian, particularly Dalkeith.

WHO CAN BENEFIT Charitable organisations.

WHAT IS FUNDED The trust supports young people, local community organisations and medical research.

WHAT IS NOT FUNDED No grants are made directly to individuals.

RANGE OF GRANTS £1,000–£5,000.

SAMPLE GRANTS The Edinburgh Sick Kids Friends Foundation (£5,000); Brass in the Park

(£3,000); CHAS, Maggie's Centre and Mercy Ships (£2,000 each); and British Red Cross, Lothian Special Olympics, Newtongrange Children's Gala Day, the Princess Royal Trust for Carers and Save the Children Fund (£1,000 each).

FINANCES *Year* 2011–12 *Income* £15,520

TRUSTEES Douglas A. Connell; Elizabeth Thomson.

OTHER INFORMATION In 2011–12 the trust had a total expenditure of £39,700.

HOW TO APPLY The trust does not reply to unsolicited applications.

WHO TO APPLY TO Douglas A. Connell, Trustee, Turcan Connell WS, Princes Exchange, 1 Earl Grey Street, Edinburgh EH3 9EE *Tel.* 01312 288111 *email* dac@turcanconnell.com

■ The Sue Thomson Foundation

CC NO 298808   **ESTABLISHED** 1988

WHERE FUNDING CAN BE GIVEN UK, Sussex, London or Surrey.

WHO CAN BENEFIT Organisations.

WHAT IS FUNDED (i) Major grants – The majority of the funds went to Christ's Hospital, which received £101,000. The foundation nominates one new entrant each year from a needy background to the school, subject to the child meeting Christ's Hospital's own admissions criteria academically, socially and in terms of need. The foundation commits to contributing to the child's costs at a level agreed with Christ's Hospital for as long as each of them remains in the school. (ii) Regular grants – It is the policy of the trustees to provide up to 10% of the foundation's available income each year for grants in this category, subject to the foundation's commitments to Christ's Hospital having been satisfied. Charities eligible for consideration for grants at this level include: charities related to Christ's Hospital including the sister school, King Edward's – Witley; UK book trade charities, including the charities of the Worshipful Company of Stationers and Newspaper Makers; suitable grantmaking charities selected in recognition of pro-bono professional work done for the foundation by its trustees or others; special situations or other applications at the trustees' discretion. Grants in this category may be spread over a period of years. (iii) Special grants – It is the policy of the trustees to set aside a further 10% of available income each year for this programme, subject to its commitments in the major and medium categories and other financial needs having been met. Special grants are confined to fund education or welfare projects that aim to help people who are in need and cannot be readily helped by statutory bodies. They are confined to charities in Sussex, Surrey or London.

WHAT IS NOT FUNDED No grants to large, national charities (except Christ's Hospital) or individuals, except as part of a specific scheme. No research projects, charities concerned with animals, birds, the environment, gardens or historic buildings.

TYPE OF GRANT Major grants which are above £5,000; regular grants which can be from £500 to £5,000; special grants which can be up to £3,000 per year.

RANGE OF GRANTS £1,000–£3,000.

SAMPLE GRANTS The Leonard Sainer Legal Education Foundation (£3,000); Book Trade Benevolent Society (£2,500); The Bridewell Foundation (£2,000); Hoskings House Trust, Broadfield Children's Project and Parent and Carers

Support Association (£1,000 each) and The Stationers' Foundation (£500).

FINANCES *Year* 2011–12 *Income* £214,117 *Grants* £122,018 *Assets* £2,654,542

TRUSTEES Susan M. Mitchell, Chair; Timothy J. Binnington; Charles L. Corman; Kathleen Duncan; Susannah Holliman.

OTHER INFORMATION The grant total includes £7,000 paid to individual students.

HOW TO APPLY In writing to the correspondent. Preliminary telephone or email enquiries are encouraged. Unsolicited applications are not acknowledged, unless accompanied by an sae or an email address. Grantmaking policies are published in the annual report and accounts, available from the Charity Commission website, and in relevant charity sector publications when the trustees are able to do so free of charge. This statement of policies is provided to anyone on request.

WHO TO APPLY TO Susannah Holliman, Administrator, Arcadia, 58a Woodland Way, Kingswood, Surrey KT20 6NW *email* stfsusannah@aol.com

■ The Sir Jules Thorn Charitable Trust

CC NO 233838 **ESTABLISHED** 1964
WHERE FUNDING CAN BE GIVEN UK.

WHO CAN BENEFIT Registered charities engaged in medical research (universities/hospitals only); medically related work; and humanitarian work which tackles serious illness, disability or disadvantage or helps overcome adversity.

WHAT IS FUNDED Medical research with strong clinical relevance, medicine generally, and small grants for humanitarian appeals.

WHAT IS NOT FUNDED The trust does not fund: research which is considered unlikely to provide clinical benefit within five years; research which could reasonably be expected to be supported by a disease specific funder, unless there is a convincing reason why the trust has been approached; research into cancer or AIDS, for the sole reason that they are relatively well funded elsewhere; 'top up' grants for ongoing projects; research which will also involve other funders, apart from the institution itself; individuals – except in the context of a project undertaken by an approved institution which is in receipt of a grant from the trust; research or data collection overseas; research institutions which are not registered charities; third parties raising resources to fund research themselves.

TYPE OF GRANT Medical research projects usually covering a period of up to five years, plus one-off donations to other charities.

SAMPLE GRANTS Newcastle University received the Sir Jules Thord Award for Biomedical research worth £1.5 million over a period of up to five years for a proposed study of 'Bringing the next generation sequencing to the next generation: early diagnosis of inherited immune deficiency'. PhD scholarships totalling £244,500 were awarded to the universities of Liverpool, Dundee and Southampton.

Capital grants to hospitals and universities were made to: Southampton Hospital Charity 'Red and White' Appeal (£100,000) towards the creation of a specialist Day Case Treatment Unit for patients with leukaemia and other forms of life threatening blood cancer; Queen Elizabeth Hospital Birmingham (£50,000) towards the purchase of a CyberKnife robotic radiotherapy system to improve the treatment of cancer patients and Yeovil Hospital (£50,000) towards the Flying

Colours appeal for a new Special Care Baby Unit at the Women's Hospital. Other medically related grants included: North East Autism Society and Kirkwood Hospice (£100,000 each); Sunfield Children's Homes (£80,000); The Meath Epilepsy Trust, Sue Ryder Thorpe Hall Hospice, Bury Hospice and Tenovus (£50,000 each).

Small grants included: Willen Hospice (£5,000); Changing Faces, Ian Rennie Grove House Hospice Care, The Air Ambulance Service and The Rossendale Trust (£1,500 each); Bliss – The National Charity for the Newborn, Bolton Hospice, British Liver Trust, Friends of the Elderly, Scottish Huntington's Association and St Wilfred's Hospice Foundation (£1,250 each); Autism Bedfordshire, Beating Bowel Cancer, Dogs for the Disabled and British Refugee Council (£1,000 each); Guildford Action for Community Care, Launchpad Reading, Music in Hospitals (Scotland) and Relate Avon (£750 each) and Dyspraxia Foundation, East Bristol Advice and Information Centres, Sportability and Sailor's Society (£500 each).

FINANCES *Year* 2012 *Income* £2,463,236 *Grants* £3,039,547 *Assets* £105,618,690

TRUSTEES Elizabeth S. Charal, Chair; Prof. Sir Ravinder Maini; Sir Bruce McPhail; Nancy V. Pearcey; Christopher Sporborg; William Sporborg; John Rhodes; Prof. David Russell-Jones.

HOW TO APPLY The Sir Jules Thorn Award: applicants should first contact the trust to discuss their proposal before applying. Full guidance notes are available online and the deadline for applications is usually in the autumn.

The Sir Jules Thorn PhD Scholarship Programme: scholarships are available only through medical schools invited to participate.

Medically related donations: 'Organisations seeking a medically related donation should download, complete and return the expression of interest form as an e-mail attachment to donations@julesthorntrust.org.uk'. Applicants should also attach an electronic copy of their latest trustee's report and financial statements. The trust chair and director review all expressions of interest to decide whether a full application will be request for consideration by the board of trustees. The final decision as to whether an award is made and the amount rests with the trustees.'

Ann Rylands small donations programme: applications are accepted, and preferred, online. However application forms can also be downloaded and sent to the trust by email or post. However, the trust does advise that online applications save both time and money.

WHO TO APPLY TO David H. Richings, Director, 24 Manchester Square, London W1U 3TH *Tel.* 020 7487 5851 *Fax* 020 7224 3976 *email* info@julesthorntrust.org.uk *Website* www.julesthorntrust.org.uk

■ The Thornton Foundation

CC NO 326383 **ESTABLISHED** 1983
WHERE FUNDING CAN BE GIVEN UK.

WHO CAN BENEFIT Charities which are personally known to the trustees.

WHAT IS FUNDED General charitable purposes.

SAMPLE GRANTS Institute of Cancer Research (£111,000); Great Ormond Street Hospital (£25,000); The Cirdan Sailing Trust (£10,000); Helen House (£7,000); Action for Blind People, Help for Heroes, Keble College – Oxford and Prisoners of Conscience (£5,000 each); The Tait Memorial Trust (£2,000); Museum of London

(£1,500) and Arrow Riding Centre and UCL HD Research (£1,000 each).

FINANCES *Year* 2011–12 *Income* £89,614 *Grants* £204,203 *Assets* £4,219,686

TRUSTEES R. C. Thornton, Chair; A. H. Isaacs; H. D. C. Thornton; S. J. Thornton.

HOW TO APPLY The trust strongly emphasises that it does not accept unsolicited applications and only organisations that are known to one of the trustees will be considered for support. Any unsolicited applications will not receive a reply.

WHO TO APPLY TO A. H. Isaacs, Jordans, Eashing, Surrey GU7 2QA

■ The Thornton Trust

CC NO 205357   **ESTABLISHED** 1962

WHERE FUNDING CAN BE GIVEN UK and overseas.

WHO CAN BENEFIT Charitable organisations.

WHAT IS FUNDED 'The promotion and furthering of education and the Evangelical Christian faith, and assisting in the relief of sickness, suffering and poverty'. The 2011/12 trustees' annual report states: 'Some organisations are involved in all of the activities referred to in the deed, but generally one third in supporting the Christian church, training and associated societies in the UK; a third in Christian missions and relief work overseas; and the balance in education, youth work, medical and other.'

SAMPLE GRANTS Africa Inland Mission (£20,000); Saffron Walden Baptist Church (£10,000); Redcliffe Missionary College (£6,000); London Institute for Contemporary Christianity and London City Mission (£5,000 each); Hertford Community Church (£4,000); Bible Society and Young Life YHT (£3,000 each); Daughters Cambodia and Middle East Christian Outreach Ltd (£2,000 each); Abbeyfield Free Church (£1,000); and Alzheimer's Society and Guiding Herts (£100 each).

FINANCES *Year* 2011–12 *Income* £69,913 *Grants* £125,915 *Assets* £824,374

TRUSTEES Douglas Thornton; Betty Thornton; James Thornton.

HOW TO APPLY The trust states: 'Our funds are fully committed and we regret that we are unable to respond to the many unsolicited calls for assistance we are now receiving.'

WHO TO APPLY TO Douglas Thornton, Trustee, Hunters Cottage, Hunters Yard, Debden Road, Saffron Walden, Essex CB11 4AA *Tel.* 01799 526712

■ The Thousandth Man – Richard Burns Charitable Trust (formerly known as The Hammonds Charitable Trust)

CC NO 1064028   **ESTABLISHED** 1997

WHERE FUNDING CAN BE GIVEN Mainly Birmingham, London, Leeds, Bradford and Manchester.

WHO CAN BENEFIT Registered charities only.

WHAT IS FUNDED General charitable purposes directed towards the young, elderly and disabled.

WHAT IS NOT FUNDED The charity generally supports smaller charities local to the firm's offices.

RANGE OF GRANTS Usually up to £10,000.

SAMPLE GRANTS Crohn's and Colitis in Children (£5,000); Paddington Law Centre Limited (£3,000); Help for Heroes (£2,300); Marie Curie Cancer Care (£1,200); the Prince's Trust and East Anglia's Children's Hospices (£1,000 each); Wooden Spoon Society (£700); Bowel Cancer and Research, Samaritan's Purse International Limited and Action for Children (£500 each); Rett Syndrome Research Trust UK and Minge's Gift (£250 each); the Ickle Pickle Partnership Ltd and Royal Commonwealth Society for the Blind (£100 each); and the Candlelighters Trust (£50).

FINANCES *Year* 2011–12 *Income* £118,038 *Grants* £39,415 *Assets* £141,008

TRUSTEES John Forrest; Simon Miller; Susan Nickson; Robert Weekes; Robert Elvin.

OTHER INFORMATION The Thousandth Man – Richard Burns Charitable Trust was formerly known as The Hammonds Charitable Trust.

HOW TO APPLY This trust does not accept unsolicited applications.

WHO TO APPLY TO Linda Sylvester, Administrator, Squire Sanders (UK) LLP, Rutland House, 148 Edmund Street, Birmingham B3 2JR *Tel.* 01212 223318 *email* linda.sylvester@ squiresanders.com *Website* www. squiresanders.com

---

■ The Three Guineas Trust

CC NO 1059652   **ESTABLISHED** 1996

WHERE FUNDING CAN BE GIVEN Worldwide, in practice mainly UK.

WHO CAN BENEFIT Currently, registered charities working with people suffering from autism and Asperger's Syndrome.

WHAT IS FUNDED Initiatives related to autism and Asperger's Syndrome. Climate change research projects.

WHAT IS NOT FUNDED No grants for individuals or for research (except where it has an immediate benefit).

TYPE OF GRANT One off and recurrent.

RANGE OF GRANTS Typically up to £100,000.

SAMPLE GRANTS University of Cambridge (£581,000); Autism Cymru (£139,500); Turning the Red Lights Green (£72,000); Action for ASD (£45,000); Resources for Autism (£25,000); Blackpool Tiggers (£9,000); Killamarsh Autistic and PDA Support Group (£6,000); Disabilities and Self Help and Project Art Works (£5,000 each); and Helping Hands Autism Support Group (£3,500).

FINANCES *Year* 2011–12 *Income* £1,509,429 *Grants* £1,037,807 *Assets* £14,878,146

TRUSTEES Clare Sainsbury; Bernard Willis; Dominic Flynn.

OTHER INFORMATION The trust is one of the Sainsbury Family Charitable Trusts which share a common administration. An application to one is taken as an application to all.

HOW TO APPLY See the guidance for applicants in the entry for the Sainsbury Family Charitable Trusts. A single application will be considered for support by all the trusts in the group. 'The trustees do not at present wish to invite applications, except in the field of autism and Asperger's syndrome, where they will examine unsolicited proposals alongside those that result from their own research and contacts with expert individuals and organisations working in this field. The trustees prefer to support innovative schemes that can be successfully replicated or become self-sustaining. They are also keen that, wherever possible, schemes supporting adults and teenagers on the autistic spectrum should include clients/service users in decision-making.'

WHO TO APPLY TO Alan Bookbinder, Director, The Peak, 5 Wilton Road, London SW1V 1AP *Tel.* 020 7410 0330 *Fax* 020 7410 0332 *Website* www.sfct.org.uk

---

Think carefully about every application. Is it justified?

949

■ The Three Oaks Trust

CC NO 297079 **ESTABLISHED** 1987
WHERE FUNDING CAN BE GIVEN UK and overseas, with a preference for West Sussex.
WHO CAN BENEFIT Organisations that promote the welfare of individuals and families. Grants are also made to individuals via statutory authorities or voluntary agencies.
WHAT IS FUNDED The trust regularly supports the same welfare organisations in the UK and overseas each year.
WHAT IS NOT FUNDED No direct applications from individuals. Applications from students for gap year activities are not a priority and will not be funded.
SAMPLE GRANTS Raynauds and Scleroderma Association (£15,000); Crawley Open House (£10,000); Basildon Community Resource Centre, Wendy Gough Cancer Awareness Foundation and Springboard Project (£5,000 each); and MIND Brighton and Hove (£4,000).
FINANCES *Year* 2011–12 *Income* £221,072 *Grants* £130,000 *Assets* £6,339,089
TRUSTEES Dianne Margaret Ward; Polly Elizabeth Hobbs; Carol Vivian Foreman; Carol Johnson; Pam Wilkinson; Dr P. Kane; Sarah A. Kane; Giles Duncan Wilkinson; Three Oaks Family Trust Co Ltd.
OTHER INFORMATION Additionally, in 2011–12, donations were made to 353 individuals totalling £63,000.
HOW TO APPLY The following guidelines are taken from the 2011/12 annual accounts: 'Grants are made to organisations that promote the welfare of individuals and families. In general, the trustees intend to continue supporting the organisations that they have supported in the past. Periodically and generally annually the trustees review the list of registered charities and institutions to which grants have been given and consider additions and deletions from the list. To save on administration, the trustees do not respond to requests unless they are considering making a donation. Requests from organisations for donations in excess of £2,000 are considered by the trustees on a quarterly basis in meetings usually held in January, April, July and September.' For the full guidelines, visit the trust's website.
WHO TO APPLY TO The Trustees, P. O. Box 893, Horsham, West Sussex RH12 9JD
email contact@thethreeoakstrust.co.uk
Website www.thethreeoakstrust.co.uk

■ The Thriplow Charitable Trust

CC NO 1025531 **ESTABLISHED** 1993
WHERE FUNDING CAN BE GIVEN Preference for British institutions.
WHO CAN BENEFIT Universities, university colleges and other places of learning benefiting young adults and older people, academics, research workers and students.
WHAT IS FUNDED Advancement of higher and further education, the promotion of research and the dissemination of the results of such research.
WHAT IS NOT FUNDED Grants can only be made to charitable bodies or component parts of charitable bodies. In no circumstances can grants be made to individuals.
TYPE OF GRANT Research study funds, research fellowships, certain academic training schemes, computer facilities and building projects related to research.
RANGE OF GRANTS Generally £1,000–£5,000.

SAMPLE GRANTS Previous beneficiaries have included: Cambridge University Library, Centre of South Asian Studies, Computer Aid International, Fight for Sight, Fitzwilliam Museum, Foundation for Prevention of Blindness, Foundation of Research Students, Hearing Research Trust, Inspire Foundation, Loughborough University, Marie Curie Cancer Care, Royal Botanic Gardens, Royal College of Music, Transplant Trust and University of Reading.
FINANCES *Year* 2011–12 *Income* £458,267 *Grants* £87,400 *Assets* £4,012,699
TRUSTEES Sir Peter Swinnerton-Dyer, Chair; Dr Harriet Crawford; Prof. Christopher Bayly; Sir David Wallace; Dame Jean Thomas.
HOW TO APPLY There is no application form. A letter of application should specify the purpose for which funds are sought and the costings of the project. It should be indicated whether other applications for funds are pending and, if the funds are to be channelled to an individual or a small group, what degree of supervision over the quality of the work would be exercised by the institution. Trustee meetings are held twice a year – in spring and in autumn.
WHO TO APPLY TO The Trustees, PO Box 225, Royston SG8 1BG

■ The John Raymond Tijou Charitable Trust

CC NO 1146260 **ESTABLISHED** 2012
WHERE FUNDING CAN BE GIVEN UK.
WHO CAN BENEFIT Registered charities.
WHAT IS FUNDED General charitable purposes, health and medical research.
TRUSTEE HSBC Trust Company (UK) Ltd.
HOW TO APPLY In writing to the correspondent.
WHO TO APPLY TO HSBC Trust Company (UK) Ltd, 10th Floor, Norwich House, Nelson Gate, Commercial Road, Southampton SO15 1GX
Tel. 02380 722739

■ Mrs R. P. Tindall's Charitable Trust

CC NO 250558 **ESTABLISHED** 1966
WHERE FUNDING CAN BE GIVEN Wiltshire, Dorset and Africa.
WHO CAN BENEFIT Charitable organisations, churches, students in need and members of the clergy in Africa, Wiltshire and Dorset.
WHAT IS FUNDED Relief of poverty, furtherance of the work of the Christian church and advancement of education. Grants are also made to students in need and for the welfare of the clergy and their dependants.
TYPE OF GRANT One-off and recurrent grants.
RANGE OF GRANTS £500–£20,000.
SAMPLE GRANTS Sarum College (£10,000); Salisbury Diocesan Bd Finance (£9,000); Woodford Valley Primary School – Centre for Autism (£2,000); and Salisbury – Sudan Medical Link (£1,500).
FINANCES *Year* 2012 *Income* £95,304 *Grants* £61,202 *Assets* £2,617,927
TRUSTEES Giles Fletcher; Michael Newman; Canon Ann Philp; Nicola Halls; Stephen Herbert; Claire Newman.
OTHER INFORMATION Grants totalling just over £3,500 were paid to individuals.
HOW TO APPLY According to the trust's annual report, the trust invites applications for funding by advertising in charitable trusts' registers.

WHO TO APPLY TO Giles Fletcher, Trustee, Appletree House, Wishford Road, Middle Woodford, Salisbury SP4 6NG *Tel.* 01722 782329

■ The Tinsley Foundation
CC NO 1076537   **ESTABLISHED** 1999
WHERE FUNDING CAN BE GIVEN UK and overseas.
WHO CAN BENEFIT Charitable organisations.
WHAT IS FUNDED The foundation will support: charities which promote human rights and democratisation and/or which educate against racism, discrimination and oppression; charities which promote self-help in fighting poverty and homelessness; and charities which provide reproductive health education in underdeveloped countries, but specifically excluding charities whose policy is against abortion or birth control.
SAMPLE GRANTS SURF Survivors Fund (£50,000); Client Earth (£35,000); Network for Africa and Technoserve Europe (£25,000 each); Medact (£15,000); Article 1 Charitable Trust and Searchlight Education Trust (£10,000 each); and Computer Aid International, English National Opera, Fairtrade Foundation and Oxford Research Group (£1,000 each).
FINANCES *Year* 2011–12 *Income* £194,387 *Grants* £180,250 *Assets* £2,591,871
TRUSTEES H. C. Tinsley; R. C. Tinsley; T. A. Jones.
HOW TO APPLY While the charity welcomes applications from eligible potential grantees, the trustees seek out organisations that will effectively fulfil the foundation's objectives.
WHO TO APPLY TO Henry Tinsley, Trustee, 14 St Mary's Street, Stamford, Lincolnshire PE9 2DF *Tel.* 01780 762056 *Fax* 01780 767594 *email* hctinsley@aol.com

■ The Tisbury Telegraph Trust
CC NO 328595   **ESTABLISHED** 1990
WHERE FUNDING CAN BE GIVEN UK and overseas.
WHO CAN BENEFIT Registered charities and churches.
WHAT IS FUNDED Christian, overseas aid and general charitable purposes. Most distributions are to charities of which the trustees have personal knowledge. Other applications are unlikely to be successful.
WHAT IS NOT FUNDED No applications from individuals for expeditions or courses can be considered.
TYPE OF GRANT Core costs, one-off, project, research and running costs will be considered.
SAMPLE GRANTS Crisis and Tear Fund (£22,000 each); World Vision (£20,000); All Saints Church, Peckham (£15,500); Friends of Kiwoko Hospital (£15,000); Practical Action (£10,500); Helen and Douglas House (£10,000); Christian Aid and Wycliffe Bible Translators (£2,000 each); and Friends of the Earth, Habitat for Humanity, Pecan, Traidcraft and Salvation Army (£1,000 each).
FINANCES *Year* 2011–12 *Income* £335,115 *Grants* £185,970 *Assets* £327,134
TRUSTEES Alison Davidson; John Davidson; Eleanor Orr; Roger Orr; Sonia Phippard; Michael Hartley.
HOW TO APPLY In writing to the correspondent. However, it is extremely rare that unsolicited applications are successful and the trust does not respond to applicants unless an sae is included. No telephone applications please.
WHO TO APPLY TO Eleanor Orr, Trustee, 35 Kitto Road, Telegraph Hill, London SE14 5TW *email* tisburytelegraphtrust@gmail.com

■ The Tobacco Pipe Makers and Tobacco Trade Benevolent Fund
CC NO 1135646   **ESTABLISHED** 1961
WHERE FUNDING CAN BE GIVEN City of London and Sevenoaks School.
WHO CAN BENEFIT Educational establishments benefiting children, young adults, students, and people disadvantaged by poverty.
WHAT IS FUNDED To assist in the education of those who would not otherwise be able to afford it. To support only those charities with which the company can have an active relationship.
WHAT IS NOT FUNDED No grants to individuals.
TYPE OF GRANT Ongoing scholarships.
RANGE OF GRANTS £500–£12,000
SAMPLE GRANTS Speech and Language Hearing Centre (£26,000); Oxford and Bermondsey Youth Club (£10,000); Guildhall School of Music Awards (£8,000); Riding for the Disabled – Barrow Farm (£4,000); Children's Country Holidays (£2,000); St Lawrence Jewry (St Botolph's) (£600); Corporation of the Sons of the Clergy (£500).
The trust also gave one off grants totalling £12,000
FINANCES *Year* 2011–12 *Income* £362,274 *Grants* £86,000 *Assets* £5,292,820
TRUSTEES Roger Merton; Stephen Preedy; Fiona Adler; George Lankester; Derek Harris; Alan Henderson; Graham Blashill; David Glynn-Jones; Nigel Rich.
OTHER INFORMATION The trust also runs a welfare support scheme for individuals with links to the tobacco trade. See the trust's website for further information.
HOW TO APPLY The trust prefers applications from small charities and organisations that have links, including geographically, to the city of London. Applications in writing to the secretary. The committee meets regularly during the year to review and approve grants.
WHO TO APPLY TO Paul D. Bethel, Clerk, 23 Florence Road, Sanderstead, Surrey CR2 0PQ *Tel.* 020 8763 1063 *email* tobaccoclerk@btinternet.com *Website* www.tobaccocharity.org.uk

■ The Tolkien Trust
CC NO 1150801   **ESTABLISHED** 1977
WHERE FUNDING CAN BE GIVEN UK, with some preference for Oxfordshire, and overseas.
WHO CAN BENEFIT Registered charities.
WHAT IS FUNDED General charitable purposes including charities and charitable causes supporting children, young people, families, older people, homeless people, socially disadvantaged people, organisations supporting overseas aid and development, refugees, medical aid, research, education, the arts and religion.
WHAT IS NOT FUNDED No grants to individuals.
RANGE OF GRANTS £2,500–£100,000.
SAMPLE GRANTS Previous beneficiaries include: Bodleian Library; Rebuilding Sri Lanka; Medical Foundation; Friends of the Connection at St Martin-in-the-Fields; Prisoners' Education Trust; Music in Lyddington; Cancer Active; Friends of Cardigan Bay; Shakespeare Link; and Marymount of Santa Barbara.
FINANCES *Year* 2012–13 *Income* £1,700,000 *Grants* £650,000 *Assets* £27,000,000
TRUSTEES Christopher Reuel Tolkien; Priscilla Mary Anne Reuel Tolkien; Michael Reuel Tolkien; Baillie Tolkien.
OTHER INFORMATION In May 2013 the Tolkien Trust (Charity Commission no. 273615) ceased to

exist, with funds being transferred to create this trust. No accounts were available for the new incarnation of the trust at the time of writing (December 2013), but for reference the previous trust held assets of around £27 million, with an annual income of around £1.7 million, mostly from royalties. The level of grantmaking was around £650,000 per year. Given the recent production of a new trilogy of films based on *The Hobbit*, it is likely that assets and income for this trust will increase.

HOW TO APPLY In writing to the correspondent. Applications must be posted and email applications will not be accepted. The majority of donations are made to charities or causes selected by the trustees. There are no guidelines for applicants and the trust does not enter into correspondence with applicants in the interests of controlling administrative costs. It is left to the discretion of applicants how they feel they can best present their case for support. Decisions about donations annually at the end of March/beginning of April. Therefore, any applications should be timed to reach the trust by no later than 15 December in the preceding year.

WHO TO APPLY TO Cathleen Blackburn, Administrator, c/o Maier Blackburn LLP, Prama House, 267 Banbury Road, Oxford OX2 7HT *Website* www.tolkientrust.org

---

■ Tollemache (Buckminster) Charitable Trust

CC NO 271795   **ESTABLISHED** 1976
WHERE FUNDING CAN BE GIVEN UK.
WHO CAN BENEFIT Voluntary organisations and charitable groups only.
WHAT IS FUNDED General charitable purposes.
WHAT IS NOT FUNDED No grants to individuals.
SAMPLE GRANTS Alzheimer's Society, Bassingthorpe Parochial Church Council, Brooke Hospital for Animals, Buckminster Primary School, Buckminster United Football Club, Cancer Research, Cats Protection League, Coldstream Guards Association, Coston Parochial Church Council, Ex Services Mental Welfare, NSPCC, Oxfam, Parkinson's Disease Society, Rainbows, Royal Hospital for Neuro-Disability, Royal Star and Garter Home, Rutland House School for Parents, Sight Savers, Society for the Protection of Animals Abroad, South Witham Parochial Church Council, Springfield Rifle Club, St Peter's Church and WSPA.
FINANCES *Year* 2011–12 *Income* £25,699 *Grants* £24,900 *Assets* £719,258
TRUSTEES Richard Tollemache; William Wilks.
HOW TO APPLY In writing to the secretary. No acknowledgements sent.
WHO TO APPLY TO Roger Stafford, Estate Office, Buckminster, Grantham, Lincolnshire NG33 5SD *Tel.* 01476 860471 *Fax* 01476 861235

■ Tomchei Torah Charitable Trust

CC NO 802125   **ESTABLISHED** 1989
WHERE FUNDING CAN BE GIVEN UK and Israel.
WHO CAN BENEFIT Jewish people and organisations.
WHAT IS FUNDED Jewish causes.
RANGE OF GRANTS Average £5,000.
SAMPLE GRANTS Previous beneficiaries included: Friends of Mir; MST College; Friends of Sanz Institutions; United Talmudical Associates; Ezer North West; Menorah Grammar School; Friends

of Torah Ohr; Ruzin Sadagora Trust; Achisomoch Aid Co and Chesed Charity Trust.
FINANCES *Year* 2011–12 *Income* £125,767 *Grants* £60,227 *Assets* £70,820
TRUSTEES Israel Kohn; Sandra Kohn; Daniel Netzer.
HOW TO APPLY In writing to the correspondent at any time.
WHO TO APPLY TO Israel Kohn, 36 Cranbourne Gardens, London NW11 0HP *Tel.* 020 8458 5706

■ The Tompkins Foundation

CC NO 281405   **ESTABLISHED** 1980
WHERE FUNDING CAN BE GIVEN UK, with a preference for the parishes of Hampstead Norreys, Berkshire and West Grinstead, West Sussex.
WHO CAN BENEFIT Registered charities, including schools, hospitals and churches.
WHAT IS FUNDED Health, education, religion and community purposes.
WHAT IS NOT FUNDED Grants are not given to individuals.
TYPE OF GRANT One-off and recurring.
RANGE OF GRANTS £500–£50,000
SAMPLE GRANTS Arthroplasty for Arthritis (£50,000); Great Ormond Street Hospital Children's Charity (£30,000); Foundation of Nursing Studies and Chicken Shed Theatre (£25,000 each); Order of Malta Volunteers (£20,000); British Association for Adoption and Fostering and Toynbee Hall (£10,000 each); Anna Freud Centre (£5,000); and Momentum Skills (£2,000).
FINANCES *Year* 2011–12 *Income* £349,216 *Grants* £345,550 *Assets* £11,043,063
TRUSTEES Elizabeth Tompkins; Peter Vaines.
HOW TO APPLY In writing to the correspondent, although unsolicited applications are unlikely to be successful as the trust has a regular list of charities which receive support. 'The trustees aim to respond to need and therefore consider that more specific plans [for the future] would be too restrictive.'
WHO TO APPLY TO Richard Geoffrey Morris, 7 Belgrave Square, London SW1X 8PH *Tel.* 020 7235 9322 *Fax* 020 7259 5129

■ Toni and Guy Charitable Foundation Limited

CC NO 1095285   **ESTABLISHED** 2002
WHERE FUNDING CAN BE GIVEN England and Wales.
WHO CAN BENEFIT Registered charities and hospitals and Toni and Guy employees.
WHAT IS FUNDED General charitable purposes.
RANGE OF GRANTS £1,000–£50,000
SAMPLE GRANTS Macmillan (£31,000); Variety Club (£25,000); Italian Church Charity (£4,500); Crimestoppers (£1,000); British Red Cross (£600) and Prostate Cancer (£100).
FINANCES *Year* 2010–11 *Income* £131,507 *Grants* £61,881 *Assets* £21,000
TRUSTEES Richard Freeman; Pauline Mascolo; Rupert Berrow; James McDonnell; Toni Mascolo.
OTHER INFORMATION The 2011–12 accounts, at the Charity Commission, appear to be the same as the 2010–11.
HOW TO APPLY See the foundation's website for details of the application process.
WHO TO APPLY TO Cameron Tewson, Fundraising and Charity Manager, 58–60 Stamford St, London SE1 9LX *Tel.* 020 7921 9000 *email* cameron. tewson@toniandguy.co.uk *Website* toniandguy. com

---

■ The Torah Temimah Trust

CC NO 802390   **ESTABLISHED** 1989
WHERE FUNDING CAN BE GIVEN UK.
WHO CAN BENEFIT Orthodox Jewish organisations.
WHAT IS FUNDED Orthodox Jewish religious education and religion.
FINANCES *Year* 2011–12 *Income* £38,214 *Grants* £28,110 *Assets* £127,431
TRUSTEES E. Bernath; M. Bernath; A. Grunfeld.
HOW TO APPLY In writing to the correspondent.
WHO TO APPLY TO E. Bernath, Trustee, 16 Reizel Close, Stamford Hill, London N16 5GY *Tel.* 020 8800 3021

■ Toras Chesed (London) Trust

CC NO 1110653   **ESTABLISHED** 2005
WHERE FUNDING CAN BE GIVEN Worldwide.
WHO CAN BENEFIT Jewish organisations.
WHAT IS FUNDED the objects of the charity are: the advancement of the Orthodox Jewish faith; the advancement of Orthodox Jewish religious education; the relief of poverty and infirmity among persons of the Jewish faith; to provide a safe and user friendly environment to share mutual problems and experiences; to encourage active parental participation in their children's education.
FINANCES *Year* 2011–12 *Income* £289,519 *Grants* £276,592
TRUSTEES Akiva Stern; Simon Stern; Aaron Langberg.
OTHER INFORMATION There are no assets, income is received from donations.
HOW TO APPLY 'Applications for grants are considered by the trustees and reviewed in depth for final approval.'
WHO TO APPLY TO Aaron Langberg, Trustee, 14 Lampard Grove, London N16 6UZ *Tel.* 020 8806 9589 *email* ari@toraschesed.co.uk

■ The Tory Family Foundation

CC NO 326584   **ESTABLISHED** 1984
WHERE FUNDING CAN BE GIVEN Worldwide, but principally Folkestone.
WHO CAN BENEFIT Charitable organisations and individuals.
WHAT IS FUNDED 'The charity was formed to provide financial assistance to a wide range of charitable needs. It is currently supporting a wide range of causes both from a national perspective and an international perspective. These causes include educational, religious, social and medical subjects and the donees themselves are often registered charities.'
WHAT IS NOT FUNDED Priority is given to applications from east Kent.
TYPE OF GRANT Capital costs, research. The trust does not usually fund full projects.
RANGE OF GRANTS Up to £10,000, mostly £1,000 or less.
SAMPLE GRANTS Previous beneficiaries have included: Ashford YMCA, Bletchley Park, Canterbury Cathedral, Concern Worldwide, Deal Festival, Disability Law Service, Folk Rainbow Club, Foresight, Friends of Birzett, Gurkha Welfare, Kent Cancer Trust, Royal British Legion, Uppingham Foundation and Youth Action Wiltshire.
FINANCES *Year* 2011–12 *Income* £100,751 *Grants* £82,150 *Assets* £3,118,668
TRUSTEES James Tory; Paul Tory; S. Tory; David Callister; Jill Perkins.

OTHER INFORMATION Some beneficiaries receive more than one grant during the year and many have been supported in previous years.
HOW TO APPLY In writing to the correspondent. Applications are considered throughout the year. To keep costs down, unsuccessful applicants will not be notified.
WHO TO APPLY TO Paul Tory, Trustee, The Estate Office, Etchinghill Golf Club, Canterbury Road, Etchinghill, Folkestone CT18 8FA *Tel.* 01303 862280

■ Tottenham Grammar School Foundation

CC NO 312634   **ESTABLISHED** 1989
WHERE FUNDING CAN BE GIVEN The borough of Haringey.
WHO CAN BENEFIT Individuals under 25 who are in education in the borough, schools and voluntary organisations.
WHAT IS FUNDED Equipment and activities not provided by local authorities. Activities supported include youth clubs, Saturday schools and sports promotion. Grants are also made to individuals under 25 who, or whose parents, normally live in the borough, or who have attended school in the borough.
WHAT IS NOT FUNDED The foundation cannot fund: the direct delivery of the National Curriculum; the employment of staff; the construction, adaptation, repair and maintenance of buildings; the repair and maintenance of equipment.
SAMPLE GRANTS Haringey Sports Development Trust (£42,000); Chaverim Youth Organisation (£19,000); Riverside Secondary Special School (£17,000); Markfield Project and The Brook Primary Special School (£15,000 each); Haringey Young Musicians (£10,000); Lubavitch Youth Groups (£6,500); London Skolars Junior Rugby League Club and Jackson Lane Community Arts Centre Association (£2,800 each); London Boxing Academy Trust (£2,250); White Hart Lane Tennis Club (£2,000) and Bruce Grove Primary School (£1,800).
FINANCES *Year* 2011–12 *Income* £271,769 *Grants* £750,232 *Assets* £17,852,918
TRUSTEES Keith Brown; Terry Clarke; Paul Compton; Roger Knight; Frederick Gruncell; Peter Jones; Graham Kantorowicz; Keith McGuinness; Victoria Phillips; Andrew Krokou; John Fowl.
OTHER INFORMATION In 2011–12 grants to institutions totalled £337,000 and grants to individuals totalled £413,000.
HOW TO APPLY On a form available from the foundation's website, together with guidelines and criteria.
WHO TO APPLY TO Graham Chappell, Clerk, PO Box 34098, London N13 5XU *Tel.* 020 8882 2999 *Fax* 020 8882 9724 *email* trustees@tgsf.org.uk *Website* www.tgsf.org.uk

■ The Tower Hill Trust

CC NO 206225   **ESTABLISHED** 1938
WHERE FUNDING CAN BE GIVEN Tower Hill and St Katherine's ward in Tower Hamlets.
WHO CAN BENEFIT Community-based organisations and appeals benefiting children and young adults, at risk groups, people disadvantaged by poverty and socially isolated people.
WHAT IS FUNDED Organisations working for the relief of need or sickness, the provision of leisure and recreation facilities for social welfare and in

Think carefully about every application. Is it justified?

953

support of education, and to provide and maintain gardens and open spaces.

WHAT IS NOT FUNDED No grants to individuals.

TYPE OF GRANT General and capital projects involving building renovation will be considered.

RANGE OF GRANTS Generally £300–£25,000.

SAMPLE GRANTS Osmani Trust; Crisis UK; both receive a grant of (£25,000); Valliance Community Sports Association; All Hallows Church both receive a grant of (£10,000); Old Ford Primary School (£7,000) and Newton Fusion (£4,000).

FINANCES *Year* 2011–12 *Income* £207,996 *Grants* £115,000 *Assets* £4,696,464

TRUSTEES Maj.Gen.Geoffrey Field; John Polk; John Burton-Hall; Susan Wood; Ken Clunie; Jonathan Solomon; Davina Walter.

HOW TO APPLY 'We have a two-stage application process. Stage One – Initial Proposal: Initially we ask you to send in a proposal (up to three pages) that covers the points below. We also ask for certain additional documents. When we receive your proposal we will send you an acknowledgement and may ask you for further clarification. You may submit your proposal at any time. Every three months (February, May, August and November), trustees will look at all of the initial proposals we have received and draw up a shortlist. All proposals that are not on the shortlist will be rejected. Stage Two – Further Information: If your proposal is successfully shortlisted, you move on to stage two of the process and will be asked for further information. You may also receive a visit from our Grant Officer. Your proposal will then be presented to a trustees' meeting, which will make the final decision about your request. Not all shortlisted organisations will receive funding, as the trust considers more proposals than we are able to support. Note that the whole process (stage one and stage two) is likely to take up to four months.'

WHO TO APPLY TO Roland Smith, Attlee House, 28 Commercial Street, London E1 6LR *Tel.* 020 7377 6614 *Fax* 020 7377 9822 *email* enquiries@towerhilltrust.org.uk *Website* www.towerhilltrust.org.uk

■ **The Towry Law Charitable Trust**

(also known as the Castle Educational Trust)

CC NO 278880   **ESTABLISHED** 1979

WHERE FUNDING CAN BE GIVEN UK, with a slight preference for the south of England.

WHO CAN BENEFIT Organisations benefiting people of all ages and disabled people.

WHAT IS FUNDED Education, medical research and social welfare.

WHAT IS NOT FUNDED No grants to individuals, bodies which are not UK-registered charities, local branches or associates of UK charities.

RANGE OF GRANTS £45–£100,000

SAMPLE GRANTS The Prince's Trust (£100,000); The Scouts Association; The Teenage Cancer Trust; The Three Counties Council Ride; Walk the Walk; Yorkshire Air Ambulance; Orangutan Appeal; Race for Life; Rainbow Trust; Richmond Borough Mind; Rotary Club of Leatherhead; East Berkshire Operatic Society; Exeter YMCA; Friends of St Michael's and Guide Dogs for the Blind.

FINANCES *Year* 2012–13 *Income* £52,074 *Grants* £125,130 *Assets* £1,385,138

TRUSTEES Andrew Fisher; David Middleton; Alex Rickard; Jill Pinington.

HOW TO APPLY The trust has stated that unsolicited applications are not considered. The trust currently states: 'The Towry Charitable Trust is a Silver Patron of The Prince's Trust and, as such, is committed to supporting The Prince's Trust for the next three years. Once grants have been paid to The Prince's Trust each year, the Towry Consultative Committee (an employee Consultative Committee) determines the appropriate charities to which remaining funds may be paid by way of grant and support is given to charitable causes supported by individual employees. The Towry Consultative Committee will also determine the duration of the grant, which may vary from a one-off grant to grants for longer periods. In view of this programme of activities, the Towry Charitable Trust does not tend to consider ad hoc requests for grants.'

WHO TO APPLY TO Jacqueline Gregory, c/o Towry Group, 6 New Street Square, London EC4A 3BF *Tel.* 020 7936 7236 *email* jacqui.gregory@towry.com

■ **The Toy Trust**

CC NO 1001634   **ESTABLISHED** 1991

WHERE FUNDING CAN BE GIVEN UK.

WHO CAN BENEFIT Children's charities.

WHAT IS FUNDED Projects benefiting children

SAMPLE GRANTS Medic Malawi (£135,000); Toybox Charity (£10,000); Blaen Wern Farm Trust and Disability Challengers (£5,000 each); and Eden Rose Coppice Trust (£4,000).

FINANCES *Year* 2012 *Income* £356,832 *Grants* £340,622 *Assets* £68,551

TRUSTEES The British Toy and Hobby Association Ltd; Clive Jones; Frank Martin; Kevin Jones; Philip Ratcliffe.

OTHER INFORMATION This trust was registered in 1991 to centralise the giving of the British Toy and Hobby Association.

HOW TO APPLY In writing to the correspondent.

WHO TO APPLY TO Roland Earl, c/o British Toy and Hobby Association, 80 Camberwell Road, London SE5 0EG *Tel.* 020 7701 7271 *email* admin@btha.co.uk *Website* www.btha.co.uk

■ **The Toye Foundation**

CC NO 1147256   **ESTABLISHED** 2012

WHERE FUNDING CAN BE GIVEN UK, with a preference for Essex.

WHO CAN BENEFIT Registered charities.

WHAT IS FUNDED General charitable purposes.

TRUSTEES William Toye; Rosemarie Toye; John Worby.

OTHER INFORMATION The settlor of the foundation, William Toye, co-founded transport company Allport Group, which has since been sold to CS Logistics. Mr Toye is also active in the Christian community in Essex, and this may influence future funding from the foundation.

HOW TO APPLY In writing to the correspondent.

WHO TO APPLY TO William Toye, Trustee, Hazel Cottage, Epping Green, Epping, Essex CM16 6QL

■ **The TPO Foundation**

CC NO 1149917   **ESTABLISHED** 2012

WHERE FUNDING CAN BE GIVEN UK.

WHO CAN BENEFIT Registered charities.

WHAT IS FUNDED General charitable purposes.

954

Does the trust you have chosen match your needs? Haphazard applications waste postage and time

TRUSTEES Andrew Rosenfeld; Kevin Curley; Christopher Kelly.

HOW TO APPLY In writing to the correspondent.

WHO TO APPLY TO Andrew Rosenfeld, Trustee, c/o Airnet Limited, Bond House, 19–20 Woodstock Street, London W1C 2AN *Tel.* 020 7268 2600

■ The Mayor of Trafford's Charity Fund

CC NO 512299   **ESTABLISHED** 1982

WHERE FUNDING CAN BE GIVEN The borough of Trafford.

WHO CAN BENEFIT Voluntary organisations and charitable groups only.

WHAT IS FUNDED The mayor/mayoress chooses a single charity (occasionally two) to support the year before he/she takes office; the charity must benefit the inhabitants of the borough of Trafford.

TYPE OF GRANT Capital; one-off; one year or less.

SAMPLE GRANTS Victim Support (£18,000); Intergen (£1,000) and 'Earthquake Appeal' (£500).

FINANCES *Year* 2011–12 *Income* £26,081 *Grants* £26,081

TRUSTEES Ian Duncan; Jane Baugh; Jane Le Fevre.

HOW TO APPLY As the recipient charity is selected before the mayor takes office, it is unlikely that applications to this trust will be successful.

WHO TO APPLY TO The Mayor's Office, Mayor's Office, Trafford Borough Council, Trafford Town Hall, Talbot Road, Stretford, Manchester M32 0TH *Tel.* 01619 124221 *email* mayors.office@trafford.gov.uk

■ Annie Tranmer Charitable Trust

CC NO 1044231   **ESTABLISHED** 1989

WHERE FUNDING CAN BE GIVEN UK, particularly Suffolk and adjacent counties.

WHO CAN BENEFIT Organisations and individuals.

WHAT IS FUNDED The objectives of the trust are to: make grants in the county of Suffolk and adjacent counties; make grants to national charities according to the wishes of Mrs Tranmer during her lifetime; advance education and historical research relating to the national monument known as the Sutton Hoo burial site and Sutton Hoo estate; to further the education of children and young people in Suffolk; make grants for general charitable purposes.

RANGE OF GRANTS Up to £129,000.

SAMPLE GRANTS Royal National Lifeboat Institution (£128,500); Mid Essex Hospital Services NHS Trust, Macmillan Cancer and Marie Curie Cancer (£5,000 each); St Elizabeth Hospice, Ovarian Cancer Action and the Salvation Army (£2,000 each); the National Strings Academy, Raynauds and Scleroderma Association and Wellbeing for Women (£1,000 each); and Wendy Gough Awareness Foundation and Missing People (£500 each).

FINANCES *Year* 2012–13 *Income* £119,033 *Grants* £229,553 *Assets* £3,536,992

TRUSTEES John Miller; Valerie Lewis; Nigel Bonham-Carter; Patrick Grieve.

OTHER INFORMATION Grants were made totalling £229,000 of which £216,500 was donated to 74 organisations and £13,000 to 17 individuals.

HOW TO APPLY This trust does not accept unsolicited applications.

WHO TO APPLY TO M. Kirby, Administrator, 51 Bennett Road, Ipswich IP1 5HX

■ The Constance Travis Charitable Trust

CC NO 294540   **ESTABLISHED** 1986

WHERE FUNDING CAN BE GIVEN UK (national charities only); Northamptonshire (all sectors).

WHO CAN BENEFIT UK-wide organisations and local groups in Northamptonshire.

WHAT IS FUNDED General charitable purposes.

WHAT IS NOT FUNDED No grants to individuals or non-registered charities.

TYPE OF GRANT One-off grants for core, capital and project support.

RANGE OF GRANTS Up to £30,000.

SAMPLE GRANTS Royal Academy of Music (£210,000); Delapre Abbey Preservation Trust (£150,000); Northamptonshire Community Foundation (£115,000); Royal Albert Hall (£50,000); UCL Cancer Institute Research Trust (£20,000); Volunteer Reading Help (£15,000); and Alzheimer's Research Trust (£10,000).

FINANCES *Year* 2012 *Income* £2,416,705 *Grants* £1,158,464 *Assets* £74,377,330

TRUSTEES Constance M. Travis; Ernest R. A. Travis; Peta J. Travis; Matthew Travis.

HOW TO APPLY In writing to the correspondent. The trust's 2012 accounts note that though the trustees make grants with no formal application, they may invite organisations to submit a formal application.

WHO TO APPLY TO Ernest R. A. Travis, Trustee, Quinton Rising, Quinton, Northampton NN7 2EF

■ The Treeside Trust

CC NO 1061586   **ESTABLISHED** 1997

WHERE FUNDING CAN BE GIVEN UK, but mainly local in Oldham

WHO CAN BENEFIT Mainly small local charities, as well as a few UK-wide charities which are supported on a regular basis.

WHAT IS FUNDED General charitable purposes.

RANGE OF GRANTS The trust states: 'In the main the trustees intend to make a limited number of substantial grants each year, rather than a larger number of smaller ones, in order to make significant contributions to some of the causes supported.'

SAMPLE GRANTS Footprints Theatre Trust (£12,500).

FINANCES *Year* 2011–12 *Income* £29,931 *Grants* £75,000 *Assets* £2,038,734

TRUSTEES Catherine Gould; Diana Ives; Richard Gould; Roger Gould; Richard Ives.

HOW TO APPLY The trust has stated that they 'do not welcome unsolicited applications'.

WHO TO APPLY TO John Beresford Gould, 4 The Park, Grasscroft, Oldham OL4 4ES *Tel.* 01457 876422

■ The Trefoil Trust (formerly known as Anona Winn Charitable Trust)

CC NO 1044101   **ESTABLISHED** 1995

WHERE FUNDING CAN BE GIVEN UK.

WHO CAN BENEFIT Charitable organisations.

WHAT IS FUNDED Health; young people; disability; the arts; armed forces.

WHAT IS NOT FUNDED No applications are considered from individuals.

TYPE OF GRANT Mostly one-off.

RANGE OF GRANTS Mostly £1,000–£5,000.

SAMPLE GRANTS Charities Aid Foundation (£30,000); COPS (£5,000); Sussex Snowdrop Trust (£4,000); the Fire Fighters' Charity, Friends of

Newmarket Day Centre and Gurkha Welfare Trust (£2,500 each); Sarah Greene Breakthrough Tribute Fund (£1,500); and ABF the Soldiers Charity, Alzheimer's Research and Crisis at Christmas (£1,000 each).

FINANCES *Year* 2012 *Income* £49,762 *Grants* £90,000 *Assets* £1,052,958

TRUSTEE Trefoil Trustees Ltd.

OTHER INFORMATION Grants to 26 organisations totalled £90,000.

HOW TO APPLY Applications will only be considered if received in writing and accompanied by the organisation's latest report and full accounts. The trustees usually meet in February and July to decide on distributions.

WHO TO APPLY TO Rupert Hughes, Administrator, New Inn Cottage, Croft Lane, Winstone, Cirencester GL7 7LN *Tel.* 01285 821338

....

■ The Tresillian Trust

CC NO 1105826   **ESTABLISHED** 2004

WHERE FUNDING CAN BE GIVEN Worldwide.

WHO CAN BENEFIT Charitable organisations.

WHAT IS FUNDED Overseas aid and welfare causes. In the UK, community based projects supporting the elderly and young people; in Africa, Asia and South America, projects supporting the education and health of women and children; and worldwide projects dealing with conflict and disaster areas and the environment.

SAMPLE GRANTS Target TB (£6,000); St Andrew's Clinic for Children and Christian Friends of Korea (£5,000 each); Alive and Kicking UK and Blacksmith Institute (£2,000 each) and Homes for Zimbabwe (£1,000.)

FINANCES *Year* 2011–12 *Income* £67,350 *Grants* £39,500 *Assets* £2,679,602

TRUSTEES G. E. S. Robinson; P. W. Bate; M. D. Willcox.

HOW TO APPLY In writing to the correspondent. 'The trust is very selective in the grantmaking process and applications are reviewed by the trustees personally.'

WHO TO APPLY TO M. D. Willcox, Trustee, Old Coach House, Sunnyside, Bergh Apton, Norwich NR15 1DD *Tel.* 01508 480100 *email* info@willcoxlewis.co.uk

....

■ The Triangle Trust (1949) Fund

CC NO 222860   **ESTABLISHED** 1949

WHERE FUNDING CAN BE GIVEN Worldwide. In practice UK.

WHO CAN BENEFIT Registered charities, CICs and social enterprises.

WHAT IS FUNDED Specialist organisations working with carers or the rehabilitation of ex-offenders.

WHAT IS NOT FUNDED The trust will not fund the following: overseas charities or projects outside the UK; charities for the promotion of religion; medical research; environmental, wildlife or heritage appeals. Also refer to the trust's eligibility criteria on its website.

TYPE OF GRANT One-off, recurring, salaries and running costs.

RANGE OF GRANTS Up to £40,000.

FINANCES *Year* 2012–13 *Income* £630,216 *Grants* £343,116 *Assets* £17,681,645

TRUSTEES Melanie Burfitt, Chair; Dr Robert Hale; Mark Powell; Bruce Newbigging; Kate Purcell; Jamie Dicks; Helen Evans; Andrew Pitt.

OTHER INFORMATION The grant total includes commitments from previous years within themes and purposes the trust no longer supports, and £31,000 to individuals.

HOW TO APPLY The following information was taken from the trust's website:

'We will be holding one round of development grants per year for organisations working with carers, and one round per year for organisations working with the rehabilitation of offenders or ex-offenders. This will ensure applicants have a higher success rate and high quality applications are not rejected, compared to holding two or more rounds with lower success rates. The application process will be two-stage. Following the submission of your initial online application, shortlisted applicants will be asked to host a visit from the Triangle Trust where they will be required to present their strategic plan for the next few years. Only complete applications submitted using the online form by 5 pm on the published closing date will be accepted. Ensure you meet all the criteria before deciding to apply.' Check the trust's website for application deadlines.

WHO TO APPLY TO Dr Joanne Knight, Director, Foundation House, 2–4 Forum Place, Fiddlebridge Lane, Hatfield, Hertfordshire AL10 0RN *Tel.* 01707 707078 *email* info@triangletrust.org.uk *Website* www.triangletrust.org.uk

....

■ The True Colours Trust

CC NO 1089893   **ESTABLISHED** 2001

WHERE FUNDING CAN BE GIVEN UK and Africa.

WHO CAN BENEFIT Registered charities.

WHAT IS FUNDED Grantmaking is focused in three areas: children and young people with complex disabilities in the UK; palliative care for children and young people in the UK; and palliative care in sub-Saharan Africa. The trust also makes small grants to local charities supporting disabled children, children with life-limiting conditions, their siblings and their families.

WHAT IS NOT FUNDED No grants to individuals.

TYPE OF GRANT One-off and recurring. Local grants tend to be one-off and for capital expenditure.

RANGE OF GRANTS Up to £250,000. Small grants up to £10,000.

SAMPLE GRANTS Childhood Bereavement Network (£405,000), towards the organisation's core costs over three years; Council for Disabled Children (£312,000), towards the core costs of the Every Disabled Child Matters campaign over three years and the development of resources to help parents understand Health and Safety legislation and their child's rights in this context; African Palliative Care Association (£200,000), towards the organisation's core costs over two years; Jessie May Trust (£150,000), towards the salary of a band 5 nurse and a contribution towards core costs over three years; Kenya Hospices and Palliative Care Association (£120,500), towards the costs of establishing integrated palliative care services in Kenya's 11 national referral hospitals and towards the development of a higher diploma in palliative care at Kenya Medical Training College; St Oswald's Hospice (£60,000), towards a two-year appointment of a part-time consultant in Paediatric Palliative Care to work across North East England; Heart n Soul (£28,000), a one-off grant towards the organisation's core costs; Julia's House (£11,500), towards its sibling support programme; Chicken Shed Theatre Company (£10,000), towards the purchase of a specially adapted minibus; Go Kids Go – Association of Wheelchair Children (£6,500), towards the cost of wheelchair training workshops; and Noah's

Ark – The Children's Hospice (£5,000), towards its siblings support programme.

FINANCES *Year* 2011–12 *Income* £1,757,245 *Grants* £1,675,701 *Assets* £9,858,392

TRUSTEES Lucy Sainsbury; Dominic Flynn; Bernard Willis; Tim Price.

HOW TO APPLY The following information is taken from the trust's website:

'Programme Grants: the trust only funds registered charities or activities with clearly defined charitable purposes. Trustees only consider unsolicited applications for their Small Grants Programmes (UK and Africa) and for their Individual Grants UK programme. Proposals for the trust's other programmes are invited by the trustees or initiated at their request. The trustees are keen to learn more about organisations whose work fits into the categories above but unsolicited applications are not encouraged and are unlikely to be successful. Information about your organisation and project should be sent by post to The True Colours Trust, The Peak, 5 Wilton Road, London SW1V 1AP, do not send more than two pages of A4 covering: the organisation – explaining its charitable aims and objectives, and giving its most recent annual income and expenditure, and current financial position. Do not send a full set of accounts; the project requiring funding – why it is needed, who will benefit and in what way; the funding – breakdown of costs, any money raised so far, and how the balance will be raised; at this stage do not send supporting books, brochures, DVDs, annual reports or accounts. All correspondence will be acknowledged by post. If your organisation is a candidate for support, you will hear from us within 12 weeks of the acknowledgement. Applicants who do not hear from us within this time must assume they have been unsuccessful.'

'Small Grants – UK and Africa: the trustees welcome unsolicited applications for their small grants programmes, both in the UK and in Africa. Trustees are keen to make these programmes available to as many organisations as possible; it is therefore unlikely that they will fund any organisation in consecutive years.'

'UK: the trustees are committed to supporting a large number of excellent local organisations and projects that work with disabled children and their families on a daily basis. This is done through the trust's small grants programme. It provides grants of up to £10,000 to help smaller organisations develop and deliver programmes for children, their siblings and families. It is open to applications at any time. Grants in this category are usually one-off contributions rather than multi-year grants for ongoing revenue costs. Note the following: this programme is for UK organisations and projects only; the programme is unable to provide support to local authorities; trustees are keen to make the grant programme available to as many organisations as possible; it is therefore unlikely that they will fund organisations in consecutive years.'

'Upon submission of your application you will receive an acknowledgement letter or email. If you do not hear from us within twelve weeks of the date of this acknowledgement accept that the trustees, with regret, have not been able to make a grant in response to your appeal. You will not receive a letter explaining that your application has been unsuccessful. Applications for small grants should be made using our online application form or alternatively you may complete the downloadable version of the form and either return to us by post or email.'

WHO TO APPLY TO Alan Bookbinder, Director, The Peak, 5 Wilton Road, London SW1V 1AP *Tel.* 020 7410 0330 *Fax* 020 7410 0332 *email* truecolours@sfct.org.uk *Website* www.truecolourstrust.org.uk

■ Truedene Co. Ltd

CC NO 248268   **ESTABLISHED** 1966

WHERE FUNDING CAN BE GIVEN UK and overseas.

WHO CAN BENEFIT Organisations benefiting children, young adults, students and Jewish people.

WHAT IS FUNDED Educational, religious and other charitable institutions, principally Jewish.

RANGE OF GRANTS £1,000–£150,000

SAMPLE GRANTS Previous beneficiaries have included: Beis Ruchel D'Satmar Girls School Ltd, British Friends of Tchernobyl, Congregation Paile Yoetz, Cosmon Belz Limited, Friends of Mir, Kolel Shomrei Hachomoth, Mesifta Talmudical College, Mosdos Ramou, Orthodox Council of Jerusalem, Tevini Limited, United Talmudical Associates Limited, VMCT and Yeshivo Horomo Talmudical College.

FINANCES *Year* 2011–12 *Income* £444,686 *Grants* £788,378 *Assets* £4,100,974

TRUSTEES Sarah Klein, Chair; Samuel Berger; Solomon Laufer; Sije Berger; Zelda Sternlicht.

OTHER INFORMATION No list of grant beneficiaries was included in the accounts.

HOW TO APPLY In writing to the correspondent

WHO TO APPLY TO The Trustees, c/o Cohen Arnold and Co., 1075 Finchley Road, London NW11 0PU *Tel.* 020 8731 0777

■ The Truemark Trust

CC NO 265855   **ESTABLISHED** 1973

WHERE FUNDING CAN BE GIVEN UK.

WHO CAN BENEFIT Registered charities with preference for small local charities, neighbourhood-based community projects and innovative work with less popular groups.

WHAT IS FUNDED 'The relief of all kinds of social distress and disadvantage.'

WHAT IS NOT FUNDED Grants are made to registered charities only. Applications from individuals, including students, are ineligible. No grants are made in response to general appeals from large national charities. Grants are seldom available for churches or church buildings or for scientific or medical research projects.

TYPE OF GRANT Usually one-off for a specific project or part of a project. Core funding and/or salaries rarely considered.

RANGE OF GRANTS Average grant £1,000.

SAMPLE GRANTS Iris Trust (£11,000); Music and Health in the Community and West Midlands Quaker Peace Education Project (£10,000 each); Unite and Wardens Centre for Disabled People (£5,000 each); Cape UK and Forces Support (£3,000 each); Hibiscus Caribbean Elderly Association (£2,500); Cranford Job Seekers Club and Meridian Money Advice (£2,000 each); and Coventry Tamil Association, College of Psychic Studies, Playback Youth Theatre, Shetland Youth Information Service, South Copeland Disability Group and Young People Taking Action (£1,000 each).

FINANCES *Year* 2011–12 *Income* £549,894 *Grants* £404,000 *Assets* £12,033,194

TRUSTEES Sharon Knight; Wendy Collett; Judy Hayward; Stuart Neil; Sir Thomas Lucas.

HOW TO APPLY In writing to the correspondent, including the most recent set of accounts, clear details of the need the project is designed to meet and an outline budget. Trustees meet four times a year. Only successful applicants receive a reply.

WHO TO APPLY TO Clare Pegden, Administrator, PO Box 2, Liss, Hampshire GU33 6YP *Tel.* 01730 894120

■ Truemart Limited

CC NO 1090586   **ESTABLISHED** 1984
WHERE FUNDING CAN BE GIVEN UK-wide and overseas, with a preference for Greater London.
WHO CAN BENEFIT Charitable organisations.
WHAT IS FUNDED The advancement of religion in accordance with the Orthodox Jewish faith, the relief of poverty and general charitable purposes.
FINANCES *Year* 2011–12 *Income* £232,304 *Grants* £175,430 *Assets* £82,769
TRUSTEES I. Heitner; S. Heitner.
OTHER INFORMATION No list of grant beneficiaries was included in the accounts.
HOW TO APPLY In writing to the correspondent.
WHO TO APPLY TO S. Heitner, Trustee, 34 The Ridgeway, London NW11 8QS *Tel.* 020 8455 4456

■ Trumros Limited

CC NO 285533   **ESTABLISHED** 1982
WHERE FUNDING CAN BE GIVEN UK.
WHO CAN BENEFIT Jewish organisations.
WHAT IS FUNDED Jewish religious and educational organisations.
SAMPLE GRANTS Emuno Educational Centre (£51,000); Before Trust (£32,000); Ichud Mosdos Gur (£31,000); Chevras Mo'oz Ladol (£25,500); Am Ha Chessed (£20,000); Beis Yosef Zvi (£12,500); Gesher Charitable Trust and Ozer Gemillas Chasodim (£10,000 each).
FINANCES *Year* 2012 *Income* £1,149,148 *Grants* £513,521 *Assets* £9,119,258
TRUSTEES Ronald Hofbauer; Hannah Hofbauer.
HOW TO APPLY In writing to the correspondent.
WHO TO APPLY TO Ronald Hofbauer, Trustee, 282 Finchley Road, London NW3 7AD *Tel.* 020 7431 3282 *email* r.hofbauer@btconnect.com

■ The Trusthouse Charitable Foundation

CC NO 1063945   **ESTABLISHED** 1997
WHERE FUNDING CAN BE GIVEN Unrestricted, but mainly UK.
WHO CAN BENEFIT Registered charities and other not-for-profit organisations.
WHAT IS FUNDED Within the trust's overarching themes, there are three broad areas of funding: community support; disability and healthcare; arts, education and heritage.
WHAT IS NOT FUNDED The foundation will not normally consider supporting the following: animal welfare; applications for revenue funding for more than one year; capital appeals for places of worship; grantmaking organisations or umbrella groups; grants for individuals (including bursaries through a third party organisation); feasibility studies and evaluations; local authorities; Local Education Authority schools or their Parent Teachers Associations, except if those schools are solely for students with Special Needs; medical research projects; office IT equipment including software costs; organisations that have received a grant for

three consecutive years from the foundation; projects involving the start-up or piloting of new services; projects where the primary objective is environmental or conservation; projects where the primary objective is the promotion of a particular religion; renovation or alteration projects to make a building compliant with the Disability and Discrimination Act; revenue funding for organisations with an income of over £300,000 per annum; services operated by the NHS; social research; training of professionals within the UK; universities. Under normal circumstances, the foundation is not currently funding projects which are for: the purchase of computers, other electronic equipment or software for delivery of the charity's work (e.g. for an IT suite in a youth centre); PR or other awareness raising campaigns, including the publication of leaflets or events calendars, websites.
TYPE OF GRANT One-off for specific purposes.
RANGE OF GRANTS Generally up to £30,000.
SAMPLE GRANTS KIND: towards the cost of creating a healthy living and wellbeing centre for disadvantaged children and their families in Toxteth, Liverpool; Glasgow Building Preservation Trust: towards the cost of repairing a listed railway station building in Pollokshaws, Glasgow, to create a base for a charity recycling bikes and giving sporting/training opportunities to young people; and Daviot Village Hall: towards the cost of building a new hall at a small village in Aberdeenshire (£30,000 each).
FINANCES *Year* 2011–12 *Income* £1,020,000 *Grants* £2,058,374 *Assets* £61,374,000
TRUSTEES Sir Jeremy Beecham; Baroness Sarah Hogg; The Duke of Marlborough; Anthony Peel; The Hon. Olga Polizzi; Sir Hugh Rossi; Lady Janet Balfour of Burleigh; Sir John Nutting; Howell Harris-Hughes; Revd Rose Hudson-Wilkin; Lady Hamilton.
HOW TO APPLY On an application form available from the foundation's website, accessed following the completion of a brief eligibility questionnaire, which also identifies which type of grant may be most suitable. Details of additional information to be included with the application are given on the form. Applications must be made by post.
WHO TO APPLY TO Judith Leigh, Grants Manager, 6th Floor, 65 Leadenhall Street, London EC3A 2AD *Tel.* 020 7264 4990 *Website* www. trusthousecharitablefoundation.org.uk

■ The Tsukanov Family Foundation

CC NO 1148772   **ESTABLISHED** 2012
WHERE FUNDING CAN BE GIVEN UK and Russia.
WHO CAN BENEFIT Charities and community groups.
WHAT IS FUNDED General charitable purposes, education and the arts, with a preference for organisations working with children and young people
TRUSTEES Igor Tsukanov; Natalia Tsukanova; Viktoria Grigoreva.
HOW TO APPLY In writing to the correspondent.
WHO TO APPLY TO Igor Tsukanov, Trustee, 2nd Floor, Audley House, 13 Palace Street, London W1K 5JH *Tel.* 020 7937 6153

■ The James Tudor Foundation

CC NO 1105916   **ESTABLISHED** 2004
WHERE FUNDING CAN BE GIVEN UK and overseas.
WHO CAN BENEFIT Institutions and registered charities.

Does the trust you have chosen match your needs? Haphazard applications waste postage and time

WHAT IS FUNDED The foundation's six programme areas are: palliative care; medical research; health education, awards and scholarship; the direct relief of sickness; the fulfilment of the foundation's charitable objects by other means; overseas work for the relief of sickness.

WHAT IS NOT FUNDED Grants are not made: that directly replace, or negatively affect, statutory funding; for work that has already taken place; for endowment funds; for economic, community development or employment use; for adventure or residential courses, expeditions or overseas travel; for sport or recreation uses, including festivals; for environmental, conservation or heritage causes; for animal welfare; from applicants who have applied within the last 12 months.

TYPE OF GRANT Project funding, awards and scholarships, capital projects and equipment and staffing costs.

RANGE OF GRANTS Mostly up to £10,000

SAMPLE GRANTS World Health Organisation (£50,000); University of Nottingham (£47,500); Children's Hospice South West (£30,000); Islet Research (£21,500); University of Bath (£19,500); Special Effects (£18,500); British Liver Trust (£16,500); GivingWorldOnLine (£13,500); Youth Net (£8,000); and West Cumbria Hospice at Home (£5,000).

FINANCES *Year* 2011–12 *Income* £997,066 *Grants* £573,563 *Assets* £24,132,532

TRUSTEES Martin G. Wren, Chair; Richard R. G. Esler; Malcolm R. Field; Roger K. Jones; Cedric B. Nash.

HOW TO APPLY On an application form available from the foundation's website. Comprehensive guidelines for applicant are also available from there. Potential applicants must first complete an initial eligibility check.

WHO TO APPLY TO Rod Shaw, Chief Executive, WestPoint, 78 Queens Road, Clifton, Bristol BS8 1QU *Tel.* 01179 858715 *Fax* 01179 858716 *email* admin@jamestudor.org.uk *Website* www.jamestudor.org.uk

---

■ Tudor Rose Ltd

CC NO 800576   **ESTABLISHED** 1987

WHERE FUNDING CAN BE GIVEN UK.

WHO CAN BENEFIT Registered charities benefiting Jewish people and people disadvantaged by poverty.

WHAT IS FUNDED Advancement of religion (Orthodox Jewish), relief of poverty and other charitable purposes.

SAMPLE GRANTS Previously: Lolev Charitable Trust; Woodlands Charity; KTV; Bell Synagogue; Hatzola; Lubavitch Centre; and TCT.

FINANCES *Year* 2011–12 *Income* £418,069 *Grants* £252,406 *Assets* £3,167,473

TRUSTEES Miriam Lehrfield; Sylvie Taub.

OTHER INFORMATION A list of grant beneficiaries was not included in the accounts.

HOW TO APPLY In writing to the correspondent.

WHO TO APPLY TO Samuel Taub, Secretary, c/o Martin and Heller, 5 North End Road, London NW11 7RJ

■ The Tudor Trust

CC NO 1105580   **ESTABLISHED** 1955

WHERE FUNDING CAN BE GIVEN UK and sub-Saharan Africa.

WHO CAN BENEFIT Registered charities and other charitable organisations.

WHAT IS FUNDED Organisations working directly with people who are on the margins of society; a focus on building stronger communities by overcoming isolation and fragmentation and encouraging inclusion, connection and integration; organisations which are embedded in and have developed out of their community – whether the local area or a 'community of interest' high levels of user involvement, and an emphasis on self-help where this is appropriate; work which addresses complex and multi-stranded problems in unusual or imaginative ways; organisations which are thoughtful in their use of resources and which foster community resilience in the face of environmental, economic or social change.

WHAT IS NOT FUNDED The trust does not make grants to: individuals, or organisations applying on behalf of individuals; larger charities (both national and local) enjoying widespread support; statutory bodies; hospitals, health authorities or hospices; medical care, medical equipment or medical research; universities, colleges or schools; academic research, scholarships or bursaries; nurseries, playgroups or crèches; one-off holidays, residentials, trips, exhibitions, conferences, events etc.; animal charities; the promotion of religion; the restoration or conservation of buildings or habitats (where there isn't a strong social welfare focus); work outside the UK. The trust runs a targeted grants programme promoting sustainable agriculture in sub-Saharan Africa. They do not consider unsolicited proposals from groups working overseas; endowment appeals; and work that has already taken place. Applicants are encouraged to call the information team for advice concerning applications.

TYPE OF GRANT Capital and revenue grants, core funding.

RANGE OF GRANTS There is no minimum or maximum grant. Average grant in 2012–13 was £51,000.

SAMPLE GRANTS UK beneficiaries included: Gatwick Detainees Welfare Group (£160,000); Personal Support Unit (£150,000); Coalition for Independent Action and Female Prisoners Welfare Project Hibiscus (£120,000 each); Amber Foundation and Carefree Foster Independence – Cornwall (£105,000 each); Bankside Open Spaces Trust (£85,000); Be Attitude, Brighton Unemployed Centre Families Project and Latin Americas Women's Rights Service (£75,000 each); Alcohol Concern, Angelou Centre and Edinburgh Garden Partners (£60,000 each); Basement Studio, Broomhouse Centre and Green Light Trust (£50,000 each); Making Communities Work and Grow and Men's Action Network (£45,000 each); Age UK Haringey and Bath City Farm Ltd (£20,000 each); Plymouth Youth Sailing (£15,000); and Allsorts Youth Project (£6,500). Overseas beneficiaries included: EMESCO Development Foundation (£90,000); Build It International (£70,000); Organic Agriculture Centre of Kenya – OACK (£40,000); Rammed Earth Consulting CIC and Youth Action for Rural Development (£20,000 each); Find Your Feet (£15,000); and Resources Orientated Development Initiatives – RODI (£2,000).

FINANCES *Year* 2012–13 *Income* £7,694,000 *Grants* £17,460,000 *Assets* £238,585,000

TRUSTEES James Long; Dr Desmond Graves; Catherine Antcliff; Monica Barlow; Nell Buckler; Louise Collins; Elizabeth Crawshaw; Ben Dunwell; Helen Dunwell; Matt Dunwell; Christopher Graves; Mary Graves; Francis Runacres; Vanessa James; Rosalind Dunwell.

OTHER INFORMATION Excellent annual report and accounts are available from the trust. The trust's website also includes full, clear guidelines for applicants.

HOW TO APPLY According to the trust's website, the application process is made up of two stages. A first stage application must include the following: a brief introductory letter; a completed organisation details sheet (available from the funding section of the trust's website); a copy of your most recent annual accounts, and annual report if you produce one; and answers to the following questions, on no more than two sides of A4: what difference do you want to make, and how will your organisation achieve this?; why are you the right organisation to do this work?; how do you know there is a need for your work, and who benefits from the work that you do?; and how would you use funding from Tudor? The proposal should be addressed to the trustees and sent via post. Proposals will be acknowledged within a few days of being received. If the first-stage proposal is successful, applicants will receive an acknowledgement letter plus details about the second-stage of the process. The second stage will be conducted via telephone or a visit. The trust aims to let applicants know within a month whether or not they have progressed to the second stage application. The trust aims to make a decision on most applications three months after progressing to the second stage. Trustees and staff meet every three weeks to consider applications. More information is available on the trust's website.

WHO TO APPLY TO Nicky Lappin, Research and Information Manager, 7 Ladbroke Grove, London W11 3BD *Tel.* 020 7727 8522 *email* general@tudortrust.org.uk *Website* www.tudortrust.org.uk

···

■ The Tufton Charitable Trust

CC NO 801479 **ESTABLISHED** 1989
WHERE FUNDING CAN BE GIVEN UK.
WHO CAN BENEFIT Individuals and charitable organisations.
WHAT IS FUNDED Christian activity supporting evangelism.
WHAT IS NOT FUNDED No grants for repair or maintenance of buildings.
TYPE OF GRANT One-off and project-related.
SAMPLE GRANTS Stowe School Foundation (£60,000); St Michael's Hospice (£45,000); London Institute of Contemporary Christianity (£30,000); Soul Survivor (£25,000); Off the Fence, Mission Aviation Fellowship and Vincent's Appeal Trust (£15,000 each); Royal Opera House and Jesus College – Cambridge (£10,000 each); ReSource and Theos (£7,500 each); and the British Library and Spinnaker Trust (£5,000 each).
FINANCES *Year* 2012 *Income* £241,063 *Grants* £292,900 *Assets* £163,815
TRUSTEES Lady Georgina Wates; Sir Christopher Wates; Joseph Lulham; Wates Charitable Trustees Ltd.
OTHER INFORMATION Grants were given to over 14 organisations and totalled £293,000.
HOW TO APPLY In writing to the correspondent, including an sae. The trustees meet regularly to review applications.
WHO TO APPLY TO The Trustees, Tufton Place, Ewhurst Place, Northiam, East Sussex TN31 6HL

···

■ Tuixen Foundation

CC NO 1081124 **ESTABLISHED** 2000
WHERE FUNDING CAN BE GIVEN Worldwide.
WHO CAN BENEFIT Charitable organisations.
WHAT IS FUNDED General charitable purposes.
WHAT IS NOT FUNDED No grants to individuals.
RANGE OF GRANTS Up to £150,000.
SAMPLE GRANTS Previous beneficiaries included: Impetus Trust (£175,500); University of Manchester (£100,000); Camfed (£50,000); Chance UK, Facing the World, School Home Support and Street League (£30,000 each); Sports Aid Trust (£25,000); First Step Trust (£20,000); and the Shannon Trust (£10,000).
FINANCES *Year* 2011–12 *Income* £3,047,624 *Grants* £805,000 *Assets* £19,770,906
TRUSTEES Peter D. Englander; Dr Leanda Kroll; Stephen M. Rosefield; Peter Clements.
OTHER INFORMATION A list of grants was not available to view with the current accounts.
HOW TO APPLY The foundation has previously stated that 'unsolicited applications are not sought and correspondence will not be entered into'.
WHO TO APPLY TO Paul Clements, Trustee, c/o Coutts and Co., 27th Floor, St Mary Axe, London EC3 8BF *Tel.* 020 7649 2903

···

■ The R. D. Turner Charitable Trust

CC NO 263556 **ESTABLISHED** 1971
WHERE FUNDING CAN BE GIVEN UK, with a preference for the Worcestershire area.
WHO CAN BENEFIT Registered charities only.
WHAT IS FUNDED General charitable purposes. The trustees have resolved that the following objectives be adopted: to support by means of grants and loans other registered charities, particularly in the Worcestershire area; to maintain and enhance the amenities of the villages of Arley and Upper Arley; such other general charitable purposes in connection with the villages of Arley and Upper Arley as the trustees shall in their absolute discretion determine/decide.
WHAT IS NOT FUNDED No grants to non-registered charities or to individuals.
TYPE OF GRANT One-off and recurrent.
RANGE OF GRANTS £500–£15,000.
SAMPLE GRANTS Previous beneficiaries have included: St Richard's Hospice (£15,000); Worcestershire and Dudley Historic Churches Trust (£12,000); British Red Cross Hereford and Worcester (£10,000); ARCOS, Cobalt Appeal Fund and Motor Neurone Disease Association (£5,000 each); County Air Ambulance Trust and Relate Worcestershire (£3,000); Sunfield Children's Homes (£2,000); Listening Books (£1,000); and Talking Newspapers of the UK (£500).
FINANCES *Year* 2011–12 *Income* £565,819 *Grants* £70,500 *Assets* £29,093,122
TRUSTEES John Del Mar; David Pearson; Stephen Preedy; Peter Millward; James Fea.
OTHER INFORMATION Financial information taken from the accounts for the nine months ending December 2012.
HOW TO APPLY The trust does not have a grant application form. Applicant Charities are requested to send a letter of no more than two pages describing their appeal, together with a copy of their latest accounts, to the Trust Administrator at the Grants Office. Phone calls and emails are welcome prior to submitting an application. Appeal guidelines are available on request.

WHO TO APPLY TO Timothy Patrickson, Administrator, 3 Poplar Piece, Inkberrow, Worcester WR7 4JD *Tel.* 01386 792014 *email* timpatrickson@ hotmail.co.uk

....

■ The Douglas Turner Trust

CC NO 227892   ESTABLISHED 1964

WHERE FUNDING CAN BE GIVEN UK and overseas; however, in practice, there is a strong preference for Birmingham and the West Midlands.

WHO CAN BENEFIT Registered charities.

WHAT IS FUNDED Mainly local charities including charities supporting: youth and children; work in the community; health and people with disabilities; hospices; older people; international aid; environment and heritage; social support; the arts; and medical research.

WHAT IS NOT FUNDED No grants to individuals or unregistered charities.

TYPE OF GRANT Recurring and one-off donations, capital and core costs.

RANGE OF GRANTS £500–£20,000

SAMPLE GRANTS St Mary's Hospice Ltd (£18,000); Birmingham Boys' and Girls' Union (£10,000); and WaterAid (£4,000 each). Previous beneficiaries included: 870 House Youth Movement; Gingerbread; Listening Books; Dial Walsall; Compton Hospice; Gracewell Homes Foster Trust; Cotteridge Church Day Centre; Busoga Trust; Birmingham Botanical Gardens; Midlands Actors' Theatre; and Action Medical Research.

FINANCES *Year* 2011–12 *Income* £394,812 *Grants* £383,000 *Assets* £14,769,815

TRUSTEES John Del Mar, Chair; Peter Millward; David Pearson; Stephen Preedy; James Grindall.

HOW TO APPLY In writing to the correspondent, 'on applicant letterhead, two pages or less, and preferably not stapled together', with a copy of the latest annual report and accounts. There are no application forms. The trustees usually meet in February, May, August and December to consider applications, which should be submitted in the month prior to each meeting. Telephone enquiries may be made before submitting an appeal. All applications are acknowledged.

WHO TO APPLY TO Tim Patrickson, Administrator, 3 Poplar Piece, Inkberrow, Worcester WR7 4JD *Tel.* 01386 792014 *email* timpatrickson@ hotmail.co.uk

....

■ The G. J. W. Turner Trust

CC NO 258615   ESTABLISHED 1969

WHERE FUNDING CAN BE GIVEN Birmingham and the Midlands area.

WHO CAN BENEFIT Charitable organisations.

WHAT IS FUNDED General charitable purposes

RANGE OF GRANTS Up to £40,000

SAMPLE GRANTS Birmingham St Mary's Hospice and Sunfield Children's Homes (£40,000 each); Birmingham Rathbone Society (£30,000); Victoria School and Shakespeare's Hospice (£15,000 each); Elmhurst Ballet School Bursary Fund and The Diabetic Foot Trust Fund (£10,000 each); Barnardo's, Birmingham Hippodrome, Children's Hand and Arm Surgery, County Air Ambulance and Queen Alexandra College (£5,000 each); Saltley Neighbourhood Pensioner's Centre (£3,000); St Margaret's Church Short Heath (£2,000) and The National Children's Orchestra of Great Britain (£1,000).

FINANCES *Year* 2011–12 *Income* £365,115 *Grants* £435,500 *Assets* £9,406,793

TRUSTEES David Pearson; Andrew Inglis; Hugh Carslake.

HOW TO APPLY In writing to the correspondent. The trustees meet annually, usually in July.

WHO TO APPLY TO Chrissy Norgrove, Administrator, c/o SGH Martineau LLP, 1 Colmore Square, Birmingham B4 6AA *Tel.* 0870 763 1000 *Fax* 0870 763 2001

....

■ The Florence Turner Trust

CC NO 502721   ESTABLISHED 1973

WHERE FUNDING CAN BE GIVEN UK, but with a strong preference for Leicestershire.

WHO CAN BENEFIT Smaller projects are favoured where donations will make a 'quantifiable difference to the recipients rather than favouring large national charities whose income is measured in millions rather than thousands.' Grants are made for the benefit of individuals through a referring agency such as social services, NHS trusts or similar responsible bodies.

WHAT IS FUNDED 'It is usual practice to make grants for the benefit of individuals through a referring agency such as Social Services, NHS Trusts or similar responsible bodies, and rather

WHAT IS NOT FUNDED The trust does not support individuals for educational purposes.

SAMPLE GRANTS Leicester Charity Link (£12,000); Leicester Grammar School – Bursary (£10,000); Age Concern Leicester, Leicester and Leicestershire Historic Churches Preservation Trust and VISTA (£2,400 each); LOROS (£2,000); New Parks Club for Young People (£1,500); and Four Twelve Ministries and Help for Heroes (£1,000 each).

FINANCES *Year* 2011–12 *Income* £157,906 *Grants* £99,277 *Assets* £5,909,373

TRUSTEES Roger Bowder; Allan A. Veasey; Caroline A. Macpherson.

OTHER INFORMATION Grants totalled £99,000. Support costs were £17,000; auditor's remuneration £3,400 and 'trustees remuneration' was £6,000.

HOW TO APPLY In writing to the correspondent. Trustees meet every eight or nine weeks.

WHO TO APPLY TO Pamela Fowle, Administrator, Shakespeares, Two Colton Square, Leicester LE1 1 QH *Tel.* 01162 576129 *email* paula. fowle@Shakespeares.co.uk

....

■ The Turtleton Charitable Trust

SC NO SC038018   ESTABLISHED 2007

WHERE FUNDING CAN BE GIVEN Scotland

WHO CAN BENEFIT Registered charities.

WHAT IS FUNDED Arts, heritage, poverty, education

FINANCES *Year* 2012–13 *Grants* £75,000

HOW TO APPLY The following information is given by the trust:

'Applications should be made in writing on no more than three sides of A4 by email to turtletontrust@turcanconnell.com. If your charity does not have access to email, a hard copy application may be sent. If this is the first time that you have applied to The Turtleton Charitable Trust, the most recent set of accounts for your charity should also be submitted, preferably by email, along with your application. Do not send additional literature or materials such as DVDs, compact discs, etc., as additional materials will not be passed on to the trustees. The trustees meet once a year in Spring to decide on grants for the following 12 months. Applications should reach us by email or in hard copy not later than 31 January. The trustees normally pay grants prior to 30 June in each year. Note that applications are not normally acknowledged on receipt. A note will be posted [on the administrator's website] once the trustees have met and successful applicants will be contacted after the trustees have held their annual meeting.'

WHO TO APPLY TO Kenneth Pinkerton, Clerk to the Trustees, Turcan Connell, Princes Exchange, 1 Earl Grey Street, Edinburgh EH3 9EE *Tel.* 01312 288111 *email* turtletontrust@turcanconnell.com *Website* www.turcanconnell.com/turtleton

■ Miss S. M. Tutton Charitable Trust

CC NO 298774   ESTABLISHED 1988
WHERE FUNDING CAN BE GIVEN Throughout England and Wales.
WHO CAN BENEFIT Individuals on postgraduate opera courses and organisations involved in music education.
WHAT IS FUNDED Awards and grants for postgraduate opera studies and grants to music colleges, charities and opera companies.
TYPE OF GRANT Grants to individuals through the Sybil Tutton Awards and financial support to educational organisations.
RANGE OF GRANTS Not specified.
SAMPLE GRANTS As stated in the previous system entry, past beneficiaries have included: British Youth Opera, The Britten-Pears Young Artist Programme, Clonter Opera, The National Opera Studio and Young Concert Artists Trust.
FINANCES *Year* 2012 *Income* £96,384 *Grants* £39,000 *Assets* £2,976,118
TRUSTEE Musicians Benevolent Fund.
HOW TO APPLY As the trust's website states, applications from individuals are no longer accepted. 'Candidates will be selected on a nominations only basis, by heads of voice from the conservatoires, music colleges and National Opera Studio. Institutions will be fully informed of the nomination process.' Applications by the organisations for financial support are not specified.
WHO TO APPLY TO Musicians Benevolent Fund, 7–11 Britannia Street, London WC1X 9JS *Tel.* 020 7239 9100 *email* info@helpmusicians.org.uk *Website* www.helpmusicians.org.uk

■ The TUUT Charitable Trust

CC NO 258665   ESTABLISHED 1969
WHERE FUNDING CAN BE GIVEN Worldwide.
WHO CAN BENEFIT Small to medium-sized organisations, particularly those having close associations with trade unions.
WHAT IS FUNDED General at trustees' discretion, with an overriding priority to charities with strong trade union connections or interests.
The trustees stated in their 2011/12 annual report that they are:
'adopting a fresh approach which in the main and over perhaps a four year period, will provide support for one specific cause or project in the UK and one overseas.'
WHAT IS NOT FUNDED No grants to individuals or to charities based overseas.
RANGE OF GRANTS Up to £40,000
SAMPLE GRANTS React (£1,700); Happy Days Children's' Charity (£1,200); Cares, Hope and

Happy Homes for Children and Second Chance (£1,000); CICRA (£950); Derby Toc H Camp (£780) and RNLI and Royal British Legion (£500).
FINANCES *Year* 2011–12 *Income* £29,381 *Grants* £9,120 *Assets* £2,055,622
TRUSTEES Lord Christopher; M. Walsh; M. Bradley; B. Barber; Lord Brookman; E. Sweeney.
HOW TO APPLY 'To apply for a grant, charitable organisations should apply for a Form of Request and submit this, duly completed. The Trustees meet three times a year to consider requests received.'
WHO TO APPLY TO Stephanie Ellis, TU Fund Managers Ltd, Congress House, Great Russell Street, London WC1B 3LQ *Tel.* 020 7637 7116 *email* stephanie@tufm.co.uk *Website* www.tufm.co.uk

■ TVML Foundation

CC NO 1135495   ESTABLISHED 2010
WHERE FUNDING CAN BE GIVEN UK and overseas, with preference towards Brazil and Israel.
WHO CAN BENEFIT Charities and community groups.
WHAT IS FUNDED Educational and lifehood initiatives.
FINANCES *Year* 2012 *Income* £102,635 *Grants* £466,072 *Assets* £4,601,385
TRUSTEES Vivian Lederman; Marcos Lederman; Marcelo Steuer.
OTHER INFORMATION Grants are made to organisations and individuals. A list of grant beneficiaries was not included in the accounts.
HOW TO APPLY In writing to the correspondent.
WHO TO APPLY TO Tania Lima, Administrator, 8 Sand Ridge, Ridgewood, Uckfield, East Sussex TN22 5ET

■ Two Ridings Community Foundation

CC NO 1084043   ESTABLISHED 2000
WHERE FUNDING CAN BE GIVEN York and North Yorkshire.
WHO CAN BENEFIT Charities and community groups.
WHAT IS FUNDED Health and social welfare.
RANGE OF GRANTS Usually up to £10,000.
SAMPLE GRANTS Hull and East Riding Development Company Limited (£10,000); Selby Globe Community Cinema and Burton Regeneration Group (£5,000 each); Beal Village Hall Trust (£3,900); Sherburn White Rose Junior Football Club (£2,250); Thirsk and Sowerby Hard of Hearing Club (£1,600); Poppleton Under Fives (£550); Greenfields – School and Community Garden Project (£300) and Poppleton Road Out Of School Club (£100).
FINANCES *Year* 2011–12 *Income* £394,170 *Grants* £425,170 *Assets* £2,364,117
TRUSTEES Wendy Bundy; Maureen Macleod; Joe Goodhart; Philip Ingham; Gil Richardson; Richard Fletcher.
OTHER INFORMATION Grant schemes change frequently. Consult the foundation's website for details of current programmes.
HOW TO APPLY The foundation's website has details of the grant schemes currently being administered and how to apply.
WHO TO APPLY TO Jan Norton, Grants Manager, Primrose Hill, Buttercrambe Road, Stamford Bridge, York YO41 1AW *Tel.* 01759 377400 *email* office@trcf.org.uk *Website* www.trcf.org.uk

■ The Tyche Charitable Trust

cc no 1148078   **established** 2012
where funding can be given UK.
who can benefit Charities and community groups.
what is funded Health and social welfare, support for the armed forces and the emergency services. There is a preference for organisations working with children and young people, older people and people with a disability.
trustees Barclays Bank Trust Co. Ltd (Walter Coxon; David Currie; Graham Nicoll; Thomas Rostron; David Blizzard).
how to apply In writing to the correspondent.
who to apply to Barclays Bank Trust Co. Ltd, Osborne Court, Gadbrook Park, Rudheath, Cheshire CW9 7UE *Tel.* 01606 313386

■ Community Foundation Serving Tyne and Wear and Northumberland

cc no 700510   **established** 1988
where funding can be given Tyne and Wear and Northumberland.
who can benefit Voluntary organisations benefiting the local community and individuals.
what is funded The funds generally have a specific cause as their individual funding priority, but overall the foundation has social welfare as its predominant cause to support. Projects that help communities and individuals who are disadvantaged because of poverty, poor health or disability are of particular interest.
what is not funded The foundation supports applications for general running costs; specific projects or activities; and capital developments or equipment. According to the trustees' report for 2011/12, 'the board has agreed certain exclusions for grants with its general funds and these are detailed in grant application materials available on request.'
type of grant Mostly single grants, but some grants recurrent for up to three years. Will consider capital, core costs, recurring, running and start-up costs, as well as one-off, feasibility studies and salaries.
range of grants Usually up to £5,000, exceptionally up to £100,000.
finances *Year* 2011–12 *Income* £5,370,104 *Grants* £4,509,128 *Assets* £47,982,385
trustees Prof. Christopher Drinkwater; Susan Winfield; Ashley Winter; Alastair Conn; Jamie Martin; Jo Curry; Colin Seccombe; Dean Higgins; Prof. Charles Harvey; Jane Robinson; John Clough; Gev Pringle; Fiona Cruickshank; Kate Roe.
publications Yearbooks and various reports.
other information 234 individuals were given grants that totalled £113,500.
how to apply There is one application form for the general Community Foundation grants and generally, separate forms for the other rolling grants programmes and one-off funds. Funds that support individuals are advertised separately. All of these plus application guidelines are available on the website under the 'apply' section. Some of the programmes have deadlines and some do not; also, programmes change regularly so the trust's website should be checked for the most recent information. If a grant is approved, there are terms and conditions that must be adhered to and a project report is to be submitted. Organisations that are not registered charities can apply to get a grant, but grants can only be distributed for activities that are charitable in law. CICs or other social enterprises with a good business plan can apply for help with start-up or expansion, but help with general running costs is not usually supported. Applicants must provide a copy of the bank statement; a copy of the latest annual accounts; constitution or set of rules; Child Protection or Vulnerable Adult Policy (if applicable); and copies of written estimates or catalogue pages if applying for grants regarding equipment or capital items. Email this information where possible to documents@communityfoundation.org.uk and write the name of the organisation making the application in the subject line of the email. Alternatively, send this information to the correspondent. Mark each of the documents clearly with the name of the organisation making the application.
who to apply to Sonia Waugh, Deputy Chief Executive, Cale Cross House, 156 Pilgrim Street, Newcastle upon Tyne NE1 6SU *Tel.* 01912 220945 *email* general@communityfoundation.org.uk *Website* www.communityfoundation.org.uk

■ Trustees of Tzedakah

cc no 251897   **established** 1966
where funding can be given Worldwide, in practice mainly UK and Israel.
who can benefit Mainly Jewish religious institutions and people disadvantaged by poverty.
what is funded The relief of poverty; advancement of education; advancement of religion; and general charitable purposes.
what is not funded Grants only to registered charities. No grants to individuals.
range of grants £25–£35,000.
sample grants Previous beneficiaries include: Hasmonean High School Charitable Trust; Gertner Charitable Trust; Society of Friends of the Torah; Hendon Adath Yisroel Synagogue; Medrash Shmuel Theological College; Torah Temimoh; Willow Foundation; Tifferes Girls School; Sage Home for the Aged; Wizo; and Torah Movement of Great Britain.
finances *Year* 2011–12 *Grants* £450,000
trustee Trustees of Tzedakah Ltd.
other information Up-to-date information is usually unavailable as accounts are consistently filed late with the Charity Commission.
how to apply **This trust states that it does not respond to unsolicited applications.**
who to apply to Michael Lebrett, Brentmead House, Britannia Road, London N12 9RU *Tel.* 020 8446 6767

■ The Udlington Trust

CC NO 1129443   **ESTABLISHED** 2009
WHERE FUNDING CAN BE GIVEN UK and overseas.
WHO CAN BENEFIT Registered charities.
WHAT IS FUNDED General charitable purposes.
FINANCES *Year* 2012 *Income* £264,000
Grants £145,543 *Assets* £150,811
TRUSTEES Bruce Blackledge; Richard Blackledge;
Robert Blackledge; Rebecca Blackledge.
OTHER INFORMATION In 2012 grants were awarded to
four organisations.
HOW TO APPLY In writing to the correspondent.
WHO TO APPLY TO Richard Blackledge, Trustee,
Udlington Manor, Isle Lane, Bicton, Shrewsbury,
Shropshire SY3 8DY *Tel.* 01743 850270
email theudlingtontrust@talktalk.com

■ UKI Charitable Foundation

CC NO 1071978   **ESTABLISHED** 1998
WHERE FUNDING CAN BE GIVEN UK.
WHO CAN BENEFIT Registered charities and
individuals.
WHAT IS FUNDED General charitable purposes,
education training, medical/health/sickness,
disability, the relief of poverty and religious
activities.
FINANCES *Year* 2011–12 *Income* £365,221
Grants £125,052 *Assets* £1,946,779
TRUSTEES Jacob Schimmel; Vered Schimmel; Anna
Schimmel.
HOW TO APPLY In writing to the correspondent.
WHO TO APPLY TO Jacob Schimmel, Trustee, UKI
International, 54–56 Euston Street, London
NW1 2ES *Tel.* 020 7387 0155

■ Ulster Garden Villages Ltd

ESTABLISHED 1946
WHERE FUNDING CAN BE GIVEN Northern Ireland
WHO CAN BENEFIT Organisations and individuals.
WHAT IS FUNDED Financial assistance is given to aid
housing for people who are disadvantaged,
elderly or have disabilities as well as donations
to assist improvements in quality of life for such
people. There are also interests in helping youth
organisations and movements, preservation of
heritage and organisations seeking to improve
health in the community.
WHAT IS NOT FUNDED Grants are not made to:
individuals; organisations whose application is
not charitable and with public benefit; activities
which are primarily the responsibility of central
and local government; sponsorship or marketing
appeals; promotion of religion; expeditions or
overseas travel; charities who collect funds for
distribution to other charities.
RANGE OF GRANTS Usually £1,000 to £5,000; up to
£250,000 is considered.
SAMPLE GRANTS Royal Victoria Hospital – Institute of
Vision Science; Royal Victoria Hospital –
Percutaneous Aortic Valve Replacement; Belfast
City Hospital – the Garden Village Suite; the
Northern Ireland Children's Hospice; QUB
Foundation Great Hall; Belmont Tower; the Lyric
Theatre, Camphill Communities in Northern
Ireland; Croft Community; Disability Sport NI;

Clifton Nursing Home; Habitat for Humanity
Northern Ireland; the Scout Association; Ulster
Waterways Group; Rams Island.
FINANCES *Year* 2011–12
TRUSTEES Tony Hopkins; Kevin Baird; Martie Boyd;
Drew Crawford; Susan Crowe; Brian Garrett;
Erskine Holmes; Sir Desmond Lorimer; William
Webb.
OTHER INFORMATION No current financial information
was available. Previously grants have totalled
around £1 million.
HOW TO APPLY On an application form available from
the charity's website. Guidelines on how to
apply are also on the website. Applications
should be posted or delivered to the office
which is normally attended on Tuesday,
Wednesday and Thursday between 9am and
1pm.
WHO TO APPLY TO The Administration Officer,
Forestview, Purdy's Lane, Newtonbreda, Belfast
BT8 7AR *Tel.* 02890 491111 *Fax* 02890
491007 *email* admin@ulstergardenvillages.co.
uk *Website* www.ulstergardenvillages.co.uk

■ Ultach Trust

IR NO XN83581   **ESTABLISHED** 1989
WHERE FUNDING CAN BE GIVEN Northern Ireland.
WHO CAN BENEFIT Generally voluntary Irish-language
or cross-community groups based in Northern
Ireland. Irish medium schools benefiting children
and young adults.
WHAT IS FUNDED The trust normally funds new or
established groups based in Northern Ireland
involved in the promotion of the Irish language.
Grants are normally aimed at specific projects
and schemes rather than ongoing costs.
Particular consideration is given to groups
developing inter-community Irish-language
activities. The trustees also, in exceptional
cases, support projects aimed at improving the
position of Irish people in the community and
promoting knowledge of the language.
WHAT IS NOT FUNDED Generally the following are not
supported: individuals, ongoing running costs,
major capital programmes, to substitute
cutbacks in statutory funding, travel expenses,
publications or videos.
TYPE OF GRANT Except with regard to Irish-medium
education, funding is generally restricted to
starter finances and single projects.
FINANCES *Year* 2011–12 *Grants* £50,000
TRUSTEES Ruairí Ó Bléine; Bill Boyd; Réamonn Ó
Ciaráin; Déaglán Ó Doibhlín; Risteard Mac
Gabhann; Joyce Gibson; Sue Pentel; Robin
Glendinning; Barry Kinghan.
PUBLICATIONS Titles of publications and Irish
courses available on request.
OTHER INFORMATION No financial information for
2011–12 was available, although grants usually
total about £50,000.
HOW TO APPLY An application form and conditions of
funding are available from the trust's website.
WHO TO APPLY TO Róise Ní-Bhaoill, Deputy Director,
6/10 William Street, Cathedral Quarter, Belfast
BT1 1PR *Tel.* 02890 230749 *Fax* 02890
231245 *email* eolas@ultach.org *Website* www.
ultach.org

■ Ulting Overseas Trust

CC NO 294397   **ESTABLISHED** 1986
WHERE FUNDING CAN BE GIVEN The developing world
(mostly, but not exclusively, Asia, Africa and
South and Central America).

WHO CAN BENEFIT Christian workers in the developing world undergoing further training for Christian service.

WHAT IS FUNDED Bursaries, normally via grants to Christian theological training institutions or organisations with a training focus, for those in the developing world who wish to train for the Christian ministry, or for those who wish to improve their ministry skills. It gives priority to the training of students in their home countries or continents.

WHAT IS NOT FUNDED No grants are given for capital projects such as buildings or library stock, nor for training in subjects other than Biblical, theological and missionary studies.

TYPE OF GRANT One-off, bursary.

RANGE OF GRANTS Up to £15,000.

SAMPLE GRANTS International Fellowship of Evangelical Students (£15,000); Scripture Union International (£14,000); Langham Trust (£13,000); Interserve (£6,000); Asian Theological Seminary (£4,700); Evangelical Seminary Southern Africa, Discipleship Training Centre – Singapore and Langham Preaching (£2,000 each); University of Aberdeen and Alliance Development Fund (£1,000 each); and Bangladesh Bible Correspondence College (£750).

FINANCES *Year* 2011–12 *Income* £103,850 *Grants* £106,250 *Assets* £3,419,902

TRUSTEES Tim Warren; Donald Ford; Mary Brinkley; Alan Bale; John Heyward; Dr Jean Kessler; Revd Joseph Kapolyo; Nicholas Durlacher; Roger Pearce; Dr Kang San Tan.

OTHER INFORMATION There were 32 organisational grants and one individual grant made in the year totalling £106,000.

HOW TO APPLY In writing to the correspondent. Each application is examined against strict criteria.

WHO TO APPLY TO Timothy Buckland, Administrator, Pothecary, Witham Weld, 70 St George's Square, London SW1V 3RD *Tel.* 020 7821 8211

■ The Ulverscroft Foundation

CC NO 264873   **ESTABLISHED** 1972

WHERE FUNDING CAN BE GIVEN Worldwide.

WHO CAN BENEFIT Projects which will have a positive effect on the quality of life of visually impaired people (blind and partially sighted). Funding is channelled via recognised organisations which help the visually impaired, for example, libraries, hospitals, clinics, schools and colleges, and social and welfare organisations.

WHAT IS FUNDED To support sick and disabled people, particularly those with defective eyesight, and to promote or conduct medical research. Grants are given to hospitals for research, and to libraries and groups of visually impaired people for items such as computer equipment.

WHAT IS NOT FUNDED Applications from individuals are not encouraged. Generally, assistance towards salaries and general running costs are not given.

TYPE OF GRANT Annual for up to and more than three years. Buildings; capital; project and research; one-off and recurring grants.

SAMPLE GRANTS Ulverscroft Vision Research Group – Great Ormond Street Hospital (£446,000); University of Leicester (£130,000); Sightsavers and Force Foundation Netherlands (£10,000 each); Deafblind UK (£5,000); Cardiff Institute for the Blind (£3,000); Sight Support Derbyshire (£2,000) and Scarborough Blind and PS Society,

Association Blind Asians Leeds and North Lanarkshire Libraries (£1,000 each).

FINANCES *Year* 2011–12 *Income* £11,669,882 *Grants* £642,337 *Assets* £18,356,382

TRUSTEES John Bush; Peter Carr; Pat Beech; David Owen; Roger Crooks; John Sanford-Smith; Robert Gent.

OTHER INFORMATION The foundation controls a trading subsidiary which republishes books in a form accessible by people with partial sight.

HOW TO APPLY In writing to the correspondent including latest annual report and accounts. Applicants are advised to make their proposal as detailed as possible, to include details of the current service to people who are visually impaired, if any, and how the proposed project will be integrated or enhanced. If possible the trust asks for an estimate of how many people who are visually impaired use/will use the service, the amount of funding obtained to date, if any, and the names of other organisations to which they have applied. The success of any appeal is dependent on the level of funding at the time of consideration. The trustees meet quarterly to consider appeals in January, April, July and October each year; deadlines for appeals are the fifteenth (15th) day of the previous month.

WHO TO APPLY TO Joyce Sumner, Secretary, 1 The Green, Bradgate Road, Anstey, Leicester LE7 7FU *Tel.* 01162 361595 *Fax* 01162 361594 *email* foundation@ulverscroft.co.uk *Website* www.foundation.ulverscroft.com

---

■ Ulverston Town Lands Charity

CC NO 215779   **ESTABLISHED** 1963

WHERE FUNDING CAN BE GIVEN The urban district of Ulverston.

WHO CAN BENEFIT Local organisations and schools.

WHAT IS FUNDED Youth, health, welfare, disability.

WHAT IS NOT FUNDED No grants outside the beneficial area. Grants are generally given to organisations and not to individuals. The trust prefers to support grants for specific items or equipment rather than running costs.

TYPE OF GRANT One-off grants for specific items or equipment.

RANGE OF GRANTS Up to £3,000.

SAMPLE GRANTS St Mary's Hospice, Prince's Trust and Cumbria Flood Recovery Fund (£3,000 each); Sandside Lodge School (£2,000); Sir John Barrow School Hardship Fund (£1,700); Rotary Club of Ulverston (£1,000); St Mary's Catholic Primary School, CADAS, Age Concern and Furness Youth Theatre (£500 each); WRVS for meals on wheels (£350); Churchwalk Infant School (£300); Ulverston Blind Class and Marsh House Amenities Fund (£200 each).

FINANCES *Year* 2011–12 *Income* £41,414

TRUSTEES Edwin Twentyman; Cllr J. W. Prosser; Cllr Janette Jenkinson; Anthony Bryson; Margaret Hornby; Cllr Norman Bishop-Rowe; Colin Pickthall; Doreen Fell; Cllr Paul Smith.

OTHER INFORMATION In 2011–12 the charity had a total expenditure of £40,260.

HOW TO APPLY In writing to the correspondent. Trustees meet four or five times a year.

WHO TO APPLY TO J. Going, Secretary to the Trustees, c/o Hart Jackson and Sons, PO Box 2, 8 and 10 New Market Street, Ulverston, Cumbria LA12 7LW *Tel.* 01229 583291 *Fax* 01229 581136

■ The Underwood Trust

cc no 266164   **established** 1973

where funding can be given Worldwide. In practice UK with a preference for Scotland and Wiltshire.

who can benefit Registered charities only, or bodies with equivalent status such as universities or churches.

what is funded Medicine and health, social welfare, education, arts, environment and wildlife.

what is not funded Individuals directly; political activities; commercial ventures or publications; the purchase of vehicles including minibuses; overseas travel or holidays; retrospective grants or loans; direct replacement of statutory funding or activities that are primarily the responsibility of central or local government; large capital, endowment or widely distributed appeals.

sample grants Restorative Solutions (£1.43 million in total); Community Foundation for Wiltshire and Swindon – One Degree More Project (£1 million); Wiltshire Wildlife Trust (£850,000 to fund the acquisition of Raines House); Greenpeace Environmental Trust (£253,000 in total); I Can (£124,000); Counsel and Care (£100,000); Living Paintings Trust (£56,500 in total); Shooting Star Chase and Friends of the Earth (£50,000 each); Bristol Children's Hospital Grand Appeal and DEC East Africa Crisis Appeal (£25,000 each); Music for Youth (£16,500); and the Limbless Association (£5,000).

finances *Year* 2011–12 *Income* £371,966 *Grants* £4,336,500 *Assets* £25,003,437

trustees Robin Clark, Chair; Jack C. Taylor; Briony Wilson; Reg Harvey.

how to apply 'The resources of the trust are limited and inevitably there are many more good causes that it can possibly fund. All the available funds are allocated pro-actively by the trustees. We are keen that applicants do not waste both their own and our limited resources in applications which have little chance of success, and therefore DO NOT apply to the trust. Currently the trust has no free funds.' **Do not apply to the trust unless invited to do so.** The trust's website further states that: 'Due to the current economic situation and the reduction in interest rates our income has been greatly reduced. As such there are currently no free funds in the trust and therefore THE TRUST IS UNABLE TO ACCEPT UNSOLICITED APPLICATIONS. This position is expected to continue for the foreseeable future, but any changes to this will be posted on [its] website at the time'. Note: the trust is unable to deal with telephone or email enquiries about an application.'

who to apply to John Dippie, Trust Manager, c/o Tcp Atlantic Square Limited, Fourth Floor South, 35 Portman Square, London W1H 6LR *Tel.* 020 7486 0100 *Website* www.theunderwoodtrust. org.uk

■ The Union of Orthodox Hebrew Congregation

cc no 249892   **established** 1966

where funding can be given UK.

who can benefit Jewish organisations.

what is funded To protect and to further in every way the interests of traditional Judaism in Great Britain and to establish and support such institutions as will serve this object.

sample grants Previous beneficiaries have included: Addas Yisoroel Mikva Foundation, Achieve Trust, Atereth Shau, Beis Malka, Beis Shmuel, Belz Nursery, Bnos Yerushaim, Chesed Charity Trust, London Board of Schechita, Mutual Trust, Maoz Ladol, North West London Mikvah, Needy Families and Poor Families Pesach, Society of Friends of the Torah, Talmud Centre Trust and VMCT.

finances *Year* 2012 *Income* £1,104,945 *Grants* £467,847 *Assets* £1,658,670

trustees Benzion Se Freshwater; Chaim Konig; Rabbi A. Pinter.

other information £437,847 was given in grants to organisations and £30,000 to individuals.

how to apply In writing to the correspondent.

who to apply to The Administrator, Landau Morley, Lanmor House, 370–386 High Road, Wembley HA9 6AX *Tel.* 020 8903 5122

■ The United Society for the Propagation of the Gospel

cc no 234518   **established** 1701

where funding can be given Mainly churches in Africa, West Indies, South Pacific, South America, Pakistan, India, Indian Ocean, Myanmar (Burma), Bangladesh, East Asia, but also UK.

who can benefit Overseas Anglican provinces and dioceses and churches in communion with the Anglican Church which benefit Christians and other disadvantaged groups.

what is funded The promotion of the Christian religion and related charitable works.

what is not funded Direct applications from individuals are not considered.

type of grant One-off grants; bursaries; loans.

sample grants Church for the Province of Central Africa (£441,000); Anglican Church of Tanzania (£286,000); Anglican Church of Southern Africa (£92,000); Selly Oak Centre for Mission Studies (SOCMS) (£81,000); Igreja Episcopal church of Brazil (£57,000); Church of South India (£15,000); Development of Programmes for Britain and Ireland (£12,000) and Experience Exchange Programme (£9,000).

finances *Year* 2012 *Income* £3,816,000 *Grants* £1,823,000 *Assets* £38,831,000

trustees Rt Revd Cannon Christopher Chivers; Revd Cannon Richard Bartlett; Revd Dr John Perumbalath; Nigel Wildish; Revd Cannon Christopher Burke; Rt Revd Michael Burrows; Revd Dr Ian E. Rock; Dr Jane Watkeys; Rt Revd Dr Jacob Ayeebo; Rt Revd Edward Pacyaya Malecdan; Rosemary Kempsell; Dr Joabe Gomes Cavalcanti; Simon Gill; Jaqueline Humphreys; John Chilver.

other information The charity is now known as United Society.

how to apply Applications must be submitted by Anglican Archbishops or Bishops to the Finance in Mission Officer.

who to apply to Finance in Mission Officer, Harling House, 47/51 Great Suffolk Street, London SE1 0BS *Tel.* 020 7921 2200 *email* info@ weareUS.org.uk *Website* www.weareus.org.uk

■ United Utilities Trust Fund

cc no 1108296   **established** 2005

where funding can be given The area supplied by United Utilities Water plc (predominantly the north west of England).

who can benefit Mainly individuals, but also organisations.

what is funded Social welfare and debt advice.

WHAT IS NOT FUNDED The trust will not fund: existing projects; charities which appear to the trustees to have sufficient unrestricted or free reserves, or are in serious deficit; projects outside the geographical area; national charities that do not have the facility to accept the funding on a regional basis; grantmaking bodies seeking to distribute grants on UUTF's behalf; general appeals, sponsorship and marketing appeals; replacement of existing programmes or statutory funding.

TYPE OF GRANT Small one-off donations and larger grants for up to two years.

RANGE OF GRANTS Usually up to £30,000.

SAMPLE GRANTS Speke CAB (£51,000); VENUS and Age Concern Manchester (£30,000 each); Stockport and District MIND (£28,000); Age Concern Barrow and District and North Liverpool CAB (£7,000 each) and Sefton CAB (£1,500).

FINANCES *Year* 2011–12 *Income* £5,002,761 *Grants* £4,019,435 *Assets* £721,981

TRUSTEES Deborah Moreton; Alastair Richards; Simon Dewsnip; Allen Mackie; David Burdis; Nick Pearson; Carl Smith.

OTHER INFORMATION During the year £3.8 million was paid in grants to individuals. A further £239,000 was donated to 15 debt counselling organisations.

HOW TO APPLY On an application form available from the correspondent or the trust's website.

WHO TO APPLY TO The Secretary (Auriga Services Limited), FREEPOST RLYY-JHEJ-XCXS, Sutton Coldfield B72 1TJ *Tel.* 0845 179 1791 *email* contact@uutf.org.uk *Website* www.uutf.org.uk

··

■ Unity Theatre Trust

CC NO 210387　　　**ESTABLISHED** 1964

WHERE FUNDING CAN BE GIVEN UK

WHO CAN BENEFIT Registered charities and theatres.

WHAT IS FUNDED Drama and theatre related activities; performing arts.

WHAT IS NOT FUNDED The trust does not give grants for core funding, i.e. for annual running costs of an organisation, such as rent, telephone, salaries, etc. The trust also prefers not to be the sole funder of a project but rather the junior partner in such funding.

TYPE OF GRANT Project funding and bursaries.

RANGE OF GRANTS £1,000 and £2,000.

FINANCES *Year* 2011–12 *Income* £39,094 *Grants* £25,000

TRUSTEES Ann Mitchell; Harry Landis; Clive Gehle; Jack Grossman; John Burgess; Kate O'Donoghue; Maureen Coman; Maggie McCarthy; Kayelle O'Donoghue.

OTHER INFORMATION A list of beneficiaries was not available.

HOW TO APPLY On an application form which can be downloaded from the trust's website. Full details are as follows: 'A grant request will only be considered on completion of an application form supplied by the trust. All successful applicants must keep detailed accounts in relation to the disbursement of the grant received and make these available to the trust for inspection at all reasonable times. Any unused grant must be returned, unless prior permission has been given by the trust for any other use. In their efforts to monitor the effectiveness of their grant strategy, the trustees expect all recipients of grant to inform the trust of the success or otherwise of the activities for which the grant was given. They also expect to be invited to the performance of plays or events the trust awards grants to. No

grant may be used for any other purpose than that for which it was approved for without the prior permission of the trust. All applicants, by accepting receipt of any grant, agree not to contravene the charitable aims of the trust as summarised in the section of this website called 'The Theatre' and as restated in the guidance notes supplied with the application form. All successful applicants will be asked to confirm in writing their agreement as above before any grant is released.

There will usually be FOUR decision dates in any one year, one in each of the following quarters, unless the trustees deem it necessary to meet outside these dates – 1st Quarter: January, February, March; 2nd Quarter: April, May, June; 3rd Quarter: July, August, September; 4th Quarter: October, November, December. Applications should be received 30 days prior to the planned trust meeting. The trustees will inform successful applicants how their grant will be administered but it will usually be done in one of the following ways: total grant in advance with invoices or accounts on request by the trustees; total grant after receipt of invoices or accounts; by instalments, with or without progress reports or account details of the preceding period; a progress report should be submitted to the trust by all successful projects.'

WHO TO APPLY TO Andreas Michaelides, Secretary, 37 Dunsmure Road, London N16 5PT *Tel.* 020 8802 6437 *email* secretary@unitytheatre.org.uk *Website* www.unitytheatre.org.uk

··

■ The Michael Uren Foundation

CC NO 1094102　　　**ESTABLISHED** 2002

WHERE FUNDING CAN BE GIVEN UK.

WHO CAN BENEFIT Registered charities.

WHAT IS FUNDED General charitable purposes. 'The trustees are particularly keen on making grants for specific large projects. This could mean that, to satisfy this objective, no significant grants are paid in one year. With the resultant reserves retained a large grant could be made in the following year.'

TYPE OF GRANT Mainly large project grants.

RANGE OF GRANTS £500–£500,000.

SAMPLE GRANTS International Animal Rescue (£980,000); The Gurkha Welfare Trust and Moorfields Eye Charity (£500,000 each); Imperial College Trust (£300,000); Royal Naval Benevolent Fund (£250,000); WAVE Heritage Fund (£200,000); Royal British Legion (£111,000); City of London Royal Fusiliers Volunteers Trust (£100,000); Royal Society of Wildlife Trusts (£50,000); Magdalen and Lasher Trust and Afghan Appeal Fund (£20,000 each); Royal Navy Submarine Museum (£10,000); and Friends of St Mary's, Kenardington (£5,000).

FINANCES *Year* 2011–12 *Income* £2,401,104 *Grants* £3,046,111 *Assets* £63,400,606

TRUSTEES Michael Uren; Anne Gregory-Jones; Janis Bennett; Alastair McDonald.

HOW TO APPLY In writing to the correspondent.

WHO TO APPLY TO Anne Gregory-Jones, Trustee, Haysmacintyre, Fairfax House, 15 Fulwood Place, London WC1V 6AY *email* agregory-jones@haysmacintyre.com

■ The David Uri Memorial Trust

cc no 327810 **ESTABLISHED** 1988

WHERE FUNDING CAN BE GIVEN Worldwide.

WHO CAN BENEFIT Registered charities benefiting Jewish people, at risk groups and people who are disadvantaged by poverty or social isolation.

WHAT IS FUNDED Mainly Jewish organisations; also welfare and education charities.

WHAT IS NOT FUNDED No grants to individuals.

SAMPLE GRANTS Previous beneficiaries have included: National Jewish Chaplaincy Board, Age Concern, Crisis at Christmas, Jefferies Research Wing Trust, NSPCC and Yakar Education Foundation.

FINANCES *Year* 2011–12 *Income* £117,228 *Grants* £0 *Assets* £3,173,269

TRUSTEES Benjamin Blackman; Bianca Roden; Sandra Blackman.

HOW TO APPLY In writing to the correspondent.

WHO TO APPLY TO The Trustees, 244 Vauxhall Bridge Road, London SW1V 1AU

■ Uxbridge United Welfare Trust

cc no 217066 **ESTABLISHED** 1991

WHERE FUNDING CAN BE GIVEN Former urban district of Uxbridge, including Uxbridge, Hillingdon, Ickenham, Harefield and Cowley.

WHO CAN BENEFIT Local organisations benefiting children, young adults and people disadvantaged by poverty and individuals.

WHAT IS FUNDED Education, relief of poverty, including the provision of almshouses.

WHAT IS NOT FUNDED No grants are made outside the beneficial area.

SAMPLE GRANTS A list of beneficiaries was not available.

FINANCES *Year* 2012 *Income* £583,162 *Grants* £100,000

TRUSTEES John Childs; David Routledge; Peter Ryerson; Gerda Driver; Raymond Graham; Duncan Struthers; Susan James; Alan Morris.

HOW TO APPLY On a form available from the correspondent. Applications are considered at the trustee's monthly meetings.

WHO TO APPLY TO Josie Duffy, Grants Officer, Woodbridge House, New Windsor Street, Uxbridge UB8 2TY *Tel.* 01895 232976 *email* info@uuwt.org *Website* www.uuwt.org

■ The Vail Foundation

cc no 1089579　　　**established** 2001
where funding can be given UK and overseas.
who can benefit Registered charities.
what is funded Jewish causes.
range of grants Up to £400,000.
sample grants KKL Charity Limited (£472,500 in total); United Jewish Israel Appeal (£270,000 in total); London School of Jewish Studies (£135,000 in total); Community Security Trust (£60,000); Finchley Jewish Primary School Trust (£50,000); Jewish Leadership Council (£25,000); Kisharon Charitable Trust (£20,000); Chai Lifeline Cancer Care (£10,000); and the Chicken Soup Shelter (£5,000).
finances *Year* 2011–12 *Income* £243,005 *Grants* £1,444,500 *Assets* £7,053,996
trustees Michael S. Bradfield; Paul Brett; Michael H. Goldstein.
how to apply In writing to the correspondent. 'The trustees consider all requests which they receive and make such donations as they feel appropriate.'
who to apply to Michael S. Bradfield, Trustee, 5 Fitzhardinge Street, London W1H 6ED *Tel.* 020 7317 3000

■ Vale of Glamorgan – Welsh Church Fund

cc no 506628　　　**established** 1996
where funding can be given Vale of Glamorgan and City of Cardiff council areas.
who can benefit Organisations benefiting children, young adults, students and local communities may all be considered.
what is funded Restoration of churches and memorials; education and training, particularly vocational or religious; health; social welfare; arts and culture; recreation and sport; environment and animals; faith activities; science and technology; social sciences, policy and research; and philanthropy and the voluntary sector.
what is not funded No grants to individuals.
type of grant One-off.
range of grants 'Whilst no maximum/minimum grant levels are stipulated, awards are usually in the region of £1,500.'
sample grants Ewenny Prior Church (£7,000); St Nicholas Parish Church (£5,000); All Saints Church, Barry (£3,000); Bethania Presbyterian Church (£2,300); All Saints Church, Llandaff North (£1,500); Tabernacle Baptist Church (£1,000) and Beacon Church cardiff and Ararat Baptist Church, Whitchurch (£500 each).
finances *Year* 2011–12 *Income* £42,000 *Grants* £29,000 *Assets* £3,699,000
trustee The Vale of Glamorgan County Borough Council.
other information In practise grants are made solely to churches.
how to apply For organisations based in the Vale of Glamorgan, further information can be obtained from the correspondent. For organisations based in Cardiff, contact Robert Giddings at Cardiff County Council (029 20 853 7484/voluntarysectorgrants@cardiff.gov.uk). Applications are accepted throughout the year.
who to apply to A. D. Williams, Director of Finance, ICT and Property, The Vale of Glamorgan Council, Civic Offices, Holton Rd, Barry CF63 4RU *Tel.* 01446 709250 *email* adwilliams@valeofglamorgan.gov.uk *Website* www.valeofglamorgan.gov.uk/en/living/life_in_the_community/community_grants/welsh_church_act

■ The Valentine Charitable Trust

cc no 1001782　　　**established** 1990
where funding can be given Unrestricted, but mainly Dorset, UK.
who can benefit Registered charities in the UK with preference to Dorset and sometimes overseas.
what is funded General charitable purposes.
what is not funded No grants to individuals. The trust would not normally fund appeals for village halls or the fabric of church buildings.
type of grant Core, capital and project support is given as well as loan finance. One-off grants are preferred, but funding can be for longer periods.
range of grants Up to £20,000.
sample grants Lewis-Manning Cancer Trust (£20,000); Kerala India, Bournemouth Nightclub Outreach Work, Bournemouth Symphony Orchestra, Game and Wildlife Conservation Trust and St John of Jerusalem Eye Hospital (£10,000 each); Faithworks and National Coastwatch Institution (£7,500 each); Hope House Training and Support Ltd, St Philip's Church Community Project and Vitalise (£6,000 each); Jubilee Sailing Trust, Parkstone Sports and Arts Centre, Shelter, Sports Forum for the Disabled and Tree Aid (£5,000 each); Poole Christian Fellowship, React and Smile Connect (£2,000 each); Traffic of the Stage (£1,000); Purbeck Strings (£300); Youth Action for Holistic Development (£200).
finances *Year* 2011–12 *Income* £819,492 *Grants* £532,125 *Assets* £26,932,406
trustees Douglas Neville-Jones; Patricia Walker; Peter Leatherdale; Susan Patterson; Roger Gregory; Diana Tory; Sheila Cox; Wing Cdr Donald Jack; Susan Ridley.
how to apply In writing to the correspondent. The trust provides the following insight into its application process in its annual report: 'All applications will be acknowledged with standard letters, even those that are not appropriate for receiving a grant. This responsibility is delegated to Douglas J E Neville-Jones who then provides a report to the next trustees' meeting. The following general comments summarise some of the considerations the trustees seek to apply when considering applications for funding: The trustees look for value for money. While this concept is difficult to apply in a voluntary sector it can certainly be used on a comparative basis and subjectively. If the trustees have competing applications they will usually decide to support just one of them as they believe that to concentrate the charity's donations is more beneficial than to dilute them. Regular contact with the charities to which donations are made is considered essential. Reports and accounts are also requested from charities which are supported and the trustees consider those at their meetings. The trustees take great comfort from the fact that they employ the policy of only making donations to other charities or similar bodies. However they are not complacent about the need to review all donations made and the objects to which those have been given. The

trustees are conscious that, particularly with the smaller and local charities, the community of those working for and with the charity is an important consideration. The trustees regularly review the classifications to which donations have been made so that they can obtain an overview of the charity's donations and assess whether their policies are being implemented in practice. They are conscious that when dealing with individual donations it is easy to lose sight of the overall picture.'

WHO TO APPLY TO Douglas Neville-Jones, Trustee, Preston Redman, Hinton House, Hinton Road, Bournemouth BH1 2EN *Tel.* 01202 292424

....

■ The Valiant Charitable Trust

CC NO 1135810 ESTABLISHED 2010
WHERE FUNDING CAN BE GIVEN UK.
WHO CAN BENEFIT Registered charities.
WHAT IS FUNDED General, older people, people with disabilities.
RANGE OF GRANTS £10,000–£36,000
SAMPLE GRANTS Leech Hospice Care (£36,000) and Lord Lieutenant's Fund (£11,000).
FINANCES *Year* 2011–12 *Income* £245,646 *Grants* £46,250 *Assets* £1,203,209
TRUSTEES Roger Woolfe; Lady Valarie Dixon; Paul Brenham.
OTHER INFORMATION The settlor of the trust is Lady Valerie Dixon, widow of the late Sir Ian Dixon, former chair of the Willmott Dixon construction group.
HOW TO APPLY In writing to the correspondent.
WHO TO APPLY TO Roger Woolfe, Trustee, Collyer Bristow Solicitors, 4 Bedford Row, London WC1R 4DF *Tel.* 020 7242 7363 *email* roger. woolfe@collyerbristow.com

....

■ The Albert Van Den Bergh Charitable Trust

CC NO 296885 ESTABLISHED 1987
WHERE FUNDING CAN BE GIVEN UK and overseas.
WHO CAN BENEFIT Charitable organisations.
WHAT IS FUNDED Medical research, disability, community, care of the elderly, children, ex-service personnel and general charitable purposes.
SAMPLE GRANTS Previous beneficiaries have included: BLISS, Bishop of Guildford's Charity, British Heart Foundation, Counsel and Care for the Elderly, Leukaemia Research Trust, Multiple Sclerosis Society, Parentline Surrey, National Osteoporosis Society, RNID, Riding for the Disabled – Cranleigh Age Concern, SSAFA, St John Ambulance and United Charities Fund – Liberal Jewish Synagogue.
FINANCES *Year* 2011–12 *Income* £111,200 *Grants* £103,200 *Assets* £3,145,742
TRUSTEES Jane Hartley; Nicola Glover; Bruce Hopkins.
HOW TO APPLY In writing to the correspondent, including accounts and budgets.
WHO TO APPLY TO Jane Hartley, Trustee, Trevornick Farmhouse, Holywell Bay, Newquay, Cornwall TR8 5PW

....

■ The Van Neste Foundation

CC NO 201951 ESTABLISHED 1959
WHERE FUNDING CAN BE GIVEN UK (especially the Bristol area) and overseas.
WHO CAN BENEFIT Registered charities.

WHAT IS FUNDED Currently the main areas of interest are: developing world; people who are disabled or elderly; advancement of religion; community and 'Christian family life' and 'respect for the sanctity and dignity of life'.
WHAT IS NOT FUNDED No grants to individuals or to large, well-known charities. Applications are only considered from registered charities.
TYPE OF GRANT Usually one-off for a specific project or part of a project. Core funding is rarely considered.
SAMPLE GRANTS CAFOD, DEKI and St James Priory (£25,000 each); CHAS Bristol (£21,000); Emmaus House Bristol (£10,000); African Promise, Bristol and District Tranquiliser Project and The Salvation Army (£5,000 each); For Ethiopia (£4,000); Mentoring Plus (£3,500); Cerebral Palsy Plus (£3,000); Avon Riding Centre (£1,000) and Have a Stick will Travel (£500).
FINANCES *Year* 2011–12 *Income* £260,502 *Grants* £205,000 *Assets* £6,862,582
TRUSTEES M. T. M. Appleby, Chair; F. J. F. Lyons; G. J. Walker; J. F. Lyons; B. M. Appleby; Michael Lyons; Tom Appleby.
HOW TO APPLY Applications should be in the form of a concise letter setting out the clear objectives to be obtained, which must be charitable. Information must be supplied concerning agreed funding from other sources together with a timetable for achieving the objectives of the appeal and a copy of the latest accounts. The foundation does not normally make grants on a continuing basis. To keep overheads to a minimum, only successful applications are acknowledged. Appeals are considered by the trustees at their meetings in January, June and October.
WHO TO APPLY TO Fergus Lyons, Secretary, 15 Alexandra Road, Clifton, Bristol BS8 2DD *Tel.* 01179 735167

....

■ Mrs Maud Van Norden's Charitable Foundation

CC NO 210844 ESTABLISHED 1962
WHERE FUNDING CAN BE GIVEN UK.
WHO CAN BENEFIT Registered UK charities only.
WHAT IS FUNDED General charitable purposes, particularly aid to younger or older people. Also preservation of the environment and heritage, disability and animal welfare.
WHAT IS NOT FUNDED No grants to individuals, expeditions or scholarships. The trustees make donations to registered UK charities only.
TYPE OF GRANT One-off and research.
RANGE OF GRANTS Most grants are for £1,500 each.
SAMPLE GRANTS Salvation Army (£4,000); Women's Royal Voluntary Service (£3,000); Royal Hospital for Neuro-disability and Crisis UK (£2,500) and Action on Elder Abuse, Humane Slaughter Association, Gurkha Welfare Trust, Calibre Audio Library, The Cure Parkinson's Trust, Police Community Clubs of Great Britain and Princess Alice Hospice (£1,500 each).
FINANCES *Year* 2012 *Income* £39,571 *Grants* £40,500 *Assets* £1,127,662
TRUSTEES Ena Dukler; John Gordon; Elizabeth Humphryes; Neil Wingerath.
HOW TO APPLY All appeals should be by letter containing the following: aims and objectives of the charity; nature of the appeal; total target, if for a specific project; contributions received against target; registered charity number; any other factors. Letters should be accompanied by

....

a copy of the applicant's latest reports and accounts.

WHO TO APPLY TO The Trustees, BM Box 2367, London WC1N 3XX

....

■ The Vandervell Foundation

CC NO 255651   **ESTABLISHED** 1968

WHERE FUNDING CAN BE GIVEN UK.

WHO CAN BENEFIT Individuals and organisations.

WHAT IS FUNDED General charitable purposes.

RANGE OF GRANTS £1,000–£30,000.

SAMPLE GRANTS The Big Issue Foundation (£30,000); Prisoners Education Trust (£20,000); PMS Foundation and Nottingham Trent University (£15,000 each); Kenwood Dairy Restoration Trust, The Outward Bound Trust and Weekend Arts College (£10,000 each); FareShare (£6,000) and London Air Ambulance, Royal National Theatre, Mayor of London and Salisbury Cathedral School (£5,000 each).

FINANCES *Year* 2012 *Income* £301,458 *Grants* £350,500 *Assets* £6,707,051

TRUSTEE The Vandervell Foundation Limited Trustee Company.

OTHER INFORMATION There was also one grant to an individual of £750.

HOW TO APPLY In writing to the correspondent. Trustees meet every two months to consider major grant applications; smaller grants are considered more frequently.

WHO TO APPLY TO Valerie Kaye, Administrator, Hampstead Town Hall Centre, 213 Haverstock Hill, London NW3 4QP *Tel.* 020 7435 7546

....

■ The Vardy Foundation

CC NO 328415   **ESTABLISHED** 1987

WHERE FUNDING CAN BE GIVEN UK and overseas, with a preference to the north east of England.

WHO CAN BENEFIT Registered charities and individuals.

WHAT IS FUNDED General charitable purposes; education in north east England; young people; social welfare and the arts

WHAT IS NOT FUNDED The foundation will not fund: applications for more than a three year commitment; animal welfare projects; health related charities; projects normally provided by central or local government; individuals (including requests for educational support costs) (: the foundation does award grants to individuals, however these are likely to already be connected to the foundation or one of the educational institutions that receive funding from the foundation); projects that do not demonstrate an element of self-funding or other funding; contribute to an organisation's healthy reserves or endowments.

TYPE OF GRANT One-off and recurrent for up to two years.

RANGE OF GRANTS Up to £125,000.

SAMPLE GRANTS A Way Out (£123,000); Reverend Norman Drummond (£100,000); Betel International (£97,000); Christians Against Poverty (£50,000); and Premier Radio (£40,000).

FINANCES *Year* 2011–12 *Income* £1,093,850 *Grants* £1,358,714 *Assets* £21,840,095

TRUSTEES Lady Margaret Vardy; Peter Vardy; Richard Vardy; Sir Peter Vardy; Victoria Vardy.

OTHER INFORMATION Individual grants totalled £173,500.

HOW TO APPLY In writing to the correspondent

WHO TO APPLY TO Sir Peter Vardy, Trustee, Venture House, Aykley Heads, Durham DH1 5TS *Tel.* 01913 744744

....

■ The Variety Club Children's Charity

CC NO 209259   **ESTABLISHED** 1949

WHERE FUNDING CAN BE GIVEN UK.

WHO CAN BENEFIT Hospitals, schools, individuals, charities and other organisations.

WHAT IS FUNDED The welfare of children and young people who are disadvantaged or have disabilities.

WHAT IS NOT FUNDED Examples of grants outside the guidelines: repayment of loans; garden adaptions; cost of a family/wheelchair adapted vehicle; administrative/salary costs; maintenance or ongoing costs; distribution to other organisations; reimbursement of funds already paid out; hire, rental costs or down payments; computers; trips abroad or holiday costs; medical treatment or research; and education/tuition fees.

TYPE OF GRANT One-off and recurring. Money and equipment, including coaches, to organisations. Individual children have received money, electric wheelchairs, toys and holidays.

RANGE OF GRANTS Up to £125,000.

SAMPLE GRANTS Young Epilepsy – Surrey (£38,500); Oakfield School – Pontefract, Heritage House School – Buckinghamshire and Garth School – Lincolnshire (£37,000 each); Oak View School – Essex, The Village School – London and Milestone Academy – Kent (£32,000 each); Elmwood School – Somerset and Pennfields School – Wolverhampton (£27,000 each); Bradstow School – Kent and Waltham Forest Asian Mothers Group – London (£25,00 each); Wandle Valley School – Surrey (£24,000); and Wicksteed Leisure – Northants (£5,500).

FINANCES *Year* 2011–12 *Income* £6,199,759 *Grants* £2,453,585 *Assets* £1,006,885

TRUSTEES Jarvis Astaire; Raymond Curtis; Stanley Salter; Anthony Harris; Anthony Hatch; Lionel Rosenblatt; Pamela Sinclair; Ronald Nathan; Russell Kahn; Trevor Green; Jonathan Shalit; Laurence Davis; Norman Kaphan; Keith Andrews; Malcolm Brenner; Lloyd Barr; Jason Lewis; Ronald Sinclair; Nicholas Shattock; William Sangster; Rodney Natkiel; Jane Kerner.

OTHER INFORMATION A total of just over £45,000 was given in grants of less than £5,000 to organisations.

A further £343,000 was made in grants to individuals.

HOW TO APPLY According to the application guidelines at the time of writing (August 2013), 'there are application forms for each programme available – with application guidelines – from the charity or through its website.' General application guidelines are as follows: 'applications can be made on behalf of individual children, but these must be supported by a letter from an appropriately qualified professional, e.g. family doctor, occupational therapist, social worker, school teacher; applications can also be made from non-profit making groups and organisations working with children up to, and including, the physical age of 18 years. These include statutory bodies (schools and hospitals) and registered charities; applications can be made by parents, medical professionals, a school or organisation, hospitals and registered charities; applications for specialist items of equipment, i.e. walking frames, seating systems, specialist beds should be accompanied by a supporting letter from a physiotherapist or occupational therapist; quotations for equipment should accompany an application; applicants are advised to think carefully before submitting a more substantial request. Variety will need to be convinced of the high quality and efficiency of your organisation before consideration is given to making a donation. The grants committee meets six times per year; therefore, there is no deadline for applications to be made. In some cases a member of the grants committee will contact you to discuss your application more fully. Notification of the outcome of applications will be by letter, and the decision of the trustees is final.'

WHO TO APPLY TO Stanley Salter, Trustee, Variety Club House, 93 Bayham Street, London NW1 0AG *email* info@varietyclub.org.uk *Website* www.varietyclub.org.uk

....

■ Veneziana Fund

CC NO 1061760   **ESTABLISHED** 1997
WHERE FUNDING CAN BE GIVEN Venice and the UK.
WHO CAN BENEFIT Charitable organisations working with old buildings or art.
WHAT IS FUNDED This trust gives half its grant total to the Venice in Peril Fund (amounting to £35,000 in 2009–10), and in the UK or the preservation, restoration, repair and maintenance of: buildings originally constructed before 1750; the fixtures and fittings of such buildings; and works of art made before 1750 (including the purchase of such items).
WHAT IS NOT FUNDED No grants are made towards heating systems or toilets.
TYPE OF GRANT One-off capital grants.
RANGE OF GRANTS Up to £2,000.
SAMPLE GRANTS Venice in Peril (£26,250); Holburne Museum of Art (£2,000); The Bowes Museum (£1,250); National Trust, Portsmouth Cathedral, Chipping Warden Church Bell Fund and Kings College London and Somerset House Trust (£1,000 each) and St Mary-at-Hill, Billingsgate (£750).
FINANCES *Year* 2011–12 *Income* £63,434 *Grants* £52,500 *Assets* £279
TRUSTEES Peter Boizot MBE; Timothy Warren; Jackie Freeman; Jane Botros.
HOW TO APPLY The trustee's consider appeals twice a year in spring and autumn. Applications should be submitted online via www.pwwsolicitors.co.uk. The trustees require applicants to have raised two thirds of the total required from other sources before applying to the fund.
WHO TO APPLY TO Jayne Day, The Trust Administrator, c/o Pothecary Witham Weld Solicitors, 70 St George's Square, London SW1V 3RD *Tel.* 020 7821 8211 *email* charities@pwwsolicitors.co.uk *Website* www.pwwsolicitors.co.uk

....

■ The William and Patricia Venton Charitable Trust

CC NO 1103884   **ESTABLISHED** 2004
WHERE FUNDING CAN BE GIVEN UK.
WHO CAN BENEFIT Older people, day centres, animal welfare.
WHAT IS FUNDED Relief in need for older people, particularly day centre provision and the

prevention of cruelty and suffering among animals.
RANGE OF GRANTS £1,000–£10,000
SAMPLE GRANTS Age Concern Plymouth and Kettering General Hospital Charity Fund (£10,000 each); Age UK Solihull, Sudbury (Middlesex) Neighbourhood Centre, SPECIAL and Homelink – Day respite care (£5,000 each); Battersea Dogs and Cats Home, the Council for Music in Hospitals, SERVE and Abbey Field Bromley Society Ltd (£5,000 each); Aylesham and District Care Trust (£4,500); RSPCA Cornwall (£4,000); Essex Horse and Pony Protection Society (£3,000) and Tillington Local Centre (£2,000).
FINANCES *Year* 2011–12 *Income* £127,438 *Grants* £53,131 *Assets* £2,444,304
TRUSTEES George Hillman-Liggett; Christopher Saunby; Graham Cudlipp.
HOW TO APPLY In writing to the correspondent.
WHO TO APPLY TO The Trustees, c/o Laytons Solicitors, Carmelite, 50 Victoria Embankment, Blackfriars, London EC4Y 0LS *Tel.* 01590 623818

....

■ The Verdon-Smith Family Charitable Settlement

CC NO 284919   **ESTABLISHED** 1983
WHERE FUNDING CAN BE GIVEN South West England, mainly Bristol, Somerset, South Gloucestershire, Dorset and Wiltshire.
WHO CAN BENEFIT Registered charities with emphasis on local activity and needs benefiting: people of all ages; ex-service and service people; seafarers and fishermen; musicians; widows and widowers; Church of England; disabled people; disaster victims; and homeless people.
WHAT IS FUNDED This trust will consider funding: almshouses and respite accommodation; architecture; music; visual arts; arts education; orchestras; cultural activities; religious buildings; acute health care; hospices and hospice at home; respite care for carers; cancer and MS research; conservation; animal welfare; church schools; independent schools; care in the community and day centres. There is a quarterly review of regular donations with occasional addition of new donations.
WHAT IS NOT FUNDED No grants to individuals, or for salaries or running costs. Grants to organisations with recognized charitable status only.
TYPE OF GRANT Recurrent, occasional one-off, buildings, capital, core costs, project and research. Funding is available for one year or less.
RANGE OF GRANTS £50–£500.
SAMPLE GRANTS Corsham Festival; Devon Wildlife Trust; Gloucestershire Society; Salisbury Trust for the Homeless; Shaw Trust; Royal Hospital for Children – Bristol; Jubilee Sailing Trust; West Lavington Youth Club; Canine Partners for Independence; Motability for Somerset; Arthritis Research Campaign; Royal British Legion; Building of Bath Museum Appeal; Salisbury Cathedral Choral Foundation; Grateful Society; Genesis Trust; and Avon Outward Bound Association.
FINANCES *Year* 2011–12 *Income* £34,440 *Grants* £27,310 *Assets* £557,049
TRUSTEES William Verdon-Smith; Elizabeth White; Diana Verdon-Smith.

HOW TO APPLY In writing to the correspondent. The trustees meet quarterly and applications will not be acknowledged unless successful.

WHO TO APPLY TO Elizabeth White, Trustee, Church Farm House, Hawkesbury, Badminston, Gloucestershire GL9 1BN

....

■ Roger Vere Foundation

CC NO 1077559   **ESTABLISHED** 1999

WHERE FUNDING CAN BE GIVEN UK and worldwide, with a special interest in High Wycombe.

WHO CAN BENEFIT Charitable organisations.

WHAT IS FUNDED The relief of financial hardship in and around, but not restricted to, High Wycombe; advancement of education; advancement of religion; advancement of scientific and medical research; conservation and protection of the natural environment and endangered plants and animals; relief of natural and civil disasters; and general charitable purposes.

RANGE OF GRANTS In 2009–10 no single grant exceeded £1,000.

SAMPLE GRANTS Previously: Cord Blood Charity, the Leprosy Mission, Claire House Children's Hospice, Angels International, Signalong Group, Changing Faces, Women's Aid, St John Water Wing, UK Youth and Jubilee Plus.

FINANCES *Year* 2011–12 *Income* £138,346 *Grants* £262,207 *Assets* £3,260,888

TRUSTEES Rosemary Vere, Chair; Marion Lyon; Peter Allen.

HOW TO APPLY In writing to the correspondent. The trustees meet regularly to consider requests.

WHO TO APPLY TO Peter Allen, Trustee, 19 Berwick Road, Marlow, Buckinghamshire SL7 3AR *Tel.* 01628 471702

....

■ Victoria Homes Trust

IR NO XN45474   **ESTABLISHED** 1892

WHERE FUNDING CAN BE GIVEN Northern Ireland.

WHO CAN BENEFIT Registered charities benefiting children and young people.

WHAT IS FUNDED Voluntary projects in the fields of homelessness, alcohol and drug abuse and counselling.

WHAT IS NOT FUNDED The following activities are not normally supported: projects whose beneficiaries are outside Northern Ireland; projects which do not target the needs of children and young people; projects for which expenditure has already been incurred; applications to support playgroups are discouraged; the trust is unlikely to contribute towards core running costs of charities and voluntary organisations.

RANGE OF GRANTS Usually £500–£2,500

FINANCES *Year* 2013 *Grants* £45,000

OTHER INFORMATION Grants usually total between £40,000 and £50,000 a year,

HOW TO APPLY On a form available from the correspondent or from the charity's website. A copy of the most recent audited accounts should be included. Applications should be typed or written in block capital letters using black ink. If the project requires work which involves planning permission, evidence that the permission has been granted should be enclosed. The trust asks that pamphlets or other printed matter should not be sent. Trustees meet in June and January. Applications should be submitted before 30 April and 30 November respectively.

WHO TO APPLY TO Derek H. Catney, Secretary, 2 Tudor Court, Rochester Road, Belfast BT6 9LB *Tel.* 02890 794306 *email* derek. catney@victoriahomestrust.org.uk *Website* www. victoriahomestrust.org.uk

....

■ The Nigel Vinson Charitable Trust

CC NO 265077   **ESTABLISHED** 1973

WHERE FUNDING CAN BE GIVEN UK, with a preference for north east England.

WHO CAN BENEFIT Individuals and organisations.

WHAT IS FUNDED Economic/community development and employment; and general charitable purposes.

TYPE OF GRANT Capital (including buildings), one-off, project and research. Funding is for one year or less.

SAMPLE GRANTS The Injustice Foundation (£50,000); The Christian Institute (£37,000); Politics and Economics Research Trust (£30,000); Civitas (£15,000); Young Briton's Foundation and Chillingham Wild Cattle Association (£10,000 each); Northumberland and Newcastle Society, Christian Concern for our Nation, The Wing Appeal, Renewable Energy Research Foundation and Family Education Trust (£5,000 each) and European Foundation (£2,500).

FINANCES *Year* 2011–12 *Income* £5,616,611 *Grants* £281,825 *Assets* £10,056,511

TRUSTEES Hon. Rowena A. Cowan; Rt Hon. Lord Vinson of Roddam Dene; Thomas O. C. Harris; Hon. Bettina C. Witheridge; Hon. Antonia C. Bennett; Miss E. Passey; C. Hoare and Co Trustees.

HOW TO APPLY In writing to the correspondent. The trustees meet periodically to consider applications for grants of £1,000 and above. All grants below £1,000 are decided by The Rt. Hon. Nigel Lord Vinson on behalf of the trustees.

WHO TO APPLY TO The Trustees, Hoare Trustees, 37 Fleet Street, London EC4P 4DQ *Tel.* 020 7353 4522

....

■ The William and Ellen Vinten Trust

CC NO 285758   **ESTABLISHED** 1982

WHERE FUNDING CAN BE GIVEN UK, but mostly Bury St Edmunds.

WHO CAN BENEFIT Individuals, schools and colleges; and industrial firms and companies. There is a strong preference for Bury St Edmunds.

WHAT IS FUNDED The trustees' report states that: ' The principal activity of the trust during the year was continuing to pursue initiatives to increase the interest of schools and college students in the Bury St Edmunds' area in science and technology subjects, with a view to increasing the numbers who might consider careers related to the subjects and improving their attainment.'

SAMPLE GRANTS A list of beneficiaries was not available.

FINANCES *Year* 2011–12 *Income* £58,266 *Grants* £47,195 *Assets* £1,582,268

TRUSTEES Adrian Williams; David Youngman; Emma Bass; Robin Crosher; Igor Wowk; Alan Bonnett; James Guest; Keith Honeyman.

OTHER INFORMATION Grants were given towards education (£24,700) and training (£22,500).

HOW TO APPLY The trust stated that as a proactive charity it does not seek unsolicited applications. Such applications are now so significant in number that the trust has decided not to respond to them, however discourteous this may seem.

WHO TO APPLY TO D. Marriott, Valhalla, School Road, Thurston, Bury St Edmunds, Suffolk IP31 3SY *email* vinten@vintentrust.org *Website* www. vintentrust.org.uk

■ The Vintners' Company Charitable Foundation

CC NO 1015212   **ESTABLISHED** 1992
WHERE FUNDING CAN BE GIVEN Greater London only.
WHO CAN BENEFIT Schools and charitable organisations.
WHAT IS FUNDED Prevention of drug and alcohol abuse. Funding for schools can be for general purposes.
WHAT IS NOT FUNDED No grants to UK-wide or research charities.
TYPE OF GRANT One-off.
RANGE OF GRANTS Up to £5,000.
SAMPLE GRANTS Stepney Greencoat C.E. Primary School and PSP Association (£5,000 each); The Nehemiah Project (£3,500); Wine and Spirit Education Trust (£3,300); East Coast Hospice Project; Anchor House; The Prnce's Trust (Fairbridge Programe Kennington) and St Mungo's; (£3,000 each); The Single Homeless Project (£2,500) and The University of Toronto; Mary Rose Trust Appeal; St John's Notting Hill and St Paul's Church Erith, Kent (£1,000 each).
FINANCES *Year* 2011–12 *Income* £156,718 *Grants* £36,800 *Assets* £756,482
TRUSTEES Michael Cox; Brigadier Jonathan Bourne-May; Anthony Sykes; Rupert Clevely.
HOW TO APPLY In writing to the correspondent.
WHO TO APPLY TO Andrew Ling, Charities Secretary, Vintners' Company, Vintners' Hall, Upper Thames Street, London EC4V 3BG *Tel.* 020 7236 1863 *Fax* 020 7236 8177 *email* stephen.freeth@vintershall.co.uk *Website* www.vintnershall.co.uk

■ Vintners' Gifts Charity

CC NO 1091238   **ESTABLISHED** 1992
WHERE FUNDING CAN BE GIVEN Greater London.
WHO CAN BENEFIT Hospices, hospitals and organisations benefiting older people, people with disabilities, those who have experienced abuse or addiction, young people, the homeless and the disadvantaged.
WHAT IS FUNDED The Company has recently decided to focus on trade related charities involved with the abuse and misuse of alcohol.
WHAT IS NOT FUNDED No grants to national charities, research organisations or charities that help buildings (as opposed to people).
TYPE OF GRANT One-off.
RANGE OF GRANTS Up to £12,000.
SAMPLE GRANTS Action on Addiction, Chain Reaction Theatre Company, Brandon Centre, Coram Foundation, Enfield Parents and Children and One North East London (£5,000 each) and Springfield Community Flat (£2,500).
FINANCES *Year* 2011–12 *Income* £115,131 *Grants* £72,421 *Assets* £2,154,851
TRUSTEES The Master and Wardens of the Vintners' Company. Martin Mason; Sam Dow; Michael Cox; Brigadier Michael Smythe OBE; Michael Turner.
HOW TO APPLY In writing to the correspondent, giving details of the charity and a brief description of the project, if applicable, together with a copy of

the latest audited accounts. Applicants must be prepared to be visited by a member of The Vintners' Company. The Charities Committee Meetings are in May and November. Applications should be received by 14 February for May Meetings and 14 August for November Meetings.
WHO TO APPLY TO Stephen Freeth, Charities Secretary, Vintners' Company, Vintners' Hall, Upper Thames Street, London EC4V 3BG *Tel.* 020 7236 1863 *Fax* 020 7236 8177 *email* stephen.freeth@vintnershall.co.uk *Website* www.vintnershall.co.uk

■ Vision Charity

CC NO 1075630   **ESTABLISHED** 1976
WHERE FUNDING CAN BE GIVEN UK and overseas.
WHO CAN BENEFIT 'Registered institutional charities and other organisations and individuals involved in helping blind, dyslexic or visually impaired children.'
WHAT IS FUNDED Welfare of children with dyslexia or visual difficulties.
TYPE OF GRANT 'The monies raised are used expressly to purchase equipment, goods or specialist services. The Vision Charity will make cash donations only in very exceptional circumstances, as approved by its Board of Trustees.'
SAMPLE GRANTS New College Worcester (£29,000); Priestley Smith School, Birmingham (£26,000 in two grants); VICTA (£20,000); Churchwood CP School (£12,000); Joseph Clarke School, London (£10,000); SENSE (£7,000); Autism Independent UK (£2,600) and The Bloomfield Learning Centre for Children (£1,600).
FINANCES *Year* 2013 *Income* £252,101 *Grants* £112,299 *Assets* £219,459
TRUSTEE William Vestey.
PUBLICATIONS *Vision Charity News* (published twice yearly).
HOW TO APPLY A brief summary of the request should be sent to the correspondent. If the request is of interest to the trustees, further details will be requested. If the request has not been acknowledged within three months of submission, the applicant should assume that it has not been successful. The charity is interested to receive such applications but regrets that it is not able to acknowledge every unsuccessful submission.
WHO TO APPLY TO Peter Thompson, President, 59 Victoria Road, Surbiton, Surrey KT6 4NQ *Tel.* 01296 655227 *email* info@visioncharity. co.uk *Website* www.visioncharity.co.uk

■ Vivdale Ltd

CC NO 268505   **ESTABLISHED** 1974
WHERE FUNDING CAN BE GIVEN UK.
WHO CAN BENEFIT Jewish people.
WHAT IS FUNDED The advancement of religion in accordance with the Orthodox Jewish faith and general charitable purposes.
TYPE OF GRANT One-off, one year grants.
SAMPLE GRANTS Previous beneficiaries have included: Achisomach Aid Company Ltd, Beis Soroh Schneirer, Beis Yaakov Town, Beis Yisroel Tel Aviv, Comet Charities Ltd, Friends of Harim Bnei Brak, Jewish Teachers Training College Gateshead, Mosdos Bnei Brak, Torah Vechesed Ashdod and Woodstock Sinclair Trust.
FINANCES *Year* 2011–12 *Income* £102,906 *Grants* £67,318 *Assets* £2,375,813

TRUSTEES David Henry Marks; Francesca Zipporah Sinclair; Loretta Marks.

OTHER INFORMATION No list of grant beneficiaries was included in the accounts.

HOW TO APPLY In writing to the correspondent.

WHO TO APPLY TO David Henry Marks, Trustee, 17 Cheyne Walk, London NW4 3QH *Tel.* 020 8202 9367

■ The Viznitz Foundation

CC NO 326581   **ESTABLISHED** 1984

WHERE FUNDING CAN BE GIVEN UK and abroad.

WHO CAN BENEFIT Organisations, including schools and registered charities.

WHAT IS FUNDED 'The objects of the charity are to pay and apply and appropriate the whole of the trust fund to those purposes both in the UK and abroad recognised as charitable by English Law and in accordance with the trust deed and the wishes of the Grand Rabbi of Viznitz.'

FINANCES *Year* 2011–12 *Income* £204,039 *Grants* £119,707 *Assets* £2,204,856

TRUSTEES Heinrich Feldman; Shulom Feldman.

HOW TO APPLY In writing to the correspondent.

WHO TO APPLY TO Heinrich Feldman, Trustee, 23 Overlea Road, London E5 9BG *Tel.* 020 8557 9557

■ The Vodafone Foundation

CC NO 1089625   **ESTABLISHED** 2002

WHERE FUNDING CAN BE GIVEN Uk and Worldwide (where Vodaphone operates).

WHO CAN BENEFIT Registered charities and community groups.

WHAT IS FUNDED Social welfare.

WHAT IS NOT FUNDED No grant to individuals.

RANGE OF GRANTS £500–£2 million

SAMPLE GRANTS Grants to local Vodafone Foundations totalled £15.6 million. Beneficiaries of 'Direct Grants' include: World of Difference – UK (£1.4 million); United Nations World Food Programme and Health Alliance (£438,000); Telecoms Sans Frontieres (£288,000); Foundation of the Hellenic World (£81,000); Democratic Republic of Congo – Charitable Fund (£73,000); Red Cross – Kenya (£64,000); Tatra Mountain Rescue Service (£34,000); Animals Asia Foundation (£15,000) and Avenues Youth Project (£10,000).

FINANCES *Year* 2011–12 *Income* £22,140,637 *Grants* £22,412,155 *Assets* £11,292,096

TRUSTEES Nick Land; Margherita Della Valle; Elizabeth Filkin; Lord Hastings of Scarisbrick; Matthew Kirk; Guy Laurence; Ronald Schellekens; Tina Southall; Hatem Dowidar; Francisco Roman; Mwamvita Makamba; Andrew Dunnett.

HOW TO APPLY Contact the foundation or see the website for details of all application processes.

WHO TO APPLY TO Andrew Dunnett, Director, Vodafone House, The Connection, Newbury, Berkshire RG14 2FN *email* groupfoundation@vodafone.com *Website* www.vodafone.com/content/index/about/foundation

■ Volant Charitable Trust

SC NO SC030790   **ESTABLISHED** 2000

WHERE FUNDING CAN BE GIVEN UK and overseas, with a preference for Scotland.

WHO CAN BENEFIT Organisations benefiting women, children, the relief of poverty, the alleviation of social deprivation and the provision of social benefit to the community.

WHAT IS FUNDED Research and teaching related to the treatment, cure and nursing of Multiple Sclerosis and related conditions; charitable organisations involved in the support and protection of women, children, relief of poverty and alleviating social deprivation and the provision of social benefit to the community and the public at large

WHAT IS NOT FUNDED The trust will not provide grants to individuals or major capital projects.

TYPE OF GRANT One-off and recurrent grants.

RANGE OF GRANTS Up to £100,000.

SAMPLE GRANTS Foundation Scotland (£350,000); Médecins Sans Frontières – Congo, Save the Children – Ivory Coast (£100,000 each); The Place2Be (£90,000); The Roses Charitable Trust (£75,000); Women Onto Work (£60,000); and Kids Company (£50,000).

FINANCES *Year* 2011–12 *Income* £2,626,418 *Grants* £1,176,068 *Assets* £51,309,645

TRUSTEES J. K. Rowling; Dr N. S. Murray; G. C. Smith; R. D. Fulton.

HOW TO APPLY Applications for funding requests of up to and including £10,000 per annum, for those projects based in Scotland only, are dealt with by the appointed agents, Foundation Scotland (www.foundationscotland.org.uk). According to Foundation Scotland's website, 'the fund's primary focus is to support women, children and young people who are at risk and facing social deprivation. There is limited funding available, so only those projects that closely match the above criteria are likely to be considered for support. Projects must demonstrate a strong focus on supporting women affected by hardship or disadvantage and on tackling the issues they face in order to make a lasting difference to their lives and life chances. Projects which tackle serious issues and help people to turn their lives around are given priority.' Organisations who are currently in receipt of a grant may not apply. Groups that will distribute funds as grants or bursaries to other groups may not apply. An outline of the project using the enquiry form should be sent to: grants@foundationscotland.org.uk. Any questions should be directed towards Jane Martin on 0131 524 0301. All other requests for funding are dealt with via an application form available from the Volant Trust's website. Complete and return the application form, plus any supporting materials by post. Applications should not be hand delivered. If an application is hand delivered, management at mail boxes are not in a position to discuss applications and will not be expected to provide any form of receipt.

WHO TO APPLY TO Christine Collingwood, Trust Administrator, Box 8, 196 Rose Street, Edinburgh EH2 4AT *email* admin@volanttrust.com *Website* www.volanttrust.com

■ Voluntary Action Fund (VAF)

SC NO SC035037   **ESTABLISHED** 2003

WHERE FUNDING CAN BE GIVEN Scotland.

WHO CAN BENEFIT Registered charities and organisations with a constitution and activities that could be considered charitable.

WHAT IS FUNDED VAF manages funds that are open to application from eligible groups and organisations. The funding and support VAF provides enables community based organisations to involve volunteers, undertake projects that challenge inequalities and overcome barriers to being involved in community life.

WHAT IS NOT FUNDED See the fund's website for details of any individual exclusions for each fund.

TYPE OF GRANT Check the individual scheme guidelines.

RANGE OF GRANTS Up to about £165,000.

SAMPLE GRANTS Scottish Equality Disability Forum – policy and information (£165,000); EHRC – Independent Living in Scotland (£140,000); Scottish Transgender Alliance (£125,000); Scottish Alliance of Regional Equality Councils and Show Racism the Red Card (£120,000 each); Bridges Programme (£95,000); Maryhill CAB (£80,000); Positive Action in Housing (£60,000); Multi Ethnic Aberdeen Ltd (MEAL), Glasgow Wood Recycling and Faith in Community Scotland (£40,000 each); British Deaf Association – Building Capacity (£30,000); Homelink Family Support (£23,000); Alzheimer Scotland/Glasgow and E Dumbartonshire (£17,000); and Brighter Horizons – Banff (£9,000).

FINANCES *Year* 2011–12 *Income* £6,168,149 *Grants* £5,672,757 *Assets* £232,548

TRUSTEES Ron Daniel; Dorothy MacLauchlin; Michael Cunningham; Pam Judson; John McDonald; Douglas Guest; Shirley Grieve; Gail Edwards; Andrew Marshall-Roberts; Bridgid Corr; Sid Wales.

PUBLICATIONS Programme evaluations.

HOW TO APPLY Application forms and guidance notes for open programmes are available on the fund's website. The fund recommends that interested parties contact them to discuss the project before making any application. Funds may open and close so applicants should check the website for the most recent updates. Different funds have different application guidance.

WHO TO APPLY TO Keith Wimbles, Chief Executive, Suite 3, Forth House, Burnside Business Court, North Road, Inverkeithing, Fife KY11 1NZ *Tel.* 01383 620780 *Fax* 01383 626314 *email* info@voluntaryactionfund.org.uk *Website* www.voluntaryactionfund.org.uk

■ Wade's Charity

CC NO 224939   **ESTABLISHED** 1530

WHERE FUNDING CAN BE GIVEN Leeds, within the pre-1974 boundary of the city (approximately LS1 to LS17 postcodes).

WHO CAN BENEFIT Charities benefiting people of all ages and those living in urban areas. Mainly youth organisations and community centres. (Grants are only a part of the charity's activities.)

WHAT IS FUNDED 'The provision of facilities for recreation, amusement, entertainment and general social intercourse for citizens of every age of areas of population in the City of Leeds occupied in the main by the working classes including in any such objects the establishment of what are commonly known as community centres and youth centres.' See the charity's website for full guidelines.

WHAT IS NOT FUNDED No grants given to: applications from outside the beneficial area, i.e. from outside the pre-1974 boundary of the city of Leeds covered roughly by postcodes LS1 to LS17; applications from non-charitable organisations; applications from individuals; applications for church repairs (unless there is proven significant community use); circulars or general appeals from high profile national charities; applications which do not offer benefit within the terms of the trust; applications for activities which are the responsibility of statutory or local authority funding, particularly within health or education; applications to fund salaries.

TYPE OF GRANT The majority of grants are given on a one-off basis.

RANGE OF GRANTS Average grant around £2,000.

SAMPLE GRANTS Al-Haqq Supplementary School, Hawksworth Wood YMCA, Youth Theatres Leeds, 10th Leeds Girls' Brigade, Leeds University Union, Richmond Hill Elderly Action, Armley Helping Hands, Kirkstall Educational Cricket Club, Hunslet Baptist Church, Spacious Places, Leeds Asylum Seekers Support Network and Headingley Music Festival.

FINANCES *Year* 2012 *Income* £219,074

TRUSTEES Bernard Atha; Susan Reddington; John Tinker; Ann Chadwick; Ann Blackburn; John Roberts; John Stoddart-Scott; Hilary Finnigan; Kenneth Jones; Bruce Smith; Mark Pullan; Martin Hamilton; Nicholas Mercer; John Pike; David Richardson; The Rector of Leeds; The Lord Mayor of Leeds.

OTHER INFORMATION A small grants programme has been operating through Voluntary Action Leeds for many years. This programme enables small community groups (with an annual income of less than £10,000) who may not be a registered charity to apply for funds of up to £100 to contribute towards their administrative costs.

HOW TO APPLY Main grants – In writing to the correspondent, including the following information: the name, address and telephone number of both the applicant and the organisations they are applying on behalf of; registered charity number; an outline of what the organisation does; an outline of the purpose for which the grant is being sought; a copy of the latest signed accounts. If an application potentially fulfils at least one of the charity's primary charitable objectives, an appointment will then be made for the Grants Adviser to visit the organisation to establish further relevant information about the application. The application will then be considered by the board of trustees at one of their grants meetings, these are usually held in April, July and November. The deadline for inclusion at any meeting is four weeks prior to the meeting date. The charity is happy to discuss ideas before a formal application is made. Applicants may only submit an application once per calendar year. Voluntary Action Leeds advertises the small grants programme in their newsletter at the start of each year.

WHO TO APPLY TO Kathryn Hodges, Grants Adviser and Administrator, 5 Grimston Park Mews, Grimston Park, Tadcaster LS24 9DB *Tel.* 01937 830295 *email* wadescharity@btinernet.com *Website* www.wadescharity.org

■ The Scurrah Wainwright Charity

CC NO 1002755   **ESTABLISHED** 1991

WHERE FUNDING CAN BE GIVEN Preference for Yorkshire, South Africa and Zimbabwe.

WHO CAN BENEFIT Charitable organisations.

WHAT IS FUNDED The charity 'looks for innovative work in the field of social reform, with a preference for 'root-cause' rather than palliative projects. It favours causes that are outside the mainstream, and unlikely to be funded by other charities.'

WHAT IS NOT FUNDED No support is given to: individuals; animal welfare; buildings; medical research or support for individual medical conditions; substitution for Government funding (e.g. in education and health); charities who send unsolicited general appeal letters; activities that have already happened; applicants who do not have a UK bank into which a grant can be paid.

TYPE OF GRANT Contributions to core costs. Rarely funds for more than one year.

RANGE OF GRANTS Typically £1,000–£5,000, but in 'cases of exceptional merit' larger grants may be awarded.

SAMPLE GRANTS Heads Together Productions (£25,000); War on Want and Leeds Refuge Forum (£5,000 each); 32 Degrees East Ugandan Arts Trust (£4,500); HALE – Healthy Action Local Engagement (£4,000); Food Aware (£3,500); The Global Native (£3,000); Public Interest Investigations (£2,500); Helena Kennedy Foundation and Barnardo's Yorkshire (£2,000 each); Northern Indymedia – 1 in 12 Library Collective (£1,500) and Womankind Worldwide (£1,000).

FINANCES *Year* 2011–12 *Income* £62,186 *Grants* £112,420 *Assets* £1,567,658

TRUSTEES M. S. Wainwright, Chair; R. R. Bhaskar; H. P. I. Scott; H. A. Wainwright; P. Wainwright; T. M. Wainwright.

OTHER INFORMATION 'The Wainwright family runs two trusts, one charitable [The Scurrah Wainwright Charity], one non-charitable [The Andrew Wainwright Reform Trust Ltd]. The trusts are based on the family's traditions of liberal values and support for the socially disempowered. The trustees are all family members, based in West Yorkshire.'

HOW TO APPLY Follow these preliminary steps: check that your aims meet the charity's criteria; check that the amount of money you need falls within the charity's limits; check deadlines: the trustees meet three times a year – in March, July and November – and applications must be submitted by 1 February, 1 June or 1 October respectively.

Write a succinct but complete application that should include: an opening section that gives the name and postal address of your organisation, details of a named contact for the application and where you heard about the Charity; background information about you and/or your organisation; the nature of the project you wish to pursue and what it seeks to achieve; your plans for practical implementation of the work and a budget; your most recent accounts and details of any additional sources of funding already secured or to be sought; whether you will accept a contribution to the amount requested.

If the above information (excluding your accounts) takes up more than two sides of A4, include a summary of that information on no more than two sides of A4, using a font no smaller than 12-point.

Applicants may contact the administrator, preferably by email, for any clarification. If you have not heard from the administrator by the end of the month in which the trustees' meeting was held you must assume your application was not successful.

WHO TO APPLY TO Kerry McQuade, Administrator, 16 Blenheim Street, Hebden Bridge, West Yorkshire HX7 8BU *email* admin@wainwrighttrusts.org.uk *Website* www.wainwrighttrusts.org.uk

....

■ The Wakefield and Tetley Trust

CC NO 1121779   **ESTABLISHED** 2008
WHERE FUNDING CAN BE GIVEN London boroughs of Tower Hamlets, Southwark and the City of London.
WHO CAN BENEFIT Community groups and charities.
WHAT IS FUNDED Social welfare and general charitable purposes.
WHAT IS NOT FUNDED The trust will not support: grants to individuals; work that has already taken place; applicants who have been rejected by the trust within the last six months; organisations with significant unrestricted reserves; organisations in serious financial deficit; the promotion of religion; animal charities; statutory bodies and work that is primarily the responsibility of central or local government; health trusts, health authorities and hospices (or any sort of medical equipment or medical research). The trust is unlikely to support: building restoration or conservation; uniformed youth groups; schools, supplementary schools or vocational training; environmental improvements.
TYPE OF GRANT Up to three years for project costs and core costs.
RANGE OF GRANTS Grants range from £500 to £65,000 over one year; the average grant awarded in 2009–10 was £7,000.
SAMPLE GRANTS All Hallows (£49,500); Southwark Daycentre for Asylum Seekers (£10,000); Eclectic Productions (£7,000); Tower Hamlets Parents Centre (£6,000); Bishop Ho Ming Wah Association, Docklands Youth Service, Ernest Foundation and First Love Foundation (£2,500 each) and East London Chinese Community Centre (£1,500).
FINANCES *Year* 2011–12 *Income* £390,182 *Grants* £243,703 *Assets* £5,980,499
TRUSTEES Peter Delaney, Chair; Patrick Kelly; Lady Judy Moody-Stuart; Stuart Morganstein; Clare Murphy; Kenneth Prideaux-Brune; Helal Rahman; Susan Reardon-Smith

HOW TO APPLY You will need to demonstrate that your organisation: benefits people resident or working in Tower Hamlets and/or Southwark and/or the City of London; undertakes charitable work (however you do not have to be a registered charity); has a constitution or a set of rules which governs its activities; has its own bank or building society account where two or more named people (including one trustee or management committee member) have to sign all the cheques; can provide annual accounts for the previous year (if your organisation is new, copies of your most recent bank or building society statements will suffice).

'The trust is likely to receive many more proposals than we are able to fund so the following funding priorities have been agreed. The trust particularly welcomes applications for: cross-cultural and intergenerational projects that help to bring people together, reduce barriers and support community cohesion; new initiatives that address emerging needs new methods of tackling existing problems.

The trust will prioritise: projects with local support and beneficiary involvement; projects that have a well-considered plan and demonstrate the difference that will be made; organisations with an annual turnover of less than £500,000; organisations with a relevant track record and experience. These priorities will be subject to regular review. We are happy to consider requests to fund project costs, relevant core costs and associated training. However the trust is unlikely to support equipment or capital costs. We usually make grants over one, two or three years, however, funding cannot continue indefinitely as we are keen to support a range of projects and organisations, including those which are new to us.'

WHO TO APPLY TO Elaine Crush, Grant Officer, Attlee House, 28 Commercial Street, London E1 6LR *Tel.* 020 7377 6614 *email* enquiries@wakefieldtrust.org.uk *Website* www.wakefieldtrust.org.uk

....

■ Wakeham Trust

CC NO 267495   **ESTABLISHED** 1974
WHERE FUNDING CAN BE GIVEN UK.
WHO CAN BENEFIT Registered charities.
WHAT IS FUNDED 'We provide grants to help people rebuild their communities. We are particularly interested in neighbourhood projects, community arts projects, projects involving community service by young people, or projects set up by those who are socially excluded. We also support innovative projects to promote excellence in teaching (at any level, from primary schools to universities), though we never support individuals.'
WHAT IS NOT FUNDED No grants to individuals or large, well-established charities, or towards buildings and transport.
RANGE OF GRANTS Normally £75–£750.
SAMPLE GRANTS A furniture reclamation and delivery enterprise (£500); A group of elderly and disabled volunteers for a children's cafe (£350); New youth club and The Kaiama Community Association (£250 each); Community garden and toy boxes for DHSS offices (£200 each); Martin Youth Bikers (£150); and Community football (£50).
FINANCES *Year* 2011–12 *Income* £23,494 *Grants* £70,000

TRUSTEES Harold Carter; Barnaby Newbolt; Tess Silkstone.

HOW TO APPLY By letter or by completing the form on the trust's website (online applications are preferred). Full guidelines are also available on the trust's website.

WHO TO APPLY TO Laura Gosling, Administrator, Wakeham Lodge, Rogate, Petersfield, Hampshire GU31 5EJ *Tel.* 01730 821748 *email* wakehamtrust@mac.com *Website* www. wakehamtrust.org

■ The Community Foundation in Wales

CC NO 1074655   **ESTABLISHED** 1999
WHERE FUNDING CAN BE GIVEN Wales.

WHO CAN BENEFIT Local charities, community groups and voluntary organisations that are engaged in tackling social need and economic disadvantage at a grass-roots level.

WHAT IS FUNDED The promotion of any charitable purposes for the benefit of communities within Wales. Projects providing worthwhile service to the community. The foundation manages a number of funds, many with their own individual criteria and some which relate to specific geographical areas of Wales. Community cohesion; the environment; older people; minority groups; young people; economic disadvantage; social exclusion; rural isolation; crime reduction; substance misuse and addiction; skills development and confidence-building; education and lifelong learning; and sport as a vehicle for social inclusion.

WHAT IS NOT FUNDED Political organisations and pressure groups; religious organisations, where the primary aim of the project is the promotion of faith; individuals, unless the specific focus of a fund; general appeals; sports organisations where no obvious charitable element exists; medical research; statutory bodies e.g. schools, local authorities and councils, although the foundation will consider applications from school PTAs if the intended project is non-statutory in nature; animal welfare; arts and heritage projects unless there exists a clear, demonstrable community benefit; large capital projects; retrospective applications for projects that have taken place.

RANGE OF GRANTS The majority of grants awarded are under £5,000

FINANCES *Year* 2011–12 *Income* £2,364,644 *Grants* £1,716,307 *Assets* £8,403,610

TRUSTEES Janet Lewis-Jones; David Dudley; Michael Westerman; Julian Smith; Frank Learner; Dr Caryl Cresswell; Jonathan Hollins; Henry Robertson; Lulu Burridge; Sheila Maxwell; Thomas Jones.

OTHER INFORMATION 'The Community Foundation in Wales promotes the cause of philanthropy in Wales by creating and managing relationships between donors and those who are running life-enhancing initiatives. We are dedicated to strengthening local communities by providing a permanent source of funding, building endowment and *immediate impact* funds to link donors to local needs.'

HOW TO APPLY Visit the 'how to apply' page of its website. If an organisation is uncertain about whether it meets the criteria for any of its named funds a general application may be completed at any time during the year. The foundation aims to match proposals to available funding and make contact if further information is required.

WHO TO APPLY TO Liza Kellett, St Andrew's House, 24 St Andrew's Crescent, Cardiff CF10 3DD *Tel.* 02920 379580 *email* mail@cfiw.org.uk *Website* www.cfiw.org.uk

■ Wales Council for Voluntary Action

CC NO 218093   **ESTABLISHED** 1963
WHERE FUNDING CAN BE GIVEN Wales.

WHO CAN BENEFIT Registered charities and voluntary organisations only.

WHAT IS FUNDED Local community, volunteering, social welfare, environment, regeneration.

WHAT IS NOT FUNDED Grants are made to constituted voluntary organisations only. Check the WCVA website for specific exclusions for individual funds.

TYPE OF GRANT Capital, core costs, one-off, project, recurring costs, running costs, start-up costs.

SAMPLE GRANTS Gwent Association of Voluntary Organisations – Newport (£658,500); Powys Association of Voluntary Organisations (£403,000); Swansea Council for Voluntary Service (£246,000); Vale Centre for Voluntary Service (£127,500); British Trust for Conservation Volunteers (£42,500); RSPB Cymru (£37,500); CTC Challenge for Change (£25,500); Scope (£18,500); and the SAFE Foundation and Community First (£16,500 each).

FINANCES *Year* 2011–12 *Income* £43,407,139 *Grants* £11,532,348 *Assets* £15,849,628

TRUSTEES Margaret McCarter; Catriona Williams; Pauline Young; Lydia Stephens; Peter Davies; Dilys Jackson; Eurwen Edwards; Fran Targett; Walter Dickie; Louise Bennett; Simon Harris; Michael Hewlett Williams; Philip Avery; Win Griffiths; Efa Jones; Chad Patel; John Jones; Anne Stephenson; Clive Wolfendale; Joy Kent; Paul Glaze; Janet Walsh; Rocio Cifuentes; Hilary Stevens; Liza Kellett; Martin Pollard; Mike Denman; Thomas Williams; Catherine Gwynant; Roy Norris; Moira Lockitt; Cherrie Galvin; Judy Leering.

PUBLICATIONS Guidance notes for applicants available on request. Visit www.wcva.org.uk or call the Helpdesk on 0800 2888 329.

OTHER INFORMATION Grants were made to 1,829 organisations.

HOW TO APPLY There are separate application forms for each scheme. Contact WCVA on 0800 2888 329, or visit its website, for further information.

WHO TO APPLY TO Tracey Lewis, Secretary, Baltic House, Mount Stuart Square, Cardiff CF10 5FH *Tel.* 02920 431734 *email* help@wcva.org.uk *Website* www.wcva.org.uk

■ Robert and Felicity Waley-Cohen Charitable Trust

CC NO 272126   **ESTABLISHED** 1976
WHERE FUNDING CAN BE GIVEN Throughout England and Wales with a preference for Warwickshire and Oxfordshire.

WHO CAN BENEFIT Charitable organisations, schools and those of the Jewish faith.

WHAT IS FUNDED Jewish, children, education, fine arts, health

WHAT IS NOT FUNDED No grants to individuals.

TYPE OF GRANT One off grant

RANGE OF GRANTS £50–£16,667

SAMPLE GRANTS Serpentine Trust (£16,667); The Place 28e (£11,000); The EORTC Charitable Trust (£10,000); The Injured Jockeys Fund

(£10,350); Racing Welfare (£5,500); TATE Foundation (£5,000); Cancer Research Ltd; RADA; Rainbow Hospice (£100 each); The Order of St John (£50)

FINANCES *Year* 2011–12 *Income* £104,204 *Grants* £80,045 *Assets* £1,831,345

TRUSTEES R. B. Waley-Cohen; Hon F. A. Waley-Cohen.

HOW TO APPLY In writing to the Correspondent.

WHO TO APPLY TO R. Waley-Cohen, Trustee, 18 Gilston Road, London SW10 9SR *Tel.* 020 7244 6022 *email* ccopeman@alliance.co.uk

....

■ The Walker Trust

CC NO 215479   **ESTABLISHED** 1897

WHERE FUNDING CAN BE GIVEN Shropshire.

WHO CAN BENEFIT Individuals and organisations benefiting children and young adults who are in care, fostered and adopted.

WHAT IS FUNDED The establishment or towards maintenance of any hospital, infirmary, convalescent home or other institution having for its object the relief of sickness or promoting convalescence; the provision of medical or surgical aid or appliance; any institution for the maintenance and education of orphans.

WHAT IS NOT FUNDED No grants to individuals for second degrees or postgraduate courses. Appeals from outside Shropshire will not be considered or replied to.

TYPE OF GRANT Funding given up to one year. Part project funding and capital costs.

RANGE OF GRANTS Up to £100,000.

SAMPLE GRANTS The Music Hall Education Suite (£100,000); Shropshire Jubilee Pageant (£50,000); The Ark (25,000); Shrewsbury and Oswestry Crucial Crew (£4,000); Shropshire Schools and Colleges Athletics Association (£3,000); Clun Valley AED Scheme and RNIB (£2,500 each); Haughton Special School (£1,500) and Vitalise, Compton Hospice and Arthritis Research UK (£1,000 each).

FINANCES *Year* 2011–12 *Income* £200,141 *Grants* £285,118 *Assets* £5,680,669

TRUSTEES A. Herber-Percy; Caroline Paton-Smith; David Lloyd; Malcolm Pate; Shirley Reynolds; Lady Lydia Forester.

OTHER INFORMATION The grant total in 2011–12 includes £81,000 that was given in grants to individuals.

HOW TO APPLY In writing to the correspondent. Details of other assistance applied for must be given and, in the case of organisations, the latest annual report and accounts. The trustees meet in January, April, July and October each year, but arrangements can be made for urgent applications to receive consideration between meetings. Applications must reach the clerk not less than one month before a decision is required.

WHO TO APPLY TO Edward Hewitt, Clerk, 2 Breidden Way, Bayston Hill, Shrewsbury SY3 0LN *Tel.* 01743 873866

....

■ The Thomas Wall Trust

CC NO 206121   **ESTABLISHED** 1920

WHERE FUNDING CAN BE GIVEN UK.

WHO CAN BENEFIT Individuals and registered charities. Small charities and small schemes are preferred to large national ones.

WHAT IS FUNDED 'The object must be in a broad sense educational and/or concerned with social service.'

WHAT IS NOT FUNDED Grants are not made: towards the erection, upkeep or renovation of buildings; to hospitals, almshouses or similar institutions; for objects which are purely medical; for projects outside of the UK; for charities that have received a grant from the trust in the last five years.

TYPE OF GRANT Project, activity or one-off costs.

RANGE OF GRANTS £250–£1,100

SAMPLE GRANTS Crossroads Counselling (£1,100); Action Foundation; Barnet Lone Person Centre; Cued Speech Association; Foyle Down Syndrome Trust; Get Set Girls; Gospel Oak Action Link; Lincoln Toy Library; Westcliff Drop-In Centre (£1,000 each); Community Development Support (£900); Ulverston Inshore Rescue (£800) and Tho0mas Wall Nursery (£250).

FINANCES *Year* 2011–12 *Income* £118,185 *Grants* £27,046 *Assets* £2,800,968

TRUSTEES Dr G. M. Copland; M. A. Barrie; P. Bellamy; C. R. Broomfield; Miss A. S. Kennedy; A. Mullins; Revd Dr R. Waller; Paola Morris.

OTHER INFORMATION An additional £44,000 was given to 41 individuals.

HOW TO APPLY On a form available from the website which must be completed and returned via post or email along with a copy of the most recent audited accounts (if they are not available on the Charity Commission website). Charities will only be contacted if the application is successful. The trustees meet twice a year, in July and November. Applications for the July meeting must be received by mid-May and for the November meeting by end of September.

WHO TO APPLY TO Louise Pooley, Skinners' Hall, 8 Dowgate Hill, London EC4R 2SP *Tel.* 020 7213 0564 *email* information@thomaswalltrust.org.uk *Website* www.thomaswalltrust.org.uk

....

■ Wallace and Gromit's Children's Foundation

CC NO 1096483   **ESTABLISHED** 2003

WHERE FUNDING CAN BE GIVEN UK.

WHO CAN BENEFIT Children's hospitals, hospices and healthcare organisations.

WHAT IS FUNDED Wallace and Gromit's Children's Foundation is a national charity raising funds to improve the quality of life for children in hospitals and hospices throughout the UK. The foundation provides funding to support projects such as: (i) Arts, music play and entertainment programmes to stimulate young minds and divert attention away from illness. (ii) Providing welcoming and accessible environments and surroundings, designed specifically for children in a fun and engaging way. (iii) Funding Education and Information Programmes to educate young people and recognising the importance of self-help and health related issues. (iv) Helping to fund the acquisition of medical facilities, which can help to improve diagnosis and treatment of a wide range of conditions and illnesses in children. (v) Sustaining family relationships helping to keep families together during emotionally difficult times. (vi) Helping to meet the cost of care in a children's hospice where children and their families are cared for during good days, difficult days and last days. (vii) Supporting children with physical and emotional difficulties empowering and increasing confidence.

WHAT IS NOT FUNDED No support for; charities not supporting children's healthcare; organisations that do not have charitable status; animal, religious or international charities; retrospective funding; organisations that do not work within a hospital or hospice environment; organisations that provide excursions, holidays or away days; no grants will be made to individuals; no retrospective funding and no funding for Clown Doctors.

SAMPLE GRANTS University Hospital Coventry and Warwickshire CW Charity, Coventry (£13,000); Alexander Devine Children's Hospice Service (£10,000); Wallace and Gromit's Grand Appeal (£9,000); Northern Ireland Children's Hospice (£7,700); The Sick Kids Friends Foundation, Alder Hey IMAGINE Appeal and Leeds Children's Hospital (£5,000 each); Little Havens Children's Hospice (£4,300); Chestnut Tree Children's Hospice (£3,500) and Chelsea Children's Hospital School (£1,000).

FINANCES *Year* 2011–12 *Income* £221,178 *Grants* £100,331 *Assets* £57,520

TRUSTEES I. Hannah, Chair; S. Cooper; P. Lord; J. Moule; N. Park; D. Sproxton.

OTHER INFORMATION The charity raises its income through various fundraising activities such as the Wrong Trousers Day and Wallace and Gromit's BIG Bake

HOW TO APPLY Grants are distributed on an annual basis. Application forms and guidelines are posted on the foundation's website from October and the closing date for applications is usually in December. All awards are made by the end of March.

WHO TO APPLY TO Anna Shepherd, Deputy Director, 24 Upper Maudlin Street, Bristol BS2 8DJ *Tel.* 01179 252744 *email* info@wallaceandgromitcharity.org *Website* www.wallaceandgromitfoundation.org

---

■ **Wallington Missionary Mart and Auctions**

CC NO 289030   **ESTABLISHED** 1965
WHERE FUNDING CAN BE GIVEN Overseas.

WHO CAN BENEFIT Missionary societies working overseas benefiting Christians.

WHAT IS FUNDED Christian education and outreach.

WHAT IS NOT FUNDED Only registered Christian charities may receive support. Applications from individuals are only considered if funds will go to a Christian missionary society or Christian charity.

TYPE OF GRANT Usually one-off grants for core costs. Fully committed for charities selected by the trustees.

RANGE OF GRANTS £1,500–£7,000

SAMPLE GRANTS Wycliffe Bible Translators (£6,800); Youth with a mission (£6,000); OMF International UK (£5,500); Operation Mobilisation (£3,800); SIM UK (£3,500); Tear Fund (£2,400); Limuru Children's Centre (£1,700); International Fellowship Evangelical Students (£1,500); London City Mission (£1,200).

FINANCES *Year* 2012 *Income* £178,147 *Grants* £67,000

TRUSTEES Stephen Crawley; Brian Chapman; Geoffrey Willey; Sylvia Symes; Pat Collett.

OTHER INFORMATION This trust receives its income through receiving donated goods from the public, which are sold at the auctions it stages four to six times a year. For further information on these auctions, see its website.

HOW TO APPLY The trustees meet to consider grants throughout the year but do not consider unsolicited applications.

WHO TO APPLY TO Brian E. Chapman, Trustee, 99 Woodmansterne Road, Carshalton Beeches, Surrey SM5 4EG *Tel.* 020 8643 3616 *email* enq@wmma.org.uk *Website* www.wallingtonmissionary.org.uk

---

■ **The F. J. Wallis Charitable Settlement**

CC NO 279273   **ESTABLISHED** 1979
WHERE FUNDING CAN BE GIVEN UK, with some interest in Hampshire and Surrey.

WHO CAN BENEFIT Charitable organisations, including both headquarters and branches of large UK charities.

WHAT IS FUNDED General charitable purposes.

WHAT IS NOT FUNDED No grants to individuals or to local charities except those in Surrey or in Hampshire. The same organisation is not supported twice within a 24-month period.

TYPE OF GRANT Mostly one-off but there are some recurring grants.

RANGE OF GRANTS Usually £500–£1,000.

SAMPLE GRANTS Our Lady's Nursery (£3,000); and RNLI (£1,000).

FINANCES *Year* 2011–12 *Income* £48,619 *Grants* £4,480 *Assets* £1,243,532

TRUSTEES Francis Hughes; Alan Hills; Revd John Archer.

OTHER INFORMATION There was also a donation of £70,000 made to 4th New Forest North (Eling) Sea Scouts towards their new aquativity centre – this had been accrued for in the previous year's accounts.

HOW TO APPLY In writing to the correspondent. No telephone calls. Applications are not acknowledged and unsuccessful applicants will only be contacted if an sae is provided. Trustees meet in March and September and applications need to be received the month prior to the trustees' meeting. Consideration is given to those charities supported by the Wallis family or the trustees.

WHO TO APPLY TO Francis Hughes, Trustee, c/o Bridge House, 11 Creek Road, Hampton Court, East Molesey, Surrey KT8 9BE *Tel.* 020 8941 4455 *email* francis@hughescollett.co.uk

---

■ **War on Want**

CC NO 208724   **ESTABLISHED** 1959
WHERE FUNDING CAN BE GIVEN Developing countries only.

WHO CAN BENEFIT Typically, War on Want directly funds the work of labour organisations and NGOs in developing countries, usually trade unions or similar workers' organisations, and women's organisations.

WHAT IS FUNDED Overseas development projects that address the root causes of poverty, oppression and injustice in developing countries.

WHAT IS NOT FUNDED War on Want is an overseas development agency and does not make grants to organisations in the UK.

TYPE OF GRANT Continuous project funding.

SAMPLE GRANTS Sweatshops and Plantations (£155,000); Informal Economies (£113,500); Food Sovereignty (£6,000); Economic Justice (£52,000); Global Justice (£12,000); Conflict Zones (Zero).

FINANCES *Year* 2011–12 *Income* £1,599,051 *Grants* £338,377 *Assets* £1,532,605

TRUSTEES Sue Branford; Polly Jones; David Hillman; Mark Luetchford; Guillermo Rogel; Steve Preston; Gaynelle Samuel; Atif Choudhury;

Branislava Milosevic; Anna Morser; Tony McMullan.

PUBLICATIONS Upfront (a regular newsletter); publications list – covering subjects such as health, women, trade, aid, Asia, Latin America and Africa.

HOW TO APPLY Unsolicited applications are not accepted and will not be acknowledged.

WHO TO APPLY TO The Executive Director, 44–48 Shepherdess Walk, London N1 7JP *Tel.* 020 7324 5040 *Fax* 020 7324 5041 *email* mailroom@waronwant.org *Website* www. waronwant.org

■ Sir Siegmund Warburg's Voluntary Settlement

CC NO 286719 **ESTABLISHED** 1983

WHERE FUNDING CAN BE GIVEN UK, especially London.

WHO CAN BENEFIT Registered charities only.

WHAT IS FUNDED The arts.

WHAT IS NOT FUNDED No grants to individuals.

TYPE OF GRANT Revenue funding and capital projects.

RANGE OF GRANTS Up to £250,000.

SAMPLE GRANTS British Museum, English National Opera and the National Gallery (£250,000 each); York Minster (£150,000); Bristol Old Vic (£100,000); Bush Theatre, Central School of Speech and Drama, Manchester Camerata and Salisbury and South Wiltshire Museum (£50,000 each); Hepworth Wakefield (£25,000); Cambridge Music Festival and the Sainsbury Institute for the Study of Japanese Art and Culture (£5,000 each); and St Paul's Girls' School (£2,000).

FINANCES *Year* 2011–12 *Income* £188,572 *Grants* £2,205,000 *Assets* £8,339,518

TRUSTEES Sir Hugh Stevenson; Doris Wasserman; Dr Michael Harding; Christopher Purvis.

OTHER INFORMATION Following the trustees decision to start planning for the eventual wind-down of the trust, they have begun withdrawing larger amounts from the invested portfolio and distributing this in grants.

HOW TO APPLY Organisations are invited to send applications by email to applications@sswvs.org. It is requested that initial applications should be no more than four sides and should be accompanied by the latest audited accounts. Applications sent by post will not be considered.

WHO TO APPLY TO The Secretary, 19 Norland Square, London W11 4PU *email* applications@sswvs.org

■ The Ward Blenkinsop Trust

CC NO 265449 **ESTABLISHED** 1972

WHERE FUNDING CAN BE GIVEN UK, with a special interest in Merseyside and surrounding counties.

WHO CAN BENEFIT Charitable organisations.

WHAT IS FUNDED General charitable purposes with emphasis on support for medical research, social welfare, arts and education.

WHAT IS NOT FUNDED No grants to individuals.

SAMPLE GRANTS Previous beneficiaries have included Action on Addiction, BID, Chase Children's Hospice, Clatterbridge Cancer Research, Clod Ensemble, Comic Relief, Depaul Trust, Fairley House, Give Youth a Break, Halton Autistic Family Support Group, Hope HIV, Infertility Network, George Martin Music Foundation, Royal Academy of Dance, St Joseph's Family Centre, Strongbones Children's Charitable Trust, Walk

the Walk, Winchester Visitors Group and Wirral Holistic Care Services.

FINANCES *Year* 2011–12 *Income* £136,960 *Grants* £126,108 *Assets* £1,799,198

TRUSTEES Andrew Blenkinsop; Sarah Blenkinsop; Charlotte Blenkinsop; Frances Stormer; Haidee Millin.

OTHER INFORMATION Brief accounts available at the Charity Commission.

HOW TO APPLY In writing to the correspondent.

WHO TO APPLY TO Charlotte Blenkinsop, Trustee, PO Box 28840, London SW13 0WZ *Tel.* 020 8878 9975

■ The George Ward Charitable Trust

CC NO 516954 **ESTABLISHED** 1985

WHERE FUNDING CAN BE GIVEN The area covered by Hinckley and Bosworth Borough Council.

WHO CAN BENEFIT Organisations and former employees of George Ward (Barwell) Ltd and George Geary and Son Ltd, and their dependants.

WHAT IS FUNDED General charitable purposes.

RANGE OF GRANTS Up to £3,000

SAMPLE GRANTS Get Thomas To America (£3,000); William Bradford Community College (£1,800); St Mary's Church Barwell and Garden Landscape Groundwork (£1,000 each); The Royal British Legion, Barwell (£750); Barwell Carnival, British Red Cross and Concordia Theatre, Hinckley (£500 each); Hinckley and District Museum Limited, Mayflower Court Residence Association and Voluntary Action Hinckley and Bosworth – Christmas Toy Appeal (£350 each) and Barwell Flower Festival (£90).

FINANCES *Year* 2011–12 *Income* £43,461 *Grants* £28,475 *Assets* £994,006

TRUSTEES David Radford; Sarah Major.

OTHER INFORMATION In 2011–12 grants were given to 49 organisations.

HOW TO APPLY In writing to the correspondent at any time.

WHO TO APPLY TO Stephanie Hiom, Secretary, c/o Grant Thornton Chartered Accountants, Regent House, 80 Regent Road, Leicester LE1 7NH *Tel.* 01162 471234 *email* stephanie.e.hiom@ uk.gt.com

■ The Barbara Ward Children's Foundation

CC NO 1089783 **ESTABLISHED** 2001

WHERE FUNDING CAN BE GIVEN England and Wales.

WHO CAN BENEFIT Registered charities and other institutions.

WHAT IS FUNDED Mostly work with children who are seriously or terminally ill, disadvantaged or otherwise.

TYPE OF GRANT Grants given range from one-off donations to project-related grants that run for two to five years.

SAMPLE GRANTS Friendship Works (£34,000) The Bubble Foundation (£27,000); Dame Vera Lynn Trust (£20,000); The Food Chain (£16,000); BIME – Bath Institute of Medical Engineering (£10,000); Wirral Swallows and Amazons (£6,500); Autism Bedfordshire, The Eyeless Trust and Stubbers Adventure Centre (£5,000 each); 4 Seasons Activity Group (£3,000); Friends of Mapledown School (£2,000) and Saffron Walden Opportunity Playgroup (£1,000).

FINANCES *Year* 2012 *Income* £532,351 *Grants* £516,327 *Assets* £8,298,142

TRUSTEES Barbara Irene Ward, Chair; D. C. Bailey; J. C. Banks; A. M. Gardner; K. R. Parker; B. M. Walters.

HOW TO APPLY In writing to the correspondent including latest set of audited financial statements. The trustees usually meet quarterly.

WHO TO APPLY TO Christopher Banks, Trustee, 5 Great College Street, London SW1P 3SJ *Tel.* 020 7222 7040 *Fax* 020 7222 6208 *email* info@bwcf.org.uk *Website* www.bwcf.org.uk

■ The John Warren Foundation

CC NO 201522   **ESTABLISHED** 1949
WHERE FUNDING CAN BE GIVEN Lincolnshire, then Bedfordshire, Northamptonshire and Nottinghamshire.
WHO CAN BENEFIT Churches.
WHAT IS FUNDED Church fabric repairs.
WHAT IS NOT FUNDED No support for major cathedral appeals.
TYPE OF GRANT One-off grants.
FINANCES *Year* 2011–12 *Income* £25,867 *Grants* £19,991 *Assets* £729,088
TRUSTEES Edward Lamb; Robert Lamb; Brian Marshall.
HOW TO APPLY In writing to the correspondent.
WHO TO APPLY TO The Trustees, c/o Lamb and Holmes Solicitors, West Street, Kettering, Northamptonshire NN16 0AZ *Tel.* 01536 513195 *email* jelamb@lamb-holmes.co.uk

■ The Waterloo Foundation

CC NO 1117535   **ESTABLISHED** 2007
WHERE FUNDING CAN BE GIVEN UK and overseas.
WHO CAN BENEFIT Organisations working on childhood development, in the developing world, the environment, and projects in Wales.
WHAT IS FUNDED 'We welcome applications from registered charities and organisations with projects that have a recognisable charitable purpose. Your project has to be allowed within the terms of your constitution or rules and, if you are not a registered charity, you will need to send us a copy of your constitution or set of rules. We make grants for all types of projects; start-up, initial stages and valuable ongoing funding. This can include running costs and overheads as well as posts; particularly under the World Development and Projects in Wales. We do not have any upper or lower limit on the amount of grant we offer but it is unlikely that we would offer a grant of more than £100,000.'
WHAT IS NOT FUNDED The foundation will not support: 'applications for grants for work that has already taken place; applications for grants that replace or subsidise statutory funding. We will not consider applications for grants in the following areas: the arts and heritage, except in Wales; animal welfare; the promotion of religious or political causes; general appeals or circulars. We are unlikely to support projects in the following areas: from individuals; for the benefit of an individual; medical charities (except under certain aspects of our 'Child Development' programme, particularly mental health); festivals, sports and leisure activities; websites, publications, conferences or seminars, except under our 'Child Development' programme.'
TYPE OF GRANT Project and core costs; one-off and recurrent grants.
RANGE OF GRANTS Up to £100,000.

FINANCES *Year* 2012 *Income* £4,964,016 *Grants* £5,912,493 *Assets* £102,363,692
TRUSTEES Heather Stevens; David Stevens; Janet Alexander; Caroline Oakes.
OTHER INFORMATION Detailed information is available on beneficiaries on the foundation's website.
HOW TO APPLY 'We hope to make applying for a grant fairly painless and fairly quick. However it will help us a great deal if you could follow the simple rules below when sending in an application (there are no application forms). Email applications to applications@waterloofoundation.org.uk (nowhere else please!). Include a BRIEF description (equivalent to two sides of A4) within your e-mail, but NOT as an attachment, of your project or the purpose for which you want the funding, detailing: your charity's name, address and charity number; email, phone and name of a person to reply to; a link to your website; what it's for; who it benefits; how much you want and when; what happens if you don't get our help; the programme under which you are applying. Don't write long flowery sentences – we won't read them. Do be brief, honest, clear and direct. Use abbreviations if you like! Don't send attachments to your email – your website will give us an introduction to you so you don't need to cover that.
Who can apply? We welcome applications from registered charities and organisations with projects that have a recognisable charitable purpose. Your project has to be allowed within the terms of your constitution or rules and, if you are not a registered charity, you will need to send us a copy of your constitution or set of rules. We make grants for all types of projects; start-up, initial stages and valuable ongoing funding. This can include running costs and overheads as well as posts; particularly under the World Development and Projects in Wales. We do not have any upper or lower limit on the amount of grant we offer but it is unlikely that we would offer a grant of more that £100,000.'
Applicants outside the UK: consult the trust's website for special application guidance.
WHO TO APPLY TO Janice Matthews, Finance Manager, c/o 46–48 Cardiff Road, Llandaff, Cardiff CF5 2DT *Tel.* 02920 838980 *email* info@waterloofoundation.org.uk *Website* www.waterloofoundation.org.uk

■ G. R. Waters Charitable Trust 2000

CC NO 1091525   **ESTABLISHED** 2000
WHERE FUNDING CAN BE GIVEN UK, also North and Central America.
WHO CAN BENEFIT Registered charities.
WHAT IS FUNDED General charitable purposes.
RANGE OF GRANTS £100–£132,000
SAMPLE GRANTS Mandeville School (£50,000); Fundacion Decimo Cuarta Compania (£16,000); Wessex Children's Hospital rust, Freedom from Torture, Dream Holidays, Brecon District disABLEd Club, React and Dream Connection (£5,000 each) and Lambourne Housing Trust (£100).
FINANCES *Year* 2011–12 *Income* £323,000 *Grants* £100,631 *Assets* £1,418,715
TRUSTEES M. Fenwick; C. Organ.
OTHER INFORMATION This trust was registered with the Charity Commission in 2002, replacing Roger Waters 1989 Charitable Trust (Charity Commission number 328574), which transferred its assets to this new trust. (The

2000 in the title refers to when the declaration of trust was made.) Like the former trust, it receives a share of the Pink Floyd's royalties as part of its annual income. It has general charitable purposes throughout the UK, as well as North and Central America.

HOW TO APPLY In writing to the correspondent.

WHO TO APPLY TO Michael Lewis, Finers Stephens Innocent, 179–185 Great Portland Street, London W1W 5LS *Tel.* 020 7323 4000

■ The Wates Foundation

CC NO 247941   **ESTABLISHED** 1966

WHERE FUNDING CAN BE GIVEN Berkshire; Bristol, Avon and Somerset; Buckinghamshire; Cambridgeshire; Dorset; Gloucestershire; Hampshire; Middlesex; Nottinghamshire; Oxfordshire; Surrey; Sussex; Warwickshire (not including the Greater Birmingham area) and the Greater London Metropolitan Area as defined by the M25 motorway.

WHO CAN BENEFIT Projects with charitable status. Practical projects involving people are preferred especially those benefiting young and disadvantaged people.

WHAT IS FUNDED The foundation currently awards grants under the following programmes, although they may be subject to change after it reopens to new applicants in 2015: Building Family Values; Community Health; Safer Communities; Life Transitions; Strengthening the Charitable and Voluntary Sectors.

WHAT IS NOT FUNDED See 'applications'.

TYPE OF GRANT Grants may be one-off and for salaries, although buildings, capital, project, research, start-up, core, running and recurring costs will also be considered.

RANGE OF GRANTS Normally up to £50,000.

FINANCES *Year* 2012–13 *Income* £492,777 *Grants* £1,159,873 *Assets* £17,115,283

TRUSTEES Richard Wates; Emily King; Kate Minch; William Wates; Jonathan Heynes; Claire Spotwood-Brown.

OTHER INFORMATION The foundation regularly reviews its activities and programmes – check the foundation's website for current information.

HOW TO APPLY **Note the following statement from the foundation:**

'The Wates Foundation reviewed its grantmaking policy in November 2011 in the light of a range of factors, including finance and levels of demand for support.

As a result of this review, the foundation has adopted a wholly pro-active grantmaking strategy and will no longer take applications or bids for support from external organisations. Any unsolicited applications or bids will be rejected automatically.

This strategy will be in place for three years until 31 March 2015.'

WHO TO APPLY TO Brian Wheelwright, Director, Wates House, Station Approach, Leatherhead, Surrey KT22 7SW *Tel.* 01372 861000 *Fax* 01372 861252 *email* director@watesfoundation.org.uk *Website* www.watesfoundation.org.uk

■ Blyth Watson Charitable Trust

CC NO 1071390   **ESTABLISHED** 1997

WHERE FUNDING CAN BE GIVEN UK.

WHO CAN BENEFIT Charitable organisations.

WHAT IS FUNDED The trust dedicates its grant-giving policy in the area of humanitarian causes based in the UK.

TYPE OF GRANT Mainly one-off. Occasional loans

RANGE OF GRANTS £1,000–£5,000.

SAMPLE GRANTS St Martin-in-the-Fields Endowment Fund (£10,000 in two grants); Trinity Hospice (£8,000 in two grants); St John's Hospice (£6,500 in two grants); Bread and Water for Africa (£5,000 in two grants); Royal Academy of Music (£3,000); Hospices of Hope (£2,500); Initiatives for Change (£1,500) and Comitato Fiori di Lavanda Onlus and Pace Centre (£1,000 each).

FINANCES *Year* 2011–12 *Income* £99,930 *Grants* £76,000 *Assets* £3,051,803

TRUSTEES Nicholas Brown; Ian McCulloch.

OTHER INFORMATION The grant total provided includes support costs.

HOW TO APPLY In writing to the correspondent. Trustees usually meet twice during the year in June and December.

WHO TO APPLY TO The Trustees, c/o Bircham Dyson Bell Solicitors, 50 Broadway, Westminster, London SW1H 0BL *Tel.* 020 7227 7000

■ The Howard Watson Symington Memorial Charity

CC NO 512708   **ESTABLISHED** 1946

WHERE FUNDING CAN BE GIVEN The former urban district of Market Harborough.

WHO CAN BENEFIT Residents of Market Harborough.

WHAT IS FUNDED The trust has a particular interest towards relief of need, welfare, recreation, leisure and education.

RANGE OF GRANTS Up to £5,000.

SAMPLE GRANTS St Nicholas Church (£5,000); Marshall Court (£3,000); Arts Fresco (£1,500); Global Young Leaders Conference (£500) and Robert Smyth Cricket Festival (£100).

FINANCES *Year* 2011–12 *Income* £232,071 *Grants* £284,588 *Assets* £2,278,580

TRUSTEES Harborough District Council; Cllr Roger Dunton.

OTHER INFORMATION In 2011–12 the charity made a single charitable contribution of £284,588 towards the maintenance and repair of Brooklands Gardens.

HOW TO APPLY In writing to the correspondent. Applications are considered in early autumn. 'The Charity has devised a standard form for applications for financial assistance and all applications are subjected to a validation process undertaken by the Clerk to the Trustee.'

WHO TO APPLY TO Anne Cowan, Clerk to the Trustees, 17 Thatch Meadow Drive, Market Harborough, Leicestershire LE16 7XH *Tel.* 01838 821291

■ John Watson's Trust

SC NO SC014004   **ESTABLISHED** 1984

WHERE FUNDING CAN BE GIVEN Scotland, with a strong preference for Lothian.

WHO CAN BENEFIT Individuals, charitable organisations, ad hoc groups, research bodies or individuals. Beneficiaries must be under 21 years of age. People in care, fostered or adopted; children of one-parent families; people with disabilities; and people disadvantaged by poverty will be considered.

WHAT IS FUNDED (a) Grants to children and young people under 21, physically or mentally disabled or socially disadvantaged, for education and training, equipment, travel, and educational, social, recreational and cultural activities. Grants can be made to charitable organisations and ad hoc groups in this field and to bodies

and individuals for educational research.
(b) Grants for boarding education to orphans and children subject to some other special family difficulty.

WHAT IS NOT FUNDED No general appeals. Grants are not given for running or capital costs.

TYPE OF GRANT Equipment, small capital expenditure, tuition, student support, personal equipment (such as special wheelchairs, special typewriters), projects and activities including travel. One year only, but can be extended.

RANGE OF GRANTS Up to £5,000

SAMPLE GRANTS Dunedin School (£5,000); Lothian Special Olympics (£3,500); Craigroyston High School, Nancy Ovens Trust and Scouts Scotland (£2,000 each); Gracemount Primary School and Multicultural Family Base (£1,500 each); and Cosgrove Care, Ferryhill Primary School and Sleep Scotland (£1,000 each).

FINANCES *Year* 2012 *Income* £202,907
Grants £150,000

TRUSTEES Six representatives of the Society of Writers to Her Majesty's Signet; two nominated by the City of Edinburgh Council; one nominated by the Lothian Association of Youth Clubs; one nominated by the Merchant Company Education Board; one co-opted trustee.

PUBLICATIONS Background notes and application forms available.

HOW TO APPLY On forms available to download, together with criteria and guidelines, on the trust's website.

WHO TO APPLY TO Laura Campbell, Administrator, The Signet Library, Parliament Square, Edinburgh EH1 1RF *Tel.* 01312 250658 *email* lcampbell@wssociety.co.uk *Website* www.wssociety.co.uk

---

■ Waynflete Charitable Trust

CC NO 1068892   **ESTABLISHED** 1998

WHERE FUNDING CAN BE GIVEN UK, with a preference for Lincolnshire.

WHO CAN BENEFIT Lincolnshire based charities and organisations; national charities and organisations where Lincolnshire residents are involved and new individual initiatives.

WHAT IS FUNDED General charitable purposes, with a particular interest in the training of volunteers.

TYPE OF GRANT Core costs.

SAMPLE GRANTS Previous beneficiaries include: Lincolnshire Blind Society (£6,000); Canine Partners, Lincolnshire and Nottinghamshire Air Ambulance and the Order of St John (£4,000 each); Deaf Blind (£2,500); Action for Kids, Gurka Welfare Trust and Marine Conservation Society (£1,000); Braille Chess Association, Children's Safety Education Foundation and Royal National Lifeboat Fund (£500 each) and Mouth and Foot Painting Artists (£100).

FINANCES *Year* 2011–12 *Income* £762,439
Grants £151,900 *Assets* £1,334,886

TRUSTEES Michael Worth; Graham Scrimshaw.

HOW TO APPLY In writing to the correspondent. Criteria are available to view on the trust's website.

WHO TO APPLY TO Michael Worth, Chair, PO Box 9986, Grantham, Lincolnshire NG31 0FJ *Tel.* 01400 250210 *email* info@waynfletecharity.com *Website* www.waynfletecharity.com

---

■ Weatherley Charitable Trust

CC NO 1079267   **ESTABLISHED** 1999

WHERE FUNDING CAN BE GIVEN Unrestricted.

WHO CAN BENEFIT Grants to individuals and organisations.

WHAT IS FUNDED General charitable purposes.

FINANCES *Year* 2012–13 *Income* £0
Grants £196,542

TRUSTEES Christine Weatherley; Richard Weatherley; Neil Weatherley

OTHER INFORMATION In 2013 there had been no income for the past four years, suggesting the trust may be spending out.

HOW TO APPLY This trust does not accept unsolicited applications.

WHO TO APPLY TO Christine Weatherley, Trustee, Northampton Science Park Ltd, Newton House, Kings Park Road Moulton Park, Northampton NN3 6LG *Tel.* 01604 821841

■ The Weavers' Company Benevolent Fund

CC NO 266189   **ESTABLISHED** 1973

WHERE FUNDING CAN BE GIVEN UK.

WHO CAN BENEFIT Registered charities; preference to small, community-based groups, rather than larger, established charities. 'To be eligible for funding, local organisations such as those working in a village, estate or small town should normally have an income of less than about £100,000. Those working across the UK should normally have an income of not more than about £250,000.'

WHAT IS FUNDED Supporting work with: disadvantaged young people; and offenders and ex-offenders, particularly those under 30 years of age. 'We like to encourage new ideas and to fund projects that could inspire similar work in other areas of the country.'

WHAT IS NOT FUNDED Funding is not given for the following: '(i) Long-term support – We will not normally provide long-term support. (ii) General appeals – We will not support sponsorship, marketing or other fundraising activities. (iii) Endowment funds – We will not support endowment funds, nor bursaries or long-term capital projects. (iv) Grant-giving charities. (v) Retrospective funding – We will not make grants for work that has been completed or will be completed while the application is being considered. (vi) Replacement funding – We will not provide grants for work that should be covered by statutory funding. (vii) Building projects – We will not fund building work but may help with the cost of equipment or furnishings. (viii) Disability Discrimination Act – We will not fund capital projects to provide access in compliance with the DDA (ix) Personal appeals – We will not make grants to individuals. Applicants must be registered charities, in the process of registering, or qualified as charitable. (x) Umbrella bodies or large, established organisations – We will not normally support projects in which the charity is collaborating or working in partnership with umbrella bodies or large, established organisations. (xi) Overseas – We will not support organisations outside the UK, nor overseas expeditions or travel. Funding is not usually given for the following: (i) Work with children under five years of age. (ii) Universities or colleges. (iii) Medical charities or those involved in medical care. (iv) Organisations of and for disabled people. (v) Environmental projects. (vi) Work in promotion of religious or political causes.'

TYPE OF GRANT Grants may be awarded for up to three years. The trust particularly welcomes applications for pump-priming grants from small community-based organisations where a grant would form a major element of the funding. It prefers to support projects where our grant will be used for an identified purpose. Applications for core funding will be considered, such as general administration and training that enable an organisation to develop and maintain expertise. The trust appreciates the importance of providing ongoing funding for successful projects, which have 'proved their worth'. Salaries are normally funded for up to three years but payment of the second and third year grants are subject to satisfactory progress reports. In exceptional circumstances, the trust may provide emergency or deficit funding for an established organisation. Applicants most likely to be granted emergency funding are charities which the company knows or has previously supported.

RANGE OF GRANTS Usually up to £15,000, but applications for smaller amounts from small or new organisations are welcomed.

SAMPLE GRANTS Weavers' Company Textile Education Fund (£90,000); Keep Out/Coldingly Crime Prevention Scheme (£13,000); The Helping Hands Trust (Gangsline) (£12,000); Trailblazers and Footprints (£10,000 each); Recycle Project (£8,500); Youth Empowerment (£7,800); The Ulysses Trust (£6,000); Grange Primary School and get Hooked on Fishing (£5,000 each); Prisoners' Penfriends (£4,700); Koestler Trust (£1,000) and Framlington Area Youth Action Partnership (£500).

FINANCES *Year* 2012 *Income* £382,524 *Grants* £263,500 *Assets* £8,412,469

TRUSTEE The Worshipful Company of Weavers.

HOW TO APPLY Detailed *Guidelines for Applicants* are available from the Weaver's Company website. Application forms can be downloaded from the fund's website, or by post or e-mail. The grants committee meets in February, June and October of each year. Deadlines are available on the website, they are typically about three months prior to the meetings.

WHO TO APPLY TO Susie Williams, Charities Assistant, The Weavers Company, Saddlers' House, Gutter Lane, London EC2V 6BR *Tel.* 020 7606 1155 *Fax* 020 7606 1119 *email* charity@weavers.org.uk *Website* www.weavers.org.uk

....

■ Webb Memorial Trust

CC NO 313760   **ESTABLISHED** 1944

WHERE FUNDING CAN BE GIVEN UK and Eastern Europe.

WHO CAN BENEFIT Individuals, universities and other organisations.

WHAT IS FUNDED The trust is set up with the aims of the advancement of education and learning with respect to the history and problem of government and social policy (including socialism, trade unionism and co-operation) in Great Britain and elsewhere by: research; lectures, scholarships and educational grants; such other educational means as the trustees may from time to time approve.

WHAT IS NOT FUNDED No grants in support of any political party. No grants for individuals including students.

SAMPLE GRANTS Centris (£74,000); Smith Institute (£56,000); Children North East (£51,000); New Statesman (£20,000); Fabian Society, London School of Economics and Fair Pay Network (£15,000 each); Essays and Writings (£13,000); Campaign Transport (£8,500) and Northern Upstart (£5,700).

FINANCES *Year* 2011–12 *Income* £47,218 *Grants* £275,970 *Assets* £1,429,102

TRUSTEES Richard Rawes, Chair; Mike Parker; Robert Lloyd-Davies; Dianne Hayter; Mike Gapes; Mike Gapes; Robert Lloyd-Davies; Katherine Green.

OTHER INFORMATION The Webb Memorial Trust was established as a memorial to the socialist pioneer Beatrice Webb. In 2011 the trustees decided to spend down the remaining resources using at least 85% of the budget for a co-ordinated programme leaving a legacy worthy of Beatrice Webb. As such most of its funding resources are committed to a structured programme that will concentrate on the issues of poverty and inequality on the UK. Funding Applications outside of these programmes may be considered if they reflect the original aims and ambitions of the Webbs.

HOW TO APPLY Via the online form. Applications by post or email will not be accepted. Trustees meet three to four times a year.

WHO TO APPLY TO Mike Parker, Secretary, Crane House, Unit 19 Apex Business Village, Annitsford, Newcastle NE23 7BF *email* webb@cranehouse.eu *Website* www.webbmemorialtrust.org.uk

....

■ The David Webster Charitable Trust

CC NO 1055111   **ESTABLISHED** 1995

WHERE FUNDING CAN BE GIVEN UK.

WHO CAN BENEFIT Charitable organisations.

WHAT IS FUNDED General, mainly ecological and broadly environmental projects.

SAMPLE GRANTS Bird Life International (£100,000); Natural History Museum and National Trust White Cliffs of Dover (£25,000 each); High Cross Church (£15,000); Isabel Hospice and Future Trees Trust (£10,000 each); National Churches Trust, Museum of the Broads, Berks, Beds and Oxford Wildlife Trust, National Trust and CPRE (£5,000 each) and Bat Conservation Trust and Norfolk Wherry Trust (£2,000 each).

FINANCES *Year* 2011–12 *Income* £201,823 *Grants* £214,000 *Assets* £3,317,259

TRUSTEES Thomas Webster; Nikola Thompson.

HOW TO APPLY In writing to the correspondent.

WHO TO APPLY TO Nikola Thompson, Trustee, Marshalls, Marshalls Lane, High Cross, Ware, Hertfordshire SG11 1AJ *Tel.* 01920 462001

....

■ The William Webster Charitable Trust

CC NO 259848   **ESTABLISHED** 1969

WHERE FUNDING CAN BE GIVEN North East England.

WHO CAN BENEFIT Registered charitable organisations in the north east of England, or for the benefit of branches in the north east of England.

WHAT IS FUNDED General charitable purposes.

WHAT IS NOT FUNDED No grants to individuals or to non-charitable organisations. Core/running costs are not funded.

TYPE OF GRANT One-off only, for capital projects.

SAMPLE GRANTS Bubble Foundation and the Derwentside Hospice Care Foundation (£4,000 each), the National Rheumatoid Arthritis Society

Richmond (£2,500), YMCA, St Columbus United Reformed Church (£2,000 each), Teesdale Disability Access Forum (£1,500), Different Strokes and Longframlington Memorial Hall (£1,000 each) and Aidis Trust (£500).

FINANCES *Year* 2012–13 *Income* £88,977 *Grants* £84,000

TRUSTEE Barclays Bank Trust Company Limited.

HOW TO APPLY Applications should be submitted by the end of May for consideration in July; by the end of September for consideration in November; and by the end of January for consideration in March. They should include details of the costings of capital projects, of funding already raised, a set of the latest annual accounts and details of the current charity registration.

WHO TO APPLY TO Graham Prew, Trust Officer, c/o Barclays Bank Trust Co. Ltd, Osborne Court, Gadbrook Park, Rudheath, Cheshire CW9 7UE *Tel.* 01606 313179 *Fax* 01606 313005

....

■ Weedon Family Trust

CC NO 1147085   **ESTABLISHED** 2012
WHERE FUNDING CAN BE GIVEN UK.
WHO CAN BENEFIT Charities and community groups.
WHAT IS FUNDED General charitable purposes.
TRUSTEES David Weedon; Ruth Weedon; Gordon Clarke.
HOW TO APPLY No grants to unsolicited applications.
WHO TO APPLY TO David Weedon, Trustee, Gainslaw House, Gasden Copse, Witley, Godalming, Surrey GU8 5QE *Tel.* 01428 685503

....

■ The Weinberg Foundation

CC NO 273308   **ESTABLISHED** 1971
WHERE FUNDING CAN BE GIVEN UK and overseas.
WHO CAN BENEFIT Registered charities.
WHAT IS FUNDED General charitable purposes.
SAMPLE GRANTS Previous beneficiaries included: Natan Foundation; Friends of EORTC; Amnesty International; Community Security Trust; Ability Net; Philharmonia Orchestra; Royal Shakespeare Theatre; St James's Palace Foundation; University of Cambridge; UJIA Campaign; South Bank Foundation; and the Elton John AIDS Foundation.
FINANCES *Year* 2011–12 *Income* £2,590 *Grants* £75,434
TRUSTEES Sir Mark Weinberg; Joy Whitehouse.
HOW TO APPLY In writing to the correspondent.
WHO TO APPLY TO Nathan Steinberg, Administrator, Munslows, 2nd Floor, Manfield House, 1 Southampton Street, London WC2R 0LR *Tel.* 020 7845 7500

....

■ The Weinstein Foundation

CC NO 277779   **ESTABLISHED** 1979
WHERE FUNDING CAN BE GIVEN Worldwide.
WHO CAN BENEFIT Registered charities.
WHAT IS FUNDED Jewish, medical and welfare causes.
WHAT IS NOT FUNDED No grants to individuals.
TYPE OF GRANT Recurrent.
RANGE OF GRANTS Up to £20,000.
SAMPLE GRANTS Previously: Chevras Evas Nitzrochim Trust; Friends of Mir; SOFT UK; Chesed Charitable Trust; and Youth Aliyah.
FINANCES *Year* 2011–12 *Income* £49,113 *Grants* £65,905 *Assets* £1,561,994
TRUSTEES Stella Weinstein; Michael Weinstein; Philip Weinstein; Lea Anne Newman.

HOW TO APPLY In writing to the correspondent.
WHO TO APPLY TO Michael Weinstein, Trustee, 32 Fairholme Gardens, Finchley, London N3 3EB *Tel.* 020 8346 1257

....

■ The Weinstock Fund

CC NO 1150031   **ESTABLISHED** 2012
WHERE FUNDING CAN BE GIVEN UK
WHO CAN BENEFIT Registered charities.
WHAT IS FUNDED General charitable purposes.
TRUSTEES Dr Susan Lacroix; Patricia Milner; The Hon. Laura Weinstock.
OTHER INFORMATION This fund was established by Laura Weinstock, who had another fund of the same name (charity number 222376) which was removed from the Charity Commission register in May 2013.
HOW TO APPLY In writing to the correspondent.
WHO TO APPLY TO Sally Barber, Administrator, PO Box 2318, Salisbury SP2 2JX *email* enquiries@ weinstockfund.org.uk

....

■ The James Weir Foundation

CC NO 251764   **ESTABLISHED** 1967
WHERE FUNDING CAN BE GIVEN UK, with a preference for Ayrshire and Glasgow.
WHO CAN BENEFIT Registered charities in the UK, mainly Scottish charities.
WHAT IS FUNDED The foundation has general charitable purposes, giving priority to Scottish organisations, especially local charities in Ayrshire and Glasgow.
WHAT IS NOT FUNDED No grants to individuals.
TYPE OF GRANT One-off and recurrent. Capital and core costs.
RANGE OF GRANTS Mostly £1,000–£3,000.
SAMPLE GRANTS Addaction, Age Scotland, Ayrshire Community Trust, Macmillan Cancer Support and Outward Bound Trust (£3,000 each); British Red Cross (£2,000); Kilbryde Hospice, Glasgow Women's Aid, Help for Heroes, Wiltshire Wildlife Trust and Scottish Refugee Council (£1,000 each); and St John Ambulance (£500).
FINANCES *Year* 2012 *Income* £225,023 *Grants* £209,676 *Assets* £6,804,930
TRUSTEES Simon Bonham; Elizabeth Bonham; William Ducas.
OTHER INFORMATION The following six charities are listed in the trust deed as potential beneficiaries: the Royal Society; the British Science Association; the RAF Benevolent Fund; the Royal College of Surgeons; the Royal College of Physicians; and the University of Strathclyde.
HOW TO APPLY The trustees' report for 2012 states that 'applications should be received by letter with supporting evidence and a copy of the latest annual report. No applications can be received by email. The trustees meet twice a year in furtherance of the trust's objective of making grants to charitable bodies. Successful applicants are not able to submit a further application for two years.'
WHO TO APPLY TO The Trustees, Mercer and Hole Trustees Ltd, Gloucester House, 72 London Road, St Albans, Herts AL1 1NS *Tel.* 01727 869141

■ The Joir and Kato Weisz Foundation

CC NO 1134632   **ESTABLISHED** 2010

WHERE FUNDING CAN BE GIVEN Worldwide, with a preference for England, Wales, France, Hungary, Italy and Israel

WHO CAN BENEFIT Registered charities.

WHAT IS FUNDED General charitable purposes.

SAMPLE GRANTS The Jake Gittlen Cancer Research Foundation (£150,000); British Friends of Igud Hakolelim B'Yerushalaim and Beth Shalom Reform Synagogue – Cambridge (£10,000 each); Ben Uri Gallery and Museum (£5,000); Spanish and Portuguese Synagogue (£3,500); Danson Sports Football Club (£1,000) and Circular Foundation (£500).

FINANCES *Year* 2011–12 *Income* £201,032 *Grants* £184,000 *Assets* £186,858

TRUSTEES George Weisz; Gideon Wittenberg; Thomas Kardos.

OTHER INFORMATION The following is taken from the 2011–12 accounts: 'While retaining its general scope, it is intended that the charity will make grants to any individual, group, organisation or institution to provide and assist in the provision of conferences, courses of instruction, exhibitions, lectures and other educational activities.'

HOW TO APPLY In writing to the correspondent.

WHO TO APPLY TO The Trustees, c/o SG Hambros Bank Limited, Norfolk House, 31 St James's Square, London SW1Y 4JR *Tel.* 020 7597 3000

■ The Barbara Welby Trust

CC NO 252973   **ESTABLISHED** 1967

WHERE FUNDING CAN BE GIVEN UK, with a preference for Lincolnshire.

WHO CAN BENEFIT Charitable organisations.

WHAT IS FUNDED General charitable purposes, especially for charitable organisations located in Lincolnshire.

WHAT IS NOT FUNDED The trust has stated that: 'Donations are generally made to established charitable organisations and not to individuals as the trustees have limited funds available to donate each year. In addition to providing regular support for a number of organisations, they consider all applications and, when possible, support exceptional appeals e.g. disaster funds.'

RANGE OF GRANTS £500–£7,500.

SAMPLE GRANTS Lincolnshire Agricultural Society (£5,000); Community Action Northumberland (£2,500); Be Your Best Foundation, CAFOD and Stroxton Church (£1,000 each); and MS Therapy Centre, DEMAND, St Barnabas Hospice and Linkage Community Trust (£500 each).

FINANCES *Year* 2011–12 *Income* £35,392 *Grants* £30,500 *Assets* £1,007,313

TRUSTEES Nicolas Robertson; Charles Welby; Nevil Barker.

OTHER INFORMATION Grants were made to 38 organisations totalling almost £31,000.

HOW TO APPLY In writing to the correspondent.

WHO TO APPLY TO Hunters, 9 New Square, Lincoln's Inn, London WC2A 3QN

■ The Wellcome Trust

CC NO 210183   **ESTABLISHED** 1936

WHERE FUNDING CAN BE GIVEN UK and overseas.

WHO CAN BENEFIT Academic researchers working in the fields of human and veterinary medicine, bio-ethics, public understanding of science and the history of medicine.

WHAT IS FUNDED The support of clinical and basic scientific research into human and veterinary medicine; support of research in tropical medicine; the social and ethical implications of medical advances; and the history of medicine. Grants to individuals are usually given via a university, although small grants for travel or developing public understanding of science may be given directly.

WHAT IS NOT FUNDED The trust does not normally consider support for the extension of professional education or experience, the care of patients or clinical trials. Contributions are not made towards overheads and not normally towards office expenses. The trust does not supplement support provided by other funding bodies, nor does it donate funds for other charities to use, nor does it respond to general appeals.

TYPE OF GRANT All types of grant including project grants, programme grants, fellowships, research expenses, travel grants, equipment and occasionally laboratory equipment for research in human and veterinary medicine and the history of medicine. Grants may last for more than three years.

SAMPLE GRANTS University of Oxford (£56 million); University College London (£47.1 million); Insight: Research for Mental Health (£20.7 million); London School of Hygiene and Tropical Medicine (£16 million); Myscience.Co Ltd (£10 million); University of Birmingham (£7.3 million); Cardiff University (£6.9 million); Institute of Cancer Research (£5.4 million); University of Liverpool (£4.7 million); University of Ghana (£3.4 million).

FINANCES *Year* 2011–12 *Income* £222,600,000 *Grants* £511,100,000 *Assets* £13,239,000,000

TRUSTEES Sir William Castell; Prof. Dame Kay Davies; Prof. Richard Hynes; Baroness Eliza Manningham-Buller; Prof. Peter Rigby; Prof. Peter Smith; Prof. Anne Johnson; Damon Buffini; Prof. Michael Ferguson; Alan Brown.

PUBLICATIONS The trust produces various reports and publications, all of which are available from its website.

OTHER INFORMATION The Wellcome Trust is one of the world's leading biomedical research charities and is the UK's largest non-governmental source of funds for biomedical research – it is also the UK's largest charity. The trust has a revised strategic plan for 2010–2020.

HOW TO APPLY **eGrants – online application:** The eGrants system enables applicants to apply for grants online. The system provides workflow to steer the application through head of department and university administration approval steps until final submission to the Wellcome Trust. Most applicants for Science Funding and Medical Humanities grants are required to submit their applications via the trust's eGrants system. However, Word forms are still available for: preliminary applications; Public Engagement grants; Technology Transfer grants; and applicants who have limited/unreliable access to the internet – email the eGrants helpdesk – ga-formsupport@wellcome.ac.uk – if this is the case.

'If you haven't applied using eGrants before, here is what you need to do: make sure your institution (or the institution that would be administering the grant, if you are not already based there) is registered with the trust; access the eGrants

accessing this page.'

'**Registration status of institutions:** If you wish to register with eGrants but are not sure whether your institution is registered, you can check the list of registered institutions on the trust's website. If your institution is not on this list you should contact your administration office directly for further information.'

'**Frequently asked questions:** A list of frequently asked questions for eGrants is available from the trust's website.'

WHO TO APPLY TO Jonathan Best, Grants Operations Manager, Gibbs Building, 215 Euston Road, London NW1 2BE *Tel.* 020 7611 8888 *Fax* 020 7611 8545 *email* grantenquiries@ wellcome.ac.uk *Website* www.wellcome.ac.uk

---

■ Welsh Church Fund – Dyfed area (Carmarthenshire, Ceredigion and Pembrokeshire)

CC NO 506583　　　　**ESTABLISHED** 1977

WHERE FUNDING CAN BE GIVEN Carmarthenshire, Ceredigion and Pembrokeshire.

WHO CAN BENEFIT Individuals, churches, chapels, and registered charities, particularly those concerned with health and welfare.

WHAT IS FUNDED General charitable purposes, particularly religious work, health and welfare.

TYPE OF GRANT One-off and recurrent

RANGE OF GRANTS Up to £10,000.

SAMPLE GRANTS Carmarthenshire: Ammanford Bible Church, The Community of the Many Names of God and Pontyberem Community Council (£3,000 each); and St Lleian's Church Gorslas (£1,500).
Ceredigion: Cwmni Theatr Arad Goch (£5,000); Mentro Lluest (£4,000) and Musicfest (£1,500).
Pembrokeshire: North Road Baptist Church and St Cawrda's Church, Jordanston (£3,000 each); Uzmaston and Boulton Community Project (£1,400) and Llawhaden Y F C Hall and Community Centre (£1,000).

FINANCES *Year* 2011–12 *Income* £67,885 *Grants* £60,525 *Assets* £5,505,502

TRUSTEE Selected members of Carmarthenshire, Ceredigion and Pembrokeshire County Councils.

HOW TO APPLY For Ceredigion and Pembrokeshire, in writing to the correspondent. For Carmarthenshire, an application form needs to be downloaded from the website and returned to: Welsh Church Fund, Business and Community Grants, Economic Development, Directorate of Regeneration, Carmarthenshire County Council, Business Resource Centre, Parc Amanwy, Ammanford, SA18 3EP. For further information contact Sally Doughton on 01269 590218 or community.grants@sirgar.gov.uk

---

purposes considered include education, welfare and arts organisations.

WHAT IS NOT FUNDED Grants only to registered charities and organisations with a charitable purpose.

TYPE OF GRANT Some recurrent funding and several small and large donations.

RANGE OF GRANTS £450,000–£500.

SAMPLE GRANTS National Heart and Lung Institute (£450,000); Multiple System Atrophy Trust (£100,000); Psychiatry Research Trust (£79,500); University of Cape Town and Sheffield Institute for Translational Neuroscience (£50,000 each); National Society for Epilepsy (£20,000); Salisbury Cathedral Fund and Mary Rose Trust (£10,000 each); Aidis Trust and Combat Stress (£7,500 each); Tricycle Theatre (£5,000); and Cystic Fibrosis Trust (£500).

FINANCES *Year* 2011–12 *Income* £202,210 *Grants* £985,355 *Assets* £5,034,698

TRUSTEES H. A. Stevenson; D. B. Vaughan; Dr Michael Harding.

OTHER INFORMATION Grants totalling £985,500 were made to 26 organisations.

HOW TO APPLY The trustees meet regularly to review grant applications.

WHO TO APPLY TO The Trustees, Old Waterfield, Winkfield Road, Ascot, Berkshire SL5 7LJ

■ The Wessex Youth Trust

CC NO 1076003　　　　**ESTABLISHED** 1999

WHERE FUNDING CAN BE GIVEN Worldwide.

WHO CAN BENEFIT Registered charities with which the Earl and Countess have a personal interest.

WHAT IS FUNDED General charitable purposes. 'The trust is particularly, although not exclusively, interested in supporting projects which provide opportunities to help, support and advance young people.'

WHAT IS NOT FUNDED Grants are not made: to organisations or groups which are not registered as charities or charitable causes; in response to applications by, or for the benefit of, individuals; by means of sponsorship for individuals undertaking fundraising activities on behalf of any charity; to organisations or groups whose main objects are to fund or support other charitable bodies; generally not to charities whose accounts disclose substantial financial resources and which have well established and ample fundraising capabilities; and to charities with religious objectives, political, industrial or commercial appeal.

TYPE OF GRANT One-off grants. Capital costs and full project funding.

SAMPLE GRANTS Freewheelers Theatre; New Horizon Youth Centre; Caring for Life; Adventure Unlimited; Ignito; Wessex Autistic Society; HopScotch Children's Charity; Carers Lewisham; and Carmarthen Women's Aid Limited.

Think carefully about every application. Is it justified?

989

FINANCES *Year* 2011–12 *Income* £106,188
Grants £122,412 *Assets* £436,041

TRUSTEES Robert Clinton; Mark Foster-Brown; Mary
Poulton; Richard Parry; Kathryn Cavelle;
Francesca Schwarzenbach.

OTHER INFORMATION The accounts stated: the
Charity Commission has been supplied with
details of amounts given to each charity
together with an explanation of the reason for
the non-disclosure of individual amounts in the
financial statements.

HOW TO APPLY Applicants must complete an
application form which can be downloaded from
the trust's website. Completed forms need to
be submitted by 1 May or 1 November. Clarity
of presentation and provision of financial details
are among the qualities which impress the
trustees. Successful applicants will receive a
letter stating that acceptance of funding is
conditional on an update report received within
six months. Unsuccessful applications will
receive a letter of notification following the
trustees' meeting. The trust cannot enter any
further communication with applicants.

WHO TO APPLY TO Jenny Cannon, Administrator,
Chelwood, Rectory Road, East Carleton, Norwich
NR14 8HT *Tel.* 01508 571230 *email* j.
cannon@wessexyouthtrust.org.uk *Website* www.
wessexyouthtrust.org.uk

■ The West Derby Wastelands Charity

CC NO 223623   ESTABLISHED 1964

WHERE FUNDING CAN BE GIVEN The ancient township
of West Derby in Liverpool.

WHO CAN BENEFIT Local organisations and local
branches of national organisations benefiting
volunteers; at-risk groups; carers; people
disadvantaged by poverty; socially isolated
people; and victims of abuse, crime or domestic
violence.

WHAT IS FUNDED Health and welfare; carers
organisations; education and training; victim
support and volunteer organisations.

WHAT IS NOT FUNDED The trust has stated that
'education or maintenance during education is
not funded'.

RANGE OF GRANTS £200–£3,000.

SAMPLE GRANTS Deysbrook Village Centre (£3,000);
West Derby Village History Project and
Bohemians Tennis Club (£2,500 each);
Tuebrook Community Centre, St Christopher's
Rosebuds, Brownies, Guides and Boys Brigade
and Lister Junior School (£2,000 each); RNIB
and Tuebrook Amateur Boxing Club (£1,500
each); Macmillan Cancer Support (£1,000);
MedEquip4Kids and Anchor Women's Club
(£500 each) and Ernest Cookson School
(£200).

FINANCES *Year* 2012 *Income* £57,676
Grants £47,141 *Assets* £1,676,267

TRUSTEES Joan Driscoll; Barry Flynn; John Kerr;
Barbara Kerr; Peter North; Barbara Shacklady;
Derek Corlett; Barbara Antrobus; Anthony Heath.

OTHER INFORMATION The grant total includes £1,500
given to individuals.

HOW TO APPLY In writing to the correspondent.

WHO TO APPLY TO Lawrence Downey, Secretary,
Ripley House, 56 Freshfield Road, Formby,
Liverpool L37 3HW *Tel.* 01704 879330
email lawrencedowney@btconnect.com

■ West London Synagogue Charitable Fund

CC NO 209778   ESTABLISHED 1959

WHERE FUNDING CAN BE GIVEN UK.

WHO CAN BENEFIT Registered charities only.

WHAT IS FUNDED General charitable purposes.

WHAT IS NOT FUNDED No grants to individuals.

RANGE OF GRANTS Up to £8,000.

SAMPLE GRANTS Supporting Children with Diabetes
(£5,000); Asylum Seekers Drop-In Centre
(£4,000); Macmillan Nurses (£1,000); Fortune
Riding Centre for the Disabled (£900); and
Downs Syndrome Association, Helen House
Hospice, OCD Action and Pets as Therapy (£500
each).

FINANCES *Year* 2012 *Income* £29,939
Grants £23,380 *Assets* £6,783

TRUSTEES Michael Cutter; Simon Raperport; Vivien
Feather; Jacqui Green; Jane Cutter; Jean Regen;
Monica Jankel; Ruth Jacobs; Elizabeth Shrager;
Hermy Jankel; Francine Epstein; Elaine Parry;
Vivien Rose; Rabbi Debbie Young-Somers; Lucy
Heath.

OTHER INFORMATION Grants were given to 24
organisations totalling £23,000.

HOW TO APPLY In writing to the correspondent.

WHO TO APPLY TO Simon Raperport, Trustee,
45 Arden Road, London N3 3AD *Tel.* 020 7723
4404

■ The West Yorkshire Police Community Trust

CC NO 1057368   ESTABLISHED 1996

WHERE FUNDING CAN BE GIVEN West Yorkshire.

WHO CAN BENEFIT Charitable and community
organisations.

WHAT IS FUNDED Awareness of crime prevention,
promotion of road safety and education in all
matters relating to drug, alcohol and other
substance misuse.

WHAT IS NOT FUNDED The Community Trust will not
support: national charities or general appeals,
work outside West Yorkshire, pure academic
research, educational bursaries, travel projects,
individuals or work that forms part of a statutory
requirement.

RANGE OF GRANTS Up to £2,500.

SAMPLE GRANTS Cardigan Centre and City of Leeds
School (£1,850); Halifax Boxing Sport and
Fitness Club, The Old Quarry Adventure
Playground, Crofton Fishing Club and Friends of
Bradford Youth Players (£1,750 each);
Huddersfield Pakistani Community Alliance
(£1,700); Cardinal Community Enterprise Project
(£1,000); Almondbury South Tenants and
Residents, Lower Fields Primary School (£375
each); Masjid-E-Bilal Learning Academy (£250)
and St Mary's School (£75)

FINANCES *Year* 2011–12 *Income* £90,238
Grants £70,380 *Assets* £161,409

TRUSTEES Mark Burns-Williamson; Alison Bainbridge;
Sir Norman Bettison; Bob Lewis; Andrew Walker;
Lesley Hastings; Brendan McLaughlin; Canon
Yaqub Masih.

OTHER INFORMATION The trust has a different
'theme' for grant-giving each year. In 2011–12
the main theme was: 'Activities which
discourage Anti-Social Behaviour in 11–25year
olds throughout West Yorkshire'

HOW TO APPLY Application forms, guidelines and
grant round information is available on the
trust's website.

WHO TO APPLY TO Jane Mills, Administrator, West
Yorkshire Police HQ, PO Box 9, Wakefield, West

Yorkshire WF1 3QP Tel. 01924 151588
Fax 01924 292595 *email* communitytrust@
westyorkshire.pnn.police.uk *Website* www.
westyorkshire.police.uk

■ Mrs S. K. West's Charitable Trust

CC NO 294755 **ESTABLISHED** 1986
WHERE FUNDING CAN BE GIVEN UK
WHO CAN BENEFIT Registered charities.
WHAT IS FUNDED Charities are selected by the trustees. General charitable purposes.
RANGE OF GRANTS £2,000 £5,000.
SAMPLE GRANTS Spen Valley Faith in Schools Trust (£5,000); Go Africa (£4,000); OMF International (£2,500); and BLESMA and Turning Point (£2,000 each).
FINANCES *Year* 2011–12 *Income* £34,545
Grants £25,000 *Assets* £960,000
TRUSTEES Peter Schoon; Richard Blakeborough; Judith Grandage; John Schoon; Rachel Grandage.
OTHER INFORMATION The trust owns a shop in St Annes, Lancashire, which provides most of its income.
HOW TO APPLY The trust states that it does not respond to unsolicited applications and would prefer not to receive any such applications asking for support.
WHO TO APPLY TO Peter Schoon, Trustee, 20 Beech Road, Garstang, Preston PR3 1FS

■ The Westcroft Trust

CC NO 212931 **ESTABLISHED** 1947
WHERE FUNDING CAN BE GIVEN Unrestricted, but with a special interest in Shropshire.
WHO CAN BENEFIT Registered charities only.
WHAT IS FUNDED Currently the trustees have four main areas of interest: international understanding, including conflict resolution and the material needs of the third world; religious causes, particularly of social outreach, usually of the Society of Friends (Quakers) but also for those originating in Shropshire; development of the voluntary sector in Shropshire; and special needs of people with disabilities, primarily in Shropshire. Medical aid, education and relief work in developing countries are supported but mainly through UK agencies; international disasters may be helped in response to public appeals.
WHAT IS NOT FUNDED Grants are given to charities only. No grants to individuals or for medical electives, sport, the arts (unless specifically for people with disabilities in Shropshire) or armed forces charities. Requests for sponsorship are not supported. Annual grants are withheld if recent accounts are not available or do not satisfy the trustees as to continuing need.
TYPE OF GRANT Single or annual with or without specified time limit. Few grants for capital or endowment. One-off, research, recurring costs, running costs and start-up costs. Funding for up to and over three years will be considered.
RANGE OF GRANTS £500–£3,500.
SAMPLE GRANTS Northern Friends Peace Board (£3,600); British Epilepsy Association (£3,000); Community Council of Shropshire (£1,500); Institute of Orthopaedics (£1,300); Quaker Bolivia Link (£1,100); Disasters Emergency Committee (£1,000); BuildIT International and Bethseda Leprosy Hospital (£750 each) and

Tolerance Internati
(£500 each).
FINANCES *Year* 20
Grants £91
TRUSTEES Mar
James F
HOW TO AP
is no
app'
of
r
w.
Prime
and gloss,
[illegible]
Applications are dean
months. No acknowledge
Replies to relevant but unsu
will be sent only if a stamped-a
envelope is enclosed. As some an
are made by Bank Telepay, details o[illegible] IK
name, branch, sort code, and account name
and number should be sent in order to save
time and correspondence.
WHO TO APPLY TO Martin Beardwell, Clerk, 32 Hampton Road, Oswestry, Shropshire SY11 1SJ

■ The Westminster Foundation

CC NO 267618 **ESTABLISHED** 1974
WHERE FUNDING CAN BE GIVEN Unrestricted, in practice mainly UK. Local interests in central London (SW1 and W1 and immediate environs), North West England, especially rural Lancashire and the Chester area, and the Sutherland area of Scotland.
WHO CAN BENEFIT Registered charities.
WHAT IS FUNDED Social welfare, military charities, education, environment and conservation.
WHAT IS NOT FUNDED No grants to individuals, 'holiday' charities, student expeditions, or research projects.
TYPE OF GRANT Usually one-off, but any type is considered. Larger grants are awarded over several years. Core costs and rents.
SAMPLE GRANTS Community Foundation for Merseyside (£300,000), a multi-year grant towards the Liverpool ONE Fund, administered by the foundation, to provide grants to local community projects that meet the local priority needs; Veterans' Aid (£61,500), towards the rent of the charity's London offices over three years; Fine Cell Work (£54,500), towards the rent of the charity's London offices over three years; Richard House Hospice (£35,000), towards running costs; West Sutherland Fisheries Trust (£25,000), towards running costs; and Farms for City Children (£20,000), towards running costs.
FINANCES *Year* 2012 *Income* £2,814,305
Grants £1,343,729 *Assets* £38,771,347
TRUSTEES The Duke of Westminster, Chair; Jeremy H. M. Newsum; Mark Loveday.
HOW TO APPLY In writing to the correspondent, 'as succinctly as possible and including only the most relevant details relating to the application'. The trustees meet four times a year. Full guidelines and details of current application deadlines are published on the foundation's website.
WHO TO APPLY TO Jane Sandars, Administrator, 70 Grosvenor Street, London W1K 3JP *Tel.* 020 7408 0988 *Fax* 020 7312 6244
email westminster.foundation@grosvenor.com
Website www.westminsterfoundation.org.uk

■ The Garfield Weston Foundation

CC NO 230260 ESTABLISHED 1958
WHERE FUNDING CAN BE GIVEN UK.

WHO CAN BENEFIT The beneficiaries include:
Independent schools, housing corporations and
churches.

WHAT IS FUNDED A broad range of activities in the
fields of education, the arts, health (including
research), welfare, environment, youth, religion
and other areas of general benefit to the
community.

WHAT IS NOT FUNDED According to the foundation's
guidelines, which can be found on its website,
the foundation does not fund the areas
indicated here: any funding request made within
12 months of the outcome of a previous
application, whether a grant was received or
not; UK registered charities only (unless it being
exempt status as a church, educational
establishment, hospital or housing corporation);
overseas projects; individual applicants,
individual research or study including gap year
activities, study trips, fundraising expeditions
and sponsorship; animal welfare charities; one-
off events such as galas or festivals, even if for
fundraising purposes; specific salaries and
positions, however core operating costs are
supported where general salary costs are
recognised; funding commitments over several
years – grants made are typically for a single
year; and organisations who cannot
demonstrate significant progress with
fundraising.

TYPE OF GRANT Capital (including buildings), core
costs, endowments, one-off, research, recurring
costs, running costs and start-up costs. Funding
is given by means of a single cash donation.

RANGE OF GRANTS Up to £3 million.

SAMPLE GRANTS Westminster Abbey (£3 million);
Imperial War Museum, King's College London
and the Foundation and Friends of the Royal
Botanic Gardens – Kew (£1 million each); New
Schools Network and Cancer Research UK
(£500,000 each); the Outward Bound Trust
(£375,000); Square Chapel Trust and
Shakespeare's Globe (£300,000 each); Lyric
Hammersmith and South Georgia Heritage Trust
(£250,000 each); the Pennies Foundation,
University of Hertfordshire and National Portrait
Gallery (£150,000 each); the Whitworth Gallery
and the New Marlowe Theatre Development
Trust (£100,000 each); Welsh National Opera,
Maidstone Museums' Foundation and the
National Hospital Development Foundation
(£75,000 each); Academy of Ancient Music,
Asthma UK and the Public Catalogue Foundation
(£50,000 each); Music for Youth, the Cartoon
Museum and SANE (£30,000 each); and Norfolk
Concerts and Eco Centre Wales (£20,000
each); Little Angel Theatre, the Hangleton and
Knoll Project and British Stammering
Association (£15,000 each); Sheffield Wildlife
Trust, Hearts and Minds Ltd and Gracious
Street Methodist Church (£10,000 each); the
Actors' Workshop Youth Theatre, the Solent
Stream Packet Limited and Prospects
Kensington Ltd (£7,500 each); Rook Lane Arts
Trust, Number One Community Trust and Life
Education Centres Thames Valley (£5,000
each); Colliery Mission, the Temple Trust and
Moyraverty HUB Playgroup (£1,000 each); and
Shoestring (£500).

FINANCES Year 2011–12 Income £42,233,000
Grants £46,078,000 Assets £4,948,533,000

TRUSTEES Jana Khayat; Camilla Dalglish; Kate
Hobhouse; Eliza Mitchell; Galen Weston; George
Weston; Sophia Mason; Melissa Murdoch.

OTHER INFORMATION In 2011–12 the foundation
received 1,988 grants.

HOW TO APPLY The trust's website states that
applications are accepted at any time during the
year and that there are no formal deadlines for
the submission of applications. Organisations
should allow approximately four months for a
final full decision but an acknowledgement or an
application will be received within four weeks.
The trust asks that applications are sent as
hard copies only through the post.

WHO TO APPLY TO Philippa Charles, Director, Weston
Centre, 10 Grosvenor Street, London W1K 4QY
Tel 020 7399 6565 email gdaroche@
garfieldweston.org Website www.garfieldweston.
org

■ The Barbara Whatmore Charitable Trust

CC NO 283336 ESTABLISHED 1981
WHERE FUNDING CAN BE GIVEN UK.

WHO CAN BENEFIT Charitable organisations.

WHAT IS FUNDED The arts and music; relief of
poverty; other general charitable purposes.

RANGE OF GRANTS Up to £3,500.

SAMPLE GRANTS City and Guilds of London Art
School (£4,500); Aldeburgh Music (£4,000);
Campaign for Drawing (£3,500); National Youth
Orchestra (£3,200); Edward Barnsley
Educational Trust, the Garden Museum and
Textile Conservation Centre (£2,000 each);
Hereford Cathedral and Pro Corda (£1,500
each); English National Opera and the Old
Operating Theatre (£1,000 each); Finchocks
Musical Museum and Jericho House Productions
(£500 each); and New Lanark Conservation
(£250).

FINANCES Year 2011–12 Income £57,449
Grants £49,875 Assets £1,452,888

TRUSTEES David Eldridge; Denis Borrow; Gillian
Lewis; Luke Gardiner; Patricia Cooke-
Yarborough; Sally Carter; Stephen Bate.

HOW TO APPLY In writing to the correspondent.

WHO TO APPLY TO Denise Gardiner, Administrator,
3 Honeyhanger, Hindhead Road, Hindhead
GU26 6BA email denise@bwct.org

■ The Whitaker Charitable Trust

CC NO 234491 ESTABLISHED 1964
WHERE FUNDING CAN BE GIVEN UK, but mostly East
Midlands and Scotland.

WHO CAN BENEFIT UK-wide organisations and local
organisations (registered charities only)

WHAT IS FUNDED The trust has general charitable
objects, although with stated preferences in the
following fields: local charities in
Nottinghamshire and the east Midlands; music;
agriculture and silviculture; countryside
conservation; Scottish charities.

WHAT IS NOT FUNDED Support is given to registered
charities only. No grants are given to individuals
or for the repair or maintenance of individual
churches.

SAMPLE GRANTS A substantial grant of £250,000
was made to The Jasmine Trust. Other
beneficiaries included: Atlantic College
(£42,000); Leith School of Art, Opera North
Education and Royal Forestry Society (£10,000
each); Live Music Now (£5,000); Bassetlaw
Hospice and Lincoln Cathedral Fabric Fund
(£3,000 each); Bassetlaw Homestart and
Prisoner Education Trust (£2,000 each);

Babworth Church and Reality Adventure Works (£1,000 each); and Baronet's Trust (£500).

FINANCES *Year* 2011–12 *Income* £229,275 *Grants* £375,274 *Assets* £7,119,156

TRUSTEES David Price; Edward Perks; Lady Elizabeth Whitaker.

HOW TO APPLY In writing to the correspondent. Applications should include clear details of the need the intended project is designed to meet plus a copy of the latest accounts available and an outline budget. If an acknowledgement of the application, or notification in the event of the application not being accepted is required, an sae should be enclosed. Trustees meet on a regular basis.

WHO TO APPLY TO The Trustees, c/o Currey and Co., 21 Buckingham Gate, London SW1E 6LS *Tel.* 020 7802 2700

■ The Colonel W. H. Whitbread Charitable Trust

CC NO 210496   **ESTABLISHED** 1953

WHERE FUNDING CAN BE GIVEN UK, with an interest in Gloucestershire.

WHO CAN BENEFIT Charitable organisations.

WHAT IS FUNDED The promotion of education and in particular: (a) the provision of financial assistance towards the maintenance and development of Aldenham School, and (b) the creation of Colonel W H Whitbread scholarships or bursaries or prizes to be awarded to pupils at Aldenham School; charitable organisations within Gloucestershire; the preservation, protection and improvement for the public benefit of places of historic interest and natural beauty. The trustees make charitable distributions on an arbitrary basis, having reviewed all applications and considered other charities that they wish to benefit.

RANGE OF GRANTS The trustees will only in exceptional circumstances consider grant applications for purposes which fall outside its stated areas of support. In these cases, the trustees will distribute a minimum of £500 per distribution.

SAMPLE GRANTS Previous beneficiaries have included: 1st Queen's Dragon Guards Regimental Trust, Abbey School Tewkesbury, Army Benevolent Fund, CLIC Sargent, DEC Tsunami Earthquake Appeal, Friends of Alderman Knights School, Gloucestershire Historic Churches Trust, Great Ormond Street Hospital Children's Charity, Household Cavalry Museum Appeal, Hunt Servants' Fund, Queen Mary's Clothing Guild, Royal Hospital Chelsea and St Richard's Hospice.

FINANCES *Year* 2012 *Income* £160,481 *Grants* £118,737 *Assets* £7,397,000

TRUSTEES H. F. Whitbread; Jeremy Barkes; Rupert Foley.

HOW TO APPLY A brief summary (no more than one side of A4) in writing (by e-mail if possible) to the correspondent. It is not necessary to send any accompanying paperwork at this stage. Should the trustees wish to consider any application further, then an application form would be sent out.

WHO TO APPLY TO Susan Smith, Administrator, Fir Tree Cottage, World's End, Sinton Green *Tel.* 07812 454321 *email* whwhitbread.trust@googlemail.com

■ The Simon Whitbread Charitable Trust

CC NO 200412   **ESTABLISHED** 1961

WHERE FUNDING CAN BE GIVEN UK, with a preference for Bedfordshire.

WHO CAN BENEFIT Registered charities, or bodies with similar status.

WHAT IS FUNDED General charitable purposes.

WHAT IS NOT FUNDED Generally no support for local projects outside Bedfordshire.

TYPE OF GRANT One-off.

RANGE OF GRANTS £1,000– £5,000.

SAMPLE GRANTS Fun 4 Young People and St John Ambulance Bedfordshire (£10,000 each); Elizabeth Finn Care and Turn 2 Us and Stepping Stones Luton (£5,000 each); Bedfordshire Festival of Music, Speech and Drama, Age UK Milton Keynes and Onset Trust (£3,000 each); Young People of the Year and Victim Support Kempston (£2,000 each); Traffic of the Stage and Brainwave Centre Ltd (£1,000 each); and Goldington Family Centre (£500).

FINANCES *Year* 2011–12 *Income* £129,210 *Grants* £97,315 *Assets* £2,948,105

TRUSTEES Sir Samuel Whitbread; Edward Martineau; Elizabeth Bennett.

HOW TO APPLY In writing to the correspondent. The trust has stated the following: 'when it is felt more appropriate, grantees are asked to report back. To minimise the costs, applicants are given no feedback or even acknowledgement unless they (a) are sent an application form or (b) specifically request feedback in which case it is given.'

WHO TO APPLY TO Matthew Yates, Administrator, Hunters, 9 New Square, Lincoln's Inn, London WC2A 3QN

■ The Melanie White Foundation Limited

CC NO 1077150   **ESTABLISHED** 1999

WHERE FUNDING CAN BE GIVEN Unrestricted.

WHO CAN BENEFIT Charitable organisations.

WHAT IS FUNDED General charitable purposes. 'The charity's principal activity during the year was the support of charities through the payments of donations. The objects of the charity are to promote any charitable purpose or support any charity selected by the directors. It is expressly contemplated that CLIC Sargent may be a beneficiary of the application of some or all funds or other benefits by the charity.'

SAMPLE GRANTS Community Foundation for the CSRA (£50,000); CLIC Sargent (£30,000); Alfred Dunhill Foundation (£25,000); Dyslexia Association (£10,000); RNIB (£7,500); Right to Play (£1,000); Air Ambulance for Children (£500) and Centrepoint (£100).

FINANCES *Year* 2011–12 *Income* £313,820 *Grants* £131,340 *Assets* £10,532,776

TRUSTEES Melanie White; Andrew White.

HOW TO APPLY This trust does not accept unsolicited applications.

WHO TO APPLY TO Paula Doraisamy, 61 Grosvenor Street, London W1k 3JE *Tel.* 020 3011 1041 *email* melaniewhitefoundation@gmail.com

■ White Stuff Foundation

CC NO 1134754   **ESTABLISHED** 2010

WHERE FUNDING CAN BE GIVEN UK

WHO CAN BENEFIT Registered charities, which are local to a White Stuff shop, office, warehouse or manufacturer (operating at county or local authority level, rather than nationally or internationally), and have an annual income of less than £1 million. Potential partners must not be political or religious or conflict with the foundation values.

WHAT IS FUNDED Projects supporting disadvantaged children and/or young people.

WHAT IS NOT FUNDED No grants are made to non-partner charities.

SAMPLE GRANTS Into University (£80,000); Wishes 4 Kids (£23,000); Lothian Autistic Society (£8,000); Milton Hospice, Bath Opportunity pre-school and Voice of Young People in Care (£4,000 each); Sail 4 Cancer and Norfolk Wildlife Trust (£3,000 each); and Trinity Hospice and Angels Support Group (£2,000 each).

FINANCES *Year* 2011–12 *Income* £538,166 *Grants* £254,293 *Assets* £262,476

TRUSTEES Sally Bailey; Rebecca Kong; Sean Thomas; Victoria Hodges; Louise McGarr; Immanuel Mensik; Nigel Wreford-Brown.

OTHER INFORMATION The foundation runs a partnering scheme between White Stuff shops and small charities supporting disadvantaged children and young people. There are currently over 75 partner charities across the UK and one in India, which receive regular grants and support.

HOW TO APPLY On a form available to download via the foundation's website.

WHO TO APPLY TO Sally Crane, Foundation Manager, Canterbury Court, 1–3 Brixton Road, London SW9 6DE *Tel.* 020 7091 8501 *Fax* 020 7091 8599 *email* giving@whitestufffoundation.org *Website* www.whitestuff.com

■ The Whitecourt Charitable Trust

CC NO 1000012   **ESTABLISHED** 1990

WHERE FUNDING CAN BE GIVEN UK and overseas, with a preference for South Yorkshire.

WHO CAN BENEFIT Organisations benefiting Christians.

WHAT IS FUNDED General charitable purposes. Trustees prefer to support Christian projects, especially near Sheffield.

WHAT IS NOT FUNDED No support for animal or conservation organisations or for campaigning on social issues.

RANGE OF GRANTS £25–£10,000.

SAMPLE GRANTS Christ Church Fulwood (£7,000); Monkton Combe School Bursary Fund (£5,000); TEAR Fund (£2,500); Overseas Missionary Fellowship (£2,000); Church Pastoral Aid Society, Help for Heroes and Sudan Interior Mission (£1,000 each); The Cathedral Archer Project, Just 42, Riverside Church and VSO (£100 each); and The Prison Fellowship (£30).

FINANCES *Year* 2011–12 *Income* £40,222 *Grants* £52,342 *Assets* £64,020

TRUSTEES Peter Lee; Gillian Lee; Martin Lee.

HOW TO APPLY In writing to the correspondent, at any time. However, the trust states very little money is available for unsolicited applications, due to advance commitments.

WHO TO APPLY TO Gillian Lee, Trustee, 48 Canterbury Avenue, Fulwood, Sheffield S10 3RU *Tel.* 01142 305555

■ A. H. and B. C. Whiteley Charitable Trust

CC NO 1002220   **ESTABLISHED** 1990

WHERE FUNDING CAN BE GIVEN England, Scotland and Wales, with a special interest in Nottinghamshire.

WHO CAN BENEFIT Registered charities.

WHAT IS FUNDED General charitable purposes, particularly those causes based in Nottinghamshire.

RANGE OF GRANTS Up to £10,000.

SAMPLE GRANTS Lincolnshire and Nottinghamshire Air Ambulance and Macmillan Cancer Support (£10,000 each); Home Start Mansfield and Mansfield Choral Society (£5,000 each); Nottingham Churches Holding Fund (£3,000); and Southwell Minster (£2,500).

FINANCES *Year* 2012–13 *Income* £45,678 *Grants* £35,500 *Assets* £1,445,559

TRUSTEES Ted Aspley; Keith Clayton.

HOW TO APPLY The trust does not seek applications.

WHO TO APPLY TO Ted Aspley, Trustee, Marchant and Co, Regent Chambers, 2A Regent Street, Mansfield NG18 1SW *Tel.* 01623 655111

■ The Norman Whiteley Trust

CC NO 226445   **ESTABLISHED** 1963

WHERE FUNDING CAN BE GIVEN Worldwide, although in practice mainly Cumbria.

WHO CAN BENEFIT Organisations benefiting Christians and evangelists.

WHAT IS FUNDED To help evangelical Christian causes primarily.

TYPE OF GRANT One-off, recurrent, capital, running costs.

SAMPLE GRANTS Capernwray Miss Fellowship of Torchbearer and International Aid (£6,500 each); New Life Church (£5,000); Kinder Und Jugendwerk (£4,500); International Teams Austria (£2,700); Salvation Army and Christians Against Poverty (£1,000 each) and Baptisten Germeinde (£800).

FINANCES *Year* 2011–12 *Income* £91,327 *Grants* £68,217 *Assets* £2,696,865

TRUSTEES Miss P. Whiteley; P. Whiteley; D. Dickson; J. Ratcliff.

HOW TO APPLY In writing to the correspondent along with an application form, available to download from the trust's Dropbox account which can be accessed by sending an email to the trust. Applications should be made on headed paper or accompanied by a suitable reference. Applications are considered throughout the year.

WHO TO APPLY TO D. Foster, Bovil Barn, Newbiggin-on-Lune, Kirkby Stephen, Cumbria CA17 4NT *email* normanwhiteleytrust@gmail.com

■ The Whitewater Charitable Trust

CC NO 1146069   **ESTABLISHED** 2012

WHERE FUNDING CAN BE GIVEN UK and overseas.

WHO CAN BENEFIT Registered charities.

WHAT IS FUNDED General charitable purposes.

SAMPLE GRANTS Action for ME; and Homes for Zimbabwe.

FINANCES *Year* 2012–13 *Income* £28,737 *Grants* £23,750

TRUSTEES John McMonigall; Coutts and Co.

HOW TO APPLY In writing to the correspondent.

WHO TO APPLY TO Coutts and Co, Trustee Department, 440 Strand, London WC2R 0QS *Tel.* 020 7663 6826

■ The Whitley Animal Protection Trust

CC NO 236746   **ESTABLISHED** 1964
WHERE FUNDING CAN BE GIVEN UK and overseas, with a preference for Scotland.
WHO CAN BENEFIT Registered charities only.
WHAT IS FUNDED Animal welfare; conservation.
WHAT IS NOT FUNDED No grants to non-registered charities.
TYPE OF GRANT Core and project grants, one-off but usually recurring grants that last for several years.
RANGE OF GRANTS Generally £1,000–£20,000, although larger grants are also given.
SAMPLE GRANTS Whitley Fund for Nature (£100,000); Shropshire Wildlife Trust (£25,000); WILDCRU Wildlife Conservation Research Unit (£20,000); Sustainable Inshore Fisheries Trust (£15,000); Songbird Survival (£10,000); Orangutan Foundation (£7,000); Tusk Trust and RSPC Scotland (£5,000 each); National Great Dane Rescue (£2,000); and Eden Rivers Trust and the Wye and Usk Foundation (£1,000 each).
FINANCES *Year* 2012 *Income* £373,806 *Grants* £227,993 *Assets* £8,882,192
TRUSTEES Edward Whitley; Edward Whitley; Jeremy Whitley; Penelope Whitley.
HOW TO APPLY The trust has previously stated that: 'the trust honours existing commitments and initiates new ones through its own contacts rather than responding to unsolicited applications.'
WHO TO APPLY TO Michael Gwynne, Administrator, Padmore House, Hall Court, Hall Park Way, Telford TF3 4LX *Tel.* 01952 641651

■ The Whittlesey Charity

CC NO 1005069   **ESTABLISHED** 1990
WHERE FUNDING CAN BE GIVEN The parishes of Whittlesey Urban and Whittlesey Rural.
WHO CAN BENEFIT Charitable organisations within the beneficial area.
WHAT IS FUNDED General charitable purposes.
TYPE OF GRANT Capital costs; core costs; full project funding. Funding of up to three years and more.
RANGE OF GRANTS £250–£5,000.
SAMPLE GRANTS St Andrew's Church, Friends of Holy Trinity Church and Friends of St Mary's Church (£6,000 each); Hospital at Home and Whittlesey Christmas Lights (£1,000 each); St Mary's House Community Fund, FAC Transport and Coates Silver Lining Club (£500 each) and Whittlesey Widows Contact Group and Whittlesey Social Dancing Group (£300 each).
FINANCES *Year* 2011–12 *Income* £63,383 *Grants* £36,153 *Assets* £1,773,052
TRUSTEES Pearl Beeby; Ralph Butcher; David W. Green; Geoffrey Oldfield; Gordon Ryall; Revd Nigel A. Whitehouse; David Wright; Philip Oldfield; Gill Lawrence; Claire Smith.
HOW TO APPLY Charities in the parishes of Whittlesey Urban and Whittlesey Rural should apply in writing for consideration in February, May or September (although urgent requests can be dealt with more quickly). Charities from outside these parishes should not apply as they will not receive any response.
WHO TO APPLY TO P. Gray, Secretary, 33 Bellamy Road, Oundle, Peterborough PE8 4NE *Tel.* 01832 273085 *Fax* 01832 273085

■ The Lionel Wigram Memorial Trust

CC NO 800533   **ESTABLISHED** 1988
WHERE FUNDING CAN BE GIVEN UK, with a preference for Greater London.
WHO CAN BENEFIT Registered charities and voluntary organisations.
WHAT IS FUNDED General charitable purposes. The trustees 'have particular regard to projects which will commemorate the life of Major Lionel Wigram who was killed in action in Italy in 1944'. The trust makes grants to a wide range of organisations in the UK, especially those providing services or support for people who are disabled, particularly those who are blind or deaf.
WHAT IS NOT FUNDED No support for individuals, building projects or charities which do not have a three year record.
TYPE OF GRANT One-off and recurrent.
RANGE OF GRANTS £50–£8,000. Average grant under £1,000.
SAMPLE GRANTS U Can Do IT (£32,000 in four grants); The New English Ballet Theatre (£3,500); The Second World War Experience Centre (£1,500); The Cure Parkinson's Trust and Vision North Somerset (£750 each); Braille Chess Association; Finsbury Park Community Hub Ltd; The National Lobster Hatchery; The Trust Women's Project; Forest Sensory Services and The Anorexia and Bulimia Charitable Care Trust (£400 each).
FINANCES *Year* 2011–12 *Income* £68,517 *Grants* £65,320 *Assets* £677,021
TRUSTEES Antony Wigram; Sally A. Wigram.
HOW TO APPLY On a form available on the website. Applications are considered in December each year and successful applicants will receive a cheque at this time. Apart from this the trust does not communicate with applicants.
WHO TO APPLY TO Tracy Pernice, PA to A. F. Wigram, Highfield House, 4 Woodfall Street, London SW3 4DJ *Tel.* 020 7730 6820

■ The Felicity Wilde Charitable Trust

CC NO 264404   **ESTABLISHED** 1972
WHERE FUNDING CAN BE GIVEN UK.
WHO CAN BENEFIT Registered charities only.
WHAT IS FUNDED Children's charities and medical research, particularly into asthma.
WHAT IS NOT FUNDED No grants to individuals or non-registered charities.
RANGE OF GRANTS £1,000–£10,000.
SAMPLE GRANTS Kings College London – Respiratory Medicine and Allergy (£10,000); Hearing Dogs for Deaf People (£5,000); Action Medical Research and Cystic Fibrosis Trust (£3,000 each); The Roy Castle Lung Cancer Foundation and Prostate Campaign (£2,000 each); The Sick Children's Trust (£1,500) and The Dream Team, The Stagecoach Charitable Trust, Autism Initiatives UK and Meningitis Trust (£1,000 each).
FINANCES *Year* 2011–12 *Income* £70,020 *Grants* £69,000 *Assets* £1,883,388
TRUSTEE Barclays Bank Trust Co Ltd.
HOW TO APPLY In writing to the correspondent at any time. Applications are usually considered quarterly.
WHO TO APPLY TO S. Wakefield, Trustee, Barclays Bank Trust Co. Ltd, Osborne Court, Gadbrook Park, Rudheath, Cheshire CW9 7UE *Tel.* 01606 313179

■ The Wilkinson Charitable Foundation

CC NO 276214   **ESTABLISHED** 1978
WHERE FUNDING CAN BE GIVEN UK.
WHO CAN BENEFIT Academic institutions, medical research organisations.
WHAT IS FUNDED The trust was set up for the advancement of scientific knowledge and education at Imperial College – University of London. The trustees have continued their policy of supporting research and initiatives commenced in the founder's lifetime and encouraging work in similar fields to those he was interested in.
WHAT IS NOT FUNDED No grants to individuals.
RANGE OF GRANTS £250–£5,000
SAMPLE GRANTS Imperial College, London (£5,000); Lady Margaret Hall Development Fund (£2,500); University College, London (£1,000); Breast Cancer Campaign (£1,000) Blond McIndoe Research Foundation, Centre of the Cell, Forces Support and Wellbeing of Women (£500 each) and Elimination of Leukaemia Fund, Headstart, Murray Edwards College, The Smile Train UK and World Cancer Research Fund (£250 each).
FINANCES *Year* 2011–12 *Income* £39,631 *Grants* £16,250 *Assets* £1,420,183
TRUSTEES Glenn Hurstfield; Barry Lock; Anne Hardy.
HOW TO APPLY In writing to the correspondent.
WHO TO APPLY TO Barry Lock, Trustee, c/o Berkeley Law, 4th Floor, 19 Berkeley Street, London W1J 8ED *Tel.* 020 7399 0930

■ The Will Charitable Trust

CC NO 801682   **ESTABLISHED** 1989
WHERE FUNDING CAN BE GIVEN UK.
WHO CAN BENEFIT UK charities benefiting people with sight loss and the prevention and cure of blindness, services for people suffering from cancer and their families and the provision of residential care for people with mental disabilities.
WHAT IS FUNDED Care of and services for blind people, and the prevention and cure of blindness; care of people with learning disabilities in a way that provides lifelong commitment; care of and services for people suffering from cancer, and their families.
WHAT IS NOT FUNDED Grants are only given to registered or exempt charities. 'It is unlikely that applications relating to academic or research projects will be successful. The trustees recognise the importance of research, but lack the resources and expertise required to judge its relevance and value.'
TYPE OF GRANT One-off.
RANGE OF GRANTS £5,000–£20,000
SAMPLE GRANTS Bury Hospice and St David's Foundation Hospice Care (£20,000 each); Cam Sight, L'Arche and CLIC Sargent Care for Children (£15,000 each); Weston Hospice Care and West Northumberland Citizens Advice (£12,000 each) County Durham Society for the Blind and FORCE Cancer Charity (£10,000 each); Mousetrap Theatre Projects and Livability (£8,000 each); Music in Hospitals and Talking Newspaper Association of the UK (£5,000 each).
FINANCES *Year* 2011–12 *Income* £644,111 *Grants* £575,400 *Assets* £17,645,389
TRUSTEES Alastair McDonald; Rodney Luff; Vanessa Reburn.
HOW TO APPLY In writing to the correspondent; there are no application forms. The trust offers the following advice on its website on how applications should be presented: 'We are not necessarily looking for glossy professional bids and understand that your application to us will vary according to the size of organisation you are, and the size of the proposed project. It can be a professionally prepared presentation pack, but can equally be a short letter with supporting information. Both will receive equal consideration. Whatever the presentation, the following lists the areas that must be covered. Failure to do so will affect your chances of success: organisation overview – this paragraph/section must include a short background to the charity and a summary of activities. Include relevant information on your clients/beneficiaries (this might include numbers helped, geographic location, age group etc.) and numbers of employees and volunteers. Give us this information every time you apply; project description – tell us what you want a grant for/towards. Explain why it is necessary, what you hope to achieve, who will benefit and how; costs – tell us the total cost of your project and give us a breakdown including at least the main items of expenditure. Tell us how you intend to fund it, and how much you have raised so far. If the project is part of a larger one, explain the wider context; contingency plan. Explain what you intend to do if you fail to raise all the funds you need; a timetable – tell us your timescale for raising funds and when you aim to have the project up and running; annual accounts – your latest audited accounts and annual review (if you have one) must be included; other information – include any other information which you feel will assist us in judging your application. This could include for example a copy of your newsletter, or short promotional/advertising leaflets. Such publications often help give a flavour of an organisation. If you wish to discuss your application, or have other queries, contact the Grants Administrator, Christine Dix, either by email or by telephone on 020 8941 0450. Note if you telephone that the office is open part-time and you may need to leave a message. Blind people and Learning disabilities applications should be submitted from November and by 31 January at the latest. Decisions are made in the following April and successful applicants will be notified by the end of the month. Cancer care applications should be submitted from June and by 31 August at the latest. Decisions are made in the following November and successful applicants will be notified by the end of the month. Applications will normally be acknowledged within three weeks. Successful applicants will be notified before 30 April or 30 November as applicable. If you have not heard by those dates, you should assume that your application has been unsuccessful. We ask charities to whom we have awarded grants to submit a short update on their project by the application deadline the following year. Note that although the requirement to update us is not a formal grant condition, failure to do so will be taken into accounts when we consider future applications.'
WHO TO APPLY TO Christine Dix, Grants Administrator, Haysmacintyre, 26 Red Lion Square, London WC1R 4AG *email* admin@willcharitabletrust.org.uk *Website* willcharitabletrust.org.uk

■ Will to Win Foundation Ltd. (previously Tennis for a Life)

CC NO 1147881   **ESTABLISHED** 2012
WHERE FUNDING CAN BE GIVEN UK
WHO CAN BENEFIT Community sports clubs and youth organisations.
WHAT IS FUNDED The foundation aims to promote community participation in healthy recreation in the interest of social welfare by providing support and assistance for the coaching and playing of tennis and other sports as a means of improving health.
TRUSTEES Steve Riley; Emily Taylor; Nicholas Welman; Faye Andrews.
HOW TO APPLY Contact the correspondent in the first instance to discuss an application.
WHO TO APPLY TO Steve Riley, Trustee, 30 Thorney Hedge Road, Chiswick W4 5SD *Tel.* 020 7224 1625 *email* info@tennisforalife.org.uk *Website* www.tennisforalife.com

■ The William Barrow's Charity

CC NO 307574   **ESTABLISHED** 1965
WHERE FUNDING CAN BE GIVEN The parish of Borden, Kent.
WHO CAN BENEFIT Residents of Borden, Kent.
WHAT IS FUNDED The charity distributes its income equally between the Barrows Eleemosynary Charity and Barrows Educational Foundation. The latter supports local schools, one of which is supported each year in accordance with the trust deed. No other organisations were supported.
WHAT IS NOT FUNDED No grants outside the parish of Borden.
FINANCES *Year* 2012 *Income* £204,741 *Grants* £56,678 *Assets* £6,079,504
TRUSTEES SJ. Mair, Chair; PE. Cole; EG. Doubleday; DA. Jarrett; JJ. Jefferiss; D. Jordan; Fr J. Lewis; C. Ford; JM. Scott.
OTHER INFORMATION Some grants were also made to individuals.
HOW TO APPLY In writing to the correspondent for consideration at quarterly meetings of the trustees.
WHO TO APPLY TO c/o George Webb Finn, 43 Park Road, Sittingbourne, Kent ME10 1DX *Tel.* 01795 470556 *email* stuart@georgewebbfinn.com

■ The Charity of William Williams

CC NO 202188   **ESTABLISHED** 1621
WHERE FUNDING CAN BE GIVEN The ancient parishes of Blandford, Shaftesbury and Sturminster Newton.
WHO CAN BENEFIT Primarily individuals, also some local organisations benefiting people in need, children, young adults, at risk groups, and people disadvantaged by poverty or socially isolated.
WHAT IS FUNDED People in need, youth organisations, schools and welfare charities.
SAMPLE GRANTS Pramacare (£8,500); North Dorset CAB (£6,000); and Blandford Food Bank and Youth Aid (£2,000 each).
FINANCES *Year* 2012 *Income* £322,475 *Grants* £164,500 *Assets* £7,894,379
TRUSTEES Robert Cowley; Richard Prideaux-Brune; Leo Williams; Carole Sharpe; Richard Gillam; Ray Humphries; Haydn White; Joe Rose.
OTHER INFORMATION The grant total included £138,000 to individuals and £26,500 to organisations.
HOW TO APPLY In writing to the correspondent.

WHO TO APPLY TO Ian Winsor, Steward, Stafford House, 10 Prince of Wales Road, Dorchester, Dorset DT1 1PW *Tel.* 01305 264573 *email* enquiries@williamwilliams.org.uk *Website* www.williamwilliams.org.uk

■ The Kay Williams Charitable Foundation

CC NO 1047947   **ESTABLISHED** 1995
WHERE FUNDING CAN BE GIVEN UK.
WHO CAN BENEFIT Registered charities.
WHAT IS FUNDED General charitable purposes including medical research, disability causes and animal welfare.
SAMPLE GRANTS Royal Opera House Trust (£4,500); Cancer Research Campaign (£3,000); Help the Aged, RSPCA and The River Thames Boat Project (£2,000 each); Richmond Concert Society, Shooting Star Children's Hospice and The Campbell Village Trust (£1,000 each); The Mission to Seafarers (£500) and English National Opera (£300).
FINANCES *Year* 2011–12 *Income* £8,244 *Grants* £36,000
TRUSTEES Richard Cantor; Margaret Williams.
OTHER INFORMATION In 2011–12 the foundation had a total expenditure of £44,000.
HOW TO APPLY In writing to the correspondent.
WHO TO APPLY TO Richard Cantor, Trustee, BDO LLP, Kings Wharf, 20–30 Kings Road, Reading, Berkshire RG1 3EX *Tel.* 01189 254400

■ The Williams Charitable Trust

CC NO 1086668   **ESTABLISHED** 2001
WHERE FUNDING CAN BE GIVEN UK.
WHO CAN BENEFIT Charitable organisations.
WHAT IS FUNDED 'The objects of the trust are to support education and training, the advancement of medicine and general charitable purposes.'
RANGE OF GRANTS £500–£25,000
SAMPLE GRANTS Donmar Warehouse (£24,000); Wilton's Music Hall Trust (£11,000); Royal Court Theatre and Children's Musical Theatre (£10,000); Fight for Peace (£6,000); The Shakespeare Globe Trust (£5,000); The Production Works – The Changeling (£2,500); The Soho Theatre (£2,000) and Mousetrap Theatre Project and British Film Institute (£1,000 each).
FINANCES *Year* 2011–12 *Income* £82,886 *Grants* £77,450 *Assets* £2,320,678
TRUSTEES Stuart Williams; Hilary Williams; Andrew Williams; Matthew Williams; Keith Percival Eyre-Varnier.
OTHER INFORMATION Five grants of less than £1,000 totalled £4,100.
HOW TO APPLY In writing to the correspondent. 'The trustees adopt a proactive approach in seeking worthy causes requiring support.'
WHO TO APPLY TO Stuart Williams, Trustee, Flat 85 Capital Wharf, 50 Wapping High Street, London E1W 1LY

■ The Williams Family Charitable Trust

CC NO 255452   **ESTABLISHED** 1959
WHERE FUNDING CAN BE GIVEN Worldwide.
WHO CAN BENEFIT Jewish people.
WHAT IS FUNDED Organisations benefiting Jewish people.

RANGE OF GRANTS Generally less than £1,000.
SAMPLE GRANTS Previous beneficiaries include: But Chabad, Friends of Mifalhtorah for Shiloh, Holon Association for Absorption of Immigrants, Ingun Yedidut, Israel Concern Society, Karen Denny Pincus, Mogdal Un, Yedidut Maabeh Eliahu and Yesodrey Hetorah Schools.
FINANCES *Year* 2012 *Income* £47,776 *Grants* £52,000
TRUSTEES Barry Landy; Arnon Levy; Rabbi Shimon Bension.
HOW TO APPLY In writing to the correspondent.
WHO TO APPLY TO Barry Landy, Trustee, 192 Gilbert Road, Cambridge CB4 3PB *Tel.* 01223 570417 *email* bl10@cam.ac.uk

---

■ Williams Serendipity Trust

CC NO 1114631   **ESTABLISHED** 2006
WHERE FUNDING CAN BE GIVEN UK and overseas, with a preference for London.
WHO CAN BENEFIT Charitable organisations and individuals.
WHAT IS FUNDED General charitable purposes; education; social welfare; arts and culture; young people; people with disabilities; older people.
RANGE OF GRANTS £100–£500,000
SAMPLE GRANTS YMCA (£37,500); Care for Children (£16,000); Y Care International, Cambridge Community Fund and Home Farm Trust (£10,000 each); Gorilla Organisation, Kids, Save the Children UK and Bomber Command Association (£5,000 each); Prostate Cancer and Papworth Trust (£1,000 each); East Anglian Air Ambulance (£500); and ACT Friends (£100).
FINANCES *Year* 2011 *Income* £148,708 *Grants* £129,800 *Assets* £477,720
TRUSTEES Colin Williams; Alexander Williams; Sophie Williams; Gerlinde Williams.
OTHER INFORMATION Grants totalled £130,000 and were given to 20 different charities including, educational charities and the YMCA.
HOW TO APPLY In writing to the correspondent. Trustees' meetings are held at least twice each year.
WHO TO APPLY TO The Trustees, c/o 4 The Sanctuary, Westminster, London SW1P 3JS

■ The HDH Wills 1965 Charitable Trust

CC NO 1117747   **ESTABLISHED** 1965
WHERE FUNDING CAN BE GIVEN Mainly UK, occasionally overseas.
WHO CAN BENEFIT Registered or recognised charities only.
WHAT IS FUNDED General charitable purposes. The Martin Wills fund gives particular favour to wildlife conservation projects in years three and four of its seven year funding priority cycle.
WHAT IS NOT FUNDED Registered or recognised charities only.
TYPE OF GRANT One-off grants. Grants may be made towards revenue, capital or project expenditure.
RANGE OF GRANTS The vast majority of grants from the General Fund total £500 or less.
SAMPLE GRANTS Salzburg Seminar and 21st Century Trust (£3,000 each); Countryside Learning, CMRF – Katie Nugent Fund and Break (£2,000 each); and Ashmolean Museum, First Story, Leonard Cheshire Disability and Refugee Resource (£1,000 each).
FINANCES *Year* 2011–12 *Income* £2,755,960 *Grants* £986,868 *Assets* £57,731,634

TRUSTEES Dr Catherine Wills; John Burrell Carson; Lord Victor Killearn; Charles Francklin; Martin Fiennes; Thomas Nelson.
OTHER INFORMATION The trust runs two separate funds: the General Fund and the Martin Wills Fund. The two funds operate in different areas of grantmaking and, in the case of the Martin Wills Fund, on a seven-year cycle. 114 grants of £1,000 were made in 2011–12.
HOW TO APPLY An online submission form is available from the trust's website. Only one application from a given charity will be considered in any 18-month period. According to the trust's website, 'on application you will be asked to supply the following information: contact name, address, telephone number and email address; organisation's charitable status and charity registration number; brief description of the organisation and its work; the organisation's most recent set of accounts; and a project document containing the following: a description of the project; a budget for the project; and how the project will be monitored and evaluated.'
According to the trust's website, the current grantmaking policy of the trust for the general fund is as follows: charities only; generally no grants are made to an organisation that it has supported within the previous eighteen months; no support for individuals seeking personal support; the fund seeks to make donations to charities which are small enough in size, or which apply for support for a modest project, to benefit substantially from a donation of £250 or £500, though it will consider grants of up to £5,000; grants may be made towards revenue, capital or project expenditure; and grants are made on a rolling basis and there is no deadline for applications. The current grantmaking policy of the trust for the Martin Wills fund is as follows: charities only; grants may be made towards revenue, capital or project expenditure; grants are distributed after the end of each financial year (the trust's financial year runs from 1 April to 31 March); and applications must be received by the trust before the end of the appropriate financial year.
WHO TO APPLY TO Wendy Cooper, Administrator, Henley Knapp Barn, Fulwell, Chipping Norton, Oxon OX7 4EN *Tel.* 01608 678051 *email* hdhwills@btconnect.com *Website* www.hdhwills.org

---

■ Dame Violet Wills Charitable Trust

CC NO 219485   **ESTABLISHED** 1955
WHERE FUNDING CAN BE GIVEN UK and overseas.
WHO CAN BENEFIT Registered evangelical Christian charities.
WHAT IS FUNDED Evangelical Christian activities.
WHAT IS NOT FUNDED Grants are not given to individuals.
TYPE OF GRANT One-off and recurrent. Capital and core costs. Full-project funding.
RANGE OF GRANTS Mainly £1,000–£5,000.
SAMPLE GRANTS WC and SWET Evangelists Fund (£12,000); Wycliffe Bibles Translators (£1,800); Bristol International Student Centre (£1,600); SWYM – the Rise Up Project, OMF and Sat-7 Trust (£1,500 each); Living Water Radio Ministry (£1,200); Open Air Campaigners (£800); True Freedom Trust, Open Doors and Eurovangelism (£500 each); France Mission Trust (£200); and Wales Evangelical School of Theology (£80).

FINANCES *Year* 2012 *Income* £71,126 *Grants* £57,027 *Assets* £1,753,601

TRUSTEES Julian Marsh; Revd Dr Ernest Lucas; Revd Alexander Cooper; Revd Ray Lockhart; Derek Cleave; John Dean; Rosalind Peskett; Janet Persson; Rachel Daws; Revd David Caporn; E. Street; Yme Potjewijd; Tim Kevan.

HOW TO APPLY In writing to the correspondent. Trustees meet in March and in September.

WHO TO APPLY TO Julian Marsh, Trustee, 3 Cedar Way, Portishead, Bristol BS20 6TT *Tel.* 01275 848770

■ The Dame Violet Wills Will Trust

CC NO 262251   ESTABLISHED 1965

WHERE FUNDING CAN BE GIVEN Bristol and south Devon areas.

WHO CAN BENEFIT Registered charities.

WHAT IS FUNDED The support of homes established privately by the late Dame Violet Wills and charities active in Bristol and south Devon.

TYPE OF GRANT Single donations.

SAMPLE GRANTS Amos Vale, Bristol and the Colston Society, Bristol Cathedral Trust, Church of the Good Shepherd, Clifton Gateway Club, Guide Dogs for the Blind, Lord Mamhead Homes, RNLI, Rainbow Centre, Rowcroft Hospice, Samaritans, St Loye's Foundation and WRVS.

FINANCES *Year* 2011–12 *Income* £110,132 *Grants* £98,500 *Assets* £2,665,237

TRUSTEES J. Brooks; D. P. L. Howe; T. J. Baines.

HOW TO APPLY In writing to the correspondent. The trustees meet four times per year to consider applications.

WHO TO APPLY TO D. P. L. Howe, Trustee, 7 Christchurch Road, Clifton, Bristol BS8 4EE

■ The Wilmcote Charitrust

CC NO 503837   ESTABLISHED 1974

WHERE FUNDING CAN BE GIVEN Birmingham and Midlands.

WHO CAN BENEFIT Registered charities and voluntary organisations.

WHAT IS FUNDED General charitable purposes.

TYPE OF GRANT Mainly recurrent

RANGE OF GRANTS £95–£2,500; mainly around £500.

SAMPLE GRANTS **Ex-Service charities** – Gurkha Welfare Trust, Queen Alexander Hospital Home and Royal British Legion (£500 each) and SSAFA (£250). **Medical charities** – Douglas House Hospice (£2,000); Kissing It Better (£1,500); Conductive Education (£1,000); Alzheimer's Research UK, Cyclists Fighting Cancer, Mercia MS Therapy Centre and Oesophageal Patients Association (£500 each) and Multiple Sclerosis Society UK (£250). **Children's and Young Person's charities** – 1st Wilmcote Scout Group, Edward Russ Trust, CBSO Education Programme, National Youth Orchestra of Great Britain (£500 each); Butterfly Tree, Youth Aliyah (£250 each); Birmingham Children's Hospital(£100). **General charities** – Birmingham Botanical Gardens and Cotswold Canals Trust (£500 each); and RNLI (£100). **Religious charities** – Salvation Army (£500); Trinity Christian Centre (£250) and Jewish Childs Day (£100). **Aged charities** – Princess Royal Trust (£2,000) and Home from Hospital Care and Age Concern Solihull (£500 each).

FINANCES *Year* 2011–12 *Income* £76,599 *Grants* £58,350 *Assets* £1,689,639

TRUSTEES Carol Worrall; Anabel Murphy; Roseamond Whiteside; Graham Beach.

HOW TO APPLY In writing to the correspondent.

WHO TO APPLY TO Carol Worrall, Trust Administrator, Warren Chase, Billesley Road, Wilmcote, Stratford-upon-Avon CV37 9XG *Tel.* 01789 298472

■ Sumner Wilson Charitable Trust

CC NO 1018852   ESTABLISHED 1992

WHERE FUNDING CAN BE GIVEN UK.

WHO CAN BENEFIT Registered charities.

WHAT IS FUNDED General charitable purposes.

RANGE OF GRANTS Mostly under £2,000.

SAMPLE GRANTS St James's Place Foundation (£21,200); Lewisham Youth Theatre (£13,300); St Mungo's Community Housing Association (£3,000); Friends of Young Carers (£2,300); Mental Health Foundation, West London Centre for Counselling and Bramay Trust (£1,000 each); Land Aid (£900); Help for Heroes and SOS Children's Village (£800); and Tongole Foundation (£300).

FINANCES *Year* 2011–12 *Income* £67,551 *Grants* £70,101 *Assets* £3,073,296

TRUSTEES Michael Wilson; Amanda Christie; Anne-Marie Challen.

OTHER INFORMATION Over 24 grants totalling £70,000 were made to organisations.

HOW TO APPLY In writing to the correspondent, or to the trustees.

WHO TO APPLY TO N. Steinberg, Administrator, Munslows, 2nd Floor, Manfield House, 1 Southampton Street, London WC2R 0LR *Tel.* 020 7845 7500 *email* mail@munslows.co. uk

■ David Wilson Foundation

CC NO 1049047   ESTABLISHED 1995

WHERE FUNDING CAN BE GIVEN UK with a strong preference for the Leicestershire and Rutland area.

WHO CAN BENEFIT Primarily organisations which benefit the Leicestershire and Rutland area.

WHAT IS FUNDED General charitable purposes, with a preference for training in the construction industry and sport.

WHAT IS NOT FUNDED No support for general appeals and one-off events.

SAMPLE GRANTS University of Leicester Cardiovascular Research Centre (£500,000).

FINANCES *Year* 2011–12 *Income* £202,242 *Grants* £500,000 *Assets* £6,895,498

TRUSTEES James Wilson; Thomas Neiland; Laura Wilson; Richard Wilson; Robert Wilson; Sarah Carley.

OTHER INFORMATION No grants were made to individuals.

HOW TO APPLY In writing to the correspondent. See the website for criteria.

WHO TO APPLY TO John Gillions, Secretary, c/o Fisher Solicitors, 4–8 Kilwardby Street, Ashby-de-la-Zouch, Leicestershire LE65 2FU *Tel.* 01530 412167 *email* john.gillions@fisherslaw.co.uk *Website* www.davidwilsonfoundation.com

■ The Wilson Foundation

CC NO 1074414   ESTABLISHED 1999

WHERE FUNDING CAN BE GIVEN Northamptonshire.

WHO CAN BENEFIT Organisations working with people aged 10 to 21.

WHAT IS FUNDED Educational purposes, including activity-based courses/centres.

TYPE OF GRANT Recurrent project funding, one-off scholarships, running costs.

RANGE OF GRANTS £100–£20,000.

SAMPLE GRANTS Oakham School (£21,500); Naseby Battlefield Project (£20,000); Bunbury ESCA Festival (£5,000); Wooden Spoon (£3,000); Sports Aid Midlands (£2,000); Abbey Primary School (£1,500); Tall Ships Youth Trusts (£600); Northampton Carers (£400) and Northampton Hospital Show (£100).

FINANCES *Year* 2011–12 *Income* £26,227 *Grants* £64,263 *Assets* £4,669,394

TRUSTEES Anthony Hewitt; Giles Wilson; Nicholas Wilson; Fiona Wilson; Adam Welch; Pollyanna Wilson.

OTHER INFORMATION The grant total includes £2,000 that was donated to 11 individuals.

HOW TO APPLY Individuals: application forms are available on the trust's website. Organisations should apply in writing to the trustees.

WHO TO APPLY TO Nick Wilson, Chair, The Maltings, Tithe Farm, Moulton Road, Holcot, Northamptonshire NN6 9SH *Tel.* 01604 782240 *email* polly@tithefarm.com *Website* www.thewilsonfoundation.co.uk

....

■ **J. and J. R. Wilson Trust**

SC NO SC007411   **ESTABLISHED** 1989

WHERE FUNDING CAN BE GIVEN Mainly Scotland, particularly Glasgow and the west coast of Scotland.

WHO CAN BENEFIT Organisations benefiting older people and animals and birds.

WHAT IS FUNDED Grants are given to charitable bodies which are concerned with older people, or the care of both domestic and wild animals and birds.

WHAT IS NOT FUNDED No grants to individuals.

SAMPLE GRANTS Royal Society for the Protection of Birds (£4,500); Cancer Bacup (£4,000); St Margaret's Hospice – Clydebank and SSPCA (£3,000 each); Maggie's Cancer Care – Glasgow and Marine Connection (£2,000 each); Accord Hospice – Paisley, Ardgowan Hospice – Greenock, British Red Cross, Princess Royal Trust for Carers, Royal National Institute of Blind People, Royal Zoological Society Scotland and Trees for Life (£1,000 each).

FINANCES *Year* 2012–13 *Income* £135,658 *Grants* £160,000

TRUSTEES H. M. K. Hopkins; J. G. L. Robinson; K. H. Mackenzie; R. N. C. Douglas; G. I. M. Chapman.

HOW TO APPLY In writing to the correspondent. The trustees meet at least once a year.

WHO TO APPLY TO Beth Hamilton, c/o Tho and JW Barty Solicitors, 61 High Street, Dunblane FK15 0EH *Tel.* 01786 822296

....

■ **The Community Foundation for Wiltshire and Swindon**

CC NO 1123126   **ESTABLISHED** 1991

WHERE FUNDING CAN BE GIVEN Wiltshire and Swindon only.

WHO CAN BENEFIT Local voluntary and community groups.

WHAT IS FUNDED The primary focus is on disadvantage including, supporting community care, tackling isolation and investing in young people. There are other funds, see the foundation's website for details of up-to-date schemes.

WHAT IS NOT FUNDED The foundation will not fund: groups that have more than 12 months running costs in unrestricted (free) reserves; projects operating outside the County of Wiltshire / Borough of Swindon; organisations delivering services in Wiltshire or Swindon who do not have a local management structure; sponsored events; general large appeals; the advancement of religion; medical research and equipment; animal welfare; party political activities; schools; preschools; CICs (apart from start-up funds).

TYPE OF GRANT Project, core costs and capital grants.

RANGE OF GRANTS Main grants: £500–£10,000 per year for three years. Small grants: £50–£750 on a one-off basis.

FINANCES *Year* 2011–12 *Income* £2,451,343 *Grants* £483,897 *Assets* £9,966,006

TRUSTEES Richard Handover, Chair; Elizabeth Webbe; Denise Bentley; Christopher Bromfield; Clare Evans; David Holder; Andrew Kerr; Angus Macpherson; Dame Elizabeth Neville; Tim Odoire; Alison Radevsky; John Rendell; Dr Fiona Richards; Ram Thiagarajah; Sarah Troughton; John Woodget; Simon Wright.

OTHER INFORMATION The foundation has a Main Grants and a Small Grants programme. Check the foundation's website for details of other current programmes.

HOW TO APPLY The foundation describes its application process as follows: '1. to ensure that you do not waste time unnecessarily, we strongly recommend that you read the [exclusions] carefully before you start your expression of interest form; 2. if after step 1, you feel that your project is eligible, fill in our expression of interest form [available from the foundation's website]. We will let you know if you are eligible and send you an application pack. We make our application forms as straightforward and as short as possible. If your project is not eligible to apply to one of our funds, we will aim to put you in touch with someone who can help you; 3. complete the form and return it, within the deadline shown on the front of the pack. If you have any problems completing it, call us for assistance; 4. a member of the Grants Team will assess your application and will either visit or telephone you. This meeting also provides the opportunity to discuss the application further and answer any questions; 5. your application and our assessment report go forward to the relevant Local Grants Committee. The committee then makes the decisions and these are ratified by our Trustees; 6. if we turn you down, you will get details in writing of the reason why. Contact us by telephone or email and we will let you know if you can re-apply; 7. if you are awarded a grant, you will be asked to report back to us on how the money is spent and has been achieved.'

WHO TO APPLY TO Heidi Yorke, Grants Programme Director, Sandcliffe, 21 Northgate Street, Devizes, Wiltshire SN10 1JX *Tel.* 01380 729284 *email* info@wscf.org.uk *Website* www.wscf.org.uk

....

■ **The Windruff Charitable Trust**

CC NO 1147510   **ESTABLISHED** 2012

WHERE FUNDING CAN BE GIVEN UK.

WHO CAN BENEFIT Charities and community groups.

WHAT IS FUNDED General charitable purposes.

TRUSTEES Derek Pratt; Joan Pratt; Clifford Pratt; Roger Pratt; Barbara Pratt; David Pratt; Rosaleen Pratt.

HOW TO APPLY In writing to the correspondent.

WHO TO APPLY TO Joan Pratt, Trustee, c/o Windruff Holdings Limited, 22 Felpham Road, Bognor Regis, West Sussex PO22 7AZ *Tel.* 01243 863454

■ The Benjamin Winegarten Charitable Trust

CC NO 271442   ESTABLISHED 1976

WHERE FUNDING CAN BE GIVEN UK.

WHO CAN BENEFIT Individuals and organisations benefiting Jewish people and people disadvantaged by poverty.

WHAT IS FUNDED Relief of poverty and the advancement of Jewish religion and religious education.

SAMPLE GRANTS Previous beneficiaries have included Hechal Hatovah Institute, the Jewish Educational Trust, the Mechinah School, Merkaz Lechinuch Torani Zichron Ya'akov, Ohr Someach Friends, Or Akiva Community Centre, Yeshivo Hovomo Talmudical College and ZSVT.

FINANCES *Year* 2011–12 *Income* £138,793 *Grants* £71,900 *Assets* £941,617

TRUSTEES Benjamin Winegarten; Esther Winegarten.

OTHER INFORMATION The grant total in 2011–12 includes £13,000 donated to individuals.

HOW TO APPLY In writing to the correspondent.

WHO TO APPLY TO Benjamin Winegarten, Trustee, 25 St Andrew's Grove, Stoke Newington, London N16 5NF *Tel.* 020 8800 6669

■ The Harold Hyam Wingate Foundation

CC NO 264114   ESTABLISHED 1960

WHERE FUNDING CAN BE GIVEN UK and developing world.

WHO CAN BENEFIT Registered charities and organisations working in developing countries.

WHAT IS FUNDED Jewish life and learning, performing arts, music, education and social exclusion, overseas development and medical research (travel costs).

WHAT IS NOT FUNDED No grants to individuals (the scholarship fund is administered separately). The foundation will not normally make grants to the general funds of large charitable bodies, wishing instead to focus support on specific projects.

TYPE OF GRANT Either one-off or recurrent for a limited period. Also capital projects on a highly selective basis.

RANGE OF GRANTS Generally £10,000 or less.

SAMPLE GRANTS Whitechapel Society for the Advancement of Knowledge of Gastroenterology (£100,000); Queen Mary and Westfield College (£96,000); World Ort Union (£30,000); Donmar Warehouse (£15,000); Chichester Festival Theatre (£12,000); Jewish Community Centre London and the Young Vic (£10,000 each); FilmClubUK (£8,000); ReSurge Africa (£7,500); Tree Aid (£6,000); Cardboard Citizens, Computer Aid International and Village Water (£5,000 each); Arvon Foundation (£4,000); Classical Opera Company (£3,000); and the University of Glasgow (£1,000).

FINANCES *Year* 2011–12 *Income* £247,946 *Grants* £1,095,875 *Assets* £7,990,979

TRUSTEES Roger Wingate; Tony Wingate; Prof. Robert Cassen; Prof. David Wingate; Prof. Jonathon Drori; Daphne Hyman; Emily Kasriel; Dr Richard Wingate.

OTHER INFORMATION The foundation also operates a scholarship scheme, under the name of Wingate Scholarships. Further details can be found at www.wingatescholarships.org.uk. In 2011–12 scholarships totalled £408,000.

HOW TO APPLY On an application form available from the foundation's website. Applications are only acknowledged if a stamped addressed envelope is enclosed or if the application is successful. The administrator of the foundation only deals with enquiries by post and it is hoped that the guidelines and examples of previous support for successful applicants, given on the foundation's website, provides sufficient information. There is no email address for the foundation. Trustee meetings are held quarterly and further information on upcoming deadlines can be found on the foundation's website.

WHO TO APPLY TO Karen Marshall, Trust Administrator, 2nd Floor, 20–22 Stukeley Street, London WC2B 5LR *Website* www. wingatefoundation.org.uk

■ The Francis Winham Foundation

CC NO 278092   ESTABLISHED 1979

WHERE FUNDING CAN BE GIVEN England.

WHO CAN BENEFIT Older people.

WHAT IS FUNDED Organisations, institutions and foundations benefiting older people.

SAMPLE GRANTS Butterwick Hospice Care (£50,000); Age UK (£23,000 in eight donations); Help the Hospices and King Edward VII's Hospital (£20,000 each); U Can Do It (£10,000); and British Heart Foundation and Independence at Home (£5,000 each).

FINANCES *Year* 2011–12 *Income* £340,891 *Grants* £435,101 *Assets* £2,443,867

TRUSTEES Francine Winham; Josephine Winham; Elsa Peters.

HOW TO APPLY In writing to the correspondent. The trust regrets it cannot send replies to applications outside its specific field of help for older people. Applications should be made through registered charities or social services departments only.

WHO TO APPLY TO Josephine Winham, Trustee, 41 Langton Street, London SW10 0JL *Tel.* 020 7795 1261 *email* francinetrust@btopenworld. com

■ The Winton Charitable Foundation

CC NO 1110131   ESTABLISHED 2005

WHERE FUNDING CAN BE GIVEN National and overseas.

WHO CAN BENEFIT Academic institutions and other organisations.

WHAT IS FUNDED Academic, recreation, health and welfare.

SAMPLE GRANTS AfriKids (£21,000); The Helen and Douglas Trust (£18,000); Centraid of Great Montreal, UNICEF (£10,000 each).

FINANCES *Year* 2012 *Income* £300,064 *Grants* £266,682

TRUSTEES David Winton; Martin Hunt.

HOW TO APPLY In writing to the correspondent.

WHO TO APPLY TO Martin Hunt, Trustee, 1–5 St Mary Abbot's Place, London W8 6LS *Tel.* 020 7610 5350

Wirral Mayor's Charity

CC NO 518288   **ESTABLISHED** 1986

WHERE FUNDING CAN BE GIVEN Wirral.

WHO CAN BENEFIT Local organisations, and local branches of UK organisations.

WHAT IS FUNDED A large variety of causes including welfare and medical charities, children and youth organisations, and disability groups. Many are community-based or local branches of UK charities.

RANGE OF GRANTS £50–£15,000

SAMPLE GRANTS Wirral Women and Children's Aid (£14,500); Wirral Hospice St John (£12,000); Age UK Devonshire Centre (£8,000); Tomorrow's Women (£2,000); Wirral Foodbank (£600); Mercian Regimental Charity, 20th Rainbow Guides and Sevenoaks Community Group (£100 each) and Deafblind Uk, Wallasey Festival of Stage Dance and Bebington Hard of Hearing Club (£50 each).

FINANCES *Year* 2011–12 *Income* £69,172 *Grants* £38,924

TRUSTEES Cllr Gerry Ellis; Peter Timmins; Cllr Moira McLaughlin; Graham Burgess.

HOW TO APPLY In writing to the correspondent.

WHO TO APPLY TO The Mayor's Secretary, Wirral Borough Council, Town Hall, Brighton Street, Wallasey, Wirral CH44 8ED *Tel.* 01516 918527 *Fax* 01516 918468 *email* mayor@wirral.gov.uk

The James Wise Charitable Trust

CC NO 273853   **ESTABLISHED** 1977

WHERE FUNDING CAN BE GIVEN UK, but mainly Surrey and Hampshire.

WHO CAN BENEFIT Charitable organisations and individuals.

WHAT IS FUNDED General charitable purposes.

TYPE OF GRANT Generally one-off grants.

RANGE OF GRANTS Up to £25,000.

SAMPLE GRANTS MNDA (£2,000); PDSA, Royal Berks Charity, Chiddingford Village Hall and Recreational Ground Charity and County Air Ambulance Trust (£1,000 each); ABF The Soldiers Charity (£600); Godalming Museum, Canine Partners, Peter Pan Nursery and National Talking Newspaper (£500 each); The Eyeless Trust (£300); Streatham Youth 8 Community Trust and Global Rescue Services (£200 each); Finsbury Park Community Hub (£150) and Alzheimer's Society and Godalming Parochial Church Council (£100 each).

FINANCES *Year* 2012–13 *Income* £58,097 *Grants* £48,014 *Assets* £1,904,745

TRUSTEES Lisa Rabinowitz; Barry Kilburn; Sara Coate.

HOW TO APPLY In writing to the correspondent.

WHO TO APPLY TO Claire Burnett, c/o Marshalls Solicitors, 102 High Street, Godalming, Surrey GU7 1DS *Tel.* 01483 416101

The Witzenfeld Foundation

CC NO 1115034   **ESTABLISHED** 2006

WHERE FUNDING CAN BE GIVEN UK and Israel.

WHO CAN BENEFIT Charitable organisations.

WHAT IS FUNDED General charitable purposes, Jewish.

FINANCES *Year* 2011–12 *Income* £56,205 *Grants* £71,488 *Assets* £5,482

TRUSTEES Alan Witzenfeld; Lyetta Witzenfeld; Emma Witzenfeld-Saigh; Mark Witzenfeld.

OTHER INFORMATION 22 grants totalling £72,000 were made during 2011–12.

HOW TO APPLY In writing to the correspondent.

WHO TO APPLY TO Alan Witzenfeld, Trustee, Porters House, Station Court, Radford Way, Billericay, Essex *Tel.* 01702 330032

The Michael and Anna Wix Charitable Trust

CC NO 207863   **ESTABLISHED** 1955

WHERE FUNDING CAN BE GIVEN UK.

WHO CAN BENEFIT Registered charities (mainly UK) benefiting students, at risk groups, and people who are disabled, disadvantaged by poverty or socially isolated.

WHAT IS FUNDED Main areas of interest are older people, disability, education, medicine and health, poverty and welfare and Jewish.

WHAT IS NOT FUNDED Applications from individuals are not considered. Grants are to national bodies rather than local branches or local groups.

TYPE OF GRANT 'Modest semi-regular' donations. Also one-off for part or all of a specific project.

RANGE OF GRANTS Mostly for smaller amounts in the range of £100 and £500 each.

SAMPLE GRANTS Weizmann UK (£3,000); British Friends of the Hebrew University and Jewish Care (£2,000 each) Pinhas Rutenberg Educational Trust and UJIA (£1,000 each). The remaining funds were distributed among over 200 beneficiaries in small grants of between £100–500. Beneficiaries included: YMCA, Ro-Ro Sailing Project, No Panic, Motability, Mencap, Meningitis Trust, Rehab UK, Independence at Home, Forces Support and Concern Worldwide.

FINANCES *Year* 2011–12 *Income* £66,639 *Grants* £53,200 *Assets* £1,720,354

TRUSTEES J. B. Bloch; D. B. Flynn; Judith Portrait.

HOW TO APPLY In writing to the trustees. Applications are considered half-yearly. Only applications from registered charities are acknowledged. Frequent applications by a single charity are not appreciated.

WHO TO APPLY TO Sarah Hovil, Administrator, c/o Portrait Solicitors, 21 Whitefriars Street, London EC4Y 8JJ *Tel.* 020 7092 6985

The Wixamtree Trust

CC NO 210089   **ESTABLISHED** 1949

WHERE FUNDING CAN BE GIVEN UK and overseas, in practice mainly Bedfordshire.

WHO CAN BENEFIT Local charities, a small number of national and overseas charities with a focus on family social issues and some overseas. Applicants must be a registered charity or considered to be charitable in nature by the Inland Revenue.

WHAT IS FUNDED General charitable purposes. In particular, social welfare; environment and conservation; medicine and health; the arts; education; and sports and leisure.

WHAT IS NOT FUNDED No grants to individuals.

TYPE OF GRANT One-off projects, capital, core costs and research.

RANGE OF GRANTS Usually grants between £1,000 and £10,000 with a small number of donations outside this range.

SAMPLE GRANTS Beneficiaries were not listed in the accounts but could be viewed on the trust's website. Beneficiaries included: British Epilepsy Association; Narcolepsy UK; Keech Hospice Care; Leighton Linslade Homeless Service; Barton Scouts and Guides Headquarters Management Committee; Farms for City Children; Bibles for Children; British Association for Adoption and Fostering (BAAF); Mitalee Youth Association; Oakley Rural Day Care Centre; Bedfordshire African Community Centre; Dunstable and District Citizens Advice; Luton West Indian Community Association; Autism Bedfordshire; Special Needs Out Of School Club in Beds (SNOOSC); Whizz-Kidz; Child Bereavement UK; Road Victims Trust; Westminster College – Cambridge; Bedford Creative Arts; Music First; Bedfordshire Historical Record Society; Bedfordshire Wildlife Rescue; European Squirrel Initiative; Campaign to Protect Rural England (CPRE); Fauna and Flora International; Wheelchair Dance Sport Association (UK); and Sandy Cricket Club.

FINANCES *Year* 2011–12 *Income* £762,618 *Grants* £958,199 *Assets* £22,196,037

TRUSTEES Sir Samuel Whitbread; Lady Whitbread; H. F. Whitbread; Charles Whitbread; Ian Pilkington; Geoff McMullen.

HOW TO APPLY Application forms can be downloaded from the website or requested via email or post. The method of submission must be via email: wixamtree@thetrustpartnership.com. Future meeting dates and application deadlines are listed on the trust's website. Along with the application form, applicants must provide a copy of their latest audited report and accounts. If the organisation is not a charity, then a copy of its constitution must also be provided. Applicants are permitted to provide additional information to support their application if they wish to do so. According to the trust's website, 'the trustees have entered into an arrangement with the trustees of the Beds and Herts Historic Churches Trust (BHHCT) who consider applications from Bedfordshire churches which are seeking support for repairs to the fabric of their buildings. It was felt that the BHHCT had more expertise in this area and by using their network of assessors to decide what projects should be supported. Bedfordshire churches seeking such support should therefore complete a different application form and, once submitted to the Administrator of the BHHCT, a site visit will be arranged to evaluate the project.' Successful applicants will be notified within 14 days of the trustees' meeting of the amount that has been approved. Unsuccessful applicants will receive a letter detailing the trustees' decision within seven days of the meeting. Before another application can be submitted, the trust asks previously successful organisations who already hold grants to submit an annual report on how the earlier grant has been used.

WHO TO APPLY TO Paul Patten, Administrator, 148 The Grove, West Wickham, Kent BR4 9JZ *Tel.* 020 8777 4140 *email* wixamtree@ thetrustpartnership.com *Website* www. wixamtree.org

■ The Woburn 1986 Charitable Trust

CC NO 295525 **ESTABLISHED** 1986
WHERE FUNDING CAN BE GIVEN Primarily Woburn.
WHO CAN BENEFIT Primarily older people; also welfare and medical charities.
WHAT IS FUNDED The provision and maintenance of housing for Woburn estate pensioners in need; research into, and the provision of facilities for, the welfare of elephants.
TYPE OF GRANT Recurrent and single donations.
RANGE OF GRANTS Up to £23,000.

SAMPLE GRANTS Bedfordshire and Luton Community Foundation (£23,000); St Francis Children's Society, All Saints Dunterton and Marie Curie Cancer Care (£1,000 each); Red Squirrel Survival Trust (£500); Action for Blind People, Addenbrookes Charitable Trust and Mercy Corps, (£250 each); Woburn Sands Christmas Carnival (£100).

FINANCES *Year* 2011–12 *Income* £78,084
TRUSTEES The Duke of Bedford; David Fox; Peter Pemberton; The Duchess of Bedford.
OTHER INFORMATION In 2011–12 the trust had a total expenditure of £45,469.
HOW TO APPLY In writing to the correspondent.
WHO TO APPLY TO K. Shurrock, Administrator, The Bedford Office, Woburn, Milton Keynes, Bedfordshire MK17 9WA *Tel.* 01525 290333 *email* kshurrock@woburnabbey.co.uk

■ The Maurice Wohl Charitable Foundation

CC NO 244519 **ESTABLISHED** 1965
WHERE FUNDING CAN BE GIVEN UK and Israel.
WHO CAN BENEFIT In practice, Jewish groups and health, welfare and medical organisations.
WHAT IS FUNDED Support is given to organisations in the UK with particular emphasis on the following areas: the care, welfare and support of children (including education); the promotion of health, welfare and the advancement of medical services; the relief of poverty, indigence and distress; the care, welfare and support of the aged, infirm and disabled; the support of the arts.
WHAT IS NOT FUNDED The trustees do not in general entertain applications for grants for ongoing maintenance projects. The trustees do not administer any schemes for individual awards or scholarships and they do not, therefore, entertain any individual applications for grants.
TYPE OF GRANT One-off grants.
RANGE OF GRANTS £861,000–£900.
SAMPLE GRANTS King's College London Dental Institute (£861,000); King's College London (£245,000); The Interlink Foundation (£98,500); The University of Glasgow – Beatson Translational Research Centre (£64,000); Yad Harav Herzog (£45,000); The London School of Jewish Studies (£33,000); Bayis Sheli Limited (£21,500); Friends of Ohel Torah (£15,000); Jewish Women's Aid and Helenslea Tsedoko Limited (£10,000 each); Keren Shabbos and Michael Sobell Sinai School (£5,000 each); Spinal Research (£2,500); and Best Beginnings and Friends of Israel Educational Foundation (£945 each).
FINANCES *Year* 2011–12 *Income* £1,703,372 *Grants* £1,956,527 *Assets* £81,243,916
TRUSTEES Ella Latchman; Martin Paisner; Prof. David Latchman; Sir Ian Gainsford; Daniel Dover.
HOW TO APPLY In writing to the correspondent. The trustees meet regularly throughout the year.
WHO TO APPLY TO Joseph Houri, Secretary, Fitzrovia House, 2nd Floor, 153 - 157 Cleveland Street, London W1T 6QW *Tel.* 020 7383 5111 *email* josephhouri@wohl.co.uk

■ The Charles Wolfson Charitable Trust

cc no 238043   **ESTABLISHED** 1960

WHERE FUNDING CAN BE GIVEN Unrestricted, mainly UK.

WHO CAN BENEFIT Registered charities, hospitals and schools. Particular, but not exclusive regard is given to the Jewish community.

WHAT IS FUNDED Medical and scientific research and facilities, education and welfare.

WHAT IS NOT FUNDED No grants to individuals.

TYPE OF GRANT Mostly capital or fixed term projects and the provision of rent-free premises. Grants may be made for up to three years.

RANGE OF GRANTS Up to £500,000.

SAMPLE GRANTS Previous beneficiaries included: Addenbrookes Charitable Trust and Yavneh College Trust (£500,000 each); Jewish Care (£350,000); Cure Parkinson's Trust (£200,000); Huntingdon Foundation (£125,000); Royal Marsden Cancer Campaign (£50,000); Sir George Pinker Appeal (£30,000); Zoological Society of London (£25,000); Priors Court Foundation (£10,000); Tavistock Trust for Aphasia (£5,000); and the Roundhouse Trust (£1,000).

FINANCES *Year* 2011–12 *Income* £7,901,101 *Grants* £6,492,936 *Assets* £155,899,025

TRUSTEES Lord Simon Wolfson; Dr Sara Levene; The Hon Andrew Wolfson; Lord David Wolfson.

OTHER INFORMATION A list of beneficiaries was not available.

HOW TO APPLY In writing to the correspondent.

WHO TO APPLY TO Cynthia Crawford, Administrator, 129 Battenhall Road, Worcester WR5 2BU

■ The Wolfson Family Charitable Trust

cc no 228382   **ESTABLISHED** 1958

WHERE FUNDING CAN BE GIVEN UK; mostly Israel.

WHO CAN BENEFIT Particularly Jewish groups and Israeli institutions.

WHAT IS FUNDED Science, technology and medicine; education; medical research and care and welfare; arts and humanities.

WHAT IS NOT FUNDED Exclusions, as stated on the trust's website, are as follows: 'grants direct to individuals or through conduit organisations; overheads, maintenance costs, VAT and professional fees; non-specific appeals (including circulars) and endowment funds; costs of meetings, exhibitions, concerts, expeditions, etc.; the purchase of land or existing buildings (including a building's freehold); film or promotional materials; repayment of loans and projects that have already been completed or will be by the time of award.'

TYPE OF GRANT One-off for capital costs and equipment.

RANGE OF GRANTS Up to £200,000

SAMPLE GRANTS Israel Museum (£200,000); Technion – Israel Institute of Technology and Weizmann Institute of Science (£171,000 each); Tel Aviv University (£162,000); The Hebrew University of Jerusalem (£126,000); The Academy of Medical Sciences (£100,000); Central Synagogue and Yemin Orde Wingate Academy (£50,000 each); Beit Issie Shapiro and Foundation for the Benefit of Holocaust Survivors (£20,000 each); The Langdon Foundation and Ezrra U'Marpeh (£15,000 each); Technoda Dorset (£7,500); Carmel Zvulun and

Yuri Shtern Foundation (£5,000 each); and Min Ajliki (£2,500).

FINANCES *Year* 2011–12 *Income* £842,000 *Grants* £1,513,000 *Assets* £30,360,000

TRUSTEES Martin Paisner; Sir Ian Gainsford; Sir Bernard Rix; Sir Eric Ash; The Hon Laura Wolfson Townsley; The Hon Janet De Botton; Lord Turnberg; The Hon Elizabeth Wolfson Peltz.

OTHER INFORMATION It took £79,000 to distribute £1.5 million worth of grants.

HOW TO APPLY According to the trust's website, awards are made once or twice a year. Awards for Israeli universities and hospitals are made in conjunction with designated programmes. Organisations should be charities or have a charitable purpose, generally have an income of above £50,000 and show evidence of long-term financial viability. Within the cultural field, organisations should have a national reputation for excellence. In the area of heritage, the trust is particularly interested in historic synagogues. Funding is provided for capital projects and applicants should guarantee matched funding. Requests should generally be in the range of £5,000–£25,000. Applications can be made online via the trust's website.

WHO TO APPLY TO Paul Ramsbottom, Chief Executive, 8 Queen Anne Street, London W1G 9LD *Tel.* 020 7323 5730 *Fax* 020 7323 3241 *Website* www.wolfson.org.uk

■ The Wolfson Foundation

cc no 206495   **ESTABLISHED** 1955

WHERE FUNDING CAN BE GIVEN Mainly UK, but also Israel.

WHO CAN BENEFIT Registered charities and exempt charities (such as universities and schools), benefiting people of all ages, especially academics, scientists and terminally ill people.

WHAT IS FUNDED Renovation of historic buildings; libraries; museums; support for preventative medicine; science and technology; programmes for people with special needs, and education. Grants for university research are awarded through competitive programmes.

WHAT IS NOT FUNDED The following are ineligible for funding: individuals; conduit organisations; overheads, maintenance cost (including for software), VAT and professional fees; VAT and professional fees; non-specific appeals (including circulars) and endowment funds; costs of meetings, exhibitions, concerts, expeditions, etc.; purchasing of land or existing buildings (including a building's freehold); film or promotional materials; repayment of loans; completed projects; and projects where the total cost is below £15,000.

TYPE OF GRANT Capital, equipment.

RANGE OF GRANTS £5,000–£2,000,000.

SAMPLE GRANTS Wolfson Neurology Initiative (£20 million); University of Manchester – cancer research building (£2 million); Epilepsy Society – epilepsy research centre, Royal Botanic Gardens – Kew and National Theatre (£1 million each); English Heritage (£810,000); Design Museum (£500,000); University of Leicester – cardiovascular research laboratories and Royal College of Art – printmaking machine hall (£400,000 each); Rambert Dance Company (£250,000); The Hebrew University of Jerusalem (£210,000); Stroke Association (£150,000); Sutton Trust (£135,000); Manchester Historic Buildings Trust (£65,000); John Spendluffe Technology College and High Wycombe Royal Grammar School (£45,000 each); Old Castle Lachlan – Argyll and Sir William Turner's Almshouses (£20,000 each); Mausolea and Monuments Trust (£10,000); and All Saints – Salop, On Course Foundation and St Peter – Brighton (£5,000 each).

FINANCES *Year* 2011–12 *Income* £24,113,000 *Grants* £49,664,000 *Assets* £633,134,000

TRUSTEES Sir David Cannadine; Sir Eric Ash; Sir David Weatherall; Lord McColl of Dulwich; The Hon Janet De Botton; The Hon Laura Wolfson Townsley; Lord Turnberg; The Hon Deborah Wolfson Davis; Prof. Hermione Lee; Sir Michael Pepper.

OTHER INFORMATION The foundation made 267 grants.

HOW TO APPLY The foundation's website states the following: 'The Wolfson Foundation has a two stage application process. Details of eligibility and what we fund are contained within the various funding programme pages. Note that, under some funding programmes, applicants are asked to submit via partner organisations, and so the application process and deadlines may vary from those described here. Such cases are signposted within the relevant programme area pages.'

'We are committed to rigorous assessment in order to fund high quality projects. All applications undergo detailed internal review and assessment by external experts. As such, the time between submission of a stage 1 application and a funding decision on a Stage 2 application will be a minimum of some five months (and may in some cases be substantially longer). As we do not make retrospective grants (i.e. your project will need to be ongoing at the time that it is considered by our trustees), it is important to plan carefully the timing of your application.'

'Grants are generally given for capital infrastructure (new build, refurbishment and equipment) supporting excellence in the fields of science and medicine, health and disability, education and the arts and humanities.'

'The large majority of our funding is allocated through open programmes (i.e. programmes which are open for any applicant to apply, albeit within defined eligibility criteria). We also run a small number of closed programmes (i.e. programmes where the particular field being funded is tightly defined and where we work with a number of carefully selected organisations). Generally our capital infrastructure programmes are open programmes and our closed programmes are all bursary, scholarship or salary schemes focussed on people rather than buildings or equipment. We welcome applications under our open programmes but do not accept unsolicited applications under our closed programmes.'

'The foundation is committed to working, where possible, in partnership with other funders and expert bodies. A number of our funding programmes are administered by other organisations and this website provides details of those programmes, including links to the relevant information on how to apply (which is generally via the partner organisation rather than direct to us). By partnership programmes we mean all programmes that are administered and/or co-funded by other organisations.'

All stage applications should be submitted online through the foundation's website. For more information visit the website's funding pages. Charities are encouraged to apply only once in a five year period.

WHO TO APPLY TO Paul Ramsbottom, Chief Executive, 8 Queen Anne Street, London W1G 9LD *Tel.* 020 7323 5730 *Fax* 020 7323 3241 *Website* www.wolfson.org.uk

■ The Wolseley Charitable Trust

CC NO 326607   **ESTABLISHED** 1984

WHERE FUNDING CAN BE GIVEN UK.

WHO CAN BENEFIT Grants are made to organisations and individuals situated locally to the businesses of Wolseley plc and its subsidiary companies, or for causes recommended by employees of such subsidiary companies.

WHAT IS FUNDED General charitable purposes that benefit the communities in which the business of Wolseley plc and its subsidiary companies operate.

RANGE OF GRANTS Up to £28,000.

SAMPLE GRANTS Prince's Foundation for the Built Environment (£10,000); Help for Heroes (£1,500); Cancer Research UK (£800); Southampton Hospital Charity (£600); Make-a-Wish Foundation (£500); Royal British Legion Women's Section Lambourn Branch (£250); Scope (£100) and St Wilfrid's Association (£50).

FINANCES *Year* 2011–12 *Income* £51,745 *Grants* £15,150

TRUSTEES Richard Shoylekov; Graham Middlemiss.

OTHER INFORMATION The 2011–12 grant total was significantly lower than in previous years (2010/11: £124,000). However, the trust states that the 'at the Trust's current level of funds, income and grants, trustees do not foresee any significant risks that could materially impact on the Trust's activities.'

HOW TO APPLY In writing to the correspondent.

WHO TO APPLY TO The Trustees, Parkview 1220, Arlington Business Park, Theale, Reading RG7 4GA *Tel.* 01189 298700

■ The James Wood Bequest Fund

SC NO SC000459   **ESTABLISHED** 1932

WHERE FUNDING CAN BE GIVEN Glasgow and the 'central belt of Scotland'.

WHO CAN BENEFIT Registered charities.

WHAT IS FUNDED General charitable purposes. Church of Scotland, historic buildings and other registered charities based in Scotland with preference being given to the central belt.

WHAT IS NOT FUNDED Registered charities only. Grants cannot be made to individuals.

TYPE OF GRANT Capital.

RANGE OF GRANTS £500–£4,000.

SAMPLE GRANTS Society of Friends of Glasgow Cathedral, Scottish Brass Band Association, Shelter Scotland, Children 1st, Princess Royal Trust for Carers, Erskine Hospital and Scottish Spina Bifida Association; Glasgow and West of Scotland Society for the Blind, Mental Health Foundation, Aberlour Child Care Trust, RSPB Scotland, Hopscotch Theatre Company, Reality at Work in Scotland and Sense Scotland.

FINANCES *Year* 2011–12 *Income* £72,042

TRUSTEES Eric Webster; David Ballantine; Alistair Campbell.

OTHER INFORMATION In 2011–12 the fund had a total expenditure of £80,500.

HOW TO APPLY In writing to the correspondent, including if possible a copy of the latest accounts, a budget for the project, sources of funding received and other relevant financial information. Trustees meet in January, April, July and October. Applications should be received by the preceding month.

WHO TO APPLY TO David Ballantine, Trustee, Mitchells Roberton Solicitors, George House, 36 North Hanover Street, Glasgow G1 2AD *Tel.* 01415 523422 *Fax* 01415 522935 *email* darb@mitchells-roberton.co.uk

■ The Wood Family Trust

SC NO SC037957 **ESTABLISHED** 2007
WHERE FUNDING CAN BE GIVEN UK, with a preference for Scotland; developing countries.
WHO CAN BENEFIT Organisations and individuals.
WHAT IS FUNDED The Wood Family Trust has three clear areas of investment focus: (1) Making Markets Work for the Poor Sub Saharan Africa (anticipated to be 75% of the overall investment); (2) Volunteering Overseas and Global Citizenship (anticipated to be 12.5% of the overall investment); (3) Developing Young People in Scotland (anticipated to be 12.5% of the overall investment).
SAMPLE GRANTS Grants were made totalling just over £1 million, of which £857,000 was designated to the cause of 'developing young people in Scotland', £146,000 was designated to institutions with the purpose of 'making markets work for the poor', £34,000 was designated to overseas volunteering and £2,000 was designated as 'miscellaneous grants'. No grants were made to individuals.
FINANCES *Year* 2011–12 *Income* £29,163,000 *Grants* £1,039,000 *Assets* £71,038,000
TRUSTEES Sir Ian Wood, Chair; Lady Helen Wood; Garreth Wood; Graham Good.
OTHER INFORMATION This trust became operational in September 2007. During 2011–12 no grants were awarded to individuals.
HOW TO APPLY 'The trust is proactive by nature and will only accept applications through our Volunteering Overseas investment programme.' Contact the trust for further information on how to make an application.
WHO TO APPLY TO Jo Mackie, Chief Executive, John Wood House, Greenwell Road, Aberdeen AB12 3AX *email* info@woodfamilytrust.org.uk *Website* www.woodfamilytrust.org.uk

■ The Woodcock Charitable Trust

CC NO 1110896 **ESTABLISHED** 2005
WHERE FUNDING CAN BE GIVEN UK.
WHO CAN BENEFIT Charitable organisations.
WHAT IS FUNDED General charitable purposes and children's charities.
SAMPLE GRANTS Previous beneficiaries have included: Egmont Trust, RNIB, George Adamson Wildlife Preservation Trust, Kids Company, Walden Spoon, Surrey Air Ambulance, Tusk Trust and Action on Addiction.
FINANCES *Year* 2012–13 *Income* £31 *Grants* £30,000
TRUSTEES Martin Woodcock; Sally Woodcock.
HOW TO APPLY In writing to the correspondent.
WHO TO APPLY TO Lucy Gibson, Administrator, Harcus Sinclair, 3 Lincoln's Inn Fields, London WC2A 3AA *Tel.* 020 7242 9700

■ Wooden Spoon Society

CC NO 326691 **ESTABLISHED** 1984
WHERE FUNDING CAN BE GIVEN UK
WHO CAN BENEFIT Charitable and community organisations that support people under the age of 25.
WHAT IS FUNDED 1.) Capital Projects with a particular interest in rugby for disabled young people and recreational and sporting facilities. Grants are currently awarded for such things as buildings and extensions, equipment and activity aids, sensory rooms/gardens, playgrounds, sports areas, transport and soft play rooms. 2.) Community Projects that support disenfranchised young people back into education, employment or training.
WHAT IS NOT FUNDED Grants will not be considered for salaries, administration costs, professional fees and ongoing overheads related to a capital project. No grants to individuals.
RANGE OF GRANTS Usually up to £100,000
SAMPLE GRANTS Noah's Ark (Cardiff Royal Infirmary) – Sensory garden/room (£250,000); Great Britain Wheelchair Rugby Ltd (£75,000); Scottish Rugby Union (£60,000); Northern Ireland Cancer Fund for Children (£54,000); Brantwood School (£40,000); Lochend Amateur Boxing Club (£34,000); Loanhead After Schools Care Club (£25,000); Fuse Youth Cafe (£18,000) and Witchford Village College (£5,000).
FINANCES *Year* 2011–12 *Income* £4,228,524 *Grants* £1,491,487
TRUSTEES David Allen; Stephen Bellamy-James; John Gibson; Steuart Howie; Alison Lowe; Fiona Morris; Martin Sanders; Stephen Scott; Peter Scott; Nigel Timson; Richard Smith; Brian Whitefoot.
HOW TO APPLY Application forms, full guidelines and criteria are available to download on the website. For applications regarding Community Projects contact Jai Purewal: jpurewal@woodenspoon.com and for applications regarding Capital Projects contact the correspondent.
WHO TO APPLY TO The Trustees, 115–117 Fleet Road, Fleet, Hampshire GU51 3PD *Tel.* 01252 773720 *Fax* 01252 773721 *email* bhodges@woodenspoon.com *Website* www.woodenspoon.com

■ The F. Glenister Woodger Trust

CC NO 802642 **ESTABLISHED** 1990
WHERE FUNDING CAN BE GIVEN West Witting and surrounding areas.
WHO CAN BENEFIT Charities and other community organisations
WHAT IS FUNDED General charitable purposes in West Wittering and surrounding areas
WHAT IS NOT FUNDED No grants to individuals.
TYPE OF GRANT Capital costs
RANGE OF GRANTS Up to £165,000.
SAMPLE GRANTS West Wittering Cycle Route Construction (£165,000); New Park Community and Arts Association (£135,000); West Wittering Parochial Church Council (£50,000); West Wittering Croquet Club (£26,000); Chichester Counselling Services (£22,000); West Wittering Cricket Club and Chichester Ship Canal (£20,000 each); RNIB (£1,775); West Wittering Eleemosynary (£1,500); National Talking Newspapers and Magazines (£1,000); Calibre Audio Library (£700) and Patient Information Centre (£675).
FINANCES *Year* 2011–12 *Income* £1,607,012 *Grants* £461,141 *Assets* £32,971,150
TRUSTEES Richard Shrubb, Chair; Rosamund Champ; William Craven; Stuart Dobbin; Maxine Thompson; Tamaris Thompson.
OTHER INFORMATION Grants were given to 14 organisations.
HOW TO APPLY In writing to the correspondent. Trustees meet quarterly.
WHO TO APPLY TO Richard Shrubb, Chair, Wicks Farm Holiday Park, Redlands Lane, West Wittering, West Sussex PO20 8QE *Tel.* 01243 513116

1006

Does the trust you have chosen match your needs? Haphazard applications waste postage and time

■ Woodlands Green Ltd

CC NO 277299   **ESTABLISHED** 1979
WHERE FUNDING CAN BE GIVEN Worldwide.
WHO CAN BENEFIT Organisations benefiting Jewish people.
WHAT IS FUNDED Jewish charities performing educational projects.
WHAT IS NOT FUNDED No grants to individuals, or for expeditions or scholarships.
SAMPLE GRANTS Previous beneficiaries have included Achisomoch Aid Co, Beis Soro Schneirer, Friends of Beis Yisroel Trust, Friends of Mir, Friends of Seret Wiznitz, Friends of Toldos Avrohom Yitzchok, JET, Kahal Imrei Chaim, Oizer Dalim Trust, NWLCM, TYY Square and UTA.
FINANCES *Year* 2010–11 *Income* £262,567 *Grants* £202,067 *Assets* £1,353,362
TRUSTEES Daniel Ost; E. Ost; A. Ost; J. A. Ost; A. Hepner.
HOW TO APPLY In writing to the correspondent.
WHO TO APPLY TO Daniel Ost, Trustee, 19 Green Walk, London NW4 2AL

■ Woodlands Trust

CC NO 259569   **ESTABLISHED** 1969
WHERE FUNDING CAN BE GIVEN West Midlands, Warwickshire, London within the boundaries of the M25.
WHO CAN BENEFIT Organisations benefiting young adults and older people; at risk groups; carers; disabled people; people disadvantaged by poverty; ex-offenders and those at risk of offending; homeless people; people living in rural and urban areas; socially isolated people; refugees; victims of abuse, crime or domestic violence.
WHAT IS FUNDED Preference to charities which the trust has special interest in, knowledge of, or association with. Particularly charities working in the fields of hospice at home; respite care and care for carers; support and self-help groups; woodlands and horticulture.
WHAT IS NOT FUNDED No grant for the cost of buildings. No grants to individuals.
TYPE OF GRANT Core costs, one-off, project, research, running costs, recurring costs, salaries and start-up costs. Funding of up to two years will be considered.
RANGE OF GRANTS Mostly £1,000–£5,000.
SAMPLE GRANTS Bromley Mencap and Daylight Christian Prison Trust (£3,500 each); Fight for Peace, Coventry Boys Club and The Limes Community and Children's Centre (£3,000 each); Arts for All and Warwickshire Crimebeat (£2,500 each); and Contact the Elderly, Stubbers Adventure Centre and Better Understanding of Dementia for Sandwell (£2,000 each).
FINANCES *Year* 2011–12 *Income* £66,954 *Grants* £57,383 *Assets* £1,775,446
TRUSTEES Judith Steele; Rosalind Bagshaw; Josephine Houston; Thomas Steele; Duncan Bagshaw; Elizabeth Brennan.
HOW TO APPLY On a form available to download, together with criteria and guidelines, from the website. The trustees meet to consider applications in April and October each year, and applications should be submitted in January and July. If you have any queries email the correspondent.
WHO TO APPLY TO Jayne Day, Administrator, c/o PWW Solicitors, 70 St George's Square, London SW1V 3RD *email* charities@pwwsolicitors.co.uk *Website* www.pwwsolicitors.co.uk/charitable-applications

■ Woodroffe Benton Foundation

CC NO 1075272   **ESTABLISHED** 1988
WHERE FUNDING CAN BE GIVEN UK.
WHO CAN BENEFIT Any charitable organisation based in the UK is eligible to apply for a grant, as are any educational institutions (schools, universities, etc.) whether or not they have charitable status.
WHAT IS FUNDED Financial assistance in times of disaster on behalf of individuals in need within the UK through registered charitable bodies; accommodation and housing; promotion of education – especially through scholarships at Queen Elizabeth Grammar School in Ashbourne; conservation and environment; and community services and facilities.
WHAT IS NOT FUNDED The trustees do not usually make grants for: organisations that operate primarily outside the UK or for the benefit of non-UK residents; places of worship seeking funds for restoration or upgrade of facilities; students requesting a grant for tertiary education or a gap year; educational organisations based outside the Derbyshire region – although the trustees may choose to do so; museums, historical or heritage organisations; medical research or palliative care; animal welfare organisations whose primary purpose is not conservation of the environment; bodies affiliated to or a local 'branch' of a national organisation, even when registered as a separate charity – if you are unsure whether you would fall within this category, submit a query via the foundation's website.
TYPE OF GRANT Starter finances, recurrent, research, project, one-off, core costs, feasibility studies and running costs. Funding is available for one year or less.
RANGE OF GRANTS Most grants are for less than £2,000–the trust does not normally make more than one grant to the same charity in a 12 month period.
SAMPLE GRANTS Beneficiaries of grants which receive ongoing support included: Queen Elizabeth's Grammar School (£18,000 in four grants); Community Links (£12,000); Action for Stammering Children, Friendship Works, Prisoners' Families and Friends Service and Young Peoples Trust for the Environment (£5,000 each); Beauchamp Lodge Settlement (£4,000); DEMAND (£3,000); and Theatre Peckham (£1,500).
FINANCES *Year* 2011–12 *Income* £226,250 *Grants* £240,220 *Assets* £6,123,883
TRUSTEES James Hope, Chair; Philip Miles; Colin Russell; Rita Drew; Peter Foster; Richard Page.
HOW TO APPLY Applications are made via an online form on the foundation's website – no supporting documentation is required. 'Meetings of the trustees are held quarterly, in the second or third week of January, April, July and October. The deadline for the receipt of applications is approximately three weeks prior to each meeting. Applications are not considered between meetings but any received after the deadline are automatically carried forward.'
WHO TO APPLY TO Alan King, Secretary, 44 Leasway, Wickford, Essex SS12 0HE *Tel.* 01268 562941 *email* secretary@woodroffebenton.org.uk *Website* www.woodroffebenton.org.uk

■ The Woodward Charitable Trust

CC NO 299963   **ESTABLISHED** 1988
WHERE FUNDING CAN BE GIVEN Unrestricted.
WHO CAN BENEFIT Registered charities.
WHAT IS FUNDED Arts, community and social welfare (including children's summer holiday schemes), disability, health, education, environment. Priority to smaller-scale, locally based initiatives.
WHAT IS NOT FUNDED Trustees will not fund: charities whose annual turnover exceeds £300,000; construction projects such as playgrounds, village halls, and disabled accesses; general school appeals including out of hours provision; hospices; medical research; parish facilities; playgroups and pre-school groups; requests for vehicles; individuals in any capacity or educational fees.
TYPE OF GRANT Usually one-off.
RANGE OF GRANTS Up to £30,000. Average grant £1,000 –£5,000.
SAMPLE GRANTS Trialogue Educational Trust (£30,000); Noah's Ark Children's Venture and Jamie's Farm (£10,000 each); Story Museum (£7,500); Deafness Research UK (£5,000); Proteus Theatre Company (£3,000); West Euston Time Bank (£2,200); Lambeth Summer Projects Trust and British Trust for Conservation Volunteers (£2,000 each); Lift People and Aylesbury Youth Action (£1,500); Action for Sustainable Living (£1,000) and African Caribbean Forum (£500).
FINANCES *Year* 2011–12 *Income* £205,585 *Grants* £242,771 *Assets* £10,052,324
TRUSTEES Camilla Woodward; Rt Hon. Shaun A. Woodward; Judith Portrait.
OTHER INFORMATION The trust is one of the Sainsbury Family Charitable Trusts which share a common administration. An application to one is taken as an application to all.
HOW TO APPLY On simple application forms available from the trust, or via its website. Potential applicants whose project falls within the criteria are invited to telephone the administrator in advance to discuss the advisability of making an application. Do not skip sections on the application form and refer instead to supplementary material. Only send your accounts if they are not already available on the Charity Commission website. Further advice on how to best complete the form is available on the website.
Main grants are allocated following trustees' meetings in January and July each year, with the exception of summer schemes, which are considered at the beginning of May each year. All application forms are assessed on arrival and if additional information is required you will be contacted. The website has a useful diary of trustees' meetings and of the cut-off dates for applications. The trust advises that only around 15% of applicants are successful and the majority of grants are for less than £5,000.
WHO TO APPLY TO Karin Hooper, Administrator, The Peak, 5 Wilton Road, London SW1V 1AP *Tel.* 020 7410 0330 *Fax* 020 7410 0332 *email* contact@woodwardcharitabletrust.org.uk *Website* www.woodwardcharitabletrust.org.uk

■ The A. and R. Woolf Charitable Trust

CC NO 273079   **ESTABLISHED** 1977
WHERE FUNDING CAN BE GIVEN Worldwide; UK, mainly in Hertfordshire.
WHO CAN BENEFIT Registered charities and voluntary organisations only.

WHAT IS FUNDED The trust supports a range of causes, including Jewish organisations, animal welfare and conservation causes, children and health and welfare charities.
WHAT IS NOT FUNDED No grants to individuals or non-registered charities unless schools, hospices and so on.
RANGE OF GRANTS Mostly £100–£5,000.
SAMPLE GRANTS Previous beneficiaries include: Central British Fund for World Jewish Relief, the Peace Hospice, United Nations International Children's Emergency Fund, University of Hertfordshire Charitable Trust, Northwood Pinner Liberal Synagogue, RSPCA, WWF UK, the Multiple Sclerosis Society, Jewish Child's Day, Wellbeing for Women, National Schizophrenia Fellowship, International Primate Protection League UK, the Hertfordshire and Middlesex Wildlife Trust and Senahasa Trust.
FINANCES *Year* 2011–12 *Income* £44,227 *Grants* £32,736 *Assets* £2,683,312
TRUSTEES Andrew Rose; Dr Gillian Edmonds; Stephen Rose; Joyce Rose.
HOW TO APPLY Support is only given to projects/organisations/causes personally known to the trustees. The trust does not respond to unsolicited applications.
WHO TO APPLY TO The Trustees, c/o Griffiths Preston Accountants, Aldbury House, Dower Mews, 108 High Street, Berkhamsted, Hertfordshire HP4 2BL *Tel.* 01442 870277

■ ME Woolfe Charitable Trust

CC NO 1135193   **ESTABLISHED** 2010
WHERE FUNDING CAN BE GIVEN UK, with some preference for Merseyside.
WHO CAN BENEFIT Charitable organisations.
WHAT IS FUNDED This trust was registered with the Charity Commission in March 2010. Provdes funding for projects working with young people through education and those supporting animal welfare.
FINANCES *Year* 2010–11 *Income* £7,235 *Grants* £2,882
TRUSTEES Carol Mason; Nicholas Pye.
HOW TO APPLY In writing to the correspondent.
WHO TO APPLY TO Carol Mason, Trustee, Morecrofts LLP, 1–5 Tithebarn Street, Liverpool L2 2NZ *Tel.* 01512 368871 *email* cm@morecrofts.co.uk

■ Worcester Municipal Charities

CC NO 205299   **ESTABLISHED** 1836
WHERE FUNDING CAN BE GIVEN The city of Worcester.
WHO CAN BENEFIT Poorer people, individually or generally, in Worcester City.
WHAT IS FUNDED Grants to relieve need. Purchase of household equipment, clothes, food and so on, help with bills. Donations to organisations that help poorer people. Grants to poorer students.
WHAT IS NOT FUNDED No grants to organisations of over 49% of their annual income. No grants to individuals unless all statutory sources have been exhausted. Requests for furniture (except bunk beds) are referred to the 'Armchair Project'. Requests for clothes are referred to the 'Lydia Project'.
TYPE OF GRANT Cheque or purchase of item.
RANGE OF GRANTS £1,000–£35,000 for running costs; £100–£100,000 for capital costs; £50–£1,000 for individuals.
SAMPLE GRANTS Worcester CAB and W H A B A C (£124,000); Worcester Municipal Exhibitions Foundation (£54,000); Maggs Day Centre

(£16,000); Shopmobility (£11,000) and Headway Worcester Trust (£9,500).
FINANCES *Year* 2012 *Income* £904,973 *Grants* £369,879 *Assets* £14,149,571
TRUSTEES Paul Griffith; P. Denham; Margaret Jones; Bob Kington; Stanley Markwell; G. Hughes; Sue Osborne; Martyn Saunders; Brenda Sheridan; Dr David Tibbutt; Robert Peachey; R. Berry; C. Lord; C. Panter; A. Whitcher; J. Whitehouse; Miss M. Kirk; Ron Rust; Jess Bird.
OTHER INFORMATION The grants total includes £127,000 that was given to 605 individuals.
HOW TO APPLY In writing to the correspondent requesting an application form.
WHO TO APPLY TO Ian Pugh, Clerk to the Trustees, Kateryn Heywood House, Berkeley Court, The Foregate, Worcester WR1 3QG *Tel.* 01905 317117 *email* admin@wmcharities.org.uk

■ The Worcestershire and Dudley Historic Churches Trust
CC NO 1035156 **ESTABLISHED** 1993
WHERE FUNDING CAN BE GIVEN The diocese and county of Worcester.
WHO CAN BENEFIT Christian churches.
WHAT IS FUNDED The trust gives grants for the preservation, repair and improvement of churches in the beneficial area and of the monuments, fittings and furniture etc., of such churches.
WHAT IS NOT FUNDED No grants for new building projects, organs or bells.
RANGE OF GRANTS £500–£5,000.
SAMPLE GRANTS St Mary RC, Harvington (£2,500); St Leonard, Newland (£5,000); St Kenelem, Clifton-upon-Teme (£5,800); St John the Baptist, Wickhamford (£3,000); St Peter, Astley (£3,500); Bewdley Methodist (£2,300); Holy Trinity, Malvern (£5,000); St Cassian, Chaddesley Corbett (£3,000); St John URC, Stourbridge (£1,200); St Michael, Dines Green (£2,000).
FINANCES *Year* 2012 *Income* £13,805 *Grants* £41,000
TRUSTEES Tim Bridges – Chair; John Davies; Jean Crabbe; John Bailey; John Colley; Sam White; Andrew Grant; Annette Leech; Richard Slawson; Michael Thomas.
HOW TO APPLY Requests for grants should be discussed with the secretary who will advise as to whether the project meets the criteria. An application form will then be sent. Decisions on grants are made at the trust's quarterly meetings and following a visit by a trustee.
WHO TO APPLY TO John Davies, Secretary, Yarrington's, Alfrick, Worcestershire WR6 5EX *Tel.* 01886 884336 *email* flora.donald@virgin. net *Website* www.worcestershirechurches. blogspot.com

■ The Wragge and Co. Charitable Trust
CC NO 803009 **ESTABLISHED** 1990
WHERE FUNDING CAN BE GIVEN Mainly West Midlands.
WHO CAN BENEFIT Local and national charities operating in the area.
WHAT IS FUNDED General charitable purposes, with an interest in health.
WHAT IS NOT FUNDED No grants to individuals or to organisations which are not charities.
RANGE OF GRANTS Usually £50–£1,000
SAMPLE GRANTS Macmillan Cancer Support (£5,000); Sense (£2,000); Court Based

Personal Support (£1,000); Feed the Children UK, Medical Foundation for the Care of Victims of Torture and New College Worcester (£500 each); Marie Curie Cancer Care (£300); Shelter and The Black Country Living Museum Trust (£200 each) and The Gurkha Welfare Trust (£50).
FINANCES *Year* 2011–12 *Income* £25,015 *Grants* £23,810 *Assets* £22,653
TRUSTEES Quentin Poole; Philip Clissitt; Lee Nuttall.
HOW TO APPLY In writing to the correspondent with a copy of the most recent accounts.
WHO TO APPLY TO Lee Nuttall, Trustee, Wragge and Co., 55 Colmore Row, Birmingham B3 2AS *Tel.* 01212 331000

■ The Diana Edgson Wright Charitable Trust
CC NO 327737 **ESTABLISHED** 1987
WHERE FUNDING CAN BE GIVEN UK with some preference for Kent.
WHO CAN BENEFIT Registered charities.
WHAT IS FUNDED General charitable purposes and animal conservation and social welfare causes.
SAMPLE GRANTS Shooting Star Children's Hospice and British Heart Foundation (£3,000 each); Friends of Canterbury Museum (£2,500); Gurkha Welfare Trust, The Donkey Sanctuary and Royal National Lifeboat Institution (£2,000 each); Campaign to Protect Rural England, Kent (£1,200); Friends of St Margaret's Church Bethersden and International Fund for Animal Welfare (£1,000 each) and The MFPA Trust for the Training of Handicapped Children in the Arts and War Memorial Trust (£500 each).
FINANCES *Year* 2012 *Income* £63,197 *Grants* £67,500 *Assets* £1,313,862
TRUSTEES Robert Moorhead; G. Edgson Wright; Henry Moorhead.
OTHER INFORMATION In 2012 grants were awarded to 52 organisations.
HOW TO APPLY In writing to the correspondent.
WHO TO APPLY TO Henry Moorhead, Trustee, c/o Henry Moorhead and Company Solicitors, 2 Stade Street, Hythe, Kent CT21 6BD *email* henmo4@talktalk.net

■ The Wright Vigar Charitable Trust
CC NO 1149552 **ESTABLISHED** 2012
WHERE FUNDING CAN BE GIVEN UK and overseas.
WHO CAN BENEFIT Registered charities.
WHAT IS FUNDED General charitable purposes.
TRUSTEES Christopher Shelbourne; Bridget Starling; James Sewell; Jon O'Hern; Kevin Shaw; Neil Roberts; Peter Harrison.
OTHER INFORMATION This is the charitable trust of chartered accountants Wright Vigars, with all of the trustees being directors of the firm.
HOW TO APPLY No grants to unsolicited applications.
WHO TO APPLY TO Bridget Starling, Trustee, Wright Vigar Ltd, 15 Newland, Lincoln LN1 1XG *Tel.* 01522 531341 *email* wvct@wrightvigar.co. uk

■ The Matthews Wrightson Charity Trust
CC NO 262109 **ESTABLISHED** 1970
WHERE FUNDING CAN BE GIVEN UK and some overseas.
WHO CAN BENEFIT Smaller charities and individuals.

WHAT IS FUNDED General charitable purposes, with preference towards young people; disability; Christian causes; rehabilitation; the arts; social welfare; health; the elderly.

WHAT IS NOT FUNDED Gap year projects; maintenance and repair of the fabric of church buildings; animal charities.

TYPE OF GRANT One-off cash grants, on annual basis.

RANGE OF GRANTS The standard 'unit' donation for 2012 was £500, with a few larger grants made to regular beneficiaries.

SAMPLE GRANTS Previously: Tools for Self-Reliance (£2,400); and the Butler Trust, Childhood First, the Daneford Trust, DEMAND, Live Music Now! New Bridge and Practical Action (£1,200 each). Most other donations, with a few exceptions, were for £400 or £500 each.

FINANCES *Year* 2012 *Income* £62,589 *Grants* £49,650 *Assets* £1,449,129

TRUSTEES Isabelle White; Guy Garmondsay Wrightson; Priscilla Wilmot Wrightson; Maria de Broe Ferguson; Robert Partridge.

OTHER INFORMATION There were 96 grants made totalling £50,000, including grants to individuals. Grants were made to two individuals totalling £1,000.

HOW TO APPLY In writing to the correspondent including a set of accounts. Applications received are considered by the trustees on a monthly basis. Applicants who wish to be advised of the outcome of their application must include an sae. Successful applicants are advised of the trustees' decision at the earliest opportunity.

WHO TO APPLY TO Jon Mills, Administrator, The Old School House, Church Lane, Easton, Winchester SO21 1EH *Tel.* 0845 241 2574 *email* matthewswrightson@gmail.com

■ Miss E. B. Wrightson's Charitable Settlement

CC NO 1002147   **ESTABLISHED** 1990

WHERE FUNDING CAN BE GIVEN Throughout the UK.

WHO CAN BENEFIT Organisations and individual young people with musical talent.

WHAT IS FUNDED General charitable purposes, inshore rescue services, multiple sclerosis and musical education. Circumstances related to financial hardship and social deprivation receive preferential consideration.

WHAT IS NOT FUNDED Applicants over 21 and post/undergraduates are not normally supported.

TYPE OF GRANT Mainly one-off or renewable grants (up to three grants per individual) to individuals, however organisations may be supported as well.

RANGE OF GRANTS £140–£4,000.

SAMPLE GRANTS Beneficiaries included: Frenford (£4,000); Cancer Research (£500) and Chernobyl Children's BBQ (£400). Individual grants ranged from £140 to £800.

FINANCES *Year* 2011–12 *Income* £30,475 *Grants* £19,825 *Assets* £1,096,571

TRUSTEES Tony Callard; Elizabeth Clarke; Patrick Dorking.

HOW TO APPLY Application forms can be obtained from the funder's website. Individual applicants are requested to provide the following: two copies of a completed application form; evidence of worthiness and financial hardship with supporting documentation; references; a brief musical CV for those over 12; two letters of support from applicant's teachers as to the suitability of the application for a grant from the

trust; reasons for applying; details of applications to other grant giving bodies.

WHO TO APPLY TO N. Hickman, Administrator, Swangles Farm, Cold Christmas Lane, Thundridge, Ware SG12 7SP *email* info@wrightsontrust.co.uk *Website* www.wrightsontrust.co.uk

■ The Joan Wyatt Charitable Trust

CC NO 1136314   **ESTABLISHED** 2010

WHERE FUNDING CAN BE GIVEN Worldwide.

WHO CAN BENEFIT Registered charities.

WHAT IS FUNDED General charitable purposes.

FINANCES *Year* 2012–13 *Income* £20,800 *Grants* £19,000

TRUSTEE NatWest Trust Services.

HOW TO APPLY In writing to the correspondent.

WHO TO APPLY TO NatWest Trust Services, 5th Floor, Trinity Quay 2, Avon Street, Bristol BS2 0PT *Tel.* 05516577371

■ Wychdale Ltd

CC NO 267447   **ESTABLISHED** 1974

WHERE FUNDING CAN BE GIVEN UK and abroad.

WHO CAN BENEFIT Jewish people.

WHAT IS FUNDED Jewish educational institutions.

WHAT IS NOT FUNDED Non-Jewish organisations are not supported.

SAMPLE GRANTS M and R Gross Charitable Trust (£50,000); Friends of the Yeshivat Shaar Hashamayim (£43,000); Friends of Beis Abraham (£21,000); and Chevras Machzikei Mesifta and Emuno Education (£20,000 each)

FINANCES *Year* 2011–12 *Income* £276,798 *Grants* £253,251 *Assets* £1,419,547

TRUSTEES C. D. Schlaff; J. Schlaff; Z. Schlaff.

HOW TO APPLY In writing to the correspondent.

WHO TO APPLY TO Sugarwhite Associates, 5 Windus Road, London N16 6UT

■ Wychville Ltd

CC NO 267584   **ESTABLISHED** 1973

WHERE FUNDING CAN BE GIVEN UK.

WHO CAN BENEFIT Organisations benefiting Jewish people.

WHAT IS FUNDED Jewish organisations, education and general charitable purposes.

SAMPLE GRANTS No information available regarding beneficiaries despite the high level of giving.

FINANCES *Year* 2011–12 *Income* £734,895 *Grants* £1,093,980 *Assets* -£139,000

TRUSTEES S. Englander; E. Englander; B. R. Englander.

HOW TO APPLY In writing to the correspondent.

WHO TO APPLY TO S. Englander, Trustee, 44 Leweston Place, London N16 6RH

■ The Wyndham Charitable Trust

CC NO 259313   **ESTABLISHED** 1969

WHERE FUNDING CAN BE GIVEN UK and developing countries.

WHO CAN BENEFIT Charitable organisations.

WHAT IS FUNDED General charitable purposes. The trust's main interest lies with helping to bring about the abolition of modern-day slavery through supporting charities connected with this cause.

WHAT IS NOT FUNDED No grants to organisations not known to the trustees, or to any individuals.

RANGE OF GRANTS Up to £10,000.

SAMPLE GRANTS Anti-Slavery International (£10,000); Surgical Research Fund (£3,200); St Thomas's Church Lymington (£1,300); Dalit Solidarity Network of the UK (£1,000); and Centrepoint (£350).

FINANCES *Year* 2012–13 *Income* £55,906 *Grants* £48,990 *Assets* £133,983

TRUSTEES John Gaselee; Juliet Gaselee; David Gaselee; Sarah Gaselee.

HOW TO APPLY The trust stated that unsolicited applications are unlikely to be supported and they do not encourage requests.

WHO TO APPLY TO John Gaselee, Trustee, 34a Westfield Road, Lymington, Hampshire SO41 3QA *email* wyndham_ct@yahoo.co.uk *Website* www.wyndham-ct.org

■ The Wyseliot Charitable Trust

CC NO 257219 **ESTABLISHED** 1968

WHERE FUNDING CAN BE GIVEN UK.

WHO CAN BENEFIT Registered charities only.

WHAT IS FUNDED Medical, welfare, arts organisations, including music, visual arts and literature.

WHAT IS NOT FUNDED Local charities are not supported. No support for individuals; grants are only made to registered charities of national significance.

RANGE OF GRANTS Up to £5,000.

SAMPLE GRANTS Avenues Youth Project and Time and Talents Association (£5,000 each); Royal Marsden Cancer Fund, Trinity Hospice and Macmillan (£4,000 each); Musicians Benevolent Fund (£3,000) and Brains Trust, Vitiligo Society and International Glaucoma Association (£2,000 each).

FINANCES *Year* 2011–12 *Income* £87,180 *Grants* £102,000 *Assets* £1,544,828

TRUSTEES Jonathan Rose; Emma Rose; Adam Raphael.

HOW TO APPLY In writing to the correspondent; however, note that the trust states that the same charities are supported each year, with perhaps one or two changes. It is unlikely new charities sending circular appeals will be supported and large UK charities are generally not supported. Currently approximately one application is successful each year.

WHO TO APPLY TO Jonathan Rose, Trustee, 17 Chelsea Square, London SW3 6LF

■ The Xerox (UK) Trust

CC NO 284698 **ESTABLISHED** 1982

WHERE FUNDING CAN BE GIVEN UK.

WHO CAN BENEFIT Usually local or mid-sized organisations benefiting children, young adults, at risk groups, and people who are disabled, disadvantaged by poverty or socially isolated.

WHAT IS FUNDED The advancement of equality of opportunity, working with people who are disabled, disadvantaged or terminally ill; and young people.

WHAT IS NOT FUNDED No grants to individuals, religious or political organisations or national bodies.

TYPE OF GRANT One-off grants.

SAMPLE GRANTS Gobo Theatre Foundation (£2,500); Hertfordshire Multiple Sclerosis Therapy Centre (£2,000); Clapton Common Boys Club (£1,600); Holidays For Disabled People and Special Needs Adventure Playground (£1,000 each); The Respite Association (£600) and Birmingham Youth Foundation, Debtford Action Group for the Elderly, Mid Sussex Community Support Association and Cerebral Palsy Plus (£500 each).

FINANCES *Year* 2012 *Income* £56,795 *Grants* £21,122 *Assets* £821,509

TRUSTEES Francis Mooney; John Edwards; John Hopwood.

HOW TO APPLY In writing to the correspondent, preferably supported by a Xerox employee. Applications are considered in April and October, for payment in June and December respectively.

WHO TO APPLY TO Cheryl Walsh, Trust Secretary, Xerox Ltd, Bridge House, Oxford Road, Uxbridge UB8 1HS *Tel.* 01895 251133

Yankov Charitable Trust

CC NO 1106703   **ESTABLISHED** 2004
WHERE FUNDING CAN BE GIVEN Worldwide.
WHO CAN BENEFIT Jewish organisations.
WHAT IS FUNDED Jewish causes and community.
SAMPLE GRANTS Previous grant beneficiaries include: European Yarchei Kalloh (£53,000); Keren Machzikei Torah (£23,000); Kollel Tiferes Chaim (£21,000); Agudas Israel Housing Association (£12,000); Ponovez Hachnosos Kalloh (£7,600); Freiman Appeal (£7,200); Beth Jacob Grammar School (£4,000); British Friends of Tiferes Chaim (£3,000); Yeshiva Tzemach Yisroel (£2,000); British Friends of Rinat Ahsron (£1,500); and Yeshivat Givat Shaul (£1,000).
FINANCES *Year* 2011–12 *Income* £129,532 *Grants* £81,061 *Assets* £236,993
TRUSTEES Jacob Schonberg; Bertha Schonberg; Aryeh Schonberg.
OTHER INFORMATION A list of beneficiaries was unavailable.
HOW TO APPLY In writing to the correspondent.
WHO TO APPLY TO Jacob Schonberg, Trustee, 40 Wellington Avenue, London N15 6AS Tel. 020 3150 1227

The Yapp Charitable Trust

CC NO 1076803   **ESTABLISHED** 1999
WHERE FUNDING CAN BE GIVEN England and Wales.
WHO CAN BENEFIT It is the trustees' policy to focus their support on smaller charities (local rather than UK), and to offer grants only in situations where a small grant will make a significant difference. The trust therefore only considers applications from charities whose normal turnover is less than £40,000 in the year of application. Grants are only made to applicants who have charitable status. 'We concentrate on sustaining existing work rather than funding new work because many funders prefer new projects.'
WHAT IS FUNDED Older people; children and young people aged 5–25; people with disabilities or mental health problems; moral welfare, e.g. people trying to overcome life-limiting problems such as addiction, relationship difficulties, abuse or a history of offending; education and learning (including lifelong learning); and scientific or medical research. The trust gives priority to work that is unattractive to the general public or unpopular with other funders, particularly when it helps improve the lives of marginalised, disadvantaged or isolated people. Within these areas the trust gives preference to charities that can demonstrate the effective use of volunteers. Grantmaking policies are kept under review – current priorities and exclusions are publicised on the trust's website.
WHAT IS NOT FUNDED The trust's website states that the trustees cannot fund: charities with a total annual expenditure of more than £40,000; charities that are not registered with the Charity Commission in England and Wales. You must have your own charity number or be excepted from registration. Industrial Provident Societies and Community Interest Companies are not eligible to apply; work that is based in Scotland and Northern Ireland – we can only fund charities that are operating in England or Wales; charities with unrestricted reserves that equate to more than 12 months expenditure; branches of national charities. You must have your own charity number, not a shared national registration; new organisations – you must have been operating as a fully constituted organisation for at least three years, even though you may have registered as a charity more recently; new work that has not been occurring for at least a year; new paid posts – even if the work is now being done by volunteers; additional activities, expansion or development plans; special events, trips or outings; capital expenditure – including equipment, buildings, renovations, furnishings, minibuses; work with under-5s; childcare; holidays and holiday centres; core funding of charities that benefit the wider community such as general advice services and community centres unless a significant element of their work focuses on one of the trust's priority groups; bereavement support; debt advice; community safety initiatives; charities raising money to give to another organisation, such as schools, hospitals or other voluntary groups; individuals – including charities raising funds to purchase equipment for or make grants to individuals.
TYPE OF GRANT Running costs and salaries
RANGE OF GRANTS Grants are normally for a maximum of £3,000 per year. Most grants are for more than one year because priority is given to ongoing needs.
SAMPLE GRANTS BCU Life Skills Centre (£7,500); Community Based Training Limited, St George's Pop In and Sandwell Asian Development Association (£6,000 each); African Women's Health Group, Soundwaves Music Project and WHEAT Mentor Support Trust (£4,500 each); Llandrindod Wells YMCA (£3,000); and Eastern Enfield Good Neighbours, The Muslim Women's Organisation and Yeovil Shopmobility (£1,000 each).
FINANCES *Year* 2011–12 *Income* £197,157 *Grants* £178,000 *Assets* £5,408,851
TRUSTEES Revd Timothy C. Brooke; Ron Lis; Alfred Hill; Jane Fergusson; Andrew Burgen; Lisa Suchet.
OTHER INFORMATION The Yapp Welfare Trust (two-thirds share) and The Yapp Education and Research Trust (one-third share) merged in September 1999 to become The Yapp Charitable Trust. In 2011–12 the largest number of grants was awarded in the London region (14 totalling £50,000) and most grants were to support work undertaken for people with disabilities.
HOW TO APPLY 'We have a simple application form which we ask you to send in by post, together with a copy of your most recent annual report and accounts and any other information you wish to send. Applications are processed continuously. When we receive your application we will be in touch, usually within two weeks: to ask for more information; or to tell you the application will be going forward to the next stage of assessment and give an idea of when you can expect a decision; or to let you know we can't help. The time it takes to process an application and make a grant is usually between two months and six months. We always write to let you know the decision. We will accept an application only once each year and you can have only one grant at a time from us. Current grant-holders may make a new application when their grant is coming to an end. If we refused

your last application you must wait a year before applying again.' The application form and guidelines can be downloaded in Word or pdf format from the trust's website. Alternatively they can be obtained from the trust's administrator.

WHO TO APPLY TO Joanne Anderson, Administrator, 8 Leyburn Close, Ouston, Chester le Street DH2 1TD *Tel.* 01914 922118 *email* info@yappcharitabletrust.org.uk *Website* www.yappcharitabletrust.org.uk

■ The Yardley Great Trust

CC NO 216082   **ESTABLISHED** 1355

WHERE FUNDING CAN BE GIVEN The ancient parish of Yardley now part of the County of West Midlands. This includes the wards of Yardley, Acocks Green, Fox Hollies, Billesley, Hall Green and parts of the wards of Hodge Hill, Shard End, Sheldon, Small Heath, Sparkhill, Moseley, Stechford, Sparkbrook and Brandwood. (A map is available on request.)

WHO CAN BENEFIT Individuals and organisations benefiting people of all ages in the ancient parish of Yardley in Birmingham.

WHAT IS FUNDED Individuals in need, hardship or distress. Projects which benefit the community, particularly charities working in the fields of support for voluntary and community organisations, community centres and village halls, community transport, day centres, holidays and outings, meals provision and play schemes.

TYPE OF GRANT Usually one-off. Buildings, capital, feasibility studies, project and start-up costs funded for one year or less will be considered.

RANGE OF GRANTS £250–£7,500.

SAMPLE GRANTS The Springfield Project (£5,000); The Feast (£3,000); Fox Hollies Community Association (£2,500); St Richard's Lea Hall/Worth Unlimited (£2,000); St Thomas Church, Garrets Green (£1,300); Birmingham and Solihull Women's Aid (£1,000); St Richard's Church and Centre, Lea Hall (£700) and Hallmoor School, Yardley, Sport 4 Life UK and Yardley Church Forward Club (£500 each).

FINANCES *Year* 2012 *Income* £2,206,908 *Grants* £55,582 *Assets* £8,707,800

TRUSTEES Iris Aylin; Revd Andrew Bullock; Jean Hayes; Joy Holt; Cllr Barbara Jackson; Conrad James; Revd John Ray; Revd John Richards; Keith Rollins; Revd John Self; Revd Paul Leckey; Malcolm Cox; Revd William Sands; Andrew Veitch; Robert Jones.

OTHER INFORMATION The grant total includes £27,500 that was disbursed in grants of less than £500 to individuals and £3,000 given to residents of Yardley Great Trust.

HOW TO APPLY On a form available from the correspondent. Applications from individuals should be via a third party such as Neighbourhood Offices or Citizens Advice. Applications are considered on the second Thursday of each month.

WHO TO APPLY TO K. L. Grice, Clerk to the Trustees, Old Brookside, Yardley Fields Road, Stechford, Birmingham B33 8QL *Tel.* 01217 847889 *Fax* 01217 851386 *email* enquiries@ygtrust.org.uk *Website* www.yardley-great-trust.org.uk

■ The Dennis Alan Yardy Charitable Trust

CC NO 1039719   **ESTABLISHED** 1993

WHERE FUNDING CAN BE GIVEN Overseas and UK with a preference for the East Midlands.

WHO CAN BENEFIT Major UK and international charities.

WHAT IS FUNDED General charitable purposes.

WHAT IS NOT FUNDED No grants to individuals or non-registered charities.

SAMPLE GRANTS None available.

FINANCES *Year* 2011–12 *Income* £25,444 *Grants* £15,950 *Assets* £557,257

TRUSTEES Dennis Alan Yardy; Christine Anne Yardy; Jeffrey Creek; Joanne Stoney; Simon Bown.

OTHER INFORMATION A grants list was not included in the latest accounts.

HOW TO APPLY In writing to the correspondent.

WHO TO APPLY TO The Secretary, PO Box 5039, Spratton, Northampton NN6 8YH

■ The W. Wing Yip and Brothers Foundation

CC NO 326999   **ESTABLISHED** 1986

WHERE FUNDING CAN BE GIVEN Birmingham, Manchester, Croydon and Cricklewood.

WHO CAN BENEFIT Chinese organisations benefiting children, young adults, students and people disadvantaged by poverty.

WHAT IS FUNDED Chinese organisations especially those concerned with education, relief of poverty, Chinese students, and education of Chinese children living in the above stated areas.

TYPE OF GRANT One-off, project and start-up costs. Funding for up to two years will be considered.

RANGE OF GRANTS Up to £100,000.

SAMPLE GRANTS Churchill College Cambridge (£24,600); Overseas ChineseAssociation School, Host UK and Chinese Education Cultural Community Centre (£3,000 each); Croydon Chinese School (£2,500); Birmingham Chinese School and United Kingdom Chinese Education Foundation (£2,500 each); Royal British Legion (£450); Chung Wah Chinese School and Brainwave Centre (£300 each); London Air Ambulance (£100) and The Smile Train (£50).

FINANCES *Year* 2011–12 *Income* £215,587 *Grants* £168,187 *Assets* £1,420,183

TRUSTEES Robert Brittain; Jenny Loynton; Git Ying Yap; Hon Yuen Yap; Brian Win Yip; Woon Wing Yip; Albert Yip.

OTHER INFORMATION The grant total includes £120,000 that was given in bursaries to 81 students.

HOW TO APPLY In writing to the correspondent.

WHO TO APPLY TO Robert Brittain, Trustee, c/o W. Wing Yip plc, The Wing Yip Centre, 375 Nechells Park Road, Birmingham B7 5NT *Tel.* 01213 276618 *Fax* 01213 276612

■ Yorkshire Agricultural Society

CC NO 513238   **ESTABLISHED** 1837

WHERE FUNDING CAN BE GIVEN Yorkshire and Humbershire; occasionally extending into Durham, Northumberland and the former county of Cleveland.

WHO CAN BENEFIT Primarily local activities and organisations, particularly those in farming and related industries, and those living in rural areas. Priority is given to charities in Yorkshire

Think carefully about every application. Is it justified?

1013

and former Cleveland, with some activities extending into Durham and Northumberland.

WHAT IS FUNDED (a) Promotion of agriculture and allied industries, related research and education. (b) Protection and safeguarding of the environment. (c) Holding of an annual agricultural show. (d) Appropriate charitable purposes. Environmental projects normally require relevance to agriculture to attract support. The trust will consider giving support to religious umbrella bodies, schools and colleges, and rural crime prevention schemes, all within the context of farming and the rural economy.

WHAT IS NOT FUNDED No support to students. Overseas projects are seldom supported.

TYPE OF GRANT Most usually once only or starter/pump priming finance. Buildings, capital, core costs, feasibility studies, projects, research, running costs, recurring costs and salaries will be considered. Funding may be given for up to three years.

RANGE OF GRANTS £200–£10,000, typical grant under £1,000.

SAMPLE GRANTS Yorkshire Rural Support Network (£18,000); Nuffield Farming Scholarship Trust (£10,000); Food and Farming Forum (£7,000); University of Newcastle (£6,000); University of Northumbria (£4,000); Leeds University (£2,500) and Borreliosis and Associated Diseases awareness (£1,000).

FINANCES *Year* 2012 *Income* £6,029,328 *Grants* £59,705 *Assets* £23,062,341

TRUSTEES Charles Forbes Adam; Raymond Twiddle; William Cowling; Simon Theakston; George Lane-Fox; Charles Mills; John Crabtree; Robert Copley.

PUBLICATIONS Quarterly newsletter.

OTHER INFORMATION In 2012 grants were made to 23 organisations.

HOW TO APPLY In writing to the correspondent, to be considered quarterly. Applications should include accounts, proposed budget, details of confirmed and anticipated funding and ongoing management and costs.

WHO TO APPLY TO Nigel Pulling, Chief Executive, Yorkshire Agricultural Society, Regional Agricultural Centre, Great Yorkshire Showground, Railway Road, HARROGATE HG2 8NZ *Tel.* 01423 541000 *email* info@yas.co.uk *Website* www.yas.co.uk

....

■ Yorkshire Building Society Charitable Foundation

CC NO 1069082   **ESTABLISHED** 1998

WHERE FUNDING CAN BE GIVEN UK, with a preference for grantmaking in branch localities.

WHO CAN BENEFIT Charitable organisations/good causes meeting foundation criteria.

WHAT IS FUNDED General charitable purposes/specific items to maximum donation of £2,000.

WHAT IS NOT FUNDED 'We do not support any activity which is not carried out by a registered charity or which does not otherwise count as being a good cause. Additionally, there may be projects or activities that could be considered as registered charities or good causes but which do not fall within our priorities or meet other criteria. Examples of these are: Applications for general ongoing funding, running costs, research, sponsorship, payment of salaries or expenses; Requests for any administration equipment such as telephones, security systems or computers, for a charity's own use; Causes serving only a specific sector of the community selected on the basis of ethnic,

racial, political or religious grounds/advancement; Overseas travel, expeditions or educational expenses, including causes that would otherwise qualify for support but require funds for activities outside the UK; Support of activities in, or equipment for mainstream schools, sports clubs, scouts/guides groups, local/government funded bodies (unless for special needs groups).'

TYPE OF GRANT Money for specific items.

RANGE OF GRANTS Usually around £2,000 but can be up to £201,000.

SAMPLE GRANTS RNLI (201,000); Age UK (£35,000); Wellsprirgs (Inn Churches) (£18,500); Macmillan Cancer Support (£5,000); Guide Dogs for the Blind Association (£4,000); Yorkshire Air Ambulance (£3,000); RSPCA (£2,300) and Gloucestershire Wildlife Trust, The Afghanistan Trust, Troop Aid and Willows Animal Sanctuary (£2,000 each).

FINANCES *Year* 2012 *Income* £552,492 *Grants* £669,571 *Assets* £147,706

TRUSTEES Christopher Faulkner; Sarah Wildon; Christopher Parrish; Andy Caton; Linda Oakes.

OTHER INFORMATION During the year the foundation made 2,042 grants.

HOW TO APPLY Application forms can be downloaded, together with guidelines and criteria, from the society's website. Alternatively, you can apply in your local branch of Yorkshire Building Society.

WHO TO APPLY TO Ann Fitzpatrick, Yorkshire Building Society, Yorkshire House, Yorkshire Drive, Bradford, West Yorkshire BD5 8LJ *Tel.* 01274 472512 *email* charitable@ybs.co.uk *Website* www.ybs.co.uk/your-society/charity/charitable-foundation/apply

....

■ The South Yorkshire Community Foundation

CC NO 1140947   **ESTABLISHED** 1986

WHERE FUNDING CAN BE GIVEN South Yorkshire wide, with specific reference to Barnsley, Doncaster, Rotherham, Sheffield.

WHO CAN BENEFIT Community and voluntary organisations benefiting people disadvantaged by poverty children and young people.

WHAT IS FUNDED General charitable purposes, particularly social welfare.

WHAT IS NOT FUNDED Groups that have substantial unrestricted funds, national charities, activities promoting political or religious beliefs or where people are excluded on political or religious grounds, statutory bodies e.g. schools, local councils, colleges, projects outside of South Yorkshire, endowments, small contributions to large projects, projects for personal profit, minibuses or other vehicle purchases, projects that have already happened, animals, sponsorship and fundraising events.

TYPE OF GRANT The main grants programme is for amounts under £1,000. Capital and revenue costs. South Yorkshire Key Fund grants are for similar purposes for larger amounts.

RANGE OF GRANTS Generally up to £10,000.

SAMPLE GRANTS A wide range of organisations across all of the foundation's areas of operation were supported under various programmes, some of which may no longer be running. Many organisations received grants from more than one fund.

FINANCES *Year* 2011–12 *Income* £8,745,197 *Grants* £712,712 *Assets* £8,156,161

TRUSTEES Jonathan Hunt, Chair; David Moody; Sir Hugh Neill; Peter W. Lee; Martin P. W. Lee; Peter Hollis; Frank Carter; Jackie Drayton; Galen

Ives; Christopher Jewitt; Michael Mallett; Sue Scholey; Maureen Shah; Allan Sherriff; Lady R. Sykes; R. J. Giles Bloomer; Timothy M. Greenacre; Allan Jackson; Jane Kemp; Jane Marshall; William Warrack.

HOW TO APPLY Applications are initiated online via the foundation's website. The foundation provides the following information there:
'To apply online, click on the link [on the foundation's website] which asks for your email address. You will be emailed a unique link to your own application form which is Stage 1 of the process. Assistance with how to fill in the application form is available when you access that link and you will be able to save the application if you cannot complete it in one go. Once you have completed Part A and submitted it to us, you will also receive a copy by email for your records. We will inform you within one month if you have been successful in moving to Stage 2 of our application process, when you will be invited to complete Part B of our standard application form and asked to submit supporting documents. Part B requests your organisation's bank details and other information to back up what you told us in Part A. Two members of your organisation must also sign Part B to accept the Terms and Conditions if a grant is made.'
'Application Part B should then be posted to South Yorkshire Community Foundation together with the following documentation: a copy of your last year's accounts; a photocopy of a bank statement no more than three months old; quotes (as appropriate); any other material you consider relevant to your application (do not send material you want returned) e.g. leaflets, flyers, press cuttings.'
'Decision making: all applications are assessed against South Yorkshire Community Foundation's criteria and the criteria of the relevant funder(s). Those meeting eligibility will be invited to complete Part B of the application form. The complete application form is then assessed and then passed to a panel of independent volunteer decision makers that meets approximately every 12 weeks, and their decision is final.'
'Monitoring: we have to ensure that funding has been appropriately spent and therefore require monitoring information. A monitoring form will be posted or emailed to you with the letter confirming that your application has been successful. It will ask you to report on the difference the grant has made to your group and beneficiaries. This must be returned six weeks after the grant has been spent or the activity has finished.'
'Your project may also be subject to a monitoring visit and any audit requirements of the programme. You must retain and return with your monitoring copies of all receipts, invoices and all expenditure relating to your grants including any capital items. South Yorkshire Community Foundation will only consider further applications if a satisfactory monitoring form is returned. Feel free to contact the Grants team on 0114 242 4294 Tuesday to Thursday during office hours to discuss your application.'

WHO TO APPLY TO Sue Wragg, Fund Manager, Unit 3 - G1 Building, 6 Leeds Road, Attercliffe, Sheffield S9 3TY *Tel.* 01142 424294 *Fax* 01142 424605 *email* grants@sycf.org.uk *Website* www.sycf.org.uk

■ The Yorkshire Dales Millennium Trust

CC NO 1061687   **ESTABLISHED** 1996
WHERE FUNDING CAN BE GIVEN The Yorkshire Dales.
WHO CAN BENEFIT Voluntary organisations, community groups, farmers and other individuals, Yorkshire Dales National Park Authority, estates, National Trust, parish councils, district councils and English Nature.
WHAT IS FUNDED The conservation and regeneration of the natural and built heritage and community life of the Yorkshire Dales, for example, planting new and restoring old woods, the restoration of dry stone walls and field barns, conservation of historical features and community projects.
FINANCES *Year* 2011–12 *Income* £1,037,625 *Grants* £800,954 *Assets* £233,350
TRUSTEES Stephen Macare; Joseph Pearlman; Carl Lis; Colin Speakman; Dorothy Fairburn; Dorothy Fairburn; Hazel Cambers; David Sanders Rees-Jones; Jane Roberts; Peter Charlesworth; David Joy; Thomas Wheelwright; Margaret Billing; Andrew Campbell; David Shaw; Wendy Hull; Karen Cowley; Christine Leigh.
HOW TO APPLY In writing to the correspondent.
WHO TO APPLY TO Isobel Hall, Projects and Grants Manager, The Old Post Office, Main Street, Clapham, Lancaster LA2 8DP *Tel.* 01524 251002 *Fax* 01524 251150 *email* info@ydmt.org *Website* www.ydmt.org

■ The Yorkshire Historic Churches Trust

CC NO 700639   **ESTABLISHED** 1988
WHERE FUNDING CAN BE GIVEN Yorkshire (the historic county of Yorkshire before local government reorganisation in 1974).
WHO CAN BENEFIT All Christian churches.
WHAT IS FUNDED The repair, restoration, preservation and maintenance of churches in the area stated above.
WHAT IS NOT FUNDED No grants for the reordering of churches or any other new work including provision of disabled facilities.
TYPE OF GRANT Capital building grants. Funding of up to three years will be considered.
RANGE OF GRANTS £250–£6,000.
SAMPLE GRANTS Trinity Methodist – Ossett (£6,000); Harehills Lane Baptist Church – Leeds (£4,000); Wakefield Cathedral (£2,500); Gledholt Methodist – Huddersfield (£1,000) and St Mary – Myton-on-Swale (£500).
FINANCES *Year* 2012 *Income* £144,765 *Grants* £102,500 *Assets* £919,874
TRUSTEES Prof. Clyde Binfield; Richard Carr-Archer; The Lord Crathorne; Malcolm Warburton; Tom Ramsden; David Quick; Rory Wardroper; John Smith; Peter Johnston; Anthony Hesselwood; Jane Hedley.
HOW TO APPLY Application forms and guidelines are available from the Trust's website.
WHO TO APPLY TO J. K. Stamp, Grants Secretary, c/o 11 Ovington Close, Templetown, Consett, Co Durham DH8 7NY *Tel.* 07594 578665 *email* yhctgrants@sky.com *Website* www.yhct.org.uk

■ You Gossip Foundation

CC NO 1149841   **ESTABLISHED** 2012
WHERE FUNDING CAN BE GIVEN UK.
WHO CAN BENEFIT Registered charities.
WHAT IS FUNDED General charitable purposes.

TRUSTEES Glenn Morgan; Alastair Waite; Michael Mannion; Nancy Hallam-Wright.
HOW TO APPLY In writing to the correspondent.
WHO TO APPLY TO Glenn Morgan, Trustee, 3 Chartwell Close, Ingleby Barwick, Stockton-On-Tees, Cleveland TS17 0XQ

■ The John Young Charitable Settlement

CC NO 283254   ESTABLISHED 1981
WHERE FUNDING CAN BE GIVEN UK and overseas.
WHO CAN BENEFIT Charitable organisations.
WHAT IS FUNDED General charitable purposes.
RANGE OF GRANTS £120–£13,000.
SAMPLE GRANTS Previously: Caius House (£13,000); the Boulase Smart, Médecins du Monde, Pancreatic Cancer Research Fund, RSBP and St Barnabas Hospice Trust (£5,000 each); Chichester Harbour Trust (£2,000); and Action Aid (£250).
FINANCES Year 2011–12 Income £8,223 Grants £35,000
TRUSTEES John Young; Patrick Burgess.
HOW TO APPLY In writing to the correspondent.
WHO TO APPLY TO Ken Hawkins, c/o H. W. Lee Associates LLP, New Derwent House, 69–73 Theobalds Road, London WC1X 8TA Tel. 020 7025 4600

■ The William Allen Young Charitable Trust

CC NO 283102   ESTABLISHED 1978
WHERE FUNDING CAN BE GIVEN UK, with a preference for South London, occasionally overseas.
WHO CAN BENEFIT Registered charities.
WHAT IS FUNDED General charitable purposes, with a preference for health and social welfare.
SAMPLE GRANTS Anti-Slavery International (£20,000); St Mary's Wrestwood Children's Trust (£10,000); Somerset Otter Group (£7,000); Trinity Hospice (£4,000); 2boats (Halow Project) (£3,000); Back to Work, Canine Partners, Community Housing and Therapy, Dementia Concern, Fight for Sight, Jumbulance and Tall Ships Youth Trust (£2,000 each); and Age Concern Wandsworth, Battersea United Charities, Breast Cancer Care, Friends of the Elderly, Listening Books in South London, Stroke Association and Wisborough Green Cricket Club (£1,000 each).
FINANCES Year 2012–13 Income £465,787 Grants £231,552 Assets £24,537,894
TRUSTEES Torquil Sligo-Young; James Young; Thomas Young.
HOW TO APPLY The trust has stressed that all funds are committed and consequently unsolicited applications will not be supported.
WHO TO APPLY TO Torquil Sligo-Young, Trustee, Young and Co.'s Brewery plc, Riverside House, 26 Osiers Road, London SW18 1NH Tel. 020 8875 7000

■ The John K. Young Endowment Fund

SC NO SC002264   ESTABLISHED 1992
WHERE FUNDING CAN BE GIVEN Edinburgh.
WHO CAN BENEFIT Registered charities.
WHAT IS FUNDED Grants are given to support medical and surgical research and research in chemistry as an aid to UK industry. Also to fund charities which are concerned with the physical wellbeing

of the youth of Edinburgh or with restoring people who are sick to health.
WHAT IS NOT FUNDED No grants to individuals or non-registered charities.
TYPE OF GRANT One-off grants are awarded. Funding is available for up to one year.
RANGE OF GRANTS £500–£2,000.
SAMPLE GRANTS Previous beneficiaries have included: Alzheimer's Scotland, Kidney Kids Scotland and Tommy's (£2,000 each); Alzheimer's Research Trust, British Institute for Brian Injured Children, Capability Scotland, Maggie's Cancer Caring Centres and Lee Smith Foundation (£1,000 each); Bethany Christian Trust and Fairbridge in Scotland (£1,500 each); and Guide Dogs for the Blind Association, PBC Foundation and Youth Scotland (£500 each).
FINANCES Year 2011–12 Income £40,492
TRUSTEES A. J. R. Ferguson; R. J. S. Morton; S. F. J. Judson; D. J. Hamilton.
OTHER INFORMATION In 2011–12 the fund had a total expenditure of £58,000.
HOW TO APPLY In writing to the correspondent. Trustees meet to consider grants in the autumn.
WHO TO APPLY TO The Trust Administrator, Quartermile Two, 2 Lister Square, Edinburgh EH3 9GL

■ Youth Music (previously known as National Foundation for Youth Music)

CC NO 1075032   ESTABLISHED 1999
WHERE FUNDING CAN BE GIVEN UK.
WHO CAN BENEFIT Music organisations, singing groups, nursery schools, nursery departments of large organisations, schools, after-school clubs, youth groups, recording studios, local authority departments and other organisations providing music-making opportunities to children and young people of any age up to 18.
WHAT IS FUNDED The Youth Music Programme is a grantmaking process, targeting a specific element of youth music. Its main aim is to support music-making opportunities for children and young people in England and, in particular, for those in challenging circumstances.
WHAT IS NOT FUNDED Funding is not available towards: organisations overseas; individuals; companies limited by shares; activities that are not related to music; activities that work with young people aged 19 to 25; wider performing arts activities beyond music; activities that aim to promote party political or religious beliefs; land, building, refurbishment, landscaping, vehicle or property costs.
TYPE OF GRANT Project duration can be from one year up to three years and longer. Core costs and salaries.
RANGE OF GRANTS £2,000– £400,000
SAMPLE GRANTS National Youth Orchestra (£351,500); Youth Music Theatre: UK (£243,000); The Garage Trust Ltd (£237,000); Merseyside Youth Association (£160,000); Southend YMCA (£104,000); St Paul's Bursey School (£20,000); The South Down Community (£15,000); London Sitar Ensemble (£12,500); Mid Pennine Arts (£8,500); AFRIL (Action For Refugees in Lewisham (£6,500); and Association of British Orchestras (£2,500).
FINANCES Year 2011–12 Income £14,920,827 Grants £8,322,783 Assets £3,574,811
TRUSTEES Richard Stilgoe; Richard Peel; David Poole; Nicholas Cleobury; Sean Gregory; Clive Grant; Constance Agyeman; Timothy Berg; Rafi Gokay

OTHER INFORMATION This trust is funded each year by a £10 million payment from the National Lottery, channelled through Arts Council England.

HOW TO APPLY There are two application deadlines per year, usually in March and October. There are two stages to the application process. Applicants will be notified of the outcome of their first stage application around eight weeks after the submission date. If successful, applicants will be provided with the second stage application form and guidance and have around one month to complete their stage two application. It is important that potential applicants check Youth Music's website for up-to-date criteria, priorities and guidelines prior to applications being completed.

WHO TO APPLY TO Angela Linton, Suites 3–5, Swan Court, 9 Tanner Street, London SE1 3LE *Tel.* 020 7902 1060 *email* info@youthmusic.org.uk *Website* www.youthmusic.org.uk

■ Youth United Foundation

CC NO 1147952   **ESTABLISHED** 2012
WHERE FUNDING CAN BE GIVEN UK
WHO CAN BENEFIT Uniformed youth groups. This charity exists for the benefit of all uniformed youth groups including The Scouts Association; Girlguiding UK; St John Ambulance; Army Cadets; Sea Cadets; Boy's Brigade; Girl's Brigade; Volunteer Police Cadets; Community Fire Cadets and Air Training Corps.
WHAT IS FUNDED Social welfare, with a particular interest in disadvantaged communities. Grants can be made for any need that a member organisation might have.
SAMPLE GRANTS Beneficiaries included the following Youth United organisations: Emergency Services Cadets, Fire Cadets, St John Ambulance, Reserve Forces and Cadets Association (RFCA), Voluntary Police Cadets, Marine Society and Sea Cadets, The Scout Association, The Guide Association, Girls' Brigade and Boys' Brigade.
FINANCES *Year* 2012–13 *Income* £3,820,230 *Grants* £3,243,933 *Assets* £62,757
TRUSTEES Susan Lomas; Rt Hon. David Blunkett; Adam Hale; Martin Coles; Shyama Perera; David Feldman.
OTHER INFORMATION The charity is expanding to set up local branches. So far these include Wales, London, Greater Manchester, Cheshire, Ayrshire, Derbyshire and Avon. Ultimately they aim to have a branch in each county in the UK.
HOW TO APPLY Organisations can apply to their local branch, if one exists and otherwise to the national charity, who will refer the application to the trustees of a local branch if necessary. The foundation welcomes contact by email.
WHO TO APPLY TO Rosie Thomas, Director, 202 Lambert Road, London SE1 7JW *Tel.* 020 7401 7601 *email* youth.united@yuf.org.uk *Website* www.youthunited.org.uk

■ Suha Yusuf Charitable Trust

CC NO 1137655   **ESTABLISHED** 2010
WHERE FUNDING CAN BE GIVEN Worldwide.
WHO CAN BENEFIT Registered charities.
WHAT IS FUNDED General charitable purposes.
FINANCES *Year* 2011–12 *Income* £2,500 *Grants* £0
TRUSTEES Vivienne Clyde-Eckhardt; S. Kornfeld.
HOW TO APPLY In writing to the correspondent.
WHO TO APPLY TO Vivienne Clyde-Eckhardt, Trustee, 29 Montpelier Square, London SW7 1JY *Tel.* 020 7581 1544

■ Zephyr Charitable Trust

CC NO 1003234 **ESTABLISHED** 1991
WHERE FUNDING CAN BE GIVEN UK and worldwide.
WHO CAN BENEFIT Organisations.
WHAT IS FUNDED The trust's grants are particularly targeted towards three areas: enabling lower income communities to be self-sustaining; the protection and improvement of the environment; providing relief and support for those in need, particularly from medical conditions or social or financial disadvantage.
WHAT IS NOT FUNDED No grants to individuals, expeditions or scholarships.
TYPE OF GRANT Mainly annual 'subscriptions' decided by the trustees.
RANGE OF GRANTS £500–£3,500.
SAMPLE GRANTS Friends of the Earth Trust; Medical Foundation for the Victims of Torture (£2,500 each); Organic Research Centre – Elm Farm; Hearing Research Trust (Deafness Research UK), UNICEF and Womankind (£2,000 each); Margaret Pyke Trust and MERLIN (Medical Emergency Relief International) (£1,500 each).
FINANCES *Year* 2012–13 *Income* £62,847 *Grants* £43,625 *Assets* £1,596,415
TRUSTEES Elizabeth Breeze; Marigo Harries; David Baldock; Donald I. Watson.
HOW TO APPLY In writing to the correspondent. The trustees usually meet to consider grants in July each year. Unsolicited applications are unlikely to be successful, since the trust makes annual donations to a list of beneficiaries. However, the trust stated that unsolicited applications are considered on a quarterly basis by the trustees and very occasional support is given. Telephone applications are not accepted.
WHO TO APPLY TO The Trust Administrator, Luminary Finance LLP, PO Box 135, Longfield, Kent DA3 8WF *Tel.* 01732 822114

■ The Marjorie and Arnold Ziff Charitable Foundation

CC NO 249368 **ESTABLISHED** 1964
WHERE FUNDING CAN BE GIVEN UK, with a preference for Yorkshire, especially Leeds and Harrogate.
WHO CAN BENEFIT There are no restrictions regarding which organisations can benefit.
WHAT IS FUNDED This trust likes to support causes that will provide good value for the money donated by benefiting a large number of people, as well as encouraging others to make contributions to the work. This includes a wide variety of schemes that involve the community at many levels, including education, public places, the arts and helping people who are disadvantaged.
WHAT IS NOT FUNDED No grants to individuals.
TYPE OF GRANT Capital costs and building work are particularly favoured by the trustees.
RANGE OF GRANTS £50–£60,000.
SAMPLE GRANTS United Jewish Israel Appeal (£53,000); Leeds Jewish Welfare Board (£34,000); The Haven (£30,000); Chief Rabbinate Trust (£10,000); Leeds University, Community Security Trust and Youth Aliyah – Child Rescue (£5,000 each); Association for Research into Stammering (£1,000); Little

Sisters of the Poor (£400) and MS Society (£150).
FINANCES *Year* 2011–12 *Income* £648,646 *Grants* £256,342 *Assets* £6,856,330
TRUSTEES Marjorie E. Ziff; Michael A. Ziff; Edward M. Ziff; Ann L. Manning.
HOW TO APPLY In writing to the correspondent. Replies will only be given to a request accompanied by an sae. Note that funds available from the trust are limited and requests not previously supported are unlikely to be successful. Initial telephone calls are welcome but note the foregoing comments.
WHO TO APPLY TO Sharon Hall, Secretary, Town Centre House, The Merrion Centre, Leeds LS2 8LY *Tel.* 01132 221234

■ Stephen Zimmerman Charitable Trust

CC NO 1038310 **ESTABLISHED** 1994
WHERE FUNDING CAN BE GIVEN UK.
WHO CAN BENEFIT Jewish organisations.
WHAT IS FUNDED Jewish causes.
SAMPLE GRANTS Previous beneficiaries have included: British ORT, Cancer Research, CIS Development Fund, London Youth, Jewish Association of Business Ethics, Jewish Care, Norwood Ltd, RNIB, United Jewish Israel Appeal and United Synagogue.
FINANCES *Year* 2011–12 *Income* £49,588 *Grants* £107,348 *Assets* £26,624
TRUSTEES L. J. Zimmerman; M. Marks; Stephen Zimmerman.
HOW TO APPLY The trust does not respond to unsolicited applications.
WHO TO APPLY TO S. Zimmerman, Trustee, S. Zimmerman, 35 Stormont Road, London N6 4NR *Tel.* 020 7518 3849

■ The Zochonis Charitable Trust

CC NO 274769 **ESTABLISHED** 1977
WHERE FUNDING CAN BE GIVEN UK, particularly Greater Manchester, and overseas, particularly Africa.
WHO CAN BENEFIT Registered charities only.
WHAT IS FUNDED General charitable purposes, with some preference for education and the welfare of children.
WHAT IS NOT FUNDED No grants for individuals.
TYPE OF GRANT One-off and recurrent.
RANGE OF GRANTS £2,000–£150,000.
SAMPLE GRANTS Cancer Research UK and Corpus Christi College Oxford (£150,000 each); VSO (£100,000); Police Foundation (£75,000); Manchester Art Gallery (£60,000); Gaddum Centre (£50,000); MENCAP (£30,000); Missing Foundation (£15,000); Royal Court Liverpool Trust (£10,000); Centrepoint (£5,000); Music and the Deaf (£3,000); and Live Music Now North West (£2,000).
FINANCES *Year* 2011–12 *Income* £3,362,376 *Grants* £3,396,750 *Assets* £157,853,812
TRUSTEES Sir John Zochonis; Christopher Nigel Green; Archibald G. Calder; Joseph J. Swift; Paul Milner.
HOW TO APPLY In writing to the correspondent.
WHO TO APPLY TO Ruth Barron, Administrator, DWF LLP, 1 Scott Place, 2 Hardman Street, Manchester M3 3AA *Tel.* 01618 380487 *email* ruth.barron@dwf.co.uk

■ The Zolfo Cooper Foundation

cc no 1134913   **established** 2010
where funding can be given Not defined. In practice, UK.
who can benefit Registered charities.
what is funded General charitable purposes.
range of grants Up to £5,000
sample grants University of Birmingham, London Music Masters and Pedal 2 Africa (£5,000 each); Happy Days' Charity (£2,500); Shelter and NSPCC (£2,000 each); The Lord's Taverners (£1,700); Habitat for Humanity (£1,500); Breakthrough Breast Cancer Suffolk (£1,000) and British Heart Foundation (£500). Smaller donations, totalling £18,600, were given to 167 organisations.
finances *Year* 2011–12 *Income* £50,450 *Grants* £59,297 *Assets* £108,418
trustees Nick Gittings; Anne O'Keefe; Anne-Marie Laing; Peter Saville; Ryan Grant; Luke Hartley.
how to apply In writing to the correspondent.
who to apply to The Trustees, c/o Zolfo Cooper LLP, 10 Fleet Place, London EC4M 7RB *Tel.* 020 7332 5000 *Fax* 020 7332 5001

■ Zurich Community Trust (UK) Limited

cc no 266983   **established** 1973
where funding can be given UK and overseas. Mainly focused in Wiltshire, Hampshire and Gloucestershire. Other areas include Birmingham, Brighton, Cardiff, Glasgow, Leeds, London, Manchester, Nottingham, Reigate, Southampton, Sutton, Watford and Wilmslow. (See general section).
who can benefit Registered charities, voluntary organisations and non-governmental organisations that help people who are disadvantaged achieve a better quality of life by moving from dependence to independence.
what is funded National programmes that create sustainable change, tackle issues in disadvantaged areas or work with disadvantaged groups of older people, such as those who are homeless or abused. Projects aiming to break the cycle of generational drug abuse by focusing on children and the family. Work with children under 18 years of age who are disadvantaged. Work to deal with mental health issues and youth. Relief of poverty in India.
what is not funded No grants made for: Statutory organisations (including mainstream schools and hospitals), unless exclusively for a special needs unit; Fundraising events including appeals or events for national charities; Expeditions, exchanges or study tours; Playgroups and mother and toddler groups, unless for special needs groups; Medical research, animal welfare charities, conservation or environmental projects; Sports clubs, village halls, political or religious organisations (including the upkeep and repair of places of worship); or Advertising or sponsorship connected with charitable events or appeals.
type of grant One-off, or partnership grants for three to five years; core costs; project costs; revenues; salaries; seed funding; capital.
range of grants Local grants: £100–£3,000,000; partnership grants: £20,000–£100,000.
sample grants Young People's Mental Health (£484,000); Breaking the Cycle (Addaction) (£207,000); India Programme (£113,000); Children's Hospices UK, Philippine Community Trust (£100,000 each); Calvert Trust (£68,000); Hope and Homes for Children (£63,000); Foundation for Conductive Education, Canine Partners (£40,000 each); NSPCC (ChildLine) and Marie Curie Cancer Care (£25,000 each).
finances *Year* 2012 *Income* £2,833,000
trustees Tim Culling; Gary Shaughnessy; Eileen Hopkins; Ian Lovett; Andrew Moore; Vinicio Cellerini; Stephen Lewis; Kay Martin; Peter Campbell.
how to apply In the first instance, visit the trust's website and follow the links to check eligibility and download the guidelines and application forms. Note: The trust runs a variety of grant programmes and for some of these the trust only accepts applications from organisations that have been invited to apply.
who to apply to Pam Webb, Head of Zurich Community Trust (UK), PO Box 1288, Swindon, Wiltshire SN1 1FL *Tel.* 01793 502450 *Fax* 01793 506982 *email* pam.webb@zct.org.uk *Website* www.zurich.co.uk/zurichcommunitytrust/home/home